# SELECTED VALUES OF PHYSICAL AND THERMODYNAMIC PROPERTIES OF HYDROCARBONS AND RELATED COMPOUNDS

COMPRISING THE TABLES OF THE

AMERICAN PETROLEUM INSTITUTE RESEARCH PROJECT 44

EXTANT AS OF DECEMBER 31, 1952

*By*

Frederick D. Rossini
*Silliman Professor and Head of the Department of Chemistry and
Director of the Petroleum Research Laboratory at the
Carnegie Institute of Technology*

Kenneth S. Pitzer
*Professor and Dean of the College of Chemistry at the University of California
Formerly Associate Director of the American Petroleum Institute Research Project 44*

Raymond L. Arnett
*Formerly Supervisor on the American Petroleum Institute Research Project 44
at the Carnegie Institute of Technology*

Rita M. Braun
*Assistant Research Chemist on the American Petroleum Institute Research Project 44
at the Carnegie Institute of Technology*

George C. Pimentel
*Assistant Professor of Chemistry at the University of California
Formerly Supervisor on the American Petroleum Institute Research Project 44*

*with contributions from*

KUN LI
HARRY J. RIES
PHYLLIS A. COWIE
JANET MITCHELL
LOUISE A. PARCELLA

MORTON B. EPSTEIN
AUDREY L. McCLELLAN
MARY H. SARAO
CORINNE R. DeCELLES
HELEN M. FLANAGAN

Published for the American Petroleum Institute by

## CARNEGIE PRESS

Carnegie Institute of Technology          Pittsburgh, Pennsylvania

1953

Price, Seven Dollars
on order from
CARNEGIE PRESS
CARNEGIE INSTITUTE OF TECHNOLOGY
Pittsburgh, Pennsylvania


Printed in the United States of America
by Edwards Brothers, Inc.

# FOREWORD

Since 1926, the American Petroleum Institute (API) has sponsored a fundamental research program whose purpose and policy is well phrased by Robert E. Wilson, Chairman of the Research Committee of the API Board of Directors, in his paper entitled "API Wildcatting in Some Interesting Areas", presented at the 1949 annual API meeting: "The primary purpose of the Institute's program of fundamental research is the determination and publication of basic facts relating to the occurrence, recovery, composition, and properties of petroleum. The several projects are established in fields in which our industry has broad, but primarily non-competitive, interests. The information resulting from the research work ordinarily is not directly applicable to industrial operations or processes, but is useful to individuals and corporations as basic data and background information of real value in the planning and development of new or improved methods for the discovery, production, or refining of petroleum."

As the various individual research programs took shape and gained momentum, the results of the coordinated efforts appeared in special papers or reports in the technical journals. Important new physical and thermodynamic data were made available to the technical world. It soon became apparent that an additional invaluable service could be rendered to those working in technical fields if all the physical and thermodynamic properties of known hydrocarbons, including the new data being reported as a result of the American Petroleum Institute's programs, could be assembled in a consolidated form. The API Advisory Committee on Fundamental Research on the Composition and Properties of Petroleum (ACFRCPP), one of the two advisory committees responsible to the Research Committee of the API Board of Directors, were fully cognizant of the fact that a mechanical compilation of such information would have little value, but rather a painstaking critical analysis would be necessary to assure unimpeachable reliability of the data. Selection of the most authentic values must be paramount in such an undertaking. This, then, was the basis for the establishment in 1942 of the new API Research Project 44, entitled "Data on Hydrocarbons and Related Compounds", which would report to the ACFRCPP, of which the Chairmen have been J. Bennett Hill, 1931–45, William J. Sweeney, 1946–49, and Howard G. Vesper, 1949–present.

The individual API projects are placed in the most competent hands possible by the careful selection of a Research Director for each project. The man must be of known scientific ability and achievement and with unquestionable technical integrity. In turn, as liaison between it and the main committee, a project Advisory Committee is established. This project Advisory Committee, composed of representatives of the petroleum industry, is responsible for counselling with the Director in the formation of the project program and for reviewing periodically the scope and progress of the work.

Since its establishment in 1942, the API Research Project 44 has been under the direction of Frederick D. Rossini, formerly Chief of the Section on Thermochemistry and Hydrocarbons at the National Bureau of Standards and since June, 1950, Silliman Professor and Head of the Department of Chemistry at the Carnegie Institute of Technology. Kenneth S. Pitzer, Professor and Dean of the College of Chemistry at the University of California, and formerly Director of Research for the U. S. Atomic Energy Commission, joined the project, first as Consultant, and then, as Associate Director. On July 1, 1952, the unit of the API Research Project 44 which was at the University of California was incorporated as part of the new API Research Project 50 established there under the direction of Dean Pitzer.

Those who have served as members of the Advisory Committee for the API Research Project 44 since its beginning ten years ago are the following: Wayne E. Kuhn (Chairman to December 31, 1952), 1942 to present; Otto Beeck, 1942 to 1950; Gustav Egloff, 1942 to present; Stewart S. Kurtz, Jr., 1942 to present; R. Robert Brattain, 1950 to present; Arthur L. Lyman (Chairman beginning January 1, 1953), 1951 to present. The Advisory Committee and Project Staff suffered a severe loss on July 3, 1950, in the death of Otto Beeck, who had been particularly helpful and instrumental in promoting the work of the Project dealing with spectral properties.

The outstanding accomplishments of the staff of the API Research Project 44 are readily apparent by the recognition and acceptance of the work by all of industry and by virtually every major educational institution in the world today. The project has made available, for hydrocarbons and related compounds, selected values of physical and thermodynamic properties and infrared, ultraviolet, Raman, and mass spectral data. The Advisory Committee believes that this volume serves as today's standard of physical and thermodynamic data on hydrocarbons.

December 31, 1952
New York, New York

Wayne E. Kuhn, Chairman, 1942–1952, Advisory Committee,
American Petroleum Institute Research Project 44

iii

## PREFACE

The American Petroleum Institute Research Project 44 has in 1952 completed ten years of work, operating at the National Bureau of Standards from its beginning in July, 1942 until June, 1950, and since then at the Carnegie Institute of Technology. From July, 1947 to June, 1952, a unit of the Project was maintained at the University of California, which unit has since become a part of the newly established API Research Project 50 at that institution under the direction of Kenneth S. Pitzer, who formerly served as Associate Director for the API Research Project 44.

The API Research Project 44 serves as the central agency of the American Petroleum Institute for collecting, calculating, and compiling data of interest to the petroleum industry, covering physical, thermodynamic, and infrared, ultraviolet, Raman, and mass spectral properties of hydrocarbons and all related compounds. The overall purpose of the Project is to maintain up-to-date a complete set of data, critically selected and internally consistent, on the physical, thermodynamic, and spectral properties of petroleum-derived compounds, to aid the petroleum industry to utilize its raw material to the greatest possible advantage.

With regard to the physical and thermodynamic properties, the aims of the Project are as follows: To examine all the pertinent original data in the literature, plus all available unpublished data, and to appraise them critically; to correlate values of given properties, with temperature or pressure to obtain values for temperatures or pressures for which no data are available, and with molecular structure to obtain values for compounds for which no data are available; to make original calculations of thermodynamic and physical properties as necessary; to select and tabulate "best" values of the properties; to prepare the selected values in a convenient form for use by industrial and scientific laboratories; to publish descriptions of the original calculations and correlations; and to keep the tables of selected values of properties up-to-date with revisions at appropriate intervals.

The properties being investigated include the following: Boiling point, and pressure coefficient of the boiling point, at 1 atmosphere; refractive index at 20° and 25°C; density at 20° and 25°C; specific gravity at 60°F; freezing point, in air at 1 atmosphere, in °C and °F; molecular volume, molecular refraction, specific refraction, refractivity intercept, and specific dispersion, at 20° and 25°C; viscosity, in centipoises, for the normal liquid range, at given temperatures in °C; kinematic viscosity, in centistokes, for the normal liquid range, at given temperatures in °C and °F; vapor pressures and boiling points, in °C, at 10 to 1,500 mm pressure, and, in °F, at 0.2 to 31 psi pressure; critical pressure, temperature, density, volume, and compressibility factor; surface tension at various temperatures; P-V-T and related properties; heat of vaporization at 25°C and, at the normal boiling point, at 1 atmosphere; entropy of vaporization at the normal boiling point; heat of combustion, at 25°C, for both the liquid and gaseous states, in kilocalories per mole, calories per gram, and BTU per lb; heat of formation, entropy, and free energy of formation, at 25°C, for both the liquid and gaseous states; standard heat, entropy, and free energy of vaporization, at 25°C; heat-content function, free-energy function, entropy, and heat capacity, for the ideal gaseous state, to high temperatures in calories per degree mole; heat content, for the ideal gaseous state, to high temperatures in calories per mole, calories per gram, and BTU per lb; heat of formation, and free energy of formation, in kilocalories per mole, and the logarithm of the equilibrium constant of formation, for the ideal gaseous state, to high temperatures; the cryoscopic constants (first and second), freezing point at saturation pressure (triple point) and in air at 1 atm., and heat and entropy of fusion.

The compounds covered or to be covered in the work of the Project include hydrocarbons of all types and molecular weights, and all non-hydrocarbon compounds of importance to the petroleum industry. The latter include organic sulfur compounds, organic oxygen compounds, simple nitrogen compounds, and certain halogens and halogenated hydrocarbons.

The extent of the coverage of the scientific and technical literature by the Project is indicated by the fact that the number of papers included in the list of references is now well over 2500.

It is to be emphasized that selection of the "best" value of a given property of a given compound involves consideration and appraisal of both the accuracy of the physical measurements and of the purity of the substance on which the measurements were made.

In order that the tables of data of the Project may be of greatest usefulness to engineers as well as chemists and physicists, the selected values are converted to engineering units, as appropriate. Beginning in 1952, the Project has actively embarked on a program of compiling data on P-V-T and associated properties of hydrocarbons and related compounds, which data will be of primary importance for engineering and process calculations.

The tables compiled by the API Research Project 44 are printed on loose-leaf sheets, 8" x 10-1/2" in size, one side only, and are distributed once or more each year, as prepared. Since one of the important jobs of the Project is to maintain its tables of data up-to-date by revision at appropriate intervals, the distribution each year includes revisions of previously issued tables as well as new tables.

Distribution of the loose-leaf data sheets is made to three categories of recipients: (1) complimentary copies to contributors to the fundamental research fund of the American Petroleum Institute; (2) gratis copies, one set each, to libraries and departments of chemistry, physics, and engineering in universities, to non-profit research institutions, and to government organizations; and (3) copies by sale to industrial purchasers or to recipients of the preceding categories who may wish to receive additional copies. Information concerning the loose-leaf data sheets on physical and thermodynamic properties and on the infrared, ultraviolet, Raman, and mass spectral data, as well as the IBM punch cards mentioned below, may be obtained from the American Petroleum Institute Research Project 44, attention of Frederick D. Rossini, Carnegie Institute of Technology, Pittsburgh 13, Pennsylvania.

As of December 31, 1952, the Project has issued a total of 5526 loose-leaf data sheets, including 2064 on physical and thermodynamic properties, and 1759 on infrared, 594 on ultraviolet, 246 on Raman, and 863 on mass spectral data. As of this same date, the number of valid sheets extant in the several categories of data are as follows: physical and thermodynamic properties, 1045 sheets; infrared, 1450 sheets; ultraviolet, 512 sheets; Raman, 226 sheets; and mass, 799 sheets. The status of the tables of physical and thermodynamic properties of hydrocarbons and related compounds as of December 31, 1952 is shown on the two pages following this Preface.

A new development that occurred in the work of the Project in 1952 was that of placing on IBM punch cards the data on physical and thermodynamic properties extant as of June 30, 1952. This work, carried on by a special subcommittee under the chairmanship of Jack Sherman, involved 35,905 cards containing over 110,000 numerical entries on 935 different hydrocarbons and related compounds. The new and revised data will be placed on IBM cards as they become available.

In addition to the uninterrupted distribution of loose-leaf data sheets as prepared, the Project also arranges, at intervals of about 5 years, to issue in bound book form the data on physical and thermodynamic properties which are extant in the loose-leaf sheets as of a given date. The present bound volume contains all of the material on physical and thermodynamic properties extant as of December 31, 1952.

It is to be emphasized that the distribution of the loose-leaf data sheets as prepared is independent of the preparation of this bound volume. The issuance of the loose-leaf data sheets continues unabated. Those who may wish to consult the latest information compiled are referred to the collection of loose-leaf data sheets of the API Research Project 44 on file in most of the libraries and research organizations of the free world.

The operations of the API Research Project 44 involve many man-years of work. Following are the former full-time professional members of the headquarters staff of the Project, with their dates of service: William J. Taylor, September, 1942, to September, 1947; Anthony J. Urbanic, September, 1942, to December, 1942; Joan Pignocco Ebert, June, 1943, to August, 1948; John E. Kilpatrick, April, 1944, to August, 1947; Mary Greaney Williams, July, 1945, to June, 1947; Helene Gilliaert Werner, June, 1946, to May, 1947; Marie T. Lynch, July, 1947, to January, 1950; Mary Helm Sarao, July, 1947, to May, 1950; Morton B. Epstein, September, 1947, to May, 1949; Corinne R. DeCelles, July, 1948, to April, 1950; Alberta L. Kelvie, July, 1948, to June, 1950; Raymond L. Arnett, May, 1949, to April, 1952; Helen M. Flanagan, July, 1949, to June, 1950; M. Elizabeth Janes Carlin, June, 1950, to September, 1952. Graduate students formerly serving with the Project at the Carnegie Institute of Technology have included Holwell K. Land, September, 1950, to June, 1951.

The former full-time professional members of the unit of the Project at Berkeley, under the direction of Kenneth S. Pitzer, January, 1944, to June, 1952, and the supervision of William D. Gwinn, January, 1949, to March, 1951, and of George C. Pimentel, July, 1949, to June, 1952, are as follows: Chia-Si Lu, April, 1945, to September, 1945; Charles W. Beckett, July, 1945, to December, 1947; Audrey L. McClellan, November, 1948, to August, 1950. Graduate students formerly serving with the unit of the Project at the University of California have included the following: N. K. Freeman, July, 1947, to June, 1949; William Weltner, July, 1947, to December, 1949; Gordon M. Barrow, September, 1948, to July, 1950; Henry J. Hrowstowski, July, 1950, to June, 1952; Willis P. Person, July, 1950, to June, 1952; Isamu C. Hisatsune, February, 1951, to July, 1951; William A. Klemperer, August, 1951, to January, 1952. From the beginning of the Project until June, 1952, Kenneth S. Pitzer was associated with the work, first as a Consultant and later as Associate Director in charge of the unit of the Project at the University of California. This unit, on July 1, 1952, became part of the new API Research Project 50 under his direction.

The staff of the API Research Project 44 at the Carnegie Institute of Technology as of December 31, 1952, consists of the following full-time professional members, with their initial date of connection with the Project: Frederick D. Rossini, July 1, 1942, Director; Kun Li, July 1, 1952, Research Chemist; Harry J. Ries, July 1, 1952, Assistant Research Chemist; Rita M. Braun, July 1, 1947, Assistant Research Chemist; Mary Cauffield Hinman, July 1, 1951, Junior Research Chemist and Editor; Phyllis A. Cowie, July 1, 1952, Junior Research Chemist; Janet Mitchell, July 1, 1951, Junior Research Chemist; Louise A. Parcella, July 1, 1951, Junior Research Chemist; Shirlee J. Ploeger, July 1, 1952, Junior Research Chemist; Ellen T. Drake, September 16, 1952, Junior Research Chemist and Assistant Editor. Lawrence N. Canjar, Assistant Professor of Chemical Engineering, has served part-time with the Project as Research Chemical Engineer beginning July 1, 1952. Graduate students currently serving with the Project, with their first dates of appointment, are as follows: John B. Greenshields, September 16, 1950; C. Marilyn Spath, June 25, 1951; Shui-Shen Hu, July 1, 1952; Nilda Zegarra Paz, September 8, 1952.

In addition to the important services performed in the work of the Project by the past and present professional members of the staff, I wish to record here our great indebtedness to the many faithful assistants that the Project has had over the years, and more recently also to our graduate student assistants.

It is important to emphasize that the fruits of the fundamental research which the American Petroleum Institute supports under the API Research Project 44 and other similar projects are made available promptly without cost to the entire scientific public of the free world. It is with sincere gratitude that I record here on behalf of the Project our thanks for the generous cooperation which the API Research Project 44 has had over the years from the headquarters staff of the American Petroleum Institute, particularly from the following with whom we had had important contacts: Lacey Walker, David V. Stroop, and Elmer O. Mattocks.

Contact with the members of the Advisory Committee has constituted one of the most pleasant and profitable features of the work of the API Research Project 44. All of the members of the Advisory Committee have given unstintedly of their time and have provided the staff of the Project with important suggestions and necessary encouragement in difficult periods. On behalf of the staff of the Project, I herewith gratefully acknowledge our debt to the following present or former members of the Advisory and higher Committees: Robert E. Wilson, Howard G. Vesper, William J. Sweeney, J. Bennett Hill, Albert E. Miller, Otto Beeck (deceased), Gustav Egloff, Stewart S. Kurtz, Jr., R. Robert Brattain, and Arthur L. Lyman (Chairman beginning January 1, 1953). In particular, I wish to acknowledge our great indebtedness to Wayne E. Kuhn, who served as the Chairman of the Advisory Committee of the Project from its very beginning to December 31, 1952, the date of closing of this bound volume, and who aided the Project in innumerable ways over the years as can only one who possesses a deep and sincere interest in its work.

I wish finally to acknowledge the important help received from the former Editors of the Project, Joan Pignocco Ebert, Marie T. Lynch, Alberta L. Kelvie, and M. Elizabeth Janes Carlin, and the very practical and immediate assistance received in preparing this book for the printer from Mary C. Hinman, Editor, and Ellen T. Drake, Assistant Editor, who were ably assisted by Shirley J. McIlree, Vari-Typist, and Marcella M. Prusak and Kathryn G. Chieffalo, Editorial Assistants.

In closing this Preface, I invite with thanks in advance notices of any errors that may be found in the volume as well as criticism of its contents.

Frederick D. Rossini
Director, American Petroleum Institute
Research Project 44

December 31, 1952
Carnegie Institute of Technology
Pittsburgh 13, Pennsylvania

Note in block indicates number of pages.

**Compound groups (GROUP NO. — COMPOUNDS):**

- 00 — O,H,N,C
- 00 — $O_2, H_2, OH, H_2O, N_2, NO, C, CO, CO_2$
- 20 — Normal Paraffins, $C_1$ to $C_{40}$
- 1 — Paraffins, $C_1$ to $C_7$
- 2 — Paraffins, $C_6$ and $C_7$
- 3 — Paraffins, $C_8$
- 4 — Paraffins, $C_9$
- 17 — Paraffins, $C_{10}$
- 22 — Normal Alkyl Cyclopentanes, $C_5$ to $C_{41}$
- 15 — Alkyl Cyclopentanes, $C_8$
- 6 — Alkyl Cyclohexanes, $C_6$ to $C_8$
- 23 — Normal Alkyl Cyclohexanes, $C_6$ to $C_{42}$
- 7 — Alkyl Cyclohexanes, $C_9$
- 16 — Alkyl Cyclohexanes
- 24 — Normal Monoolefins (1-Alkenes), $C_2$ to $C_{40}$
- 8 — Monoolefins, $C_2$ to $C_6$
- 9 — Monoolefins, $C_7$
- 10 — Monoolefins, $C_8$
- 11 — Diolefins, $C_3$ to $C_6$
- 18 — Alkyl Cyclopentenes, $C_5$ to $C_7$
- 19 — Alkyl Cyclohexenes, $C_6$ to $C_8$
- 25 — Normal Acetylenes (1-Alkynes), $C_2$ to $C_{40}$
- 12 — Acetylenes, $C_2$ to $C_5$
- 21 — Normal Alkyl Benzenes, $C_6$ to $C_{42}$
- 5 — Alkyl Benzenes, $C_6$ to $C_9$
- 14 — Alkyl Benzenes, $C_{10}$
- 26 — Alkyl Benzenes, $C_{11}$
- 13 — Styrenes, $C_8$ and $C_9$
- 30 — 1-Normal Alkyl Naphthalenes, $C_{10}$ to $C_{22}$
- 31 — 2-Normal Alkyl Naphthalenes, $C_{10}$ to $C_{22}$
- 27 — Naphthalenes, $C_{10}$ to $C_{12}$
- 28 — Tetrahydronaphthalenes, $C_{10}$ to $C_{12}$
- 29 — Decahydronaphthalenes, $C_{10}$ to $C_{12}$
- 101 — Normal 1-Alkanethiols, $C_1$ to $C_{20}$
- 102 — Normal 2-Alkanethiols, $C_3$ to $C_{20}$
- 103 — Alkanethiols, $C_1$ to $C_5$
- 104 — Alkyl Benzenethiols, $C_6$ to $C_8$
- 105 — 2-Thiaalkanes, $C_2$ to $C_{20}$
- 107 — Thiaalkanes, $C_2$ to $C_5$
- 108 — Thiaalkanes, $C_6$
- 109 — Alkyl (1-Thiaalkyl) Benzenes, $C_7$ and $C_8$
- 110 — Alkyl (1-Thiaalkyl) Benzenes, $C_9$
- 111 — Alkyl Thiacyclopropanes, $C_2$ to $C_4$
- 112 — Alkyl Thiacyclopentanes, $C_4$ to $C_6$
- 113 — Alkyl Thiacyclohexanes, $C_5$ to $C_7$
- 114 — Alkyl Thiophenes, $C_4$ to $C_6$
- 115 — Alkyl Thiophenes, $C_7$

**Properties (PROPERTIES — UNITS — LETTER — Total):**

| PROPERTIES | UNITS | LETTER | Total |
|---|---|---|---|
| BOILING POINT, at 1 atm; dt/dP, at 1 atm | °C; °C/mm Hg | a | 64 |
| REFRACTIVE INDEX, $n_D$, at 20° and 25°C | | a | |
| DENSITY, at 20° and 25°C | g/ml | a | |
| FREEZING POINT, in air at 1 atm | °C | a | |
| BOILING POINT, at 1 atm; dt/dP, at 1 atm | °F; °F/in Hg | a-E | 64 |
| REFRACTIVE INDEX, $n_D$, at 68° and 77°F | | a-E | |
| DENSITY, at 60°, 68°, and 77°F | lb/ft³; lb/gal | a-E | |
| SPECIFIC GRAVITY, 60°F/60°F | | a-E | |
| FREEZING POINT, in air at 1 atm | °F | a-E | |
| MOLECULAR VOLUME at 20°C | ml/mole | b | 64 |
| MOLECULAR REFRACTION | ml/mole | b | |
| SPECIFIC REFRACTION and 25°C | ml/g | b | |
| REFRACTIVITY INTERCEPT | | b | |
| SPECIFIC DISPERSION | ml/g | b | |
| SPECIFIC REFERENCES for Tables a, a-E, and b | | | 77 |
| VISCOSITY (ABSOLUTE) at given temperatures in °C | centipoises | c | 21 |
| KINEMATIC VISCOSITY at given temperatures in °F | centistokes | c-E | 19 |
| KINEMATIC VISCOSITY at given temperatures in °C | centistokes | c-K | 21 |
| SPECIFIC REFERENCES for Tables c, c-E, and c-K | | | 8 |
| DENSITY at given temperatures in °C | g/ml | d | 12 |
| DENSITY at given temperatures in °F | lb/ft³ | d-E | 19 |
| SPECIFIC REFERENCES for Tables d and d-E | | | 7 |
| SURFACE TENSION at given temperatures in °C | dyne/cm | e | 8 |
| SPECIFIC REFERENCES for Tables e | | | 6 |
| CRITICAL TEMPERATURE | °K; °C; °R; °F | | 10 |
| CRITICAL PRESSURE | atm; lb/ft² | | |
| CRITICAL DENSITY | g/ml; lb/ft³ | | |
| CRITICAL VOLUME | liter/mole; ft³/lb mole | | |
| CRITICAL COMPRESSIBILITY FACTOR | | i | |
| P-V-T AND RELATED DATA | | j | 10 |
| SPECIFIC REFERENCES for Tables i | | | |
| SPECIFIC REFERENCES for Tables j | | | |
| VAPOR PRESSURES at 10 to 1500 mm Hg | mm Hg | k | 32 |
| BOILING POINTS | °C | k | 67 |
| VAPOR PRESSURES at given temperatures | lb/in² | k-E | |
| BOILING POINTS | °F | k-E | 16 |
| SPECIFIC REFERENCES for Tables k and k-E | | | |

vii

# PAGE 2 OF STATUS OF TABLES OF PHYSICAL AND THERMODYNAMIC PROPERTIES OF HYDROCARBONS AND RELATED COMPOUNDS
## AS OF DECEMBER 31, 19xx

Number in block indicates number of pages

| PROPERTIES | UNITS | LETTER | O,H,N,C | $O_2,H_2,OH,H_2O,N_2,NO,C,CO,CO_2$ | Normal Paraffins, $C_1$ to $C_{40}$ | Paraffins, $C_1$ to $C_5$ | Paraffins, $C_6$ and $C_7$ | Paraffins, $C_8$ | Paraffins, $C_9$ | Paraffins, $C_{10}$ | Normal Alkyl Cyclopentanes, $C_5$ to $C_{41}$ | Alkyl Cyclopentanes, $C_8$ | Normal Alkyl Cyclohexanes, $C_6$ to $C_{42}$ | Alkyl Cyclohexanes, $C_9$ | Normal Monoolefins (1-Alkenes), $C_2$ to $C_{40}$ | Monoolefins, $C_2$ to $C_6$ | Monoolefins, $C_7$ | Monoolefins, $C_8$ | Diolefins, $C_3$ to $C_6$ | Alkyl Cyclopentenes, $C_5$ to $C_7$ | Alkyl Cyclohexenes, $C_6$ to $C_8$ | Normal Acetylenes (1-Alkynes), $C_2$ to $C_{40}$ | Acetylenes, $C_2$ to $C_5$ | Normal Alkyl Benzenes, $C_6$ to $C_{42}$ | Alkyl Benzenes, $C_6$ to $C_9$ | Alkyl Benzenes, $C_{10}$ | Alkyl Benzenes, $C_{11}$ | Styrenes, $C_8$ and $C_9$ | Normal 1-Alkyl Naphthalenes, $C_{10}$ to $C_{22}$ | Normal 2-Alkyl Naphthalenes, $C_{10}$ to $C_{22}$ | Naphthalenes, $C_{10}$ to $C_{12}$ | Tetrahydronaphthalenes, $C_{10}$ to $C_{12}$ | Decahydronaphthalenes, $C_{10}$ to $C_{12}$ | Normal 1-Alkanethiols, $C_1$ to $C_{20}$ | Normal 2-Alkanethiols, $C_3$ to $C_{20}$ | Alkanethiols, $C_1$ to $C_5$ | Alkyl Benzenethiols, $C_6$ to $C_8$ | 2-Thiaalkanes, $C_2$ to $C_{20}$ | Thiaalkanes, $C_2$ to $C_5$ | Thiaalkanes, $C_6$ | Alkyl (1-Thiaalkyl) Benzenes, $C_7$ and $C_8$ | Alkyl (1-Thiaalkyl) Benzenes, $C_9$ | Alkyl Thiacyclopropanes, $C_2$ to $C_4$ | Alkyl Thiacyclopentanes, $C_4$ to $C_6$ | Alkyl Thiacyclohexanes, $C_5$ to $C_7$ | Alkyl Thiophenes, $C_4$ to $C_6$ | Alkyl Thiophenes, $C_7$ | Total |
|---|---|---|---|---|---|---|---|---|---|---|---|---|---|---|---|---|---|---|---|---|---|---|---|---|---|---|---|---|---|---|---|---|---|---|---|---|---|---|---|---|---|---|---|---|---|---|---|

(Group No. / column reference numbers: 00, 0, 20, 1, 2, 3, 4, 17, 22, 6, 23, 7, 16, 24, 8, 9, 10, 11, 15, 18, 25, 19, 21, 12, 5, 14, 26, 13, 30, 31, 27, 28, 29, 100, 101, 102, 103, 104, 105, 106, 107, 108, 109, 110, 111, 112, 113, 114, 115)

Data rows (selected readable values; number in block = number of pages):

| Property | Letter | Total |
|---|---|---|
| HEAT OF VAPORIZATION at 25°C and normal boiling point; ENTROPY OF VAPORIZATION at normal boiling point (kcal/mole; cal/g; cal/deg mole) | e | 9 |
| SPECIFIC REFERENCES for Tables m | | 9 |
| HEAT OF COMBUSTION at 25°C, for liquid and gas (kcal/mole; cal/g, BTU/lb) | n | 20 |
| SPECIFIC REFERENCES for Tables n | | 1 |
| HEAT OF FORMATION / FREE ENERGY OF FORMATION at 25°C for liquid and gas; ENTROPY (kcal/mole; cal/deg mole) | p | 20 |
| SPECIFIC REFERENCES for Tables p | | 20 |
| STANDARD HEAT / STANDARD FREE ENERGY / STANDARD ENTROPY of vaporization at 25°C (kcal/mole; kcal/mole; cal/deg mole) | q | 7 |
| SPECIFIC REFERENCES for Tables q | | 1 |
| HEAT CONTENT FUNCTION, 0° to 1500°K (cal/mole) | r | 22 |
| FREE ENERGY FUNCTION, 0° to 1500°K (cal/deg mole) | s | 22 |
| ENTROPY, 0° to 1500°K (cal/deg mole) | u | 22 |
| HEAT CONTENT, 0° to 1500°K (cal/mole) | u-E | 22 |
| HEAT CONTENT, −459.69° to 2200°F (BTU/lb) | u-G | 31 |
| HEAT CONTENT, −273.16° to 1200°C (cal/g) | v | 20 |
| HEAT CAPACITY, 0° to 1500°K (cal/deg mole) | v-E | 22 |
| HEAT CAPACITY, −459.69° to 2200°F (BTU/lb deg F) | v-G | 31 |
| HEAT CAPACITY, −273.16° to 1200°C (cal/g deg C) | w | 20 |
| HEAT OF FORMATION, 0° to 1500°K (kcal/mole) | x | 22 |
| FREE ENERGY OF FORMATION, 0° to 1500°K (kcal/mole) | y | 22 |
| LOGARITHM OF EQUILIBRIUM CONSTANT OF FORMATION, 0° to 1500°K | y | 22 |
| SPECIFIC REFERENCES for Tables r,s,t,u,u-E,u-G,v,v-E,v-G,w,x, and y | | 24 |
| HEAT OF FUSION / ENTROPY OF FUSION / CRYOSCOPIC CONSTANTS / FREEZING POINTS, at saturation pressure and in air at 1 atm (kcal/mole; cal/deg mole; mole fraction/deg; °C; °F) | z | 12 |
| SPECIFIC REFERENCES for Tables z | | 12 |
| TOTAL | | 938 |

| | Letter | Total |
|---|---|---|
| FUNDAMENTAL CONSTANTS | | 3 |
| CONVERSION FACTORS | α | 5 |
| USEFUL EQUATIONS WITH NUMERICAL CONSTANTS | γ | 1 |
| MOLECULAR WEIGHTS | ε | 18 |
| TITLE, STATUS, INTRODUCTION | | 4 |
| GENERAL REFERENCES | | 68 |
| LIST OF PUBLICATIONS | | 3 |
| GRAND TOTAL | | 1045 |

# CONTENTS

## FUNDAMENTAL CONSTANTS AND CONVERSION FACTORS

The values of the fundamental constants used in these tables are those recommended by the Subcommittee on Fundamental Constants of the Committee on Physical Chemistry of the National Research Council (see Rossini, Gucker, Johnston, Pauling, and Vinal[1]). The constants are classified as basic, derived, and defined (see Rossini[22]).

## SCALES OF TEMPERATURE

In these tables, temperatures given in degrees Celsius (Centigrade), °C, which are based on experimental measurements, as for example, boiling points and freezing points, are referred to the International Temperature Scale (see Burgess[1], Mueller[1], and Stimson[1]). As appropriate, these temperatures have been converted to degrees Kelvin, °K, by the relation,

number of degrees Kelvin = 273.160 + number of degrees Celsius,

and to degrees Fahrenheit, °F, by the relation,

number of degrees Fahrenheit = 32 + 1.8 (number of degrees Celsius).

The differences between temperatures on the international and the thermodynamic scales are discussed by Mueller[1], Stimson[1], and Rossini[22].

Temperatures given in degrees Kelvin, °K, in the tables of thermodynamic functions (tables designated by the letters r,s,t,u,v,w,x, and y) are on the Kelvin thermodynamic scale. These temperatures have been converted to degrees Celsius, °C, in the u-G and v-G tables by the relation,

number of degrees Celsius = number of degrees Kelvin −273.160,

and to degrees Fahrenheit, °F, in the u-E and v-E tables, by the relation,

number of degrees Fahrenheit = 1.8 (number of degrees Kelvin) −459.688.

## THERMODYNAMIC SYMBOLS AND CALCULATIONS

The thermodynamic symbols used in these tables are defined as follows (see Rossini[22]):

$P$ is the pressure.

$V$ is the volume, usually per mole.

$T$ is the absolute temperature.

$E$ is the energy, internal or intrinsic.

$H = E+PV$ is the heat content (or enthalpy).

$F = E+PV-TS = H-TS$ is the free energy.

$K$ is the equilibrium constant.

$C_p = (\partial H/\partial T)_p$ is the heat capacity at constant pressure.

$R$ is the gas constant, per mole.

Circular superscript, $^\circ$, denotes the standard state (thermodynamic standard reference state, see Rossini[22]).

The italicized letters, $f$, $m$, $v$, and $c$, used as modifiers immediately following (with no space between) the symbols $\Delta H$, $\Delta F$, or $\Delta S$, refer respectively to the following processes: formation from the elements, fusion or melting, vaporization, and combustion.

Numeral subscript, as $_{298.16}$ or $_0$, denotes the absolute temperature in degrees Kelvin.

$H^\circ-H^\circ_0$ is the heat content (or enthalpy) in the standard state at the temperature $T$ less the heat content in the standard state at 0°K.

$(H^\circ-H^\circ_0)/T$ is the heat content function, which is the heat content (or enthalpy) in the standard state at the temperature $T$ less the heat content in the standard state at 0°K, all divided by $T$.

$(F^\circ-H^\circ_0)/T$ is the free energy function, which is the free energy in the standard state at the temperature $T$ less the heat content in the standard state at 0°K, all divided by T.

$S^\circ$ is the entropy of the given substance in the standard state at the indicated temperature, omitting nuclear contributions, as isotopic mixing, nuclear spins, etc., which contributions cancel out in all reactions of practical importance.

$\Delta$ denotes the increment of a given property for a given process or reaction, taken as the value for the final state (sum of products) less that for the initial state (sum of reactants).

$\Delta H$, $\Delta F$, $\Delta S$, $\Delta C_p$ is the increment in heat content, free energy, entropy, and heat capacity, respectively, for the given process or reaction, with each substance in a specified thermodynamic state.

$\Delta H^o$, $\Delta F^o$, $\Delta S^o$, $\Delta C_p{}^o$ is the standard increment in heat content, free energy, entropy, and heat capacity, respectively, for the given process or reaction, with each substance in its standard state.

$K$ is the equilibrium constant for a given process or reaction, defined as the proper quotient of activities ($a$), of the substances involved in the reaction, at thermodynamic equilibrium at the given temperature, pressure, etc. For example, for the reaction,

$$bB + cC = mM + nN,$$

with each of the reactants and products at equilibrium,

$$K = \frac{(a_M)^m (a_N)^n}{(a_B)^b (a_C)^c} .$$

For all gases, the activity is exactly equal to the fugacity. For the ideal gas, the fugacity is equal to the pressure. For real gases at low pressures and at ordinary and high temperatures, the fugacity of each gas is approximately equal to its pressure, so that, under these conditions,

$$K = \frac{(f_M)^m (f_N)^n}{(f_B)^b (f_C)^c} \simeq \frac{(p_M)^m (p_N)^n}{(p_B)^b (p_C)^c} .$$

The equilibrium constant for a given process or reaction is related to the standard change in free energy for that process or reaction at the same temperature by the relation,

$$\log_{10} K = -\Delta F^o / (2.302585 RT).$$

$\Delta H f^o$ is the standard heat of formation, which is the increment in heat content associated with the reaction of forming the given compound from its elements, with each substance in its standard state at the given temperature.

$\Delta F f^o$ is the standard free energy of formation, which is the increment in free energy associated with the reaction of forming the given compound from its elements, with each substance in its standard state at the given temperature.

$\log_{10} Kf$ is the logarithm (to the base 10) of the equilibrium constant of formation, for the reaction of forming one mole of the given compound from its elements, with each substance in its standard state at the given temperature. The equilibrium constant of formation is related to the standard free energy of formation, per mole, by the relation:

$$\log_{10} Kf = - \Delta Kf^o / (2.302585 RT).$$

$\Delta Hm$, $\Delta Sm$ are the increment in heat content and entropy, respectively, for the process of fusion, as B (crystal) = B (liquid), with the crystal and liquid each in a specified thermodynamic state, as at saturation pressure. With superscripts indicating standard states, as $\Delta Hm^o$ and $\Delta Sm^o$, the process refers to one in which the crystal and liquid are in their respective standard states, and the increments represent the standard heat of fusion and the standard entropy of fusion, respectively. For the process of fusion, the values of the standard heat and entropy of fusion usually do not differ significantly from the heat and entropy of fusion, respectively, at saturation pressure.

$\Delta Hv$, $\Delta Sv$ are the increment in heat content and entropy, respectively, for the process of vaporization, as B(liquid) = B(gas), with the liquid and the gas in a specified thermodynamic state, as at saturation pressure. With superscripts indicating standard states, as $\Delta Hv^o$ and $\Delta Sv^o$, the process refers to one in which the liquid and gas are in their respective standard states, and the increments represent the standard heat of vaporization and the standard entropy of vaporization, respectively. For the process of vaporization, the value of the standard heat of vaporization usually differs only by a small amount from the value of the heat of vaporization at saturation pressures of 1 atmosphere or less, whereas the value of the standard entropy of vaporization may differ considerably from the value of the entropy of vaporization at saturation pressure.

$\Delta Hc^o$ is the increment in heat content for the reaction of combustion of the given substance (compound containing C, H, O, N) in gaseous oxygen to form gaseous carbon dioxide, gaseous or liquid water, and gaseous nitrogen, as indicated, at constant temperature and pressure, with all the reactants and products in their appropriate standard states.

For a detailed description of methods of utilizing the data given in these tables for calculating thermodynamic equilibria etc., the reader is referred to Rossini[22].

## SOURCES OF DATA, SPECIFIC REFERENCES, GENERAL REFERENCES

The sources of data are given specifically for each property of each compound, as appropriate, in the section on Specific References, which gives the name or names of the author or authors of each publication, together with a numeral superscript on the last author's name, indicating the number of the publication for that particular author or group of authors'. From this, the complete reference to the publication in the literature is obtained from the section on the General List of References, in which the names are arranged alphabetically, with the publications of each author or group of authors listed in numerical order. Initials of authors are not given unless two or more authors or groups of authors have identical surnames.

## INTERNAL CONSISTENCY

These tables of the API Research Project 44 are internally consistent in the sense that all the known physical and thermodynamic relations existing between the properties in the several tables are satisfied by the tabulated values of these properties. Thus, the values in the a-E and b tables, are based on the appropriate values in the a tables, and the boiling and freezing points in the a tables are, insofar as possible, consistent with the corresponding values in the k and z tables, respectively. The thermodynamic relations that exist between the properties in the $k, m, n, p, q, r, s, t, u, u-E, u-G, v, v-E, v-G, w, x, y,$ and $z$ tables are satisfied by the tabulated values, and they therefore form an internally consistent set of tables of the thermodynamic properties.

## DATING OF THE TABLES

The dates appearing in the heading of each table establishes the time of issue of the given table. Where more than one date appears, the second and additional dates each apply to dates of revision of the table. Where the same property for the same compound is covered in two different tables, as for $n$-octane in Tables 3a and 20a, and the values are not identical, the value in the table of later date is assumed to be better, and the other table will in due course be revised accordingly. The appearance of "(Corrected)" following a date in the heading indicates that an error occurring in the table was corrected by issuance of a replacement sheet bearing the same date but having added the notation "(Corrected)".

## EXPLANATION OF NUMBERS IN THE TITLES OF THE TABLES

The numbers in the titles of the tables represent the following groups of compounds:

| NUMBER | COMPOUNDS |
|---|---|
| 00 | O, H, N, C |
| 0 | $O_2$, $H_2$, OH, $H_2O$, $N_2$, NO, C, CO, $CO_2$ |
| 1 | Paraffins, $C_1$ to $C_5$ |
| 2 | Paraffins, $C_6$ and $C_7$ |
| 3 | Paraffins, $C_8$ |
| 4 | Paraffins, $C_9$ |
| 5 | Alkyl benzenes, $C_6$ to $C_9$ |
| 6 | Alkyl cyclopentanes, $C_5$ to $C_7$ |
| 7 | Alkyl cyclohexanes, $C_6$ to $C_8$ |
| 8 | Monoolefins, $C_2$ to $C_6$ |
| 9 | Monoolefins, $C_7$ |
| 10 | Monoolefins, $C_8$ |
| 11 | Diolefins, $C_3$ to $C_6$ |
| 12 | Acetylenes, $C_2$ to $C_5$ |
| 13 | Styrenes, $C_8$ and $C_9$ |
| 14 | Alkyl benzenes, $C_{10}$ |
| 15 | Alkyl cyclopentanes, $C_8$ |
| 17 | Paraffins. $C_{10}$ |
| 18 | Alkyl cyclopentenes, $C_5$ to $C_7$ |
| 19 | Alkyl cyclohexenes, $C_6$ to $C_8$ |
| 20 | Normal paraffins, $C_1$ to $C_{40}$ |
| 21 | Normal alkyl benzenes, $C_6$ to $C_{42}$ |
| 22 | Normal alkyl cyclopentanes, $C_5$ to $C_{41}$ |
| 23 | Normal alkyl cyclohexanes, $C_6$ to $C_{42}$ |
| 24 | Normal monoolefins, (1-Alkenes), $C_2$ to $C_{40}$ |
| 25 | Normal acetylenes, (1-Alkynes), $C_2$ to $C_{40}$ |
| 26 | Alkyl benzenes, $C_{11}$ |
| 27 | Naphthalenes, $C_{10}$ to $C_{12}$ |
| 28 | Tetrahydronaphthalenes, $C_{10}$ to $C_{12}$ |
| 29 | Decahydronaphthalenes, $C_{10}$ to $C_{12}$ |
| 30 | 1-Normal alkyl naphthalenes, $C_{10}$ to $C_{12}$ |
| 31 | 2-Normal alkyl naphthalenes, $C_{10}$ to $C_{12}$ |
| 101 | Normal 1-alkanethiols, $C_1$ to $C_{20}$ |
| 102 | Normal 2-alkanethiols, $C_3$ to $C_{20}$ |
| 103 | Alkanethiols, $C_1$ to $C_5$ |
| 104 | Alkyl benzenethiols, $C_6$ to $C_8$ |
| 105 | 2-Thiaalkanes, $C_2$ to $C_{20}$ |
| 107 | Thiaalkanes, $C_2$ to $C_5$ |
| 108 | Thiaalkanes, $C_6$ |
| 109 | Alkyl (1-thiaalkyl) benzenes, $C_7$ and $C_8$ |
| 110 | Alkyl (1-thiaalkyl) benzenes, $C_9$ |
| 111 | Alkyl thiacyclopropanes, $C_2$ to $C_4$ |
| 112 | Alkyl thiacyclopentanes, $C_4$ to $C_7$ |
| 113 | Alkyl thiacyclohexanes, $C_5$ to $C_7$ |
| 114 | Alkyl thiophenes, $C_4$ to $C_6$ |
| 115 | Alkyl thiophenes. $C_7$ |

Where a number has been assigned to a group of compounds which is subsequently subdivided into two or more subgroups of compounds, for purposes of simplifying the arrangement of compounds and the presentation of the data, the subgroups will be labeled Part 1, Part 2, etc., of the given group number, as Table 20 (Part 1). Where the tabulation for a given group or subgroup of compounds occupies more than one page, the pages are indicated as Page 1, Page 2, etc.

## EXPLANATION OF LETTERS IN THE TITLES OF THE TABLES

The letters in the titles of the tables represent the following properties:

| LETTER | PROPERTIES |
|---|---|
| $\alpha$ | Values of fundamental constants. |
| $\beta$ | Conversion factors. |
| $\gamma$ | Useful equations with numerical constants. |
| $\delta$ | Molecular weights of hydrocarbons. |
| a | Boiling point ($^o$C), dt/dp ($^o$C/mm Hg), refractive index, density (g/ml), and freezing point ($^o$C). |
| a–E | Boiling point ($^o$F), dt/dp ($^o$F/in Hg), refractive index, density (lb/ft$^3$ and lb/gal), specific gravity (60$^o$F/60$^o$F), and freezing point ($^o$F). |
| b | Molecular volume (ml/mole), molecular refraction (ml/mole), specific refraction (ml/g), refractivity intercept, and specific dispersion (ml/g). |
| c | Viscosity (absolute) (centipoises), at temperatures in $^o$C. |
| c–E | Kinematic viscosity (centistokes), at temperatures in $^o$F. |
| c–K | Kinematic viscosity (centistokes), at temperatures in $^o$C. |
| d | Density (g/ml), at temperatures in $^o$C. |
| d–E | Density (lb/ft$^3$), at temperatures in $^o$F. |
| e | Surface tension (dyne/cm), at temperatures in $^o$C. |
| i | Critical temperature ($^o$K, $^o$C, $^o$R and $^o$F), critical pressure (atm and lb/in$^2$), critical density (g/ml, lb/ft$^3$), critical volume (liter/mole and ft$^3$/lb mole) and compressibility. |
| k | Vapor pressures (mm Hg) and boiling points ($^o$C) at 10 to 1500 mm Hg. |
| k–E | Vapor pressures (lb/in$^2$) and boiling points ($^o$F) at 0.2 to 30 lb/in$^2$. |
| m | Heat of vaporization (kcal/mole, cal/g, and BTU/lb) and entropy of vaporization (cal/deg mole), at 25$^o$C and the normal boiling point. |
| n | Heat of combustion (kcal/mole, cal/g, and BTU/lb), at 25$^o$C. |
| p | Heat of formation (kcal/mole), entropy (cal/deg mole), and free energy of formation (kcal/mole), at 25$^o$C. |
| q | Standard heat of vaporization (kcal/mole), entropy of vaporization (cal/deg mole), and free energy of formation (kcal/mole), at 25$^o$C. |
| r | Heat content function, $(H^o - H^o_0)/T$, (cal/deg mole) at 0$^o$ to 1500$^o$K. |
| s | Free energy function, $(F^o - H^o_0)/T$, (cal/deg mole) at 0$^o$ to 1500$^o$K. |
| t | Entropy, $S^o$, (cal/deg mole) at 0$^o$ to 1500$^o$K. |
| u | Heat content, $H^o - H^o_0$, (cal/mole), at 0$^o$ to 1500$^o$K. |
| u–E | Heat content, $H^o - H^o_0$, (BTU/lb), at −459.69$^o$ to 2200$^o$F. |
| u–G | Heat content, $H^o - H^o_0$, (cal/g), at −273.16$^o$ to 1200$^o$C. |
| v | Heat capacity, $C_p{}^o$, (cal/deg mole), at 0$^o$ to 1500$^o$K. |
| v–E | Heat capacity, $C_p{}^o$, (BTU/lb $^o$F), at −459.69$^o$ to 2200$^o$F. |
| v–G | Heat capacity, $C_p{}^o$, (cal/g $^o$C), at −273.16$^o$ to 1200$^o$C. |
| w | Heat of formation, $\Delta H f^o$, (kcal/mole), at 0$^o$ to 1500$^o$K. |
| x | Free energy of formation, $\Delta F f^o$, (kcal/mole), at 0$^o$ to 1500$^o$K. |
| y | Logarithm of equilibrium constant of formation, $\log_{10} K f$, at 0$^o$ to 1500$^o$K. |
| z | Heat of fusion (kcal/mole), entropy of fusion (cal/deg mole), freezing points ($^o$C and $^o$K), and cryoscopic constants (deg$^{-1}$). |

INTRODUCTION, Page 6

June 30, 1945; March 31, 1947; December 31, 1948; December 31, 1952

## MAGNITUDE OF ESTIMATED UNCERTAINTIES

It is not feasible to give estimated uncertainties for each of the individual numerical values of the physical and thermodynamic properties. However, an indication of the magnitude of the estimated uncertainties is given in the following table:

| Property | Units | When value is written to: | | | | | |
|---|---|---|---|---|---|---|---|
| | | 1. | 0.1 | 0.01 | 0.001 | 0.0001 | 0.00001 |
| | | Uncertainty is estimated to be: | | | | | |
| Boiling Point <br><br> Freezing Point | °C | >1. | 0.2 to 1.0 | 0.03 to 0.15 | 0.005 to 0.020 | | |
| Refractive Index <br><br> Density | <br><br> g/ml | | | >0.02 | 0.003 to 0.020 | 0.0002 to 0.0020 | 0.00005 to 0.00015 |
| Viscosity (Absolute) <br><br> Kinmatic Viscosity | centipoise <br><br> centistoke | | >0.1 | 0.03 to 0.30 | 0.003 to 0.030 | 0.0010 to 0.0030 | |
| Surface Tension | dyne/cm | >1. | 0.2 to 1.0 | 0.02 to 0.20 | | | |
| Critical Temperature | °K (°C) | >1. | 0.2 to 1.5 | 0.02 to 0.20 | | | |
| Critical Pressure | atm | >1. | 0.2 to 1.0 | 0.02 to 0.20 | | | |
| Critical Density | g/ml | | | >0.02 | 0.003 to 0.020 | 0.0002 to 0.0030 | |
| Heat Content Function[a] <br> Free Energy Function[a] <br> Entropy[a] <br> Heat Capacity[a] | cal/deg mole | | >0.75 | 0.10 to 0.75 | 0.005 to 0.050 | | |
| Heat of Formation <br><br> Free Energy of Formation | kcal/mole | | >1.0 | 0.20 to 1.00 | 0.015 to 0.200 | | |
| Heat of Vaporization | kcal/mole | | >0.2 | 0.04 to 0.20 | 0.010 to 0.040 | | |
| Heat of Fusion | kcal/mole | | >0.2 | 0.04 to 0.20 | 0.004 to 0.040 | 0.0010 to 0.0040 | |

[a] The values at 298.16° and 300°K are frequently given to one more decimal place than are the corresponding values at higher temperatures. In these cases the estimated uncertainty is indicated by the number of decimal places retained at the next higher temperature.

TABLE a, Page 1 - VALUES OF CONSTANTS

December 31, 1944; March 31, 1945; December 31, 1947; April 30, 1952

## BASIC CONSTANTS[a]

| Name | Symbol | Value | Units | Uncertainty |
|---|---|---|---|---|
| Velocity of light | $c$ | $2.997902 \times 10^{10}$ | cm/sec | $\pm 0.000013 \times 10^{10}$ |
| Planck constant | $h$ | $6.62377 \times 10^{-27}$ | erg sec/molecule | $\pm 0.00027 \times 10^{-27}$ |
| Avogadro constant | $N$ | $6.02380 \times 10^{23}$ | number of molecules/mole | $\pm 0.00016 \times 10^{23}$ |
| Faraday constant | $\mathscr{F}$ | 96,493.1 | coulombs/equivalent | $\pm 1.0$ |
| Absolute temperature of the "ice" point, $0°C$ | $T_{0°C}$ | 273.160 | °K | $\pm 0.010$ |
| Pressure-volume product for one mole of a gas at $0°C$ and zero pressure | $(PV)_{T_{0°C}}^{P=0}$ | 2271.16 | joules/mole | $\pm 0.04$ |

## DERIVED CONSTANTS

| Name | Symbol | Relation | Value | Units | Uncertainty |
|---|---|---|---|---|---|
| Electronic charge | $e$ | $= \mathscr{F}/N$ | $1.601864 \times 10^{-19}$ | coulomb | $\pm 0.000036 \times 10^{-19}$ |
| Gas constant | $R$ | $= \dfrac{(PV)_{T_{0°C}}^{P=0}}{T_{0°C}}$ | 8.31439 | joules/deg mole | $\pm 0.00034$ |
| Boltzmann constant | $k$ | $= R/N$ | $1.380257 \times 10^{-16}$ | erg/deg molecule | $\pm 0.000067 \times 10^{-16}$ |
| Second radiation constant | $c_2$ | $= hc/k$ | 1.438676 | cm deg | $\pm 0.000091$ |
| Constant relating wave number, $\tilde{v}$, and energy per mole, $E$, in the relation, $(\Delta E) = Nhc(\Delta \tilde{v}) = Z(\Delta \tilde{v})$ | $Z$ | $= Nhc$ | 11.96171 | joule cm/mole | $\pm 0.00026$ |
| Constant relating energy, $E$, and mass, $m$, in the Einstein relation, $(\Delta E) = c^2 (\Delta m) = Y (\Delta m)$ | $Y$ | $= c^2$ | $8.987416 \times 10^{13}$ | joules/g | $\pm 0.000081 \times 10^{13}$ |

## DEFINED CONSTANTS

| Name | Symbol | Value and units |
|---|---|---|
| Standard gravity | $g_0$ | $980.665$ cm/sec$^2$ |
| Standard atmosphere | atm | 1,013,250 dynes/cm$^2$ |
| Standard millimeter of mercury pressure | mm Hg | 1/760 atm |
| Calorie (thermochemical) | cal | 4.1840 joules |

[a]For details regarding the values of constants, see the following entries in the General List of References: Birge[1,2]; Burgess[1]; Cragoe[3]; Curtis[1]; Mueller and Rossini[1]; National Bureau of Standards[2,3]; Peffer and Mulligan[1]; DuMond and Cohen[1,2]; Bearden and Watts[1]; National Research Council[1,2]; Rossini, Gucker, Johnston, Pauling, and Vinal[1].

TABLE α, Page 2 – VALUES OF CONSTANTS

December 31, 1944; March 31, 1945; December 31, 1947; April 30, 1952

### AUXILIARY RELATIONS[b]

| | | |
|---|---|---|
| 1 second (mean solar) | = 1.00273791 sidereal second | |
| 1 joule | = 0.999835 $\pm$ 0.000052 | international joule (NBS) |
| 1 ohm | = 0.999505 $\pm$ 0.000015 | international ohm (NBS) |
| 1 ampere | = 1.000165 $\pm$ 0.000025 | international ampere (NBS) |
| 1 volt | = 0.999670 $\pm$ 0.000029 | international volt (NBS) |
| 1 coulomb | = 1.000165 $\pm$ 0.000025 | international coulomb (NBS) |
| 1 watt | = 0.999835 $\pm$ 0.000052 | international watt (NBS) |
| 1 liter | = 1000.028 $\pm$ 0.004 | $cm^3$. |

### BASIC, DERIVED, AND DEFINED CONSTANTS EXPRESSED IN DIFFERENT UNITS

| Constant | Values and units |
|---|---|
| $(PV)^{P=0}_{T \ 0°C}$ | 2271.16 joules/mole |
| | 22,414.6 $cm^3$ atm/mole |
| | 22.4140 liter atm/mole |
| $\mathcal{F}$ | 96,493.1 coul/equiv, or joules/volt equiv |
| | 96,509.0 int coul/equiv, or int joules/int volt equiv |
| | 23,062.4 cal/volt equiv |
| | 23,070.0 cal/int volt equiv |
| $e$ | $1.601864 \times 10^{-19}$ coulomb |
| | $1.601864 \times 10^{-20}$ emu |
| | $4.802232 \times 10^{-10}$ esu |
| $R$ | 8.31439 joules/deg mole |
| | 1.98719 cal/deg mole |
| | 82.0567 $cm^3$ atm/deg mole |
| | 0.0820544 liter atm/deg mole |
| $k$ | $1.380257 \times 10^{-16}$ erg/deg molecule |
| | $8.61657 \times 10^{-5}$ electron-volt/deg molecule |
| $Z$ | 11.96171 joule cm/mole |
| | 2.858917 cal cm/mole |
| $Y$ | $8.987416 \times 10^{13}$ joules/g |
| | $2.148044 \times 10^{13}$ cal/g |
| 1 cal | 4.1840 (exact) joules |
| | 4.18331 int joules |
| | 41.2929 $cm^3$ atm |
| | 0.0412917 liter atm |

[b] The electrical units in these tables are those in terms of which certification of standard cells, standard resistances, etc., is made by the National Bureau of Standards. Unless otherwise indicated, all electrical units are absolute.

TABLE α, Page 3 — VALUES OF CONSTANTS

December 31, 1944; March 31, 1945; December 31, 1947; April 30, 1952

## SOME USEFUL CONSTANTS

| Name | Symbol | Value | Units | Uncertainty |
|------|--------|-------|-------|-------------|
| Constant relating wave number and energy per molecule | $hc$ | $1.239644 \times 10^{-4}$ | electron-volt cm/molecule | $\pm 0.000062 \times 10^{-4}$ |
| | | $1.239235 \times 10^{-4}$ | int electron-volt cm/molecule | $\pm 0.000062 \times 10^{-4}$ |
| Constant in rotational partition function of gases | $\dfrac{h^2}{8\pi^2 k}$ | $4.02588 \times 10^{-39}$ | g cm$^2$ deg/molecule | $\pm 0.00030 \times 10^{-39}$ |
| Constant relating wave number and moment of inertia | $\dfrac{h}{8\pi^2 c}$ | $2.798325 \times 10^{-39}$ | g cm/molecule | $\pm 0.000115 \times 10^{-39}$ |
| Natural logarithm (base e) | $\ln 10$ | $2.30258509$ | | |
| | $R\ln x$ | $19.14460 \log_{10} x$ | joules/deg mole | $\pm 0.00078 \log_{10} x$ |
| | | $4.57567 \log_{10} x$ | cal/deg mole | $\pm 0.00019 \log_{10} x$ |
| | $RT_{298.16}\ln 10$ | $5708.154$ | joules/mole | |
| | | $1364.282$ | cal/mole | |

## CONSTANTS IN ENGLISH AND ENGINEERING UNITS

1 in. = (1/0.3937) = 2.54000508 cm     Definition; in. = U.S. inch

1 ft = 30.4800610 cm     U.S. foot (1ft = 12 in.)

1 lb = 453.5924277 g     Definition; lb = avoirdupois pound

1 gal = 231 cu in.     Definition; gal = U.S. gallon

= 0.133680555 cu ft

= 3785.43449 cm$^3$

= 3.785329 liter

1 I.T. cal = (1/860) = 0.00116279 int watt-hr     Definition; I.T. = International Steam Tables

= 4.18674 joules

= 4.18605 int joules

= 1.000654 cal     cal = thermochemical calorie

1 BTU/lb = (1/1.8) = 0.5555556 I.T. cal/g     Definition; BTU = I.T. British Thermal Unit

1 BTU = 251.996 I.T. cal

= 1055.040 joules

= 1054.866 int joules

= 0.293018 int watt-hr

= 252.161 cal     cal = thermochemical calorie

1 horsepower = 550 ft-lb (wt)/sec     Definition; lb (wt) = weight of 1 lb at standard gravity

= 745.701 watts

= 745.578 int watts

## TABLE 8, Page 1 – CONVERSION FACTORS

January 31, 1945; March 31, 1945; December 31, 1947; April 30, 1952

To convert the numerical value of a property expressed in one of the units in the left-hand column of a table to the numerical value of the same property expressed in one of the units in the top row of the same table, multiply the former value by the factor in the block common to both units.

### UNITS OF LENGTH

| Units | | cm | u | mu | A |
|---|---|---|---|---|---|
| 1 centimeter (cm) | = | 1 | $10^{-4}$ | $10^7$ | $10^8$ |
| 1 micron (u) | = | $10^{-4}$ | 1 | $10^3$ | $10^4$ |
| 1 millimicron (mu) | = | $10^{-7}$ | $10^{-3}$ | 1 | 10 |
| 1 Angstrom unit (A) | = | $10^{-8}$ | $10^{-4}$ | $10^{-1}$ | 1 |

### UNITS OF LENGTH

| Units | | cm | m | in. | ft | yd |
|---|---|---|---|---|---|---|
| 1 cm | = | 1 | 0.01 | 0.3937 | 0.032808333 | 0.010936111 |
| 1 m | = | 100. | 1 | 39.37 | 3.2808333 | 1.0936111 |
| 1 in. | = | 2.5400051 | 0.025400051 | 1 | 0.083333333 | 0.027777778 |
| 1 ft | = | 30.480061 | 0.30480061 | 12. | 1 | 0.33333333 |
| 1 yd | = | 91.440183 | 0.91440183 | 36. | 3. | 1 |

### UNITS OF AREA

| Units | = | $cm^2$ | $m^2$ | sq in. | sq ft | sq yd |
|---|---|---|---|---|---|---|
| 1 $cm^2$ | = | 1 | $10^{-4}$ | 0.15499969 | $1.0763867 \times 10^{-3}$ | $1.1959853 \times 10^{-4}$ |
| 1 $m^2$ | = | $10^4$ | 1 | 1549.9969 | 10.763967 | 1.1959853 |
| 1 sq in. | = | 6.4516258 | $6.4516258 \times 10^{-4}$ | 1 | $6.9444444 \times 10^{-3}$ | $7.7160494 \times 10^{-4}$ |
| 1 sq ft | = | 929.03412 | 0.092903412 | 144. | 1 | 0.11111111 |
| 1 sq yd | = | 8361.3070 | 0.83613070 | 1296. | 9. | 1 |

## TABLE B, Page 2 – CONVERSION FACTORS

### January 31, 1945; March 31, 1945; December 31, 1947; April 30, 1952

To convert the numerical value of a property expressed in one of the units in the left-hand column of a table to the numerical value of the same property expressed in one of the units in the top row of the same table, multiply the former value by the factor in the block common to both units.

### UNITS OF VOLUME

| Units | | $cm^3$ | liter | cu in. | cu ft | gal |
|---|---|---|---|---|---|---|
| 1 $cm^3$ | = | 1 | $0.9999720 \times 10^{-3}$ | 0.061023378 | $3.5314455 \times 10^{-5}$ | $2.6417047 \times 10^{-4}$ |
| 1 liter | = | 1000.028 | 1 | 61.02509 | 0.03531544 | 0.2641779 |
| 1 cu in. | = | 16.387162 | $1.638670 \times 10^{-2}$ | 1 | $5.7870370 \times 10^{-4}$ | $4.3290043 \times 10^{-3}$ |
| 1 cu ft | = | 28317.017 | 28.31622 | 1728. | 1 | 7.4805195 |
| 1 gal | = | 3785.4345 | 3.785329 | 231. | 0.13368056 | 1 |

### UNITS OF MASS

| Units | | g | kg | lb | metric ton | ton |
|---|---|---|---|---|---|---|
| 1 g | = | 1 | $10^{-3}$ | $2.2046223 \times 10^{-3}$ | $10^{-6}$ | $1.1023112 \times 10^{-6}$ |
| 1 kg | = | $10^3$ | 1 | 2.2046223 | $10^{-3}$ | $1.1023112 \times 10^{-3}$ |
| 1 lb | = | 453.59243 | 0.45359243 | 1 | $4.5359243 \times 10^{-4}$ | 0.0005 |
| 1 metric ton | = | $10^6$ | $10^3$ | 2204.6223 | 1 | 1.1023112 |
| 1 ton | = | 907184.86 | 907.18486 | 2000. | 0.90718486 | 1 |

### UNITS OF DENSITY

| Units | | $g/cm^3$ | g/ml | lb/cu in. | lb/cu ft | lb/gal |
|---|---|---|---|---|---|---|
| 1 $g/cm^3$ | = | 1 | 1.000028 | 0.036127504 | 62.428327 | 8.3454535 |
| 1 g/ml | = | 0.9999720 | 1 | 0.03612649 | 62.42658 | 8.345220 |
| 1 lb/cu in. | = | 27.679742 | 27.68052 | 1 | 1728. | 231. |
| 1 lb/cu ft | = | 0.016018369 | 0.01601882 | $5.7870370 \times 10^{-4}$ | 1 | 0.13368056 |
| 1 lb/gal | = | 0.11982572 | 0.1198291 | $4.3290043 \times 10^{-3}$ | 7.4805195 | 1 |

TABLE 3, Page 3 – CONVERSION FACTORS

January 31, 1945; March 31, 1945; December 31, 1947; April 30, 1952

To convert the numerical value of a property expressed in one of the units in the left-hand column of a table to the numerical value of the same property expressed in one of the units in the top row of the same table, multiply the former value by the factor in the block common to both units.

## UNITS OF PRESSURE

| Units | $dyne/cm^2$ | bar | atm | $kg(wt)/cm^2$ | mm Hg | in. Hg | lb(wt)/sq in. |
|---|---|---|---|---|---|---|---|
| 1 dyne/cm$^2$ = | 1 | $10^{-6}$ | $0.9869233 \times 10^{-6}$ | $1.0197162 \times 10^{-6}$ | $7.500617 \times 10^{-4}$ | $2.952993 \times 10^{-5}$ | $1.4503830 \times 10^{-5}$ |
| 1 bar = | $10^6$ | 1 | 0.9869233 | 1.0197162 | 750.0617 | 29.52993 | 14.503830 |
| 1 atm = | 1013250. | 1.013250 | 1 | 1.0332275 | 760. | 29.92120 | 14.696006 |
| 1 kg(wt)/cm$^2$ = | 980665. | 0.980665 | 0.9678411 | 1 | 735.5592 | 28.95897 | 14.223398 |
| 1 mm Hg = | 1333.2237 | $1.3332237 \times 10^{-3}$ | $1.3157895 \times 10^{-3}$ | $1.3595098 \times 10^{-3}$ | 1 | 0.03937 | 0.019336850 |
| 1 in. Hg = | 33863.95 | 0.03386395 | 0.03342112 | 0.03453162 | 25.40005 | 1 | 0.4911570 |
| 1 lb(wt)/ sq in. = | 68947.31 | 0.06894731 | 0.06804570 | 0.07030669 | 51.71473 | 2.036009 | 1 |

## UNITS OF MOLECULAR ENERGY[a]

| Units | erg/molecule | joule/mole | international joule/mole | cal/mole | electron-volt/molecule | international electron-volt/molecule | wave number (cm$^{-1}$) |
|---|---|---|---|---|---|---|---|
| 1 erg/molecule= | 1 | $6.02380 \times 10^{16}$ | $6.02281 \times 10^{16}$ | $1.439723 \times 10^{16}$ | $6.242726 \times 10^{11}$ | $6.240666 \times 10^{11}$ | $5.035903 \times 10^{15}$ |
| 1 joule/mole = | $1.660082 \times 10^{-17}$ | 1 | 0.999835 | 0.239006 | $1.036344 \times 10^{-5}$ | $1.036002 \times 10^{-5}$ | $8.360010 \times 10^{-2}$ |
| 1 international joule/mole = | $1.660356 \times 10^{-17}$ | 1.000165 | 1 | 0.239045 | $1.036515 \times 10^{-5}$ | $1.036173 \times 10^{-5}$ | $8.361389 \times 10^{-2}$ |
| 1 cal/mole = | $6.945782 \times 10^{-17}$ | 4.1840 | 4.18331 | 1 | $4.336061 \times 10^{-5}$ | $4.334631 \times 10^{-5}$ | 0.349783 |
| 1 electron-volt/molecule = | $1.601864 \times 10^{-12}$ | 96493.1 | 96477.2 | 23062.4 | 1 | 0.999670 | 8066.83 |
| 1 international electron-volt/molecule = | $1.602393 \times 10^{-12}$ | 96524.95 | 96509.02 | 23070.02 | 1.000330 | 1 | 8069.49 |
| 1 wave number (cm$^{-1}$) = | $1.985741 \times 10^{-16}$ | 11.96171 | 11.95973 | 2.85892 | $1.239644 \times 10^{-4}$ | $1.239235 \times 10^{-4}$ | 1 |

[a] The electrical units in these tables are those in terms of which certification of standard cells, standard resistances, etc., is made by the National Bureau of Standards. Unless otherwise indicated, all electrical units are absolute.

TABLE B, Page 4 — CONVERSION FACTORS

January 31, 1945; March 31, 1945; December 31, 1947; April 30, 1952

To convert the numerical value of a property expressed in one of the units in the left-hand column of a table to the numerical value of the same property expressed in one of the units in the top row of the same table, multiply the former value by the factor in the block common to both units.

## UNITS OF ENERGY[a]

| Units | g mass (energy equiv) | joule | int joule | cal | I.T. cal | BTU | kilo-watt-hr | horse-power-hr | ft-lb(wt) | cu ft-lb(wt)/ sq in. | liter-atm |
|---|---|---|---|---|---|---|---|---|---|---|---|
| 1 g mass = (energy equiv) | 1 | $8.987416 \times 10^{13}$ | $8.985933 \times 10^{13}$ | $2.1480444 \times 10^{13}$ | $2.146640 \times 10^{13}$ | $8.518554 \times 10^{10}$ | $2.496505 \times 10^{7}$ | $3.347861 \times 10^{7}$ | $6.628764 \times 10^{13}$ | $4.603308 \times 10^{11}$ | $8.869642 \times 10^{11}$ |
| 1 joule = | $1.112667 \times 10^{-14}$ | 1 | 0.999835 | 0.239006 | 0.238849 | $0.947831 \times 10^{-3}$ | $2.777778 \times 10^{-7}$ | $3.72505 \times 10^{-7}$ | 0.737561 | $5.12195 \times 10^{-3}$ | $9.86896 \times 10^{-3}$ |
| 1 int joule = | $1.112850 \times 10^{-14}$ | 1.000165 | 1 | 0.239045 | 0.238889 | $0.947988 \times 10^{-3}$ | $2.778236 \times 10^{-7}$ | $3.72567 \times 10^{-7}$ | 0.737682 | $5.12279 \times 10^{-3}$ | $9.87058 \times 10^{-3}$ |
| 1 cal = | $4.655398 \times 10^{-14}$ | 4.1840 | 4.18331 | 1 | 0.999346 | $3.96573 \times 10^{-3}$ | $1.162222 \times 10^{-6}$ | $1.558562 \times 10^{-6}$ | 3.08595 | $2.14302 \times 10^{-2}$ | $4.12917 \times 10^{-2}$ |
| 1 I.T. cal = | $4.658444 \times 10^{-14}$ | 4.18674 | 4.18605 | 1.000654 | 1 | $3.96832 \times 10^{-3}$ | $1.162983 \times 10^{-6}$ | $1.559582 \times 10^{-6}$ | 3.08797 | $2.14443 \times 10^{-2}$ | $4.13187 \times 10^{-2}$ |
| 1 BTU = | $1.173908 \times 10^{-11}$ | 1055.040 | 1054.866 | 252.161 | 251.996 | 1 | $2.930667 \times 10^{-4}$ | $3.93008 \times 10^{-4}$ | 778.156 | 5.40386 | 10.41215 |
| 1 kilo-watt-hr = | $4.005601 \times 10^{-8}$ | 3,600,000 | 3,599,406 | 860,421 | 859,858 | 3412.19 | 1 | 1.341019 | 2,655,218 | 18439.01 | 35528.2 |
| 1 horse-power-hr = | $2.986982 \times 10^{-8}$ | 2,684,525 | 2,684,082 | 641,617 | 641,197 | 2544.48 | 0.745701 | 1 | 1,980,000 | 13750. | 26493.5 |
| 1 ft-lb (wt) = | $1.508577 \times 10^{-14}$ | 1.355821 | 1.355597 | 0.324049 | 0.323837 | $1.285089 \times 10^{-3}$ | $3.766169 \times 10^{-7}$ | $5.05051 \times 10^{-7}$ | 1 | $6.94444 \times 10^{-3}$ | $1.338054 \times 10^{-2}$ |
| 1 cu ft-lb(wt)/ sq in. = | $2.172351 \times 10^{-12}$ | 195.2382 | 195.2060 | 46.6630 | 46.6325 | 0.1850529 | $5.423283 \times 10^{-5}$ | $7.27273 \times 10^{-5}$ | 144. | 1 | 1.926797 |
| 1 liter-atm = | $1.127441 \times 10^{-12}$ | 101.3278 | 101.3111 | 24.2179 | 24.2021 | 0.0960417 | $2.814662 \times 10^{-5}$ | $3.77452 \times 10^{-5}$ | 74.7354 | 0.518996 | 1 |

[a] The electrical units in these tables are those in terms of which certification of standard cells, standard resistances, etc., is made by the National Bureau of Standards. Unless otherwise indicated, all electrical units are absolute.

TABLE B, Page 5 – CONVERSION FACTORS

January 31, 1945; March 31, 1945; December 31, 1947; April 30, 1952

To convert the numerical value of a property expressed in one of the units in the left-hand column of a table to the numerical value of the same property expressed in one of the units in the top row of the same table, multiply the former value by the factor in the block common to both units.

## UNITS OF SPECIFIC ENERGY[a]

| Units | joule/g | international joule/g | cal/g | I.T. cal/g | BTU/lb |
|---|---|---|---|---|---|
| 1 joule/g = | 1 | 0.999835 | 0.239006 | 0.238849 | 0.429929 |
| 1 international joule/g = | 1.000165 | 1 | 0.2390452 | 0.238889 | 0.430000 |
| 1 cal/g = | 4.1840 | 4.18331 | 1 | 0.999346 | 1.798823 |
| 1 I.T. cal/g = | 4.18674 | 4.18605 | 1.000654 | 1 | 1.8 |
| 1 BTU/lb = | 2.32597 | 2.32558 | 0.555919 | 0.555556 | 1 |

## UNITS OF SPECIFIC ENERGY PER DEGREE[a]

| Units | joule/g deg C | international joule/g deg C | cal/g deg C | I.T. cal/g deg C | BTU/lb deg F |
|---|---|---|---|---|---|
| 1 joule/g deg C = | 1 | 0.999835 | 0.239006 | 0.238849 | 0.238849 |
| 1 international joule/g deg C = | 1.000165 | 1 | 0.2390452 | 0.238889 | 0.238889 |
| 1 cal/g deg C = | 4.1840 | 4.18331 | 1 | 0.999346 | 0.999346 |
| 1 I.T. cal/g deg C = | 4.18674 | 4.18605 | 1.000654 | 1 | 1 |
| 1 BTU/lb deg F = | 4.18674 | 4.18605 | 1.000654 | 1 | 1 |

[a] The electrical units in these tables are those in terms of which certification of standard cells, standard resistances, etc., is made by the National Bureau of Standards. Unless otherwise indicated, all electrical units are absolute.

## TABLE $\Upsilon$ — USEFUL EQUATIONS WITH NUMERICAL CONSTANTS

January 31, 1945; December 31, 1947; April 30, 1952

### EQUATIONS FOR CALCULATING THERMODYNAMIC FUNCTIONS

### FOR TRANSLATION FOR ALL MOLECULES AND ROTATION FOR RIGID MOLECULES

The equations in this table may be used to calculate the translational and rotational contributions to the heat content function, $(H^\circ - H_0^\circ)/T$, the free energy function, $(F^\circ - H_0^\circ)/T$, and the entropy, $S^\circ$, the translational heat capacity at constant pressure, $C_p^\circ$, and the rotational heat capacity, $C^\circ$; all for a gas in the thermodynamic standard gaseous state of unit fugacity (1 atmosphere), at the given absolute temperature $T$ (in °K). $M$ is the molecular weight (g/mole). $I$ (g-cm$^2$) is the value of the two equal moments of inertia of a linear molecule about axes perpendicular to the axis of the molecule; and $I_1$, $I_2$, and $I_3$ (g-cm$^2$) are the three principal moments of inertia of a nonlinear molecule. The symmetry number, $\sigma$ (a dimensionless integer), is the number of ways the molecule may be superimposed upon itself by rotation of the entire molecule. See Tolman[1], Mayer and Mayer[1], and Rossini[22].

### TRANSLATION
### FOR ALL MOLECULES

$$\frac{(H^\circ - H_0^\circ)}{T} = C_p^\circ = 4.96797 \qquad \text{cal/deg mole}$$

$$\frac{(F^\circ - H_0^\circ)}{T} = -6.86350 \log_{10} M + 7.28295 - 11.43917 \log_{10} T \qquad \text{cal/deg mole}$$

$$S^\circ = 6.86350 \log_{10} M - 2.31498 + 11.43917 \log_{10} T \qquad \text{cal/deg mole}$$

### ROTATION
### FOR RIGID MOLECULES
#### I. Diatomic or linear polyatomic molecules

$$\frac{(H^\circ - H_0^\circ)}{T} = C^\circ = 1.98719 \qquad \text{cal/deg mole}$$

For $\sigma = 1$:

$$\frac{(F^\circ - H_0^\circ)}{T} = -4.57567 \log_{10}(I \times 10^{39}) + 2.76764 - 4.57567 \log_{10} T \qquad \text{cal/deg mole}$$

$$S^\circ = 4.57567 \log_{10}(I \times 10^{39}) - 0.78045 + 4.57567 \log_{10} T \qquad \text{cal/deg mole}$$

For $\sigma = 2$:

$$\frac{(F^\circ - H_0^\circ)}{T} = -4.57567 \log_{10}(I \times 10^{39}) + 4.14506 - 4.57567 \log_{10} T \qquad \text{cal/deg mole}$$

$$S^\circ = 4.57567 \log_{10}(I \times 10^{39}) - 2.15787 + 4.57567 \log_{10} T \qquad \text{cal/deg mole}$$

#### II. Nonlinear polyatomic molecules

$$\frac{(H^\circ - H_0^\circ)}{T} = C^\circ = 2.98078 \qquad \text{cal/deg mole}$$

$$\frac{(F^\circ - H_0^\circ)}{T} = -2.28783 \log_{10}(I_1 I_2 I_3 \times 10^{117}) + 4.57567 \log_{10} \sigma + 3.01407 - 6.86350 \log_{10} T \qquad \text{cal/deg mole}$$

$$S^\circ = 2.28783 \log_{10}(I_1 I_2 I_3 \times 10^{117}) - 4.57567 \log_{10} \sigma - 0.03329 + 6.86350 \log_{10} T \qquad \text{cal/deg mole}$$

## TABLE 8, Page 1 – MOLECULAR WEIGHTS OF HYDROCARBONS [a]

Range: $C_1$ to $C_{26}$; $H_1$ to $H_{18}$

December 31, 1946; October 31, 1952

| No. of Carbon Atoms | Number of Hydrogen Atoms | | | | | | | | | | | | | | | | | |
|---|---|---|---|---|---|---|---|---|---|---|---|---|---|---|---|---|---|---|
| | 1 | 2 | 3 | 4 | 5 | 6 | 7 | 8 | 9 | 10 | 11 | 12 | 13 | 14 | 15 | 16 | 17 | 18 |
| 1 | 13.018 | 14.026 | 15.034 | 16.042 | ---- | ---- | ---- | ---- | ---- | ---- | ---- | ---- | ---- | ---- | ---- | ---- | ---- | ---- |
| 2 | 25.028 | 26.036 | 27.044 | 28.052 | 29.060 | 30.068 | ---- | ---- | ---- | ---- | ---- | ---- | ---- | ---- | ---- | ---- | ---- | ---- |
| 3 | 37.038 | 38.046 | 39.054 | 40.062 | 41.070 | 42.078 | 43.086 | 44.094 | ---- | ---- | ---- | ---- | ---- | ---- | ---- | ---- | ---- | ---- |
| 4 | 49.048 | 50.056 | 51.064 | 52.072 | 53.080 | 54.088 | 55.096 | 56.104 | 57.112 | 58.120 | ---- | ---- | ---- | ---- | ---- | ---- | ---- | ---- |
| 5 | 61.058 | 62.066 | 63.074 | 64.082 | 65.090 | 66.098 | 67.106 | 68.114 | 69.122 | 70.130 | 71.138 | 72.146 | ---- | ---- | ---- | ---- | ---- | ---- |
| 6 | 73.068 | 74.076 | 75.084 | 76.092 | 77.100 | 78.108 | 79.116 | 80.124 | 81.132 | 82.140 | 83.148 | 84.156 | 85.164 | 86.172 | ---- | ---- | ---- | ---- |
| 7 | 85.078 | 86.086 | 87.094 | 88.102 | 89.110 | 90.118 | 91.126 | 92.134 | 93.142 | 94.150 | 95.158 | 96.166 | 97.174 | 98.182 | 99.190 | 100.198 | ---- | ---- |
| 8 | 97.088 | 98.096 | 99.104 | 100.112 | 101.120 | 102.128 | 103.136 | 104.144 | 105.152 | 106.160 | 107.168 | 108.176 | 109.184 | 110.192 | 111.200 | 112.208 | 113.216 | 114.224 |
| 9 | 109.098 | 110.106 | 111.114 | 112.122 | 113.130 | 114.138 | 115.146 | 116.154 | 117.162 | 118.170 | 119.178 | 120.186 | 121.194 | 122.202 | 123.210 | 124.218 | 125.226 | 126.234 |
| 10 | 121.108 | 122.116 | 123.124 | 124.132 | 125.140 | 126.148 | 127.156 | 128.164 | 129.172 | 130.180 | 131.188 | 132.196 | 133.204 | 134.212 | 135.220 | 136.228 | 137.236 | 138.244 |
| 11 | 133.118 | 134.126 | 135.134 | 136.142 | 137.150 | 138.158 | 139.166 | 140.174 | 141.182 | 142.190 | 143.198 | 144.206 | 145.214 | 146.222 | 147.230 | 148.238 | 149.246 | 150.254 |
| 12 | 145.128 | 146.136 | 147.144 | 148.152 | 149.160 | 150.168 | 151.176 | 152.184 | 153.192 | 154.200 | 155.208 | 156.216 | 157.224 | 158.232 | 159.240 | 160.248 | 161.256 | 162.264 |
| 13 | 157.138 | 158.146 | 159.154 | 160.162 | 161.170 | 162.178 | 163.186 | 164.194 | 165.202 | 166.210 | 167.218 | 168.226 | 169.234 | 170.242 | 171.250 | 172.258 | 173.266 | 174.274 |
| 14 | 169.148 | 170.156 | 171.164 | 172.172 | 173.180 | 174.188 | 175.196 | 176.204 | 177.212 | 178.220 | 179.228 | 180.236 | 181.244 | 182.252 | 183.260 | 184.268 | 185.276 | 186.284 |
| 15 | 181.158 | 182.166 | 183.174 | 184.182 | 185.190 | 186.198 | 187.206 | 188.214 | 189.222 | 190.230 | 191.238 | 192.246 | 193.254 | 194.262 | 195.270 | 196.278 | 197.286 | 198.294 |
| 16 | 193.168 | 194.176 | 195.184 | 196.192 | 197.200 | 198.208 | 199.216 | 200.224 | 201.232 | 202.240 | 203.248 | 204.256 | 205.264 | 206.272 | 207.280 | 208.288 | 209.296 | 210.304 |
| 17 | 205.178 | 206.186 | 207.194 | 208.202 | 209.210 | 210.218 | 211.226 | 212.234 | 213.242 | 214.250 | 215.258 | 216.266 | 217.274 | 218.282 | 219.290 | 220.298 | 221.306 | 222.314 |
| 18 | 217.188 | 218.196 | 219.204 | 220.212 | 221.220 | 222.228 | 223.236 | 224.244 | 225.252 | 226.260 | 227.268 | 228.276 | 229.284 | 230.292 | 231.300 | 232.308 | 233.316 | 234.324 |
| 19 | 229.198 | 230.206 | 231.214 | 232.222 | 233.230 | 234.238 | 235.246 | 236.254 | 237.262 | 238.270 | 239.278 | 240.286 | 241.294 | 242.302 | 243.310 | 244.318 | 245.326 | 246.334 |
| 20 | 241.208 | 242.216 | 243.224 | 244.232 | 245.240 | 246.248 | 247.256 | 248.264 | 249.272 | 250.280 | 251.288 | 252.296 | 253.304 | 254.312 | 255.320 | 256.328 | 257.336 | 258.344 |
| 21 | 253.218 | 254.226 | 255.234 | 256.242 | 257.250 | 258.258 | 259.266 | 260.274 | 261.282 | 262.290 | 263.298 | 264.306 | 265.314 | 266.322 | 267.330 | 268.338 | 269.346 | 270.354 |
| 22 | 265.228 | 266.236 | 267.244 | 268.252 | 269.260 | 270.268 | 271.276 | 272.284 | 273.292 | 274.300 | 275.308 | 276.316 | 277.324 | 278.332 | 279.340 | 280.348 | 281.356 | 282.364 |
| 23 | 277.238 | 278.246 | 279.254 | 280.262 | 281.270 | 282.278 | 283.286 | 284.294 | 285.302 | 286.310 | 287.318 | 288.326 | 289.334 | 290.342 | 291.350 | 292.358 | 293.366 | 294.374 |
| 24 | 289.248 | 290.256 | 291.264 | 292.272 | 293.280 | 294.288 | 295.296 | 296.304 | 297.312 | 298.320 | 299.328 | 300.336 | 301.344 | 302.352 | 303.360 | 304.368 | 305.376 | 306.384 |
| 25 | 301.258 | 302.266 | 303.274 | 304.282 | 305.290 | 306.298 | 307.306 | 308.314 | 309.322 | 310.330 | 311.338 | 312.346 | 313.354 | 314.362 | 315.370 | 316.378 | 317.386 | 318.394 |
| 26 | 313.268 | 314.276 | 315.284 | 316.292 | 317.300 | 318.308 | 319.316 | 320.324 | 321.332 | 322.340 | 323.348 | 324.356 | 325.364 | 326.372 | 327.380 | 328.388 | 329.396 | 330.404 |

[a] The values of molecular weights in this table are based on the atomic weights, $C = 12.010$, $H = 1.0080$.

TABLE 6, Page 2 – MOLECULAR WEIGHTS OF HYDROCARBONS

Range: $C_1$ to $C_{26}$; $H_{19}$ to $H_{36}$

December 31, 1946; October 31, 1952

| No. of Carbon Atoms | Number of Hydrogen Atoms | | | | | | | | | | | | | | | | | |
|---|---|---|---|---|---|---|---|---|---|---|---|---|---|---|---|---|---|---|
| | 19 | 20 | 21 | 22 | 23 | 24 | 25 | 26 | 27 | 28 | 29 | 30 | 31 | 32 | 33 | 34 | 35 | 36 |
| 1 | | | | | | | | | | | | | | | | | | |
| 2 | | | | | | | | | | | | | | | | | | |
| 3 | | | | | | | | | | | | | | | | | | |
| 4 | | | | | | | | | | | | | | | | | | |
| 5 | | | | | | | | | | | | | | | | | | |
| 6 | | | | | | | | | | | | | | | | | | |
| 7 | | | | | | | | | | | | | | | | | | |
| 8 | | | | | | | | | | | | | | | | | | |
| 9 | 127.242 | 128.250 | | | | | | | | | | | | | | | | |
| 10 | 139.252 | 140.260 | 141.268 | 142.276 | | | | | | | | | | | | | | |
| 11 | 151.262 | 152.270 | 153.278 | 154.286 | 155.294 | 156.302 | | | | | | | | | | | | |
| 12 | 163.272 | 164.280 | 165.288 | 166.296 | 167.304 | 168.312 | 169.320 | 170.328 | | | | | | | | | | |
| 13 | 175.282 | 176.290 | 177.298 | 178.306 | 179.314 | 180.322 | 181.330 | 182.338 | 183.346 | 184.354 | | | | | | | | |
| 14 | 187.292 | 188.300 | 189.308 | 190.316 | 191.324 | 192.332 | 193.340 | 194.348 | 195.356 | 196.364 | 197.372 | 198.380 | | | | | | |
| 15 | 199.302 | 200.310 | 201.318 | 202.326 | 203.334 | 204.342 | 205.350 | 206.358 | 207.366 | 208.374 | 209.382 | 210.390 | 211.398 | 212.406 | | | | |
| 16 | 211.312 | 212.320 | 213.328 | 214.336 | 215.344 | 216.352 | 217.360 | 218.368 | 219.376 | 220.384 | 221.392 | 222.400 | 223.408 | 224.416 | 225.424 | 226.432 | | |
| 17 | 223.322 | 224.330 | 225.338 | 226.346 | 227.354 | 228.362 | 229.370 | 230.378 | 231.386 | 232.394 | 233.402 | 234.410 | 235.418 | 236.426 | 237.434 | 238.442 | 239.450 | 240.458 |
| 18 | 235.332 | 236.340 | 237.348 | 238.356 | 239.364 | 240.372 | 241.380 | 242.388 | 243.396 | 244.404 | 245.412 | 246.420 | 247.428 | 248.436 | 249.444 | 250.452 | 251.460 | 252.468 |
| 19 | 247.342 | 248.350 | 249.358 | 250.366 | 251.374 | 252.382 | 253.390 | 254.398 | 255.406 | 256.414 | 257.422 | 258.430 | 259.438 | 260.446 | 261.454 | 262.462 | 263.470 | 264.478 |
| 20 | 259.352 | 260.360 | 261.368 | 262.376 | 263.384 | 264.392 | 265.400 | 266.408 | 267.416 | 268.424 | 269.432 | 270.440 | 271.448 | 272.456 | 273.464 | 274.472 | 275.480 | 276.488 |
| 21 | 271.362 | 272.370 | 273.378 | 274.386 | 275.394 | 276.402 | 277.410 | 278.418 | 279.426 | 280.434 | 281.442 | 282.450 | 283.458 | 284.466 | 285.474 | 286.482 | 287.490 | 288.498 |
| 22 | 283.372 | 284.380 | 285.388 | 286.396 | 287.404 | 288.412 | 289.420 | 290.428 | 291.436 | 292.444 | 293.452 | 294.460 | 295.468 | 296.476 | 297.484 | 298.492 | 299.500 | 300.508 |
| 23 | 295.382 | 296.390 | 297.398 | 298.406 | 299.414 | 300.422 | 301.430 | 302.438 | 303.446 | 304.454 | 305.462 | 306.470 | 307.478 | 308.486 | 309.494 | 310.502 | 311.510 | 312.518 |
| 24 | 307.392 | 308.400 | 309.408 | 310.416 | 311.424 | 312.432 | 313.440 | 314.448 | 315.456 | 316.464 | 317.472 | 318.480 | 319.488 | 320.496 | 321.504 | 322.512 | 323.520 | 324.528 |
| 25 | 319.402 | 320.410 | 321.418 | 322.426 | 323.434 | 324.442 | 325.450 | 326.458 | 327.466 | 328.474 | 329.482 | 330.490 | 331.498 | 332.506 | 333.514 | 334.522 | 335.530 | 336.538 |
| 26 | 331.412 | 332.420 | 333.428 | 334.436 | 335.444 | 336.452 | 337.460 | 338.468 | 339.476 | 340.484 | 341.492 | 342.500 | 343.508 | 344.516 | 345.524 | 346.532 | 347.540 | 348.548 |

TABLE 6, Page 3 – MOLECULAR WEIGHTS OF HYDROCARBONS

Range: $C_1$ to $C_{26}$; $H_{37}$ to $H_{54}$

December 31, 1946; October 31, 1952

| No. of Carbon Atoms | Number of Hydrogen Atoms | | | | | | | | | | | | | | | | | | No. of Carbon Atoms |
|---|---|---|---|---|---|---|---|---|---|---|---|---|---|---|---|---|---|---|---|
| | 37 | 38 | 39 | 40 | 41 | 42 | 43 | 44 | 45 | 46 | 47 | 48 | 49 | 50 | 51 | 52 | 53 | 54 | |
| 1 | -- | -- | -- | -- | -- | -- | -- | -- | -- | -- | -- | -- | -- | -- | -- | -- | -- | -- | 1 |
| 2 | -- | -- | -- | -- | -- | -- | -- | -- | -- | -- | -- | -- | -- | -- | -- | -- | -- | -- | 2 |
| 3 | -- | -- | -- | -- | -- | -- | -- | -- | -- | -- | -- | -- | -- | -- | -- | -- | -- | -- | 3 |
| 4 | -- | -- | -- | -- | -- | -- | -- | -- | -- | -- | -- | -- | -- | -- | -- | -- | -- | -- | 4 |
| 5 | -- | -- | -- | -- | -- | -- | -- | -- | -- | -- | -- | -- | -- | -- | -- | -- | -- | -- | 5 |
| 6 | -- | -- | -- | -- | -- | -- | -- | -- | -- | -- | -- | -- | -- | -- | -- | -- | -- | -- | 6 |
| 7 | -- | -- | -- | -- | -- | -- | -- | -- | -- | -- | -- | -- | -- | -- | -- | -- | -- | -- | 7 |
| 8 | -- | -- | -- | -- | -- | -- | -- | -- | -- | -- | -- | -- | -- | -- | -- | -- | -- | -- | 8 |
| 9 | -- | -- | -- | -- | -- | -- | -- | -- | -- | -- | -- | -- | -- | -- | -- | -- | -- | -- | 9 |
| 10 | -- | -- | -- | -- | -- | -- | -- | -- | -- | -- | -- | -- | -- | -- | -- | -- | -- | -- | 10 |
| 11 | -- | -- | -- | -- | -- | -- | -- | -- | -- | -- | -- | -- | -- | -- | -- | -- | -- | -- | 11 |
| 12 | -- | -- | -- | -- | -- | -- | -- | -- | -- | -- | -- | -- | -- | -- | -- | -- | -- | -- | 12 |
| 13 | -- | -- | -- | -- | -- | -- | -- | -- | -- | -- | -- | -- | -- | -- | -- | -- | -- | -- | 13 |
| 14 | -- | -- | -- | -- | -- | -- | -- | -- | -- | -- | -- | -- | -- | -- | -- | -- | -- | -- | 14 |
| 15 | -- | -- | -- | -- | -- | -- | -- | -- | -- | -- | -- | -- | -- | -- | -- | -- | -- | -- | 15 |
| 16 | -- | -- | -- | -- | -- | -- | -- | -- | -- | -- | -- | -- | -- | -- | -- | -- | -- | -- | 16 |
| 17 | -- | -- | -- | -- | -- | -- | -- | -- | -- | -- | -- | -- | -- | -- | -- | -- | -- | -- | 17 |
| 18 | 253.476 | 254.484 | -- | -- | -- | -- | -- | -- | -- | -- | -- | -- | -- | -- | -- | -- | -- | -- | 18 |
| 19 | 265.486 | 266.494 | 267.502 | 268.510 | -- | -- | -- | -- | -- | -- | -- | -- | -- | -- | -- | -- | -- | -- | 19 |
| 20 | 277.496 | 278.504 | 279.512 | 280.520 | 281.528 | 282.536 | -- | -- | -- | -- | -- | -- | -- | -- | -- | -- | -- | -- | 20 |
| 21 | 289.506 | 290.514 | 291.522 | 292.530 | 293.538 | 294.546 | 295.554 | 296.562 | -- | -- | -- | -- | -- | -- | -- | -- | -- | -- | 21 |
| 22 | 301.516 | 302.524 | 303.532 | 304.540 | 305.548 | 306.556 | 307.564 | 308.572 | 309.580 | 310.588 | -- | -- | -- | -- | -- | -- | -- | -- | 22 |
| 23 | 313.526 | 314.534 | 315.542 | 316.550 | 317.558 | 318.566 | 319.574 | 320.582 | 321.590 | 322.598 | 323.606 | 324.614 | -- | -- | -- | -- | -- | -- | 23 |
| 24 | 325.536 | 326.544 | 327.552 | 328.560 | 329.568 | 330.576 | 331.584 | 332.592 | 333.600 | 334.608 | 335.616 | 336.624 | 337.632 | 338.640 | -- | -- | -- | -- | 24 |
| 25 | 337.546 | 338.554 | 339.562 | 340.570 | 341.578 | 342.586 | 343.594 | 344.602 | 345.610 | 346.618 | 347.626 | 348.634 | 349.642 | 350.650 | 351.658 | 352.666 | -- | -- | 25 |
| 26 | 349.556 | 350.564 | 351.572 | 352.580 | 353.588 | 354.596 | 355.604 | 356.612 | 357.620 | 358.628 | 359.636 | 360.644 | 361.652 | 362.660 | 363.668 | 364.676 | 365.684 | 366.692 | 26 |

TABLE 6, Page 4 – MOLECULAR WEIGHTS OF HYDROCARBONS

Range: $C_{27}$ to $C_{52}$; $H_1$ to $H_{18}$

December 31, 1946; October 31, 1952

| No. of Carbon Atoms | Number of Hydrogen Atoms | | | | | | | | | | | | | | | | | | No. of Carbon Atoms |
|---|---|---|---|---|---|---|---|---|---|---|---|---|---|---|---|---|---|---|---|
| | 1 | 2 | 3 | 4 | 5 | 6 | 7 | 8 | 9 | 10 | 11 | 12 | 13 | 14 | 15 | 16 | 17 | 18 | |
| 27 | 325.278 | 326.286 | 327.294 | 328.302 | 329.310 | 330.318 | 331.326 | 332.334 | 333.342 | 334.350 | 335.358 | 336.366 | 337.374 | 338.382 | 339.390 | 340.398 | 341.406 | 342.414 | 27 |
| 28 | 337.288 | 338.296 | 339.304 | 340.312 | 341.320 | 342.328 | 343.336 | 344.344 | 345.352 | 346.360 | 347.368 | 348.376 | 349.384 | 350.392 | 351.400 | 352.408 | 353.416 | 354.424 | 28 |
| 29 | 349.298 | 350.306 | 351.314 | 352.322 | 353.330 | 354.338 | 355.346 | 356.354 | 357.362 | 358.370 | 359.378 | 360.386 | 361.394 | 362.402 | 363.410 | 364.418 | 365.426 | 366.434 | 29 |
| 30 | 361.308 | 362.316 | 363.324 | 364.332 | 365.340 | 366.348 | 367.356 | 368.364 | 369.372 | 370.380 | 371.388 | 372.396 | 373.404 | 374.412 | 375.420 | 376.428 | 377.436 | 378.444 | 30 |
| 31 | 373.318 | 374.326 | 375.334 | 376.342 | 377.350 | 378.358 | 379.366 | 380.374 | 381.382 | 382.390 | 383.398 | 384.406 | 385.414 | 386.422 | 387.430 | 388.438 | 389.446 | 390.454 | 31 |
| 32 | 385.328 | 386.336 | 387.344 | 388.352 | 389.360 | 390.368 | 391.376 | 392.384 | 393.392 | 394.400 | 395.408 | 396.416 | 397.424 | 398.432 | 399.440 | 400.448 | 401.456 | 402.464 | 32 |
| 33 | 397.338 | 398.346 | 399.354 | 400.362 | 401.370 | 402.378 | 403.386 | 404.394 | 405.402 | 406.410 | 407.418 | 408.426 | 409.434 | 410.442 | 411.450 | 412.458 | 413.466 | 414.474 | 33 |
| 34 | 409.348 | 410.356 | 411.364 | 412.372 | 413.380 | 414.388 | 415.396 | 416.404 | 417.412 | 418.420 | 419.428 | 420.436 | 421.444 | 422.452 | 423.460 | 424.468 | 425.476 | 426.484 | 34 |
| 35 | 421.358 | 422.366 | 423.374 | 424.382 | 425.390 | 426.398 | 427.406 | 428.414 | 429.422 | 430.430 | 431.438 | 432.446 | 433.454 | 434.462 | 435.470 | 436.478 | 437.486 | 438.494 | 35 |
| 36 | 433.368 | 434.376 | 435.384 | 436.392 | 437.400 | 438.408 | 439.416 | 440.424 | 441.432 | 442.440 | 443.448 | 444.456 | 445.464 | 446.472 | 447.480 | 448.488 | 449.496 | 450.504 | 36 |
| 37 | 445.378 | 446.386 | 447.394 | 448.402 | 449.410 | 450.418 | 451.426 | 452.434 | 453.442 | 454.450 | 455.458 | 456.466 | 457.474 | 458.482 | 459.490 | 460.498 | 461.506 | 462.514 | 37 |
| 38 | 457.388 | 458.396 | 459.404 | 460.412 | 461.420 | 462.428 | 463.436 | 464.444 | 465.452 | 466.460 | 467.468 | 468.476 | 469.484 | 470.492 | 471.500 | 472.508 | 473.516 | 474.524 | 38 |
| 39 | 469.398 | 470.406 | 471.414 | 472.422 | 473.430 | 474.438 | 475.446 | 476.454 | 477.462 | 478.470 | 479.478 | 480.486 | 481.494 | 482.502 | 483.510 | 484.518 | 485.526 | 486.534 | 39 |
| 40 | 481.408 | 482.416 | 483.424 | 484.432 | 485.440 | 486.448 | 487.456 | 488.464 | 489.472 | 490.480 | 491.488 | 492.496 | 493.504 | 494.512 | 495.520 | 496.528 | 497.536 | 498.544 | 40 |
| 41 | 493.418 | 494.426 | 495.434 | 496.442 | 497.450 | 498.458 | 499.466 | 500.474 | 501.482 | 502.490 | 503.498 | 504.506 | 505.514 | 506.522 | 507.530 | 508.538 | 509.546 | 510.554 | 41 |
| 42 | 505.428 | 506.436 | 507.444 | 508.452 | 509.460 | 510.468 | 511.476 | 512.484 | 513.492 | 514.500 | 515.508 | 516.516 | 517.524 | 518.532 | 519.540 | 520.548 | 521.556 | 522.564 | 42 |
| 43 | 517.438 | 518.446 | 519.454 | 520.462 | 521.470 | 522.478 | 523.486 | 524.494 | 525.502 | 526.510 | 527.518 | 528.526 | 529.534 | 530.542 | 531.550 | 532.558 | 533.566 | 534.574 | 43 |
| 44 | 529.448 | 530.456 | 531.464 | 532.472 | 533.480 | 534.488 | 535.496 | 536.504 | 537.512 | 538.520 | 539.528 | 540.536 | 541.544 | 542.552 | 543.560 | 544.568 | 545.576 | 546.584 | 44 |
| 45 | 541.458 | 542.466 | 543.474 | 544.482 | 545.490 | 546.498 | 547.506 | 548.514 | 549.522 | 550.530 | 551.538 | 552.546 | 553.554 | 554.562 | 555.570 | 556.578 | 557.586 | 558.594 | 45 |
| 46 | 553.468 | 554.476 | 555.484 | 556.492 | 557.500 | 558.508 | 559.516 | 560.524 | 561.532 | 562.540 | 563.548 | 564.556 | 565.564 | 566.572 | 567.580 | 568.588 | 569.596 | 570.604 | 46 |
| 47 | 565.478 | 566.486 | 567.494 | 568.502 | 569.510 | 570.518 | 571.526 | 572.534 | 573.542 | 574.550 | 575.558 | 576.566 | 577.574 | 578.582 | 579.590 | 580.598 | 581.606 | 582.614 | 47 |
| 48 | 577.488 | 578.496 | 579.504 | 580.512 | 581.520 | 582.528 | 583.536 | 584.544 | 585.552 | 586.560 | 587.568 | 588.576 | 589.584 | 590.592 | 591.600 | 592.608 | 593.616 | 594.624 | 48 |
| 49 | 589.498 | 590.506 | 591.514 | 592.522 | 593.530 | 594.538 | 595.546 | 596.554 | 597.562 | 598.570 | 599.578 | 600.586 | 601.594 | 602.602 | 603.610 | 604.618 | 605.626 | 606.634 | 49 |
| 50 | 601.508 | 602.516 | 603.524 | 604.532 | 605.540 | 606.548 | 607.556 | 608.564 | 609.572 | 610.580 | 611.588 | 612.596 | 613.604 | 614.612 | 615.620 | 616.628 | 617.636 | 618.644 | 50 |
| 51 | 613.518 | 614.526 | 615.534 | 616.542 | 617.550 | 618.558 | 619.566 | 620.574 | 621.582 | 622.590 | 623.598 | 624.606 | 625.614 | 626.622 | 627.630 | 628.638 | 629.646 | 630.654 | 51 |
| 52 | 625.528 | 626.536 | 627.544 | 628.552 | 629.560 | 630.568 | 631.576 | 632.584 | 633.592 | 634.600 | 635.608 | 636.616 | 637.624 | 638.632 | 639.640 | 640.648 | 641.656 | 642.664 | 52 |

TABLE 6, Page 5 - MOLECULAR WEIGHTS OF HYDROCARBONS

Range: C₂₇ to C₅₂; H₁₉ to H₃₆

December 31, 1946; October 31, 1952

| No. of Carbon Atoms | Number of Hydrogen Atoms | | | | | | | | | | | | | | | | | | No. of Carbon Atoms |
|---|---|---|---|---|---|---|---|---|---|---|---|---|---|---|---|---|---|---|---|
| | 19 | 20 | 21 | 22 | 23 | 24 | 25 | 26 | 27 | 28 | 29 | 30 | 31 | 32 | 33 | 34 | 35 | 36 | |
| 27 | 343.422 | 344.430 | 345.438 | 346.446 | 347.454 | 348.462 | 349.470 | 350.478 | 351.486 | 352.494 | 353.502 | 354.510 | 355.518 | 356.526 | 357.534 | 358.542 | 359.550 | 360.558 | 27 |
| 28 | 355.432 | 356.440 | 357.448 | 358.456 | 359.464 | 360.472 | 361.480 | 362.488 | 363.496 | 364.504 | 365.512 | 366.520 | 367.528 | 368.536 | 369.544 | 370.552 | 371.560 | 372.568 | 28 |
| 29 | 367.442 | 368.450 | 369.458 | 370.466 | 371.474 | 372.482 | 373.490 | 374.498 | 375.506 | 376.514 | 377.522 | 378.530 | 379.538 | 380.546 | 381.554 | 382.562 | 383.570 | 384.578 | 29 |
| 30 | 379.452 | 380.460 | 381.468 | 382.476 | 383.484 | 384.492 | 385.500 | 386.508 | 387.516 | 388.524 | 389.532 | 390.540 | 391.548 | 392.556 | 393.564 | 394.572 | 395.580 | 396.588 | 30 |
| 31 | 391.462 | 392.470 | 393.478 | 394.486 | 395.494 | 396.502 | 397.510 | 398.518 | 399.526 | 400.534 | 401.542 | 402.550 | 403.558 | 404.566 | 405.574 | 406.582 | 407.590 | 408.598 | 31 |
| 32 | 403.472 | 404.480 | 405.488 | 406.496 | 407.504 | 408.512 | 409.520 | 410.528 | 411.536 | 412.544 | 413.552 | 414.560 | 415.568 | 416.576 | 417.584 | 418.592 | 419.600 | 420.608 | 32 |
| 33 | 415.482 | 416.490 | 417.498 | 418.506 | 419.514 | 420.522 | 421.530 | 422.538 | 423.546 | 424.554 | 425.562 | 426.570 | 427.578 | 428.586 | 429.594 | 430.602 | 431.610 | 432.618 | 33 |
| 34 | 427.492 | 428.500 | 429.508 | 430.516 | 431.524 | 432.532 | 433.540 | 434.548 | 435.556 | 436.564 | 437.572 | 438.580 | 439.588 | 440.596 | 441.604 | 442.612 | 443.620 | 444.628 | 34 |
| 35 | 439.502 | 440.510 | 441.518 | 442.526 | 443.534 | 444.542 | 445.550 | 446.558 | 447.566 | 448.574 | 449.582 | 450.590 | 451.598 | 452.606 | 453.614 | 454.622 | 455.630 | 456.638 | 35 |
| 36 | 451.512 | 452.520 | 453.528 | 454.536 | 455.544 | 456.552 | 457.560 | 458.568 | 459.576 | 460.584 | 461.592 | 462.600 | 463.608 | 464.616 | 465.624 | 466.632 | 467.640 | 468.648 | 36 |
| 37 | 463.522 | 464.530 | 465.538 | 466.546 | 467.554 | 468.562 | 469.570 | 470.578 | 471.586 | 472.594 | 473.602 | 474.610 | 475.618 | 476.626 | 477.634 | 478.642 | 479.650 | 480.658 | 37 |
| 38 | 475.532 | 476.540 | 477.548 | 478.556 | 479.564 | 480.572 | 481.580 | 482.588 | 483.596 | 484.604 | 485.612 | 486.620 | 487.628 | 488.636 | 489.644 | 490.652 | 491.660 | 492.668 | 38 |
| 39 | 487.542 | 488.550 | 489.558 | 490.566 | 491.574 | 492.582 | 493.590 | 494.598 | 495.606 | 496.614 | 497.622 | 498.630 | 499.638 | 500.646 | 501.654 | 502.662 | 503.670 | 504.678 | 39 |
| 40 | 499.552 | 500.560 | 501.568 | 502.576 | 503.584 | 504.592 | 505.600 | 506.608 | 507.616 | 508.624 | 509.632 | 510.640 | 511.648 | 512.656 | 513.664 | 514.672 | 515.680 | 516.688 | 40 |
| 41 | 511.562 | 512.570 | 513.578 | 514.586 | 515.594 | 516.602 | 517.610 | 518.618 | 519.626 | 520.634 | 521.642 | 522.650 | 523.658 | 524.666 | 525.674 | 526.682 | 527.690 | 528.698 | 41 |
| 42 | 523.572 | 524.580 | 525.588 | 526.596 | 527.604 | 528.612 | 529.620 | 530.628 | 531.636 | 532.644 | 533.652 | 534.660 | 535.668 | 536.676 | 537.684 | 538.692 | 539.700 | 540.708 | 42 |
| 43 | 535.582 | 536.590 | 537.598 | 538.606 | 539.614 | 540.622 | 541.630 | 542.638 | 543.646 | 544.654 | 545.662 | 546.670 | 547.678 | 548.686 | 549.694 | 550.702 | 551.710 | 552.718 | 43 |
| 44 | 547.592 | 548.600 | 549.608 | 550.616 | 551.624 | 552.632 | 553.640 | 554.648 | 555.656 | 556.664 | 557.672 | 558.680 | 559.688 | 560.696 | 561.704 | 562.712 | 563.720 | 564.728 | 44 |
| 45 | 559.602 | 560.610 | 561.618 | 562.626 | 563.634 | 564.642 | 565.650 | 566.658 | 567.666 | 568.674 | 569.682 | 570.690 | 571.698 | 572.706 | 573.714 | 574.722 | 575.730 | 576.738 | 45 |
| 46 | 571.612 | 572.620 | 573.628 | 574.636 | 575.644 | 576.652 | 577.660 | 578.668 | 579.676 | 580.684 | 581.692 | 582.700 | 583.708 | 584.716 | 585.724 | 586.732 | 587.740 | 588.748 | 46 |
| 47 | 583.622 | 584.630 | 585.638 | 586.646 | 587.654 | 588.662 | 589.670 | 590.678 | 591.686 | 592.694 | 593.702 | 594.710 | 595.718 | 596.726 | 597.734 | 598.742 | 599.750 | 600.758 | 47 |
| 48 | 595.632 | 596.640 | 597.648 | 598.656 | 599.664 | 600.672 | 601.680 | 602.688 | 603.696 | 604.704 | 605.712 | 606.720 | 607.728 | 608.736 | 609.744 | 610.752 | 611.760 | 612.768 | 48 |
| 49 | 607.642 | 608.650 | 609.658 | 610.666 | 611.674 | 612.682 | 613.690 | 614.698 | 615.706 | 616.714 | 617.722 | 618.730 | 619.738 | 620.746 | 621.754 | 622.762 | 623.770 | 624.778 | 49 |
| 50 | 619.652 | 620.660 | 621.668 | 622.676 | 623.684 | 624.692 | 625.700 | 626.708 | 627.716 | 628.724 | 629.732 | 630.740 | 631.748 | 632.756 | 633.764 | 634.772 | 635.780 | 636.788 | 50 |
| 51 | 631.662 | 632.670 | 633.678 | 634.686 | 635.694 | 636.702 | 637.710 | 638.718 | 639.726 | 640.734 | 641.742 | 642.750 | 643.758 | 644.766 | 645.774 | 646.782 | 647.790 | 648.798 | 51 |
| 52 | 643.672 | 644.680 | 645.688 | 646.696 | 647.704 | 648.712 | 649.720 | 650.728 | 651.736 | 652.744 | 653.752 | 654.760 | 655.768 | 656.776 | 657.784 | 658.792 | 659.800 | 660.808 | 52 |

## TABLE 6, Page 6 – MOLECULAR WEIGHTS OF HYDROCARBONS
### Range: $C_{27}$ to $C_{52}$; $H_{37}$ to $H_{54}$
### December 31, 1946; October 31, 1952

| No. of Carbon Atoms | Number of Hydrogen Atoms | | | | | | | | | | | | | | | | | | No. of Carbon Atoms |
|---|---|---|---|---|---|---|---|---|---|---|---|---|---|---|---|---|---|---|---|
| | 37 | 38 | 39 | 40 | 41 | 42 | 43 | 44 | 45 | 46 | 47 | 48 | 49 | 50 | 51 | 52 | 53 | 54 | |
| 27 | 361.566 | 362.574 | 363.582 | 364.590 | 365.598 | 366.606 | 367.614 | 368.622 | 369.630 | 370.638 | 371.646 | 372.654 | 373.662 | 374.670 | 375.678 | 376.686 | 377.694 | 378.702 | 27 |
| 28 | 373.576 | 374.584 | 375.592 | 376.600 | 377.608 | 378.616 | 379.624 | 380.632 | 381.640 | 382.648 | 383.656 | 384.664 | 385.672 | 386.680 | 387.688 | 388.696 | 389.704 | 390.712 | 28 |
| 29 | 385.586 | 386.594 | 387.602 | 388.610 | 389.618 | 390.626 | 391.634 | 392.642 | 393.650 | 394.658 | 395.666 | 396.674 | 397.682 | 398.690 | 399.698 | 400.706 | 401.714 | 402.722 | 29 |
| 30 | 397.596 | 398.604 | 399.612 | 400.620 | 401.628 | 402.636 | 403.644 | 404.652 | 405.660 | 406.668 | 407.676 | 408.684 | 409.692 | 410.700 | 411.708 | 412.716 | 413.724 | 414.732 | 30 |
| 31 | 409.606 | 410.614 | 411.622 | 412.630 | 413.638 | 414.646 | 415.654 | 416.662 | 417.670 | 418.678 | 419.686 | 420.694 | 421.702 | 422.710 | 423.718 | 424.726 | 425.734 | 426.742 | 31 |
| 32 | 421.616 | 422.624 | 423.632 | 424.640 | 425.648 | 426.656 | 427.664 | 428.672 | 429.680 | 430.688 | 431.696 | 432.704 | 433.712 | 434.720 | 435.728 | 436.736 | 437.744 | 438.752 | 32 |
| 33 | 433.626 | 434.634 | 435.642 | 436.650 | 437.658 | 438.666 | 439.674 | 440.682 | 441.690 | 442.698 | 443.706 | 444.714 | 445.722 | 446.730 | 447.738 | 448.746 | 449.754 | 450.762 | 33 |
| 34 | 445.636 | 446.644 | 447.652 | 448.660 | 449.668 | 450.676 | 451.684 | 452.692 | 453.700 | 454.708 | 455.716 | 456.724 | 457.732 | 458.740 | 459.748 | 460.756 | 461.764 | 462.772 | 34 |
| 35 | 457.646 | 458.654 | 459.662 | 460.670 | 461.678 | 462.686 | 463.694 | 464.702 | 465.710 | 466.718 | 467.726 | 468.734 | 469.742 | 470.750 | 471.758 | 472.766 | 473.774 | 474.782 | 35 |
| 36 | 469.656 | 470.664 | 471.672 | 472.680 | 473.688 | 474.696 | 475.704 | 476.712 | 477.720 | 478.728 | 479.736 | 480.744 | 481.752 | 482.760 | 483.768 | 484.776 | 485.784 | 486.792 | 36 |
| 37 | 481.666 | 482.674 | 483.682 | 484.690 | 485.698 | 486.706 | 487.714 | 488.722 | 489.730 | 490.738 | 491.746 | 492.754 | 493.762 | 494.770 | 495.778 | 496.786 | 497.794 | 498.802 | 37 |
| 38 | 493.676 | 494.684 | 495.692 | 496.700 | 497.708 | 498.716 | 499.724 | 500.732 | 501.740 | 502.748 | 503.756 | 504.764 | 505.772 | 506.780 | 507.788 | 508.796 | 509.804 | 510.812 | 38 |
| 39 | 505.686 | 506.694 | 507.702 | 508.710 | 509.718 | 510.726 | 511.734 | 512.742 | 513.750 | 514.758 | 515.766 | 516.774 | 517.782 | 518.790 | 519.798 | 520.806 | 521.814 | 522.822 | 39 |
| 40 | 517.696 | 518.704 | 519.712 | 520.720 | 521.728 | 522.736 | 523.744 | 524.752 | 525.760 | 526.768 | 527.776 | 528.784 | 529.792 | 530.800 | 531.808 | 532.816 | 533.824 | 534.832 | 40 |
| 41 | 529.706 | 530.714 | 531.722 | 532.730 | 533.738 | 534.746 | 535.754 | 536.762 | 537.770 | 538.778 | 539.786 | 540.794 | 541.802 | 542.810 | 543.818 | 544.826 | 545.834 | 546.842 | 41 |
| 42 | 541.716 | 542.724 | 543.732 | 544.740 | 545.748 | 546.756 | 547.764 | 548.772 | 549.780 | 550.788 | 551.796 | 552.804 | 553.812 | 554.820 | 555.828 | 556.836 | 557.844 | 558.852 | 42 |
| 43 | 553.726 | 554.734 | 555.742 | 556.750 | 557.758 | 558.766 | 559.774 | 560.782 | 561.790 | 562.798 | 563.806 | 564.814 | 565.822 | 566.830 | 567.838 | 568.846 | 569.854 | 570.862 | 43 |
| 44 | 565.736 | 566.744 | 567.752 | 568.760 | 569.768 | 570.776 | 571.784 | 572.792 | 573.800 | 574.808 | 575.816 | 576.824 | 577.832 | 578.840 | 579.848 | 580.856 | 581.864 | 582.872 | 44 |
| 45 | 577.746 | 578.754 | 579.762 | 580.770 | 581.778 | 582.786 | 583.794 | 584.802 | 585.810 | 586.818 | 587.826 | 588.834 | 589.842 | 590.850 | 591.858 | 592.866 | 593.874 | 594.882 | 45 |
| 46 | 589.756 | 590.764 | 591.772 | 592.780 | 593.788 | 594.796 | 595.804 | 596.812 | 597.820 | 598.828 | 599.836 | 600.844 | 601.852 | 602.860 | 603.868 | 604.876 | 605.884 | 606.892 | 46 |
| 47 | 601.766 | 602.774 | 603.782 | 604.790 | 605.798 | 606.806 | 607.814 | 608.822 | 609.830 | 610.838 | 611.846 | 612.854 | 613.862 | 614.870 | 615.878 | 616.886 | 617.894 | 618.902 | 47 |
| 48 | 613.776 | 614.784 | 615.792 | 616.800 | 617.808 | 618.816 | 619.824 | 620.832 | 621.840 | 622.848 | 623.856 | 624.864 | 625.872 | 626.880 | 627.888 | 628.896 | 629.904 | 630.912 | 48 |
| 49 | 625.786 | 626.794 | 627.802 | 628.810 | 629.818 | 630.826 | 631.834 | 632.842 | 633.850 | 634.858 | 635.866 | 636.874 | 637.882 | 638.890 | 639.898 | 640.906 | 641.914 | 642.922 | 49 |
| 50 | 637.796 | 638.804 | 639.812 | 640.820 | 641.828 | 642.836 | 643.844 | 644.852 | 645.860 | 646.868 | 647.876 | 648.884 | 649.892 | 650.900 | 651.908 | 652.916 | 653.924 | 654.932 | 50 |
| 51 | 649.806 | 650.814 | 651.822 | 652.830 | 653.838 | 654.846 | 655.854 | 656.862 | 657.870 | 658.878 | 659.886 | 660.894 | 661.902 | 662.910 | 663.918 | 664.926 | 665.934 | 666.942 | 51 |
| 52 | 661.816 | 662.824 | 663.832 | 664.840 | 665.848 | 666.856 | 667.864 | 668.872 | 669.880 | 670.888 | 671.896 | 672.904 | 673.912 | 674.920 | 675.928 | 676.936 | 677.944 | 678.952 | 52 |

TABLE 6, Page 7 – MOLECULAR WEIGHTS OF HYDROCARBONS

Range: $C_{27}$ to $C_{52}$; $H_{55}$ to $H_{72}$

December 31, 1946; October 31, 1952

| No. of Carbon Atoms | Number of Hydrogen Atoms | | | | | | | | | | | | | | | | | | No. of Carbon Atoms |
|---|---|---|---|---|---|---|---|---|---|---|---|---|---|---|---|---|---|---|---|
| | 55 | 56 | 57 | 58 | 59 | 60 | 61 | 62 | 63 | 64 | 65 | 66 | 67 | 68 | 69 | 70 | 71 | 72 | |
| 27 | 379.710 | 380.718 | ---- | ---- | ---- | ---- | ---- | ---- | ---- | ---- | ---- | ---- | ---- | ---- | ---- | ---- | ---- | ---- | 27 |
| 28 | 391.720 | 392.728 | 393.736 | 394.744 | ---- | ---- | ---- | ---- | ---- | ---- | ---- | ---- | ---- | ---- | ---- | ---- | ---- | ---- | 28 |
| 29 | 403.730 | 404.738 | 405.746 | 406.754 | 407.762 | 408.770 | ---- | ---- | ---- | ---- | ---- | ---- | ---- | ---- | ---- | ---- | ---- | ---- | 29 |
| 30 | 415.740 | 416.748 | 417.756 | 418.764 | 419.772 | 420.780 | 421.788 | 422.796 | ---- | ---- | ---- | ---- | ---- | ---- | ---- | ---- | ---- | ---- | 30 |
| 31 | 427.750 | 428.758 | 429.766 | 430.774 | 431.782 | 432.790 | 433.798 | 434.806 | 435.814 | 436.822 | ---- | ---- | ---- | ---- | ---- | ---- | ---- | ---- | 31 |
| 32 | 439.760 | 440.768 | 441.776 | 442.784 | 443.792 | 444.800 | 445.808 | 446.816 | 447.824 | 448.832 | 449.840 | 450.848 | ---- | ---- | ---- | ---- | ---- | ---- | 32 |
| 33 | 451.770 | 452.778 | 453.786 | 454.794 | 455.802 | 456.810 | 457.818 | 458.826 | 459.834 | 460.842 | 461.850 | 462.858 | 463.866 | 464.874 | ---- | ---- | ---- | ---- | 33 |
| 34 | 463.780 | 464.788 | 465.796 | 466.804 | 467.812 | 468.820 | 469.828 | 470.836 | 471.844 | 472.852 | 473.860 | 474.868 | 475.876 | 476.884 | 477.892 | 478.900 | ---- | ---- | 34 |
| 35 | 475.790 | 476.798 | 477.806 | 478.814 | 479.822 | 480.830 | 481.838 | 482.846 | 483.854 | 484.862 | 485.870 | 486.878 | 487.886 | 488.894 | 489.902 | 490.910 | 491.918 | 492.926 | 35 |
| 36 | 487.800 | 488.808 | 489.816 | 490.824 | 491.832 | 492.840 | 493.848 | 494.856 | 495.864 | 496.872 | 497.880 | 498.888 | 499.896 | 500.904 | 501.912 | 502.920 | 503.928 | 504.936 | 36 |
| 37 | 499.810 | 500.818 | 501.826 | 502.834 | 503.842 | 504.850 | 505.858 | 506.866 | 507.874 | 508.882 | 509.890 | 510.898 | 511.906 | 512.914 | 513.922 | 514.930 | 515.938 | 516.946 | 37 |
| 38 | 511.820 | 512.828 | 513.836 | 514.844 | 515.852 | 516.860 | 517.868 | 518.876 | 519.884 | 520.892 | 521.900 | 522.908 | 523.916 | 524.924 | 525.932 | 526.940 | 527.948 | 528.956 | 38 |
| 39 | 523.830 | 524.838 | 525.846 | 526.854 | 527.862 | 528.870 | 529.878 | 530.886 | 531.894 | 532.902 | 533.910 | 534.918 | 535.926 | 536.934 | 537.942 | 538.950 | 539.958 | 540.966 | 39 |
| 40 | 535.840 | 536.848 | 537.856 | 538.864 | 539.872 | 540.880 | 541.888 | 542.896 | 543.904 | 544.912 | 545.920 | 546.928 | 547.936 | 548.944 | 549.952 | 550.960 | 551.968 | 552.976 | 40 |
| 41 | 547.850 | 548.858 | 549.866 | 550.874 | 551.882 | 552.890 | 553.898 | 554.906 | 555.914 | 556.922 | 557.930 | 558.938 | 559.946 | 560.954 | 561.962 | 562.970 | 563.978 | 564.986 | 41 |
| 42 | 559.860 | 560.868 | 561.876 | 562.884 | 563.892 | 564.900 | 565.908 | 566.916 | 567.924 | 568.932 | 569.940 | 570.948 | 571.956 | 572.964 | 573.972 | 574.980 | 575.988 | 576.996 | 42 |
| 43 | 571.870 | 572.878 | 573.886 | 574.894 | 575.902 | 576.910 | 577.918 | 578.926 | 579.934 | 580.942 | 581.950 | 582.958 | 583.966 | 584.974 | 585.982 | 586.990 | 587.998 | 589.006 | 43 |
| 44 | 583.880 | 584.888 | 585.896 | 586.904 | 587.912 | 588.920 | 589.928 | 590.936 | 591.944 | 592.952 | 593.960 | 594.968 | 595.976 | 596.984 | 597.992 | 599.000 | 600.008 | 601.016 | 44 |
| 45 | 595.890 | 596.898 | 597.906 | 598.914 | 599.922 | 600.930 | 601.938 | 602.946 | 603.954 | 604.962 | 605.970 | 606.978 | 607.986 | 608.994 | 610.002 | 611.010 | 612.018 | 613.026 | 45 |
| 46 | 607.900 | 608.908 | 609.916 | 610.924 | 611.932 | 612.940 | 613.948 | 614.956 | 615.964 | 616.972 | 617.980 | 618.988 | 619.996 | 621.004 | 622.012 | 623.020 | 624.028 | 625.036 | 46 |
| 47 | 619.910 | 620.918 | 621.926 | 622.934 | 623.942 | 624.950 | 625.958 | 626.966 | 627.974 | 628.982 | 629.990 | 630.998 | 632.006 | 633.014 | 634.022 | 635.030 | 636.038 | 637.046 | 47 |
| 48 | 631.920 | 632.928 | 633.936 | 634.944 | 635.952 | 636.960 | 637.968 | 638.976 | 639.984 | 640.992 | 642.000 | 643.008 | 644.016 | 645.024 | 646.032 | 647.040 | 648.048 | 649.056 | 48 |
| 49 | 643.930 | 644.938 | 645.946 | 646.954 | 647.962 | 648.970 | 649.978 | 650.986 | 651.994 | 653.002 | 654.010 | 655.018 | 656.026 | 657.034 | 658.042 | 659.050 | 660.058 | 661.066 | 49 |
| 50 | 655.940 | 656.948 | 657.956 | 658.964 | 659.972 | 660.980 | 661.988 | 662.996 | 664.004 | 665.012 | 666.020 | 667.028 | 668.036 | 669.044 | 670.052 | 671.060 | 672.068 | 673.076 | 50 |
| 51 | 667.950 | 668.958 | 669.966 | 670.974 | 671.982 | 672.990 | 673.998 | 675.006 | 676.014 | 677.022 | 678.030 | 679.038 | 680.046 | 681.054 | 682.062 | 683.070 | 684.078 | 685.086 | 51 |
| 52 | 679.960 | 680.968 | 681.976 | 682.984 | 683.992 | 685.000 | 686.008 | 687.016 | 688.024 | 689.032 | 690.040 | 691.048 | 692.056 | 693.064 | 694.072 | 695.080 | 696.088 | 697.096 | 52 |

TABLE 6, Page 8 — MOLECULAR WEIGHTS OF HYDROCARBONS

Range: C_{27} to C_{52}; H_{73} to H_{90}

December 31, 1946; October 31, 1952

Number of Hydrogen Atoms

| No. of Carbon Atoms | 73 | 74 | 75 | 76 | 77 | 78 | 79 | 80 | 81 | 82 | 83 | 84 | 85 | 86 | 87 | 88 | 89 | 90 | No. of Carbon Atoms |
|---|---|---|---|---|---|---|---|---|---|---|---|---|---|---|---|---|---|---|---|
| 27 | — | — | — | — | — | — | — | — | — | — | — | — | — | — | — | — | — | — | 27 |
| 28 | — | — | — | — | — | — | — | — | — | — | — | — | — | — | — | — | — | — | 28 |
| 29 | — | — | — | — | — | — | — | — | — | — | — | — | — | — | — | — | — | — | 29 |
| 30 | — | — | — | — | — | — | — | — | — | — | — | — | — | — | — | — | — | — | 30 |
| 31 | — | — | — | — | — | — | — | — | — | — | — | — | — | — | — | — | — | — | 31 |
| 32 | — | — | — | — | — | — | — | — | — | — | — | — | — | — | — | — | — | — | 32 |
| 33 | — | — | — | — | — | — | — | — | — | — | — | — | — | — | — | — | — | — | 33 |
| 34 | — | 506.952 | — | — | — | — | — | — | — | — | — | — | — | — | — | — | — | — | 34 |
| 35 | — | — | — | — | — | — | — | — | — | — | — | — | — | — | — | — | — | — | 35 |
| 36 | 505.944 | 506.952 | — | 520.978 | — | — | — | — | — | — | — | — | — | — | — | — | — | — | 36 |
| 37 | 517.954 | 518.962 | 519.970 | 520.978 | — | — | — | — | — | — | — | — | — | — | — | — | — | — | 37 |
| 38 | 529.964 | 530.972 | 531.980 | 532.988 | 533.996 | 535.004 | — | — | — | — | — | — | — | — | — | — | — | — | 38 |
| 39 | 541.974 | 542.982 | 543.990 | 544.998 | 546.006 | 547.014 | 548.022 | 549.030 | — | — | — | — | — | — | — | — | — | — | 39 |
| 40 | 553.984 | 554.992 | 556.000 | 557.008 | 558.016 | 559.024 | 560.032 | 561.040 | 562.048 | 563.056 | — | — | — | — | — | — | — | — | 40 |
| 41 | 565.994 | 567.002 | 568.010 | 569.018 | 570.026 | 571.034 | 572.042 | 573.050 | 574.058 | 575.066 | 576.074 | 577.082 | — | — | — | — | — | — | 41 |
| 42 | 578.004 | 579.012 | 580.020 | 581.028 | 582.036 | 583.044 | 584.052 | 585.060 | 586.068 | 587.076 | 588.084 | 589.092 | 590.100 | 591.108 | — | — | — | — | 42 |
| 43 | 590.014 | 591.022 | 592.030 | 593.038 | 594.046 | 595.054 | 596.062 | 597.070 | 598.078 | 599.086 | 600.094 | 601.102 | 602.110 | 603.118 | 604.126 | 605.134 | — | — | 43 |
| 44 | 602.024 | 603.032 | 604.040 | 605.048 | 606.056 | 607.064 | 608.072 | 609.080 | 610.088 | 611.096 | 612.104 | 613.112 | 614.120 | 615.128 | 616.136 | 617.144 | 618.152 | 619.160 | 44 |
| 45 | 614.034 | 615.042 | 616.050 | 617.058 | 618.066 | 619.074 | 620.082 | 621.090 | 622.098 | 623.106 | 624.114 | 625.122 | 626.130 | 627.138 | 628.146 | 629.154 | 630.162 | 631.170 | 45 |
| 46 | 626.044 | 627.052 | 628.060 | 629.068 | 630.076 | 631.084 | 632.092 | 633.100 | 634.108 | 635.116 | 636.124 | 637.132 | 638.140 | 639.148 | 640.156 | 641.164 | 642.172 | 643.180 | 46 |
| 47 | 638.054 | 639.062 | 640.070 | 641.078 | 642.086 | 643.094 | 644.102 | 645.110 | 646.118 | 647.126 | 648.134 | 649.142 | 650.150 | 651.158 | 652.166 | 653.174 | 654.182 | 655.190 | 47 |
| 48 | 650.064 | 651.072 | 652.080 | 653.088 | 654.096 | 655.104 | 656.112 | 657.120 | 658.128 | 659.136 | 660.144 | 661.152 | 662.160 | 663.168 | 664.176 | 665.184 | 666.192 | 667.200 | 48 |
| 49 | 662.074 | 663.082 | 664.090 | 665.098 | 666.106 | 667.114 | 668.122 | 669.130 | 670.138 | 671.146 | 672.154 | 673.162 | 674.170 | 675.178 | 676.186 | 677.194 | 678.202 | 679.210 | 49 |
| 50 | 674.084 | 675.092 | 676.100 | 677.108 | 678.116 | 679.124 | 680.132 | 681.140 | 682.148 | 683.156 | 684.164 | 685.172 | 686.180 | 687.188 | 688.196 | 689.204 | 690.212 | 691.220 | 50 |
| 51 | 686.094 | 687.102 | 688.110 | 689.118 | 690.126 | 691.134 | 692.142 | 693.150 | 694.158 | 695.166 | 696.174 | 697.182 | 698.190 | 699.198 | 700.206 | 701.214 | 702.222 | 703.230 | 51 |
| 52 | 698.104 | 699.112 | 700.120 | 701.128 | 702.136 | 703.144 | 704.152 | 705.160 | 706.168 | 707.176 | 708.184 | 709.192 | 710.200 | 711.208 | 712.216 | 713.224 | 714.232 | 715.240 | 52 |

TABLE 6, Page 9 – MOLECULAR WEIGHTS OF HYDROCARBONS

Range: $C_{27}$ to $C_{52}$; $H_{91}$ to $H_{106}$

December 31, 1946; October 31, 1952

Number of Hydrogen Atoms

| No. of Carbon Atoms | 91 | 92 | 93 | 94 | 95 | 96 | 97 | 98 | 99 | 100 | 101 | 102 | 103 | 104 | 105 | 106 | No. of Carbon Atoms |
|---|---|---|---|---|---|---|---|---|---|---|---|---|---|---|---|---|---|
| 27 | | | | | | | | | | | | | | | | | 27 |
| 28 | | | | | | | | | | | | | | | | | 28 |
| 29 | | | | | | | | | | | | | | | | | 29 |
| 30 | | | | | | | | | | | | | | | | | 30 |
| 31 | | | | | | | | | | | | | | | | | 31 |
| 32 | | | | | | | | | | | | | | | | | 32 |
| 33 | | | | | | | | | | | | | | | | | 33 |
| 34 | | | | | | | | | | | | | | | | | 34 |
| 35 | | | | | | | | | | | | | | | | | 35 |
| 36 | | | | | | | | | | | | | | | | | 36 |
| 37 | | | | | | | | | | | | | | | | | 37 |
| 38 | | | | | | | | | | | | | | | | | 38 |
| 39 | | | | | | | | | | | | | | | | | 39 |
| 40 | | | | | | | | | | | | | | | | | 40 |
| 41 | | | | | | | | | | | | | | | | | 41 |
| 42 | | | | | | | | | | | | | | | | | 42 |
| 43 | | | | | | | | | | | | | | | | | 43 |
| 44 | | | | | | | | | | | | | | | | | 44 |
| 45 | 632.178 | 633.186 | | | | | | | | | | | | | | | 45 |
| 46 | 644.188 | 645.196 | 646.204 | 647.212 | | | | | | | | | | | | | 46 |
| 47 | 656.198 | 657.206 | 658.214 | 659.222 | 660.230 | 661.238 | | | | | | | | | | | 47 |
| 48 | 668.208 | 669.216 | 670.224 | 671.232 | 672.240 | 673.248 | 674.256 | 675.264 | | | | | | | | | 48 |
| 49 | 680.218 | 681.226 | 682.234 | 683.242 | 684.250 | 685.258 | 686.266 | 687.274 | 688.282 | 689.290 | | | | | | | 49 |
| 50 | 692.228 | 693.236 | 694.244 | 695.252 | 696.260 | 697.268 | 698.276 | 699.284 | 700.292 | 701.300 | 702.308 | 703.316 | | | | | 50 |
| 51 | 704.238 | 705.246 | 706.254 | 707.262 | 708.270 | 709.278 | 710.286 | 711.294 | 712.302 | 713.310 | 714.318 | 715.326 | 716.334 | 717.342 | | | 51 |
| 52 | 716.248 | 717.256 | 718.264 | 719.272 | 720.280 | 721.288 | 722.296 | 723.304 | 724.312 | 725.320 | 726.328 | 727.336 | 728.344 | 729.352 | 730.360 | 731.368 | 52 |

TABLE 8, Page 10 – MOLECULAR WEIGHTS OF HYDROCARBONS

Range: $C_{53}$ to $C_{78}$; $H_1$ to $H_{18}$

December 31, 1946; October 31, 1952

| No. of Carbon Atoms | Number of Hydrogen Atoms | | | | | | | | | | | | | | | | | | No. of Carbon Atoms |
|---|---|---|---|---|---|---|---|---|---|---|---|---|---|---|---|---|---|---|---|
| | 1 | 2 | 3 | 4 | 5 | 6 | 7 | 8 | 9 | 10 | 11 | 12 | 13 | 14 | 15 | 16 | 17 | 18 | |
| 53 | 637.538 | 638.546 | 639.554 | 640.562 | 641.570 | 642.578 | 643.586 | 644.594 | 645.602 | 646.610 | 647.618 | 648.626 | 649.634 | 650.642 | 651.650 | 652.658 | 653.666 | 654.674 | 53 |
| 54 | 649.548 | 650.556 | 651.564 | 652.572 | 653.580 | 654.588 | 655.596 | 656.604 | 657.612 | 658.620 | 659.628 | 660.636 | 661.644 | 662.652 | 663.660 | 664.668 | 665.676 | 666.684 | 54 |
| 55 | 661.556 | 662.566 | 663.574 | 664.582 | 665.590 | 666.598 | 667.606 | 668.614 | 669.622 | 670.630 | 671.638 | 672.646 | 673.654 | 674.662 | 675.670 | 676.678 | 677.686 | 678.694 | 55 |
| 56 | 673.568 | 674.576 | 675.584 | 676.592 | 677.600 | 678.608 | 679.616 | 680.624 | 681.632 | 682.640 | 683.648 | 684.656 | 685.664 | 686.672 | 687.680 | 688.688 | 689.696 | 690.704 | 56 |
| 57 | 685.578 | 686.586 | 687.594 | 688.602 | 689.610 | 690.618 | 691.626 | 692.634 | 693.642 | 694.650 | 695.658 | 696.666 | 697.674 | 698.682 | 699.690 | 700.698 | 701.706 | 702.714 | 57 |
| 58 | 697.588 | 698.596 | 699.604 | 700.612 | 701.620 | 702.628 | 703.636 | 704.644 | 705.652 | 706.660 | 707.668 | 708.676 | 709.684 | 710.692 | 711.700 | 712.708 | 713.716 | 714.724 | 58 |
| 59 | 709.598 | 710.606 | 711.614 | 712.622 | 713.630 | 714.638 | 715.646 | 716.654 | 717.662 | 718.670 | 719.678 | 720.686 | 721.694 | 722.702 | 723.710 | 724.718 | 725.726 | 726.734 | 59 |
| 60 | 721.608 | 722.616 | 723.624 | 724.632 | 725.640 | 726.648 | 727.656 | 728.664 | 729.672 | 730.680 | 731.688 | 732.696 | 733.704 | 734.712 | 735.720 | 736.728 | 737.736 | 738.744 | 60 |
| 61 | 733.618 | 734.626 | 735.634 | 736.642 | 737.650 | 738.658 | 739.666 | 740.674 | 741.682 | 742.690 | 743.698 | 744.706 | 745.714 | 746.722 | 747.730 | 748.738 | 749.746 | 750.754 | 61 |
| 62 | 745.628 | 746.636 | 747.644 | 748.652 | 749.660 | 750.668 | 751.676 | 752.684 | 753.692 | 754.700 | 755.708 | 756.716 | 757.724 | 758.732 | 759.740 | 760.748 | 761.756 | 762.764 | 62 |
| 63 | 757.638 | 758.646 | 759.654 | 760.662 | 761.670 | 762.678 | 763.686 | 764.694 | 765.702 | 766.710 | 767.718 | 768.726 | 769.734 | 770.742 | 771.750 | 772.758 | 773.766 | 774.774 | 63 |
| 64 | 769.648 | 770.656 | 771.664 | 772.672 | 773.680 | 774.688 | 775.696 | 776.704 | 777.712 | 778.720 | 779.728 | 780.736 | 781.744 | 782.752 | 783.760 | 784.768 | 785.776 | 786.784 | 64 |
| 65 | 781.658 | 782.666 | 783.674 | 784.682 | 785.690 | 786.698 | 787.706 | 788.714 | 789.722 | 790.730 | 791.738 | 792.746 | 793.754 | 794.762 | 795.770 | 796.778 | 797.786 | 798.794 | 65 |
| 66 | 793.668 | 794.676 | 795.684 | 796.692 | 797.700 | 798.708 | 799.716 | 800.724 | 801.732 | 802.740 | 803.748 | 804.756 | 805.764 | 806.772 | 807.780 | 808.788 | 809.796 | 810.804 | 66 |
| 67 | 805.678 | 806.686 | 807.694 | 808.702 | 809.710 | 810.718 | 811.726 | 812.734 | 813.742 | 814.750 | 815.758 | 816.766 | 817.774 | 818.782 | 819.790 | 820.798 | 821.806 | 822.814 | 67 |
| 68 | 817.688 | 818.696 | 819.704 | 820.712 | 821.720 | 822.728 | 823.736 | 824.744 | 825.752 | 826.760 | 827.768 | 828.776 | 829.784 | 830.792 | 831.800 | 832.808 | 833.816 | 834.824 | 68 |
| 69 | 829.698 | 830.706 | 831.714 | 832.722 | 833.730 | 834.738 | 835.746 | 836.754 | 837.762 | 838.770 | 839.778 | 840.786 | 841.794 | 842.802 | 843.810 | 844.818 | 845.826 | 846.834 | 69 |
| 70 | 841.708 | 842.716 | 843.724 | 844.732 | 845.740 | 846.748 | 847.756 | 848.764 | 849.772 | 850.780 | 851.788 | 852.796 | 853.804 | 854.812 | 855.820 | 856.828 | 857.836 | 858.844 | 70 |
| 71 | 853.718 | 854.726 | 855.734 | 856.742 | 857.750 | 858.758 | 859.766 | 860.774 | 861.782 | 862.790 | 863.798 | 864.806 | 865.814 | 866.822 | 867.830 | 868.838 | 869.846 | 870.854 | 71 |
| 72 | 865.728 | 866.736 | 867.744 | 868.752 | 869.760 | 870.768 | 871.776 | 872.784 | 873.792 | 874.800 | 875.808 | 876.816 | 877.824 | 878.832 | 879.840 | 880.848 | 881.856 | 882.864 | 72 |
| 73 | 877.738 | 878.746 | 879.754 | 880.762 | 881.770 | 882.778 | 883.786 | 884.794 | 885.802 | 886.810 | 887.818 | 888.826 | 889.834 | 890.842 | 891.850 | 892.858 | 893.866 | 894.874 | 73 |
| 74 | 889.748 | 890.756 | 891.764 | 892.772 | 893.780 | 894.788 | 895.796 | 896.804 | 897.812 | 898.820 | 899.828 | 900.836 | 901.844 | 902.852 | 903.860 | 904.868 | 905.876 | 906.884 | 74 |
| 75 | 901.758 | 902.766 | 903.774 | 904.782 | 905.790 | 906.798 | 907.806 | 908.814 | 909.822 | 910.830 | 911.838 | 912.846 | 913.854 | 914.862 | 915.870 | 916.878 | 917.886 | 918.894 | 75 |
| 76 | 913.768 | 914.776 | 915.784 | 916.792 | 917.800 | 918.808 | 919.816 | 920.824 | 921.832 | 922.840 | 923.848 | 924.856 | 925.864 | 926.872 | 927.880 | 928.888 | 929.896 | 930.904 | 76 |
| 77 | 925.778 | 926.786 | 927.794 | 928.802 | 929.810 | 930.818 | 931.826 | 932.834 | 933.842 | 934.850 | 935.858 | 936.866 | 937.874 | 938.882 | 939.890 | 940.898 | 941.906 | 942.914 | 77 |
| 78 | 937.788 | 938.796 | 939.804 | 940.812 | 941.820 | 942.828 | 943.836 | 944.844 | 945.852 | 946.860 | 947.868 | 948.876 | 949.884 | 950.892 | 951.900 | 952.908 | 953.916 | 954.924 | 78 |

TABLE 6, Page 11 – MOLECULAR WEIGHTS OF HYDROCARBONS

Range: $C_{53}$ to $C_{78}$: $H_{19}$ to $H_{36}$

December 31, 1946; October 31, 1952

| No. of Carbon Atoms | Number of Hydrogen Atoms | | | | | | | | | | | | | | | | | |
|---|---|---|---|---|---|---|---|---|---|---|---|---|---|---|---|---|---|---|
| | 19 | 20 | 21 | 22 | 23 | 24 | 25 | 26 | 27 | 28 | 29 | 30 | 31 | 32 | 33 | 34 | 35 | 36 |
| 53 | 655.682 | 656.690 | 657.698 | 658.706 | 659.714 | 660.722 | 661.730 | 662.738 | 663.746 | 664.754 | 665.762 | 666.770 | 667.778 | 668.786 | 669.794 | 670.802 | 671.810 | 672.818 |
| 54 | 667.692 | 668.700 | 669.708 | 670.716 | 671.724 | 672.732 | 673.740 | 674.748 | 675.756 | 676.764 | 677.772 | 678.780 | 679.788 | 680.796 | 681.804 | 682.812 | 683.820 | 684.828 |
| 55 | 679.702 | 680.710 | 681.718 | 682.726 | 683.734 | 684.742 | 685.750 | 686.758 | 687.766 | 688.774 | 689.782 | 690.790 | 691.798 | 692.806 | 693.814 | 694.822 | 695.830 | 696.838 |
| 56 | 691.712 | 692.720 | 693.728 | 694.736 | 695.744 | 696.752 | 697.760 | 698.768 | 699.776 | 700.784 | 701.792 | 702.800 | 703.808 | 704.816 | 705.824 | 706.832 | 707.840 | 708.848 |
| 57 | 703.722 | 704.730 | 705.738 | 706.746 | 707.754 | 708.762 | 709.770 | 710.778 | 711.786 | 712.794 | 713.802 | 714.810 | 715.818 | 716.826 | 717.834 | 718.842 | 719.850 | 720.858 |
| 58 | 715.732 | 716.740 | 717.748 | 718.756 | 719.764 | 720.772 | 721.780 | 722.788 | 723.796 | 724.804 | 725.812 | 726.820 | 727.828 | 728.836 | 729.844 | 730.852 | 731.860 | 732.868 |
| 59 | 727.742 | 728.750 | 729.758 | 730.766 | 731.774 | 732.782 | 733.790 | 734.798 | 735.806 | 736.814 | 737.822 | 738.830 | 739.838 | 740.846 | 741.854 | 742.862 | 743.870 | 744.878 |
| 60 | 739.752 | 740.760 | 741.768 | 742.776 | 743.784 | 744.792 | 745.800 | 746.808 | 747.816 | 748.824 | 749.832 | 750.840 | 751.848 | 752.856 | 753.864 | 754.872 | 755.880 | 756.888 |
| 61 | 751.762 | 752.770 | 753.778 | 754.786 | 755.794 | 756.802 | 757.810 | 758.818 | 759.826 | 760.834 | 761.842 | 762.850 | 763.858 | 764.866 | 765.874 | 766.882 | 767.890 | 768.898 |
| 62 | 763.772 | 764.780 | 765.788 | 766.795 | 767.804 | 768.812 | 769.820 | 770.828 | 771.836 | 772.844 | 773.852 | 774.860 | 775.868 | 776.876 | 777.884 | 778.892 | 779.900 | 780.908 |
| 63 | 775.782 | 776.790 | 777.798 | 778.806 | 779.814 | 780.822 | 781.830 | 782.838 | 783.846 | 784.854 | 785.862 | 786.870 | 787.878 | 788.886 | 789.894 | 790.902 | 791.910 | 792.918 |
| 64 | 787.792 | 788.800 | 789.808 | 790.816 | 791.824 | 792.832 | 793.840 | 794.848 | 795.856 | 796.864 | 797.872 | 798.880 | 799.888 | 800.896 | 801.904 | 802.912 | 803.920 | 804.928 |
| 65 | 799.802 | 800.810 | 801.818 | 802.826 | 803.834 | 804.842 | 805.850 | 806.858 | 807.866 | 808.874 | 809.882 | 810.890 | 811.898 | 812.906 | 813.914 | 814.922 | 815.930 | 816.938 |
| 66 | 811.812 | 812.820 | 813.828 | 814.836 | 815.844 | 816.852 | 817.860 | 818.868 | 819.876 | 820.884 | 821.892 | 822.900 | 823.908 | 824.916 | 825.924 | 826.932 | 827.940 | 828.948 |
| 67 | 823.822 | 824.830 | 825.838 | 826.846 | 827.854 | 828.862 | 829.870 | 830.878 | 831.886 | 832.894 | 833.902 | 834.910 | 835.918 | 836.926 | 837.934 | 838.942 | 839.950 | 840.958 |
| 68 | 835.832 | 836.840 | 837.848 | 838.856 | 839.864 | 840.872 | 841.880 | 842.888 | 843.896 | 844.904 | 845.912 | 846.920 | 847.928 | 848.936 | 849.944 | 850.952 | 851.960 | 852.968 |
| 69 | 847.842 | 848.850 | 849.858 | 850.866 | 851.874 | 852.882 | 853.890 | 854.898 | 855.906 | 856.914 | 857.922 | 858.930 | 859.938 | 860.946 | 861.954 | 862.962 | 863.970 | 864.978 |
| 70 | 859.852 | 860.860 | 861.868 | 862.876 | 863.884 | 864.892 | 865.900 | 866.908 | 867.916 | 868.924 | 869.932 | 870.940 | 871.948 | 872.956 | 873.964 | 874.972 | 875.980 | 876.988 |
| 71 | 871.862 | 872.870 | 873.878 | 874.886 | 875.894 | 876.902 | 877.910 | 878.918 | 879.926 | 880.934 | 881.942 | 882.950 | 883.958 | 884.966 | 885.974 | 886.982 | 887.990 | 888.998 |
| 72 | 883.872 | 884.880 | 885.888 | 886.896 | 887.904 | 888.912 | 889.920 | 890.928 | 891.936 | 892.944 | 893.952 | 894.960 | 895.968 | 896.976 | 897.984 | 898.992 | 900.000 | 901.008 |
| 73 | 895.882 | 896.890 | 897.898 | 898.906 | 899.914 | 900.922 | 901.930 | 902.938 | 903.946 | 904.954 | 905.962 | 906.970 | 907.978 | 908.986 | 909.994 | 911.002 | 912.010 | 913.018 |
| 74 | 907.892 | 908.900 | 909.908 | 910.916 | 911.924 | 912.932 | 913.940 | 914.948 | 915.956 | 916.964 | 917.972 | 918.980 | 919.988 | 920.996 | 922.004 | 923.012 | 924.020 | 925.028 |
| 75 | 919.902 | 920.910 | 921.918 | 922.926 | 923.934 | 924.942 | 925.950 | 926.958 | 927.966 | 928.974 | 929.982 | 930.990 | 931.998 | 933.006 | 934.014 | 935.022 | 936.030 | 937.038 |
| 76 | 931.912 | 932.920 | 933.928 | 934.936 | 935.944 | 936.952 | 937.960 | 938.968 | 939.976 | 940.984 | 941.992 | 943.000 | 944.008 | 945.016 | 946.024 | 947.032 | 948.040 | 949.048 |
| 77 | 943.922 | 944.930 | 945.938 | 946.946 | 947.954 | 948.962 | 949.970 | 950.978 | 951.986 | 952.994 | 954.002 | 955.010 | 956.018 | 957.026 | 958.034 | 959.042 | 960.050 | 961.058 |
| 78 | 955.932 | 956.940 | 957.948 | 958.956 | 959.964 | 960.972 | 961.980 | 962.988 | 963.996 | 965.004 | 966.012 | 967.020 | 968.028 | 969.036 | 970.044 | 971.052 | 972.060 | 973.068 |

27

## TABLE 6, Page 12 - MOLECULAR WEIGHTS OF HYDROCARBONS

Range $C_{53}$ to $C_{78}$; $H_{37}$ to $H_{54}$

December 31, 1946; October 31, 1952

| No. of Carbon Atoms | Number of Hydrogen Atoms | | | | | | | | | | | | | | | | | | No. of Carbon Atoms |
| --- | 37 | 38 | 39 | 40 | 41 | 42 | 43 | 44 | 45 | 46 | 47 | 48 | 49 | 50 | 51 | 52 | 53 | 54 | --- |
| 53 | 673.826 | 674.834 | 675.842 | 676.850 | 677.858 | 678.866 | 679.874 | 680.882 | 681.890 | 682.898 | 683.906 | 684.914 | 685.922 | 686.930 | 687.938 | 688.946 | 689.954 | 690.962 | 53 |
| 54 | 685.836 | 686.844 | 687.852 | 688.860 | 689.868 | 690.876 | 691.884 | 692.892 | 693.900 | 694.908 | 695.916 | 696.924 | 697.932 | 698.940 | 699.948 | 700.956 | 701.964 | 702.972 | 54 |
| 55 | 697.846 | 698.854 | 699.862 | 700.870 | 701.878 | 702.886 | 703.894 | 704.902 | 705.910 | 706.918 | 707.926 | 708.934 | 709.942 | 710.950 | 711.958 | 712.966 | 713.974 | 714.982 | 55 |
| 56 | 709.856 | 710.864 | 711.872 | 712.880 | 713.888 | 714.896 | 715.904 | 716.912 | 717.920 | 718.928 | 719.936 | 720.944 | 721.952 | 722.960 | 723.968 | 724.976 | 725.984 | 726.992 | 56 |
| 57 | 721.866 | 722.874 | 723.882 | 724.890 | 725.898 | 726.906 | 727.914 | 728.922 | 729.930 | 730.938 | 731.946 | 732.954 | 733.962 | 734.970 | 735.978 | 736.986 | 737.994 | 739.002 | 57 |
| 58 | 733.876 | 734.884 | 735.892 | 736.900 | 737.908 | 738.916 | 739.924 | 740.932 | 741.940 | 742.948 | 743.956 | 744.964 | 745.972 | 746.980 | 747.988 | 748.996 | 750.004 | 751.012 | 58 |
| 59 | 745.886 | 746.894 | 747.902 | 748.910 | 749.918 | 750.926 | 751.934 | 752.942 | 753.950 | 754.958 | 755.966 | 756.974 | 757.982 | 758.990 | 759.998 | 761.006 | 762.014 | 763.022 | 59 |
| 60 | 757.896 | 758.904 | 759.912 | 760.920 | 761.928 | 762.936 | 763.944 | 764.952 | 765.960 | 766.968 | 767.976 | 768.984 | 769.992 | 771.000 | 772.008 | 773.016 | 774.024 | 775.032 | 60 |
| 61 | 769.906 | 770.914 | 771.922 | 772.930 | 773.938 | 774.946 | 775.954 | 776.962 | 777.970 | 778.978 | 779.986 | 780.994 | 782.002 | 783.010 | 784.018 | 785.026 | 786.034 | 787.042 | 61 |
| 62 | 781.916 | 782.924 | 783.932 | 784.940 | 785.948 | 786.956 | 787.964 | 788.972 | 789.980 | 790.988 | 791.996 | 793.004 | 794.012 | 795.020 | 796.028 | 797.036 | 798.044 | 799.052 | 62 |
| 63 | 793.926 | 794.934 | 795.942 | 796.950 | 797.958 | 798.966 | 799.974 | 800.982 | 801.990 | 802.998 | 804.006 | 805.014 | 806.022 | 807.030 | 808.038 | 809.046 | 810.054 | 811.062 | 63 |
| 64 | 805.936 | 806.944 | 807.952 | 808.960 | 809.968 | 810.976 | 811.984 | 812.992 | 814.000 | 815.008 | 816.016 | 817.024 | 818.032 | 819.040 | 820.048 | 821.056 | 822.064 | 823.072 | 64 |
| 65 | 817.946 | 818.954 | 819.962 | 820.970 | 821.978 | 822.986 | 823.994 | 825.002 | 826.010 | 827.018 | 828.026 | 829.034 | 830.042 | 831.050 | 832.058 | 833.066 | 834.074 | 835.082 | 65 |
| 66 | 829.956 | 830.964 | 831.972 | 832.980 | 833.988 | 834.996 | 836.004 | 837.012 | 838.020 | 839.028 | 840.036 | 841.044 | 842.052 | 843.060 | 844.068 | 845.076 | 846.084 | 847.092 | 66 |
| 67 | 841.966 | 842.974 | 843.982 | 844.990 | 845.998 | 847.006 | 848.014 | 849.022 | 850.030 | 851.038 | 852.046 | 853.054 | 854.062 | 855.070 | 856.078 | 857.086 | 858.094 | 859.102 | 67 |
| 68 | 853.976 | 854.984 | 855.992 | 857.000 | 858.008 | 859.016 | 860.024 | 861.032 | 862.040 | 863.048 | 864.056 | 865.064 | 866.072 | 867.080 | 868.088 | 869.096 | 870.104 | 871.112 | 68 |
| 69 | 865.986 | 866.994 | 868.002 | 869.010 | 870.018 | 871.026 | 872.034 | 873.042 | 874.050 | 875.058 | 876.066 | 877.074 | 878.082 | 879.090 | 880.098 | 881.106 | 882.114 | 883.122 | 69 |
| 70 | 877.996 | 879.004 | 880.012 | 881.020 | 882.028 | 883.036 | 884.044 | 885.052 | 886.060 | 887.068 | 888.076 | 889.084 | 890.092 | 891.100 | 892.108 | 893.116 | 894.124 | 895.132 | 70 |
| 71 | 890.006 | 891.014 | 892.022 | 893.030 | 894.038 | 895.046 | 896.054 | 897.062 | 898.070 | 899.078 | 900.086 | 901.094 | 902.102 | 903.110 | 904.118 | 905.126 | 906.134 | 907.142 | 71 |
| 72 | 902.016 | 903.024 | 904.032 | 905.040 | 906.048 | 907.056 | 908.064 | 909.072 | 910.080 | 911.088 | 912.096 | 913.104 | 914.112 | 915.120 | 916.128 | 917.136 | 918.144 | 919.152 | 72 |
| 73 | 914.026 | 915.034 | 916.042 | 917.050 | 918.058 | 919.066 | 920.074 | 921.082 | 922.090 | 923.098 | 924.106 | 925.114 | 926.122 | 927.130 | 928.138 | 929.146 | 930.154 | 931.162 | 73 |
| 74 | 926.036 | 927.044 | 928.052 | 929.060 | 930.068 | 931.076 | 932.084 | 933.092 | 934.100 | 935.108 | 936.116 | 937.124 | 938.132 | 939.140 | 940.148 | 941.156 | 942.164 | 943.172 | 74 |
| 75 | 938.046 | 939.054 | 940.062 | 941.070 | 942.078 | 943.086 | 944.094 | 945.102 | 946.110 | 947.118 | 948.126 | 949.134 | 950.142 | 951.150 | 952.158 | 953.166 | 954.174 | 955.182 | 75 |
| 76 | 950.056 | 951.064 | 952.072 | 953.080 | 954.088 | 955.096 | 956.104 | 957.112 | 958.120 | 959.128 | 960.136 | 961.144 | 962.152 | 963.160 | 964.168 | 965.176 | 966.184 | 967.192 | 76 |
| 77 | 962.066 | 963.074 | 964.082 | 965.090 | 966.098 | 967.106 | 968.114 | 969.122 | 970.130 | 971.138 | 972.146 | 973.154 | 974.162 | 975.170 | 976.178 | 977.186 | 978.194 | 979.202 | 77 |
| 78 | 974.076 | 975.084 | 976.092 | 977.100 | 978.108 | 979.116 | 980.124 | 981.132 | 982.140 | 983.148 | 984.156 | 985.164 | 986.172 | 987.180 | 988.188 | 989.196 | 990.204 | 991.212 | 78 |

TABLE 6, Page 13 – MOLECULAR WEIGHTS OF HYDROCARBONS

Range: $C_{53}$ to $C_{78}$; $H_{55}$ to $H_{72}$

December 31, 1946; October 31, 1952

| No. of Carbon Atoms | Number of Hydrogen Atoms | | | | | | | | | | | | | | | | | | No. of Carbon Atoms |
|---|---|---|---|---|---|---|---|---|---|---|---|---|---|---|---|---|---|---|---|
| | 55 | 56 | 57 | 58 | 59 | 60 | 61 | 62 | 63 | 64 | 65 | 66 | 67 | 68 | 69 | 70 | 71 | 72 | |
| 53 | 691.970 | 692.978 | 693.986 | 694.994 | 696.002 | 697.010 | 698.018 | 699.026 | 700.034 | 701.042 | 702.050 | 703.058 | 704.066 | 705.074 | 706.082 | 707.090 | 708.098 | 709.106 | 53 |
| 54 | 703.980 | 704.988 | 705.996 | 707.004 | 708.012 | 709.020 | 710.028 | 711.036 | 712.044 | 713.052 | 714.060 | 715.068 | 716.076 | 717.084 | 718.092 | 719.100 | 720.108 | 721.116 | 54 |
| 55 | 715.990 | 716.998 | 718.006 | 719.014 | 720.022 | 721.030 | 722.038 | 723.046 | 724.054 | 725.062 | 726.070 | 727.078 | 728.086 | 729.094 | 730.102 | 731.110 | 732.118 | 733.126 | 55 |
| 56 | 728.000 | 729.008 | 730.016 | 731.024 | 732.032 | 733.040 | 734.048 | 735.056 | 736.064 | 737.072 | 738.080 | 739.088 | 740.096 | 741.104 | 742.112 | 743.120 | 744.128 | 745.136 | 56 |
| 57 | 740.010 | 741.018 | 742.026 | 743.034 | 744.042 | 745.050 | 746.058 | 747.066 | 748.074 | 749.082 | 750.090 | 751.098 | 752.106 | 753.114 | 754.122 | 755.130 | 756.138 | 757.146 | 57 |
| 58 | 752.020 | 753.028 | 754.036 | 755.044 | 756.052 | 757.060 | 758.068 | 759.076 | 760.084 | 761.092 | 762.100 | 763.108 | 764.116 | 765.124 | 766.132 | 767.140 | 768.148 | 769.156 | 58 |
| 59 | 764.030 | 765.038 | 766.046 | 767.054 | 768.062 | 769.070 | 770.078 | 771.086 | 772.094 | 773.102 | 774.110 | 775.118 | 776.126 | 777.134 | 778.142 | 779.150 | 780.158 | 781.166 | 59 |
| 60 | 776.040 | 777.048 | 778.056 | 779.064 | 780.072 | 781.080 | 782.088 | 783.096 | 784.104 | 785.112 | 786.120 | 787.128 | 788.136 | 789.144 | 790.152 | 791.160 | 792.168 | 793.176 | 60 |
| 61 | 788.050 | 789.058 | 790.066 | 791.074 | 792.082 | 793.090 | 794.098 | 795.106 | 796.114 | 797.122 | 798.130 | 799.138 | 800.146 | 801.154 | 802.162 | 803.170 | 804.178 | 805.186 | 61 |
| 62 | 800.060 | 801.068 | 802.076 | 803.084 | 804.092 | 805.100 | 806.108 | 807.116 | 808.124 | 809.132 | 810.140 | 811.148 | 812.156 | 813.164 | 814.172 | 815.180 | 816.188 | 817.196 | 62 |
| 63 | 812.070 | 813.078 | 814.086 | 815.094 | 816.102 | 817.110 | 818.118 | 819.126 | 820.134 | 821.142 | 822.150 | 823.158 | 824.166 | 825.174 | 826.182 | 827.190 | 828.198 | 829.206 | 63 |
| 64 | 824.080 | 825.088 | 826.096 | 827.104 | 828.112 | 829.120 | 830.128 | 831.136 | 832.144 | 833.152 | 834.160 | 835.168 | 836.176 | 837.184 | 838.192 | 839.200 | 840.208 | 841.216 | 64 |
| 65 | 836.090 | 837.098 | 838.106 | 839.114 | 840.122 | 841.130 | 842.138 | 843.146 | 844.154 | 845.162 | 846.170 | 847.178 | 848.186 | 849.194 | 850.202 | 851.210 | 852.218 | 853.226 | 65 |
| 66 | 848.100 | 849.108 | 850.116 | 851.124 | 852.132 | 853.140 | 854.148 | 855.156 | 856.164 | 857.172 | 858.180 | 859.188 | 860.196 | 861.204 | 862.212 | 863.220 | 864.228 | 865.236 | 66 |
| 67 | 860.110 | 861.118 | 862.126 | 863.134 | 864.142 | 865.150 | 866.158 | 867.166 | 868.174 | 869.182 | 870.190 | 871.198 | 872.206 | 873.214 | 874.222 | 875.230 | 876.238 | 877.246 | 67 |
| 68 | 872.120 | 873.128 | 874.136 | 875.144 | 876.152 | 877.160 | 878.168 | 879.176 | 880.184 | 881.192 | 882.200 | 883.208 | 884.216 | 885.224 | 886.232 | 887.240 | 888.248 | 889.256 | 68 |
| 69 | 884.130 | 885.138 | 886.146 | 887.154 | 888.162 | 889.170 | 890.178 | 891.186 | 892.194 | 893.202 | 894.210 | 895.218 | 896.226 | 897.234 | 898.242 | 899.250 | 900.258 | 901.266 | 69 |
| 70 | 896.140 | 897.148 | 898.156 | 899.164 | 900.172 | 901.180 | 902.188 | 903.196 | 904.204 | 905.212 | 906.220 | 907.228 | 908.236 | 909.244 | 910.252 | 911.260 | 912.268 | 913.276 | 70 |
| 71 | 908.150 | 909.158 | 910.166 | 911.174 | 912.182 | 913.190 | 914.198 | 915.206 | 916.214 | 917.222 | 918.230 | 919.238 | 920.246 | 921.254 | 922.262 | 923.270 | 924.278 | 925.286 | 71 |
| 72 | 920.160 | 921.168 | 922.176 | 923.184 | 924.192 | 925.200 | 926.208 | 927.216 | 928.224 | 929.232 | 930.240 | 931.248 | 932.256 | 933.264 | 934.272 | 935.280 | 936.288 | 937.296 | 72 |
| 73 | 932.170 | 933.178 | 934.186 | 935.194 | 936.202 | 937.210 | 938.218 | 939.226 | 940.234 | 941.242 | 942.250 | 943.258 | 944.266 | 945.274 | 946.282 | 947.290 | 948.298 | 949.306 | 73 |
| 74 | 944.180 | 945.188 | 946.196 | 947.204 | 948.212 | 949.220 | 950.228 | 951.236 | 952.244 | 953.252 | 954.260 | 955.268 | 956.276 | 957.284 | 958.292 | 959.300 | 960.308 | 961.316 | 74 |
| 75 | 956.190 | 957.198 | 958.206 | 959.214 | 960.222 | 961.230 | 962.238 | 963.246 | 964.254 | 965.262 | 966.270 | 967.278 | 968.286 | 969.294 | 970.302 | 971.310 | 972.318 | 973.326 | 75 |
| 76 | 968.200 | 969.208 | 970.216 | 971.224 | 972.232 | 973.240 | 974.248 | 975.256 | 976.264 | 977.272 | 978.280 | 979.288 | 980.296 | 981.304 | 982.312 | 983.320 | 984.328 | 985.336 | 76 |
| 77 | 980.210 | 981.218 | 982.226 | 983.234 | 984.242 | 985.250 | 986.258 | 987.266 | 988.274 | 989.282 | 990.290 | 991.298 | 992.306 | 993.314 | 994.322 | 995.330 | 996.338 | 997.346 | 77 |
| 78 | 992.220 | 993.228 | 994.236 | 995.244 | 996.252 | 997.260 | 998.268 | 999.276 | 1000.284 | 1001.292 | 1002.300 | 1003.308 | 1004.316 | 1005.324 | 1006.332 | 1007.340 | 1008.348 | 1009.356 | 78 |

TABLE 6, Page 14 – MOLECULAR WEIGHTS OF HYDROCARBONS

Range: $C_{53}$ to $C_{78}$: $H_{73}$ to $H_{90}$

December 31, 1946; October 31, 1952

| No. of Carbon Atoms | Number of Hydrogen Atoms | | | | | | | | | | | | | | | | | | No. of Carbon Atoms |
|---|---|---|---|---|---|---|---|---|---|---|---|---|---|---|---|---|---|---|---|
| | 73 | 74 | 75 | 76 | 77 | 78 | 79 | 80 | 81 | 82 | 83 | 84 | 85 | 86 | 87 | 88 | 89 | 90 | |
| 53 | 710.114 | 711.122 | 712.130 | 713.138 | 714.146 | 715.154 | 716.162 | 717.170 | 718.178 | 719.186 | 720.194 | 721.202 | 722.210 | 723.218 | 724.226 | 725.234 | 726.242 | 727.250 | 53 |
| 54 | 722.124 | 723.132 | 724.140 | 725.148 | 726.156 | 727.164 | 728.172 | 729.180 | 730.188 | 731.196 | 732.204 | 733.212 | 734.220 | 735.228 | 736.236 | 737.244 | 738.252 | 739.260 | 54 |
| 55 | 734.134 | 735.142 | 736.150 | 737.158 | 738.166 | 739.174 | 740.182 | 741.190 | 742.198 | 743.206 | 744.214 | 745.222 | 746.230 | 747.238 | 748.246 | 749.254 | 750.262 | 751.270 | 55 |
| 56 | 746.144 | 747.152 | 748.160 | 749.168 | 750.176 | 751.184 | 752.192 | 753.200 | 754.208 | 755.216 | 756.224 | 757.232 | 758.240 | 759.248 | 760.256 | 761.264 | 762.272 | 763.280 | 56 |
| 57 | 758.154 | 759.162 | 760.170 | 761.178 | 762.186 | 763.194 | 764.202 | 765.210 | 766.218 | 767.226 | 768.234 | 769.242 | 770.250 | 771.258 | 772.266 | 773.274 | 774.282 | 775.290 | 57 |
| 58 | 770.164 | 771.172 | 772.180 | 773.188 | 774.196 | 775.204 | 776.212 | 777.220 | 778.228 | 779.236 | 780.244 | 781.252 | 782.260 | 783.268 | 784.276 | 785.284 | 786.292 | 787.300 | 58 |
| 59 | 782.174 | 783.182 | 784.190 | 785.198 | 786.206 | 787.214 | 788.222 | 789.230 | 790.238 | 791.246 | 792.254 | 793.262 | 794.270 | 795.278 | 796.286 | 797.294 | 798.302 | 799.310 | 59 |
| 60 | 794.184 | 795.192 | 796.200 | 797.208 | 798.216 | 799.224 | 800.232 | 801.240 | 802.248 | 803.256 | 804.264 | 805.272 | 806.280 | 807.288 | 808.296 | 809.304 | 810.312 | 811.320 | 60 |
| 61 | 806.194 | 807.202 | 808.210 | 809.218 | 810.226 | 811.234 | 812.242 | 813.250 | 814.258 | 815.266 | 816.274 | 817.282 | 818.290 | 819.298 | 820.306 | 821.314 | 822.322 | 823.330 | 61 |
| 62 | 818.204 | 819.212 | 820.220 | 821.228 | 822.236 | 823.244 | 824.252 | 825.260 | 826.268 | 827.276 | 828.284 | 829.292 | 830.300 | 831.308 | 832.316 | 833.324 | 834.332 | 835.340 | 62 |
| 63 | 830.214 | 831.222 | 832.230 | 833.238 | 834.246 | 835.254 | 836.262 | 837.270 | 838.278 | 839.286 | 840.294 | 841.302 | 842.310 | 843.318 | 844.326 | 845.334 | 846.342 | 847.350 | 63 |
| 64 | 842.224 | 843.232 | 844.240 | 845.248 | 846.256 | 847.264 | 848.272 | 849.280 | 850.288 | 851.296 | 852.304 | 853.312 | 854.320 | 855.328 | 856.336 | 857.344 | 858.352 | 859.360 | 64 |
| 65 | 854.234 | 855.242 | 856.250 | 857.258 | 858.266 | 859.274 | 860.282 | 861.290 | 862.298 | 863.306 | 864.314 | 865.322 | 866.330 | 867.338 | 868.346 | 869.354 | 870.362 | 871.370 | 65 |
| 66 | 866.244 | 867.252 | 868.260 | 869.268 | 870.276 | 871.284 | 872.292 | 873.300 | 874.308 | 875.316 | 876.324 | 877.332 | 878.340 | 879.348 | 880.356 | 881.364 | 882.372 | 883.380 | 66 |
| 67 | 878.254 | 879.262 | 880.270 | 881.278 | 882.286 | 883.294 | 884.302 | 885.310 | 886.318 | 887.326 | 888.334 | 889.342 | 890.350 | 891.358 | 892.366 | 893.374 | 894.382 | 895.390 | 67 |
| 68 | 890.264 | 891.272 | 892.280 | 893.288 | 894.296 | 895.304 | 896.312 | 897.320 | 898.328 | 899.336 | 900.344 | 901.352 | 902.360 | 903.368 | 904.376 | 905.384 | 906.392 | 907.400 | 68 |
| 69 | 902.274 | 903.282 | 904.290 | 905.298 | 906.306 | 907.314 | 908.322 | 909.330 | 910.338 | 911.346 | 912.354 | 913.362 | 914.370 | 915.378 | 916.386 | 917.394 | 918.402 | 919.410 | 69 |
| 70 | 914.284 | 915.292 | 916.300 | 917.308 | 918.316 | 919.324 | 920.332 | 921.340 | 922.348 | 923.356 | 924.364 | 925.372 | 926.380 | 927.388 | 928.396 | 929.404 | 930.412 | 931.420 | 70 |
| 71 | 926.294 | 927.302 | 928.310 | 929.318 | 930.326 | 931.334 | 932.342 | 933.350 | 934.358 | 935.366 | 936.374 | 937.382 | 938.390 | 939.398 | 940.406 | 941.414 | 942.422 | 943.430 | 71 |
| 72 | 938.304 | 939.312 | 940.320 | 941.328 | 942.336 | 943.344 | 944.352 | 945.360 | 946.368 | 947.376 | 948.384 | 949.392 | 950.400 | 951.408 | 952.416 | 953.424 | 954.432 | 955.440 | 72 |
| 73 | 950.314 | 951.322 | 952.330 | 953.338 | 954.346 | 955.354 | 956.362 | 957.370 | 958.378 | 959.386 | 960.394 | 961.402 | 962.410 | 963.418 | 964.426 | 965.434 | 966.442 | 967.450 | 73 |
| 74 | 962.324 | 963.332 | 964.340 | 965.348 | 966.356 | 967.364 | 968.372 | 969.380 | 970.388 | 971.396 | 972.404 | 973.412 | 974.420 | 975.428 | 976.436 | 977.444 | 978.452 | 979.460 | 74 |
| 75 | 974.334 | 975.342 | 976.350 | 977.358 | 978.366 | 979.374 | 980.382 | 981.390 | 982.398 | 983.406 | 984.414 | 985.422 | 986.430 | 987.438 | 988.446 | 989.454 | 990.462 | 991.470 | 75 |
| 76 | 986.344 | 987.352 | 988.360 | 989.368 | 990.376 | 991.384 | 992.392 | 993.400 | 994.408 | 995.416 | 996.424 | 997.432 | 998.440 | 999.448 | 1000.456 | 1001.464 | 1002.472 | 1003.480 | 76 |
| 77 | 998.354 | 999.362 | 1000.370 | 1001.378 | 1002.386 | 1003.394 | 1004.402 | 1005.410 | 1006.418 | 1007.426 | 1008.434 | 1009.442 | 1010.450 | 1011.458 | 1012.466 | 1013.474 | 1014.482 | 1015.490 | 77 |
| 78 | 1010.364 | 1011.372 | 1012.380 | 1013.388 | 1014.396 | 1015.404 | 1016.412 | 1017.420 | 1018.428 | 1019.436 | 1020.444 | 1021.452 | 1022.460 | 1023.468 | 1024.476 | 1025.484 | 1026.492 | 1027.500 | 78 |

TABLE 6, Page 15 – MOLECULAR WEIGHTS OF HYDROCARBONS

Range: $C_{53}$ to $C_{78}$; $H_{91}$ to $H_{108}$

December 31, 1946; October 31, 1952

| No. of Carbon Atoms | Number of Hydrogen Atoms | | | | | | | | | | | | | | | | | | No. of Carbon Atoms |
|---|---|---|---|---|---|---|---|---|---|---|---|---|---|---|---|---|---|---|---|
| | 91 | 92 | 93 | 94 | 95 | 96 | 97 | 98 | 99 | 100 | 101 | 102 | 103 | 104 | 105 | 106 | 107 | 108 | |
| 53 | 728.258 | 729.266 | 730.274 | 731.282 | 732.290 | 733.298 | 734.306 | 735.314 | 736.322 | 737.330 | 738.338 | 739.346 | 740.354 | 741.362 | 742.370 | 743.378 | 744.386 | 745.394 | 53 |
| 54 | 740.268 | 741.276 | 742.284 | 743.292 | 744.300 | 745.308 | 746.316 | 747.324 | 748.332 | 749.340 | 750.348 | 751.356 | 752.364 | 753.372 | 754.380 | 755.388 | 756.396 | 757.404 | 54 |
| 55 | 752.278 | 753.286 | 754.294 | 755.302 | 756.310 | 757.318 | 758.326 | 759.334 | 760.342 | 761.350 | 762.358 | 763.366 | 764.374 | 765.382 | 766.390 | 767.398 | 768.406 | 769.414 | 55 |
| 56 | 764.288 | 765.296 | 766.304 | 767.312 | 768.320 | 769.328 | 770.336 | 771.344 | 772.352 | 773.360 | 774.368 | 775.376 | 776.384 | 777.392 | 778.400 | 779.408 | 780.416 | 781.424 | 56 |
| 57 | 776.298 | 777.306 | 778.314 | 779.322 | 780.330 | 781.338 | 782.346 | 783.354 | 784.362 | 785.370 | 786.378 | 787.386 | 788.394 | 789.402 | 790.410 | 791.418 | 792.426 | 793.434 | 57 |
| 58 | 788.308 | 789.316 | 790.324 | 791.332 | 792.340 | 793.348 | 794.356 | 795.364 | 796.372 | 797.380 | 798.388 | 799.396 | 800.404 | 801.412 | 802.420 | 803.428 | 804.436 | 805.444 | 58 |
| 59 | 800.318 | 801.326 | 802.334 | 803.342 | 804.350 | 805.358 | 806.366 | 807.374 | 808.382 | 809.390 | 810.398 | 811.406 | 812.414 | 813.422 | 814.430 | 815.438 | 816.446 | 817.454 | 59 |
| 60 | 812.328 | 813.336 | 814.344 | 815.352 | 816.360 | 817.368 | 818.376 | 819.384 | 820.392 | 821.400 | 822.408 | 823.416 | 824.424 | 825.432 | 826.440 | 827.448 | 828.456 | 829.464 | 60 |
| 61 | 824.338 | 825.346 | 826.354 | 827.362 | 828.370 | 829.378 | 830.386 | 831.394 | 832.402 | 833.410 | 834.418 | 835.426 | 836.434 | 837.442 | 838.450 | 839.458 | 840.466 | 841.474 | 61 |
| 62 | 836.348 | 837.356 | 838.364 | 839.372 | 840.380 | 841.388 | 842.396 | 843.404 | 844.412 | 845.420 | 846.428 | 847.436 | 848.444 | 849.452 | 850.460 | 851.468 | 852.476 | 853.484 | 62 |
| 63 | 848.358 | 849.366 | 850.374 | 851.382 | 852.390 | 853.398 | 854.406 | 855.414 | 856.422 | 857.430 | 858.438 | 859.446 | 860.454 | 861.462 | 862.470 | 863.478 | 864.486 | 865.494 | 63 |
| 64 | 860.368 | 861.376 | 862.384 | 863.392 | 864.400 | 865.408 | 866.416 | 867.424 | 868.432 | 869.440 | 870.448 | 871.456 | 872.464 | 873.472 | 874.480 | 875.488 | 876.496 | 877.504 | 64 |
| 65 | 872.378 | 873.386 | 874.394 | 875.402 | 876.410 | 877.418 | 878.426 | 879.434 | 880.442 | 881.450 | 882.458 | 883.466 | 884.474 | 885.482 | 886.490 | 887.498 | 888.506 | 889.514 | 65 |
| 66 | 884.388 | 885.396 | 886.404 | 887.412 | 888.420 | 889.428 | 890.436 | 891.444 | 892.452 | 893.460 | 894.468 | 895.476 | 896.484 | 897.492 | 898.500 | 899.508 | 900.516 | 901.524 | 66 |
| 67 | 896.398 | 897.406 | 898.414 | 899.422 | 900.430 | 901.438 | 902.446 | 903.454 | 904.462 | 905.470 | 906.478 | 907.486 | 908.494 | 909.502 | 910.510 | 911.518 | 912.526 | 913.534 | 67 |
| 68 | 908.408 | 909.416 | 910.424 | 911.432 | 912.440 | 913.448 | 914.456 | 915.464 | 916.472 | 917.480 | 918.488 | 919.496 | 920.504 | 921.512 | 922.520 | 923.528 | 924.536 | 925.544 | 68 |
| 69 | 920.418 | 921.426 | 922.434 | 923.442 | 924.450 | 925.458 | 926.466 | 927.474 | 928.482 | 929.490 | 930.498 | 931.506 | 932.514 | 933.522 | 934.530 | 935.538 | 936.546 | 937.554 | 69 |
| 70 | 932.428 | 933.436 | 934.444 | 935.452 | 936.460 | 937.468 | 938.476 | 939.484 | 940.492 | 941.500 | 942.508 | 943.516 | 944.524 | 945.532 | 946.540 | 947.548 | 948.556 | 949.564 | 70 |
| 71 | 944.438 | 945.446 | 946.454 | 947.462 | 948.470 | 949.478 | 950.486 | 951.494 | 952.502 | 953.510 | 954.518 | 955.526 | 956.534 | 957.542 | 958.550 | 959.558 | 960.566 | 961.574 | 71 |
| 72 | 956.448 | 957.456 | 958.464 | 959.472 | 960.480 | 961.488 | 962.496 | 963.504 | 964.512 | 965.520 | 966.528 | 967.536 | 968.544 | 969.552 | 970.560 | 971.568 | 972.576 | 973.584 | 72 |
| 73 | 968.458 | 969.466 | 970.474 | 971.482 | 972.490 | 973.498 | 974.506 | 975.514 | 976.522 | 977.530 | 978.538 | 979.546 | 980.554 | 981.562 | 982.570 | 983.578 | 984.586 | 985.594 | 73 |
| 74 | 980.468 | 981.476 | 982.484 | 983.492 | 984.500 | 985.508 | 986.516 | 987.524 | 988.532 | 989.540 | 990.548 | 991.556 | 992.564 | 993.572 | 994.580 | 995.588 | 996.596 | 997.604 | 74 |
| 75 | 992.478 | 993.486 | 994.494 | 995.502 | 996.510 | 997.518 | 998.526 | 999.534 | 1000.542 | 1001.550 | 1002.558 | 1003.566 | 1004.574 | 1005.582 | 1006.590 | 1007.598 | 1008.606 | 1009.614 | 75 |
| 76 | 1004.488 | 1005.496 | 1006.504 | 1007.512 | 1008.520 | 1009.528 | 1010.536 | 1011.544 | 1012.552 | 1013.560 | 1014.568 | 1015.576 | 1016.584 | 1017.592 | 1018.600 | 1019.608 | 1020.616 | 1021.624 | 76 |
| 77 | 1016.498 | 1017.506 | 1018.514 | 1019.522 | 1020.530 | 1021.538 | 1022.546 | 1023.554 | 1024.562 | 1025.570 | 1026.578 | 1027.586 | 1028.594 | 1029.602 | 1030.610 | 1031.618 | 1032.626 | 1033.634 | 77 |
| 78 | 1028.508 | 1029.516 | 1030.524 | 1031.532 | 1032.540 | 1033.548 | 1034.556 | 1035.564 | 1036.572 | 1037.580 | 1038.588 | 1039.596 | 1040.604 | 1041.612 | 1042.620 | 1043.628 | 1044.636 | 1045.644 | 78 |

TABLE 6, Page 16 — MOLECULAR WEIGHTS OF HYDROCARBONS

Range: $C_{53}$ to $C_{78}$; $H_{109}$ to $H_{126}$
December 31, 1946; October 31, 1952

Number of Hydrogen Atoms

| No. of Carbon Atoms | 109 | 110 | 111 | 112 | 113 | 114 | 115 | 116 | 117 | 118 | 119 | 120 | 121 | 122 | 123 | 124 | 125 | 126 | No. of Carbon Atoms |
|---|---|---|---|---|---|---|---|---|---|---|---|---|---|---|---|---|---|---|---|
| 53 | ---- | ---- | ---- | ---- | ---- | ---- | ---- | ---- | ---- | ---- | ---- | ---- | ---- | ---- | ---- | ---- | ---- | ---- | 53 |
| 54 | 758.412 | 759.420 | ---- | ---- | ---- | ---- | ---- | ---- | ---- | ---- | ---- | ---- | ---- | ---- | ---- | ---- | ---- | ---- | 54 |
| 55 | 770.422 | 771.430 | 772.438 | 773.446 | ---- | ---- | ---- | ---- | ---- | ---- | ---- | ---- | ---- | ---- | ---- | ---- | ---- | ---- | 55 |
| 56 | 782.432 | 783.440 | 784.448 | 785.456 | 786.464 | 787.472 | ---- | ---- | ---- | ---- | ---- | ---- | ---- | ---- | ---- | ---- | ---- | ---- | 56 |
| 57 | 794.442 | 795.450 | 796.458 | 797.466 | 798.474 | 799.482 | 800.490 | 801.498 | ---- | ---- | ---- | ---- | ---- | ---- | ---- | ---- | ---- | ---- | 57 |
| 58 | 806.452 | 807.460 | 808.468 | 809.476 | 810.484 | 811.492 | 812.500 | 813.508 | 814.516 | 815.524 | ---- | ---- | ---- | ---- | ---- | ---- | ---- | ---- | 58 |
| 59 | 818.462 | 819.470 | 820.478 | 821.486 | 822.494 | 823.502 | 824.510 | 825.518 | 826.526 | 827.534 | 828.542 | 829.550 | ---- | ---- | ---- | ---- | ---- | ---- | 59 |
| 60 | 830.472 | 831.480 | 832.488 | 833.496 | 834.504 | 835.512 | 836.520 | 837.528 | 838.536 | 839.544 | 840.552 | 841.560 | 842.568 | 843.576 | ---- | ---- | ---- | ---- | 60 |
| 61 | 842.482 | 843.490 | 844.498 | 845.506 | 846.514 | 847.522 | 848.530 | 849.538 | 850.546 | 851.554 | 852.562 | 853.570 | 854.578 | 855.586 | 856.594 | 857.602 | ---- | ---- | 61 |
| 62 | 854.492 | 855.500 | 856.508 | 857.516 | 858.524 | 859.532 | 860.540 | 861.548 | 862.556 | 863.564 | 864.572 | 865.580 | 866.588 | 867.596 | 868.604 | 869.612 | 870.620 | 871.628 | 62 |
| 63 | 866.502 | 867.510 | 868.518 | 869.526 | 870.534 | 871.542 | 872.550 | 873.558 | 874.566 | 875.574 | 876.582 | 877.590 | 878.598 | 879.606 | 880.614 | 881.622 | 882.630 | 883.638 | 63 |
| 64 | 878.512 | 879.520 | 880.528 | 881.536 | 882.544 | 883.552 | 884.560 | 885.568 | 886.576 | 887.584 | 888.592 | 889.600 | 890.608 | 891.616 | 892.624 | 893.632 | 894.640 | 895.648 | 64 |
| 65 | 890.522 | 891.530 | 892.538 | 893.546 | 894.554 | 895.562 | 896.570 | 897.578 | 898.586 | 899.594 | 900.602 | 901.610 | 902.618 | 903.626 | 904.634 | 905.642 | 906.650 | 907.658 | 65 |
| 66 | 902.532 | 903.540 | 904.548 | 905.556 | 906.564 | 907.572 | 908.580 | 909.588 | 910.596 | 911.604 | 912.612 | 913.620 | 914.628 | 915.636 | 916.644 | 917.652 | 918.660 | 919.668 | 66 |
| 67 | 914.542 | 915.550 | 916.558 | 917.566 | 918.574 | 919.582 | 920.590 | 921.598 | 922.606 | 923.614 | 924.622 | 925.630 | 926.638 | 927.646 | 928.654 | 929.662 | 930.670 | 931.678 | 67 |
| 68 | 926.552 | 927.560 | 928.568 | 929.576 | 930.584 | 931.592 | 932.600 | 933.608 | 934.616 | 935.624 | 936.632 | 937.640 | 938.648 | 939.656 | 940.664 | 941.672 | 942.680 | 943.688 | 68 |
| 69 | 938.562 | 939.570 | 940.578 | 941.586 | 942.594 | 943.602 | 944.610 | 945.618 | 946.626 | 947.634 | 948.642 | 949.650 | 950.658 | 951.666 | 952.674 | 953.682 | 954.690 | 955.698 | 69 |
| 70 | 950.572 | 951.580 | 952.588 | 953.596 | 954.604 | 955.612 | 956.620 | 957.628 | 958.636 | 959.644 | 960.652 | 961.660 | 962.668 | 963.676 | 964.684 | 965.692 | 966.700 | 967.708 | 70 |
| 71 | 962.582 | 963.590 | 964.598 | 965.606 | 966.614 | 967.622 | 968.630 | 969.638 | 970.646 | 971.654 | 972.662 | 973.670 | 974.678 | 975.686 | 976.694 | 977.702 | 978.710 | 979.718 | 71 |
| 72 | 974.592 | 975.600 | 976.60b | 977.616 | 978.624 | 979.632 | 980.640 | 981.648 | 982.656 | 983.664 | 984.672 | 985.680 | 986.688 | 987.696 | 988.704 | 989.712 | 990.720 | 991.728 | 72 |
| 73 | 986.602 | 987.610 | 988.618 | 989.626 | 990.634 | 991.642 | 992.650 | 993.658 | 994.666 | 995.674 | 996.682 | 997.690 | 998.698 | 999.706 | 1000.714 | 1001.722 | 1002.730 | 1003.738 | 73 |
| 74 | 998.612 | 999.620 | 1000.628 | 1001.636 | 1002.644 | 1003.652 | 1004.660 | 1005.668 | 1006.676 | 1007.684 | 1008.692 | 1009.700 | 1010.708 | 1011.716 | 1012.724 | 1013.732 | 1014.740 | 1015.748 | 74 |
| 75 | 1010.622 | 1011.630 | 1012.638 | 1013.646 | 1014.654 | 1015.662 | 1016.670 | 1017.676 | 1018.686 | 1019.694 | 1020.702 | 1021.710 | 1022.718 | 1023.726 | 1024.734 | 1025.742 | 1026.750 | 1027.758 | 75 |
| 76 | 1022.632 | 1023.640 | 1024.648 | 1025.656 | 1026.664 | 1027.672 | 1028.680 | 1029.688 | 1030.696 | 1031.704 | 1032.712 | 1033.720 | 1034.728 | 1035.736 | 1036.744 | 1037.752 | 1038.760 | 1039.768 | 76 |
| 77 | 1034.642 | 1035.650 | 1036.658 | 1037.666 | 1038.674 | 1039.682 | 1040.690 | 1041.698 | 1042.706 | 1043.714 | 1044.722 | 1045.730 | 1046.738 | 1047.746 | 1048.754 | 1049.762 | 1050.770 | 1051.778 | 77 |
| 78 | 1046.652 | 1047.660 | 1048.668 | 1049.676 | 1050.684 | 1051.692 | 1052.700 | 1053.708 | 1054.716 | 1055.724 | 1056.732 | 1057.740 | 1058.748 | 1059.756 | 1060.764 | 1061.772 | 1062.780 | 1063.788 | 78 |

32

TABLE 6, Page 17 – MOLECULAR WEIGHTS OF HYDROCARBONS

Range: C53 to C78; H127 to H144

December 31, 1946; October 31, 1952

| No. of Carbon Atoms | Number of Hydrogen Atoms | | | | | | | | | | | | | | | | | |
|---|---|---|---|---|---|---|---|---|---|---|---|---|---|---|---|---|---|---|
| | 127 | 128 | 129 | 130 | 131 | 132 | 133 | 134 | 135 | 136 | 137 | 138 | 139 | 140 | 141 | 142 | 143 | 144 |
| 53 | | | | | | | | | | | | | | | | | | |
| 54 | | | | | | | | | | | | | | | | | | |
| 55 | | | | | | | | | | | | | | | | | | |
| 56 | | | | | | | | | | | | | | | | | | |
| 57 | | | | | | | | | | | | | | | | | | |
| 58 | | | | | | | | | | | | | | | | | | |
| 59 | | | | | | | | | | | | | | | | | | |
| 60 | | | | | | | | | | | | | | | | | | |
| 61 | | | | | | | | | | | | | | | | | | |
| 62 | | | | | | | | | | | | | | | | | | |
| 63 | 884.646 | 885.654 | | | | | | | | | | | | | | | | |
| 64 | 896.656 | 897.664 | 898.672 | 899.680 | | | | | | | | | | | | | | |
| 65 | 908.666 | 909.674 | 910.682 | 911.690 | 912.698 | 913.706 | | | | | | | | | | | | |
| 66 | 920.676 | 921.684 | 922.692 | 923.700 | 924.708 | 925.716 | 926.724 | 927.732 | | | | | | | | | | |
| 67 | 932.686 | 933.694 | 934.702 | 935.710 | 936.718 | 937.726 | 938.734 | 939.742 | 940.750 | 941.758 | | | | | | | | |
| 68 | 944.696 | 945.704 | 946.712 | 947.720 | 948.728 | 949.736 | 950.744 | 951.752 | 952.760 | 953.768 | 954.776 | 955.784 | | | | | | |
| 69 | 956.706 | 957.714 | 958.722 | 959.730 | 960.738 | 961.746 | 962.754 | 963.762 | 964.770 | 965.778 | 966.786 | 967.794 | 968.802 | 969.810 | | | | |
| 70 | 968.716 | 969.724 | 970.732 | 971.740 | 972.748 | 973.756 | 974.764 | 975.772 | 976.780 | 977.788 | 978.796 | 979.804 | 980.812 | 981.820 | 982.828 | 983.836 | | |
| 71 | 980.726 | 981.734 | 982.742 | 983.750 | 984.758 | 985.766 | 986.774 | 987.782 | 988.790 | 989.798 | 990.806 | 991.814 | 992.822 | 993.830 | 994.838 | 995.846 | 996.854 | 997.862 |
| 72 | 992.736 | 993.744 | 994.752 | 995.760 | 996.768 | 997.776 | 998.784 | 999.792 | 1000.800 | 1001.808 | 1002.816 | 1003.824 | 1004.832 | 1005.840 | 1006.848 | 1007.856 | 1008.864 | 1009.872 |
| 73 | 1004.746 | 1005.754 | 1006.762 | 1007.770 | 1008.778 | 1009.786 | 1010.794 | 1011.802 | 1012.810 | 1013.818 | 1014.826 | 1015.834 | 1016.842 | 1017.850 | 1018.858 | 1019.866 | 1020.874 | 1021.882 |
| 74 | 1016.756 | 1017.764 | 1018.772 | 1019.780 | 1020.788 | 1021.796 | 1022.804 | 1023.812 | 1024.820 | 1025.828 | 1026.836 | 1027.844 | 1028.852 | 1029.860 | 1030.868 | 1031.876 | 1032.884 | 1033.892 |
| 75 | 1028.766 | 1029.774 | 1030.782 | 1031.790 | 1032.798 | 1033.806 | 1034.814 | 1035.822 | 1036.830 | 1037.838 | 1038.846 | 1039.854 | 1040.862 | 1041.870 | 1042.878 | 1043.886 | 1044.894 | 1045.902 |
| 76 | 1040.776 | 1041.784 | 1042.792 | 1043.800 | 1044.808 | 1045.816 | 1046.824 | 1047.832 | 1048.840 | 1049.848 | 1050.856 | 1051.864 | 1052.872 | 1053.880 | 1054.888 | 1055.896 | 1056.904 | 1057.912 |
| 77 | 1052.786 | 1053.794 | 1054.802 | 1055.810 | 1056.818 | 1057.826 | 1058.834 | 1059.842 | 1060.850 | 1061.858 | 1062.866 | 1063.874 | 1064.882 | 1065.890 | 1066.898 | 1067.906 | 1068.914 | 1069.922 |
| 78 | 1064.796 | 1065.804 | 1066.812 | 1067.820 | 1068.828 | 1069.836 | 1070.844 | 1071.852 | 1072.860 | 1073.868 | 1074.876 | 1075.884 | 1076.892 | 1077.900 | 1078.908 | 1079.916 | 1080.924 | 1081.932 |

TABLE 6, Page 18 – MOLECULAR WEIGHTS OF HYDROCARBONS

Range: $C_{53}$ to $C_{78}$; $H_{145}$ to $H_{158}$

December 31, 1946; October 31, 1952

| No. of Carbon Atoms | Number of Hydrogen Atoms | | | | | | | | | | | | | |
|---|---|---|---|---|---|---|---|---|---|---|---|---|---|---|
| | 145 | 146 | 147 | 148 | 149 | 150 | 151 | 152 | 153 | 154 | 155 | 156 | 157 | 158 |
| 53 | — | — | — | — | — | — | — | — | — | — | — | — | — | — |
| 54 | — | — | — | — | — | — | — | — | — | — | — | — | — | — |
| 55 | — | — | — | — | — | — | — | — | — | — | — | — | — | — |
| 56 | — | — | — | — | — | — | — | — | — | — | — | — | — | — |
| 57 | — | — | — | — | — | — | — | — | — | — | — | — | — | — |
| 58 | — | — | — | — | — | — | — | — | — | — | — | — | — | — |
| 59 | — | — | — | — | — | — | — | — | — | — | — | — | — | — |
| 60 | — | — | — | — | — | — | — | — | — | — | — | — | — | — |
| 61 | — | — | — | — | — | — | — | — | — | — | — | — | — | — |
| 62 | — | — | — | — | — | — | — | — | — | — | — | — | — | — |
| 63 | — | — | — | — | — | — | — | — | — | — | — | — | — | — |
| 64 | — | — | — | — | — | — | — | — | — | — | — | — | — | — |
| 65 | — | — | — | — | — | — | — | — | — | — | — | — | — | — |
| 66 | — | — | — | — | — | — | — | — | — | — | — | — | — | — |
| 67 | — | — | — | — | — | — | — | — | — | — | — | — | — | — |
| 68 | — | — | — | — | — | — | — | — | — | — | — | — | — | — |
| 69 | — | — | — | — | — | — | — | — | — | — | — | — | — | — |
| 70 | — | — | — | — | — | — | — | — | — | — | — | — | — | — |
| 71 | — | — | — | — | — | — | — | — | — | — | — | — | — | — |
| 72 | 1010.880 | 1011.888 | — | — | — | — | — | — | — | — | — | — | — | — |
| 73 | 1022.890 | 1023.898 | 1024.906 | 1025.914 | — | — | — | — | — | — | — | — | — | — |
| 74 | 1034.900 | 1035.908 | 1036.916 | 1037.924 | 1038.932 | 1039.940 | — | — | — | — | — | — | — | — |
| 75 | 1046.910 | 1047.918 | 1048.926 | 1049.934 | 1050.942 | 1051.950 | 1052.958 | 1053.966 | — | — | — | — | — | — |
| 76 | 1058.920 | 1059.928 | 1060.936 | 1061.944 | 1062.952 | 1063.960 | 1064.968 | 1065.976 | 1066.984 | 1067.992 | — | — | — | — |
| 77 | 1070.930 | 1071.938 | 1072.946 | 1073.954 | 1074.962 | 1075.970 | 1076.978 | 1077.986 | 1078.994 | 1080.002 | 1081.010 | 1082.018 | — | — |
| 78 | 1082.940 | 1083.948 | 1084.956 | 1085.964 | 1086.972 | 1087.980 | 1088.988 | 1089.996 | 1091.004 | 1092.012 | 1093.020 | 1094.028 | 1095.036 | 1096.044 |

TABLE 20a (PART 1) – NORMAL PARAFFINS, $C_1$ TO $C_{20}$
BOILING POINT, $dt/dp$, REFRACTIVE INDEX, DENSITY, AND FREEZING POINT
June 30, 1948; December 31, 1950; October 31, 1952

| Compound | Formula | Boiling Point 760 mm Hg (°C) | dt/dp 760 mm Hg (°C/mm Hg) | Refractive Index[a] 20°C ($n_D$) | Refractive Index[a] 25°C ($n_D$) | Density[a] 20°C (g/ml) | Density[a] 25°C (g/ml) | Freezing Point In air at 1 atm (°C) |
|---|---|---|---|---|---|---|---|---|
| Methane | $CH_4$ | -161.49 | 0.0160 | ——— | ——— | ——— | ——— | -182.48[c] |
| Ethane | $C_2H_6$ | - 88.63 | 0.0244 | ——— | ——— | ——— | ——— | -183.27[c] |
| Propane | $C_3H_8$ | - 42.07 | 0.0298 | | 1.3292[b] | 0.5005[b] | 0.4928[b] | -187.69[c] |
| n-Butane | $C_4H_{10}$ | - 0.50 | 0.0347 | 1.3326[b] | | 0.5788[b] | 0.5730[b] | -138.350 |
| n-Pentane | $C_5H_{12}$ | +36.074 | 0.03856 | 1.35748 | 1.35472 | 0.62624 | 0.62139 | -129.721 |
| n-Hexane | $C_6H_{14}$ | 68.740 | 0.04191 | 1.37486 | 1.37226 | 0.65937 | 0.65481 | - 95.348 |
| n-Heptane | $C_7H_{16}$ | 98.427 | 0.04479 | 1.38764 | 1.38511 | 0.68376 | 0.67951 | - 90.610 |
| n-Octane | $C_8H_{18}$ | 125.665 | 0.04738 | 1.39743 | 1.39505 | 0.70252 | 0.69849 | - 56.795 |
| n-Nonane | $C_9H_{20}$ | 150.798 | 0.04967 | 1.40542 | 1.40311 | 0.71763 | 0.71381 | - 53.519 |
| n-Decane | $C_{10}H_{22}$ | 174.123 | 0.05172 | 1.41189 | 1.40967 | 0.73005 | 0.72625 | - 29.661 |
| n-Undecane | $C_{11}H_{24}$ | 195.890 | 0.05356 | 1.41716 | 1.41500 | 0.74017 | 0.73655 | - 25.594 |
| n-Dodecane | $C_{12}H_{26}$ | 216.278 | 0.05528 | 1.42160 | 1.41949 | 0.74869 | 0.74516 | - 9.587 |
| n-Tridecane | $C_{13}H_{28}$ | 235.44 | 0.0568 | 1.4256 | 1.4234 | 0.7564 | 0.7528 | - 5.392 |
| n-Tetradecane | $C_{14}H_{30}$ | 253.57 | 0.0582 | 1.4289 | 1.4268 | 0.7628 | 0.7593 | + 5.863 |
| n-Pentadecane | $C_{15}H_{32}$ | 270.63 | 0.0595 | 1.4319 | 1.4298 | 0.7685 | 0.7650 | 9.926 |
| n-Hexadecane | $C_{16}H_{34}$ | 286.793 | 0.06077 | 1.43453 | 1.43250 | 0.77344 | 0.76996 | 18.165 |
| n-Heptadecane | $C_{17}H_{36}$ | 301.82 | 0.0619 | 1.4369[d] | 1.4348 | 0.7780[d] | 0.7745 | 21.980 |
| n-Octadecane | $C_{18}H_{38}$ | 316.12 | 0.0630 | 1.4390[d] | 1.4369[d] | 0.7819[d] | 0.7785[d] | 28.180 |
| n-Nonadecane | $C_{19}H_{40}$ | 329.7 | 0.064 | 1.4409[d] | 1.4388[d] | 0.7855[d] | 0.7821[d] | 32.1 |
| n-Eicosane | $C_{20}H_{42}$ | 342.7 | 0.065 | 1.4426[d] | 1.4405[d] | 0.7887[d] | 0.7853[d] | 36.8 |

[a] See footnote a of Table 1a.   [b] At saturation pressure.   [c] At saturation pressure (triple point).   [d] For the undercooled liquid below the normal freezing point.

TABLE 20a (PART 2) - NORMAL PARAFFINS, $C_{21}$ TO $C_{40}$
BOILING POINT, $dt/dp$, REFRACTIVE INDEX, DENSITY, AND FREEZING POINT
December 31, 1950

| Compound | Formula | Boiling Point 760 mm Hg °C | $dt/dp$ 760 mm Hg °C/mm Hg | Refractive Index[a] 20°C $n_D$ | Refractive Index[a] 25°C $n_D$ | Density[a] 20°C g/ml | Density[a] 25°C g/ml | Freezing Point In air at 1 atm °C |
|---|---|---|---|---|---|---|---|---|
| n-Heneicosane | $C_{21}H_{44}$ | 355.1 | 0.07 | 1.4441[b] | 1.4420[b] | 0.7917[b] | 0.7883[b] | 40.5 |
| n-Docosane | $C_{22}H_{46}$ | 367.0 | 0.07 | 1.4455[b] | 1.4435[b] | 0.7944[b] | 0.7910[b] | 44.4 |
| n-Tricosane | $C_{23}H_{48}$ | 378.3 | 0.07 | 1.4466[b] | 1.4448[b] | 0.7969[b] | 0.7935[b] | 47.6 |
| n-Tetracosane | $C_{24}H_{50}$ | 389.2 | 0.07 | 1.4480[b] | 1.4460[b] | 0.7991[b] | 0.7958[b] | 50.9 |
| n-Pentacosane | $C_{25}H_{52}$ | 399.7 | 0.07 | 1.4491[b] | 1.4471[b] | 0.8012[b] | 0.7979[b] | 53.7 |
| n-Hexacosane | $C_{26}H_{54}$ | 409.7 | 0.07 | 1.4501[b] | 1.4481[b] | 0.8032[b] | 0.7998[b] | 56.4 |
| n-Heptacosane | $C_{27}H_{56}$ | 419.4 | 0.07 | 1.4511[b] | 1.4491[b] | 0.8050[b] | 0.8016[b] | 59.0 |
| n-Octacosane | $C_{28}H_{58}$ | 428.7 | 0.07 | 1.4520[b] | 1.4500[b] | 0.8067[b] | 0.8033[b] | 61.4 |
| n-Nonacosane | $C_{29}H_{60}$ | 437.7 | 0.07 | 1.4529[b] | 1.4508[b] | 0.8083[b] | 0.8049[b] | 63.7 |
| n-Triacontane | $C_{30}H_{62}$ | 446.4 | 0.07 | 1.4536[b] | 1.4516[b] | 0.8097[b] | 0.8064[b] | 65.8 |
| n-Hentriacontane | $C_{31}H_{64}$ | 455. | 0.07 | 1.4543[b] | 1.4523[b] | 0.8111[b] | 0.8078[b] | 67.9 |
| n-Dotriacontane | $C_{32}H_{66}$ | 463. | 0.07 | 1.4550[b] | 1.4530[b] | 0.8124[b] | 0.8091[b] | 69.7 |
| n-Tritriacontane | $C_{33}H_{66}$ | 471. | 0.07 | 1.4557[b] | 1.4536[b] | 0.8136[b] | 0.8103[b] | 71.4 |
| n-Tetratriacontane | $C_{34}H_{70}$ | 478. | 0.07 | 1.4563[b] | 1.4542[b] | 0.8148[b] | 0.8115[b] | 73.1 |
| n-Pentatriacontane | $C_{35}H_{72}$ | 486. | 0.08 | 1.4568[b] | 1.4548[b] | 0.8159[b] | 0.8126[b] | 74.7 |
| n-Hexatriacontane | $C_{36}H_{74}$ | 493. | 0.08 | 1.4573[b] | 1.4554[b] | 0.8169[b] | 0.8136[b] | 76.2 |
| n-Heptatriacontane | $C_{37}H_{76}$ | 500. | 0.08 | 1.4578[b] | 1.4559[b] | 0.8179[b] | 0.8146[b] | 77.7 |
| n-Octatriacontane | $C_{38}H_{78}$ | 507. | 0.08 | 1.4583[b] | 1.4564[b] | 0.8188[b] | 0.8155[b] | 79.0 |
| n-Nonatriacontane | $C_{39}H_{80}$ | 513. | 0.08 | 1.4588[b] | 1.4568[b] | 0.8197[b] | 0.8164[b] | 80.3 |
| n-Tetracontane | $C_{40}H_{82}$ | 520. | 0.08 | 1.4593[b] | 1.4573[b] | 0.8205[b] | 0.8172[b] | 81.5 |

a See footnote a of Table 1a.  b For the undercooled liquid below the normal freezing point.

TABLE 1a - PARAFFINS, C$_1$ TO C$_5$

BOILING POINT, $dt/dp$, REFRACTIVE INDEX, DENSITY, AND FREEZING POINT

June 30, 1945; June 30, 1948; October 31, 1952

| Compound | Formula | Boiling Point 760 mm Hg °C | $dt/dp$ 760 mm Hg °C/mm Hg | Refractive Index[a] 20°C $n_D$ | Refractive Index[a] 25°C $n_D$ | Density[a] 20°C g/ml | Density[a] 25°C g/ml | Freezing Point In air at 1 atm °C |
|---|---|---|---|---|---|---|---|---|
| Methane | CH$_4$ | -161.49 | 0.0160 | — | — | — | — | -182.48[c] |
| Ethane | C$_2$H$_6$ | -88.63 | 0.0244 | — | — | — | — | -183.27[c] |
| Propane | C$_3$H$_8$ | -42.07 | 0.0298 | — | — | 0.5005[b] | 0.4928[b] | -187.69[c] |
| n-Butane | C$_4$H$_{10}$ | -0.50 | 0.0347 | 1.3326[b] | 1.3292[b] | 0.5788[b] | 0.5730[b] | -138.350 |
| 2-Methylpropane (Isobutane) | " | -11.73 | 0.0337 | — | — | 0.5572[b] | 0.5510[b] | -159.600 |
| n-Pentane | C$_5$H$_{12}$ | +36.074 | 0.03856 | 1.35748 | 1.35472 | 0.62624 | 0.62139 | -129.721 |
| 2-Methylbutane (Isopentane) | " | 27.852 | 0.03815 | 1.35373 | 1.35088 | 0.61967 | 0.61462 | -159.900 |
| 2,2-Dimethylpropane (Neopentane) | " | 9.503 | 0.0361 | 1.342[b] | 1.339[b] | 0.5910[b] | 0.5851[b] | -16.550 |

[a] Values are given for the air-saturated hydrocarbon in the liquid state at one atmosphere. Values of the refractive index are for the sodium D line, for which the wave length is taken to be 5892.6 Angstrom units, which is the intensity weighted mean of the wave lengths of the D$_1$ and D$_2$ lines.

[b] At saturation pressure.

[c] At saturation pressure (triple point).

TABLE 2a (PART 1) - PARAFFINS, C$_6$

BOILING POINT, d$t$/d$p$, REFRACTIVE INDEX, DENSITY, AND FREEZING POINT

June 30, 1945; December 30, 1948; October 31, 1952

| Compound | Formula | Boiling Point 760 mm Hg °C | d$t$/d$p$ 760 mm Hg °C/mm Hg | Refractive Index[a] 20°C $n_D$ | 25°C $n_D$ | Density[a] 20°C g/ml | 25°C g/ml | Freezing Point In air at 1 atm °C |
|---|---|---|---|---|---|---|---|---|
| n-Hexane | C$_6$H$_{14}$ | 68.740 | 0.04191 | 1.37486 | 1.37226 | 0.65937 | 0.65481 | -95.348 |
| 2-Methylpentane | " | 60.271 | 0.04141 | 1.37145 | 1.36873 | 0.65315 | 0.64852 | -153.670 |
| 3-Methylpentane | " | 63.282 | 0.04182 | 1.37652 | 1.37386 | 0.66431 | 0.65976 | |
| 2,2-Dimethylbutane | " | 49.741 | 0.04117 | 1.36876 | 1.36595 | 0.64916 | 0.64446 | -99.870 |
| 2,3-Dimethylbutane | " | 57.988 | 0.04173 | 1.37495 | 1.37231 | 0.66164 | 0.65702 | -128.538 |

a See footnote a of Table 1a.

TABLE 2a (PART 2) — PARAFFINS, $C_7$

BOILING POINT, $dt/dp$, REFRACTIVE INDEX, DENSITY, AND FREEZING POINT

June 30, 1945; December 31, 1948; October 31, 1952

| Compound | Formula[a] | Boiling Point 760 mm Hg °C | $dt/dp$ 760 mm Hg °C/mm Hg | Refractive Index[a] 20°C $n_D$ | Refractive Index[a] 25°C $n_D$ | Density[a] 20°C g/ml | Density[a] 25°C g/ml | Freezing Point In air at 1 atm °C |
|---|---|---|---|---|---|---|---|---|
| n-Heptane | $C_7H_{16}$ | 98.427 | 0.04479 | 1.38764 | 1.38511 | 0.68376 | 0.67951 | -90.610 |
| 2-Methylhexane | " | 90.052 | 0.04431 | 1.38485 | 1.38227 | 0.67859 | 0.67439 | -118.276 |
| 3-Methylhexane | " | 91.850 | 0.04459 | 1.38864 | 1.38609 | 0.68713 | 0.68295 | |
| 3-Ethylpentane | " | 93.475 | 0.04482 | 1.39339 | 1.39084 | 0.69816 | 0.69395 | -118.604 |
| 2,2-Dimethylpentane | " | 79.197 | 0.04394 | 1.38215 | 1.37955 | 0.67385 | 0.66953 | -123.811 |
| 2,3-Dimethylpentane | " | 89.784 | 0.04482 | 1.39196 | 1.38945 | 0.69508 | 0.69091 | |
| 2,4-Dimethylpentane | " | 80.500 | 0.04376 | 1.38145 | 1.37882 | 0.67270 | 0.66832 | -119.242 |
| 3,3-Dimethylpentane | " | 86.064 | 0.04509 | 1.39092 | 1.38842 | 0.69327 | 0.68908 | -134.46[b] |
| 2,2,3-Trimethylbutane | " | 80.882 | 0.04484 | 1.38944 | 1.38692 | 0.69011 | 0.68588 | -24.912 |

a See footnote a of Table 1a.    b See Table 2z (Part 2) for the freezing points of the metastable crystalline forms.

TABLE 3a - PARAFFINS, $C_8$

BOILING POINT, $dt/dp$, REFRACTIVE INDEX, DENSITY, AND FREEZING POINT

June 30, 1945; December 31, 1948; October 31, 1952

| Compound | Formula | Boiling Point 760 mm Hg °C | $dt/dp$ 760 mm Hg °C/mm Hg | Refractive Index[a] 25°C $n_D$ | Refractive Index[a] 20°C $n_D$ | Density[a] 20°C g/ml | Density[a] 25°C g/ml | Freezing Point In air at 1 atm °C |
|---|---|---|---|---|---|---|---|---|
| n-Octane | $C_8H_{18}$ | 125.665 | 0.04738 | 1.39505 | 1.39743 | 0.70252 | 0.69849 | -56.795 |
| 2-Methylheptane | " | 117.647 | 0.04691 | 1.39257 | 1.39494 | 0.69792 | 0.69392 | -109.040 |
| 3-Methylheptane | " | 118.925 | 0.04712 | 1.39610 | 1.39848 | 0.70582 | 0.70175 | -120.50 |
| 4-Methylheptane | " | 117.709 | 0.04695 | 1.39553 | 1.39792 | 0.70463 | 0.70055 | -120.955 |
| 3-Ethylhexane | " | 118.534 | 0.04719 | 1.39919 | 1.40162 | 0.71358 | 0.70948 | |
| 2,2-Dimethylhexane | " | 106.840 | 0.04650 | 1.39104 | 1.39349 | 0.69528 | 0.69112 | -121.18 |
| 2,3-Dimethylhexane | " | 115.607 | 0.04724 | 1.39880 | 1.40113 | 0.71214 | 0.70809 | |
| 2,4-Dimethylhexane | " | 109.429 | 0.04664 | 1.39291 | 1.39534 | 0.70036 | 0.69620 | |
| 2,5-Dimethylhexane | " | 109.103 | 0.04646 | 1.39004 | 1.39246 | 0.69954 | 0.68934 | -91.200 |
| 3,3-Dimethylhexane | " | 111.969 | 0.04741 | 1.39782 | 1.40009 | 0.71000 | 0.70596 | -126.10 |
| 3,4-Dimethylhexane | " | 117.725 | 0.04752 | 1.40180 | 1.40406 | 0.71923 | 0.71516 | |
| 2-Methyl-3-ethylpentane | " | 115.650 | 0.04748 | 1.40167 | 1.40401 | 0.71932 | 0.71522 | -114.960 |
| 3-Methyl-3-ethylpentane | " | 118.259 | 0.04844 | 1.40549 | 1.40775 | 0.72742 | 0.72354 | -90.870 |
| 2,2,3-Trimethylpentane | " | 109.841 | 0.04755 | 1.40066 | 1.40295 | 0.71602 | 0.71207 | -112.27 |
| 2,2,4-Trimethylpentane | " | 99.238 | 0.04651 | 1.38901 | 1.39145 | 0.69192 | 0.68777 | -107.380 |
| 2,3,3-Trimethylpentane | " | 114.760 | 0.04833 | 1.40522 | 1.40750 | 0.72619 | 0.72232 | -100.70 |
| 2,3,4-Trimethylpentane | " | 113.467 | 0.04761 | 1.40198 | 1.40422 | 0.71906 | 0.71503 | -109.210 |
| 2,2,3,3-Tetramethylbutane | " | 106.47 | 0.0476 | — | — | — | — | +100.69 |

[a] See footnote a of Table 1a.

TABLE 4a, Page 1 — PARAFFINS, C9

BOILING POINT, *dt/dp*, REFRACTIVE INDEX, DENSITY, AND FREEZING POINT

June 30, 1945; March 31, 1949; October 31, 1952

| Compound | Formula | Boiling Point 760 mm Hg °C | dt/dp 760 mm Hg °C/mm Hg | Refractive Index[a] 20°C $n_D$ | 25°C $n_D$ | Density[a] 20°C g/ml | 25°C g/ml | Freezing Point In air at 1 atm °C |
|---|---|---|---|---|---|---|---|---|
| *n*-Nonane | C₉H₂₀ | 150.798 | 0.04967 | 1.40542 | 1.40311 | 0.71763 | 0.71381 | −53.519 |
| 2-Methyloctane | " | 143.26 | 0.049 | 1.4031 | 1.4008 | 0.7134 | 0.7095 | −80.4 |
| 3-Methyloctane | " | 144.18 | 0.049 | 1.4062 | 1.4039 | 0.7207 | 0.7168 | −107.6 |
| 4-Methyloctane | " | 142.48 | 0.049 | 1.4061 | 1.4038 | 0.7199 | 0.7160 | −113.2 |
| 3-Ethylheptane | " | 143.0 | 0.050 | 1.4093 | 1.4070 | 0.727 | 0.723 | |
| 4-Ethylheptane | " | 141.2 | 0.050 | 1.4096 | 1.4073 | 0.730 | 0.726 | −113.00 |
| 2,2-Dimethylheptane | " | 132.69 | 0.049 | 1.4016 | 1.3993 | 0.7105 | 0.7066 | |
| 2,3-Dimethylheptane | " | 140.5 | 0.050 | 1.4085 | 1.4062 | 0.7260 | 0.7221 | |
| 2,4-Dimethylheptane | " | 133.5 | 0.049 | 1.4033 | 1.4010 | 0.716 | 0.712 | |
| 2,5-Dimethylheptane | " | 136.0 | 0.049 | 1.4038 | 1.4015 | 0.715 | 0.711 | |
| 2,6-Dimethylheptane | " | 135.21 | 0.049 | 1.4007 | 1.3983 | 0.7089 | 0.7049 | −102.9 |
| 3,3-Dimethylheptane | " | 137.3 | 0.049 | 1.4085 | 1.4062 | 0.725 | 0.721 | |
| 3,4-Dimethylheptane | " | 140.6 | 0.050 | 1.4111 | 1.4089 | 0.7314 | 0.7275 | |
| 3,5-Dimethylheptane | " | 136.0 | 0.049 | 1.4067 | 1.4044 | 0.723 | 0.719 | |
| 4,4-Dimethylheptane | " | 135.2 | 0.049 | 1.4076 | 1.4053 | 0.725 | 0.721 | |

[a] See footnote a of Table 1a.

## TABLE 4a, Page 2 – PARAFFINS, C$_9$
### BOILING POINT, $dt/dp$, REFRACTIVE INDEX, DENSITY, AND FREEZING POINT
June 30, 1945; March 31, 1949; October 31, 1952

| Compound | Formula[a] | Boiling Point 760 mm Hg °C | $dt/dp$ 760 mm Hg °C/mm Hg | Refractive Index[a] $n_D$ 20°C | Refractive Index[a] $n_D$ 25°C | Density[a] 20°C g/ml | Density[a] 25°C g/ml | Freezing Point In air at 1 atm °C |
|---|---|---|---|---|---|---|---|---|
| 2-Methyl-3-ethylhexane | C$_9$H$_{20}$ | 138.0 | 0.050 | 1.4120 | 1.4097 | 0.731 | 0.727 | |
| 2-Methyl-4-ethylhexane | " | 133.8 | 0.049 | 1.4068 | 1.4046 | 0.723 | 0.719 | |
| 3-Methyl-3-ethylhexane | " | 140.6 | 0.050 | 1.4142 | 1.4120 | 0.741 | 0.737 | |
| 3-Methyl-4-ethylhexane | " | 140.4 | 0.050 | 1.416 | 1.414 | 0.742 | 0.738 | |
| 2,2,3-Trimethylhexane | " | 133.60 | 0.049 | 1.4105 | 1.4082 | 0.7292 | 0.7254 | |
| 2,2,4-Trimethylhexane | " | 126.54 | 0.049 | 1.4033 | 1.4010 | 0.7156 | 0.7118 | -120.0 |
| 2,2,5-Trimethylhexane | " | 124.084 | 0.04838 | 1.39972 | 1.39728 | 0.70721 | 0.70322 | -105.730 |
| 2,3,3-Trimethylhexane | " | 137.68 | 0.049 | 1.4141 | 1.4119 | 0.738 | 0.734 | -116.800 |
| 2,3,4-Trimethylhexane | " | 139.0 | 0.050 | 1.4144 | 1.4120 | 0.7392 | 0.7354 | |
| 2,3,5-Trimethylhexane | " | 131.34 | 0.049 | 1.4061 | 1.4037 | 0.7219 | 0.7179 | -127.8 |
| 2,4,4-Trimethylhexane | " | 130.648 | 0.04960 | 1.40745 | 1.40515 | 0.72381 | 0.72007 | -113.380 |
| 3,3,4-Trimethylhexane | " | 140.46 | 0.049 | 1.4178 | 1.4154 | 0.7454 | 0.7414 | -101.20 |
| 3,3-Diethylpentane | " | 146.168 | 0.05153 | 1.42051 | 1.41837 | 0.75359 | 0.75000 | -33.110 |
| 2,2-Dimethyl-3-ethylpentane | " | 133.83 | 0.050 | 1.4123 | 1.4102 | 0.7348 | 0.7310 | -99.2 |
| 2,3-Dimethyl-3-ethylpentane | " | 142. | 0.050 | 1.419 | 1.417 | 0.754 | 0.750 | |
| 2,4-Dimethyl-3-ethylpentane | " | 136.73 | 0.0504 | 1.4137 | 1.4115 | 0.7379 | 0.7341 | -122.2 |
| 2,2,3,3-Tetramethylpentane | " | 140.274 | 0.05124 | 1.42360 | 1.42140 | 0.75666 | 0.75299 | -9.90 |
| 2,2,3,4-Tetramethylpentane | " | 133.016 | 0.05030 | 1.41472 | 1.41246 | 0.73895 | 0.73524 | -121.09 |
| 2,2,4,4-Tetramethylpentane | " | 122.284 | 0.04932 | 1.40694 | 1.40459 | 0.71947 | 0.71563 | -66.54 |
| 2,3,3,4-Tetramethylpentane | " | 141.551 | 0.04223 | 1.42222 | 1.42003 | 0.75473 | 0.75113 | -102.123 |

a See footnote a of Table 1a.

TABLE 17a, Page 1 - PARAFFINS, C$_{10}$

BOILING POINT, *dt/dp*, REFRACTIVE INDEX, DENSITY, AND FREEZING POINT

October 31, 1950; October 31, 1952

| Compound | Formula | Boiling Point 760 mm Hg °C | dt/dp 760 mm Hg °C/mm Hg | Refractive Index[a] 20°C $n_D$ | Refractive Index[a] 25°C $n_D$ | Density[a] 20°C g/ml | Density[a] 25°C g/ml | Freezing Point In air at 1 atm °C |
|---|---|---|---|---|---|---|---|---|
| n-Decane | C$_{10}$H$_{22}$ | 174.123 | 0.05172 | 1.41189 | 1.40967 | 0.73005 | 0.72625 | -29.661 |
| 2-Methylnonane | " | 166.8 | 0.051 | 1.4099 | 1.4076 | 0.7281 | 0.7242 | -74.50 |
| 3-Methylnonane | " | 167.8 | 0.052 | 1.4125 | 1.4103 | 0.7334 | 0.7296 | -84.80 |
| 4-Methylnonane | " | 165.7 | 0.051 | 1.4123 | 1.4100 | 0.7323 | 0.7284 | -98.7 |
| 5-Methylnonane | " | 165.1 | 0.051 | 1.4122 | 1.4100 | 0.7326 | 0.7288 | -87.70 |
| 3-Ethyloctane | " | 168. | 0.052 | 1.416 | 1.414 | 0.740 | 0.736 | |
| 4-Ethyloctane | " | 168. | 0.052 | 1.416 | 1.414 | 0.740 | 0.736 | -54. |
| 2,2-Dimethyloctane | " | 155. | 0.051 | 1.4082 | 1.4060 | 0.7245 | 0.7208 | |
| 2,3-Dimethyloctane | " | 163.3 | 0.052 | 1.4148 | 1.4125 | 0.7376 | 0.7337 | |
| 2,4-Dimethyloctane | " | 153. | 0.050 | 1.4093 | 1.4069 | 0.7264 | 0.7224 | |
| 2,5-Dimethyloctane | " | 158. | 0.051 | 1.414 | 1.412 | 0.736 | 0.732 | |
| 2,6-Dimethyloctane | " | 158.54 | 0.0521 | 1.4113 | 1.4089 | 0.7285 | 0.7245 | |
| 2,7-Dimethyloctane | " | 159.87 | 0.051 | 1.4086 | 1.4062 | 0.7242 | 0.7202 | |
| 3,3-Dimethyloctane | " | 161.2 | 0.052 | 1.4165 | 1.4142 | 0.7390 | 0.7351 | |
| 3,4-Dimethyloctane | " | 166. | 0.052 | 1.4182 | 1.4159 | 0.746 | 0.742 | |
| 3,5-Dimethyloctane | " | 160. | 0.051 | 1.413 | 1.411 | 0.736 | 0.732 | |
| 3,6-Dimethyloctane | " | 160. | 0.051 | 1.4145 | 1.4122 | 0.7363 | 0.7324 | |
| 4,4-Dimethyloctane | " | 161. | 0.052 | 1.414 | 1.412 | 0.737 | 0.733 | |
| 4,5-Dimethyloctane | " | 162.13 | 0.052 | 1.4190 | 1.4167 | 0.7470 | 0.7432 | |
| 4-Propylheptane | " | 162. | 0.051 | 1.4150 | 1.4127 | 0.7364 | 0.7326 | |
| 4-Isopropylheptane | " | 160. | 0.051 | 1.417 | 1.415 | 0.741 | 0.737 | |
| 2-Methyl-3-ethylheptane | " | 166. | 0.052 | 1.418 | 1.416 | 0.746 | 0.742 | |
| 2-Methyl-4-ethylheptane | " | 160. | 0.051 | 1.413 | 1.411 | 0.736 | 0.732 | |
| 2-Methyl-5-ethylheptane | " | 159.7 | 0.051 | 1.4134 | 1.4109 | 0.736 | 0.732 | |
| 3-Methyl-3-ethylheptane | " | 163.8 | 0.053 | 1.4208 | 1.4190 | 0.7501 | 0.7463 | |

a See footnote a of Table 1a.

# TABLE 17a, Page 2 – PARAFFINS, $C_{10}$

## BOILING POINT, dt/dp, REFRACTIVE INDEX, DENSITY, AND FREEZING POINT

October 31, 1950; October 31, 1952

| Compound | Formula | Boiling Point 760 mm Hg °C | dt/dp 760 mm Hg °C/mm Hg | Refractive Index[a] $n_D$ 20°C | Refractive Index[a] $n_D$ 25°C | Density[a] 20°C g/ml | Density[a] 25°C g/ml | Freezing Point In air at 1 atm °C |
|---|---|---|---|---|---|---|---|---|
| 3-Methyl-4-ethylheptane | $C_{10}H_{22}$ | 167. | 0.052 | 1.422 | 1.419 | 0.753 | 0.749 | |
| 3-Methyl-b-ethylheptane | " | 161. | 0.051 | 1.416 | 1.414 | 0.743 | 0.739 | |
| 4-Methyl-3-ethylheptane | " | 167. | 0.052 | 1.422 | 1.419 | 0.753 | 0.749 | |
| 4-Methyl-4-ethylheptane | " | 167. | 0.053 | 1.421 | 1.419 | 0.752 | 0.748 | |
| 2,2,3-Trimethylheptane | " | 158. | 0.052 | 1.417 | 1.414 | 0.742 | 0.738 | |
| 2,2,4-Trimethylheptane | " | 147.7 | 0.051 | 1.4092 | 1.4070 | 0.7275 | 0.7237 | |
| 2,2,5-Trimethylheptane | " | 149. | 0.051 | 1.409 | 1.407 | 0.726 | 0.722 | |
| 2,2,6-Trimethylheptane | " | 148.2 | 0.051 | 1.4059 | 1.4036 | 0.7195 | 0.715b | |
| 2,3,3-Trimethylheptane | " | 160. | 0.053 | 1.4202 | 1.4178 | 0.7488 | 0.7448 | |
| 2,3,4-Trimethylheptane | " | 163. | 0.052 | 1.421 | 1.418 | 0.751 | 0.747 | |
| 2,3,5-Trimethylheptane | " | 157. | 0.051 | 1.416 | 1.414 | 0.741 | 0.737 | |
| 2,3,6-Trimethylheptane | " | 155.7 | 0.051 | 1.4125 | 1.4101 | 0.7345 | 0.7305 | |
| 2,4,4-Trimethylheptane | " | 153. | 0.052 | 1.412 | 1.410 | 0.733 | 0.729 | |
| 2,4,5-Trimethylheptane | " | 157. | 0.051 | 1.4160 | 1.4137 | 0.741 | 0.737 | |
| 2,4,6-Trimethylheptane | " | 144.8 | 0.050 | 1.4071 | 1.4046 | 0.7225 | 0.7184 | |
| 2,5,5-Trimethylheptane | " | 152.80 | 0.052 | 1.4136 | 1.4112 | 0.7368 | 0.7328 | |
| 3,3,4-Trimethylheptane | " | 164. | 0.053 | 1.424 | 1.422 | 0.757 | 0.753 | |
| 3,3,5-Trimethylheptane | " | 155.68 | 0.052 | 1.4170 | 1.4146 | 0.7428 | 0.7388 | |
| 3,4,4-Trimethylheptane | " | 164. | 0.053 | 1.424 | 1.422 | 0.757 | 0.753 | |
| 3,4,5-Trimethylheptane | " | 164. | 0.052 | 1.424 | 1.422 | 0.759 | 0.755 | |
| 2-Methyl-3-isopropylhexane | " | 163. | 0.052 | 1.421 | 1.418 | 0.751 | 0.747 | |
| 3,3-Diethylhexane | " | 166.3 | 0.053 | 1.428 | 1.426 | 0.767 | 0.763 | |
| 3,4-Diethylhexane | " | 162. | 0.052 | 1.420 | 1.418 | 0.754 | 0.750 | |
| 2,2-Dimethyl-3-ethylhexane | " | 159. | 0.052 | 1.420 | 1.413 | 0.749 | 0.745 | |
| 2,2-Dimethyl-4-ethylhexane | " | 147. | 0.051 | 1.4131 | 1.4107 | 0.733 | 0.729 | |

a See footnote a of Table 1a.

TABLE 17a, Page 3 - PARAFFINS, C$_{10}$

BOILING POINT, dt/dp, REFRACTIVE INDEX, DENSITY, AND FREEZING POINT

October 31, 1950; October 31, 1952

| Compound | Formula | Boiling Point 760 mm Hg °C | dt/dp 760 mm Hg °C/mm Hg | Refractive Index[a] 20°C $n_D$ | Refractive Index[a] 25°C $n_D$ | Density[a] 20°C g/ml | Density[a] 25°C g/ml | Freezing Point In air at 1 atm °C |
|---|---|---|---|---|---|---|---|---|
| 2,3-Dimethyl-3-ethylhexane | C$_{10}$H$_{22}$ | 169. | 0.054 | 1.427 | 1.424 | 0.765 | 0.760 | |
| 2,3-Dimethyl-4-ethylhexane | " | 164. | 0.052 | 1.424 | 1.422 | 0.759 | 0.755 | |
| 2,4-Dimethyl-3-ethylhexane | " | 164. | 0.052 | 1.424 | 1.422 | 0.759 | 0.755 | |
| 2,4-Dimethyl-4-ethylhexane | " | 158. | 0.052 | 1.419 | 1.417 | 0.747 | 0.743 | |
| 2,5-Dimethyl-3-ethylhexane | " | 157. | 0.051 | 1.416 | 1.414 | 0.741 | 0.737 | |
| 3,3-Dimethyl-4-ethylhexane | " | 165. | 0.053 | 1.427 | 1.425 | 0.764 | 0.760 | |
| 3,4-Dimethyl-3-ethylhexane | " | 170. | 0.054 | 1.431 | 1.429 | 0.772 | 0.768 | |
| 2,2,3,3-Tetramethylhexane | " | 160.31 | 0.0538 | 1.42818 | 1.42600 | 0.76446 | 0.76039 | -54.00 |
| 2,2,3,4-Tetramethylhexane | " | 154.9 | 0.052 | 1.4226 | 1.4202 | 0.7548 | 0.7503 | |
| 2,2,3,5-Tetramethylhexane | " | 148.4 | 0.051 | 1.4142 | 1.4117 | 0.7378 | 0.7336 | |
| 2,2,4,4-Tetramethylhexane | " | 153.3 | 0.051 | 1.4208 | 1.4183 | 0.7470 | 0.7428 | |
| 2,2,4,5-Tetramethylhexane | " | 147.88 | 0.0512 | 1.41318 | 1.41095 | 0.73346 | 0.73161 | -12.60 |
| 2,2,5,5-Tetramethylhexane | " | 137.46 | 0.0500 | 1.40550 | 1.40316 | 0.71875 | 0.71480 | |
| 2,3,3,4-Tetramethylhexane | " | 164.59 | 0.054 | 1.4297 | 1.4269 | 0.7694 | 0.7648 | |
| 2,3,3,5-Tetramethylhexane | " | 153. | 0.052 | 1.4196 | 1.4172 | 0.746 | 0.742 | |
| 2,3,4,4-Tetramethylhexane | " | 162.2 | 0.054 | 1.4270 | 1.4244 | 0.7639 | 0.7596 | |
| 2,3,4,5-Tetramethylhexane | " | 161. | 0.053 | 1.424 | 1.422 | 0.757 | 0.753 | |
| 3,3,4,4-Tetramethylhexane | " | 170.0 | 0.054 | 1.4368 | 1.4344 | 0.7824 | 0.7783 | -81.70 |
| 2,4-Dimethyl-3-isopropylpentane | " | 157.04 | 0.0544 | 1.42263 | 1.42243 | 0.75830 | 0.75457 | |
| 2-Methyl-3,3-diethylpentane | " | 174. | 0.055 | 1.435 | 1.432 | 0.780 | 0.775 | |
| 2,2,3-Trimethyl-3-ethylpentane | " | 168. | 0.054 | 1.436 | 1.434 | 0.781 | 0.777 | |
| 2,2,4-Trimethyl-3-ethylpentane | " | 155.3 | 0.053 | 1.4223 | 1.4199 | 0.7571 | 0.7531 | |
| 2,3,4-Trimethyl-3-ethylpentane | " | 169.44 | 0.054 | 1.4333 | 1.4310 | 0.7773 | 0.7733 | |
| 2,2,3,3,4-Pentamethylpentane | " | 166.05 | 0.0552 | 1.43606 | 1.43412 | 0.78009 | 0.77675 | -36.45 |
| 2,2,3,4,4-Pentamethylpentane | " | 159.29 | 0.0537 | 1.43069 | 1.4286b | 0.76703 | 0.76361 | -38.75 |

a See footnote a of Table 1a.

TABLE 22a (PART 1) – NORMAL ALKYL CYCLOPENTANES, $C_5$ TO $C_{21}$
BOILING POINT, $dt/dp$, REFRACTIVE INDEX, DENSITY, AND FREEZING POINT
December 31, 1948; June 30, 1949; September 30, 1951 (Corrected)

| Compound | Formula | Boiling Point 760 mm Hg °C | $dt/dp$ 760 mm Hg °C/mm Hg | Refractive Index[a] 20°C $n_D$ | 25°C $n_D$ | Density[a] 20°C g/ml | 25°C g/ml | Freezing Point In air at 1 atm °C |
|---|---|---|---|---|---|---|---|---|
| Cyclopentane | $C_5H_{10}$ | 49.262 | 0.04003 | 1.40645 | 1.40363 | 0.74538 | 0.74045 | −93.879 |
| Methylcyclopentane | $C_6H_{12}$ | 71.812 | 0.04274 | 1.40970 | 1.40700 | 0.74864 | 0.74394 | −142.455 |
| Ethylcyclopentane | $C_7H_{14}$ | 103.466 | 0.04623 | 1.41981 | 1.41730 | 0.76647 | 0.76217 | −138.446[c] |
| n-Propylcyclopentane | $C_8H_{16}$ | 130.949 | 0.04888 | 1.42626 | 1.42389 | 0.77633 | 0.77229 | −117.340 |
| n-Butylcyclopentane | $C_9H_{18}$ | 156.56 | 0.0512 | 1.4316 | 1.4293 | 0.7846 | 0.7808 | −107.985 |
| n-Pentylcyclopentane | $C_{10}H_{20}$ | 180. | 0.05 | 1.4358 | 1.4336 | 0.7912 | 0.7874 | − 83. |
| n-Hexylcyclopentane | $C_{11}H_{22}$ | 203. | 0.05 | 1.4392 | 1.4370 | 0.7965 | 0.7927 | − 73. |
| n-Heptylcyclopentane | $C_{12}H_{24}$ | 224. | 0.06 | 1.4421 | 1.4400 | 0.8010 | 0.7973 | − 53. |
| n-Octylcyclopentane | $C_{13}H_{26}$ | 243. | 0.06 | 1.4446 | 1.4425 | 0.8048 | 0.8011 | − 44. |
| n-Nonylcyclopentane | $C_{14}H_{28}$ | 262. | 0.06 | 1.4467 | 1.4446 | 0.8081 | 0.8045 | − 29. |
| n-Decylcyclopentane | $C_{15}H_{30}$ | 279.2 | 0.061 | 1.44662 | 1.44659 | 0.81097 | 0.80739 | − 22.13 |
| n-Undecylcyclopentane | $C_{16}H_{32}$ | 296. | 0.06 | 1.4503 | 1.4482 | 0.8135 | 0.8100 | − 10. |
| n-Dodecylcyclopentane | $C_{17}H_{34}$ | 312. | 0.06 | 1.4518 | 1.4497 | 0.8158 | 0.8123 | − 5. |
| n-Tridecylcyclopentane | $C_{18}H_{36}$ | 327. | 0.06 | 1.4531 | 1.4510 | 0.8178 | 0.8143 | + 5. |
| n-Tetradecylcyclopentane | $C_{19}H_{38}$ | 341. | 0.07 | 1.4543 | 1.4522 | 0.8196 | 0.8162 | 9. |
| n-Pentadecylcyclopentane | $C_{20}H_{40}$ | 355. | 0.07 | 1.4554 | 1.4533 | 0.8213 | 0.8178 | 17. |
| n-Hexadecylcyclopentane | $C_{21}H_{42}$ | 368. | 0.07 | 1.4564[b] | 1.4543 | 0.8228[b] | 0.8194 | 21. |

[a] See footnote a of Table 1a.   [b] For the undercooled liquid below the normal freezing point.   [c] See Table 6z for the freezing point of the metastable crystalline form.

TABLE 22a (PART 2) - NORMAL ALKYL CYCLOPENTANES, $C_{22}$ TO $C_{41}$
BOILING POINT, $dt/dp$, REFRACTIVE INDEX, DENSITY, AND FREEZING POINT
September 30, 1951

| Compound | Formula | Boiling Point 760 mm Hg °C | $dt/dp$ 760 mm Hg °C/mm Hg | Refractive Index[a] 20°C $n_D$ | 25°C $n_D$ | Density[a] 20°C g/ml | 25°C g/ml | Freezing Point In air at 1 atm °C |
|---|---|---|---|---|---|---|---|---|
| n-Heptadecylcyclopentane | $C_{22}H_{44}$ | 380. | 0.07 | 1.4572[b] | 1.4552[b] | 0.8241[b] | 0.8207[b] | 27. |
| n-Octadecylcyclopentane | $C_{23}H_{46}$ | 391. | 0.07 | 1.4581[b] | 1.4560[b] | 0.8254[b] | 0.8220[b] | 30. |
| n-Nonadecylcyclopentane | $C_{24}H_{48}$ | 402. | 0.07 | 1.4588[b] | 1.4568[b] | 0.8266[b] | 0.8232[b] | 35. |
| n-Eicosylcyclopentane | $C_{25}H_{50}$ | 413. | 0.07 | 1.4595[b] | 1.4575[b] | 0.8276[b] | 0.8242[b] | 38. |
| n-Heneicosylcyclopentane | $C_{26}H_{52}$ | 423. | 0.07 | 1.4602[b] | 1.4582[b] | 0.8286[b] | 0.8252[b] | 42. |
| n-Docosylcyclopentane | $C_{27}H_{54}$ | 433. | 0.07 | 1.4608[b] | 1.4588[b] | 0.8295[b] | 0.8262[b] | 45. |
| n-Tricosylcyclopentane | $C_{28}H_{56}$ | 442. | 0.07 | 1.4614[b] | 1.4593[b] | 0.8304[b] | 0.8270[b] | 49. |
| n-Tetracosylcyclopentane | $C_{29}H_{58}$ | 451. | 0.07 | 1.4619[b] | 1.4599[b] | 0.8312[b] | 0.8278[b] | 51. |
| n-Pentacosylcyclopentane | $C_{30}H_{60}$ | 460. | 0.07 | 1.4624[b] | 1.4604[b] | 0.8319[b] | 0.8286[b] | 54. |
| n-Hexacosylcyclopentane | $C_{31}H_{62}$ | 468. | 0.07 | 1.4628[b] | 1.4608[b] | 0.8326[b] | 0.8293[b] | 56. |
| n-Heptacosylcyclopentane | $C_{32}H_{64}$ | 476. | 0.07 | 1.4633[b] | 1.4612[b] | 0.8333[b] | 0.8299[b] | 59. |
| n-Octacosylcyclopentane | $C_{33}H_{66}$ | 483. | 0.08 | 1.4637[b] | 1.4617[b] | 0.8339[b] | 0.8306[b] | 61. |
| n-Nonacosylcyclopentane | $C_{34}H_{68}$ | 491. | 0.08 | 1.4640[b] | 1.4620[b] | 0.8345[b] | 0.8312[b] | 63. |
| n-Triacontylcyclopentane | $C_{35}H_{70}$ | 498. | 0.08 | 1.4644[b] | 1.4624[b] | 0.8350[b] | 0.8317[b] | 65. |
| n-Hentriacontylcyclopentane | $C_{36}H_{72}$ | 505. | 0.08 | 1.4648[b] | 1.4628[b] | 0.8356[b] | 0.8322[b] | 67. |
| n-Dotriacontylcyclopentane | $C_{37}H_{74}$ | 512. | 0.08 | 1.4651[b] | 1.4631[b] | 0.8360[b] | 0.8327[b] | 69. |
| n-Tritriacontylcyclopentane | $C_{38}H_{76}$ | 518. | 0.08 | 1.4654[b] | 1.4634[b] | 0.8365[b] | 0.8332[b] | 70. |
| n-Tetratriacontylcyclopentane | $C_{39}H_{78}$ | 525. | 0.08 | 1.4657[b] | 1.4637[b] | 0.8370[b] | 0.8336[b] | 72. |
| n-Pentatriacontylcyclopentane | $C_{40}H_{80}$ | 531. | 0.08 | 1.4660[b] | 1.4640[b] | 0.8374[b] | 0.8341[b] | 74. |
| n-Hexatriacontylcyclopentane | $C_{41}H_{82}$ | 537. | 0.08 | 1.4662[b] | 1.4642[b] | 0.8378[b] | 0.8345[b] | 75. |

a See footnote a of Table 1a.

b For the undercooled liquid below the normal freezing point.

TABLE 6a — ALKYL CYCLOPENTANES, C$_5$ TO C$_7$

BOILING POINT, dt/dp, REFRACTIVE INDEX, DENSITY, AND FREEZING POINT

June 30, 1945; February 28, 1947; June 30, 1949 (Corrected)

| Compound | Formula | Boiling Point 760 mm Hg °C | dt/dp 760 mm Hg °C/mm Hg | Refractive Index[a] 20°C $n_D$ | Refractive Index[a] 25°C $n_D$ | Density[a] 20°C g/ml | Density[a] 25°C g/ml | Freezing Point In air at 1 atm °C |
|---|---|---|---|---|---|---|---|---|
| Cyclopentane | C$_5$H$_{10}$ | 49.262 | 0.04003 | 1.40645 | 1.40363 | 0.74538 | 0.74045 | -93.879 |
| Methylcyclopentane | C$_6$H$_{12}$ | 71.812 | 0.04274 | 1.40970 | 1.40700 | 0.74864 | 0.74394 | -142.455 |
| Ethylcyclopentane | C$_7$H$_{14}$ | 103.466 | 0.04623 | 1.41981 | 1.41730 | 0.76647 | 0.76217 | -138.446[b] |
| 1,1-Dimethylcyclopentane | " | 87.846 | 0.04497 | 1.41356 | 1.41091 | 0.75448 | 0.74991 | -69.795 |
| 1,cis-2-Dimethylcyclopentane | " | 99.532 | 0.04603 | 1.42217 | 1.41963 | 0.77262 | 0.76807 | -53.896 |
| 1,trans-2-Dimethylcyclopentane | " | 91.869 | 0.04521 | 1.41200 | 1.40941 | 0.75144 | 0.74686 | -117.58 |
| 1,cis-3-Dimethylcyclopentane | " | 91.725 | 0.04525 | 1.41074 | 1.40813 | 0.74880 | 0.74435 | -133.975 |
| 1,trans-3-Dimethylcyclopentane | " | 90.773 | 0.04518 | 1.40894 | 1.40633 | 0.74479 | 0.74025 | -133.702 |

a See footnote a of Table 1a.   b See Table 6z for the freezing point of the metastable crystalline form.

TABLE 15a – ALKYL CYCLOPENTANES, $C_8$
BOILING POINT, $dt/dp$, REFRACTIVE INDEX, DENSITY, AND FREEZING POINT
February 28, 1947; June 30, 1949; October 31, 1952

| Compound | Formula[a] | Boiling Point 760 mm Hg | dt/dp 760 mm Hg | Refractive Index[a] | | Density[a] | | Freezing Point In air at 1 atm |
|---|---|---|---|---|---|---|---|---|
| | | °C | °C/mm Hg | 20°C $n_D$ | 25°C $n_D$ | 20°C g/ml | 25°C g/ml | °C |
| n-Propylcyclopentane | $C_8H_{16}$ | 130.949 | 0.04888 | 1.42626 | 1.42389 | 0.77633 | 0.77229 | -117.340 |
| isopropylcyclopentane | " | 126.419 | 0.04913 | 1.42582 | 1.42350 | 0.77653 | 0.77259 | -111.375 |
| 1-Methyl-1-ethylcyclopentane | " | 121.522 | 0.04863 | 1.42718 | 1.42476 | 0.78093 | 0.77670 | -143.800 |
| 1-Methyl-cis-2-ethylcyclopentane | " | 128.050 | 0.04897 | 1.42933 | 1.42695 | 0.78522 | 0.78113 | -105.95 |
| 1-Methyl-trans-2-ethylcyclopentane | " | 121.2 | 0.049 | 1.4219 | 1.4195 | 0.7690 | 0.7649 | |
| 1-Methyl-cis-3-ethylcyclopentane | " | 121.4 | 0.049 | 1.4203 | 1.4179 | 0.7724 | 0.7681 | |
| 1-Methyl-trans-3-ethylcyclopentane | " | 120.8 | 0.049 | 1.4186 | 1.4162 | 0.7619 | 0.7577 | -108. |
| 1,1,2-Trimethylcyclopentane | " | 113.729 | 0.04818 | 1.42298 | 1.42051 | 0.77252 | 0.76817 | -21.64 |
| 1,1,3-Trimethylcyclopentane | " | 104.893 | 0.04724 | 1.41119 | 1.40870 | 0.74825 | 0.74392 | -142.44 |
| 1,cis-2,cis-3-Trimethylcyclopentane | " | 123.0 | 0.049 | 1.4262 | 1.4238 | 0.7792 | 0.7751 | -116.430 |
| 1,cis-2,trans-3-Trimethylcyclopentane | " | 117.5 | 0.048 | 1.4218 | 1.4194 | 0.7704 | 0.7661 | -112. |
| 1,trans-2,cis-3-Trimethylcyclopentane | " | 110.2 | 0.048 | 1.4138 | 1.4114 | 0.7535 | 0.7492 | -112.705 |
| 1,cis-2,cis-4-Trimethylcyclopentane | " | 118. | 0.048 | 1.422 | 1.420 | 0.766 | 0.762 | |
| 1,cis-2,trans-4-Trimethylcyclopentane | " | 116.731 | 0.04827 | 1.41855 | 1.41612 | 0.76345 | 0.75920 | -132.55 |
| 1,trans-2,cis-4-Trimethylcyclopentane | " | 109.290 | 0.04738 | 1.41060 | 1.40812 | 0.74727 | 0.74302 | -130.78 |

[a] See footnote a of Table 1a.

### TABLE 23a (PART 1) – NORMAL ALKYL CYCLOHEXANES, $C_6$ TO $C_{22}$
### BOILING POINT, $dt/dp$, REFRACTIVE INDEX, DENSITY, AND FREEZING POINT
December 31, 1948; September 30, 1951; October 31, 1952

| Compound | Formula[a] | Boiling Point 760 mm Hg °C | $dt/dp$ 760 mm Hg °C/mm Hg | Refractive Index[a] 20°C $n_D$ | 25°C $n_D$ | Density[a] 20°C g/ml | 25°C g/ml | Freezing Point In air at 1 atm °C |
|---|---|---|---|---|---|---|---|---|
| Cyclohexane | $C_6H_{12}$ | 80.738 | 0.0476 | 1.42623 | 1.42354 | 0.77855 | 0.77389 | + 6.554 |
| Methylcyclohexane | $C_7H_{14}$ | 100.934 | 0.04671 | 1.42312 | 1.42058 | 0.76939 | 0.76506 | −126.593 |
| Ethylcyclohexane | $C_8H_{16}$ | 131.783 | 0.04969 | 1.43304 | 1.43073 | 0.78792 | 0.78390 | −111.323 |
| n-Propylcyclohexane | $C_9H_{18}$ | 156.724 | 0.05200 | 1.43705 | 1.43478 | 0.79960 | 0.78977 | − 94.900 |
| n-Butylcyclohexane | $C_{10}H_{20}$ | 180.947 | 0.05412 | 1.44075 | 1.43855 | 0.79918 | 0.79551 | − 74.725 |
| n-Pentylcyclohexane | $C_{11}H_{22}$ | 202.8 | 0.354 | 1.4437 | 1.4416 | 0.8037 | 0.8002 | − 57.5 |
| n-Hexylcyclohexane | $C_{12}H_{24}$ | 224.0 | 0.056 | 1.4462 | 1.4441 | 0.8076 | 0.8041 | − 43.0 |
| n-Heptylcyclohexane | $C_{13}H_{26}$ | 244. | 0.06 | 1.4484 | 1.4463 | 0.8109 | 0.8074 | − 30.5 |
| n-Octylcyclohexane | $C_{14}H_{28}$ | 264. | 0.06 | 1.4503 | 1.4483 | 0.8138 | 0.8104 | − 19.7 |
| n-Nonylcyclohexane | $C_{15}H_{30}$ | 282. | 0.36 | 1.4519 | 1.4499 | 0.8163 | 0.8129 | − 10.2 |
| n-Decylcyclohexane | $C_{16}H_{32}$ | 299. | 0.06 | 1.45338 | 1.45141 | 0.81958 | 0.81517 | − 1.726 |
| n-Undecylcyclohexane | $C_{17}H_{34}$ | 316. | 0.06 | 1.4547 | 1.4527 | 0.8206 | 0.8172 | + 5.8 |
| n-Dodecylcyclohexane | $C_{18}H_{36}$ | 331. | 0.06 | 1.4559 | 1.4539 | 0.8223 | 0.8190 | 12.5 |
| n-Tridecylcyclohexane | $C_{19}H_{38}$ | 346. | 0.07 | 1.4570 | 1.4550 | 0.8239 | 0.8206 | 16.5 |
| n-Tetradecylcyclohexane | $C_{20}H_{40}$ | 360. | 0.07 | 1.4579[b] | 1.4559 | 0.8254[b] | 0.8221 | 24.0 |
| n-Pentadecylcyclohexane | $C_{21}H_{42}$ | 373. | 0.07 | 1.4588[b] | 1.4568[b] | 0.8267[b] | 0.8234[b] | 29.0 |
| n-Hexadecylcyclohexane | $C_{22}H_{44}$ | 385. | 0.07 | 1.4596[b] | 1.4576[b] | 0.8279[b] | 0.8246[b] | 33.6 |

a See footnote a of Table 1a.    b For the undercooled liquid below the normal freezing point.

50

TABLE 23a (PART 2) – NORMAL ALKYL CYCLOHEXANES, $C_{23}$ TO $C_{42}$
BOILING POINT, $dt/dp$, REFRACTIVE INDEX, DENSITY, AND FREEZING POINT

September 30, 1951

| Compound | Formula | Boiling Point 760 mm Hg °C | dt/dp 760 mm Hg °C/mm Hg | Refractive Index[a] 20°C $n_D$ | 25°C $n_D$ | Density[a] 20°C g/ml | 25°C g/ml | Freezing Point In air at 1 atm °C |
|---|---|---|---|---|---|---|---|---|
| n-Heptadecylcyclohexane | $C_{23}H_{46}$ | 397. | 0.07 | 1.4603[b] | 1.4583[b] | 0.8290[b] | 0.8257[b] | 37.8 |
| n-Octadecylcyclohexane | $C_{24}H_{48}$ | 409. | 0.07 | 1.4610[b] | 1.4590[b] | 0.8300[b] | 0.8267[b] | 41.6 |
| n-Nonadecylcyclohexane | $C_{25}H_{50}$ | 420. | 0.07 | 1.4616[b] | 1.4596[b] | 0.8310[b] | 0.8277[b] | 45.2 |
| n-Eicosylcyclohexane | $C_{26}H_{52}$ | 430. | 0.07 | 1.4622[b] | 1.4602[b] | 0.8318[b] | 0.8285[b] | 48.5 |
| n-Heneicosylcyclohexane | $C_{27}H_{54}$ | 440. | 0.07 | 1.4627[b] | 1.4607[b] | 0.8326[b] | 0.8294[b] | 51.5 |
| n-Docosylcyclohexane | $C_{28}H_{56}$ | 449. | 0.07 | 1.4632[b] | 1.4612[b] | 0.8334[b] | 0.8301[b] | 54.4 |
| n-Tricosylcyclohexane | $C_{29}H_{58}$ | 459. | 0.07 | 1.4637[b] | 1.4617[b] | 0.8341[b] | 0.8308[b] | 57.0 |
| n-Tetracosylcyclohexane | $C_{30}H_{60}$ | 467. | 0.07 | 1.4641[b] | 1.4621[b] | 0.8347[b] | 0.8315[b] | 59.5 |
| n-Pentacosylcyclohexane | $C_{31}H_{62}$ | 476. | 0.07 | 1.4645[b] | 1.4626[b] | 0.8353[b] | 0.8321[b] | 61.9 |
| n-Hexacosylcyclohexane | $C_{32}H_{64}$ | 484. | 0.08 | 1.4649[b] | 1.4629[b] | 0.8359[b] | 0.8326[b] | 64.0 |
| n-Heptacosylcyclohexane | $C_{33}H_{66}$ | 492. | 0.08 | 1.4653[b] | 1.4633[b] | 0.8365[b] | 0.8332[b] | 66.1 |
| n-Octacosylcyclohexane | $C_{34}H_{68}$ | 499. | 0.08 | 1.4656[b] | 1.4636[b] | 0.8370[b] | 0.8337[b] | 68.0 |
| n-Nonacosylcyclohexane | $C_{35}H_{70}$ | 507. | 0.08 | 1.4659[b] | 1.4640[b] | 0.8374[b] | 0.8342[b] | 69.9 |
| n-Triacontylcyclohexane | $C_{36}H_{72}$ | 514. | 0.08 | 1.4662[b] | 1.4643[b] | 0.8379[b] | 0.8346[b] | 71.6 |
| n-Hentriacontylcyclohexane | $C_{37}H_{74}$ | 520. | 0.08 | 1.4665[b] | 1.4645[b] | 0.8383[b] | 0.8351[b] | 73.3 |
| n-Dotriacontylcyclohexane | $C_{38}H_{76}$ | 527. | 0.08 | 1.4668[b] | 1.4648[b] | 0.8388[b] | 0.8355[b] | 74.8 |
| n-Tritriacontylcyclohexane | $C_{39}H_{78}$ | 533. | 0.08 | 1.4670[b] | 1.4651[b] | 0.8391[b] | 0.8359[b] | 76.3 |
| n-Tetratriacontylcyclohexane | $C_{40}H_{80}$ | 540. | 0.08 | 1.4673[b] | 1.4653[b] | 0.8395[b] | 0.8363[b] | 77.7 |
| n-Pentatriacontylcyclohexane | $C_{41}H_{82}$ | 546. | 0.08 | 1.4675[b] | 1.4656[b] | 0.8399[b] | 0.8366[b] | 79.1 |
| n-Hexatriacontylcyclohexane | $C_{42}H_{84}$ | 551. | 0.08 | 1.4678[b] | 1.4658[b] | 0.8402[b] | 0.8370[b] | 80.4 |

[a] See footnote a of Table 1a.   [b] For the undercooled liquid below the normal freezing point.

TABLE 7a — ALKYL CYCLOHEXANES, C$_6$ TO C$_8$
BOILING POINT, dt/dp, REFRACTIVE INDEX, DENSITY, AND FREEZING POINT
June 30, 1943; June 30, 1945; March 31, 1947; June 30, 1949; October 31, 1952

| Compound | Formula[a] | Boiling Point 760 mm Hg °C | dt/dp 760 mm Hg °C/mm Hg | Refractive Index[a] 20°C $n_D$ | Refractive Index[a] 25°C $n_D$ | Density[a] 20°C g/ml | Density[a] 25°C g/ml | Freezing Point In air at 1 atm °C |
|---|---|---|---|---|---|---|---|---|
| Cyclohexane | C$_6$H$_{12}$ | 80.738 | 0.04376 | 1.42623 | 1.42354 | 0.77855 | 0.77389 | +6.554 |
| Methylcyclohexane | C$_7$H$_{14}$ | 100.934 | 0.04671 | 1.42312 | 1.42058 | 0.76939 | 0.76506 | -126.593 |
| Ethylcyclohexane | C$_8$H$_{16}$ | 131.783 | 0.04969 | 1.43304 | 1.43073 | 0.78792 | 0.78390 | -111.323 |
| 1,1-Dimethylcyclohexane | " | 119.543 | 0.04920 | 1.42900 | 1.42662 | 0.78094 | 0.77677 | -33.495 |
| 1,cis-2-Dimethylcyclohexane | " | 129.728 | 0.04988 | 1.43596 | 1.43358 | 0.79627 | 0.79222 | -50.023 |
| 1,trans-2-Dimethylcyclohexane | " | 123.419 | 0.04951 | 1.42695 | 1.42470 | 0.77601 | 0.77204 | -88.194 |
| 1,cis-3-Dimethylcyclohexane[b] | " | 120.088 | 0.04880 | 1.42294 | 1.42063 | 0.76603 | 0.76196 | -75.573 |
| 1,trans-3-Dimethylcyclohexane[c] | " | 124.450 | 0.04910 | 1.43085 | 1.42843 | 0.78472 | 0.78055 | -90.108 |
| 1,cis-4-Dimethylcyclohexane | " | 124.321 | 0.04921 | 1.42966 | 1.42731 | 0.78285 | 0.77870 | -87.436 |
| 1,trans-4-Dimethylcyclohexane | " | 119.351 | 0.04903 | 1.42090 | 1.41853 | 0.76255 | 0.75835 | -36.962 |

a See footnote a of Table 1a.
b This isomer, formerly labled "*trans*", has the following properties: boiling point at 1 atm., 120.09°C; refractive index, $n_D$ at 25°C, 1.4206; density at 25°C, 0.7620 g/ml.
c This isomer, formerly labeled "*cis*", has the following properties: boiling point at 1 atm., 124.45°C; refractive index, $n_D$ at 25°C, 1.4284; density at 25°C, 0.7806 g/ml.

51

52

TABLE 24a (PART 1) – NORMAL MONOOLEFINS (1-ALKENES), C₂ TO C₂₀
BOILING POINT, dt/dp, REFRACTIVE INDEX, DENSITY, AND FREEZING POINT

February 28, 1949; December 31, 1950; October 31, 1952

| Compound | Formula | Boiling Point 760 mm Hg °C | dt/dp 760 mm Hg °C/mm Hg | Refractive Index[a] $n_D$ 20°C | Refractive Index[a] $n_D$ 25°C | Density[a] 20°C g/ml | Density[a] 25°C g/ml | Freezing Point In air at 1 atm °C |
|---|---|---|---|---|---|---|---|---|
| Ethene (Ethylene) | $C_2H_4$ | -103.71 | 0.0224 | — | — | — | — | -169.15[c] |
| Propene (Propylene) | $C_3H_6$ | - 47.70 | 0.0289 | — | — | 0.5139[b] | 0.5053[b] | -185.25[c] |
| 1-Butene | $C_4H_8$ | - 6.26 | 0.0337 | — | — | 0.5951[b] | 0.5888[b] | -185.35[c] |
| 1-Pentene | $C_5H_{10}$ | + 29.968 | 0.03801 | 1.37148 | 1.36835 | 0.64050 | 0.63533 | -165.220 |
| 1-Hexene | $C_6H_{12}$ | 63.485 | 0.04149 | 1.38798 | 1.38502 | 0.67317 | 0.66848 | -139.819 |
| 1-Heptene | $C_7H_{14}$ | 93.643 | 0.04447 | 1.39980 | 1.39713 | 0.69698 | 0.69267 | -119.029 |
| 1-Octene | $C_8H_{16}$ | 121.280 | 0.04711 | 1.40870 | 1.40620 | 0.71492 | 0.71085 | -101.736 |
| 1-Nonene | $C_9H_{18}$ | 146.868 | 0.04944 | 1.41572 | 1.41333 | 0.72922 | 0.72531 | - 81.37 |
| 1-Decene | $C_{10}H_{20}$ | 170.570 | 0.05157 | 1.42146 | 1.41913 | 0.74081 | 0.73693 | - 66.310 |
| 1-Undecene | $C_{11}H_{22}$ | 192.671 | 0.05348 | 1.42609 | 1.42383 | 0.75032 | 0.74655 | - 49.185 |
| 1-Dodecene | $C_{12}H_{24}$ | 213.357 | 0.05522 | 1.43002 | 1.42782 | 0.75896 | 0.75474 | - 35.230 |
| 1-Tridecene | $C_{13}H_{26}$ | 232.78 | 0.0569 | 1.4335 | 1.4313 | 0.7653 | 0.7617 | - 23.070 |
| 1-Tetradecene | $C_{14}H_{28}$ | 251.01 | 0.0583 | 1.4364 | 1.4342 | 0.7713 | 0.7677 | - 12.85 |
| 1-Pentadecene | $C_{15}H_{30}$ | 268.17 | 0.0597 | 1.4389 | 1.4368 | 0.7765 | 0.7730 | - 3.730 |
| 1-Hexadecene | $C_{16}H_{32}$ | 284.4 | 0.061 | 1.44120 | 1.43907 | 0.78112 | 0.77759 | + 4.120 |
| 1-Heptadecene | $C_{17}H_{34}$ | 299.7 | 0.062 | 1.4432 | 1.4411 | 0.7852 | 0.7817 | 11.2 |
| 1-Octadecene | $C_{18}H_{36}$ | 314.2 | 0.063 | 1.4450 | 1.4429 | 0.7888 | 0.7853 | 17.6 |
| 1-Nonadecene | $C_{19}H_{38}$ | 328.0 | 0.064 | 1.4466[d] | 1.4445 | 0.7920[d] | 0.7886 | 23.4 |
| 1-Eicosene | $C_{20}H_{40}$ | 341.2 | 0.065 | 1.4481[d] | 1.4460[d] | 0.7950[d] | 0.7916[d] | 28.6 |

[a] See footnote a of Table 1a.  [b] At saturation pressure.  [c] At saturation pressure (triple point).  [d] For the undercooled liquid below the normal freezing point.

53

TABLE 24a (PART 2) – NORMAL MONOOLEFINS (1-ALKENES), $C_{21}$ TO $C_{40}$
BOILING POINT, $dt/dp$, REFRACTIVE INDEX, DENSITY, AND FREEZING POINT
December 31, 1950

| Compound | Formula | Boiling Point 760 mm Hg °C | $dt/dp$ 760 mm Hg °C/mm Hg | Refractive Index[a] 20°C $n_D$ | 25°C $n_D$ | Density[a] 20°C g/ml | 25°C g/ml | Freezing Point In air at 1 atm °C |
|---|---|---|---|---|---|---|---|---|
| 1-Heneicosene | $C_{21}H_{42}$ | 354. | 0.07 | 1.4494[b] | 1.4473[b] | 0.7977[b] | 0.7943[b] | 33.3 |
| 1-Docosene | $C_{22}H_{44}$ | 366. | 0.07 | 1.4506[b] | 1.4485[b] | 0.8002[b] | 0.7968[b] | 37.8 |
| 1-Tricosene | $C_{23}H_{46}$ | 377. | 0.07 | 1.4517[b] | 1.4496[b] | 0.8024[b] | 0.7991[b] | 41.6 |
| 1-Tetracosene | $C_{24}H_{48}$ | 388. | 0.07 | 1.4527[b] | 1.4506[b] | 0.8045[b] | 0.8011[b] | 45.3 |
| 1-Pentacosene | $C_{25}H_{50}$ | 398. | 0.07 | 1.4537[b] | 1.4516[b] | 0.8064[b] | 0.8031[b] | 48.7 |
| 1-Hexacosene | $C_{26}H_{52}$ | 408. | 0.07 | 1.4545[b] | 1.4524[b] | 0.8082[b] | 0.8048[b] | 51.8 |
| 1-Heptacosene | $C_{27}H_{54}$ | 418. | 0.07 | 1.4553[b] | 1.4533[b] | 0.8098[b] | 0.8065[b] | 54.7 |
| 1-Octacosene | $C_{28}H_{56}$ | 427. | 0.07 | 1.4561[b] | 1.4540[b] | 0.8114[b] | 0.8080[b] | 57.5 |
| 1-Nonacosene | $C_{29}H_{58}$ | 436. | 0.07 | 1.4568[b] | 1.4547[b] | 0.8128[b] | 0.8095[b] | 60.0 |
| 1-Triacontene | $C_{30}H_{60}$ | 445. | 0.07 | 1.4574[b] | 1.4554[b] | 0.8141[b] | 0.8108[b] | 62.4 |
| 1-Hentriacontene | $C_{31}H_{62}$ | 453. | 0.07 | 1.4580[b] | 1.4560[b] | 0.8154[b] | 0.8121[b] | 64.6 |
| 1-Dotriacontene | $C_{32}H_{64}$ | 461. | 0.07 | 1.4586[b] | 1.4566[b] | 0.8166[b] | 0.8133[b] | 66.7 |
| 1-Tritriacontene | $C_{33}H_{66}$ | 469. | 0.07 | 1.4592[b] | 1.4571[b] | 0.8177[b] | 0.8144[b] | 68.7 |
| 1-Tetratriacontene | $C_{34}H_{68}$ | 477. | 0.07 | 1.4596[b] | 1.4576[b] | 0.8187[b] | 0.8154[b] | 70.5 |
| 1-Pentatriacontene | $C_{35}H_{70}$ | 484. | 0.08 | 1.4602[b] | 1.4581[b] | 0.8197[b] | 0.8164[b] | 72.3 |
| 1-Hexatriacontene | $C_{36}H_{72}$ | 491. | 0.08 | 1.4606[b] | 1.4586[b] | 0.8206[b] | 0.8173[b] | 73.9 |
| 1-Heptatriacontene | $C_{37}H_{74}$ | 498. | 0.08 | 1.4610[b] | 1.4590[b] | 0.8215[b] | 0.8182[b] | 75.5 |
| 1-Octatriacontene | $C_{38}H_{76}$ | 505. | 0.08 | 1.4614[b] | 1.4594[b] | 0.8224[b] | 0.8191[b] | 77.0 |
| 1-Nonatriacontene | $C_{39}H_{78}$ | 511. | 0.08 | 1.4618[b] | 1.4598[b] | 0.8232[b] | 0.8199[b] | 78.4 |
| 1-Tetracontene | $C_{40}H_{80}$ | 517. | 0.08 | 1.4622[b] | 1.4602[b] | 0.8239[b] | 0.8206[b] | 79.8 |

a See footnote a of Table 1a.    b For the undercooled liquid below the normal freezing point.

TABLE 8a (PART 1) - MONOOLEFINS, C$_2$ TO C$_5$

BOILING POINT, dt/dp, REFRACTIVE INDEX, DENSITY, AND FREEZING POINT

September 30, 1943; June 30, 1945; May 31, 1947; October 31, 1952

| Compound | Formula[a] | Boiling Point 760 mm Hg °C | dt/dp 760 mm Hg °C/mm Hg | Refractive Index[a] 20°C $n_D$ | 25°C $n_D$ | Density[a] 20°C g/ml | 25°C g/ml | Freezing Point In air at 1 atm °C |
|---|---|---|---|---|---|---|---|---|
| Ethene (Ethylene) | C$_2$H$_4$ | -103.71 | 0.0224 | — | — | — | — | -169.15[c] |
| Propene (Propylene) | C$_3$H$_6$ | -47.70 | 0.0289 | — | — | 0.5139[b] | 0.5053[b] | -185.25[c] |
| 1-Butene | C$_4$H$_8$ | -6.26 | 0.0337 | — | — | 0.5951[b] | 0.5888[b] | -185.35[c] |
| cis-2-Butene | " | +3.720 | 0.0345 | — | — | 0.6213[b] | 0.6154[b] | -138.910 |
| trans-2-Butene | " | 0.88 | 0.0345 | — | — | 0.6042[b] | 0.5984[b] | -105.550 |
| 2-Methylpropene (Isobutene) | " | -6.900 | 0.0336 | — | — | 0.5942[b] | 0.5879[b] | -140.350 |
| 1-Pentene | C$_5$H$_{10}$ | 29.968 | 0.03801 | 1.37148 | 1.36835 | 0.64050 | 0.63533 | -165.220 |
| cis-2-Pentene | " | 36.942 | 0.03830 | 1.3830 | 1.3798 | 0.6556 | 0.6504 | -151.390 |
| trans-2-Pentene | " | 36.353 | 0.03824 | 1.3793 | 1.3761 | 0.6482 | 0.6431 | -140.244 |
| 2-Methyl-1-butene | " | 31.163 | 0.03778 | 1.3778 | 1.3746 | 0.6504 | 0.6451 | -137.470 |
| 3-Methyl-1-butene | " | 20.061 | 0.03721 | 1.3643 | — | 0.6272 | — | -168.528 |
| 2-Methyl-2-butene | " | 38.568 | 0.03844 | 1.3874 | 1.3842 | 0.6623 | 0.6570 | -133.768 |

a See footnote a of Table 1a.  b At saturation pressure.  c At saturation pressure (triple point).

TABLE 8a (PART 2) - MONOOLEFINS, $C_6$

BOILING POINT, $dt/dp$, REFRACTIVE INDEX, DENSITY, AND FREEZING POINT

June 30, 1945; October 31, 1952

| Compound | Formula | Boiling Point 760 mm Hg °C | $dt/dp$ 760 mm Hg °C/mm Hg | Refractive Index[a] 20°C $n_D$ | Refractive Index[a] 25°C $n_D$ | Density[a] 20°C g/ml | Density[a] 25°C g/ml | Freezing Point In air at 1 atm °C |
|---|---|---|---|---|---|---|---|---|
| 1-Hexene | $C_6H_{12}$ | 63.485 | 0.04149 | 1.38788 | 1.38502 | 0.67317 | 0.66848 | -139.819 |
| cis-2-Hexene | " | 68.84 | 0.041 | 1.3977 | 1.3948 | 0.6869 | 0.6823 | -141.135 |
| trans-2-Hexene | " | 67.87 | 0.041 | 1.3935 | 1.3907 | 0.6784 | 0.6738 | -132.970 |
| cis-3-Hexene | " | 66.44 | 0.041 | 1.3947 | 1.3920 | 0.6796 | 0.6749 | -137.820 |
| trans-3-Hexene | " | 67.08 | 0.041 | 1.3943 | 1.3916 | 0.6772 | 0.6725 | -113.430 |
| 2-Methyl-1-pentene | " | 60.7 | 0.040 | 1.3915 | 1.3884 | 0.6817 | 0.6769 | -135.760 |
| 3-Methyl-1-pentene | " | 54.14 | 0.040 | 1.3842 | 1.3814 | 0.6675 | 0.6628 | -153.0 |
| 4-Methyl-1-pentene | " | 53.88 | 0.040 | 1.3828 | 1.3799 | 0.6642 | 0.6594 | -153.63 |
| 2-Methyl-2-pentene | " | 67.29 | 0.041 | 1.4004 | 1.3976 | 0.6863 | 0.6815 | -135.070 |
| 3-Methyl-cis-2-pentene | " | 70.45 | 0.041 | 1.4045 | 1.4018 | 0.6986 | 0.6942 | -138.445 |
| 3-Methyl-trans-2-pentene | " | 67.63 | 0.041 | 1.4016 | 1.3989 | 0.6942 | 0.6898 | -134.840 |
| 4-Methyl-cis-2-pentene | " | 56.30 | 0.040 | 1.3880 | 1.3849 | 0.6690 | 0.6642 | -134.430 |
| 4-Methyl-trans-2-pentene | " | 58.55 | 0.040 | 1.3889 | 1.3859 | 0.6686 | 0.6638 | -140.810 |
| 2-Ethyl-1-butene | " | 64.66 | 0.041 | 1.3969 | 1.3941 | 0.6894 | 0.6847 | -131.530 |
| 2,3-Dimethyl-1-butene | " | 55.67 | 0.043 | 1.3904 | 1.3874 | 0.6779 | 0.6731 | -157.27 |
| 3,3-Dimethyl-1-butene | " | 41.24 | 0.040 | 1.3760 | 1.3730 | 0.6529 | 0.6479 | -115.20 |
| 2,3-Dimethyl-2-butene | " | 73.21 | 0.042 | 1.4122 | 1.4094 | 0.7080 | 0.7034 | -74.280 |

[a] See footnote a of Table 1a.

TABLE 9a, Page 1 - MONOOLEFINS, $C_7$

BOILING POINT, $dt/dp$, REFRACTIVE INDEX, DENSITY, AND FREEZING POINT

June 30, 1945; October 31, 1952

| Compound[b] | Formula | Boiling Point 760 mm Hg °C | $dt/dp$ 760 mm Hg °C/mm Hg | Refractive Index[a] 20°C $n_D$ | Refractive Index[a] 25°C $n_D$ | Density[a] 20°C g/ml | Density[a] 25°C g/ml | Freezing Point In air at 1 atm °C |
|---|---|---|---|---|---|---|---|---|
| 1-Heptene | $C_7H_{14}$ | 93.643 | 0.04447 | 1.39980 | 1.39713 | 0.69698 | 0.69267 | −119.029 |
| cis-2-Heptene | " | 98.5 | 0.044 | 1.406 | 1.403 | 0.708 | 0.704 | |
| trans-2-Heptene | " | 97.95 | 0.044 | 1.4045 | 1.4020 | 0.7012 | 0.6969 | −109.480 |
| cis-3-Heptene | " | 95.75 | 0.044 | 1.4059 | 1.4033 | 0.7030 | 0.6987 | −136.63 |
| trans-3-Heptene | " | 95.67 | 0.044 | 1.4043 | 1.4017 | 0.6981 | 0.6938 | −102.840 |
| 2-Methyl-1-hexene | " | 92.00 | 0.044 | 1.4034 | 1.4007 | 0.7030 | 0.6986 | |
| 3-Methyl-1-hexene | " | 84. | 0.044 | 1.397 | 1.394 | 0.695 | 0.691 | |
| 4-Methyl-1-hexene | " | 86.73 | 0.044 | 1.4000 | 1.3973 | 0.6985 | 0.6942 | −141.45 |
| 5-Methyl-1-hexene | " | 85.31 | 0.044 | 1.3966 | 1.3940 | 0.6920 | 0.6876 | |
| 2-Methyl-2-hexene | " | 95.41 | 0.044 | 1.4106 | 1.4079 | 0.7082 | 0.7038 | −130.350 |
| 3-Methyl-cis-2-hexene | " | 94. | 0.044 | 1.410 | 1.407 | 0.712 | 0.708 | |
| 3-Methyl-trans-2-hexene | " | | 0.044 | | | | | |
| 4-Methyl-cis-2-hexene | " | 87.37 | 0.044 | 1.4024 | 1.3997* | 0.6996 | 0.6953 | −126.5 |
| 4-Methyl-trans-2-hexene | " | 87.6 | 0.044 | 1.4023 | 1.3997 | 0.6975 | 0.6932 | |
| 5-Methyl-cis-2-hexene | " | 91. | 0.044 | 1.400 | 1.397 | 0.700 | 0.696 | |
| 5-Methyl-trans-2-hexene | " | 86. | 0.044 | 1.400 | 1.397 | 0.700 | 0.696 | |
| 2-Methyl-cis-3-hexene | " | 86. | 0.044 | 1.399 | 1.396 | 0.694 | 0.690 | |
| 2-Methyl-trans-3-hexene | " | | 0.044 | | | | | |
| 3-Methyl-cis-3-hexene | " | 95.35 | 0.044 | 1.4123 | 1.4096 | 0.7132 | 0.7089 | |
| 3-Methyl-trans-3-hexene | " | 93.55 | 0.044 | 1.4107 | 1.4080 | 0.7099 | 0.7056 | |

a See footnote a of Table 1a.

b For completeness, all isomers are listed. However, where the data are inadequate, approximate values are given for mixtures of the cis and trans forms, as indicated by the braces.

TABLE 9a, Page 2 — MONOOLEFINS, C$_7$

BOILING POINT, $dt/dp$, REFRACTIVE INDEX, DENSITY, AND FREEZING POINT

June 30, 1945; October 31, 1952

| Compound [b] | Formula | Boiling Point 760 mm Hg | $dt/dp$ 760 mm Hg | Refractive Index[a] 20°C | Refractive Index[a] 25°C | Density[a] 20°C | Density[a] 25°C | Freezing Point In air at 1 atm |
|---|---|---|---|---|---|---|---|---|
| | | °C | °C/mm Hg | $n_D$ | $n_D$ | g/ml | g/ml | °C |
| 2-Ethyl-1-pentene | C$_7$H$_{14}$ | 94. | 0.044 | 1.405 | 1.402 | 0.708 | 0.704 | |
| 3-Ethyl-1-pentene | " | 85.13 | 0.044 | 1.3980 | 1.3954 | 0.6962 | 0.6917 | -127.4 |
| 2,3-Dimethyl-1-pentene | " | 84.26 | 0.044 | 1.4033 | 1.4007 | 0.7051 | 0.7008 | -134.8 |
| 2,4-Dimethyl-1-pentene | " | 81.64 | 0.044 | 1.3996 | 1.3959 | 0.6943 | 0.6898 | -123.8 |
| 3,3-Dimethyl-1-pentene | " | 77.54 | 0.044 | 1.3984 | 1.3958 | 0.6974 | 0.6932 | -134.3 |
| 3,4-Dimethyl-1-pentene | " | 81. | 0.044 | 1.3995 | 1.3969 | 0.701 | 0.697 | |
| 4,4-Dimethyl-1-pentene | " | 72.49 | 0.044 | 1.3918 | 1.3892 | 0.6827 | 0.6785 | -136.600 |
| 3-Ethyl-2-pentene | " | 96.01 | 0.044 | 1.4148 | 1.4122 | 0.7204 | 0.7159 | |
| 2,3-Dimethyl-2-pentene | " | 97.46 | 0.044 | 1.4208 | 1.4182 | 0.7277 | 0.7224 | -118.3 |
| 2,4-Dimethyl-2-pentene | " | 83.44 | 0.044 | 1.4040 | 1.4013 | 0.6955 | 0.6912 | |
| 3,4-Dimethyl-cis-2-pentene | " | 87. | 0.044 | 1.407 | 1.404 | 0.713 | 0.709 | |
| 3,4-Dimethyl-trans-2-pentene | " | 87. | | | | | | |
| 4,4-Dimethyl-cis-2-pentene | " | 80.42 | 0.044 | 1.4024 | 1.3998 | 0.6996 | 0.6952 | -135.46 |
| 4,4-Dimethyl-trans-2-pentene | " | 76.75 | 0.044 | 1.3962 | 1.3953 | 0.6889 | 0.6845 | -115.235 |
| 3-Methyl-2-ethyl-1-butene | " | 89. | 0.044 | 1.410 | 1.407 | 0.715 | 0.711 | |
| 2,3,3-Trimethyl-1-butene | " | 77.87 | 0.044 | 1.4029 | 1.4000 | 0.7050 | 0.7005 | -109.85 |

[a] See footnote a of Table 1a.   [b] See footnote b of Table 9a, Page 1.

TABLE 10a, Page 1 — MONOOLEFINS, $C_8$

BOILING POINT, $dt/dp$, REFRACTIVE INDEX, DENSITY, AND FREEZING POINT

June 30, 1945; October 31, 1952

| Compound[b] | Formula | Boiling Point 760 mm Hg °C | $dt/dp$ 760 mm Hg °C/mm Hg | Refractive Index[a] 20°C $n_D$ | Refractive Index[a] 25°C $n_D$ | Density[a] 20°C g/ml | Density[a] 25°C g/ml | Freezing Point In air at 1 atm °C |
|---|---|---|---|---|---|---|---|---|
| 1-Octene | $C_8H_{16}$ | 121.280 | 0.04711 | 1.40870 | 1.40620 | 0.71492 | 0.71085 | -101.736 |
| cis-2-Octene | " | 125.64 | 0.046 | 1.4150 | 1.4125 | 0.7243 | 0.7201 | -100.2 |
| trans-2-Octene | " | 125.0 | 0.046 | 1.4132 | 1.4107 | 0.7199 | 0.7157 | -87.7 |
| cis-3-Octene | " | 122.9 | 0.046 | 1.4135 | 1.4111 | 0.721 | 0.717 | |
| trans-3-Octene | " | 123.3 | 0.046 | 1.4126 | 1.4102 | 0.7152 | 0.7110 | -110. |
| cis-4-Octene | " | 122.54 | 0.046 | 1.4148 | 1.4124 | 0.7212 | 0.7170 | -118.7 |
| trans-4-Octene | " | 122.25 | 0.046 | 1.4118 | 1.4093 | 0.7141 | 0.7099 | -93.810 |
| 2-Methyl-1-heptene | " | 119.3 | 0.046 | 1.4123 | 1.4098 | 0.7205 | 0.7164 | -90.0 |
| 3-Methyl-1-heptene | " | 111. | 0.045 | 1.406 | 1.404 | 0.711 | 0.707 | |
| 4-Methyl-1-heptene | " | 112.8 | 0.045 | 1.410 | 1.408 | 0.717 | 0.713 | |
| 5-Methyl-1-heptene | " | 113.3 | 0.045 | 1.4094 | 1.4069 | 0.7164 | 0.7122 | |
| 6-Methyl-1-heptene | " | 113.2 | 0.045 | 1.4070 | 1.4045 | 0.7120 | 0.7079 | |
| 2-Methyl-2-heptene | " | 122.6 | 0.046 | 1.4170 | 1.4145 | 0.7241 | 0.7200 | |
| 3-Methyl-cis-2-heptene | " | 122. | 0.046 | 1.419 | 1.417 | 0.729 | 0.725 | |
| 3-Methyl-trans-2-heptene | " | | | | | | | |
| 4-Methyl-cis-2-heptene | " | 114. | 0.045 | 1.410 | 1.408 | 0.716 | 0.712 | |
| 4-Methyl-trans-2-heptene | " | | | | | | | |
| 5-Methyl-cis-2-heptene | " | 118. | 0.046 | 1.414 | 1.412 | 0.723 | 0.719 | |
| 5-Methyl-trans-2-heptene | " | | | | | | | |
| 6-Methyl-cis-2-heptene | " | 117. | 0.046 | 1.412 | 1.410 | 0.718 | 0.714 | |
| 6-Methyl-trans-2-heptene | " | | | | | | | |
| 2-Methyl-cis-3-heptene | " | 112. | 0.045 | 1.407 | 1.405 | 0.706 | 0.702 | |
| 2-Methyl-trans-3-heptene | " | | | | | | | |

a See footnote a of Table 1a.

b See footnote b of Table 9a.

TABLE 10a, Page 2 — MONOOLEFINS, C$_8$

BOILING POINT, dt/dp, REFRACTIVE INDEX, DENSITY, AND FREEZING POINT

June 30, 1945; October 31, 1952

| Compound [b] | Formula | Boiling Point 760 mm Hg (°C) | dt/dp 760 mm Hg (°C/mm Hg) | Refractive Index[a] 20°C ($n_D$) | Refractive Index[a] 25°C ($n_D$) | Density[a] 20°C (g/ml) | Density[a] 25°C (g/ml) | Freezing Point In air at 1 atm (°C) |
|---|---|---|---|---|---|---|---|---|
| 3-Methyl-cis-3-heptene | C$_8$H$_{16}$ | 121. | 0.046 | 1.418 | 1.416 | 0.728 | 0.724 | |
| 3-Methyl-trans-3-heptene | " | 122. | 0.046 | 1.417 | 1.415 | 0.725 | 0.721 | |
| 4-Methyl-cis-3-heptene | " | 112. | 0.045 | 1.410 | 1.408 | 0.713 | 0.709 | |
| 4-Methyl-trans-3-heptene | " | 115. | 0.045 | 1.410 | 1.408 | 0.713 | 0.709 | |
| 5-Methyl-cis-3-heptene | " | 120. | 0.046 | 1.4157 | 1.4132 | 0.7270 | 0.7228 | |
| 5-Methyl-trans-3-heptene | " | 110.3 | 0.046 | 1.407 | 1.405 | 0.715 | 0.711 | |
| 6-Methyl-cis-3-heptene | " | 113. | 0.046 | 1.412 | 1.410 | 0.726 | 0.722 | |
| 6-Methyl-trans-3-heptene | " | 110.5 | 0.046 | 1.4113 | 1.4089 | 0.7214 | 0.7172 | |
| 2-Ethyl-1-hexene | " | 111.2 | 0.046 | 1.411 | 1.409 | 0.720 | 0.716 | |
| 3-Ethyl-1-hexene | " | 111.6 | 0.046 | 1.4105 | 1.4080 | 0.7172 | 0.7129 | |
| 4-Ethyl-1-hexene | " | 104. | 0.046 | 1.4070 | 1.4046 | 0.7140 | 0.7099 | |
| 2,3-Dimethyl-1-hexene | " | 112. | 0.046 | 1.413 | 1.411 | 0.724 | 0.720 | |
| 2,4-Dimethyl-1-hexene | " | 104. | 0.045 | 1.404 | 1.402 | 0.708 | 0.704 | |
| 2,5-Dimethyl-1-hexene | " | 107.2 | 0.046 | 1.4102 | 1.4078 | 0.7198 | 0.7157 | |
| 3,3-Dimethyl-1-hexene | " | 109. | 0.046 | 1.414 | 1.412 | 0.728 | 0.724 | |
| 3,4-Dimethyl-1-hexene | " | 102.5 | 0.047 | 1.4049 | 1.4024 | 0.709 | 0.705 | |
| 3,5-Dimethyl-1-hexene | " | | | | | | | |
| 4,4-Dimethyl-1-hexene | " | | | | | | | |
| 4,5-Dimethyl-1-hexene | " | | | | | | | |
| 5,5-Dimethyl-1-hexene | " | | | | | | | |
| 3-Ethyl-cis-2-hexene | " | 121. | 0.046 | 1.424 | 1.422 | 0.737 | 0.733 | |
| 3-Ethyl-trans-2-hexene | " | | | | | | | |
| 4-Ethyl-cis-2-hexene | " | 113. | 0.046 | 1.412 | 1.410 | 0.725 | 0.721 | |
| 4-Ethyl-trans-2-hexene | " | | | | | | | |

a See footnote a of Table 1a.  b See footnote b of Table 9a.

• TABLE 10a, Page 3 – MONOOLEFINS, C$_8$

BOILING POINT, *dt/dp*, REFRACTIVE INDEX, DENSITY, AND FREEZING POINT

June 30, 1945; October 31, 1952

| Compound b | Formula | Boiling Point 760 mm Hg °C | dt/dp 760 mm Hg °C/mm Hg | Refractive Index[a] $n_D$ 20°C | Refractive Index[a] $n_D$ 25°C | Density[a] 20°C g/ml | Density[a] 25°C g/ml | Freezing Point In air at 1 atm °C |
|---|---|---|---|---|---|---|---|---|
| 2,3-Dimethyl-2-hexene | C$_8$H$_{16}$ | 121.77 | 0.046 | 1.4268 | 1.4244 | 0.7408 | 0.7366 | -115.1 |
| 2,4-Dimethyl-2-hexene | " | 110.6 | 0.047 | 1.4118 | 1.4094 | 0.7213 | 0.7171 | |
| 2,5-Dimethyl-2-hexene | " | 112.2 | 0.045 | 1.4140 | 1.4115 | 0.720 | 0.716 | |
| 3,4-Dimethyl-*cis*-2-hexene | " | 116. | 0.046 | 1.418 | 1.416 | 0.737 | 0.733 | |
| 3,4-Dimethyl-*trans*-2-hexene | " | | | | | | | |
| 3,5-Dimethyl-*cis*-2-hexene | " | 112. | 0.045 | 1.416 | 1.414 | 0.725 | 0.721 | |
| 3,5-Dimethyl-*trans*-2-hexene | " | | | | | | | |
| 4,4-Dimethyl-*cis*-2-hexene | " | 106. | 0.046 | 1.413 | 1.411 | 0.722 | 0.718 | |
| 4,4-Dimethyl-*trans*-2-hexene | " | | | | | | | |
| 4,5-Dimethyl-*cis*-2-hexene | " | 110. | 0.046 | 1.413 | 1.411 | 0.725 | 0.721 | |
| 4,5-Dimethyl-*trans*-2-hexene | " | | | | | | | |
| 5,5-Dimethyl-*cis*-2-hexene | " | 106.9 | 0.047 | 1.4113 | 1.4088 | 0.7169 | 0.7125 | |
| 5,5-Dimethyl-*trans*-2-hexene | " | 104.1 | 0.046 | 1.4055 | 1.4030 | 0.7066 | 0.7023 | |
| 3-Ethyl-2-hexene | " | 116. | 0.046 | 1.418 | 1.416 | 0.729 | 0.725 | |
| 2,2-Dimethyl-*cis*-3-hexene | " | 105.43 | 0.045 | 1.4099 | 1.4074 | 0.7128 | 0.7086 | -137.350 |
| 2,2-Dimethyl-*trans*-3-hexene | " | 100 85 | 0.045 | 1.4063 | 1.4037 | 0.7039 | 0.6995 | |
| 2,3-Dimethyl-*cis*-3-hexene | " | 114. | 0.046 | 1.416 | 1.414 | 0.728 | 0.724 | |
| 2,3-Dimethyl-*trans*-3-hexene | " | | | | | | | |
| 2,4-Dimethyl-*cis*-3-hexene | " | 109.0 | 0.045 | 1.4140 | 1.4114 | 0.7178 | 0.7135 | |
| 2,4-Dimethyl-*trans*-3-hexene | " | 107.6 | 0.046 | 1.4126 | 1.4101 | 0.7145 | 0.7101 | |
| 2,5-Dimethyl-*cis*-3-hexene | " | 102. | 0.045 | 1.406 | 1.404 | 0.710 | 0.706 | |
| 2,5-Dimethyl-*trans*-3-hexene | " | | | | | | | |
| 3,4-Dimethyl-*cis*-3-hexene | " | 122. | 0.046 | 1.430 | 1.428 | 0.747 | 0.743 | |
| 3,4-Dimethyl-*trans*-3-hexene | " | | | | | | | |

a See footnote a of Table 1a.   b See footnote b of Table 9a.

TABLE 10a, Pane 4 – MONOOLEFINS, C$_8$

BOILING POINT, $dt/dp$, REFRACTIVE INDEX, DENSITY, AND FREEZING POINT

June 30, 1945; October 31, 1952

| Compound[b] | Formula | Boiling Point 760 mm Hg °C | $dt/dp$ 760 mm Hg °C/mm Hg | Refractive Index[a] 20°C $n_D$ | Refractive Index[a] 25°C $n_D$ | Density[a] 20°C g/ml | Density[a] 25°C g/ml | Freezing Point In air at 1 atm °C |
|---|---|---|---|---|---|---|---|---|
| 2-n-Propyl-1-pentene | C$_8$H$_{16}$ | 117.7 | 0.046 | 1.4136 | 1.4111 | 0.7240 | 0.7198 | |
| 2-Isopropyl-1-pentene | " | 113. | 0.046 | 1.414 | 1.412 | 0.725 | 0.721 | |
| 3-Methyl-2-ethyl-1-pentene | " | 112.5 | 0.046 | 1.4142 | 1.4118 | 0.729 | 0.725 | |
| 4-Methyl-2-ethyl-1-pentene | " | 110.3 | 0.046 | 1.4105 | 1.4080 | 0.7195 | 0.7152 | |
| 2-Methyl-3-ethyl-1-pentene | " | 110. | 0.046 | 1.415 | 1.413 | 0.730 | 0.726 | |
| 3-Methyl-3-ethyl-1-pentene | " | 112. | 0.047 | 1.418 | 1.416 | 0.7305 | 0.7264 | |
| 4-Methyl-3-ethyl-1-pentene | " | 107.5 | 0.047 | 1.4097 | 1.4072 | 0.7200 | 0.7158 | -69. |
| 2,3,3-Trimethyl-1-pentene | " | 108.31 | 0.047 | 1.4174 | 1.4151 | 0.7352 | 0.7308 | |
| 2,3,4-Trimethyl-1-pentene | " | 108. | 0.046 | 1.415 | 1.413 | 0.729 | 0.725 | -93.480 |
| 2,4,4-Trimethyl-1-pentene | " | 101.44 | 0.046 | 1.4086 | 1.4060 | 0.7150 | 0.7108 | |
| 3,3,4-Trimethyl-1-pentene | " | 105. | 0.047 | 1.4144 | 1.4120 | 0.729 | 0.725 | |
| 3,4,4-Trimethyl-1-pentene | " | 104. | 0.046 | 1.412 | 1.410 | 0.719 | 0.715 | |
| 2-Methyl-3-ethyl-2-pentene | " | 117.0 | 0.045 | 1.4247 | 1.4222 | 0.739 | 0.735 | |
| 4-Methyl-3-ethyl-cis-2-pentene | " | 116. | 0.047 | 1.424 | 1.422 | 0.739 | 0.735 | |
| 4-Methyl-3-ethyl-trans-2-nentene | " | 114.3 | 0.047 | 1.4210 | 1.4183 | 0.7350 | 0.7308 | -113.3 |
| 2,3,4-Trimethyl-2-pentene | " | 116.26 | 0.046 | 1.4275 | 1.4249 | 0.7434 | 0.7391 | |
| 2,4,4-Trimethyl-2-pentene | " | 104.91 | 0.047 | 1.4160 | 1.4135 | 0.7218 | 0.7176 | -106.330 |
| 3,4,4-Trimethyl-cis-2-nentene | " | 112. | 0.046 | 1.423 | 1.421 | 0.739 | 0.735 | |
| 3,4,4-Trimethyl-trans-2-pentene | " | 104. | 0.046 | 1.4085 | 1.4061 | 0.722 | 0.718 | |
| 3-Methyl-2-isopropyl-1-butene | " | 110. | 0.046 | 1.4159 | 1.4135 | 0.728 | 0.724 | |
| 3,3-Dimethyl-2-ethyl-1-butene | " | | | | | | | |

a See footnote a of Table 1a.   b See footnote b of Table 9a.

TABLE 11a (PART 1) – DIOLEFINS, C$_3$ TO C$_5$

BOILING POINT, $dt/dp$, REFRACTIVE INDEX, DENSITY, AND FREEZING POINT

June 30, 1945; September 30, 1951; October 31, 1952

| Compound | Formula | Boiling Point 760 mm Hg °C | $dt/dp$ 760 mm Hg °C/mm Hg | Refractive Index[a] 20°C $n_D$ | 25°C $n_D$ | Density[a] 20°C g/ml | 25°C g/ml | Freezing Point In air at 1 atm °C |
|---|---|---|---|---|---|---|---|---|
| Propadiene (Allene) | C$_3$H$_4$ | −34.5 | 0.033 | — | — | — | — | −136. |
| 1,2-Butadiene | C$_4$H$_6$ | +10.85 | 0.0351 | — | — | 0.652[b] | 0.646[b] | −136.190 |
| 1,3-Butadiene | " | − 4.413 | 0.03377 | — | — | 0.6211[b] | 0.6149[b] | −108.915 |
| 1,2-Pentadiene | C$_5$H$_8$ | +44.856 | 0.03867 | 1.42091 | 1.41773 | 0.69257 | 0.68760 | −137.26 |
| 1,*cis*-3-Pentadiene | " | 44.068 | 0.03875 | 1.43634 | 1.43291 | 0.69102 | 0.68592 | −140.820 |
| 1,*trans*-3-Pentadiene | " | 42.032 | 0.03879 | 1.43008 | 1.42669 | 0.67603 | 0.67102 | − 87.470 |
| 1,4-Pentadiene | " | 25.967 | 0.03720 | 1.38876 | 1.38542 | 0.66076 | 0.65571 | −148.275 |
| 2,3-Pentadiene | " | 48.265 | 0.03871 | 1.42842 | 1.42509 | 0.69502 | 0.69000 | −125.650 |
| 3-Methyl-1,2-butadiene | " | 40. | 0.04 | 1.410 | 1.407 | 0.660 | 0.675 | |
| 2-Methyl-1,3-butadiene (Isoprene) | " | 34.067 | 0.03818 | 1.42194 | 1.41852 | 0.66095 | 0.67587 | −145.950 |

a See footnote a of Table 1a.    b At saturation pressure.

TABLE 11a (PART 2) – DIOLEFINS, $C_6$

BOILING POINT, $dt/dp$, REFRACTIVE INDEX, DENSITY, AND FREEZING POINT

June 30, 1945; October 31, 1952

| Compound [b] | Formula | Boiling Point 760 mm Hg °C | $dt/dp$ 760 mm Hg °C/mm Hg | Refractive Index[a] 20°C $n_D$ | 25°C $n_D$ | Density[a] 20°C g/ml | 25°C g/ml | Freezing Point In air at 1 atm °C |
|---|---|---|---|---|---|---|---|---|
| 1,2-Hexadiene | $C_6H_{10}$ | 76. | 0.044 | 1.4282 | 1.4252 | 0.7149 | 0.7102 | |
| 1,cis-3-Hexadiene | " | 73. | 0.043 | 1.438 | 1.435 | 0.705 | 0.700 | |
| 1,trans-3-Hexadiene | " | | | | | | | |
| 1,cis-4-Hexadiene | " | 65. | 0.042 | 1.415 | 1.412 | 0.700 | 0.695 | |
| 1,trans-4-Hexadiene | " | 59.46 | 0.042 | 1.4042 | 1.4010 | 0.6923 | 0.6878 | -140.680 |
| 1,5-Hexadiene | " | 68.0 | 0.043 | 1.395 | 1.392 | 0.680 | 0.675 | |
| 2,3-Hexadiene | " | | | | | | | |
| cis-2,cis-4-Hexadiene | " | 80. | 0.044 | 1.450 | 1.447 | 0.720 | 0.715 | |
| cis-2,trans-4-Hexadiene | " | | | | | | | |
| trans-2,trans-4-Hexadiene | " | | | | | | | |
| 3-Methyl-1,2-pentadiene | " | 70. | 0.043 | 1.425 | 1.422 | 0.715 | 0.710 | |
| 4-Methyl-1,2-pentadiene | " | 70. | 0.043 | 1.424 | 1.421 | 0.708 | 0.703 | |
| 2-Methyl-1,cis-3-pentadiene | " | 76. | 0.044 | 1.446 | 1.443 | 0.719 | 0.714 | |
| 2-Methyl-1,trans-3-pentadiene | " | | | | | | | |
| 3-Methyl-1,cis-3-pentadiene | " | 77. | 0.044 | 1.452 | 1.449 | 0.735 | 0.730 | |
| 3-Methyl-1,trans-3-pentadiene | " | | | | | | | |
| 4-Methyl-1,3-pentadiene | " | 76.3 | 0.044 | 1.451 | 1.448 | 0.719 | 0.714 | |
| 2-Methyl-1,4-pentadiene | " | 56. | 0.041 | 1.405 | 1.402 | 0.694 | 0.689 | |
| 3-Methyl-1,4-pentadiene | " | 55. | 0.041 | 1.405 | 1.402 | 0.695 | 0.690 | |
| 2-Methyl-2,3-pentadiene | " | 72. | 0.043 | 1.425 | 1.422 | 0.711 | 0.706 | |
| 2-Ethyl-1,3-butadiene | " | 75. | 0.044 | 1.445 | 1.442 | 0.717 | 0.712 | |
| 2,3-Dimethyl-1,3-butadiene | " | 68.78 | 0.043 | 1.4394 | 1.4362 | 0.7267 | 0.7222 | -76.005 |

a See footnote a of Table 1a.

b See footnote b of Table 9a.

TABLE 18a – ALKYL CYCLOPENTENES, $C_5$ TO $C_7$

BOILING POINT, dt/dp, REFRACTIVE INDEX, DENSITY, AND FREEZING POINT

October 31, 1950; October 31, 1952

| Compound | Formula | Boiling Point 760 mm Hg °C | dt/dp 760 mm Hg °C/mm Hg | Refractive Index[a] 20°C $n_D$ | Refractive Index[a] 25°C $n_D$ | Density[a] 20°C g/ml | Density[a] 25°C g/ml | Freezing Point In air at 1 atm °C |
|---|---|---|---|---|---|---|---|---|
| Cyclopentene | $C_5H_8$ | 44.242 | 0.03928 | 1.42246 | 1.41940 | 0.77199 | 0.76653 | -135.076 |
| 1-Methylcyclopentene | $C_6H_{10}$ | 75.8 | 0.0431 | 1.4330 | 1.4302 | 0.7802 | 0.7752 | -127. |
| 3-Methylcyclopentene | " | 65.0 | 0.0418 | 1.4207 | 1.4179 | 0.7622 | 0.7572 | . |
| 4-Methylcyclopentene | " | 75.2 | 0.0430 | 1.4306 | 1.4278 | 0.7796 | 0.7747 | |
| 1-Ethylcyclopentene | $C_7H_{12}$ | 106.3 | 0.0467 | 1.4410 | 1.4384 | 0.7982 | 0.7936 | -118.4 |
| 3-Ethylcyclopentene | " | 98.1 | 0.0458 | 1.4319 | 1.4293 | 0.7830 | 0.7784 | |
| 4-Ethylcyclopentene | " | 106. | 0.047 | 1.440 | 1.437 | 0.798 | 0.793 | |
| 1,2-Dimethylcyclopentene | " | 105.8 | 0.0467 | 1.4448 | 1.4420 | 0.7976 | 0.7928 | -90.4. |
| 1,3-Dimethylcyclopentene | " | 92. | 0.045 | 1.428 | 1.425 | 0.766 | 0.761 | |
| 1,4-Dimethylcyclopentene | " | 93.2 | 0.046 | 1.4283 | 1.4255 | 0.779 | 0.774 | |
| 1,5-Dimethylcyclopentene | " | 102. | 0.046 | 1.4331 | 1.4304 | 0.780 | 0.775 | -118. |
| 3,3-Dimethylcyclopentene | " | 88. | 0.045 | 1.423 | 1.420 | 0.771 | 0.766 | |
| 3,cis-4-Dimethylcyclopentene | " | | | 1.4300 | 1.4272 | 0.777 | .0.772 | |
| 3,trans-4-Dimethylcyclopentene | " | | | | | | | |
| 3,cis-5-Dimethylcyclopentene | " | | | | | | | |
| 3,trans-5-Dimethylcyclopentene | " | | | | | | | |
| 4,4-Dimethylcyclopentene | " | 88. | 0.045 | 1.423 | 1.420 | 0.771 | 0.766 | |

a See footnote a of Table 1a.

TABLE 19a – ALKYL CYCLOHEXENES, $C_6$ TO $C_8$

BOILING POINT, $dt/dp$, REFRACTIVE INDEX, DENSITY, AND FREEZING POINT

October 31, 1950

| Compound | Formula | Boiling Point 760 mm Hg °C | dt/dp 760 mm Hg °C/mm Hg | Refractive Index[a] 20°C $n_D$ | 25°C $n_D$ | Density[a] 20°C g/ml | 25°C g/ml | Freezing Point In air at 1 atm °C |
|---|---|---|---|---|---|---|---|---|
| Cyclohexene | $C_6H_{10}$ | 82.979 | 0.04381 | 1.44654 | 1.44377 | 0.81096 | 0.80609 | −103.512 |
| 1-Methylcyclohexene | $C_7H_{12}$ | 110.0 | 0.0470 | 1.4503 | 1.4478 | 0.8102 | 0.8058 | −121. |
| 3-Methylcyclohexene | " | 104.0 | 0.0463 | 1.4444 | 1.4419 | 0.8010 | 0.7966 | −115.5 |
| 4-Methylcyclohexene | " | 102.74 | 0.0461 | 1.4414 | 1.4389 | 0.7991 | 0.7947 | |
| 1-Ethylcyclohexene | $C_8H_{14}$ | 136. | 0.050 | 1.4575 | 1.4552 | 0.823 | 0.819 | |
| 3-Ethylcyclohexene | " | 134. | 0.050 | 1.451 | 1.449 | 0.814 | 0.810 | |
| 4-Ethylcyclohexene | " | 133. | 0.049 | 1.449 | 1.447 | 0.810 | 0.806 | |
| 1,2-Dimethylcyclohexene | " | 137. | 0.050 | 1.4588 | 1.4564 | 0.8250 | 0.8208 | −59. |
| 1,3-Dimethylcyclohexene | " | 137. | 0.050 | 1.445 | 1.443 | 0.802 | 0.798 | |
| 1,4-Dimethylcyclohexene | " | 128. | 0.049 | 1.446 | 1.444 | 0.802 | 0.798 | |
| 1,5-Dimethylcyclohexene | " | 128. | 0.049 | 1.448 | 1.446 | 0.8051 | 0.8009 | |
| 1,6-Dimethylcyclohexene | " | 133. | 0.049 | 1.454 | 1.452 | 0.815 | 0.811 | |
| 3,3-Dimethylcyclohexene | " | 119. | 0.048 | 1.445 | 1.443 | 0.804 | 0.800 | |
| 3,cis-4-Dimethylcyclohexene | " | | | | | | | |
| 3,trans-4-Dimethylcyclohexene | " | | | | | | | |
| 3,cis-5-Dimethylcyclohexene | " | | | | | | | |
| 3,trans-5-Dimethylcyclohexene | " | | | | | | | |
| 3,cis-6-Dimethylcyclohexene | " | | | | | | | |
| 3,trans-6-Dimethylcyclohexene | " | 116.93 | 0.0477 | 1.4420 | 1.4396 | 0.7996 | 0.7956 | −80.5 |
| 4,4-Dimethylcyclohexene | " | | | | | | | |
| 4,cis-5-Dimethylcyclohexene | " | | | | | | | |
| 4,trans-5-Dimethylcyclohexene | " | | | | | | | |

[a] See footnote a of Table 1a.

## TABLE 25a (PART 1) — NORMAL ACETYLENES (1-ALKYNES) $C_2$ TO $C_{20}$
## BOILING POINT, $dt/dp$, REFRACTIVE INDEX, DENSITY, AND FREEZING POINT

April 30, 1949; September 30, 1951; October 31, 1952

| Compound | Formula[a] | Boiling Point 760 mm Hg °C | $dt/dp$ 760 mm Hg °C/mm Hg | Refractive Index[a] 20°C $n_D$ | Refractive Index[a] 25°C $n_D$ | Density[a] 20°C g/ml | Density[a] 25°C g/ml | Freezing Point In air at 1 atm °C |
|---|---|---|---|---|---|---|---|---|
| Ethyne (Acetylene) | $C_2H_2$ | − 84.[b] | 0.018 | — | — | — | — | − 81.[c] |
| Propyne (Methylacetylene) | $C_3H_4$ | − 23.22 | 0.030 | — | — | — | — | −102.7 |
| 1-Butyne (Ethylacetylene) | $C_4H_6$ | + 8.07 | 0.036 | — | — | 0.65[d] | 0.65[d] | −125.720 |
| 1-Pentyne | $C_5H_8$ | 40.18 | 0.039 | 1.3852 | 1.3826 | 0.6901 | 0.6849 | −105.7 |
| 1-Hexyne | $C_6H_{10}$ | 71.33 | 0.042 | 1.3989 | 1.3960 | 0.7155 | 0.7106 | −131.9 |
| 1-Heptyne | $C_7H_{12}$ | 99.7 | 0.045 | 1.4087 | 1.4060 | 0.7328 | 0.7283 | − 80.9 |
| 1-Octyne | $C_8H_{14}$ | 126.2 | 0.047 | 1.4159 | 1.4134 | 0.7461 | 0.7419 | − 79.3 |
| 1-Nonyne | $C_9H_{16}$ | 150.8 | 0.050 | 1.4217 | 1.4193 | 0.7568 | 0.7527 | − 50. |
| 1-Decyne | $C_{10}H_{18}$ | 174. | 0.05 | 1.4265 | 1.4242 | 0.7655 | 0.7616 | − 44. |
| 1-Undecyne | $C_{11}H_{20}$ | 195. | 0.05 | 1.4306 | 1.4284 | 0.7728 | 0.7690 | − 25. |
| 1-Dodecyne | $C_{12}H_{22}$ | 215. | 0.06 | 1.4340 | 1.4318 | 0.7788 | 0.7751 | − 19. |
| 1-Tridecyne | $C_{13}H_{24}$ | 234. | 0.06 | 1.4371 | 1.4349 | 0.7842 | 0.7806 | − 5. |
| 1-Tetradecyne | $C_{14}H_{26}$ | 252. | 0.06 | 1.4396 | 1.4375 | 0.7888 | 0.7852 | + 0. |
| 1-Pentadecyne | $C_{15}H_{28}$ | 268. | 0.06 | 1.4419 | 1.4398 | 0.7928 | 0.7893 | 10. |
| 1-Hexadecyne | $C_{16}H_{30}$ | 284. | 0.06 | 1.4440 | 1.4419 | 0.7965 | 0.7930 | 15. |
| 1-Heptadecyne | $C_{17}H_{32}$ | 299. | 0.06 | 1.4457[e] | 1.4437 | 0.7996[e] | 0.7961 | 22. |
| 1-Octadecyne | $C_{18}H_{34}$ | 313. | 0.06 | 1.4474[e] | 1.4453[e] | 0.8025[e] | 0.7990[e] | 27. |
| 1-Nonadecyne | $C_{19}H_{36}$ | 327. | 0.06 | 1.4488[e] | 1.4467[e] | 0.8050[e] | 0.8016[e] | 33. |
| 1-Eicosyne | $C_{20}H_{38}$ | 340. | 0.06 | 1.4501[e] | 1.4481[e] | 0.8073[e] | 0.8039[e] | 36. |

a See footnote a of Table 1a.   b Sublimation point.   c At saturation pressure (triple point).   d At saturation pressure.   e For the undercooled liquid below the normal freezing point.

TABLE 25a (PART 2) – NORMAL ACETYLENES (1-ALKYNES) $C_{21}$ TO $C_{40}$
BOILING POINT, $dt/dp$, REFRACTIVE INDEX, DENSITY, AND FREEZING POINT
September 30, 1951

| Compound | Formula[a] | Boiling Point 760 mm Hg °C | $dt/dp$ 760 mm Hg °C/mm Hg | Refractive Index[a] 20°C $n_D$ | 25°C $n_D$ | Density[a] 20°C g/ml | 25°C g/ml | Freezing Point In air at 1 atm °C |
|---|---|---|---|---|---|---|---|---|
| 1-Heneicosyne | $C_{21}H_{40}$ | 352. | 0.07 | 1.4513[b] | 1.4493[b] | 0.8094[b] | 0.8060[b] | 41. |
| 1-Docosyne | $C_{22}H_{42}$ | 363. | 0.07 | 1.4524[b] | 1.4504[b] | 0.8114[b] | 0.8080[b] | 45. |
| 1-Tricosyne | $C_{23}H_{44}$ | 374. | 0.07 | 1.4534[b] | 1.4514[b] | 0.8131[b] | 0.8100[b] | 49. |
| 1-Tetracosyne | $C_{24}H_{46}$ | 385. | 0.07 | 1.4544[b] | 1.4523[b] | 0.8148[b] | 0.8114[b] | 52. |
| 1-Pentacosyne | $C_{25}H_{48}$ | 395. | 0.07 | 1.4552[b] | 1.4532[b] | 0.8163[b] | 0.8129[b] | 55. |
| 1-Hexacosyne | $C_{26}H_{50}$ | 405. | 0.07 | 1.4560[b] | 1.4540[b] | 0.8177[b] | 0.8143[b] | 57. |
| 1-Heptacosyne | $C_{27}H_{52}$ | 415. | 0.07 | 1.4568[b] | 1.4548[b] | 0.8190[b] | 0.8156[b] | 60. |
| 1-Octacosyne | $C_{28}H_{54}$ | 424. | 0.07 | 1.4575[b] | 1.4555[b] | 0.8202[b] | 0.8168[b] | 62. |
| 1-Nonacosyne | $C_{29}H_{56}$ | 432. | 0.07 | 1.4581[b] | 1.4561[b] | 0.8213[b] | 0.8180[b] | 65. |
| 1-Triacontyne | $C_{30}H_{58}$ | 441. | 0.07 | 1.4587[b] | 1.4567[b] | 0.8224[b] | 0.8190[b] | 67. |
| 1-Hentriacontyne | $C_{31}H_{60}$ | 449. | 0.07 | 1.4593[b] | 1.4573[b] | 0.8234[b] | 0.8200[b] | 69. |
| 1-Dotriacontyne | $C_{32}H_{62}$ | 457. | 0.07 | 1.4598[b] | 1.4578[b] | 0.8243[b] | 0.8210[b] | 71. |
| 1-Tritriacontyne | $C_{33}H_{64}$ | 464. | 0.07 | 1.4603[b] | 1.4583[b] | 0.8252[b] | 0.8218[b] | 73. |
| 1-Tetratriacontyne | $C_{34}H_{66}$ | 472. | 0.07 | 1.4608[b] | 1.4588[b] | 0.8260[b] | 0.8227[b] | 74. |
| 1-Pentatriacontyne | $C_{35}H_{68}$ | 479. | 0.07 | 1.4612[b] | 1.4593[b] | 0.8268[b] | 0.8235[b] | 76. |
| 1-Hexatriacontyne | $C_{36}H_{70}$ | 486. | 0.08 | 1.4617[b] | 1.4597[b] | 0.8275[b] | 0.8242[b] | 77. |
| 1-Heptatriacontyne | $C_{37}H_{72}$ | 493. | 0.08 | 1.4621[b] | 1.4601[b] | 0.8282[b] | 0.8249[b] | 79. |
| 1-Octatriacontyne | $C_{38}H_{74}$ | 499. | 0.08 | 1.4625[b] | 1.4605[b] | 0.8289[b] | 0.8256[b] | 80. |
| 1-Nonatriacontyne | $C_{39}H_{76}$ | 505. | 0.08 | 1.4628[b] | 1.4608[b] | 0.8295[b] | 0.8262[b] | 82. |
| 1-Tetracontyne | $C_{40}H_{78}$ | 512. | 0.08 | 1.4632[b] | 1.4612[b] | 0.8301[b] | 0.8268[b] | 83. |

[a] See footnote a of Table 1a.   [b] For the undercooled liquid below the normal freezing point.

TABLE 12a - ACETYLENES, $C_2$ TO $C_5$

BOILING POINT, $dt/dp$, REFRACTIVE INDEX, DENSITY, AND FREEZING POINT

June 30, 1945; October 31, 1950; October 31, 1952

| Compound | Formula | Boiling Point 760 mm Hg °C | $dt/dp$ 760 mm Hg °C/mm Hg | Refractive Index[a] | | Density[a] | | Freezing Point In air at 1 atm °C |
|---|---|---|---|---|---|---|---|---|
| | | | | 20°C $n_D$ | 25°C $n_D$ | 20°C g/ml | 25°C g/ml | |
| Ethyne (Acetylene) | $C_2H_2$ | -84.[b] | 0.018 | — | — | — | — | -81.[c] |
| Propyne (Methylacetylene) | $C_3H_4$ | -23.22 | 0.030 | — | — | — | — | -102.7 |
| 1-Butyne (Ethylacetylene) | $C_4H_6$ | 8.07 | 0.036 | — | — | 0.65[d] | 0.65[d] | -125.720 |
| 2-Butyne (Dimethylacetylene) | " | 26.99 | 0.037 | 1.3921 | 1.3893 | 0.6910 | 0.6856 | -32.260 |
| 1-Pentyne | $C_5H_8$ | 40.18 | 0.039 | 1.3852 | 1.3826 | 0.6901 | 0.6849 | -105.7 |
| 2-Pentyne | " | 56.07 | 0.041 | 1.4039 | 1.4009 | 0.7107 | 0.7055 | -109.3 |
| 3-Methyl-1-butyne | " | 26.35 | 0.038 | 1.3723 | 1.3695 | 0.666 | 0.660 | -89.7 |

a See footnote a of Table 1a.   b Sublimation point.   c At saturation pressure (triple point).   d At saturation pressure.

TABLE 21a (PART 1) – NORMAL ALKYL BENZENES, $C_6$ TO $C_{22}$

BOILING POINT, $dt/dp$, REFRACTIVE INDEX, DENSITY, AND FREEZING POINT

June 30, 1948; September 30, 1951

| Compound | Formula [a] | Boiling Point 760 mm Hg °C | $dt/dp$ 760 mm Hg °C/mm Hg | Refractive Index [a] 20°C $n_D$ | Refractive Index [a] 25°C $n_D$ | Density [a] 20°C g/ml | Density [a] 25°C g/ml | Freezing Point [a] In air at 1 atm °C |
|---|---|---|---|---|---|---|---|---|
| Benzene | $C_6H_6$ | 80.100 | 0.04271 | 1.50112 | 1.49792 | 0.87901 | 0.87370 | + 5.533 |
| Methylbenzene (Toluene) | $C_7H_8$ | 110.625 | 0.04630 | 1.49693 | 1.49414 | 0.86694 | 0.86230 | -94.991 |
| Ethylbenzene | $C_8H_{10}$ | 136.186 | 0.04898 | 1.49588 | 1.49320 | 0.86702 | 0.86264 | -94.975 |
| n-Propylbenzene | $C_9H_{12}$ | 159.217 | 0.05143 | 1.49202 | 1.48951 | 0.86204 | 0.65780 | -99.500 |
| n-Butylbenzene | $C_{10}H_{14}$ | 183.270 | 0.05358 | 1.48979 | 1.48742 | 0.86013 | 0.85607 | -87.970 |
| n-Pentylbenzene | $C_{11}H_{16}$ | 205.4 | 0.055 | 1.4878 | 1.4855 | 0.8565 | 0.8546 | -75. |
| n-Hexylbenzene | $C_{12}H_{18}$ | 226.1 | 0.056 | 1.4864 | 1.4842 | 0.8575 | 0.8537 | -61. |
| n-Heptylbenzene | $C_{13}H_{20}$ | 245.5 | 0.058 | 1.4854 | 1.4832 | 0.8567 | 0.8530 | -48. |
| n-Octylbenzene | $C_{14}H_{22}$ | 264.5 | 0.059 | 1.4845 | 1.4824 | 0.8562 | 0.8525 | -36. |
| n-Nonylbenzene | $C_{15}H_{24}$ | 282.0 | 0.061 | 1.4838 | 1.4817 | 0.8558 | 0.8522 | -24. |
| n-Decylbenzene | $C_{16}H_{26}$ | 300. | 0.06 | 1.48319 | 1.48112 | 0.85553 | 0.85189 | -14.38 |
| n-Undecylbenzene | $C_{17}H_{28}$ | 316. | 0.06 | 1.4828 | 1.4807 | 0.8553 | 0.8517 | - 5. |
| n-Dodecylbenzene | $C_{18}H_{30}$ | 331. | 0.06 | 1.4824 | 1.4803 | 0.8551 | 0.8516 | + 3. |
| n-Tridecylbenzene | $C_{19}H_{32}$ | 346. | 0.07 | 1.4821 | 1.4800 | 0.8550 | 0.8515 | 10. |
| n-Tetradecylbenzene | $C_{20}H_{34}$ | 359. | 0.07 | 1.4818 | 1.4797 | 0.8549 | 0.8514 | 16. |
| n-Pentadecylbenzene | $C_{21}H_{36}$ | 373. | 0.07 | 1.4815[b] | 1.4794 | 0.8546[b] | 0.8513 | 22. |
| n-Hexadecylbenzene | $C_{22}H_{38}$ | 385. | 0.07 | 1.4813[b] | 1.4792[b] | 0.8547[b] | 0.8512[b] | 27. |

a See footnote a of Table 1a.

b For the undercooled liquid below the normal freezing point.

TABLE 21a (PART 2) - NORMAL ALKYL BENZENES, $C_{23}$ TO $C_{42}$

BOILING POINT, $dt/dp$, REFRACTIVE INDEX, DENSITY, AND FREEZING POINT

September 30, 1951

| Compound | Formula | Boiling Point 760 mm Hg (°C) | $dt/dp$ 760 mm Hg (°C/mm Hg) | Refractive Index[a] 20°C ($n_D$) | 25°C ($n_D$) | Density[a] 20°C (g/ml) | 25°C (g/ml) | Freezing Point In air at 1 atm (°C) |
|---|---|---|---|---|---|---|---|---|
| n-Heptadecylbenzene | $C_{23}H_{40}$ | 397. | 0.07 | 1.4810[b] | 1.4790[b] | 0.8546[b] | 0.8512[b] | 32. |
| n-Octadecylbenzene | $C_{24}H_{42}$ | 408. | 0.07 | 1.4809[b] | 1.4788[b] | 0.8546[b] | 0.8511[b] | 36. |
| n-Nonadecylbenzene | $C_{25}H_{44}$ | 419. | 0.07 | 1.4807[b] | 1.4786[b] | 0.8545[b] | 0.8511[b] | 40. |
| n-Eicosylbenzene | $C_{26}H_{46}$ | 429. | 0.07 | 1.4805[b] | 1.4785[b] | 0.8545[b] | 0.8511[b] | 44. |
| n-Heneicosylbenzene | $C_{27}H_{48}$ | 439. | 0.07 | 1.4804[b] | 1.4783[b] | 0.8545[b] | 0.8510[b] | 48. |
| n-Docosylbenzene | $C_{28}H_{50}$ | 448. | 0.07 | 1.4802[b] | 1.4782[b] | 0.8544[b] | 0.8510[b] | 51. |
| n-Tricosylbenzene | $C_{29}H_{52}$ | 457. | 0.07 | 1.4801[b] | 1.4781[b] | 0.8544[b] | 0.8510[b] | 54. |
| n-Tetracosylbenzene | $C_{30}H_{54}$ | 466. | 0.07 | 1.4800[b] | 1.4780[b] | 0.8544[b] | 0.8510[b] | 57. |
| n-Pentacosylbenzene | $C_{31}H_{56}$ | 474. | 0.07 | 1.4799[b] | 1.4779[b] | 0.8544[b] | 0.8510[b] | 59. |
| n-Hexacosylbenzene | $C_{32}H_{58}$ | 482. | 0.08 | 1.4798[b] | 1.4778[b] | 0.8543[b] | 0.8510[b] | 62. |
| n-Heptacosylbenzene | $C_{33}H_{60}$ | 490. | 0.08 | 1.4797[b] | 1.4777[b] | 0.8543[b] | 0.8510[b] | 64. |
| n-Octacosylbenzene | $C_{34}H_{62}$ | 498. | 0.08 | 1.4796[b] | 1.4776[b] | 0.8543[b] | 0.8510[b] | 66. |
| n-Nonacosylbenzene | $C_{35}H_{64}$ | 505. | 0.08 | 1.4796[b] | 1.4775[b] | 0.8543[b] | 0.8509[b] | 68. |
| n-Triacontylbenzene | $C_{36}H_{66}$ | 512. | 0.08 | 1.4795[b] | 1.4775[b] | 0.8543[b] | 0.8509[b] | 70. |
| n-Hentriacontylbenzene | $C_{37}H_{68}$ | 519. | 0.08 | 1.4794[b] | 1.4774[b] | 0.8543[b] | 0.8509[b] | 72 |
| n-Dotriacontylbenzene | $C_{38}H_{70}$ | 525. | 0.08 | 1.4794[b] | 1.4773[b] | 0.8543[b] | 0.8509[b] | 74. |
| n-Tritriacontylbenzene | $C_{39}H_{72}$ | 532. | 0.08 | 1.4793[b] | 1.4773[b] | 0.8543[b] | 0.8509[b] | 75. |
| n-Tetratriacontylbenzene | $C_{40}H_{74}$ | 538. | 0.08 | 1.4792[b] | 1.4772[b] | 0.8543[b] | 0.8509[b] | 77. |
| n-Pentatriacontylbenzene | $C_{41}H_{76}$ | 544. | 0.08 | 1.4792[b] | 1.4772[b] | 0.8543[b] | 0.8509[b] | 79. |
| n-Hexatriacontylbenzene | $C_{42}H_{78}$ | 549. | 0.08 | 1.4791[b] | 1.4771[b] | 0.8542[b] | 0.8509[b] | 80. |

[a] See footnote a of Table 1a.

[b] For the undercooled liquid below the normal freezing point.

TABLE 5a — ALKYL BENZENES, $C_6$ TO $C_9$

BOILING POINT, $dt/dp$, REFRACTIVE INDEX, DENSITY, AND FREEZING POINT

March 31, 1943; June 30, 1945; May 31, 1947; October 31, 1950 (Corrected)

| Compound | Formula | Boiling Point 760 mm Hg °C | $dt/dp$ 760 mm Hg °C/mm Hg | Refractive Index[a] 20°C $n_D$ | 25°C $n_D$ | Density[a] 20°C g/ml | 25°C g/ml | Freezing Point In air at 1 atm °C |
|---|---|---|---|---|---|---|---|---|
| Benzene | $C_6H_6$ | 80.100 | 0.04271 | 1.50112 | 1.49792 | 0.87901 | 0.87370 | 5.533 |
| Methylbenzene (Toluene) | $C_7H_8$ | 110.625 | 0.04630 | 1.49693 | 1.49414 | 0.86694 | 0.86230 | -94.991 |
| Ethylbenzene | $C_8H_{10}$ | 136.186 | 0.04898 | 1.49588 | 1.49320 | 0.86702 | 0.86264 | -94.975 |
| 1,2-Dimethylbenzene (o-Xylene) | " | 144.411 | 0.04969 | 1.50545 | 1.50295 | 0.88020 | 0.87596 | -25.182 |
| 1,3-Dimethylbenzene (m-Xylene) | " | 139.103 | 0.04903 | 1.49722 | 1.49464 | 0.86417 | 0.85990 | -47.872 |
| 1,4-Dimethylbenzene (p-Xylene) | " | 138.351 | 0.04917 | 1.49582 | 1.49325 | 0.86105 | 0.85669 | 13.263 |
| n-Propylbenzene | $C_9H_{12}$ | 159.217 | 0.05143 | 1.49202 | 1.48951 | 0.86204 | 0.85780 | -99.500 |
| Isopropylbenzene | " | 152.392 | 0.05074 | 1.49145 | 1.48890 | 0.86179 | 0.85751 | -96.035 |
| 1-Methyl-2-ethylbenzene | " | 165.153 | 0.05163 | 1.50456 | 1.50208 | 0.88069 | 0.87657 | -80.833 |
| 1-Methyl-3-ethylbenzene | " | 161.305 | 0.05111 | 1.49660 | 1.49406 | 0.86452 | 0.86040 | -95.55 |
| 1-Methyl-4-ethylbenzene | " | 161.989 | 0.05148 | 1.49500 | 1.49244 | 0.86118 | 0.85702 | -62.350 |
| 1,2,3-Trimethylbenzene | " | 176.084 | 0.05263 | 1.51393 | 1.51150 | 0.89438 | 0.89044 | -25.375 |
| 1,2,4-Trimethylbenzene | " | 169.351 | 0.05187 | 1.50484 | 1.50237 | 0.87582 | 0.87180 | -43.80 |
| 1,3,5-Trimethylbenzene | " | 164.716 | 0.05100 | 1.49937 | 1.49684 | 0.86518 | 0.86111 | -44.720 |

a See footnote a of Table 1a.

### TABLE 14a – ALKYL BENZENES, C$_{10}$
### BOILING POINT, $dt/dp$, REFRACTIVE INDEX, DENSITY, AND FREEZING POINT

January 31, 1946; May 31, 1947; April 30, 1952

| Compound | Formula | Boiling Point 760 mm Hg °C | $dt/dp$ 760 mm Hg °C/mm Hg | Refractive Index[a] 20°C $n_D$ | Refractive Index[a] 25°C $n_D$ | Density[a] 20°C g/ml | Density[a] 25°C g/ml | Freezing Point In air at 1 atm °C |
|---|---|---|---|---|---|---|---|---|
| n-Butylbenzene (1-Phenylbutane) | C$_{10}$H$_{14}$ | 183.270 | 0.05558 | 1.48979 | 1.48742 | 0.86013 | 0.85607 | -87.970 |
| Isobutylbenzene (1-Phenyl-2-methylpropane) | " | 172.759 | 0.05319 | 1.48646 | 1.48400 | 0.85321 | 0.84907 | -51.48 |
| sec-Butylbenzene (2-Phenylbutane) | " | 173.305 | 0.05313 | 1.49020 | 1.48779 | 0 86207 | 0.85797 | -75.470 |
| tert-Butylbenzene (2-Phenyl-2-methylpropane) | " | 169.119 | 0.05269 | 1.49266 | 1.49024 | 0.86650 | 0.86240 | -57.850 |
| 1-Methyl-2-propylbenzene | " | 184.80 | 0.0535 | 1.4998 | 1.4974 | 0.8744 | 0.8705 | -60.2 |
| 1-Methyl-3-propylbenzene | " | 181.80 | 0.0530 | 1.4956 | 1.4912 | 0.8610 | 0.8570 | |
| 1-Methyl-4-propylbenzene | " | 183.30 | 0.0535 | 1.4919 | 1.4895 | 0.8584 | 0.8544 | -63.6 |
| 1-Methyl-2-isopropylbenzene (o-Cymene) | " | 178.15 | 0.0529 | 1.5006 | 1.4982 | 0.8766 | 0.8726 | -71.540 |
| 1-Methyl-3-isopropylbenzene (m-Cymene) | " | 175.14 | 0.0524 | 1.4930 | 1.4906 | 0.8610 | 0.8570 | -63.745 |
| 1-Methyl-4-isopropylbenzene (p-Cymene) | " | 177.10 | 0.0528 | 1.4909 | 1.4885 | 0.8573 | 0.8533 | -67.935 |
| 1,2-Diethylbenzene | " | 183.423 | 0.05340 | 1.50346 | 1.50106 | 0.87996 | 0.87592 | -31.240 |
| 1,3-Diethylbenzene | " | 181.102 | 0.05293 | 1.49552 | 1.49310 | 0.86394 | 0.85993 | -83.920 |
| 1,4-Diethylbenzene | " | 183.752 | 0.05351 | 1.49483 | 1.49245 | 0.86196 | 0.85794 | -42.850 |
| 1,2-Dimethyl-3-ethylbenzene | " | 193.91 | 0.0554 | 1.5117 | 1.5095 | 0.8921 | 0.8881 | -49.5 |
| 1,2-Dimethyl-4-ethylbenzene | " | 189.75 | 0.0563 | 1.5031 | 1.5009 | 0.8745 | 0.8706 | -67.0 |
| 1,3-Dimethyl-2-ethylbenzene | " | 190.01 | 0.0561 | 1.5107 | 1.5085 | 0.8904 | 0.8864 | -16.3 |
| 1,3-Dimethyl-4-ethylbenzene | " | 188.41 | 0.0555 | 1.5038 | 1.5016 | 0.8763 | 0.8723 | -63.0 |
| 1,3-Dimethyl-5-ethylbenzene | " | 183.75 | 0.0542 | 1.4981 | 1.4958 | 0.8648 | 0.8608 | -84.325 |
| 1,4-Dimethyl-2-ethylbenzene | " | 186.91 | 0.0533 | 1.5043 | 1.5020 | 0.8772 | 0.8732 | -53.7 |
| 1,2,3,4-Tetramethylbenzene (Prehnitene) | " | 205.04 | 0.055 | 1.5203 | 1.5181 | 0.9052 | 0.9015 | - 6.25 |
| 1,2,3,5-Tetramethylbenzene (Isodurene) | " | 198.00 | 0.055 | 1.5130 | 1.5107 | 0.8903 | 0.8865 | -23.685 |
| 1,2,4,5-Tetramethylbenzene (Durene) | " | 196.80 | 0.054 | 1.5116[b] | 1.5093[b] | 0.8875[b] | 0.8837[b] | +79.240 |

a See footnote a of Table 1a.  b For the undercooled liquid below the normal freezing point.

TABLE 26a, Page 1 - ALKYL BENZENES, C$_{11}$

BOILING POINT, $dt/dp$, REFRACTIVE INDEX, DENSITY, AND FREEZING POINT

April 30, 1952

| Compound | Formula | Boiling Point 760 mm Hg °C | dt/dp 760 mm Hg °C/mm Hg | Refractive Index[a] 20°C $n_D$ | Refractive Index[a] 25°C $n_D$ | Density[a] 20°C g/ml | Density[a] 25°C g/ml | Freezing Point In air at 1 atm °C |
|---|---|---|---|---|---|---|---|---|
| n-Pentylbenzene | C$_{11}$H$_{16}$ | 205.4 | 0.055 | 1.4878 | 1.4855 | 0.8585 | 0.8546 | -75. |
| 2-Phenylpentane | " | 193. | 0.05 | 1.4876 | 1.4853 | 0.8585 | 0.8546 | |
| 3-Phenylpentane | " | 191. | 0.05 | 1.4877 | 1.4854 | 0.860 | 0.856 | |
| 1-Phenyl-2-methylbutane | " | 197. | 0.05 | 1.486 | 1.484 | 0.859 | 0.855 | |
| 1-Phenyl-3-methylbutane | " | 198.9 | 0.054 | 1.484 | 1.482 | 0.856 | 0.852 | |
| 2-Phenyl-2-methylbutane | " | 192.38 | 0.053 | 1.4958 | 1.4935 | 0.8748 | 0.8709 | |
| 2-Phenyl-3-methylbutane | " | 188. | 0.05 | 1.486 | 1.484 | 0.870 | 0.866 | |
| 1-Phenyl-2,2-dimethylpropane | " | 186. | 0.05 | 1.488 | 1.486 | 0.858 | 0.854 | |
| 1-Methyl-2-n-butylbenzene | " | 208. | 0.05 | 1.496 | 1.494 | 0.871 | 0.867 | |
| 1-Methyl-3-n-butylbenzene | " | 205. | 0.05 | 1.491 | 1.489 | 0.859 | 0.855 | |
| 1-Methyl-4-n-butylbenzene | " | 207. | 0.05 | 1.490 | 1.488 | 0.857 | 0.853 | |
| 1-Methyl-2-sec-butylbenzene | " | 196. | 0.05 | 1.497 | 1.495 | 0.873 | 0.869 | |
| 1-Methyl-3-sec-butylbenzene | " | 194. | 0.05 | 1.490 | 1.488 | 0.858 | 0.854 | |
| 1-Methyl-4-sec-butylbenzene | " | 197. | 0.05 | 1.493 | 1.491 | 0.866 | 0.862 | |
| 1-Methyl-2-isobutylbenzene | " | 196. | 0.05 | 1.4935 | 1.4912 | 0.8649 | 0.8610 | |
| 1-Methyl-3-isobutylbenzene | " | 194. | 0.05 | 1.4888 | 1.4865 | 0.8536 | 0.8497 | |
| 1-Methyl-4-isobutylbenzene | " | 196. | 0.05 | 1.4674 | 1.4851 | 0.8517 | 0.8478 | |
| 1-Methyl-2-tert-butylbenzene | " | 200.45 | 0.054 | 1.5076 | 1.5053 | 0.8897 | 0.8858 | -50.32 |
| 1-Methyl-3-tert-butylbenzene | " | 189.26 | 0.053 | 1.4944 | 1.4921 | 0.8657 | 0.8618 | -41.370 |
| 1-Methyl-4-tert-butylbenzene | " | 192.76 | 0.053 | 1.4918 | 1.4895 | 0.8612 | 0.8573 | -52.515 |
| 1-Ethyl-2-n-propylbenzene | " | 203. | 0.05 | 1.4992 | 1.4969 | 0.8744 | 0.8705 | |
| 1-Ethyl-3-n-propylbenzene | " | 201. | 0.05 | 1.4930 | 1.4907 | 0.8607 | 0.8568 | |
| 1-Ethyl-4-n-propylbenzene | " | 205. | 0.05 | 1.4921 | 1.4898 | 0.8594 | 0.8555 | |
| 1-Ethyl-2-isopropylbenzene | " | 193. | 0.05 | 1.508 | 1.506 | 0.888 | 0.884 | |
| 1-Ethyl-3-isopropylbenzene | " | 192.0 | 0.053 | 1.492 | 1.490 | 0.859 | 0.855 | |
| 1-Ethyl-4-isopropylbenzene | " | 196.6 | 0.054 | 1.4923 | 1.4900 | 0.8585 | 0.8546 | |

a See footnote a of Table 1a.

TABLE 26a, Page 2 - ALKYL BENZENES, $C_{11}$

BOILING POINT, dt/dp, REFRACTIVE INDEX, DENSITY, AND FREEZING POINT

April 30, 1952

| Compound | Formula | Boiling Point 760 mm Hg °C | dt/dp 760 mm Hg °C/mm Hg | Refractive Index[a] 20°C $n_D$ | 25°C $n_D$ | Density[a] 20°C g/ml | 25°C g/ml | Freezing Point In air at 1 atm °C |
|---|---|---|---|---|---|---|---|---|
| 1,2-Dimethyl-3-n-propylbenzene | $C_{11}H_{16}$ | 210.7 | 0.055 | 1.5075 | 1.5053 | 0.8864 | 0.8825 | |
| 1,2-Dimethyl-4-n-propylbenzene | " | 208.9 | 0.055 | 1.5000 | 1.4978 | 0.8715 | 0.8676 | |
| 1,3-Dimethyl-2-n-propylbenzene | " | 207.6 | 0.055 | 1.5063 | 1.5041 | 0.8856 | 0.8817 | |
| 1,3-Dimethyl-4-n-propylbenzene | " | 206.6 | 0.055 | 1.4998 | 1.4976 | 0.8723 | 0.8684 | |
| 1,3-Dimethyl-5-n-propylbenzene | " | 202.24 | 0.054 | 1.4952 | 1.4930 | 0.8607 | 0.8568 | -59.1 |
| 1,4-Dimethyl-2-n-propylbenzene | " | 204.3 | 0.054 | 1.4999 | 1.4977 | 0.8717 | 0.8678 | |
| 1,2-Dimethyl-3-isopropylbenzene | " | 202.6 | 0.054 | 1.508 | 1.506 | 0.888 | 0.884 | |
| 1,2-Dimethyl-4-isopropylbenzene | " | 201.8 | 0.054 | 1.4993 | 1.4971 | 0.8699 | 0.8660 | |
| 1,3-Dimethyl-2-isopropylbenzene | " | 199. | 0.05 | 1.509 | 1.507 | 0.890 | 0.886 | |
| 1,3-Dimethyl-4-isopropylbenzene | " | 199.1 | 0.054 | 1.500 | 1.498 | 0.873 | 0.869 | |
| 1,3-Dimethyl-5-isopropylbenzene | " | 194.5 | 0.053 | 1.495 | 1.493 | 0.862 | 0.858 | |
| 1,4-Dimethyl-2-isopropylbenzene | " | 196.2 | 0.054 | 1.5010 | 1.4988 | 0.8738 | 0.8699 | |
| 1-Methyl-2,3-diethylbenzene | " | 206.6 | 0.055 | 1.5105 | 1.5083 | 0.8910 | 0.8871 | |
| 1-Methyl-2,4-diethylbenzene | " | 205.0 | 0.054 | 1.5027 | 1.5005 | 0.8748 | 0.8709 | |
| 1-Methyl-2,5-diethylbenzene | " | 207.1 | 0.055 | 1.5034 | 1.5012 | 0.8758 | 0.8719 | |
| 1-Methyl-2,6-diethylbenzene | " | 208.8 | 0.055 | 1.5106 | 1.5084 | 0.8907 | 0.8868 | |
| 1-Methyl-3,4-diethylbenzene | " | 203.6 | 0.054 | 1.5039 | 1.5017 | 0.8762 | 0.8723 | |
| 1-Methyl-3,5-diethylbenzene | " | 200.70 | 0.054 | 1.4969 | 1.4947 | 0.8630 | 0.8591 | -74.12 |
| 1,2,3-Trimethyl-4-ethylbenzene | " | 220.4 | 0.056 | 1.5180 | 1.5158 | 0.9019 | 0.8980 | |
| 1,2,3-Trimethyl-5-ethylbenzene | " | 215.8 | 0.055 | 1.5101 | 1.5079 | 0.8863 | 0.8824 | |
| 1,2,4-Trimethyl-3-ethylbenzene | " | 216.6 | 0.055 | 1.5133 | 1.5111 | 0.895 | 0.891 | |
| 1,2,4-Trimethyl-5-ethylbenzene | " | 213.0 | 0.055 | 1.5075 | 1.5053 | 0.883 | 0.879 | -13.5 |
| 1,2,4-Trimethyl-6-ethylbenzene | " | 213.0 | 0.055 | 1.5118 | 1.5096 | 0.8897 | 0.8858 | |
| 1,3,5-Trimethyl-2-ethylbenzene | " | 212.4 | 0.055 | 1.5074 | 1.5052 | 0.883 | 0.879 | -15.5 |
| Pentamethylbenzene | " | 231.8 | 0.057 | 1.527[b] | 1.525[b] | 0.917[b] | 0.913[b] | +54.3 |

a See footnote a of Table 1a.

b For the undercooled liquid below the normal freezing point.

TABLE 13a – STYRENES, $C_8$ AND $C_9$

BOILING POINT, $dt/dp$, REFRACTIVE INDEX, DENSITY, AND FREEZING POINT

September 30, 1943; June 30, 1945; May 31, 1947; June 30, 1948; October 31, 1952

| Compound | Formula[a] | Boiling Point 760 mm Hg °C | $dt/dp$ 760 mm Hg °C/mm Hg | Refractive Index[a] 20°C $n_D$ | Refractive Index[a] 25°C $n_D$ | Density[a] 20°C g/ml | Density[a] 25°C g/ml | Freezing Point In air at 1 atm °C |
|---|---|---|---|---|---|---|---|---|
| Ethenylbenzene (Styrene; Vinylbenzene; Phenylethylene) | $C_8H_8$ | 145.2 | 0.049 | 1.54682 | 1.54395 | 0.90600 | 0.90122 | −30.628 |
| Isopropenylbenzene (α-Methylstyrene; 2-Phenyl-1-propene) | $C_9H_{10}$ | 165.38 | 0.052 | 1.5386 | 1.5358 | 0.9106 | 0.9062 | −23.21 |
| cis-1-Propenylbenzene (cis-β-Methylstyrene; cis-1-Phenyl-1-propene) | " | 170. | 0.051 | 1.549 | 1.546 | 0.911 | 0.907 | |
| trans-1-Propenylbenzene (trans-β-Methylstyrene; trans-1-Phenyl-1-propene) | | | | | | | | |
| 1-Methyl-2-ethenyl benzene (o-Methyl styrene) | " | 171. | 0.051 | 1.5450 | 1.5422 | 0.9106 | 0.9060 | |
| 1-Methyl-3-ethenyl benzene (m-Methyl styrene) | " | 168. | 0.051 | 1.5419 | 1.5391 | 0.8989 | 0.8943 | |
| 1-Methyl-4-ethenyl benzene (p-Methyl styrene) | " | 169. | 0.051 | 1.5428 | 1.5400 | 0.897 | 0.892 | |

a See footnote a of Table 1a.

TABLE 30a -1- NORMAL ALKYL NAPHTHALENES, $C_{10}$ TO $C_{22}$
BOILING POINT, $dt/dp$, REFRACTIVE INDEX, DENSITY, AND FREEZING POINT

October 31, 1952

| Compound | Formula | Boiling Point 760 mm Hg °C | $dt/dp$ 760 mm Hg °C/mm Hg | Refractive Index[a] 20°C $n_D$ | Refractive Index[a] 25°C $n_D$ | Density[a] 20°C g/ml | Density[a] 25°C g/ml | Freezing Point In air at 1 atm °C |
|---|---|---|---|---|---|---|---|---|
| Naphthalene | $C_{10}H_8$ | 217.955 | 0.0584 | — | 1.5898[b] | — | 0.9752[b] | +80.290 |
| 1-Methylnaphthalene | $C_{11}H_{10}$ | 244.642 | 0.0604 | 1.6174 | 1.6149 | 1.02015 | 1.01630 | -30.57 |
| 1-Ethylnaphthalene | $C_{12}H_{12}$ | 258.67 | 0.0615 | 1.6062 | 1.6040 | 1.00816 | 1.00446 | -13.88 |
| 1-n-Propylnaphthalene | $C_{13}H_{14}$ | 272.5 | 0.06 | 1.5952 | 1.5930 | 0.9918 | 0.9882 | -10. |
| 1-n-Butylnaphthalene | $C_{14}H_{16}$ | 289.34 | 0.06 | 1.5819 | 1.5798 | 0.97673 | 0.97324 | -19.76 |
| 1-n-Pentylnaphthalene | $C_{15}H_{18}$ | 307. | 0.06 | 1.5725 | 1.5704 | 0.9656 | 0.9622 | -22. |
| 1-n-Hexylnaphthalene | $C_{16}H_{20}$ | 322. | 0.06 | 1.5647 | 1.5626 | 0.9566 | 0.9532 | -18. |
| 1-n-Heptylnaphthalene | $C_{17}H_{22}$ | 340. | 0.07 | 1.5582 | 1.5561 | 0.9491 | 0.9458 | -8. |
| 1-n-Octylnaphthalene | $C_{18}H_{24}$ | 356. | 0.07 | 1.5526 | 1.5505 | 0.9427 | 0.9394 | -2. |
| 1-n-Nonylnaphthalene | $C_{19}H_{26}$ | 372. | 0.07 | 1.5477 | 1.5456 | 0.9371 | 0.9339 | +8. |
| 1-n-Decylnaohthalene | $C_{20}H_{28}$ | 387. | 0.07 | 1.5435 | 1.5414 | 0.9322 | 0.9290 | 15. |
| 1-n-Undecylnaphthalene | $C_{21}H_{30}$ | 401. | 0.07 | 1.5399[c] | 1.5379 | 0.9279[c] | 0.9248 | 23. |
| 1-n-Dodecylnaphthalene | $C_{22}H_{32}$ | 415. | 0.07 | 1.5364[c] | 1.5344[c] | 0.9240[c] | 0.9209[c] | 27. |

a See footnote a of Table 1a.    b At 85°C.    c For the undercooled liquid below the normal freezing point.

TABLE 31a -2- NORMAL ALKYL NAPHTHALENES, $C_{10}$ TO $C_{22}$

BOILING POINT, $dt/dp$, REFRACTIVE INDEX, DENSITY, AND FREEZING POINT

October 31, 1952

| Compound | Formula | Boiling Point 760 mm Hg | $dt/dp$ 760 mm Hg | Refractive Index[a] | | Density[a] | | Freezing Point In air at 1 atm |
|---|---|---|---|---|---|---|---|---|
| | | °C | °C/mm Hg | 20°C $n_D$ | 25°C $n_D$ | 20°C g/ml | 25°C g/ml | °C |
| Naphthalene | $C_{10}H_8$ | 217.955 | 0.0584 | — | 1.5898[b] | — | 0.9752[b] | 80.290 |
| 2-Methylnaphthalene | $C_{11}H_{10}$ | 241.052 | 0.0600 | — | 1.6019[c] | — | 0.9904[c] | +34.58 |
| 2-Ethylnaphthalene | $C_{12}H_{12}$ | 257.9 | 0.062 | 1.5999 | 1.5977 | 0.9922 | 0.9885 | -7.4 |
| 2-*n*-Propylnaphthalene | $C_{13}H_{14}$ | 273.5 | 0.06 | 1.5872 | 1.5850 | 0.9770 | 0.9734 | -3. |
| 2-*n*-Butylnaphthalene | $C_{14}H_{16}$ | 292. | 0.06 | 1.5776 | 1.5755 | 0.9659 | 0.9624 | -5. |
| 2-*n*-Pentylnaphthalene | $C_{15}H_{18}$ | 310. | 0.06 | 1.5694 | 1.5673 | 0.9561 | 0.9527 | -4. |
| 2-*n*-Hexylnaphthalene | $C_{16}H_{20}$ | 324. | 0.06 | 1.5620 | 1.5599 | 0.9479 | 0.9445 | -3. |
| 2-*n*-Heptylnaphthalene | $C_{17}H_{22}$ | 341. | 0.07 | 1.5556 | 1.5535 | 0.9410 | 0.9377 | +1. |
| 2-*n*-Octylnaphthalene | $C_{18}H_{24}$ | 357. | 0.07 | 1.5501 | 1.5480 | 0.9350 | 0.9317 | 12. |
| 2-*n*-Nonylnaphthalene | $C_{19}H_{26}$ | 372. | 0.07 | 1.5454 | 1.5433 | 0.9298 | 0.9266 | 12. |
| 2-*n*-Decylnaphthalene | $C_{20}H_{28}$ | 387. | 0.07 | 1.5413 | 1.5392 | 0.9253 | 0.9221 | 20. |
| 2-*n*-Undecylnaphthalene | $C_{21}H_{30}$ | 401. | 0.07 | 1.5376 | 1.5356 | 0.9213 | 0.9182 | 20. |
| 2-*n*-Dodecylnaphthalene | $C_{22}H_{32}$ | 414. | 0.07 | 1.5343 | 1.5323 | 0.9177 | 0.9146 | 26. |

a See footnote a of Table 1a.  b At 85°C.  c At 40°C.

TABLE 27a - NAPHTHALENES, C₁₀ TO C₁₂

BOILING POINT, $dt/dp$, REFRACTIVE INDEX, DENSITY, AND FREEZING POINT

February 28, 1949; October 31, 1952

| Compound | Formula | Boiling Point 760 mm Hg °C | $dt/dp$ 760 mm Hg °C/mm Hg | Refractive Index [a] 20°C $n_D$ | Refractive Index [a] 25°C $n_D$ | Density [a] 20°C g/ml | Density [a] 25°C g/ml | Freezing Point In air at 1 atm °C |
|---|---|---|---|---|---|---|---|---|
| Naphthalene | $C_{10}H_8$ | 217.955 | 0.0584 | — | (1.5698) [b] | — | (0.9752) [b] | +80.290 |
| 1-Methylnaphthalene | $C_{11}H_{10}$ | 244.642 | 0.0604 | 1.6174 | 1.6149 | 1.02015 | 1.01630 | -30.57 |
| 2-Methylnaphthalene | " | 241.052 | 0.0600 | — | (1.6019) [c] | — | (0.9904) [c] | +34.58 |
| 1-Ethylnaphthalene | $C_{12}H_{12}$ | 258.67 | 0.0615 | 1.6062 | 1.6040 | 1.00816 | 1.00446 | -13.88 |
| 2-Ethylnaphthalene | " | 257.9 | 0.062 | 1.5999 | 1.5977 | 0.9922 | 0.9885 | -7.4 |
| 1,2-Dimethylnaphthalene | " | 266. | 0.057 | 1.6164 | 1.6142 | 1.013 | 1.009 | -1.0 |
| 1,3-Dimethylnaphthalene | " | 263. | 0.057 | 1.6090 | 1.6068 | 1.0063 | 1.0026 | -4.0 |
| 1,4-Dimethylnaphthalene | " | 268. | 0.057 | 1.6127 | 1.6105 | 1.0166 | 1.0129 | +7.66 |
| 1,5-Dimethylnaphthalene | " | 265. | 0.057 | | | | | 82.0 |
| 1,6-Dimethylnaphthalene | " | 263. | 0.057 | 1.6073 | 1.6051 | 1.003 | 0.999 | -14. |
| 1,7-Dimethylnaphthalene | " | 263. | 0.057 | 1.607 | 1.605 | 1.003 | 0.999 | -13. d |
| 1,8-Dimethylnaphthalene | " | 270. | 0.057 | | | | | +65. |
| 2,3-Dimethylnaphthalene | " | 268. | 0.057 | | | | | 105.0 |
| 2,6-Dimethylnaphthalene | " | 262. | 0.057 | | | | | 112.0 |
| 2,7-Dimethylnaphthalene | " | 263. | 0.057 | | | | | 98.0 |

a See footnote a of Table 1a.  b At 85°C.  c At 40°C.  d For the metastable crystalline form IIu, the freezing point is -28. °C.

## TABLE 28a, Page 1 - TETRAHYDRONAPHTHALENES, $C_{10}$ TO $C_{12}$
## BOILING POINT, $dt/dp$, REFRACTIVE INDEX, DENSITY, AND FREEZING POINT
August 31, 1949; October 31, 1952

| Compound | Formula[a] | Boiling Point 760 mm Hg °C | dt/dp 760 mm Hg °C/mm Hg | Refractive Index[a] 20°C $n_D$ | Refractive Index[a] 25°C $n_D$ | Density[a] 20°C g/ml | Density[a] 25°C g/ml | Freezing Point In air at 1 atm °C |
|---|---|---|---|---|---|---|---|---|
| 1,2,3,4-Tetrahydronaphthalene | $C_{10}H_{12}$ | 207.57 | 0.0575 | 1.54135 | 1.53919 | 0.9702 | 0.9662 | -35.790 |
| 1-Methyl-[1,2,3,4-tetrahydronaphthalene] | $C_{11}H_{14}$ | 219. | 0.058 | 1.5357 | 1.5336 | 0.9580 | 0.9543 | |
| 2-Methyl-[1,2,3,4-tetrahydronaphthalene] | " | 218. | 0.058 | 1.531 | 1.529 | 0.952 | 0.948 | |
| 5-Methyl-[1,2,3,4-tetrahydronaphthalene] | " | 234.35 | 0.058 | 1.54395 | 1.54190 | 0.9720 | 0.9683 | -22.90 |
| 6-Methyl-[1,2,3,4-tetrahydronaphthalene] | " | 229.03 | 0.058 | 1.53572 | 1.53365 | 0.9537 | 0.9500 | -39.75 |
| 1-Ethyl-[1,2,3,4-tetrahydronaphthalene] | $C_{12}H_{16}$ | 236. | 0.059 | 1.5321 | 1.5300 | 0.9535 | 0.9498 | |
| 2-Ethyl-[1,2,3,4-tetrahydronaphthalene] | " | 235. | 0.059 | 1.523 | 1.521 | 0.938 | 0.934 | |
| 5-Ethyl-[1,2,3,4-tetrahydronaphthalene] | " | 242. | 0.059 | 1.540 | 1.538 | 0.973 | 0.969 | |
| 6-Ethyl-[1,2,3,4-tetrahydronaphthalene] | " | 241. | 0.059 | 1.5331 | 1.5310 | 0.9568 | 0.9531 | |
| 1,1-Dimethyl-[1,2,3,4-tetrahydronaphthalene] | " | 221. | 0.059 | 1.5292 | 1.5271 | 0.950 | 0.946 | |
| 1,cis-2-Dimethyl-[1,2,3,4-tetrahydronaphthalene] | " | } 235. | 0.059 | 1.5286 | 1.5265 | 0.9470 | 0.9433 | |
| 1,trans-2-Dimethyl-[1,2,3,4-tetrahydronaphthalene] | " | | | | | | | |
| 1,cis-3-Dimethyl-[1,2,3,4-tetrahydronaphthalene] | " | } 234. | 0.059 | 1.525 | 1.523 | 0.940 | 0.936 | |
| 1,trans-3-Dimethyl-[1,2,3,4-tetrahydronaphthalene] | " | | | | | | | |
| 1,cis-4-Dimethyl-[1,2,3,4-tetrahydronaphthalene] | " | } 234. | 0.059 | 1.528 | 1.526 | 0.940 | 0.936 | |
| 1,trans-4-Dimethyl-[1,2,3,4-tetrahydronaphthalene] | " | | | | | | | |

a See footnote a of Table 1a.

80

TABLE 28a, Page 2 – TETRAHYDRONAPHTHALENES, $C_{10}$ TO $C_{12}$
BOILING POINT, dt/dp, REFRACTIVE INDEX, DENSITY, AND FREEZING POINT
August 31, 1949; October 31, 1952

| Compound | Formula[a] | Boiling Point 760 mm Hg °C | dt/dp 760 mm Hg °C/mm Hg | Refractive Index[a] 20°C $n_D$ | 25°C $n_D$ | Density[a] 20°C g/ml | 25°C g/ml | Freezing Point In air at 1 atm °C |
|---|---|---|---|---|---|---|---|---|
| 2,2-Dimethyl-[1,2,3,4-tetrahydronaphthalene] | $C_{12}H_{16}$ | 230. | 0.059 | 1.5200 | 1.5180 | 0.935 | 0.931 | |
| 2,cis-3-Dimethyl-[1,2,3,4-tetrahydronaphthalene] | " | 232 | 0.059 | 1.523 | 1.521 | 0.940 | 0.936 | 10. |
| 2,trans-3-Dimethyl-[1,2,3,4-tetrahydronaphthalene] | " | | | | | | | |
| 1,5-Dimethyl-[1,2,3,4-tetrahydronaphthalene] | " | 239. | 0.059 | 1.526 | 1.524 | 0.941 | 0.937 | |
| 1,6-Dimethyl-[1,2,3,4-tetrahydronaphthalene] | " | | | | | 0.939 | 0.935 | |
| 1,7-Dimethyl-[1,2,3,4-tetrahydronaphthalene] | " | | | 1.526 | 1.524 | 0.941 | 0.937 | |
| 1,8-Dimethyl-[1,2,3,4-tetrahydronaphthalene] | " | | | | | 0.941 | 0.937 | |
| 2,5-Dimethyl-[1,2,3,4-tetrahydronaphthalene] | " | 236. | 0.059 | 1.526 | 1.524 | 0.946 | 0.942 | 20. |
| 2,6-Dimethyl-[1,2,3,4-tetrahydronaphthalene] | " | 238. | 0.059 | 1.526 | 1.524 | 0.941 | 0.937 | |
| 2,7-Dimethyl-[1,2,3,4-tetrahydronaphthalene] | " | 237. | 0.059 | 1.526 | 1.524 | 0.941 | 0.937 | |
| 2,8-Dimethyl-[1,2,3,4-tetrahydronaphthalene] | " | 236. | 0.059 | 1.526 | 1.524 | 0.941 | 0.937 | |
| 5,6-Dimethyl-[1,2,3,4-tetrahydronaphthalene] | " | 252. | 0.059 | 1.552 | 1.550 | 0.975 | 0.971 | |
| 5,7-Dimethyl-[1,2,3,4-tetrahydronaphthalene] | " | 253.1 | 0.059 | 1.5405 | 1.5384 | 0.9583 | 0.9537 | -6. |
| 5,8-Dimethyl-[1,2,3,4-tetrahydronaphthalene] | " | 254. | 0.059 | 1.547 | 1.545 | 0.967 | 0.963 | |
| 6,7-Dimethyl-[1,2,3,4-tetrahydronaphthalene] | " | 252. | 0.059 | 1.538 | 1.536 | 0.954 | 0.950 | 10. |

a See footnote a of Table 1a.

TABLE 29a (PART 1) - DECAHYDRONAPHTHALENES, $C_{10}$ AND $C_{11}$
BOILING POINT, $dt/dp$, REFRACTIVE INDEX, DENSITY, AND FREEZING POINT
October 31, 1950

| Compound | Formula | Boiling Point | $dt/dp$ | Refractive Index[a] | | Density[a] | | Freezing Point |
|---|---|---|---|---|---|---|---|---|
| | | 760 mm Hg | 760 mm Hg | 20°C | 25°C | 20°C | 25°C | In air at 1 atm |
| | | °C | °C/mm Hg | $n_D$ | $n_D$ | g/ml | g/ml | °C |
| cis-Decahydronaphthalene | $C_{10}H_{18}$ | 195.69 | 0.0550 | 1.4810 | 1.4788 | 0.8965 | 0.8925 | -43.01 |
| trans-Decahydronaphthalene | " | 187.25 | 0.0564 | 1.4695 | 1.4672 | 0.8699 | 0.8659 | -30.400 |
| 1-Methyl-[cis-decahydronaphthalene] | $C_{11}H_{20}$ | 243. | 0.06 | | | | | |
| 1-Methyl-[trans-decahydronaphthalene] | " | 235. | 0.06 | 1.4720 | 1.4698 | | | |
| 2-Methyl-[cis-decahydronaphthalene] | " | 216. | 0.06 | | | | | |
| 2-Methyl-[trans-decahydronaphthalene] | " | 208. | 0.06 | | | 0.891 | 0.887 | |
| 9-Methyl-[cis-decahydronaphthalene] | " | 215. | 0.06 | 1.4804 | 1.4782 | | | |
| 9-Methyl-[trans-decahydronaphthalene] | " | 205. | 0.06 | 1.4651 | 1.4619 | 0.862 | 0.858 | |

a See footnote a of Table 1a.

TABLE 29a (PART 2) – DECAHYDRONAPHTHALENES, $C_{12}$

BOILING POINT, $dt/dp$, REFRACTIVE INDEX, DENSITY, AND FREEZING POINT

October 31, 1950

| Compound | Formula | Boiling Point 760 mm Hg °C | $dt/dp$ 760 mm Hg °C/mm Hg | Refractive Index[a] 20°C $n_D$ | Refractive Index[a] 25°C $n_D$ | Density[a] 20°C g/ml | Density[a] 25°C g/ml | Freezing Point In air at 1 atm °C |
|---|---|---|---|---|---|---|---|---|
| 1-Ethyl-[cis-decahydronaphthalene] | $C_{12}H_{22}$ | 260. | 0.06 | | | | | |
| 1-Ethyl-[trans-decahydronaphthalene] | " | 255. | 0.06 | | | | | |
| 2-Ethyl-[cis-decahydronaphthalene] | " | 235. | 0.06 | | | | | |
| 2-Ethyl-[trans-decahydronaphthalene] | " | 228. | 0.06 | | | | | |
| 9-Ethyl-[cis-decahydronaphthalene] | " | 253. | 0.06 | 1.480 | 1.478 | 0.886 | 0.883 | |
| 9-Ethyl-[trans-decahydronaphthalene] | " | 225. | 0.06 | 1.466 | 1.464 | 0.861 | 0.857 | |
| 1,1-Dimethyl-[cis-decahydronaphthalene] | | | | | | | | |
| 1,1-Dimethyl-[trans-decahydronaphthalene] | | | | | | | | |
| 1,cis-2-Dimethyl-[cis-decahydronaphthalene] | | | | | | | | |
| 1,cis-2-Dimethyl-[trans-decahydronaphthalene] | | | | | | | | |
| 1,trans-2-Dimethyl-[cis-decahydronaphthalene] | | | | | | | | |
| 1,trans-2-Dimethyl-[trans-decahydronaphthalene] | | | | | | | | |
| 1,cis-3-Dimethyl-[cis-decahydronaphthalene] | | | | | | | | |
| 1,cis-3-Dimethyl-[trans-decahydronaphthalene] | | | | | | | | |
| 1,trans-3-Dimethyl-[cis-decahydronaphthalene] | | | | | | | | |
| 1,trans-3-Dimethyl-[trans-decahydronaphthalene] | | | | | | | | |
| 1,cis-4-Dimethyl-[cis-decahydronaphthalene] | | | | | | | | |
| 1,cis-4-Dimethyl-[trans-decahydronaphthalene] | | | | | | | | |
| 1,trans-4-Dimethyl-[cis-decahydronaphthalene] | | | | | | | | |
| 1,trans-4-Dimethyl-[trans-decahydronaphthalene] | | | | | | | | |
| 1,cis-5-Dimethyl-[cis-decahydronaphthalene] | | | | | | | | |
| 1,cis-5-Dimethyl-[trans-decahydronaphthalene] | | | | | | | | |
| 1,trans-5-Dimethyl-[cis-decahydronaphthalene] | | | | | | | | |
| 1,trans-5-Dimethyl-[trans-decahydronaphthalene] | | | | | | | | |
| 1,cis-6-Dimethyl-[cis-decahydronaphthalene] | | | | | | | | |
| 1,cis-6-Dimethyl-[trans-decahydronaphthalene] | | | | | | | | |
| 1,trans-6-Dimethyl-[cis-decahydronaphthalene] | | | | | | | | |
| 1,trans-6-Dimethyl-[trans-decahydronaphthalene] | | | | | | | | |
| 1,cis-7-Dimethyl-[cis-decahydronaphthalene] | | | | | | | | |
| 1,cis-7-Dimethyl-[trans-decahydronaphthalene] | | | | | | | | |
| 1,trans-7-Dimethyl-[cis-decahydronaphthalene] | | | | | | | | |
| 1,trans-7-Dimethyl-[trans-decahydronaphthalene] | | | | | | | | |

a See footnote a of Table 1a.

TABLE 29a (PART 3) – DECAHYDRONAPHTHALENES, $C_{12}$

BOILING POINT, $dt/dp$, REFRACTIVE INDEX, DENSITY, AND FREEZING POINT

October 31, 1950

| Compound | Formula | Boiling Point 760 mm Hg °C | $dt/dp$ 760 mm Hg °C/mm Hg | Refractive Index[a] 20°C $n_D$ | Refractive Index[a] 25°C $n_D$ | Density[a] 20°C g/ml | Density[a] 25°C g/ml | Freezing Point In air at 1 atm °C |
|---|---|---|---|---|---|---|---|---|
| 1,cis-8-Dimethyl-[cis-decahydronaphthalene] | $C_{12}H_{22}$ | | | | | | | |
| 1,cis-8-Dimethyl-[trans-decahydronaphthalene] | " | | | | | | | |
| 1,trans-8-Dimethyl-[cis-decahydronaphthalene] | " | | | | | | | |
| 1,trans-8-Dimethyl-[cis-decahydronaphthalene] | " | | | | | | | |
| 1,9-Dimethyl-[cis-decahydronaphthalene] | " | | | | | | | |
| 1,9-Dimethyl-[trans-decahydronaphthalene] | " | | | | | | | |
| 1,10-Dimethyl-[cis-decahydronaphthalene] | " | 220. | 0.06 | 1.4812 | 1.4790 | 0.8896 | 0.8856 | |
| 1,10-Dimethyl-[trans-decahydronaphthalene] | " | 213. | 0.06 | 1.4659 | 1.4637 | 0.8633 | 0.8593 | |
| 2,2-Dimethyl-[cis-decahydronaphthalene] | " | | | | | | | |
| 2,2-Dimethyl-[trans-decahydronaphthalene] | " | | | | | | | |
| 2,cis-3-Dimethyl-[cis-decahydronaphthalene] | " | | | | | | | |
| 2,cis-3-Dimethyl-[trans-decahydronaphthalene] | " | | | | | | | |
| 2,trans-3-Dimethyl-[cis-decahydronaphthalene] | " | | | | | | | |
| 2,trans-3-Dimethyl-[trans-decahydronaphthalene] | " | | | | | | | |
| 2,cis-6-Dimethyl-[cis-decahydronaphthalene] | " | | | | | | | |
| 2,cis-6-Dimethyl-[trans-decahydronaphthalene] | " | | | | | | | |
| 2,trans-6-Dimethyl-[cis-decahydronaphthalene] | " | | | | | | | |
| 2,trans-6-Dimethyl-[trans-decahydronaphthalene] | " | | | | | | | |
| 2,cis-7-Dimethyl-[cis-decahydronaphthalene] | " | | | | | | | |
| 2,cis-7-Dimethyl-[trans-decahydronaphthalene] | " | | | | | | | |
| 2,trans-7-Dimethyl-[cis-decahydronaphthalene] | " | | | | | | | |
| 2,trans-7-Dimethyl-[trans-decahydronaphthalene] | " | | | | | | | |
| 2,9-Dimethyl-[cis-decahydronaphthalene] | " | | | | | | | |
| 2,9-Dimethyl-[trans-decahydronaphthalene] | " | | | | | | | |
| 2,10-Dimethyl-[cis-decahydronaphthalene] | " | | | | | | | |
| 2,10-Dimethyl-[trans-decahydronaphthalene] | " | | | | | | | |
| 9,10-Dimethyl-[cis-decahydronaphthalene] | " | | | | | | | |
| 9,10-Dimethyl-[trans-decahydronaphthalene] | " | | | | | | | |

a See footnote a of Table 1a.

TABLE 101a -1- ALKANETHIOLS, $C_1$ TO $C_{20}$

BOILING POINT, $dt/dp$, REFRACTIVE INDEX, DENSITY, AND FREEZING POINT

April 30, 1952; December 31, 1952

| Compound | Formula[a] | Boiling Point 760 mm Hg °C | $dt/dp$ 760 mm Hg °C/mm Hg | Refractive Index[a] | | Density[a] | | Freezing Point In air at 1 atm °C |
|---|---|---|---|---|---|---|---|---|
| | | | | 20°C $n_D$ | 25°C $n_D$ | 20°C g/ml | 25°C g/ml | |
| Methanethiol (Methyl mercaptan) | $CH_4S$ | 5.95 | 0.0336 | — | — | 0.8665[b] | 0.8600[b] | -123.02 |
| Ethanethiol (Ethyl mercaptan) | $C_2H_6S$ | 35.00 | 0.0374 | 1.43105 | 1.42779 | 0.83914 | 0.83316 | -147.90 |
| 1-Propanethiol (n-Propyl mercaptan) | $C_3H_8S$ | 67.6 | 0.042 | 1.4380 | 1.4351 | 0.8411 | 0.8359 | -113.06 |
| 1-Butanethiol (n-Butyl mercaptan) | $C_4H_{10}S$ | 98.46 | 0.0447 | 1.44298 | 1.44034 | 0.84161 | 0.83676 | -115.67 |
| 1-Pentanethiol | $C_5H_{12}S$ | 126.64 | 0.0477 | 1.44692 | 1.44439 | 0.84209 | 0.83763 | - 75.70 |
| 1-Hexanethiol | $C_6H_{14}S$ | 151.5 | 0.047 | 1.4496 | 1.4471 | 0.8424 | 0.8381 | - 80.0 |
| 1-Heptanethiol | $C_7H_{16}S$ | 176.2 | 0.049 | 1.4521 | 1.4497 | 0.8427 | 0.8387 | - 43.1 |
| 1-Octanethiol | $C_8H_{18}S$ | 199.1 | 0.051 | 1.4540 | 1.4517 | 0.8433 | 0.8394 | - 49.2 |
| 1-Nonanethiol | $C_9H_{20}S$ | 220.2 | 0.052 | 1.4560 | 1.4537 | 0.8438 | 0.8399 | - 20.1 |
| 1-Decanethiol | $C_{10}H_{22}S$ | 240.6 | 0.053 | 1.4572 | 1.4550 | 0.8443 | 0.8405 | - 26. |
| 1-Undecanethiol | $C_{11}H_{24}S$ | 259.5 | 0.054 | 1.4585 | 1.4563 | 0.8448 | 0.8411 | - 3. |
| 1-Dodecanethiol | $C_{12}H_{26}S$ | 277.3 | 0.055 | 1.4597 | 1.4575 | 0.8453 | 0.8416 | - 8. |
| 1-Tridecanethiol | $C_{13}H_{28}S$ | 294.1 | 0.056 | 1.4608 | 1.4586 | 0.8457 | 0.8421 | + 9. |
| 1-Tetradecanethiol | $C_{14}H_{30}S$ | 310. | 0.06 | 1.4617 | 1.4595 | 0.8461 | 0.8425 | 6. |
| 1-Pentadecanethiol | $C_{15}H_{32}S$ | 325. | 0.06 | 1.4624 | 1.4603 | 0.8465 | 0.8429 | 18. |
| 1-Hexadecanethiol | $C_{16}H_{34}S$ | 339. | 0.06 | 1.4632 | 1.4611 | 0.8468 | 0.8433 | 18. |
| 1-Heptadecanethiol | $C_{17}H_{36}S$ | 353. | 0.06 | 1.4639[c] | 1.4618[c] | 0.8471[c] | 0.8436[c] | 27. |
| 1-Octadecanethiol | $C_{18}H_{38}S$ | 366. | 0.06 | 1.4645[c] | 1.4624[c] | 0.8475[c] | 0.8440[c] | 28. |
| 1-Nonadecanethiol | $C_{19}H_{40}S$ | 378. | 0.06 | 1.4650[c] | 1.4629[c] | 0.8477[c] | 0.8442[c] | 34. |
| 1-Eicosanethiol | $C_{20}H_{42}S$ | 389. | 0.06 | 1.4655[c] | 1.4634[c] | 0.8480[c] | 0.8445[c] | 37. |

[a] See footnote a of Table 1a.　　[b] At saturation pressure.　　[c] For the undercooled liquid below the normal freezing point.

TABLE 102a – 2-ALKANETHIOLS, $C_3$ TO $C_{20}$

BOILING POINT, $dt/dp$, REFRACTIVE INDEX, DENSITY, AND FREEZING POINT

April 30, 1952; December 31

| Compound | Formula | Boiling Point 760 mm Hg °C | $dt/dp$ 760 mm Hg °C/mm Hg | Refractive Index[a] 20°C $n_D$ | 25°C $n_D$ | Density[a] 20°C g/ml | 25°C g/ml | Freezing Point In air at 1 atm °C |
|---|---|---|---|---|---|---|---|---|
| 2-Propanethiol (isopropyl mercaptan) | $C_3H_8S$ | 52.56 | 0.0399 | 1.42554 | 1.42251 | 0.81431 | 0.80864 | -130.54 |
| 2-Butanethiol (sec-Butyl mercaptan) | $C_4H_{10}S$ | 84.98 | 0.0438 | 1.43663 | 1.43385 | 0.82947 | 0.82457 | -140.2 |
| 2-Pentanethiol | $C_5H_{12}S$ | 122.9 | 0.045 | 1.4412 | 1.4386 | 0.83268 | 0.82813 | -112.8 |
| 2-Hexanethiol | $C_6H_{14}S$ | 138.9 | 0.046 | 1.4451 | 1.4426 | 0.8345 | 0.8302 | -147. |
| 2-Heptanethiol | $C_7H_{16}S$ | 163.6 | 0.049 | 1.4478 | 1.4454 | 0.8352 | 0.8311 | -141. |
| 2-Octanethiol | $C_8H_{18}S$ | 186.4 | 0.050 | 1.4504 | 1.4481 | 0.8366 | 0.8327 | - 79. |
| 2-Nonanethiol | $C_9H_{20}S$ | 208.2 | 0.052 | 1.4523 | 1.4500 | 0.8377 | 0.8338 | - 69. |
| 2-Decanethiol | $C_{10}H_{22}S$ | 228.9 | 0.053 | 1.4539 | 1.4516 | 0.8386 | 0.8348 | - 42. |
| 2-Undecanethiol | $C_{11}H_{24}S$ | 248.3 | 0.054 | 1.4554 | 1.4532 | 0.8396 | 0.8358 | - 34. |
| 2-Dodecanethiol | $C_{12}H_{26}S$ | 266.6 | 0.055 | 1.4567 | 1.4545 | 0.8403 | 0.8366 | - 17. |
| 2-Tridecanethiol | $C_{13}H_{28}S$ | 284. | 0.06 | 1.4578 | 1.4557 | 0.8411 | 0.8374 | - 10. |
| 2-Tetradecanethiol | $C_{14}H_{30}S$ | 300. | 0.06 | 1.4589 | 1.4568 | 0.8417 | 0.8381 | + 1. |
| 2-Pentadecanethiol | $C_{15}H_{32}S$ | 316. | 0.06 | 1.4600 | 1.4578 | 0.8423 | 0.8387 | 7. |
| 2-Hexadecanethiol | $C_{16}H_{34}S$ | 330. | 0.06 | 1.4608 | 1.4587 | 0.8429 | 0.8393 | 15. |
| 2-Heptadecanethiol | $C_{17}H_{36}S$ | 344. | 0.06 | 1.4617 | 1.4595 | 0.8434 | 0.8398 | 20. |
| 2-Octadecanethiol | $C_{18}H_{38}S$ | 357. | 0.06 | 1.4623[b] | 1.4602[b] | 0.8438[b] | 0.8403[b] | 26. |
| 2-Nonadecanethiol | $C_{19}H_{40}S$ | 370. | 0.06 | 1.4629[b] | 1.4608[b] | 0.8443[b] | 0.8408[b] | 31. |
| 2-Eicosanethiol | $C_{20}H_{42}S$ | 381. | 0.06 | 1.4635[b] | 1.4614[b] | 0.8447[b] | 0.8412[b] | 35. |

a See footnote a of Table 1a.　　b For the undercooled liquid below the normal freezing point.

TABLE 103a - ALKANETHIOLS, $C_1$ TO $C_5$

BOILING POINT, $dt/dp$, REFRACTIVE INDEX, DENSITY, AND FREEZING POINT

April 30, 1952; December 31, 1952

| Compound | Formula | Boiling Point 760 mm Hg °C | $dt/dp$ 760 mm Hg °C/mm Hg | Refractive Index[a] 20°C $n_D$ | Refractive Index[a] 25°C $n_D$ | Density[a] 20°C g/ml | Density[a] 25°C g/ml | Freezing Point In air at 1 atm °C |
|---|---|---|---|---|---|---|---|---|
| Methanethiol (Methyl mercaptan) | $CH_4S$ | 5.95 | 0.0336 | ---------- | ---------- | 0.8665[b] | 0.8600[b] | -123.00 |
| Ethanethiol (Ethyl mercaptan) | $C_2H_6S$ | 35.00 | 0.0374 | 1.43105 | 1.42779 | 0.83914 | 0.83316 | -147.90 |
| 1-Propanethiol (n-Propyl mercaptan) | $C_3H_8S$ | 67.6 | 0.042 | 1.4380 | 1.4351 | 0.8411 | 0.8359 | -113.06 |
| 2-Propanethiol (Isopropyl mercaptan) | " | 52.56 | 0.0399 | 1.42554 | 1.42251 | 0.81431 | 0.80864 | -130.54 |
| 1-Butanethiol (n-Butyl mercaptan) | $C_4H_{10}S$ | 98.46 | 0.0447 | 1.44298 | 1.44034 | 0.84161 | 0.83676 | -115.67 |
| 2-Butanethiol (sec-Butyl mercaptan) | " | 84.98 | 0.0438 | 1.43663 | 1.43385 | 0.82947 | 0.82457 | -140.2 |
| 2-Methyl-1-propanethiol (Isobutyl mercaptan) | " | 88.72 | 0.044 | 1.4387 | 1.4358 | 0.8339 | 0.8288 |  |
| 2-Methyl-2-propanethiol (tert-Butyl mercaptan) | " | 64.22 | 0.0418 | 1.42320 | 1.42007 | 0.80020 | 0.79472 | + 1.11 |
| 1-Pentanethiol | $C_5H_{12}S$ | 126.64 | 0.0477 | 1.44692 | 1.44439 | 0.84209 | 0.83763 | -75.70 |
| 2-Pentanethiol | " | 112.9 | 0.045 | 1.4412 | 1.4386 | 0.83268 | 0.82813 | -112.8 |
| 3-Pentanethiol | " | 105. | 0.04 | 1.4447 | 1.4421 | 0.8410 | 0.8365 | -110.8 |
| 2-Methyl-1-butanethiol | " | 118.2 | 0.047 | 1.444 | 1.442 | 0.842 | 0.837 |  |
| 3-Methyl-1-butanethiol | " | 118. | 0.04 | 1.4415 | 1.4389 | 0.8350 | 0.8305 |  |
| 2-Methyl-2-butanethiol | " | 99.0 | 0.043 | 1.4379 | 1.4353 | 0.812 | 0.807 |  |
| 3-Methyl-2-butanethiol | " |  |  | 1.4446 | 1.4420 | 0.8409 | 0.8364 | - 67.3 |
| 2,2-Dimethyl-1-propanethiol | " |  |  |  |  |  |  |  |

a See footnote a of Table 1a.   b At saturation pressure.

TABLE 104a – ALKYL BENZENETHIOLS, $C_6$ TO $C_8$
BOILING POINT, $dt/dp$, REFRACTIVE INDEX, DENSITY, AND FREEZING POINT
October 31, 1952

| Compound | Formula | Boiling Point | $dt/dp$ | Refractive Index[a] | | Density[a] | | Freezing Point |
|---|---|---|---|---|---|---|---|---|
| | | 760 mm Hg | 760 mm Hg | 20°C | 25°C | 20°C | 25°C | In air at 1 atm |
| | | °C | °C/mm Hg | $n_D$ | $n_D$ | g/ml | g/ml | °C |
| Benzenethiol (Thiophenol) | $C_6H_6S$ | 168.7 | 0.055 | 1.5893 | 1.5864 | 1.0766 | 1.0724 | −14.8 |
| 2-Methylbenzenethiol (o-Methylthiophenol) | $C_7H_8S$ | 194.2 | 0.055 | 1.570 | 1.568 | 1.041 | 1.037 | 15. |
| 3-Methylbenzenethiol (m-Methylthiophenol) | " | 195.1 | 0.054 | 1.572 | 1.569 | 1.044 | 1.040 | |
| 4-Methylbenzenethiol (p-Methylthiophenol) | " | 194.9 | 0.055 | 1.572 | 1.569 | | | 44. |
| 2-Ethylbenzenethiol (o-Ethylthiophenol) | $C_8H_{10}S$ | 210. | 0.06 | 1.5700 | 1.5680 | 1.0349 | 1.0309 | |
| 3-Ethylbenzenethiol (m-Ethylthiophenol) | " | 211. | 0.06 | 1.572 | 1.569 | 1.038 | 1.034 | |
| 4-Ethylbenzenethiol (p-Ethylthiophenol) | " | 211. | 0.06 | 1.572 | 1.569 | 1.036 | 1.034 | |
| 2,3-Dimethylbenzenethiol (2,3-Dimethylthiophenol) | " | | 0.06 | | | | | |
| 2,4-Dimethylbenzenethiol (2,4-Dimethylthiophenol) | " | 208. | | | | | | |
| 2,5-Dimethylbenzenethiol (2,5-Dimethylthiophenol) | " | 205. | 0.06 | | | | | |
| 2,6-Dimethylbenzenethiol (2,6-Dimethylthiophenol) | " | | | | | | | |
| 3,4-Dimethylbenzenethiol (3,4-Dimethylthiophenol) | " | | | | | | | |
| 3,5-Dimethylbenzenethiol (3,5-Dimethylthiophenol) | " | | | | | | | |

a See footnote a of Table 1a.

TABLE 105a – 2-$n$-THIAALKANES, $C_2$ TO $C_{20}$

BOILING POINT, $dt/dp$, REFRACTIVE INDEX, DENSITY, AND FREEZING POINT

April 30, 1952; December 31, 1952

| Compound | Formula | Boiling Point 760 mm Hg °C | $dt/dp$ 760 mm Hg °C/mm Hg | Refractive Index[a] | | Density[a] | | Freezing Point[a] In air at 1 atm °C |
|---|---|---|---|---|---|---|---|---|
| | | | | 20°C $n_D$ | 25°C $n_D$ | 20°C g/ml | 25°C g/ml | |
| 2-Thiapropane (Dimethyl sulfide) | $C_2H_6S$ | 37.34 | 0.0376 | 1.43547 | 1.43231 | 0.84825 | 0.84290 | -98.27 |
| 2-Thiabutane (Methyl ethyl sulfide) | $C_3H_8S$ | 66.65 | 0.0410 | 1.44035 | 1.43737 | 0.84221 | 0.83679 | -105.93 |
| 2-Thiapentane (Methyl $n$-propyl sulfide) | $C_4H_{10}S$ | 95.54 | 0.0442 | 1.4442 | 1.4415 | 0.8424 | 0.8375 | -112.97 |
| 2-Thiahexane | $C_5H_{12}S$ | 123.2 | 0.047 | 1.4477 | 1.4452 | 0.8426 | 0.8381 | - 97.8 |
| 2-Thiaheptane | $C_6H_{14}S$ | 145. | 0.05 | 1.4506 | 1.4482 | 0.8431 | 0.8389 | - 94. |
| 2-Thiaoctane | $C_7H_{16}S$ | 171. | 0.05 | 1.4529 | 1.4505 | 0.8434 | 0.8393 | - 66.5 |
| 2-Thianonane | $C_8H_{18}S$ | 195. | 0.05 | 1.4548 | 1.4525 | 0.8437 | 0.8398 | - 63.3 |
| 2-Thiadecane | $C_9H_{20}S$ | 218. | 0.06 | 1.4564 | 1.4541 | 0.8441 | 0.8403 | - 42. |
| 2-Thiaundecane | $C_{10}H_{22}S$ | 240. | 0.06 | 1.4578 | 1.4556 | 0.8447 | 0.8409 | - 35. |
| 2-Thiadodecane | $C_{11}H_{24}S$ | 260. | 0.06 | 1.4591 | 1.4569 | 0.8451 | 0.8414 | - 18.5 |
| 2-Thiatridecane | $C_{12}H_{26}S$ | 279. | 0.06 | 1.4602 | 1.4580 | 0.8456 | 0.8419 | - 14. |
| 2-Thiatetradecane | $C_{13}H_{28}S$ | 297. | 0.06 | 1.4612 | 1.4590 | 0.8460 | 0.8424 | - 2. |
| 2-Thiapentadecane | $C_{14}H_{30}S$ | 314. | 0.06 | 1.4621 | 1.4599 | 0.8464 | 0.8428 | + 3. |
| 2-Thiahexadecane | $C_{15}H_{32}S$ | 330. | 0.06 | 1.4628 | 1.4607 | 0.8468 | 0.8432 | 11. |
| 2-Thiaheptadecane | $C_{16}H_{34}S$ | 345. | 0.06 | 1.4636 | 1.4615 | 0.8471 | 0.8435 | 15. |
| 2-Thiaoctadecane | $C_{17}H_{36}S$ | 359. | 0.07 | 1.4642[b] | 1.4621 | 0.8473[b] | 0.8438 | 21. |
| 2-Thianonadecane | $C_{18}H_{38}S$ | 373. | 0.07 | 1.4648[b] | 1.4627 | 0.8476[b] | 0.8441 | 25. |
| 2-Thiaeicosane | $C_{19}H_{40}S$ | 386. | 0.07 | 1.4654[b] | 1.4633[b] | 0.8479[b] | 0.8444[b] | 30. |
| 2-Thiaheneicosane | $C_{20}H_{42}S$ | 398. | 0.07 | 1.4659[b] | 1.4638[b] | 0.8482[b] | 0.8447[b] | 35. |

a See footnote a of Table 1a.   b For the undercooled liquid below the normal freezing point.

## TABLE 107a – THIAALKANES, $C_2$ TO $C_5$
### BOILING POINT, $dt/dp$, REFRACTIVE INDEX, DENSITY, AND FREEZING POINT
April 30, 1952; December 31, 1952

| Compound | Formula | Boiling Point 760 mm Hg °C | $dt/dp$ 760 mm Hg °C/mm Hg | Refractive Index[a] 20°C $n_D$ | Refractive Index[a] 25°C $n_D$ | Density[a] 20°C g/ml | Density[a] 25°C g/ml | Freezing Point In air at 1 atm °C |
|---|---|---|---|---|---|---|---|---|
| 2-Thiapropane (Dimethyl sulfide) | $C_2H_6S$ | 37.34 | 0.0376 | 1.43547 | 1.43231 | 0.84825 | 0.84230 | -98.27 |
| 2-Thiabutane (Methyl ethyl sulfide) | $C_3H_8S$ | 66.65 | 0.0410 | 1.44035 | 1.43737 | 0.84221 | 0.83679 | -105.93 |
| 2-Thiapentane (Methyl $n$-propyl sulfide) | $C_4H_{10}S$ | 95.54 | 0.0442 | 1.4442 | 1.4415 | 0.8424 | 0.8375 | -112.97 |
| 3-Thiapentane (Diethyl sulfide) | " | 92.10 | 0.0439 | 1.44298 | 1.44017 | 0.83623 | 0.83120 | -103.95 |
| 3-Methyl-2-thiabutane (Methyl isopropyl sulfide) | " | 84.75 | 0.0435 | 1.4392 | 1.4362 | 0.8291 | 0.8251 | -101.51 |
| 2-Thiahexane | $C_5H_{12}S$ | 123.2 | 0.047 | 1.4477 | 1.4452 | 0.8426 | 0.8381 | -97.8 |
| 3-Thiahexane | " | 118.50 | 0.0467 | 1.4462 | 1.4435 | 0.8370 | 0.8324 | -117.04 |
| 3-Methyl-2-thiapentane | " | 112. | 0.05 | 1.442 | 1.440 | 0.831 | 0.827 | |
| 4-Methyl-2-thiapentane | " | 112.5 | 0.047 | 1.4433 | 1.4410 | 0.8335 | 0.8293 | -109.1 |
| 2-Methyl-3-thiapentane | " | 107.38 | 0.0459 | 1.4407 | 1.4382 | 0.8246 | 0.8199 | -122.19 |
| 3,3-Dimethyl-2-thiabutane | " | 99. | 0.04 | 1.4403 | 1.4376 | 0.8255 | 0.8208 | -82.3 |

a See footnote a of Table 1a.

TABLE 108a – THIAALKANES, $C_6$

BOILING POINT, dt/dp, REFRACTIVE INDEX, DENSITY, AND FREEZING POINT

April 30, 1952

| Compound | Formula | Boiling Point 760 mm Hg °C | dt/dp 760 mm Hg °C/mm Hg | Refractive Index[a] 20°C $n_D$ | Refractive Index[a] 25°C $n_D$ | Density[a] 20°C g/ml | Density[a] 25°C g/ml | Freezing Point In air at 1 atm °C |
|---|---|---|---|---|---|---|---|---|
| 2-Thiaheptane | $C_6H_{14}S$ | 145. | 0.05 | 1.4506 | 1.4482 | 0.8431 | 0.8389 | -94. |
| 3-Thiaheptane | " | 144.24 | 0.0492 | 1.4491 | 1.4463 | 0.8376 | 0.8332 | -95.13 |
| 4-Thiaheptane | " | 142.83 | 0.0491 | 1.4487 | 1.4461 | 0.8377 | 0.8332 | -102.5 |
| 3-Methyl-2-thiahexane | " | 139. | 0.05 | | | | | |
| 4-Methyl-2-thiahexane | " | 140. | 0.05 | 1.452 | 1.449 | 0.842 | 0.838 | |
| 5-Methyl-2-thiahexane | " | 138. | 0.05 | | | | | |
| 2-Methyl-3-thiahexane | " | 132.05 | 0.0484 | 1.4440 | 1.4414 | 0.8269 | 0.8225 | |
| 4-Methyl-3-thiahexane | " | 133.65 | 0.0486 | 1.4477 | 1.4451 | 0.8353 | 0.8307 | |
| 5-Methyl-3-thiahexane | " | 134.22 | 0.0486 | 1.4450 | 1.4424 | 0.8306 | 0.8261 | |
| 3,3-Dimethyl-2-thiapentane | " | | | | | | | |
| 3,4-Dimethyl-2-thiapentane | " | | | | | | | |
| 4,4-Dimethyl-2-thiapentane | " | | | | | | | |
| 2,2-Dimethyl-3-thiapentane | " | 120.41 | 0.0480 | 1.4417 | 1.4390 | 0.8206 | 0.8161 | -88.95 |
| 2,4-Dimethyl-3-thiapentane | " | 120.02 | 0.0476 | 1.4388 | 1.4362 | 0.8146 | 0.8104 | -78.08 |

a See footnote a of Table 1a.

TABLE 109a – ALKYL (1-THIAALKYL) BENZENES, $C_7$ AND $C_8$

BOILING POINT, $dt/dp$, REFRACTIVE INDEX, DENSITY, AND FREEZING POINT

October 31, 1952

| Compound | Formula | Boiling Point 760 mm Hg °C | $dt/dp$ 760 mm Hg °C/mm Hg | Refractive Index[a] 20°C $n_D$ | Refractive Index[a] 25°C $n_D$ | Density[a] 20°C g/ml | Density[a] 25°C g/ml | Freezing Point In air at 1 atm °C |
|---|---|---|---|---|---|---|---|---|
| (1-Thiaethyl)-benzene (Methyl phenyl sulfide) | $C_7H_8S$ | 193. | 0.05 | 1.5868 | 1.5840 | 1.0579 | 1.0535 | |
| (1-Thiapropyl)-benzene (Ethyl phenyl sulfide) | $C_8H_{10}S$ | 205. | 0.05 | 1.5670 | 1.5644 | 1.0211 | 1.0166 | |
| 2-Methyl-(1-thiaethyl)-benzene | " | | | | | | | |
| 3-Methyl-(1-thiaethyl)-benzene | " | | | 1.5757 | 1.5731 | 1.030 | 1.026 | |
| 4-Methyl-(1-thiaethyl)-benzene | " | 217. | 0.05 | 1.5733 | 1.5707 | 1.027 | 1.023 | |

[a] See footnote a of Table 1a.

TABLE 110a — ALKYL (1-THIAALKYL) BENZENES, $C_9$

BOILING POINT, $dt/dp$, REFRACTIVE INDEX, DENSITY, AND FREEZING POINT

October 31, 1952

| Compound | Formula | Boiling Point 760 mm Hg (°C) | $dt/dp$ 760 mm Hg (°C/mm Hg) | Refractive Index[a] 20°C ($n_D$) | Refractive Index[a] 25°C ($n_D$) | Density[a] 20°C (g/ml) | Density[a] 25°C (g/ml) | Freezing Point In air at 1 atm (°C) |
|---|---|---|---|---|---|---|---|---|
| (1-Thiabutyl)-benzene (n-Propyl phenyl sulfide) | $C_9H_{12}S$ | 220. | 0.05 | 1.5571 | 1.5551 | 0.9995 | 0.9952 | |
| (2-Methyl-1-thiapropyl)-benzene (Isopropyl phenyl sulfide) | " | 208. | 0.05 | 1.5464 | 1.5446 | 0.9852 | 0.9810 | |
| 2-Methyl-(1-thiapropyl)-benzene | " | | | | | | | |
| 3-Methyl-(1-thiapropyl)-benzene | " | 219. | 0.05 | 1.5590 | 1.5570 | 0.9987 | 0.9947 | |
| 4-Methyl-(1-thiapropyl)-benzene | " | 220. | 0.05 | 1.555 | 1.553 | 0.9996 | 0.9956 | |
| 2-Ethyl-(1-thiaethyl)-benzene | " | 228. | 0.05 | 1.5708 | 1.5688 | 1.025 | 1.021 | |
| 3-Ethyl-(1-thiaethyl)-benzene | " | | | | | | | |
| 4-Ethyl-(1-thiaethyl)-benzene | " | | | | | | | |
| 2,3-Dimethyl-(1-thiaethyl)-benzene | " | | | 1.575 | 1.573 | 1.019 | 1.015 | |
| 2,4-Dimethyl-(1-thiaethyl)-benzene | " | | | | | | | |
| 2,5-Dimethyl-(1-thiaethyl)-benzene | " | | | | | | | |
| 2,6-Dimethyl-(1-thiaethyl)-benzene | " | | | | | | | |
| 3,4-Dimethyl-(1-thiaethyl)-benzene | " | | | | | | | |
| 3,5-Dimethyl-(1-thiaethyl)-benzene | " | | | | | | | |

[a] See footnote a of Table 1a.

TABLE 111a – ALKYL THIACYCLOPROPANES, $C_2$ TO $C_4$

BOILING POINT, $dt/dp$, REFRACTIVE INDEX, DENSITY, AND FREEZING POINT

October 31, 1952

| Compound | Formula | Boiling Point 760 mm Hg | $dt/dp$ 760 mm Hg | Refractive Index[a] | | Density[a] | | Freezing Point In air at 1 atm |
|---|---|---|---|---|---|---|---|---|
| | | | | 20°C | 25°C | 20°C | 25°C | |
| | | °C | °C/mm Hg | $n_D$ | $n_D$ | g/ml | g/ml | °C |
| Thiacyclopropane (Ethylene sulfide) | $C_2H_4S$ | 54.93 | 0.0395 | 1.490 | 1.487 | 1.013 | 1.007 | −109. |
| 2-Methylthiacyclopropane | $C_3H_6S$ | 74.4 | 0.041 | 1.475 | 1.472 | 0.944 | 0.939 | −91. |
| 2-Ethylthiacyclopropane | $C_4H_8S$ | 105. | 0.04 | 1.472 | 1.470 | 0.927 | 0.922 | |
| 2,2-Dimethylthiacyclopropane | " | 86. | 0.04 | 1.464 | 1.462 | | | |
| 2,cis-3-Dimethylthiacyclopropane | " | | | | | | | |
| 2,trans-3-Dimethylthiacyclopropane | " | | | | | | | |

[a] See footnote a of Table 1a.

TABLE 112a – ALKYL THIACYCLOPENTANES, $C_4$ TO $C_6$

BOILING POINT, $dt/dp$, REFRACTIVE INDEX, DENSITY, AND FREEZING POINT

October 31, 1952

| Compound | Formula | Boiling Point 760 mm Hg °C | $dt/dp$ 760 mm Hg °C/mm Hg | Refractive Index[a] 20°C $n_D$ | Refractive Index[a] 25°C $n_D$ | Density[a] 20°C g/ml | Density[a] 25°C g/ml | Freezing Point In air at 1 atm °C |
|---|---|---|---|---|---|---|---|---|
| Thiacyclopentane (Tetrahydrothiophene) | $C_4H_8S$ | 121.117 | 0.04732 | 1.50483 | 1.50217 | 0.99869 | 0.99379 | -96.16 |
| 2-Methylthiacyclopentane | $C_5H_{10}S$ | 133.23 | 0.0490 | 1.4909 | 1.4884 | 0.9552 | 0.9512 | -100.71 |
| 3-Methylthiacyclopentane | " | 138.67 | 0.0495 | 1.4924 | 1.4902 | 0.9634 | 0.9585 | -81.16 |
| 2-Ethylthiacyclopentane | $C_6H_{12}S$ | 157. | 0.05 | 1.490 | 1.487 | 0.944 | 0.939 | |
| 3-Ethylthiacyclopentane | " | 165. | 0.05 | 1.491 | 1.489 | 0.950 | 0.945 | |
| 2,2-Dimethylthiacyclopentane | " | | | | | | | |
| 2,cis-3-Dimethylthiacyclopentane | " | | | | | | | |
| 2,trans-3-Dimethylthiacyclopentane | " | | | | | | | |
| 2,cis-4-Dimethylthiacyclopentane | " | | | | | | | |
| 2,trans-4-Dimethylthiacyclopentane | " | | | | | | | |
| 2,cis-5-Dimethylthiacyclopentane | " | 142.28 | 0.0500 | 1.4799 | 1.4774 | 0.9222 | 0.9177 | -89.4 |
| 2,trans-5-Dimethylthiacyclopentane | " | 142.0 | 0.050 | 1.4776 | 1.4152 | 0.9188 | 0.9142 | -76.35 |
| 3,3-Dimethylthiacyclopentane | " | | | | | | | |
| 3,cis-4-Dimethylthiacyclopentane | " | | | | | | | |
| 3,trans-4-Dimethylthiacyclopentane | " | | | | | | | |

a See footnote a of Table 1a.

TABLE 113a – ALKYL THIACYCLOHEXANES, $C_5$ TO $C_7$
BOILING POINT, $dt/dp$, REFRACTIVE INDEX, DENSITY, AND FREEZING POINT
October 31, 1952

| Compound | Formula | Boiling Point 760 mm Hg | $dt/dp$ 760 mm Hg | Refractive Index[a] 20°C | Refractive Index[a] 25°C | Density[a] 20°C | Density[a] 25°C | Freezing Point In air at 1 atm |
|---|---|---|---|---|---|---|---|---|
| | | °C | °C/mm Hg | $n_D$ | $n_D$ | g/ml | g/ml | °C |
| Thiacyclohexane | $C_5H_{10}S$ | 141.75 | 0.0502 | 1.5067 | 1.5041 | 0.9856 | 0.9810 | 18.99 |
| 2-Methylthiacyclohexane | $C_6H_{12}S$ | 153.04 | 0.0521 | 1.4905 | 1.4881 | 0.9428 | 0.9381 | −58.14 |
| 3-Methylthiacyclohexane | " | 158.04 | 0.0524 | 1.4922 | 1.4899 | 0.9473 | 0.9430 | −60.17 |
| 4-Methylthiacyclohexane | " | 156.64 | 0.0527 | 1.4923 | 1.4899 | 0.9471 | 0.9427 | −28.1 |
| | | | | | | | | |
| 2-Ethylthiacyclohexane | $C_7H_{14}S$ | | | | | | | |
| 3-Ethylthiacyclohexane | " | | | | | | | |
| 4-Ethylthiacyclohexane | " | | | | | | | |
| 2,2-Dimethylthiacyclohexane | " | | | | | | | |
| 2,cis-3-Dimethylthiacyclohexane | " | | | | | | | |
| 2,trans-3-Dimethylthiacyclohexane | " | | | | | | | |
| 2,cis-4-Dimethylthiacyclohexane | " | | | | | | | |
| 2,trans-4-Dimethylthiacyclohexane | " | | | | | | | |
| 2,cis-5-Dimethylthiacyclohexane | " | | | | | | | |
| 2,trans-5-Dimethylthiacyclohexane | " | | | | | | | |
| 2,cis-6-Dimethylthiacyclohexane | " | | | | | | | |
| 2,trans-6-Dimethylthiacyclohexane | " | | | | | | | |
| 3,3-Dimethylthiacyclohexane | " | | | | | | | |
| 3,cis-4-Dimethylthiacyclohexane | " | | | | | | | |
| 3,trans-4-Dimethylthiacyclohexane | " | | | | | | | |
| 3,cis-5-Dimethylthiacyclohexane | " | | | | | | | |
| 3,trans-5-Dimethylthiacyclohexane | " | | | | | | | |
| 4,4-Dimethylthiacyclohexane | " | | | | | | | |

a See footnote a of Table 1a.

TABLE 114a – ALKYL THIOPHENES, C$_4$ TO C$_6$
BOILING POINT, $dt/dp$, REFRACTIVE INDEX, DENSITY, AND FREEZING POINT
April 30, 1952; December 31, 1952

| Compound | Formula | Boiling Point 760 mm Hg °C | dt/dp 760 mm Hg °C/mm Hg | Refractive Index[a] 20°C $n_D$ | 25°C $n_D$ | Density[a] 20°C g/ml | 25°C g/ml | Freezing Point In air at 1 atm °C |
|---|---|---|---|---|---|---|---|---|
| Thiophene | C$_4$H$_4$S | 84.16 | 0.0428 | 1.52890 | 1.52572 | 1.06485 | 1.05887 | −38.21 |
| 2-Methylthiophene | C$_5$H$_6$S | 112.56 | 0.0460 | 1.5203 | 1.5174 | 1.0193 | 1.0139 | −63.38 |
| 3-Methylthiophene | " | 115.43 | 0.0462 | 1.52042 | 1.51758 | 1.02183 | 1.01647 | −68.97 |
| 2-Ethylthiophene | C$_6$H$_8$S | 134. | 0.05 | 1.5122 | 1.5094 | 0.9930 | 0.9880 | −89.1 |
| 3-Ethylthiophene | " | 136. | 0.05 | 1.5146 | 1.5120 | 0.9980 | 0.9931 | −49.0 |
| 2,3-Dimethylthiophene | " | 141.6 | 0.049 | 1.5192 | 1.5166 | 1.0021 | 0.9970 | |
| 2,4-Dimethylthiophene | " | 140.7 | 0.05 | 1.5104 | 1.5078 | 0.9956 | 0.9905 | −62.6 |
| 2,5-Dimethylthiophene | " | 136.7 | 0.049 | 1.5129 | 1.5104 | 0.9850 | 0.9799 | |
| 3,4-Dimethylthiophene | " | 145. | 0.05 | 1.5212 | 1.5187 | 1.008 | 1.003 | |

a See footnote a of Table 1a.

TABLE 115a — ALKYL THIOPHENES, $C_7$

BOILING POINT, $dt/dp$, REFRACTIVE INDEX, DENSITY, AND FREEZING POINT

April 30, 1952

| Compound | Formula | Boiling Point 760 mm Hg °C | $dt/dp$ 760 mm Hg °C/mm Hg | Refractive Index[a] 20°C $n_D$ | Refractive Index[a] 25°C $n_D$ | Density[a] 20°C g/ml | Density[a] 25°C g/ml | Freezing Point In air at 1 atm °C |
|---|---|---|---|---|---|---|---|---|
| 2-Propylthiophene | $C_7H_{10}S$ | 158.5 | 0.051 | 1.5049 | 1.5023 | 0.9687 | 0.9639 | |
| 3-Propylthiophene | " | 161. | 0.05 | 1.5057 | 1.5031 | 0.9716 | 0.9669 | |
| 2-Isopropylthiophene | " | 153. | 0.05 | 1.5038 | 1.5013 | 0.9678 | 0.9633 | |
| 3-Isopropylthiophene | " | 157. | 0.05 | 1.5052 | 1.5027 | 0.9733 | 0.9688 | |
| 2-Methyl-3-ethylthiophene | " | 157. | 0.05 | | | | | |
| 2-Methyl-4-ethylthiophene | " | 163. | 0.05 | 1.5098 | 1.5073 | 0.9742 | 0.9696 | −59. |
| 2-Methyl-5-ethylthiophene | " | 160.1 | 0.051 | 1.5073 | 1.5048 | 0.9661 | 0.9618 | −68.5 |
| 3-Methyl-2-ethylthiophene | " | 161. | 0.05 | 1.5105 | 1.5080 | 0.9815 | 0.9769 | |
| 3-Methyl-4-ethylthiophene | " | | | | | | | |
| 3-Methyl-5-ethylthiophene | " | | | | | | | |
| 2,3,4-Trimethylthiophene | " | 172.7 | 0.052 | 1.5208 | 1.5183 | 0.995 | 0.991 | |
| 2,3,5-Trimethylthiophene | " | 164.5 | 0.051 | 1.5112 | 1.5088 | 0.9753 | 0.9708 | |

a See footnote a of Table 1a.

## TABLE 20a-E (PART 1) – NORMAL PARAFFINS, $C_1$ TO $C_{20}$
## BOILING POINT, $dt/dp$, REFRACTIVE INDEX, DENSITY, AND FREEZING POINT

June 30, 1948; December 31, 1950; October 31, 1952

| Compound | Formula | Boiling Point 29.921 in Hg °F | $dt/dp$ 29.921 in.Hg °F/in.Hg | Refractive Index[a] $n_D$ 68°F | Refractive Index[a] $n_D$ 77°F | Density[a] lb/cu ft 60°F | Density[a] lb/cu ft 68°F | Density[a] lb/cu ft 77°F | Density[a] lb/gal 60°F | Density[a] lb/gal 68°F | Density[a] lb/gal 77°F | Specific Gravity[a] 60°F/60°F | Freezing Point In air at 1 atm °F |
|---|---|---|---|---|---|---|---|---|---|---|---|---|---|
| Methane | $CH_4$ | −258.68 | 0.732 | — | — | — | — | — | — | — | — | — | −296.46[c] |
| Ethane | $C_2H_6$ | −127.53 | 1.116 | — | — | — | — | — | — | — | — | — | −297.89[c] |
| Propane | $C_3H_8$ | −43.73 | 1.362 | — | — | 31.64[b] | 31.24[b] | 30.76[b] | 4.233[b] | 4.177[b] | 4.113[b] | 0.5077[b] | −305.84[c] |
| n-Butane | $C_4H_{10}$ | +31.10 | 1.586 | 1.3326[b] | 1.3292[b] | 36.46[b] | 36.13[b] | 35.77[b] | 4.872[b] | 4.830[b] | 4.762[b] | 0.5844[b] | −217.03 |
| n-Pentane | $C_5H_{12}$ | 96.93 | 1.763 | 1.35748 | 1.35472 | 39.35 | 39.094 | 38.791 | 5.262 | 5.2261 | 5.1856 | 0.6312 | −201.50 |
| n-Hexane | $C_6H_{14}$ | 155.73 | 1.916 | 1.37486 | 1.37226 | 41.41 | 41.162 | 40.878 | 5.536 | 5.5026 | 5.4646 | 0.6640 | −139.63 |
| n-Heptane | $C_7H_{16}$ | 209.17 | 2.048 | 1.38764 | 1.38511 | 42.92 | 42.685 | 42.419 | 5.738 | 5.7061 | 5.6707 | 0.6882 | −131.10 |
| n-Octane | $C_8H_{18}$ | 258.20 | 2.166 | 1.39743 | 1.39505 | 44.08 | 43.856 | 43.604 | 5.893 | 5.8627 | 5.8291 | 0.7068 | −70.23 |
| n-Nonane | $C_9H_{20}$ | 303.44 | 2.271 | 1.40542 | 1.40311 | 45.01 | 44.799 | 44.561 | 6.017 | 5.9888 | 5.9569 | 0.7217 | −64.33 |
| n-Decane | $C_{10}H_{22}$ | 345.42 | 2.365 | 1.41189 | 1.40967 | 45.79 | 45.575 | 45.337 | 6.121 | 6.0924 | 6.0607 | 0.7341 | −21.39 |
| n-Undecane | $C_{11}H_{24}$ | 384.60 | 2.449 | 1.41716 | 1.41500 | 46.42 | 46.206 | 45.980 | 6.204 | 6.1769 | 6.1467 | 0.7441 | −14.07. |
| n-Dodecane | $C_{12}H_{26}$ | 421.30 | 2.527 | 1.42160 | 1.41949 | 46.95 | 46.738 | 46.518 | 6.274 | 6.2480 | 6.2185 | 0.7526 | +14.74 |
| n-Tridecane | $C_{13}H_{28}$ | 455.79 | 2.597 | 1.4256 | 1.4234 | 47.42 | 47.22 | 46.99 | 6.339 | 6.312 | 6.282 | 0.7603 | 22.29 |
| n-Tetradecane | $C_{14}H_{30}$ | 488.43 | 2.661 | 1.4289 | 1.4266 | 47.82 | 47.62 | 47.40 | 6.392 | 6.366 | 6.337 | 0.7667 | 42.55 |
| n-Pentadecane | $C_{15}H_{32}$ | 519.13 | 2.720 | 1.4319 | 1.4298 | 48.17 | 47.96 | 47.76 | 6.439 | 6.413 | 6.384 | 0.7724 | 49.87 |
| n-Hexadecane | $C_{16}H_{34}$ | 548.23 | 2.778 | 1.43453 | 1.43250 | 48.47[d] | 48.283 | 48.066 | 6.4808[d] | 6.4545 | 6.4255 | 0.7773[d] | 64.70 |
| n-Heptadecane | $C_{17}H_{36}$ | 575.28 | 2.830 | 1.4369[d] | 1.4348 | 48.76[d] | 48.57[d] | 48.35 | 6.518[d] | 6.492[d] | 6.463 | 0.7818[d] | 71.56 |
| n-Octadecane | $C_{18}H_{38}$ | 601.02 | 2.880 | 1.4390[d] | 1.4369[d] | 49.00[d] | 48.81[d] | 48.60[d] | 6.551[d] | 6.525[d] | 6.497[d] | 0.7858[d] | 82.72 |
| n-Nonadecane | $C_{19}H_{40}$ | 625.5 | 2.83 | 1.4409[d] | 1.4388[d] | 49.23[d] | 49.04[d] | 48.82[d] | 6.581[d] | 6.555[d] | 6.527[d] | 0.7893[d] | 89.8 |
| n-Eicosane | $C_{20}H_{42}$ | 648.9 | 2.97 | 1.4426[d] | 1.4405 | 49.42[d] | 49.24[d] | 49.02[d] | 6.607[d] | 6.582[d] | 6.554[d] | 0.7925[d] | 98.2 |

a See footnote a of Table 1a-E.  b At saturation pressure.  c At saturation pressure (triple point.)  d For the undercooled liquid below the normal freezing point.

## TABLE 20a-E (PART 2) - NORMAL PARAFFINS, C$_{21}$ TO C$_{40}$
## BOILING POINT, $dt/dp$, REFRACTIVE INDEX, DENSITY, AND FREEZING POINT
### December 31, 1950 (Corrected)

| Compound | Formula | Boiling Point 29.921 in Hg °F | $dt/dp$ 29.921 in Hg °F/in Hg | Refractive Index[a] $n_D$ 68°F | Refractive Index[a] $n_D$ 77°F | Density[a] lb/cu ft 60°F | Density[a] lb/cu ft 68°F | Density[a] lb/cu ft 77°F | Density[a] lb/gal 60°F | Density[a] lb/gal 68°F | Density[a] lb/gal 77°F | Specific Gravity[a] 60°F/60°F | Freezing Point In air at 1 atm °F |
|---|---|---|---|---|---|---|---|---|---|---|---|---|---|
| n-Heneicosane | C$_{21}$H$_{44}$ | 671.2 | 3.0 | 1.4441[b] | 1.4420[b] | 49.61[b] | 49.42[b] | 49.21[b] | 6.632[b] | 6.607[b] | 6.578[b] | 0.7955[b] | 104.9 |
| n-Docosane | C$_{22}$H$_{46}$ | 692.6 | 3.1 | 1.4455[b] | 1.4435[b] | 49.78[b] | 49.59[b] | 49.38[b] | 6.654[b] | 6.629[b] | 6.601[b] | 0.7981[b] | 111.9 |
| n-Tricosane | C$_{23}$H$_{48}$ | 712.9 | 3.1 | 1.4468[b] | 1.4448[b] | 49.93[b] | 49.74[b] | 49.53[b] | 6.675[b] | 6.650[b] | 6.622[b] | 0.8006[b] | 117.7 |
| n-Tetracosane | C$_{24}$H$_{50}$ | 732.6 | 3.1 | 1.4480[b] | 1.4460[b] | 50.07[b] | 49.89[b] | 49.68[b] | 6.694[b] | 6.669[b] | 6.641[b] | 0.8029[b] | 123.6 |
| n-Pentacosane | C$_{25}$H$_{52}$ | 751.5 | 3.2 | 1.4491[b] | 1.4471[b] | 50.20[b] | 50.02[b] | 49.81[b] | 6.711[b] | 6.686[b] | 6.658[b] | 0.8050[b] | 128.7 |
| n-Hexacosane | C$_{26}$H$_{54}$ | 769.5 | 3.2 | 1.4501[b] | 1.4481[b] | 50.33[b] | 50.14[b] | 49.93[b] | 6.728[b] | 6.703[b] | 6.675[b] | 0.8069[b] | 133.5 |
| n-Heptacosane | C$_{27}$H$_{56}$ | 786.9 | 3.2 | 1.4511[b] | 1.4491[b] | 50.44[b] | 50.25[b] | 50.04[b] | 6.743[b] | 6.718[b] | 6.690[b] | 0.8087[b] | 138.2 |
| n-Octacosane | C$_{28}$H$_{58}$ | 803.7 | 3.3 | 1.4520[b] | 1.4500[b] | 50.54[b] | 50.36[b] | 50.15[b] | 6.757[b] | 6.732[b] | 6.704[b] | 0.8104[b] | 142.5 |
| n-Nonacosane | C$_{29}$H$_{60}$ | 819.9 | 3.3 | 1.4529[b] | 1.4508[b] | 50.64[b] | 50.46[b] | 50.25[b] | 6.770[b] | 6.745[b] | 6.717[b] | 0.8120[b] | 146.7 |
| n-Triacontane | C$_{30}$H$_{62}$ | 835.5 | 3.3 | 1.4536[b] | 1.4516[b] | 50.73[b] | 50.55[b] | 50.34[b] | 6.782[b] | 6.757[b] | 6.730[b] | 0.8135[b] | 150.4 |
| n-Hentriacontane | C$_{31}$H$_{64}$ | 851. | 3. | 1.4543[b] | 1.4523[b] | 50.82[b] | 50.63[b] | 50.43[b] | 6.794[b] | 6.769[b] | 6.741[b] | 0.8148[b] | 154.2 |
| n-Dotriacontane | C$_{32}$H$_{66}$ | 865. | 3. | 1.4550[b] | 1.4530[b] | 50.90[b] | 50.72[b] | 50.51[b] | 6.804[b] | 6.780[b] | 6.752[b] | 0.8161[b] | 157.5 |
| n-Tritriacontane | C$_{33}$H$_{68}$ | 880. | 3. | 1.4557[b] | 1.4536[b] | 50.98[b] | 50.79[b] | 50.59[b] | 6.814[b] | 6.790[b] | 6.762[b] | 0.8174[b] | 160.5 |
| n-Tetratriacontane | C$_{34}$H$_{70}$ | 892. | 3. | 1.4563[b] | 1.4542[b] | 51.05[b] | 50.86[b] | 50.66[b] | 6.824[b] | 6.800[b] | 6.772[b] | 0.8185[b] | 163.6 |
| n-Pentatriacontane | C$_{35}$H$_{72}$ | 907. | 3. | 1.4568[b] | 1.4548[b] | 51.12[b] | 50.93[b] | 50.73[b] | 6.833[b] | 6.809[b] | 6.781[b] | 0.8196[b] | 166.5 |
| n-Hexatriacontane | C$_{36}$H$_{74}$ | 919. | 3. | 1.4573[b] | 1.4554[b] | 51.18[b] | 51.00[b] | 50.79[b] | 6.842[b] | 6.817[b] | 6.790[b] | 0.8206[b] | 169.2 |
| n-Heptatriacontane | C$_{37}$H$_{76}$ | 932. | 3. | 1.4578[b] | 1.4559[b] | 51.24[b] | 51.06[b] | 50.85[b] | 6.850[b] | 6.825[b] | 6.798[b] | 0.8216[b] | 171.9 |
| n-Octatriacontane | C$_{38}$H$_{78}$ | 945. | 4. | 1.4583[b] | 1.4564[b] | 51.30[b] | 51.11[b] | 50.91[b] | 6.857[b] | 6.833[b] | 6.806[b] | 0.8225[b] | 174.2 |
| n-Nonatriacontane | C$_{39}$H$_{80}$ | 955. | 4. | 1.4588[b] | 1.456b[b] | 51.35[b] | 51.17[b] | 50.96[b] | 6.865[b] | 6.840[b] | 6.813[b] | 0.8234[b] | 176.5 |
| n-Tetracontane | C$_{40}$H$_{82}$ | 968. | 4. | 1.4593[b] | 1.4573[b] | 51.40[b] | 51.22[b] | 51.02[b] | 6.872[b] | 6.847[b] | 6.820[b] | 0.8242[b] | 178.7 |

a See footnote a of Table 1a-E.    b For the undercooled liquid below the normal freezing point.

TABLE 1a-E – PARAFFINS, C$_1$ TO C$_5$

BOILING POINT, dt/dp, REFRACTIVE INDEX, DENSITY, AND FREEZING POINT

June 30, 1945; June 30, 1948; October 31, 1952

| Compound | Formula | Boiling Point 29.921 in Hg (°F) | dt/dp 29.921 in Hg (°F/in.Hg) | Refractive Index[a] $n_D$ 68°F | Refractive Index[a] $n_D$ 77°F | Density[a] lb/cu ft 60°F | Density[a] lb/cu ft 68°F | Density[a] lb/cu ft 77°F | Density[a] lb/gal 60°F | Density[a] lb/gal 68°F | Density[a] lb/gal 77°F | Specific Gravity[a] 60°F/60°F | Freezing Point[a] In air at 1 atm (°F) |
|---|---|---|---|---|---|---|---|---|---|---|---|---|---|
| Methane | CH$_4$ | -258.68 | 0.732 | — | — | — | — | — | — | — | — | — | -296.46[c] |
| Ethane | C$_2$H$_6$ | -127.53 | 1.116 | — | — | — | — | — | — | — | — | — | -297.89 |
| Propane | C$_3$H$_8$ | -43.73 | 1.362 | — | — | 31.64[b] | 31.24[b] | 30.76[b] | 4.233[b] | 4.177[b] | 4.113[b] | 0.5077[b] | -305.84 |
| n-Butane | C$_4$H$_{10}$ | +31.10 | 1.586 | 1.3326[b] | 1.3292[b] | 36.46[b] | 36.13[b] | 35.77[b] | 4.872[b] | 4.830[b] | 4.782[b] | 0.5844[b] | -217.03 |
| 2-Methylpropane (Isobutane) | " | 10.89 | 1.541 | — | — | 35.12[b] | 34.78[b] | 34.40[b] | 4.695[b] | 4.650[b] | 4.598[b] | 0.5631[b] | -255.28 |
| n-Pentane | C$_5$H$_{12}$ | 96.93 | 1.763 | 1.35748 | 1.35472 | 39.35 | 39.094 | 38.791 | 5.262 | 5.2261 | 5.1856 | 0.6312 | -201.50 |
| 2-Methylbutane (Isopentane) | " | 82.13 | 1.744 | 1.35373 | 1.35088 | 38.96 | 38.684 | 38.369 | 5.209 | 5.1713 | 5.1291 | 0.6248 | -255.82 |
| 2,2-Dimethylpropane (Neopentane) | " | 49.10 | 1.650 | 1.342[b] | 1.339[b] | 37.21[b] | 36.89[b] | 36.53[b] | 4.975[b] | 4.932[b] | 4.883[b] | 0.5967 | +2.21 |

a Values are given for the air-saturated hydrocarbon in the liquid state at one atmosphere. Values of the refractive index are for the sodium D line, for which the wave length is taken to be 5892.6 Angstrom units, which is the intensity weighted mean of the wave lengths of the $D_1$ and $D_2$ lines. Values of the specific gravity, 60°F/60°F, are referred to a value of 0.99904 g/ml for water at 60°F (15.556°C).

b At saturation pressure.

c At saturation pressure (triple point).

TABLE 2a-E (PART 1) – PARAFFINS, $C_6$

BOILING POINT, $dt/dp$, REFRACTIVE INDEX, DENSITY, AND FREEZING POINT

June 30, 1945; December 31, 1948; October 31, 1952

| Compound | Formula | Boiling Point 29.921 in Hg °F | $dt/dp$ 29.921 in Hg °F/in Hg | Refractive Index[a] 68°F $n_D$ | 77°F $n_D$ | Density[a] 600°F | 68°F lb/cu ft | 77°F | 600°F | 68°F lb/gal | 77°F | Specific Gravity[a] 60°F/60°F | Freezing Point In air at 1 atm °F |
|---|---|---|---|---|---|---|---|---|---|---|---|---|---|
| n-Hexane | $C_6H_{14}$ | 155.73 | 1.916 | 1.37486 | 1.37226 | 41.41 | 41.162 | 40.878 | 5.536 | 5.5026 | 5.4645 | 0.6640 | -139.63 |
| 2-Methylpentane | " | 140.49 | 1.893 | 1.37145 | 1.36873 | 41.03 | 40.774 | 40.485 | 5.485 | 5.4507 | 5.4120 | 0.6579 | -244.61 |
| 3-Methylpentane | " | 145.91 | 1.912 | 1.37652 | 1.37386 | 41.72 | 41.471 | 41.187 | 5.578 | 5.5438 | 5.5058 | 0.6690 | |
| 2,2-Dimethylbutane | " | 121.53 | 1.882 | 1.36876 | 1.36595 | 40.79 | 40.525 | 40.231 | 5.452 | 5.4174 | 5.3782 | 0.6540 | -147.77 |
| 2,3-Dimethylbutane | " | 136.38 | 1.908 | 1.37495 | 1.37231 | 41.56 | 41.304 | 41.016 | 5.556 | 5.5215 | 5.4830 | 0.6664 | -199.37 |

a See footnote a of Table 1a-E.

TABLE 2a-E (PART 2) — PARAFFINS, C$_7$
BOILING POINT, dt/dp, REFRACTIVE INDEX, DENSITY, AND FREEZING POINT
June 30, 1945; December 31, 1948; October 31, 1952

| Compound | Formula | Boiling Point 29.921 in Hg (°F) | dt/dp 29.921 in Hg (°F/in Hg) | Refractive Index[a] 68°F ($n_D$) | 77°F ($n_D$) | Density[a] 60°F (lb/cu ft) | 68°F | 77°F | 60°F (lb/gal) | 68°F | 77°F | Specific Gravity[a] 60°F/60°F | Freezing Point In air at 1 atm (°F) |
|---|---|---|---|---|---|---|---|---|---|---|---|---|---|
| n-Heptane | C$_7$H$_{16}$ | 209.17 | 2.049 | 1.38764 | 1.38511 | 42.92 | 42.685 | 42.419 | 5.738 | 5.7061 | 5.6707 | 0.6882 | −131.10 |
| 2-Methylhexane | " | 194.09 | 2.026 | 1.38485 | 1.38227 | 42.60 | 42.362 | 42.100 | 5.694 | 5.6630 | 5.6279 | 0.6830 | −180.90 |
| 3-Methylhexane | " | 197.33 | 2.039 | 1.38864 | 1.38609 | 43.14 | 42.895 | 42.634 | 5.765 | 5.7343 | 5.6994 | 0.6915 | |
| 3-Ethylpentane | " | 200.26 | 2.049 | 1.39339 | 1.39084 | 43.82 | 43.584 | 43.321 | 5.858 | 5.8263 | 5.7912 | 0.7026 | −181.49 |
| 2,2-Dimethylpentane | " | 174.55 | 2.009 | 1.38215 | 1.37955 | 42.30 | 42.066 | 41.796 | 5.655 | 5.6234 | 5.5874 | 0.6783 | −190.86 |
| 2,3-Dimethylpentane | " | 193.61 | 2.049 | 1.39196 | 1.38945 | 43.63 | 43.391 | 43.131 | 5.832 | 5.8006 | 5.7658 | 0.6994 | |
| 2,4-Dimethylpentane | " | 176.90 | 2.001 | 1.38145 | 1.37882 | 42.24 | 41.994 | 41.721 | 5.646 | 5.6138 | 5.5773 | 0.6772 | −182.64 |
| 3,3-Dimethylpentane | " | 186.92 | 2.062 | 1.39092 | 1.38842 | 43.51 | 43.278 | 43.017 | 5.817 | 5.7855 | 5.7505 | 0.6977 | −210.03[b] |
| 2,2,3-Trimethylbutane | " | 177.59 | 2.050 | 1.38944 | 1.38692 | 43.32 | 43.081 | 42.817 | 5.790 | 5.7591 | 5.7238 | 0.6945 | −12.84 |

a See footnote a of Table 1a-E.   b See Table 2z (Part 2) for the freezing points of the metastable crystalline forms.

TABLE 3a-E – PARAFFINS, $C_8$

BOILING POINT, $dt/dp$, REFRACTIVE INDEX, DENSITY, AND FREEZING POINT

June 30, 1945; December 31, 1948; October 31, 1952

| Compound | Formula | Boiling Point 29.921 in Hg | $dt/dp$ 29.921 in Hg | Refractive Index[a] | | Density[a] | | | | | | | | Specific Gravity[a] | Freezing Point |
|---|---|---|---|---|---|---|---|---|---|---|---|---|---|---|---|
| | | | | 68°F $n_D$ | 77°F $n_D$ | 60°F | 68°F | 77°F | 60°F | 68°F | 77°F | | | 60°F/60°F | In air at 1 atm |
| | | °F | °F/in Hg | | | lb/cu ft | | | | | | lb/gal | | | °F |
| $n$-Octane | $C_8H_{18}$ | 258.20 | 2.166 | 1.39743 | 1.39505 | 44.08 | 43.856 | 43.604 | 5.893 | 5.8627 | 5.8291 | | | 0.7068 | -70.24 |
| 2-Methylheptane | " | 243.76 | 2.145 | 1.39494 | 1.39257 | 43.79 | 43.569 | 43.319 | 5.854 | 5.8243 | 5.7909 | | | 0.7021 | -164.27 |
| 3-Methylheptane | " | 246.06 | 2.154 | 1.39848 | 1.39610 | 44.29 | 44.062 | 43.808 | 5.920 | 5.8902 | 5.8563 | | | 0.7101 | -184.90 |
| 4-Methylheptane | " | 243.88 | 2.147 | 1.39792 | 1.39553 | 44.22 | 43.988 | 43.733 | 5.911 | 5.8803 | 5.8462 | | | 0.7090 | -185.72 |
| 3-Ethylhexane | " | 245.36 | 2.158 | 1.40162 | 1.39919 | 44.77 | 44.546 | 44.290 | 5.985 | 5.9550 | 5.9208 | | | 0.7179 | |
| 2,2-Dimethylhexane | " | 224.31 | 2.126 | 1.39349 | 1.39104 | 43.64 | 43.404 | 43.144 | 5.833 | 5.8023 | 5.7675 | | | 0.6996 | -186.12 |
| 2,3-Dimethylhexane | " | 240.09 | 2.160 | 1.40113 | 1.39880 | 44.69 | 44.456 | 44.204 | 5.973 | 5.9430 | 5.9092 | | | 0.7165 | |
| 2,4-Dimethylhexane | " | 228.97 | 2.132 | 1.39534 | 1.39291 | 43.95 | 43.721 | 43.461 | 5.876 | 5.8447 | 5.8099 | | | 0.7047 | |
| 2,5-Dimethylhexane | " | 228.39 | 2.124 | 1.39246 | 1.39004 | 43.53 | 43.295 | 43.033 | 5.819 | 5.7877 | 5.7527 | | | 0.6980 | -132.16 |
| 3,3-Dimethylhexane | " | 233.54 | 2.168 | 1.40009 | 1.39782 | 44.55 | 44.323 | 44.071 | 5.955 | 5.9251 | 5.8914 | | | 0.7143 | -194.98 |
| 3,4-Dimethylhexane | " | 243.90 | 2.173 | 1.40406 | 1.40180 | 45.13 | 44.899 | 44.645 | 6.032 | 6.0021 | 5.9682 | | | 0.7236 | |
| 2-Methyl-3-ethylpentane | " | 240.17 | 2.171 | 1.40401 | 1.40167 | 45.13 | 44.905 | 44.649 | 6.033 | 6.0029 | 5.9687 | | | 0.7237 | -174.93 |
| 3-Methyl-3-ethylpentane | " | 244.87 | 2.215 | 1.40775 | 1.40549 | 45.62 | 45.410 | 45.168 | 6.099 | 6.0705 | 6.0381 | | | 0.7315 | -131.57 |
| 2,2,3-Trimethylpentane | " | 229.71 | 2.174 | 1.40295 | 1.40066 | 44.92 | 44.699 | 44.452 | 6.005 | 5.9753 | 5.9424 | | | 0.7203 | -170.09 |
| 2,2,4-Trimethylpentane | " | 210.63 | 2.126 | 1.39145 | 1.38901 | 43.42 | 43.194 | 42.935 | 5.805 | 5.7742 | 5.7396 | | | 0.6962 | -161.28 |
| 2,3,3-Trimethylpentane | " | 238.57 | 2.210 | 1.40750 | 1.40522 | 45.55 | 45.334 | 45.092 | 6.089 | 6.0602 | 6.0279 | | | 0.7304 | -149.26 |
| 2,3,4-Trimethylpentane | " | 236.24 | 2.177 | 1.40422 | 1.40198 | 45.11 | 44.888 | 44.637 | 6.030 | 6.0007 | 5.9671 | | | 0.7233 | -164.58 |
| 2,2,3,3-Tetramethylbutane | " | 223.65 | 2.18 | | | | | | | | | | | | +213.24 |

[a] See footnote a of Table 1a-E.

104

TABLE 4a-E, Page 1 - PARAFFINS, C$_9$

BOILING POINT, dt/dp, REFRACTIVE INDEX, DENSITY, AND FREEZING POINT

June 30, 1945; March 31, 1949; October 31, 1952

| Compound | Formula | Boiling Point 29.921 in Hg °F | dt/dp 29.921 in Hg °F/in Hg | Refractive Index[a] $n_D$ 68°F | $n_D$ 77°F | Density[a] lb/cu ft 60°F | 68°F | 77°F | lb/gal 60°F | 68°F | 77°F | Specific Gravity[a] 60°F/60°F | Freezing Point In air at 1 atm °F |
|---|---|---|---|---|---|---|---|---|---|---|---|---|---|
| n-Nonane | C$_9$H$_{20}$ | 303.44 | 2.271 | 1.40542 | 1.40311 | 45.01 | 44.800 | 44.561 | 6.017 | 5.9888 | 5.9569 | 0.7217 | -64.33 |
| 2-Methyloctane | " | 289.87 | 2.2 | 1.4031 | 1.4008 | 44.75 | 44.54 | 44.29 | 5.983 | 5.954 | 5.921 | 0.7175 | -112.7 |
| 3-Methyloctane | " | 291.52 | 2.2 | 1.4062 | 1.4039 | 45.21 | 44.99 | 44.75 | 6.044 | 6.014 | 5.982 | 0.7249 | -161.7 |
| 4-Methyloctane | " | 288.46 | 2.2 | 1.4061 | 1.4038 | 45.16 | 44.94 | 44.70 | 6.037 | 6.008 | 5.975 | 0.7241 | -171.8 |
| 3-Ethylheptane | " | 289.4 | 2.3 | 1.4093 | 1.4070 | 45.6 | 45.4 | 45.1 | 6.10 | 6.07 | 6.03 | 0.731 | -174.8 |
| 4-Ethylheptane | " | 286.2 | 2.3 | 1.4096 | 1.4073 | 45.8 | 45.6 | 45.3 | 6.12 | 6.09 | 6.06 | 0.734 |  |
| 2,2-Dimethylheptane | " | 270.84 | 2.2 | 1.4016 | 1.3993 | 44.57 | 44.35 | 44.11 | 5.958 | 5.929 | 5.897 | 0.7146 | -171.40 |
| 2,3-Dimethylheptane | " | 284.9 | 2.3 | 1.4085 | 1.4062 | 45.54 | 45.32 | 45.08 | 6.088 | 6.059 | 6.026 | 0.7302 |  |
| 2,4-Dimethylheptane | " | 272.3 | 2.2 | 1.4033 | 1.4010 | 44.9 | 44.7 | 44.4 | 6.01 | 5.98 | 5.94 | 0.720 |  |
| 2,5-Dimethylheptane | " | 276.8 | 2.2 | 1.4038 | 1.4015 | 44.9 | 44.6 | 44.4 | 6.00 | 5.97 | 5.93 | 0.720 |  |
| 2,6-Dimethylheptane | " | 275.38 | 2.2 | 1.4007 | 1.3983 | 44.48 | 44.25 | 44.00 | 5.946 | 5.916 | 5.882 | 0.7131 | -153.2 |
| 3,3-Dimethylheptane | " | 279.1 | 2.2 | 1.4085 | 1.4062 | 45.5 | 45.3 | 45.0 | 6.08 | 6.05 | 6.02 | 0.730 |  |
| 3,4-Dimethylheptane | " | 285.1 | 2.3 | 1.4111 | 1.4089 | 45.88 | 45.66 | 45.42 | 6.133 | 6.104 | 6.071 | 0.7356 |  |
| 3,5-Dimethylheptane | " | 276.8 | 2.2 | 1.4067 | 1.4044 | 45.4 | 45.1 | 44.9 | 6.06 | 6.03 | 6.00 | 0.728 |  |
| 4,4-Dimethylheptane | " | 275.4 | 2.2 | 1.4076 | 1.4053 | 45.5 | 45.3 | 45.0 | 6.08 | 6.05 | 6.02 | 0.730 |  |

[a] See footnote a of Table 1a-E.

TABLE 4a-E, Page 2 – PARAFFINS, C$_9$

BOILING POINT, $dt/dp$, REFRACTIVE INDEX, DENSITY, AND FREEZING POINT

June 30, 1945; March 31, 1949; October 31, 1952

| Compound | Formula | Boiling Point 29.921 in Hg °F | $dt/dp$ 29.921 in Hg °F/in Hg | Refractive Index[a] $n_D$ 68°F | Refractive Index[a] $n_D$ 77°F | Density[a] 60°F lb/cu ft | Density[a] 68°F lb/cu ft | Density[a] 77°F lb/cu ft | Density[a] 60°F lb/gal | Density[a] 68°F lb/gal | Density[a] 77°F lb/gal | Specific Gravity[a] 60°F/60°F | Freezing Point In air at 1 atm °F |
|---|---|---|---|---|---|---|---|---|---|---|---|---|---|
| 2-Methyl-3-ethylhexane | C$_9$H$_{20}$ | 280.4 | 2.3 | 1.4120 | 1.4097 | 45.9 | 45.6 | 45.4 | 6.13 | 6.10 | 6.07 | 0.736 | |
| 2-Methyl-4-ethylhexane | " | 272.8 | 2.2 | 1.4068 | 1.4046 | 45.4 | 45.1 | 44.9 | 6.06 | 6.03 | 6.00 | 0.728 | |
| 3-Methyl-3-ethylhexane | " | 296.1 | 2.3 | 1.4142 | 1.4120 | 46.5 | 46.3 | 46.0 | 6.21 | 6.18 | 6.15 | 0.746 | |
| 3-Methyl-4-ethylhexane | " | 284.7 | 2.3 | 1.416 | 1.414 | 46.6 | 46.3 | 46.1 | 6.23 | 6.19 | 6.16 | 0.747 | |
| 2,2,3-Trimethylhexane | " | 272.48 | 2.2 | 1.4105 | 1.4082 | 45.73 | 45.52 | 45.28 | 6.114 | 6.085 | 6.054 | 0.7332 | |
| 2,2,4-Trimethylhexane | " | 259.77 | 2.2 | 1.4033 | 1.4010 | 44.88 | 44.67 | 44.44 | 6.000 | 5.972 | 5.940 | 0.7196 | −184.0 |
| 2,2,5-Trimethylhexane | " | 255.35 | 2.212 | 1.39972 | 1.39728 | 44.74 | 44.149 | 43.900 | 5.931 | 5.9018 | 5.8685 | 0.7174 | −158.40 |
| 2,3,3-Trimethylhexane | " | 279.82 | 2.2 | 1.4141 | 1.4119 | 46.3 | 46.1 | 45.8 | 6.19 | 6.16 | 6.13 | 0.742 | −178.24 |
| 2,3,4-Trimethylhexane | " | 282.2 | 2.3 | 1.4144 | 1.4120 | 46.36 | 46.15 | 45.91 | 6.197 | 6.169 | 6.137 | 0.7433 | |
| 2,3,5-Trimethylhexane | " | 268.41 | 2.2 | 1.4061 | 1.4037 | 45.29 | 45.07 | 44.82 | 6.054 | 6.024 | 5.991 | 0.7262 | −198.0 |
| 2,4,4-Trimethylhexane | " | 267.17 | 2.268 | 1.40745 | 1.40515 | 45.39 | 45.185 | 44.952 | 6.068 | 6.0404 | 6.0091 | 0.7278 | −172.08 |
| 3,3,4-Trimethylhexane | " | 284.83 | 2.24 | 1.4178 | 1.4154 | 46.76 | 46.53 | 46.28 | 6.251 | 6.221 | 6.187 | 0.7497 | −150.16 |
| 3,3-Diethylpentane | " | 295.10 | 2.356 | 1.42051 | 1.41837 | 47.24 | 47.044 | 46.820 | 6.316 | 6.2889 | 6.2589 | 0.7575 | −27.60 |
| 2,2-Dimethyl-3-ethylpentane | " | 272.89 | 2.3 | 1.4123 | 1.4102 | 46.08 | 45.87 | 45.63 | 6.160 | 6.132 | 6.100 | 0.7389 | −146.6 |
| 2,3-Dimethyl-3-ethylpentane | " | 288. | 2.3 | 1.419 | 1.417 | 47.3 | 47.1 | 46.8 | 6.32 | 6.29 | 6.26 | 0.758 | |
| 2,4-Dimethyl-3-ethylpentane | " | 276.11 | 2.30 | 1.4137 | 1.4115 | 46.28 | 46.06 | 45.83 | 6.186 | 6.158 | 6.126 | 0.7421 | −188.0 |
| 2,2,3,3-Tetramethylpentane | " | 284.49 | 2.343 | 1.42360 | 1.42140 | 47.44 | 47.236 | 47.007 | 6.342 | 6.3145 | 6.2839 | 0.7607 | +14.18 |
| 2,2,3,4-Tetramethylpentane | " | 271.43 | 2.30 | 1.41472 | 1.41246 | 46.34 | 46.130 | 45.899 | 6.194 | 6.1667 | 6.1357 | 0.7429 | −185.96 |
| 2,2,4,4-Tetramethylpentane | " | 252.11 | 2.255 | 1.40694 | 1.40459 | 45.13 | 44.914 | 44.674 | 6.032 | 6.0041 | 5.9721 | 0.7236 | −87.77 |
| 2,3,3,4-Tetramethylpentane | " | 286.79 | 1.931 | 1.42222 | 1.42003 | 47.32 | 47.115 | 46.890 | 6.326 | 6.2984 | 6.2683 | 0.7587 | −151.82 |

a See footnote a of Table 1a-E.

## TABLE 17a-E, Page 1 - PARAFFINS, C$_{10}$

### BOILING POINT, dt/dp, REFRACTIVE INDEX, DENSITY, AND FREEZING POINT

October 31, 1950; October 31, 1952

| Compound | Formula | Boiling Point 29.921 in Hg °F | dt/dp 29.921 in Hg °F/in Hg | Refractive Index[a] 68°F $n_D$ | Refractive Index[a] 77°F $n_D$ | Density[a] 60°F lb/cu ft | Density[a] 68°F lb/cu ft | Density[a] 77°F lb/cu ft | Density[a] 60°F lb/gal | Density[a] 68°F lb/gal | Density[a] 77°F lb/gal | Specific Gravity[a] 60°F/60°F | Freezing Point In air at 1 atm °F |
|---|---|---|---|---|---|---|---|---|---|---|---|---|---|
| n-Decane | C$_{10}$H$_{22}$ | 345.42 | 2.365 | 1.41189 | 1.40967 | 45.78 | 45.575 | 45.337 | 6.121 | 6.0924 | 6.0607 | 0.7341 | -21.39 |
| 2-Methylnonane | " | 332.2 | 2.3 | 1.4099 | 1.4076 | 45.67 | 45.45 | 45.21 | 6.105 | 6.076 | 6.044 | 0.7323 | -102.10 |
| 3-Methylnonane | " | 334.0 | 2.4 | 1.4125 | 1.4103 | 45.99 | 45.78 | 45.55 | 6.149 | 6.120 | 6.089 | 0.7375 | -120.64 |
| 4-Methylnonane | " | 330.3 | 2.3 | 1.4123 | 1.4100 | 45.93 | 45.71 | 45.47 | 6.140 | 6.111 | 6.079 | 0.7365 | -145.86 |
| 5-Methylnonane | " | 329.2 | 2.3 | 1.4122 | 1.4100 | 45.94 | 45.73 | 45.50 | 6.142 | 6.114 | 6.082 | 0.7367 | -125.86 |
| 3-Ethyloctane | " | 334. | 2.4 | 1.416 | 1.414 | 46.4 | 46.2 | 45.9 | 6.21 | 6.18 | 6.14 | 0.744 | |
| 4-Ethyloctane | " | 334. | 2.4 | 1.416 | 1.414 | 46.4 | 46.2 | 45.9 | 6.21 | 6.18 | 6.14 | 0.744 | |
| 2,2-Dimethyloctane | " | 311. | 2.3 | 1.4082 | 1.4060 | 45.43 | 45.23 | 45.00 | 6.074 | 6.046 | 6.015 | 0.7285 | |
| 2,3-Dimethyloctane | " | 326.8 | 2.4 | 1.4146 | 1.4125 | 46.26 | 46.05 | 45.80 | 6.184 | 6.155 | 6.123 | 0.7418 | |
| 2,4-Dimethyloctane | " | 307. | 2.3 | 1.4093 | 1.4069 | 45.57 | 45.35 | 45.10 | 6.092 | 6.062 | 6.029 | 0.7307 | |
| 2,5-Dimethyloctane | " | 316. | 2.3 | 1.414 | 1.412 | 46.2 | 45.9 | 45.7 | 6.17 | 6.14 | 6.11 | 0.740 | |
| 2,6-Dimethyloctane | " | 317.37 | 2.38 | 1.4113 | 1.4089 | 45.70 | 45.48 | 45.23 | 6.109 | 6.079 | 6.046 | 0.7328 | |
| 2,7-Dimethyloctane | " | 319.77 | 2.3 | 1.4086 | 1.4082 | 45.43 | 45.21 | 44.96 | 6.073 | 6.044 | 6.010 | 0.7285 | - 65. |
| 3,3-Dimethyloctane | " | 322.2 | 2.4 | 1.4145 | 1.4142 | 46.35 | 46.13 | 45.89 | 6.196 | 6.167 | 6.135 | 0.7432 | |
| 3,4-Dimethyloctane | " | 331. | 2.4 | 1.4182 | 1.4159 | 46.8 | 46.6 | 46.3 | 6.26 | 6.23 | 6.19 | 0.750 | |
| 3,5-Dimethyloctane | " | 320. | 2.3 | 1.413 | 1.411 | 46.2 | 45.9 | 45.7 | 6.17 | 6.14 | 6.11 | 0.740 | |
| 3,6-Dimethyloctane | " | 320. | 2.3 | 1.4145 | 1.4122 | 46.18 | 45.96 | 45.72 | 6.174 | 6.145 | 6.112 | 0.7405 | |
| 4,4-Dimethyloctane | " | 322. | 2.4 | 1.414 | 1.412 | 46.2 | 46.0 | 45.3 | 6.18 | 6.15 | 6.12 | 0.741 | |
| 4,5-Dimethyloctane | " | 323.83 | 2.4 | 1.4190 | 1.4167 | 46.84 | 46.63 | 46.40 | 6.262 | 6.234 | 6.202 | 0.7511 | |
| 4-Propylheptane | " | 324. | 2.3 | 1.4150 | 1.4127 | 46.18 | 45.97 | 45.73 | 6.174 | 6.145 | 6.114 | 0.740b | |
| 4-Isopropylheptane | " | 320. | 2.3 | 1.417 | 1.415 | 46.5 | 46.3 | 46.0 | 6.21 | 6.18 | 6.15 | 0.745 | |
| 2-Methyl-3-ethylheptane | " | 331. | 2.4 | 1.418 | 1.416 | 46.8 | 46.6 | 46.3 | 6.26 | 6.23 | 6.19 | 0.750 | |
| 2-Methyl-4-ethylheptane | " | 320. | 2.3 | 1.413 | 1.411 | 46.2 | 45.9 | 45.7 | 6.17 | 6.14 | 6.11 | 0.740 | |
| 2-Methyl-5-ethylheptane | " | 319.5 | 2.3 | 1.4134 | 1.4109 | 46.2 | 45.9 | 45.7 | 6.17 | 6.14 | 6.11 | 0.740 | |
| 3-Methyl-3-ethylheptane | " | 326.8 | 2.4 | 1.4208 | 1.4190 | 47.04 | 46.83 | 46.59 | 6.288 | 6.260 | 6.228 | 0.7542 | |

a See footnote a of Table 1a-E.

TABLE 17a-E, Page 2 - PARAFFINS, $C_{10}$

BOILING POINT, $dt/dp$, REFRACTIVE INDEX, DENSITY, AND FREEZING POINT

October 31, 1950; October 31, 1952

| Compound | Formula | Boiling Point 29.921 in Hg °F | dt/dp 29.921 in Hg °F/in Hg | Refractive Index[a] $n_D$ 68°F | Refractive Index[a] $n_D$ 77°F | Density[a] lb/cu ft 60°F | Density[a] lb/cu ft 68°F | Density[a] lb/cu ft 77°F | Density[a] lb/gal 60°F | Density[a] lb/gal 68°F | Density[a] lb/gal 77°F | Specific Gravity[a] 60°F/60°F | Freezing Point In air at 1 atm °F |
|---|---|---|---|---|---|---|---|---|---|---|---|---|---|
| 3-Methyl-4-ethylheptane | $C_{10}H_{22}$ | 333. | 2.4 | 1.422 | 1.419 | 47.2 | 47.0 | 46.8 | 6.31 | 6.28 | 6.25 | 0.757 | |
| 3-Methyl-5-ethylheptane | " | 322. | 2.3 | 1.416 | 1.414 | 46.6 | 46.4 | 46.1 | 6.23 | 6.20 | 6.17 | 0.747 | |
| 4-Methyl-3-ethylheptane | " | 333. | 2.4 | 1.422 | 1.419 | 47.2 | 47.0 | 46.8 | 6.31 | 6.28 | 6.25 | 0.757 | |
| 4-Methyl-4-ethylheptane | " | 333. | 2.4 | 1.421 | 1.419 | 47.2 | 46.9 | 46.7 | 6.31 | 6.28 | 6.24 | 0.756 | |
| 2,2,3-Trimethylheptane | " | 316. | 2.4 | 1.417 | 1.414 | 46.5 | 46.3 | 46.1 | 6.22 | 6.19 | 6.16 | 0.746 | |
| 2,2,4-Trimethylheptane | " | 297.9 | 2.3 | 1.4092 | 1.4070 | 45.63 | 45.42 | 45.18 | 6.099 | 6.071 | 6.039 | 0.7316 | |
| 2,2,5-Trimethylheptane | " | 298. | 2.3 | 1.409 | 1.407 | 45.5 | 45.3 | 45.1 | 6.09 | 6.06 | 6.03 | 0.730 | |
| 2,2,6-Trimethylheptane | " | 298.8 | 2.3 | 1.4059 | 1.4036 | 45.13 | 44.92 | 44.67 | 6.033 | 6.004 | 5.972 | 0.7237 | |
| 2,3,3-Trimethylheptane | " | 320. | 2.4 | 1.4202 | 1.4178 | 46.97 | 46.74 | 46.50 | 6.279 | 6.249 | 6.216 | 0.7531 | |
| 2,3,4-Trimethylheptane | " | 325. | 2.4 | 1.421 | 1.418 | 47.1 | 46.9 | 46.6 | 6.30 | 6.27 | 6.23 | 0.755 | |
| 2,3,5-Trimethylheptane | " | 315. | 2.3 | 1.416 | 1.414 | 46.5 | 46.3 | 46.0 | 6.21 | 6.18 | 6.15 | 0.745 | |
| 2,3,6-Trimethylheptane | " | 312.3 | 2.3 | 1.4125 | 1.4101 | 46.07 | 45.85 | 45.60 | 6.159 | 6.130 | 6.096 | 0.7388 | |
| 2,4,4-Trimethylheptane | " | 307. | 2.4 | 1.412 | 1.410 | 46.0 | 45.8 | 45.5 | 6.15 | 6.12 | 6.08 | 0.737 | |
| 2,4,5-Trimethylheptane | " | 315. | 2.3 | 1.4160 | 1.4137 | 46.5 | 46.3 | 46.0 | 6.21 | 6.18 | 6.15 | 0.745 | |
| 2,4,6-Trimethylheptane | " | 292.6 | 2.3 | 1.4071 | 1.4046 | 45.33 | 45.10 | 44.85 | 6.060 | 6.029 | 5.995 | 0.7268 | |
| 2,5,5-Trimethylheptane | " | 307.04 | 2.4 | 1.4136 | 1.4112 | 46.22 | 46.00 | 45.75 | 6.178 | 6.150 | 6.115 | 0.7411 | |
| 3,3,4-Trimethylheptane | " | 327. | 2.4 | 1.424 | 1.422 | 47.5 | 47.3 | 47.0 | 6.35 | 6.32 | 6.28 | 0.761 | |
| 3,3,5-Trimethylheptane | " | 312.22 | 2.4 | 1.4170 | 1.4146 | 46.60 | 46.37 | 46.12 | 6.229 | 6.199 | 6.165 | 0.7471 | |
| 3,4,4-Trimethylheptane | " | 327. | 2.4 | 1.424 | 1.422 | 47.5 | 47.3 | 47.0 | 6.35 | 6.32 | 6.28 | 0.761 | |
| 3,4,5-Trimethylheptane | " | 327. | 2.4 | 1.424 | 1.422 | 47.6 | 47.4 | 47.1 | 6.36 | 6.33 | 6.30 | 0.763 | |
| 2-Methyl-3-isopropylhexane | " | 325. | 2.4 | 1.421 | 1.413 | 47.1 | 46.9 | 46.6 | 6.30 | 6.27 | 6.23 | 0.755 | |
| 3,3-Diethylhexane | " | 331.3 | 2.4 | 1.428 | 1.426 | 48.1 | 47.9 | 47.6 | 6.43 | 6.40 | 6.37 | 0.771 | |
| 3,4-Diethylhexane | " | 324. | 2.4 | 1.420 | 1.418 | 47.3 | 47.1 | 46.8 | 6.32 | 6.29 | 6.26 | 0.758 | |
| 2,2-Dimethyl-3-ethylhexane | " | 318. | 2.4 | 1.420 | 1.418 | 47.0 | 46.8 | 46.5 | 6.28 | 6.25 | 6.22 | 0.753 | |
| 2,2-Dimethyl-4-ethylhexane | " | 297. | 2.3 | 1.4131 | 1.4107 | 46.0 | 45.8 | 45.5 | 6.15 | 6.12 | 6.08 | 0.737 | |

a See footnote a of Table 1a-E.

TABLE 17a-E, Page 3 — PARAFFINS, $C_{10}$

BOILING POINT, $dt/dp$, REFRACTIVE INDEX, DENSITY, AND FREEZING POINT

October 31, 1950; October 31, 1952

| Compound | Formula | Boiling Point 29.921 in Hg °F | dt/dp 29.921 in Hg °F/in Hg | Refractive Index[a] $n_D$ 68°F | $n_D$ 77°F | Density[a] lb/cu ft 60°F | 68°F | 77°F | lb/gal 60°F | 68°F | 77°F | Specific Gravity[a] 60°F/60°F | Freezing Point In air at 1 atm °F |
|---|---|---|---|---|---|---|---|---|---|---|---|---|---|
| 2,3-Dimethyl-3-ethylhexane | $C_{10}H_{22}$ | 336. | 2.5 | 1.427 | 1.424 | 48.0 | 47.8 | 47.4 | 6.42 | 6.38 | 6.34 | 0.770 | |
| 2,3-Dimethyl-4-ethylhexane | " | 327. | 2.4 | 1.424 | 1.422 | 47.6 | 47.4 | 47.1 | 6.36 | 6.33 | 6.30 | 0.763 | |
| 2,4-Dimethyl-3-ethylhexane | " | 327. | 2.4 | 1.424 | 1.422 | 47.6 | 47.4 | 47.1 | 6.36 | 6.33 | 6.30 | 0.763 | |
| 2,4-Dimethyl-4-ethylhexane | " | 316. | 2.4 | 1.419 | 1.417 | 46.9 | 46.6 | 46.4 | 6.26 | 6.23 | 6.20 | 0.751 | |
| 2,5-Dimethyl-3-ethylhexane | " | 315. | 2.3 | 1.416 | 1.414 | 46.5 | 46.3 | 46.0 | 6.21 | 6.18 | 6.15 | 0.745 | |
| 3,3-Dimethyl-4-ethylhexane | " | 329. | 2.4 | 1.427 | 1.425 | 47.9 | 47.7 | 47.4 | 6.41 | 6.38 | 6.34 | 0.768 | |
| 3,4-Dimethyl-3-ethylhexane | " | 338. | 2.5 | 1.431 | 1.429 | 48.4 | 48.2 | 47.9 | 6.47 | 6.44 | 6.41 | 0.776 | −65.20 |
| 2,2,3,3-Tetramethylhexane | " | 320.56 | 2.46 | 1.42818 | 1.42600 | 47.92 | 47.723 | 47.500 | 6.406 | 6.3796 | 6.3498 | 0.7684 | |
| 2,2,3,4-Tetramethylhexane | " | 310.8 | 2.4 | 1.4226 | 1.4202 | 47.34 | 47.12 | 46.87 | 6.329 | 6.299 | 6.266 | 0.7591 | |
| 2,2,3,5-Tetramethylhexane | " | 299.1 | 2.3 | 1.4142 | 1.4117 | 46.29 | 46.06 | 45.80 | 6.188 | 6.157 | 6.122 | 0.7422 | |
| 2,2,4,4-Tetramethylhexane | " | 307.9 | 2.3 | 1.4208 | 1.4183 | 46.86 | 46.63 | 46.37 | 6.264 | 6.234 | 6.199 | 0.7514 | |
| 2,2,4,5-Tetramethylhexane | " | 298.18 | 2.34 | 1.41318 | 1.41095 | 46.13 | 45.912 | 45.672 | 6.166 | 6.1376 | 6.1054 | 0.7396 | |
| 2,2,5,5-Tetramethylhexane | " | 279.43 | 2.29 | 1.40550 | 1.40316 | 45.09 | 44.869 | 44.623 | 6.027 | 5.9981 | 5.9652 | 0.7230 | 9.32 |
| 2,3,3,4-Tetramethylhexane | " | 328.26 | 2.5 | 1.4297 | 1.4269 | 48.29 | 48.03 | 47.74 | 6.455 | 6.421 | 6.382 | 0.7742 | |
| 2,3,3,5-Tetramethylhexane | " | 307. | 2.4 | 1.4196 | 1.4172 | 46.8 | 46.6 | 46.3 | 6.26 | 6.23 | 6.19 | 0.750 | |
| 2,3,4,4-Tetramethylhexane | " | 324.0 | 2.5 | 1.4270 | 1.4244 | 47.92 | 47.69 | 47.42 | 6.407 | 6.375 | 6.339 | 0.7684 | |
| 2,3,4,5-Tetramethylhexane | " | 322. | 2.4 | 1.424 | 1.422 | 47.5 | 47.3 | 47.0 | 6.35 | 6.32 | 6.28 | 0.761 | |
| 3,3,4,4-Tetramethylhexane | " | 338.0 | 2.5 | 1.4368 | 1.4344 | 49.07 | 48.84 | 48.59 | 6.560 | 6.529 | 6.495 | 0.7868 | |
| 2,4-Dimethyl-3-isopropylpentane | " | 314.67 | 2.49 | 1.42463 | 1.42248 | 47.54 | 47.338 | 47.105 | 6.356 | 6.3282 | 6.2971 | 0.7624 | −115.06 |
| 2-Methyl-3,3-diethylpentane | " | 345. | 2.5 | 1.435 | 1.432 | 49.0 | 48.7 | 48.4 | 6.55 | 6.51 | 6.47 | 0.785 | |
| 2,2,3-Trimethyl-3-ethylpentane | " | 334. | 2.5 | 1.436 | 1.434 | 49.0 | 48.8 | 48.5 | 6.55 | 6.52 | 6.48 | 0.785 | |
| 2,2,4-Trimethyl-3-ethylpentane | " | 311.5 | 2.4 | 1.4223 | 1.4199 | 47.49 | 47.26 | 47.01 | 6.348 | 6.318 | 6.285 | 0.7614 | |
| 2,3,4-Trimethyl-3-ethylpentane | " | 336.99 | 2.5 | 1.4333 | 1.4310 | 48.75 | 48.52 | 48.27 | 6.517 | 6.487 | 6.453 | 0.7816 | |
| 2,2,3,3,4-Pentamethylpentane | " | 330.89 | 2.52 | 1.43606 | 1.43412 | 48.88 | 48.698 | 48.490 | 6.535 | 6.5100 | 6.4821 | 0.7838 | −33.61 |
| 2,2,3,4,4-Pentamethylpentane | " | 318.72 | 2.46 | 1.43069 | 1.42868 | 48.07 | 47.883 | 47.670 | 6.426 | 6.4010 | 6.3725 | 0.7708 | −37.75 |

[a] See footnote a of Table 1a-E.

## TABLE 22a-E (PART 1) — NORMAL ALKYL CYCLOPENTANES, $C_5$ TO $C_{21}$
### BOILING POINT, $dt/dp$, REFRACTIVE INDEX, DENSITY, AND FREEZING POINT
(December 31, 1948; June 30, 1949; September 30, 1951 (Corrected))

| Compound | Formula | Boiling Point 29.921 in Hg °F | $dt/dp$ 29.921 in Hg °F/in Hg | Refractive Index[a] $n_D$ 68°F | Refractive Index[a] $n_D$ 77°F | Density[a] lb/cu ft 60°F | Density[a] lb/cu ft 68°F | Density[a] lb/cu ft 77°F | Density[a] lb/gal 60°F | Density[a] lb/gal 68°F | Density[a] lb/gal 77°F | Specific Gravity[a] 60°F/60°F | Freezing Point In air at 1 atm °F |
|---|---|---|---|---|---|---|---|---|---|---|---|---|---|
| Cyclopentane | $C_5H_{10}$ | 120.67 | 1.830 | 1.40645 | 1.40363 | 46.80 | 46.532 | 46.224 | 6.257 | 6.2204 | 6.1792 | 0.7505 | −136.98 |
| Methylcyclopentane | $C_6H_{12}$ | 161.26 | 1.954 | 1.40970 | 1.40700 | 47.00 | 46.735 | 46.442 | 6.282 | 6.2476 | 6.2083 | 0.7535 | −224.42 |
| Ethylcyclopentane | $C_7H_{14}$ | 218.24 | 2.114 | 1.41981 | 1.41730 | 48.09 | 47.848 | 47.580 | 6.428 | 6.3964 | 6.3605 | 0.7710 | −217.20[c] |
| n-Propylcyclopentane | $C_8H_{16}$ | 267.71 | 2.235 | 1.42626 | 1.42389 | 48.69 | 48.464 | 48.211 | 6.509 | 6.4786 | 6.4449 | 0.7807 | −179.21 |
| n-Butylcyclopentane | $C_9H_{18}$ | 313.81 | 2.341 | 1.4316 | 1.4293 | 49.19 | 48.98 | 48.74 | 6.576 | 6.548 | 6.516 | 0.7888 | −162.37 |
| n-Pentylcyclopentane | $C_{10}H_{20}$ | 356. | 2. | 1.4358 | 1.4336 | 49.61 | 49.39 | 49.15 | 6.631 | 6.603 | 6.571 | 0.7954 | −117. |
| n-Hexylcyclopentane | $C_{11}H_{22}$ | 397. | 2. | 1.4392 | 1.4370 | 49.93 | 49.72 | 49.49 | 6.675 | 6.647 | 6.615 | 0.8006 | − 99. |
| n-Heptylcyclopentane | $C_{12}H_{24}$ | 435. | 3. | 1.4421 | 1.4400 | 50.21 | 50.00 | 49.77 | 6.712 | 6.685 | 6.654 | 0.8051 | − 63. |
| n-Octylcyclopentane | $C_{13}H_{26}$ | 469. | 3. | 1.4446 | 1.4425 | 50.44 | 50.24 | 50.01 | 6.743 | 6.716 | 6.685 | 0.8088 | − 47. |
| n-Nonylcyclopentane | $C_{14}H_{28}$ | 504. | 3. | 1.4467 | 1.4446 | 50.65 | 50.45 | 50.22 | 6.771 | 6.744 | 6.714 | 0.8121 | − 20. |
| n-Decylcyclopentane | $C_{15}H_{30}$ | 534.6 | 2.8 | 1.44862 | 1.44659 | 50.82 | 50.626 | 50.403 | 6.794 | 6.7677 | 6.7378 | 0.8149 | − 7.83 |
| n-Undecylcyclopentane | $C_{16}H_{32}$ | 565. | 3. | 1.4503 | 1.4482 | 50.98 | 50.78 | 50.57 | 6.816 | 6.789 | 6.760 | 0.8175 | + 14. |
| n-Dodecylcyclopentane | $C_{17}H_{34}$ | 594. | 3. | 1.4518 | 1.4497 | 51.12 | 50.93 | 50.71 | 6.834 | 6.808 | 6.779 | 0.8197 | 23. |
| n-Tridecylcyclopentane | $C_{18}H_{36}$ | 621. | 3. | 1.4531 | 1.4510 | 51.25 | 51.05 | 50.83 | 6.851 | 6.825 | 6.796 | 0.8217 | 41. |
| n-Tetradecylcyclopentane | $C_{19}H_{38}$ | 646. | 3. | 1.4543 | 1.4522 | 51.36 | 51.16 | 50.95 | 6.866 | 6.840 | 6.811 | 0.8235 | 48. |
| n-Pentadecylcyclopentane | $C_{20}H_{40}$ | 671. | 3. | 1.4554 | 1.4533 | 51.47[b] | 51.27 | 51.05 | 6.880[b] | 6.854 | 6.825 | 0.8252[b] | 63. |
| n-Hexadecylcyclopentane | $C_{21}H_{42}$ | 694. | 3. | 1.4564[b] | 1.4543 | 51.56[b] | 51.36[b] | 51.15 | 6.892[b] | 6.866[b] | 6.838 | 0.8267[b] | 70. |

a See footnote a of Table 1a-E.    b For the undercooled liquid below the normal freezing point.    c See Table 6z-E for the freezing point of the metastable crystalline form.

TABLE 22a-E (PART 2) - NORMAL ALKYL CYCLOPENTANES, $C_{22}$ TO $C_{41}$
BOILING POINT, $dt/dp$, REFRACTIVE INDEX, DENSITY, AND FREEZING POINT

September 30, 1951 (Corrected)

| Compound | Formula | Boiling Point 29.921 in Hg | $dt/dp$ 29.921 in Hg | Refractive Index[a] 68°F | 77°F | Density[a] 60°F | 68°F | 77°F | 60°F | 68°F | 77°F | Specific Gravity[a] 60°F/60°F | Freezing Point In air at 1 atm |
|---|---|---|---|---|---|---|---|---|---|---|---|---|---|
| | | °F | °F/in Hg | $n_D$ | $n_D$ | lb/cu ft | | | lb/gal | | | | °F |
| n-Heptadecylcyclopentane | $C_{22}H_{44}$ | 716. | 3. | 1.4572[b] | 1.4552[b] | 51.64[b] | 51.45[b] | 51.24[b] | 6.903[b] | 6.878[b] | 6.849[b] | 0.8280[b] | 81. |
| n-Octadecylcyclopentane | $C_{23}H_{46}$ | 736. | 3. | 1.4581[b] | 1.4560[b] | 51.72[b] | 51.53[b] | 51.31[b] | 6.914[b] | 6.888[b] | 6.860[b] | 0.8293[b] | 86. |
| n-Nonadecylcyclopentane | $C_{24}H_{48}$ | 756. | 3. | 1.4588[b] | 1.4568[b] | 51.79[b] | 51.60[b] | 51.39[b] | 6.923[b] | 6.898[b] | 6.870[b] | 0.8304[b] | 95. |
| n-Eicosylcyclopentane | $C_{25}H_{50}$ | 775. | 3. | 1.4595[b] | 1.4575[b] | 51.86[b] | 51.67[b] | 51.45[b] | 6.932[b] | 6.907[b] | 6.878[b] | 0.8315[b] | 100. |
| n-Heneicosylcyclopentane | $C_{26}H_{52}$ | 793. | 3. | 1.4602[b] | 1.4582[b] | 51.92[b] | 51.73[b] | 51.52[b] | 6.940[b] | 6.915[b] | 6.887[b] | 0.8324[b] | 108. |
| n-Docosylcyclopentane | $C_{27}H_{54}$ | 811. | 3. | 1.4608[b] | 1.4588[b] | 51.97[b] | 51.79[b] | 51.57[b] | 6.948[b] | 6.923[b] | 6.894[b] | 0.8333[b] | 113. |
| n-Tricosylcyclopentane | $C_{28}H_{56}$ | 828. | 3. | 1.4614[b] | 1.4593[b] | 52.03[b] | 51.84[b] | 51.63[b] | 6.955[b] | 6.930[b] | 6.902[b] | 0.8342[b] | 120. |
| n-Tetracosylcyclopentane | $C_{29}H_{58}$ | 844. | 3. | 1.4619[b] | 1.4599[b] | 52.07[b] | 51.89[b] | 51.68[b] | 6.961[b] | 6.936[b] | 6.908[b] | 0.8350[b] | 124. |
| n-Pentacosylcyclopentane | $C_{30}H_{60}$ | 860. | 3. | 1.4624[b] | 1.4604[b] | 52.12[b] | 51.94[b] | 51.73[b] | 6.968[b] | 6.943[b] | 6.915[b] | 0.8357[b] | 129. |
| n-Hexacosylcyclopentane | $C_{31}H_{62}$ | 874. | 3. | 1.4628[b] | 1.4608[b] | 52.16[b] | 51.98[b] | 51.77[b] | 6.973[b] | 6.948[b] | 6.921[b] | 0.8364[b] | 133. |
| n-Heptacosylcyclopentane | $C_{32}H_{64}$ | 889. | 3. | 1.4633[b] | 1.4612[b] | 52.20[b] | 52.02[b] | 51.81[b] | 6.979[b] | 6.954[b] | 6.926[b] | 0.8371[b] | 138. |
| n-Octacosylcyclopentane | $C_{33}H_{66}$ | 901. | 3. | 1.4637[b] | 1.4617[b] | 52.24[b] | 52.06[b] | 51.85[b] | 6.984[b] | 6.959[b] | 6.931[b] | 0.8377[b] | 142. |
| n-Nonacosylcyclopentane | $C_{34}H_{68}$ | 916. | 3. | 1.4640[b] | 1.4620[b] | 52.28[b] | 52.09[b] | 51.89[b] | 6.989[b] | 6.964[b] | 6.936[b] | 0.8382[b] | 145. |
| n-Triacontylcyclopentane | $C_{35}H_{70}$ | 928. | 3. | 1.4644[b] | 1.4624[b] | 52.31[b] | 52.13[b] | 51.92[b] | 6.993[b] | 6.969[b] | 6.941[b] | 0.8388[b] | 149. |
| n-Hentriacontylcyclopentane | $C_{36}H_{72}$ | 941. | 3. | 1.4648[b] | 1.4628[b] | 52.35[b] | 52.16[b] | 51.95[b] | 6.997[b] | 6.973[b] | 6.945[b] | 0.8393[b] | 153. |
| n-Dotriacontylcyclopentane | $C_{37}H_{74}$ | 954. | 4. | 1.4651[b] | 1.4631[b] | 52.38[b] | 52.19[b] | 51.98[b] | 7.002[b] | 6.977[b] | 6.949[b] | 0.8398[b] | 156. |
| n-Tritriacontylcyclopentane | $C_{38}H_{76}$ | 964. | 4. | 1.4654[b] | 1.4634[b] | 52.41[b] | 52.22[b] | 52.01[b] | 7.006[b] | 6.981[b] | 6.953[b] | 0.8403[b] | 158. |
| n-Tetratriacontylcyclopentane | $C_{39}H_{78}$ | 977. | 4. | 1.4657[b] | 1.4637[b] | 52.43[b] | 52.25[b] | 52.04[b] | 7.009[b] | 6.985[b] | 6.957[b] | 0.8407[b] | 162. |
| n-Pentatriacontylcyclopentanee | $C_{40}H_{80}$ | 988. | 4. | 1.4660[b] | 1.4640[b] | 52.46[b] | 52.27[b] | 52.07[b] | 7.013[b] | 6.988[b] | 6.960[b] | 0.8411[b] | 165. |
| n-Hexatriacontylcyclopentane | $C_{41}H_{82}$ | 999. | 4. | 1.4662[b] | 1.4642[b] | 52.48[b] | 52.30[b] | 52.09[b] | 7.016[b] | 6.991[b] | 6.964[b] | 0.8415[b] | 167. |

a See footnote a of Table 1a-E.   b For the undercooled liquid below the normal freezing point.

## TABLE 6a-E — ALKYL CYCLOPENTANES, $C_5$ TO $C_7$

### BOILING POINT, $dt/dp$, REFRACTIVE INDEX, DENSITY, AND FREEZING POINT

June 30, 1945; February 28, 1947; June 30, 1949 (Corrected)

| Compound | Formula | Boiling Point 29.921 in Hg (°F) | $dt/dp$ 29.921 in Hg (°F/in Hg) | Refractive Index[a] 68°F $n_D$ | 77°F $n_D$ | Density[a] 60°F (lb/cu ft) | 68°F | 77°F | 60°F (lb/gal) | 68°F | 77°F | Specific Gravity[a] 60°F/60°F | Freezing Point In air at 1 atm (°F) |
|---|---|---|---|---|---|---|---|---|---|---|---|---|---|
| Cyclopentane | $C_5H_{10}$ | 120.67 | 1.830 | 1.40645 | 1.40363 | 46.80 | 46.532 | 46.224 | 6.257 | 6.2204 | 6.1792 | 0.7505 | −136.98 |
| Methylcyclopentane | $C_6H_{12}$ | 161.26 | 1.954 | 1.40970 | 1.40700 | 47.00 | 46.735 | 46.442 | 6.282 | 6.2476 | 6.2083 | 0.7535 | −224.42 |
| Ethylcyclopentane | $C_7H_{14}$ | 218.24 | 2.114 | 1.41981 | 1.41730 | 48.09 | 47.848 | 47.580 | 6.428 | 6.3964 | 6.3605 | 0.7710 | −217.20[b] |
| 1,1-Dimethylcyclopentane | " | 190.12 | 2.056 | 1.41356 | 1.41091 | 47.35 | 47.100 | 46.814 | 6.330 | 6.2963 | 6.2582 | 0.7593 | −93.63 |
| 1,*cis*-2-Dimethylcyclopentane | " | 211.16 | 2.104 | 1.42217 | 1.41963 | 48.48 | 48.232 | 47.948 | 6.481 | 6.4477 | 6.4097 | 0.7774 | −65.01 |
| 1,*trans*-2-Dimethylcyclopentane | " | 197.36 | 2.067 | 1.41200 | 1.40941 | 47.16 | 46.910 | 46.624 | 6.305 | 6.2709 | 6.2327 | 0.7562 | −179.64 |
| 1,*cis*-3-Dimethylcyclopentane | " | 197.10 | 2.069 | 1.41074 | 1.40813 | 46.99 | 46.745 | 46.467 | 6.282 | 6.2489 | 6.2118 | 0.7535 | −209.16 |
| 1,*trans*-3-Dimethylcyclopentane | " | 195.39 | 2.066 | 1.40894 | 1.40633 | 46.75 | 46.495 | 46.211 | 6.249 | 6.2154 | 6.1775 | 0.7496 | −208.66 |

a See footnote a of Table 1a-E.

b See Table 6z for the freezing point of the metastable crystalline form.

TABLE 15a-E – ALKYL CYCLOPENTANES, C$_8$

BOILING POINT, dt/dp, REFRACTIVE INDEX, DENSITY, AND FREEZING POINT

February 28, 1947; June 30, 1949; October 31, 1952

| Compound | Formula | Boiling Point 29.921 in Hg °F | dt/dp 29.921 in Hg °F/in Hg | Refractive Index[a] $n_D$ 68°F | Refractive Index[a] $n_D$ 77°F | Density[a] lb/cu ft 60°F | Density[a] lb/cu ft 68°F | Density[a] lb/cu ft 77°F | Density[a] lb/gal 60°F | Density[a] lb/gal 68°F | Density[a] lb/gal 77°F | Specific Gravity[a] 60°F/60°F | Freezing Point In air at 1 atm °F |
|---|---|---|---|---|---|---|---|---|---|---|---|---|---|
| n-Propylcyclopentane | C$_8$H$_{16}$ | 267.71 | 2.235 | 1.42626 | 1.42389 | 48.69 | 48.464 | 48.211 | 6.509 | 6.4786 | 6.4449 | 0.7807 | -179.21 |
| Isopropylcyclopentane | " | 259.55 | 2.246 | 1.42582 | 1.42350 | 48.69 | 48.476 | 48.230 | 6.510 | 6.4803 | 6.4474 | 0.7808 | -168.48 |
| 1-Methyl-1-ethylcyclopentane | " | 250.74 | 2.223 | 1.42718 | 1.42476 | 48.99 | 48.751 | 48.487 | 6.548 | 6.5170 | 6.4817 | 0.7854 | -226.84 |
| 1-Methyl-cis-2-ethylcyclopentane | " | 262.49 | 2.239 | 1.42933 | 1.42695 | 49.25 | 49.019 | 48.763 | 6.583 | 6.5528 | 6.5187 | 0.7896 | -158.71 |
| 1-Methyl-trans-2-ethylcyclopentane | " | 250.2 | 2.2 | 1.4219 | 1.4195 | 48.23 | 48.01 | 47.75 | 6.448 | 6.417 | 6.383 | 0.7733 | |
| 1-Methyl-cis-3-ethylcyclopentane | " | 250.5 | 2.2 | 1.4203 | 1.4179 | 48.46 | 48.22 | 47.95 | 6.478 | 6.446 | 6.410 | 0.7769 | |
| 1-Methyl-trans-3-ethylcyclopentane | " | 249.4 | 2.2 | 1.4186 | 1.4162 | 47.79 | 47.56 | 47.30 | 6.389 | 6.358 | 6.323 | 0.7663 | -162. |
| 1,1,2-Trimethylcyclopentane | " | 236.71 | 2.203 | 1.42298 | 1.42051 | 48.47 | 48.226 | 47.954 | 6.479 | 6.4468 | 6.4105 | 0.7771 | -6.95. |
| 1,1,3-Trimethylcyclopentane | " | 220.81 | 2.160 | 1.41119 | 1.40870 | 46.95 | 46.711 | 46.440 | 6.276 | 6.2443 | 6.2082 | 0.7528 | -224.39 |
| 1,cis-2,cis-3-Trimethylcyclopentane | " | 253.4 | 2.2 | 1.4262 | 1.4238 | 48.87 | 48.64 | 48.39 | 6.534 | 6.503 | 6.468 | 0.7836 | -177.57 |
| 1,cis-2,trans-3-Trimethylcyclopentane | " | 243.5 | 2.2 | 1.4218 | 1.4194 | 48.33 | 48.09 | 47.82 | 6.461 | 6.429 | 6.393 | 0.7749 | -170. |
| 1,trans-2,cis-3-Trimethylcyclopentane | " | 230.4 | 2.2 | 1.4138 | 1.4114 | 47.28 | 47.04 | 46.77 | 6.320 | 6.288 | 6.252 | 0.7580 | -170.87 |
| 1,cis-2,cis-4-Trimethylcyclopentane | " | 244. | 2.2 | 1.422 | 1.420 | 48.1 | 47.8 | 47.6 | 6.43 | 6.40 | 6.36 | 0.771 | |
| 1,cis-2,trans-4-Trimethylcyclopentane | " | 242.12 | 2.207 | 1.41855 | 1.41612 | 47.90 | 47.660 | 47.394 | 6.403 | 6.3712 | 6.3357 | 0.7680 | -206.59 |
| 1,trans-2,cis-4-Trimethylcyclopentane | " | 228.72 | 2.166 | 1.41060 | 1.40812 | 46.89 | 46.650 | 46.384 | 6.268 | 6.2361 | 6.2007 | 0.7518 | -203.40 |

a See footnote a of Table 1a-E.

TABLE 23a-E (PART 1) – NORMAL ALKYL CYCLOHEXANES, $C_6$ TO $C_{22}$

BOILING POINT, $dt/dp$, REFRACTIVE INDEX, DENSITY, AND FREEZING POINT

December 31, 1948; September 30, 1951; October 31, 1952

| Compound | Formula | Boiling Point 29.921 in Hg (°F) | $dt/dp$ 29.921 in Hg (°F/in Hg) | Refractive Index[a] 68°F ($n_D$) | 77°F ($n_D$) | Density[a] 60°F (lb/cu ft) | 68°F (lb/cu ft) | 77°F (lb/cu ft) | 60°F (lb/gal) | 68°F (lb/gal) | 77°F (lb/gal) | Specific Gravity[a] 60°F/60°F | Freezing Point In air at 1 atm (°F) |
|---|---|---|---|---|---|---|---|---|---|---|---|---|---|
| Cyclohexane | $C_6H_{12}$ | 177.33 | 2.001 | 1.42623 | 1.42354 | 48.86 | 48.602 | 48.311 | 6.532 | 6.4972 | 6.4583 | 0.7834 | +43.80 |
| Methylcyclohexane | $C_7H_{14}$ | 213.68 | 2.136 | 1.42312 | 1.42058 | 48.27 | 48.030 | 47.760 | 6.453 | 6.4207 | 6.3846 | 0.7740 | -195.87 |
| Ethylcyclohexane | $C_8H_{16}$ | 269.21 | 2.272 | 1.43304 | 1.43073 | 49.41 | 49.187 | 48.936 | 6.605 | 6.5754 | 6.5418 | 0.7922 | -168.38 |
| n-Propylcyclohexane | $C_9H_{18}$ | 314.10 | 2.377 | 1.43705 | 1.43478 | 49.75 | 49.542 | 49.302 | 6.651 | 6.6228 | 6.5908 | 0.7978 | -138.82 |
| n-Butylcyclohexane | $C_{10}H_{20}$ | 357.70 | 2.474 | 1.44075 | 1.43855 | 50.09 | 49.890 | 49.661 | 6.696 | 6.6693 | 6.6387 | 0.8032 | -102.50 |
| n-Pentylcyclohexane | $C_{11}H_{22}$ | 397.0 | 2.5 | 1.4437 | 1.4416 | 50.37 | 50.17 | 49.95 | 6.734 | 6.707 | 6.677 | 0.8077 | - 71.6 |
| n-Hexylcyclohexane | $C_{12}H_{24}$ | 435.2 | 2.6 | 1.4462 | 1.4441 | 50.61 | 50.42 | 50.20 | 6.766 | 6.740 | 6.710 | 0.8115 | - 45.5 |
| n-Heptylcyclohexane | $C_{13}H_{26}$ | 471. | 3. | 1.4484 | 1.4463 | 50.82 | 50.62 | 50.41 | 6.793 | 6.767 | 6.738 | 0.8148 | - 23.0 |
| n-Octylcyclohexane | $C_{14}H_{28}$ | 507. | 3. | 1.4503 | 1.4483 | 50.99 | 50.80 | 50.59 | 6.817 | 6.791 | 6.763 | 0.8176 | - 3.4 |
| n-Nonylcyclohexane | $C_{15}H_{30}$ | 540. | 3. | 1.4519 | 1.4499 | 51.15 | 50.96 | 50.75 | 6.838 | 6.813 | 6.784 | 0.8201 | + 13.7 |
| n-Decylcyclohexane | $C_{16}H_{32}$ | 570. | 3. | 1.45338 | 1.45141 | 51.29 | 51.101 | 50.888 | 6.856 | 6.8312 | 6.8028 | 0.8224 | 28.87 |
| n-Undecylcyclohexane | $C_{17}H_{34}$ | 601. | 3. | 1.4547 | 1.4527 | 51.41 | 51.22 | 51.02 | 6.873 | 6.848 | 6.820 | 0.8243 | 42.4 |
| n-Dodecylcyclohexane | $C_{18}H_{36}$ | 628. | 3. | 1.4559 | 1.4539 | 51.52 | 51.34 | 51.13 | 6.887 | 6.863 | 6.835 | 0.8261 | 54.5 |
| n-Tridecylcyclohexane | $C_{19}H_{38}$ | 655. | 3. | 1.4570 | 1.4550 | 51.62[b] | 51.44 | 51.23 | 6.901[b] | 6.876 | 6.84[b] | 0.8277[b] | 65.4 |
| n-Tetradecylcyclohexane | $C_{20}H_{40}$ | 680. | 3. | 1.4579[b] | 1.4559 | 51.71[b] | 51.53[b] | 51.32 | 6.913[b] | 6.888[b] | 6.860 | 0.8291[b] | 75.2 |
| n-Pentadecylcyclohexane | $C_{21}H_{42}$ | 703. | 3. | 1.4588[b] | 1.4568[b] | 51.79[b] | 51.61[b] | 51.40[b] | 6.924[b] | 6.899[b] | 6.871[b] | 0.8304[b] | 84.3 |
| n-Hexadecylcyclohexane | $C_{22}H_{44}$ | 725. | 3. | 1.4596[b] | 1.4576[b] | 51.87[b] | 51.66[b] | 51.45[b] | 6.953[b] | 6.909[b] | 6.881[b] | 0.8316[b] | 92.5 |

[a] See footnote a of Table 1a-E.   [b] For the undercooled liquid below the normal freezing point.

TABLE 23a-E (PART 2) – NORMAL ALKYL CYCLOHEXANES, C$_{23}$ TO C$_{42}$
BOILING POINT, $dt/dp$, REFRACTIVE INDEX, DENSITY, AND FREEZING POINT
September 30, 1951 (Corrected)

| Compound | Formula | Boiling Point 29.921 in Hg °F | $dt/dp$ 29.921 in Hg °F/in Hg | Refractive Index[a] $n_D$ 68°F | Refractive Index[a] $n_D$ 77°F | Density[a] lb/cu ft 68°F | Density[a] lb/cu ft 77°F | Density[a] lb/cu ft 60°F | Density[a] lb/gal 68°F | Density[a] lb/gal 77°F | Density[a] lb/gal 60°F | Specific Gravity[a] 60°F/60°F | Freezing Point In air at 1 atm °F |
|---|---|---|---|---|---|---|---|---|---|---|---|---|---|
| n-Heptadecylcyclohexane | C$_{23}$H$_{46}$ | 747. | 3. | 1.4603[b] | 1.4583[b] | 51.75[b] | 51.55[b] | 51.94[b] | 6.918[b] | 6.891[b] | 6.943[b] | 0.8327[b] | 100.0 |
| n-Octadecylcyclohexane | C$_{24}$H$_{48}$ | 768. | 3. | 1.4610[b] | 1.4590[b] | 51.81[b] | 51.61[b] | 52.00[b] | 6.927[b] | 6.899[b] | 6.951[b] | 0.8337[b] | 106.9 |
| n-Nonadecylcyclohexane | C$_{25}$H$_{50}$ | 788. | 3. | 1.4616[b] | 1.4596[b] | 51.88[b] | 51.67[b] | 52.06[b] | 6.935[b] | 6.907[b] | 6.959[b] | 0.8347[b] | 113.4 |
| n-Eicosylcyclohexane | C$_{26}$H$_{52}$ | 806. | 3. | 1.4622[b] | 1.4602[b] | 51.93[b] | 51.72[b] | 52.11[b] | 6.942[b] | 6.914[b] | 6.966[b] | 0.8355[b] | 119.3 |
| n-Heneicosylcyclohexane | C$_{27}$H$_{54}$ | 824. | 3. | 1.4627[b] | 1.4607[b] | 51.98[b] | 51.78[b] | 52.16[b] | 6.948[b] | 6.921[b] | 6.973[b] | 0.8363[b] | 124.7 |
| n-Docosylcyclohexane | C$_{28}$H$_{56}$ | 840. | 3. | 1.4632[b] | 1.4612[b] | 52.03[b] | 51.82[b] | 52.21[b] | 6.955[b] | 6.927[b] | 6.979[b] | 0.8371[b] | 129.9 |
| n-Tricosylcyclohexane | C$_{29}$H$_{58}$ | 858. | 3. | 1.4637[b] | 1.4617[b] | 52.07[b] | 51.86[b] | 52.25[b] | 6.960[b] | 6.933[b] | 6.985[b] | 0.8378[b] | 134.6 |
| n-Tetracosylcyclohexane | C$_{30}$H$_{60}$ | 873. | 3. | 1.4641[b] | 1.4621[b] | 52.11[b] | 51.91[b] | 52.29[b] | 6.966[b] | 6.939[b] | 6.990[b] | 0.8384[b] | 139.1 |
| n-Pentacosylcyclohexane | C$_{31}$H$_{62}$ | 889. | 3. | 1.4645[b] | 1.4626[b] | 52.14[b] | 51.95[b] | 52.33[b] | 6.971[b] | 6.944[b] | 6.995[b] | 0.8390[b] | 143.4 |
| n-Hexacosylcyclohexane | C$_{32}$H$_{64}$ | 903. | 3. | 1.4649[b] | 1.4629[b] | 52.18[b] | 51.98[b] | 52.36[b] | 6.976[b] | 6.949[b] | 7.000[b] | 0.8396[b] | 147.2 |
| n-Heptacosylcyclohexane | C$_{33}$H$_{66}$ | 918. | 3. | 1.4653[b] | 1.4633[b] | 52.22[b] | 52.01[b] | 52.40[b] | 6.980[b] | 6.953[b] | 7.005[b] | 0.8402[b] | 151.0 |
| n-Octacosylcyclohexane | C$_{34}$H$_{68}$ | 930. | 3. | 1.4656[b] | 1.4636[b] | 52.25[b] | 52.05[b] | 52.43[b] | 6.985[b] | 6.957[b] | 7.009[b] | 0.8407[b] | 154.4 |
| n-Nonacosylcyclohexane | C$_{35}$H$_{70}$ | 945. | 4. | 1.4659[b] | 1.4640[b] | 52.28[b] | 52.08[b] | 52.46[b] | 6.989[b] | 6.961[b] | 7.013[b] | 0.8411[b] | 157.8 |
| n-Triacontylcyclohexane | C$_{36}$H$_{72}$ | 957. | 4. | 1.4662[b] | 1.4643[b] | 52.31[b] | 52.10[b] | 52.49[b] | 6.992[b] | 6.965[b] | 7.017[b] | 0.8416[b] | 160.9 |
| n-Hentriacontylcyclohexane | C$_{37}$H$_{74}$ | 968. | 4. | 1.4665[b] | 1.4645[b] | 52.33[b] | 52.13[b] | 52.52[b] | 6.996[b] | 6.969[b] | 7.020[b] | 0.8420[b] | 163.9 |
| n-Dotriacontylcyclohexane | C$_{38}$H$_{76}$ | 981. | 4. | 1.4668[b] | 1.4648[b] | 52.36[b] | 52.16[b] | 52.54[b] | 7.000[b] | 6.972[b] | 7.024[b] | 0.8424[b] | 166.6 |
| n-Tritriacontylcyclohexane | C$_{39}$H$_{78}$ | 991. | 4. | 1.4670[b] | 1.4651[b] | 52.38[b] | 52.18[b] | 52.57[b] | 7.003[b] | 6.976[b] | 7.027[b] | 0.8428[b] | 169.3 |
| n-Tetratriacontylcyclohexane | C$_{40}$H$_{80}$ | 1004. | 4. | 1.4673[b] | 1.4653[b] | 52.41[b] | 52.21[b] | 52.59[b] | 7.006[b] | 6.979[b] | 7.030[b] | 0.8432[b] | 171.9 |
| n-Pentatriacontylcyclohexane | C$_{41}$H$_{82}$ | 1025. | 4. | 1.4675[b] | 1.4656[b] | 52.43[b] | 52.23[b] | 52.61[b] | 7.009[b] | 6.982[b] | 7.033[b] | 0.8436[b] | 174.4 |
| n-Hexatriacontylcyclohexane | C$_{42}$H$_{84}$ | 1024. | 4. | 1.4678[b] | 1.4658[b] | 52.45[b] | 52.25[b] | 52.63[b] | 7.012[b] | 6.985[b] | 7.036[b] | 0.8439[b] | 176.7 |

[a] See footnote a of Table 1a-E.

[b] For the undercooled liquid below the normal freezing point.

TABLE 7a-E — ALKYL CYCLOHEXANES, $C_6$ TO $C_8$

BOILING POINT, $dt/dp$, REFRACTIVE INDEX, DENSITY, AND FREEZING POINT

June 30, 1945; March 31, 1947; June 30, 1949; October 31, 1952

| Compound | Formula | Boiling Point 29.921 in Hg °F | $dt/dp$ 29.921 in Hg °F/in Hg | Refractive Index[a] 68°F $n_D$ | 77°F $n_D$ | Density[a] 60°F lb/cu ft | 68°F lb/cu ft | 77°F lb/cu ft | 60°F lb/gal | 68°F lb/gal | 77°F lb/gal | Specific Gravity[a] 60°F/60°F | Freezing Point In air at 1 atm °F |
|---|---|---|---|---|---|---|---|---|---|---|---|---|---|
| Cyclohexane | $C_6H_{12}$ | 177.33 | 2.001 | 1.42623 | 1.42354 | 48.86 | 48.602 | 48.311 | 6.532 | 6.4972 | 6.4583 | 0.7834 | +43.80 |
| Methylcyclohexane | $C_7H_{14}$ | 213.68 | 2.136 | 1.42312 | 1.42058 | 48.27 | 48.030 | 47.760 | 6.453 | 6.4207 | 6.3846 | 0.7740 | −195.87 |
| Ethylcyclohexane | $C_8H_{16}$ | 269.21 | 2.272 | 1.43304 | 1.43073 | 49.41 | 49.187 | 48.936 | 6.605 | 6.5754 | 6.5418 | 0.7922 | −168.38 |
| 1,1-Dimethylcyclohexane | " | 247.18 | 2.249 | 1.42900 | 1.42662 | 48.98 | 48.751 | 48.491 | 6.548 | 6.5171 | 6.4623 | 0.7854 | −28.29 |
| 1,cis-2-Dimethylcyclohexane | " | 265.51 | 2.281 | 1.43596 | 1.43358 | 49.93 | 49.708 | 49.456 | 6.675 | 6.6451 | 6.6113 | 0.8006 | −58.04 |
| 1,trans-2-Dimethylcyclohexane | " | 254.15 | 2.264 | 1.42695 | 1.42470 | 48.66 | 48.444 | 48.196 | 6.505 | 6.4760 | 6.4428 | 0.7803 | −126.75 |
| 1,cis-3-Dimethylcyclohexane[b] | " | 248.16 | 2.231 | 1.42294 | 1.42063 | 48.05 | 47.821 | 47.567 | 6.423 | 6.3927 | 6.3587 | 0.7704 | −104.03 |
| 1,trans-3-Dimethylcyclohexane[c] | " | 256.01 | 2.245 | 1.43085 | 1.42843 | 49.22 | 48.987 | 48.727 | 6.580 | 6.5487 | 6.5139 | 0.7892 | −130.19 |
| 1,cis-4-Dimethylcyclohexane | " | 255.78 | 2.250 | 1.42966 | 1.42731 | 49.10 | 48.871 | 48.612 | 6.564 | 6.5331 | 6.4984 | 0.7873 | −125.38 |
| 1,trans-4-Dimethylcyclohexane | " | 246.83 | 2.242 | 1.42090 | 1.41853 | 47.84 | 47.603 | 47.341 | 6.395 | 6.3637 | 6.3286 | 0.7670 | −34.53 |

a See footnote a of Table 1a-E.  b Formerly labeled "trans"; see footnote b of Table 7a.  c Formerly labeled "cis"; see footnote c of Table 7a.

TABLE 24a-E (PART 1) - NORMAL MONOOLEFINS (1-ALKENES), $C_2$ TO $C_{20}$
BOILING POINT, dt/dp, REFRACTIVE INDEX, DENSITY, AND FREEZING POINT

February 28, 1949; December 31, 1950; October 31, 1952

| Compound | Formula | Boiling Point 29.921 in Hg °F | dt/dp 29.921 in Hg °F/in Hg | Refractive Index[a] $n_D$ 68°F | Refractive Index[a] $n_D$ 77°F | Density[a] lb/cu ft 60°F | Density[a] lb/cu ft 68°F | Density[a] lb/cu ft 77°F | Density[a] lb/gal 60°F | Density[a] lb/gal 68°F | Density[a] lb/gal 77°F | Specific Gravity[a] 60°F/60°F | Freezing Point In air at 1 atm °F |
|---|---|---|---|---|---|---|---|---|---|---|---|---|---|
| Ethene (Ethylene) | $C_2H_4$ | -154.68 | 1.024 | — | — | | | | | | | — | -272.47[c] |
| Propene (Propylene) | $C_3H_6$ | -53.86 | 1.321 | — | — | 32.56[b] | 32.08[b] | 31.54[b] | 4.352[b] | 4.289[b] | 4.217[b] | 0.5220[b] | -301.45[c] |
| 1-Butene | $C_4H_8$ | +20.73 | 1.541 | — | — | 37.50[b] | 37.15[b] | 36.76[b] | 5.013[b] | 4.966[b] | 4.914[b] | 0.6013[b] | -301.63[c] |
| 1-Pentene | $C_5H_{10}$ | 85.94 | 1.737 | 1.37148 | 1.36635 | 40.27 | 39.984 | 39.661 | 5.384 | 5.3451 | 5.3020 | 0.6457 | -265.40 |
| 1-Hexene | $C_6H_{12}$ | 146.27 | 1.897 | 1.38788 | 1.38502 | 42.28 | 42.024 | 41.731 | 5.653 | 5.6178 | 5.5786 | 0.6780 | -219.67 |
| 1-Heptene | $C_7H_{14}$ | 200.56 | 2.034 | 1.39980 | 1.39713 | 43.75 | 43.510 | 43.241 | 5.848 | 5.8165 | 5.7805 | 0.7015 | -182.25 |
| 1-Octene | $C_8H_{16}$ | 250.30 | 2.153 | 1.40870 | 1.40620 | 44.86 | 44.630 | 44.376 | 5.996 | 5.9662 | 5.9322 | 0.7192 | -151.12 |
| 1-Nonene | $C_9H_{18}$ | 296.36 | 2.259 | 1.41572 | 1.41333 | 45.74 | 45.523 | 45.279 | 6.114 | 6.0855 | 6.0529 | 0.7334 | -114.47 |
| 1-Decene | $C_{10}H_{20}$ | 339.03 | 2.359 | 1.42146 | 1.41913 | 46.46 | 46.246 | 46.004 | 6.211 | 6.1822 | 6.1498 | 0.7450 | -87.36 |
| 1-Undecene | $C_{11}H_{22}$ | 378.81 | 2.446 | 1.42609 | 1.42383 | 47.05 | 46.840 | 46.605 | 6.290 | 6.2616 | 6.2301 | 0.7544 | -56.53 |
| 1-Dodecene | $C_{12}H_{24}$ | 416.04 | 2.524 | 1.43002 | 1.42782 | 47.54 | 47.342 | 47.116 | 6.356 | 6.3287 | 6.2985 | 0.7623 | -31.41 |
| 1-Tridecene | $C_{13}H_{26}$ | 451.00 | 2.602 | 1.4335 | 1.4313 | 47.98 | 47.78 | 47.55 | 6.414 | 6.387 | 6.357 | 0.7693 | -9.53 |
| 1-Tetradecene | $C_{14}H_{28}$ | 483.82 | 2.666 | 1.4364 | 1.4342 | 48.35 | 48.15 | 47.92 | 6.463 | 6.436 | 6.407 | 0.7752 | +8.87 |
| 1-Pentadecene | $C_{15}H_{30}$ | 514.71 | 2.73 | 1.4389 | 1.4368 | 48.67 | 48.48 | 48.26 | 6.507 | 6.480 | 6.451 | 0.7804 | 25.29 |
| 1-Hexadecene | $C_{16}H_{32}$ | 543.9 | 2.79 | 1.44120 | 1.43907 | 48.96 | 48.763 | 48.542 | 6.545 | 6.5186 | 6.4892 | 0.7850 | 39.42 |
| 1-Heptadecene | $C_{17}H_{34}$ | 571.5 | 2.84 | 1.4432 | 1.4411 | 49.21 | 49.02 | 48.80 | 6.578 | 6.552 | 6.523 | 0.7890 | 52.2 |
| 1-Octadecene | $C_{18}H_{36}$ | 597.6 | 2.88 | 1.4450 | 1.4429 | 49.43[d] | 49.24 | 49.02 | 6.608[d] | 6.582 | 6.554 | 0.7926[d] | 63.7 |
| 1-Nonadecene | $C_{19}H_{38}$ | 622.4 | 2.93 | 1.4466[d] | 1.4445 | 49.64[d] | 49.44[d] | 49.23 | 6.635[d] | 6.610[d] | 6.58. | 0.7959[d] | 74.1 |
| 1-Eicosene | $C_{20}H_{40}$ | 646.2 | 2.97 | 1.4481[d] | 1.4460 | 49.82[d] | 49.63[d] | 49.42[d] | 6.660 | 6.635[d] | 6.606[d] | 0.7968[d] | 83.5 |

a See footnote a of Table 1a-E.   b At saturation pressure.   c At saturation pressure (triple point).   d For the undercooled liquid below the normal freezing point.

TABLE 24a-E (PART 2) – NORMAL MONOOLEFINS (1-ALKENES), $C_{21}$ TO $C_{40}$
BOILING POINT, dt/dp, REFRACTIVE INDEX, DENSITY, AND FREEZING POINT
December 31, 1950

| Compound | Formula | Boiling Point 29.921 in Hg °F | dt/dp 29.921 in Hg °F/in Hg | Refractive Index[a] $n_D$ 68°F | $n_D$ 77°F | Density[a] 60°F lb/cu ft | 68°F | 77°F | 60°F lb/gal | 68°F | 77°F | Specific Gravity[a] 60°F/60°F | Freezing Point In air at 1 atm °F |
|---|---|---|---|---|---|---|---|---|---|---|---|---|---|
| 1-Heneicosene | $C_{21}H_{42}$ | 669. | 3. | 1.4494[b] | 1.4473[b] | 49.99[b] | 49.80[b] | 49.59[b] | 6.683[b] | 6.657[b] | 6.629[b] | 0.8015[b] | 91.9 |
| 1-Docosene | $C_{22}H_{44}$ | 691. | 3. | 1.4506[b] | 1.4485[b] | 50.14[b] | 49.95[b] | 49.74[b] | 6.703[b] | 6.678[b] | 6.649[b] | 0.8040[b] | 100.0 |
| 1-Tricosene | $C_{23}H_{46}$ | 711. | 3. | 1.4517[b] | 1.4496[b] | 50.28[b] | 50.09[b] | 49.88[b] | 6.722[b] | 6.697[b] | 6.668[b] | 0.8062[b] | 106.9 |
| 1-Tetracosene | $C_{24}H_{48}$ | 730. | 3. | 1.4527[b] | 1.4506[b] | 50.41[b] | 50.22[b] | 50.01[b] | 6.739[b] | 6.714[b] | 6.686[b] | 0.8083[b] | 113.5 |
| 1-Pentacosene | $C_{25}H_{50}$ | 748. | 3. | 1.4537[b] | 1.4516[b] | 50.53[b] | 50.34[b] | 50.13[b] | 6.755[b] | 6.730[b] | 6.702[b] | 0.8102[b] | 119.7 |
| 1-Hexacosene | $C_{26}H_{52}$ | 766. | 3. | 1.4545[b] | 1.4524[b] | 50.64[b] | 50.45[b] | 50.24[b] | 6.769[b] | 6.745[b] | 6.717[b] | 0.8120[b] | 125.2 |
| 1-Heptacosene | $C_{27}H_{54}$ | 784. | 3. | 1.4553[b] | 1.4533[b] | 50.74[b] | 50.56[b] | 50.35[b] | 6.783[b] | 6.758[b] | 6.730[b] | 0.8136[b] | 130.5 |
| 1-Octacosene | $C_{28}H_{56}$ | 801. | 3. | 1.4561[b] | 1.4540[b] | 50.84[b] | 50.65[b] | 50.44[b] | 6.796[b] | 6.771[b] | 6.743[b] | 0.8151[b] | 135.5 |
| 1-Nonacosene | $C_{29}H_{58}$ | 817. | 3. | 1.4568[b] | 1.4547[b] | 50.93[b] | 50.74[b] | 50.53[b] | 6.808[b] | 6.783[b] | 6.755[b] | 0.8165[b] | 140.0 |
| 1-Triacontene | $C_{30}H_{60}$ | 833. | 3. | 1.4574[b] | 1.4554[b] | 51.01[b] | 50.82[b] | 50.62[b] | 6.819[b] | 6.794[b] | 6.766[b] | 0.8179[b] | 144.3 |
| 1-Hentriacontene | $C_{31}H_{62}$ | 847. | 3. | 1.4580[b] | 1.4560[b] | 51.09[b] | 50.90[b] | 50.69[b] | 6.829[b] | 6.805[b] | 6.777[b] | 0.8191[b] | 148.3 |
| 1-Dotriacontene | $C_{32}H_{64}$ | 862. | 3. | 1.4586[b] | 1.4566[b] | 51.16[b] | 50.98[b] | 50.77[b] | 6.839[b] | 6.815[b] | 6.787[b] | 0.8203[b] | 152.1 |
| 1-Tritriacontene | $C_{33}H_{66}$ | 876. | 3. | 1.4592[b] | 1.4571[b] | 51.23[b] | 51.04[b] | 50.84[b] | 6.848[b] | 6.824[b] | 6.796[b] | 0.8214[b] | 155.7 |
| 1-Tetratriacontene | $C_{34}H_{68}$ | 891. | 3. | 1.4596[b] | 1.4576[b] | 51.29[b] | 51.11[b] | 50.90[b] | 6.857[b] | 6.832[b] | 6.805[b] | 0.8225[b] | 158.9 |
| 1-Pentatriacontene | $C_{35}H_{70}$ | 903. | 3. | 1.4602[b] | 1.4581[b] | 51.35[b] | 51.17[b] | 50.97[b] | 6.865[b] | 6.841[b] | 6.813[b] | 0.8234[b] | 162.1 |
| 1-Hexatriacontene | $C_{36}H_{72}$ | 916. | 3. | 1.4606[b] | 1.4586[b] | 51.41[b] | 51.23[b] | 51.02[b] | 6.873[b] | 6.848[b] | 6.821[b] | 0.8244[b] | 165.0 |
| 1-Heptatriacontene | $C_{37}H_{74}$ | 928. | 3. | 1.4610[b] | 1.4590[b] | 51.47[b] | 51.29[b] | 51.08[b] | 6.880[b] | 6.856[b] | 6.828[b] | 0.8252[b] | 167.9 |
| 1-Octatriacontene | $C_{38}H_{76}$ | 941. | 3. | 1.4614[b] | 1.4594[b] | 51.52[b] | 51.34[b] | 51.13[b] | 6.887[b] | 6.863[b] | 6.835[b] | 0.8261[b] | 170.6 |
| 1-Nonatriacontene | $C_{39}H_{78}$ | 952. | 4. | 1.4618[b] | 1.4598[b] | 51.57[b] | 51.39[b] | 51.18[b] | 6.894[b] | 6.869[b] | 6.842[b] | 0.8269[b] | 173.1 |
| 1-Tetracontene | $C_{40}H_{80}$ | 963. | 4. | 1.4622[b] | 1.4602[b] | 51.62[b] | 51.43[b] | 51.23[b] | 6.900[b] | 6.876[b] | 6.848[b] | 0.8276[b] | 175.6 |

a See footnote a of Table 1a-E.    b For the undercooled liquid below the normal freezing point.

TABLE 8a-E (PART 1) – MONOOLEFINS, $C_2$ TO $C_5$
BOILING POINT, $dt/dp$, REFRACTIVE INDEX, DENSITY, AND FREEZING POINT
June 30, 1945; May 31, 1947; October 31, 1952

| Compound | Formula | Boiling Point 29.921 in Hg °F | $dt/dp$ 29.921 in Hg °F/in Hg | Refractive Index[a] $n_D$ 68°F | $n_D$ 77°F | Density[a] lb/cu ft 60°F | 68°F | 77°F | lb/gal 60°F | 68°F | 77°F | Specific Gravity[a] 60°F/60°F | Freezing Point In air at 1 atm °F |
|---|---|---|---|---|---|---|---|---|---|---|---|---|---|
| Ethene (Ethylene) | $C_2H_4$ | -154.68 | 1.02 | --- | --- | --- | --- | --- | --- | --- | --- | --- | -272.47[c] |
| Propene (Propylene) | $C_3H_6$ | -53.86 | 1.321 | | | 32.56[b] | 32.08[b] | 31.54[b] | 4.352[b] | 4.289[b] | 4.217[b] | 0.5220[b] | -301.45[c] |
| 1-Butene | $C_4H_8$ | +20.73 | 1.541 | --- | --- | 37.50[b] | 37.15[b] | 36.76[b] | 5.013[b] | 4.966[b] | 4.914[b] | 0.6013[b] | -301.63[c] |
| cis-2-Butene | " | 38.70 | 1.577 | --- | --- | 39.12[b] | 38.79[b] | 38.42[b] | 5.229[b] | 5.185[b] | 5.135[b] | 0.6272[b] | -218.04 |
| trans-2-Butene | " | 33.58 | 1.577 | --- | --- | 38.04[b] | 37.72[b] | 37.36[b] | 5.085[b] | 5.042[b] | 4.993[b] | 0.6100[b] | -157.99 |
| 2-Methylpropene (Isobutene) | " | 19.58 | 1.536 | --- | --- | 37.43[b] | 37.09[b] | 36.70[b] | 5.004[b] | 4.958[b] | 4.907[b] | 0.6002[b] | -220.63 |
| 1-Pentene | $C_5H_{10}$ | 85.94 | 1.737 | 1.37148 | 1.3683[b] | 40.27 | 39.984 | 39.661 | 5.384 | 5.3451 | 5.3020 | 0.6457 | -265.40 |
| cis-2-Pentene | " | 98.50 | 1.751 | 1.3830 | 1.3798 | 41.21 | 40.93 | 40.60 | 5.510 | 5.471 | 5.428 | 0.6408 | -240.50 |
| trans-2-Pentene | " | 97.42 | 1.748 | 1.3793 | 1.3761 | 40.75 | 40.46 | 40.15 | 5.447 | 5.409 | 5.367 | 0.6533 | -220.44 |
| 2-Methyl-1-butene | " | 88.09 | 1.727 | 1.3778 | 1.3746 | 40.90 | 40.60 | 40.27 | 5.467 | 5.428 | 5.384 | 0.6557 | -215.45 |
| 3-Methyl-1-butene | " | 68.11 | 1.701 | 1.3643 | --- | 39.45 | 39.15 | --- | 5.273 | 5.234 | --- | 0.6325 | -271.35 |
| 2-Methyl-2-butene | " | 101.42 | 1.757 | 1.3874 | 1.3842 | 41.64 | 41.35 | 41.01 | 5.566 | 5.527 | 5.483 | 0.6676 | -208.78 |

a See footnote a of Table 1a-E.  
b At saturation pressure.  
c At saturation pressure (triple point).

## TABLE 8a-E (PART 2) – MONOOLEFINS, $C_6$
### BOILING POINT, $dt/dp$, REFRACTIVE INDEX, DENSITY, AND FREEZING POINT
June 30, 1945; October 31, 1952

| Compound | Formula | Boiling Point 29.921 in Hg °F | $dt/dp$ 29.921 in Hg °F/in Hg | Refractive Index$^a$ $n_D$ 68°F | Refractive Index$^a$ $n_D$ 77°F | Density$^a$ lb/cu ft 60°F | Density$^a$ lb/cu ft 68°F | Density$^a$ lb/cu ft 77°F | Density$^a$ lb/gal 60°F | Density$^a$ lb/gal 68°F | Density$^a$ lb/gal 77°F | Specific Gravity$^a$ 60°F/60°F | Freezing Point In air at 1 atm °F |
|---|---|---|---|---|---|---|---|---|---|---|---|---|---|
| 1-Hexene | $C_6H_{12}$ | 146.27 | 1.897 | 1.38788 | 1.38502 | 42.28 | 42.024 | 41.731 | 5.653 | 5.6178 | 5.5786 | 0.6780 | -219.67 |
| cis-2-Hexene | " | 155.91 | 1.87 | 1.3977 | 1.3948 | 43.14 | 42.88 | 42.59 | 5.767 | 5.732 | 5.694 | 0.6916 | -222.04 |
| trans-2-Hexene | " | 154.17 | 1.87 | 1.3935 | 1.3907 | 42.61 | 42.35 | 42.06 | 5.696 | 5.661 | 5.623 | 0.6832 | -207.35 |
| cis-3-Hexene | " | 151.59 | 1.87 | 1.3947 | 1.3920 | 42.69 | 42.43 | 42.13 | 5.706 | 5.671 | 5.632 | 0.6845 | -216.08 |
| trans-3-Hexene | " | 152.74 | 1.87 | 1.3943 | 1.3916 | 42.54 | 42.28 | 41.98 | 5.686 | 5.651 | 5.612 | 0.6820 | -172.17 |
| 2-Methyl-1-pentene | " | 141.3 | 1.83 | 1.3915 | 1.3884 | 42.82 | 42.56 | 42.26 | 5.725 | 5.689 | 5.649 | 0.6867 | -212.37 |
| 3-Methyl-1-pentene | " | 129.45 | 1.83 | 1.3842 | 1.3814 | 41.93 | 41.67 | 41.38 | 5.605 | 5.570 | 5.531 | 0.6723 | -243.4 |
| 4-Methyl-1-pentene | " | 128.98 | 1.83 | 1.3828 | 1.3799 | 41.73 | 41.46 | 41.16 | 5.579 | 5.553 | 5.503 | 0.6691 | -244.53 |
| 2-Methyl-2-pentene | " | 153.12 | 1.87 | 1.4004 | 1.3976 | 43.11 | 42.84 | 42.54 | 5.763 | 5.727 | 5.687 | 0.6911 | -211.13 |
| 3-Methyl-cis-2-pentene | " | 158.81 | 1.87 | 1.4045 | 1.4018 | 43.86 | 43.61 | 43.34 | 5.863 | 5.830 | 5.793 | 0.7032 | -217.20 |
| 3-Methyl-trans-2-pentene | " | 153.73 | 1.87 | 1.4016 | 1.3989 | 43.58 | 43.34 | 43.06 | 5.826 | 5.793 | 5.757 | 0.6988 | -210.71 |
| 4-Methyl-cis-2-pentene | " | 133.33 | 1.83 | 1.3880 | 1.3849 | 42.03 | 41.76 | 41.46 | 5.619 | 5.582 | 5.543 | 0.6739 | -209.97 |
| 4-Methyl-trans-2-pentene | " | 137.39 | 1.83 | 1.3889 | 1.3859 | 42.01 | 41.74 | 41.45 | 5.615 | 5.580 | 5.540 | 0.6735 | -204.75 |
| 2-Ethyl-1-butene | " | 148.39 | 1.87 | 1.3969 | 1.3941 | 43.30 | 43.04 | 42.74 | 5.788 | 5.753 | 5.714 | 0.6943 | -251.09 |
| 2,3-Dimethyl-1-butene | " | 132.21 | 1.87 | 1.3904 | 1.3874 | 42.59 | 42.32 | 42.02 | 5.693 | 5.657 | 5.617 | 0.6828 | -220.0 |
| 3,3-Dimethyl-1-butene | " | 106.23 | 1.83 | 1.3760 | 1.3730 | 41.03 | 40.76 | 40.45 | 5.485 | 5.449 | 5.407 | 0.6579 | -175.36 |
| 2,3-Dimethyl-2-butene | " | 163.78 | 1.87 | 1.4122 | 1.4094 | 44.45 | 44.20 | 43.91 | 5.942 | 5.908 | 5.870 | 0.7127 | -101.70 |

$^a$ See footnote a of Table 1a-E.

TABLE 9a-E, Page 1 – MONOOLEFINS, C7

BOILING POINT, $dt/dp$, REFRACTIVE INDEX, DENSITY, AND FREEZING POINT

June 30, 1945; October 31, 1952

| Compound [b] | Formula | Boiling Point 29.921 in Hg (°F) | $dt/dp$ 29.921 in Hg (°F/in Hg) | Refractive Index [a] $n_D$ 68°F | $n_D$ 77°F | Density [a] lb/cu ft 60°F | 68°F | 77°F | lb/gal 60°F | 68°F | 77°F | Specific Gravity [a] 60°F/60°F | Freezing Point In air at 1 atm (°F) |
|---|---|---|---|---|---|---|---|---|---|---|---|---|---|
| 1-Heptene | $C_7H_{14}$ | 200.56 | 2.034 | 1.39980 | 1.39713 | 43.75 | 43.510 | 43.241 | 5.848 | 5.8165 | 5.7805 | 0.7015 | -182.25 |
| cis-2-Heptene | " | 209.3 | 2.01 | 1.406 | 1.403 | 44.4 | 44.2 | 43.9 | 5.94 | 5.91 | 5.88 | 0.712 | |
| trans-2-Heptene | " | 208.31 | 2.01 | 1.4045 | 1.4020 | 44.01 | 43.77 | 43.51 | 5.883 | 5.852 | 5.816 | 0.7057 | -165.06 |
| cis-3-Heptene | " | 204.35 | 2.01 | 1.4059 | 1.4033 | 44.12 | 43.89 | 43.62 | 5.898 | 5.867 | 5.831 | 0.7075 | |
| trans-3-Heptene | " | 204.21 | 2.01 | 1.4043 | 1.4017 | 43.82 | 43.58 | 43.31 | 5.858 | 5.826 | 5.790 | 0.7026 | -213.93 |
| 2-Methyl-1-hexene | " | 197.60 | 2.01 | 1.4034 | 1.4007 | 44.13 | 43.89 | 43.61 | 5.899 | 5.867 | 5.830 | 0.7076 | -153.11 |
| 3-Methyl-1-hexene | " | 183. | 2.01 | 1.397 | 1.394 | 43.6 | 43.4 | 43.1 | 5.83 | 5.80 | 5.77 | 0.699 | |
| 4-Methyl-1-hexene | " | 188.11 | 2.01 | 1.4000 | 1.3973 | 43.84 | 43.60 | 43.34 | 5.861 | 5.829 | 5.793 | 0.7030 | -222.61 |
| 5-Methyl-1-hexene | " | 185.56 | 2.01 | 1.3966 | 1.3940 | 43.44 | 43.20 | 42.92 | 5.807 | 5.775 | 5.738 | 0.6986 | |
| 2-Methyl-2-hexene | " | 203.74 | 2.01 | 1.4106 | 1.4079 | 44.45 | 44.21 | 43.94 | 5.943 | 5.910 | 5.873 | 0.7128 | -202.63 |
| 3-Methyl-cis-2-hexene { 3-Methyl-trans-2-hexene | " | 201. | 2.01 | 1.410 | 1.407 | 44.7 | 44.4 | 44.2 | 5.97 | 5.94 | 5.91 | 0.716 | |
| 4-Methyl-cis-2-hexene | " | 189.27 | 2.01 | 1.4024 | 1.3997 | 43.91 | 43.67 | 43.41 | 5.870 | 5.838 | 5.802 | 0.7041 | |
| 4-Methyl-trans-2-hexene | " | 189.7 | 2.01 | 1.4023 | 1.3997 | 43.78 | 43.54 | 43.27 | 5.853 | 5.821 | 5.785 | 0.7020 | -195.7 |
| 5-Methyl-cis-2-hexene | " | 196. | 2.01 | 1.400 | 1.397 | 43.9 | 43.7 | 43.4 | 5.87 | 5.84 | 5.81 | 0.704 | |
| 5-Methyl-trans-2-hexene | " | 187. | 2.01 | 1.400 | 1.397 | 43.9 | 43.7 | 43.4 | 5.87 | 5.84 | 5.81 | 0.704 | |
| 2-Methyl-cis-3-hexene { 2-Methyl-trans-3-hexene | " | 187. | 2.01 | 1.399 | 1.396 | 43.5 | 43.3 | 43.1 | 5.82 | 5.79 | 5.76 | 0.698 | |
| 3-Methyl-cis-3-hexene | " | 203.63 | 2.01 | 1.4123 | 1.4096 | 44.76 | 44.52 | 44.25 | 5.983 | 5.952 | 5.916 | 0.7177 | |
| 3-Methyl-trans-3-hexene | " | 200.39 | 2.01 | 1.4107 | 1.4080 | 44.55 | 44.32 | 44.05 | 5.956 | 5.924 | 5.888 | 0.7144 | |

[a] See footnote a of Table 1a-E.

[b] For completeness, all isomers are listed. However, where the data are inadequate, approximate values are given for mixtures of the cis and trans forms, as indicated by the braces.

TABLE 9a-E, Page 2 — MONOOLEFINS, C₇

BOILING POINT, dt/dp, REFRACTIVE INDEX, DENSITY, AND FREEZING POINT

June 30, 1945; October 31, 1952

| Compound [b] | Formula | Boiling Point 29.921 in Hg °F | dt/dp 29.921 in Hg °F/in Hg | Refractive Index[a] $n_D$ 68°F | Refractive Index[a] $n_D$ 77°F | Density[a] lb/cu ft 60°F | Density[a] lb/cu ft 68°F | Density[a] lb/cu ft 77°F | Density[a] lb/gal 60°F | Density[a] lb/gal 68°F | Density[a] lb/gal 77°F | Specific Gravity[a] 60°F/60°F | Freezing Point In air at 1 atm °F |
|---|---|---|---|---|---|---|---|---|---|---|---|---|---|
| 2-Ethyl-1-pentene | C₇H₁₄ | 201. | 2.01 | 1.405 | 1.402 | 44.4 | 44.2 | 43.9 | 5.94 | 5.91 | 5.88 | 0.712 | |
| 3-Ethyl-1-pentene | " | 185.23 | 2.01 | 1.3980 | 1.3954 | 43.71 | 43.46 | 43.18 | 5.843 | 5.810 | 5.772 | 0.7009 | -197.32 |
| 2,3-Dimethyl-1-pentene | " | 183.67 | 2.01 | 1.4033 | 1.4007 | 44.25 | 44.02 | 43.75 | 5.916 | 5.884 | 5.848 | 0.7096 | -210.6 |
| 2,4-Dimethyl-1-pentene | " | 178.95 | 2.01 | 1.3986 | 1.3959 | 43.59 | 43.34 | 43.06 | 5.827 | 5.794 | 5.757 | 0.6990 | -190.8 |
| 3,3-Dimethyl-1-pentene | " | 171.57 | 2.01 | 1.3984 | 1.3958 | 43.77 | 43.54 | 43.27 | 5.851 | 5.820 | 5.785 | 0.7018 | -209.7 |
| 3,4-Dimethyl-1-pentene | " | 178. | 2.01 | 1.3995 | 1.3969 | 44.0 | 43.8 | 43.5 | 5.88 | 5.85 | 5.82 | 0.705 | |
| 4,4-Dimethyl-1-pentene | " | 162.48 | 2.01 | 1.3918 | 1.3892 | 42.85 | 42.62 | 42.36 | 5.728 | 5.697 | 5.662 | 0.6871 | -213.88 |
| 3-Ethyl-2-pentene | " | 204.82 | 2.01 | 1.4148 | 1.4122 | 45.22 | 44.97 | 44.69 | 6.045 | 6.012 | 5.974 | 0.7251 | |
| 2,3-Dimethyl-2-pentene | " | 207.43 | 2.01 | 1.4208 | 1.4182 | 45.67 | 45.43 | 45.16 | 6.105 | 6.073 | 6.037 | 0.7322 | -180.9 |
| 2,4-Dimethyl-2-pentene | " | 182.19 | 2.01 | 1.4040 | 1.4013 | 43.65 | 43.42 | 43.15 | 5.836 | 5.804 | 5.768 | 0.7000 | |
| 3,4-Dimethyl-cis-2-pentene | " | 189. | 2.01 | 1.407 | 1.404 | 44.7 | 44.5 | 44.3 | 5.98 | 5.95 | 5.92 | 0.717 | |
| 3,4-Dimethyl-trans-2-pentene | " | | 2.01 | | | | | | | | | | |
| 4,4-Dimethyl-cis-2-pentene | " | 176.76 | 2.01 | 1.4024 | 1.3998 | 43.92 | 43.67 | 43.40 | 5.871 | 5.838 | 5.802 | 0.7042 | -211.83 |
| 4,4-Dimethyl-trans-2-pentene | " | 170.15 | 2.01 | 1.3982 | 1.3953 | 43.25 | 43.01 | 42.73 | 5.782 | 5.749 | 5.712 | 0.6935 | -175.42 |
| 3-Methyl-2-ethyl-1-butene | " | 192. | 2.01 | 1.410 | 1.407 | 44.9 | 44.6 | 44.4 | 6.00 | 5.97 | 5.93 | 0.719 | |
| 2,3,3-Trimethyl-1-butene | " | 172.17 | 2.06 | 1.4029 | 1.4000 | 44.26 | 44.01 | 43.73 | 5.913 | 5.883 | 5.846 | 0.7097 | -165.73 |

[a] See footnote a of Table 1a-E.

[b] See footnote b of Table 9a-E, Page 1.

TABLE 10a-E, Page 1 - MONOOLEFINS, C$_8$

BOILING POINT, dt/dp, REFRACTIVE INDEX, DENSITY, AND FREEZING POINT

June 30, 1945; October 31, 1952

| Compound [b] | Formula | Boiling Point 29.921 in Hg (°F) | dt/dp 29.921 in Hg (°F/in Hg) | Refractive Index [a] 68°F ($n_D$) | Refractive Index [a] 77°F ($n_D$) | Density [a] 60°F (lb/cu ft) | Density [a] 68°F (lb/cu ft) | Density [a] 77°F (lb/cu ft) | Density [a] 60°F (lb/gal) | Density [a] 68°F (lb/gal) | Density [a] 77°F (lb/gal) | Specific Gravity [a] 60°F/60°F | Freezing Point In air at 1 atm (°F) |
|---|---|---|---|---|---|---|---|---|---|---|---|---|---|
| 1-Octene | C$_8$H$_{16}$ | 250.30 | 2.153 | 1.40870 | 1.40620 | 44.86 | 44.630 | 44.376 | 5.996 | 5.9662 | 5.9322 | 0.7194 | -151.12 |
| cis-2-Octene | " | 258.15 | 2.10 | 1.4150 | 1.4125 | 45.45 | 45.22 | 44.95 | 6.075 | 6.044 | 6.009 | 0.7287 | -148.4 |
| trans-2-Octene | " | 257.0 | 2.10 | 1.4132 | 1.4107 | 45.17 | 44.94 | 44.68 | 6.039 | 6.008 | 5.973 | 0.7243 | -125.9 |
| cis-3-Octene | " | 253.2 | 2.10 | 1.4135 | 1.4111 | 45.2 | 45.0 | 44.8 | 6.05 | 6.02 | 5.98 | 0.725 | -166. |
| trans-3-Octene | " | 253.9 | 2.10 | 1.4126 | 1.4102 | 44.88 | 44.65 | 44.39 | 5.999 | 5.969 | 5.933 | 0.7196 | -181.7 |
| cis-4-Octene | " | 252.57 | 2.10 | 1.4148 | 1.4124 | 45.25 | 45.02 | 44.76 | 6.049 | 6.019 | 5.984 | 0.7256 | -136.86 |
| trans-4-Octene | " | 252.05 | 2.10 | 1.4118 | 1.4093 | 44.81 | 44.58 | 44.32 | 5.990 | 5.959 | 5.924 | 0.7185 | -130.0 |
| 2-Methyl-1-heptene | " | 246.7 | 2.10 | 1.4123 | 1.4098 | 45.20 | 44.98 | 44.72 | 6.043 | 6.013 | 5.979 | 0.7248 | |
| 3-Methyl-1-heptene | " | 232. | 2.06 | 1.406 | 1.404 | 44.6 | 44.4 | 44.1 | 5.96 | 5.93 | 5.90 | 0.715 | |
| 4-Methyl-1-heptene | " | 235.0 | 2.06 | 1.410 | 1.408 | 45.0 | 44.8 | 44.5 | 6.01 | 5.98 | 5.95 | 0.721 | |
| 5-Methyl-1-heptene | " | 235.9 | 2.06 | 1.4094 | 1.4069 | 44.95 | 44.72 | 44.46 | 6.009 | 5.979 | 5.943 | 0.7208 | |
| 6-Methyl-1-heptene | " | 235.8 | 2.06 | 1.4070 | 1.4045 | 44.67 | 44.45 | 44.19 | 5.972 | 5.942 | 5.908 | 0.7163 | |
| 2-Methyl-2-heptene | " | 252.7 | 2.10 | 1.4170 | 1.4145 | 45.43 | 45.20 | 44.95 | 6.073 | 6.043 | 6.009 | 0.7284 | |
| 3-Methyl-cis-2-heptene | " | 252. | 2.10 | 1.419 | 1.417 | 45.7 | 45.5 | 45.3 | 6.11 | 6.08 | 6.05 | 0.733 | |
| 3-Methyl-trans-2-heptene | " | | | | | | | | | | | | |
| 4-Methyl-cis-2-heptene | " | 237. | 2.06 | 1.410 | 1.408 | 44.9 | 44.7 | 44.4 | 6.01 | 5.98 | 5.94 | 0.720 | |
| 4-Methyl-trans-2-heptene | " | | | | | | | | | | | | |
| 5-Methyl-cis-2-heptene | " | 244. | 2.10 | 1.414 | 1.412 | 45.4 | 45.1 | 44.9 | 6.06 | 6.03 | 6.00 | 0.727 | |
| 5-Methyl-trans-2-heptene | " | | | | | | | | | | | | |
| 6-Methyl-cis-2-heptene | " | 243. | 2.10 | 1.412 | 1.410 | 45.0 | 44.8 | 44.6 | 6.02 | 5.99 | 5.96 | 0.722 | |
| 6-Methyl-trans-2-heptene | " | | | | | | | | | | | | |
| 2-Methyl-cis-3-heptene | " | 234. | 2.06 | 1.407 | 1.405 | 44.3 | 44.1 | 43.8 | 5.92 | 5.89 | 5.86 | 0.710 | |
| 2-Methyl-trans-3-heptene | " | | | | | | | | | | | | |

a See footnote a of Table 1a-E.    b See footnote b of Table 9a-E.

TABLE 10a-E, Page 2 — MONOOLEFINS, C$_8$

## BOILING POINT, $dt/dp$, REFRACTIVE INDEX, DENSITY, AND FREEZING POINT

June 30, 1945; October 31, 1952

| Compound [b] | Formula [a] | Boiling Point 29.921 in Hg (°F) | $dt/dp$ 29.921 in Hg (°F/in Hg) | Refractive Index [a] $n_D$ 68°F | $n_D$ 77°F | Density [a] 60°F (lb/cu ft) | 68°F (lb/cu ft) | 77°F (lb/cu ft) | 60°F (lb/gal) | 68°F (lb/gal) | 77°F (lb/gal) | Specific Gravity [a] 60°F/60°F | Freezing Point In air at 1 atm (°F) |
|---|---|---|---|---|---|---|---|---|---|---|---|---|---|
| 3-Methyl-*cis*-3-heptene | C$_8$H$_{16}$ | 250. | 2.10 | 1.418 | 1.416 | 45.7 | 45.4 | 45.2 | 6.11 | 6.08 | 6.04 | 0.732 | |
| 3-Methyl-*trans*-3-heptene | " | (250.) | | | | | | | | | | | |
| 4-Methyl-*cis*-3-heptene | " | 252. | 2.10 | 1.417 | 1.415 | 45.5 | 45.3 | 45.1 | 6.08 | 6.05 | 6.02 | 0.729 | |
| 4-Methyl-*trans*-3-heptene | " | (252.) | | | | | | | | | | | |
| 5-Methyl-*cis*-3-heptene | " | 234. | 2.06 | 1.410 | 1.408 | 44.7 | 44.5 | 44.3 | 5.98 | 5.95 | 5.92 | 0.717 | |
| 5-Methyl-*trans*-3-heptene | " | (234.) | | | | | | | | | | | |
| 6-Methyl-*cis*-3-heptene | " | 239. | 2.06 | 1.410 | 1.408 | 44.7 | 44.5 | 44.3 | 5.98 | 5.95 | 5.92 | 0.717 | |
| 6-Methyl-*trans*-3-heptene | " | (239.) | | | | | | | | | | | |
| 2-Ethyl-1-hexene | " | 248. | 2.10 | 1.4157 | 1.4132 | 45.62 | 45.38 | 45.12 | 6.098 | 6.067 | 6.032 | 0.7314 | |
| 3-Ethyl-1-hexene | " | 230.5 | 2.10 | 1.407 | 1.405 | 44.9 | 44.6 | 44.4 | 6.00 | 5.97 | 5.93 | 0.719 | |
| 4-Ethyl-1-hexene | " | 235. | 2.10 | 1.412 | 1.410 | 45.5 | 45.3 | 45.1 | 6.09 | 6.06 | 6.03 | 0.730 | |
| 2,3-Dimethyl-1-hexene | " | 230.9 | 2.10 | 1.4113 | 1.4089 | 45.27 | 45.03 | 44.77 | 6.051 | 6.020 | 5.985 | 0.7321 | |
| 2,4-Dimethyl-1-hexene | " | 232.2 | 2.10 | 1.411 | 1.409 | 45.2 | 44.9 | 44.7 | 6.04 | 6.01 | 5.98 | 0.724 | |
| 2,5-Dimethyl-1-hexene | " | 232.9 | 2.10 | 1.4105 | 1.4080 | 45.01 | 44.77 | 44.50 | 6.017 | 5.985 | 5.949 | 0.7217 | |
| 3,3-Dimethyl-1-hexene | " | 219. | 2.10 | 1.4070 | 1.4046 | 44.80 | 44.57 | 44.32 | 5.989 | 5.958 | 5.924 | 0.7183 | |
| 3,4-Dimethyl-1-hexene | " | 234. | 2.10 | 1.413 | 1.411 | 45.4 | 45.2 | 44.9 | 6.07 | 6.04 | 6.01 | 0.728 | |
| 3,5-Dimethyl-1-hexene | " | 219. | 2.06 | 1.404 | 1.402 | 44.4 | 44.2 | 43.9 | 5.94 | 5.91 | 5.88 | 0.712 | |
| 4,4-Dimethyl-1-hexene | " | 225.0 | 2.10 | 1.4102 | 1.4078 | 45.16 | 44.93 | 44.68 | 6.037 | 6.007 | 5.973 | 0.7241 | |
| 4,5-Dimethyl-1-hexene | " | 228. | 2.10 | 1.414 | 1.412 | 45.7 | 45.4 | 45.2 | 6.10 | 6.07 | 6.04 | 0.732 | |
| 5,5-Dimethyl-1-hexene | " | 216.5 | 2.15 | 1.4049 | 1.4024 | 44.5 | 44.3 | 44.0 | 5.95 | 5.92 | 5.88 | 0.713 | |
| 3-Ethyl-*cis*-2-hexene | " | 250. | 2.10 | 1.424 | 1.422 | 46.2 | 46.0 | 45.8 | 6.18 | 6.15 | 6.12 | 0.741 | |
| 3-Ethyl-*trans*-2-hexene | " | (250.) | | | | | | | | | | | |
| 4-Ethyl-*cis*-2-hexene | " | 235. | 2.10 | 1.412 | 1.410 | 45.5 | 45.3 | 45.0 | 6.08 | 6.05 | 6.02 | 0.729 | |
| 4-Ethyl-*trans*-2-hexene | " | (235.) | | | | | | | | | | | |

a See footnote a of Table 1a-E.  b See footnote b of Table 9a-E.

TABLE 10a–E, Page 3 – MONOOLEFINS, $C_8$

BOILING POINT, *dt/dp*, REFRACTIVE INDEX, DENSITY, AND FREEZING POINT

June 30, 1945; October 31, 1952

| Compound [b] | Formula | Boiling Point 29.921 in Hg (°F) | *dt/dp* 29.921 in Hg (°F/in Hg) | Refractive Index [a] 68°F ($n_D$) | 77°F ($n_D$) | Density [a] lb/cu ft 60°F | lb/cu ft 68°F | lb/cu ft 77°F | lb/gal 60°F | lb/gal 68°F | lb/gal 77°F | Specific Gravity [a] 60°F/60°F | Freezing Point In air at 1 atm (°F) |
|---|---|---|---|---|---|---|---|---|---|---|---|---|---|
| 2,3-Dimethyl-2-hexene | $C_8H_{16}$ | 251.19 | 2.10 | 1.4268 | 1.4244 | 46.48 | 46.25 | 45.98 | 6.213 | 6.182 | 6.147 | 0.7452 | −175.2 |
| 2,4-Dimethyl-2-hexene | " | 231.1 | 2.15 | 1.4118 | 1.4094 | 45.26 | 45.03 | 44.77 | 6.050 | 6.019 | 5.984 | 0.7257 | |
| 2,5-Dimethyl-2-hexene | " | 234.0 | 2.06 | 1.4140 | 1.4115 | 45.2 | 44.9 | 44.7 | 6.04 | 6.01 | 5.98 | 0.724 | |
| 3,4-Dimethyl-cis-2-hexene / 3,4-Dimethyl-trans-2-hexene | " | 241. | 2.10 | 1.418 | 1.416 | 46.2 | 46.0 | 45.8 | 6.18 | 6.15 | 6.12 | 0.741 | |
| 3,5-Dimethyl-cis-2-hexene / 3,5-Dimethyl-trans-2-hexene | " | 234. | 2.06 | 1.416 | 1.414 | 45.5 | 45.3 | 45.0 | 6.08 | 6.05 | 6.02 | 0.729 | |
| 4,4-Dimethyl-cis-2-hexene / 4,4-Dimethyl-trans-2-hexene | " | 223. | 2.10 | 1.413 | 1.411 | 45.3 | 45.1 | 44.8 | 6.06 | 6.03 | 5.99 | 0.726 | |
| 4,5-Dimethyl-cis-2-hexene / 4,5-Dimethyl-trans-2-hexene | " | 230. | 2.10 | 1.413 | 1.411 | 45.5 | 45.3 | 45.0 | 6.08 | 6.05 | 6.02 | 0.729 | |
| 5,5-Dimethyl-cis-2-hexene | " | 224.4 | 2.15 | 1.4113 | 1.4088 | 45.00 | 44.75 | 44.48 | 6.015 | 5.983 | 5.946 | 0.7215 | |
| 5,5-Dimethyl-trans-2-hexene | " | 219.4 | 2.10 | 1.4055 | 1.4030 | 44.35 | 44.11 | 43.84 | 5.928 | 5.897 | 5.861 | 0.7111 | |
| 3-Ethyl-3-hexene | " | 241. | 2.10 | 1.418 | 1.416 | 45.7 | 45.5 | 45.3 | 6.11 | 6.08 | 6.05 | 0.733 | |
| 2,2-Dimethyl-cis-3-hexene | " | 221.77 | 2.06 | 1.4099 | 1.4074 | 44.73 | 44.50 | 44.24 | 5.979 | 5.948 | 5.913 | 0.7172 | −215.23 |
| 2,2-Dimethyl-trans-3-hexene | " | 213.53 | 2.06 | 1.4063 | 1.4037 | 44.19 | 43.94 | 43.67 | 5.907 | 5.874 | 5.837 | 0.7085 | |
| 2,3-Dimethyl-cis-3-hexene / 2,3-Dimethyl-trans-3-hexene | " | 237. | 2.10 | 1.416 | 1.414 | 45.7 | 45.4 | 45.2 | 6.11 | 6.08 | 6.04 | 0.732 | |
| 2,4-Dimethyl-cis-3-hexene | " | 228.2 | 2.06 | 1.4140 | 1.4114 | 45.05 | 44.81 | 44.54 | 6.022 | 5.990 | 5.954 | 0.7223 | |
| 2,4-Dimethyl-trans-3-hexene | " | 225.7 | 2.10 | 1.4126 | 1.4101 | 44.85 | 44.60 | 44.33 | 5.995 | 5.963 | 5.926 | 0.7191 | |
| 2,5-Dimethyl-cis-3-hexene / 2,5-Dimethyl-trans-3-hexene | " | 216. | 2.06 | 1.406 | 1.404 | 44.5 | 44.3 | 44.1 | 5.96 | 5.93 | 5.89 | 0.714 | |
| 3,4-Dimethyl-cis-3-hexene / 3,4-Dimethyl-trans-3-hexene | " | 252. | 2.10 | 1.430 | 1.428 | 46.9 | 46.6 | 46.4 | 6.26 | 6.23 | 6.20 | 0.751 | |

[a] See footnote a of Table 1a–E.

[b] See footnote b of Table 9a–E.

TABLE 10a-E, Page 4 — MONOOLEFINS, $C_8$

BOILING POINT, $dt/dp$, REFRACTIVE INDEX, DENSITY, AND FREEZING POINT

June 30, 1945; October 31, 1952

| Compound[b] | Formula[a] | Boiling Point 29.921 in Hg (°F) | dt/dp 29.921 in Hg (°F/in Hg) | Refractive Index[a] 68°F ($n_D$) | Refractive Index[a] 77°F ($n_D$) | Density[a] lb/cu ft 60°F | Density[a] lb/cu ft 68°F | Density[a] lb/cu ft 77°F | Density[a] lb/gal 60°F | Density[a] lb/gal 68°F | Density[a] lb/gal 77°F | Specific Gravity[a] 60°F/60°F | Freezing Point In air at 1 atm (°F) |
|---|---|---|---|---|---|---|---|---|---|---|---|---|---|
| 2-n-Propyl-1-pentene | $C_8H_{16}$ | 243.9 | 2.10 | 1.4136 | 1.4111 | 45.43 | 45.20 | 44.93 | 6.073 | 6.042 | 6.007 | 0.7284 | |
| 2-Isopropyl-1-pentene | " | 235. | 2.10 | 1.414 | 1.412 | 45.5 | 45.3 | 45.0 | 6.08 | 6.05 | 6.02 | 0.729 | |
| 3-Methyl-2-ethyl-1-pentene | " | 234.5 | 2.10 | 1.4142 | 1.4118 | 45.7 | 45.5 | 45.2 | 6.11 | 6.08 | 6.05 | 0.733 | |
| 4-Methyl-2-ethyl-1-pentene | " | 230.5 | 2.10 | 1.4105 | 1.4080 | 45.15 | 44.92 | 44.65 | 6.036 | 6.004 | 5.969 | 0.7240 | |
| 2-Methyl-3-ethyl-1-pentene | " | 230. | 2.10 | 1.415 | 1.413 | 45.8 | 45.6 | 45.3 | 6.12 | 6.09 | 6.06 | 0.734 | |
| 3-Methyl-3-ethyl-1-pentene | " | 234. | 2.15 | 1.418 | 1.416 | 45.83 | 45.60 | 45.35 | 6.126 | 6.096 | 6.062 | 0.7348 | |
| 4-Methyl-3-ethyl-1-pentene | " | 225.5 | 2.15 | 1.4097 | 1.4072 | 45.18 | 44.94 | 44.68 | 6.039 | 6.009 | 5.974 | 0.7244 | -92. |
| 2,3,3-Trimethyl-1-pentene | " | 226.96 | 2.15 | 1.4174 | 1.4151 | 46.14 | 45.90 | 45.62 | 6.168 | 6.135 | 6.099 | 0.7398 | |
| 2,3,4-Trimethyl-1-pentene | " | 226. | 2.10 | 1.415 | 1.413 | 45.7 | 45.5 | 45.3 | 6.11 | 6.08 | 6.05 | 0.733 | |
| 2,4,4-Trimethyl-1-pentene | " | 214.59 | 2.10 | 1.4086 | 1.4060 | 44.87 | 44.64 | 44.37 | 5.998 | 5.967 | 5.932 | 0.7194 | -136.26 |
| 3,3,4-Trimethyl-1-pentene | " | 221. | 2.15 | 1.4144 | 1.4120 | 45.7 | 45.5 | 45.3 | 6.11 | 6.08 | 6.05 | 0.733 | |
| 3,4,4-Trimethyl-1-pentene | " | 219. | 2.10 | 1.412 | 1.410 | 45.1 | 44.9 | 44.6 | 6.03 | 6.00 | 5.97 | 0.723 | |
| 2-Methyl-3-ethyl-2-pentene | " | 242.6 | 2.10 | 1.4247 | 1.4222 | 46.4 | 46.1 | 45.9 | 6.20 | 6.17 | 6.13 | 0.743 | |
| 4-Methyl-3-ethyl-cis-2-pentene | " | 241. | 2.15 | 1.424 | 1.422 | 46.4 | 46.1 | 45.9 | 6.20 | 6.17 | 6.13 | 0.743 | |
| 4-Methyl-3-ethyl-trans-2-pentene | " | 237.7 | 2.15 | 1.4210 | 1.4183 | 46.11 | 45.88 | 45.62 | 6.165 | 6.134 | 6.099 | 0.7394 | |
| 2,3,4-Trimethyl-2-pentene | " | 241.27 | 2.10 | 1.4275 | 1.4249 | 46.65 | 46.41 | 46.14 | 6.236 | 6.204 | 6.168 | 0.7479 | -171.9 |
| 2,4,4-Trimethyl-2-pentene | " | 220.84 | 2.15 | 1.4160 | 1.4135 | 45.29 | 45.06 | 44.80 | 6.054 | 6.024 | 5.989 | 0.7262 | -159.39 |
| 3,4,4-Trimethyl-cis-2-pentene | " | 234. | 2.10 | 1.423 | 1.421 | 46.4 | 46.1 | 45.9 | 6.20 | 6.17 | 6.13 | 0.743 | |
| 3,4,4-Trimethyl-trans-2-pentene | " | | | | | | | | | | | | |
| 3-Methyl-2-isopropyl-1-butene | " | 219. | 2.10 | 1.4085 | 1.4061 | 45.3 | 45.1 | 44.8 | 6.06 | 6.03 | 5.99 | 0.726 | |
| 3,3-Dimethyl-2-ethyl-1-butene | " | 230. | 2.10 | 1.4159 | 1.4135 | 45.7 | 45.4 | 45.2 | 6.11 | 6.08 | 6.04 | 0.732 | |

a See footnote a of Table 1a-E.

b See footnote b of Table 9a-E.

TABLE 11a-E (PART 1) – DIOLEFINS, $C_3$ TO $C_5$

BOILING POINT, $dt/dp$, REFRACTIVE INDEX, DENSITY, AND FREEZING POINT

June 30, 1945; September 30, 1951; October 31, 1952

| Compound | Formula | Boiling Point 29.921 in Hg °F | $dt/dp$ 29.921 in Hg °F/in Hg | Refractive Index[a] $n_D$ 68°F | $n_D$ 77°F | Density[a] lb/cu ft 60°F | 68°F | 77°F | lb/gal 60°F | 68°F | 77°F | Specific Gravity[a] 60°F/60°F | Freezing Point In air at 1 atm °F |
|---|---|---|---|---|---|---|---|---|---|---|---|---|---|
| Propadiene (Allene) | $C_3H_4$ | -30.1 | 1.51 | ----- | ----- | ----- | ----- | ----- | ----- | ----- | ----- | ----- | -213. |
| 1,2-Butadiene | $C_4H_6$ | +51.53 | 1.60 | ----- | ----- | 41.0b | 40.7b | 40.3b | 5.49b | 5.44b | 5.39b | 0.658b | -213.14 |
| 1,3-Butadiene | " | 24.06 | 1.544 | ----- | ----- | 39.12b | 38.77b | 38.39b | 5.229b | 5.183b | 5.131b | 0.6272b | -164.05 |
| 1,2-Pentadiene | $C_5H_8$ | 112.74 | 1.768 | 1.42091 | 1.41773 | 43.51 | 43.235 | 42.925 | 5.816 | 5.7796 | 5.7382 | 0.6977 | -215.07 |
| 1,cis-3-Pentadiene | " | 111.32 | 1.772 | 1.43634 | 1.43291 | 43.42 | 43.138 | 42.820 | 5.804 | 5.7667 | 5.7242 | 0.6962 | -221.48 |
| 1,trans-3-Pentadiene | " | 107.66 | 1.773 | 1.43008 | 1.42669 | 42.48 | 42.202 | 41.889 | 5.679 | 5.6416 | 5.5998 | 0.6811 | -125.45 |
| 1,4-Pentadiene | " | 78.74 | 1.701 | 1.38876 | 1.38542 | 41.53 | 41.249 | 40.934 | 5.552 | 5.5142 | 5.4720 | 0.6659 | -234.90 |
| 2,3-Pentadiene | " | 118.88 | 1.770 | 1.42842 | 1.42509 | 43.67 | 43.388 | 43.074 | 5.837 | 5.8001 | 5.7582 | 0.7002 | -194.17 |
| 3-Methyl-1,2-butadiene | " | 104. | 2. | 1.410 | 1.407 | 42.7 | 42.5 | 42.1 | 5.71 | 5.67 | 5.63 | 0.685 | |
| 2-Methyl-1,3-butadiene (Isoprene) | " | 93.32 | 1.746 | 1.42194 | 1.41852 | 42.79 | 42.509 | 42.192 | 5.720 | 5.6827 | 5.6403 | 0.6861 | -230.71 |

a See footnote a of Table 1a-E.   b At saturation pressure.

TABLE 11a-E (PART 2) – DIOLEFINS, C₆

BOILING POINT, $dt/dp$, REFRACTIVE INDEX, DENSITY, AND FREEZING POINT

June 30, 1945; October 31, 1952

| Compound [b] | Formula | Boiling Point 29.921 in Hg °F | $dt/dp$ 29.921 in Hg °F/in Hg | Refractive Index [a] $n_D$ 68°F | $n_D$ 77°F | Density [a] lb/cu ft 60°F | 68°F | 77°F | Density [a] lb/gal 60°F | 68°F | 77°F | Specific Gravity [a] 60°F/60°F | Freezing Point In air at 1 atm °F |
|---|---|---|---|---|---|---|---|---|---|---|---|---|---|
| 1,2-Hexadiene | $C_6H_{10}$ | 169. | 2.01 | 1.4282 | 1.4252 | 44.89 | 44.63 | 44.34 | 6.001 | 5.966 | 5.927 | 0.7198 | |
| 1,cis-3-Hexadiene | " | 163. | 1.97 | 1.438 | 1.435 | 44.3 | 44.0 | 43.7 | 5.92 | 5.88 | 5.84 | 0.710 | |
| 1,trans-3-Hexadiene | " | 149.0 | 1.92 | 1.415 | 1.412 | 43.9 | 43.7 | 43.4 | 5.88 | 5.84 | 5.80 | 0.705 | |
| 1,cis-4-Hexadiene | " | 139.03 | 1.92 | 1.4042 | 1.4010 | 43.47 | 43.22 | 42.94 | 5.811 | 5.777 | 5.740 | 0.6970 | |
| 1,trans-4-Hexadiene | " | 154.4 | 1.97 | 1.395 | 1.392 | 42.7 | 42.4 | 42.1 | 5.71 | 5.67 | 5.63 | 0.685 | -221.22 |
| 1,5-Hexadiene | " | 176. | 2.01 | 1.450 | 1.447 | 45.2 | 44.9 | 44.6 | 6.05 | 6.01 | 5.97 | 0.725 | |
| 2,3-Hexadiene | " | 158. | 1.97 | 1.425 | 1.422 | 44.9 | 44.6 | 44.3 | 6.00 | 5.97 | 5.93 | 0.720 | |
| cis-2,cis-4-Hexadiene } | " | 158. | 1.97 | 1.424 | 1.421 | 44.5 | 44.2 | 43.9 | 5.95 | 5.91 | 5.87 | 0.713 | |
| cis-2,trans-4-Hexadiene } | " | | | | | | | | | | | | |
| trans-2,trans-4-Hexadiene } | " | | | | | | | | | | | | |
| 3-Methyl-1,2-pentadiene | " | 169. | 2.01 | 1.446 | 1.443 | 45.2 | 44.9 | 44.6 | 6.04 | 6.00 | 5.96 | 0.724 | |
| 4-Methyl-1,2-pentadiene | " | 171. | 2.01 | 1.452 | 1.449 | 46.2 | 45.9 | 45.6 | 6.17 | 6.13 | 6.09 | 0.740 | |
| 2-Methyl-1,cis-3-pentadiene } | " | 169.3 | 2.01 | 1.451 | 1.448 | 45.2 | 44.9 | 44.6 | 6.04 | 6.00 | 5.96 | 0.724 | |
| 2-Methyl-1,trans-3-pentadiene } | " | | | | | | | | | | | | |
| 3-Methyl-1,cis-3-pentadiene } | " | 133. | 1.67 | 1.405 | 1.402 | 43.6 | 43.3 | 43.0 | 5.83 | 5.79 | 5.75 | 0.699 | |
| 3-Methyl-1,trans-3-pentadiene } | " | | | | | | | | | | | | |
| 4-Methyl-1,3-pentadiene | " | 131. | 1.87 | 1.405 | 1.402 | 43.7 | 43.4 | 43.1 | 5.84 | 5.80 | 5.76 | 0.700 | |
| 2-Methyl-1,4-pentadiene | " | 162. | 1.97 | 1.425 | 1.422 | 44.7 | 44.4 | 44.1 | 5.97 | 5.93 | 5.89 | 0.716 | |
| 3-Methyl-1,4-pentadiene | " | 167. | 2.01 | 1.445 | 1.442 | 45.0 | 44.8 | 44.4 | 6.02 | 5.98 | 5.94 | 0.722 | |
| 2-Methyl-2,3-pentadiene | " | | | | | | | | | | | | |
| 2-Ethyl-1,3-butadiene | " | | | | | | | | | | | | |
| 2,3-Dimethyl-1,3-butadiene | " | 155.60 | 1.97 | 1.4394 | 1.4362 | 45.62 | 45.37 | 45.08 | 6.098 | 6.064 | 6.027 | 0.7314 | -104.81 |

a See footnote a of Table 1a-E.   b See footnote b of Table 9a-E.

TABLE 1a3-E – ALKYL CYCLOPENTENES, C$_5$ TO C$_7$

BOILING POINT, $dt/dp$, REFRACTIVE INDEX, DENSITY, AND FREEZING POINT

October 31, 1950; October 31, 1952

| Compound | Formula | Boiling Point 29.921 in Hg °F | $dt/dp$ 29.921 in Hg °F/in Hg | Refractive Index[a] $n_D$ 68°F | $n_D$ 77°F | Density[a] lb/cu ft 600F | lb/cu ft 68°F | lb/cu ft 77°F | lb/gal 600F | lb/gal 68°F | lb/gal 77°F | Specific Gravity[a] 60°F/60°F | Freezing Point In air at 1 atm °F |
|---|---|---|---|---|---|---|---|---|---|---|---|---|---|
| Cyclopentene | C$_5$H$_8$ | 111.64 | 1.796 | 1.42246 | 1.41940 | 48.49 | 48.193 | 47.852 | 6.482 | 6.4424 | 6.3969 | 0.7775 | -211.14 |
| 1-Methylcyclopentene | C$_6$H$_{10}$ | 188.4 | 1.97 | 1.4330 | 1.4302 | 48.98 | 48.71 | 48.39 | 6.548 | 6.511 | 6.4692 | 0.7854 | -197. |
| 3-Methylcyclopentene | " | 149.0 | 1.91 | 1.4207 | 1.4179 | 47.86 | 47.58 | 47.27 | 6.397 | 6.361 | 6.319 | 0.7673 | |
| 4-Methylcyclopentene | " | 167.4 | 1.97 | 1.430b | 1.4278 | 48.94 | 48.67 | 48.3b | 6.543 | 6.50b | 6.465 | 0.7848 | |
| 1-Ethylcyclopentene | C$_7$H$_{12}$ | 223.3 | 2.14 | 1.4410 | 1.4384 | 50.08 | 49.83 | 49.54 | 6.695 | 6.661 | 6.623 | 0.8031 | -181.1 |
| 3-Ethylcyclopentene | " | 208.6 | 2.09 | 1.4319 | 1.4293 | 49.14 | 48.88 | 48.59 | 6.569 | 6.534 | 6.496 | 0.7879 | |
| 4-Ethylcyclopentene | " | 223. | 2.1 | 1.440 | 1.437 | 50.1 | 49.3 | 49.5 | 6.69 | 6.66 | 6.62 | 0.803 | |
| 1,2-Dimethylcyclopentene | " | 222.4 | 2.14 | 1.4448 | 1.4420 | 50.06 | 49.79 | 49.49 | 6.692 | 6.656 | 6.616 | 0.8027 | -130.7 |
| 1,3-Dimethylcyclopentene | " | 198. | 2.1 | 1.428 | 1.425 | 48.1 | 47.8 | 47.5 | 6.43 | 6.39 | 6.35 | 0.771 | |
| 1,4-Dimethylcyclopentene | " | 199.8 | 2.1 | 1.4283 | 1.4255 | 48.9 | 48.6 | 48.3 | 6.53 | 6.50 | 6.46 | 0.784 | |
| 1,5-Dimethylcyclopentene | " | 216. | 2.1 | 1.4331 | 1.4304 | 48.9 | 48.7 | 48.4 | 6.54 | 6.51 | 6.47 | 0.785 | -180. |
| 3,3-Dimethylcyclopentene | " | 190. | 2.1 | 1.423 | 1.420 | 48.4 | 48.1 | 47.8 | 6.47 | 6.43 | 6.39 | 0.776 | |
| 3,cis-4-Dimethylcyclopentene | " | | | 1.4300 | 1.4272 | 48.8 | 48.5 | 48.2 | 6.52 | 6.48 | 6.44 | 0.782 | |
| 3,trans-4-Dimethylcyclopentene | " | | | | | | | | | | | | |
| 3,cis-5-Dimethylcyclopentene | " | | | | | | | | | | | | |
| 3,trans-5-Dimethylcyclopentene | " | | | | | | | | | | | | |
| 4,4-Dimethylcyclopentene | " | 190. | 2.1 | 1.423 | 1.420 | 48.4 | 48.1 | 47.8 | 6.47 | 6.43 | 6.39 | 0.776 | |

a See footnote a of Table 1a-E.

TABLE 19a-E – ALKYL CYCLOHEXENES, $C_6$ TO $C_8$
BOILING POINT, $dt/dp$, REFRACTIVE INDEX, DENSITY, AND FREEZING POINT

October 31, 1950

| Compound | Formula | Boiling Point 29.921 in Hg °F | $dt/dp$ 29.921 in Hg °F/in Hg | Refractive Index[a] $n_D$ 68°F | Refractive Index[a] $n_D$ 77°F | Density[a] lb/cu ft 60°F | Density[a] lb/cu ft 68°F | Density[a] lb/cu ft 77°F | Density[a] lb/gal 60°F | Density[a] lb/gal 68°F | Density[a] lb/gal 77°F | Specific Gravity[a] 60°F/60°F | Freezing Point In air at 1 atm °F |
|---|---|---|---|---|---|---|---|---|---|---|---|---|---|
| Cyclohexene | $C_6H_{10}$ | 181.36 | 2.003 | 1.44654 | 1.44377 | 50.89 | 50.625 | 50.321 | 6.803 | 6.7676 | 6.7270 | 0.8159 | -154.32 |
| 1-Methylcyclohexene | $C_7H_{12}$ | 230.0 | 2.15 | 1.4503 | 1.4478 | 50.82 | 50.58 | 50.30 | 6.794 | 6.761 | 6.725 | 0.8149 | -186. |
| 3-Methylcyclohexene | " | 219.2 | 2.12 | 1.4444 | 1.4419 | 50.25 | 50.00 | 49.73 | 6.717 | 6.685 | 6.648 | 0.8057 | |
| 4-Methylcyclohexene | " | 216.93 | 2.11 | 1.4414 | 1.4389 | 50.13 | 49.89 | 49.61 | 6.701 | 6.669 | 6.632 | 0.8038 | -175.9 |
| 1-Ethylcyclohexene | $C_8H_{14}$ | 277. | 2.3 | 1.4575 | 1.4552 | 51.6 | 51.4 | 51.1 | 6.90 | 6.87 | 6.83 | 0.829 | |
| 3-Ethylcyclohexene | " | 273 | 2.3 | 1.451 | 1.449 | 51.1 | 50.8 | 50.6 | 6.83 | 6.79 | 6.76 | 0.819 | |
| 4-Ethylcyclohexene | " | 271. | 2.2 | 1.449 | 1.447 | 50.8 | 50.6 | 50.3 | 6.79 | 6.76 | 6.73 | 0.815 | |
| 1,2-Dimethylcyclohexene | " | 279. | 2.3 | 1.4588 | 1.4564 | 51.73 | 51.5 | 51.24 | 6.916 | 6.885 | 6.850 | 0.8295 | |
| 1,3-Dimethylcyclohexene | " | 279. | 2.3 | 1.445 | 1.443 | 50.3 | 50.1 | 49.8 | 6.73 | 6.69 | 6.66 | 0.807 | |
| 1,4-Dimethylcyclohexene | " | 262. | 2.2 | 1.446 | 1.444 | 50.29 | 50.1 | 49.8 | 6.723 | 6.69 | 6.66 | 0.806 | - 74. |
| 1,5-Dimethylcyclohexene | " | 262. | 2.2 | 1.448 | 1.446 | 50.49 | 50.26 | 50.00 | 6.750 | 6.719 | 6.684 | 0.8096 | |
| 1,6-Dimethylcyclohexene | " | 271. | 2.2 | 1.454 | 1.452 | 51.1 | 50.9 | 50.6 | 6.83 | 6.80 | 6.77 | 0.820 | |
| 3,3-Dimethylcyclohexene | " | 246. | 2.2 | 1.445 | 1.443 | 50.4 | 50.2 | 49.9 | 6.74 | 6.71 | 6.68 | 0.809 | |
| 3,cis-4-Dimethylcyclohexene | " | | | | | | | | | | | | |
| 3,trans-4-Dimethylcyclohexene | " | | | | | | | | | | | | |
| 3,cis-5-Dimethylcyclohexene | " | | | | | | | | | | | | |
| 3,trans-5-Dimethylcyclohexene | " | | | | | | | | | | | | |
| 3,cis-6-Dimethylcyclohexene | " | | | | | | | | | | | | |
| 3,trans-6-Dimethylcyclohexene | " | | | | | | | | | | | | |
| 4,4-Dimethylcyclohexene | " | 242.56 | 2.18 | 1.4420 | 1.4396 | 50.14 | 49.92 | 49.67 | 6.703 | 6.673 | 6.639 | 0.8040 | -112.9 |
| 4,cis-5-Dimethylcyclohexene | " | | | | | | | | | | | | |
| 4,trans-5-Dimethylcyclohexene | " | | | | | | | | | | | | |

a  See footnote a of Table 1a-E.

## TABLE 25a-E (PART 1) – NORMAL ACETYLENES (1-ALKYNES) $C_2$ TO $C_{20}$
### BOILING POINT, $dt/dp$, REFRACTIVE INDEX, DENSITY, AND FREEZING POINT
April 30, 1949; September 30, 1951; October 31, 1952

| Compound | Formula | Boiling Point 29.921 in Hg °F | $dt/dp$ 29.921 in Hg °F/in Hg | Refractive Index[a] $n_D$ 68°F | Refractive Index[a] $n_D$ 77°F | Density[a] lb/cu ft 60°F | Density[a] lb/cu ft 68°F | Density[a] lb/cu ft 77°F | Density[a] lb/gal 60°F | Density[a] lb/gal 68°F | Density[a] lb/gal 77°F | Specific Gravity[a] 60°F/60°F | Freezing Point In air at 1 atm °F |
|---|---|---|---|---|---|---|---|---|---|---|---|---|---|
| Ethyne (Acetylene) | $C_2H_2$ | -119.[b] | 0.82 | — | — | — | — | — | — | — | — | — | -114.[c] |
| Propyne (Methylacetylene) | $C_3H_4$ | -9.80 | 1.37 | — | — | — | — | — | — | — | — | 0.65[d] | -152.9 |
| 1-Butyne (Ethylacetylene) | $C_4H_6$ | +46.53 | 1.65 | 1.3852 | 1.3826 | 41.[d] | 41.[d] | 41.[d] | 5.4[d] | 5.4[d] | 5.4[d] | 0.65[d] | -194.30 |
| 1-Pentyne | $C_5H_8$ | 104.32 | 1.78 | 1.3989 | 1.3960 | 43.37 | 43.08 | 42.76 | 5.797 | 5.759 | 5.716 | 0.6954 | -156.3 |
| 1-Hexyne | $C_6H_{10}$ | 160.5 | 1.9 | 1.4087 | 1.4060 | 44.94 | 44.67 | 44.36 | 6.007 | 5.971 | 5.930 | 0.7205 | -205.4 |
| 1-Heptyne | $C_7H_{12}$ | 211.5 | 2.1 | 1.4159 | 1.4134 | 46.00 | 45.75 | 45.47 | 6.149 | 6.115 | 6.078 | 0.7375 | -113.6 |
| 1-Octyne | $C_8H_{14}$ | 259.2 | 2.1 | 1.4217 | 1.4193 | 46.81 | 46.58 | 46.31 | 6.258 | 6.226 | 6.191 | 0.7506 | -110.7 |
| 1-Nonyne | $C_9H_{16}$ | 303.4 | 2.3 | 1.4265 | 1.4242 | 47.47 | 47.24 | 46.99 | 6.346 | 6.316 | 6.282 | 0.7611 | -58. |
| 1-Decyne | $C_{10}H_{18}$ | 345. | 2.4 | 1.4306 | 1.4284 | 48.00 | 47.79 | 47.54 | 6.417 | 6.388 | 6.356 | 0.7697 | -47. |
| 1-Undecyne | $C_{11}H_{20}$ | 383. | 2.5 | 1.4340 | 1.4318 | 48.45 | 48.24 | 48.00 | 6.477 | 6.449 | 6.417 | 0.7769 | -13. |
| 1-Dodecyne | $C_{12}H_{22}$ | 419. | 2.5 | 1.4371 | 1.4349 | 48.83 | 48.62 | 48.39 | 6.527 | 6.500 | 6.468 | 0.7829 | -2. |
| 1-Tridecyne | $C_{13}H_{24}$ | 453. | 2.6 | 1.4396 | 1.4375 | 49.16 | 48.96 | 48.73 | 6.572 | 6.545 | 6.514 | 0.7882 | +23. |
| 1-Tetradecyne | $C_{14}H_{26}$ | 486. | 2.7 | 1.4419 | 1.4398 | 49.44 | 49.24 | 49.02 | 6.610 | 6.583 | 6.553 | 0.7928 | 32. |
| 1-Pentadecyne | $C_{15}H_{28}$ | 514. | 2.7 | 1.4440 | 1.4419 | 49.69 | 49.49 | 49.27 | 6.643 | 6.616 | 6.587 | 0.7968 | 50. |
| 1-Hexadecyne | $C_{16}H_{30}$ | 543. | 2.8 | 1.4457[e] | 1.4437 | 49.92 | 49.72 | 49.50 | 6.673 | 6.647 | 6.618 | 0.8004 | 59. |
| 1-Heptadecyne | $C_{17}H_{32}$ | 570. | 2.8 | 1.4474[e] | 1.4453[e] | 50.11[e] | 49.92[e] | 49.70 | 6.698[e] | 6.673[e] | 6.644 | 0.8034[e] | 72. |
| 1-Octadecyne | $C_{18}H_{34}$ | 595. | 2.9 | 1.4488[e] | 1.4467[e] | 50.29[e] | 50.09[e] | 49.88[e] | 6.722[e] | 6.697[e] | 6.668[e] | 0.8063[e] | 81. |
| 1-Nonadecyne | $C_{19}H_{36}$ | 621. | 2.9 | 1.4501[e] | 1.4481[e] | 50.44[e] | 50.25[e] | 50.04[e] | 6.743[e] | 6.718[e] | 6.689[e] | 0.8088[e] | 91. |
| 1-Eicosyne | $C_{20}H_{38}$ | 644. | 3.0 | — | — | 50.59[e] | 50.40[e] | 50.18[e] | 6.763[e] | 6.737[e] | 6.709[e] | 0.8111[e] | 97. |

a See footnote a of Table 1a-E.  b Sublimation point.  c At saturation pressure (triple point).  d At saturation pressure.  e For the undercooled liquid below the normal freezing point.

TABLE 25a-E (PART 2) – NORMAL ACETYLENES (1-ALKYNES) $C_{21}$ TO $C_{40}$
BOILING POINT, $dt/dp$, REFRACTIVE INDEX, DENSITY, AND FREEZING POINT
September 30, 1951

| Compound | Formula | Boiling Point 29.921 in Hg °F | $dt/dp$ 29.921 in Hg °F/in Hg | Refractive Index[a] $n_D$ 68°F | Refractive Index[a] $n_D$ 77°F | Density[a] lb/cu ft 60°F | Density[a] lb/cu ft 68°F | Density[a] lb/cu ft 77°F | Density[a] lb/gal 60°F | Density[a] lb/gal 68°F | Density[a] lb/gal 77°F | Specific Gravity[a] 60°F/60°F | Freezing Point In air at 1 atm °F |
|---|---|---|---|---|---|---|---|---|---|---|---|---|---|
| 1-Heneicosyne | $C_{21}H_{40}$ | 666. | 3. | 1.4513[b] | 1.4493[b] | 50.72[b] | 50.53[b] | 50.32[b] | 6.780[b] | 6.755[b] | 6.726[b] | 0.8133[b] | 106. |
| 1-Docosyne | $C_{22}H_{42}$ | 685. | 3. | 1.4524[b] | 1.4504[b] | 50.84[b] | 50.65[b] | 50.44[b] | 6.796[b] | 6.771[b] | 6.743[b] | 0.8152[b] | 113. |
| 1-Tricosyne | $C_{23}H_{44}$ | 705. | 3. | 1.4534[b] | 1.4514[b] | 50.95[b] | 50.76[b] | 50.55[b] | 6.811[b] | 6.786[b] | 6.758[b] | 0.8169[b] | 120. |
| 1-Tetracosyne | $C_{24}H_{46}$ | 725. | 3. | 1.4544[b] | 1.4523[b] | 51.05[b] | 50.86[b] | 50.65[b] | 6.824[b] | 6.799[b] | 6.771[b] | 0.8186[b] | 126. |
| 1-Pentacosyne | $C_{25}H_{48}$ | 743. | 3. | 1.4552[b] | 1.4532[b] | 51.14[b] | 50.96[b] | 50.75[b] | 6.837[b] | 6.812[b] | 6.784[b] | 0.8200[b] | 131. |
| 1-Hexacosyne | $C_{26}H_{50}$ | 761. | 3. | 1.4560[b] | 1.4540[b] | 51.23[b] | 51.04[b] | 50.84[b] | 6.848[b] | 6.824[b] | 6.796[b] | 0.8214[b] | 135. |
| 1-Heptacosyne | $C_{27}H_{52}$ | 779. | 3. | 1.4568[b] | 1.4548[b] | 51.31[b] | 51.13[b] | 50.92[b] | 6.859[b] | 6.834[b] | 6.807[b] | 0.8227[b] | 140. |
| 1-Octacosyne | $C_{28}H_{54}$ | 795. | 3. | 1.4575[b] | 1.4555[b] | 51.39[b] | 51.20[b] | 50.99[b] | 6.869[b] | 6.845[b] | 6.817[b] | 0.8239[b] | 144. |
| 1-Nonacosyne | $C_{29}H_{56}$ | 810. | 3. | 1.4581[b] | 1.4561[b] | 51.46[b] | 51.27[b] | 51.06[b] | 6.879[b] | 6.854[b] | 6.826[b] | 0.8251[b] | 149. |
| 1-Triacontyne | $C_{30}H_{58}$ | 826. | 3. | 1.4587[b] | 1.4567[b] | 51.52[b] | 51.34[b] | 51.13[b] | 6.887[b] | 6.863[b] | 6.835[b] | 0.8261[b] | 153. |
| 1-Hentriacontyne | $C_{31}H_{60}$ | 840. | 3. | 1.4593[b] | 1.4573[b] | 51.58[b] | 51.40[b] | 51.19[b] | 6.896[b] | 6.871[b] | 6.843[b] | 0.8271[b] | 156. |
| 1-Dotriacontyne | $C_{32}H_{62}$ | 855. | 3. | 1.4598[b] | 1.4578[b] | 51.64[b] | 51.46[b] | 51.25[b] | 6.903[b] | 6.879[b] | 6.851[b] | 0.8280[b] | 160. |
| 1-Tritriacontyne | $C_{33}H_{64}$ | 867. | 3. | 1.4603[b] | 1.4583[b] | 51.70[b] | 51.51[b] | 51.30[b] | 6.911[b] | 6.886[b] | 6.858[b] | 0.8289[b] | 163. |
| 1-Tetratriacontyne | $C_{34}H_{66}$ | 882. | 3. | 1.4608[b] | 1.4588[b] | 51.75[b] | 51.56[b] | 51.36[b] | 6.918[b] | 6.893[b] | 6.865[b] | 0.8297[b] | 165. |
| 1-Pentatriacontyne | $C_{35}H_{68}$ | 894. | 3. | 1.4612[b] | 1.4593[b] | 51.79[b] | 51.61[b] | 51.41[b] | 6.924[b] | 6.899[b] | 6.872[b] | 0.8305[b] | 169. |
| 1-Hexatriacontyne | $C_{36}H_{70}$ | 907. | 3. | 1.4617[b] | 1.4597[b] | 51.84[b] | 51.66[b] | 51.45[b] | 6.930[b] | 6.906[b] | 6.878[b] | 0.8312[b] | 171. |
| 1-Heptatriacontyne | $C_{37}H_{72}$ | 919. | 3. | 1.4621[b] | 1.4601[b] | 51.89[b] | 51.70[b] | 51.50[b] | 6.936[b] | 6.912[b] | 6.884[b] | 0.8319[b] | 174. |
| 1-Octatriacontyne | $C_{38}H_{74}$ | 930. | 3. | 1.4625[b] | 1.4605[b] | 51.93[b] | 51.74[b] | 51.54[b] | 6.941[b] | 6.917[b] | 6.890[b] | 0.826[b] | 176. |
| 1-Nonatriacontyne | $C_{39}H_{76}$ | 941. | 4. | 1.4628[b] | 1.4608[b] | 51.97[b] | 51.78[b] | 51.58[b] | 6.947[b] | 6.922[b] | 6.895[b] | 0.8332[b] | 180. |
| 1-Tetracontyne | $C_{40}H_{78}$ | 954. | 4. | 1.4632[b] | 1.4612[b] | 52.00[b] | 51.82[b] | 51.61[b] | 6.952[b] | 6.927[b] | 6.900[b] | 0.8338[b] | 181. |

a See footnote a of Table 1a-E.   b For the undercooled liquid below the normal freezing point.

TABLE 12a–E, ACETYLENES, $C_2$ TO $C_5$

BOILING POINT, $dt/dp$, REFRACTIVE INDEX, DENSITY, AND FREEZING POINT

June 30, 1945; October 31, 1950; October 31, 1952

| Compound | Formula | Boiling Point 29.921 in Hg °F | $dt/dp$ 29.921 in Hg °F/in Hg | Refractive Index[a] 68°F $n_D$ | Refractive Index[a] 77°F $n_D$ | Density[a] 600°F | Density[a] 68°F lb/cu ft | Density[a] 77°F | Density[a] 600°F | Density[a] 68°F lb/gal | Density[a] 79°F | Specific Gravity[a] 600°F/600°F | Freezing Point In air at 1 atm °F |
|---|---|---|---|---|---|---|---|---|---|---|---|---|---|
| Ethyne (Acetylene) | $C_2H_2$ | -119.[b] | 0.82 | — | — | — | — | — | — | — | — | — | -114.[c] |
| Propyne (Methylacetylene) | $C_3H_4$ | - 9.60 | 1.37 | — | — | — | — | — | — | — | — | — | -152.9 |
| 1-Butyne (Ethylacetylene) | $C_4H_6$ | 46.53 | 1.65 | — | — | 41.[d] | 41.[d] | 41.[d] | 5.4[d] | 5.4[d] | 5.4[d] | 0.65[d] | -194.30 |
| 2-Butyne (Dimethylacetylene) | " | 80.58 | 1.69 | 1.3921 | 1.3893 | 43.44 | 43.14 | 42.80 | 5.807 | 5.767 | 5.721 | 0.696[b] | -26.07 |
| 1-Pentyne | $C_5H_8$ | 104.32 | 1.73 | 1.3852 | 1.3826 | 43.37 | 43.08 | 42.76 | 5.797 | 5.759 | 5.716 | 0.6954 | -158.3 |
| 2-Pentyne | " | 132.93 | 1.87 | 1.4039 | 1.4009 | 44.65 | 44.37 | 44.04 | 5.969 | 5.931 | 5.888 | 0.7160 | -164.7 |
| 3-Methyl-1-butyne | " | 79.43 | 1.74 | 1.3723 | 1.3695 | 41.9 | 41.6 | 41.2 | 5.60 | 5.56 | 5.51 | 0.672 | -130.5 |

a See footnote a of Table 1a-E.   b Sublimation Point.   c At saturation pressure (triple point).   d At saturation pressure.

TABLE 21a-E (PART 1) – NORMAL ALKYL BENZENES, $C_6$ TO $C_{22}$

BOILING POINT, $dt/dp$, REFRACTIVE INDEX, DENSITY, AND FREEZING POINT

June 30, 1948; September 30, 1951 (Corrected)

| Compound | Formula | Boiling Point 29.921 in Hg (°F) | $dt/dp$ 29.921 in Hg (°F/in Hg) | Refractive Index[a] $n_D$ 68°F | $n_D$ 77°F | Density[a] (lb/cu ft) 60°F | 68°F | 77°F | Density[a] (lb/gal) 60°F | 68°F | 77°F | Specific Gravity[a] 60°F/60°F | Freezing Point In air at 1 atm (°F) |
|---|---|---|---|---|---|---|---|---|---|---|---|---|---|
| Benzene | $C_6H_6$ | 176.18 | 1.954 | 1.50112 | 1.49792 | 55.16 | 54.874 | 54.542 | 7.375 | 7.3355 | 7.2912 | 0.8846 | + 41.96 |
| Methylbenzene (Toluene) | $C_7H_8$ | 231.12 | 2.117 | 1.49693 | 1.49414 | 54.37 | 54.120 | 53.830 | 7.269 | 7.2348 | 7.1961 | 0.8719 | −138.98 |
| Ethylbenzene | $C_8H_{10}$ | 277.13 | 2.239 | 1.49588 | 1.49320 | 54.37 | 54.125 | 53.852 | 7.268 | 7.2355 | 7.1989 | 0.8718 | −138.96 |
| n-Propylbenzene | $C_9H_{12}$ | 318.59 | 2.351 | 1.49202 | 1.48951 | 54.04 | 53.814 | 53.550 | 7.225 | 7.1939 | 7.1585 | 0.8666 | −147.10 |
| n-Butylbenzene | $C_{10}H_{14}$ | 361.89 | 2.450 | 1.48979 | 1.48742 | 53.92 | 53.695 | 53.442 | 7.208 | 7.1780 | 7.1441 | 0.8646 | −126.35 |
| n-Pentylbenzene | $C_{11}H_{16}$ | 401.7 | 2.5 | 1.4878 | 1.4855 | 53.81 | 53.60 | 53.35 | 7.194 | 7.165 | 7.132 | 0.8628 | −103. |
| n-Hexylbenzene | $C_{12}H_{18}$ | 439.0 | 2.6 | 1.4864 | 1.4842 | 53.74 | 53.53 | 53.29 | 7.184 | 7.156 | 7.124 | 0.8617 | − 78. |
| n-Heptylbenzene | $C_{13}H_{20}$ | 473.9 | 2.7 | 1.4854 | 1.4832 | 53.69 | 53.48 | 53.25 | 7.177 | 7.150 | 7.118 | 0.8609 | − 54. |
| n-Octylbenzene | $C_{14}H_{22}$ | 508.1 | 2.7 | 1.4845 | 1.4824 | 53.65 | 53.45 | 53.22 | 7.172 | 7.145 | 7.114 | 0.8603 | − 33. |
| n-Nonylbenzene | $C_{15}H_{24}$ | 539.6 | 2.8 | 1.4838 | 1.4817 | 53.63 | 53.42 | 53.20 | 7.169 | 7.142 | 7.111 | 0.8599 | − 11. |
| n-Decylbenzene | $C_{16}H_{26}$ | 572. | 3. | 1.48319 | 1.48112 | 53.61 | 53.408 | 53.181 | 7.167 | 7.1396 | 7.1092 | 0.8596 | + 6.12 |
| n-Undecylbenzene | $C_{17}H_{28}$ | 601. | 3. | 1.4828 | 1.4807 | 53.59 | 53.39 | 53.17 | 7.164 | 7.138 | 7.108 | 0.8593 | 23. |
| n-Dodecylbenzene | $C_{18}H_{30}$ | 628. | 3. | 1.4824 | 1.4803 | 53.58 | 53.38 | 53.16 | 7.162 | 7.136 | 7.107 | 0.8591 | 37. |
| n-Tridecylbenzene | $C_{19}H_{32}$ | 655. | 3. | 1.4821 | 1.4800 | 53.57 | 53.37 | 53.15 | 7.161 | 7.135 | 7.106 | 0.8589 | 50. |
| n-Tetradecylbenzene | $C_{20}H_{34}$ | 678. | 3. | 1.4818 | 1.4797 | 53.56[b] | 53.37 | 53.15 | 7.160[b] | 7.134 | 7.105 | 0.8588[b] | 61. |
| n-Pentadecylbenzene | $C_{21}H_{36}$ | 703. | 3. | 1.4815[b] | 1.4794 | 53.55[b] | 53.36[b] | 53.14 | 7.159[b] | 7.133[b] | 7.104 | 0.8587[b] | 72. |
| n-Hexadecylbenzene | $C_{22}H_{38}$ | 725. | 3. | 1.4813[b] | 1.4792[b] | 53.55[b] | 53.36[b] | 53.14[b] | 7.158[b] | 7.133[b] | 7.104[b] | 0.8586[b] | 81. |

a See footnote a of Table 1a-E.  b For the undercooled liquid below the normal freezing point.

TABLE 21a-E (PART 2) – NORMAL ALKYL BENZENES, $C_{23}$ TO $C_{42}$

BOILING POINT, $dt/dp$, REFRACTIVE INDEX, DENSITY, AND FREEZING POINT

September 30, 1951

| Compound | Formula | Boiling Point 29.921 in Hg °F | $dt/dp$ 29.921 in Hg °F/in Hg | Refractive Index[a] $n_D$ 68°F | Refractive Index[a] $n_D$ 77°F | Density[a] lb/cu ft 60°F | Density[a] lb/cu ft 68°F | Density[a] lb/cu ft 77°F | Density[a] lb/gal 60°F | Density[a] lb/gal 68°F | Density[a] lb/gal 77°F | Specific Gravity[a] 60°F/60°F | Freezing Point In air at 1 atm °F |
|---|---|---|---|---|---|---|---|---|---|---|---|---|---|
| n-Heptadecylbenzene | $C_{23}H_{40}$ | 747. | 3. | 1.4810[b] | 1.4790[b] | 53.54[b] | 53.35[b] | 53.14[b] | 7.158[b] | 7.132[b] | 7.103[b] | 0.8585[b] | 90. |
| n-Octadecylbenzene | $C_{24}H_{42}$ | 766. | 3. | 1.4809[b] | 1.4788[b] | 53.54[b] | 53.35[b] | 53.13[b] | 7.157[b] | 7.132[b] | 7.103[b] | 0.8585[b] | 97. |
| n-Nonadecylbenzene | $C_{25}H_{44}$ | 786. | 3. | 1.4807[b] | 1.4786[b] | 53.54[b] | 53.35[b] | 53.13[b] | 7.157[b] | 7.131[b] | 7.103[b] | 0.8584[b] | 104. |
| n-Eicosylbenzene | $C_{26}H_{46}$ | 804. | 3. | 1.4805[b] | 1.4785[b] | 53.53[b] | 53.34[b] | 53.13[b] | 7.156[b] | 7.131[b] | 7.102[b] | 0.8584[b] | 111. |
| n-Heneicosylbenzene | $C_{27}H_{48}$ | 822. | 3. | 1.4804[b] | 1.4783[b] | 53.53[b] | 53.34[b] | 53.13[b] | 7.156[b] | 7.131[b] | 7.102[b] | 0.8583[b] | 118. |
| n-Docosylbenzene | $C_{28}H_{50}$ | 838. | 3. | 1.4802[b] | 1.4782[b] | 53.53[b] | 53.34[b] | 53.13[b] | 7.156[b] | 7.130[b] | 7.102[b] | 0.8583[b] | 124. |
| n-Tricosylbenzene | $C_{29}H_{52}$ | 855. | 3. | 1.4801[b] | 1.4781[b] | 53.53[b] | 53.34[b] | 53.13[b] | 7.155[b] | 7.130[b] | 7.102[b] | 0.8582[b] | 129. |
| n-Tetracosylbenzene | $C_{30}H_{54}$ | 871. | 3. | 1.4800[b] | 1.4780[b] | 53.52[b] | 53.34[b] | 53.13[b] | 7.155[b] | 7.130[b] | 7.102[b] | 0.8582[b] | 135. |
| n-Pentacosylbenzene | $C_{31}H_{56}$ | 885. | 3. | 1.4799[b] | 1.4779[b] | 53.52[b] | 53.34[b] | 53.12[b] | 7.155[b] | 7.130[b] | 7.102[b] | 0.8582[b] | 138 |
| n-Hexacosylbenzene | $C_{32}H_{58}$ | 900. | 3. | 1.4798[b] | 1.4778[b] | 53.52[b] | 53.33[b] | 53.12[b] | 7.155[b] | 7.130[b] | 7.102[b] | 0.8582[b] | 144. |
| n-Heptacosylbenzene | $C_{33}H_{60}$ | 914. | 3. | 1.4797[b] | 1.4777[b] | 53.52[b] | 53.33[b] | 53.12[b] | 7.155[t] | 7.129[b] | 7.101[b] | 0.8581[b] | 147. |
| n-Octacosylbenzene | $C_{34}H_{62}$ | 928. | 3. | 1.4796[b] | 1.4776[b] | 53.52[b] | 53.33[b] | 53.12[b] | 7.154[b] | 7.129[b] | 7.101[b] | 0.8581[b] | 151. |
| n-Nonacosylbenzene | $C_{35}H_{64}$ | 941. | 3. | 1.4796[b] | 1.4775[b] | 53.52[b] | 53.33[b] | 53.12[b] | 7.154[b] | 7.129[b] | 7.101[b] | 0.8581[b] | 154. |
| n-Triacontylbenzene | $C_{36}H_{66}$ | 954. | 4. | 1.4795[b] | 1.4775[b] | 53.52[b] | 53.33[b] | 53.12[b] | 7.154[b] | 7.129[b] | 7.101[b] | 0.8581[b] | 158. |
| n-Hentriacontylbenzene | $C_{37}H_{68}$ | 966. | 4. | 1.4794[b] | 1.4774[b] | 53.52[b] | 53.33[b] | 53.12[b] | 7.154[b] | 7.129[b] | 7.101[b] | 0.8581[b] | 162. |
| n-Dotriacontylbenzene | $C_{38}H_{70}$ | 977. | 4. | 1.4794[b] | 1.4773[b] | 53.52[b] | 53.33[b] | 53.12[b] | 7.154[b] | 7.129[b] | 7.101[b] | 0.8581[b] | 165. |
| n-Tritriacontylbenzene | $C_{39}H_{72}$ | 990. | 4. | 1.4793[b] | 1.4773[b] | 53.51[b] | 53.33[b] | 53.12[b] | 7.154[b] | 7.129[b] | 7.101[b] | 0.8581[b] | 167. |
| n-Tetratriacontylbenzene | $C_{40}H_{74}$ | 1000. | 4. | 1.4792[b] | 1.4772[b] | 53.51[b] | 53.33[b] | 53.12[b] | 7.154[b] | 7.129[b] | 7.101[b] | 0.8581[b] | 171. |
| n-Pentatriacontylbenzene | $C_{41}H_{76}$ | 1011. | 4. | 1.4792[b] | 1.4772[b] | 53.51[b] | 53.33[b] | 53.12[b] | 7.154[b] | 7.129[b] | 7.101[b] | 0.8581[b] | 174. |
| n-Hexatriacontylbenzene | $C_{42}H_{78}$ | 1020. | 4. | 1.4791[b] | 1.4771[b] | 53.51[b] | 53.33[b] | 53.12[b] | 7.154[b] | 7.129[b] | 7.101[b] | 0.8581[b] | 176. |

a See footnote a of Table 1a-E.　b For the undercooled liquid below the normal freezing point.

TABLE 5a-E - ALKYL BENZENES, $C_6$ TO $C_9$

BOILING POINT, $dt/dp$, REFRACTIVE INDEX, DENSITY, AND FREEZING POINT

June 30, 1945; May 31, 1947; October 31, 1950 (Corrected)

| Compound | Formula | Boiling Point 29.921 in Hg °F | $dt/dp$ 29.921 in Hg °F/in Hg | Refractive Index[a] 68°F $n_D$ | 77°F $n_D$ | Density[a] 60°F lb/cu ft | 68°F lb/cu ft | 77°F lb/cu ft | 60°F lb/gal | 68°F lb/gal | 77°F lb/gal | Specific Gravity[a] 60°F/60°F | Freezing Point In air at 1 atm °F |
|---|---|---|---|---|---|---|---|---|---|---|---|---|---|
| Benzene | $C_6H_6$ | 176.18 | 1.954 | 1.50112 | 1.49792 | 55.16 | 54.874 | 54.542 | 7.375 | 7.3355 | 7.2912 | 0.8846 | +41.96 |
| Methylbenzene (Toluene) | $C_7H_8$ | 231.12 | 2.117 | 1.49693 | 1.49414 | 54.37 | 54.120 | 53.830 | 7.269 | 7.2348 | 7.1961 | 0.8719 | −138.98 |
| Ethylbenzene | $C_8H_{10}$ | 277.13 | 2.239 | 1.49588 | 1.49320 | 54.37 | 54.125 | 53.852 | 7.268 | 7.2355 | 7.1989 | 0.8718 | −138.96 |
| 1,2-Dimethylbenzene (o-Xylene) | " | 291.94 | 2.272 | 1.50545 | 1.50295 | 55.18 | 54.948 | 54.683 | 7.377 | 7.3455 | 7.3101 | 0.8848 | − 13.33 |
| 1,3-Dimethylbenzene (m-Xylene) | " | 282.39 | 2.242 | 1.49722 | 1.49464 | 54.18 | 53.947 | 53.681 | 7.243 | 7.2117 | 7.1761 | 0.8687 | − 54.17 |
| 1,4-Dimethylbenzene (p-Xylene) | " | 281.03 | 2.248 | 1.49582 | 1.49325 | 53.99 | 53.752 | 53.480 | 7.218 | 7.1857 | 7.1493 | 0.8657 | + 55.87 |
| n-Propylbenzene | $C_9H_{12}$ | 318.59 | 2.351 | 1.49202 | 1.48951 | 54.04 | 53.814 | 53.550 | 7.225 | 7.1939 | 7.1585 | 0.8666 | −147.10 |
| Isopropylbenzene | " | 306.31 | 2.320 | 1.49145 | 1.48890 | 54.03 | 53.799 | 53.531 | 7.224 | 7.1918 | 7.1561 | 0.8663 | −140.86 |
| 1-Methyl-2-ethylbenzene | " | 329.28 | 2.360 | 1.50456 | 1.50208 | 55.20 | 54.978 | 54.721 | 7.380 | 7.3496 | 7.3152 | 0.8852 | −113.50 |
| 1-Methyl-3-ethylbenzene | " | 322.35 | 2.337 | 1.49660 | 1.49406 | 54.20 | 53.969 | 53.712 | 7.245 | 7.2145 | 7.1802 | 0.8690 | −139.99 |
| 1-Methyl-4-ethylbenzene | " | 323.58 | 2.354 | 1.49500 | 1.49244 | 53.99 | 53.761 | 53.501 | 7.218 | 7.1867 | 7.1520 | 0.8657 | − 80.23 |
| 1,2,3-Trimethylbenzene | " | 348.95 | 2.406 | 1.51303 | 1.51150 | 56.05 | 55.833 | 55.587 | 7.493 | 7.4638 | 7.4309 | 0.8987 | − 13.68 |
| 1,2,4-Trimethylbenzene | " | 336.83 | 2.372 | 1.50484 | 1.50237 | 54.90 | 54.674 | 54.423 | 7.339 | 7.3089 | 7.2754 | 0.8802 | − 46.84 |
| 1,3,5-Trimethylbenzene | " | 328.49 | 2.332 | 1.49937 | 1.49684 | 54.23 | 54.010 | 53.756 | 7.250 | 7.2201 | 7.1862 | 0.8696 | − 48.50 |

[a] See footnote a of Table 1a-E.

TABLE 14a-E – ALKYL BENZENES, C$_{10}$

BOILING POINT, dt/dp, REFRACTIVE INDEX, DENSITY, AND FREEZING POINT

January 31, 1946; May 31, 1947; April 30, 1952

| Compound | Formula | Boiling Point 29.921 in Hg | dt/dp 29.921 in Hg | Refractive Index[a] 68°F | 77°F | Density[a] (lb/cu ft) 60°F | 68°F | 77°F | Density[a] (lb/gal) 60°F | 68°F | 77°F | Specific Gravity[a] 60°F/60°F | Freezing Point In air at 1 atm |
|---|---|---|---|---|---|---|---|---|---|---|---|---|---|
| | | °F | °F/in.Hg | $n_D$ | $n_D$ | | | | | | | | °F |
| n-Butylbenzene (1-Phenylbutane) | C$_{10}$H$_{14}$ | 361.89 | 2.450 | 1.48979 | 1.48742 | 53.92 | 53.695 | 53.442 | 7.208 | 7.1780 | 7.1441 | 0.8646 | -126.35 |
| Isobutylbenzene (1-Phenyl-2-methylpropane) | " | 342.97 | 2.432 | 1.48646 | 1.48400 | 53.49 | 53.263 | 53.005 | 7.151 | 7.1202 | 7.0857 | 0.8576 | -60.66 |
| sec-Butylbenzene (2-Phenylbutane) | " | 343.95 | 2.429 | 1.49020 | 1.48779 | 54.04 | 53.816 | 53.560 | 7.225 | 7.1942 | 7.1599 | 0.8664 | -103.85 |
| tert-Butylbenzene (2-Phenyl-2-methylpropane) | " | 336.41 | 2.409 | 1.49266 | 1.49024 | 54.32 | 54.093 | 53.837 | 7.262 | 7.2311 | 7.1969 | 0.8710 | -72.13 |
| 1-Methyl-2-propylbenzene | " | 364.64 | 2.446 | 1.4998 | 1.4974 | 54.80 | 54.59 | 54.34 | 7.326 | 7.297 | 7.265 | 0.8787 | -76.4 |
| 1-Methyl-3-propylbenzene | " | 359.24 | 2.423 | 1.4936 | 1.4912 | 53.97 | 53.75 | 53.50 | 7.215 | 7.185 | 7.152 | 0.8654 | |
| 1-Methyl-4-propylbenzene | " | 361.94 | 2.446 | 1.4919 | 1.4895 | 53.81 | 53.59 | 53.34 | 7.194 | 7.164 | 7.130 | 0.8628 | -82.5 |
| 1-Methyl-2-isopropylbenzene (o-Cymene) | " | 352.67 | 2.419 | 1.5006 | 1.4982 | 54.95 | 54.72 | 54.47 | 7.345 | 7.315 | 7.282 | 0.8810 | -96.77 |
| 1-Methyl-3-isopropylbenzene (m-Cymene) | " | 347.25 | 2.396 | 1.4930 | 1.4906 | 53.97 | 53.75 | 53.50 | 7.215 | 7.185 | 7.152 | 0.8654 | -82.74 |
| 1-Methyl-4-isopropylbenzene (p-Cymene) | " | 350.78 | 2.414 | 1.4909 | 1.4885 | 53.74 | 53.52 | 53.27 | 7.184 | 7.154 | 7.121 | 0.8617 | -90.28 |
| 1,2-Diethylbenzene | " | 362.16 | 2.441 | 1.50346 | 1.50106 | 55.15 | 54.933 | 54.681 | 7.373 | 7.3435 | 7.3097 | 0.8843 | -24.23 |
| 1,3-Diethylbenzene | " | 357.98 | 2.420 | 1.49552 | 1.49310 | 54.16 | 53.933 | 53.682 | 7.239 | 7.2098 | 7.1763 | 0.8683 | -119.06 |
| 1,4-Diethylbenzene | " | 362.75 | 2.446 | 1.49483 | 1.49245 | 54.03 | 53.809 | 53.558 | 7.223 | 7.1932 | 7.1597 | 0.8663 | -45.13 |
| 1,2-Dimethyl-3-ethylbenzene | " | 381.04 | 2.533 | 1.5117 | 1.5095 | 55.91 | 55.69 | 55.44 | 7.474 | 7.445 | 7.411 | 0.8965 | -57.1 |
| 1,2-Dimethyl-4-ethylbenzene | " | 373.55 | 2.574 | 1.5031 | 1.5009 | 54.81 | 54.59 | 54.35 | 7.327 | 7.298 | 7.265 | 0.8788 | -88.6 |
| 1,3-Dimethyl-2-ethylbenzene | " | 374.02 | 2.565 | 1.5107 | 1.5085 | 55.81 | 55.58 | 55.33 | 7.460 | 7.431 | 7.397 | 0.8948 | + 2.7 |
| 1,3-Dimethyl-4-ethylbenzene | " | 371.14 | 2.537 | 1.5038 | 1.5016 | 54.93 | 54.70 | 54.45 | 7.343 | 7.313 | 7.280 | 0.8807 | -81.4 |
| 1,3-Dimethyl-5-ethylbenzene | " | 362.75 | 2.478 | 1.4981 | 1.4958 | 54.21 | 53.99 | 53.74 | 7.247 | 7.217 | 7.184 | 0.8692 | -119.78 |
| 1,4-Dimethyl-2-ethylbenzene | " | 368.44 | 2.437 | 1.5043 | 1.5020 | 54.98 | 54.76 | 54.51 | 7.350 | 7.320 | 7.287 | 0.8816 | -64.7 |
| 1,2,3,4-Tetramethylbenzene (Prehnitene) | " | 401.07 | 2.51 | 1.5203 | 1.5181 | 56.71 | 56.51 | 56.28 | 7.582 | 7.554 | 7.523 | 0.9094 | ± 20.75 |
| 1,2,3,5-Tetramethylbenzene (Isodurene) | " | 388.40 | 2.51 | 1.5130 | 1.5107 | 55.79 | 55.58 | 55.34 | 7.458 | 7.430 | 7.398 | 0.8946 | -10.63 |
| 1,2,4,5-Tetramethylbenzene (Durene) | " | 386.24 | 2.47 | 1.5116[b] | 1.5093[b] | 55.60[b] | 55.40[b] | 55.17[b] | 7.434[b] | 7.406[b] | 7.375[b] | 0.8918[b] | +174.63 |

a See footnote a of Table 1a-E.    b For the undercooled liquid below the normal freezing point.

TABLE 26a-E, Page 1 – ALKYL BENZENES, C$_{11}$

BOILING POINT, dt/dp, REFRACTIVE INDEX, DENSITY, AND FREEZING POINT

April 30, 1952

| Compound | Formula | Boiling Point 29.921 in Hg (°F) | dt/dp 29.921 in Hg (°F/in Hg) | Refractive Index$^a$ $n_D$ 68°F | Refractive Index$^a$ $n_D$ 77°F | Density$^a$ (lb/cu ft) 60°F | 68°F | 77°F | Density$^a$ (lb/gal) 60°F | 68°F | 77°F | Specific Gravity$^a$ 60°F/60°F | Freezing Point In air at 1 atm (°F) |
|---|---|---|---|---|---|---|---|---|---|---|---|---|---|
| n-Pentylbenzene | C$_{11}$H$_{16}$ | 401.7 | 2.5 | 1.4878 | 1.4855 | 53.81 | 53.60 | 53.35 | 7.194 | 7.165 | 7.132 | 0.8628 | −103. |
| 2-Phenylpentane | " | 379. | 2. | 1.4876 | 1.4853 | 53.81 | 53.60 | 53.35 | 7.194 | 7.165 | 7.132 | 0.8628 | |
| 3-Phenylpentane | " | 376. | 2. | 1.4877 | 1.4854 | 53.9 | 53.7 | 53.4 | 7.20 | 7.18 | 7.14 | 0.864 | |
| 1-Phenyl-2-methylbutane | " | 386. | 2. | 1.486 | 1.484 | 53.8 | 53.6 | 53.4 | 7.20 | 7.17 | 7.14 | 0.863 | |
| 1-Phenyl-3-methylbutane | " | 388. | 2.5 | 1.484 | 1.482 | 53.6 | 53.4 | 53.2 | 7.17 | 7.14 | 7.11 | 0.860 | |
| 2-Phenyl-2-methylbutane | " | 378.28 | 2.4 | 1.4958 | 1.4935 | 54.83 | 54.61 | 54.37 | 7.330 | 7.300 | 7.268 | 0.8792 | |
| 2-Phenyl-3-methylbutane | " | 370. | 2. | 1.486 | 1.484 | 54.5 | 54.3 | 54.1 | 7.29 | 7.26 | 7.23 | 0.874 | |
| 1-Phenyl-2,2-dimethylpropane | " | 367. | 2. | 1.488 | 1.486 | 53.7 | 53.6 | 53.3 | 7.19 | 7.16 | 7.13 | 0.862 | |
| 1-Methyl-2-n-butylbenzene | " | 406. | 2. | 1.496 | 1.494 | 54.6 | 54.4 | 54.1 | 7.30 | 7.27 | 7.24 | 0.875 | |
| 1-Methyl-3-n-butylbenzene | " | 401. | 2. | 1.491 | 1.489 | 53.8 | 53.6 | 53.4 | 7.20 | 7.17 | 7.14 | 0.863 | |
| 1-Methyl-4-n-butylbenzene | " | 405. | 2. | 1.490 | 1.488 | 53.7 | 53.5 | 53.2 | 7.18 | 7.15 | 7.12 | 0.861 | |
| 1-Methyl-2-sec-butylbenzene | " | 385. | 2. | 1.497 | 1.495 | 54.7 | 54.5 | 54.2 | 7.31 | 7.28 | 7.25 | 0.877 | |
| 1-Methyl-3-sec-butylbenzene | " | 381. | 2. | 1.490 | 1.488 | 53.8 | 53.6 | 53.4 | 7.19 | 7.16 | 7.13 | 0.863 | |
| 1-Methyl-4-sec-butylbenzene | " | 387. | 2. | 1.493 | 1.491 | 54.3 | 54.1 | 53.8 | 7.26 | 7.23 | 7.19 | 0.870 | |
| 1-Methyl-2-isobutylbenzene | " | 385. | 2. | 1.4935 | 1.4912 | 54.21 | 53.99 | 53.75 | 7.247 | 7.218 | 7.185 | 0.8693 | |
| 1-Methyl-3-isobutylbenzene | " | 381. | 2. | 1.4888 | 1.4865 | 53.51 | 53.29 | 53.04 | 7.153 | 7.123 | 7.091 | 0.8580 | |
| 1-Methyl-4-isobutylbenzene | " | 385. | 2. | 1.4874 | 1.4851 | 53.39 | 53.17 | 52.93 | 7.137 | 7.108 | 7.075 | 0.8560 | |
| 1-Methyl-2-tert-butylbenzene | " | 392.81 | 2.5 | 1.5076 | 1.5053 | 55.76 | 55.54 | 55.30 | 7.454 | 7.425 | 7.392 | 0.8941 | −58.58 |
| 1-Methyl-3-tert-butylbenzene | " | 372.67 | 2.4 | 1.4944 | 1.4921 | 54.26 | 54.04 | 53.80 | 7.254 | 7.224 | 7.192 | 0.8701 | −42.47 |
| 1-Methyl-4-tert-butylbenzene | " | 378.97 | 2.4 | 1.4918 | 1.4895 | 53.98 | 53.76 | 53.52 | 7.216 | 7.187 | 7.154 | 0.8656 | −62.53 |
| 1-Ethyl-2-n-propylbenzene | " | 397. | 2. | 1.4992 | 1.4969 | 54.80 | 54.59 | 54.34 | 7.326 | 7.297 | 7.265 | 0.8788 | |
| 1-Ethyl-3-n-propylbenzene | " | 394. | 2. | 1.4930 | 1.4907 | 53.95 | 53.73 | 53.49 | 7.212 | 7.183 | 7.150 | 0.8651 | |
| 1-Ethyl-4-n-propylbenzene | " | 401. | 2. | 1.4921 | 1.4898 | 53.87 | 53.65 | 53.41 | 7.201 | 7.172 | 7.139 | 0.8638 | |
| 1-Ethyl-2-isopropylbenzene | " | 379. | 2. | 1.508 | 1.506 | 55.6 | 55.4 | 55.2 | 7.44 | 7.41 | 7.37 | 0.892 | |
| 1-Ethyl-3-isopropylbenzene | " | 377.6 | 2.4 | 1.492 | 1.490 | 53.3 | 53.6 | 53.4 | 7.20 | 7.17 | 7.14 | 0.864 | |
| 1-Ethyl-4-isopropylbenzene | " | 385.9 | 2.5 | 1.4923 | 1.4900 | 53.81 | 53.59 | 53.35 | 7.194 | 7.164 | 7.132 | 0.8628 | |

$^a$ See footnote a of Table 1a-E.

TABLE 26a-E, Page 2 – ALKYL BENZENES, C$_{11}$

BOILING POINT, $dt/dp$, REFRACTIVE INDEX, DENSITY, AND FREEZING POINT

April 30, 1952

| Compound | Formula | Boiling Point 29.921 in Hg (°F) | $dt/dp$ 29.921 in Hg (°F/in Hg) | Refractive Index[a] $n_D$ 68°F | $n_D$ 77°F | Density[a] (lb/cu ft) 60°F | 68°F | 77°F | Density (lb/gal) 60°F | 68°F | 77°F | Specific Gravity[a] 60°F/60°F | Freezing Point In air at 1 atm (°F) |
|---|---|---|---|---|---|---|---|---|---|---|---|---|---|
| 1,2-Dimethyl-3-n-propylbenzene | C$_{11}$H$_{16}$ | 411.3 | 2.5 | 1.5075 | 1.5053 | 55.55 | 55.33 | 55.09 | 7.426 | 7.397 | 7.365 | 0.8908 | |
| 1,2-Dimethyl-4-n-propylbenzene | " | 408.0 | 2.5 | 1.5000 | 1.4978 | 54.62 | 54.40 | 54.16 | 7.302 | 7.273 | 7.240 | 0.8758 | |
| 1,3-Dimethyl-2-n-propylbenzene | " | 405.7 | 2.5 | 1.5063 | 1.5041 | 55.50 | 55.28 | 55.04 | 7.420 | 7.391 | 7.358 | 0.8900 | |
| 1,3-Dimethyl-4-n-propylbenzene | " | 403.9 | 2.5 | 1.4998 | 1.4976 | 54.67 | 54.45 | 54.21 | 7.309 | 7.280 | 7.247 | 0.8767 | |
| 1,3-Dimethyl-5-n-propylbenzene | " | 396.03 | 2.5 | 1.4952 | 1.4930 | 53.95 | 53.73 | 53.49 | 7.212 | 7.183 | 7.150 | 0.8651 | − 74.4 |
| 1,4-Dimethyl-2-n-propylbenzene | " | 399.7 | 2.5 | 1.4999 | 1.4977 | 54.63 | 54.41 | 54.17 | 7.304 | 7.275 | 7.242 | 0.8761 | |
| 1,2-Dimethyl-3-isopropylbenzene | " | 396.7 | 2.5 | 1.508 | 1.506 | 55.6 | 55.4 | 55.2 | 7.44 | 7.41 | 7.38 | 0.892 | |
| 1,2-Dimethyl-4-isopropylbenzene | " | 395.2 | 2.5 | 1.4993 | 1.4971 | 54.52 | 54.30 | 54.06 | 7.289 | 7.260 | 7.227 | 0.8743 | |
| 1,3-Dimethyl-2-isopropylbenzene | " | 390. | 2. | 1.509 | 1.507 | 55.7 | 55.5 | 55.3 | 7.47 | 7.43 | 7.39 | 0.894 | |
| 1,3-Dimethyl-4-isopropylbenzene | " | 390.4 | 2.5 | 1.500 | 1.498 | 54.6 | 54.4 | 54.2 | 7.32 | 7.29 | 7.25 | 0.877 | |
| 1,3-Dimethyl-5-isopropylbenzene | " | 382.1 | 2.4 | 1.495 | 1.493 | 54.0 | 53.8 | 53.6 | 7.22 | 7.19 | 7.16 | 0.866 | |
| 1,4-Dimethyl-2-isopropylbenzene | " | 385.2 | 2.5 | 1.5010 | 1.4988 | 54.76 | 54.54 | 54.30 | 7.321 | 7.292 | 7.260 | 0.8782 | |
| 1-Methyl-2,3-diethylbenzene | " | 403.9 | 2.5 | 1.5105 | 1.5083 | 55.84 | 55.62 | 55.38 | 7.465 | 7.436 | 7.403 | 0.8954 | |
| 1-Methyl-2,4-diethylbenzene | " | 401.0 | 2.5 | 1.5027 | 1.5005 | 54.83 | 54.61 | 54.37 | 7.330 | 7.300 | 7.268 | 0.8792 | |
| 1-Methyl-2,5-diethylbenzene | " | 404.8 | 2.5 | 1.5034 | 1.5012 | 54.89 | 54.67 | 54.43 | 7.338 | 7.309 | 7.276 | 0.8802 | |
| 1-Methyl-2,6-diethylbenzene | " | 407.8 | 2.5 | 1.5106 | 1.5084 | 55.82 | 55.60 | 55.36 | 7.462 | 7.433 | 7.401 | 0.8951 | |
| 1-Methyl-3,4-diethylbenzene | " | 398.5 | 2.5 | 1.5039 | 1.5017 | 54.91 | 54.69 | 54.45 | 7.341 | 7.312 | 7.280 | 0.8806 | |
| 1-Methyl-3,5-diethylbenzene | " | 393.26 | 2.5 | 1.4969 | 1.4947 | 54.09 | 53.87 | 53.63 | 7.231 | 7.202 | 7.169 | 0.8674 | −101.42 |
| 1,2,3-Trimethyl-4-ethylbenzene | " | 428.7 | 2.6 | 1.5180 | 1.5158 | 56.52 | 56.30 | 56.06 | 7.556 | 7.527 | 7.494 | 0.9063 | |
| 1,2,3-Trimethyl-5-ethylbenzene | " | 420.4 | 2.5 | 1.5101 | 1.5079 | 55.55 | 55.33 | 55.09 | 7.426 | 7.396 | 7.364 | 0.8907 | |
| 1,2,4-Trimethyl-3-ethylbenzene | " | 421.9 | 2.5 | 1.5133 | 1.5111 | 56.0 | 55.8 | 55.6 | 7.50 | 7.47 | 7.44 | 0.899 | |
| 1,2,4-Trimethyl-5-ethylbenzene | " | 415.4 | 2.5 | 1.5075 | 1.5053 | 55.3 | 55.1 | 54.9 | 7.40 | 7.37 | 7.34 | 0.887 | 7.7 |
| 1,2,4-Trimethyl-6-ethylbenzene | " | 415.4 | 2.5 | 1.5118 | 1.5096 | 55.76 | 55.54 | 55.30 | 7.454 | 7.425 | 7.392 | 0.8941 | |
| 1,3,5-Trimethyl-2-ethylbenzene | " | 414.3 | 2.5 | 1.5074 | 1.5052 | 55.3 | 55.1 | 54.9 | 7.40 | 7.37 | 7.34 | 0.887 | 4.1 |
| Pentamethylbenzene | " | 449.2 | 2.6 | 1.527$^b$ | 1.525$^b$ | 57.4$^b$ | 57.2$^b$ | 57.0$^b$ | 7.68$^b$ | 7.65$^b$ | 7.62$^b$ | 0.921$^b$ | 129.7 |

a See footnote a of Table 1a-E.  b For the undercooled liquid below the normal freezing point.

138

TABLE 13a-E – STYRENES, $C_8$ AND $C_9$

BOILING POINT, $dt/dp$, REFRACTIVE INDEX, DENSITY, AND FREEZING POINT

September 30, 1943; June 30, 1945; May 31, 1947; June 30, 1948; October 31, 1952

| Compound | Formula | Boiling Point 29.921 in Hg °F | $dt/dp$ 29.921 in Hg °F/in Hg | Refractive Index[a] $n_D$ 68°F | $n_D$ 77°F | Density[a] lb/cu ft 60°F | 68°F | 77°F | lb/gal 60°F | 68°F | 77°F | Specific Gravity[a] 60°F/60°F | Freezing Point In air at 1 atm °F |
|---|---|---|---|---|---|---|---|---|---|---|---|---|---|
| Ethenylbenzene (Styrene; Vinylbenzene; Phenylethylene) | $C_8H_8$ | 293.4 | 2.24 | 1.54682 | 1.54395 | 56.82 | 56.558 | 56.260 | 7.596 | 7.5608 | 7.5209 | 0.9111 | −23.13 |
| Isopropenylbenzene (α-Methylstyrene; 2-Phenyl-1-propene) | $C_9H_{10}$ | 329.68 | 2.38 | 1.5386 | 1.5358 | 57.09 | 56.85 | 56.57 | 7.632 | 7.599 | 7.562 | 0.9154 | −9.78 |
| cis-1-Propenylbenzene (cis-β-Methylstyrene; cis-1-Phenyl-1-propene) | " | 338. | 2.33 | 1.549 | 1.546 | 57.1 | 56.9 | 56.6 | 7.63 | 7.60 | 7.57 | 0.915 | |
| trans-1-Propenylbenzene (trans-β-Methylstyrene; trans-1-Phenyl-1-propene) | | | | | | | | | | | | | |
| 1-Methyl-2-ethenylbenzene (o-Methylstyrene) | " | 340. | 2.33 | 1.5450 | 1.5422 | 57.10 | 56.04 | 56.56 | 7.633 | 7.599 | 7.561 | 0.9156 | |
| 1-Methyl-3-ethenylbenzene (m-Methylstyrene) | " | 334. | 2.33 | 1.5419 | 1.5391 | 56.37 | 56.12 | 55.83 | 7.536 | 7.502 | 7.463 | 0.9039 | |
| 1-Methyl-4-ethenylbenzene (p-Methylstyrene) | " | 336. | 2.33 | 1.5428 | 1.5400 | 56.3 | 56.0 | 55.7 | 7.52 | 7.49 | 7.44 | 0.902 | |

[a] See footnote a of Table 1a-E.

TABLE 30a-E -1- NORMAL ALKYL NAPHTHALENES, $C_{10}$ TO $C_{22}$
BOILING POINT, $dt/dp$, REFRACTIVE INDEX, DENSITY, AND FREEZING POINT

October 31, 1952

| Compound | Formula | Boiling Point 29.921 in Hg °F | $dt/dp$ 29.921 in Hg °F/in Hg | Refractive Index[a] $n_D$ 68°F | $n_D$ 77°F | Density[a] lb/cu ft 60°F | lb/cu ft 68°F | lb/cu ft 77°F | lb/gal 60°F | lb/gal 68°F | lb/gal 77°F | Specific Gravity[a] 60°F/60°F | Freezing Point In air at 1 atm °F |
|---|---|---|---|---|---|---|---|---|---|---|---|---|---|
| Naphthalene | $C_{10}H_8$ | 424.32 | 2.67 | — | 1.5898[b] | ——— | ——— | 60.88[b] | ——— | ——— | 8.138[b] | — | +176.52 |
| 1-Methylnaphthalene | $C_{11}H_{10}$ | 472.36 | 2.76 | 1.6174 | 1.6149 | 63.90 | 63.684 | 63.444 | 8.542 | 8.5134 | 8.4812 | 1.0246 | -23.03 |
| 1-Ethylnaphthalene | $C_{12}H_{12}$ | 497.61 | 2.81 | 1.6062 | 1.6040 | 63.14 | 62.996 | 62.705 | 8.441 | 8.4133 | 8.3824 | 1.0124 | +7.02 |
| 1-$n$-Propylnaphthalene | $C_{13}H_{14}$ | 522.5 | 3. | 1.5952 | 1.5930 | 62.11 | 61.91 | 61.69 | 8.303 | 8.277 | 8.247 | 0.9960 | 14. |
| 1-$n$-Butylnaphthalene | $C_{14}H_{16}$ | 552.81 | 3. | 1.5819 | 1.5798 | 61.17 | 60.974 | 60.756 | 8.177 | 8.1510 | 8.1219 | 0.9808 | -3.57 |
| 1-$n$-Pentylnaphthalene | $C_{15}H_{18}$ | 585. | 3. | 1.5725 | 1.5704 | 60.47 | 60.28 | 60.07 | 8.083 | 8.058 | 8.030 | 0.9695 | -8. |
| 1-$n$-Hexylnaphthalene | $C_{16}H_{20}$ | 612. | 3. | 1.5647 | 1.5626 | 59.90 | 59.72 | 59.51 | 8.008 | 7.983 | 7.955 | 0.9605 | 0. |
| 1-$n$-Heptylnaphthalene | $C_{17}H_{22}$ | 644. | 3. | 1.5582 | 1.5561 | 59.43 | 59.25 | 59.04 | 7.945 | 7.920 | 7.893 | 0.9529 | 18. |
| 1-$n$-Octylnaphthalene | $C_{18}H_{24}$ | 673. | 3. | 1.5526 | 1.5505 | 59.03 | 58.85 | 58.64 | 7.891 | 7.867 | 7.839 | 0.9465 | 28. |
| 1-$n$-Nonylnaphthalene | $C_{19}H_{26}$ | 702. | 3. | 1.5477 | 1.5456 | 58.68 | 58.50 | 58.30 | 7.845 | 7.820 | 7.794 | 0.9409 | 46. |
| 1-$n$-Decylnaphthalene | $C_{20}H_{28}$ | 729. | 3. | 1.5435 | 1.5414 | 58.37[c] | 58.19 | 57.99 | 7.803[c] | 7.779 | 7.753 | 0.9359[c] | 59. |
| 1-$n$-Undecylnaphthalene | $C_{21}H_{30}$ | 754. | 3. | 1.5399[c] | 1.5379 | 58.10[c] | 57.93[c] | 57.73 | 7.767[c] | 7.744[c] | 7.718 | 0.9316[c] | 73. |
| 1-$n$-Dodecylnaphthalene | $C_{22}H_{32}$ | 779. | 3. | 1.5364[c] | 1.5344[c] | 57.86 | 57.68[c] | 57.49[c] | 7.734[c] | 7.711[c] | 7.685[c] | 0.9277[c] | 81. |

[a] See footnote a of Table 1a-E.  [b] At 185°F.  [c] For the undercooled liquid below the normal freezing point.

TABLE 31a-E -2- NORMAL ALKYL NAPHTHALENES, C$_{10}$ TO C$_{22}$

BOILING POINT, dt/dp, REFRACTIVE INDEX, DENSITY, AND FREEZING POINT

October 31, 1952

| Compound | Formula | Boiling Point 29.921 in Hg °F | dt/dp 29.921 in Hg °F/in Hg | Refractive Index[a] $n_D$ 68°F | Refractive Index[a] $n_D$ 77°F | Density[a] lb/cu ft 60°F | Density[a] lb/cu ft 68°F | Density[a] lb/cu ft 77°F | Density[a] lb/gal 60°F | Density[a] lb/gal 68°F | Density[a] lb/gal 77°F | Specific Gravity[a] 60°F/60°F | Freezing Point In air at 1 atm °F |
|---|---|---|---|---|---|---|---|---|---|---|---|---|---|
| Naphthalene | C$_{10}$H$_8$ | 424.32 | 2.67 | --- | 1.5898[b] | --- | --- | 60.88[b] | --- | --- | 8.138[b] | --- | 176.52 |
| 2-Methylnaphthalene | C$_{11}$H$_{10}$ | 465.89 | 2.74 | --- | 1.6019[c] | --- | --- | 61.83[c] | --- | --- | 8.265[c] | --- | 94.24 |
| 2-Ethylnaphthalene | C$_{12}$H$_{12}$ | 496.2 | 2.8 | 1.5999 | 1.5977 | 62.15 | 61.94 | 61.71 | 8.308 | 8.280 | 8.249 | 0.9965 | 18.7 |
| 2-$n$-Propylnaphthalene | C$_{13}$H$_{14}$ | 524.3 | 3. | 1.5872 | 1.5850 | 61.19 | 60.99 | 60.77 | 8.180 | 8.153 | 8.123 | 0.9811 | 27. |
| 2-$n$-Butylnaphthalene | C$_{14}$H$_{16}$ | 558. | 3. | 1.5776 | 1.5755 | 60.49 | 60.30 | 60.08 | 8.087 | 8.061 | 8.031 | 0.9699 | 23. |
| 2-$n$-Pentylnaphthalene | C$_{15}$H$_{18}$ | 590. | 3. | 1.5694 | 1.5673 | 59.87 | 59.69 | 59.47 | 8.004 | 7.979 | 7.950 | 0.9600 | 25. |
| 2-$r$-Hexylnaphthalene | C$_{16}$H$_{20}$ | 615. | 3. | 1.5620 | 1.5599 | 59.36 | 59.17 | 58.96 | 7.935 | 7.910 | 7.882 | 0.9518 | 27. |
| 2-$n$-Heptylnaphthalene | C$_{17}$H$_{22}$ | 646. | 3. | 1.5556 | 1.5535 | 58.92 | 58.74 | 58.54 | 7.877 | 7.853 | 7.825 | 0.9448 | 34. |
| 2-$n$-Octylnaphthalene | C$_{18}$H$_{24}$ | 675. | 3. | 1.5501 | 1.5480 | 58.55 | 58.37 | 58.16 | 7.827 | 7.803 | 7.775 | 0.9388 | 54. |
| 2-$n$-Nonylnaphthalene | C$_{19}$H$_{26}$ | 702. | 3. | 1.5454 | 1.5433 | 58.23 | 58.04 | 57.84 | 7.784 | 7.759 | 7.733 | 0.9336 | 54. |
| 2-$n$-Decylnaphthalene | C$_{20}$H$_{28}$ | 729. | 3. | 1.5413 | 1.5392 | 57.94 | 57.76 | 57.56 | 7.745 | 7.722 | 7.695 | 0.9290 | 68. |
| 2-$n$-Undecylnaphthalene | C$_{21}$H$_{30}$ | 754. | 3. | 1.5376 | 1.5356 | 57.69 | 57.51 | 57.32 | 7.712 | 7.688 | 7.663 | 0.9250 | 68. |
| 2-$n$-Dodecylnaphthalene | C$_{22}$H$_{32}$ | 777. | 3. | 1.5343 | 1.5323 | 57.46 | 57.29 | 57.10 | 7.682 | 7.658 | 7.633 | 0.9214 | 79. |

[a] See footnote a of Table 1a-E.    [b] At 185°F.    [c] At 104°F.

## TABLE 27a-E — NAPHTHALENES, $C_{10}$ TO $C_{12}$
### BOILING POINT, *dt/dp*, REFRACTIVE INDEX, DENSITY, AND FREEZING POINT
February 28, 1949; October 31, 1952

| Compound | Formula | Boiling Point 29.921 in Hg °F | dt/dp 29.921 in Hg °F/in Hg | Refractive Index[a] $n_D$ 68°F | Refractive Index[a] $n_D$ 77°F | Density[a] lb/cu ft 60°F | Density[a] lb/cu ft 68°F | Density[a] lb/cu ft 77°F | Density[a] lb/gal 60°F | Density[a] lb/gal 68°F | Density[a] lb/gal 77°F | Specific Gravity[a] 60°F/60°F | Freezing Point In air at 1 atm °F |
|---|---|---|---|---|---|---|---|---|---|---|---|---|---|
| Naphthalene | $C_{10}H_8$ | 424.32 | 2.67 | —— | (1.5698)[b] | —— | —— | (60.88)[b] | —— | —— | (8.138)[b] | —— | 176.52 |
| 1-Methylnaphthalene | $C_{11}H_{10}$ | 472.36 | 2.76 | 1.6174 | 1.6149 | 63.90 | 63.684 | 63.444 | 8.542 | 8.5134 | 8.4812 | 1.0246 | -23.03 |
| 2-Methylnaphthalene | " | 465.89 | 2.74 | | (1.6019)[b] | | | (61.83)[c] | | | (8.265)[c] | | +94.24 |
| 1-Ethylnaphthalene | $C_{12}H_{12}$ | 497.61 | 2.81 | 1.6062 | 1.6040 | 63.14 | 62.936 | 62.705 | 8.441 | 8.4133 | 8.3824 | 1.0124 | 7.02 |
| 2-Ethylnaphthalene | " | 496.2 | 2.8 | 1.5999 | 1.5977 | 62.17 | 61.93 | 61.71 | 8.311 | 8.280 | 8.249 | 0.9969 | 18.7 |
| 1,2-Dimethylnaphthalene | " | 511. | 2.6 | 1.6164 | 1.6142 | 63.5 | 63.2 | 63.0 | 8.49 | 8.45 | 8.42 | 1.018 | 30.2 |
| 1,3-Dimethylnaphthalene | " | 505. | 2.6 | 1.6090 | 1.6068 | 63.03 | 62.82 | 62.59 | 8.425 | 8.398 | 8.367 | 1.0106 | 24.8 |
| 1,4-Dimethylnaphthalene | " | 514. | 2.6 | 1.6127 | 1.6105 | 63.67 | 63.46 | 63.23 | 8.511 | 8.484 | 8.453 | 1.0209 | 45.79 |
| 1,5-Dimethylnaphthalene | " | 509. | 2.6 | —— | —— | —— | —— | —— | —— | —— | —— | —— | 179.6 |
| 1,6-Dimethylnaphthalene | " | 505. | 2.6 | 1.6073 | 1.6051 | 62.9 | 62.6 | 62.4 | 8.40 | 8.37 | 8.34 | 1.008 | 7. |
| 1,7-Dimethylnaphthalene | " | 505. | 2.6 | 1.607 | 1.605 | 62.9 | 62.6 | 62.4 | 8.40 | 8.37 | 8.34 | 1.008 | 9. d |
| 1,8-Dimethylnaphthalene | " | 518. | 2.6 | —— | —— | —— | —— | —— | —— | —— | —— | —— | 149. |
| 2,3-Dimethylnaphthalene | " | 514. | 2.6 | —— | —— | —— | —— | —— | —— | —— | —— | —— | 221.0 |
| 2,6-Dimethylnaphthalene | " | 504. | 2.6 | —— | —— | —— | —— | —— | —— | —— | —— | —— | 233.6 |
| 2,7-Dimethylnaphthalene | " | 505. | 2.6 | —— | —— | —— | —— | —— | —— | —— | —— | —— | 208.4 |

a See footnote a of Table 1a-E.  b At 185°F.  c At 104°F.  d For the metastable crystalline form IIu, the freezing point is -18. °F.

143

TABLE 28a-E, Page 1 – TETRAHYDRONAPHTHALENES, $C_{10}$ TO $C_{12}$
BOILING POINT, $dt/dp$, REFRACTIVE INDEX, DENSITY, AND FREEZING POINT
August 31, 1949; October 31, 1952

| Compound | Formula | Boiling Point 29.921 in Hg (°F) | $dt/dp$ 29.921 in Hg (°F/in Hg) | Refractive Index[a] 68°F $n_D$ | 77°F $n_D$ | Density[a] 60°F (lb/cu ft) | 68°F | 77°F | 60°F (lb/gal) | 68°F | -77°F | Specific Gravity[a] 60°F/60°F | Freezing Point In air at 1 atm (°F) |
|---|---|---|---|---|---|---|---|---|---|---|---|---|---|
| 1,2,3,4-Tetrahydronaphthalene | $C_{10}H_{12}$ | 405.63 | 2.63 | 1.54135 | 1.53919 | 60.79 | 60.57 | 60.32 | 81.27 | 80.97 | 80.63 | 0.9747 | -32.42 |
| 1-Methyl-[1,2,3,4-tetrahydronaphthalene] | $C_{11}H_{14}$ | 426. | 2.7 | 1.5357 | 1.5336 | 60.01 | 59.80 | 59.57 | 80.22 | 79.95 | 79.64 | 0.9622 | |
| 2-Methyl-[1,2,3,4-tetrahydronaphthalene] | " | 424. | 2.7 | 1.531 | 1.529 | 59.7 | 59.4 | 59.2 | 79.8 | 79.4 | 79.1 | 0.957 | |
| 5-Methyl-[1,2,3,4-tetrahydronaphthalene] | " | 453.83 | 2.7 | 1.54395 | 1.54190 | 60.88 | 60.68 | 60.45 | 81.39 | 81.12 | 80.81 | 0.9762 | -9.22 |
| 6-Methyl-[1,2,3,4-tetrahydronaphthalene] | " | 444.25 | 2.7 | 1.53572 | 1.53365 | 59.74 | 59.54 | 59.31 | 79.86 | 79.59 | 79.28 | 0.9579 | -39.55 |
| 1-Ethyl-[1,2,3,4-tetrahydronaphthalene] | $C_{12}H_{16}$ | 457. | 2.7 | 1.5321 | 1.5300 | 59.73 | 59.52 | 59.29 | 79.85 | 79.57 | 79.26 | 0.9577 | |
| 2-Ethyl-[1,2,3,4-tetrahydronaphthalene] | " | 457. | 2.7 | 1.523 | 1.521 | 58.8 | 59.6 | 58.3 | 78.6 | 78.3 | 77.9 | 0.943 | |
| 5-Ethyl-[1,2,3,4-tetrahydronaphthalene] | " | 468. | 2.7 | 1.540 | 1.538 | 61.0 | 60.7 | 60.5 | 81.5 | 81.2 | 80.9 | 0.978 | |
| 6-Ethyl-[1,2,3,4-tetrahydronaphthalene] | " | 468. | 2.7 | 1.5331 | 1.5310 | 59.94 | 59.73 | 59.50 | 80.12 | 79.85 | 79.54 | 0.9610 | |
| 1,1-Dimethyl-[1,2,3,4-tetrahydronaphthalene] | " | 430. | 2.7 | 1.5292 | 1.5271 | 59.6 | 59.3 | 59.1 | 79.6 | 79.3 | 78.9 | 0.955 | |
| 1,cis-2-Dimethyl-[1,2,3,4-tetrahydronaphthalene] | " | 455. | 2.7 | 1.5286 | 1.5265 | 59.32 | 59.12 | 58.89 | 79.30 | 79.03 | 78.72 | 0.9512 | |
| 1,trans-2-Dimethyl-[1,2,3,4-tetrahydronaphthalene] | " | | | | | | | | | | | | |
| 1,cis-3-Dimethyl-[1,2,3,4-tetrahydronaphthalene] | " | 453. | 2.7 | 1.525 | 1.523 | 58.9 | 58.7 | 58.4 | 78.8 | 78.4 | 78.1 | 0.945 | |
| 1,trans-3-Dimethyl-[1,2,3,4-tetrahydronaphthalene] | " | | | | | | | | | | | | |
| 1,cis-4-Dimethyl-[1,2,3,4-tetrahydronaphthalene] | " | 453. | 2.7 | 1.528 | 1.526 | 58.9 | 58.7 | 58.4 | 78.8 | 78.4 | 78.1 | 0.945 | |
| 1,trans-4-Dimethyl-[1,2,3,4-tetrahydronaphthalene] | " | | | | | | | | | | | | |

a See footnote a of Table 1a-E.

TABLE 2ba-E, Page 2 - TETRAHYDRONAPHTHALENES, $C_{10}$ TO $C_{12}$
BOILING POINT, $dt/dp$, REFRACTIVE INDEX, DENSITY, AND FREEZING POINT
August 31, 1949; October 31, 1952

| Compound | Formula | Boiling Point 29.921 in Hg (°F) | $dt/dp$ 29.921 in Hg (°F/in Hg) | Refractive Index[a] $n_D$ 68°F | Refractive Index[a] $n_D$ 77°F | Density[a] 60°F (lb/cu ft) | Density[a] 68°F (lb/cu ft) | Density[a] 77°F (lb/cu ft) | Density[a] 60°F (lb/gal) | Density[a] 68°F (lb/gal) | Density[a] 77°F (lb/gal) | Specific Gravity[a] 60°F/60°F | Freezing Point In air at 1 atm (°F) |
|---|---|---|---|---|---|---|---|---|---|---|---|---|---|
| 2,2-Dimethyl-[1,2,3,4-tetrahydronaphthalene] | $C_{12}H_{16}$ | 446. | 2.7 | 1.5200 | 1.5180 | 58.6 | 58.4 | 58.1 | 7.84 | 7.80 | 7.77 | 0.940 | |
| 2,cis-3-Dimethyl-[1,2,3,4-tetrahydronaphthalene] | " | 450. | 2.7 | 1.523 | 1.521 | 58.9 | 58.7 | 58.4 | 7.88 | 7.84 | 7.81 | 0.945 | 50. |
| 2,trans-3-Dimethyl-[1,2,3,4-tetrahydronaphthalene] | " | | | | | 59.0 | 58.7 | 58.5 | 7.89 | 7.85 | 7.82 | 0.946 | |
| 1,5-Dimethyl-[1,2,3,4-tetrahydronaphthalene] | " | 462. | 2.7 | 1.526 | 1.524 | 58.9 | 58.6 | 58.4 | 7.87 | 7.84 | 7.80 | 0.944 | |
| 1,6-Dimethyl-[1,2,3,4-tetrahydronaphthalene] | " | | | | | 59.0 | 58.7 | 58.5 | 7.89 | 7.85 | 7.82 | 0.946 | |
| 1,7-Dimethyl-[1,2,3,4-tetrahydronaphthalene] | " | | | | | 59.0 | 58.7 | 58.5 | 7.89 | 7.85 | 7.82 | 0.946 | |
| 1,8-Dimethyl-[1,2,3,4-tetrahydronaphthalene] | " | 457. | 2.7 | 1.526 | 1.524 | 59.3 | 59.1 | 58.8 | 7.93 | 7.89 | 7.86 | 0.951 | |
| 2,5-Dimethyl-[1,2,3,4-tetrahydronaphthalene] | " | 460. | 2.7 | 1.526 | 1.524 | 59.0 | 58.7 | 58.5 | 7.89 | 7.85 | 7.82 | 0.946 | |
| 2,6-Dimethyl-[1,2,3,4-tetrahydronaphthalene] | " | 459. | 2.7 | 1.526 | 1.524 | 59.0 | 58.7 | 58.5 | 7.89 | 7.85 | 7.82 | 0.946 | 68. |
| 2,7-Dimethyl-[1,2,3,4-tetrahydronaphthalene] | " | 457. | 2.7 | 1.526 | 1.524 | 59.0 | 58.7 | 58.5 | 7.89 | 7.85 | 7.82 | 0.946 | |
| 2,8-Dimethyl-[1,2,3,4-tetrahydronaphthalene] | " | 486. | 2.7 | 1.552 | 1.550 | 61.1 | 60.9 | 60.6 | 8.17 | 8.14 | 8.10 | 0.980 | |
| 5,6-Dimethyl-[1,2,3,4-tetrahydronaphthalene] | " | 487.6 | 2.7 | 1.5405 | 1.5384 | 60.08 | 59.82 | 59.54 | 8.031 | 7.997 | 7.959 | 0.9633 | |
| 5,7-Dimethyl-[1,2,3,4-tetrahydronaphthalene] | " | 489. | 2.7 | 1.547 | 1.545 | 60.6 | 60.4 | 60.1 | 8.10 | 8.07 | 8.04 | 0.972 | 17. |
| 5,8-Dimethyl-[1,2,3,4-tetrahydronaphthalene] | " | 486. | 2.7 | 1.538 | 1.536 | 59.8 | 59.5 | 59.3 | 7.99 | 7.96 | 7.93 | 0.959 | 50. |
| 6,7-Dimethyl-[1,2,3,4-tetrahydronaphthalene] | " | | | | | | | | | | | | |

[a] See footnote a of Table 1a-E.

TABLE 23a-E (PART 1) – DECAHYDRONAPHTHALENES, $C_{10}$ AND $C_{11}$
BOILING POINT, $dt/dp$, REFRACTIVE INDEX, DENSITY, AND FREEZING POINT

October 31, 1950 (Corrected)

| Compound | Formula | Boiling Point 29.921 in Hg | $dt/dp$ 29.921 in Hg | Refractive Index[a] | | Density[a] | | | | | | Specific Gravity[a] | Freezing Point In air at 1 atm |
|---|---|---|---|---|---|---|---|---|---|---|---|---|---|
| | | °F | °F/in Hg | $n_D$ 68°F | $n_D$ 77°F | lb/cu ft 60°F | 68°F | 77°F | lb/gal 60°F | 68°F | 77°F | 60°F/60°F | °F |
| cis-Decahydronaphthalene | $C_{10}H_{18}$ | 384.24 | 2.515 | 1.4810 | 1.4788 | 56.19 | 55.97 | 55.72 | 7.512 | 7.481 | 7.448 | 0.9010 | −45.42 |
| trans-Decahydronaphthalene | " | 369.05 | 2.579 | 1.4695 | 1.4672 | 54.53 | 54.30 | 54.06 | 7.290 | 7.260 | 7.226 | 0.8743 | −22.72 |
| 1-Methyl-[cis-decahydronaphthalene] | $C_{11}H_{20}$ | 469. | 2.7 | 1.4720 | 1.4698 | | | | | | | | |
| 1-Methyl-[trans-decahydronaphthalene] | " | 455. | 2.7 | | | | | | | | | | |
| 2-Methyl-[cis-decahydronaphthalene] | " | 421. | 2.7 | | | | | | | | | | |
| 2-Methyl-[trans-decahydronaphthalene] | " | 406. | 2.7 | | | | | | | | | | |
| 9-Methyl-[cis-decahydronaphthalene] | " | 419. | 2.7 | 1.4804 | 1.4782 | 55.9 | 55.6 | 55.4 | 7.47 | 7.44 | 7.40 | 0.896 | |
| 9-Methyl-[trans-decahydronaphthalene] | " | 401. | 2.7 | 1.4631 | 1.4619 | 54.1 | 53.8 | 53.6 | 7.23 | 7.19 | 7.16 | 0.867 | |

[a] See footnote a of Table 1a-E.

TABLE 29a-E (PART 2) - DECAHYDRONAPHTHALENES, C$_{12}$

BOILING POINT, $dt/dp$, REFRACTIVE INDEX, DENSITY, AND FREEZING POINT

October 31, 1950

| Compound | Formula | Boiling Point 29.921 in Hg °F | $dt/dp$ 29.921 in Hg °F/in Hg | Refractive Index[a] $n_D$ 68°F | Refractive Index[a] $n_D$ 77°F | Density[a] lb/cu ft 60°F | Density[a] lb/cu ft 68°F | Density[a] lb/cu ft 77°F | Density[a] lb/gal 60°F | Density[a] lb/gal 68°F | Density[a] lb/gal 77°F | Specific Gravity[a] 60°F/60°F | Freezing Point In air at 1 atm °F |
|---|---|---|---|---|---|---|---|---|---|---|---|---|---|
| 1-Ethyl-[cis-decahydronaphthalene] | C$_{12}$H$_{22}$ | 500. | 2.7 | | | | | | | | | | |
| 1-Ethyl-[trans-decahydronaphthalene] | " | 491. | 2.7 | | | | | | | | | | |
| 2-Ethyl-[cis-decahydronaphthalene] | " | 455. | 2.7 | | | | | | | | | | |
| 2-Ethyl-[trans-decahydronaphthalene] | " | 442. | 2.7 | | | | | | | | | | |
| 9-Ethyl-[cis-decahydronaphthalene] | " | 451. | 2.7 | 1.480 | 1.478 | 55.5 | 55.3 | 55.1 | 7.42 | 7.40 | 7.37 | 0.891 | |
| 9-Ethyl-[trans-decahydronaphthalene] | " | 437. | 2.7 | 1.466 | 1.464 | 53.9 | 53.7 | 53.5 | 7.21 | 7.18 | 7.15 | 0.865 | |
| 1,1-Dimethyl-[cis-decahydronaphthalene] | " | | | | | | | | | | | | |
| 1,1-Dimethyl-[trans-decahydronaphthalene] | " | | | | | | | | | | | | |
| 1,cis-2-Dimethyl-[cis-decahydronaphthalene] | " | | | | | | | | | | | | |
| 1,cis-2-Dimethyl-[trans-decahydronaphthalene] | " | | | | | | | | | | | | |
| 1,trans-2-Dimethyl-[cis-decahydronaphthalene] | " | | | | | | | | | | | | |
| 1,trans-2-Dimethyl-[trans-decahydronaphthalene] | " | | | | | | | | | | | | |
| 1,cis-3-Dimethyl-[cis-decahydronaphthalene] | " | | | | | | | | | | | | |
| 1,cis-3-Dimethyl-[trans-decahydronaphthalene] | " | | | | | | | | | | | | |
| 1,trans-3-Dimethyl-[cis-decahydronaphthalene] | " | | | | | | | | | | | | |
| 1,trans-3-Dimethyl-[trans-decahydronaphthalene] | " | | | | | | | | | | | | |
| 1,cis-4-Dimethyl-[cis-decahydronaphthalene] | " | | | | | | | | | | | | |
| 1,cis-4-Dimethyl-[trans-decahydronaphthalene] | " | | | | | | | | | | | | |
| 1,trans-4-Dimethyl-[cis-decahydronaphthalene] | " | | | | | | | | | | | | |
| 1,trans-4-Dimethyl-[trans-decahydronaphthalene] | " | | | | | | | | | | | | |
| 1,cis-5-Dimethyl-[cis-decahydronaphthalene] | " | | | | | | | | | | | | |
| 1,cis-5-Dimethyl-[trans-decahydronaphthalene] | " | | | | | | | | | | | | |
| 1,trans-5-Dimethyl-[cis-decahydronaphthalene] | " | | | | | | | | | | | | |
| 1,trans-5-Dimethyl-[trans-decahydronaphthalene] | " | | | | | | | | | | | | |
| 1,cis-6-Dimethyl-[cis-decahydronaphthalene] | " | | | | | | | | | | | | |
| 1,cis-6-Dimethyl-[trans-decahydronaphthalene] | " | | | | | | | | | | | | |
| 1,trans-6-Dimethyl-[cis-decahydronaphthalene] | " | | | | | | | | | | | | |
| 1,trans-6-Dimethyl-[trans-decahydronaphthalene] | " | | | | | | | | | | | | |
| 1,cis-7-Dimethyl-[cis-decahydronaphthalene] | " | | | | | | | | | | | | |
| 1,cis-7-Dimethyl-[trans-decahydronaphthalene] | " | | | | | | | | | | | | |
| 1,trans-7-Dimethyl-[cis-decahydronaphthalene] | " | | | | | | | | | | | | |
| 1,trans-7-Dimethyl-[trans-decahydronaphthalene] | " | | | | | | | | | | | | |

[a] See footnote a of Table 1a-E.

147

TABLE 23a-E (PART 3) — DECAHYDRONAPHTHALENES, $C_{12}$

BOILING POINT, dt/dp, REFRACTIVE INDEX, DENSITY, AND FREEZING POINT

October 31, 1950

| Compound | Formula | Boiling Point 29.921 in Hg °F | dt/dp 29.921 in Hg °F/in.Hg | Refractive Index[a] $n_D$ 68°F | $n_D$ 77°F | Density[a] (lb/cu ft) 60°F | 68°F | 77°F | Density[a] (lb/gal) 60°F | 68°F | 77°F | Specific Gravity[a] 60°F/60°F | Freezing Point In air at 1 atm °F |
|---|---|---|---|---|---|---|---|---|---|---|---|---|---|
| 1,cis-8-Dimethyl-[cis-decahydronaphthalene] | $C_{12}H_{22}$ | 428. | 2.7 | 1.4812 | 1.4790 | 55.76 | 55.53 | 55.28 | 7.454 | 7.424 | 7.391 | 0.8941 | |
| 1,cis-8-Dimethyl-[trans-decahydronaphthalene] | " | 415. | 2.7 | 1.4659 | 1.4637 | 54.12 | 53.89 | 53.64 | 7.234 | 7.204 | 7.171 | 0.8677 | |
| 1,trans-8-Dimethyl-[cis-decahydronaphthalene] | " | | | | | | | | | | | | |
| 1,trans-8-Dimethyl-[trans-decahydronaphthalene] | " | | | | | | | | | | | | |
| 1,9-Dimethyl-[cis-decahydronaphthalene] | " | | | | | | | | | | | | |
| 1,9-Dimethyl-[trans-decahydronaphthalene] | " | | | | | | | | | | | | |
| 1,10-Dimethyl-[cis-decahydronaphthalene] | " | | | | | | | | | | | | |
| 1,10-Dimethyl-[trans-decahydronaphthalene] | " | | | | | | | | | | | | |
| 2,2-Dimethyl-[cis-decahydronaphthalene] | " | | | | | | | | | | | | |
| 2,2-Dimethyl-[trans-decahydronaphthalene] | " | | | | | | | | | | | | |
| 2,cis-3-Dimethyl-[cis-decahydronaphthalene] | " | | | | | | | | | | | | |
| 2,cis-3-Dimethyl-[trans-decahydronaphthalene] | " | | | | | | | | | | | | |
| 2,trans-3-Dimethyl-[cis-decahydronaphthalene] | " | | | | | | | | | | | | |
| 2,trans-3-Dimethyl-[trans-decahydronaphthalene] | " | | | | | | | | | | | | |
| 2,cis-6-Dimethyl-[cis-decahydronaphthalene] | " | | | | | | | | | | | | |
| 2,cis-6-Dimethyl-[trans-decahydronaphthalene] | " | | | | | | | | | | | | |
| 2,trans-6-Dimethyl-[cis-decahydronaphthalene] | " | | | | | | | | | | | | |
| 2,trans-6-Dimethyl-[trans-decahydronaphthalene] | " | | | | | | | | | | | | |
| 2,cis-7-Dimethyl-[cis-decahydronaphthalene] | " | | | | | | | | | | | | |
| 2,cis-7-Dimethyl-[trans-decahydronaphthalene] | " | | | | | | | | | | | | |
| 2,trans-7-Dimethyl-[cis-decahydronaphthalene] | " | | | | | | | | | | | | |
| 2,trans-7-Dimethyl-[trans-decahydronaphthalene] | " | | | | | | | | | | | | |
| 2,9-Dimethyl-[cis-decahydronaphthalene] | " | | | | | | | | | | | | |
| 2,9-Dimethyl-[trans-decahydronaphthalene] | " | | | | | | | | | | | | |
| 2,10-Dimethyl-[cis-decahydronaphthalene] | " | | | | | | | | | | | | |
| 2,10-Dimethyl-[trans-decahydronaphthalene] | " | | | | | | | | | | | | |
| 9,10-Dimethyl-[cis-decahydronaphthalene] | " | | | | | | | | | | | | |
| 9,10-Dimethyl-[trans-decahydronaphthalene] | " | | | | | | | | | | | | |

a See footnote a of Table 1a-E.

## TABLE 101a-E -1- ALKANETHIOLS, $C_1$ TO $C_{20}$
## BOILING POINT, $dt/dp$, REFRACTIVE INDEX, DENSITY, AND FREEZING POINT

April 30, 1952; December 31, 1952

| Compound | Formula | Boiling Point 29.921 in Hg °F | $dt/dp$ 29.921 in Hg °F/in.Hg | Refractive Index[a] $n_D$ 68°F | Refractive Index[a] $n_D$ 77°F | Density[a] lb/cu ft 60°F | Density[a] lb/cu ft 68°F | Density[a] lb/cu ft 77°F | Density[a] lb/gal 60°F | Density[a] lb/gal 68°F | Density[a] lb/gal 77°F | Specific Gravity[a] 60°F/60°F | Freezing Point In air at 1 atm °F |
|---|---|---|---|---|---|---|---|---|---|---|---|---|---|
| Methanethiol (Methyl mercaptan) | $CH_4S$ | 42.71 | 1.54 | ——— | ——— | 54.45[b] | 54.09[b] | 53.68[b] | 7.273[b] | 7.231[b] | 7.177[b] | 0.8731[b] | -189.44 |
| Ethanethiol (Ethyl mercaptan) | $C_2H_6S$ | 95.00 | 1.71 | 1.43105 | 1.42779 | 52.72 | 52.385 | 52.011 | 7.047 | 7.0028 | 6.9529 | 0.8453 | -234.22 |
| 1-Propanethiol ($n$-Propyl mercaptan) | $C_3H_8S$ | 153.7 | 1.9 | 1.4380 | 1.4351 | 52.79 | 52.51 | 52.18 | 7.058 | 7.019 | 6.976 | 0.8465 | -171.51 |
| 1-Butanethiol ($n$-Butyl mercaptan) | $C_4H_{10}S$ | 209.23 | 2.04 | 1.44298 | 1.44034 | 52.81 | 52.539 | 52.236 | 7.059 | 7.0234 | 6.9829 | 0.8467 | -176.21 |
| 1-Pentanethiol | $C_5H_{12}S$ | 259.95 | 2.18 | 1.44692 | 1.44439 | 52.82 | 52.569 | 52.290 | 7.060 | 7.0274 | 6.9902 | 0.8469 | -104.26 |
| 1-Hexanethiol | $C_6H_{14}S$ | 304.7 | 2.1 | 1.4496 | 1.4471 | 52.83 | 52.59 | 52.32 | 7.062 | 7.030 | 6.994 | 0.8470 | -112.0 |
| 1-Heptanethiol | $C_7H_{16}S$ | 349.2 | 2.2 | 1.4521 | 1.4497 | 52.83 | 52.61 | 52.36 | 7.063 | 7.033 | 6.999 | 0.8471 | -45.6 |
| 1-Octanethiol | $C_8H_{18}S$ | 390.4 | 2.3 | 1.4540 | 1.4517 | 52.86 | 52.64 | 52.40 | 7.067 | 7.038 | 7.005 | 0.8476 | -56.6 |
| 1-Nonanethiol | $C_9H_{20}S$ | 428.3 | 2.4 | 1.4560 | 1.4537 | 52.89 | 52.68 | 52.43 | 7.070 | 7.042 | 7.009 | 0.8480 | -4.2 |
| 1-Decanethiol | $C_{10}H_{22}S$ | 465.1 | 2.4 | 1.4572 | 1.4550 | 52.91 | 52.71 | 52.47 | 7.073 | 7.046 | 7.014 | 0.8484 | -14. |
| 1-Undecanethiol | $C_{11}H_{24}S$ | 499.1 | 2.5 | 1.4585 | 1.4563 | 52.94 | 52.73 | 52.51 | 7.078 | 7.050 | 7.019 | 0.8489 | +27. |
| 1-Dodecanethiol | $C_{12}H_{26}S$ | 531.1 | 2.5 | 1.4597 | 1.4575 | 52.98 | 52.77 | 52.54 | 7.082 | 7.054 | 7.023 | 0.8494 | 18. |
| 1-Tridecanethiol | $C_{13}H_{28}S$ | 561.4 | 2.6 | 1.4608 | 1.4586 | 52.99 | 52.79 | 52.57 | 7.084 | 7.058 | 7.028 | 0.8497 | 48. |
| 1-Tetradecanethiol | $C_{14}H_{30}S$ | 590. | 3. | 1.4617 | 1.4595 | 53.02 | 52.81 | 52.59 | 7.088 | 7.061 | 7.031 | 0.8501 | 43. |
| 1-Pentadecanethiol | $C_{15}H_{32}S$ | 617. | 3. | 1.4624 | 1.4603 | 53.04[c] | 52.84 | 52.62 | 7.091[c] | 7.064 | 7.034 | 0.8505[c] | 64. |
| 1-Hexadecanethiol | $C_{16}H_{34}S$ | 642. | 3. | 1.4632 | 1.4611 | 53.06[c] | 52.86 | 52.64 | 7.093[c] | 7.067 | 7.038 | 0.8507[c] | 64. |
| 1-Heptadecanethiol | $C_{17}H_{36}S$ | 667. | 3. | 1.4639[c] | 1.4618[c] | 53.08[c] | 52.88[c] | 52.66[c] | 7.095[c] | 7.069[c] | 7.040[c] | 0.8510[c] | 81. |
| 1-Octadecanethiol | $C_{18}H_{38}S$ | 691. | 3. | 1.4645[c] | 1.4624[c] | 53.10[c] | 52.91[c] | 52.69[c] | 7.098[c] | 7.073[c] | 7.043[c] | 0.8514[c] | 82. |
| 1-Nonadecanethiol | $C_{19}H_{40}S$ | 712. | 3. | 1.4650[c] | 1.4629[c] | 53.11[c] | 52.92[c] | 52.70[c] | 7.100[c] | 7.074[c] | 7.045[c] | 0.8516[c] | 93. |
| 1-Eicosanethiol | $C_{20}H_{42}S$ | 732. | 3. | 1.4655[c] | 1.4634[c] | 53.13[c] | 52.94[c] | 52.72[c] | 7.103[c] | 7.077[c] | 7.048[c] | 0.8519[c] | 99. |

a See footnote a of Table 1a-E.  b At saturation pressure.  c For the undercooled liquid below the normal freezing point.

## TABLE 102a-E – 2-ALKANETHIOLS, $C_3$ TO $C_{20}$
## BOILING POINT, dt/dp, REFRACTIVE INDEX, DENSITY, AND FREEZING POINT
April 30, 1952; December 31, 1952

| Compound | Formula | Boiling Point 29.921 in Hg °F | dt/dp 29.921 in Hg °F/in Hg | Refractive Index[a] $n_D$ 68°F | Refractive Index[a] $n_D$ 77°F | Density[a] lb/cu ft 60°F | Density[a] lb/cu ft 68°F | Density[a] lb/cu ft 77°F | Density[a] lb/gal 60°F | Density[a] lb/gal 68°F | Density[a] lb/gal 77°F | Specific Gravity[a] 60°F/60°F | Freezing Point In air at 1 atm °F |
|---|---|---|---|---|---|---|---|---|---|---|---|---|---|
| 2-Propanethiol (Isopropyl mercaptan) | $C_3H_8S$ | 126.61 | 1.82 | 1.42554 | 1.42251 | 51.14 | 50.835 | 50.481 | 6.837 | 6.7956 | 6.7483 | 0.8201 | -202.97 |
| 2-Butanethiol (sec-Butyl mercaptan) | $C_4H_{10}S$ | 184.96 | 2.00 | 1.43663 | 1.43385 | 52.05 | 51.781 | 51.475 | 6.358 | 6.9221 | 6.8812 | 0.8346 | -220.4 |
| 2-Pentanethiol | $C_5H_{12}S$ | 235.3 | 2.1 | 1.4412 | 1.4386 | 52.23 | 51.981 | 51.697 | 6.983 | 6.9489 | 6.9109 | 0.8375 | -171.0 |
| 2-Hexanethiol | $C_6H_{14}S$ | 282.0 | 2.1 | 1.4451 | 1.4426 | 52.33 | 52.09 | 51.83 | 6.996 | 6.364 | 6.928 | 0.8391 | -233. |
| 2-Heptanethiol | $C_7H_{16}S$ | 326.5 | 2.2 | 1.4478 | 1.4454 | 52.37 | 52.14 | 51.88 | 7.001 | 6.970 | 6.936 | 0.8397 | -222. |
| 2-Octanethiol | $C_8H_{18}S$ | 367.5 | 2.3 | 1.4504 | 1.4481 | 52.45 | 52.23 | 51.98 | 7.011 | 6.982 | 6.949 | 0.8410 | -110. |
| 2-Nonanethiol | $C_9H_{20}S$ | 406.8 | 2.4 | 1.4523 | 1.4500 | 52.51 | 52.29 | 52.05 | 7.020 | 6.991 | 6.958 | 0.8420 | -92. |
| 2-Decanethiol | $C_{10}H_{22}S$ | 444.0 | 2.4 | 1.4539 | 1.4516 | 52.56 | 52.35 | 52.11 | 7.027 | 6.998 | 6.967 | 0.8428 | -44. |
| 2-Undecanethiol | $C_{11}H_{24}S$ | 478.9 | 2.5 | 1.4554 | 1.4532 | 52.62 | 52.41 | 52.18 | 7.034 | 7.007 | 6.975 | 0.8437 | -29. |
| 2-Dodecanethiol | $C_{12}H_{26}S$ | 511.9 | 2.5 | 1.4567 | 1.4545 | 52.66 | 52.46 | 52.23 | 7.040 | 7.012 | 6.982 | 0.8444 | +1. |
| 2-Tridecanethiol | $C_{13}H_{28}S$ | 543. | 3. | 1.4578 | 1.4557 | 52.71 | 52.51 | 52.28 | 7.046 | 7.019 | 6.988 | 0.8451 | 14. |
| 2-Tetradecanethiol | $C_{14}H_{30}S$ | 572. | 3. | 1.4589 | 1.4568 | 52.75 | 52.54 | 52.32 | 7.052 | 7.024 | 6.994 | 0.8458 | 34. |
| 2-Pentadecanethiol | $C_{15}H_{32}S$ | 601. | 3. | 1.4600 | 1.4578 | 52.78 | 52.58 | 52.36 | 7.056 | 7.029 | 6.999 | 0.8463 | 45. |
| 2-Hexadecanethiol | $C_{16}H_{34}S$ | 626. | 3. | 1.4608 | 1.4587 | 52.82 | 52.62 | 52.39 | 7.061 | 7.034 | 7.004 | 0.8469 | 59. |
| 2-Heptadecanethiol | $C_{17}H_{36}S$ | 651. | 3. | 1.4617 | 1.4595 | 52.84[b] | 52.65 | 52.43 | 7.064[b] | 7.038 | 7.008 | 0.8473[b] | 68. |
| 2-Octadecanethiol | $C_{18}H_{38}S$ | 675. | 3. | 1.4623[b] | 1.4602[b] | 52.88[b] | 52.68[b] | 52.46[b] | 7.068[b] | 7.042[b] | 7.012[b] | 0.8478[b] | 79. |
| 2-Nonadecanethiol | $C_{19}H_{40}S$ | 698. | 3. | 1.4629[b] | 1.4608[b] | 52.90[b] | 52.71[b] | 52.49[b] | 7.072[b] | 7.046[b] | 7.017[b] | 0.8482[b] | 88. |
| 2-Eicosanethiol | $C_{20}H_{42}S$ | 718. | 3. | 1.4635[b] | 1.4614[b] | 52.93[b] | 52.73[b] | 52.51[b] | 7.075[b] | 7.049[b] | 7.020[b] | 0.8486[b] | 95. |

[a] See footnote a of Table 1a-E.   [b] For the undercooled liquid below the normal freezing point.

TABLE 103a-E — ALKANETHIOLS, C$_1$ TO C$_5$

BOILING POINT, $dt/dp$, REFRACTIVE INDEX, DENSITY, AND FREEZING POINT

April 30, 1952; December 31, 1952

| Compound | Formula | Boiling Point 29.921 in Hg (°F) | $dt/dp$ 29.921 in Hg (°F/in Hg) | Refractive Index[a] $n_D$ 68°F | $n_D$ 77°F | Density[a] lb/cu ft 60°F | 68°F | 77°F | lb/gal 60°F | 68°F | 77°F | Specific Gravity[a] 60°F/60°F | Freezing Point In air at 1 atm (°F) |
|---|---|---|---|---|---|---|---|---|---|---|---|---|---|
| Methanethiol (Methyl mercaptan) | CH$_4$S | 42.71 | 1.54 | ----- | ----- | 54.45[b] | 54.09[b] | 53.68[b] | 7.279[b] | 7.231[b] | 7.177[b] | 0.8731[b] | -189.44 |
| Ethanethiol (Ethyl mercaptan) | C$_2$H$_6$S | 95.00 | 1.71 | 1.43105 | 1.42779 | 52.72 | 53.385 | 52.011 | 7.047 | 7.0028 | 6.9529 | 0.8453 | -234.22 |
| 1-Propanethiol (n-Propyl mercaptan) | C$_3$H$_8$S | 153.7 | 1.9 | 1.4380 | 1.4351 | 52.79 | 52.51 | 52.18 | 7.058 | 7.019 | 6.976 | 0.8465 | -171.50 |
| 2-Propanethiol (Isopropyl mercaptan) | " | 126.61 | 1.82 | 1.42554 | 1.42251 | 51.14 | 50.835 | 50.487 | 6.837 | 6.7956 | 6.7483 | 0.8201 | -202.97 |
| 1-Butanethiol (n-Butyl mercaptan) | C$_4$H$_{10}$S | 209.23 | 2.04 | 1.44298 | 1.44034 | 52.81 | 52.59 | 52.236 | 7.059 | 7.0234 | 6.9829 | 0.8467 | -176.21 |
| 2-Butanethiol (sec-Butyl mercaptan) | " | 184.96 | 2.00 | 1.43663 | 1.43385 | 52.05 | 51.781 | 51.475 | 6.958 | 6.9221 | 6.8812 | 0.8346 | -220.4 |
| 2-Methyl-1-propanethiol (Isobutyl mercaptan) | " | 191.70 | 2.0 | 1.4387 | 1.4358 | 52.34 | 52.06 | 51.74 | 6.997 | 6.959 | 6.917 | 0.8392 | |
| 2-Methyl-2-propanethiol (tert-Butyl mercaptan) | " | 147.60 | 1.91 | 1.42320 | 1.42007 | 50.2b | 49.954 | 49.612 | 6.718 | 6.6778 | 6.6321 | 0.8058 | + 34.00 |
| 1-Pentanethiol | C$_5$H$_{12}$S | 259.95 | 2.18 | 1.44692 | 1.44439 | 52.82 | 52.569 | 52.290 | 7.060 | 7.0274 | 6.9902 | 0.8469 | -104.26 |
| 2-Pentanethiol | " | 235.3 | 2.1 | 1.4412 | 1.4386 | 52.23 | 51.981 | 51.697 | 6.983 | 6.9489 | 6.9109 | 0.8375 | -171.0 |
| 3-Pentanethiol | " | 221. | 2. | 1.4447 | 1.4421 | 52.75 | 52.50 | 52.22 | 7.052 | 7.018 | 6.981 | 0.8458 | -166.4 |
| 2-Methyl-1-butanethiol | " | 244.8 | 2.1 | 1.444 | 1.442 | 52.8 | 52.6 | 52.3 | 7.06 | 7.03 | 6.98 | 0.847 | |
| 3-Methyl-1-butanethiol | " | 244. | 2. | 1.4415 | 1.4389 | 52.38 | 52.13 | 51.85 | 7.002 | 6.968 | 6.931 | 0.8398 | |
| 2-Methyl-2-butanethiol | " | 210.2 | 2.0 | 1.4379 | 1.4353 | 50.9 | 50.7 | 50.4 | 6.81 | 6.78 | 6.73 | 0.817 | |
| 3-Methyl-2-Butanethiol | " | | | 1.4446 | 1.4420 | 52.74 | 52.49 | 52.21 | 7.051 | 7.017 | 6.980 | 0.8457 | |
| 2,2-Dimethyl-1-propanethiol | " | | | | | | | | | | | | - 89.1 |

[a] See footnote a of Table 1a-E.   [b] At saturation pressure.

151

TABLE 104a-E – ALKYL BENZENETHIOLS, $C_6$ TO $C_8$
BOILING POINT, dt/dp, REFRACTIVE INDEX, DENSITY, AND FREEZING POINT
October 31, 1952

| Compound | Formula | Boiling Point 29.921 in Hg (°F) | dt/dp 29.921 in Hg (°F/in Hg) | Refractive Index[a] $n_D$ 68°F | Refractive Index[a] $n_D$ 77°F | Density[a] lb/cu ft 60°F | 68°F | 77°F | Density[a] lb/gal 60°F | 68°F | 77°F | Specific Gravity[a] 60°F/60°F | Freezing Point In air at 1 atm (°F) |
|---|---|---|---|---|---|---|---|---|---|---|---|---|---|
| Benzenethiol (Thiophenol) | $C_6H_6S$ | 335.7 | 2.5 | 1.5893 | 1.5864 | 67.44 | 67.21 | 66.95 | 9.016 | 8.984 | 8.949 | 1.0814 | 5.4 |
| 2-Methylbenzenethiol (o-Methylthiophenol) | $C_7H_8S$ | 381.6 | 2.5 | 1.570 | 1.568 | 65.2 | 65.0 | 64.7 | 8.72 | 8.69 | 8.65 | 1.046 | 59. |
| 3-Methylbenzenethiol (m-Methylthiophenol) | " | 383.2 | 2.5 | 1.572 | 1.569 | 65.4 | 65.2 | 64.9 | 8.74 | 8.71 | 8.68 | 1.049 | |
| 4-Methylbenzenethiol (p-Methylthiophenol) | " | 382.8 | 2.5 | — | — | — | — | — | — | — | — | — | 111. |
| 2-Ethylbenzenethiol (o-Ethylthiophenol) | $C_8H_{10}S$ | 410. | 2. | 1.5700 | 1.5680 | 64.83 | 64.61 | 64.36 | 8.666 | 8.636 | 8.603 | 1.0394 | |
| 3-Ethylbenzenethiol (m-Ethylthiophenol) | " | 412. | 2. | 1.572 | 1.569 | 65.0 | 64.8 | 64.5 | 8.69 | 8.66 | 8.63 | 1.043 | |
| 4-Ethylbenzenethiol (p-Ethylthiophenol) | " | 412. | 2. | 1.572 | 1.569 | 65.0 | 64.8 | 64.5 | 8.69 | 8.66 | 8.63 | 1.043 | |
| 2,3-Dimethylbenzenethiol (2,3-Dimethylthiophenol) | " | | 2. | | | | | | | | | | |
| 2,4-Dimethylbenzenethiol (2,4-Dimethylthiophenol) | " | 406. | | | | | | | | | | | |
| 2,5-Dimethylbenzenethiol (2,5-Dimethylthiophenol) | " | 402. | 2. | | | | | | | | | | |
| 2,6-Dimethylbenzenethiol (2,6-Dimethylthiophenol) | " | | | | | | | | | | | | |
| 3,4-Dimethylbenzenethiol (3,4-Dimethylthiophenol) | " | | | | | | | | | | | | |
| 3,5-Dimethylbenzenethiol (3,5-Dimethylthiophenol) | " | | | | | | | | | | | | |

a See footnote a of Table 1a-E.

TABLE 105a-E — 2-n-THIAALKANES, $C_2$ TO $C_{20}$

BOILING POINT, $dt/dp$, REFRACTIVE INDEX, DENSITY, AND FREEZING POINT

April 30, 1952; December 31, 1952

| Compound | Formula | Boiling Point 29.921 in Hg °F | $dt/dp$ 29.921 in Hg °F/in Hg | Refractive Index[a] $n_D$ 68°F | Refractive Index[a] $n_D$ 77°F | Density[a] lb/cu ft 60°F | Density[a] lb/cu ft 68°F | Density[a] lb/cu ft 77°F | Density[a] lb/gal 60°F | Density[a] lb/gal 68°F | Density[a] lb/gal 77°F | Specific Gravity[a] 60°F/60°F | Freezing Point In air at 1 atm °F |
|---|---|---|---|---|---|---|---|---|---|---|---|---|---|
| 2-Thiapropane (Dimethyl sulfide) | $C_2H_6S$ | 99.21 | 1.72 | 1.43547 | 1.43231 | 53.28 | 52.953 | 52.582 | 7.123 | 7.0788 | 7.0292 | 0.8544 | -144.89 |
| 2-Thiabutane (Methyl ethyl sulfide) | $C_3H_8S$ | 151.97 | 1.87 | 1.44035 | 1.43737 | 52.88 | 52.576 | 52.238 | 7.069 | 7.0284 | 6.9832 | 0.8478 | -158.67 |
| 2-Thiapentane (Methyl n-propyl sulfide) | $C_4H_{10}S$ | 203.97 | 2.02 | 1.4442 | 1.4415 | 52.86 | 52.59 | 52.28 | 7.066 | 7.030 | 6.989 | 0.8476 | -171.35 |
| 2-Thiahexane | $C_5H_{12}S$ | 253.8 | 2.1 | 1.4477 | 1.4452 | 52.62 | 52.60 | 52.32 | 7.035 | 7.032 | 6.994 | 0.8438 | -144.0 |
| 2-Thiaheptane | $C_6H_{14}S$ | 293. | 2. | 1.4506 | 1.4482 | 52.87 | 52.63 | 52.37 | 7.067 | 7.036 | 7.001 | 0.8477 | -137. |
| 2-Thiaoctane | $C_7H_{16}S$ | 340. | 2. | 1.4529 | 1.4505 | 52.87 | 52.65 | 52.39 | 7.068 | 7.038 | 7.004 | 0.8478 | -87.7 |
| 2-Thianonane | $C_8H_{18}S$ | 383. | 2. | 1.4548 | 1.4525 | 52.89 | 52.67 | 52.43 | 7.070 | 7.041 | 7.008 | 0.8481 | -81.9 |
| 2-Thiadecane | $C_9H_{20}S$ | 424. | 3. | 1.4564 | 1.4541 | 52.91 | 52.69 | 52.46 | 7.073 | 7.044 | 7.012 | 0.8483 | -44. |
| 2-Thiaundecane | $C_{10}H_{22}S$ | 464. | 3. | 1.4578 | 1.4556 | 52.94 | 52.73 | 52.49 | 7.077 | 7.049 | 7.017 | 0.8489 | -31. |
| 2-Thiadodecane | $C_{11}H_{24}S$ | 500. | 3. | 1.4591 | 1.4569 | 52.97 | 52.76 | 52.53 | 7.081 | 7.053 | 7.022 | 0.8493 | -1.3 |
| 2-Thiatridecane | $C_{12}H_{26}S$ | 534. | 3. | 1.4602 | 1.4580 | 52.99 | 52.79 | 52.56 | 7.084 | 7.057 | 7.026 | 0.8497 | +7. |
| 2-Thiatetradecane | $C_{13}H_{28}S$ | 567. | 3. | 1.4612 | 1.4590 | 53.02 | 52.81 | 52.59 | 7.087 | 7.060 | 7.030 | 0.8501 | 28. |
| 2-Thiapentadecane | $C_{14}H_{30}S$ | 597. | 3. | 1.4621 | 1.4599 | 53.04 | 52.84 | 52.61 | 7.090 | 7.063 | 7.033 | 0.8504 | 37. |
| 2-Thiahexadecane | $C_{15}H_{32}S$ | 626. | 3. | 1.4628 | 1.4607 | 53.06 | 52.86 | 52.64 | 7.093 | 7.067 | 7.037 | 0.8508 | 52. |
| 2-Thiaheptadecane | $C_{16}H_{34}S$ | 653. | 3. | 1.4636 | 1.4615 | 53.08 | 52.88 | 52.66 | 7.095 | 7.069 | 7.039 | 0.8510 | 59. |
| 2-Thiaoctadecane | $C_{17}H_{36}S$ | 678. | 3. | 1.4642 | 1.4621[b] | 53.09[b] | 52.89[b] | 52.68 | 7.097[b] | 7.071[b] | 7.042 | 0.8513 | 70. |
| 2-Thianonadecane | $C_{18}H_{38}S$ | 703. | 3. | 1.4648 | 1.4627[b] | 53.11[b] | 52.91[b] | 52.69 | 7.100[b] | 7.073[b] | 7.044 | 0.8516 | 77. |
| 2-Thiaeicosane | $C_{19}H_{40}S$ | 727. | 3. | 1.4654[b] | 1.4633[b] | 53.13[b] | 52.93[b] | 52.71[b] | 7.102[b] | 7.076[b] | 7.047[b] | 0.8518[b] | 86. |
| 2-Thiaheneicosane | $C_{20}H_{42}S$ | 748. | 3. | 1.4659[b] | 1.4638[b] | 53.14[b] | 52.95[b] | 52.73[b] | 7.104[b] | 7.078[b] | 7.049[b] | 0.8521[b] | 95. |

a See footnote a of Table 1a-E.

b For the undercooled liquid below the normal freezing point.

TABLE 107a-E — THIAALKANES, $C_2$ TO $C_5$

BOILING POINT, $dt/dp$, REFRACTIVE INDEX, DENSITY, AND FREEZING POINT

April 30, 1952; December 31, 1952

| Compound | Formula | Boiling Point 29.921 in Hg (°F) | $dt/dp$ 29.921 in Hg (°F/in Hg) | Refractive Index[a] 68°F $n_D$ | 77°F $n_D$ | Density[a] 60°F (lb/cu ft) | 68°F | 77°F | 60°F (lb/gal) | 68°F | 77°F | Specific Gravity[a] 60°F/60°F | Freezing Point In air at 1 atm (°F) |
|---|---|---|---|---|---|---|---|---|---|---|---|---|---|
| 2-Thiapropane (Dimethyl sulfide) | $C_2H_6S$ | 99.21 | 1.72 | 1.43547 | 1.43231 | 53.28 | 52.953 | 52.582 | 7.123 | 7.0788 | 7.0292 | 0.8544 | -144.89 |
| 2-Thiabutane (Methyl ethyl sulfide) | $C_3H_8S$ | 151.97 | 1.87 | 1.44035 | 1.43737 | 52.88 | 52.576 | 52.238 | 7.069 | 7.0284 | 6.9832 | 0.8478 | -158.67 |
| 2-Thiapentane (Methyl n-propyl sulfide) | $C_4H_{10}S$ | 203.97 | 2.02 | 1.4442 | 1.4415 | 52.86 | 52.59 | 52.28 | 7.066 | 7.030 | 6.989 | 0.8476 | -171.35 |
| 3-Thiapentane (Diethyl sulfide) | " | 197.78 | 2.01 | 1.44298 | 1.44017 | 52.48 | 52.203 | 51.889 | 7.016 | 6.9785 | 6.9365 | 0.8415 | -155.11 |
| 3-Methyl-2-thiabutane (Methyl isopropyl sulfide) | " | 184.55 | 1.99 | 1.4392 | 1.4362 | 51.98 | 51.76 | 51.51 | 6.949 | 6.919 | 6.886 | 0.8335 | -150.71 |
| 2-Thiahexane | $C_5H_{12}S$ | 253.8 | 2.1 | 1.4477 | 1.4452 | 52.62 | 52.60 | 52.32 | 7.035 | 7.032 | 6.994 | 0.8438 | -144.0 |
| 3-Thiahexane | " | 245.30 | 2.14 | 1.4462 | 1.4435 | 52.51 | 52.25 | 51.96 | 7.019 | 6.985 | 6.947 | 0.8419 | -178.67 |
| 3-Methyl-2-thiapentane | " | 234. | 2. | 1.442 | 1.440 | 52.1 | 51.9 | 51.6 | 6.96 | 6.93 | 6.90 | 0.835 | -164.4 |
| 4-Methyl-2-thiapentane | " | 234.5 | 2.1 | 1.4433 | 1.4410 | 52.27 | 52.03 | 51.77 | 6.987 | 6.956 | 6.921 | 0.8380 | -164.4 |
| 2-Methyl-3-thiapentane | " | 225.28 | 2.10 | 1.4407 | 1.4382 | 51.74 | 51.48 | 51.18 | 6.916 | 6.881 | 6.842 | 0.8296 | -187.94 |
| 3,3-Dimethyl-2-thiabutane | " | 210.2 | 2. | 1.4403 | 1.4376 | 51.79 | 51.53 | 51.24 | 6.924 | 6.889 | 6.850 | 0.8305 | -116.1 |

[a] See footnote a of Table 1a-E.

TABLE 108a-E – THIAALKANES, C$_6$

BOILING POINT, dt/dp, REFRACTIVE INDEX, DENSITY, AND FREEZING POINT

April 30, 1952

| Compound | Formula | Boiling Point 29.921 in Hg °F | dt/dp 29.921 in Hg °F/in Hg | Refractive Index[a] 68°F $n_D$ | Refractive Index[a] 77°F $n_D$ | Density[a] lb/cu ft 60°F | Density[a] lb/cu ft 68°F | Density[a] lb/cu ft 77°F | Density[a] lb/gal 60°F | Density[a] lb/gal 68°F | Density[a] lb/gal 77°F | Specific Gravity[a] 60°F/60°F | Freezing Point In air at 1 atm °F |
|---|---|---|---|---|---|---|---|---|---|---|---|---|---|
| 2-Thiaheptane | C$_6$H$_{14}$S | 293. | 2. | 1.4506 | 1.4482 | 52.87 | 52.63 | 52.37 | 7.067 | 7.036 | 7.001 | 0.8477 | -137. |
| 3-Thiaheptane | " | 291.63 | 2.29 | 1.4491 | 1.4463 | 52.53 | 52.29 | 52.01 | 7.023 | 6.990 | 6.953 | 0.8423 | -139.23 |
| 4-Thiaheptane | " | 289.09 | 2.24 | 1.4487 | 1.4461 | 52.54 | 52.29 | 52.01 | 7.024 | 6.991 | 6.953 | 0.8425 | -152.5 |
| 3-Methyl-2-thiahexane | " | 284. | 2. | | | | | | | | | | |
| 4-Methyl-2-thiahexane | " | 280. | 2. | 1.452 | 1.449 | 52.8 | 52.6 | 52.3 | 7.06 | 7.03 | 6.99 | 0.846 | |
| 5-Methyl-2-thiahexane | " | | | | | | | | | | | | |
| 2-Methyl-3-thiahexane | " | 269.69 | 2.21 | 1.4440 | 1.4414 | 51.86 | 51.62 | 51.35 | 6.933 | 6.901 | 6.864 | 0.8316 | |
| 4-Methyl-3-thiahexane | " | 272.57 | 2.22 | 1.4477 | 1.4451 | 52.40 | 52.14 | 51.86 | 7.005 | 6.971 | 6.932 | 0.8402 | |
| 5-Methyl-3-thiahexane | " | 273.60 | 2.22 | 1.4450 | 1.4424 | 52.10 | 51.85 | 51.57 | 6.965 | 6.932 | 6.894 | 0.8354 | |
| 3,3-Dimethyl-2-thiapentane | " | | | | | | | | | | | | |
| 3,4-Dimethyl-2-thiapentane | " | | | | | | | | | | | | |
| 4,4-Dimethyl-2-thiapentane | " | | | | | | | | | | | | |
| 2,2-Dimethyl-3-thiapentane | " | 248.74 | 2.19 | 1.4417 | 1.4390 | 51.48 | 51.23 | 50.95 | 6.881 | 6.848 | 6.811 | 0.8254 | -128.11 |
| 2,4-Dimethyl-3-thiapentane | " | 248.04 | 2.18 | 1.4388 | 1.4362 | 51.09 | 50.85 | 50.59 | 6.829 | 6.798 | 6.763 | 0.8191 | -108.54 |

[a] See footnote a of Table 1a-E.

TABLE 109a-E – ALKYL (1-THIAALKYL) BENZENES, C₇ AND C₈
BOILING POINT, $dt/dp$, REFRACTIVE INDEX, DENSITY, AND FREEZING POINT

October 31, 1952

| Compound | Formula | Boiling Point 29.921 in Hg °F | $dt/dp$ 29.921 in Hg °F/in Hg | Refractive Index[a] 68°F $n_D$ | 77°F $n_D$ | Density[a] 60°F lb/cu ft | 68°F lb/cu ft | 77°F lb/cu ft | 60°F lb/gal | 68°F lb/gal | 77°F lb/gal | Specific Gravity[a] 60°F/60°F | Freezing Point In air at 1 atm °F |
|---|---|---|---|---|---|---|---|---|---|---|---|---|---|
| (1-Thiaethyl)-benzene (Methyl phenyl sulfide) | $C_7H_8S$ | 379. | 2. | 1.5868 | 1.5840 | 66.29 | 66.04 | 65.77 | 8.861 | 8.826 | 8.792 | 1.0628 | |
| (1-Thiapropyl)-benzene (Ethyl phenyl sulfide) | $C_8H_{10}S$ | 401. | 2. | 1.5670 | 1.5644 | 63.99 | 63.74 | 63.46 | 8.555 | 8.521 | 8.484 | 1.0261 | |
| 2-Methyl-(1-thiaethyl)-benzene | " | | | 1.5757 | 1.5731 | 64.5 | 64.3 | 64.0 | 8.63 | 8.60 | 8.56 | 1.035 | |
| 3-Methyl-(1-thiaethyl)-benzene | " | 423. | 2. | 1.5733 | 1.5707 | 64.3 | 64.1 | 63.9 | 8.60 | 8.57 | 8.54 | 1.032 | |
| 4-Methyl-(1-thiaethyl)-benzene | " | | | | | | | | | | | | |

[a] See footnote a of Table 1a-E.

TABLE 110a-E – ALKYL (1-THIAALKYL) BENZENES, $C_9$

BOILING POINT, $dt/dp$, REFRACTIVE INDEX, DENSITY, AND FREEZING POINT

October 31, 1952

| Compound | Formula | Boiling Point 29.921 in Hg °F | $dt/dp$ 29.921 in Hg °F/in Hg | Refractive Index[a] 68°F $n_D$ | 77°F $n_D$ | Density[a] lb/cu ft 60°F | 68°F | 77°F | lb/gal 60°F | 68°F | 77°F | Specific Gravity[a] 60°F/60°F | Freezing Point In air at 1 atm °F |
|---|---|---|---|---|---|---|---|---|---|---|---|---|---|
| (1-Thiabutyl)-benzene (n-Propyl phenyl sulfide) | $C_9H_{12}S$ | 428. | 2. | 1.5571 | 1.5551 | 62.63 | 62.40 | 62.13 | 8.373 | 8.341 | 8.305 | 1.0043 | |
| (2-Methyl-1-thiapropyl)-benzene (Isopropyl phenyl sulfide) | " | 406. | 2. | 1.5464 | 1.5446 | 61.74 | 61.50 | 61.24 | 8.253 | 8.222 | 8.187 | 0.9899 | |
| 2-Methyl-(1-thiapropyl)-benzene | " | 427. | 2. | 1.5590 | 1.5570 | 62.57 | 62.35 | 62.10 | 8.364 | 8.334 | 8.301 | 1.0032 | |
| 3-Methyl-(1-thiapropyl)-benzene | " | 428. | 2. | 1.555 | 1.553 | 62.62 | 62.40 | 62.15 | 8.372 | 8.342 | 8.309 | 1.0041 | |
| 4-Methyl-(1-thiapropyl)-benzene | " | 442. | 2. | 1.5708 | 1.5688 | 64.2 | 64.0 | 63.7 | 8.58 | 8.55 | 8.52 | 1.030 | |
| 2-Ethyl-(1-thiaethyl)-benzene | " | | | | | | | | | | | | |
| 3-Ethyl-(1-thiaethyl)-benzene | " | | | | | | | | | | | | |
| 4-Ethyl-(1-thiaethyl)-benzene | " | | | | | | | | | | | | |
| 2,3-Dimethyl-(1-thiaethyl)-benzene | " | | | | | | | | | | | | |
| 2,4-Dimethyl-(1-thiaethyl)-benzene | " | | | 1.575 | 1.573 | 63.8 | 63.6 | 63.4 | 8.53 | 8.50 | 8.47 | 1.024 | |
| 2,5-Dimethyl-(1-thiaethyl)-benzene | " | | | | | | | | | | | | |
| 2,6-Dimethyl-(1-thiaethyl)-benzene | " | | | | | | | | | | | | |
| 3,4-Dimethyl-(1-thiaethyl)-benzene | " | | | | | | | | | | | | |
| 3,5-Dimethyl-(1-thiaethyl)-benzene | " | | | | | | | | | | | | |

[a] See footnote a of Table 1a-E.

TABLE 111a-E - ALKYL THIACYCLOPROPANES, $C_2$ TO $C_4$

BOILING POINT, $dt/dp$, REFRACTIVE INDEX, DENSITY, AND FREEZING POINT

October 31, 1952

| Compound | Formula[a] | Boiling Point 29.921 in Hg °F | $dt/dp$ 29.921 in Hg °F/in Hg | Refractive Index[a] 68°F $n_D$ | Refractive Index[a] 77°F $n_D$ | Density[a] lb/cu ft 60°F | Density[a] lb/cu ft 68°F | Density[a] lb/cu ft 77°F | Density[a] lb/gal 60°F | Density[a] lb/gal 68°F | Density[a] lb/gal 77°F | Specific Gravity[a] 60°F/60°F | Freezing Point In air at 1 atm °F |
|---|---|---|---|---|---|---|---|---|---|---|---|---|---|
| Thiacyclopropane (Ethylene sulfide) | $C_2H_4S$ | 130.87 | 1.81 | 1.490 | 1.487 | 63.6 | 63.2 | 62.9 | 8.50 | 8.45 | 8.40 | 1.019 | -162. |
| 2-Methylthiacyclopropane | $C_3H_6S$ | 165.9 | 1.9 | 1.475 | 1.472 | 59.2 | 58.9 | 58.6 | 7.91 | 7.88 | 7.84 | 0.949 | -132. |
| 2-Ethylthiacyclopropane | $C_4H_8S$ | 221. | 2. | 1.472 | 1.470 | 58.1 | 57.9 | 57.6 | 7.77 | 7.74 | 7.69 | 0.932 | |
| 2,2-Dimethylthiacyclopropane | " | 187. | 2. | 1.464 | 1.462 | | | | | | | | |
| 2,cis-3-Dimethylthiacyclopropane | " | | | | | | | | | | | | |
| 2,trans-3-Dimethylthiacyclopropane | " | | | | | | | | | | | | |

a See footnote a of Table 1a-E.

TABLE 112a-E – ALKYL THIACYCLOPENTANES, $C_4$ TO $C_6$

BOILING POINT, $dt/dp$, REFRACTIVE INDEX, DENSITY, AND FREEZING POINT

October 31, 1952

| Compound | Formula | Boiling Point 29.921 in Hg °F | $-dt/dp$ 29.921 in Hg °F/in Hg | Refractive Index[a] 68°F $n_D$ | Refractive Index[a] 77°F $n_D$ | Density[a] lb/cu ft 600°F | Density[a] lb/cu ft 68°F | Density[a] lb/cu ft 77°F | Density[a] lb/gal 600°F | Density[a] lb/gal 68°F | Density[a] lb/gal 77°F | Specific Gravity[a] 60°F/60°F | Freezing Point In air at 1 atm °F |
|---|---|---|---|---|---|---|---|---|---|---|---|---|---|
| Thiacyclopentane (Tetrahydrothiophene) | $C_4H_8S$ | 250.01 | 2.163 | 1.50483 | 1.50217 | 62.62 | 62.345 | 62.039 | 8.371 | 8.3343 | 8.2934 | 1.0040 | -141.09 |
| 2-Methylthiacyclopentane | $C_5H_{10}S$ | 271.81 | 2.24 | 1.4909 | 1.4884 | 59.85 | 59.63 | 59.38 | 8.001 | 7.971 | 7.938 | 0.9597 | -149.28 |
| 3-Methylthiacyclopentane | " | 281.61 | 2.26 | 1.4924 | 1.4902 | 60.41 | 60.14 | 59.84 | 8.076 | 8.040 | 7.999 | 0.9687 | -114.09 |
| 2-Ethylthiacyclopentane | $C_6H_{12}S$ | 315. | 2. | 1.490 | 1.487 | 59.2 | 58.9 | 58.6 | 7.91 | 7.88 | 7.84 | 0.949 | |
| 3-Ethylthiacyclopentane | " | 329. | 2. | 1.491 | 1.489 | 59.6 | 59.3 | 59.0 | 7.97 | 7.93 | 7.89 | 0.955 | |
| 2,2-Dimethylthiacyclopentane | " | | | | | | | | | | | | |
| 2,cis-3-Dimethylthiacyclopentane | " | | | | | | | | | | | | |
| 2,trans-3-Dimethylthiacyclopentane | " | | | | | | | | | | | | |
| 2,cis-4-Dimethylthiacyclopentane | " | | | | | | | | | | | | |
| 2,trans-4-Dimethylthiacyclopentane | " | | | | | | | | | | | | |
| 2,cis-5-Dimethylthiacyclopentane | " | 288.10 | 2.29 | 1.4799 | 1.4774 | 57.82 | 57.57 | 57.29 | 7.729 | 7.696 | 7.658 | 0.9271 | -128.9 |
| 2,trans-5-Dimethylthiacyclopentane | " | 287.6 | 2.3 | 1.4776 | 1.4752 | 57.61 | 57.36 | 57.07 | 7.702 | 7.668 | 7.629 | 0.9238 | -105.43 |
| 3,3-Dimethylthiacyclopentane | " | | | | | | | | | | | | |
| 3,cis-4-Dimethylthiacyclopentane | " | | | | | | | | | | | | |
| 3,trans-4-Dimethylthiacyclopentane | " | | | | | | | | | | | | |

a See footnote a of Table 1a-E.

158

TABLE 113a-E – ALKYL THIACYCLOHEXANES, C$_5$ TO C$_7$,
BOILING POINT, dt/dp, REFRACTIVE INDEX, DENSITY, AND FREEZING POINT

October 31, 1952

| Compound | Formula | Boiling Point 29.921 in Hg °F | dt/dp 29.921 in Hg °F/in Hg | Refractive Index[a] 68°F $n_D$ | 77°F $n_D$ | Density[a] lb/cu ft 60°F | 68°F | 77°F | lb/gal 60°F | 68°F | 77°F | Specific Gravity[a] 60°F/60°F | Freezing Point In air at 1 atm °F |
|---|---|---|---|---|---|---|---|---|---|---|---|---|---|
| Thiacyclohexane | C$_5$H$_{10}$S | 287.15 | 2.30 | 1.5067 | 1.5041 | 61.78 | 61.53 | 61.24 | 8.259 | 8.225 | 8.187 | 0.9906 | 66.18 |
| 2-Methylthiacyclohexane | C$_6$H$_{12}$S | 307.47 | 2.38 | 1.4905 | 1.4881 | 59.12 | 58.86 | 58.56 | 7.903 | 7.868 | 7.829 | 0.9479 | -72.65 |
| 3-Methylthiacyclohexane | " | 316.47 | 2.40 | 1.4922 | 1.4899 | 59.38 | 59.14 | 58.87 | 7.937 | 7.905 | 7.870 | 0.9520 | -76.31 |
| 4-Methylthiacyclohexane | " | 317.55 | 2.41 | 1.4923 | 1.4899 | 59.37 | 59.12 | 58.85 | 7.936 | 7.904 | 7.867 | 0.9519 | -18.60 |
| 2-Ethylthiacyclohexane | C$_7$H$_{14}$S | | | | | | | | | | | | |
| 3-Ethylthiacyclohexane | " | | | | | | | | | | | | |
| 4-Ethylthiacyclohexane | " | | | | | | | | | | | | |
| 2,2-Dimethylthiacyclohexane | " | | | | | | | | | | | | |
| 2,cis-3-Dimethylthiacyclohexane | " | | | | | | | | | | | | |
| 2,trans-3-Dimethylthiacyclohexane | " | | | | | | | | | | | | |
| 2,cis-4-Dimethylthiacyclohexane | " | | | | | | | | | | | | |
| 2,trans-4-Dimethylthiacyclohexane | " | | | | | | | | | | | | |
| 2,cis-5-Dimethylthiacyclohexane | " | | | | | | | | | | | | |
| 2,trans-5-Dimethylthiacyclohexane | " | | | | | | | | | | | | |
| 2,cis-6-Dimethylthiacyclohexane | " | | | | | | | | | | | | |
| 2,trans-6-Dimethylthiacyclohexane | " | | | | | | | | | | | | |
| 3,3-Dimethylthiacyclohexane | " | | | | | | | | | | | | |
| 3,cis-4-Dimethylthiacyclohexane | " | | | | | | | | | | | | |
| 3,trans-4-Dimethylthiacyclohexane | " | | | | | | | | | | | | |
| 3,cis-5-Dimethylthiacyclohexane | " | | | | | | | | | | | | |
| 3,trans-5-Dimethylthiacyclohexane | " | | | | | | | | | | | | |
| 4,4-Dimethylthiacyclohexane | " | | | | | | | | | | | | |

a See footnote a of Table 1a-E.

TABLE 114a-E – ALKYL THIOPHENES, C₄ TO C₆

BOILING POINT, dt/dp, REFRACTIVE INDEX, DENSITY, AND FREEZING POINT

April 30, 1952; December 31, 1952

| Compound | Formula | Boiling Point 29.921 in Hg °F | dt/dp 29.921 in Hg °F/in Hg | Refractive Index[a] 68°F $n_D$ | 77°F $n_D$ | Density[a] 60°F lb/cu ft | 68°F lb/cu ft | 77°F lb/cu ft | 60°F lb/gal | 68°F lb/gal | 77°F lb/gal | Specific Gravity[a] 60°F/60°F | Freezing Point In air at 1 atm °F |
|---|---|---|---|---|---|---|---|---|---|---|---|---|---|
| Thiophene | $C_4H_4S$ | 183.49 | 1.96 | 1.52890 | 1.52572 | 66.81 | 66.475 | 66.102 | 8.931 | 8.8864 | 8.8365 | 1.0712 | -36.78 |
| 2-Methylthiophene | $C_5H_6S$ | 234.61 | 2.10 | 1.5203 | 1.5174 | 63.93 | 63.63 | 63.29 | 8.546 | 8.506 | 8.461 | 1.0251 | -82.08 |
| 3-Methylthiophene | " | 239.77 | 2.11 | 1.52042 | 1.51758 | 64.09 | 63.789 | 63.455 | 8.567 | 8.5274 | 8.4827 | 1.0276 | -92.15 |
| 2-Ethylthiophene | $C_6H_8S$ | 273. | 2. | 1.5122 | 1.5094 | 62.27 | 61.99 | 61.68 | 8.324 | 8.287 | 8.245 | 0.9984 | |
| 3-Ethylthiophene | " | 277. | 2. | 1.5146 | 1.5120 | 62.57 | 62.30 | 62.00 | 8.365 | 8.329 | 8.288 | 1.0033 | -128.4 |
| 2,3-Dimethylthiophene | " | 286.9 | 2.2 | 1.5192 | 1.5166 | 62.84 | 62.56 | 62.24 | 8.401 | 8.363 | 8.320 | 1.0076 | - 56.2 |
| 2,4-Dimethylthiophene | " | 285.3 | 2. | 1.5104 | 1.5078 | 62.43 | 62.15 | 61.83 | 8.346 | 8.309 | 8.266 | 1.0011 | |
| 2,5-Dimethylthiophene | " | 278.1 | 2.2 | 1.5129 | 1.5104 | 61.77 | 61.49 | 61.17 | 8.258 | 8.220 | 8.177 | 0.9905 | -80.7 |
| 3,4-Dimethylthiophene | " | 293. | 2. | 1.5212 | 1.5187 | 63.2 | 62.9 | 62.6 | 8.45 | 8.41 | 8.37 | 1.013 | |

[a] See footnote a of Table 1a-E.

TABLE 115a-E – ALKYL THIOPHENES, $C_7$

BOILING POINT, $dt/dp$, REFRACTIVE INDEX, DENSITY, AND FREEZING POINT

April 30, 1952

| Compound | Formula | Boiling Point 29.921 in Hg °F | $dt/dp$ 29.921 in Hg °F/in Hg | Refractive Index[a] $n_D$ 68°F | $n_D$ 77°F | Density[a] (lb/cu ft) 60°F | 68°F | 77°F | Density[a] (lb/gal) 60°F | 68°F | 77°F | Specific Gravity[a] 60°F/60°F | Freezing Point In air at 1 atm °F |
|---|---|---|---|---|---|---|---|---|---|---|---|---|---|
| 2-Propylthiophene | $C_7H_{10}S$ | 317.3 | 2.3 | 1.5049 | 1.5023 | 60.74 | 60.47 | 60.17 | 8.120 | 8.084 | 8.044 | 0.9739 | |
| 3-Propylthiophene | " | 322. | 2. | 1.5057 | 1.5031 | 60.91 | 60.65 | 60.36 | 8.143 | 8.108 | 8.069 | 0.9767 | |
| 2-Isopropylthiophene | " | 307. | 2. | 1.5038 | 1.5013 | 60.67 | 60.42 | 60.14 | 8.110 | 8.077 | 8.039 | 0.9727 | |
| 3-Isopropylthiophene | " | 315. | 2. | 1.5052 | 1.5027 | 61.01 | 60.76 | 60.48 | 8.156 | 8.122 | 8.085 | 0.9782 | |
| 2-Methyl-3-ethylthiophene | " | 315. | 2. | | | | | | | | | | |
| 2-Methyl-4-ethylthiophene | " | 325. | 2. | 1.5098 | 1.5073 | 61.07 | 60.82 | 60.53 | 8.164 | 8.130 | 8.092 | 0.9792 | -74. |
| 2-Methyl-5-ethylthiophene | " | 320.2 | 2.3 | 1.5073 | 1.5048 | 60.55 | 60.31 | 60.04 | 8.094 | 8.062 | 8.026 | 0.9709 | -91.3 |
| 3-Methyl-2-ethylthiophene | " | 322. | 2. | 1.5105 | 1.5080 | 61.53 | 61.27 | 60.98 | 8.225 | 8.191 | 8.152 | 0.9865 | |
| 3-Methyl-4-ethylthiophene | " | | | | | | | | | | | | |
| 3-Methyl-5-ethylthiophene | " | | | | | | | | | | | | |
| 2,3,4-Trimethylthiophene | " | 342.9 | 2.4 | 1.5208 | 1.5183 | 62.3 | 62.1 | 61.9 | 8.33 | 8.30 | 8.27 | 1.000 | |
| 2,3,5-Trimethylthiophene | " | 328.1 | 2.3 | 1.5112 | 1.5088 | 61.13 | 60.88 | 60.60 | 8.172 | 8.139 | 8.102 | 0.9802 | |

a See footnote a of Table 1a-E.

TABLE 20b (PART 1) – NORMAL PARAFFINS, $C_1$ TO $C_{20}$

MOLECULAR VOLUME, MOLECULAR REFRACTION, SPECIFIC REFRACTION, REFRACTIVITY INTERCEPT, AND SPECIFIC DISPERSION

June 30, 1948; December 31, 1950; October 31, 1952

| Compound | Formula | Molecular Volume[a] $V = M/d$ (ml/mole) | | Molecular Refraction[a] $V(n_D^2-1)/(n_D^2+2)$ (ml/mole) | | Specific Refraction[a] $(1/d)(n_D^2-1)/(n_D^2+2)$ (ml/g) | | Refractivity Intercept[a] $n_D - d/2$ | | Specific Dispersion[a] $10^4(n_F-n_C)/d$ (ml/g) | |
|---|---|---|---|---|---|---|---|---|---|---|---|
| | | 20°C | 25°C | 20°C | 25°C | 20°C | 25°C | 20°C | 25°C | 20°C | 25°C |
| Methane | $CH_4$ | — | — | — | — | — | — | — | — | — | — |
| Ethane | $C_2H_6$ | — | — | — | — | — | — | — | — | — | — |
| Propane | $C_3H_8$ | 88.10[b] | 89.48[b] | — | — | — | — | — | — | — | — |
| n-Butane | $C_4H_{10}$ | 100.41[b] | 101.43[b] | 20.63[b] | 20.64[b] | 0.3550[b] | 0.3552[b] | 1.0432[b] | 1.0426[b] | — | — |
| n-Pentane | $C_5H_{12}$ | 115.205 | 116.104 | 25.266 | 25.286 | 0.35020 | 0.35048 | 1.04436 | 1.04402 | 98.1 | 98.0 |
| n-Hexane | $C_6H_{14}$ | 130.688 | 131.598 | 29.907 | 29.928 | 0.34706 | 0.34730 | 1.04518 | 1.04486 | 98.1 | 98.0 |
| n-Heptane | $C_7H_{16}$ | 146.540 | 147.456 | 34.550 | 34.565 | 0.34482 | 0.34496 | 1.04576 | 1.04536 | 97.8 | 97.7 |
| n-Octane | $C_8H_{18}$ | 162.592 | 163.530 | 39.192 | 39.209 | 0.34312 | 0.34327 | 1.04617 | 1.04580 | 98.1 | 98.0 |
| n-Nonane | $C_9H_{20}$ | 178.713 | 179.670 | 43.842 | 43.855 | 0.34185 | 0.34195 | 1.04660 | 1.04620 | 97.4 | 97.2 |
| n-Decane | $C_{10}H_{22}$ | 194.865 | 195.905 | 48.481 | 48.503 | 0.34075 | 0.34091 | 1.04686 | 1.04654 | 98.1 | 98.0 |
| n-Undecane | $C_{11}H_{24}$ | 211.170 | 212.208 | 53.122 | 53.140 | 0.33987 | 0.33998 | 1.04709 | 1.04672 | 98.1 | 98.0 |
| n-Dodecane | $C_{12}H_{26}$ | 227.501 | 228.579 | 57.764 | 57.783 | 0.33913 | 0.33925 | 1.04726 | 1.04691 | 98.1 | 98.0 |
| n-Tridecane | $C_{13}H_{28}$ | 243.73 | 244.89 | 62.39 | 62.41 | 0.3384 | 0.3385 | 1.0474 | 1.0470 | 98. | 98. |
| n-Tetradecane | $C_{14}H_{30}$ | 260.05 | 261.27 | 67.03 | 67.05 | 0.3379 | 0.3380 | 1.0475 | 1.0472 | 98. | 98. |
| n-Pentadecane | $C_{15}H_{32}$ | 276.39 | 277.65 | 71.67 | 71.70 | 0.3374 | 0.3375 | 1.0476 | 1.0473 | 98. | 98. |
| n-Hexadecane | $C_{16}H_{34}$ | 292.760 | 294.083 | 76.333 | 76.354 | 0.33711 | 0.33720 | 1.04788 | 1.04752 | 98. | 98. |
| n-Heptadecane | $C_{17}H_{36}$ | 309.09[c] | 310.47 | 80.96[c] | 80.98 | 0.3367[c] | 0.3368 | 1.0479[c] | 1.0476[c] | 98. | 98. |
| n-Octadecane | $C_{18}H_{38}$ | 325.45[c] | 326.89[c] | 85.60[c] | 85.62[c] | 0.3364[c] | 0.3365[c] | 1.0480[c] | 1.0476[c] | 98.[c] | 98.[c] |
| n-Nonadecane | $C_{19}H_{40}$ | 341.82[c] | 343.32[c] | 90.24[c] | 90.27[c] | 0.3361[c] | 0.3362[c] | 1.0481[c] | 1.0478[c] | 98.[c] | 98.[c] |
| n-Eicosane | $C_{20}H_{42}$ | 358.23[c] | 359.78[c] | 94.89[c] | 94.91[c] | 0.3358[c] | 0.3359[c] | 1.0482[c] | 1.0478[c] | 98.[c] | 98.[c] |

[a] See footnote a of Table 1b.  [b] At saturation pressure.  [c] For the undercooled liquid below the normal freezing point.

TABLE 20b (PART 2) - NORMAL PARAFFINS, $C_{21}$ TO $C_{40}$

MOLECULAR VOLUME, MOLECULAR REFRACTION, SPECIFIC REFRACTION, REFRACTIVITY INTERCEPT, AND SPECIFIC DISPERSION

December 31, 1950

| Compound | Formula | Molecular Volume[a] $V=M/d$ (ml/mole) | | Molecular Refraction[a] $V(n_D^2-1)/(n_D^2+2)$ (ml/mole) | | Specific Refraction[a] $(1/d)(n_D^2-1)/(n_D^2+2)$ (ml/g) | | Refractivity Intercept[a] $n_D-d/2$ | | Specific Dispersion[a] $10^4(n_F-n_C)/d$ (ml/g) | |
|---|---|---|---|---|---|---|---|---|---|---|---|
| | | 20°C | 25°C | 20°C | 25°C | 20°C | 25°C | 20°C | 25°C | 20°C | 25°C |
| n-Heneicosane | $C_{21}H_{44}$ | 374.59[b] | 376.21[b] | 99.52[b] | 99.55[b] | 0.3356[b] | 0.3357[b] | 1.0483[b] | 1.0479[b] | 98.[b] | 98.[b] |
| n-Docosane | $C_{22}H_{46}$ | 390.98[b] | 392.66[b] | 104.16[b] | 104.19[b] | 0.3354[b] | 0.3355[b] | 1.0483[b] | 1.0480[b] | 98.[b] | 98.[b] |
| n-Tricosane | $C_{23}H_{48}$ | 407.36[b] | 409.10[b] | 108.80[b] | 108.83[b] | 0.3352[b] | 0.3353[b] | 1.0484[b] | 1.0480[b] | 98.[b] | 98.[b] |
| n-Tetracosane | $C_{24}H_{50}$ | 423.75[b] | 425.55[b] | 113.44[b] | 113.48[b] | 0.3350[b] | 0.3351[b] | 1.0484[b] | 1.0481[b] | 98.[b] | 98.[b] |
| n-Pentacosane | $C_{25}H_{52}$ | 440.15[b] | 442.01[b] | 118.09[b] | 118.12[b] | 0.3348[b] | 0.3349[b] | 1.0485[b] | 1.0481[b] | 98.[b] | 98.[b] |
| n-Hexacosane | $C_{26}H_{54}$ | 456.54[b] | 458.46[b] | 122.73[b] | 122.76[b] | 0.3347[b] | 0.3348[b] | 1.0485[b] | 1.0482[b] | 98.[b] | 98.[b] |
| n-Heptacosane | $C_{27}H_{56}$ | 472.94[b] | 474.92[b] | 127.37[b] | 127.40[b] | 0.3345[b] | 0.3346[b] | 1.0486[b] | 1.0482[b] | 98.[b] | 98.[b] |
| n-Octacosane | $C_{28}H_{58}$ | 489.34[b] | 491.38[b] | 132.01[b] | 132.04[b] | 0.3344[b] | 0.3345[b] | 1.0487[b] | 1.0483[b] | 98.[b] | 98.[b] |
| n-Nonacosane | $C_{29}H_{60}$ | 505.7[b] | 507.8[b] | 136.65[b] | 136.68[b] | 0.3343[b] | 0.3344[b] | 1.0487[b] | 1.0483[b] | 98.[b] | 98.[b] |
| n-Triacontane | $C_{30}H_{62}$ | 522.1[b] | 524.3[b] | 141.29[b] | 141.33[b] | 0.3342[b] | 0.3343[b] | 1.0487[b] | 1.0484[b] | 98.[b] | 98.[b] |
| n-Hentriacontane | $C_{31}H_{64}$ | 538.5[b] | 540.8[b] | 145.93[b] | 145.97[b] | 0.3341[b] | 0.3342[b] | 1.0487[b] | 1.0484[b] | 98.[b] | 98.[b] |
| n-Dotriacontane | $C_{32}H_{66}$ | 554.9[b] | 557.2[b] | 150.57[b] | 150.61[b] | 0.3340[b] | 0.3341[b] | 1.0488[b] | 1.0484[b] | 98.[b] | 98.[b] |
| n-Tritriacontane | $C_{33}H_{68}$ | 571.4[b] | 573.7[b] | 155.21[b] | 155.25[b] | 0.3339[b] | 0.3340[b] | 1.0488[b] | 1.0485[b] | 98.[b] | 98.[b] |
| n-Tetratriacontane | $C_{34}H_{70}$ | 587.8[b] | 590.2[b] | 159.85[b] | 159.89[b] | 0.3338[b] | 0.3339[b] | 1.0488[b] | 1.0485[b] | 98.[b] | 98.[b] |
| n-Pentatriacontane | $C_{35}H_{72}$ | 604.2[b] | 606.6[b] | 164.49[b] | 164.53[b] | 0.3337[b] | 0.3338[b] | 1.0489[b] | 1.0485[b] | 98.[b] | 98.[b] |
| n-Hexatriacontane | $C_{36}H_{74}$ | 620.6[b] | 623.1[b] | 169.13[b] | 169.17[b] | 0.3336[b] | 0.3337[b] | 1.0489[b] | 1.0486[b] | 98.[b] | 98.[b] |
| n-Heptatriacontane | $C_{37}H_{76}$ | 637.0[b] | 639.6[b] | 173.77[b] | 173.82[b] | 0.3335[b] | 0.3336[b] | 1.0489[b] | 1.0486[b] | 98.[b] | 98.[b] |
| n-Octatriacontane | $C_{38}H_{78}$ | 653.4[b] | 656.0[b] | 178.41[b] | 178.46[b] | 0.3335[b] | 0.3336[b] | 1.0489[b] | 1.0486[b] | 98.[b] | 98.[b] |
| n-Nonatriacontane | $C_{39}H_{80}$ | 669.8[b] | 672.5[b] | 183.05[b] | 183.10[b] | 0.3334[b] | 0.3335[b] | 1.0490[b] | 1.0486[b] | 98.[b] | 98.[b] |
| n-Tetracontane | $C_{40}H_{82}$ | 686.2[b] | 689.0[b] | 187.69[b] | 187.74[b] | 0.3333[b] | 0.3334[b] | 1.0490[b] | 1.0487[b] | 98.[b] | 98.[b] |

a See footnote a of Table 1b.

b For the undercooled liquid below the normal freezing point.

TABLE 1b — PARAFFINS, $C_1$ TO $C_5$

MOLECULAR VOLUME, MOLECULAR REFRACTION, SPECIFIC REFRACTION, REFRACTIVITY INTERCEPT, AND SPECIFIC DISPERSION

June 30, 1945; June 30 1949; October 31, 1952

| Compound | Formula | Molecular Volume[a] $V = M/d$ ml/mole | | Molecular Refraction[a] $V(n_D^2-1)/(n_D^2+2)$ ml/mole | | Specific Refraction[a] $(1/d)(n_D^2-1)/(n_D^2+2)$ ml/g | | Refractivity Intercept[a] $n_D - d/2$ | | Specific Dispersion[a] $10^4(n_F - n_C)/d$ ml/g | |
|---|---|---|---|---|---|---|---|---|---|---|---|
| | | 20°C | 25°C | 20°C | 25°C | 20°C | 25°C | 20°C | 25°C | 20°C | 25°C |
| Methane | $CH_4$ | — | — | — | — | — | — | — | — | — | — |
| Ethane | $C_2H_6$ | — | — | — | — | — | — | — | — | — | — |
| Propane | $C_3H_8$ | 88.10[b] | 89.48[b] | — | — | — | — | — | — | — | — |
| n-Butane | $C_4H_{10}$ | 100.41[b] | 101.43[b] | 20.63[b] | 20.64[b] | 0.3550[b] | 0.3552[b] | 1.0432[b] | 1.0426[b] | — | — |
| 2-Methylpropane (Isobutane) | " | 104.31[b] | 105.48[b] | — | — | — | — | — | — | — | — |
| n-Pentane | $C_5H_{12}$ | 115.205 | 116.104 | 25.266 | 25.286 | 0.35020 | 0.35048 | 1.04436 | 1.04402 | 98.1 | 98.0 |
| 2-Methylbutane (Isopentane) | " | 116.426 | 117.383 | 25.292 | 25.315 | 0.35057 | 0.35089 | 1.04390 | 1.04357 | 98.7 | 98.6 |
| 2,2-Dimethylpropane (Neopentane) | " | 122.07[b] | 123.31[b] | 25.72[b] | 25.78[b] | 0.356[b] | 0.3573[b] | 1.046[b] | 1.046[b] | 98.[b] | 98.[b] |

a Values are given for the air-saturated hydrocarbon in the liquid state at one atmosphere. $n_D$, $n_F$, and $n_C$ are the refractive indices for the sodium D (5892.6 Angstrom units), the hydrogen F (4861.3 Angstrom units) and the hydrogen C (6562.8 Angstrom units) lines, respectively.

b At saturation pressure.

165

TABLE 2b (PART 1) - PARAFFINS, $C_6$

MOLECULAR VOLUME, MOLECULAR REFRACTION, SPECIFIC REFRACTION, REFRACTIVITY INTERCEPT, AND SPECIFIC DISPERSION

June 30, 1945; December 31, 1948; December 31, 1948; October 31, 1952

| Compound | Formula | Molecular Volume[a] $V = M/d$ ml/mole | | Molecular Refraction[a] $V(n_D^2-1)/(n_D^2+2)$ ml/mole | | Specific Refraction[a] $(1/d)(n_D^2-1)/(n_D^2+2)$ ml/g | | Refractivity Intercept[a] $n_D-d/2$ | | Specific Dispersion[a] $10^4(n_F-n_C)/d$ ml/g | |
|---|---|---|---|---|---|---|---|---|---|---|---|
| | | 20°C | 25°C | 20°C | 25°C | 20°C | 25°C | 20°C | 25°C | 20°C | 25°C |
| n-Hexane | $C_6H_{14}$ | 130.688 | 131.598 | 29.907 | 29.928 | 0.34706 | 0.34730 | 1.04518 | 1.04486 | 98.1 | 98.0 |
| 2-Methylpentane | " | 131.933 | 132.875 | 29.946 | 29.962 | 0.34751 | 0.34770 | 1.04488 | 1.04447 | 98.7 | 98.6 |
| 3-Methylpentane | " | 129.717 | 130.611 | 29.802 | 29.818 | 0.34584 | 0.34602 | 1.04436 | 1.04398 | 97.2 | 97.1 |
| 2,2-Dimethylbutane | " | 132.744 | 133.712 | 29.935 | 29.947 | 0.34738 | 0.34753 | 1.04418 | 1.04372 | 99.9 | 99.8 |
| 2,3-Dimethylbutane | " | 130.240 | 131.156 | 29.810 | 29.831 | 0.34594 | 0.34618 | 1.04413 | 1.04380 | 98.4 | 98.3 |

[a] See footnote a of Table 1b.

TABLE 2b (PART 2) - PARAFFINS, $C_7$

MOLECULAR VOLUME, MOLECULAR REFRACTION, SPECIFIC REFRACTION, REFRACTIVITY INTERCEPT, AND SPECIFIC DISPERSION

June 30, 1945; December 31, 1948; October 31, 1952

| Compound | Formula | Molecular Volume[a] $V=M/d$ ml/mole | | Molecular Refraction[a] $V(n_D^2-1)/(n_D^2+2)$ ml/mole | | Specific Refraction[a] $(1/d)(n_D^2-1)/(n_D^2+2)$ ml/g | | Refractivity Intercept[a] $n_D-d/2$ | | Specific Dispersion[a] $10^4(n_F-n_C)/d$ ml/g | |
|---|---|---|---|---|---|---|---|---|---|---|---|
| | | 20°C | 25°C | 20°C | 25°C | 20°C | 25°C | 20°C | 25°C | 20°C | 25°C |
| n-Heptane | $C_7H_{16}$ | 146.540 | 147.456 | 34.550 | 34.565 | 0.34482 | 0.34496 | 1.04576 | 1.04536 | 97.8 | 97.7 |
| 2-Methylhexane | " | 147.656 | 148.576 | 34.591 | 34.599 | 0.34522 | 0.34530 | 1.04556 | 1.04508 | 98.4 | 98.5 |
| 3-Methylhexane | " | 145.821 | 146.714 | 34.460 | 34.469 | 0.34392 | 0.34400 | 1.04508 | 1.04462 | 97.5 | 97.4 |
| 3-Ethylpentane | " | 143.517 | 144.388 | 34.283 | 34.292 | 0.34215 | 0.34225 | 1.04431 | 1.04386 | 95.7 | 95.7 |
| 2,2-Dimethylpentane | " | 148.695 | 149.654 | 34.617 | 34.629 | 0.34548 | 0.34560 | 1.04522 | 1.04478 | 99.4 | 99.3 |
| 2,3-Dimethylpentane | " | 144.153 | 145.023 | 34.324 | 34.335 | 0.34256 | 0.34267 | 1.04442 | 1.04400 | 96.4 | 96.2 |
| 2,4-Dimethylpentane | " | 148.949 | 149.925 | 34.619 | 34.632 | 0.34551 | 0.34564 | 1.04510 | 1.04466 | 98.7 | 98.6 |
| 3,3-Dimethylpentane | " | 144.530 | 145.408 | 34.332 | 34.345 | 0.34265 | 0.34277 | 1.04428 | 1.04388 | 97.4 | 97.1 |
| 2,2,3-Trimethylbutane | " | 145.191 | 146.087 | 34.374 | 34.387 | 0.34306 | 0.34319 | 1.04438 | 1.04398 | 98.7 | 98.3 |

a See footnote a of Table 1b.

167

TABLE 3b – PARAFFINS, $C_8$

MOLECULAR VOLUME, MOLECULAR REFRACTION, SPECIFIC REFRACTION, REFRACTIVITY INTERCEPT, AND SPECIFIC DISPERSION

June 30, 1945; December 31, 1948; October 31, 1952

| Compound | Formula | Molecular Volume[a] $V=M/d$ (ml/mole) | | Molecular Refraction[a] $V(n_D^2-1)/(n_D^2+2)$ (ml/mole) | | Specific Refraction[a] $(1/d)(n_D^2-1)/(n_D^2+2)$ (ml/g) | | Refractivity Intercept[a] $n_D - d/2$ | | Specific Dispersion[a] $10^4(n_F-n_C)/d$ (ml/g) | |
|---|---|---|---|---|---|---|---|---|---|---|---|
| | | 20°C | 25°C | 20°C | 25°C | 20°C | 25°C | 20°C | 25°C | 20°C | 25°C |
| n-Octane | $C_8H_{18}$ | 162.592 | 163.530 | 39.192 | 39.209 | 0.34312 | 0.34327 | 1.04617 | 1.04580 | 98.1 | 98.0 |
| 2-Methylheptane | " | 163.663 | 164.607 | 39.231 | 39.248 | 0.34346 | 0.34360 | 1.04598 | 1.04561 | 98.6 | 98.5 |
| 3-Methylheptane | " | 161.832 | 162.770 | 39.100 | 39.119 | 0.34231 | 0.34248 | 1.04557 | 1.04523 | 97.6 | 97.5 |
| 4-Methylheptane | " | 162.105 | 163.049 | 39.117 | 39.136 | 0.34246 | 0.34263 | 1.04560 | 1.04525 | 97.6 | 97.5 |
| 3-Ethylhexane | " | 160.072 | 160.997 | 38.944 | 38.960 | 0.34094 | 0.34108 | 1.04483 | 1.04445 | 96.5 | 96.4 |
| 2,2-Dimethylhexane | " | 164.285 | 165.274 | 39.252 | 39.271 | 0.34364 | 0.34380 | 1.04585 | 1.04548 | 99.8 | 99.7 |
| 2,3-Dimethylhexane | " | 160.395 | 161.313 | 38.981 | 39.002 | 0.34127 | 0.34146 | 1.04506 | 1.04476 | 97.1 | 97.0 |
| 2,4-Dimethylhexane | " | 163.093 | 164.068 | 39.130 | 39.149 | 0.34257 | 0.34274 | 1.04516 | 1.04481 | 97.9 | 97.8 |
| 2,5-Dimethylhexane | " | 164.697 | 165.700 | 39.260 | 39.283 | 0.34371 | 0.34391 | 1.04569 | 1.04537 | 99.1 | 99.0 |
| 3,3-Dimethylhexane | " | 160.879 | 161.800 | 39.009 | 39.035 | 0.34151 | 0.34174 | 1.04509 | 1.04484 | 97.4 | 97.3 |
| 3,4-Dimethylhexane | " | 158.814 | 159.718 | 38.845 | 38.873 | 0.34008 | 0.34033 | 1.04444 | 1.04422 | 96.7 | 96.6 |
| 2-Methyl-3-ethylpentane | " | 158.794 | 159.704 | 38.836 | 38.859 | 0.34000 | 0.34020 | 1.04435 | 1.04406 | 96.2 | 96.1 |
| 3-Methyl-3-ethylpentane | " | 157.026 | 157.868 | 38.717 | 38.734 | 0.33896 | 0.33911 | 1.04404 | 1.04372 | 95.9 | 95.8 |
| 2,2,3-Trimethylpentane | " | 159.526 | 160.411 | 38.925 | 38.944 | 0.34078 | 0.34095 | 1.04494 | 1.04462 | 97.3 | 97.2 |
| 2,2,4-Trimethylpentane | " | 165.083 | 166.079 | 39.262 | 39.280 | 0.34373 | 0.34389 | 1.04549 | 1.04513 | 100.6 | 100.5 |
| 2,3,3-Trimethylpentane | " | 157.292 | 158.135 | 38.762 | 38.777 | 0.33935 | 0.33948 | 1.04440 | 1.04406 | 96.2 | 96.1 |
| 2,3,4-Trimethylpentane | " | 158.852 | 159.747 | 38.868 | 38.896 | 0.34028 | 0.34052 | 1.04469 | 1.04446 | 97.0 | 96.9 |
| 2,2,3,3-Tetramethylbutane | " | | | | | | | | | | |

[a] See footnote a of Table 1b.

TABLE 4b, Page 1 – PARAFFINS, $C_9$

MOLECULAR VOLUME, MOLECULAR REFRACTION, SPECIFIC REFRACTION, REFRACTIVITY INTERCEPT, AND SPECIFIC DISPERSION

June 30, 1945; March 31, 1949; October 31, 1952

| Compound | Formula | Molecular Volume[a] $V = M/d$ ml/mole | | Molecular Refraction[a] $V(n_D^2-1)/(n_D^2+2)$ ml/mole | | Specific Refraction[a] $(1/d)(n_D^2-1)/(n_D^2+2)$ ml/g | | Refractivity Intercept[a] $n_D - d/2$ | | Specific Dispersion[a] $10^4(n_F-n_C)/d$ ml/g | |
|---|---|---|---|---|---|---|---|---|---|---|---|
| | | 20°C | 25°C | 20°C | 25°C | 20°C | 25°C | 20°C | 25°C | 20°C | 25°C |
| n-Nonane | $C_9H_{20}$ | 178.713 | 179.670 | 43.842 | 43.855 | 0.34185 | 0.34195 | 1.04660 | 1.04620 | 97.4 | 97.2 |
| 2-Methyloctane | " | 179.77 | 180.76 | 43.88 | 43.90 | 0.3421 | 0.3423 | 1.0464 | 1.0460 | 98.5 | 98.4 |
| 3-Methyloctane | " | 177.95 | 178.92 | 43.73 | 43.75 | 0.3410 | 0.3411 | 1.0459 | 1.0455 | 97.6 | 97.5 |
| 4-Methyloctane | " | 178.15 | 179.12 | 43.77 | 43.79 | 0.3413 | 0.3414 | 1.0462 | 1.0458 | 97.6 | 97.5 |
| 3-Ethylheptane | " | 176.4 | 177.4 | 43.6 | 43.7 | 0.340 | 0.340 | 1.046 | 1.046 | 96.7 | 96.6 |
| 4-Ethylheptane | " | 175.7 | 176.7 | 43.5 | 43.5 | 0.339 | 0.339 | 1.0446 | 1.0443 | 96.7 | 96.6 |
| 2,2-Dimethylheptane | " | 180.51 | 181.50 | 43.91 | 43.93 | 0.3424 | 0.3426 | 1.0464 | 1.0460 | 99.6 | 99.5 |
| 2,3-Dimethylheptane | " | 176.65 | 177.61 | 43.63 | 43.65 | 0.3402 | 0.3403 | 1.0455 | 1.0452 | 97.3 | 97.2 |
| 2,4-Dimethylheptane | " | 179.1 | 180.1 | 43.7 | 43.7 | 0.341 | 0.341 | 1.0453 | 1.0450 | 97.9 | 97.8 |
| 2,5-Dimethylheptane | " | 179.4 | 180.4 | 43.9 | 43.9 | 0.342 | 0.342 | 1.046 | 1.046 | 97.9 | 97.8 |
| 2,6-Dimethylheptane | " | 180.91 | 181.94 | 43.92 | 43.94 | 0.3425 | 0.3426 | 1.0462 | 1.0458 | 99.0 | 98.9 |
| 3,3-Dimethylheptane | " | 176.9 | 177.9 | 43.7 | 43.7 | 0.341 | 0.341 | 1.046 | 1.046 | 97.5 | 97.4 |
| 3,4-Dimethylheptane | " | 175.35 | 176.29 | 43.55 | 43.57 | 0.3395 | 0.3398 | 1.0454 | 1.0452 | 96.9 | 96.8 |
| 3,5-Dimethylheptane | " | 177.4 | 178.4 | 43.6 | 43.7 | 0.340 | 0.340 | 1.045 | 1.045 | 97.0 | 96.9 |
| 4,4-Dimethylheptane | " | 176.9 | 177.9 | 43.6 | 43.6 | 0.340 | 0.340 | 1.045 | 1.045 | 97.5 | 97.4 |

a See footnote a of Table 1b.

TABLE 4b, Page 2 – PARAFFINS, C9

MOLECULAR VOLUME, MOLECULAR REFRACTION, SPECIFIC REFRACTION, REFRACTIVITY INTERCEPT, AND SPECIFIC DISPERSION

June 30, 1945; March 31, 1949; October 31, 1952

| Compound | Formula | Molecular Volume[a] $V=M/d$ (ml/mole) | | Molecular Refraction[a] $V(n_D^2-1)/(n_D^2+2)$ (ml/mole) | | Specific Refraction[a] $(1/d)(n_D^2-1)/(n_D^2+2)$ (ml/g) | | Refractivity Intercept[a] $n_D-d/2$ | | Specific Dispersion[a] $10^4(n_F-n_c)/d$ (ml/g) | |
|---|---|---|---|---|---|---|---|---|---|---|---|
| | | 20°C | 25°C | 20°C | 25°C | 20°C | 25°C | 20°C | 25°C | 20°C | 25°C |
| 2-Methyl-3-ethylhexane | $C_9H_{20}$ | 175.4 | 176.4 | 43.6 | 43.7 | 0.340 | 0.341 | 1.046 | 1.046 | 96.7 | 96.6 |
| 2-Methyl-4-ethylhexane | " | 177.4 | 178.4 | 43.7 | 43.7 | 0.340 | 0.341 | 1.045 | 1.045 | 97.0 | 96.9 |
| 3-Methyl-3-ethylhexane | " | 173.1 | 174.0 | 43.3 | 43.3 | 0.337 | 0.338 | 1.044 | 1.044 | 96.0 | 95.9 |
| 3-Methyl-4-ethylhexane | " | 172.8 | 173.8 | 43.4 | 43.4 | 0.338 | 0.339 | 1.045 | 1.045 | 95.6 | 95.5 |
| 2,2,3-Trimethylhexane | " | 175.88 | 176.80 | 43.62 | 43.63 | 0.3401 | 0.3402 | 1.0459 | 1.0455 | 97.4 | 97.3 |
| 2,2,4-Trimethylhexane | " | 179.22 | 180.18 | 43.76 | 43.78 | 0.3412 | 0.3413 | 1.0455 | 1.0451 | 98.9 | 98.8 |
| 2,2,5-Trimethylhexane | " | 181.346 | 182.375 | 43.935 | 43.946 | 0.34258 | 0.34266 | 1.04612 | 1.04567 | 98.8 | 99.0 |
| 2,3,3-Trimethylhexane | " | 173.8 | 174.7 | 43.4 | 43.5 | 0.339 | 0.339 | 1.045 | 1.045 | 96.4 | 96.3 |
| 2,3,4-Trimethylhexane | " | 173.50 | 174.39 | 43.39 | 43.39 | 0.3383 | 0.3383 | 1.0448 | 1.0443 | 96.5 | 96.4 |
| 2,3,5-Trimethylhexane | " | 177.66 | 178.65 | 43.64 | 43.65 | 0.3403 | 0.3404 | 1.0450 | 1.0446 | 97.9 | 97.8 |
| 2,4,4-Trimethylhexane | " | 177.187 | 178.108 | 43.660 | 43.668 | 0.34043 | 0.34049 | 1.04554 | 1.04512 | 98.2 | 98.2 |
| 3,3,4-Trimethylhexane | " | 172.06 | 172.98 | 43.34 | 43.35 | 0.3379 | 0.3380 | 1.0451 | 1.0447 | 95.4 | 95.3 |
| 3,3-Diethylpentane | " | 170.185 | 171.000 | 43.113 | 43.126 | 0.33616 | 0.33627 | 1.04372 | 1.04337 | 94.6 | 94.3 |
| 2,2-Dimethyl-3-ethylpentane | " | 174.54 | 175.44 | 43.46 | 43.49 | 0.3388 | 0.3388 | 1.0449 | 1.0447 | 96.4 | 96.3 |
| 2,3-Dimethyl-3-ethylpentane | " | 170.1 | 171.0 | 43.0 | 43.0 | 0.335 | 0.335 | 1.042 | 1.042 | 94.7 | 94.6 |
| 2,4-Dimethyl-3-ethylpentane | " | 173.80 | 174.70 | 43.40 | 43.42 | 0.3384 | 0.3386 | 1.0488 | 1.0445 | 96.5 | 96.4 |
| 2,2,3,3-Tetramethylpentane | " | 169.495 | 170.321 | 43.215 | 43.228 | 0.33696 | 0.33706 | 1.04527 | 1.04490 | 96.1 | 95.9 |
| 2,2,3,4-Tetramethylpentane | " | 173.557 | 174.433 | 43.436 | 43.446 | 0.33868 | 0.33876 | 1.04524 | 1.04484 | 96.8 | 96.8 |
| 2,2,4,4-Tetramethylpentane | " | 178.256 | 179.213 | 43.875 | 43.886 | 0.34210 | 0.34219 | 1.04720 | 1.04677 | 100.8 | 101.0 |
| 2,3,3,4-Tetramethylpentane | " | 169.928 | 170.743 | 43.201 | 43.211 | 0.33685 | 0.33693 | 1.04486 | 1.04446 | 95.5 | 95.5 |

a See footnote a of Table 1b.

TABLE 17b, Page 1 – PARAFFINS, $C_{10}$

MOLECULAR VOLUME, MOLECULAR REFRACTION, SPECIFIC REFRACTION, REFRACTIVITY INTERCEPT, AND SPECIFIC DISPERSION

October 31, 1950; October 31, 1952

| Compound | Formula | Molecular Volume[a] $V=M/d$ ml/mole | | Molecular Refraction[a] $V(n_D^2-1)/(n_D^2+2)$ ml/mole | | Specific Refraction[a] $(1/d)(n_D^2-1)/(n_D^2+2)$ ml/g | | Refractivity Intercept[a] $n_D-d/2$ | | Specific Dispersion[a] $10^4(n_F-n_C)/d$ ml/g | |
|---|---|---|---|---|---|---|---|---|---|---|---|
| | | 20°C | 25°C | 20°C | 25°C | 20°C | 25°C | 20°C | 25°C | 20°C | 25°C |
| n-Decane | $C_{10}H_{22}$ | 194.885 | 195.905 | 48.481 | 48.503 | 0.34075 | 0.34091 | 1.04686 | 1.04654 | 98.1 | 98.0 |
| 2-Methylnonane | " | 195.41 | 196.46 | 48.40 | 48.42 | 0.3402 | 0.3404 | 1.0459 | 1.0455 | 99. | 99. |
| 3-Methylnonane | " | 194.00 | 195.01 | 48.32 | 48.34 | 0.3396 | 0.3398 | 1.0458 | 1.0455 | 98. | 98. |
| 4-Methylnonane | " | 194.29 | 195.33 | 48.38 | 48.39 | 0.3400 | 0.3402 | 1.0461 | 1.0458 | 98. | 98. |
| 5-Methylnonane | " | 194.21 | 195.22 | 48.34 | 48.36 | 0.3398 | 0.3400 | 1.0459 | 1.0456 | 98. | 98. |
| 3-Ethyloctane | " | 192.3 | 193.3 | 48.3 | 48.3 | 0.339 | 0.340 | 1.046 | 1.046 | 96. | 96. |
| 4-Ethyloctane | " | 192.3 | 193.3 | 48.3 | 48.3 | 0.339 | 0.340 | 1.046 | 1.046 | 96. | 100. |
| 2,2-Dimethyloctane | " | 196.38 | 197.39 | 48.47 | 48.49 | 0.3406 | 0.3408 | 1.0460 | 1.0456 | 100. | 100. |
| 2,3-Dimethyloctane | " | 192.89 | 193.92 | 48.28 | 48.30 | 0.3394 | 0.3395 | 1.0460 | 1.0457 | 97. | 97. |
| 2,4-Dimethyloctane | " | 195.86 | 196.95 | 48.45 | 48.47 | 0.3406 | 0.3407 | 1.0461 | 1.0457 | 98. | 98. |
| 2,5-Dimethyloctane | " | 193.3 | 194.4 | 48.3 | 48.3 | 0.340 | 0.340 | 1.046 | 1.046 | 99. | 99. |
| 2,6-Dimethyloctane | " | 195.30 | 196.38 | 48.52 | 48.54 | 0.3410 | 0.3412 | 1.0471 | 1.0467 | 99. | 99. |
| 2,7-Dimethyloctane | " | 196.46 | 197.55 | 48.53 | 48.55 | 0.3411 | 0.3412 | 1.0465 | 1.0461 | 98.7 | 98.6 |
| 3,3-Dimethyloctane | " | 192.52 | 193.55 | 48.36 | 48.38 | 0.3399 | 0.3401 | 1.0470 | 1.0466 | 97. | 97. |
| 3,4-Dimethyloctane | " | 190.7 | 191.7 | 48.1 | 48.1 | 0.338 | 0.338 | 1.045 | 1.045 | 97. | 97. |
| 3,5-Dimethyloctane | " | 193.3 | 194.4 | 48.2 | 48.2 | 0.339 | 0.339 | 1.045 | 1.045 | 97. | 97. |
| 3,6-Dimethyloctane | " | 193.23 | 194.26 | 48.34 | 48.36 | 0.3397 | 0.3399 | 1.0463 | 1.0460 | 97. | 97. |
| 4,4-Dimethyloctane | " | 193.0 | 194.1 | 48.2 | 48.2 | 0.339 | 0.339 | 1.046 | 1.046 | 97. | 97. |
| 4,5-Dimethyloctane | " | 190.46 | 191.44 | 48.10 | 48.12 | 0.3381 | 0.3382 | 1.0455 | 1.0451 | 95.9 | 95.8 |
| 4-Propylheptane | " | 193.20 | 194.21 | 48.38 | 48.40 | 0.340 | 0.340 | 1.0463 | 1.0464 | 96. | 96. |
| 4-Isopropylheptane | " | 192.0 | 193.0 | 48.3 | 48.3 | 0.339 | 0.340 | 1.047 | 1.047 | 97. | 97. |
| 2-Methyl-3-ethylheptane | " | 190.7 | 191.7 | 48.1 | 48.1 | 0.338 | 0.338 | 1.045 | 1.045 | 96. | 96. |
| 2-Methyl-4-ethylheptane | " | 193.3 | 194.4 | 48.2 | 48.2 | 0.339 | 0.339 | 1.045 | 1.045 | 96. | 96. |
| 2-Methyl-5-ethylheptane | " | 193.3 | 194.4 | 48.2 | 48.3 | 0.339 | 0.339 | 1.045 | 1.045 | 96. | 96. |
| 3-Methyl-3-ethylheptane | " | 189.68 | 190.64 | 48.08 | 48.14 | 0.3379 | 0.3384 | 1.0458 | 1.0458 | 97. | 97. |

[a] See footnote a of Table 1b.

TABLE 17b, Page 2 – PARAFFINS, $C_{10}$

MOLECULAR VOLUME, MOLECULAR REFRACTION, SPECIFIC REFRACTION, REFRACTIVITY INTERCEPT, AND SPECIFIC DISPERSION

October 31, 1950; October 31, 1952

| Compound | Formula | Molecular Volume[a] $V=M/d$ (ml/mole) | | Molecular Refraction[a] $V(n_D^2-1)/(n_D^2+2)$ (ml/mole) | | Specific Refraction[a] $(1/d)(n_D^2-1)/(n_D^2+2)$ (ml/g) | | Refractivity Intercept[a] $n_D-d/2$ | | Specific Dispersion[a] $10^4(n_F-n_C)/d$ (ml/g) | |
|---|---|---|---|---|---|---|---|---|---|---|---|
| | | 20°C | 25°C | 20°C | 25°C | 20°C | 25°C | 20°C | 25°C | 20°C | 25°C |
| 3-Methyl-4-ethylheptane | $C_{10}H_{22}$ | 188.9 | 190.0 | 48.0 | 48.0 | 0.337 | 0.337 | 1.046 | 1.045 | 96. | 96. |
| 3-Methyl-5-ethylheptane | " | 191.5 | 192.5 | 48.1 | 48.1 | 0.338 | 0.338 | 1.044 | 1.044 | 96. | 96. |
| 4-Methyl-3-ethylheptane | " | 188.9 | 190.0 | 48.0 | 48.0 | 0.337 | 0.337 | 1.046 | 1.045 | 96. | 96. |
| 4-Methyl-4-ethylheptane | " | 189.2 | 190.2 | 48.0 | 48.0 | 0.338 | 0.338 | 1.045 | 1.045 | 97. | 97. |
| 2,2,3-Trimethylheptane | " | 191.7 | 192.8 | 48.2 | 48.2 | 0.339 | 0.339 | 1.046 | 1.045 | 97. | 97. |
| 2,2,4-Trimethylheptane | " | 195.57 | 196.60 | 48.37 | 48.39 | 0.3400 | 0.3401 | 1.0454 | 1.0451 | 100. | 100. |
| 2,2,5-Trimethylheptane | " | 196.0 | 197.1 | 48.5 | 48.5 | 0.341 | 0.340 | 1.046 | 1.046 | 100. | 100. |
| 2,2,6-Trimethylheptane | " | 197.74 | 198.82 | 48.56 | 48.58 | 0.3413 | 0.3415 | 1.0461 | 1.0458 | 98. | 98. |
| 2,3,3-Trimethylheptane | " | 190.00 | 191.03 | 48.10 | 48.12 | 0.3381 | 0.3382 | 1.0458 | 1.0454 | 96. | 96. |
| 2,3,4-Trimethylheptane | " | 189.4 | 190.5 | 48.0 | 48.0 | 0.338 | 0.337 | 1.045 | 1.044 | 97. | 97. |
| 2,3,5-Trimethylheptane | " | 192.0 | 193.0 | 48.2 | 48.2 | 0.339 | 0.339 | 1.046 | 1.046 | 97. | 97. |
| 2,3,6-Trimethylheptane | " | 193.70 | 194.77 | 48.25 | 48.27 | 0.3391 | 0.3392 | 1.0453 | 1.0449 | 97. | 97. |
| 2,4,4-Trimethylheptane | " | 194.1 | 195.2 | 48.3 | 48.3 | 0.340 | 0.340 | 1.046 | 1.046 | 97. | 97. |
| 2,4,5-Trimethylheptane | " | 192.0 | 193.0 | 48.2 | 48.2 | 0.339 | 0.339 | 1.046 | 1.046 | 97. | 97. |
| 2,4,6-Trimethylheptane | " | 196.92 | 198.05 | 48.48 | 48.50 | 0.3408 | 0.3409 | 1.0459 | 1.0454 | 97. | 97. |
| 2,5,5-Trimethylheptane | " | 193.10 | 194.15 | 48.21 | 48.23 | 0.3389 | 0.3390 | 1.0452 | 1.0448 | 97. | 97. |
| 3,3,4-Trimethylheptane | " | 187.9 | 188.9 | 47.9 | 48.0 | 0.337 | 0.337 | 1.046 | 1.046 | 97. | 97. |
| 3,3,5-Trimethylheptane | " | 191.54 | 192.58 | 48.17 | 48.18 | 0.3386 | 0.3387 | 1.0456 | 1.0452 | 97. | 97. |
| 3,4,4-Trimethylheptane | " | 187.9 | 188.9 | 47.9 | 48.0 | 0.337 | 0.337 | 1.046 | 1.046 | 97. | 97. |
| 3,4,5-Trimethylheptane | " | 187.5 | 188.4 | 47.8 | 47.9 | 0.336 | 0.337 | 1.044 | 1.044 | 97. | 97. |
| 2-Methyl-3-isopropylhexane | " | 189.4 | 190.5 | 48.0 | 48.0 | 0.338 | 0.337 | 1.045 | 1.044 | 98. | 98. |
| 3,3-Diethylhexane | " | 185.5 | 186.5 | 47.7 | 47.7 | 0.335 | 0.336 | 1.044 | 1.044 | 95. | 95. |
| 3,4-Diethylhexane | " | 188.7 | 189.7 | 47.8 | 47.3 | 0.336 | 0.336 | 1.043 | 1.043 | 94.7 | 94.6 |
| 2,2-Dimethyl-3-ethylhexane | " | 190.0 | 191.0 | 48.1 | 48.1 | 0.338 | 0.338 | 1.046 | 1.046 | 97. | 97. |
| 2,2-Dimethyl-4-ethylhexane | " | 194.1 | 195.2 | 48.4 | 48.4 | 0.340 | 0.340 | 1.0466 | 1.0462 | 97. | 97. |

[a] See footnote a of Table 1b.

TABLE 17b, Page 3 – PARAFFINS, C₁₀

MOLECULAR VOLUME, MOLECULAR REFRACTION, SPECIFIC REFRACTION, REFRACTIVITY INTERCEPT, AND SPECIFIC DISPERSION

October 31, 1950; October 31, 1952

| Compound | Formula[a] | Molecular Volume[a] $V=M/d$ (ml/mole) | | Molecular Refraction[a] $V(n_D^2-1)/(n_D^2+2)$ (ml/mole) | | Specific Refraction[a] $(1/d)(n_D^2-1)/(n_D^2+2)$ (ml/g) | | Refractivity Intercept[a] $n_D-d/2$ | | Specific Dispersion[a] $10^4(n_F-n_C)/d$ (ml/g) | |
|---|---|---|---|---|---|---|---|---|---|---|---|
| | | 20°C | 25°C | 20°C | 25°C | 20°C | 25°C | 20°C | 25°C | 20°C | 25°C |
| 2,3-Dimethyl-3-ethylhexane | $C_{10}H_{22}$ | 186.0 | 187.2 | 47.8 | 47.8 | 0.336 | 0.336 | 1.045 | 1.044 | 97. | 97. |
| 2,3-Dimethyl-4-ethylhexane | " | 187.5 | 188.4 | 47.8 | 47.9 | 0.336 | 0.336 | 1.044 | 1.044 | 97. | 97. |
| 2,4-Dimethyl-3-ethylhexane | " | 187.5 | 188.4 | 47.8 | 47.3 | 0.336 | 0.336 | 1.044 | 1.044 | 97. | 97. |
| 2,4-Dimethyl-4-ethylhexane | " | 190.5 | 191.5 | 48.1 | 48.1 | 0.338 | 0.333 | 1.045 | 1.045 | 97. | 97. |
| 2,5-Dimethyl-3-ethylhexane | " | 192.0 | 193.0 | 48.2 | 48.2 | 0.339 | 0.339 | 1.046 | 1.046 | 97. | 97. |
| 3,3-Dimethyl-4-ethylhexane | " | 186.2 | 187.2 | 47.8 | 47.8 | 0.336 | 0.336 | 1.045 | 1.045 | 97. | 97. |
| 3,4-Dimethyl-3-ethylhexane | " | 184.3 | 185.3 | 47.7 | 47.7 | 0.335 | 0.336 | 1.045 | 1.045 | 97. | 97. |
| 2,2,3,3-Tetramethylhexane | " | 186.103 | 187.058 | 47.892 | 47.911 | 0.33661 | 0.33674 | 1.04595 | 1.04556 | 97. | 97. |
| 2,2,3,4-Tetramethylhexane | " | 188.49 | 189.50 | 47.96 | 47.98 | 0.3371 | 0.3372 | 1.0452 | 1.0448 | 98. | 98. |
| 2,2,3,5-Tetramethylhexane | " | 192.84 | 193.94 | 48.21 | 48.23 | 0.3388 | 0.3390 | 1.0453 | 1.0449 | 98. | 98. |
| 2,2,4,4-Tetramethylhexane | " | 190.46 | 191.54 | 48.28 | 48.30 | 0.3393 | 0.3395 | 1.0473 | 1.0469 | 99. | 99. |
| 2,2,4,5-Tetramethylhexane | " | 193.462 | 194.480 | 48.262 | 48.281 | 0.33918 | 0.33934 | 1.04545 | 1.04515 | 99. | 99. |
| 2,2,5,5-Tetramethylhexane | " | 197.949 | 198.960 | 48.570 | 48.589 | 0.34137 | 0.34152 | 1.04612 | 1.04576 | 102. | 102. |
| 2,3,3,4-Tetramethylhexane | " | 184.92 | 186.03 | 47.74 | 47.75 | 0.3355 | 0.3356 | 1.0450 | 1.0445 | 97. | 97. |
| 2,3,3,5-Tetramethylhexane | " | 190.7 | 191.7 | 48.2 | 48.2 | 0.339 | 0.339 | 1.0466 | 1.0462 | 97. | 97. |
| 2,3,4,4-Tetramethylhexane | " | 186.25 | 187.30 | 47.82 | 47.83 | 0.3361 | 0.3362 | 1.0451 | 1.0446 | 97. | 97. |
| 2,3,4,5-Tetramethylhexane | " | 187.9 | 188.9 | 47.9 | 48.0 | 0.337 | 0.337 | 1.046 | 1.046 | 98. | 98. |
| 3,3,4,4-Tetramethylhexane | " | 181.85 | 182.80 | 47.62 | 47.64 | 0.3347 | 0.3349 | 1.0456 | 1.0452 | 97. | 97. |
| 2,4-Dimethyl-3-isopropylpentane | " | 187.635 | 188.617 | 47.943 | 47.979 | 0.3370 | 0.3371 | 1.04548 | 1.04520 | 97. | 97. |
| 2-Methyl-3,3-diethylpentane | " | 182.4 | 183.6 | 47.6 | 47.6 | 0.334 | 0.335 | 1.045 | 1.044 | 97. | 97. |
| 2,2,3-Trimethyl-3-ethylpentane | " | 182.2 | 183.1 | 47.6 | 47.7 | 0.335 | 0.335 | 1.046 | 1.046 | 97. | 97. |
| 2,2,4-Trimethyl-3-ethylpentane | " | 187.92 | 188.92 | 47.78 | 47.80 | 0.3359 | 0.3360 | 1.0438 | 1.0434 | 98. | 98. |
| 2,3,4-Trimethyl-3-ethylpentane | " | 183.04 | 183.98 | 47.60 | 47.62 | 0.3346 | 0.3347 | 1.0447 | 1.0444 | 97. | 97. |
| 2,2,3,3,4-Pentamethylpentane | " | 182.384 | 183.168 | 47.693 | 47.712 | 0.33521 | 0.33535 | 1.04602 | 1.04574 | 97. | 97. |
| 2,2,3,4,4-Pentamethylpentane | " | 185.492 | 186.513 | 47.984 | 48.003 | 0.33726 | 0.33739 | 1.04717 | 1.04688 | 98. | 98. |

a See footnote a of Table 1b.

TABLE 22b (PART 1) – NORMAL ALKYL CYCLOPENTANES, C$_5$ TO C$_{21}$

MOLECULAR VOLUME, MOLECULAR REFRACTION, SPECIFIC REFRACTION, REFRACTIVITY INTERCEPT, AND SPECIFIC DISPERSION

December 31, 1948; June 30, 1949; September 30, 1951

| Compound | Formula | Molecular Volume[a] $V = M/d$ ml/mole | | Molecular Refraction[a] $V(n_D^2-1)/(n_D^2+2)$ ml/mole | | Specific Refraction[a] $(1/d)(n_D^2-1)/(n_D^2+2)$ ml/g | | Refractivity Intercept[a] $n_D - d/2$ | | Specific Dispersion[a] $10^4(n_F - n_C)/d$ ml/g | |
|---|---|---|---|---|---|---|---|---|---|---|---|
| | | 20°C | 25°C | 20°C | 25°C | 20°C | 25°C | 20°C | 25°C | 20°C | 25°C |
| Cyclopentane | C$_5$H$_{10}$ | 94.086 | 94.713 | 23.133 | 23.144 | 0.32985 | 0.33002 | 1.03376 | 1.03341 | 94.3 | 94.2 |
| Methylcyclopentane | C$_6$H$_{12}$ | 112.412 | 113.122 | 27.833 | 27.847 | 0.33073 | 0.33089 | 1.03538 | 1.03503 | 96.2 | 96.1 |
| Ethylcyclopentane | C$_7$H$_{14}$ | 128.096 | 128.819 | 32.403 | 32.416 | 0.33003 | 0.33016 | 1.03657 | 1.03622 | 95.5 | 95.4 |
| n-Propylcyclopentane | C$_8$H$_{16}$ | 144.536 | 145.292 | 37.052 | 37.067 | 0.33022 | 0.33034 | 1.03810 | 1.03775 | 95.7 | 95.6 |
| n-Butylcyclopentane | C$_9$H$_{18}$ | 160.89 | 161.67 | 41.70 | 41.70 | 0.3303 | 0.3304 | 1.0393 | 1.0389 | 96. | 96. |
| n-Pentylcyclopentane | C$_{10}$H$_{20}$ | 177.28 | 178.14 | 46.33 | 46.35 | 0.3303 | 0.3305 | 1.0402 | 1.0399 | 96. | 96. |
| n-Hexylcyclopentane | C$_{11}$H$_{22}$ | 193.70 | 194.62 | 50.97 | 50.99 | 0.3304 | 0.3305 | 1.0410 | 1.0407 | 96. | 96. |
| n-Heptylcyclopentane | C$_{12}$H$_{24}$ | 210.14 | 211.11 | 55.61 | 55.64 | 0.3304 | 0.3305 | 1.0416 | 1.0413 | 96. | 96. |
| n-Octylcyclopentane | C$_{13}$H$_{26}$ | 226.57 | 227.60 | 60.25 | 60.28 | 0.3304 | 0.3306 | 1.0422 | 1.0419 | 97. | 97. |
| n-Nonylcyclopentane | C$_{14}$H$_{28}$ | 243.00 | 244.09 | 64.89 | 64.92 | 0.3305 | 0.3306 | 1.0427 | 1.0424 | 97. | 97. |
| n-Decylcyclopentane | C$_{15}$H$_{30}$ | 259.430 | 260.577 | 69.534 | 69.567 | 0.33050 | 0.33066 | 1.04314 | 1.04290 | 97.0 | 96.9 |
| n-Undecylcyclopentane | C$_{16}$H$_{32}$ | 275.86 | 277.06 | 74.18 | 74.20 | 0.3305 | 0.3306 | 1.0435 | 1.0432 | 97. | 97. |
| n-Dodecylcyclopentane | C$_{17}$H$_{34}$ | 292.29 | 293.55 | 78.82 | 78.84 | 0.3305 | 0.3307 | 1.0439 | 1.0436 | 97. | 97. |
| n-Tridecylcyclopentane | C$_{18}$H$_{36}$ | 308.71 | 310.04 | 83.46 | 83.48 | 0.3306 | 0.3307 | 1.0442 | 1.0439 | 97. | 97. |
| n-Tetradecylcyclopentane | C$_{19}$H$_{38}$ | 325.14 | 326.52 | 88.10 | 88.13 | 0.3306 | 0.3307 | 1.0445 | 1.0442 | 97. | 97. |
| n-Pentadecylcyclopentane | C$_{20}$H$_{40}$ | 341.56 | 343.00 | 92.74 | 92.77 | 0.3306 | 0.3307 | 1.0447 | 1.0444 | 97. | 97. |
| n-Hexadecylcyclopentane | C$_{21}$H$_{42}$ | 357.98[b] | 359.49 | 97.38[b] | 97.41 | 0.3306[b] | 0.3307 | 1.0450[b] | 1.0446 | 97.[b] | 97. |

a See footnote a of Table 1b.

b For the undercooled liquid below the normal freezing point.

TABLE 22b (PART 2) – NORMAL ALKYL CYCLOPENTANES, $C_{22}$ TO $C_{41}$

MOLECULAR VOLUME, MOLECULAR REFRACTION, SPECIFIC REFRACTION, REFRACTIVITY INTERCEPT, AND SPECIFIC DISPERSION

September 30, 1951

| Compound | Formula | Molecular Volume[a] $V = M/d$ (ml/mole) | | Molecular Refraction[a] $V(n_D^2-1)/(n_D^2+2)$ (ml/mole) | | Specific Refraction[a] $(1/d)(n_D^2-1)/(n_D^2+2)$ (ml/g) | | Refractivity Intercept[a] $n_D - d/2$ | | Specific Dispersion[a] $10^4(n_F-n_C)/d$ (ml/g) | |
|---|---|---|---|---|---|---|---|---|---|---|---|
| | | 20°C | 25°C | 20°C | 25°C | 20°C | 25°C | 20°C | 25°C | 20°C | 25°C |
| n-Heptadecylcyclopentane | $C_{22}H_{44}$ | 374.42[b] | 375.97[b] | 102.02[b] | 102.05[b] | 0.3306[b] | 0.3307[b] | 1.0452[b] | 1.0421[b] | 97.[b] | 97.[b] |
| n-Octadecylcyclopentane | $C_{23}H_{46}$ | 390.83[b] | 392.46[b] | 106.66[b] | 106.69[b] | 0.3306[b] | 0.3307[b] | 1.0454[b] | 1.0425[b] | 97.[b] | 97.[b] |
| n-Nonadecylcyclopentane | $C_{24}H_{48}$ | 407.25[b] | 408.94[b] | 111.30[b] | 111.33[b] | 0.3306[b] | 0.3307[b] | 1.0456[b] | 1.0429[b] | 97.[b] | 97.[b] |
| n-Eicosylcyclopentane | $C_{25}H_{50}$ | 423.67[b] | 425.42[b] | 115.94[b] | 115.98[b] | 0.3306[b] | 0.3307[b] | 1.0457[b] | 1.0432[b] | 97.[b] | 97.[b] |
| n-Heneicosylcyclopentane | $C_{26}H_{52}$ | 440.10[b] | 441.91[b] | 120.58[b] | 120.62[b] | 0.3307[b] | 0.3306[b] | 1.0459[b] | 1.0435[b] | 97.[b] | 97.[b] |
| n-Docosylcyclopentane | $C_{27}H_{54}$ | 456.52[b] | 458.39[b] | 125.22[b] | 125.26[b] | 0.3307[b] | 0.3308[b] | 1.0460[b] | 1.0438[b] | 97.[b] | 97.[b] |
| n-Tricosylcyclopentane | $C_{28}H_{56}$ | 472.94[b] | 474.87[b] | 129.86[b] | 129.90[b] | 0.3307[b] | 0.3308[b] | 1.0462[b] | 1.0441[b] | 97.[b] | 97.[b] |
| n-Tetracosylcyclopentane | $C_{29}H_{58}$ | 489.37[b] | 491.35[b] | 134.50[b] | 134.54[b] | 0.3307[b] | 0.3308[b] | 1.0463[b] | 1.0443[b] | 97.[b] | 97.[b] |
| n-Pentacosylcyclopentane | $C_{30}H_{60}$ | 505.8[b] | 507.8[b] | 139.14[b] | 139.18[b] | 0.3307[b] | 0.3308[b] | 1.0464[b] | 1.0445[b] | 98.[b] | 98.[b] |
| n-Hexacosylcyclopentane | $C_{31}H_{62}$ | 522.2[b] | 524.3[b] | 143.78[b] | 143.82[b] | 0.3307[b] | 0.3308[b] | 1.0465[b] | 1.0447[b] | 98.[b] | 98.[b] |
| n-Heptacosylcyclopentane | $C_{32}H_{64}$ | 538.6[b] | 540.8[b] | 148.42[b] | 148.47[b] | 0.3307[b] | 0.3308[b] | 1.0466[b] | 1.0449[b] | 98.[b] | 98.[b] |
| n-Octacosylcyclopentane | $C_{33}H_{66}$ | 555.0[b] | 557.3[b] | 153.06[b] | 153.11[b] | 0.3307[b] | 0.3308[b] | 1.0467[b] | 1.0451[b] | 98.[b] | 98.[b] |
| n-Nonacosylcyclopentane | $C_{34}H_{68}$ | 571.5[b] | 573.8[b] | 157.71[b] | 157.75[b] | 0.3307[b] | 0.3308[b] | 1.0468[b] | 1.0452[b] | 98.[b] | 98.[b] |
| n-Triacontylcyclopentane | $C_{35}H_{70}$ | 587.9[b] | 590.2[b] | 162.35[b] | 162.39[b] | 0.3307[b] | 0.3308[b] | 1.0469[b] | 1.0454[b] | 98.[b] | 98.[b] |
| n-Hentriacontylcyclopentane | $C_{36}H_{72}$ | 604.3[b] | 606.7[b] | 166.99[b] | 167.03[b] | 0.3307[b] | 0.3308[b] | 1.0470[b] | 1.0455[b] | 98.[b] | 98.[b] |
| n-Dotriacontylcyclopentane | $C_{37}H_{74}$ | 620.7[b] | 623.2[b] | 171.63[b] | 171.67[b] | 0.3307[b] | 0.3308[b] | 1.0471[b] | 1.0457[b] | 98.[b] | 98.[b] |
| n-Tritriacontylcyclopentane | $C_{38}H_{76}$ | 637.2[b] | 639.7[b] | 176.27[b] | 176.32[b] | 0.3307[b] | 0.3308[b] | 1.0471[b] | 1.0458[b] | 98.[b] | 98.[b] |
| n-Tetratriacontylcyclopentane | $C_{39}H_{78}$ | 653.6[b] | 656.2[b] | 180.91[b] | 180.96[b] | 0.3307[b] | 0.3308[b] | 1.0472[b] | 1.0459[b] | 98.[b] | 98.[b] |
| n-Pentatriacontylcyclopentane | $C_{40}H_{80}$ | 670.0[b] | 672.6[b] | 185.55[b] | 185.60[b] | 0.3307[b] | 0.3308[b] | 1.0473[b] | 1.0460[b] | 98.[b] | 98.[b] |
| n-Hexatriacontylcyclopentane | $C_{41}H_{82}$ | 686.4[b] | 689.1[b] | 190.19[b] | 190.24[b] | 0.3307[b] | 0.3308[b] | 1.0473[b] | 1.0461[b] | 98.[b] | 98.[b] |

[a] See footnote a of Table 1b.    [b] For the undercooled liquid below the normal freezing point.

TABLE 6b – ALKYL CYCLOPENTANES, $C_5$ TO $C_7$

MOLECULAR VOLUME, MOLECULAR REFRACTION, SPECIFIC REFRACTION, REFRACTIVITY INTERCEPT, AND SPECIFIC DISPERSION

June 30, 1945; February 28, 1947; June 30, 1949

| Compound | Formula | Molecular Volume[a] $V=M/d$ (ml/mole) | | Molecular Refraction[a] $V(n_D^2-1)/(n_D^2+2)$ (ml/mole) | | Specific Refraction[a] $(1/d)(n_D^2-1)/(n_D^2+2)$ (ml/g) | | Refractivity Intercept[a] $n_D-d/2$ | | Specific Dispersion[a] $10^4(n_F-n_C)/d$ (ml/g) | |
|---|---|---|---|---|---|---|---|---|---|---|---|
| | | 20°C | 25°C | 20°C | 25°C | 20°C | 25°C | 20°C | 25°C | 20°C | 25°C |
| Cyclopentane | $C_5H_{10}$ | 94.086 | 94.713 | 23.133 | 23.144 | 0.32985 | 0.33002 | 1.03376 | 1.03341 | 94.3 | 94.2 |
| Methylcyclopentane | $C_6H_{12}$ | 112.412 | 113.122 | 27.833 | 27.847 | 0.33073 | 0.33089 | 1.03538 | 1.03503 | 96.2 | 96.1 |
| Ethylcyclopentane | $C_7H_{14}$ | 128.096 | 128.819 | 32.403 | 32.416 | 0.33003 | 0.33016 | 1.03657 | 1.03622 | 95.5 | 95.4 |
| 1,1-Dimethylcyclopentane | " | 130.132 | 130.925 | 32.489 | 32.501 | .33090 | .33103 | 1.03632 | 1.03595 | 97.3 | 97.2 |
| 1,cis-2-Dimethylcyclopentane | " | 127.077 | 127.829 | 32.304 | 32.323 | .32902 | .32922 | 1.03586 | 1.03559 | 97.4 | 97.3 |
| 1,trans-2-Dimethylcyclopentane | " | 130.658 | 131.460 | 32.511 | 32.530 | .33114 | .33132 | 1.03628 | 1.03598 | 96.5 | 96.4 |
| 1,cis-3-Dimethylcyclopentane | " | 131.119 | 131.903 | 32.537 | 32.549 | .33140 | .33236 | 1.03634 | 1.03595 | 96.2 | 96.1 |
| 1,trans-3-Dimethylcyclopentane | " | 131.825 | 132.634 | 32.587 | 32.601 | .33190 | .33206 | 1.03654 | 1.03621 | 97.4 | 97.3 |

[a] See footnote a of Table 1b.

TABLE 15b — ALKYL CYCLOPENTANES, $C_8$

MOLECULAR VOLUME, MOLECULAR REFRACTION, SPECIFIC REFRACTION, REFRACTIVITY INTERCEPT, AND SPECIFIC DISPERSION

February 28, 1947; June 30, 1949

| Compound | Formula | Molecular Volume $V = M/d$ (ml/mole) | | Molecular Refraction $V(n_D^2-1)/(n_D^2+2)$ (ml/mole) | | Specific Refraction $(1/d)(n_D^2-1)/(n_D^2+2)$ (ml/g) | | Refractivity Intercept $n_D - d/2$ | | Specific Dispersion $10^4(n_F-n_C)/d$ (ml/g) | |
|---|---|---|---|---|---|---|---|---|---|---|---|
| | | 20°C | 25°C | 20°C | 25°C | 20°C | 25°C | 20°C | 25°C | 20°C | 25°C |
| n-Propylcyclopentane | $C_8H_{16}$ | 144.536 | 145.292 | 37.052 | 37.067 | 0.33022 | 0.33034 | 1.03810 | 1.03775 | 95.7 | 95.6 |
| Isopropylcyclopentane | " | 144.499 | 145.236 | 37.011 | 37.024 | .32984 | .32995 | 1.03756 | 1.03720 | 95.6 | 95.5 |
| 1-Methyl-1-ethylcyclopentane | " | 143.685 | 144.468 | 36.904 | 36.922 | .32890 | .32905 | 1.03672 | 1.03641 | 95.9 | 95.8 |
| 1-Methyl-*cis*-2-ethylcyclopentane | " | 142.900 | 143.648 | 36.864 | 36.877 | .32853 | .32866 | 1.03672 | 1.03639 | 94.7 | 94.6 |
| 1-Methyl-*trans*-2-ethylcyclopentane | " | 145.91 | 146.70 | 37.07 | 37.08 | .3304 | .3305 | 1.0374 | 1.0371 | 95. | 95. |
| 1-Methyl-*cis*-3-ethylcyclopentane | " | 145.27 | 146.09 | 36.79 | 36.81 | .3278 | .3280 | 1.0341 | 1.0339 | 95. | 95. |
| 1-Methyl-*trans*-3-ethylcyclopentane | " | 147.27 | 148.09 | 37.16 | 37.18 | .3312 | .3313 | 1.0376 | 1.0374 | 95. | 95. |
| 1,1,2-Trimethylcyclopentane | " | 145.249 | 146.072 | 36.986 | 37.004 | .32962 | .32978 | 1.03672 | 1.03643 | 97.0 | 96.9 |
| 1,1,3-Trimethylcyclopentane | " | 149.960 | 150.833 | 37.249 | 37.266 | .33196 | .33212 | 1.03707 | 1.03674 | 98.7 | 98.6 |
| 1,*cis*-2,*cis*-3-Trimethylcyclopentane | " | 144.00 | 144.77 | 36.91 | 36.92 | .3290 | .3291 | 1.0366 | 1.0362 | 96. | 96. |
| 1,*cis*-2,*trans*-3-Trimethylcyclopentane | " | 145.65 | 146.47 | 37.00 | 37.02 | .3297 | .3299 | 1.0366 | 1.0364 | 96. | 96. |
| 1,*trans*-2,*cis*-3-Trimethylcyclopentane | " | 148.92 | 149.77 | 37.20 | 37.22 | .3315 | .3317 | 1.0370 | 1.0368 | 96. | 96. |
| 1,*cis*-2,*cis*-4-Trimethylcyclopentane | " | 146.5 | 147.3 | 37.2 | 37.3 | .332 | .332 | 1.039 | 1.039 | 96. | 96. |
| 1,*cis*-2,*trans*-4-Trimethylcyclopentane | " | 146.975 | 147.798 | 37.082 | 37.099 | .33048 | .33063 | 1.03683 | 1.03652 | 95.8 | 95.7 |
| 1,*trans*-2,*cis*-4-Trimethylcyclopentane | " | 150.157 | 151.016 | 37.251 | 37.265 | .33198 | .33211 | 1.03696 | 1.03661 | 96.9 | 96.8 |

a See footnote a of Table 1b.

TABLE 23b (PART 1) – NORMAL ALKYL CYCLOHEXANES, $C_6$ TO $C_{22}$

MOLECULAR VOLUME, MOLECULAR REFRACTION, SPECIFIC REFRACTION, REFRACTIVITY INTERCEPT, AND SPECIFIC DISPERSION

December 31, 1948; September 30, 1951

| Compound | Formula | Molecular Volume[a] $V=M/d$ (ml/mole) | | Molecular Refraction[a] $V(n_D^2-1)/(n_D^2+2)$ (ml/mole) | | Specific Refraction[a] $(1/d)(n_D^2-1)/(n_D^2+2)$ (ml/g) | | Refractivity Intercept[a] $n_D-d/2$ | | Specific Dispersion[a] $10^4(n_F-n_c)/d$ (ml/g) | |
|---|---|---|---|---|---|---|---|---|---|---|---|
| | | 20°C | 25°C | 20°C | 25°C | 20°C | 25°C | 20°C | 25°C | 20°C | 25°C |
| Cyclohexane | $C_6H_{12}$ | 108.093 | 108.744 | 27.709 | 27.722 | 0.32926 | 0.32941 | 1.03696 | 1.03660 | 96.2 | 96.1 |
| Methylcyclohexane | $C_7H_{14}$ | 127.610 | 128.332 | 32.503 | 32.515 | 0.33105 | 0.33117 | 1.03843 | 1.03805 | 97.9 | 97.8 |
| Ethylcyclohexane | $C_8H_{16}$ | 142.410 | 143.141 | 37.015 | 37.032 | 0.32988 | 0.33003 | 1.03908 | 1.03878 | 97.5 | 97.4 |
| n-Propylcyclohexane | $C_9H_{18}$ | 159.065 | 159.836 | 41.677 | 41.690 | 0.33016 | 0.33026 | 1.04025 | 1.03990 | 97.5 | 97.4 |
| n-Butylcyclohexane | $C_{10}H_{20}$ | 175.505 | 176.314 | 46.323 | 46.334 | 0.33027 | 0.33035 | 1.04116 | 1.04080 | 97.1 | 97.0 |
| n-Pentylcyclohexane | $C_{11}H_{22}$ | 191.96 | 192.82 | 50.96 | 50.98 | 0.3303 | 0.3304 | 1.041b | 1.0415 | 98. | 98. |
| n-Hexylcyclohexane | $C_{12}H_{24}$ | 208.41 | 209.32 | 55.60 | 55.62 | 0.3303 | 0.3304 | 1.0424 | 1.0421 | 98. | 98. |
| n-Heptylcyclohexane | $C_{13}H_{26}$ | 224.85 | 225.82 | 60.24 | 60.26 | 0.3304 | 0.3305 | ·1.0429 | 1.0426 | 98. | 98. |
| n-Octylcyclohexane | $C_{14}H_{28}$ | 241.29 | 242.31 | 64.88 | 64.90 | 0.3304 | 0.3305 | 1.0434 | 1.0431 | 98. | 98. |
| n-Nonylcyclohexane | $C_{15}H_{30}$ | 257.72 | 258.80 | 69.52 | 69.54 | 0.3304 | 0.3305 | 1.0438 | 1.0435 | 98. | 98. |
| n-Decylcyclohexane | $C_{16}H_{32}$ | 274.153 | 275.300 | 74.154 | 74.1b4 | 0.33043 | 0.33057 | 1.04409 | 1.04382 | 97.9 | 97.8 |
| n-Undecylcyclohexane | $C_{17}H_{34}$ | 290.58 | 291.78 | 78.80 | 78.82 | 0.3305 | 0.3306 | 1.0444 | 1.0441 | 98. | 98. |
| n-Dodecylcyclohexane | $C_{18}H_{36}$ | 307.01 | 306.27 | 83.44 | 83.47 | 0.3305 | 0.3306 | 1.0447 | 1.0444 | 98. | 98. |
| n-Tridecylcyclohexane | $C_{19}H_{38}$ | 323.44 | 324.75 | 88.08 | 88.11 | 0.3305 | 0.3306 | 1.0450 | 1.0447 | 98. | 98. |
| n-Tetradecylcyclohexane | $C_{20}H_{40}$ | 339.86b | 341.24 | 92.72b | 92.75 | 0.3305b | 0.3306 | 1.0452b | 1.0449 | 98.b | 98. |
| n-Pentadecylcyclohexane | $C_{21}H_{42}$ | 356.00b | 357.72b | 97.36b | 97.39b | 0.3305b | 0.3306b | 1.0454b | 1.0451b | 98.b | 98.b |
| n-Hexadecylcyclohexane | $C_{22}H_{44}$ | 372.71b | 374.21b | 102.00b | 102.03b | 0.3306b | 0.3307b | 1.0456b | 1.0453b | 98.b | 96.b |

a See footnote a of Table 1b.   b For the undercooled liquid below the normal freezing point.

178

TABLE 23b (PART 2) - NORMAL ALKYL CYCLOHEXANES, $C_{23}$ TO $C_{42}$
MOLECULAR VOLUME, MOLECULAR REFRACTION, SPECIFIC REFRACTION, REFRACTIVITY INTERCEPT, AND SPECIFIC DISPERSION
September 30, 1951

| Compound | Formula | Molecular Volume[a] $V=M/d$ (ml/mole) | | Molecular Refraction[a] $V(n_D^2-1)/(n_D^2+2)$ (ml/mole) | | Specific Refraction[a] $(1/d)(n_D^2-1)/(n_D^2+2)$ (ml/g) | | Refractivity Intercept[a] $n_D-d/2$ | | Specific Dispersion[a] $10^4(n_F-n_C)/d$ (ml/g) | |
|---|---|---|---|---|---|---|---|---|---|---|---|
| | | 20°C | 25°C | 20°C | 25°C | 20°C | 25°C | 20°C | 25°C | 20°C | 25°C |
| n-Heptadecylcyclohexane | $C_{23}H_{46}$ | 389.13[b] | 390.69[b] | 106.64[b] | 106.67[b] | 0.3306[b] | 0.3307[b] | 1.0458[b] | 1.0455[b] | 98.[b] | 98.[b] |
| n-Octadecylcyclohexane | $C_{24}H_{48}$ | 405.56[b] | 407.18[b] | 111.28[b] | 111.32[b] | 0.3306[b] | 0.3307[b] | 1.0460[b] | 1.0457[b] | 98.[b] | 98.[b] |
| n-Nonadecylcyclohexane | $C_{25}H_{50}$ | 421.64[b] | 423.66[b] | 115.93[b] | 115.96[b] | 0.3306[b] | 0.3307[b] | 1.0461[b] | 1.0458[b] | 98.[b] | 98.[b] |
| n-Eicosylcyclohexane | $C_{26}H_{52}$ | 438.40[b] | 440.14[b] | 120.57[b] | 120.60[b] | 0.3306[b] | 0.3307[b] | 1.0463[b] | 1.0459[b] | 98.[b] | 98.[b] |
| n-Heneicosylcyclohexane | $C_{27}H_{54}$ | 454.82[b] | 456.63[b] | 125.21[b] | 125.24[b] | 0.3306[b] | 0.3307[b] | 1.0464[b] | 1.0461[b] | 98.[b] | 98.[b] |
| n-Docosylcyclohexane | $C_{28}H_{56}$ | 471.24[b] | 473.11[b] | 129.85[b] | 129.88[b] | 0.3306[b] | 0.3307[b] | 1.0465[b] | 1.0462[b] | 98.[b] | 98.[b] |
| n-Tricosylcyclohexane | $C_{29}H_{58}$ | 487.66[b] | 489.59[b] | 134.49[b] | 134.52[b] | 0.3306[b] | 0.3307[b] | 1.0466[b] | 1.0463[b] | 98.[b] | 98.[b] |
| n-Tetracosylcyclohexane | $C_{30}H_{60}$ | 504.1[b] | 506.1[b] | 139.13[b] | 139.16[b] | 0.3306[b] | 0.3307[b] | 1.0467[b] | 1.0464[b] | 98.[b] | 98.[b] |
| n-Pentacosylcyclohexane | $C_{31}H_{62}$ | 520.5[b] | 522.6[b] | 143.77[b] | 143.81[b] | 0.3306[b] | 0.3307[b] | 1.0468[b] | 1.0465[b] | 98.[b] | 98.[b] |
| n-Hexacosylcyclohexane | $C_{32}H_{64}$ | 536.5[b] | 539.0[b] | 148.41[b] | 148.45[b] | 0.3306[b] | 0.3307[b] | 1.0469[b] | 1.0466[b] | 98.[b] | 98.[b] |
| n-Heptacosylcyclohexane | $C_{33}H_{66}$ | 553.4[b] | 555.5[b] | 153.05[b] | 153.09[b] | 0.3307[b] | 0.3307[b] | 1.0470[b] | 1.0467[b] | 98.[b] | 98.[b] |
| n-Octacosylcyclohexane | $C_{34}H_{68}$ | 569.8[b] | 572.0[b] | 157.69[b] | 157.73[b] | 0.3307[b] | 0.3307[b] | 1.0471[b] | 1.0468[b] | 98.[b] | 98.[b] |
| n-Nonacosylcyclohexane | $C_{35}H_{70}$ | 586.2[b] | 588.5[b] | 162.33[b] | 162.37[b] | 0.3307[b] | 0.3308[b] | 1.0472[b] | 1.0469[b] | 98.[b] | 98.[b] |
| n-Triacontylcyclohexane | $C_{36}H_{72}$ | 602.6[b] | 605.0[b] | 166.97[b] | 167.01[b] | 0.3307[b] | 0.3308[b] | 1.0473[b] | 1.0470[b] | 98.[b] | 98.[b] |
| n-Hentriacontylcyclohexane | $C_{37}H_{74}$ | 619.0[b] | 621.4[b] | 171.61[b] | 171.66[b] | 0.3307[b] | 0.3308[b] | 1.0473[b] | 1.0470[b] | 98.[b] | 98.[b] |
| n-Dotriacontylcyclohexane | $C_{38}H_{76}$ | 635.4[b] | 637.9[b] | 176.25[b] | 176.30[b] | 0.3307[b] | 0.3308[b] | 1.0474[b] | 1.0471[b] | 98.[b] | 98.[b] |
| n-Tritriacontylcyclohexane | $C_{39}H_{78}$ | 651.9[b] | 654.4[b] | 180.89[b] | 180.94[b] | 0.3307[b] | 0.3308[b] | 1.0475[b] | 1.0471[b] | 98.[b] | 98.[b] |
| n-Tetratriacontylcyclohexane | $C_{40}H_{80}$ | 668.3[b] | 670.9[b] | 185.53[b] | 185.58[b] | 0.3307[b] | 0.3308[b] | 1.0475[b] | 1.0472[b] | 98.[b] | 98.[b] |
| n-Pentatriacontylcyclohexane | $C_{41}H_{82}$ | 684.7[b] | 687.4[b] | 190.17[b] | 190.22[b] | 0.3307[b] | 0.3308[b] | 1.0476[b] | 1.0472[b] | 98.[b] | 98.[b] |
| n-Hexatriacontylcyclohexane | $C_{42}H_{84}$ | 701.1[b] | 703.9[b] | 194.81[b] | 194.86[b] | 0.3307[b] | 0.3308[b] | 1.0476[b] | 1.0473[b] | 98.[b] | 98.[b] |

a See footnote a of Table 1b.  b For the undercooled liquid below the normal freezing point.

TABLE 7b – ALKYL CYCLOHEXANES, $C_6$ TO $C_8$

MOLECULAR VOLUME, MOLECULAR REFRACTION, SPECIFIC REFRACTION, REFRACTIVITY INTERCEPT, AND SPECIFIC DISPERSION

June 30, 1945; March 31, 1947; June 30, 1949

| Compound | Formula[a] | Molecular Volume[a] $V = M/d$ (ml/mole) | | Molecular Refraction[a] $V(n_D^2-1)/(n_D^2+2)$ (ml/mole) | | Specific Refraction[a] $(1/d)(n_D^2-1)/(n_D^2+2)$ (ml/g) | | Refractivity Intercept[a] $n_D - d/2$ | | Specific Dispersion[a] $10^4(n_F-n_C)/d$ (ml/g) | |
|---|---|---|---|---|---|---|---|---|---|---|---|
| | | 20°C | 25°C | 20°C | 25°C | 20°C | 25°C | 20°C | 25°C | 20°C | 25°C |
| Cyclohexane | $C_6H_{12}$ | 108.093 | 108.744 | 27.709 | 27.722 | 0.32926 | 0.32941 | 1.03696 | 1.03660 | 96.2 | 96.1 |
| Methylcyclohexane | $C_7H_{14}$ | 127.610 | 128.332 | 32.503 | 32.515 | 0.33105 | 0.33117 | 1.03843 | 1.03805 | 97.9 | 97.8 |
| Ethylcyclohexane | $C_8H_{16}$ | 142.410 | 143.141 | 37.015 | 37.032 | 0.32988 | 0.33003 | 1.03908 | 1.03878 | 97.5 | 97.4 |
| 1,1-Dimethylcyclohexane | " | 143.663 | 144.455 | 37.042 | 37.060 | .33012 | .33028 | 1.03853 | 1.03824 | 98.6 | 98.4 |
| 1,cis-2-Dimethylcyclohexane | " | 140.917 | 141.637 | 36.842 | 36.854 | .32834 | .32844 | 1.03783 | 1.03747 | 96.0 | 95.9 |
| 1,trans-2-Dimethylcyclohexane | " | 144.596 | 145.334 | 37.121 | 37.139 | .33083 | .33099 | 1.03895 | 1.03868 | 98.0 | 97.9 |
| 1,cis-3-Dimethylcyclohexane[b] | " | 146.480 | 147.262 | 37.296 | 37.316 | .33238 | .33256 | 1.03993 | 1.03965 | 99.2 | 99.1 |
| 1,trans-3-Dimethylcyclohexane[c] | " | 142.991 | 143.755 | 37.002 | 37.017 | .32976 | .32990 | 1.03849 | 1.03816 | 97.2 | 97.1 |
| 1,cis-4-Dimethylcyclohexane | " | 143.333 | 144.097 | 37.001 | 37.020 | .32975 | .32993 | 1.03824 | 1.03796 | 97.2 | 97.1 |
| 1,trans-4-Dimethylcyclohexane | " | 147.148 | 147.963 | 37.308 | 37.329 | .33249 | .33268 | 1.03963 | 1.03936 | 97.2 | 97.1 |

a See footnote a of Table 1b.  
b Formerly labeled "trans"; see footnote b of Table 7a.  
c Formerly labeled "cis"; see footnote c of Table 7a.

TABLE 24b (PART 1) - NORMAL MONOOLEFINS (1-ALKENES), $C_2$ TO $C_{20}$
MOLECULAR VOLUME, MOLECULAR REFRACTION, SPECIFIC REFRACTION, REFRACTIVITY INTERCEPT, AND SPECIFIC DISPERSION

February 28, 1949; December 31, 1950; October 31, 1952

| Compound | Formula | Molecular Volume[a] $V=M/d$ (ml/mole) | | Molecular Refraction[a] $V(n_D^2-1)/(n_D^2+2)$ (ml/mole) | | Specific Refraction[a] $(1/d)(n_D^2-1)/(n_D^2+2)$ (ml/g) | | Refractivity Intercept[a] $n_D-d/2$ | | Specific Dispersion[a] $10^4(n_F-n_C)/d$ (ml/g) | |
|---|---|---|---|---|---|---|---|---|---|---|---|
| | | 20°C | 25°C | 20°C | 25°C | 20°C | 25°C | 20°C | 25°C | 20°C | 25°C |
| Ethene (Ethylene) | $C_2H_4$ | — | — | — | — | — | — | — | — | — | — |
| Propene (Propylene) | $C_3H_6$ | 81.880[b] | 83.273[b] | — | — | — | — | — | — | — | — |
| 1-Butene | $C_4H_8$ | 94.277[b] | 95.285[b] | — | — | — | — | — | — | — | — |
| 1-Pentene | $C_5H_{10}$ | 109.493 | 110.384 | 24.854 | 24.868 | 0.35440 | 0.35459 | 1.05123 | 1.05068 | 126.2 | 126.1 |
| 1-Hexene | $C_6H_{12}$ | 125.014 | 125.892 | 29.492 | 29.504 | 0.35044 | 0.35058 | 1.05130 | 1.05078 | 122.0 | 121.9 |
| 1-Heptene | $C_7H_{14}$ | 140.868 | 141.744 | 34.135 | 34.144 | 0.34767 | 0.34776 | 1.05131 | 1.05080 | 118.3 | 118.2 |
| 1-Octene | $C_8H_{16}$ | 156.952 | 157.850 | 38.778 | 38.790 | 0.34559 | 0.34570 | 1.05124 | 1.05078 | 116.9 | 116.8 |
| 1-Nonene | $C_9H_{18}$ | 173.108 | 174.041 | 43.415 | 43.429 | 0.34392 | 0.34403 | 1.05111 | 1.05068 | 114.5 | 114.4 |
| 1-Decene | $C_{10}H_{20}$ | 189.333 | 190.330 | 48.059 | 48.078 | 0.34264 | 0.34278 | 1.05106 | 1.05066 | 113.0 | 112.9 |
| 1-Undecene | $C_{11}H_{22}$ | 205.627 | 206.665 | 52.696 | 52.717 | 0.34155 | 0.34168 | 1.05093 | 1.05056 | 112.2 | 112.1 |
| 1-Dodecene | $C_{12}H_{24}$ | 221.942 | 223.007 | 57.336 | 57.353 | 0.34065 | 0.34075 | 1.05084 | 1.05045 | 110.8 | 110.7 |
| 1-Tridecene | $C_{13}H_{26}$ | 238.25 | 239.38 | 61.98 | 62.00 | 0.3399 | 0.3400 | 1.0508 | 1.0504 | 110. | 110. |
| 1-Tetradecene | $C_{14}H_{28}$ | 254.60 | 255.78 | 66.62 | 66.64 | 0.3392 | 0.3394 | 1.0508 | 1.0504 | 109. | 109. |
| 1-Pentadecene | $C_{15}H_{30}$ | 270.93 | 272.17 | 71.25 | 71.28 | 0.3387 | 0.3388 | 1.0506 | 1.0503 | 108. | 108. |
| 1-Hexadecene | $C_{16}H_{32}$ | 287.300 | 288.605 | 75.898 | 75.922 | 0.33820 | 0.33831 | 1.05064 | 1.05028 | 107.2 | 107.1 |
| 1-Heptadecene | $C_{17}H_{34}$ | 303.68 | 305.03 | 80.54 | 80.57 | 0.3378 | 0.3379 | 1.0506 | 1.0502 | 107. | 107. |
| 1-Octadecene | $C_{18}H_{36}$ | 320.08 | 321.49 | 85.19 | 85.21 | 0.3374 | 0.3375 | 1.0506 | 1.0502 | 107. | 107. |
| 1-Nonadecene | $C_{19}H_{38}$ | 336.47[c] | 337.93 | 89.83[c] | 89.85 | 0.3371[c] | 0.3372 | 1.0506[c] | 1.0502 | 106.[c] | 106. |
| 1-Eicosene | $C_{20}H_{40}$ | 352.85[c] | 354.37[c] | 94.47[c] | 94.50[c] | 0.3368[c] | 0.3369[c] | 1.0506[c] | 1.0502[c] | 106.[c] | 106.[c] |

[a] See footnote a of Table 1b.    [b] At saturation pressure.    [c] For the undercooled liquid below the normal freezing point.

TABLE 24b (PART 2) – NORMAL MONOOLEFINS (1-ALKENES), $C_{21}$ TO $C_{40}$

MOLECULAR VOLUME, MOLECULAR REFRACTION, SPECIFIC REFRACTION, REFRACTIVITY INTERCEPT, AND SPECIFIC DISPERSION

December 31 1950 (Corrected)

| Compound | Formula | Molecular Volume[a] $V=M/d$ (ml/mole) | | Molecular Refraction[a] $V(n_D^2-1)/(n_D^2+2)$ (ml/mole) | | Specific Refraction[a] $(1/d)(n_D^2-1)/(n_D^2+2)$ (ml/g) | | Refractivity Intercept[a] $n_D-d/2$ | | Specific Dispersion[a] $10^4(n_F-n_C)/d$ (ml/g) | |
|---|---|---|---|---|---|---|---|---|---|---|---|
| | | 20°C | 25°C | 20°C | 25°C | 20°C | 25°C | 20°C | 25°C | 20°C | 25°C |
| 1-Heneicosene | $C_{21}H_{42}$ | 369.22[b] | 370.81[b] | 99.10[b] | 99.13[b] | 0.3364[b] | 0.3366[b] | 1.0505[b] | 1.0501[b] | 105.[b] | 105.[b] |
| 1-Docosene | $C_{22}H_{44}$ | 385.62[b] | 387.26[b] | 103.74[b] | 103.77[b] | 0.3362[b] | 0.3363[b] | 1.0505[b] | 1.0501[b] | 105.[b] | 105.[b] |
| 1-Tricosene | $C_{23}H_{46}$ | 402.01[b] | 403.72[b] | 108.38[b] | 108.41[b] | 0.3360[b] | 0.3361[b] | 1.0505[b] | 1.0501[b] | 105.[b] | 105.[b] |
| 1-Tetracosene | $C_{24}H_{40}$ | 418.41[b] | 420.18[b] | 113.03[b] | 113.06[b] | 0.3358[b] | 0.3358[b] | 1.0505[b] | 1.0501[b] | 104.[b] | 104.[b] |
| 1-Pentacosene | $C_{25}H_{50}$ | 434.81[b] | 436.64[b] | 117.67[b] | 117.70[b] | 0.3356[b] | 0.3357[b] | 1.0505[b] | 1.0500[b] | 104.[b] | 104.[b] |
| 1-Hexacosene | $C_{26}H_{52}$ | 451.21[b] | 453.10[b] | 122.31[b] | 122.34[b] | 0.3354[b] | 0.3355[b] | 1.0504[b] | 1.0500[b] | 104.[b] | 104.[b] |
| 1-Heptacosene | $C_{27}H_{54}$ | 467.61[b] | 469.56[b] | 126.94[b] | 126.98[b] | 0.3352[b] | 0.3353[b] | 1.0504[b] | 1.0500[b] | 104.[b] | 104.[b] |
| 1-Octacosene | $C_{28}H_{56}$ | 484.02[b] | 486.03[b] | 131.58[b] | 131.62[b] | 0.3350[b] | 0.3351[b] | 1.0504[b] | 1.0500[b] | 103.[b] | 103.[b] |
| 1-Nonacosene | $C_{29}H_{58}$ | 500.4[b] | 502.5[b] | 136.2[b] | 136.3[b] | 0.3349[b] | 0.3350[b] | 1.0504[b] | 1.0500[b] | 103.[b] | 103.[b] |
| 1-Triacontene | $C_{30}H_{60}$ | 516.8[b] | 519.0[b] | 140.9[b] | 140.9[b] | 0.3348[b] | 0.3349[b] | 1.0503[b] | 1.0500[b] | 103.[b] | 103.[b] |
| 1-Hentriacontene | $C_{31}H_{62}$ | 533.2[b] | 535.4[b] | 145.5[b] | 145.6[b] | 0.3346[b] | 0.3347[b] | 1.0503[b] | 1.0500[b] | 103.[b] | 103.[b] |
| 1-Dotriacontene | $C_{32}H_{64}$ | 549.6[b] | 551.9[b] | 150.2[b] | 150.2[b] | 0.3345[b] | 0.3346[b] | 1.0503[b] | 1.0500[b] | 103.[b] | 103.[b] |
| 1-Tritriacontene | $C_{33}H_{66}$ | 566.0[b] | 568.4[b] | 154.8[b] | 154.8[b] | 0.3344[b] | 0.3345[b] | 1.0503[b] | 1.0499[b] | 103.[b] | 103.[b] |
| 1-Tetratriacontene | $C_{34}H_{68}$ | 582.5[b] | 584.8[b] | 159.4[b] | 159.5[b] | 0.3343[b] | 0.3344[b] | 1.0503[b] | 1.0499[b] | 103.[b] | 103.[b] |
| 1-Pentatriacontene | $C_{35}H_{70}$ | 598.9[b] | 601.3[b] | 164.1[b] | 164.1[b] | 0.3342[b] | 0.3343[b] | 1.0503[b] | 1.0499[b] | 102.[b] | 102.[b] |
| 1-Hexatriacontene | $C_{36}H_{72}$ | 615.3[b] | 617.8[b] | 168.7[b] | 168.8[b] | 0.3341[b] | 0.3342[b] | 1.0503[b] | 1.0499[b] | 102.[b] | 102.[b] |
| 1-Heptatriacontene | $C_{37}H_{74}$ | 631.7[b] | 634.2[b] | 173.4[b] | 173.4[b] | 0.3340[b] | 0.3341[b] | 1.0502[b] | 1.0499[b] | 102.[b] | 102.[b] |
| 1-Octatriacontene | $C_{38}H_{76}$ | 648.1[b] | 650.7[b] | 178.0[b] | 178.0[b] | 0.3340[b] | 0.3340[b] | 1.0502[b] | 1.0499[b] | 102.[b] | 102.[b] |
| 1-Nonatriacontene | $C_{39}H_{78}$ | 664.5[b] | 667.2[b] | 182.6[b] | 182.7[b] | 0.3339[b] | 0.3340[b] | 1.0502[b] | 1.0499[b] | 102.[b] | 102.[b] |
| 1-Tetracontene | $C_{40}H_{80}$ | 680.9[b] | 683.7[b] | 187.3[b] | 187.3[b] | 0.3338[b] | 0.3339[b] | 1.0502[b] | 1.0499[b] | 102.[b] | 102.[b] |

a See footnote a of Table 1b.   b For the undercooled liquid below the normal freezing point.

TABLE 8b (PART 1) — MONOOLEFINS, $C_2$ TO $C_5$

MOLECULAR VOLUME, MOLECULAR REFRACTION, SPECIFIC REFRACTION, REFRACTIVITY INTERCEPT, AND SPECIFIC DISPERSION

June 30, 1945; May 31, 1947; October 31, 1952

| Compound | Formula | Molecular Volume[a] $V=M/d$ (ml/mole) | | Molecular Refraction[a] $V(n_D^2-1)/(n_D^2+2)$ (ml/mole) | | Specific Refraction[a] $(1/d)(n_D^2-1)/(n_D^2+2)$ (ml/g) | | Refractivity Intercept[a] $n_D-d/2$ | | Specific Dispersion[a] $10^4(n_F-n_C)/d$ (ml/g) | |
|---|---|---|---|---|---|---|---|---|---|---|---|
| | | 20°C | 25°C | 20°C | 25°C | 20°C | 25°C | 20°C | 25°C | 20°C | 25°C |
| Ethene (Ethylene) | $C_2H_4$ | ——— | ——— | ——— | ——— | ——— | ——— | ——— | ——— | ——— | ——— |
| Propene (Propylene) | $C_3H_6$ | 81.880[b] | 83.273[b] | ——— | ——— | ——— | ——— | ——— | ——— | ——— | ——— |
| 1-Butene | $C_4H_8$ | 94.277[b] | 95.285[b] | ——— | ——— | ——— | ——— | ——— | ——— | ——— | ——— |
| cis-2-Butene | " | 90.30[b] | 91.17[b] | ——— | ——— | ——— | ——— | ——— | ——— | ——— | ——— |
| trans-2-Butene | " | 92.66[b] | 93.76[b] | ——— | ——— | ——— | ——— | ——— | ——— | ——— | ——— |
| 2-Methylpropene (Isobutene) | " | 94.42[b] | 95.43[b] | ——— | ——— | ——— | ——— | ——— | ——— | ——— | ——— |
| 1-Pentene | $C_5H_{10}$ | 109.493 | 110.384 | 24.854 | 24.868 | 0.35440 | 0.35459 | 1.05123 | 1.05068 | 126.2 | 126.1 |
| cis-2-Pentene | " | 106.97 | 107.78 | 24.95 | 24.95 | 0.3558 | 0.3558 | 1.0552 | 1.0546 | 130. | 130. |
| trans-2-Pentene | " | 108.19 | 109.05 | 25.02 | 25.03 | 0.3568 | 0.3569 | 1.0552 | 1.0546 | 132. | 132. |
| 2-Methyl-1-butene | " | 107.83 | 108.71 | 24.85 | 24.86 | 0.3543 | 0.3545 | 1.0526 | 1.0520 | 133. | 133. |
| 3-Methyl-1-butene | " | 111.81 | | 24.94 | | 0.3557 | | 1.0507 | | 128. | |
| 2-Methyl-2-butene | " | 105.89 | 106.74 | 24.95 | 24.97 | 0.3558 | 0.3560 | 1.0563 | 1.0557 | 135. | 135. |

a See footnote a of Table 1b.

b At saturation pressure.

## TABLE 8b (PART 2) – MONOOLEFINS, $C_6$

### MOLECULAR VOLUME, MOLECULAR REFRACTION, SPECIFIC REFRACTION, REFRACTIVITY INTERCEPT, AND SPECIFIC DISPERSION

June 30, 1945; October 31, 1952

| Compound | Formula | Molecular Volume[a] $V = M/d$ (ml/mole) | | Molecular Refraction[a] $V(n_D^2-1)/(n_D^2+2)$ (ml/mole) | | Specific Refraction[a] $(1/d)(n_D^2-1)/(n_D^2+2)$ (ml/g) | | Refractivity Intercept[a] $n_D - d/2$ | | Specific Dispersion[a] $10^4(n_F-n_C)/d$ (ml/g) | |
|---|---|---|---|---|---|---|---|---|---|---|---|
| | | 20°C | 25°C | 20°C | 25°C | 20°C | 25°C | 20°C | 25°C | 20°C | 25°C |
| 1-Hexene | $C_6H_{12}$ | 125.014 | 125.892 | 29.492 | 29.504 | 0.35044 | 0.35058 | 1.05130 | 1.05078 | 122.0 | 121.9 |
| cis-2-Hexene | " | 122.52 | 123.34 | 29.55 | 29.56 | 0.3511 | 0.3512 | 1.0542 | 1.0536 | 125. | 125. |
| trans-2-Hexene | " | 124.05 | 124.90 | 29.64 | 29.65 | 0.3524 | 0.3524 | 1.0543 | 1.0538 | 127. | 127. |
| cis-3-Hexene | " | 123.83 | 124.69 | 29.67 | 29.69 | 0.3525 | 0.3528 | 1.0549 | 1.0546 | 126. | 126. |
| trans-3-Hexene | " | 124.27 | 125.14 | 29.75 | 29.77 | 0.3535 | 0.3538 | 1.0557 | 1.0554 | 128. | 128. |
| 2-Methyl-1-pentene | " | 123.45 | 124.33 | 29.36 | 29.36 | 0.3489 | 0.3489 | 1.0506 | 1.0500 | 129. | 129. |
| 3-Methyl-1-pentene | " | 126.08 | 126.97 | 29.49 | 29.51 | 0.3504 | 0.3506 | 1.0504 | 1.0500 | 124. | 124. |
| 4-Methyl-1-pentene | " | 126.70 | 127.63 | 29.54 | 29.56 | 0.3510 | 0.3512 | 1.0507 | 1.0502 | 124. | 124. |
| 2-Methyl-2-pentene | " | 122.62 | 123.49 | 29.75 | 29.78 | 0.3536 | 0.3538 | 1.0573 | 1.0569 | 131. | 131. |
| 3-Methyl-cis-2-pentene | " | 120.46 | 121.23 | 29.49 | 29.51 | 0.3505 | 0.3506 | 1.0552 | 1.0547 | 131. | 131. |
| 3-Methyl-trans-2-pentene | " | 121.23 | 122.00 | 29.49 | 29.50 | 0.3504 | 0.3506 | 1.0545 | 1.0540 | 131. | 131. |
| 4-Methyl-cis-2-pentene | " | 125.79 | 126.70 | 29.68 | 29.68 | 0.3517 | 0.3527 | 1.0535 | 1.0528 | 126. | 126. |
| 4-Methyl-trans-2-pentene | " | 125.87 | 126.78 | 29.76 | 29.77 | 0.3537 | 0.3538 | 1.0546 | 1.0540 | 128. | 128. |
| 2-Ethyl-1-butene | " | 122.07 | 122.91 | 29.39 | 29.41 | 0.3492 | 0.3494 | 1.0522 | 1.0517 | 128. | 128. |
| 2,3-Dimethyl-1-butene | " | 124.14 | 125.03 | 29.45 | 29.46 | 0.3500 | 0.3501 | 1.0515 | 1.0509 | 129. | 129. |
| 3,3-Dimethyl-1-butene | " | 128.90 | 129.89 | 29.58 | 29.59 | 0.3514 | 0.3516 | 1.0495 | 1.0490 | 124. | 124. |
| 2,3-Dimethyl-2-butene | " | 118.86 | 119.64 | 29.59 | 29.60 | 0.3516 | 0.3518 | 1.0582 | 1.0577 | 132. | 132. |

a See footnote a of Table 1b.

TABLE 9b, Page 1 - MONOOLEFINS, $C_7$

MOLECULAR VOLUME, MOLECULAR REFRACTION, SPECIFIC REFRACTION, REFRACTIVITY INTERCEPT, AND SPECIFIC DISPERSION

June 30, 1945; October 31, 1952

| Compound [b] | Formula | Molecular Volume [a] $V=M/d$ (ml/mole) | | Molecular Refraction [a] $V(n_D^2-1)/(n_D^2+2)$ (ml/mole) | | Specific Refraction [a] $(1/d)(n_D^2-1)/(n_D^2+2)$ (ml/g) | | Refractivity Intercept [a] $n_D-d/2$ | | Specific Dispersion [a] $10^4(n_F-n_C)/d$ (ml/g) | |
|---|---|---|---|---|---|---|---|---|---|---|---|
| | | 20°C | 25°C | 20°C | 25°C | 20°C | 25°C | 20°C | 25°C | 20°C | 25°C |
| 1-Heptene | $C_7H_{14}$ | 140.868 | 141.744 | 34.135 | 34.144 | 0.34767 | 0.34776 | 1.05131 | 1.05080 | 118.3 | 118.2 |
| cis-2-Heptene | " | 138.7 | 139.5 | 34.0 | 34.0 | 0.347 | 0.347 | 1.052 | 1.052 | 122. | 122. |
| trans-2-Heptene | " | 140.02 | 140.88 | 34.28 | 34.30 | 0.3492 | 0.3494 | 1.0539 | 1.0536 | 124. | 124. |
| cis-3-Heptene | " | 139.66 | 140.52 | 34.30 | 34.31 | 0.3494 | 0.3495 | 1.0544 | 1.0540 | 122. | 122. |
| trans-3-Heptene | " | 140.64 | 141.51 | 34.42 | 34.43 | 0.3506 | 0.3507 | 1.0553 | 1.0548 | 124. | 124. |
| 2-Methyl-1-hexene | " | 139.66 | 140.54 | 34.11 | 34.12 | 0.3474 | 0.3475 | 1.0520 | 1.0514 | 125. | 125. |
| 3-Methyl-1-hexene | " | 141.3 | 142.1 | 34.0 | 34.0 | 0.346 | 0.346 | 1.049 | 1.049 | 120. | 120. |
| 4-Methyl-1-hexene | " | 140.56 | 141.43 | 34.08 | 34.08 | 0.3471 | 0.3471 | 1.0508 | 1.0502 | 120. | 120. |
| 5-Methyl-1-hexene | " | 141.88 | 142.79 | 34.12 | 34.16 | 0.3475 | 0.3479 | 1.0506 | 1.0504 | 120. | 120. |
| 2-Methyl-2-hexene | " | 138.64 | 139.50 | 34.39 | 34.41 | 0.3503 | 0.3504 | 1.0565 | 1.0560 | 127. | 127. |
| 3-Methyl-cis-2-hexene | " | ⎰137.9 | 138.7 | 34.2 | 34.2 | 0.348 | 0.348 | 1.054 | 1.054 | 127. | 127. |
| 3-Methyl-trans-2-hexene | " | ⎱ | | | | | | | | | |
| 4-Methyl-cis-2-hexene | " | 140.34 | 141.21 | 34.20 | 34.21 | 0.3484 | 0.3484 | 1.0526 | 1.0521 | 122. | 122. |
| 4-Methyl-trans-2-hexene | " | 140.76 | 141.64 | 34.30 | 34.31 | 0.3493 | 0.3495 | 1.0536 | 1.0531 | 124. | 124. |
| 5-Methyl-cis-2-hexene | " | 140.3 | 141.1 | 34.0 | 34.0 | 0.346 | 0.346 | 1.050 | 1.050 | 122. | 122. |
| 5-Methyl-trans-2-hexene | " | 140.3 | 141.1 | 34.0 | 34.0 | 0.346 | 0.346 | 1.050 | 1.050 | 124. | 124. |
| 2-Methyl-cis-3-hexene | " | ⎰141.5 | 142.3 | 34.2 | 34.2 | 0.348 | 0.348 | 1.052 | 1.052 | 122. | 122. |
| 2-Methyl-trans-3-hexene | " | ⎱ | | | | | | | | | |
| 3-Methyl-cis-3-hexene | " | 137.66 | 138.50 | 34.28 | 34.29 | 0.3491 | 0.3492 | 1.0557 | 1.0552 | 127. | 127. |
| 3-Methyl-trans-3-hexene | " | 138.30 | 139.15 | 34.32 | 34.33 | 0.3495 | 0.3496 | 1.0558 | 1.0552 | 127. | 127. |

a See footnote a of Table 1b.

b For completeness, all isomers are listed. However, where the data are inadequate, approximate values are given for mixtures of the cis and trans forms, as indicated by the braces.

TABLE 9b, Page 2 - MONOOLEFINS, $C_7$

MOLECULAR VOLUME, MOLECULAR REFRACTION, SPECIFIC REFRACTION, REFRACTIVITY INTERCEPT, AND SPECIFIC DISPERSION

June 30, 1945; October 31, 1952

| Compound [b] | Formula [a] | Molecular Volume[a] $V=M/d$ (ml/mole) | | Molecular Refraction[a] $V(n_D^2-1)/(n_D^2+2)$ (ml/mole) | | Specific Refraction[a] $(1/d)(n_D^2-1)/(n_D^2+2)$ (ml/g) | | Refractivity Intercept[a] $n_D-d/2$ | | Specific Dispersion[a] $10^4(n_F-n_C)/d$ (ml/g) | |
|---|---|---|---|---|---|---|---|---|---|---|---|
| | | 20°C | 25°C | 20°C | 25°C | 20°C | 25°C | 20°C | 25°C | 20°C | 25°C |
| 2-Ethyl-1-pentene | $C_7H_{14}$ | 138.7 | 139.5 | 34.0 | 34.0 | 0.346 | 0.346 | 1.051 | 1.051 | 125. | 125. |
| 3-Ethyl-1-pentene | " | 141.02 | 141.94 | 34.04 | 34.06 | 0.3467 | 0.3469 | 1.0499 | 1.0496 | 121. | 121. |
| 2,3-Dimethyl-1-pentene | " | 139.25 | 140.10 | 34.00 | 34.02 | 0.3463 | 0.3465 | 1.0508 | 1.0503 | 125. | 125. |
| 2,4-Dimethyl-1-pentene | " | 141.41 | 142.33 | 34.18 | 34.19 | 0.3481 | 0.3482 | 1.0514 | 1.0510 | 125. | 125. |
| 3,3-Dimethyl-1-pentene | " | 140.78 | 141.64 | 34.01 | 34.02 | 0.3464 | 0.3465 | 1.0497 | 1.0492 | 120. | 120. |
| 3,4-Dimethyl-1-pentene | " | 140.1 | 140.9 | 33.9 | 33.9 | 0.346 | 0.346 | 1.0490 | 1.0484 | 120. | 120. |
| 4,4-Dimethyl-1-pentene | " | 143.81 | 144.70 | 34.23 | 34.24 | 0.3486 | 0.3487 | 1.0504 | 1.0500 | 120. | 120. |
| 3-Ethyl-2-pentene | " | 136.29 | 137.14 | 34.11 | 34.14 | 0.3475 | 0.3477 | 1.0546 | 1.0543 | 127. | 127. |
| 2,3-Dimethyl-2-pentene | " | 134.92 | 135.72 | 34.20 | 34.22 | 0.3483 | 0.3485 | 1.0570 | 1.0565 | 130. | 130. |
| 2,4-Dimethyl-2-pentene | " | 141.17 | 142.05 | 34.52 | 34.54 | 0.3516 | 0.3517 | 1.0562 | 1.0557 | 128. | 128. |
| 3,4-Dimethyl-*cis*-2-pentene | " | 137.7 | 138.5 | 33.9 | 33.9 | 0.345 | 0.345 | 1.050 | 1.050 | 127. | 127. |
| 3,4-Dimethyl-*trans*-2-pentene | " | | | | | | | | | | |
| 4,4-Dimethyl-*cis*-2-pentene | " | 140.34 | 141.23 | 34.20 | 34.22 | 0.3484 | 0.3486 | 1.0526 | 1.0522 | 122. | 122. |
| 4,4-Dimethyl-*trans*-2-pentene | " | 142.52 | 143.44 | 34.41 | 34.41 | 0.3505 | 0.3505 | 1.0538 | 1.0530 | 124. | 124. |
| 3-Methyl-2-ethyl-1-butene | " | 137.3 | 138.1 | 34.0 | 34.0 | 0.346 | 0.346 | 1.052 | 1.052 | 125. | 125. |
| 2,3,3-Trimethyl-1-butene | " | 139.27 | 140.16 | 33.98 | 33.98 | 0.3461 | 0.3461 | 1.0504 | 1.0498 | 124. | 124. |

[a] See footnote a of Table 1b.  [b] See footnote b of Table 9b, Page 1.

TABLE 10b, Page 1 - MONOOLEFINS, $C_8$

MOLECULAR VOLUME, MOLECULAR REFRACTION, SPECIFIC REFRACTION, REFRACTIVITY INTERCEPT, AND SPECIFIC DISPERSION

June 30, 1945; October 31, 1952

| Compound [b] | Formula [a] | Molecular Volume [a] $V=M/d$ ml/mole | | Molecular Refraction [a] $V(n_D^2-1)/(n_D^2+2)$ ml/mole | | Specific Refraction [a] $(1/d)(n_D^2-1)/(n_D^2+2)$ ml/g | | Refractivity Intercept [a] $n_D-d/2$ | | Specific Dispersion [a] $10^4(n_F-n_C)/d$ ml/g | |
|---|---|---|---|---|---|---|---|---|---|---|---|
| | | 20°C | 25°C | 20°C | 25°C | 20°C | 25°C | 20°C | 25°C | 20°C | 25°C |
| 1-Octene | $C_8H_{16}$ | 156.952 | 157.850 | 38.778 | 38.790 | 0.34559 | 0.34570 | 1.05124 | 1.05078 | 116.9 | 116.8 |
| cis-2-Octene | " | 154.92 | 155.82 | 38.79 | 38.81 | 0.3457 | 0.3459 | 1.0529 | 1.0525 | 118. | 118. |
| trans-2-Octene | " | 155.87 | 156.78 | 38.88 | 38.90 | 0.3465 | 0.3467 | 1.0533 | 1.0529 | 120. | 120. |
| cis-3-Octene | " | 155.6 | 156.5 | 38.8 | 38.8 | 0.346 | 0.346 | 1.053 | 1.053 | 119. | 119. |
| trans-3-Octene | " | 156.89 | 157.82 | 39.09 | 39.12 | 0.3484 | 0.3486 | 1.0550 | 1.0547 | 121. | 121. |
| cis-4-Octene | " | 155.59 | 156.50 | 38.95 | 38.97 | 0.3471 | 0.3473 | 1.0542 | 1.0539 | 120. | 120. |
| trans-4-Octene | " | 157.13 | 158.06 | 39.08 | 39.10 | 0.3483 | 0.3485 | 1.0548 | 1.0544 | 122. | 122. |
| 2-Methyl-1-heptene | " | 155.74 | 156.63 | 38.78 | 38.79 | 0.3456 | 0.3457 | 1.0521 | 1.0516 | 122. | 122. |
| 3-Methyl-1-heptene | " | 157.8 | 158.7 | 38.8 | 38.8 | 0.346 | 0.346 | 1.051 | 1.051 | 117. | 117. |
| 4-Methyl-1-heptene | " | 156.5 | 157.4 | 38.8 | 38.8 | 0.346 | 0.346 | 1.052 | 1.052 | 117. | 117. |
| 5-Methyl-1-heptene | " | 156.63 | 157.55 | 38.76 | 38.77 | 0.3454 | 0.3456 | 1.0512 | 1.0508 | 117. | 117. |
| 6-Methyl-1-heptene | " | 157.60 | 158.51 | 38.79 | 38.81 | 0.3457 | 0.3459 | 1.0510 | 1.0506 | 117. | 117. |
| 2-Methyl-2-heptene | " | 154.96 | 155.84 | 38.97 | 38.98 | 0.3473 | 0.3474 | 1.0550 | 1.0545 | 124. | 124. |
| 3-Methyl-cis-2-heptene | " | 153.9 | 154.8 | 38.9 | 38.9 | 0.347 | 0.347 | 1.055 | 1.055 | 124. | 124. |
| 3-Methyl-trans-2-heptene | " | | | | | | | | | | |
| 4-Methyl-cis-2-heptene | " | 156.7 | 157.6 | 38.9 | 38.9 | 0.346 | 0.346 | 1.052 | 1.052 | 119. | 119. |
| 4-Methyl-trans-2-heptene | " | | | | | | | | | 121. | 121. |
| 5-Methyl-cis-2-heptene | " | 155.2 | 156.1 | 38.8 | 38.8 | 0.346 | 0.346 | 1.053 | 1.053 | 119. | 119. |
| 5-Methyl-trans-2-heptene | " | | | | | | | | | 121. | 121. |
| 6-Methyl-cis-2-heptene | " | 156.3 | 157.2 | 38.9 | 38.9 | 0.347 | 0.347 | 1.053 | 1.053 | 119. | 119. |
| 6-Methyl-trans-2-heptene | " | | | | | | | | | 121. | 121. |
| 2-Methyl-cis-3-heptene | " | 158.9 | 159.8 | 39.1 | 39.1 | 0.349 | 0.349 | 1.054 | 1.054 | 119. | 119. |
| 2-Methyl-trans-3-heptene | " | | | | | | | | | 121. | 121. |

[a] See footnote a of Table 1b.  [b] See footnote b of Table 9b.

TABLE 10b, Page 2 — MONOOLEFINS, $C_8$

MOLECULAR VOLUME, MOLECULAR REFRACTION, SPECIFIC REFRACTION, REFRACTIVITY INTERCEPT, AND SPECIFIC DISPERSION

June 30, 1945; October 31, 1952

| Compound [b] | Formula | Molecular Volume [a] $V = M/d$ (ml/mole) | | Molecular Refraction [a] $V(n_D^2-1)/(n_D^2+2)$ (ml/mole) | | Specific Refraction [a] $(1/d)(n_D^2-1)/(n_D^2+2)$ (ml/g) | | Refractivity Intercept [a] $n_D - d/2$ | | Specific Dispersion [a] $10^4(n_F-n_C)/d$ (ml/g) | |
|---|---|---|---|---|---|---|---|---|---|---|---|
| | | 20°C | 25°C | 20°C | 25°C | 20°C | 25°C | 20°C | 25°C | 20°C | 25°C |
| 3-Methyl-cis-3-heptene | $C_8H_{16}$ | 154.1 | 155.0 | 38.9 | 38.9 | 0.346 | 0.346 | 1.054 | 1.054 | 124. | 124. |
| 3-Methyl-trans-3-heptene | " | | | | | | | | | 124. | 124. |
| 4-Methyl-cis-3-heptene | " | 154.8 | 155.6 | 38.9 | 38.9 | 0.347 | 0.347 | 1.055 | 1.055 | 119. | 119. |
| 4-Methyl-trans-3-heptene | " | | | | | | | | | 121. | 121. |
| 5-Methyl-cis-3-heptene | " | 157.4 | 158.3 | 39.0 | 39.0 | 0.348 | 0.348 | 1.054 | 1.054 | 119. | 119. |
| 5-Methyl-trans-3-heptene | " | | | | | | | | | 121. | 121. |
| 6-Methyl-cis-3-heptene | " | 157.4 | 158.3 | 39.0 | 39.0 | 0.348 | 0.348 | 1.054 | 1.054 | 119. | 119. |
| 6-Methyl-trans-3-heptene | " | | | | | | | | | 121. | 121. |
| 2-Ethyl-1-hexene | " | 154.34 | 155.24 | 38.71 | 38.73 | 0.3450 | 0.3451 | 1.0522 | 1.0518 | 121. | 121. |
| 3-Ethyl-1-hexene | " | 156.9 | 157.8 | 38.7 | 38.7 | 0.344 | 0.344 | 1.050 | 1.050 | 117. | 117. |
| 4-Ethyl-1-hexene | " | 154.6 | 155.4 | 38.5 | 38.5 | 0.343 | 0.343 | 1.049 | 1.049 | 117. | 117. |
| 2,3-Dimethyl-1-hexene | " | 155.54 | 156.45 | 38.64 | 38.67 | 0.3444 | 0.3446 | 1.0506 | 1.0503 | 122. | 122. |
| 2,4-Dimethyl-1-hexene | " | 155.8 | 156.7 | 38.7 | 38.7 | 0.345 | 0.345 | 1.051 | 1.051 | 122. | 122. |
| 2,5-Dimethyl-1-hexene | " | 156.45 | 157.40 | 38.80 | 38.83 | 0.3458 | 0.3460 | 1.0519 | 1.0515 | 122. | 122. |
| 3,3-Dimethyl-1-hexene | " | 157.15 | 158.06 | 38.68 | 38.71 | 0.3448 | 0.3450 | 1.0500 | 1.0496 | 117. | 117. |
| 3,4-Dimethyl-1-hexene | " | 155.0 | 155.8 | 38.7 | 38.7 | 0.345 | 0.345 | 1.051 | 1.051 | 117. | 117. |
| 3,5-Dimethyl-1-hexene | " | 158.5 | 159.4 | 38.8 | 38.8 | 0.346 | 0.346 | 1.050 | 1.050 | 117. | 117. |
| 4,4-Dimethyl-1-hexene | " | 155.89 | 156.78 | 38.64 | 38.66 | 0.3444 | 0.3445 | 1.0503 | 1.0499 | 117. | 117. |
| 4,5-Dimethyl-1-hexene | " | 154.1 | 155.0 | 38.5 | 38.5 | 0.344 | 0.344 | 1.050 | 1.050 | 117. | 117. |
| 5,5-Dimethyl-1-hexene | " | 158.3 | 159.2 | 38.8 | 38.8 | 0.346 | 0.346 | 1.0501 | 1.0498 | 117. | 117. |
| 3-Ethyl-cis-2-hexene | " | 152.2 | 153.1 | 38.9 | 38.9 | 0.346 | 0.346 | 1.056 | 1.056 | 124. | 124. |
| 3-Ethyl-trans-2-hexene | " | | | | | | | | | 124. | 124. |
| 4-Ethyl-cis-2-hexene | " | 154.8 | 155.6 | 38.5 | 38.5 | 0.343 | 0.343 | 1.050 | 1.050 | 119. | 119. |
| 4-Ethyl-trans-2-hexene | " | | | | | | | | | 121. | 121. |

[a] See footnote a of Table 1b.　　[b] See footnote b of Table 9b.

TABLE 10b, Page 3 – MONOOLEFINS, C₈

MOLECULAR VOLUME, MOLECULAR REFRACTION, SPECIFIC REFRACTION, REFRACTIVITY INTERCEPT, AND SPECIFIC DISPERSION

June 30, 1945; October 31, 1952

| Compound[b] | Formula[a] | Molecular Volume[a] $V=M/d$ (ml/mole) | | Molecular Refraction[a] $V(n_D^2-1)/(n_D^2+2)$ (ml/mole) | | Specific Refraction[a] $(1/d)(n_D^2-1)/(n_D^2+2)$ (ml/g) | | Refractivity Intercept[a] $n_D-d/2$ | | Specific Dispersion[a] $10^4(n_F-n_C)/d$ (ml/g) | |
|---|---|---|---|---|---|---|---|---|---|---|---|
| | | 20°C | 25°C | 20°C | 25°C | 20°C | 25°C | 20°C | 25°C | 20°C | 25°C |
| 2,3-Dimethyl-2-hexene | C₈H₁₆ | 151.47 | 152.33 | 38.87 | 38.90 | 0.3464 | 0.3467 | 1.0564 | 1.0561 | 127. | 127. |
| 2,4-Dimethyl-2-hexene | " | 155.56 | 156.47 | 38.69 | 38.72 | 0.3448 | 0.3451 | 1.0512 | 1.0508 | 124. | 124. |
| 2,5-Dimethyl-2-hexene | " | 155.8 | 156.7 | 38.9 | 38.9 | 0.347 | 0.347 | 1.054 | 1.054 | 124. | 124. |
| 3,4-Dimethyl-cis-2-hexene | " | 152.2 | 153.1 | 38.4 | 38.4 | 0.342 | 0.342 | 1.050 | 1.050 | 124. | 124. |
| 3,4-Dimethyl-trans-2-hexene | " | | | | | | | | | 124. | 124. |
| 3,5-Dimethyl-cis-2-hexene | " | 154.8 | 155.6 | 38.9 | 38.9 | 0.346 | 0.346 | 1.054 | 1.054 | 119. | 119. |
| 3,5-Dimethyl-trans-2-hexene | " | | | | | | | | | 121. | 121. |
| 4,4-Dimethyl-cis-2-hexene | " | 155.4 | 156.3 | 38.8 | 38.8 | 0.346 | 0.346 | 1.052 | 1.052 | 119. | 119. |
| 4,4-Dimethyl-trans-2-hexene | " | | | | | | | | | 121. | 121. |
| 4,5-Dimethyl-cis-2-hexene | " | 154.8 | 155.6 | 38.6 | 38.6 | 0.344 | 0.344 | 1.051 | 1.051 | 119. | 119. |
| 4,5-Dimethyl-trans-2-hexene | " | | | | | | | | | 121. | 121. |
| 5,5-Dimethyl-cis-2-hexene | " | 156.52 | 157.48 | 38.89 | 38.92 | 0.3466 | 0.3468 | 1.0528 | 1.0526 | 119. | 119. |
| 5,5-Dimethyl-trans-2-hexene | " | 158.80 | 159.77 | 38.96 | 38.99 | 0.3472 | 0.3475 | 1.0522 | 1.0518 | 121. | 121. |
| 3-Ethyl-3-hexene | " | 153.9 | 154.8 | 38.8 | 38.8 | 0.346 | 0.346 | 1.054 | 1.054 | 124. | 124. |
| 2,2-Dimethyl-cis-3-hexene | " | 157.42 | 158.35 | 38.99 | 39.01 | 0.3475 | 0.3477 | 1.0535 | 1.0531 | 119. | 119. |
| 2,2-Dimethyl-trans-3-hexene | " | 159.41 | 160.41 | 39.18 | 39.20 | 0.3492 | 0.3494 | 1.0544 | 1.0540 | 121. | 121. |
| 2,3-Dimethyl-cis-3-hexene | " | 154.1 | 155.0 | 38.7 | 38.7 | 0.345 | 0.345 | 1.052 | 1.052 | 124. | 124. |
| 2,3-Dimethyl-trans-3-hexene | " | | | | | | | | | 124. | 124. |
| 2,4-Dimethyl-cis-3-hexene | " | 156.32 | 157.26 | 39.06 | 39.08 | 0.3481 | 0.3483 | 1.0551 | 1.0546 | 124. | 124. |
| 2,4-Dimethyl-trans-3-hexene | " | 157.04 | 158.02 | 39.13 | 39.16 | 0.3487 | 0.3490 | 1.0554 | 1.0550 | 124. | 124. |
| 2,5-Dimethyl-cis-3-hexene | " | 158.0 | 158.9 | 38.8 | 38.9 | 0.346 | 0.346 | 1.051 | 1.051 | 119. | 119. |
| 2,5-Dimethyl-trans-3-hexene | " | | | | | | | | | 121. | 121. |
| 3,4-Dimethyl-cis-3-hexene | " | 150.2 | 151.0 | 38.8 | 38.8 | 0.346 | 0.346 | 1.057 | 1.057 | 127. | 127. |
| 3,4-Dimethyl-trans-3-hexene | " | | | | | | | | | | |

a See footnote a of Table 1b.   b See footnote b of Table 9b.

TABLE 10b, Page 4 — MONOOLEFINS, $C_8$

MOLECULAR VOLUME, MOLECULAR REFRACTION, SPECIFIC REFRACTION, REFRACTIVITY INTERCEPT, AND SPECIFIC DISPERSION

June 30, 1945; October 31, 1952

| Compound[b] | Formula[a] | Molecular Volume[a] $V=M/d$ (ml/mole) | | Molecular Refraction[a] $V(n_D^2-1)/(n_D^2+2)$ (ml/mole) | | Specific Refraction[a] $(1/d)(n_D^2-1)/(n_D^2+2)$ (ml/g) | | Refractivity Intercept[a] $n_D-d/2$ | | Specific Dispersion[a] $10^4(n_F-n_C)/d$ (ml/g) | |
|---|---|---|---|---|---|---|---|---|---|---|---|
| | | 20°C | 25°C | 20°C | 25°C | 20°C | 25°C | 20°C | 25°C | 20°C | 25°C |
| 2-n-Propyl-1-pentene | $C_8H_{16}$ | 154.98 | 155.89 | 38.69 | 38.71 | 0.3449 | 0.3450 | 1.0516 | 1.0512 | 123. | 123. |
| 2-Isopropyl-1-pentene | " | 154.8 | 155.6 | 38.7 | 38.7 | 0.345 | 0.345 | 1.052 | 1.052 | 122. | 122. |
| 3-Methyl-2-ethyl-1-pentene | " | 153.9 | 154.8 | 38.5 | 38.5 | 0.343 | 0.343 | 1.050 | 1.050 | 122. | 122. |
| 4-Methyl-2-ethyl-1-pentene | " | 155.95 | 156.89 | 38.68 | 38.70 | 0.3447 | 0.3449 | 1.0508 | 1.0504 | 122. | 122. |
| 2-Methyl-3-ethyl-1-pentene | " | 153.7 | 154.6 | 38.5 | 38.5 | 0.343 | 0.343 | 1.050 | 1.050 | 122. | 122. |
| 3-Methyl-3-ethyl-1-pentene | " | 153.60 | 154.47 | 38.7 | 38.7 | 0.345 | 0.345 | 1.053 | 1.053 | 117. | 117. |
| 4-Methyl-3-ethyl-1-pentene | " | 155.84 | 156.76 | 38.59 | 38.61 | 0.3439 | 0.3441 | 1.0497 | 1.0493 | 117. | 117. |
| 2,3,3-Trimethyl-1-pentene | " | 152.62 | 153.54 | 38.41 | 38.46 | 0.3423 | 0.3427 | 1.0498 | 1.0497 | 122. | 122. |
| 2,3,4-Trimethyl-1-pentene | " | 153.9 | 154.8 | 38.6 | 38.6 | 0.344 | 0.344 | 1.051 | 1.051 | 122. | 122. |
| 2,4,4-Trimethyl-1-pentene | " | 156.93 | 157.86 | 38.76 | 38.78 | 0.3455 | 0.3456 | 1.0511 | 1.0506 | 122. | 122. |
| 3,3,4-Trimethyl-1-pentene | " | 153.9 | 154.8 | 38.5 | 38.5 | 0.343 | 0.343 | 1.0499 | 1.0495 | 117. | 117. |
| 3,4,4-Trimethyl-1-pentene | " | 156.1 | 156.9 | 38.9 | 38.9 | 0.346 | 0.346 | 1.053 | 1.053 | 117. | 117. |
| 2-Methyl-3-ethyl-cis-2-pentene | " | 151.8 | 152.7 | 39.0 | 39.0 | 0.346 | 0.346 | 1.0552 | 1.0547 | 127. | 127. |
| 4-Methyl-3-ethyl-cis-2-pentene | " | 151.8 | 152.7 | 38.7 | 38.8 | 0.345 | 0.346 | 1.054 | 1.054 | 124. | 124. |
| 4-Methyl-3-ethyl-trans-2-pentene | " | 152.66 | 153.54 | 38.71 | 38.72 | 0.3450 | 0.3450 | 1.0535 | 1.0529 | 124. | 124. |
| 2,3,4-Trimethyl-2-pentene | " | 150.94 | 151.82 | 38.79 | 38.81 | 0.3457 | 0.3459 | 1.0558 | 1.0554 | 127. | 127. |
| 2,4,4-Trimethyl-2-pentene | " | 155.46 | 156.37 | 39.01 | 39.03 | 0.3477 | 0.3479 | 1.0551 | 1.0547 | 125. | 125. |
| 3,4,4-Trimethyl-cis-2-pentene | " | 151.8 | 152.7 | 38.7 | 38.7 | 0.345 | 0.345 | 1.054 | 1.054 | 124. | 124. |
| 3,4,4-Trimethyl-trans-2-pentene | " | | | | | | | | | | |
| 3-Methyl-2-isopropyl-1-butene | " | 155.4 | 156.3 | 38.4 | 38.4 | 0.342 | 0.342 | 1.0475 | 1.0471 | 122. | 122. |
| 3,3-Dimethyl-2-ethyl-1-butene | " | 154.1 | 155.0 | 38.7 | 38.7 | 0.345 | 0.345 | 1.0519 | 1.0515 | 122. | 122. |

a See footnote a of Table 1b.　　b See footnote b of Table 9b.

TABLE 11b (PART 1) – DIOLEFINS, $C_3$ TO $C_5$

MOLECULAR VOLUME, MOLECULAR REFRACTION, SPECIFIC REFRACTION, REFRACTIVITY INTERCEPT, AND SPECIFIC DISPERSION

June 30, 1945; September 30, 1951; October 31, 1952

| Compound | Formula | Molecular Volume[a] $V = M/d$ ml/mole | | Molecular Refraction[a] $V(n_D^2-1)/(n_D^2+2)$ ml/mole | | Specific Refraction[a] $(1/d)(n_D^2-1)/(n_D^2+2)$ ml/g | | Refractivity Intercept[a] $n_D - d/2$ | | Specific Dispersion[a] $10^4(n_F-n_C)/d$ ml/g | |
|---|---|---|---|---|---|---|---|---|---|---|---|
| | | 20°C | 25°C | 20°C | 25°C | 20°C | 25°C | 20°C | 25°C | 20°C | 25°C |
| Propadiene (Allene) | $C_3H_4$ | —— | —— | —— | —— | —— | —— | —— | —— | —— | —— |
| 1,2-Butadiene | $C_4H_6$ | 83.0[b] | 83.7[b] | —— | —— | —— | —— | —— | —— | —— | —— |
| 1,3-Butadiene | " | 87.08[b] | 87.96[b] | —— | —— | —— | —— | —— | —— | —— | —— |
| 1,2-Pentadiene | $C_5H_8$ | 98.350 | 99.061 | 24.936 | 24.950 | 0.36609 | 0.36629 | 1.07462 | 1.07393 | 164.7 | 164.6 |
| 1,*cis*-3-Pentadiene | " | 98.570 | 99.303 | 25.790 | 25.804 | 0.37863 | 0.37883 | 1.09083 | 1.08995 | 243.9 | 243.8 |
| 1,*trans*-3-Pentadiene | " | 100.756 | 101.508 | 26.032 | 26.046 | 0.38218 | 0.38238 | 1.09206 | 1.09118 | 245.8 | 245.7 |
| 1,4-Pentadiene | " | 103.084 | 103.878 | 24.367 | 24.367 | 0.35774 | 0.35774 | 1.05838 | 1.05756 | 153.2 | 153.1 |
| 2,3-Pentadiene | " | 98.003 | 98.716 | 25.235 | 25.246 | 0.37049 | 0.37065 | 1.08091 | 1.08009 | 174.6 | 174.5 |
| 3-Methyl-1,2-butadiene | " | 100.2 | 100.9 | 24.8 | 24.8 | 0.365 | 0.365 | 1.070 | 1.069 | | |
| 2-Methyl-1,3-butadiene (Isoprene) | " | 100.028 | 100.780 | 25.416 | 25.425 | 0.37314 | 0.37327 | 1.08146 | 1.08058 | 224.9 | 224.8 |

[a] See footnote a of Table 1b.   [b] At saturation pressure.

## TABLE 11b (PART 2) – DIOLEFINS, $C_6$
### MOLECULAR VOLUME, MOLECULAR REFRACTION, SPECIFIC REFRACTION, REFRACTIVITY INTERCEPT, AND SPECIFIC DISPERSION

June 20, 1945; October 31, 1952

Column groups:
- Molecular Volume[a]: $V=M/d$ (ml/mole)
- Molecular Refraction[a]: $V(n_D^2-1)/(n_D^2+2)$ (ml/mole)
- Specific Refraction[a]: $(1/d)(n_D^2-1)/(n_D^2+2)$ (ml/g)
- Refractivity Intercept[a]: $n_D-d/2$
- Specific Dispersion[a]: $10^4(n_F-n_C)/d$ (ml/g)

| Compound[b] | Formula | Mol Vol 20°C | Mol Vol 25°C | Mol Refr 20°C | Mol Refr 25°C | Spec Refr 20°C | Spec Refr 25°C | Refr Int 20°C | Refr Int 25°C | Spec Disp 20°C | Spec Disp 25°C |
|---|---|---|---|---|---|---|---|---|---|---|---|
| 1,2-Hexadiene | $C_6H_{10}$ | 114.90 | 115.66 | 29.57 | 29.59 | 0.360 | 0.360 | 1.0708 | 1.0700 | — | — |
| 1,*cis*-3-Hexadiene / 1,*trans*-3-Hexadiene | " | 116.5 | 117.3 | 30.6 | 30.6 | 0.373 | 0.373 | 1.086 | 1.085 | 225. | 225. |
| 1,*cis*-4-Hexadiene | " | 117.3 | 118.2 | 29.4 | 29.4 | 0.358 | 0.358 | 1.065 | 1.064 | | |
| 1,*trans*-4-Hexadiene | " | 118.65 | 119.42 | 29.03 | 29.01 | 0.3534 | 0.3532 | 1.0580 | 1.0571 | | |
| 1,5-Hexadiene | " | 120.8 | 121.7 | 29.0 | 29.0 | 0.353 | 0.353 | 1.055 | 1.054 | | |
| 2,3-Hexadiene | " | | | | | | | | | | |
| *cis*-2,*cis*-4-Hexadiene / *cis*-2,*trans*-4-Hexadiene / *trans*-2,*trans*-4-Hexadiene | " | 114.1 | 114.9 | 30.7 | 30.7 | 0.373 | 0.373 | 1.090 | 1.089 | 225. | 225. |
| 3-Methyl-1,2-pentadiene | " | 114.9 | 115.7 | 29.4 | 29.4 | 0.358 | 0.358 | 1.068 | 1.067 | | |
| 4-Methyl-1,2-pentadiene | " | 116.0 | 116.8 | 29.6 | 29.6 | 0.361 | 0.361 | 1.070 | 1.069 | | |
| 2-Methyl-1,*cis*-3-pentadiene / 2-Methyl-1,*trans*-3-pentadiene | " | 114.2 | 115.0 | 30.5 | 30.5 | 0.371 | 0.371 | 1.087 | 1.086 | 225. | 225. |
| 3-Methyl-1,*cis*-3-pentadiene / 3-Methyl-1,*trans*-3-pentadiene | " | 111.8 | 112.5 | 30.2 | 30.2 | 0.367 | 0.367 | 1.085 | 1.084 | 225. | 225. |
| 4-Methyl-1,3-pentadiene | " | 114.2 | 115.0 | 30.8 | 30.8 | 0.375 | 0.375 | 1.092 | 1.091 | 225. | 225. |
| 2-Methyl-1,4-pentadiene | " | 118.4 | 119.2 | 29.0 | 29.0 | 0.353 | 0.353 | 1.058 | 1.057 | | |
| 3-Methyl-1,4-pentadiene | " | 118.2 | 119.0 | 29.0 | 29.0 | 0.353 | 0.353 | 1.058 | 1.057 | | |
| 2-Methyl-2,3-pentadiene | " | 115.5 | 116.3 | 29.6 | 29.6 | 0.360 | 0.360 | 1.070 | 1.069 | | |
| 2-Ethyl-1,3-butadiene | " | 114.6 | 115.4 | 30.5 | 30.5 | 0.371 | 0.372 | 1.086 | 1.086 | 225. | 225. |
| 2,3-Dimethyl-1,3-butadiene | " | 113.03 | 113.74 | 29.75 | 29.75 | 0.3622 | 0.3622 | 1.0760 | 1.0751 | 225. | 225. |

[a] See footnote a of Table 1b.

[b] See footnote b of Table 9b.

TABLE 13b – ALKYL CYCLOPENTENES, $C_5$ TO $C_7$

MOLECULAR VOLUME, MOLECULAR REFRACTION, SPECIFIC REFRACTION, REFRACTIVITY INTERCEPT, AND SPECIFIC DISPERSION

October 31, 1950; October 31, 1952

| Compound | Formula | Molecular Volume[a] $V=M/d$ (ml/mole) | | Molecular Refraction[a] $V(n_D^2-1)/(n_D^2+2)$ (ml/mole) | | Specific Refraction[a] $(1/d)(n_D^2-1)/(n_D^2+2)$ (ml/g) | | Refractivity Intercept[a] $n_D-d/2$ | | Specific Dispersion[a] $10^4(n_F-n_C)/d$ (ml/g) | |
|---|---|---|---|---|---|---|---|---|---|---|---|
| | | 20°C | 25°C | 20°C | 25°C | 20°C | 25°C | 20°C | 25°C | 20°C | 25°C |
| Cyclopentene | $C_5H_8$ | 88.232 | 88.860 | 22.443 | 22.459 | 0.32949 | 0.32973 | 1.03646 | 1.03614 | 118.7 | 118.7 |
| 1-Methylcyclopentene | $C_6H_{10}$ | 105.28 | 105.96 | 27.36 | 27.38 | 0.3331 | 0.3334 | 1.0429 | 1.0426 | 124. | 124. |
| 3-Methylcyclopentene | " | 107.77 | 108.48 | 27.31 | 27.33 | 0.3325 | 0.3327 | 1.0396 | 1.0393 | 119. | 119. |
| 4-Methylcyclopentene | " | 105.36 | 106.03 | 27.25 | 27.27 | 0.3318 | 0.3320 | 1.0408 | 1.0404 | | |
| 1-Ethylcyclopentene | $C_7H_{12}$ | 120.48 | 121.18 | 31.82 | 31.84 | 0.3308 | 0.3310 | 1.0419 | 1.0416 | 119. | 119. |
| 3-Ethylcyclopentene | " | 122.82 | 123.54 | 31.85 | 31.87 | 0.3312 | 0.3314 | 1.0404 | 1.0401 | | |
| 4-Ethylcyclopentene | " | 120.5 | 121.3 | 31.8 | 31.8 | 0.330 | 0.330 | 1.041 | 1.041 | | |
| 1,2-Dimethylcyclopentene | " | 120.57 | 121.30 | 32.08 | 32.09 | 0.3336 | 0.3337 | 1.0460 | 1.0456 | 125.8 | 125.8 |
| 1,3-Dimethylcyclopentene | " | 125.5 | 126.4 | 32.3 | 32.3 | 0.336 | 0.336 | 1.045 | 1.045 | | |
| 1,4-Dimethylcyclopentene | " | 123.4 | 124.2 | 31.8 | 31.8 | 0.330 | 0.330 | 1.0388 | 1.0385 | | |
| 1,5-Dimethylcyclopentene | " | 123.3 | 124.1 | 32.1 | 32.1 | 0.333 | 0.334 | 1.043 | 1.042 | 120.8 | 120.8 |
| 3,3-Dimethylcyclopentene | " | 124.7 | 125.5 | 31.8 | 31.8 | 0.330 | 0.330 | 1.037 | 1.037 | | |
| 3,cis-4-Dimethylcyclopentene | " | 123.8 | 124.6 | 32.0 | 32.0 | 0.332 | 0.333 | 1.042 | 1.041 | | |
| 3,trans-4-Dimethylcyclopentene | " | | | | | | | | | | |
| 3,cis-5-Dimethylcyclopentene | " | | | | | | | | | | |
| 3,trans-5-Dimethylcyclopentene | " | | | | | | | | | | |
| 4,4-Dimethylcyclopentene | " | 124.7 | 125.5 | 31.8 | 31.8 | 0.330 | 0.330 | 1.037 | 1.037 | | |

[a] See footnote a of Table 1b.

## TABLE 19b – ALKYL CYCLOHEXENES, C6 TO C8

### MOLECULAR VOLUME, MOLECULAR REFRACTION, SPECIFIC REFRACTION, REFRACTIVITY INTERCEPT, AND SPECIFIC DISPERSION

October 31, 1950

| Compound | Formula | Molecular Volume[a] $V=M/d$ (ml/mole) | | Molecular Refraction[a] $V(n_D^2-1)/(n_D^2+2)$ (ml/mole) | | Specific Refraction[a] $(1/d)(n_D^2-1)/(n_D^2+2)$ (ml/g) | | Refractivity Intercept[a] $n_D-d/2$ | | Specific Dispersion[a] $10^4(n_F-n_C)/d$ (ml/g) | |
|---|---|---|---|---|---|---|---|---|---|---|---|
| | | 20°C | 25°C | 20°C | 25°C | 20°C | 25°C | 20°C | 25°C | 20°C | 25°C |
| Cyclohexene | $C_6H_{10}$ | 101.287 | 101.899 | 27.038 | 27.055 | 0.32917 | 0.32938 | 1.04106 | 1.04072 | 117.2 | 117.1 |
| 1-Methylcyclohexene | $C_7H_{12}$ | 118.69 | 119.34 | 31.91 | 31.93 | 0.3319 | 0.3321 | 1.0452 | 1.0449 | 120. | 120. |
| 3-Methylcyclohexene | " | 120.06 | 120.72 | 31.92 | 31.93 | 0.3319 | 0.3321 | 1.0439 | 1.0436 | | |
| 4-Methylcyclohexene | " | 120.34 | 121.01 | 31.80 | 31.82 | 0.3307 | 0.3309 | 1.0418 | 1.0416 | | |
| 1-Ethylcyclohexene | $C_8H_{14}$ | 133.9 | 134.5 | 36.5 | 36.5 | 0.331 | 0.331 | 1.046 | 1.045 | 117. | 117. |
| 3-Ethylcyclohexene | " | 135.4 | 136.0 | 36.5 | 36.5 | 0.331 | 0.331 | 1.044 | 1.044 | | |
| 4-Ethylcyclohexene | " | 136.0 | 136.7 | 36.5 | 36.5 | 0.331 | 0.331 | 1.044 | 1.044 | | |
| 1,2-Dimethylcyclohexene | " | 133.57 | 134.25 | 36.50 | 36.52 | 0.3312 | 0.3314 | 1.0463 | 1.046 | 123. | 123. |
| 1,3-Dimethylcyclohexene | " | 137.4 | 138.1 | 36.6 | 36.6 | 0.332 | 0.332 | 1.044 | 1.044 | 120. | 120. |
| 1,4-Dimethylcyclohexene | " | 137.4 | 138.1 | 36.6 | 36.6 | 0.333 | 0.333 | 1.045 | 1.045 | 119. | 119. |
| 1,5-Dimethylcyclohexene | " | 136.87 | 137.59 | 36.6 | 36.6 | 0.333 | 0.333 | 1.045 | 1.046 | 119. | 119. |
| 1,6-Dimethylcyclohexene | " | 135.2 | 135.9 | 36.6 | 36.6 | 0.332 | 0.331 | 1.046 | 1.046 | | |
| 3,3-Dimethylcyclohexene | " | 137.1 | 137.7 | 36.5 | 36.5 | 0.331 | 0.331 | 1.043 | 1.043 | | |
| 3,cis-4-Dimethylcyclohexene | " | | | | | | | | | | |
| 3,trans-4-Dimethylcyclohexene | " | | | | | | | | | | |
| 3,cis-5-Dimethylcyclohexene | " | | | | | | | | | | |
| 3,trans-5-Dimethylcyclohexene | " | | | | | | | | | | |
| 3,cis-6-Dimethylcyclohexene | " | | | | | | | | | | |
| 3,trans-6-Dimethylcyclohexene | " | | | | | | | | | | |
| 4,4-Dimethylcyclohexene | " | 137.81 | 138.50 | 36.46 | 36.47 | 0.3309 | 0.3310 | 1.0422 | 1.0418 | 115. | 115. |
| 4,cis-5-Dimethylcyclohexene | " | | | | | | | | | | |
| 4,trans-5-Dimethylcyclohexene | " | | | | | | | | | | |

[a] See footnote a of Table 1b.

## TABLE 25b (PART 1) – NORMAL ACETYLENES (1-ALKYNES) $C_2$ TO $C_{20}$
### MOLECULAR VOLUME, MOLECULAR REFRACTION, SPECIFIC REFRACTION, REFRACTIVITY INTERCEPT, AND SPECIFIC DISPERSION

April 30, 1949; September 30, 1951; October 31, 1952

| Compound | Formula | Molecular Volume[a] $V=M/d$ ml/mole | | Molecular Refraction[a] $V(n_D^2-1)/(n_D^2+2)$ ml/mole | | Specific Refraction[a] $(1/d)(n_D^2-1)/(n_D^2+2)$ ml/g | | Refractivity Intercept[a] $n_D-d/2$ | | Specific Dispersion[a] $10^4(n_F-n_C)/d$ ml/g | |
|---|---|---|---|---|---|---|---|---|---|---|---|
| | | 20°C | 25°C | 20°C | 25°C | 20°C | 25°C | 20°C | 25°C | 20°C | 25°C |
| Ethyne (Acetylene) | $C_2H_2$ | --- | --- | --- | --- | --- | --- | --- | --- | --- | --- |
| Propyne (Methylacetylene) | $C_3H_4$ | --- | --- | --- | --- | --- | --- | --- | --- | --- | --- |
| 1-Butyne (Ethylacetylene) | $C_4H_6$ | 83.[b] | 83.[b] | --- | --- | --- | --- | --- | --- | --- | --- |
| 1-Pentyne | $C_5H_8$ | 98.70 | 99.45 | 23.14 | 23.18 | 0.3397 | 0.3403 | 1.0402 | 1.0402 | 119. | 119. |
| 1-Hexyne | $C_6H_{10}$ | 114.80 | 115.59 | 27.76 | 27.77 | 0.3380 | 0.3381 | 1.0412 | 1.0407 | 115. | 115. |
| 1-Heptyne | $C_7H_{12}$ | 131.23 | 132.04 | 32.42 | 32.44 | 0.3372 | 0.3373 | 1.0423 | 1.0419 | 113. | 113. |
| 1-Octyne | $C_8H_{14}$ | 147.69 | 148.53 | 37.05 | 37.07 | 0.3363 | 0.3364 | 1.0428 | 1.0425 | 111. | 111. |
| 1-Nonyne | $C_9H_{16}$ | 164.14 | 165.02 | 41.68 | 41.70 | 0.3356 | 0.3357 | 1.0433 | 1.0429 | 110. | 110. |
| 1-Decyne | $C_{10}H_{18}$ | 180.60 | 181.52 | 46.32 | 46.34 | 0.3351 | 0.3352 | 1.0438 | 1.0434 | 108. | 108. |
| 1-Undecyne | $C_{11}H_{20}$ | 197.04 | 198.02 | 50.97 | 50.98 | 0.3347 | 0.3348 | 1.0442 | 1.0439 | 107. | 107. |
| 1-Dodecyne | $C_{12}H_{22}$ | 213.52 | 214.55 | 55.61 | 55.63 | 0.3344 | 0.3345 | 1.0446 | 1.0442 | 107. | 107. |
| 1-Tridecyne | $C_{13}H_{24}$ | 229.94 | 231.01 | 60.25 | 60.27 | 0.3341 | 0.3342 | 1.0449 | 1.0446 | 106. | 106. |
| 1-Tetradecyne | $C_{14}H_{26}$ | 246.38 | 247.51 | 64.89 | 64.91 | 0.3339 | 0.3340 | 1.0452 | 1.0449 | 105. | 105. |
| 1-Pentadecyne | $C_{15}H_{28}$ | 262.82 | 264.00 | 69.53 | 69.55 | 0.3337 | 0.3338 | 1.0455 | 1.0452 | 105. | 105. |
| 1-Hexadecyne | $C_{16}H_{30}$ | 279.22 | 280.45 | 74.17 | 74.19 | 0.3335 | 0.3336 | 1.0457 | 1.0454 | 104. | 104. |
| 1-Heptadecyne | $C_{17}H_{32}$ | 295.69[c] | 296.98 | 78.81[c] | 78.83 | 0.3333[c] | 0.3334 | 1.0459[c] | 1.0456 | 104.[c] | 104. |
| 1-Octadecyne | $C_{18}H_{34}$ | 312.11[c] | 313.46[c] | 83.45[c] | 83.48[c] | 0.3332[c] | 0.3333[c] | 1.0461[c] | 1.0458[c] | 104.[c] | 104.[c] |
| 1-Nonadecyne | $C_{19}H_{36}$ | 328.54[c] | 329.96[c] | 88.09[c] | 88.12[c] | 0.3331[c] | 0.3332[c] | 1.0463[c] | 1.0460[c] | 103.[c] | 103.[c] |
| 1-Eicosyne | $C_{20}H_{38}$ | 344.97[c] | 346.44[c] | 92.73[c] | 92.76[c] | 0.3330[c] | 0.3331[c] | 1.0465[c] | 1.0461[c] | 103.[c] | 103.[c] |

[a] See footnote a of Table 1b.     [b] At saturation pressure.     [c] For the undercooled liquid below the normal freezing point.

TABLE 25b (PART 2) – NORMAL ACETYLENES (1-ALKYNES) $C_{21}$ TO $C_{40}$

MOLECULAR VOLUME, MOLECULAR REFRACTION, SPECIFIC REFRACTION, REFRACTIVITY INTERCEPT, AND SPECIFIC DISPERSION

September 30, 1951

| Compound | Formula | Molecular Volume[a] $V=M/d$ (ml/mole) | | Molecular Refraction[a] $V(n_D^2-1)/(n_D^2+2)$ (ml/mole) | | Specific Refraction[a] $(1/d)(n_D^2-1)/(n_D^2+2)$ (ml/g) | | Refractivity Intercept[a] $n_D - d/2$ | | Specific Dispersion[a] $10^4(n_F-n_C)/d$ (ml/g) | |
|---|---|---|---|---|---|---|---|---|---|---|---|
| | | 20°C | 25°C | 20°C | 25°C | 20°C | 25°C | 20°C | 25°C | 20°C | 25°C |
| 1-Heneicosyne | $C_{21}H_{40}$ | 361.40[b] | 362.93[b] | 97.37[b] | 97.40[b] | 0.3329[b] | 0.3330[b] | 1.0466[b] | 1.0463[b] | 103.[b] | 103.[b] |
| 1-Docosyne | $C_{22}H_{42}$ | 377.83[b] | 379.41[b] | 102.01[b] | 102.04[b] | 0.3328[b] | 0.3329[b] | 1.0468[b] | 1.0464[b] | 103.[b] | 103.[b] |
| 1-Tricosyne | $C_{23}H_{44}$ | 394.26[b] | 395.90[b] | 106.65[b] | 106.68[b] | 0.3327[b] | 0.3328[b] | 1.0469[b] | 1.0465[b] | 103.[b] | 102.[b] |
| 1-Tetracosyne | $C_{24}H_{46}$ | 410.68[b] | 412.39[b] | 111.29[b] | 111.32[b] | 0.3326[b] | 0.3327[b] | 1.0470[b] | 1.0467[b] | 103.[b] | 102.[b] |
| 1-Pentacosyne | $C_{25}H_{48}$ | 427.11[b] | 428.87[b] | 115.93[b] | 115.97[b] | 0.3325[b] | 0.3326[b] | 1.0471[b] | 1.0468[b] | 102.[b] | 102.[b] |
| 1-Hexacosyne | $C_{26}H_{50}$ | 443.53[b] | 445.36[b] | 120.57[b] | 120.61[b] | 0.3325[b] | 0.3326[b] | 1.0472[b] | 1.0469[b] | 102.[b] | 102.[b] |
| 1-Heptacosyne | $C_{27}H_{52}$ | 459.95[b] | 461.84[b] | 125.21[b] | 125.25[b] | 0.3324[b] | 0.3325[b] | 1.0473[b] | 1.0470[b] | 102.[b] | 102.[b] |
| 1-Octacosyne | $C_{28}H_{54}$ | 476.37[b] | 478.32[b] | 129.85[b] | 129.89[b] | 0.3324[b] | 0.3325[b] | 1.0474[b] | 1.0470[b] | 102.[b] | 102.[b] |
| 1-Nonacosyne | $C_{29}H_{56}$ | 492.80[b] | 494.81[b] | 134.49[b] | 134.53[b] | 0.3323[b] | 0.3324[b] | 1.0475[b] | 1.0471[b] | 102.[b] | 101.[b] |
| 1-Triacontyne | $C_{30}H_{58}$ | 509.2[b] | 511.3[b] | 139.14[b] | 139.17[b] | 0.3323[b] | 0.3323[b] | 1.0476[b] | 1.0472[b] | 101.[b] | 101.[b] |
| 1-Hentriacontyne | $C_{31}H_{60}$ | 525.6[b] | 527.8[b] | 143.78[b] | 143.82[b] | 0.3322[b] | 0.3323[b] | 1.0476[b] | 1.0473[b] | 101.[b] | 101.[b] |
| 1-Dotriacontyne | $C_{32}H_{62}$ | 542.1[b] | 544.3[b] | 148.42[b] | 148.46[b] | 0.3322[b] | 0.3323[b] | 1.0477[b] | 1.0473[b] | 101.[b] | 101.[b] |
| 1-Tritriacontyne | $C_{33}H_{64}$ | 558.5[b] | 560.7[b] | 153.06[b] | 153.10[b] | 0.3321[b] | 0.3322[b] | 1.0477[b] | 1.0474[b] | 101.[b] | 101.[b] |
| 1-Tetratriacontyne | $C_{34}H_{66}$ | 574.9[b] | 577.2[b] | 157.70[b] | 157.74[b] | 0.3321[b] | 0.3322[b] | 1.0478[b] | 1.0475[b] | 101.[b] | 101.[b] |
| 1-Pentatriacontyne | $C_{35}H_{68}$ | 591.3[b] | 593.7[b] | 162.34[b] | 162.38[b] | 0.3321[b] | 0.3321[b] | 1.0479[b] | 1.0475[b] | 101.[b] | 101.[b] |
| 1-Hexatriacontyne | $C_{36}H_{70}$ | 607.8[b] | 610.2[b] | 166.98[b] | 167.02[b] | 0.3320[b] | 0.3321[b] | 1.0479[b] | 1.0476[b] | 101.[b] | 101.[b] |
| 1-Heptatriacontyne | $C_{37}H_{72}$ | 624.2[b] | 626.7[b] | 171.62[b] | 171.66[b] | 0.3320[b] | 0.3321[b] | 1.0480[b] | 1.0476[b] | 101.[b] | 101.[b] |
| 1-Octatriacontyne | $C_{38}H_{74}$ | 640.6[b] | 643.2[b] | 176.26[b] | 176.31[b] | 0.3320[b] | 0.3320[b] | 1.0480[b] | 1.0477[b] | 101.[b] | 101.[b] |
| 1-Nonatriacontyne | $C_{39}H_{76}$ | 657.0[b] | 659.6[b] | 180.90[b] | 180.95[b] | 0.3319[b] | 0.3320[b] | 1.0461[b] | 1.0477[b] | 101.[b] | 101.[b] |
| 1-Tetracontyne | $C_{40}H_{78}$ | 673.4[b] | 676.1[b] | 185.54[b] | 185.59[b] | 0.3319[b] | 0.3320[b] | 1.0481[b] | 1.0478[b] | 101.[b] | 101.[b] |

[a] See footnote a of Table 1b.

[b] For the undercooled liquid below the normal freezing point.

TABLE 12b – ACETYLENES, $C_2$ TO $C_5$

MOLECULAR VOLUME, MOLECULAR REFRACTION, SPECIFIC REFRACTION, REFRACTIVITY INTERCEPT, AND SPECIFIC DISPERSION

June 30, 1945; October 31, 1950; October 31, 1952

| Compound | Formula | Molecular Volume[a] $V=W/d$ ml/mole | | Molecular Refraction[a] $V(n_D^2-1)/(n_D^2+2)$ ml/mole | | Specific Refraction[a] $(1/d)(n_D^2-1)/(n_D^2+2)$ ml/g | | Refractivity Intercept[a] $n_D-d/2$ | | Specific Dispersion[a] $10^4(n_F-n_C)/d$ ml/g | |
|---|---|---|---|---|---|---|---|---|---|---|---|
| | | 20°C | 25°C | 20°C | 25°C | 20°C | 25°C | 20°C | 25°C | 20°C | 25°C |
| Ethyne (Acetylene) | $C_2H_2$ | — | — | — | — | — | — | — | — | — | — |
| Propyne (Methylacetylene) | $C_3H_4$ | — | — | — | — | — | — | — | — | — | — |
| 1-Butyne (Ethylacetylene) | $C_4H_6$ | 83.[b] | 83.[b] | — | — | — | — | — | — | — | — |
| 2-Butyne (Dimethylacetylene) | " | 78.27 | 78.89 | 18.64 | 18.67 | 0.3447 | 0.3452 | 1.0466 | 1.0465 | | |
| 1-Pentyne | $C_5H_8$ | 98.70 | 99.45 | 23.14 | 23.18 | 0.3397 | 0.3403 | 1.0402 | 1.0402 | 119. | 119. |
| 2-Pentyne | " | 95.84 | 96.55 | 23.43 | 23.45 | 0.3440 | 0.3443 | 1.0485 | 1.0481 | | |
| 3-Methyl-1-butyne | " | 102.3 | 103.2 | 23.3 | 23.3 | 0.342 | 0.342 | 1.039 | 1.040 | | |

[a] See footnote a of Table 1b.   [b] At saturation pressure.

TABLE 21b (PART 1) — NORMAL ALKYL BENZENES, $C_6$ TO $C_{22}$

MOLECULAR VOLUME, MOLECULAR REFRACTION, SPECIFIC REFRACTION, REFRACTIVITY INTERCEPT, AND SPECIFIC DISPERSION

June 30, 1948; September 30, 1951

| Compound | Formula[a] | Molecular Volume[a] $V=M/d$ ml/mole | | Molecular Refraction[a] $V(n_D^2-1)/(n_D^2+2)$ ml/mole | | Specific Refraction[a] $(1/d)(n_D^2-1)/(n_D^2+2)$ ml/g | | Refractivity Intercept[a] $n_D - d/2$ | | Specific Dispersion[a] $10^4(n_F-n_C)/d$ ml/g | |
|---|---|---|---|---|---|---|---|---|---|---|---|
| | | 20°C | 25°C | 20°C | 25°C | 20°C | 25°C | 20°C | 25°C | 20°C | 25°C |
| Benzene | $C_6H_6$ | 88.860 | 89.399 | 26.185 | 26.201 | 0.33524 | 0.33545 | 1.06162 | 1.06107 | 189.9 | 189.6 |
| Methylbenzene (Toluene) | $C_7H_8$ | 106.275 | 106.847 | 31.095 | 31.113 | 0.33749 | 0.33769 | 1.06346 | 1.06299 | 185.0 | 184.7 |
| Ethylbenzene | $C_8H_{10}$ | 122.442 | 123.064 | 35.761 | 35.777 | 0.33686 | 0.33701 | 1.06237 | 1.06188 | 175.0 | 174.7 |
| n-Propylbenzene | $C_9H_{12}$ | 139.420 | 140.110 | 40.450 | 40.474 | 0.33656 | 0.33676 | 1.06100 | 1.06061 | 166.7 | 166.4 |
| n-Butylbenzene | $C_{10}H_{14}$ | 156.037 | 156.777 | 45.096 | 45.124 | 0.33601 | 0.33621 | 1.05972 | 1.05938 | 159.6 | 159.3 |
| n-Pentylbenzene | $C_{11}H_{16}$ | 172.66 | 173.45 | 49.73 | 49.76 | 0.3355 | 0.3357 | 1.0585 | 1.0582 | 154. | 154. |
| n-Hexylbenzene | $C_{12}H_{18}$ | 189.23 | 190.08 | 54.37 | 54.40 | 0.3351 | 0.3353 | 1.0577 | 1.0574 | 149. | 149. |
| n-Heptylbenzene | $C_{13}H_{20}$ | 205.77 | 206.67 | 59.01 | 59.04 | 0.3347 | 0.3349 | 1.0570 | 1.0567 | 145. | 145. |
| n-Octylbenzene | $C_{14}H_{22}$ | 222.28 | 223.24 | 63.65 | 63.68 | 0.3344 | 0.3346 | 1.0564 | 1.0561 | 142. | 142. |
| n-Nonylbenzene | $C_{15}H_{24}$ | 238.77 | 239.79 | 68.29 | 68.32 | 0.3342 | 0.3344 | 1.0559 | 1.0556 | 139. | 139. |
| n-Decylbenzene | $C_{16}H_{26}$ | 255.243 | 256.334 | 72.920 | 72.964 | 0.33393 | 0.33413 | 1.05542 | 1.05518 | 136.9 | 136.6 |
| n-Undecylbenzene | $C_{17}H_{28}$ | 271.71 | 272.85 | 77.57 | 77.61 | 0.3338 | 0.3339 | 1.0552 | 1.0548 | 134. | 134. |
| n-Dodecylbenzene | $C_{18}H_{30}$ | 288.17 | 289.37 | 82.21 | 82.25 | 0.3336 | 0.3338 | 1.0549 | 1.0545 | 132. | 132. |
| n-Tridecylbenzene | $C_{19}H_{32}$ | 304.62 | 305.88 | 86.85 | 86.89 | 0.3335 | 0.3336 | 1.0546 | 1.0542 | 130. | 130. |
| n-Tetradecylbenzene | $C_{20}H_{34}$ | 321.07 | 322.39 | 91.49 | 91.53 | 0.3333 | 0.3335 | 1.0543 | 1.0540 | 129. | 129. |
| n-Pentadecylbenzene | $C_{21}H_{36}$ | 337.51[b] | 338.90 | 96.13[b] | 96.17 | 0.3332[b] | 0.3334 | 1.0541[b] | 1.0538 | 127.[b] | 127. |
| n-Hexadecylbenzene | $C_{22}H_{38}$ | 353.95[b] | 355.40[b] | 100.77[b] | 100.81[b] | 0.3331[b] | 0.3332[b] | 1.0539[b] | 1.0536[b] | 126.[b] | 126.[b] |

[a] See footnote a of Table 1b.

[b] For the undercooled liquid below the normal freezing point.

TABLE 21b (PART 2) – NORMAL ALKYL BENZENES $C_{23}$ TO $C_{42}$

MOLECULAR VOLUME, MOLECULAR REFRACTION, SPECIFIC REFRACTION, REFRACTIVITY INTERCEPT, AND SPECIFIC DISPERSION

September 30, 1951

| Compound | Formula | Molecular Volume[a] $V = M/d$ (ml/mole) | | Molecular Refraction[a] $V(n_D^2-1)/(n_D^2+2)$ (ml/mole) | | Specific Refraction[a] $(1/d)(n_D^2-1)/(n_D^2+2)$ (ml/g) | | Refractivity Intercept[a] $n_D - d/2$ | | Specific Dispersion[a] $10^4\,(n_F-n_C)/d$ (ml/g) | |
|---|---|---|---|---|---|---|---|---|---|---|---|
| | | 20°C | 25°C | 20°C | 25°C | 20°C | 25°C | 20°C | 25°C | 20°C | 25°C |
| n-Heptadecylbenzene | $C_{23}H_{40}$ | 370.39[b] | 371.90[b] | 105.42[b] | 105.46[b] | 0.3330[b] | 0.3331[b] | 1.0537[b] | 1.0534[b] | 125.[b] | 125.[b] |
| n-Octadecylbenzene | $C_{24}H_{42}$ | 386.82[b] | 388.39[b] | 110.06[b] | 110.10[b] | 0.3329[b] | 0.3330[b] | 1.0535[b] | 1.0532[b] | 124.[b] | 124.[b] |
| n-Nonadecylbenzene | $C_{25}H_{44}$ | 403.26[b] | 404.89[b] | 114.70[b] | 114.74[b] | 0.3328[b] | 0.3330[b] | 1.0534[b] | 1.0531[b] | 123.[b] | 123.[b] |
| n-Eicosylbenzene | $C_{26}H_{46}$ | 419.69[b] | 421.38[b] | 119.34[b] | 119.38[b] | 0.3328[b] | 0.3329[b] | 1.0533[b] | 1.0529[b] | 122.[b] | 122.[b] |
| n-Heneicosylbenzene | $C_{27}H_{48}$ | 436.12[b] | 437.88[b] | 123.98[b] | 124.02[b] | 0.3327[b] | 0.3328[b] | 1.0532[b] | 1.0528[b] | 121.[b] | 121.[b] |
| n-Docosylbenzene | $C_{28}H_{50}$ | 452.55[b] | 454.37[b] | 128.62[b] | 128.66[b] | 0.3326[b] | 0.3327[b] | 1.0531[b] | 1.0527[b] | 120.[b] | 120.[b] |
| n-Tricosylbenzene | $C_{29}H_{52}$ | 468.98[b] | 470.86[b] | 133.26[b] | 133.31[b] | 0.3326[b] | 0.3327[b] | 1.0530[b] | 1.0526[b] | 119.[b] | 119.[b] |
| n-Tetracosylbenzene | $C_{30}H_{54}$ | 485.41[b] | 487.35[b] | 137.90[b] | 137.95[b] | 0.3325[b] | 0.3326[b] | 1.0529[b] | 1.0525[b] | 118.[b] | 118.[b] |
| n-Pentacosylbenzene | $C_{31}H_{56}$ | 501.8[b] | 503.8[b] | 142.54[b] | 142.59[b] | 0.3324[b] | 0.3326[b] | 1.0527[b] | 1.0524[b] | 118.[b] | 118.[b] |
| n-Hexacosylbenzene | $C_{32}H_{58}$ | 518.3[b] | 520.3[b] | 147.18[b] | 147.23[b] | 0.3324[b] | 0.3325[b] | 1.0526[b] | 1.0523[b] | 117.[b] | 117.[b] |
| n-Heptacosylbenzene | $C_{33}H_{60}$ | 534.7[b] | 536.8[b] | 151.82[b] | 151.87[b] | 0.3324[b] | 0.3325[b] | 1.0526[b] | 1.0522[b] | 117.[b] | 117.[b] |
| n-Octacosylbenzene | $C_{34}H_{62}$ | 551.1[b] | 553.3[b] | 156.46[b] | 156.51[b] | 0.3323[b] | 0.3324[b] | 1.0524[b] | 1.0521[b] | 116.[b] | 116.[b] |
| n-Nonacosylbenzene | $C_{35}H_{64}$ | 567.5[b] | 569.8[b] | 161.10[b] | 161.15[b] | 0.3323[b] | 0.3323[b] | 1.0524[b] | 1.0521[b] | 116.[b] | 116.[b] |
| n-Triacontylbenzene | $C_{36}H_{66}$ | 584.0[b] | 586.3[b] | 165.74[b] | 165.80[b] | 0.3322[b] | 0.3323[b] | 1.0523[b] | 1.0520[b] | 115.[b] | 115.[b] |
| n-Hentriacontylbenzene | $C_{37}H_{68}$ | 600.4[b] | 602.8[b] | 170.38[b] | 170.44[b] | 0.3322[b] | 0.3323[b] | 1.0523[b] | 1.0519[b] | 115.[b] | 115.[b] |
| n-Dotriacontylbenzene | $C_{38}H_{70}$ | 616.8[b] | 619.2[b] | 175.02[b] | 175.08[b] | 0.3322[b] | 0.3323[b] | 1.0522[b] | 1.0519[b] | 114.[b] | 114.[b] |
| n-Tritriacontylbenzene | $C_{39}H_{72}$ | 633.2[b] | 635.7[b] | 179.66[b] | 179.72[b] | 0.3321[b] | 0.3322[b] | 1.0522[b] | 1.0518[b] | 114.[b] | 114.[b] |
| n-Tetratriacontylbenzene | $C_{40}H_{74}$ | 649.7[b] | 652.2[b] | 184.30[b] | 184.36[b] | 0.3321[b] | 0.3322[b] | 1.0521[b] | 1.0518[b] | 113.[b] | 113.[b] |
| n-Pentatriacontylbenzene | $C_{41}H_{76}$ | 666.1[b] | 668.7[b] | 188.95[b] | 189.00[b] | 0.3321[b] | 0.3322[b] | 1.0521[b] | 1.0517[b] | 113.[b] | 113.[b] |
| n-Hexatriacontylbenzene | $C_{42}H_{78}$ | 682.5[b] | 685.2[b] | 193.59[b] | 193.65[b] | 0.3320[b] | 0.3321[b] | 1.0520[b] | 1.0517[b] | 113.[b] | 113.[b] |

[a] See footnote a of Table 1b.     [b] For the undercooled liquid below the normal freezing point.

TABLE 5b – ALKYL BENZENES, $C_6$ TO $C_9$

MOLECULAR VOLUME, MOLECULAR REFRACTION, SPECIFIC REFRACTION, REFRACTIVITY INTERCEPT, AND SPECIFIC DISPERSION

June 30, 1945; May 31, 1947; October 31, 1950

| Compound | Formula[a] | Molecular Volume[a] $V = M/d$ (ml/mole) | | Molecular Refraction[a] $V(n_D^2-1)/(n_D^2+2)$ (ml/mole) | | Specific Refraction[a] $(1/d)(n_D^2-1)/(n_D^2+2)$ (ml/g) | | Refractivity Intercept[a] $n_D - d/2$ | | Specific Dispersion[a] $10^4(n_F-n_C)/d$ (ml/g) | |
|---|---|---|---|---|---|---|---|---|---|---|---|
| | | 20°C | 25°C | 20°C | 25°C | 20°C | 25°C | 20°C | 25°C | 20°C | 25°C |
| Benzene | $C_6H_6$ | 88.859 | 89.399 | 26.185 | 26.201 | 0.33524 | 0.33545 | 1.06162 | 1.06107 | 189.9 | 189.6 |
| Methylbenzene (Toluene) | $C_7H_8$ | 106.275 | 106.847 | 31.095 | 31.113 | 0.33749 | 0.33769 | 1.06346 | 1.06299 | 185.0 | 184.7 |
| Ethylbenzene | $C_8H_{10}$ | 122.442 | 123.064 | 35.761 | 35.777 | 0.33686 | 0.33701 | 1.06237 | 1.06188 | 175.0 | 174.7 |
| 1,2-Dimethylbenzene (o-Xylene) | " | 120.609 | 121.193 | 35.800 | 35.823 | 0.33723 | 0.33744 | 1.06535 | 1.06497 | 180.4 | 180.1 |
| 1,3-Dimethylbenzene (m-Xylene) | " | 122.846 | 123.456 | 35.961 | 35.980 | 0.33874 | 0.33892 | 1.06514 | 1.06469 | 180.9 | 180.6 |
| 1,4-Dimethylbenzene (p-Xylene) | " | 123.291 | 123.919 | 36.005 | 36.029 | 0.33916 | 0.33938 | 1.06530 | 1.06490 | 182.4 | 182.1 |
| n-Propylbenzene | $C_9H_{12}$ | 139.420 | 140.110 | 40.450 | 40.474 | 0.33656 | 0.33676 | 1.06100 | 1.06061 | 166.7 | 166.4 |
| Isopropylbenzene | " | 139.461 | 140.157 | 40.422 | 40.444 | 0.33633 | 0.33651 | 1.06055 | 1.06020 | 165.7 | 165.4 |
| 1-Methyl-2-ethylbenzene | " | 136.468 | 137.109 | 40.447 | 40.468 | 0.33654 | 0.33671 | 1.06422 | 1.06380 | 172.4 | 172.1 |
| 1-Methyl-3-ethylbenzene | " | 139.020 | 139.685 | 40.652 | 40.670 | 0.33825 | 0.33839 | 1.06434 | 1.06386 | 173.4 | 173.1 |
| 1-Methyl-4-ethylbenzene | " | 139.560 | 140.237 | 40.699 | 40.716 | 0.33863 | 0.33878 | 1.06440 | 1.06393 | 173.9 | 173.6 |
| 1,2,3-Trimethylbenzene | " | 134.379 | 134.974 | 40.451 | 40.468 | 0.33657 | 0.33671 | 1.06674 | 1.06623 | 176.0 | 175.7 |
| 1,2,4-Trimethylbenzene | " | 137.227 | 137.860 | 40.691 | 40.710 | 0.33857 | 0.33872 | 1.06693 | 1.06647 | 178.2 | 177.9 |
| 1,3,5-Trimethylbenzene | " | 138.914 | 139.571 | 40.813 | 40.830 | 0.33959 | 0.33973 | 1.06678 | 1.06628 | 177.8 | 177.5 |

a See footnote a of Table 1b.

## TABLE 14b – ALKYL BENZENES, $C_{10}$

### MOLECULAR VOLUME, MOLECULAR REFRACTION, SPECIFIC REFRACTION, REFRACTIVITY INTERCEPT, AND SPECIFIC DISPERSION

January 31, 1946; May 31, 1947; April 30, 1952

| Compound | Formula[a] | Molecular Volume[a] $V=M/d$ (ml/mole) | | Molecular Refraction[a] $V(n_D^2-1)/(n_D^2+2)$ (ml/mole) | | Specific Refraction[a] $(1/d)(n_D^2-1)/(n_D^2+2)$ (ml/g) | | Refractivity Intercept[a] $n_D-d/2$ | | Specific Dispersion[a] $10^4(n_F-n_C)/d$ (ml/g) | |
|---|---|---|---|---|---|---|---|---|---|---|---|
| | | 20°C | 25°C | 20°C | 25°C | 20°C | 25°C | 20°C | 25°C | 20°C | 25°C |
| n-Butylbenzene (1-Phenylbutane) | $C_{10}H_{14}$ | 156.037 | 156.777 | 45.096 | 45.124 | 0.33601 | 0.33621 | 1.05972 | 1.05938 | 159.6 | 159.3 |
| Isobutylbenzene (1-Phenyl-2-methylpropane) | " | 157.302 | 158.069 | 45.198 | 45.223 | 0.33677 | 0.33695 | 1.05986 | 1.05946 | 160.8 | 160.5 |
| sec-Butylbenzene (2-Phenylbutane) | " | 155.686 | 156.430 | 45.027 | 45.053 | 0.33549 | 0.33569 | 1.05916 | 1.05880 | 159.0 | 158.7 |
| tert-Butylbenzene (2-Phenyl-2-methylpropane) | " | 154.890 | 155.626 | 44.988 | 45.013 | 0.33520 | 0.33539 | 1.05941 | 1.05904 | 159.3 | 159.0 |
| 1-Methyl-2-propylbenzene | " | 153.49 | 154.18 | 45.13 | 45.15 | 0.3362 | 0.3364 | 1.0626 | 1.0622 | 166. | 166. |
| 1-Methyl-3-propylbenzene | " | 155.88 | 156.61 | 45.35 | 45.37 | 0.3379 | 0.3381 | 1.0631 | 1.0627 | 166. | 166. |
| 1-Methyl-4-propylbenzene | " | 156.35 | 157.08 | 45.34 | 45.37 | 0.3379 | 0.3380 | 1.0627 | 1.0623 | 166. | 166. |
| 1-Methyl-2-isopropylbenzene (o-Cymene) | " | 153.10 | 153.81 | 45.08 | 45.10 | 0.3359 | 0.3360 | 1.0623 | 1.0619 | 166. | 166. |
| 1-Methyl-3-isopropylbenzene (m-Cymene) | " | 155.88 | 156.61 | 45.30 | 45.32 | 0.3375 | 0.3377 | 1.0625 | 1.0621 | 166. | 166. |
| 1-Methyl-4-isopropylbenzene (p-Cymene) | " | 156.55 | 157.29 | 45.33 | 45.36 | 0.3378 | 0.3379 | 1.0623 | 1.0619 | 166. | 166. |
| 1,2-Diethylbenzene | " | 152.521 | 153.224 | 45.122 | 45.147 | 0.33620 | 0.33638 | 1.06348 | 1.06310 | 166.2 | 165.9 |
| 1,3-Diethylbenzene | " | 155.349 | 156.073 | 45.344 | 45.366 | 0.33785 | 0.33802 | 1.06355 | 1.06314 | 166.9 | 166.6 |
| 1,4-Diethylbenzene | " | 155.706 | 156.435 | 45.394 | 45.420 | 0.33823 | 0.33842 | 1.06385 | 1.06348 | 168.2 | 167.9 |
| 1,2-Dimethyl-3-ethylbenzene | " | 150.44 | 151.12 | 45.12 | 45.16 | 0.3362 | 0.3365 | 1.0656 | 1.0654 | 170. | 170. |
| 1,2-Dimethyl-4-ethylbenzene | " | 153.47 | 154.16 | 45.38 | 45.41 | 0.3381 | 0.3383 | 1.0658 | 1.0656 | 171. | 171. |
| 1,3-Dimethyl-2-ethylbenzene | " | 150.73 | 151.41 | 45.13 | 45.17 | 0.3363 | 0.3366 | 1.0655 | 1.0653 | 170. | 170. |
| 1,3-Dimethyl-4-ethylbenzene | " | 153.16 | 153.86 | 45.34 | 45.38 | 0.3378 | 0.3381 | 1.0656 | 1.0654 | 171. | 171. |
| 1,3-Dimethyl-5-ethylbenzene | " | 155.19 | 155.92 | 45.50 | 45.53 | 0.3390 | 0.3392 | 1.0657 | 1.0654 | 172. | 172. |
| 1,4-Dimethyl-2-ethylbenzene | " | 153.00 | 153.70 | 45.33 | 45.36 | 0.3377 | 0.3380 | 1.0657 | 1.0654 | 171. | 171. |
| 1,2,3,4-Tetramethylbenzene (Prehnitene) | " | 148.27 | 148.88 | 45.10 | 45.12 | 0.3360 | 0.3362 | 1.0677 | 1.0674 | 174. | 174. |
| 1,2,3,5-Tetramethylbenzene (Isodurene) | " | 150.75 | 151.40 | 45.31 | 45.33 | 0.3376 | 0.3378 | 1.0678 | 1.0675 | 174. | 174. |
| 1,2,4,5-Tetramethylbenzene (Durene) | " | 151.22[b] | 151.88[b] | 45.35[b] | 45.37[b] | 0.3379[b] | 0.3381[b] | 1.0678[b] | 1.0674[b] | 174.[b] | 174.[b] |

a See footnote a of Table 1b.   b For the undercooled liquid below the normal freezing point.

TABLE 26b, Page 1 - ALKYL BENZENES, $C_{11}$

MOLECULAR VOLUME, MOLECULAR REFRACTION, SPECIFIC REFRACTION, REFRACTIVITY INTERCEPT, AND SPECIFIC DISPERSION

April 30, 1952

| Compound | Formula | Molecular Volume[a] $V = M/d$ (ml/mole) | | Molecular Refraction[a] $V(n_D^2-1)/(n_D^2+2)$ (ml/mole) | | Specific Refraction[a] $(1/d)(n_D^2-1)/(n_D^2+2)$ (ml/g) | | Refractivity Intercept[a] $n_D - d/2$ | | Specific Dispersion[a] $10^4(n_F-n_C)/d$ (ml/g) | |
|---|---|---|---|---|---|---|---|---|---|---|---|
| | | 20°C | 25°C | 20°C | 25°C | 20°C | 25°C | 20°C | 25°C | 20°C | 25°C |
| n-Pentylbenzene | $C_{11}H_{16}$ | 172.66 | 173.45 | 49.73 | 49.76 | 0.3355 | 0.3357 | 1.0585 | 1.0582 | 154. | 154. |
| 2-Phenylpentane | " | 172.66 | 173.45 | 49.71 | 49.71 | 0.3354 | 0.3355 | 1.0584 | 1.0580 | 151. | 151. |
| 3-Phenylpentane | " | 172.4 | 173.2 | 49.6 | 49.7 | 0.335 | 0.335 | 1.0577 | 1.0574 | 149. | 149. |
| 1-Phenyl-2-methylbutane | " | 172.6 | 173.4 | 49.6 | 49.6 | 0.334 | 0.335 | 1.056 | 1.056 | 153. | 153. |
| 1-Phenyl-3-methylbutane | " | 173.2 | 174.0 | 49.6 | 49.6 | 0.334 | 0.335 | 1.056 | 1.056 | | |
| 2-Phenyl-2-methylbutane | " | 169.45 | 170.21 | 49.48 | 49.51 | 0.3338 | 0.3340 | 1.0584 | 1.0580 | 151. | 151. |
| 2-Phenyl-3-methylbutane | " | 170.4 | 171.2 | 48.9 | 49.0 | 0.330 | 0.330 | 1.051 | 1.051 | 152. | 152. |
| 1-Phenyl-2,2-dimethylpropane | " | 172.8 | 173.6 | 49.8 | 49.8 | 0.336 | 0.336 | 1.055 | 1.059 | | |
| 1-Methyl-2-n-butylbenzene | " | 170.2 | 171.0 | 49.7 | 49.8 | 0.335 | 0.336 | 1.060 | 1.060 | | |
| 1-Methyl-3-n-butylbenzene | " | 172.6 | 173.4 | 50.0 | 50.0 | 0.337 | 0.338 | 1.062 | 1.062 | | |
| 1-Methyl-4-n-butylbenzene | " | 173.0 | 173.8 | 50.0 | 50.1 | 0.337 | 0.338 | 1.062 | 1.062 | | |
| 1-Methyl-2-sec-butylbenzene | " | 169.9 | 170.6 | 49.7 | 49.8 | 0.335 | 0.336 | 1.060 | 1.060 | 160. | 160. |
| 1-Methyl-3-sec-butylbenzene | " | 172.7 | 173.5 | 50.0 | 50.0 | 0.337 | 0.337 | 1.062 | 1.061 | 161. | 161. |
| 1-Methyl-4-sec-butylbenzene | " | 171.2 | 172.0 | 49.8 | 49.8 | 0.336 | 0.336 | 1.060 | 1.060 | 158. | 158. |
| 1-Methyl-2-isobutylbenzene | " | 171.39 | 172.17 | 49.85 | 49.88 | 0.3363 | 0.3365 | 1.0610 | 1.0607 | 162. | 162. |
| 1-Methyl-3-isobutylbenzene | " | 173.66 | 174.46 | 50.10 | 50.13 | 0.3380 | 0.3382 | 1.0620 | 1.0616 | 163. | 163. |
| 1-Methyl-4-isobutylbenzene | " | 174.05 | 174.85 | 50.09 | 50.12 | 0.3379 | 0.3381 | 1.0616 | 1.0612 | | |
| 1-Methyl-2-tert-butylbenzene | " | 166.62 | 167.35 | 49.63 | 49.66 | 0.3348 | 0.3350 | 1.0628 | 1.0624 | | |
| 1-Methyl-3-tert-butylbenzene | " | 171.24 | 172.01 | 49.88 | 49.91 | 0.3365 | 0.3367 | 1.0616 | 1.0612 | | |
| 1-Methyl-4-tert-butylbenzene | " | 172.13 | 172.91 | 49.92 | 49.95 | 0.3368 | 0.3370 | 1.0612 | 1.0608 | 170. | 170. |
| 1-Ethyl-2-n-propylbenzene | " | 169.53 | 170.29 | 49.79 | 49.82 | 0.3359 | 0.3361 | 1.0620 | 1.0616 | | |
| 1-Ethyl-3-n-propylbenzene | " | 172.23 | 173.02 | 50.05 | 50.08 | 0.3377 | 0.3378 | 1.0626 | 1.0623 | | |
| 1-Ethyl-4-n-propylbenzene | " | 172.49 | 173.28 | 50.05 | 50.08 | 0.3376 | 0.3378 | 1.0624 | 1.0620 | | |
| 1-Ethyl-2-isopropylbenzene | " | 167.0 | 167.7 | 49.8 | 49.8 | 0.336 | 0.336 | 1.064 | 1.064 | 160. | 160. |
| 1-Ethyl-3-isopropylbenzene | " | 172.5 | 173.3 | 50.1 | 50.1 | 0.338 | 0.338 | 1.062 | 1.062 | 161. | 161. |
| 1-Ethyl-4-isopropylbenzene | " | 172.67 | 173.46 | 50.12 | 50.15 | 0.3381 | 0.3383 | 1.0630 | 1.0627 | 163. | 163. |

a See footnote a of Table 1b.

TABLE 26b, Page 2 - ALKYL BENZENES, $C_{11}$

MOLECULAR VOLUME, MOLECULAR REFRACTION, SPECIFIC REFRACTION, REFRACTIVITY INTERCEPT, AND SPECIFIC DISPERSION

April 30, 1952

| Compound | Formula | Molecular Volume[a] $V = M/d$ ml/mole | | Molecular Refraction[a] $V(n_D^2-1)/(n_D^2+2)$ ml/mole | | Specific Refraction[a] $(1/d)(n_D^2-1)/(n_D^2+2)$ ml/g | | Refractivity Intercept[a] $n_D - d/2$ | | Specific Dispersion[a] $10^4(n_F-n_C)/d$ ml/g | |
|---|---|---|---|---|---|---|---|---|---|---|---|
| | | 20°C | 25°C | 20°C | 25°C | 20°C | 25°C | 20°C | 25°C | 20°C | 25°C |
| 1,2-Dimethyl-3-$n$-propylbenzene | $C_{11}H_{16}$ | 167.24 | 167.98 | 49.81 | 49.85 | 0.3360 | 0.3363 | 1.0643 | 1.0640 | 166. | 166. |
| 1,2-Dimethyl-4-$n$-propylbenzene | " | 170.10 | 170.86 | 50.03 | 50.07 | 0.3375 | 0.3377 | 1.0642 | 1.0640 | 168. | 168. |
| 1,3-Dimethyl-2-$n$-propylbenzene | " | 167.39 | 168.13 | 49.76 | 49.79 | 0.3357 | 0.3359 | 1.0635 | 1.0632 | 166. | 166. |
| 1,3-Dimethyl-4-$n$-propylbenzene | " | 169.94 | 170.70 | 49.97 | 50.00 | 0.3371 | 0.3373 | 1.0637 | 1.0634 | 166. | 166. |
| 1,3-Dimethyl-5-$n$-propylbenzene | " | 172.23 | 173.01 | 50.24 | 50.28 | 0.3389 | 0.3392 | 1.0648 | 1.0646 | 168. | 168. |
| 1,4-Dimethyl-2-$n$-propylbenzene | " | 170.13 | 170.82 | 50.03 | 50.05 | 0.3375 | 0.3376 | 1.0640 | 1.0638 | 168. | 168. |
| 1,2-Dimethyl-3-isopropylbenzene | " | 166.9 | 167.7 | 49.8 | 49.8 | 0.336 | 0.336 | 1.064 | 1.064 | 166. | 166. |
| 1,2-Dimethyl-4-isopropylbenzene | " | 170.41 | 171.18 | 50.06 | 50.10 | 0.3377 | 0.3380 | 1.0644 | 1.0641 | 167. | 167. |
| 1,3-Dimethyl-2-isopropylbenzene | " | 166.6 | 167.3 | 49.7 | 49.8 | 0.336 | 0.336 | 1.064 | 1.064 | 165. | 165. |
| 1,3-Dimethyl-4-isopropylbenzene | " | 169.8 | 170.6 | 49.9 | 50.0 | 0.337 | 0.337 | 1.064 | 1.064 | 166. | 166. |
| 1,3-Dimethyl-5-isopropylbenzene | " | 172.0 | 172.8 | 50.2 | 50.2 | 0.338 | 0.338 | 1.064 | 1.064 | 168. | 168. |
| 1,4-Dimethyl-2-isopropylbenzene | " | 169.65 | 170.41 | 49.98 | 50.02 | 0.3372 | 0.3374 | 1.0641 | 1.0638 | 168. | 168. |
| 1-Methyl-2,3-diethylbenzene | " | 166.37 | 167.10 | 49.80 | 49.84 | 0.3359 | 0.3362 | 1.0650 | 1.0648 | 166. | 166. |
| 1-Methyl-2,4-diethylbenzene | " | 169.45 | 170.21 | 50.07 | 50.10 | 0.3377 | 0.3380 | 1.0653 | 1.0651 | 168. | 168. |
| 1-Methyl-2,5-diethylbenzene | " | 169.26 | 170.02 | 50.07 | 50.11 | 0.3378 | 0.3380 | 1.0655 | 1.0652 | 169. | 169. |
| 1-Methyl-2,6-diethylbenzene | " | 166.43 | 167.16 | 49.83 | 49.86 | 0.3361 | 0.3364 | 1.0652 | 1.0650 | 166. | 166. |
| 1-Methyl-3,4-diethylbenzene | " | 169.18 | 169.94 | 50.09 | 50.13 | 0.3379 | 0.3381 | 1.0658 | 1.0656 | 168. | 168. |
| 1-Methyl-3,5-diethylbenzene | " | 171.77 | 172.55 | 50.26 | 50.29 | 0.3390 | 0.3393 | 1.0654 | 1.0652 | 168. | 168. |
| 1,2,3-Trimethyl-4-ethylbenzene | " | 164.36 | 165.08 | 49.81 | 49.85 | 0.3360 | 0.3363 | 1.0670 | 1.0668 | 171. | 171. |
| 1,2,3-Trimethyl-5-ethylbenzene | " | 167.26 | 167.98 | 50.03 | 50.07 | 0.3375 | 0.3377 | 1.0670 | 1.0667 | 172. | 172. |
| 1,2,4-Trimethyl-3-ethylbenzene | " | 165.6 | 166.3 | 49.8 | 49.8 | 0.336 | 0.336 | 1.0658 | 1.0656 | 171. | 171. |
| 1,2,4-Trimethyl-5-ethylbenzene | " | 167.9 | 168.7 | 50.0 | 50.1 | 0.337 | 0.338 | 1.0660 | 1.0658 | 173. | 173. |
| 1,2,4-Trimethyl-6-ethylbenzene | " | 166.62 | 167.35 | 49.98 | 50.01 | 0.3372 | 0.3374 | 1.0670 | 1.0667 | 172. | 172. |
| 1,3,5-Trimethyl-2-ethylbenzene | " | 167.9 | 168.6 | 50.0 | 50.0 | 0.337 | 0.337 | 1.0659 | 1.0657 | 171. | 171. |
| Pentamethylbenzene | " | 161.7[b] | 162.4[b] | 49.8[b] | 49.8[b] | 0.336[b] | 0.336[b] | 1.068[b] | 1.068[b] | 174.[b] | 174.[b] |

[a] See footnote a of Table 1b.

[b] For the undercooled liquid below the normal freezing point.

## TABLE 13b – STYRENES, C$_8$ AND C$_9$
### MOLECULAR VOLUME, MOLECULAR REFRACTION, SPECIFIC REFRACTION, REFRACTIVITY INTERCEPT, AND SPECIFIC DISPERSION
September 30, 1943; June 30, 1945; May 31, 1947; June 30, 1948; October 31, 1952

| Compound | Formula[a] | Molecular Volume[a] $V=M/d$ (ml/mole) | | Molecular Refraction[a] $V(n_D^2-1)/(n_D^2+2)$ (ml/mole) | | Specific Refraction[a] $(1/d)(n_D^2-1)/(n_D^2+2)$ (ml/g) | | Refractivity Intercept[a] $n_D-d/2$ | | Specific Dispersion[a] $10^4(n_F-n_C)/d$ (ml/g) | |
|---|---|---|---|---|---|---|---|---|---|---|---|
| | | 20°C | 25°C | 20°C | 25°C | 20°C | 25°C | 20°C | 25°C | 20°C | 25°C |
| Ethenylbenzene (Styrene; Vinylbenzene; Phenylethylene) | C$_8$H$_8$ | 114.949 | 115.559 | 36.444 | 36.477 | 0.34993 | 0.35026 | 1.09382 | 1.09334 | 265. | 265. |
| Isopropenylbenzene (α-Methyl styrene; 2-Phenyl-1-propene) | C$_9$H$_{10}$ | 129.77 | 130.40 | 40.63 | 40.65 | 0.3438 | 0.3440 | 1.0833 | 1.0827 | 265. | 265. |
| cis-1-Propenylbenzene (cis-β-Methylstyrene; cis-1-Phenyl-1-propene) trans-1-Propenylbenzene (trans-β-Methylstyrene; trans-1-Phenyl-1-propene) | " | 129.7 | 130.3 | 41.3 | 41.3 | 0.349 | 0.349 | 1.094 | 1.093 | 265. | 265. |
| 1-Methyl-2-ethenylbenzene (o-Methyl styrene) | " | 129.77 | 130.43 | 41.03 | 41.06 | 0.3472 | 0.3475 | 1.0897 | 1.0892 | 265. | 265. |
| 1-Methyl-3-ethenylbenzene (m-Methyl styrene) | " | 131.46 | 132.14 | 41.37 | 41.40 | 0.3501 | 0.3504 | 1.0924 | 1.0920 | 265. | 265. |
| 1-Methyl-4-ethenylbenzene (p-Methyl styrene) | " | 131.7 | 132.5 | 41.5 | 41.6 | 0.351 | 0.352 | 1.0943 | 1.0940 | 265. | 265. |

a See footnote a of Table 1b.

TABLE 30b –1– NORMAL ALKYL NAPHTHALENES, $C_{10}$ TO $C_{22}$.

MOLECULAR VOLUME, MOLECULAR REFRACTION, SPECIFIC REFRACTION, REFRACTIVITY INTERCEPT, AND SPECIFIC DISPERSION

October 31, 1952

| Compound | Formula | Molecular Volume[a] $V = M/d$ (ml/mole) | | Molecular Refraction[a] $V(n_D^2-1)/(n_D^2+2)$ (ml/mole) | | Specific Refraction[a] $(1/d)(n_D^2-1)/(n_D^2+2)$ (ml/g) | | Refractivity Intercept[a] $n_D - d/2$ | | Specific Dispersion[a] $10^4(n_F-n_C)/d$ (ml/g) | |
|---|---|---|---|---|---|---|---|---|---|---|---|
| | | 20°C | 25°C | 20°C | 25°C | 20°C | 25°C | 20°C | 25°C | 20°C | 25°C |
| Naphthalene | $C_{10}H_8$ | — | 131.42[b] | — | 44.34[b] | — | 0.3460[b] | — | 1.1022[b] | — | 297.[b] |
| 1-Methylnaphthalene | $C_{11}H_{10}$ | 139.381 | 139.909 | 48.795 | 48.821 | 0.34317 | 0.34335 | 1.1073 | 1.1068 | 295. | 295. |
| 1-Ethylnaphthalene | $C_{12}H_{12}$ | 154.952 | 155.522 | 53.452 | 53.492 | 0.34217 | 0.34242 | 1.1021 | 1.1018 | 285. | 285. |
| 1-n-Propylnaphthalene | $C_{13}H_{14}$ | 171.65 | 172.27 | 58.34 | 58.38 | 0.3427 | 0.3429 | 1.0993 | 1.0989 | 265. | 265. |
| 1-n-Butylnaphthalene | $C_{14}H_{16}$ | 188.658 | 189.335 | 62.953 | 62.993 | 0.34164 | 0.34185 | 1.0935 | 1.0932 | 253. | 253. |
| 1-n-Pentylnaphthalene | $C_{15}H_{18}$ | 205.36 | 206.08 | 67.62 | 67.65 | 0.3410 | 0.3412 | 1.0897 | 1.0893 | 243. | 243. |
| 1-n-Hexylnaphthalene | $C_{16}H_{20}$ | 221.95 | 222.74 | 72.26 | 72.30 | 0.3404 | 0.3405 | 1.0864 | 1.0660 | 234. | 234. |
| 1-n-Heptylnaphthalene | $C_{17}H_{22}$ | 238.47 | 239.32 | 76.90 | 76.94 | 0.3398 | 0.3399 | 1.0836 | 1.0832 | 226. | 226. |
| 1-n-Octylnaphthalene | $C_{18}H_{24}$ | 254.98 | 255.88 | 81.54 | 81.58 | 0.3392 | 0.3394 | 1.0812 | 1.0808 | 219. | 219. |
| 1-n-Nonylnaphthalene | $C_{19}H_{26}$ | 271.46 | 272.40 | 86.19 | 86.20 | 0.3388 | 0.3389 | 1.0792 | 1.0786 | 212. | 212. |
| 1-n-Decylnaphthalene | $C_{20}H_{28}$ | 287.95 | 288.94 | 90.83 | 90.85 | 0.3384 | 0.3385 | 1.0774 | 1.0769 | 207. | 207. |
| 1-n-Undecylnaphthalene | $C_{21}H_{30}$ | 304.40[c] | 305.42 | 95.49[c] | 95.52 | 0.3381[c] | 0.3382 | 1.0760[c] | 1.0755 | 201.[c] | 201. |
| 1-n-Dodecylnaphthalene | $C_{22}H_{32}$ | 320.86[c] | 321.94[c] | 100.11[c] | 100.14[c] | 0.3377[c] | 0.3378[c] | 1.0744[c] | 1.0740[c] | 196.[c] | 196. |

a See footnote a of Table 1b.   b At 85°C.   c For the undercooled liquid below the normal freezing point.

TABLE 31b -2- NORMAL ALKYL NAPHTHALENES, $C_{10}$ TO $C_{22}$

MOLECULAR VOLUME, MOLECULAR REFRACTION, SPECIFIC REFRACTION, REFRACTIVITY INTERCEPT, AND SPECIFIC DISPERSION

October 31, 1952

| Compound | Formula | Molecular Volume[a] $V = M/d$ (ml/mole) | | Molecular Refraction[a] $V(n_D^2-1)/(n_D^2+2)$ (ml/mole) | | Specific Refraction[a] $(1/d)(n_D^2-1)/(n_D^2+2)$ (ml/g) | | Refractivity Intercept[a] $n_D - d/2$ | | Specific Dispersion[a] $10^4(n_F-n_C)/d$ (ml/g) | |
|---|---|---|---|---|---|---|---|---|---|---|---|
| | | 20°C | 25°C | 20°C | 25°C | 20°C | 25°C | 20°C | 25°C | 20°C | 25°C |
| Naphthalene | $C_{10}H_8$ | — | 131.42[b] | — | 44.34[b] | — | 0.3460[b] | — | 1.1022[b] | — | 297.[b] |
| 2-Methylnaphthalene | $C_{11}H_{10}$ | — | 143.57[c] | — | 49.24[c] | — | 0.3463[c] | — | 1.1067[c] | — | 293.[c] |
| 2-Ethylnaphthalene | $C_{12}H_{12}$ | 157.44 | 158.03 | 53.85 | 53.89 | 0.3447 | 0.3450 | 1.1038 | 1.1034 | 285. | 285. |
| 2-n-Propylnaphthalene | $C_{13}H_{14}$ | 174.25 | 174.89 | 58.58 | 58.61 | 0.3441 | 0.3443 | 1.0987 | 1.0983 | 265. | 265. |
| 2-n-Butylnaphthalene | $C_{14}H_{16}$ | 190.77 | 191.47 | 63.27 | 63.32 | 0.3434 | 0.3436 | 1.0946 | 1.0943 | 253. | 253. |
| 2-n-Pentylnaphthalene | $C_{15}H_{18}$ | 207.40 | 208.14 | 67.99 | 68.02 | 0.3429 | 0.3430 | 1.0914 | 1.0910 | 243. | 243. |
| 2-n-Hexylnaphthalene | $C_{16}H_{20}$ | 223.99 | 224.80 | 72.64 | 72.68 | 0.3421 | 0.3423 | 1.0880 | 1.0876 | 234. | 234. |
| 2-n-Heptylnaphthalene | $C_{17}H_{22}$ | 240.54 | 241.38 | 77.27 | 77.30 | 0.3414 | 0.3415 | 1.0851 | 1.0846 | 226. | 226. |
| 2-n-Octylnaphthalene | $C_{18}H_{24}$ | 257.08 | 257.99 | 81.91 | 81.94 | 0.3408 | 0.3409 | 1.0826 | 1.0822 | 219. | 219. |
| 2-n-Nonylnaphthalene | $C_{19}H_{26}$ | 273.61 | 274.55 | 86.56 | 86.58 | 0.3402 | 0.3403 | 1.0805 | 1.0800 | 212. | 212. |
| 2-n-Decylnaphthalene | $C_{20}H_{28}$ | 290.09 | 291.10 | 91.20 | 91.22 | 0.3398 | 0.3398 | 1.0786 | 1.0782 | 207. | 207. |
| 2-n-Undecylnaphthalene | $C_{21}H_{30}$ | 306.58 | 307.61 | 95.83 | 95.86 | 0.3393 | 0.3394 | 1.0770 | 1.0765 | 201. | 201. |
| 2-n-Dodecylnaphthalene | $C_{22}H_{32}$ | 323.06 | 324.16 | 100.47 | 100.50 | 0.3389 | 0.3390 | 1.0754 | 1.0750 | 196. | 196. |

a See footnote a of Table 1b.   b At 85°C.   c At 40°C.

TABLE 27b – NAPHTHALENES, C$_{10}$ TO C$_{12}$

MOLECULAR VOLUME, MOLECULAR REFRACTION, SPECIFIC REFRACTION, REFRACTIVITY INTERCEPT, AND SPECIFIC DISPERSION

February 28, 1949; October 31, 1952

| Compound | Formula[a] | Molecular Volume[a] $V=M/d$ ml/mole | | Molecular Refraction[a] $V(n_D^2-1)/(n_D^2+2)$ ml/mole | | Specific Refraction[a] $(1/d)(n_D^2-1)/(n_D^2+2)$ ml/g | | Refractivity Intercept[a] $n_D-d/2$ | | Specific Dispersion[a] $10^4(n_F-n_C)/d$ ml/g | |
|---|---|---|---|---|---|---|---|---|---|---|---|
| | | 20°C | 25°C | 20°C | 25°C | 20°C | 25°C | 20°C | 25°C | 20°C | 25°C |
| Naphthalene | C$_{10}$H$_8$ | ——— | (131.42)[b] | ——— | (44.34)[b] | ——— | (0.3460)[b] | ——— | (1.1022)[b] | ——— | (297.)[b] |
| 1-Methylnaphthalene | C$_{11}$H$_{10}$ | 139.381 | 139.909 | 48.795 | 48.821 | 0.34317 | 0.34335 | 1.1073 | 1.1068 | 295. | 295. |
| 2-Methylnaphthalene | " | ——— | (143.57)[c] | ——— | (49.24)[c] | ——— | (0.3463)[c] | ——— | (1.1067)[c] | | (293.)[c] |
| 1-Ethylnaphthalene | C$_{12}$H$_{12}$ | 154.95 | 155.52 | 53.45 | 53.49 | 0.3422 | 0.3424 | 1.1021 | 1.1018 | 285. | 285. |
| 2-Ethylnaphthalene | " | 157.44 | 158.03 | 53.85 | 53.89 | 0.3447 | 0.3450 | 1.1038 | 1.1034 | 285. | 285. |
| 1,2-Dimethylnaphthalene | " | 154.2 | 154.8 | 53.9 | 54.0 | 0.345 | 0.346 | 1.110 | 1.110 | 290. | 290. |
| 1,3-Dimethylnaphthalene | " | 155.24 | 155.81 | 53.75 | 53.79 | 0.3441 | 0.3443 | 1.1058 | 1.1055 | 290. | 290. |
| 1,4-Dimethylnaphthalene | " | 153.67 | 154.23 | 53.47 | 53.51 | 0.3423 | 0.3425 | 1.1044 | 1.1040 | 290. | 290. |
| 1,5-Dimethylnaphthalene | " | ——— | ——— | ——— | ——— | ——— | ——— | ——— | ——— | ——— | ——— |
| 1,6-Dimethylnaphthalene | " | 155.7 | 156.4 | 53.8 | 53.9 | 0.344 | 0.345 | 1.1058 | 1.1056 | 290. | 290. |
| 1,7-Dimethylnaphthalene | " | 155.7 | 156.4 | 53.8 | 53.9 | 0.344 | 0.345 | 1.105 | 1.105 | 290. | 290. |
| 1,8-Dimethylnaphthalene | " | ——— | ——— | ——— | ——— | ——— | ——— | ——— | ——— | ——— | ——— |
| 2,3-Dimethylnaphthalene | " | ——— | ——— | ——— | ——— | ——— | ——— | ——— | ——— | ——— | ——— |
| 2,6-Dimethylnaphthalene | " | ——— | ——— | ——— | ——— | ——— | ——— | ——— | ——— | ——— | ——— |
| 2,7-Dimethylnaphthalene | " | ——— | ——— | ——— | ——— | ——— | ——— | ——— | ——— | ——— | ——— |

a See footnote a of Table 1b.    b At 85°C.    c At 40°C.

TABLE 2db, Page 1 — TETRAHYDRONAPHTHALENES, $C_{10}$ TO $C_{12}$

MOLECULAR VOLUME, MOLECULAR REFRACTION, SPECIFIC REFRACTION, REFRACTIVITY INTERCEPT, AND SPECIFIC DISPERSION

August 31, 1949; October 31, 1952

| Compound | Formula | Molecular Volume[a] $V=M/d$ (ml/mole) | | Molecular Refraction[a] $V(n_D^2-1)/(n_D^2+2)$ (ml/mole) | | Specific Refraction[a] $(1/d)(n_D^2-1)/(n_D^2+2)$ (ml/g) | | Refractivity Intercept[a] $n_D - d/2$ | | Specific Dispersion[a] $10^4(n_F-n_C)/d$ (ml/g) | |
|---|---|---|---|---|---|---|---|---|---|---|---|
| | | 20°C | 25°C | 20°C | 25°C | 20°C | 25°C | 20°C | 25°C | 20°C | 25°C |
| 1,2,3,4-Tetrahydronaphthalene | $C_{10}H_{12}$ | 136.26 | 136.82 | 42.84 | 42.87 | 0.3241 | 0.3243 | 1.05625 | 1.05609 | 166. | 166. |
| 1-Methyl-[1,2,3,4-tetrahydronaphthalene] | $C_{11}H_{14}$ | 152.63 | 153.22 | 47.57 | 47.60 | 0.3253 | 0.3255 | 1.0567 | 1.0564 | | |
| 2-Methyl-[1,2,3,4-tetrahydronaphthalene] | " | 153.6 | 154.2 | 47.5 | 47.6 | 0.325 | 0.325 | 1.055 | 1.055 | | |
| 5-Methyl-[1,2,3,4-tetrahydronaphthalene] | " | 150.43 | 151.01 | 47.48 | 47.52 | 0.3247 | 0.3250 | 1.05795 | 1.05775 | 164. | 164. |
| 6-Methyl-[1,2,3,4-tetrahydronaphthalene] | " | 153.32 | 153.92 | 47.79 | 47.82 | 0.3268 | 0.3270 | 1.05887 | 1.05865 | 166. | 165. |
| 1-Ethyl-[1,2,3,4-tetrahydronaphthalene] | $C_{12}H_{16}$ | 168.06 | 168.72 | 52.08 | 52.12 | 0.3250 | 0.3252 | 1.0553 | 1.0551 | | |
| 2-Ethyl-[1,2,3,4-tetrahydronaphthalene] | " | 170.8 | 171.6 | 52.2 | 52.3 | 0.326 | 0.326 | 1.054 | 1.054 | | |
| 5-Ethyl-[1,2,3,4-tetrahydronaphthalene] | " | 164.7 | 165.4 | 51.7 | 51.7 | 0.322 | 0.323 | 1.054 | 1.054 | 163. | 163. |
| 6-Ethyl-[1,2,3,4-tetrahydronaphthalene] | " | 167.48 | 168.13 | 51.85 | 52.02 | 0.3244 | 0.3241 | 1.0547 | 1.0544 | 165. | 165. |
| 1,1-Dimethyl-[1,2,3,4-tetrahydronaphthalene] | " | 168.7 | 169.4 | 52.0 | 52.0 | 0.325 | 0.325 | 1.0545 | 1.0541 | | |
| 1,cis-2-Dimethyl-[1,2,3,4-tetrahydronaohthalene] | " | 169.22 | 169.88 | 52.16 | 52.19 | 0.3255 | 0.3257 | 1.0551 | 1.0549 | | |
| 1,trans-2-Dimethyl-[1,2,3,4-tetrahydronaphthalene] | " | | | | | | | | | | |
| 1,cis-3-Dimethyl-[1,2,3,4-tetrahydronaphthalene] | " | 170.5 | 171.2 | 52.3 | 52.3 | 0.326 | 0.326 | 1.055 | 1.055 | | |
| 1,trans-3-Dimethyl-[1,2,3,4-tetrahydronaphthalene] | " | | | | | | | | | | |
| 1,cis-4-Dimethyl-[1,2,3,4-tetrahydronaphthalene] | " | 170.5 | 171.2 | 52.5 | 52.5 | 0.328 | 0.328 | 1.058 | 1.058 | | |
| 1,trans-4-Dimethyl-[1,2,3,4-tetrahydronaphthalene] | " | | | | | | | | | | |

a See footnote a of Table 1b.

TABLE 28b, Page 2 – TETRAHYDRONAPHTHALENES, $C_{10}$ TO $C_{12}$

MOLECULAR VOLUME, MOLECULAR REFRACTION, SPECIFIC REFRACTION, REFRACTIVITY INTERCEPT, AND SPECIFIC DISPERSION

August 31, 1949; October 31, 1952

| Compound | Formula[a] | Molecular Volume[a] $V = M/d$ (ml/mole) | | Molecular Refraction[a] $V(n_D^2-1)/(n_D^2+2)$ (ml/mole) | | Specific Refraction[a] $(1/d)(n_D^2-1)/(n_D^2+2)$ (ml/g) | | Refractivity Intercept[a] $n_D - d/2$ | | Specific Dispersion[a] $10^4(n_F-n_C)/d$ (ml/g) | |
|---|---|---|---|---|---|---|---|---|---|---|---|
| | | 20°C | 25°C | 20°C | 25°C | 20°C | 25°C | 20°C | 25°C | 20°C | 25°C |
| 2,2-Dimethyl-[1,2,3,4-tetrahydronaphthalene] | $C_{12}H_{16}$ | 171.4 | 172.1 | 52.1 | 52.2 | 0.325 | 0.325 | 1.0525 | 1.0525 | | |
| 2,cis-3-Dimethyl-[1,2,3,4-tetrahydronaphthalene] | " | 170.5 | 171.2 | 52.1 | 52.2 | 0.325 | 0.325 | 1.053 | 1.053 | | |
| 2,trans-3-Dimethyl-[1,2,3,4-tetrahydronaphthalene] | " | 170.3 | 171.0 | 52.3 | 52.2 | 0.325 | 0.325 | 1.053 | 1.053 | | |
| 1,5-Dimethyl-[1,2,3,4-tetrahydronaphthalene] | " | 170.7 | 171.4 | 52.4 | 52.4 | 0.327 | 0.327 | 1.057 | 1.056 | | |
| 1,6-Dimethyl-[1,2,3,4-tetrahydronaphthalene] | " | 170.3 | 171.0 | 52.4 | 52.3 | 0.326 | 0.326 | 1.056 | 1.056 | | |
| 1,7-Dimethyl-[1,2,3,4-tetrahydronaphthalene] | " | | | | | | | | | | |
| 1,8-Dimethyl-[1,2,3,4-tetrahydronaphthalene] | " | 169.4 | 170.1 | 52.0 | 52.0 | 0.324 | 0.324 | 1.053 | 1.053 | | |
| 2,5-Dimethyl-[1,2,3,4-tetrahydronaphthalene] | " | 170.3 | 171.0 | 52.4 | 52.3 | 0.326 | 0.326 | 1.056 | 1.056 | | |
| 2,6-Dimethyl-[1,2,3,4-tetrahydronaphthalene] | " | | | | | | | | | | |
| 2,7-Dimethyl-[1,2,3,4-tetrahydronaphthalene] | " | | | | | | | | | | |
| 2,8-Dimethyl-[1,2,3,4-tetrahydronaphthalene] | " | | | | | | | | | | |
| 5,6-Dimethyl-[1,2,3,4-tetrahydronaphthalene] | " | 164.4 | 165.0 | 52.5 | 52.6 | 0.328 | 0.328 | 1.064 | 1.064 | | |
| 5,7-Dimethyl-[1,2,3,4-tetrahydronaphthalene] | " | 167.22 | 168.03 | 52.51 | 52.59 | 0.3277 | 0.3292 | 1.0613 | 1.0616 | 167. | 167. |
| 5,8-Dimethyl-[1,2,3,4-tetrahydronaphthalene] | " | 165.7 | 166.4 | 52.5 | 52.6 | 0.328 | 0.328 | 1.063 | 1.063 | | |
| 6,7-Dimethyl-[1,2,3,4-tetrahydronaphthalene] | " | 168.0 | 168.7 | 52.5 | 52.6 | 0.328 | 0.328 | 1.061 | 1.061 | | |

[a] See footnote a of Table 1b.

TABLE 29b (PART 1) - DECAHYDRONAPHTHALENES, $C_{10}$ AND $C_{11}$

MOLECULAR VOLUME, MOLECULAR REFRACTION, SPECIFIC REFRACTION, REFRACTIVITY INTERCEPT, AND SPECIFIC DISPERSION

October 31, 1950

| Compound | Formula | Molecular Volume[a] $V = M/d$ (ml/mole) | | Molecular Refraction[a] $V(n_D^2-1)/(n_D^2+2)$ (ml/mole) | | Specific Refraction[a] $(1/d)(n_D^2-1)/(n_D^2+2)$ (ml/g) | | Refractivity Intercept[a] $n_D - d/2$ | | Specific Dispersion[a] $10^4(n_F-n_C)/d$ (ml/g) | |
|---|---|---|---|---|---|---|---|---|---|---|---|
| | | 20°C | 25°C | 20°C | 25°C | 20°C | 25°C | 20°C | 25°C | 20°C | 25°C |
| cis-Decahydronaphthalene | $C_{10}H_{18}$ | 154.20 | 154.90 | 43.88 | 43.91 | 0.3174 | 0.3176 | 1.0328 | 1.0326 | | |
| trans-Decahydronaphthalene | " | 158.92 | 159.65 | 44.30 | 44.31 | 0.3204 | 0.3206 | 1.0345 | 1.0342 | | |
| 1-Methyl-[cis-decahydronaphthalene] | $C_{11}H_{20}$ | | | | | | | | | | |
| 1-Methyl-[trans-decahydronaphthalene] | " | | | | | | | | | | |
| 2-Methyl-[cis-decahydronaphthalene] | " | | | | | | | | | | |
| 2-Methyl-[trans-decahydronaphthalene] | " | | | | | | | | | | |
| 9-Methyl-[cis-decahydronaphthalene] | " | 170.9 | 171.7 | 48.6 | 48.6 | 0.319 | 0.319 | 1.034 | 1.034 | | |
| 9-Methyl-[trans-decahydronaphthalene] | " | 176.6 | 177.5 | 48.6 | 48.8 | 0.319 | 0.320 | 1.032 | 1.033 | | |

[a] See footnote a of Table 1b.

TABLE 23b (PART 2) - DECAHYDRONAPHTHALENES, $C_{12}$

MOLECULAR VOLUME, MOLECULAR REFRACTION, SPECIFIC REFRACTION, REFRACTIVITY INTERCEPT, AND SPECIFIC DISPERSION

October 31, 1950

| Compound | Formula | Molecular Volume [a] $V=M/d$ (ml/mole) | | Molecular Refraction [a] $V(n_D^2-1)/(n_D^2+2)$ (ml/mole) | | Specific Refraction [a] $(1/d)(n_D^2-1)/(n_D^2+2)$ (ml/g) | | Refractivity Intercept [a] $n_D-d/2$ | | Specific Dispersion [a] $10^4(n_F-n_C)/d$ (ml/g) | |
|---|---|---|---|---|---|---|---|---|---|---|---|
| | | 20°C | 25°C | 20°C | 25°C | 20°C | 25°C | 20°C | 25°C | 20°C | 25°C |
| 1-Ethyl-[cis-decahydronaphthalene] | $C_{12}H_{22}$ | | | | | | | | | | |
| 1-Ethyl-[trans-decahydronaphthalene] | " | | | | | | | | | | |
| 2-Ethyl-[cis-decahydronaphthalene] | " | | | | | | | | | | |
| 2-Ethyl-[trans-decahydronaphthalene] | " | | | | | | | | | | |
| 9-Ethyl-[cis-decahydronaphthalene] | " | 187.6 | 188.3 | 53.3 | 53.3 | 0.321 | 0.321 | 0.594 | 0.535 | | |
| 9-Ethyl-[trans-decahydronaphthalene] | " | 193.2 | 194.0 | 53.5 | 53.5 | 0.322 | 0.322 | 0.605 | 0.607 | | |
| 1,1-Dimethyl-[cis-decahydronaphthalene] | " | | | | | | | | | | |
| 1,1-Dimethyl-[trans-decahydronaphthalene] | " | | | | | | | | | | |
| 1,cis-2-Dimethyl-[cis-decahydronaphthalene] | " | | | | | | | | | | |
| 1,cis-2-Dimethyl-[trans-decahydronaphthalene] | " | | | | | | | | | | |
| 1,trans-2-Dimethyl-[cis-decahydronaphthalene] | " | | | | | | | | | | |
| 1,trans-2-Dimethyl-[trans-decahydronaphthalene] | " | | | | | | | | | | |
| 1,cis-3-Dimethyl-[cis-decahydronaphthalene] | " | | | | | | | | | | |
| 1,cis-3-Dimethyl-[trans-decahydronaphthalene] | " | | | | | | | | | | |
| 1,trans-3-Dimethyl-[cis-decahydronaphthalene] | " | | | | | | | | | | |
| 1,trans-3-Dimethyl-[trans-decahydronaphthalene] | " | | | | | | | | | | |
| 1,cis-4-Dimethyl-[cis-decahydronaphthalene] | " | | | | | | | | | | |
| 1,cis-4-Dimethyl-[trans-decahydronaphthalene] | " | | | | | | | | | | |
| 1,trans-4-Dimethyl-[cis-decahydronaphthalene] | " | | | | | | | | | | |
| 1,trans-4-Dimethyl-[trans-decahydronaphthalene] | " | | | | | | | | | | |
| 1,cis-5-Dimethyl-[cis-decahydronaphthalene] | " | | | | | | | | | | |
| 1,cis-5-Dimethyl-[trans-decahydronaphthalene] | " | | | | | | | | | | |
| 1,trans-5-Dimethyl-[cis-decahydronaphthalene] | " | | | | | | | | | | |
| 1,trans-5-Dimethyl-[trans-decahydronaphthalene] | " | | | | | | | | | | |
| 1,cis-6-Dimethyl-[cis-decahydronaphthalene] | " | | | | | | | | | | |
| 1,cis-6-Dimethyl-[trans-decahydronaphthalene] | " | | | | | | | | | | |
| 1,trans-6-Dimethyl-[cis-decahydronaphthalene] | " | | | | | | | | | | |
| 1,trans-6-Dimethyl-[trans-decahydronaphthalene] | " | | | | | | | | | | |
| 1,cis-7-Dimethyl-[cis-decahydronaphthalene] | " | | | | | | | | | | |
| 1,cis-7-Dimethyl-[trans-decahydronaphthalene] | " | | | | | | | | | | |
| 1,trans-7-Dimethyl-[cis-decahydronaphthalene] | " | | | | | | | | | | |
| 1,trans-7-Dimethyl-[trans-decahydronaphthalene] | " | | | | | | | | | | |

[a] See footnote a of Table 1b.

TABLE 29b (PART 3) – DECAHYDRONAPHTHALENES, $C_{12}$

MOLECULAR VOLUME, MOLECULAR REFRACTION, SPECIFIC REFRACTION, REFRACTIVITY INTERCEPT, AND SPECIFIC DISPERSION

October 31, 1950

| Compound | Formula[a] | Molecular Volume[a] $V=M/d$ (ml/mole) | | Molecular Refraction[a] $V(n_D^2-1)/(n_D^2+2)$ (ml/mole) | | Specific Refraction[a] $(1/d)(n_D^2-1)/(n_D^2+2)$ (ml/g) | | Refractivity Intercept[a] $n_D-d/2$ | | Specific Dispersion[a] $10^4(n_F-n_C)/d$ (ml/g) | |
|---|---|---|---|---|---|---|---|---|---|---|---|
| | | 20°C | 25°C | 20°C | 25°C | 20°C | 25°C | 20°C | 25°C | 20°C | 25°C |
| 1,cis-8-Dimethyl-[cis-decahydronaphthalene] | $C_{12}H_{22}$ | | | | | | | | | | |
| 1,cis-8-Dimethyl-[trans-decahydronaphthalene] | " | | | | | | | | | | |
| 1,trans-8-Dimethyl-[cis-decahydronaphthalene] | " | | | | | | | | | | |
| 1,trans-8-Dimethyl-[trans-decahydronaphthalene] | " | | | | | | | | | | |
| 1,9-Dimethyl-[cis-decahydronaphthalene] | " | | | | | | | | | | |
| 1,9-Dimethyl-[trans-decahydronaphthalene] | " | | | | | | | | | | |
| 1,10-Dimethyl-[cis-decahydronaphthalene] | " | 186.93 | 187.78 | 53.22 | 53.25 | 0.3200 | 0.3202 | 1.0364 | 1.0362 | | |
| 1,10-Dimethyl-[trans-decahydronaphthalene] | " | 192.63 | 193.52 | 53.34 | 53.37 | 0.3208 | 0.3209 | 1.0343 | 1.0341 | | |
| 2,2-Dimethyl-[cis-decahydronaphthalene] | " | | | | | | | | | | |
| 2,2-Dimethyl-[trans-decahydronaphthalene] | " | | | | | | | | | | |
| 2,3-Dimethyl-[cis-decahydronaphthalene] | " | | | | | | | | | | |
| 2,3-Dimethyl-[trans-decahydronaphthalene] | " | | | | | | | | | | |
| 2,trans-3-Dimethyl-[cis-decahydronaphthalene] | " | | | | | | | | | | |
| 2,trans-3-Dimethyl-[trans-decahydronaphthalene] | " | | | | | | | | | | |
| 2,cis-6-Dimethyl-[cis-decahydronaphthalene] | " | | | | | | | | | | |
| 2,cis-6-Dimethyl-[trans-decahydronaphthalene] | " | | | | | | | | | | |
| 2,trans-6-Dimethyl-[cis-decahydronaphthalene] | " | | | | | | | | | | |
| 2,trans-6-Dimethyl-[trans-decahydronaphthalene] | " | | | | | | | | | | |
| 2,cis-7-Dimethyl-[cis-decahydronaphthalene] | " | | | | | | | | | | |
| 2,trans-7-Dimethyl-[cis-decahydronaphthalene] | " | | | | | | | | | | |
| 2,trans-7-Dimethyl-[trans-decahydronaphthalene] | " | | | | | | | | | | |
| 2,9-Dimethyl-[cis-decahydronaphthalene] | " | | | | | | | | | | |
| 2,9-Dimethyl-[trans-decahydronaphthalene] | " | | | | | | | | | | |
| 2,10-Dimethyl-[cis-decahydronaphthalene] | " | | | | | | | | | | |
| 2,10-Dimethyl-[trans-decahydronaphthalene] | " | | | | | | | | | | |
| 9,10-Dimethyl-[cis-decahydronaphthalene] | " | | | | | | | | | | |
| 9,10-Dimethyl-[trans-decahydronaphthalene] | " | | | | | | | | | | |

a See footnote a of Table 1b.

212

TABLE 101b -1- ALKANETHIOLS, $C_1$ TO $C_{20}$

MOLECULAR VOLUME, MOLECULAR REFRACTION, SPECIFIC REFRACTION, REFRACTIVITY INTERCEPT, AND SPECIFIC DISPERSION

April 30, 1952

| Compound | Formula | Molecular Volume[a] $V=M/d$ (ml/mole) | | Molecular Refraction[a] $V(n_D^2-1)/(n_D^2+2)$ (ml/mole) | | Specific Refraction[a] $(1/d)(n_D^2-1)/(n_D^2+2)$ (ml/g) | | Refractivity Intercept[a] $n_D-d/2$ | | Specific Dispersion[a] $10^4(n_F-n_C)/d$ (ml/g) | |
|---|---|---|---|---|---|---|---|---|---|---|---|
| | | 20°C | 25°C | 20°C | 25°C | 20°C | 25°C | 20°C | 25°C | 20°C | 25°C |
| Methanethiol (Methyl mercaptan) | $CH_4S$ | 55.52[b] | 55.94[b] | — | — | — | — | — | — | — | — |
| Ethanethiol (Ethyl mercaptan) | $C_2H_6S$ | 74.045 | 74.576 | 19.168 | 19.178 | 0.30850 | 0.30866 | 1.01148 | 1.01121 | 122. | 122. |
| 1-Propanethiol (n-Propyl mercaptan) | $C_3H_8S$ | 90.55 | 91.11 | 23.77 | 23.78 | 0.3121 | 0.3122 | 1.0174 | 1.0172 | 116. | 116. |
| 1-Butanethiol (n-Butyl mercaptan) | $C_4H_{10}S$ | 107.159 | 107.780 | 28.408 | 28.425 | 0.31499 | 0.31518 | 1.02218 | 1.02196 | 114. | 114. |
| 1-Pentanethiol | $C_5H_{12}S$ | 123.754 | 124.413 | 33.060 | 33.073 | 0.31724 | 0.31736 | 1.02588 | 1.02558 | 112. | 112. |
| 1-Hexanethiol | $C_6H_{14}S$ | 140.36 | 141.08 | 37.69 | 37.70 | 0.3188 | 0.3189 | 1.0284 | 1.0280 | 109. | 109. |
| 1-Heptanethiol | $C_7H_{16}S$ | 156.95 | 157.70 | 42.35 | 42.36 | 0.3202 | 0.3202 | 1.0308 | 1.0304 | 108. | 108. |
| 1-Octanethiol | $C_8H_{18}S$ | 173.47 | 174.28 | 46.98 | 46.99 | 0.3211 | 0.3212 | 1.0324 | 1.0320 | 107. | 107. |
| 1-Nonanethiol | $C_9H_{20}S$ | 189.99 | 190.88 | 51.65 | 51.66 | 0.3221 | 0.3222 | 1.0341 | 1.0338 | 106. | 106. |
| 1-Decanethiol | $C_{10}H_{22}S$ | 206.49 | 207.42 | 56.26 | 56.27 | 0.3227 | 0.3228 | 1.0350 | 1.0348 | 105. | 105. |
| 1-Undecanethiol | $C_{11}H_{24}S$ | 222.97 | 223.95 | 60.90 | 60.91 | 0.3233 | 0.3234 | 1.0361 | 1.0358 | 104. | 104. |
| 1-Dodecanethiol | $C_{12}H_{26}S$ | 239.43 | 240.48 | 65.54 | 65.56 | 0.3238 | 0.3239 | 1.0370 | 1.0367 | 104. | 104. |
| 1-Tridecanethiol | $C_{13}H_{28}S$ | 255.91 | 257.00 | 70.20 | 70.20 | 0.3244 | 0.3244 | 1.0380 | 1.0376 | 103. | 103. |
| 1-Tetradecanethiol | $C_{14}H_{30}S$ | 272.36 | 273.51 | 74.83 | 74.84 | 0.3247 | 0.3248 | 1.0386 | 1.0382 | 103. | 103. |
| 1-Pentadecanethiol | $C_{15}H_{32}S$ | 288.80 | 290.02 | 79.45 | 79.48 | 0.3250 | 0.3251 | 1.0392 | 1.0388 | 103. | 103. |
| 1-Hexadecanethiol | $C_{16}H_{34}S$ | 305.26 | 306.53 | 84.11 | 84.12 | 0.3254 | 0.3254 | 1.0398 | 1.0394 | 102. | 102. |
| 1-Heptadecanethiol | $C_{17}H_{36}S$ | 321.71[c] | 323.03[c] | 88.76[c] | 88.76[c] | 0.3257[c] | 0.3257[c] | 1.0404[c] | 1.0400[c] | 102.[c] | 102.[c] |
| 1-Octadecanethiol | $C_{18}H_{38}S$ | 338.11[c] | 339.53[c] | 93.36[c] | 93.41[c] | 0.3259[c] | 0.3260[c] | 1.0408[c] | 1.0404[c] | 102.[c] | 102.[c] |
| 1-Nonadecanethiol | $C_{19}H_{40}S$ | 354.58[c] | 356.03[c] | 98.02[c] | 98.05[c] | 0.3261[c] | 0.3262[c] | 1.0412[c] | 1.0408[c] | 102.[c] | 102.[c] |
| 1-Eicosanethiol | $C_{20}H_{42}S$ | 370.99[c] | 372.53[c] | 102.66[c] | 102.69[c] | 0.3263[c] | 0.3264[c] | 1.0415[c] | 1.0412[c] | 102.[c] | 102.[c] |

[a] See footnote a of Table 1b.  [b] At saturation pressure  [c] For the undercooled liquid below the normal freezing point.

## TABLE 102b - 2-ALKANETHIOLS, $C_3$ TO $C_{20}$

### MOLECULAR VOLUME, MOLECULAR REFRACTION, SPECIFIC REFRACTION, REFRACTIVITY INTERCEPT, AND SPECIFIC DISPERSION

April 30, 1952

| Compound | Formula | Molecular Volume[a] $V = M/d$ (ml/mole) | | Molecular Refraction[a] $V(n_D^2-1)/(n_D^2+2)$ (ml/mole) | | Specific Refraction[a] $(1/d)(n_D^2-1)/(n_D^2+2)$ (ml/g) | | Refractivity Intercept[a] $n_D - d/2$ | | Specific Dispersion[a] $10^4(n_F-n_C)/d$ (ml/g) | |
|---|---|---|---|---|---|---|---|---|---|---|---|
| | | 20°C | 25°C | 20°C | 25°C | 20°C | 25°C | 20°C | 25°C | 20°C | 25°C |
| 2-Propanethiol (Isopropyl mercaptan) | $C_3H_8S$ | 93.527 | 94.183 | 23.941 | 23.959 | 0.31436 | 0.31458 | 1.01898 | 1.01819 | 118. | 118. |
| 2-Butanethiol (sec-Butyl mercaptan) | $C_4H_{10}S$ | 108.727 | 109.373 | 28.464 | 28.474 | 0.31561 | 0.31573 | 1.02190 | 1.02156 | 115. | 115. |
| 2-Pentanethiol | $C_5H_{12}S$ | 125.153 | 125.840 | 33.063 | 33.073 | 0.31727 | 0.31737 | 1.0249 | 1.0245 | 111. | 111. |
| 2-Hexanethiol | $C_6H_{14}S$ | 141.69 | 142.42 | 37.72 | 37.73 | 0.3190 | 0.3191 | 1.0278 | 1.0275 | 109. | 109. |
| 2-Heptanethiol | $C_7H_{16}S$ | 158.36 | 159.14 | 42.38 | 42.39 | 0.3204 | 0.3205 | 1.0302 | 1.0298 | 108. | 108. |
| 2-Octanethiol | $C_8H_{18}S$ | 174.85 | 175.68 | 47.03 | 47.04 | 0.3215 | 0.3216 | 1.0321 | 1.0318 | 106. | 106. |
| 2-Nonanethiol | $C_9H_{20}S$ | 191.38 | 192.28 | 51.66 | 51.67 | 0.3222 | 0.3223 | 1.0335 | 1.0331 | 105. | 105. |
| 2-Decanethiol | $C_{10}H_{22}S$ | 207.90 | 208.84 | 56.29 | 56.30 | 0.3229 | 0.3229 | 1.0346 | 1.0342 | 105. | 105. |
| 2-Undecanethiol | $C_{11}H_{24}S$ | 224.35 | 225.37 | 60.92 | 60.94 | 0.3234 | 0.3235 | 1.0356 | 1.0353 | 104. | 104. |
| 2-Dodecanethiol | $C_{12}H_{26}S$ | 240.86 | 241.92 | 65.56 | 65.58 | 0.3239 | 0.3240 | 1.0366 | 1.0362 | 104. | 104. |
| 2-Tridecanethiol | $C_{13}H_{28}S$ | 257.31 | 258.44 | 70.19 | 70.21 | 0.3243 | 0.3244 | 1.0372 | 1.0370 | 103. | 103. |
| 2-Tetradecanethiol | $C_{14}H_{30}S$ | 273.79 | 274.96 | 74.84 | 74.86 | 0.3248 | 0.3248 | 1.0380 | 1.0378 | 103. | 103. |
| 2-Pentadecanethiol | $C_{15}H_{32}S$ | 290.24 | 291.49 | 79.49 | 79.51 | 0.3251 | 0.3252 | 1.0388 | 1.0384 | 102. | 102. |
| 2-Hexadecanethiol | $C_{16}H_{34}S$ | 306.68 | 307.99 | 84.13 | 84.15 | 0.3255 | 0.3255 | 1.0394 | 1.0390 | 102. | 102. |
| 2-Heptadecanethiol | $C_{17}H_{36}S$ | 323.13 | 324.51 | 88.78 | 88.80 | 0.3258 | 0.3258 | 1.0400 | 1.0396 | 102. | 102. |
| 2-Octadecanethiol | $C_{18}H_{38}S$ | 339.59[b] | 341.01[b] | 93.41[b] | 93.43[b] | 0.3260[b] | 0.3261[b] | 1.0404[b] | 1.0400[b] | 102.[b] | 102.[b] |
| 2-Nonadecanethiol | $C_{19}H_{40}S$ | 356.01[b] | 357.49[b] | 98.04[b] | 98.06[b] | 0.3262[b] | 0.3262[b] | 1.0408[b] | 1.0404[b] | 101.[b] | 101.[b] |
| 2-Eicosanethiol | $C_{20}H_{42}S$ | 372.44[b] | 373.99[b] | 102.68[b] | 102.70[b] | 0.3264[b] | 0.3264[b] | 1.0412[b] | 1.0408[b] | 101.[b] | 101.[b] |

[a] See footnote a of Table 1b.　　[b] For the undercooled liquid below the normal freezing point.

TABLE 103b — ALKANETHIOLS, $C_1$ TO $C_5$

MOLECULAR VOLUME, MOLECULAR REFRACTION, SPECIFIC REFRACTION, REFRACTIVITY INTERCEPT, AND SPECIFIC DISPERSION

April 30, 1952; December 31, 1952

| Compound | Formula | Molecular Volume $\bar{V}=W/d$ (ml/mole) | | Molecular Refraction $\bar{V}(n_D^2-1)/(n_D^2+2)$ (ml/mole) | | Specific Refraction $(1/d)(n_D^2-1)/(n_D^2+2)$ (ml/g) | | Refractivity Intercept $n_D - d/2$ | | Specific Dispersion $10^4(n_F - n_C)/d$ (ml/g) | |
|---|---|---|---|---|---|---|---|---|---|---|---|
| | | 20°C | 25°C | 20°C | 25°C | 20°C | 25°C | 20°C | 25°C | 20°C | 25°C |
| Methanethiol (Methyl mercaptan) | $CH_4S$ | 55.52 b | 55.94 b | --- | --- | --- | --- | --- | --- | --- | --- |
| Ethanethiol (Ethyl mercaptan) | $C_2H_6S$ | 74.045 | 74.576 | 19.168 | 19.178 | 0.30850 | 0.30866 | 1.01148 | 1.01121 | 122. | 122. |
| 1-Propanethiol (n-Propyl mercaptan) | $C_3H_8S$ | 90.55 | 91.11 | 23.77 | 23.78 | 0.3121 | 0.3122 | 1.0174 | 1.0172 | 116. | 116. |
| 2-Propanethiol (Isopropyl mercaptan) | " | 93.527 | 94.183 | 23.941 | 23.959 | 0.31436 | 0.31458 | 1.01838 | 1.01819 | 118. | 118. |
| 1-Butanethiol (n-Butyl mercaptan) | $C_4H_{10}S$ | 107.159 | 107.780 | 28.408 | 28.425 | 0.31499 | 0.31518 | 1.02218 | 1.02196 | 114. | 114. |
| 2-Butanethiol (sec-Butyl mercaptan) | " | 108.727 | 109.373 | 28.464 | 28.474 | 0.31561 | 0.31573 | 1.02190 | 1.02156 | 115. | 115. |
| 2-Methyl-1-propanethiol (Isobutyl mercaptan) | " | 108.15 | 108.82 | 28.43 | 28.44 | 0.3152 | 0.3154 | 1.0218 | 1.0214 | 113. | 113. |
| 2-Methyl-2-propanethiol (tert-Butyl mercaptan) | " | 112.704 | 113.481 | 28.711 | 28.722 | 0.31836 | 0.31847 | 1.02310 | 1.02271 | 118. | 118. |
| 1-Pentanethiol | $C_5H_{12}S$ | 123.754 | 124.413 | 33.060 | 33.073 | 0.31724 | 0.31736 | 1.02588 | 1.02558 | 112. | 112. |
| 2-Pentanethiol | " | 125.153 | 125.840 | 33.063 | 33.073 | 0.31727 | 0.31736 | 1.0249 | 1.0245 | 111. | 111. |
| 3-Pentanethiol | " | 123.91 | 124.58 | 32.96 | 32.97 | 0.3163 | 0.3164 | 1.0242 | 1.0238 | | |
| 2-Methyl-1-butanethiol | " | 123.8 | 124.5 | 32.9 | 32.9 | 0.316 | 0.316 | 1.023 | 1.023 | | |
| 3-Methyl-1-butanethiol | " | 124.80 | 125.48 | 32.99 | 33.00 | 0.3166 | 0.3167 | 1.0240 | 1.0236 | 111. | 111. |
| 2-Methyl-2-butanethiol | " | 128.4 | 129.1 | 33.7 | 33.7 | 0.323 | 0.323 | 1.032 | 1.032 | | |
| 3-Methyl-2-butanethiol | " | 123.93 | 124.60 | 32.96 | 32.97 | 0.3163 | 0.3164 | 1.0242 | 1.0238 | | |
| 2,2-Dimethyl-1-propanethiol | " | | | | | | | | | | |

a See footnote a of Table 1b.    b At saturation pressure.

TABLE 104b – ALKYL BENZENETHIOLS, C$_6$ TO C$_8$

MOLECULAR VOLUME, MOLECULAR REFRACTION, SPECIFIC REFRACTION, REFRACTIVITY INTERCEPT, AND SPECIFIC DISPERSION

October 31, 1952

| Compound | Formula | Molecular Volume[a] $V=M/d$ ml/mole | | Molecular Refraction[a] $V(n_D^2-1)/(n_D^2+2)$ ml/mole | | Specific Refraction[a] $(1/d)(n_D^2-1)/(n_D^2+2)$ ml/g | | Refractivity Intercept[a] $n_0-d/2$ | | Specific Dispersion[a] $10^4(n_F-n_C)/d$ ml/g | |
|---|---|---|---|---|---|---|---|---|---|---|---|
| | | 20°C | 25°C | 20°C | 25°C | 20°C | 25°C | 20°C | 25°C | 20°C | 25°C |
| Benzenethiol (Thiophenol) | C$_6$H$_6$S | 102.34 | 102.74 | 34.50 | 34.50 | 0.3132 | 0.3131 | 1.0510 | 1.0502 | 216. | 216. |
| 2-Methylbenzenethiol (o-Methylthiophenol) | C$_7$H$_8$S | 119.3 | 119.8 | 39.1 | 39.2 | 0.315 | 0.315 | 1.050 | 1.049 | | |
| 3-Methylbenzenethiol (m-Methylthiophenol) | " | 119.0 | 119.4 | 39.2 | 39.1 | 0.315 | 0.315 | 1.050 | 1.049 | | |
| 4-Methylbenzenethiol (p-Methylthiophenol) | " | | | | | | | | | | |
| 2-Ethylbenzenethiol (o-Ethylthiophenol) | C$_8$H$_{10}$S | 133.56 | 134.08 | 43.82 | 43.86 | 0.3170 | 0.3173 | 1.0525 | 1.0525 | | |
| 3-Ethylbenzenethiol (m-Ethylthiophenol) | " | 133.2 | 133.7 | 43.8 | 43.8 | 0.317 | 0.317 | 1.053 | 1.052 | | |
| 4-Ethylbenzenethiol (p-Ethylthiophenol) | " | 133.2 | 133.7 | 43.8 | 43.8 | 0.317 | 0.317 | 1.053 | 1.052 | | |
| 2,3-Dimethylbenzenethiol (2,3-Dimethylthiophenol) | " | | | | | | | | | | |
| 2,4-Dimethylbenzenethiol (2,4-Dimethylthiophenol) | " | | | | | | | | | | |
| 2,5-Dimethylbenzenethiol (2,5-Dimethylthiophenol) | " | | | | | | | | | | |
| 2,6-Dimethylbenzenethiol (2,6-Dimethylthiophenol) | " | | | | | | | | | | |
| 3,4-Dimethylbenzenethiol (3,4-Dimethylthiophenol) | " | | | | | | | | | | |
| 3,5-Dimethylbenzenethiol (3,5-Dimethylthiophenol) | " | | | | | | | | | | |

[a] See footnote a of Table 1b.

TABLE 105b – 2-n-THIAALKANES, C$_2$ TO C$_{20}$

MOLECULAR VOLUME, MOLECULAR REFRACTION, SPECIFIC REFRACTION, REFRACTIVITY INTERCEPT, AND SPECIFIC DISPERSION

April 30, 1952

| Compound | Formula | Molecular Volume[a] $V = M/d$ (ml/mole) | | Molecular Refraction[a] $V(n_D^2-1)/(n_D^2+2)$ (ml/mole) | | Specific Refraction[a] $(1/d)(n_D^2-1)/(n_D^2+2)$ (ml/g) | | Refractivity Intercept[a] $n_D - d/2$ | | Specific Dispersion[a] $10^4(n_F-n_C)/d$ (ml/g) | |
|---|---|---|---|---|---|---|---|---|---|---|---|
| | | 20°C | 25°C | 20°C | 25°C | 20°C | 25°C | 20°C | 25°C | 20°C | 25°C |
| 2-Thiapropane (Dimethyl sulfide) | C$_2$H$_6$S | 73.250 | 73.767 | 19.132 | 19.145 | 0.30792 | 0.30813 | 1.01134 | 1.01116 | 122. | 122. |
| 2-Thiabutane (Methyl ethyl sulfide) | C$_3$H$_8$S | 90.429 | 91.014 | 23.849 | 23.862 | 0.31314 | 0.31331 | 1.01924 | 1.01898 | 120. | 120. |
| 2-Thiapentane (Methyl n-propyl sulfide) | C$_4$H$_{10}$S | 107.06 | 107.68 | 28.45 | 28.46 | 0.3155 | 0.3156 | 1.0230 | 1.0228 | 117. | 117. |
| 2-Thiahexane | C$_5$H$_{12}$S | 123.68 | 124.34 | 33.09 | 33.11 | 0.3175 | 0.3177 | 1.0264 | 1.0262 | 113. | 113. |
| 2-Thiaheptane | C$_6$H$_{14}$S | 140.24 | 140.95 | 37.73 | 37.75 | 0.3191 | 0.3193 | 1.0290 | 1.0288 | 111. | 111. |
| 2-Thiaoctane | C$_7$H$_{16}$S | 156.82 | 157.59 | 42.38 | 42.39 | 0.3204 | 0.3205 | 1.0312 | 1.0308 | 109. | 109. |
| 2-Thianonane | C$_8$H$_{18}$S | 173.39 | 174.20 | 47.03 | 47.04 | 0.3215 | 0.3216 | 1.0330 | 1.0326 | 108. | 108. |
| 2-Thiadecane | C$_9$H$_{20}$S | 189.93 | 190.77 | 51.67 | 51.67 | 0.3223 | 0.3223 | 1.0344 | 1.0340 | 107. | 107. |
| 2-Thiaundecane | C$_{10}$H$_{22}$S | 206.40 | 207.33 | 56.30 | 56.32 | 0.3229 | 0.3230 | 1.0354 | 1.0352 | 106. | 106. |
| 2-Thiadodecane | C$_{11}$H$_{24}$S | 222.89 | 223.87 | 60.94 | 60.96 | 0.3235 | 0.3236 | 1.0366 | 1.0362 | 105. | 105. |
| 2-Thiatridecane | C$_{12}$H$_{26}$S | 239.35 | 240.40 | 65.58 | 65.60 | 0.3240 | 0.3241 | 1.0374 | 1.0370 | 104. | 104. |
| 2-Thiatetradecane | C$_{13}$H$_{28}$S | 255.82 | 256.92 | 70.22 | 70.24 | 0.3245 | 0.3246 | 1.0382 | 1.0378 | 104. | 104. |
| 2-Thiapentadecane | C$_{14}$H$_{30}$S | 272.27 | 273.44 | 74.86 | 74.88 | 0.3249 | 0.3249 | 1.0389 | 1.0385 | 103. | 103. |
| 2-Thiahexadecane | C$_{15}$H$_{32}$S | 288.70 | 289.95 | 79.49 | 79.52 | 0.3251 | 0.3253 | 1.0394 | 1.0391 | 103. | 103. |
| 2-Thiaheptadecane | C$_{16}$H$_{34}$S | 305.16 | 306.46 | 84.14 | 84.17 | 0.3255 | 0.3256 | 1.0400 | 1.0398 | 103. | 103. |
| 2-Thiaoctadecane | C$_{17}$H$_{36}$S | 321.64[b] | 322.96 | 88.79[b] | 88.81 | 0.3258[b] | 0.3259 | 1.0406[b] | 1.0402 | 103.[b] | 103. |
| 2-Thianonadecane | C$_{18}$H$_{38}$S | 338.07[b] | 339.46 | 93.42[b] | 93.45 | 0.3260[b] | 0.3261 | 1.0410[b] | 1.0406 | 102.[b] | 102. |
| 2-Thiaeicosane | C$_{19}$H$_{40}$S | 354.49[b] | 355.96[b] | 98.07[b] | 98.09[b] | 0.3263[b] | 0.3263[b] | 1.0414[b] | 1.0411[b] | 102.[b] | 102.[b] |
| 2-Thiaheneicosane | C$_{20}$H$_{42}$S | 370.91[b] | 372.45[b] | 102.71[b] | 102.73[b] | 0.3265[b] | 0.3265[b] | 1.0418[b] | 1.0414[b] | 102.[b] | 102.[b] |

[a] See footnote a of Table 1b.    [b] For the undercooled liquid below the normal freezing point.

TABLE 107b – THIAALKANES, $C_2$ TO $C_5$

MOLECULAR VOLUME, MOLECULAR REFRACTION, SPECIFIC REFRACTION, REFRACTIVITY INTERCEPT, AND SPECIFIC DISPERSION

April 30, 1952

| Compound | Formula[a] | Molecular Volume[a] $V=M/d$ (ml/mole) | | Molecular Refraction[a] $V(n_D^2-1)/(n_D^2+2)$ (ml/mole) | | Specific Refraction[a] $(1/d)(n_D^2-1)/(n_D^2+2)$ (ml/g) | | Refractivity Intercept[a] $n_D - d/2$ | | Specific Dispersion[a] $10^4(n_F-n_C)/d$ (ml/g) | |
|---|---|---|---|---|---|---|---|---|---|---|---|
| | | 20°C | 25°C | 20°C | 25°C | 20°C | 25°C | 20°C | 25°C | 20°C | 25°C |
| 2-Thiapropane (Dimethyl sulfide) | $C_2H_6S$ | 73.250 | 73.767 | 19.132 | 19.145 | 0.30792 | 0.30813 | 1.01134 | 1.01116 | 122. | 122. |
| 2-Thiabutane (Methyl ethyl sulfide) | $C_3H_8S$ | 90.429 | 91.014 | 23.849 | 23.862 | 0.31314 | 0.31331 | 1.01924 | 1.01898 | 120. | 120. |
| 2-Thiapentane (Methyl n-propyl sulfide) | $C_4H_{10}S$ | 107.06 | 107.68 | 28.45 | 28.46 | 0.3155 | 0.3156 | 1.0230 | 1.0228 | 117. | 117. |
| 3-Thiapentane (Diethyl sulfide) | " | 107.848 | 108.501 | 28.591 | 28.605 | 0.31702 | 0.31718 | 1.02486 | 1.02457 | 117.6 | 117.9 |
| 3-Methyl-2-thiabutane (Methyl isopropyl sulfide) | " | 108.78 | 109.30 | 28.62 | 28.59 | 0.3174 | 0.3170 | 1.0246 | 1.0236 | 117. | 117. |
| 2-Thiahexane | $C_5H_{12}S$ | 123.68 | 124.34 | 33.09 | 33.11 | 0.3175 | 0.3177 | 1.0264 | 1.0262 | 113. | 113. |
| 3-Thiahexane | " | 124.51 | 125.19 | 33.22 | 33.22 | 0.3188 | 0.3188 | 1.0277 | 1.0273 | 116. | 116. |
| 3-Methyl-2-thiapentane | " | 125.4 | 126.0 | 33.2 | 33.2 | 0.319 | 0.319 | 1.026 | 1.026 | | |
| 4-Methyl-2-thiapentane | " | 125.03 | 125.66 | 33.17 | 33.18 | 0.3183 | 0.3184 | 1.0266 | 1.0264 | 113. | 113. |
| 2-Methyl-3-thiapentane | " | 126.38 | 127.10 | 33.35 | 33.38 | 0.3201 | 0.3203 | 1.0284 | 1.0282 | 117. | 117. |
| 3,3-Dimethyl-2-thiabutane | " | 126.24 | 126.98 | 33.29 | 33.31 | 0.3194 | 0.3196 | 1.0276 | 1.0272 | 116. | 116. |

[a] See footnote a of Table 1b.

TABLE 108b – THIAALKANES, $C_6$

MOLECULAR VOLUME, MOLECULAR REFRACTION, SPECIFIC REFRACTION, REFRACTIVITY INTERCEPT, AND SPECIFIC DISPERSION

April 30, 1952

| Compound | Formula[a] | Molecular Volume[a] $V=M/d$ ml/mole | | Molecular Refraction[a] $V(n_D^2-1)/(n_D^2+2)$ ml/mole | | Specific Refraction[a] $(1/d)(n_D^2-1)/(n_D^2+2)$ ml/g | | Refractivity Intercept[a] $n_D-d/2$ | | Specific Dispersion[a] $10^4(n_F-n_C)/d$ ml/g | |
|---|---|---|---|---|---|---|---|---|---|---|---|
| | | 20°C | 25°C | 20°C | 25°C | 20°C | 25°C | 20°C | 25°C | 20°C | 25°C |
| 2-Thiaheptane | $C_6H_{14}S$ | 140.24 | 140.95 | 37.73 | 37.75 | 0.3191 | 0.3193 | 1.0290 | 1.0288 | 111. | 111. |
| 3-Thiaheptane | " | 141.16 | 141.91 | 37.87 | 37.86 | 0.3203 | 0.3202 | 1.0303 | 1.0297 | 112. | 112. |
| 4-Thiaheptane | " | 141.15 | 141.91 | 37.84 | 37.85 | 0.3200 | 0.3201 | 1.0298 | 1.0295 | 113. | 113. |
| 3-Methyl-2-thiahexane | " | | | | | | | | | | |
| 4-Methyl-2-thiahexane | " | 140.4 | 141.1 | 37.9 | 37.9 | 0.321 | 0.321 | 1.031 | 1.030 | | . |
| 5-Methyl-2-thiahexane | " | | | | | | | | | | |
| 2-Methyl-3-thiahexane | " | 142.99 | 143.75 | 37.98 | 37.99 | 0.3212 | 0.3213 | 1.0306 | 1.0302 | 115. | 115. |
| 4-Methyl-3-thiahexane | " | 141.55 | 142.34 | 37.87 | 37.89 | 0.3203 | 0.3205 | 1.0300 | 1.0298 | 112. | 112. |
| 5-Methyl-3-thiahexane | " | 142.35 | 143.13 | 37.89 | 37.90 | 0.3204 | 0.3205 | 1.0297 | 1.0294 | 114. | 114. |
| 3,3-Dimethyl-2-thiapentane | " | | | | | | | | | | |
| 3,4-Dimethyl-2-thiapentane | " | | | | | | | | | | |
| 4,4-Dimethyl-2-thiapentane | " | | | | | | | | | | |
| 2,2-Dimethyl-3-thiapentane | " | 144.09 | 144.88 | 38.10 | 38.11 | 0.3223 | 0.3223 | 1.0314 | 1.0310 | 116. | 116. |
| 2,4-Dimethyl-3-thiapentane | " | 145.15 | 145.90 | 38.16 | 38.16 | 0.3228 | 0.3228 | 1.0315 | 1.0310 | 116. | 116. |

a See footnote a of Table 1b.

TABLE 109b – ALKYL (1-THIAALKYL) BENZENES, C$_7$ AND C$_8$

MOLECULAR VOLUME, MOLECULAR REFRACTION, SPECIFIC REFRACTION, REFRACTIVITY INTERCEPT, AND SPECIFIC DISPERSION

October 31, 1952

| Compound | Formula | Molecular Volume[a] $V = M/d$ ml/mole | | Molecular Refraction[a] $V(n_D^2-1)/(n_D^2+2)$ ml/mole | | Specific Refraction[a] $(1/d)(n_D^2-1)/(n_D^2+2)$ ml/g | | Refractivity Intercept[a] $n_D - d/2$ | | Specific Dispersion[a] $10^4(n_F-n_C)/d$ ml/g | |
|---|---|---|---|---|---|---|---|---|---|---|---|
| | | 20°C | 25°C | 20°C | 25°C | 20°C | 25°C | 20°C | 25°C | 20°C | 25°C |
| (1-Thiaethyl)-benzene (Methyl phenyl sulfide) | C$_7$H$_8$S | 117.40 | 117.89 | 39.44 | 39.45 | 0.3176 | 0.3177 | 1.0578 | 1.0572 | 221. | 221. |
| (1-Thiapropyl)-benzene (Ethyl phenyl sulfide) | C$_8$H$_{10}$S | 135.37 | 135.97 | 44.22 | 44.25 | 0.3199 | 0.3201 | 1.0564 | 1.0561 | 200. | 200. |
| 2-Methyl-(1-thiaethyl)-benzene | " | 134.2 | 134.7 | 44.4 | 44.4 | 0.321 | 0.321 | 1.061 | 1.060 | | |
| 3-Methyl-(1-thiaethyl)-benzene | " | | | | | | | | | | |
| 4-Methyl-(1-thiaethyl)-benzene | " | 134.6. | 135.1 | 44.4 | 44.4 | 0.321 | 0.321 | 1.060 | 1.059 | 215. | 215. |

[a] See footnote a of Table 1b.

TABLE 110b — ALKYL (1-THIAALKYL) BENZENES, $C_9$

MOLECULAR VOLUME, MOLECULAR REFRACTION, SPECIFIC REFRACTION, REFRACTIVITY INTERCEPT, AND SPECIFIC DISPERSION

October 31, 1952

| Compound | Formula | Molecular Volume[a] $V = M/d$ (ml/mole) | | Molecular Refraction[a] $V(n_D^2-1)/(n_D^2+2)$ (ml/mole) | | Specific Refraction[a] $(1/d)(n_D^2-1)/(n_D^2+2)$ (ml/g) | | Refractivity Intercept[a] $n_D - d/2$ | | Specific Dispersion[a] $10^4(n_F-n_C)/d$ (ml/g) | |
|---|---|---|---|---|---|---|---|---|---|---|---|
| | | 20°C | 25°C | 20°C | 25°C | 20°C | 25°C | 20°C | 25°C | 20°C | 25°C |
| (1-Thiabutyl)-benzene (n-Propyl phenyl sulfide) | $C_9H_{12}S$ | 152.33 | 152.99 | 49.05 | 49.11 | 0.3221 | 0.3226 | 1.0574 | 1.0575 | 196. | 196. |
| (2-Methyl-1-thiapropyl)-benzene (Isopropyl phenyl sulfide) | " | 154.54 | 155.20 | 48.96 | 49.03 | 0.3216 | 0.3221 | 1.0538 | 1.0541 | 192. | 192. |
| 2-Methyl-(1-thiapropyl)-benzene | " | 152.45 | 153.06 | 49.22 | 49.27 | 0.3233 | 0.3236 | 1.0596 | 1.0596 | | |
| 3-Methyl-(1-thiapropyl)-benzene | " | 152.31 | 152.92 | 49.22 | 48.9 | 0.321 | 0.321 | 1.055 | 1.055 | | |
| 4-Methyl-(1-thiapropyl)-benzene | " | 148.5 | 149.1 | 48.8 | 48.8 | 0.320 | 0.321 | 1.058 | 1.058 | | |
| 2-Ethyl-(1-thiaethyl)-benzene | " | | | | | | | | | | |
| 3-Ethyl-(1-thiaethyl)-benzene | " | | | | | | | | | | |
| 4-Ethyl-(1-thiaethyl)-benzene | " | | | | | | | | | | |
| 2,3-Dimethyl-(1-thiaethyl)-benzene | " | 149.4 | 150.0 | 49.4 | 49.4 | 0.324 | 0.324 | 1.066 | 1.066 | 208. | 208. |
| 2,4-Dimethyl-(1-thiaethyl)-benzene | " | | | | | | | | | | |
| 2,5-Dimethyl-(1-thiaethyl)-benzene | " | | | | | | | | | | |
| 2,6-Dimethyl-(1-thiaethyl)-benzene | " | | | | | | | | | | |
| 3,4-Dimethyl-(1-thiaethyl)-benzene | " | | | | | | | | | | |
| 3,5-Dimethyl-(1-thiaethyl)-benzene | " | | | | | | | | | | |

[a] See footnote a of Table 1b.

TABLE 111b – ALKYL THIACYCLOPROPANES, C$_2$ TO C$_4$

MOLECULAR VOLUME, MOLECULAR REFRACTION, SPECIFIC REFRACTION, REFRACTIVITY INTERCEPT, AND SPECIFIC DISPERSION

October 31, 1952

| Compound | Formula | Molecular Volume[a] $V = M/d$ ml/mole | | Molecular Refraction[a] $V(n_D^2-1)/(n_D^2+2)$ ml/mole | | Specific Refraction[a] $(1/d)(n_D^2-1)/(n_D^2+2)$ ml/g | | Refractivity Intercept[a] $n_D - d/2$ | | Specific Dispersion[a] $10^4(n_F-n_C)/d$ ml/g | |
|---|---|---|---|---|---|---|---|---|---|---|---|
| | | 20°C | 25°C | 20°C | 25°C | 20°C | 25°C | 20°C | 25°C | 20°C | 25°C |
| Thiacyclopropane (Ethylene sulfide) | C$_2$H$_4$S | 59.3 | 59.7 | 17.2 | 17.2 | 28.5 | 28.6 | 0.984 | 0.984 | 128. | 128. |
| 2-Methylthiacyclopropane | C$_3$H$_6$S | 78.5 | 79.0 | 22.1 | 22.1 | 29.8 | 29.8 | 1.003 | 1.003 | 126. | 126. |
| 2-Ethylthiacyclopropane | C$_4$H$_8$S | 95.1 | 95.6 | 26.6 | 26.7 | 30.2 | 30.3 | 1.009 | 1.009 | | |
| 2,2-Dimethylthiacyclopropane | " | | | | | | | | | | |
| 2,cis-3-Dimethylthiacyclopropane | " | | | | | | | | | | |
| 2,trans-3-Dimethylthiacyclopropane | " | | | | | | | | | | |

a See footnote a of Table 1b.

TABLE 112b – ALKYL THIACYCLOPENTANES, C$_4$ TO C$_6$

MOLECULAR VOLUME, MOLECULAR REFRACTION, SPECIFIC REFRACTION, REFRACTIVITY INTERCEPT, AND SPECIFIC DISPERSION

October 31, 1952

| Compound | Formula | Molecular Volume[a] $V=M/d$ (ml/mole) | | Molecular Refraction[a] $V(n_D^2-1)/(n_D^2+2)$ (ml/mole) | | Specific Refraction[a] $(1/d)(n_D^2-1)/(n_D^2+2)$ (ml/g) | | Refractivity Intercept[a] $n_D-d/2$ | | Specific Dispersion[a] $10^4(n_F-n_C)/d$ (ml/g) | |
|---|---|---|---|---|---|---|---|---|---|---|---|
| | | 20°C | 25°C | 20°C | 25°C | 20°C | 25°C | 20°C | 25°C | 20°C | 25°C |
| Thiacyclopentane (Tetrahydrothiophene) | C$_4$H$_8$S | 88.286 | 88.721 | 26.179 | 26.190 | 0.29691 | 0.29704 | 1.00548 | 1.00528 | 114.2 | 113.7 |
| 2-Methylthiacyclopentane | C$_5$H$_{10}$S | 106.99 | 107.44 | 30.98 | 30.98 | 0.3032 | 0.3031 | 1.0133 | 1.0128 | 114. | 114. |
| 3-Methylthiacyclopentane | " | 106.08 | 106.62 | 30.80 | 30.84 | 0.3014 | 0.3017 | 1.0107 | 1.0110 | 112. | 112. |
| 2-Ethylthiacyclopentane | C$_6$H$_{12}$S | 123.1 | 123.8 | 35.6 | 35.6 | 0.306 | 0.306 | 1.018 | 1.018 | | |
| 3-Ethylthiacyclopentane | " | 122.3 | 123.0 | 35.4 | 35.5 | 0.305 | 0.305 | 1.016 | 1.016 | | |
| 2,2-Dimethylthiacyclopentane | " | | | | | | | | | | |
| 2,cis-3-Dimethylthiacyclopentane | " | | | | | | | | | | |
| 2,trans-3-Dimethylthiacyclopentane | " | | | | | | | | | | |
| 2,cis-4-Dimethylthiacyclopentane | " | | | | | | | | | | |
| 2,trans-4-Dimethylthiacyclopentane | " | | | | | | | | | | |
| 2,cis-5-Dimethylthiacyclopentane | " | 126.03 | 126.64 | 35.80 | 35.81 | 0.3080 | 0.3081 | 1.0188 | 1.0186 | 114. | 114. |
| 2,trans-5-Dimethylthiacyclopentane | " | 126.49 | 127.13 | 35.78 | 35.81 | 0.3079 | 0.3081 | 1.0182 | 1.0181 | 114. | 114. |
| 3,3-Dimethylthiacyclopentane | " | | | | | | | | | | |
| 3,cis-4-Dimethylthiacyclopentane | " | | | | | | | | | | |
| 3,trans-4-Dimethylthiacyclopentane | " | | | | | | | | | | |

a See footnote a of Table 1b.

TABLE 113b – ALKYL THIACYCLOHEXANES, C$_5$ TO C$_7$

MOLECULAR VOLUME, MOLECULAR REFRACTION, SPECIFIC REFRACTION, REFRACTIVITY INTERCEPT, AND SPECIFIC DISPERSION

October 31, 1952

| Compound | Formula[a] | Molecular Volume[a] $V=M/d$ (ml/mole) | | Molecular Refraction[a] $V(n_D^2-1)/(n_D^2+2)$ (ml/mole) | | Specific Refraction[a] $(1/d)(n_D^2-1)/(n_D^2+2)$ (ml/g) | | Refractivity Intercept[a] $n_D-d/2$ | | Specific Dispersion[a] $10^4(n_F-n_c)/d$ (ml/g) | |
|---|---|---|---|---|---|---|---|---|---|---|---|
| | | 20°C | 25°C | 20°C | 25°C | 20°C | 25°C | 20°C | 25°C | 20°C | 25°C |
| Thiacyclohexane | C$_5$H$_{10}$S | 103.69 | 104.18 | 30.84 | 30.85 | 0.3018 | 0.3019 | 1.0139 | 1.0136 | 114. | 114. |
| 2-Methylthiacyclohexane | C$_6$H$_{12}$S | 123.27 | 123.89 | 35.67 | 35.70 | 0.3069 | 0.3072 | 1.0191 | 1.0190 | 114. | 114. |
| 3-Methylthiacyclohexane | " | 122.69 | 123.25 | 35.61 | 35.63 | 0.3064 | 0.3065 | 1.0186 | 1.0184 | 113. | 113. |
| 4-Methylthiacyclohexane | " | 122.71 | 123.29 | 35.62 | 35.64 | 0.3065 | 0.3066 | 1.0188 | 1.0186 | 113. | 113. |
| 2-Ethylthiacyclohexane | C$_7$H$_{14}$S | | | | | | | | | | |
| 3-Ethylthiacyclohexane | " | | | | | | | | | | |
| 4-Ethylthiacyclohexane | " | | | | | | | | | | |
| 2,2-Dimethylthiacyclohexane | " | | | | | | | | | | |
| 2,cis-3-Dimethylthiacyclohexane | " | | | | | | | | | | |
| 2,trans-3-Dimethylthiacyclohexane | " | | | | | | | | | | |
| 2,cis-4-Dimethylthiacyclohexane | " | | | | | | | | | | |
| 2,trans-4-Dimethylthiacyclohexane | " | | | | | | | | | | |
| 2,cis-5-Dimethylthiacyclohexane | " | | | | | | | | | | |
| 2,trans-5-Dimethylthiacyclohexane | " | | | | | | | | | | |
| 2,cis-6-Dimethylthiacyclohexane | " | | | | | | | | | | |
| 2,trans-6-Dimethylthiacyclohexane | " | | | | | | | | | | |
| 3,3-Dimethylthiacyclohexane | " | | | | | | | | | | |
| 3,cis-4-Dimethylthiacyclohexane | " | | | | | | | | | | |
| 3,trans-4-Dimethylthiacyclohexane | " | | | | | | | | | | |
| 3,cis-5-Dimethylthiacyclohexane | " | | | | | | | | | | |
| 3,trans-5-Dimethylthiacyclohexane | " | | | | | | | | | | |
| 4,4-Dimethylthiacyclohexane | " | | | | | | | | | | |

[a] See footnote a of Table 1b.

## TABLE 114b – ALKYL THIOPHENES, $C_4$ TO $C_6$
### MOLECULAR VOLUME, MOLECULAR REFRACTION, SPECIFIC REFRACTION, REFRACTIVITY INTERCEPT, AND SPECIFIC DISPERSION
#### April 30, 1952

| Compound | Formula | Molecular Volume[a] $V = M/d$ (ml/mole) | | Molecular Refraction[a] $V(n_0^2-1)/(n_0^2+2)$ (ml/mole) | | Specific Refraction[a] $(1/d)(n_0^2-1)/(n_0^2+2)$ (ml/g) | | Refractivity Intercept[a] $n_0-d/2$ | | Specific Dispersion[a] $10^4(n_F-n_c)/d$ (ml/g) | |
|---|---|---|---|---|---|---|---|---|---|---|---|
| | | 20°C | 25°C | 20°C | 25°C | 20°C | 25°C | 20°C | 25°C | 20°C | 25°C |
| Thiophene | $C_4H_4S$ | 79.014 | 79.460 | 24.365 | 24.379 | 0.28958 | 0.28975 | 0.99648 | 0.99628 | 162.7 | 163.1 |
| 2-Methylthiophene | $C_5H_6S$ | 96.31 | 96.82 | 29.29 | 29.31 | 0.2984 | 0.2986 | 1.0106 | 1.0104 | 160. | 160. |
| 3-Methylthiophene | " | 96.067 | 96.573 | 29.225 | 29.244 | 0.29772 | 0.29791 | 1.00950 | 1.00934 | 159.0 | 158.7 |
| 2-Ethylthiophene | $C_6H_8S$ | 112.98 | 113.55 | 33.91 | 33.93 | 0.3023 | 0.3024 | 1.0157 | 1.0154 | 154. | 154. |
| 3-Ethylthiophene | " | 112.41 | 112.97 | 33.88 | 33.90 | 0.3019 | 0.3022 | 1.0156 | 1.0154 | | |
| 2,3-Dimethylthiophene | " | 111.95 | 112.53 | 33.99 | 34.02 | 0.3030 | 0.3033 | 1.0182 | 1.0181 | | |
| 2,4-Dimethylthiophene | " | 112.69 | 113.27 | 33.73 | 33.75 | 0.3006 | 0.3009 | 1.0126 | 1.0126 | | |
| 2,5-Dimethylthiophene | " | 113.90 | 114.49 | 34.23 | 34.26 | 0.3051 | 0.3054 | 1.0204 | 1.0204 | 162. | 162. |
| 3,4-Dimethylthiophene | " | 111.3 | 111.9 | 33.9 | 34.0 | 0.302 | 0.303 | 1.017 | 1.017 | 156. | 156. |

[a] See footnote a of Table 1b.

## TABLE 115b – ALKYL THIOPHENES, $C_7$

### MOLECULAR VOLUME, MOLECULAR REFRACTION, SPECIFIC REFRACTION, REFRACTIVITY INTERCEPT, AND SPECIFIC DISPERSION

April 30, 1952

| Compound | Formula | Molecular Volume[a] $V=M/d$ (ml/mole) | | Molecular Refraction[a] $V(n_D^2-1)/(n_D^2+2)$ (ml/mole) | | Specific Refraction[a] $(1/d)(n_D^2-1)/(n_D^2+2)$ (ml/g) | | Refractivity Intercept[a] $n_D-d/2$ | | Specific Dispersion[a] $10^4(n_F-n_C)/d$ (ml/g) | |
|---|---|---|---|---|---|---|---|---|---|---|---|
| | | 20°C | 25°C | 20°C | 25°C | 20°C | 25°C | 20°C | 25°C | 20°C | 25°C |
| 2-Propylthiophene | $C_7H_{10}S$ | 130.29 | 130.94 | 38.64 | 38.66 | 0.3061 | 0.3063 | 1.0206 | 1.0204 | 149. | 149. |
| 3-Propylthiophene | " | 129.91 | 130.54 | 38.58 | 38.60 | 0.3056 | 0.3058 | 1.0199 | 1.0196 | 148. | 148. |
| 2-Isopropylthiophene | " | 130.42 | 131.02 | 38.61 | 38.62 | 0.3059 | 0.3060 | 1.0199 | 1.0196 | 150. | 150. |
| 3-Isopropylthiophene | " | 129.68 | 130.28 | 38.48 | 38.49 | 0.3048 | 0.3050 | 1.0186 | 1.0183 | 145. | 145. |
| 2-Methyl-3-ethylthiophene | " | | | | | | | | | | |
| 2-Methyl-4-ethylthiophene | " | 129.56 | 130.17 | 38.74 | 38.76 | 0.3069 | 0.3071 | 1.0227 | 1.0225 | | |
| 2-Methyl-5-ethylthiophene | " | 130.64 | 131.23 | 38.90 | 38.91 | 0.3082 | 0.3083 | 1.0242 | 1.0239 | | |
| 3-Methyl-2-ethylthiophene | " | 128.60 | 129.20 | 38.49 | 38.51 | 0.3050 | 0.3051 | 1.0198 | 1.0196 | | |
| 3-Methyl-4-ethylthiophene | " | | | | | | | | | | |
| 3-Methyl-5-ethylthiophene | " | | | | | | | 1.023 | 1.023 | | |
| 2,3,4-Trimethylthiophene | " | 126.8 | 127.3 | 38.6 | 38.6 | 0.306 | 0.306 | | | | |
| 2,3,5-Trimethylthiophene | " | 129.41 | 130.01 | 38.78 | 38.81 | 0.3073 | 0.3075 | 1.0236 | 1.0234 | | |

a See footnote a of Table 1b.

TABLE 20c (PART 1), Page 1 - NORMAL PARAFFINS, $C_1$ TO $C_{20}$

VISCOSITY (ABSOLUTE)

For the Normal Liquid Range, at Atmospheric Pressure

March 31, 1947; October 31, 1952

Viscosity (absolute) in centipoises[a]

| Compound (liquid) | Formula[a] | Temperature in °C | | | | | | | | | | | | | | | |
|---|---|---|---|---|---|---|---|---|---|---|---|---|---|---|---|---|---|
| | | -190 | -185 | -180 | -175 | -170 | -165 | -160 | -155 | -150 | -145 | -140 | -135 | -130 | -125 | -120 | -115 |
| Methane | $CH_4$ | | 0.226b | 0.188 | 0.161 | 0.142 | 0.127 | 0.115c | | | | | | | | | |
| Ethane | $C_2H_6$ | | | | 0.985 | 0.805 | 0.673 | 0.574 | 0.500 | 0.442 | 0.396 | 0.359 | 0.326 | 0.301 | 0.278 | 0.257 | 0.238 |
| Propane | $C_3H_8$ | 13.8b | 8.78 | 5.96 | 4.26 | 3.18 | 2.46 | 1.96 | 1.60 | 1.34 | 1.14 | 0.984 | 0.861 | 0.762 | 0.681 | 0.614 | 0.558 |
| n-Butane | $C_4H_{10}$ | | | | | | | | | | | | | | | | |
| n-Pentane | $C_5H_{12}$ | | | | | | | | | | | | | 3.63b | 2.89 | 2.35 | 1.96 |
| n-Hexane | $C_6H_{14}$ | | | | | | | | | | | | | | | | |
| n-Heptane | $C_7H_{16}$ | | | | | | | | | | | | | | | | |
| n-Octane | $C_8H_{18}$ | | | | | | | | | | | | | | | | |

Viscosity (absolute) in centipoises[a]

| Compound (liquid) | Formula[a] | Temperature in °C | | | | | | | | | | | | | | | |
|---|---|---|---|---|---|---|---|---|---|---|---|---|---|---|---|---|---|
| | | -110 | -105 | -100 | -95 | -90 | -85 | -80 | -75 | -70 | -65 | -60 | -55 | -50 | -45 | -40 | -35 |
| Methane | $CH_4$ | | | | | | | | | | | | | | | | |
| Ethane | $C_2H_6$ | 0.222 | 0.207 | 0.195 | 0.183 | 0.172 | 0.162c | | | | | | | | | | |
| Propane | $C_3H_8$ | 0.510 | 0.469 | 0.433 | 0.402 | 0.374 | 0.350 | 0.327 | 0.307 | 0.288 | 0.272 | 0.256 | 0.242 | 0.228 | 0.216 | 0.205c | |
| n-Butane | $C_4H_{10}$ | | | | | 0.63 | 0.58 | 0.536 | 0.497 | 0.462 | 0.431 | 0.403 | 0.378 | 0.355 | 0.335 | 0.315 | 0.298 |
| n-Pentane | $C_5H_{12}$ | 1.66 | 1.43 | 1.24 | 1.09 | 0.973 | 0.874 | 0.791 | 0.720 | 0.659 | 0.607 | 0.562 | 0.522 | 0.487 | 0.455 | 0.428 | 0.403 |
| n-Hexane | $C_6H_{14}$ | | | | | 1.83 | 1.58 | 1.38 | 1.22 | 1.09 | 0.978 | 0.888 | 0.809 | 0.741 | 0.683 | 0.632 | 0.587 |
| n-Heptane | $C_7H_{16}$ | | | | | 3.77 | 3.11 | 2.61 | 2.22 | 1.918 | 1.675 | 1.476 | 1.313 | 1.177 | 1.063 | 0.9653 | 0.8819 |
| n-Octane | $C_8H_{18}$ | | | | | | | | | | | | 2.12 | 1.86 | 1.64 | 1.46 | 1.31 |

a See footnote a of Table 1c.    b For the undercooled liquid below the normal freezing point.    c At saturation pressure.

TABLE 20c (PART 1), Page 2 - NORMAL PARAFFINS, C₁ TO C₂₀

VISCOSITY (ABSOLUTE)

For the Normal Liquid Range, at Atmospheric Pressure

March 31, 1947; October 31, 1952

| Compound (liquid) | Formula | Temperature in °C | | | | | | | | | | | | | | | |
|---|---|---|---|---|---|---|---|---|---|---|---|---|---|---|---|---|---|
| | | -30 | -25 | -20 | -15 | -10 | -5 | 0 | 5 | 10 | 15 | 20 | 25 | 30 | 35 | 40 | 45 |
| | | Viscosity (absolute) in centipoises[a] | | | | | | | | | | | | | | | |
| Methane | $CH_4$ | | | | | | | | | | | | | | | | |
| Ethane | $C_2H_6$ | | | | | | | | | | | | | | | | |
| Propane | $C_3H_8$ | | | | | | | | | | | | | | | | |
| n-Butane | $C_4H_{10}$ | 0.282 | 0.267 | 0.253 | 0.241 | 0.229 | 0.219 | 0.210[b] | | | | | | | | | |
| n-Pentane | $C_5H_{12}$ | 0.380 | 0.359 | 0.341 | 0.323 | 0.307 | 0.293 | 0.279 | 0.267 | 0.255 | 0.245 | 0.235 | 0.225 | 0.216 | 0.207 | | |
| n-Hexane | $C_6H_{14}$ | 0.547 | 0.511 | 0.480 | 0.451 | 0.426 | 0.402 | 0.3810 | 0.3615 | 0.3436 | 0.3275 | 0.3126 | 0.2985 | 0.2854 | 0.2732 | 0.2619 | 0.2512 |
| n-Heptane | $C_7H_{16}$ | 0.8098 | 0.7468 | 0.6916 | 0.6428 | 0.5995 | 0.5608 | 0.5262 | 0.4949 | 0.4666 | 0.4412 | 0.4181 | 0.3967 | 0.3772 | 0.3592 | 0.3426 | 0.3272 |
| n-Octane | $C_8H_{18}$ | 1.183 | 1.074 | 0.981 | 0.900 | 0.829 | 0.767 | 0.7125 | 0.6638 | 0.6203 | 0.5815 | 0.5466 | 0.5151 | 0.4865 | 0.4605 | 0.4368 | 0.4148 |

| Compound (liquid) | Formula | Temperature in °C | | | | | | | | | | | | | | | |
|---|---|---|---|---|---|---|---|---|---|---|---|---|---|---|---|---|---|
| | | 50 | 55 | 60 | 65 | 70 | 75 | 80 | 85 | 90 | 95 | 100 | 105 | 110 | 115 | 120 | 125 |
| | | Viscosity (absolute) in centipoises[a] | | | | | | | | | | | | | | | |
| Methane | $CH_4$ | | | | | | | | | | | | | | | | |
| Ethane | $C_2H_6$ | | | | | | | | | | | | | | | | |
| Propane | $C_3H_8$ | | | | | | | | | | | | | | | | |
| n-Butane | $C_4H_{10}$ | | | | | | | | | | | | | | | | |
| n-Pentane | $C_5H_{12}$ | | | | | | | | | | | | | | | | |
| n-Hexane | $C_6H_{14}$ | 0.2411 | 0.2314 | 0.2223 | 0.2134 | 0.2050[b] | | | | | | | | | | | |
| n-Heptane | $C_7H_{16}$ | 0.3128 | 0.2993 | 0.2867 | 0.2747 | 0.2635 | 0.2530 | 0.2431 | 0.2337 | 0.2250 | 0.2165 | 0.206[b] | | | | | |
| n-Octane | $C_8H_{18}$ | 0.3947 | 0.3760 | 0.3587 | 0.3425 | 0.3274 | 0.3134 | 0.3004 | 0.2882 | 0.2767 | 0.2658 | 0.2555 | 0.2458 | 0.2366 | 0.2278 | 0.2195 | 0.2115 |

[a] See footnote a of Table 1c.  [b] At saturation pressure.

TABLE 20c (PART 1), Page 3 - NORMAL PARAFFINS, C$_1$ TO C$_{20}$

VISCOSITY (ABSOLUTE)

For the Normal Liquid Range, at Atmospheric Pressure

March 31, 1947; October 31, 1952

Temperature in °C — Viscosity (absolute) in centipoises[a]

| Compound (liquid) | Formula | 20 | 15 | 10 | 5 | 0 | -5 | -10 | -15 | -20 | -25 | -30 | -35 | -40 | -45 | -50 | -55 |
|---|---|---|---|---|---|---|---|---|---|---|---|---|---|---|---|---|---|
| n-Nonane | C$_9$H$_{20}$ | 0.7160 | 0.7681 | 0.8267 | 0.8932 | 0.9688 | 1.055 | 1.154 | 1.269 | 1.403 | 1.561 | 1.748 | 1.97 | 2.24 | 2.58 | 2.99 | 3.52[b] |
| n-Decane | C$_{10}$H$_{22}$ | 0.9284 | 1.004 | 1.091 | 1.190 | 1.304 | 1.436 | 1.590 | 1.771 | 1.987 | 2.245 | 2.559[b] | | | | | |
| n-Undecane | C$_{11}$H$_{24}$ | 1.189 | 1.297 | 1.421 | 1.565 | 1.733 | 1.930 | 2.163 | 2.442 | 2.779 | 3.192 | | | | | | |
| n-Dodecane | C$_{12}$H$_{26}$ | 1.508 | 1.658 | 1.833 | 2.037 | 2.278 | 2.565 | 2.910[b] | | | | | | | | | |
| n-Tridecane | C$_{13}$H$_{28}$ | 1.886 | 2.089 | 2.328 | 2.611 | 2.950 | 3.358 | | | | | | | | | | |
| n-Tetradecane | C$_{14}$H$_{30}$ | 2.342 | 2.616 | 2.940 | 3.326[b] | | | | | | | | | | | | |
| n-Pentadecane | C$_{15}$H$_{32}$ | 2.872 | 3.232 | 3.663 | | | | | | | | | | | | | |
| n-Hexadecane | C$_{16}$H$_{34}$ | 3.484 | | | | | | | | | | | | | | | |
| n-Heptadecane | C$_{17}$H$_{36}$ | 4.209[b] | | | | | | | | | | | | | | | |
| n-Octadecane | C$_{18}$H$_{38}$ | | | | | | | | | | | | | | | | |
| n-Nonadecane | C$_{19}$H$_{40}$ | | | | | | | | | | | | | | | | |
| n-Eicosane | C$_{20}$H$_{42}$ | | | | | | | | | | | | | | | | |

Temperature in °C — Viscosity (absolute) in centipoises[a]

| Compound (liquid) | Formula | 100 | 95 | 90 | 85 | 80 | 75 | 70 | 65 | 60 | 55 | 50 | 45 | 40 | 35 | 30 | 25 |
|---|---|---|---|---|---|---|---|---|---|---|---|---|---|---|---|---|---|
| n-Nonane | C$_9$H$_{20}$ | 0.3100 | 0.3233 | 0.3375 | 0.3525 | 0.3687 | 0.3860 | 0.4047 | 0.4251 | 0.4472 | 0.4710 | 0.4970 | 0.5252 | 0.5562 | 0.5903 | 0.6279 | 0.6696 |
| n-Decane | C$_{10}$H$_{22}$ | 0.3715 | 0.3885 | 0.4068 | 0.4264 | 0.4476 | 0.4704 | 0.4951 | 0.5222 | 0.5517 | 0.5839 | 0.6192 | 0.6581 | 0.7010 | 0.7487 | 0.801[b] | 0.8614 |
| n-Undecane | C$_{11}$H$_{24}$ | 0.4403 | 0.4618 | 0.4850 | 0.5100 | 0.5371 | 0.5666 | 0.5988 | 0.6342 | 0.6731 | 0.7156 | 0.7627 | 0.8150 | 0.8733 | 0.9385 | 1.012 | 1.095 |
| n-Dodecane | C$_{12}$H$_{26}$ | 0.5183 | 0.5452 | 0.5743 | 0.6056 | 0.6398 | 0.6775 | 0.7188 | 0.7644 | 0.8147 | 0.8703 | 0.9321 | 1.001 | 1.079 | 1.166 | 1.265 | 1.378 |
| n-Tridecane | C$_{13}$H$_{28}$ | 0.6022 | 0.6351 | 0.6709 | 0.7099 | 0.7527 | 0.7996 | 0.8513 | 0.9087 | 0.9725 | 1.043 | 1.123 | 1.212 | 1.314 | 1.428 | 1.560 | 1.711 |
| n-Tetradecane | C$_{14}$H$_{30}$ | 0.6958 | 0.7357 | 0.7795 | 0.8272 | 0.8798 | 0.9379 | 1.002 | 1.074 | 1.154 | 1.244 | 1.345 | 1.459 | 1.590 | 1.739 | 1.910 | 2.110 |
| n-Pentadecane | C$_{15}$H$_{32}$ | 0.7949 | 0.8428 | 0.8953 | 0.9530 | 1.017 | 1.087 | 1.166 | 1.254 | 1.353 | 1.465 | 1.591 | 1.735 | 1.900 | 2.090 | 2.310 | 2.568 |
| n-Hexadecane | C$_{16}$H$_{34}$ | 0.9019 | 0.9585 | 1.021 | 1.090 | 1.166 | 1.251 | 1.346 | 1.453 | 1.573 | 1.710 | 1.866 | 2.044 | 2.250 | 2.489 | 2.766 | 3.095 |
| n-Heptadecane | C$_{17}$H$_{36}$ | 1.018 | 1.084 | 1.158 | 1.239 | 1.330 | 1.432 | 1.546 | 1.674 | 1.820 | 1.986 | 2.176 | 2.395 | 2.650 | 2.947 | 3.296 | 3.711 |
| n-Octadecane | C$_{18}$H$_{38}$ | 1.140 | 1.217 | 1.303 | 1.398 | 1.505 | 1.625 | 1.760 | 1.912 | 2.087 | 2.286 | 2.516 | 2.782 | 3.093 | 3.458 | 3.891 | |
| n-Nonadecane | C$_{19}$H$_{40}$ | 1.269 | 1.359 | 1.458 | 1.568 | 1.693 | 1.833 | 1.992 | 2.172 | 2.379 | 2.616 | 2.891 | 3.212 | 3.588 | 4.033 | 4.565[b] | |
| n-Eicosane | C$_{20}$H$_{42}$ | 1.410 | 1.513 | 1.627 | 1.755 | 1.900 | 2.063 | 2.249 | 2.461 | 2.706 | 2.998 | 3.316 | 3.701 | 4.156 | 4.699[b] | | |

a See footnote a of Table 1c.  b For the undercooled liquid below the normal freezing point.

## TABLE 20c (PART 1), Page 4 – NORMAL PARAFFINS, C₁ TO C₂₀

### VISCOSITY (ABSOLUTE)

For the Normal Liquid Range, at Atmospheric Pressure

March 31, 1947; October 31, 1952

**Temperature in °C — Viscosity (absolute) in centipoises[a]**

| Compound (liquid) | Formula | 105 | 110 | 115 | 120 | 125 | 130 | 135 | 140 | 145 | 150 | 155 | 160 | 165 | 170 | 175 | 180 |
|---|---|---|---|---|---|---|---|---|---|---|---|---|---|---|---|---|---|
| n-Nonane | $C_9H_{20}$ | 0.2975 | 0.2858 | 0.2746 | 0.2641 | 0.2540 | 0.2445 | 0.2356 | 0.2271 | 0.2191 | 0.2115 | | | | | | |
| n-Decane | $C_{10}H_{22}$ | 0.3556 | 0.3408 | 0.3268 | 0.3137 | 0.3013 | 0.2896 | 0.2786 | 0.2683 | 0.2583 | 0.2469 | 0.2399 | 0.2313 | 0.2231 | 0.2152 | 0.2075[b] | |
| n-Undecane | $C_{11}H_{24}$ | 0.4203 | 0.4018 | 0.3843 | 0.3680 | 0.3528 | 0.3385 | 0.3251 | 0.3124 | 0.3005 | 0.2892 | 0.2784 | 0.2683 | 0.2585 | 0.2493 | 0.2404 | 0.2320 |
| n-Dodecane | $C_{12}H_{26}$ | 0.4936 | 0.4706 | 0.4491 | 0.4291 | 0.4105 | 0.3932 | 0.3769 | 0.3617 | 0.3473 | 0.3338 | 0.3210 | 0.3089 | 0.2974 | 0.2865 | 0.2762 | 0.2664 |
| n-Tridecane | $C_{13}H_{28}$ | 0.5720 | 0.5441 | 0.5181 | 0.4940 | 0.4716 | 0.4508 | 0.4314 | 0.4133 | 0.3963 | 0.3803 | 0.3653 | 0.3511 | 0.3377 | 0.3251 | 0.3131 | 0.3017 |
| n-Tetradecane | $C_{14}H_{30}$ | 0.6589 | 0.6251 | 0.5941 | 0.5654 | 0.5388 | 0.5140 | 0.4910 | 0.4696 | 0.4495 | 0.4307 | 0.4131 | 0.3966 | 0.3811 | 0.3664 | 0.3526 | 0.3395 |
| n-Pentadecane | $C_{15}H_{32}$ | 0.7513 | 0.7112 | 0.6743 | 0.6403 | 0.6089 | 0.5800 | 0.5530 | 0.5280 | 0.5047 | 0.4830 | 0.4627 | 0.4437 | 0.4257 | 0.4088 | 0.3930 | 0.3781 |
| n-Hexadecane | $C_{16}H_{34}$ | 0.8504 | 0.8033 | 0.7600 | 0.7203 | 0.6837 | 0.6499 | 0.6188 | 0.5900 | 0.5632 | 0.5383 | 0.5149 | 0.4930 | 0.4726 | 0.4535 | 0.4355 | 0.4166 |
| n-Heptadecane | $C_{17}H_{36}$ | 0.9576 | 0.9026 | 0.8524 | 0.8064 | 0.7641 | 0.7251 | 0.6892 | 0.6560 | 0.6253 | 0.5968 | 0.5702 | 0.5454 | 0.5223 | 0.5006 | 0.4802 | 0.4611 |
| n-Octadecane | $C_{18}H_{38}$ | 1.070 | 1.006 | 0.948 | 0.896 | 0.847 | 0.803 | 0.762 | 0.724 | 0.689 | 0.657 | 0.627 | 0.599 | 0.573 | 0.548 | 0.526 | 0.504 |
| n-Nonadecane | $C_{19}H_{40}$ | 1.189 | 1.116 | 1.050 | 0.989 | 0.934 | 0.884 | 0.838 | 0.795 | 0.756 | 0.719 | 0.686 | 0.654 | 0.625 | 0.598 | 0.573 | 0.549 |
| n-Eicosane | $C_{20}H_{42}$ | 1.318 | 1.235 | 1.159 | 1.091 | 1.028 | 0.971 | 0.919 | 0.871 | 0.827 | 0.786 | 0.748 | 0.713 | 0.680 | 0.650 | 0.622 | 0.596 |

**Temperature in °C — Viscosity (absolute) in centipoises[a]**

| Compound (liquid) | Formula | 185 | 190 | 195 | 200 | 205 | 210 | 215 | 220 | 225 | 230 | 235 | 240 | 245 | 250 | 255 | 260 |
|---|---|---|---|---|---|---|---|---|---|---|---|---|---|---|---|---|---|
| n-Nonane | $C_9H_{20}$ | | | | | | | | | | | | | | | | |
| n-Decane | $C_{10}H_{22}$ | | | | | | | | | | | | | | | | |
| n-Undecane | $C_{11}H_{24}$ | 0.2239 | 0.2161 | 0.2087 | | | | | | | | | | | | | |
| n-Dodecane | $C_{12}H_{26}$ | 0.2570 | 0.2480 | 0.2394 | 0.2311 | 0.2230 | 0.2153 | 0.2076 | | | | | | | | | |
| n-Tridecane | $C_{13}H_{28}$ | 0.2909 | 0.2807 | 0.2709 | 0.2616 | 0.2524 | 0.2435 | 0.2350 | 0.2268 | 0.2189 | 0.2114 | 0.2040 | | | | | |
| n-Tetradecane | $C_{14}H_{30}$ | 0.3271 | 0.3153 | 0.3041 | 0.2935 | 0.2831 | 0.2733 | 0.2638 | 0.2547 | 0.2459 | 0.2375 | 0.2295 | 0.2218 | 0.2145 | 0.2074 | 0.201[b] | |
| n-Pentadecane | $C_{15}H_{32}$ | 0.3640 | 0.3506 | 0.3380 | 0.3261 | 0.3145 | 0.3034 | 0.2928 | 0.2827 | 0.2730 | 0.2638 | 0.2549 | 0.2464 | 0.2384 | 0.2307 | 0.223 | 0.216 |
| n-Hexadecane | $C_{16}H_{34}$ | 0.4026 | 0.3875 | 0.3732 | 0.3597 | 0.3468 | 0.3346 | 0.3228 | 0.3116 | 0.3009 | 0.2907 | 0.2810 | 0.2718 | 0.2629 | 0.2544 | 0.246 | 0.238 |
| n-Heptadecane | $C_{17}H_{36}$ | 0.4431 | 0.4262 | 0.4102 | 0.3951 | 0.3807 | 0.3671 | 0.3541 | 0.3417 | 0.3299 | 0.3187 | 0.3060 | 0.2978 | 0.2880 | 0.2787 | 0.270 | 0.261 |
| n-Octadecane | $C_{18}H_{38}$ | 0.484 | 0.465 | 0.448 | 0.431 | 0.415 | 0.400 | 0.385 | 0.372 | 0.359 | 0.347 | 0.335 | 0.324 | 0.313 | 0.303 | 0.29 | 0.28 |
| n-Nonadecane | $C_{19}H_{40}$ | 0.526 | 0.506 | 0.486 | 0.468 | 0.450 | 0.433 | 0.417 | 0.402 | 0.388 | 0.375 | 0.362 | 0.350 | 0.338 | 0.327 | 0.32 | 0.31 |
| n-Eicosane | $C_{20}H_{42}$ | 0.571 | 0.548 | 0.526 | 0.506 | 0.486 | 0.468 | 0.451 | 0.435 | 0.419 | 0.404 | 0.390 | 0.377 | 0.365 | 0.353 | 0.34 | 0.33 |

a See footnote a of Table 1c.

b At saturation pressure.

TABLE 20c (PART 1), Page 5— NORMAL PARAFFINS, $C_1$ TO $C_{20}$

VISCOSITY (ABSOLUTE)

For the Normal Liquid Range, at Atmospheric Pressure

March 31, 1947; October 31, 1952

Temperature in °C

Viscosity (absolute) in centipoises[a]

| Compound (liquid) | Formula | 265 | 270 | 275 | 280 | 285 | 290 | 295 | 300 | 305 | 310 | 315 | 320 | 325 | 330 | 335 | 340 |
|---|---|---|---|---|---|---|---|---|---|---|---|---|---|---|---|---|---|
| n-Nonane | $C_9H_{20}$ | | | | | | | | | | | | | | | | |
| n-Decane | $C_{10}H_{22}$ | | | | | | | | | | | | | | | | |
| n-Undecane | $C_{11}H_{24}$ | | | | | | | | | | | | | | | | |
| n-Dodecane | $C_{12}H_{26}$ | | | | | | | | | | | | | | | | |
| n-Tridecane | $C_{13}H_{28}$ | | | | | | | | | | | | | | | | |
| n-Tetradecane | $C_{14}H_{30}$ | | | | | | | | | | | | | | | | |
| n-Pentadecane | $C_{15}H_{32}$ | 0.209 | 0.202 | | | | | | | | | | | | | | |
| n-Hexadecane | $C_{16}H_{34}$ | 0.231 | 0.223 | 0.216 | 0.210 | 0.203 | | | | | | | | | | | |
| n-Heptadecane | $C_{17}H_{36}$ | 0.253 | 0.245 | 0.237 | 0.230 | 0.223 | 0.216 | 0.209 | 0.202 | | | | | | | | |
| n-Octadecane | $C_{18}H_{38}$ | 0.27 | 0.27 | 0.26 | 0.25 | 0.24 | 0.23 | 0.23 | 0.22 | 0.21 | 0.21 | 0.20 | | | | | |
| n-Nonadecane | $C_{19}H_{40}$ | 0.30 | 0.29 | 0.28 | 0.27 | 0.26 | 0.25 | 0.25 | 0.24 | 0.23 | 0.22 | 0.22 | 0.21 | 0.20 | 0.20[b] | | |
| n-Eicosane | $C_{20}H_{42}$ | 0.32 | 0.31 | 0.30 | 0.29 | 0.28 | 0.27 | 0.26 | 0.26 | 0.25 | 0.24 | 0.23 | 0.23 | 0.22 | 0.21 | 0.21 | 0.20 |

a See footnote a of Table 1c.

b At saturation pressure.

TABLE 1c, Page 1 – PARAFFINS, C$_1$ TO C$_5$

VISCOSITY (ABSOLUTE)

For the Normal Liquid Range, at Atmospheric Pressure

October 31, 1948; October 31, 1952

| Compound (liquid) | Formula | Temperature in °C | | | | | | | | | | | | | | | |
|---|---|---|---|---|---|---|---|---|---|---|---|---|---|---|---|---|---|
| | | -190 | -185 | -180 | -175 | -170 | -165 | -160 | -155 | -150 | -145 | -140 | -135 | -130 | -125 | -120 | -115 |
| | | Viscosity (absolute) in centipoises[a] | | | | | | | | | | | | | | | |
| Methane | CH$_4$ | | 0.226[b] | 0.188 | 0.161 | 0.142 | 0.127 | 0.115[c] | | | | | | | | | |
| Ethane | C$_2$H$_6$ | | | | 0.985 | 0.805 | 0.673 | 0.574 | 0.500 | 0.442 | 0.396 | 0.359 | 0.328 | 0.301 | 0.278 | 0.257 | 0.238 |
| Propane | C$_3$H$_8$ | 13.8[b] | 8.78 | 5.96 | 4.26 | 3.18 | 2.46 | 1.96 | 1.60 | 1.34 | 1.14 | 0.984 | 0.861 | 0.762 | 0.681 | 0.614 | 0.558 |
| n-Butane | C$_4$H$_{10}$ | | | | | | | | | | | | | | | | |
| 2-Methylpropane (Isobutane) | " | | | | | | | | | | | | | | | | |
| n-Pentane | C$_5$H$_{12}$ | | | | | | | | | | | | | 3.63[b] | 2.89 | 2.35 | 1.96 |
| 2-Methylbutane (Isopentane) | " | | | | | | | | | | | | | | | | |
| 2,2-Dimethylpropane (Neopentane) | " | | | | | | | | | | | | | | | | |

a  The values of absolute viscosity in this table are referred to a value of 1.005 centipoises for water at 20°C. This is the value that was used in the certification of standard viscosity samples by the National Bureau of Standards, and corresponds to the value for the kinematic viscosity of water at 20°C (68°F) that was recommended in Method of Test D-445 of the American Society for Testing Materials. Within the near future, it is expected that the American Society for Testing Materials and the National Bureau of Standards may agree upon a new value of 1.002 centipoises for the viscosity (absolute) of water at 20°C (68°F).  (See Swindells, Coe, and Godfrey[1].).

b  For the undercooled liquid below the normal freezing point.

c  At saturation pressure.

232

TABLE 1c, Page 2 – PARAFFINS, $C_1$ TO $C_5$

VISCOSITY (ABSOLUTE)

For the Normal Liquid Range, at Atmospheric Pressure

October 31, 1948; October 31, 1952

Temperature in °C

Viscosity (absolute) in centipoises[a]

| Compound (liquid) | Formula | -110 | -105 | -100 | -95 | -90 | -85 | -80 | -75 | -70 | -65 | -60 | -55 | -50 | -45 | -40 | -35 |
|---|---|---|---|---|---|---|---|---|---|---|---|---|---|---|---|---|---|
| Methane | $CH_4$ | | | | | | | | | | | | | | | | |
| Ethane | $C_2H_6$ | 0.222 | 0.207 | 0.195 | 0.183 | 0.172 | 0.162c | | | | | | | | | | |
| Propane | $C_3H_8$ | 0.510 | 0.469 | 0.433 | 0.402 | 0.374 | 0.350 | 0.327 | 0.307 | 0.288 | 0.272 | 0.256 | 0.242 | 0.228 | 0.216 | 0.205c | |
| n-Butane | $C_4H_{10}$ | | | | | 0.63 | 0.58 | 0.536 | 0.497 | 0.462 | 0.431 | 0.403 | 0.378 | 0.355 | 0.335 | 0.315 | 0.298 |
| 2-Methylpropane (Isobutane) | " | | | | | | | 0.628 | 0.576 | 0.530 | 0.489 | 0.453 | 0.421 | 0.392 | 0.366 | 0.343 | 0.321 |
| n-Pentane | $C_5H_{12}$ | 1.66 | 1.43 | 1.24 | 1.09 | 0.973 | 0.874 | 0.791 | 0.720 | 0.659 | 0.607 | 0.562 | 0.522 | 0.487 | 0.455 | 0.428 | 0.403 |
| 2-Methylbutane (Isopentane) | " | | | | | | | | | | | | | 0.55 | 0.51 | 0.47 | 0.43 |
| 2,2-Dimethylpropane (Neopentane) | " | | | | | | | | | | | | | | | | |

Temperature in °C

Viscosity (absolute) in centipoises[a]

| Compound (liquid) | Formula | -30 | -25 | -20 | -15 | -10 | -5 | 0 | 5 | 10 | 15 | 20 | 25 | 30 | 35 |
|---|---|---|---|---|---|---|---|---|---|---|---|---|---|---|---|
| Methane | $CH_4$ | | | | | | | | | | | | | | |
| Ethane | $C_2H_6$ | | | | | | | | | | | | | | |
| Propane | $C_3H_8$ | | | | | | | | | | | | | | |
| n-Butane | $C_4H_{10}$ | 0.282 | 0.267 | 0.253 | 0.241 | 0.229 | 0.219 | 0.210c | | | | | | | |
| 2-Methylpropane (Isobutane) | " | 0.302 | 0.284 | 0.268 | 0.253 | 0.239c | | | | | | | | | |
| n-Pentane | $C_5H_{12}$ | 0.380 | 0.359 | 0.341 | 0.323 | 0.307 | 0.293 | 0.279 | 0.267 | 0.255 | 0.245 | 0.235 | 0.225 | 0.216 | 0.207 |
| 2-Methylbutane (Isopentane) | " | 0.404 | 0.377 | 0.353 | 0.331 | 0.311 | 0.294 | 0.278 | 0.263 | 0.249 | 0.237 | 0.225 | 0.215 | 0.205b | |
| 2,2-Dimethylpropane (Neopentane) | " | | | | 0.431b | 0.391 | 0.357 | 0.328 | 0.303 | 0.281c | | | | | |

[a] See footnote a of Table 1c.    [b] For the undercooled liquid below the normal freezing point.    [c] At saturation pressure.

## TABLE 22c (PART 1), Page 1 – NORMAL ALKYL CYCLOPENTANES, $C_5$ TO $C_{21}$
### VISCOSITY (ABSOLUTE)
For the Normal Liquid Range, at Atmospheric Pressure

December 31, 1948

Viscosity (absolute) in centipoises[a]

| Compound (liquid) | Formula | Temperature in °C | | | | | | | | | | | | | | | |
|---|---|---|---|---|---|---|---|---|---|---|---|---|---|---|---|---|---|
| | | -25 | -20 | -15 | -10 | -5 | 0 | 5 | 10 | 15 | 20 | 25 | 30 | 35 | 40 | 45 | 50 |
| Cyclopentane | $C_5H_{10}$ | 0.78 | 0.72 | 0.67 | 0.631 | 0.591 | 0.555 | 0.522 | 0.492 | 0.464 | 0.439 | 0.416 | 0.394 | 0.374 | 0.356 | 0.339 | 0.323[c] |
| Methylcyclopentane | $C_6H_{12}$ | 0.93 | 0.86 | 0.80 | 0.745 | 0.695 | 0.650 | 0.609 | 0.572 | 0.538 | 0.507 | 0.478 | 0.452 | 0.427 | 0.405 | 0.384 | 0.365 |
| Ethylcyclopentane | $C_7H_{14}$ | | 0.96 | 0.89 | 0.829 | 0.774 | 0.724 | 0.679 | 0.639 | 0.601 | 0.567 | 0.536 | 0.507 | 0.480 | 0.456 | 0.433 | 0.412 |
| n-Propylcyclopentane | $C_8H_{16}$ | | 1.24 | 1.14 | 1.049 | 0.96 | 0.898 | 0.835 | 0.779 | 0.727 | 0.682 | 0.641 | 0.604 | 0.571 | 0.540 | 0.513 | 0.488 |
| n-Butylcyclopentane | $C_9H_{18}$ | | 1.71 | 1.56 | 1.43 | 1.310 | 1.207 | 1.111 | 1.030 | 0.956 | 0.890 | 0.830 | 0.777 | 0.728 | 0.684 | 0.644 | 0.608 |
| n-Pentylcyclopentane | $C_{10}H_{20}$ | | 2.32 | 2.12 | 1.94 | 1.78 | 1.63 | 1.494 | 1.373 | 1.257 | 1.155 | 1.065 | 0.984 | 0.915 | 0.856 | 0.802 | 0.753 |
| n-Hexylcyclopentane | $C_{11}H_{22}$ | | 3.12 | 2.84 | 2.79 | 2.36 | 2.15 | 1.962 | 1.793 | 1.632 | 1.493 | 1.367 | 1.256 | 1.161 | 1.081 | 1.005 | 0.938 |
| n-Heptylcyclopentane | $C_{12}H_{24}$ | | 4.11 | 3.73 | 3.38 | 3.07 | 2.78 | 2.53 | 2.30 | 2.08 | 1.89 | 1.727 | 1.577 | 1.449 | 1.342 | 1.241 | 1.151 |
| n-Octylcyclopentane | $C_{13}H_{26}$ | | 5.34 | 4.82 | 4.35 | 3.93 | 3.55 | 3.21 | 2.90 | 2.62 | 2.37 | 2.15 | 1.95 | 1.782 | 1.642 | 1.510 | 1.393 |
| n-Nonylcyclopentane | $C_{14}H_{28}$ | | 6.83 | 6.15 | 5.53 | 4.97 | 4.46 | 4.01 | 3.61 | 3.24 | 2.92 | 2.63 | 2.38 | 2.17 | 1.98 | 1.81 | 1.665 |
| n-Decylcyclopentane | $C_{15}H_{30}$ | | 8.63 | 7.73 | 6.92 | 6.19 | 5.54 | 4.96 | 4.45 | 3.97 | 3.56 | 3.20 | 2.87 | 2.57 | 2.37 | 2.16 | 1.97 |
| n-Undecylcyclopentane | $C_{16}H_{32}$ | | | 9.61[b] | 8.56 | 7.63 | 6.80 | 6.06 | 5.41 | 4.81 | 4.29 | 3.84 | 3.43 | 3.09 | 2.81 | 2.54 | 2.31 |
| n-Dodecylcyclopentane | $C_{17}H_{34}$ | | | | 10.49[b] | 9.31 | 8.26 | 7.34 | 6.52 | 5.77 | 5.12 | 4.56 | 4.06 | 3.64 | 3.29 | 2.96 | 2.69 |
| n-Tridecylcyclopentane | $C_{18}H_{36}$ | | | | | | 9.95[b] | 8.80 | 7.78 | 6.86 | 6.06 | 5.38 | 4.77 | 4.26 | 3.83 | 3.44 | 3.10 |
| n-Tetradecylcyclopentane | $C_{19}H_{38}$ | | | | | | | 10.45[b] | 9.21 | 8.09 | 7.13 | 6.29 | 5.56 | 4.94 | 4.43 | 3.96 | 3.55 |
| n-Pentadecylcyclopentane | $C_{20}H_{40}$ | | | | | | | | | 9.48[b] | 8.32 | 7.31 | 6.44 | 5.70 | 5.08 | 4.52 | 4.05 |
| n-Hexadecylcyclopentane | $C_{21}H_{42}$ | | | | | | | | | | 9.63[b] | 8.44 | 7.40 | 6.52 | 5.80 | 5.14 | 4.57 |

a See footnote a of Table 1c.   b For the undercooled liquid below the normal freezing point.   c For the liquid above the normal boiling point, at saturation pressure.

TABLE 22c (PART 1). Page 2 — NORMAL ALKYL CYCLOPENTANES, $C_5$ TO $C_{21}$

VISCOSITY (ABSOLUTE)

For the Normal Liquid Range, at Atmospheric Pressure

December 31, 1948

| Compound (liquid) | Formula | Temperature in °C | | | | | | | | | | | | |
|---|---|---|---|---|---|---|---|---|---|---|---|---|---|---|
| | | 50 | 55 | 60 | 65 | 70 | 75 | 80 | 85 | 90 | 95 | 100 | 105 | 110 |
| | | Viscosity (absolute) in centipoises[a] | | | | | | | | | | | | |
| Cyclopentane | $C_5H_{10}$ | 0.323[b] | | | | | | | | | | | | |
| Methylcyclopentane | $C_6H_{12}$ | 0.365 | 0.347 | 0.330 | 0.315 | 0.300 | 0.287[b] | | | | | | | |
| Ethylcyclopentane | $C_7H_{14}$ | 0.412 | 0.393 | 0.376 | 0.359 | 0.343 | 0.329 | 0.32 | 0.30 | 0.29 | 0.28 | 0.27 | 0.26[b] | |
| n-Propylcyclopentane | $C_8H_{16}$ | 0.488 | 0.465 | 0.444 | 0.424 | 0.407 | 0.390 | 0.38 | 0.36 | 0.35 | 0.34 | 0.33 | 0.31 | 0.30 |
| n-Butylcyclopentane | $C_9H_{18}$ | 0.608 | 0.575 | 0.546 | 0.518 | 0.494 | 0.471 | 0.45 | 0.43 | 0.41 | 0.40 | 0.38 | 0.37 | 0.35 |
| n-Pentylcyclopentane | $C_{10}H_{20}$ | 0.753 | 0.708 | 0.667 | 0.631 | 0.598 | 0.569 | 0.54 | 0.52 | 0.50 | 0.47 | 0.45 | 0.44 | 0.42 |
| n-Hexylcyclopentane | $C_{11}H_{22}$ | 0.938 | 0.876 | 0.822 | 0.772 | 0.729 | 0.690 | 0.65 | 0.62 | 0.59 | 0.56 | 0.54 | 0.51 | 0.49 |
| n-Heptylcyclopentane | $C_{12}H_{24}$ | 1.151 | 1.069 | 0.997 | 0.932 | 0.876 | 0.825 | 0.78 | 0.74 | 0.70 | 0.66 | 0.63 | 0.60 | 0.57 |
| n-Octylcyclopentane | $C_{13}H_{26}$ | 1.393 | 1.287 | 1.193 | 1.111 | 1.040 | 0.974 | 0.92 | 0.86 | 0.82 | 0.77 | 0.73 | 0.69 | 0.66 |
| n-Nonylcyclopentane | $C_{14}H_{28}$ | 1.665 | 1.530 | 1.413 | 1.310 | 1.220 | 1.139 | 1.07 | 1.00 | 0.94 | 0.89 | 0.84 | 0.79 | 0.75 |
| n-Decylcyclopentane | $C_{15}H_{30}$ | 1.97 | 1.80 | 1.656 | 1.529 | 1.418 | 1.319 | 1.23 | 1.15 | 1.08 | 1.02 | 0.96 | 0.90 | 0.85 |
| n-Undecylcyclopentane | $C_{16}H_{32}$ | 2.31 | 2.10 | 1.92 | 1.770 | 1.635 | 1.516 | 1.41 | 1.32 | 1.23 | 1.15 | 1.08 | 1.01 | 0.95 |
| n-Dodecylcyclopentane | $C_{17}H_{34}$ | 2.69 | 2.44 | 2.22 | 2.03 | 1.87 | 1.73 | 1.60 | 1.49 | 1.39 | 1.30 | 1.22 | 1.14 | 1.07 |
| n-Tridecylcyclopentane | $C_{18}H_{36}$ | 3.10 | 2.80 | 2.54 | 2.32 | 2.13 | 1.96 | 1.81 | 1.68 | 1.56 | 1.45 | 1.36 | 1.27 | 1.18 |
| n-Tetradecylcyclopentane | $C_{19}H_{38}$ | 3.55 | 3.19 | 2.89 | 2.63 | 2.40 | 2.20 | 2.03 | 1.88 | 1.74 | 1.62 | 1.51 | 1.40 | 1.31 |
| n-Pentadecylcyclopentane | $C_{20}H_{40}$ | 4.05 | 3.62 | 3.27 | 2.96 | 2.70 | 2.47 | 2.27 | 2.10 | 1.94 | 1.80 | 1.67 | 1.55 | 1.44 |
| n-Hexadecylcyclopentane | $C_{21}H_{42}$ | 4.57 | 4.09 | 3.67 | 3.32 | 3.02 | 2.75 | 2.52 | 2.32 | 2.14 | 1.98 | 1.84 | 1.70 | 1.58 |

a See footnote a of Table 1c.   b For the liquid above the normal boiling point, at saturation pressure.

TABLE 23c (PART 1), Page 1 - NORMAL ALKYL CYCLOHEXANES, $C_6$ TO $C_{22}$

VISCOSITY (ABSOLUTE)

For the Normal Liquid Range, at Atmospheric Pressure

December 31, 1948

| Compound (liquid) | Formula | \_ Temperature in °C | | | | | | | | | | | | | | | |
|---|---|---|---|---|---|---|---|---|---|---|---|---|---|---|---|---|---|
| | | -25 | -20 | -15 | -10 | -5 | 0 | 5 | 10 | 15 | 20 | 25 | 30 | 35 | 40 | 45 | 50 |
| | | Viscosity (absolute) in centipoises[a] | | | | | | | | | | | | | | | |
| Cyclohexane | $C_6H_{12}$ | | | | | | | 1.300[b] | 1.180 | 1.073 | 0.980 | 0.898 | 0.826 | 0.761 | 0.704 | 0.653 | 0.606 |
| Methylcyclohexane | $C_7H_{14}$ | 1.55 | 1.41 | 1.28 | 1.175 | 1.078 | 0.993 | 0.917 | 0.850 | 0.768 | 0.734 | 0.685 | 0.641 | 0.600 | 0.564 | 0.531 | 0.500 |
| Ethylcyclohexane | $C_8H_{16}$ | 1.80 | 1.63 | 1.48 | 1.356 | 1.242 | 1.142 | 1.053 | 0.976 | 0.905 | 0.843 | 0.787 | 0.737 | 0.692 | 0.651 | 0.614 | 0.581 |
| n-Propylcyclohexane | $C_9H_{18}$ | 2.35 | 2.10 | 1.88 | 1.705 | 1.546 | 1.408 | 1.287 | 1.182 | 1.088 | 1.006 | 0.934 | 0.870 | 0.812 | 0.760 | 0.714 | 0.672 |
| n-Butylcyclohexane | $C_{10}H_{20}$ | | 2.94 | 2.62 | 2.35 | 2.11 | 1.91 | 1.729 | 1.574 | 1.435 | 1.314 | 1.208 | 1.114 | 1.029 | 0.955 | 0.889 | 0.830 |
| n-Pentylcyclohexane | $C_{11}H_{22}$ | | | | 3.33 | 2.96 | 2.64 | 2.36 | 2.12 | 1.91 | 1.723 | 1.560 | 1.418 | 1.295 | 1.191 | 1.103 | 1.026 |
| n-Hexylcyclohexane | $C_{12}H_{24}$ | | | | 4.49 | 3.96 | 3.52 | 3.12 | 2.77 | 2.48 | 2.22 | 2.00 | 1.80 | 1.630 | 1.492 | 1.371 | 1.268 |
| n-Heptylcyclohexane | $C_{13}H_{26}$ | | | | 5.94 | 5.20 | 4.58 | 4.03 | 3.56 | 3.16 | 2.81 | 2.51 | 2.25 | 2.02 | 1.83 | 1.679 | 1.544 |
| n-Octylcyclohexane | $C_{14}H_{28}$ | | | | 7.72 | 6.72 | 5.88 | 5.12 | 4.51 | 3.98 | 3.51 | 3.11 | 2.77 | 2.47 | 2.24 | 2.03 | 1.86 |
| n-Nonylcyclohexane | $C_{15}H_{30}$ | | | | 9.89 | 8.55 | 7.42 | 6.45 | 5.62 | 4.92 | 4.32 | 3.80 | 3.37 | 2.99 | 2.68 | 2.43 | 2.20 |
| n-Decylcyclohexane | $C_{16}H_{32}$ | | | | | 10.73[b] | 9.26 | 8.00 | 6.93 | 6.03 | 5.26 | 4.60 | 4.05 | 3.57 | 3.19 | 2.87 | 2.59 |
| n-Undecylcyclohexane | $C_{17}H_{34}$ | | | | | | | 9.80[b] | 8.44 | 7.31 | 6.34 | 5.50 | 4.81 | 4.23 | 3.76 | 3.36 | 3.03 |
| n-Dodecylcyclohexane | $C_{18}H_{36}$ | | | | | | | | 10.19[b] | 8.76 | 7.54 | 6.53 | 5.68 | 4.96 | 4.38 | 3.91 | 3.50 |
| n-Tridecylcyclohexane | $C_{19}H_{38}$ | | | | | | | | | | 8.92 | 7.67 | 6.64 | 5.78 | 5.08 | 4.51 | 4.02 |
| n-Tetradecylcyclohexane | $C_{20}H_{40}$ | | | | | | | | | | | 8.96 | 7.71 | 6.68 | 5.85 | 5.17 | 4.59 |
| n-Pentadecylcyclohexane | $C_{21}H_{42}$ | | | | | | | | | | | | 8.91 | 7.67 | 6.69 | 5.88 | 5.21 |
| n-Hexadecylcyclohexane | $C_{22}H_{44}$ | | | | | | | | | | | | | 8.76 | 7.61 | 6.66 | 5.88 |

a See footnote a of Table 1c.　　b For the undercooled liquid below the normal freezing point.

TABLE 23c (PART 1), Page 2 – NORMAL ALKYL CYCLOHEXANES, $C_6$ TO $C_{22}$
VISCOSITY (ABSOLUTE)

For the Normal Liquid Range, at Atmospheric Pressure
December 31, 1948 (Corrected)

| Compound (liquid) | Formula[a] | Temperature in °C | | | | | | | | | | | | |
|---|---|---|---|---|---|---|---|---|---|---|---|---|---|---|
| | | Viscosity (absolute) in centipoises[a] | | | | | | | | | | | | |
| | | 50 | 55 | 60 | 65 | 70 | 75 | 80 | 85 | 90 | 95 | 100 | 105 | 110 |
| Cyclohexane | $C_6H_{12}$ | 0.606 | 0.565 | 0.528 | 0.494 | 0.464 | 0.436 | 0.411 | | | | | | |
| Methylcyclohexane | $C_7H_{14}$ | 0.500 | 0.472 | 0.446 | 0.422 | 0.400 | 0.380 | 0.36 | 0.34 | 0.33 | 0.31 | 0.30 | | |
| Ethylcyclohexane | $C_8H_{16}$ | 0.581 | 0.550 | 0.523 | 0.497 | 0.475 | 0.45 | 0.43 | 0.42 | 0.40 | 0.38 | 0.37 | 0.36 | 0.34 |
| n-Propylcyclohexane | $C_9H_{18}$ | 0.672 | 0.634 | 0.601 | 0.569 | 0.542 | 0.52 | 0.49 | 0.47 | 0.45 | 0.44 | 0.42 | 0.40 | 0.39 |
| n-Butylcyclohexane | $C_{10}H_{20}$ | 0.830 | 0.779 | 0.734 | 0.693 | 0.658 | 0.63 | 0.60 | 0.57 | 0.55 | 0.53 | 0.51 | 0.49 | 0.47 |
| n-Pentylcyclohexane | $C_{11}H_{22}$ | 1.026 | 0.958 | 0.898 | 0.843 | 0.79 | 0.75 | 0.71 | 0.67 | 0.63 | 0.60 | 0.57 | 0.54 | 0.51 |
| n-Hexylcyclohexane | $C_{12}H_{24}$ | 1.268 | 1.177 | 1.097 | 1.023 | 0.96 | 0.90 | 0.84 | 0.79 | 0.75 | 0.70 | 0.66 | 0.63 | 0.59 |
| n-Heptylcyclohexane | $C_{13}H_{26}$ | 1.544 | 1.425 | 1.320 | 1.226 | 1.14 | 1.06 | 0.99 | 0.93 | 0.87 | 0.82 | 0.77 | 0.72 | 0.68 |
| n-Octylcyclohexane | $C_{14}H_{28}$ | 1.86 | 1.702 | 1.571 | 1.450 | 1.34 | 1.25 | 1.16 | 1.08 | 1.00 | 0.94 | 0.88 | 0.82 | 0.77 |
| n-Nonylcyclohexane | $C_{15}H_{30}$ | 2.20 | 2.01 | 1.85 | 1.70 | 1.57 | 1.44 | 1.34 | 1.24 | 1.15 | 1.07 | 1.00 | 0.93 | 0.87 |
| n-Decylcyclohexane | $C_{16}H_{32}$ | 2.59 | 2.36 | 2.16 | 1.97 | 1.81 | 1.66 | 1.53 | 1.42 | 1.31 | 1.21 | 1.12 | 1.04 | 0.97 |
| n-Undecylcyclohexane | $C_{17}H_{34}$ | 3.03 | 2.74 | 2.49 | 2.27 | 2.08 | 1.90 | 1.74 | 1.60 | 1.47 | 1.36 | 1.26 | 1.16 | 1.08 |
| n-Dodecylcyclohexane | $C_{18}H_{36}$ | 3.50 | 3.16 | 2.86 | 2.60 | 2.36 | 2.15 | 1.96 | 1.80 | 1.65 | 1.52 | 1.40 | 1.29 | 1.19 |
| n-Tridecylcyclohexane | $C_{19}H_{38}$ | 4.02 | 3.61 | 3.26 | 2.94 | 2.67 | 2.42 | 2.21 | 2.02 | 1.84 | 1.69 | 1.55 | 1.42 | 1.31 |
| n-Tetradecylcyclohexane | $C_{20}H_{40}$ | 4.59 | 4.10 | 3.69 | 3.32 | 3.00 | 2.71 | 2.46 | 2.24 | 2.04 | 1.86 | 1.70 | 1.56 | 1.44 |
| n-Pentadecylcyclohexane | $C_{21}H_{42}$ | 5.21 | 4.64 | 4.15 | 3.72 | 3.36 | 3.02 | 2.74 | 2.48 | 2.25 | 2.05 | 1.87 | 1.71 | 1.57 |
| n-Hexadecylcyclohexane | $C_{22}H_{44}$ | 5.88 | 5.21 | 4.66 | 4.15 | 3.74 | 3.35 | 3.03 | 2.74 | 2.48 | 2.25 | 2.04 | 1.86 | 1.70 |

[a] See footnote a of Table 1c.

TABLE 24c, Page 1 - NORMAL MONOOLEFINS (1-ALKENES), $C_2$ TO $C_{20}$

VISCOSITY (ABSOLUTE)

For the Normal Liquid Range, at Atmospheric Pressure

August 31, 1949 (Corrected)

| Compound (liquid) | Formula | Temperature in °C — Viscosity (absolute) in centipoises[a] | | | | | | | | | | | | | | | |
|---|---|---|---|---|---|---|---|---|---|---|---|---|---|---|---|---|---|
| | | -185 | -180 | -175 | -170 | -165 | -160 | -155 | -150 | -145 | -140 | -135 | -130 | -125 | -120 | -115 | -110 |
| Ethene (Ethylene) | $C_2H_4$ | | | | 0.70[b] | 0.60 | 0.51 | 0.45 | 0.39 | 0.35 | 0.31 | 0.28 | 0.26 | 0.23 | 0.21 | 0.20 | 0.18 |
| Propene (Propylene) | $C_3H_6$ | 15.0 | 8.59 | 5.31 | 3.54 | 2.56 | 1.97 | 1.58 | 1.29 | 1.07 | 0.91 | 0.78 | 0.68 | 0.60 | 0.54 | 0.48 | 0.44 |
| 1-Butene | $C_4H_8$ | | | | | | | | | | | | | | | 0.88 | 0.79 |
| 1-Pentene | $C_5H_{10}$ | | | | | | | | | | | | | | | | |
| 1-Hexene | $C_6H_{12}$ | | | | | | | | | | | | | | | | |
| 1-Heptene | $C_7H_{14}$ | | | | | | | | | | | | | | | | |
| 1-Octene | $C_8H_{16}$ | | | | | | | | | | | | | | | | |
| 1-Nonene | $C_9H_{18}$ | | | | | | | | | | | | | | | | |
| 1-Decene | $C_{10}H_{20}$ | | | | | | | | | | | | | | | | |
| 1-Undecene | $C_{11}H_{22}$ | | | | | | | | | | | | | | | | |
| 1-Dodecene | $C_{12}H_{24}$ | | | | | | | | | | | | | | | | |
| 1-Tridecene | $C_{13}H_{26}$ | | | | | | | | | | | | | | | | |
| 1-Tetradecene | $C_{14}H_{28}$ | | | | | | | | | | | | | | | | |
| 1-Pentadecene | $C_{15}H_{30}$ | | | | | | | | | | | | | | | | |
| 1-Hexadecene | $C_{16}H_{32}$ | | | | | | | | | | | | | | | | |
| 1-Heptadecene | $C_{17}H_{34}$ | | | | | | | | | | | | | | | | |
| 1-Octadecene | $C_{18}H_{36}$ | | | | | | | | | | | | | | | | |
| 1-Nonadecene | $C_{19}H_{38}$ | | | | | | | | | | | | | | | | |
| 1-Eicosene | $C_{20}H_{40}$ | | | | | | | | | | | | | | | | |

a See footnote a of Table 1c.    b For the undercooled liquid below the normal freezing point.

## TABLE 24c, Page 2 – NORMAL MONOOLEFINS (1-ALKENES), $C_2$ TO $C_{20}$ VISCOSITY (ABSOLUTE)

For the Normal Liquid Range, at Atmospheric Pressure

August 31, 1949 (Corrected)

Temperature in °C — Viscosity (absolute) in centipoises[a]

| Compound (liquid) | Formula | -110 | -105 | -100 | -95 | -90 | -85 | -80 | -75 | -70 | -65 | -60 | -55 | -50 | -45 | -40 | -35 |
|---|---|---|---|---|---|---|---|---|---|---|---|---|---|---|---|---|---|
| Ethene (Ethylene) | $C_2H_4$ | 0.18 | 0.16 | 0.15[b] | | | | | | | | | | | | | |
| Propene (Propylene) | $C_3H_6$ | 0.44 | 0.40 | 0.37 | 0.35 | | | | | | | | | | | | |
| 1-Butene | $C_4H_8$ | 0.79 | 0.70 | 0.64 | 0.58 | 0.53 | 0.48 | 0.45 | 0.42 | 0.39 | 0.36 | 0.34 | 0.32 | 0.30 | 0.28 | 0.26 | 0.25 |
| 1-Pentene | $C_5H_{10}$ | | | | | 0.85 | 0.77 | 0.70 | 0.64 | 0.59 | 0.54 | 0.50 | 0.46 | 0.43 | 0.40 | 0.38 | 0.35 |
| 1-Hexene | $C_6H_{12}$ | | | | | | | | | | | | 0.69 | 0.63 | 0.58 | 0.54 | 0.51 |
| 1-Heptene | $C_7H_{14}$ | | | | | | | | | | | | | | | | |
| 1-Octene | $C_8H_{16}$ | | | | | | | | | | | | | | | | |
| 1-Nonene | $C_9H_{18}$ | | | | | | | | | | | | | | | | |
| 1-Decene | $C_{10}H_{20}$ | | | | | | | | | | | | | | | | |
| 1-Undecene | $C_{11}H_{22}$ | | | | | | | | | | | | | | | | |
| 1-Dodecene | $C_{12}H_{24}$ | | | | | | | | | | | | | | | | |
| 1-Tridecene | $C_{13}H_{26}$ | | | | | | | | | | | | | | | | |
| 1-Tetradecene | $C_{14}H_{28}$ | | | | | | | | | | | | | | | | |
| 1-Pentadecene | $C_{15}H_{30}$ | | | | | | | | | | | | | | | | |
| 1-Hexadecene | $C_{16}H_{32}$ | | | | | | | | | | | | | | | | |
| 1-Heptadecene | $C_{17}H_{34}$ | | | | | | | | | | | | | | | | |
| 1-Octadecene | $C_{18}H_{36}$ | | | | | | | | | | | | | | | | |
| 1-Nonadecene | $C_{19}H_{38}$ | | | | | | | | | | | | | | | | |
| 1-Eicosene | $C_{20}H_{40}$ | | | | | | | | | | | | | | | | |

a See footnote a of Table 1c.     b For the liquid above the normal boiling point, at saturation pressure.

## TABLE 24c, Page 3 — NORMAL MONOOLEFINS (1-ALKENES), $C_2$ TO $C_{20}$
### VISCOSITY (ABSOLUTE)

For the Normal Liquid Range, at Atmospheric Pressure

August 31, 1949

| Compound (liquid) | Formula | Temperature in °C | | | | | | | | | | | | | | | |
|---|---|---|---|---|---|---|---|---|---|---|---|---|---|---|---|---|---|
| | | -35 | -30 | -25 | -20 | -15 | -10 | -5 | 0 | 5 | 10 | 15 | 20 | 25 | 30 | 35 | 40 |
| | | Viscosity (absolute) in centipoises[a] | | | | | | | | | | | | | | | |
| Ethene (Ethylene) | $C_2H_4$ | | | | | | | | | | | | | | | | |
| Propene (Propylene) | $C_3H_6$ | | | | | | | | | | | | | | | | |
| 1-Butene | $C_4H_8$ | 0.25 | 0.33 | 0.31 | 0.30 | 0.28 | 0.27 | 0.25 | 0.24 | | | | | | | | |
| 1-Pentene | $C_5H_{10}$ | 0.51 | 0.47 | 0.44 | 0.42 | 0.39 | 0.37 | 0.35 | 0.33 | 0.31 | 0.29 | 0.27 | 0.26 | 0.25 | 0.24 | 0.23 | 0.22 |
| 1-Hexene | $C_6H_{12}$ | | | | | | | | 0.44 | 0.41 | 0.39 | 0.37 | 0.35 | 0.34 | 0.32 | 0.31 | 0.29 |
| 1-Heptene | $C_7H_{14}$ | | | | | | | | 0.613 | 0.571 | 0.533 | 0.498 | 0.470 | 0.447 | 0.425 | 0.403 | 0.383 |
| 1-Octene | $C_8H_{16}$ | | | | | | | | 0.839 | 0.774 | 0.715 | 0.662 | 0.620 | 0.586 | 0.554 | 0.521 | 0.492 |
| 1-Nonene | $C_9H_{18}$ | | | | | | | | 1.130 | 1.032 | 0.945 | 0.866 | 0.805 | 0.756 | 0.709 | 0.664 | 0.622 |
| 1-Decene | $C_{10}H_{20}$ | | | | | | | | 1.50 | 1.36 | 1.229 | 1.118 | 1.031 | 0.961 | 0.895 | 0.833 | 0.777 |
| 1-Undecene | $C_{11}H_{22}$ | | | | | | | | 1.96 | 1.76 | 1.58 | 1.42 | 1.30 | 1.207 | 1.117 | 1.034 | 0.959 |
| 1-Dodecene | $C_{12}H_{24}$ | | | | | | | | 2.53 | 2.25 | 2.00 | 1.79 | 1.63 | 1.50 | 1.38 | 1.270 | 1.171 |
| 1-Tridecene | $C_{13}H_{26}$ | | | | | | | | 3.23 | 2.85 | 2.51 | 2.23 | 2.01 | 1.83 | 1.68 | 1.54 | 1.41 |
| 1-Tetradecene | $C_{14}H_{28}$ | | | | | | | | 4.09 | 3.57 | 3.12 | 2.75 | 2.47 | 2.24 | 2.04 | 1.86 | 1.70 |
| 1-Pentadecene | $C_{15}H_{30}$ | | | | | | | | | 4.43 | 3.82 | 3.36 | 3.00 | 2.70 | 2.44 | 2.22 | 2.02 |
| 1-Hexadecene | $C_{16}H_{32}$ | | | | | | | | | | 4.70[b] | 4.08 | 3.61 | 3.25 | 2.93 | 2.64 | 2.38 |
| 1-Heptadecene | $C_{17}H_{34}$ | | | | | | | | | | | | 4.32 | 3.86 | 3.46 | 3.10 | 2.79 |
| 1-Octadecene | $C_{18}H_{36}$ | | | | | | | | | | | | | 4.57 | 4.08 | 3.64 | 3.26 |
| 1-Nonadecene | $C_{19}H_{38}$ | | | | | | | | | | | | | | | 4.23 | 3.77 |
| 1-Eicosene | $C_{20}H_{40}$ | | | | | | | | | | | | | | 4.77[b] | | |

a  See footnote a of Table 1c.

b  For the undercooled liquid below the normal freezing point.

TABLE 24c, Page 4 – NORMAL MONOOLEFINS (1-ALKENES) $C_2$ TO $C_{20}$
VISCOSITY (ABSOLUTE)

For the Normal Liquid Range, at Atmospheric Pressure

August 31, 1949

Temperature in $^\circ$C

Viscosity (absolute) in centipoises[a]

| Compound (liquid) | Formula | 40 | 45 | 50 | 55 | 60 | 65 | 70 | 75 | 80 | 85 | 90 | 95 | 100 | 105 | 110 | 115 |
|---|---|---|---|---|---|---|---|---|---|---|---|---|---|---|---|---|---|
| Ethene (Ethylene) | $C_2H_4$ | | | | | | | | | | | | | | | | |
| Propene (Propylene) | $C_3H_6$ | | | | | | | | | | | | | | | | |
| 1-Butene | $C_4H_8$ | | | | | | | | | | | | | | | | |
| 1-Pentene | $C_5H_{10}$ | | | | | | | | | | | | | | | | |
| 1-Hexene | $C_6H_{12}$ | 0.22 | 0.21 | 0.20 | 0.20 | 0.19 | 0.19[b] | | | | | | | | | | |
| 1-Heptene | $C_7H_{14}$ | 0.29 | 0.28 | 0.27 | 0.26 | 0.25 | 0.24 | 0.23 | 0.22 | 0.22 | 0.21 | 0.20 | 0.20[b] | | | | |
| 1-Octene | $C_8H_{16}$ | 0.383 | 0.364 | 0.347 | 0.331 | 0.317 | 0.304 | 0.292 | 0.281 | 0.271 | 0.261 | 0.251 | 0.243 | 0.235 | 0.23 | 0.22 | 0.21 |
| 1-Nonene | $C_9H_{18}$ | 0.492 | 0.465 | 0.440 | 0.418 | 0.398 | 0.380 | 0.363 | 0.348 | 0.334 | 0.320 | 0.307 | 0.296 | 0.285 | 0.27 | 0.26 | 0.26 |
| 1-Decene | $C_{10}H_{20}$ | 0.622 | 0.584 | 0.551 | 0.521 | 0.493 | 0.468 | 0.445 | 0.425 | 0.406 | 0.388 | 0.371 | 0.356 | 0.342 | 0.33 | 0.32 | 0.30 |
| 1-Undecene | $C_{11}H_{22}$ | 0.777 | 0.726 | 0.680 | 0.639 | 0.603 | 0.570 | 0.541 | 0.514 | 0.489 | 0.465 | 0.443 | 0.424 | 0.405 | 0.39 | 0.37 | 0.36 |
| 1-Dodecene | $C_{12}H_{24}$ | 0.959 | 0.891 | 0.831 | 0.778 | 0.730 | 0.686 | 0.647 | 0.612 | 0.581 | 0.551 | 0.523 | 0.498 | 0.476 | 0.45 | 0.43 | 0.41 |
| 1-Tridecene | $C_{13}H_{26}$ | 1.171 | 1.082 | 1.005 | 0.937 | 0.875 | 0.819 | 0.769 | 0.725 | 0.686 | 0.648 | 0.614 | 0.583 | 0.554 | 0.53 | 0.50 | 0.48 |
| 1-Tetradecene | $C_{14}H_{28}$ | 1.41 | 1.30 | 1.203 | 1.117 | 1.040 | 0.969 | 0.906 | 0.851 | 0.802 | 0.756 | 0.714 | 0.675 | 0.640 | 0.61 | 0.58 | 0.55 |
| 1-Pentadecene | $C_{15}H_{30}$ | 1.70 | 1.55 | 1.43 | 1.32 | 1.225 | 1.138 | 1.062 | 0.996 | 0.933 | 0.875 | 0.824 | 0.777 | 0.735 | 0.70 | 0.66 | 0.62 |
| 1-Hexadecene | $C_{16}H_{32}$ | 2.02 | 1.84 | 1.69 | 1.55 | 1.43 | 1.32 | 1.234 | 1.153 | 1.078 | 1.008 | 0.945 | 0.889 | 0.839 | 0.79 | 0.75 | 0.71 |
| 1-Heptadecene | $C_{17}H_{34}$ | 2.38 | 2.16 | 1.97 | 1.81 | 1.66 | 1.53 | 1.42 | 1.33 | 1.238 | 1.155 | 1.077 | 1.013 | 0.952 | 0.89 | 0.84 | 0.79 |
| 1-Octadecene | $C_{18}H_{36}$ | 2.79 | 2.52 | 2.29 | 2.09 | 1.92 | 1.77 | 1.65 | 1.52 | 1.41 | 1.31 | 1.221 | 1.145 | 1.074 | 1.01 | 0.95 | 0.89 |
| 1-Nonadecene | $C_{19}H_{38}$ | 3.26 | 2.93 | 2.65 | 2.42 | 2.21 | 2.02 | 1.87 | 1.73 | 1.60 | 1.48 | 1.38 | 1.29 | 1.21 | 1.13 | 1.06 | 0.99 |
| 1-Eicosene | $C_{20}H_{40}$ | 3.77 | 3.38 | 3.05 | 2.77 | 2.52 | 2.30 | 2.12 | 1.96 | 1.81 | 1.67 | 1.55 | 1.45 | 1.35 | 1.26 | 1.18 | 1.10 |

a See footnote a of Table 1c.   b For the liquid above the normal boiling point, at saturation pressure.

TABLE 21c (PART 1), Page 1 – NORMAL ALKYL BENZENES, $C_6$ TO $C_{22}$

VISCOSITY (ABSOLUTE)

For the Normal Liquid Range, at Atmospheric Pressure

October 31, 1948

| Compound (liquid) | Formula | Temperature in °C | | | | | | | | | | | | | | | |
|---|---|---|---|---|---|---|---|---|---|---|---|---|---|---|---|---|---|
| | | -25 | -20 | -15 | -10 | -5 | 0 | 5 | 10 | 15 | 20 | 25 | 30 | 35 | 40 | 45 | 50 |
| | | Viscosity (absolute) in centipoises[a] | | | | | | | | | | | | | | | |
| Benzene | $C_6H_6$ | | | | | | | 0.8260[b] | 0.7597 | 0.7004 | 0.6487 | 0.6028 | 0.5621 | 0.5252 | 0.4923 | 0.4629 | 0.4360 |
| Methylbenzene (Toluene) | $C_7H_8$ | 1.17 | 1.07 | 0.980 | 0.904 | 0.834 | 0.773 | .7184 | .6698 | .6256 | .5866 | .5516 | .5203 | .4913 | .4650 | .4411 | .4189 |
| Ethylbenzene | $C_8H_{10}$ | 1.35 | 1.24 | 1.133 | 1.045 | 0.965 | .895 | .8312 | .7751 | .7237 | .6783 | .6373 | .6003 | .5662 | .5354 | .5073 | .4814 |
| n-Propylbenzene | $C_9H_{12}$ | 1.91 | 1.72 | 1.555 | 1.416 | 1.291 | 1.182 | 1.085 | .9996 | .9234 | .8571 | .7986 | .7466 | .6993 | .6570 | .6190 | .5842 |
| n-Butylbenzene | $C_{10}H_{14}$ | 2.50 | 2.23 | 1.987 | 1.790 | 1.634 | 1.466 | 1.334 | 1.220 | 1.122 | 1.035 | .960 | .894 | .834 | .781 | .733 | .684 |
| n-Pentylbenzene | $C_{11}H_{16}$ | | 3.82 | 3.13 | 2.64 | 2.28 | 2.01 | 1.79 | 1.608 | 1.460 | 1.334 | 1.225 | 1.132 | 1.049 | .976 | .912 | .853 |
| n-Hexylbenzene | $C_{12}H_{18}$ | | 5.17 | 4.18 | 3.66 | 2.99 | 2.60 | 2.30 | 2.05 | 1.846 | 1.675 | 1.528 | 1.403 | 1.293 | 1.196 | 1.112 | 1.035 |
| n-Heptylbenzene | $C_{13}H_{20}$ | | 6.93 | 5.53 | 4.57 | 3.87 | 3.34 | 2.92 | 2.59 | 2.31 | 2.08 | 1.887 | 1.722 | 1.578 | 1.451 | 1.342 | 1.243 |
| n-Octylbenzene | $C_{14}H_{22}$ | | 9.23 | 7.28 | 5.94 | 4.98 | 4.25 | 3.69 | 3.24 | 2.87 | 2.57 | 2.31 | 2.09 | 1.907 | 1.744 | 1.605 | 1.479 |
| n-Nonylbenzene | $C_{15}H_{24}$ | | 12.20 | 9.50 | 7.66 | 6.35 | 5.36 | 4.61 | 4.02 | 3.53 | 3.14 | 2.80 | 2.53 | 2.29 | 2.08 | 1.902 | 1.745 |
| n-Decylbenzene | $C_{16}H_{26}$ | | 16.0[b] | 12.31 | 9.81 | 8.04 | 6.72 | 5.72 | 4.94 | 4.31 | 3.80 | 3.37 | 3.02 | 2.72 | 2.46 | 2.23 | 2.00 |
| n-Undecylbenzene | $C_{17}H_{28}$ | | | 15.9[b] | 12.48 | 10.11 | 8.36 | 7.06 | 6.04 | 5.23 | 4.58 | 4.03 | 3.59 | 3.21 | 2.89 | 2.62 | 2.38 |
| n-Dodecylbenzene | $C_{18}H_{30}$ | | | | | 12.62[b] | 10.34 | 8.64 | 7.33 | 6.30 | 5.47 | 4.79 | 4.24 | 3.77 | 3.37 | 3.04 | 2.75 |
| n-Tridecylbenzene | $C_{19}H_{32}$ | | | | | | 12.69[b] | 10.52 | 8.84 | 7.54 | 6.50 | 5.65 | 4.97 | 4.40 | 3.91 | 3.51 | 3.16 |
| n-Tetradecylbenzene | $C_{20}H_{34}$ | | | | | | | | 10.60[b] | 8.97 | 7.68 | 6.63 | 5.80 | 5.10 | 4.51 | 4.03 | 3.61 |
| n-Pentadecylbenzene | $C_{21}H_{36}$ | | | | | | | | | 10.61[b] | 9.02 | 7.74 | 6.72 | 5.88 | 5.18 | 4.60 | 4.11 |
| n-Hexadecylbenzene | $C_{22}H_{38}$ | | | | | | | | | | | 8.99[b] | 7.76 | 6.75 | 5.92 | 5.23 | 4.65 |

[a] See footnote a of Table 1c.   [b] Extrapolated value for the undercooled liquid below the normal freezing point.

TABLE 21c (PART 1), Page 2 – NORMAL ALKYL BENZENES, $C_6$ TO $C_{22}$
VISCOSITY (ABSOLUTE)
For the Normal Liquid Range, at Atmospheric Pressure
October 31, 1948

| Compound (liquid) | Formula | Temperature in °C. Viscosity (absolute) in centipoises[a] | | | | | | | | | | | | | | | |
|---|---|---|---|---|---|---|---|---|---|---|---|---|---|---|---|---|---|
| | | 50 | 55 | 60 | 65 | 70 | 75 | 80 | 85 | 90 | 95 | 100 | 105 | 110 | 115 | 120 | 125 |
| Benzene | $C_6H_6$ | 0.4360 | 0.412 | 0.390 | 0.369 | 0.351 | 0.333 | 0.318 | 0.302[b] | | | | | | | | |
| Methylbenzene (Toluene) | $C_7H_8$ | .4189 | .399 | .380 | .362 | .346 | .331 | .317 | .304 | .291 | .280 | .269 | .259 | .249 | | | |
| Ethylbenzene | $C_8H_{10}$ | .4814 | .458 | .436 | .416 | .397 | .380 | .364 | .348 | .334 | .321 | .308 | .296 | .286 | 0.275 | 0.265 | 0.256 |
| n-Propylbenzene | $C_9H_{12}$ | .5842 | .553 | .524 | .498 | .473 | .451 | .430 | .410 | .392 | .375 | .360 | .345 | .331 | .318 | .306 | .295 |
| n-Butylbenzene | $C_{10}H_{14}$ | .684 | .650 | .614 | .581 | .550 | .522 | .497 | .472 | .450 | .430 | .411 | .39 | .38 | .36 | .35 | .33 |
| n-Pentylbenzene | $C_{11}H_{16}$ | .853 | .801 | .756 | .711 | .674 | .636 | .602 | .572 | .543 | .516 | .492 | .47 | .45 | .43 | .41 | .39 |
| n-Hexylbenzene | $C_{12}H_{18}$ | 1.035 | .967 | .909 | .849 | .804 | .755 | .712 | .674 | .638 | .605 | .574 | .55 | .52 | .49 | .47 | .45 |
| n-Heptylbenzene | $C_{13}H_{20}$ | 1.243 | 1.157 | 1.081 | 1.008 | .949 | .887 | .834 | .786 | .742 | .701 | .664 | .63 | .60 | .57 | .54 | .51 |
| n-Octylbenzene | $C_{14}H_{22}$ | 1.479 | 1.369 | 1.274 | 1.183 | 1.111 | 1.033 | .968 | .910 | .856 | .806 | .761 | .72 | .68 | .64 | .61 | .58 |
| n-Nonylbenzene | $C_{15}H_{24}$ | 1.745 | 1.608 | 1.490 | 1.378 | 1.289 | 1.194 | 1.115 | 1.044 | .978 | .919 | .865 | .82 | .77 | .73 | .69 | .65 |
| n-Decylbenzene | $C_{16}H_{26}$ | 2.00 | 1.875 | 1.730 | 1.593 | 1.486 | 1.371 | 1.275 | 1.190 | 1.112 | 1.041 | .977 | .92 | .86 | .81 | .77 | .73 |
| n-Undecylbenzene | $C_{17}H_{28}$ | 2.38 | 2.17 | 1.995 | 1.830 | 1.701 | 1.563 | 1.449 | 1.348 | 1.255 | 1.172 | 1.098 | 1.03 | .97 | .91 | .86 | .81 |
| n-Dodecylbenzene | $C_{18}H_{30}$ | 2.75 | 2.50 | 2.29 | 2.09 | 1.935 | 1.772 | 1.637 | 1.518 | 1.410 | 1.313 | 1.226 | 1.15 | 1.07 | 1.01 | .95 | .89 |
| n-Tridecylbenzene | $C_{19}H_{32}$ | 3.16 | 2.86 | 2.61 | 2.37 | 2.19 | 1.997 | 1.839 | 1.701 | 1.575 | 1.462 | 1.362 | 1.27 | 1.19 | 1.11 | 1.04 | .98 |
| n-Tetradecylbenzene | $C_{20}H_{34}$ | 3.61 | 3.25 | 2.95 | 2.68 | 2.47 | 2.29 | 2.06 | 1.897 | 1.751 | 1.622 | 1.507 | 1.40 | 1.31 | 1.22 | 1.14 | 1.07 |
| n-Pentadecylbenzene | $C_{21}H_{36}$ | 4.11 | 3.69 | 3.33 | 3.01 | 2.76 | 2.50 | 2.29 | 2.11 | 1.938 | 1.791 | 1.660 | 1.54 | 1.43 | 1.34 | 1.25 | 1.17 |
| n-Hexadecylbenzene | $C_{22}H_{38}$ | 4.65 | 4.16 | 3.74 | 3.37 | 3.08 | 2.78 | 2.54 | 2.33 | 2.14 | 1.971 | 1.822 | 1.69 | 1.57 | 1.46 | 1.36 | 1.27 |

a See footnote a of Table 1c.   b For the liquid above the boiling point, at saturation pressure.

TABLE 21c (PART 1), Page 3 - NORMAL ALKYL BENZENES, C$_6$ TO C$_{22}$

VISCOSITY (ABSOLUTE)

For the Normal Liquid Range, at Atmospheric Pressure

October 31, 1948

| Compound (liquid) | Formula | Temperature in °C Viscosity (absolute) in centipoises[a] | | | | | | |
|---|---|---|---|---|---|---|---|---|
| | | 125 | 130 | 135 | 140 | 145 | 150 | |
| Benzene | C$_6$H$_6$ | | | | | | | |
| Methylbenzene (Toluene) | C$_7$H$_8$ | | | | | | | |
| Ethylbenzene | C$_8$H$_{10}$ | 0.256 | 0.247 | 0.238 | 0.231[b] | | | |
| n-Propylbenzene | C$_9$H$_{12}$ | .295 | .284 | .27 | .26 | 0.26 | 0.25 | |
| n-Butylbenzene | C$_{10}$H$_{14}$ | .333 | .32 | .31 | .30 | .29 | .28 | |
| n-Pentylbenzene | C$_{11}$H$_{16}$ | .39 | .37 | .36 | .34 | .33 | .32 | |
| n-Hexylbenzene | C$_{12}$H$_{18}$ | .45 | .43 | .41 | .39 | .38 | .36 | |
| n-Heptylbenzene | C$_{13}$H$_{20}$ | .51 | .49 | .47 | .45 | .43 | .40 | |
| n-Octylbenzene | C$_{14}$H$_{22}$ | .58 | .55 | .53 | .50 | .48 | .45 | |
| n-Nonylbenzene | C$_{15}$H$_{24}$ | .65 | .62 | .59 | .56 | .53 | .50 | |
| n-Decylbenzene | C$_{16}$H$_{26}$ | .73 | .69 | .65 | .62 | .59 | .56 | |
| n-Undecylbenzene | C$_{17}$H$_{28}$ | .81 | .76 | .72 | .68 | .65 | .61 | |
| n-Dodecylbenzene | C$_{18}$H$_{30}$ | .89 | .84 | .79 | .75 | .71 | .67 | |
| n-Tridecylbenzene | C$_{19}$H$_{32}$ | .98 | .92 | .87 | .82 | .77 | .73 | |
| n-Tetradecylbenzene | C$_{20}$H$_{34}$ | 1.07 | 1.01 | .95 | .89 | .84 | .79 | |
| n-Pentadecylbenzene | C$_{21}$H$_{36}$ | 1.17 | 1.09 | 1.03 | .97 | .91 | .85 | |
| n-Hexadecylbenzene | C$_{22}$H$_{38}$ | 1.27 | 1.19 | 1.11 | 1.04 | .98 | .92 | |

a See footnote a of Table 1c.

b For the liquid above the boiling point, at saturation pressure.

244

## TABLE 5c, Page 1 - ALKYL BENZENES, $C_6$ TO $C_9$
### VISCOSITY (ABSOLUTE)
For the Normal Liquid Range, at Atmospheric Pressure

November 30, 1949

Viscosity (absolute) in centipoises[a]

| Compound (liquid) | Formula | Temperature in °C | | | | | | | | | | | | | | | |
|---|---|---|---|---|---|---|---|---|---|---|---|---|---|---|---|---|---|
| | | -25 | -20 | -15 | -10 | -5 | 0 | 5 | 10 | 15 | 20 | 25 | 30 | 35 | 40 | 45 | 50 |
| Benzene | $C_6H_6$ | | | | | | | 0.8260[b] | 0.7597 | 0.7004 | 0.6487 | 0.6028 | 0.5621 | 0.5252 | 0.4923 | 0.4629 | 0.4360 |
| Methylbenzene (Toluene) | $C_7H_8$ | 1.17 | 1.07 | 0.980 | 0.904 | 0.834 | 0.773 | 0.7184 | 0.669b | 0.6256 | 0.5666 | 0.5516 | 0.5203 | 0.4913 | 0.4650 | 0.4411 | 0.4189 |
| Ethylbenzene | $C_8H_{10}$ | 1.35 | 1.24 | 1.133 | 1.045 | 0.965 | 0.895 | 0.8312 | 0.7751 | 0.7237 | 0.6783 | 0.6373 | 0.6003 | 0.5662 | 0.5354 | 0.5073 | 0.4814 |
| 1,2-Dimethylbenzene (o-Xylene) | " | | | | | 1.215 | 1.106 | 1.017 | 0.939 | 0.870 | 0.809 | 0.756 | 0.708 | 0.664 | 0.625 | 0.589 | 0.557 |
| 1,3-Dimethylbenzene (m-Xylene) | " | | | | | | 0.808 | 0.752 | 0.702 | 0.657 | 0.617 | 0.581 | 0.549 | 0.519 | 0.492 | 0.468 | 0.445 |
| 1,4-Dimethylbenzene (p-Xylene) | " | | | | | | | | | 0.687 | 0.644 | 0.605 | 0.570 | 0.537 | 0.508 | 0.482 | 0.457 |
| n-Propylbenzene | $C_9H_{12}$ | 1.91 | 1.72 | 1.555 | 1.416 | 1.291 | 1.182 | 1.085 | 0.9996 | 0.9234 | 0.8571 | 0.7986 | 0.7466 | 0.6993 | 0.6570 | 0.6190 | 0.5842 |
| Isopropylbenzene | " | | | | | | 1.076 | 0.991 | 0.917 | 0.850 | 0.791 | 0.739 | 0.693 | 0.650 | 0.612 | 0.577 | 0.545 |
| 1-Methyl-2-ethylbenzene | " | | | | | | | | | | | | | | | | |
| 1-Methyl-3-ethylbenzene | " | | | | | | | | | | | | | | | | |
| 1-Methyl-4-ethylbenzene | " | | | | | | | | 0.808 | 0.754 | 0.705 | 0.662 | 0.623 | 0.588 | 0.556 | 0.527 | 0.500 |
| 1,2,3-Trimethylbenzene | " | | | | | | | | | | | | | | | | |
| 1,2,4-Trimethylbenzene | " | | | | | | | | | | 1.011 | 0.912 | 0.812 | | | | |
| 1,3,5-Trimethylbenzene | " | | | | | | | | | | | | | | | | |

a See footnote a of Table 1c.     b For the undercooled liquid below the normal freezing point.

TABLE 5c, Page 2 — ALKYL BENZENES, C$_6$ TO C$_9$

VISCOSITY (ABSOLUTE)

For the Normal Liquid Range, at Atmospheric Pressure

November 30, 1949

| Compound (liquid) | Formula | Temperature in °C |||||||||||||||| 
|---|---|---|---|---|---|---|---|---|---|---|---|---|---|---|---|---|---|
| | | 50 | 55 | 60 | 65 | 70 | 75 | 80 | 85 | 90 | 95 | 100 | 105 | 110 | 115 | 120 | 125 |
| | | Viscosity (absolute) in centipoises[d] |||||||||||||||| 
| Benzene | C$_6$H$_6$ | 0.4360 | 0.412 | 0.390 | 0.369 | 0.351 | 0.333 | 0.318 | 0.302[b] | | | | | | | | |
| Methylbenzene (Toluene) | C$_7$H$_8$ | 0.4189 | 0.399 | 0.380 | 0.362 | 0.346 | 0.331 | 0.317 | 0.304 | 0.291 | 0.280 | 0.269 | 0.259 | 0.249 | | | |
| Ethylbenzene | C$_8$H$_{10}$ | 0.4814 | 0.458 | 0.436 | 0.416 | 0.397 | 0.380 | 0.364 | 0.348 | 0.334 | 0.321 | 0.308 | 0.296 | 0.286 | 0.275 | 0.265 | 0.256 |
| 1,2-Dimethylbenzene (o-Xylene) | " | 0.557 | 0.528 | 0.501 | 0.476 | 0.453 | 0.432 | 0.412 | 0.393 | 0.376 | 0.360 | 0.345 | 0.331 | 0.318 | 0.305 | 0.294 | 0.283 |
| 1,3-Dimethylbenzene (m-Xylene) | " | 0.445 | 0.424 | 0.405 | 0.387 | 0.370 | 0.355 | 0.340 | 0.326 | 0.314 | 0.301 | 0.290 | 0.279 | 0.269 | 0.259 | 0.250 | 0.242 |
| 1,4-Dimethylbenzene (p-Xylene) | " | 0.457 | 0.435 | 0.415 | 0.395 | 0.377 | 0.361 | 0.346 | 0.331 | 0.318 | 0.305 | 0.293 | 0.281 | 0.270 | 0.260 | 0.250 | 0.242 |
| n-Propylbenzene | C$_9$H$_{12}$ | 0.5842 | 0.553 | 0.524 | 0.498 | 0.473 | 0.451 | 0.430 | 0.410 | 0.392 | 0.375 | 0.360 | 0.345 | 0.331 | 0.318 | 0.306 | 0.295 |
| Isopropylbenzene | " | 0.545 | 0.516 | 0.490 | | | | | | | | | | | | | |
| 1-Methyl-2-ethylbenzene | " | | | | | | | | | | | | | | | | |
| 1-Methyl-3-ethylbenzene | " | | | | | | | | | | | | | | | | |
| 1-Methyl-4-ethylbenzene | " | 0.500 | 0.476 | 0.454 | 0.434 | 0.415 | 0.398 | 0.382 | | | | | | | | | |
| 1,2,3-Trimethylbenzene | " | | | | | | | | | | | | | | | | |
| 1,2,4-Trimethylbenzene | " | | | | | | | | | | | | | | | | |
| 1,3,5-Trimethylbenzene | " | | | | | | | | | | | | | | | | |

a  See footnote a of Table 1c.

b  For the liquid above the normal boiling point, at saturation pressure.

TABLE 5c, Page 3 — ALKYL BENZENES, $C_6$ TO $C_9$

VISCOSITY (ABSOLUTE)

For the Normal Liquid Range, at Atmospheric Pressure

November 30, 1949

| Compound (liquid) | Formula | Temperature in °C | | | | | |
| --- | --- | --- | --- | --- | --- | --- | --- |
| | | 125 | 130 | 135 | 140 | 145 | 150 |
| | | Viscosity (absolute) in centipoises[a] | | | | | |
| Benzene | $C_6H_6$ | | | | | | |
| Methylbenzene (Toluene) | $C_7H_8$ | | | | | | |
| Ethylbenzene | $C_8H_{10}$ | 0.256 | 0.247 | 0.238 | 0.231[b] | | |
| 1,2-Dimethylbenzene (o-Xylene) | " | 0.283 | 0.272 | 0.263 | 0.254 | 0.245[b] | |
| 1,3-Dimethylbenzene (m-Xylene) | " | 0.242 | 0.233 | 0.226 | 0.218[b] | | |
| 1,4-Dimethylbenzene (p-Xylene) | " | 0.242 | 0.233 | 0.225 | 0.217[b] | | |
| n-Propylbenzene | $C_9H_{12}$ | 0.295 | 0.284 | 0.27 | 0.26 | 0.26 | 0.25 |
| Isopropylbenzene | " | | | | | | |
| 1-Methyl-2-ethylbenzene | " | | | | | | |
| 1-Methyl-3-ethylbenzene | " | | | | | | |
| 1-Methyl-4-ethylbenzene | " | | | | | | |
| 1,2,3-Trimethylbenzene | " | | | | | | |
| 1,2,4-Trimethylbenzene | " | | | | | | |
| 1,3,5-Trimethylbenzene | " | | | | | | |

a See footnote a of Table 1c.    b For the liquid above the normal boiling point, at saturation pressure.

TABLE 20c-E (PART 1), Page 1 – NORMAL PARAFFINS, $C_1$ TO $C_{20}$

KINEMATIC VISCOSITY

For the Normal Liquid Range at Atmospheric Pressure

May 31, 1947; October 31, 1952

Temperature in °F

Kinematic viscosity in centistokes[a]

| Compound (liquid) | Formula | -310 | -300 | -290 | -280 | -270 | -260 | -250 | -240 | -230 | -220 | -210 | -200 | -190 | -180 | -170 | -160 |
|---|---|---|---|---|---|---|---|---|---|---|---|---|---|---|---|---|---|
| Methane | $CH_4$ | | 0.485[b] | 0.405 | 0.349 | 0.311 | 0.282 | 0.256[c] | | | | | | | | | |
| Ethane | $C_2H_6$ | | | | 1.42 | 1.16 | 0.967 | 0.830 | 0.728 | 0.650 | 0.588 | 0.538 | 0.496 | 0.458 | 0.426 | 0.397 | 0.372 |
| Propane | $C_3H_8$ | 18.8[b] | 11.5 | 7.62 | 5.36 | 3.96 | 3.05 | 2.43 | 1.99 | 1.68 | 1.435 | 1.247 | 1.099 | 0.982 | 0.865 | 0.806 | 0.739 |
| n-Butane | $C_4H_{10}$ | | | | | | | | | | | | | | | | |
| n-Pentane | $C_5H_{12}$ | | | | | | | | | | | | 4.53 | 3.56 | 2.88 | 2.39 | 2.02 |
| n-Hexane | $C_6H_{14}$ | | | | | | | | | | | | | | | | |
| n-Heptane | $C_7H_{16}$ | | | | | | | | | | | | | | | | |
| n-Octane | $C_8H_{18}$ | | | | | | | | | | | | | | | | |

Temperature in °F

Kinematic viscosity in centistokes[a]

| Compound (liquid) | Formula | -150 | -140 | -130 | -120 | -110 | -100 | -90 | -80 | -70 | -60 | -50 | -40 | -30 | -20 | -10 | 0 |
|---|---|---|---|---|---|---|---|---|---|---|---|---|---|---|---|---|---|
| Methane | $CH_4$ | | | | | | | | | | | | | | | | |
| Ethane | $C_2H_6$ | 0.351 | 0.332 | 0.314 | 0.296[c] | | | | | | | | | | | | |
| Propane | $C_3H_8$ | 0.682 | 0.633 | 0.590 | 0.552 | 0.518 | 0.487 | 0.460 | 0.435 | 0.412 | 0.391 | 0.372 | 0.355[c] | | | | |
| n-Butane | $C_4H_{10}$ | | | 0.91 | 0.84 | 0.76 | 0.720 | 0.670 | 0.626 | 0.586 | 0.551 | 0.520 | 0.491 | 0.465 | 0.441 | 0.419 | 0.399 |
| n-Pentane | $C_5H_{12}$ | 1.74 | 1.51 | 1.341 | 1.198 | 1.081 | 0.982 | 0.899 | 0.828 | 0.768 | 0.715 | 0.667 | 0.628 | 0.592 | 0.559 | 0.529 | 0.503 |
| n-Hexane | $C_6H_{14}$ | | 2.87[b] | 2.43 | 2.08 | 1.80 | 1.59 | 1.41 | 1.268 | 1.150 | 1.047 | 0.962 | 0.888 | 0.824 | 0.767 | 0.717 | 0.674 |
| n-Heptane | $C_7H_{16}$ | | | 4.87 | 3.96 | 3.29 | 2.77 | 2.385 | 2.075 | 1.819 | 1.620 | 1.456 | 1.315 | 1.197 | 1.097 | 1.010 | 0.9351 |
| n-Octane | $C_8H_{18}$ | | | | | | | | | 2.90 | 2.52 | 2.20 | 1.94 | 1.734 | 1.559 | 1.411 | 1.287 |

a See footnote a of Table 1c-E    b For the undercooled liquid below the normal freezing point.    c At saturation pressure.

TABLE 20c-E (PART 1), Page 2 – NORMAL PARAFFINS, $C_1$ TO $C_{20}$

KINEMATIC VISCOSITY

For the Normal Liquid Range at Atmospheric Pressure

May 31, 1947; October 31, 1952

| Compound (liquid) | Formula | Temperature in °F — Kinematic viscosity in centistokes[a] | | | | | | | | | | | | | | |
| | | 10 | 20 | 30 | 32 | 40 | 50 | 60 | 68 | 70 | 77 | 80 | 90 | 100 | 110 | 120 | 130 |
|---|---|---|---|---|---|---|---|---|---|---|---|---|---|---|---|---|---|
| Methane | $CH_4$ | | | | | | | | | | | | | | | | |
| Ethane | $C_2H_6$ | | | | | | | | | | | | | | | | |
| Propane | $C_3H_8$ | | | | | | | | | | | | | | | | |
| n-Butane | $C_4H_{10}$ | 0.382 | 0.366 | 0.353 | 0.350[b] | | | | | | | | | | | | |
| n-Pentane | $C_5H_{12}$ | 0.478 | 0.457 | 0.436 | 0.432 | 0.419 | 0.401 | 0.387 | 0.375 | 0.372 | 0.362 | 0.358 | 0.346 | 0.331[b] | | | |
| n-Hexane | $C_6H_{14}$ | 0.635 | 0.600 | 0.569 | 0.5629 | 0.5403 | 0.5144 | 0.4913 | 0.4741 | 0.4700 | 0.4559 | 0.4501 | 0.4317 | 0.4149 | 0.3993 | 0.3845 | 0.3707 |
| n-Heptane | $C_7H_{16}$ | 0.8694 | 0.8116 | 0.7606 | 0.7511 | 0.7151 | 0.6743 | 0.6379 | 0.6114 | 0.6051 | 0.5838 | 0.5751 | 0.5480 | 0.5230 | 0.5003 | 0.4792 | 0.4597 |
| n-Octane | $C_8H_{18}$ | 1.179 | 1.086 | 1.006 | 0.9911 | 0.9353 | 0.8729 | 0.8177 | 0.7781 | 0.7687 | 0.7374 | 0.7247 | 0.6852 | 0.6495 | 0.6170 | 0.5874 | 0.5603 |

| Compound (liquid) | Formula | Temperature in °F — Kinematic viscosity in centistokes[a] | | | | | | | | | | | | |
| | | 140 | 150 | 160 | 170 | 180 | 190 | 200 | 210 | 220 | 230 | 240 | 250 | 260 |
|---|---|---|---|---|---|---|---|---|---|---|---|---|---|---|
| Methane | $CH_4$ | | | | | | | | | | | | | |
| Ethane | $C_2H_6$ | | | | | | | | | | | | | |
| Propane | $C_3H_8$ | | | | | | | | | | | | | |
| n-Butane | $C_4H_{10}$ | | | | | | | | | | | | | |
| n-Pentane | $C_5H_{12}$ | | | | | | | | | | | | | |
| n-Hexane | $C_6H_{14}$ | 0.3577 | 0.3453 | 0.3338[b] | | | | | | | | | | |
| n-Heptane | $C_7H_{16}$ | 0.4416 | 0.4245 | 0.4087 | 0.3941 | 0.3802 | 0.3673 | 0.3551 | 0.3435[b] | | | | | |
| n-Octane | $C_8H_{18}$ | 0.5353 | 0.5122 | 0.4909 | 0.4712 | 0.4531 | 0.4360 | 0.4201 | 0.4051 | 0.3912 | 0.3779 | 0.3654 | 0.3537 | 0.3423[b] |

[a] See footnote a of Table 1c-E.  [b] At saturation pressure.

TABLE 20c-E (PART 1), Page 3 – NORMAL PARAFFINS, $C_1$ TO $C_{20}$

KINEMATIC VISCOSITY

For the Normal Liquid Range at Atmospheric Pressure

May 31, 1947; October 31, 1952

Temperature in °F — Kinematic viscosity in centistokes[a]

| Compound (liquid) | Formula | -60 | -50 | -40 | -30 | -20 | -10 | 0 | 20 | 30 | 32 | 40 | 50 | 60 | 68 | 70 |
|---|---|---|---|---|---|---|---|---|---|---|---|---|---|---|---|---|
| n-Nonane | $C_9H_{20}$ | 4.00 | 3.41 | 2.93 | 2.555 | 2.253 | 2.002 | 1.794 | 1.471 | 1.344 | 1.321 | 1.235 | 1.140 | 1.057 | 0.9978 | 0.9840 |
| n-Decane | $C_{10}H_{22}$ | | | | | 3.296 | 2.821 | 2.465 | 1.978 | 1.784 | 1.749 | 1.620 | 1.479 | 1.338 | 1.272 | 1.252 |
| n-Undecane | $C_{11}H_{24}$ | | | | | | 3.940 | 3.410 | 2.635 | 2.346 | 2.294 | 2.105 | 1.900 | 1.727 | 1.606 | 1.578 |
| n-Dodecane | $C_{12}H_{26}$ | | | | | | | 3.991b | 3.478 | 3.058 | 2.983 | 2.711 | 2.424 | 2.181 | 2.014 | 1.975 |
| n-Tridecane | $C_{13}H_{28}$ | | | | | | | | 4.526b | 3.932 | 3.827 | 3.448 | 3.049 | 2.718 | 2.493 | 2.441 |
| n-Tetradecane | $C_{14}H_{30}$ | | | | | | | | | | | 4.364b | 3.819 | 3.373 | 3.070 | 3.001 |
| n-Pentadecane | $C_{15}H_{32}$ | | | | | | | | | | | | 4.724 | 4.133 | 3.737 | 3.647 |
| n-Hexadecane | $C_{16}H_{34}$ | | | | | | | | | | | | | 5.006b | 4.505 | 4.390 |
| n-Heptadecane | $C_{17}H_{36}$ | | | | | | | | | | | | | | 5.410b | 5.262b |
| n-Octadecane | $C_{18}H_{38}$ | | | | | | | | | | | | | | | |
| n-Nonadecane | $C_{19}H_{40}$ | | | | | | | | | | | | | | | |
| n-Eicosane | $C_{20}H_{42}$ | | | | | | | | | | | | | | | |

Temperature in °F — Kinematic viscosity in centistokes[a]

| Compound (liquid) | Formula | 77 | 80 | 90 | 100 | 110 | 120 | 130 | 140 | 150 | 160 | 170 | 180 | 190 | 200 | 210 | 220 |
|---|---|---|---|---|---|---|---|---|---|---|---|---|---|---|---|---|---|
| n-Nonane | $C_9H_{20}$ | 0.9381 | 0.9196 | 0.8624 | 0.8111 | 0.7650 | 0.7235 | 0.6856 | 0.6515 | 0.6200 | 0.5913 | 0.5649 | 0.5407 | 0.5182 | 0.4975 | 0.4780 | 0.4600 |
| n-Decane | $C_{10}H_{22}$ | 1.186 | 1.160 | 1.079 | 1.007 | 0.9433 | 0.8861 | 0.8350 | 0.7886 | 0.7466 | 0.7085 | 0.6738 | 0.6420 | 0.6127 | 0.5857 | 0.5608 | 0.5377 |
| n-Undecane | $C_{11}H_{24}$ | 1.487 | 1.450 | 1.338 | 1.240 | 1.153 | 1.076 | 1.008 | 0.9472 | 0.8920 | 0.8424 | 0.7973 | 0.7565 | 0.7191 | 0.6849 | 0.6535 | 0.6245 |
| n-Dodecane | $C_{12}H_{26}$ | 1.849 | 1.799 | 1.648 | 1.517 | 1.402 | 1.301 | 1.211 | 1.132 | 1.061 | 0.9969 | 0.9395 | 0.8877 | 0.8408 | 0.7980 | 0.7586 | 0.7228 |
| n-Tridecane | $C_{13}H_{28}$ | 2.273 | 2.206 | 2.005 | 1.833 | 1.683 | 1.552 | 1.437 | 1.336 | 1.246 | 1.166 | 1.095 | 1.030 | 0.9721 | 0.9193 | 0.8712 | 0.8275 |
| n-Tetradecane | $C_{14}H_{30}$ | 2.779 | 2.691 | 2.428 | 2.204 | 2.011 | 1.844 | 1.699 | 1.571 | 1.458 | 1.359 | 1.270 | 1.190 | 1.119 | 1.055 | 0.9967 | 0.9435 |
| n-Pentadecane | $C_{15}H_{32}$ | 3.357 | 3.243 | 2.905 | 2.620 | 2.376 | 2.166 | 1.986 | 1.827 | 1.688 | 1.567 | 1.458 | 1.363 | 1.276 | 1.199 | 1.129 | 1.066 |
| n-Hexadecane | $C_{16}H_{34}$ | 4.020 | 3.875 | 3.448 | 3.090 | 2.785 | 2.526 | 2.303 | 2.109 | 1.941 | 1.794 | 1.664 | 1.549 | 1.446 | 1.354 | 1.272 | 1.197 |
| n-Heptadecane | $C_{17}H_{36}$ | 4.791 | 4.608 | 4.072 | 3.625 | 3.249 | 2.931 | 2.659 | 2.424 | 2.221 | 2.045 | 1.889 | 1.752 | 1.631 | 1.523 | 1.426 | 1.339 |
| n-Octadecane | $C_{18}H_{38}$ | | 5.432b | 4.769 | 4.218 | 3.760 | 3.374 | 3.045 | 2.765 | 2.521 | 2.313 | 2.129 | 1.968 | 1.826 | 1.700 | 1.588 | 1.488 |
| n-Nonadecane | $C_{19}H_{40}$ | | | 5.554 | 4.882 | 4.327 | 3.861 | 3.469 | 3.133 | 2.848 | 2.602 | 2.388 | 2.200 | 2.034 | 1.889 | 1.758 | 1.644 |
| n-Eicosane | $C_{20}H_{42}$ | | | | 5.645 | 4.972 | 4.413 | 3.946 | 3.550 | 3.211 | 2.922 | 2.671 | 2.453 | 2.262 | 2.094 | 1.945 | 1.813 |

a See footnote a of Table 1c-E    b For the undercooled liquid below the normal freezing point.

TABLE 20c-E (PART 1), Page 4 - NORMAL PARAFFINS, C₁ TO C₂₀

**KINEMATIC VISCOSITY**

For the Normal Liquid Range at Atmospheric Pressure

May 31, 1947; October 31, 1952

| Compound (liquid) | Formula | Temperature in °F — Kinematic viscosity in centistokes[a] | | | | | | | | | | | | | | | |
|---|---|---|---|---|---|---|---|---|---|---|---|---|---|---|---|---|---|
| | | 230 | 240 | 250 | 260 | 270 | 280 | 290 | 300 | 310 | 320 | 330 | 340 | 350 | 360 | 370 | 380 |
| n-Nonane | $C_9H_{20}$ | 0.4430 | 0.4271 | 0.4122 | 0.3980 | 0.3848 | 0.3723 | 0.3605 | 0.3494 | | | | | | | | |
| n-Decane | $C_{10}H_{22}$ | 0.5164 | 0.4964 | 0.4778 | 0.4602 | 0.4438 | 0.4285 | 0.4140 | 0.4002 | 0.3873 | 0.3749 | 0.3633 | 0.3521 | 0.3423[b] | | | |
| n-Undecane | $C_{11}H_{24}$ | 0.5977 | 0.5728 | 0.5496 | 0.5282 | 0.5082 | 0.4894 | 0.4718 | 0.4554 | 0.4397 | 0.4251 | 0.4111 | 0.3980 | 0.3854 | 0.3736 | 0.3622 | 0.3514 |
| n-Dodecane | $C_{12}H_{26}$ | 0.6896 | 0.6590 | 0.6307 | 0.6045 | 0.5803 | 0.5575 | 0.5364 | 0.5166 | 0.4981 | 0.4806 | 0.4641 | 0.4486 | 0.4340 | 0.4201 | 0.4068 | 0.3943 |
| n-Tridecane | $C_{13}H_{28}$ | 0.7873 | 0.7503 | 0.7163 | 0.6848 | 0.6559 | 0.6288 | 0.6038 | 0.5804 | 0.5586 | 0.5381 | 0.5188 | 0.5008 | 0.4838 | 0.4677 | 0.4526 | 0.4382 |
| n-Tetradecane | $C_{14}H_{30}$ | 0.8950 | 0.8508 | 0.8103 | 0.7730 | 0.7384 | 0.7066 | 0.6771 | 0.6496 | 0.6240 | 0.6001 | 0.5778 | 0.5568 | 0.5372 | 0.5187 | 0.5013 | 0.4848 |
| n-Pentadecane | $C_{15}H_{32}$ | 1.009 | 0.9563 | 0.9085 | 0.8646 | 0.8243 | 0.7871 | 0.7528 | 0.7210 | 0.6915 | 0.6640 | 0.6382 | 0.6141 | 0.5917 | 0.5707 | 0.5508 | 0.5322 |
| n-Hexadecane | $C_{16}H_{34}$ | 1.130 | 1.069 | 1.013 | 0.9619 | 0.9152 | 0.8723 | 0.8329 | 0.7964 | 0.7625 | 0.7309 | 0.7016 | 0.6744 | 0.6489 | 0.6251 | 0.6027 | 0.5816 |
| n-Heptadecane | $C_{17}H_{36}$ | 1.261 | 1.189 | 1.125 | 1.066 | 1.012 | 0.9632 | 0.9179 | 0.8761 | 0.8376 | 0.8018 | 0.7687 | 0.7378 | 0.7090 | 0.6821 | 0.6569 | 0.6333 |
| n-Octadecane | $C_{18}H_{38}$ | 1.396 | 1.314 | 1.242 | 1.174 | 1.113 | 1.056 | 1.005 | 0.958 | 0.914 | 0.874 | 0.837 | 0.802 | 0.770 | 0.739 | 0.711 | 0.686 |
| n-Nonadecane | $C_{19}H_{40}$ | 1.540 | 1.447 | 1.362 | 1.286 | 1.217 | 1.154 | 1.096 | 1.042 | 0.994 | 0.948 | 0.907 | 0.869 | 0.833 | 0.799 | 0.768 | 0.740 |
| n-Eicosane | $C_{20}H_{42}$ | 1.695 | 1.588 | 1.493 | 1.406 | 1.329 | 1.257 | 1.193 | 1.132 | 1.078 | 1.028 | 0.980 | 0.938 | 0.898 | 0.862 | 0.827 | 0.795 |

| Compound (liquid) | Formula | Temperature in °F — Kinematic viscosity in centistokes[a] | | | | | | | | | | | | | | | |
|---|---|---|---|---|---|---|---|---|---|---|---|---|---|---|---|---|---|
| | | 390 | 400 | 410 | 420 | 430 | 440 | 450 | 460 | 470 | 480 | 490 | 500 | 510 | 520 | 530 | 540 |
| n-Nonane | $C_9H_{20}$ | | | | | | | | | | | | | | | | |
| n-Decane | $C_{10}H_{22}$ | | | | | | | | | | | | | | | | |
| n-Undecane | $C_{11}H_{24}$ | | | | | | | | | | | | | | | | |
| n-Dodecane | $C_{12}H_{26}$ | 0.3823 | 0.3707 | 0.3597 | 0.3511 | | | | | | | | | | | | |
| n-Tridecane | $C_{13}H_{28}$ | 0.4245 | 0.4115 | 0.3987 | 0.3867 | 0.3751 | 0.3641 | 0.3535 | 0.3428[b] | | | | | | | | |
| n-Tetradecane | $C_{14}H_{30}$ | 0.4692 | 0.4543 | 0.4402 | 0.4267 | 0.4136 | 0.4012 | 0.3895 | 0.3782 | 0.3675 | 0.3572 | | | | | | |
| n-Pentadecane | $C_{15}H_{32}$ | 0.5147 | 0.4980 | 0.4819 | 0.4667 | 0.4524 | 0.4386 | 0.4256 | 0.4130 | 0.4012 | 0.3900 | 0.379 | 0.369 | 0.359 | 0.348[b] | | |
| n-Hexadecane | $C_{16}H_{34}$ | 0.5617 | 0.5430 | 0.5253 | 0.5083 | 0.4924 | 0.4771 | 0.4627 | 0.4491 | 0.4360 | 0.4235 | 0.412 | 0.400 | 0.390 | 0.378 | 0.368 | 0.359 |
| n-Heptadecane | $C_{17}H_{36}$ | 0.6112 | 0.5902 | 0.5705 | 0.5518 | 0.5340 | 0.5172 | 0.5013 | 0.4862 | 0.4718 | 0.4581 | 0.445 | 0.432 | 0.421 | 0.408 | 0.398 | 0.388 |
| n-Octadecane | $C_{18}H_{38}$ | 0.661 | 0.638 | 0.616 | 0.595 | 0.576 | 0.558 | 0.540 | 0.524 | 0.508 | 0.493 | 0.47 | 0.46 | 0.45 | 0.45 | 0.43 | 0.42 |
| n-Nonadecane | $C_{19}H_{40}$ | 0.712 | 0.687 | 0.662 | 0.639 | 0.617 | 0.597 | 0.578 | 0.561 | 0.543 | 0.527 | 0.52 | 0.50 | 0.49 | 0.46 | 0.46 | 0.45 |
| n-Eicosane | $C_{20}H_{42}$ | 0.766 | 0.737 | 0.710 | 0.686 | 0.663 | 0.640 | 0.619 | 0.599 | 0.561 | 0.564 | 0.54 | 0.53 | 0.52 | 0.50 | 0.50 | 0.47 |

[a] See footnote a of Table 1c-E.  [b] At saturation pressure.

TABLE 20c-E (PART 1), Page 5 – NORMAL PARAFFINS, $C_1$ TO $C_{20}$

KINEMATIC VISCOSITY

For the Normal Liquid Range at Atmospheric Pressure

May 31, 1947; October 31, 1952

| Compound (liquid) | Formula | Temperature in °F | | | | | | | | | | |
|---|---|---|---|---|---|---|---|---|---|---|---|---|
| | | 550 | 560 | 570 | 580 | 590 | 600 | 610 | 620 | 630 | 640 | 650 |
| | | Kinematic viscosity in centistokes[a] | | | | | | | | | | |
| n-Nonane | $C_9H_{20}$ | | | | | | | | | | | |
| n-Decane | $C_{10}H_{22}$ | | | | | | | | | | | |
| n-Undecane | $C_{11}H_{24}$ | | | | | | | | | | | |
| n-Dodecane | $C_{12}H_{26}$ | | | | | | | | | | | |
| n-Tridecane | $C_{13}H_{28}$ | | | | | | | | | | | |
| n-Tetradecane | $C_{14}H_{30}$ | | | | | | | | | | | |
| n-Pentadecane | $C_{15}H_{32}$ | | | | | | | | | | | |
| n-Hexadecane | $C_{16}H_{34}$ | 0.348[b] | | | | | | | | | | |
| n-Heptadecane | $C_{17}H_{36}$ | 0.378 | 0.367 | 0.357 | | | | | | | | |
| n-Octadecane | $C_{18}H_{38}$ | 0.40 | 0.39 | 0.38 | 0.37 | 0.37 | 0.37 | | | | | |
| n-Nonadecane | $C_{19}H_{40}$ | 0.43 | 0.42 | 0.41 | 0.40 | 0.39 | 0.38 | 0.37 | 0.36 | 0.36[b] | | |
| n-Eicosane | $C_{20}H_{42}$ | 0.45 | 0.44 | 0.44 | 0.43 | 0.41 | 0.40 | 0.40 | 0.39 | 0.38 | 0.37 | 0.36[b] |

a See footnote a of Table 1c-E.     b At saturation pressure.

TABLE 1c-E, Page 1 - PARAFFINS, C$_1$ TO C$_5$

KINEMATIC VISCOSITY

For the Normal Liquid Range at Atmospheric Pressure

October 31, 1948; October 31, 1952

Temperature in °F

Kinematic viscosity in centistokes[a]

| Compound (liquid) | Formula | -310 | -300 | -290 | -280 | -270 | -260 | -250 | -240 | -230 | -220 | -210 | -200 | -190 | -180 | -170 | -160 |
|---|---|---|---|---|---|---|---|---|---|---|---|---|---|---|---|---|---|
| Methane | CH$_4$ | | 0.465[b] | 0.405 | 0.349 | 0.311 | 0.282 | 0.258[c] | | | | | | | | | |
| Ethane | C$_2$H$_6$ | | | | 1.42 | 1.16 | 0.967 | 0.830 | 0.728 | 0.650 | 0.588 | 0.538 | 0.496 | 0.458 | 0.426 | 0.397 | 0.372 |
| Propane | C$_3$H$_8$ | 18.8[b] | 11.5 | 7.62 | 5.36 | 3.96 | 3.05 | 2.43 | 1.99 | 1.68 | 1.435 | 1.247 | 1.099 | 0.982 | 0.885 | 0.806 | 0.739 |
| n-Butane | C$_4$H$_{10}$ | | | | | | | | | | | | | | | | |
| 2-Methylpropane (Isobutane) | " | | | | | | | | | | | | | | | | |
| n-Pentane | C$_5$H$_{12}$ | | | | | | | | | | | | 4.53 | 3.56 | 2.88 | 2.39 | 2.02 |
| 2-Methylbutane (Isopentane) | " | | | | | | | | | | | | | | | | |
| 2,2-Dimethylpropane (Neopentane) | " | | | | | | | | | | | | | | | | |

Temperature in °F

Kinematic viscosity in centistokes[a]

| Compound (liquid) | Formula | -150 | -140 | -130 | -120 | -110 | -100 | -90 | -80 | -70 | -60 | -50 | -40 | -30 | -20 | -10 | 0 |
|---|---|---|---|---|---|---|---|---|---|---|---|---|---|---|---|---|---|
| Methane | CH$_4$ | | | | | | | | | | | | | | | | |
| Ethane | C$_2$H$_6$ | 0.351 | 0.332 | 0.314 | 0.298[c] | | | | | | | | | | | | |
| Propane | C$_3$H$_8$ | 0.682 | 0.633 | 0.590 | 0.552 | 0.518 | 0.487 | 0.460 | 0.435 | 0.412 | 0.391 | 0.372 | 0.355[c] | | | | |
| n-Butane | C$_4$H$_{10}$ | | | 0.91 | 0.84 | 0.78 | 0.720 | 0.670 | 0.626 | 0.586 | 0.551 | 0.520 | 0.491 | 0.465 | 0.441 | 0.419 | 0.399 |
| 2-Methylpropane (Isobutane) | " | | | | | 0.929 | 0.851 | 0.784 | 0.725 | 0.673 | 0.627 | 0.586 | 0.549 | 0.516 | 0.486 | 0.459 | 0.434 |
| n-Pentane | C$_5$H$_{12}$ | 1.74 | 1.51 | 1.341 | 1.198 | 1.081 | 0.982 | 0.899 | 0.828 | 0.768 | 0.715 | 0.667 | 0.628 | 0.592 | 0.559 | 0.529 | 0.503 |
| 2-Methylbutane (Isopentane) | " | | | | | | | | | | 0.81 | 0.74 | 0.69 | 0.64 | 0.595 | 0.556 | 0.521 |
| 2,2-Dimethylpropane (Neopentane) | " | | | | | | | | | | | | | | | | 0.712[b] |

[a] See footnote a of Table 1c.   [b] For the undercooled liquid below the normal freezing point.   [c] At saturation pressure.

TABLE 1c-E, Page 2 – PARAFFINS, $C_1$ TO $C_5$

KINEMATIC VISCOSITY

For the Normal Liquid Range at Atmospheric Pressure

October 31, 1948; October 31, 1952

| Compound (liquid) | Formula | Temperature in °F | | | | | | | | | | | | |
|---|---|---|---|---|---|---|---|---|---|---|---|---|---|---|
| | | 10 | 20 | 30 | 32 | 40 | 50 | 60 | 68 | 70 | 77 | 80 | 90 | 100 |
| | | Kinematic viscosity in centistokes[a] | | | | | | | | | | | | |
| Methane | $CH_4$ | | | | | | | | | | | | | |
| Ethane | $C_2H_6$ | | | | | | | | | | | | | |
| Propane | $C_3H_8$ | | | | | | | | | | | | | |
| n-Butane | $C_4H_{10}$ | 0.382 | 0.366 | 0.353 | | | | | | | | | | |
| 2-Methylpropane (Isobutane) | " | 0.412 | 0.392[b] | | 0.350[b] | | | | | | | | | |
| n-Pentane | $C_5H_{12}$ | 0.478 | 0.457 | 0.436 | 0.432 | 0.419 | 0.401 | 0.387 | 0.375 | 0.372 | 0.362 | 0.358 | 0.346 | 0.331[b] |
| 2-Methylbutane (Isopentane) | " | 0.491 | 0.463 | 0.438 | 0.434 | 0.416 | 0.396 | 0.377 | 0.364 | 0.361 | 0.350 | 0.345 | 0.332[b] | |
| 2,2-Dimethylpropane (Neopentane) | " | 0.651 | 0.592 | 0.543 | 0.534 | 0.502 | 0.466[b] | | | | | | | |

[a] See footnote a of Table 1c.    [b] At saturation pressure.

TABLE 22c-E (PART 1), Page 1 – NORMAL ALKYL CYCLOPENTANES, $C_5$ TO $C_{21}$

KINEMATIC VISCOSITY

For the Normal Liquid Range at Atmospheric Pressure

December 31, 1948

| Compound (liquid) | Formula | Temperature in °F — Kinematic viscosity in centistokes[a] | | | | | | | | | | | | | | | |
|---|---|---|---|---|---|---|---|---|---|---|---|---|---|---|---|---|---|
|  |  | -10 | 0 | 10 | 20 | 30 | 40 | 50 | 60 | 70 | 80 | 90 | 100 | 110 | 120 | 130 | 140 |
| Cyclopentane | $C_5H_{10}$ | 0.97 | 0.90 | 0.837 | 0.784 | 0.735 | 0.691 | 0.652 | 0.616 | 0.583 | 0.553 | 0.525 | 0.500 | 0.477 | 0.455 |  |  |
| Methylcyclopentane | $C_6H_{12}$ | 1.15 | 1.06 | 0.987 | 0.920 | 0.859 | 0.804 | 0.755 | 0.710 | 0.669 | 0.632 | 0.598 | 0.567 | 0.538 | 0.511 | 0.487 | 0.464 |
| Ethylcyclopentane | $C_7H_{14}$ | 1.26 | 1.16 | 1.077 | 1.004 | 0.937 | 0.877 | 0.824 | 0.775 | 0.731 | 0.691 | 0.655 | 0.621 | 0.590 | 0.562 | 0.536 | 0.513 |
| n-Propylcyclopentane | $C_8H_{16}$ | 1.62 | 1.48 | 1.354 | 1.246 | 1.150 | 1.066 | 0.992 | 0.926 | 0.867 | 0.815 | 0.769 | 0.726 | 0.689 | 0.655 | 0.624 | 0.597 |
| n-Butylcyclopentane | $C_9H_{18}$ | 2.24 | 2.02 | 1.83 | 1.674 | 1.554 | 1.408 | 1.300 | 1.203 | 1.118 | 1.042 | 0.973 | 0.911 | 0.857 | 0.807 | 0.763 | 0.724 |
| n-Pentylcyclopentane | $C_{10}H_{20}$ |  | 2.72 | 2.48 | 2.26 | 2.06 | 1.88 | 1.717 | 1.565 | 1.433 | 1.317 | 1.216 | 1.131 | 1.057 | 0.990 | 0.929 | 0.875 |
| n-Hexylcyclopentane | $C_{11}H_{22}$ |  | 3.61 | 3.43 | 3.06 | 2.69 | 2.45 | 2.22 | 2.01 | 1.83 | 1.674 | 1.573 | 1.419 | 1.317 | 1.224 | 1.140 | 1.068 |
| n-Heptylcyclopentane | $C_{12}H_{24}$ |  | 4.74 | 4.27 | 3.85 | 3.47 | 3.14 | 2.83 | 2.55 | 2.31 | 2.10 | 1.91 | 1.753 | 1.617 | 1.493 | 1.382 | 1.284 |
| n-Octylcyclopentane | $C_{13}H_{26}$ |  | 6.12 | 5.48 | 4.92 | 4.41 | 3.96 | 3.56 | 3.19 | 2.87 | 2.59 | 2.34 | 2.14 | 1.96 | 1.798 | 1.655 | 1.528 |
| n-Nonylcyclopentane | $C_{14}H_{28}$ |  | 7.78 | 6.95 | 6.20 | 5.53 | 4.94 | 4.41 | 3.93 | 3.52 | 3.15 | 2.84 | 2.58 | 2.35 | 2.14 | 1.96 | 1.80 |
| n-Decylcyclopentane | $C_{15}H_{30}$ |  | 9.78 | 8.69 | 7.71 | 6.85 | 6.08 | 5.41 | 4.79 | 4.27 | 3.81 | 3.39 | 3.06 | 2.79 | 2.53 | 2.30 | 2.10 |
| n-Undecylcyclopentane | $C_{16}H_{32}$ |  |  | 10.75 | 9.50 | 8.40 | 7.42 | 6.56 | 5.79 | 5.12 | 4.55 | 4.05 | 3.64 | 3.28 | 2.96 | 2.68 | 2.44 |
| n-Dodecylcyclopentane | $C_{17}H_{34}$ |  |  |  | 11.58[b] | 10.18 | 8.96 | 7.89 | 6.93 | 6.10 | 5.39 | 4.77 | 4.26 | 3.82 | 3.43 | 3.09 | 2.80 |
| n-Tridecylcyclopentane | $C_{18}H_{36}$ |  |  |  |  | 10.18 | 10.73 | 9.40 | 8.21 | 7.20 | 6.32 | 5.58 | 4.96 | 4.42 | 3.95 | 3.54 | 3.20 |
| n-Tetradecylcyclopentane | $C_{19}H_{38}$ |  |  |  |  |  |  | 11.11 | 9.67 | 8.44 | 7.38 | 6.47 | 5.73 | 5.09 | 4.52 | 4.04 | 3.63 |
| n-Pentadecylcyclopentane | $C_{20}H_{40}$ |  |  |  |  |  |  |  | 11.30[b] | 9.82 | 8.55 | 7.47 | 6.58 | 5.81 | 5.15 | 4.58 | 4.09 |
| n-Hexadecylcyclopentane | $C_{21}H_{42}$ |  |  |  |  |  |  |  |  | 11.35[b] | 9.84 | 8.56 | 7.51 | 6.60 | 5.82 | 5.16 | 4.60 |

a See footnote a of Table 1c-E   b For the undercooled liquid below the normal freezing point.

TABLE 22c-E (PART 1), Page 2 — NORMAL ALKYL CYCLOPENTANES, $C_5$ TO $C_{21}$

KINEMATIC VISCOSITY

For the Normal Liquid Range at Atmospheric Pressure

December 31, 1948

| Compound (liquid) | Formula | \multicolumn{10}{c}{Temperature in °F} |
| | | 140 | 150 | 160 | 170 | 180 | 190 | 200 | 210 | 220 | 230 |
|---|---|---|---|---|---|---|---|---|---|---|---|
| | | \multicolumn{10}{c}{Kinematic viscosity in centistokes[a]} |
| Cyclopentane | $C_5H_{10}$ | | | | | | | | | | |
| Methylcyclopentane | $C_6H_{12}$ | 0.464 | 0.443 | 0.424 | | | | | | | |
| Ethylcyclopentane | $C_7H_{14}$ | 0.513 | 0.491 | 0.470 | 0.45 | 0.43 | 0.42 | 0.40 | 0.39 | 0.38[b] | |
| n-Propylcyclopentane | $C_8H_{16}$ | 0.597 | 0.572 | 0.549 | 0.53 | 0.51 | 0.49 | 0.48 | 0.46 | 0.45 | 0.43 |
| n-Butylcyclopentane | $C_9H_{18}$ | 0.724 | 0.688 | 0.655 | 0.63 | 0.60 | 0.57 | 0.55 | 0.53 | 0.51 | 0.49 |
| n-Pentylcyclopentane | $C_{10}H_{20}$ | 0.875 | 0.826 | 0.784 | 0.75 | 0.71 | 0.68 | 0.65 | 0.62 | 0.60 | 0.58 |
| n-Hexylcyclopentane | $C_{11}H_{22}$ | 1.068 | 1.002 | 0.945 | 0.89 | 0.85 | 0.81 | 0.77 | 0.73 | 0.70 | 0.67 |
| n-Heptylcyclopentane | $C_{12}H_{24}$ | 1.284 | 1.199 | 1.125 | 1.06 | 1.00 | 0.95 | 0.90 | 0.85 | 0.81 | 0.77 |
| n-Octylcyclopentane | $C_{13}H_{26}$ | 1.528 | 1.419 | 1.326 | 1.24 | 1.17 | 1.10 | 1.04 | 0.98 | 0.93 | 0.88 |
| n-Nonylcyclopentane | $C_{14}H_{28}$ | 1.80 | 1.664 | 1.546 | 1.44 | 1.35 | 1.27 | 1.19 | 1.12 | 1.06 | 1.00 |
| n-Decylcyclopentane | $C_{15}H_{30}$ | 2.10 | 1.93 | 1.79 | 1.66 | 1.55 | 1.45 | 1.36 | 1.27 | 1.20 | 1.13 |
| n-Undecylcyclopentane | $C_{16}H_{32}$ | 2.44 | 2.23 | 2.05 | 1.90 | 1.76 | 1.64 | 1.53 | 1.44 | 1.34 | 1.26 |
| n-Dodecylcyclopentane | $C_{17}H_{34}$ | 2.80 | 2.55 | 2.34 | 2.15 | 1.99 | 1.85 | 1.72 | 1.61 | 1.50 | 1.40 |
| n-Tridecylcyclopentane | $C_{18}H_{36}$ | 3.20 | 2.90 | 2.65 | 2.43 | 2.24 | 2.08 | 1.93 | 1.79 | 1.67 | 1.55 |
| n-Tetradecylcyclopentane | $C_{19}H_{38}$ | 3.63 | 3.28 | 2.99 | 2.73 | 2.51 | 2.32 | 2.14 | 1.99 | 1.84 | 1.71 |
| n-Pentadecylcyclopentane | $C_{20}H_{40}$ | 4.09 | 3.69 | 3.34 | 3.05 | 2.79 | 2.57 | 2.37 | 2.20 | 2.03 | 1.88 |
| n-Hexadecylcyclopentane | $C_{21}H_{42}$ | 4.60 | 4.13 | 3.73 | 3.39 | 3.10 | 2.84 | 2.61 | 2.41 | 2.23 | 2.06 |

a See footnote a of Table 1c-E    b For the liquid above its normal boiling point, at saturation pressure.

TABLE 23c-E (PART 1), Pane 1 - NORMAL ALKYL CYCLOHEXANES, $C_6$ TO $C_{22}$

KINEMATIC VISCOSITY

For the Normal Liquid Range at Atmospheric Pressure

December 31, 1948

| Compound (liquid) | Formula | Temperature in °F | | | | | | | | | | | | | | | |
|---|---|---|---|---|---|---|---|---|---|---|---|---|---|---|---|---|---|
| | | -10 | 0 | 10 | 20 | 30 | 40 | 50 | 60 | 70 | 80 | 90 | 100 | 110 | 120 | 130 | 140 |
| | | Kinematic viscosity in centistokes[a] | | | | | | | | | | | | | | | |
| Cyclohexane | $C_6H_{12}$ | | | | | | 1.658[b] | 1.498 | 1.356 | 1.236 | 1.130 | 1.038 | 0.956 | 0.884 | 0.820 | 0.763 | 0.714 |
| Methylcyclohexane | $C_7H_{14}$ | 1.86 | 1.68 | 1.530 | 1.400 | 1.283 | 1.182 | 1.092 | 1.011 | 0.941 | 0.878 | 0.821 | 0.769 | 0.723 | 0.680 | 0.642 | 0.608 |
| Ethylcyclohexane | $C_8H_{16}$ | 2.12 | 1.91 | 1.732 | 1.580 | 1.446 | 1.328 | 1.226 | 1.134 | 1.054 | 0.983 | 0.921 | 0.864 | 0.814 | 0.769 | 0.728 | 0.692 |
| n-Propylcyclohexane | $C_9H_{18}$ | 2.74 | 2.43 | 2.18 | 1.96 | 1.775 | 1.614 | 1.475 | 1.353 | 1.248 | 1.156 | 1.075 | 1.003 | 0.939 | 0.882 | 0.832 | 0.787 |
| n-Butylcyclohexane | $C_{10}H_{20}$ | | 3.37 | 2.99 | 2.67 | 2.39 | 2.16 | 1.95 | 1.770 | 1.615 | 1.480 | 1.360 | 1.255 | 1.164 | 1.084 | 1.014 | 0.954 |
| n-Pentylcyclohexane | $C_{11}H_{22}$ | | | 4.24 | 3.74 | 3.31 | 2.93 | 2.61 | 2.33 | 2.10 | 1.89 | 1.711 | 1.561 | 1.436 | 1.330 | 1.238 | 1.158 |
| n-Hexylcyclohexane | $C_{12}H_{24}$ | | | 5.71 | 4.99 | 4.38 | 3.86 | 3.40 | 3.02 | 2.68 | 2.40 | 2.15 | 1.95 | 1.780 | 1.637 | 1.514 | 1.406 |
| n-Heptylcyclohexane | $C_{13}H_{26}$ | | | 7.55 | 6.55 | 5.70 | 4.97 | 4.35 | 3.83 | 3.38 | 3.00 | 2.67 | 2.39 | 2.17 | 1.99 | 1.82 | 1.683 |
| n-Octylcyclohexane | $C_{14}H_{28}$ | | | 9.81 | 8.45 | 7.30 | 6.30 | 5.49 | 4.79 | 4.19 | 3.69 | 3.26 | 2.91 | 2.62 | 2.38 | 2.17 | 1.99 |
| n-Nonylcyclohexane | $C_{15}H_{30}$ | | | 12.59 | 10.74 | 9.21 | 7.91 | 6.82 | 5.91 | 5.14 | 4.49 | 3.94 | 3.49 | 3.13 | 2.82 | 2.56 | 2.34 |
| n-Decylcyclohexane | $C_{16}H_{32}$ | | | | | 11.47 | 9.79 | 8.38 | 7.21 | 6.22 | 5.40 | 4.71 | 4.15 | 3.69 | 3.31 | 2.99 | 2.72 |
| n-Undecylcyclohexane | $C_{17}H_{34}$ | | | | | | 11.98[b] | 10.18 | 8.71 | 7.48 | 6.43 | 5.58 | 4.88 | 4.32 | 3.86 | 3.46 | 3.13 |
| n-Dodecylcyclohexane | $C_{18}H_{36}$ | | | | | | | 12.27[b] | 10.41 | 8.87 | 7.60 | 6.55 | 5.69 | 5.02 | 4.45 | 3.98 | 3.57 |
| n-Tridecylcyclohexane | $C_{19}H_{38}$ | | | | | | | | | 10.46 | 8.90 | 7.63 | 6.60 | 5.79 | 5.11 | 4.55 | 4.07 |
| n-Tetradecylcyclohexane | $C_{20}H_{40}$ | | | | | | | | | | 10.36 | 8.83 | 7.60 | 6.63 | 5.83 | 5.16 | 4.60 |
| n-Pentadecylcyclohexane | $C_{21}H_{42}$ | | | | | | | | | | 11.98[b] | 10.16 | 8.70 | 7.55 | 6.61 | 5.83 | 5.18 |
| n-Hexadecylcyclohexane | $C_{22}H_{44}$ | | | | | | | | | | | 11.60[b] | 9.90 | 8.55 | 7.45 | 6.55 | 5.80 |

a See footnote a of Table 1c-E    b For the undercooled liquid below the normal freezing point.

TABLE 23c-E (PART 1), Page 2 - NORMAL ALKYL CYCLOHEXANES, $C_6$ TO $C_{22}$

KINEMATIC VISCOSITY

For the Normal Liquid Range at Atmospheric Pressure

December 31, 1948 (Corrected)

| Compound (liquid) | Formula | Temperature in °F | | | | | | | | | |
|---|---|---|---|---|---|---|---|---|---|---|---|
| | | Kinematic viscosity in centistokes[a] | | | | | | | | | |
| | | 140 | 150 | 160 | 170 | 180 | 190 | 200 | 210 | 220 | 230 |
| Cyclohexane | $C_6H_{12}$ | 0.714 | 0.667 | 0.626 | 0.59 | 0.56[b] | | | | | |
| Methylcyclohexane | $C_7H_{14}$ | 0.608 | 0.575 | 0.546 | 0.52 | 0.49 | 0.47 | 0.45 | 0.43 | | |
| Ethylcyclohexane | $C_8H_{16}$ | 0.692 | 0.658 | 0.629 | 0.60 | 0.58 | 0.55 | 0.53 | 0.51 | 0.50 | 0.48 |
| n-Propylcyclohexane | $C_9H_{18}$ | 0.787 | 0.746 | 0.710 | 0.68 | 0.65 | 0.62 | 0.60 | 0.58 | 0.56 | 0.54 |
| n-Butylcyclohexane | $C_{10}H_{20}$ | 0.954 | 0.899 | 0.85 | 0.81 | 0.78 | 0.75 | 0.72 | 0.69 | 0.67 | 0.64 |
| n-Pentylcyclohexane | $C_{11}H_{22}$ | 1.158 | 1.086 | 1.02 | 0.96 | 0.91 | 0.86 | 0.81 | 0.77 | 0.73 | 0.69 |
| n-Hexylcyclohexane | $C_{12}H_{24}$ | 1.406 | 1.308 | 1.22 | 1.14 | 1.07 | 1.01 | 0.95 | 0.89 | 0.84 | 0.80 |
| n-Heptylcyclohexane | $C_{13}H_{26}$ | 1.683 | 1.558 | 1.44 | 1.34 | 1.25 | 1.17 | 1.10 | 1.03 | 0.96 | 0.91 |
| n-Octylcyclohexane | $C_{14}H_{28}$ | 1.99 | 1.83 | 1.70 | 1.57 | 1.45 | 1.35 | 1.25 | 1.17 | 1.09 | 1.02 |
| n-Nonylcyclohexane | $C_{15}H_{30}$ | 2.34 | 2.14 | 1.96 | 1.81 | 1.67 | 1.54 | 1.43 | 1.32 | 1.23 | 1.15 |
| n-Decylcyclohexane | $C_{16}H_{32}$ | 2.72 | 2.47 | 2.26 | 2.07 | 1.90 | 1.75 | 1.61 | 1.49 | 1.38 | 1.28 |
| n-Undecylcyclohexane | $C_{17}H_{34}$ | 3.13 | 2.83 | 2.58 | 2.35 | 2.15 | 1.97 | 1.80 | 1.66 | 1.53 | 1.41 |
| n-Dodecylcyclohexane | $C_{18}H_{36}$ | 3.57 | 3.24 | 2.92 | 2.65 | 2.41 | 2.20 | 2.01 | 1.84 | 1.69 | 1.56 |
| n-Tridecylcyclohexane | $C_{19}H_{38}$ | 4.07 | 3.65 | 3.30 | 2.98 | 2.70 | 2.45 | 2.23 | 2.04 | 1.86 | 1.71 |
| n-Tetradecylcyclohexane | $C_{20}H_{40}$ | 4.60 | 4.12 | 3.70 | 3.32 | 3.00 | 2.72 | 2.47 | 2.24 | 2.04 | 1.87 |
| n-Pentadecylcyclohexane | $C_{21}H_{42}$ | 5.18 | 4.61 | 4.13 | 3.69 | 3.33 | 3.00 | 2.71 | 2.46 | 2.23 | 2.03 |
| n-Hexadecylcyclohexane | $C_{22}H_{44}$ | 5.80 | 5.13 | 4.48 | 4.09 | 3.67 | 3.29 | 2.97 | 2.68 | 2.43 | 2.20 |

[a] See footnote a of Table 1c-E

[b] For the liquid above the normal boiling point, at saturation pressure.

TABLE 24c-E, Page 1 - NORMAL MONOOLEFINS (1-ALKENES), $C_2$ TO $C_{20}$

KINEMATIC VISCOSITY

For the Normal Liquid Range at Atmospheric Pressure

August 31, 1949 (Corrected)

Temperature in °F

Kinematic viscosity in centistokes[a]

| Compound (liquid) | Formula | -300 | -290 | -280 | -270 | -260 | -250 | -240 | -230 | -220 | -210 | -200 | -190 | -180 | -170 | -160 | -150 |
|---|---|---|---|---|---|---|---|---|---|---|---|---|---|---|---|---|---|
| Ethene (Ethylene) | $C_2H_4$ | | | | 0.99 | 0.84 | 0.72 | 0.64 | 0.57 | 0.51 | 0.46 | 0.42 | 0.38 | 0.35 | 0.32 | 0.30 | 0.27[b] |
| Propene (Propylene) | $C_3H_6$ | 18.3 | 10.0 | 6.07 | 4.04 | 2.95 | 2.30 | 1.85 | 1.50 | 1.27 | 1.08 | 0.94 | 0.83 | 0.74 | 0.67 | 0.61 | 0.57 |
| 1-Butene | $C_4H_8$ | | | | | | | | | | | | | | 1.22 | 1.03 | 0.89 |
| 1-Pentene | $C_5H_{10}$ | | | | | | | | | | | | | | | | |
| 1-Hexene | $C_6H_{12}$ | | | | | | | | | | | | | | | | |
| 1-Heptene | $C_7H_{14}$ | | | | | | | | | | | | | | | | |
| 1-Octene | $C_8H_{16}$ | | | | | | | | | | | | | | | | |
| 1-Nonene | $C_9H_{18}$ | | | | | | | | | | | | | | | | |
| 1-Decene | $C_{10}H_{20}$ | | | | | | | | | | | | | | | | |
| 1-Undecene | $C_{11}H_{22}$ | | | | | | | | | | | | | | | | |
| 1-Dodecene | $C_{12}H_{24}$ | | | | | | | | | | | | | | | | |
| 1-Tridecene | $C_{13}H_{26}$ | | | | | | | | | | | | | | | | |
| 1-Tetradecene | $C_{14}H_{28}$ | | | | | | | | | | | | | | | | |
| 1-Pentadecene | $C_{15}H_{30}$ | | | | | | | | | | | | | | | | |
| 1-Hexadecene | $C_{16}H_{32}$ | | | | | | | | | | | | | | | | |
| 1-Heptadecene | $C_{17}H_{34}$ | | | | | | | | | | | | | | | | |
| 1-Octadecene | $C_{18}H_{36}$ | | | | | | | | | | | | | | | | |
| 1-Nonadecene | $C_{19}H_{38}$ | | | | | | | | | | | | | | | | |
| 1-Eicosene | $C_{20}H_{40}$ | | | | | | | | | | | | | | | | |

a See footnote a of Table 1c-E.

b For the liquid above the normal boiling point, at saturation pressure.

## TABLE 24c-E, Page 2 — NORMAL MONOOLEFINS (1-ALKENES), $C_2$ TO $C_{20}$
### KINEMATIC VISCOSITY

For the Normal Liquid Range at Atmospheric Pressure

August 31, 1949 (Corrected)

Kinematic viscosity in centistokes[a]

| Compound (liquid) | Formula | Temperature in °F | | | | | | | | | | | | | | | |
|---|---|---|---|---|---|---|---|---|---|---|---|---|---|---|---|---|---|
| | | -150 | -140 | -130 | -120 | -110 | -100 | -90 | -80 | -70 | -60 | -50 | -40 | -30 | -20 | -10 | 0 |
| Ethene (Ethylene) | $C_2H_4$ | 0.27[b] | | | | | | | | | | | | | | | |
| Propene (Propylene) | $C_3H_6$ | 0.57 | 0.54 | | | | | | | | | | | | | | |
| 1-Butene | $C_4H_8$ | 0.89 | 0.81 | 0.74 | 0.67 | 0.62 | 0.58 | 0.54 | 0.50 | 0.47 | 0.44 | 0.42 | 0.40 | 0.38 | | | |
| 1-Pentene | $C_5H_{10}$ | | | 1.13 | 1.02 | 0.92 | 0.84 | 0.77 | 0.71 | 0.66 | 0.61 | 0.57 | 0.54 | 0.50 | 0.47 | 0.45 | 0.43 |
| 1-Hexene | $C_6H_{12}$ | | | | | | | | | 0.95 | 0.87 | 0.81 | 0.75 | 0.69 | 0.65 | 0.61 | 0.57 |
| 1-Heptene | $C_7H_{14}$ | | | | | | | | | | | | | | | | |
| 1-Octene | $C_8H_{16}$ | | | | | | | | | | | | | | | | |
| 1-Nonene | $C_9H_{18}$ | | | | | | | | | | | | | | | | |
| 1-Decene | $C_{10}H_{20}$ | | | | | | | | | | | | | | | | |
| 1-Undecene | $C_{11}H_{22}$ | | | | | | | | | | | | | | | | |
| 1-Dodecene | $C_{12}H_{24}$ | | | | | | | | | | | | | | | | |
| 1-Tridecene | $C_{13}H_{26}$ | | | | | | | | | | | | | | | | |
| 1-Tetradecene | $C_{14}H_{28}$ | | | | | | | | | | | | | | | | |
| 1-Pentadecene | $C_{15}H_{30}$ | | | | | | | | | | | | | | | | |
| 1-Hexadecene | $C_{16}H_{32}$ | | | | | | | | | | | | | | | | |
| 1-Heptadecene | $C_{17}H_{34}$ | | | | | | | | | | | | | | | | |
| 1-Octadecene | $C_{18}H_{36}$ | | | | | | | | | | | | | | | | |
| 1-Nonadecene | $C_{19}H_{38}$ | | | | | | | | | | | | | | | | |
| 1-Eicosene | $C_{20}H_{40}$ | | | | | | | | | | | | | | | | |

a See footnote a of Table 1c-E.   b For the liquid above the normal boiling point, at saturation pressure.

TABLE 24c-E, Page 3 – NORMAL MONOOLEFINS (1-ALKENES), $C_2$ TO $C_{20}$

KINEMATIC VISCOSITY

For the Normal Liquid Range at Atmospheric Pressure

August 31, 1949

| Compound (liquid) | Formula | Temperature in °F | | | | | | | | | | | | | | | |
| --- | --- | --- | --- | --- | --- | --- | --- | --- | --- | --- | --- | --- | --- | --- | --- | --- | --- |
| | | 0 | 10 | 20 | 30 | 40 | 50 | 60 | 70 | 80 | 90 | 100 | 110 | 120 | 130 | 140 | 150 |
| | | Kinematic viscosity in centistokes[a] | | | | | | | | | | | | | | | |
| Ethene (Ethylene) | $C_2H_4$ | | | | | | | | | | | | | | | | |
| Propene (Propylene) | $C_3H_6$ | | | | | | | | | | | | | | | | |
| 1-Butene | $C_4H_8$ | | | | | | | | | | | | | | | | |
| 1-Pentene | $C_5H_{10}$ | 0.43 | 0.41 | 0.39 | 0.37 | | | | | | | | | | | | |
| 1-Hexene | $C_6H_{12}$ | 0.57 | 0.54 | 0.51 | 0.48 | 0.45 | 0.43 | 0.41 | 0.38 | 0.36 | 0.35 | 0.34 | 0.33 | 0.32 | 0.31 | 0.30 | 0.29[b] |
| 1-Heptene | $C_7H_{14}$ | | | | | | 0.55 | 0.52 | 0.50 | 0.48 | 0.46 | 0.44 | 0.42 | 0.40 | 0.39 | 0.38 | 0.36 |
| 1-Octene | $C_8H_{16}$ | | | | | | 0.736 | 0.688 | 0.651 | 0.619 | 0.588 | 0.559 | 0.532 | 0.507 | 0.485 | 0.465 | 0.447 |
| 1-Nonene | $C_9H_{18}$ | | | | | | 0.972 | 0.897 | 0.841 | 0.793 | 0.748 | 0.706 | 0.667 | 0.631 | 0.599 | 0.570 | 0.545 |
| 1-Decene | $C_{10}H_{20}$ | | | | | | 1.262 | 1.158 | 1.075 | 1.004 | 0.940 | 0.880 | 0.826 | 0.777 | 0.733 | 0.694 | 0.659 |
| 1-Undecene | $C_{11}H_{22}$ | | | | | | 1.62 | 1.47 | 1.35 | 1.259 | 1.170 | 1.088 | 1.013 | 0.947 | 0.889 | 0.838 | 0.792 |
| 1-Dodecene | $C_{12}H_{24}$ | | | | | | 2.06 | 1.85 | 1.69 | 1.56 | 1.44 | 1.33 | 1.231 | 1.144 | 1.067 | 0.999 | 0.939 |
| 1-Tridecene | $C_{13}H_{26}$ | | | | | | 2.59 | 2.31 | 2.10 | 1.92 | 1.76 | 1.61 | 1.48 | 1.37 | 1.274 | 1.188 | 1.110 |
| 1-Tetradecene | $C_{14}H_{28}$ | | | | | | 3.23 | 2.85 | 2.56 | 2.32 | 2.11 | 1.93 | 1.77 | 1.63 | 1.51 | 1.40 | 1.30 |
| 1-Pentadecene | $C_{15}H_{30}$ | | | | | | 3.99 | 3.50 | 3.12 | 2.81 | 2.55 | 2.31 | 2.11 | 1.92 | 1.77 | 1.64 | 1.51 |
| 1-Hexadecene | $C_{16}H_{32}$ | | | | | | 4.86 | 4.22 | 3.75 | 3.36 | 3.03 | 2.74 | 2.48 | 2.26 | 2.07 | 1.90 | 1.75 |
| 1-Heptadecene | $C_{17}H_{34}$ | | | | | | 5.93[c] | 5.11 | 4.49 | 3.99 | 3.59 | 3.22 | 2.90 | 2.63 | 2.40 | 2.19 | 2.02 |
| 1-Octadecene | $C_{18}H_{36}$ | | | | | | | 6.02[c] | 5.34 | 4.74 | 4.22 | 3.77 | 3.37 | 3.04 | 2.76 | 2.52 | 2.31 |
| 1-Nonadecene | $C_{19}H_{38}$ | | | | | | | | | 5.58 | 4.94 | 4.38 | 3.90 | 3.51 | 3.17 | 2.88 | 2.63 |
| 1-Eicosene | $C_{20}H_{40}$ | | | | | | | | | | 5.73 | 5.06 | 4.50 | 4.04 | 3.63 | 3.28 | 2.98 |

a See footnote a of Table 1c-E.   b For the liquid above the normal boiling point, at saturation pressure.   c For the undercooled liquid below the normal freezing point.

# TABLE 24c-E, Page 4 — NORMAL MONOOLEFINS (1-ALKENES), $C_2$ TO $C_{20}$
## KINEMATIC VISCOSITY
### For the Normal Liquid Range at Atmospheric Pressure
August 31, 1949

| Compound (liquid) | Formula | Temperature in °F | | | | | | | | | |
|---|---|---|---|---|---|---|---|---|---|---|---|
| | | Kinematic viscosity in centistokes[a] | | | | | | | | | |
| | | 150 | 160 | 170 | 180 | 190 | 200 | 210 | 220 | 230 | 240 |
| Ethene (Ethylene) | $C_2H_4$ | | | | | | | | | | |
| Propene (Propylene) | $C_3H_6$ | | | | | | | | | | |
| 1-Butene | $C_4H_8$ | | | | | | | | | | |
| 1-Pentene | $C_5H_{10}$ | | | | | | | | | | |
| 1-Hexene | $C_6H_{12}$ | 0.29[b] | | | | | | | | | |
| 1-Heptene | $C_7H_{14}$ | 0.36 | 0.35 | 0.34 | 0.33 | 0.32 | 0.31 | | | | |
| 1-Octene | $C_8H_{16}$ | 0.447 | 0.431 | 0.416 | 0.402 | 0.388 | 0.376 | 0.365 | 0.35 | 0.34 | 0.33 |
| 1-Nonene | $C_9H_{18}$ | 0.545 | 0.522 | 0.501 | 0.481 | 0.463 | 0.446 | 0.430 | 0.42 | 0.40 | 0.39 |
| 1-Decene | $C_{10}H_{20}$ | 0.659 | 0.628 | 0.600 | 0.574 | 0.550 | 0.528 | 0.507 | 0.49 | 0.47 | 0.45 |
| 1-Undecene | $C_{11}H_{22}$ | 0.792 | 0.751 | 0.714 | 0.679 | 0.647 | 0.618 | 0.592 | 0.57 | 0.54 | 0.52 |
| 1-Dodecene | $C_{12}H_{24}$ | 0.939 | 0.886 | 0.839 | 0.796 | 0.756 | 0.719 | 0.685 | 0.65 | 0.62 | 0.60 |
| 1-Tridecene | $C_{13}H_{26}$ | 1.110 | 1.042 | 0.982 | 0.927 | 0.877 | 0.832 | 0.791 | 0.75 | 0.72 | 0.68 |
| 1-Tetradecene | $C_{14}H_{28}$ | 1.30 | 1.214 | 1.140 | 1.072 | 1.011 | 0.955 | 0.904 | 0.86 | 0.81 | 0.77 |
| 1-Pentadecene | $C_{15}H_{30}$ | 1.51 | 1.41 | 1.32 | 1.236 | 1.160 | 1.092 | 1.031 | 0.97 | 0.92 | 0.87 |
| 1-Hexadecene | $C_{16}H_{32}$ | 1.75 | 1.63 | 1.52 | 1.42 | 1.32 | 1.241 | 1.166 | 1.10 | 1.04 | 0.98 |
| 1-Heptadecene | $C_{17}H_{34}$ | 2.02 | 1.86 | 1.74 | 1.63 | 1.52 | 1.41 | 1.31 | 1.23 | 1.16 | 1.09 |
| 1-Octadecene | $C_{18}H_{36}$ | 2.31 | 2.14 | 1.97 | 1.83 | 1.69 | 1.58 | 1.48 | 1.39 | 1.30 | 1.22 |
| 1-Nonadecene | $C_{19}H_{38}$ | 2.63 | 2.42 | 2.23 | 2.06 | 1.91 | 1.78 | 1.66 | 1.54 | 1.44 | 1.35 |
| 1-Eicosene | $C_{20}H_{40}$ | 2.98 | 2.74 | 2.52 | 2.31 | 2.13 | 1.98 | 1.84 | 1.72 | 1.60 | 1.49 |

a See footnote a of Table 1c-E.

b For the liquid above the normal boiling point, at saturation pressure.

TABLE 21c-E (PART 1), Page 1 – NORMAL ALKYL BENZENES, $C_6$ TO $C_{22}$

KINEMATIC VISCOSITY

For the Normal Liquid Range at Atmospheric Pressure

October 31, 1948

| Compound (liquid) | Formula | Temperature in °F | | | | | | | | | | | | | | | |
|---|---|---|---|---|---|---|---|---|---|---|---|---|---|---|---|---|---|
| | | −10 | 0 | 10 | 20 | 30 | 40 | 50 | 60 | 70 | 80 | 90 | 100 | 110 | 120 | 130 | 140 |
| | | Kinematic viscosity in centistokes [a] | | | | | | | | | | | | | | | |
| Benzene | $C_6H_6$ | | | | | | 0.9310b | 0.8538 | 0.7855 | 0.7268 | 0.6751 | 0.6295 | 0.5888 | 0.5530 | 0.5209 | 0.492 | 0.467 |
| Methylbenzene (Toluene) | $C_7H_8$ | 1.25 | 1.14 | 1.045 | 0.961 | 0.887 | 0.8218 | .7645 | .7130 | .6681 | .6283 | .5926 | .5601 | .5310 | .5042 | .480 | .458 |
| Ethylbenzene | $C_8H_{10}$ | 1.45 | 1.32 | 1.208 | 1.112 | 1.027 | .9512 | .8848 | .8247 | .7723 | .7254 | .6831 | .6447 | .6104 | .5785 | .550 | .525 |
| n-Propylbenzene | $C_9H_{12}$ | 2.06 | 1.84 | 1.660 | 1.506 | 1.370 | 1.251 | 1.149 | 1.058 | .9796 | .9114 | .8510 | .7968 | .7491 | .7060 | .667 | .633 |
| n-Butylbenzene | $C_{10}H_{14}$ | 2.69 | 2.38 | 2.11 | 1.912 | 1.713 | 1.544 | 1.406 | 1.287 | 1.184 | 1.096 | 1.019 | .950 | .890 | .829 | .785 | .741 |
| n-Pentylbenzene | $C_{11}H_{16}$ | | 3.92 | 3.21 | 2.72 | 2.36 | 2.08 | 1.856 | 1.675 | 1.525 | 1.397 | 1.288 | 1.192 | 1.109 | 1.035 | .969 | .913 |
| n-Hexylbenzene | $C_{12}H_{18}$ | | 5.22 | 4.39 | 3.65 | 3.06 | 2.68 | 2.37 | 2.12 | 1.914 | 1.740 | 1.594 | 1.466 | 1.355 | 1.258 | 1.171 | 1.098 |
| n-Heptylbenzene | $C_{13}H_{20}$ | | 7.05 | 5.63 | 4.66 | 3.94 | 3.41 | 2.99 | 2.65 | 2.38 | 2.15 | 1.951 | 1.783 | 1.638 | 1.511 | 1.401 | 1.305 |
| n-Octylbenzene | $C_{14}H_{22}$ | | 9.35 | 7.36 | 6.01 | 5.04 | 4.31 | 3.75 | 3.29 | 2.93 | 2.62 | 2.37 | 2.15 | 1.964 | 1.801 | 1.659 | 1.539 |
| n-Nonylbenzene | $C_{15}H_{24}$ | | 12.30 | 9.54 | 7.70 | 6.38 | 5.40 | 4.65 | 4.05 | 3.57 | 3.17 | 2.85 | 2.57 | 2.33 | 2.13 | 1.950 | 1.800 |
| n-Decylbenzene | $C_{16}H_{26}$ | | 16.1 | 12.28 | 9.79 | 8.01 | 6.72 | 5.72 | 4.95 | 4.32 | 3.81 | 3.40 | 3.05 | 2.75 | 2.45 | 2.27 | 2.09 |
| n-Undecylbenzene | $C_{17}H_{28}$ | | | 15.7b | 12.36 | 10.00 | 8.29 | 7.00 | 5.99 | 5.20 | 4.55 | 4.03 | 3.59 | 3.22 | 2.90 | 2.63 | 2.41 |
| n-Dodecylbenzene | $C_{18}H_{30}$ | | | | 15.5b | 12.39 | 10.17 | 8.50 | 7.21 | 6.21 | 5.40 | 4.74 | 4.20 | 3.74 | 3.36 | 3.03 | 2.76 |
| n-Tridecylbenzene | $C_{19}H_{32}$ | | | | | | 12.39b | 10.25 | 8.63 | 7.36 | 6.36 | 5.55 | 4.88 | 4.33 | 3.87 | 3.47 | 3.15 |
| n-Tetradecylbenzene | $C_{20}H_{34}$ | | | | | | | 12.30b | 10.26 | 8.69 | 7.44 | 6.46 | 5.64 | 4.98 | 4.42 | 3.95 | 3.57 |
| n-Pentadecylbenzene | $C_{21}H_{36}$ | | | | | | | | 12.13b | 10.19 | 8.67 | 7.47 | 6.49 | 5.70 | 5.04 | 4.48 | 4.02 |
| n-Hexadecylbenzene | $C_{22}H_{38}$ | | | | | | | | | | 10.06 | 8.61 | 7.44 | 6.49 | 5.71 | 5.06 | 4.52 |

a See footnote a of Table 1c-E

b Extrapolated value for the undercooled liquid below the normal freezing point.

TABLE 21c-E (PART 1), Page 2 — NORMAL ALKYL BENZENES, $C_6$ TO $C_{22}$

KINEMATIC VISCOSITY

For the Normal Liquid Range at Atmospheric Pressure

October 31, 1948

| Compound (liquid) | Formula | Temperature in °F | | | | | | | | | | | | | | | |
|---|---|---|---|---|---|---|---|---|---|---|---|---|---|---|---|---|---|
| | | 150 | 160 | 170 | 180 | 190 | 200 | 210 | 220 | 230 | 240 | 250 | 260 | 270 | 280 | 290 | 300 |
| | | Kinematic viscosity in centistokes [a] | | | | | | | | | | | | | | | |
| Benzene | $C_6H_6$ | 0.442 | 0.421 | 0.401 | 0.383[b] | | | | | | | | | | | | |
| Methylbenzene (Toluene) | $C_7H_8$ | .437 | .418 | .401 | .384 | .369 | 0.355 | 0.342 | 0.329 | 0.318 | | | | | | | |
| Ethylbenzene | $C_8H_{10}$ | .501 | .479 | .459 | .440 | .422 | .406 | .391 | .376 | .363 | 0.350 | 0.339 | 0.328 | 0.317 | 0.307[b] | | |
| n-Propylbenzene | $C_9H_{12}$ | .600 | .571 | .544 | .519 | .496 | .475 | .456 | .437 | .421 | .405 | .390 | .376 | .363 | .35 | 0.34 | 0.33 |
| n-Butylbenzene | $C_{10}H_{14}$ | .700 | .663 | .630 | .599 | .571 | .544 | .520 | .498 | .48 | .46 | .44 | .42 | .41 | .39 | .38 | .37 |
| n-Pentylbenzene | $C_{11}H_{16}$ | .858 | .812 | .766 | .726 | .689 | .655 | .623 | .594 | .57 | .54 | .52 | .50 | .48 | .46 | .44 | .42 |
| n-Hexylbenzene | $C_{12}H_{18}$ | 1.025 | .968 | .907 | .857 | .810 | .767 | .727 | .691 | .66 | .63 | .60 | .57 | .54 | .52 | .50 | .48 |
| n-Heptylbenzene | $C_{13}H_{20}$ | 1.215 | 1.141 | 1.065 | 1.001 | .942 | .889 | .840 | .796 | .75 | .72 | .68 | .65 | .62 | .59 | .56 | .54 |
| n-Octylbenzene | $C_{14}H_{22}$ | 1.426 | 1.333 | 1.238 | 1.159 | 1.088 | 1.022 | .963 | .909 | .86 | .81 | .77 | .73 | .70 | .66 | .63 | .60 |
| n-Nonylbenzene | $C_{15}H_{24}$ | 1.659 | 1.546 | 1.429 | 1.333 | 1.246 | 1.166 | 1.095 | 1.031 | .97 | .92 | .87 | .82 | .78 | .74 | .70 | .67 |
| n-Decylbenzene | $C_{16}H_{26}$ | 1.917 | 1.779 | 1.638 | 1.521 | 1.417 | 1.322 | 1.238 | 1.161 | 1.09 | 1.03 | .97 | .91 | .86 | .82 | .78 | .73 |
| n-Undecylbenzene | $C_{17}H_{28}$ | 2.20 | 2.04 | 1.865 | 1.726 | 1.602 | 1.490 | 1.390 | 1.300 | 1.22 | 1.14 | 1.08 | 1.01 | .96 | .90 | .86 | .81 |
| n-Dodecylbenzene | $C_{18}H_{30}$ | 2.51 | 2.31 | 2.11 | 1.947 | 1.801 | 1.669 | 1.553 | 1.448 | 1.35 | 1.27 | 1.19 | 1.12 | 1.05 | .99 | .94 | .88 |
| n-Tridecylbenzene | $C_{19}H_{32}$ | 2.85 | 2.62 | 2.38 | 2.18 | 2.01 | 1.861 | 1.726 | 1.605 | 1.50 | 1.40 | 1.31 | 1.23 | 1.15 | 1.08 | 1.02 | .96 |
| n-Tetradecylbenzene | $C_{20}H_{34}$ | 3.22 | 2.96 | 2.71 | 2.44 | 2.24 | 2.06 | 1.910 | 1.771 | 1.65 | 1.53 | 1.43 | 1.34 | 1.26 | 1.18 | 1.11 | 1.04 |
| n-Pentadecylbenzene | $C_{21}H_{36}$ | 3.62 | 3.30 | 2.97 | 2.71 | 2.48 | 2.28 | 2.10 | 1.946 | 1.80 | 1.68 | 1.56 | 1.46 | 1.36 | 1.28 | 1.20 | 1.13 |
| n-Hexadecylbenzene | $C_{22}H_{38}$ | 4.05 | 3.68 | 3.30 | 3.00 | 2.74 | 2.51 | 2.31 | 2.13 | 1.97 | 1.83 | 1.70 | 1.58 | 1.48 | 1.38 | 1.30 | 1.21 |

a See footnote a of Table 1c-E          b For the liquid above the boiling point, at saturation pressure.

TABLE 5c-E, Page 1 – ALKYL BENZENES, $C_6$ TO $C_9$
KINEMATIC VISCOSITY
For the Normal Liquid Range at Atmospheric Pressure
November 30, 1949

Kinematic viscosity in centistokes[a]

| Compound (liquid) | Formula | Temperature in °F | | | | | | | | | | | | | | | |
|---|---|---|---|---|---|---|---|---|---|---|---|---|---|---|---|---|---|
| | | -10 | 0 | 10 | 20 | 30 | 40 | 50 | 60 | 70 | 80 | 90 | 100 | 110 | 120 | 130 | 140 |
| Benzene | $C_6H_6$ | | | | | | 0.9310[b] | 0.8538 | 0.7855 | 0.7268 | 0.6751 | 0.6295 | 0.5888 | 0.5530 | 0.5209 | 0.492 | 0.467 |
| Methylbenzene (Toluene) | $C_7H_8$ | 1.25 | 1.14 | 1.045 | 0.961 | 0.887 | 0.8218 | 0.7645 | 0.7130 | 0.6681 | 0.6283 | 0.5926 | 0.5601 | 0.5310 | 0.5042 | 0.480 | 0.458 |
| Ethylbenzene | $C_8H_{10}$ | 1.45 | 1.32 | 1.208 | 1.112 | 1.027 | 0.9512 | 0.8848 | 0.8247 | 0.7723 | 0.7254 | 0.6831 | 0.6447 | 0.6104 | 0.5785 | 0.550 | 0.525 |
| 1,2-Dimethylbenzene (o-Xylene) | " | | | | | 1.259 | 1.149 | 1.057 | 0.976 | 0.906 | 0.845 | 0.790 | 0.742 | 0.698 | 0.659 | 0.624 | 0.592 |
| 1,3-Dimethylbenzene (m-Xylene) | " | | | | | 0.932 | 0.864 | 0.805 | 0.752 | 0.705 | 0.664 | 0.627 | 0.593 | 0.563 | 0.536 | 0.511 | 0.488 |
| 1,4-Dimethylbenzene (p-Xylene) | " | | | | | | | | 0.789 | 0.738 | 0.693 | 0.653 | 0.615 | 0.583 | 0.553 | 0.526 | 0.502 |
| n-Propylbenzene | $C_9H_{12}$ | 2.06 | 1.84 | 1.660 | 1.506 | 1.370 | 1.251 | 1.149 | 1.058 | 0.9796 | 0.9114 | 0.8510 | 0.7968 | 0.7491 | 0.7060 | 0.667 | 0.633 |
| Isopropylbenzene | " | | | | | 1.246 | 1.143 | 1.054 | 0.974 | 0.905 | 0.845 | 0.791 | 0.742 | 0.699 | 0.659 | 0.623 | 0.591 |
| 1-Methyl-2-ethylbenzene | " | | | | | | | | | | | | | | | | |
| 1-Methyl-3-ethylbenzene | " | | | | | | | | | | | | | | | | |
| 1-Methyl-4-ethylbenzene | " | | | | | | | 0.930 | 0.865 | 0.808 | 0.758 | 0.713 | 0.673 | 0.637 | 0.604 | 0.575 | 0.548 |
| 1,2,3-Trimethylbenzene | " | | | | | | | | | | | | | | | | |
| 1,2,4-Trimethylbenzene | " | | | | | | | | | 1.130 | 1.009 | 0.887 | | | | | |
| 1,3,5-Trimethylbenzene | " | | | | | | | | | | | | | | | | |

a See footnote a of Table 1c-E.    b For the undercooled liquid below the normal freezing point.

TABLE 5c-E, Page 2 — ALKYL BENZENES, $C_6$ TO $C_9$

KINEMATIC VISCOSITY

For the Normal Liquid Range at Atmospheric Pressure

November 30, 1949

| Compound (liquid) | Formula | Temperature in °F — Kinematic viscosity in centistokes[a] | | | | | | | | | | | | | | | |
|---|---|---|---|---|---|---|---|---|---|---|---|---|---|---|---|---|---|
| | | 150 | 160 | 170 | 180 | 190 | 200 | 210 | 220 | 230 | 240 | 250 | 260 | 270 | 280 | 290 | 300 |
| Benzene | $C_6H_6$ | 0.442 | 0.421 | 0.401 | 0.383[b] | | | | | | | | | | | | |
| Methylbenzene (Toluene) | $C_7H_8$ | 0.437 | 0.418 | 0.401 | 0.384 | 0.369 | 0.355 | 0.342 | 0.329 | 0.318 | | | | | | | |
| Ethylbenzene | $C_8H_{10}$ | 0.501 | 0.479 | 0.459 | 0.440 | 0.422 | 0.406 | 0.391 | 0.376 | 0.363 | 0.350 | 0.339 | 0.328 | 0.317 | 0.307[b] | | |
| 1,2-Dimethylbenzene (o-Xylene) | " | 0.562 | 0.535 | 0.511 | 0.488 | 0.467 | 0.447 | 0.429 | 0.412 | 0.396 | 0.381 | 0.367 | 0.355 | 0.343 | 0.331 | 0.321 | |
| 1,3-Dimethylbenzene (m-Xylene) | " | 0.467 | 0.447 | 0.429 | 0.412 | 0.396 | 0.381 | 0.367 | 0.354 | 0.342 | 0.331 | 0.320 | 0.310 | 0.300 | 0.291 | | |
| 1,4-Dimethylbenzene (p-Xylene) | " | 0.479 | 0.458 | 0.438 | 0.420 | 0.404 | 0.388 | 0.373 | 0.359 | 0.346 | 0.334 | 0.322 | 0.312 | 0.301 | 0.293 | | |
| n-Propylbenzene | $C_9H_{12}$ | 0.600 | 0.571 | 0.544 | 0.519 | 0.496 | 0.475 | 0.456 | 0.437 | 0.421 | 0.405 | 0.390 | 0.376 | 0.363 | 0.35 | 0.34 | 0.33 |
| Isopropylbenzene | " | | | | | | | | | | | | | | | | |
| 1-Methyl-2-ethylbenzene | " | | | | | | | | | | | | | | | | |
| 1-Methyl-3-ethylbenzene | " | | | | | | | | | | | | | | | | |
| 1-Methyl-4-ethylbenzene | " | 0.524 | 0.502 | 0.482 | 0.463 | | | | | | | | | | | | |
| 1,2,3-Trimethylbenzene | " | | | | | | | | | | | | | | | | |
| 1,2,4-Trimethylbenzene | " | | | | | | | | | | | | | | | | |
| 1,3,5-Trimethylbenzene | " | | | | | | | | | | | | | | | | |

a See footnote a of Table 1c-E.

b For the liquid above the normal boiling point, at saturation pressure.

TABLE 20c–K (PART 1), Page 1 – NORMAL PARAFFINS, C$_1$ TO C$_{20}$

KINEMATIC VISCOSITY

For the Normal Liquid Range at Atmospheric Pressure

March 31, 1947; October 31, 1952

Temperature in °C

Kinematic viscosity in centistokes [a]

| Compound (liquid) | Formula | -190 | -185 | -180 | -175 | -170 | -165 | -160 | -155 | -150 | -145 | -140 | -135 | -130 | -125 | -120 | -115 |
|---|---|---|---|---|---|---|---|---|---|---|---|---|---|---|---|---|---|
| Methane | CH$_4$ | | 0.495[b] | 0.418 | 0.364 | 0.325 | 0.295 | 0.272[c] | | | | | | | | | |
| Ethane | C$_2$H$_6$ | | | | 1.52 | 1.25 | 1.05 | 0.907 | 0.796 | 0.711 | 0.643 | 0.588 | 0.542 | 0.504 | 0.469 | 0.438 | 0.411 |
| Propane | C$_3$H$_8$ | 18.8[b] | 12.1 | 8.24 | 5.93 | 4.45 | 3.46 | 2.78 | 2.28 | 1.92 | 1.65 | 1.435 | 1.264 | 1.126 | 1.015 | 0.922 | 0.844 |
| n-Butane | C$_4$H$_{10}$ | | | | | | | | | | | | | | | | |
| n-Pentane | C$_5$H$_{12}$ | | | | | | | | | | | | | 4.76[b] | 3.82 | 3.12 | 2.62 |
| n-Hexane | C$_6$H$_{14}$ | | | | | | | | | | | | | | | | |
| n-Heptane | C$_7$H$_{16}$ | | | | | | | | | | | | | | | | |
| n-Octane | C$_8$H$_{18}$ | | | | | | | | | | | | | | | | |

Temperature in °C

Kinematic viscosity in centistokes [a]

| Compound (liquid) | Formula | -110 | -105 | -100 | -95 | -90 | -85 | -80 | -75 | -70 | -65 | -60 | -55 | -50 | -45 | -40 | -35 |
|---|---|---|---|---|---|---|---|---|---|---|---|---|---|---|---|---|---|
| Methane | CH$_4$ | 0.387 | 0.365 | 0.348 | 0.330 | 0.314 | 0.299[c] | | | | | | | | | | |
| Ethane | C$_2$H$_6$ | 0.77[b] | 0.721 | 0.671 | 0.628 | 0.590 | 0.555 | 0.524 | 0.496 | 0.470 | 0.447 | 0.425 | 0.406 | 0.387 | 0.370 | 0.355[c] | |
| Propane | C$_3$H$_8$ | | | | | | | | | | | | | | | | |
| n-Butane | C$_4$H$_{10}$ | | | | | 0.91 | 0.85 | 0.79 | 0.736 | 0.689 | 0.647 | 0.609 | 0.576 | 0.545 | 0.517 | 0.491 | 0.468 |
| n-Pentane | C$_5$H$_{12}$ | 2.23 | 1.93 | 1.69 | 1.49 | 1.341 | 1.211 | 1.103 | 1.010 | 0.930 | 0.862 | 0.803 | 0.751 | 0.705 | 0.663 | 0.628 | 0.595 |
| n-Hexane | C$_6$H$_{14}$ | | | | 2.82 | 2.43 | 2.11 | 1.85 | 1.65 | 1.48 | 1.335 | 1.219 | 1.117 | 1.029 | 0.954 | 0.888 | 0.830 |
| n-Heptane | C$_7$H$_{16}$ | | | | | 4.87 | 4.04 | 3.41 | 2.91 | 2.530 | 2.221 | 1.968 | 1.752 | 1.566 | 1.440 | 1.315 | 1.208 |
| n-Octane | C$_8$H$_{18}$ | | | | | | | | | | | | 2.78 | 2.45 | 2.17 | 1.94 | 1.75 |

a See footnote a of Table 1c–K    b For the undercooled liquid below the normal freezing point.    c At saturation pressure.

TABLE 20c-K (PART 1), Page 2 – NORMAL PARAFFINS, $C_1$ TO $C_{20}$

KINEMATIC VISCOSITY

For the Normal Liquid Range at Atmospheric Pressure

March 31, 1947; October 31, 1952

| Compound (liquid) | Formula | Temperature in °C [a] | | | | | | | | | | | | | | | |
|---|---|---|---|---|---|---|---|---|---|---|---|---|---|---|---|---|---|
| | | Kinematic viscosity in centistokes [a] | | | | | | | | | | | | | | | |
| | | -30 | -25 | -20 | -15 | -10 | -5 | 0 | 5 | 10 | 15 | 20 | 25 | 30 | 35 | 40 | 45 |
| Methane | $CH_4$ | | | | | | | | | | | | | | | | |
| Ethane | $C_2H_6$ | | | | | | | | | | | | | | | | |
| Propane | $C_3H_8$ | | | | | | | | | | | | | | | | |
| n-Butane | $C_4H_{10}$ | 0.446 | 0.426 | 0.407 | 0.390 | 0.375 | 0.362 | 0.350 [b] | | | | | | | | | |
| n-Pentane | $C_5H_{12}$ | 0.565 | 0.557 | 0.514 | 0.490 | 0.469 | 0.451 | 0.432 | 0.417 | 0.401 | 0.388 | 0.375 | 0.362 | 0.351 | 0.339 | | |
| n-Hexane | $C_6H_{14}$ | 0.778 | 0.731 | 0.691 | 0.655 | 0.621 | 0.590 | 0.5629 | 0.5376 | 0.5144 | 0.4935 | 0.4741 | 0.4559 | 0.4389 | 0.4231 | 0.4065 | 0.3946 |
| n-Heptane | $C_7H_{16}$ | 1.116 | 1.035 | 0.9659 | 0.9012 | 0.8454 | 0.7956 | 0.7511 | 0.7108 | 0.6743 | 0.6414 | 0.6114 | 0.5836 | 0.5586 | 0.5352 | 0.5137 | 0.4938 |
| n-Octane | $C_8H_{18}$ | 1.592 | 1.453 | 1.334 | 1.251 | 1.140 | 1.061 | 0.9911 | 0.9287 | 0.8729 | 0.8230 | 0.7781 | 0.7374 | 0.7005 | 0.6669 | 0.6382 | 0.6078 |

| Compound (liquid) | Formula | Temperature in °C | | | | | | | | | | | | | | | |
|---|---|---|---|---|---|---|---|---|---|---|---|---|---|---|---|---|---|
| | | Kinematic viscosity in centistokes [a] | | | | | | | | | | | | | | | |
| | | 50 | 55 | 60 | 65 | 70 | 75 | 80 | 85 | 90 | 95 | 100 | 105 | 110 | 115 | 120 | 125 |
| Methane | $CH_4$ | | | | | | | | | | | | | | | | |
| Ethane | $C_2H_6$ | | | | | | | | | | | | | | | | |
| Propane | $C_3H_8$ | | | | | | | | | | | | | | | | |
| n-Butane | $C_4H_{10}$ | | | | | | | | | | | | | | | | |
| n-Pentane | $C_5H_{12}$ | | | | | | | | | | | | | | | | |
| n-Hexane | $C_6H_{14}$ | 0.3817 | 0.3694 | 0.3577 | 0.3465 | 0.3360 [b] | | | | | | | | | | | |
| n-Heptane | $C_7H_{16}$ | 0.4752 | 0.4578 | 0.4416 | 0.4262 | 0.411 [b] | 0.3984 | 0.3857 | 0.3736 | 0.3624 | 0.3515 | 0.3414 [b] | | | | | |
| n-Octane | $C_8H_{18}$ | 0.5818 | 0.5577 | 0.5353 | 0.5145 | 0.4950 | 0.4769 | 0.4602 | 0.4444 | 0.4295 | 0.4155 | 0.4022 | 0.3898 | 0.3779 | 0.3666 | 0.3560 | 0.3457 |

a See footnote a of Table 1c-K.   b At saturation pressure.

TABLE 20c-K (PART 1), Page 5 — NORMAL PARAFFINS, C$_1$ TO C$_{20}$

KINEMATIC VISCOSITY

For the Normal Liquid Range at Atmospheric Pressure

March 31, 1947; October 31, 1952

Kinematic viscosity in centistokes [a]

| Compound (liquid) | Formula | Temperature in °C | | | | | | | | | | | | | | | |
|---|---|---|---|---|---|---|---|---|---|---|---|---|---|---|---|---|---|
| | | -55 | -50 | -45 | -40 | -35 | -30 | -25 | -20 | -15 | -10 | -5 | 0 | 5 | 10 | 15 | 20 |
| n-Nonane | C$_9$H$_{20}$ | 4.54[b] | 3.87 | 3.36 | 2.93 | 2.59 | 2.309 | 2.073 | 1.872 | 1.703 | 1.557 | 1.431 | 1.321 | 1.224 | 1.140 | 1.065 | 0.9978 |
| n-Decane | C$_{10}$H$_{22}$ | | | | | | 3.330[b] | 2.936 | 2.612 | 2.340 | 2.111 | 1.917 | 1.749 | 1.605 | 1.479 | 1.368 | 1.272 |
| n-Undecane | C$_{11}$H$_{24}$ | | | | | | | 4.124 | 3.606 | 3.186 | 2.836 | 2.543 | 2.294 | 2.053 | 1.900 | 1.743 | 1.606 |
| n-Dodecane | C$_{12}$H$_{26}$ | | | | | | | | | | 3.774[b] | 3.343 | 2.983 | 2.680 | 2.424 | 2.204 | 2.014 |
| n-Tridecane | C$_{13}$H$_{28}$ | | | | | | | | | | | 4.336 | 3.827 | 3.404 | 3.049 | 2.749 | 2.493 |
| n-Tetradecane | C$_{14}$H$_{30}$ | | | | | | | | | | | | | 4.304[b] | 3.819 | 3.414 | 3.070 |
| n-Pentadecane | C$_{15}$H$_{32}$ | | | | | | | | | | | | | | 4.724 | 4.187 | 3.737 |
| n-Hexadecane | C$_{16}$H$_{34}$ | | | | | | | | | | | | | | | | 4.505 |
| n-Heptadecane | C$_{17}$H$_{36}$ | | | | | | | | | | | | | | | | 5.410[b] |
| n-Octadecane | C$_{18}$H$_{38}$ | | | | | | | | | | | | | | | | |
| n-Nonadecane | C$_{19}$H$_{40}$ | | | | | | | | | | | | | | | | |
| n-Eicosane | C$_{20}$H$_{42}$ | | | | | | | | | | | | | | | | |

Kinematic viscosity in centistokes [a]

| Compound (liquid) | Formula | Temperature in °C | | | | | | | | | | | | | | | |
|---|---|---|---|---|---|---|---|---|---|---|---|---|---|---|---|---|---|
| | | 25 | 30 | 35 | 40 | 45 | 50 | 55 | 60 | 65 | 70 | 75 | 80 | 85 | 90 | 95 | 100 |
| n-Nonane | C$_9$H$_{20}$ | 0.9381 | 0.8845 | 0.8361 | 0.7921 | 0.7521 | 0.7157 | 0.6822 | 0.6515 | 0.6231 | 0.5968 | 0.5726 | 0.5502 | 0.5292 | 0.5098 | 0.4915 | 0.4743 |
| n-Decane | C$_{10}$H$_{22}$ | 1.186 | 1.110 | 1.042 | 0.9806 | 0.9255 | 0.8754 | 0.8301 | 0.7886 | 0.7507 | 0.7158 | 0.6839 | 0.6544 | 0.6270 | 0.6017 | 0.5780 | 0.5561 |
| n-Undecane | C$_{11}$H$_{24}$ | 1.487 | 1.381 | 1.287 | 1.204 | 1.129 | 1.062 | 1.002 | 0.9472 | 0.8973 | 0.8519 | 0.8104 | 0.7724 | 0.7374 | 0.7051 | 0.6752 | 0.6475 |
| n-Dodecane | C$_{12}$H$_{26}$ | 1.849 | 1.706 | 1.580 | 1.469 | 1.370 | 1.282 | 1.203 | 1.132 | 1.068 | 1.009 | 0.9562 | 0.9078 | 0.8637 | 0.8233 | 0.7858 | 0.7512 |
| n-Tridecane | C$_{13}$H$_{28}$ | 2.273 | 2.082 | 1.915 | 1.771 | 1.641 | 1.528 | 1.426 | 1.336 | 1.255 | 1.182 | 1.116 | 1.055 | 1.000 | 0.9504 | 0.9044 | 0.8621 |
| n-Tetradecane | C$_{14}$H$_{30}$ | 2.779 | 2.527 | 2.312 | 2.124 | 1.958 | 1.813 | 1.665 | 1.571 | 1.469 | 1.378 | 1.296 | 1.221 | 1.154 | 1.093 | 1.037 | 0.9857 |
| n-Pentadecane | C$_{15}$H$_{32}$ | 3.357 | 3.033 | 2.757 | 2.518 | 2.310 | 2.128 | 1.969 | 1.827 | 1.701 | 1.590 | 1.489 | 1.400 | 1.318 | 1.244 | 1.177 | 1.116 |
| n-Hexadecane | C$_{16}$H$_{34}$ | 4.020 | 3.609 | 3.262 | 2.962 | 2.703 | 2.479 | 2.282 | 2.109 | 1.957 | 1.822 | 1.701 | 1.593 | 1.496 | 1.408 | 1.328 | 1.256 |
| n-Heptadecane | C$_{17}$H$_{36}$ | 4.791 | 4.275 | 3.839 | 3.467 | 3.148 | 2.873 | 2.634 | 2.424 | 2.240 | 2.078 | 1.934 | 1.805 | 1.690 | 1.586 | 1.493 | 1.408 |
| n-Octadecane | C$_{18}$H$_{38}$ | | 5.020 | 4.481 | 4.025 | 3.637 | 3.304 | 3.015 | 2.765 | 2.544 | 2.353 | 2.182 | 2.030 | 1.895 | 1.774 | 1.665 | 1.567 |
| n-Nonadecane | C$_{19}$H$_{40}$ | | 5.862[b] | 5.202 | 4.648 | 4.178 | 3.777 | 3.433 | 3.136 | 2.875 | 2.649 | 2.449 | 2.272 | 2.114 | 1.974 | 1.849 | 1.734 |
| n-Eicosane | C$_{20}$H$_{42}$ | | | 6.034[b] | 5.360 | 4.793 | 4.313 | 3.903 | 3.550 | 3.243 | 2.977 | 2.743 | 2.537 | 2.354 | 2.192 | 2.048 | 1.917 |

[a] See footnote a of Table 1c-K.

[b] For the undercooled liquid below the normal freezing point.

TABLE 20c-K (PART 1), Page 4 – NORMAL PARAFFINS, $C_1$ TO $C_{20}$

KINEMATIC VISCOSITY

For the Normal Liquid Range at Atmospheric Pressure

March 31, 1947; October 31, 1952

Temperature in °C — Kinematic viscosity in centistokes [a]

| Compound (liquid) | Formula | 105 | 110 | 115 | 120 | 125 | 130 | 135 | 140 | 145 | 150 | 155 | 160 | 165 | 170 | 175 | 180 |
|---|---|---|---|---|---|---|---|---|---|---|---|---|---|---|---|---|---|
| n-Nonane | $C_9H_{20}$ | 0.4582 | 0.4430 | 0.4286 | 0.4151 | 0.4021 | 0.3900 | 0.3785 | 0.3675 | 0.3571 | 0.3473 | | | | | | |
| n-Decane | $C_{10}H_{22}$ | 0.5355 | 0.5164 | 0.4983 | 0.4814 | 0.4654 | 0.4502 | 0.4360 | 0.4227 | 0.4097 | 0.3976 | 0.3860 | 0.3749 | 0.3645 | 0.3543 | 0.3444[b] | |
| n-Undecane | $C_{11}H_{24}$ | 0.6217 | 0.5977 | 0.5752 | 0.5541 | 0.5345 | 0.5160 | 0.4987 | 0.4822 | 0.4668 | 0.4522 | 0.4382 | 0.4251 | 0.4125 | 0.4006 | 0.3891 | 0.3783 |
| n-Dodecane | $C_{12}H_{26}$ | 0.7193 | 0.6696 | 0.6620 | 0.6362 | 0.6121 | 0.5898 | 0.5687 | 0.5489 | 0.5303 | 0.5128 | 0.4963 | 0.4806 | 0.4657 | 0.4516 | 0.4383 | 0.4256 |
| n-Tridecane | $C_{13}H_{28}$ | 0.8233 | 0.7873 | 0.7539 | 0.7229 | 0.6940 | 0.6672 | 0.6421 | 0.6186 | 0.5966 | 0.5759 | 0.5565 | 0.5381 | 0.5207 | 0.5043 | 0.4888 | 0.4740 |
| n-Tetradecane | $C_{14}H_{30}$ | 0.9364 | 0.8950 | 0.8551 | 0.8181 | 0.7839 | 0.7519 | 0.7222 | 0.6946 | 0.6686 | 0.6443 | 0.6215 | 0.6001 | 0.5800 | 0.5609 | 0.5430 | 0.5260 |
| n-Pentadecane | $C_{15}H_{32}$ | 1.060 | 1.009 | 0.9614 | 0.9177 | 0.8773 | 0.8401 | 0.8053 | 0.7731 | 0.7430 | 0.7149 | 0.6886 | 0.6640 | 0.6407 | 0.6188 | 0.5983 | 0.5789 |
| n-Hexadecane | $C_{16}H_{34}$ | 1.190 | 1.130 | 1.075 | 1.024 | 0.9768 | 0.9334 | 0.8933 | 0.8562 | 0.8216 | 0.7894 | 0.7592 | 0.7309 | 0.7045 | 0.6797 | 0.6564 | 0.6344 |
| n-Heptadecane | $C_{17}H_{36}$ | 1.331 | 1.261 | 1.196 | 1.138 | 1.083 | 1.033 | 0.9873 | 0.9446 | 0.9050 | 0.8682 | 0.8339 | 0.8018 | 0.7719 | 0.7436 | 0.7174 | 0.6927 |
| n-Octadecane | $C_{18}H_{38}$ | 1.478 | 1.396 | 1.322 | 1.256 | 1.193 | 1.137 | 1.084 | 1.035 | 0.990 | 0.949 | 0.910 | 0.874 | 0.841 | 0.808 | 0.780 | 0.751 |
| n-Nonadecane | $C_{19}H_{40}$ | 1.633 | 1.540 | 1.456 | 1.378 | 1.308 | 1.244 | 1.185 | 1.130 | 1.080 | 1.032 | 0.989 | 0.948 | 0.911 | 0.876 | 0.844 | 0.812 |
| n-Eicosane | $C_{20}H_{42}$ | 1.801 | 1.695 | 1.598 | 1.512 | 1.431 | 1.359 | 1.292 | 1.231 | 1.174 | 1.121 | 1.073 | 1.028 | 0.985 | 0.946 | 0.910 | 0.876 |

Temperature in °C — Kinematic viscosity in centistokes [a]

| Compound (liquid) | Formula | 185 | 190 | 195 | 200 | 205 | 210 | 215 | 220 | 225 | 230 | 235 | 240 | 245 | 250 | 255 | 260 |
|---|---|---|---|---|---|---|---|---|---|---|---|---|---|---|---|---|---|
| n-Nonane | $C_9H_{20}$ | | | | | | | | | | | | | | | | |
| n-Decane | $C_{10}H_{22}$ | | | | | | | | | | | | | | | | |
| n-Undecane | $C_{11}H_{24}$ | 0.3679 | 0.3578 | 0.3483 | | | | | | | | | | | | | |
| n-Dodecane | $C_{12}H_{26}$ | 0.4134 | 0.4017 | 0.3907 | 0.3800 | 0.3696 | 0.3597 | 0.3500 | | | | | | | | | |
| n-Tridecane | $C_{13}H_{28}$ | 0.4600 | 0.4466 | 0.4340 | 0.4219 | 0.4102 | 0.3987 | 0.3879 | 0.3774 | 0.3673 | 0.3577 | 0.3482 | | | | | |
| n-Tetradecane | $C_{14}H_{30}$ | 0.5099 | 0.4946 | 0.4800 | 0.4662 | 0.4528 | 0.4402 | 0.4280 | 0.4162 | 0.4049 | 0.3941 | 0.3838 | 0.3736 | 0.3644 | 0.3552 | 0.347[b] | |
| n-Pentadecane | $C_{15}H_{32}$ | 0.5606 | 0.5432 | 0.5268 | 0.5113 | 0.4963 | 0.4819 | 0.4662 | 0.4552 | 0.4426 | 0.4308 | 0.4192 | 0.4082 | 0.3978 | 0.3878 | 0.378 | 0.369 |
| n-Hexadecane | $C_{16}H_{34}$ | 0.6137 | 0.5941 | 0.5755 | 0.5579 | 0.5412 | 0.5253 | 0.5100 | 0.4955 | 0.4816 | 0.4684 | 0.4558 | 0.4438 | 0.4322 | 0.4211 | 0.410 | 0.400 |
| n-Heptadecane | $C_{17}H_{36}$ | 0.6693 | 0.6473 | 0.6265 | 0.6069 | 0.5882 | 0.5705 | 0.5536 | 0.5375 | 0.5222 | 0.5076 | 0.4937 | 0.4804 | 0.4676 | 0.4555 | 0.444 | 0.433 |
| n-Octadecane | $C_{18}H_{38}$ | 0.725 | 0.701 | 0.679 | 0.656 | 0.636 | 0.616 | 0.597 | 0.580 | 0.563 | 0.547 | 0.532 | 0.517 | 0.503 | 0.490 | 0.47 | 0.46 |
| n-Nonadecane | $C_{19}H_{40}$ | 0.783 | 0.757 | 0.731 | 0.707 | 0.684 | 0.662 | 0.641 | 0.621 | 0.603 | 0.586 | 0.569 | 0.554 | 0.538 | 0.524 | 0.52 | 0.50 |
| n-Eicosane | $C_{20}H_{42}$ | 0.844 | 0.814 | 0.786 | 0.760 | 0.734 | 0.710 | 0.688 | 0.667 | 0.647 | 0.627 | 0.609 | 0.592 | 0.576 | 0.560 | 0.54 | 0.53 |

[a] See footnote a of Table 1c-K.   [b] At saturation pressure.

TABLE 20c-K (PART 1), Page 5 - NORMAL PARAFFINS, $C_1$ TO $C_{20}$

KINEMATIC VISCOSITY

For the Normal Liquid Range at Atmospheric Pressure

March 31, 1947; October 31, 1952

| Compound (liquid) | Formula | Temperature in °C | | | | | | | | | | | | | | | |
|---|---|---|---|---|---|---|---|---|---|---|---|---|---|---|---|---|---|
| | | 265 | 270 | 275 | 280 | 285 | 290 | 295 | 300 | 305 | 310 | 315 | 320 | 325 | 330 | 335 | 340 |
| | | Kinematic viscosity in centistokes [a] | | | | | | | | | | | | | | | |
| n-Nonane | $C_9H_{20}$ | | | | | | | | | | | | | | | | |
| n-Decane | $C_{10}H_{22}$ | | | | | | | | | | | | | | | | |
| n-Undecane | $C_{11}H_{24}$ | | | | | | | | | | | | | | | | |
| n-Dodecane | $C_{12}H_{26}$ | | | | | | | | | | | | | | | | |
| n-Tridecane | $C_{13}H_{28}$ | | | | | | | | | | | | | | | | |
| n-Tetradecane | $C_{14}H_{30}$ | | | | | | | | | | | | | | | | |
| n-Pentadecane | $C_{15}H_{32}$ | 0.360 | 0.351 | | | | | | | | | | | | | | |
| n-Hexadecane | $C_{16}H_{34}$ | 0.391 | 0.360 | 0.371 | 0.363 | 0.354 | | | | | | | | | | | |
| n-Heptadecane | $C_{17}H_{36}$ | 0.422 | 0.411 | 0.401 | 0.392 | 0.383 | 0.374 | 0.365 | 0.355 | | | | | | | | |
| n-Octadecane | $C_{18}H_{38}$ | 0.45 | 0.45 | 0.43 | 0.42 | 0.41 | 0.39 | 0.39 | 0.38 | 0.37 | 0.37 | 0.36 | | | | | |
| n-Nonadecane | $C_{19}H_{40}$ | 0.49 | 0.48 | 0.46 | 0.45 | 0.44 | 0.42 | 0.42 | 0.41 | 0.40 | 0.39 | 0.38 | 0.37 | 0.36 | 0.36[b] | | |
| n-Eicosane | $C_{20}H_{42}$ | 0.52 | 0.50 | 0.49 | 0.48 | 0.46 | 0.45 | 0.44 | 0.44 | 0.43 | 0.41 | 0.40 | 0.40 | 0.39 | 0.38 | 0.37 | 0.36 |

a See footnote a of Table 1c-K     b At saturation pressure.

TABLE 1c-K, Page 1 – PARAFFINS, C$_1$ TO C$_5$

KINEMATIC VISCOSITY

For the Normal Liquid Range at Atmospheric Pressure

October 31, 1948; October 31, 1952

Temperature in °C — Kinematic viscosity in centistokes [a]

| Compound (liquid) | Formula | -115 | -120 | -125 | -130 | -135 | -140 | -145 | -150 | -155 | -160 | -165 | -170 | -175 | -180 | -185 | -190 |
|---|---|---|---|---|---|---|---|---|---|---|---|---|---|---|---|---|---|
| Methane | CH$_4$ | | | | | | | | | | 0.272[c] | 0.295 | 0.325 | 0.364 | 0.416[b] | 0.495[b] | |
| Ethane | C$_2$H$_6$ | 0.411 | 0.438 | 0.469 | 0.504 | 0.542 | 0.588 | 0.643 | 0.711 | 0.796 | 0.907 | 1.05 | 1.25 | 1.52 | | | |
| Propane | C$_3$H$_8$ | 0.844 | 0.922 | 1.015 | 1.126 | 1.264 | 1.435 | 1.65 | 1.92 | 2.28 | 2.78 | 3.46 | 4.45 | 5.93 | 8.24 | 12.1 | 18.8[b] |
| n–Butane | C$_4$H$_{10}$ | | | | | | | | | | | | | | | | |
| 2–Methylpropane (Isobutane) | " | | | | | | | | | | | | | | | | |
| n–Pentane | C$_5$H$_{12}$ | 2.62 | 3.12 | 3.82 | 4.76 | | | | | | | | | | | | |
| 2–Methylbutane (Isopentane) | " | | | | | | | | | | | | | | | | |
| 2,2–Dimethylpropane (Neopentane) | " | | | | | | | | | | | | | | | | |

Temperature in °C — Kinematic viscosity in centistokes [a]

| Compound (liquid) | Formula | -35 | -40 | -45 | -50 | -55 | -60 | -65 | -70 | -75 | -80 | -85 | -90 | -95 | -100 | -105 | -110 |
|---|---|---|---|---|---|---|---|---|---|---|---|---|---|---|---|---|---|
| Methane | CH$_4$ | | | | | | | | | | | | | | | | |
| Ethane | C$_2$H$_6$ | | | | | | | | | | | 0.299[c] | 0.314 | 0.330 | 0.348 | 0.365 | 0.367 |
| Propane | C$_2$H$_8$ | | 0.355[c] | 0.370 | 0.387 | 0.406 | 0.425 | 0.447 | 0.470 | 0.496 | 0.524 | 0.555 | 0.590 | 0.628 | 0.671 | 0.721 | 0.778 |
| n–Butane | C$_4$H$_{10}$ | 0.468 | 0.491 | 0.517 | 0.545 | 0.576 | 0.609 | 0.647 | 0.689 | 0.736 | 0.79 | 0.85 | 0.91 | | | | |
| 2–Methylpropane (Isobutane) | " | 0.519 | 0.549 | 0.582 | 0.619 | 0.659 | 0.703 | 0.753 | 0.810 | 0.874 | 0.946 | | | | | | |
| n–Pentane | C$_5$H$_{12}$ | 0.595 | 0.628 | 0.663 | 0.705 | 0.751 | 0.803 | 0.862 | 0.930 | 1.010 | 1.103 | 1.211 | 1.341 | 1.49 | 1.69 | 1.93 | 2.23 |
| 2–Methylbutane (Isopentane) | " | 0.64 | 0.69 | 0.74 | 0.79 | | | | | | | | | | | | |
| 2,2–Dimethylpropane (Neopentane) | " | | | | | | | | | | | | | | | | |

a See footnote a of Table 1c.   b For the undercooled liquid below the normal freezing point.   c At saturation pressure.

TABLE 1c-K, Page 2 – PARAFFINS, $C_1$ TO $C_5$

KINEMATIC VISCOSITY

For the Normal Liquid Range at Atmospheric Pressure

October 31, 1948; October 31, 1952

| Compound (liquid) | Formula | Temperature in °C |||||||||||||| 
|---|---|---|---|---|---|---|---|---|---|---|---|---|---|---|---|
| | | -30 | -25 | -20 | -15 | -10 | -5 | 0 | 5 | 10 | 15 | 20 | 25 | 30 | 35 |
| | | Kinematic viscosity in centistokes [a] |||||||||||||
| Methane | $CH_4$ | | | | | | | | | | | | | | |
| Ethane | $C_2H_6$ | | | | | | | | | | | | | | |
| Propane | $C_3H_8$ | | | | | | | | | | | | | | |
| n-Butane | $C_4H_{10}$ | 0.446 | 0.426 | 0.407 | 0.390 | 0.375 | 0.362 | 0.350[b] | | | | | | | |
| 2-Methylpropane (Isobutane) | " | 0.491 | 0.466 | 0.443 | 0.423 | 0.403[b] | | | | | | | | | |
| n-Pentane | $C_5H_{12}$ | 0.565 | 0.537 | 0.514 | 0.490 | 0.469 | 0.451 | 0.432 | 0.417 | 0.401 | 0.388 | 0.375 | 0.362 | 0.351 | 0.339 |
| 2-Methylbutane (Isopentane) | " | 0.603 | 0.567 | 0.535 | 0.506 | 0.479 | 0.455 | 0.434 | 0.414 | 0.396 | 0.379 | 0.364 | 0.350 | 0.337[b] | |
| 2,2-Dimethylpropane (Neopentane) | " | | | | 0.684[c] | 0.626 | 0.576 | 0.534 | 0.498 | 0.466[b] | | | | | |

[a] See footnote a of Table 1c.    [b] At saturation pressure.    [c] For the undercooled liquid below the normal freezing point.

273

TABLE 22c-K (PART 1), Page 1 - NORMAL ALKYL CYCLOPENTANES, C$_5$ TO C$_{21}$

KINEMATIC VISCOSITY

For the Normal Liquid Range at Atmospheric Pressure

December 31, 1948

Temperature in °C — Kinematic viscosity in centistokes [a]

| Compound (liquid) | Formula | -25 | -20 | -15 | -10 | -5 | 0 | 5 | 10 | 15 | 20 | 25 | 30 | 35 | 40 | 45 | 50 |
|---|---|---|---|---|---|---|---|---|---|---|---|---|---|---|---|---|---|
| Cyclopentane | C$_5$H$_{10}$ | 0.99 | 0.92 | 0.87 | 0.815 | 0.768 | 0.726 | 0.687 | 0.652 | 0.619 | 0.589 | 0.562 | 0.536 | 0.512 | 0.490 | 0.470 | 0.451[c] |
| Methylcyclopentane | C$_6$H$_{12}$ | 1.18 | 1.10 | 1.02 | 0.960 | 0.901 | 0.847 | 0.798 | 0.755 | 0.714 | 0.677 | 0.643 | 0.612 | 0.582 | 0.555 | 0.530 | 0.506 |
| Ethylcyclopentane | C$_7$H$_{14}$ | 1.29 | 1.20 | 1.12 | 1.047 | 0.983 | 0.924 | 0.872 | 0.824 | 0.780 | 0.740 | 0.703 | 0.669 | 0.637 | 0.608 | 0.582 | 0.557 |
| n-Propylcyclopentane | C$_8$H$_{16}$ | 1.67 | 1.53 | 1.41 | 1.310 | 1.216 | 1.133 | 1.058 | 0.992 | 0.932 | 0.878 | 0.830 | 0.787 | 0.747 | 0.711 | 0.678 | 0.648 |
| n-Butylcyclopentane | C$_9$H$_{18}$ | 2.31 | 2.10 | 1.92 | 1.768 | 1.629 | 1.508 | 1.396 | 1.300 | 1.212 | 1.134 | 1.064 | 1.000 | 0.941 | 0.889 | 0.842 | 0.798 |
| n-Pentylcyclopentane | C$_{10}$H$_{20}$ | | 2.82 | 2.59 | 2.39 | 2.19 | 2.02 | 1.86 | 1.717 | 1.579 | 1.458 | 1.350 | 1.254 | 1.171 | 1.102 | 1.036 | 0.978 |
| n-Hexylcyclopentane | C$_{11}$H$_{22}$ | | 3.77 | 3.45 | 3.40 | 2.88 | 2.64 | 2.42 | 2.22 | 2.03 | 1.87 | 1.719 | 1.587 | 1.473 | 1.378 | 1.287 | 1.207 |
| n-Heptylcyclopentane | C$_{12}$H$_{24}$ | | 4.94 | 4.50 | 4.10 | 3.73 | 3.40 | 3.10 | 2.83 | 2.58 | 2.35 | 2.16 | 1.98 | 1.83 | 1.698 | 1.578 | 1.470 |
| n-Octylcyclopentane | C$_{13}$H$_{26}$ | | 6.39 | 5.79 | 5.25 | 4.76 | 4.32 | 3.92 | 3.56 | 3.22 | 2.93 | 2.67 | 2.43 | 2.23 | 2.07 | 1.91 | 1.769 |
| n-Nonylcyclopentane | C$_{14}$H$_{28}$ | | 8.14 | 7.35 | 6.64 | 5.99 | 5.41 | 4.88 | 4.41 | 3.98 | 3.60 | 3.26 | 2.96 | 2.70 | 2.49 | 2.28 | 2.10 |
| n-Decylcyclopentane | C$_{15}$H$_{30}$ | | 10.25 | 9.22 | 8.28 | 7.44 | 6.69 | 6.01 | 5.41 | 4.85 | 4.37 | 3.94 | 3.56 | 3.20 | 2.96 | 2.70 | 2.48 |
| n-Undecylcyclopentane. | C$_{16}$H$_{32}$ | | | 11.43[b] | 10.23 | 9.15 | 8.19 | 7.33 | 6.56 | 5.86 | 5.25 | 4.71 | 4.24 | 3.83 | 3.49 | 3.17 | 2.90 |
| n-Dodecylcyclopentane | C$_{17}$H$_{34}$ | | | | 12.50[b] | 11.14 | 9.92 | 8.85 | 7.89 | 7.02 | 6.25 | 5.59 | 5.00 | 4.50 | 4.08 | 3.69 | 3.36 |
| n-Tridecylcyclopentane | C$_{18}$H$_{36}$ | | | | | | 11.93[b] | 10.59 | 9.40 | 8.33 | 7.39 | 6.58 | 5.86 | 5.25 | 4.74 | 4.27 | 3.87 |
| n-Tetradecylcyclopentane | C$_{19}$H$_{38}$ | | | | | | | 12.56[b] | 11.11 | 9.80 | 8.67 | 7.68 | 6.82 | 6.08 | 5.47 | 4.91 | 4.42 |
| n-Pentadecylcyclopentane | C$_{20}$H$_{40}$ | | | | | | | | | 11.47[b] | 10.10 | 8.91 | 7.88 | 7.00 | 6.27 | 5.60 | 5.03 |
| n-Hexadecylcyclopentane | C$_{21}$H$_{42}$ | | | | | | | | | | 11.68[b] | 10.27 | 9.04 | 8.00 | 7.14 | 6.35 | 5.68 |

a See footnote a of Table 1c-K    b For the undercooled liquid below the normal freezing point.    c For the liquid above the normal boiling point, at saturation pressure.

TABLE 22c-K (PART 1), Page 2 - NORMAL ALKYL CYCLOPENTANES, $C_5$ TO $C_{21}$

KINEMATIC VISCOSITY

For the Normal Liquid Range at Atmospheric Pressure

December 31, 1948

| Compound (liquid) | Formula | Temperature in °C [a] | | | | | | | | | | | | |
|---|---|---|---|---|---|---|---|---|---|---|---|---|---|---|
| | | Kinematic viscosity in centistokes [a] | | | | | | | | | | | | |
| | | 50 | 55 | 60 | 65 | 70 | 75 | 80 | 85 | 90 | 95 | 100 | 105 | 110 |
| Cyclopentane | $C_5H_{10}$ | 0.451[b] | | | | | | | | | | | | |
| Methylcyclopentane | $C_6H_{12}$ | 0.506 | 0.484 | 0.464 | 0.445 | 0.428 | 0.411[b] | | | | | | | |
| Ethylcyclopentane | $C_7H_{14}$ | 0.557 | 0.534 | 0.513 | 0.493 | 0.474 | 0.457 | 0.44 | 0.43 | 0.41 | 0.40 | 0.39 | 0.38[b] | |
| n-Propylcyclopentane | $C_8H_{16}$ | 0.648 | 0.621 | 0.597 | 0.574 | 0.553 | 0.534 | 0.52 | 0.50 | 0.48 | 0.47 | 0.46 | 0.44 | 0.43 |
| n-Butylcyclopentane | $C_9H_{18}$ | 0.798 | 0.759 | 0.724 | 0.691 | 0.661 | 0.634 | 0.61 | 0.59 | 0.56 | 0.54 | 0.53 | 0.51 | 0.49 |
| n-Pentylcyclopentane | $C_{10}H_{20}$ | 0.978 | 0.923 | 0.875 | 0.831 | 0.792 | 0.757 | 0.72 | 0.70 | 0.67 | 0.64 | 0.62 | 0.60 | 0.58 |
| n-Hexylcyclopentane | $C_{11}H_{22}$ | 1.207 | 1.132 | 1.068 | 1.008 | 0.956 | 0.909 | 0.87 | 0.83 | 0.79 | 0.76 | 0.73 | 0.70 | 0.70 |
| n-Heptylcyclopentane | $C_{12}H_{24}$ | 1.470 | 1.371 | 1.284 | 1.207 | 1.139 | 1.078 | 1.02 | 0.97 | 0.93 | 0.88 | 0.84 | 0.81 | 0.77 |
| n-Octylcyclopentane | $C_{13}H_{26}$ | 1.769 | 1.641 | 1.528 | 1.430 | 1.344 | 1.265 | 1.19 | 1.13 | 1.07 | 1.02 | 0.97 | 0.92 | 0.88 |
| n-Nonylcyclopentane | $C_{14}H_{28}$ | 2.10 | 1.94 | 1.80 | 1.677 | 1.568 | 1.471 | 1.38 | 1.31 | 1.24 | 1.17 | 1.11 | 1.06 | 1.00 |
| n-Decylcyclopentane | $C_{15}H_{30}$ | 2.48 | 2.28 | 2.10 | 1.95 | 1.82 | 1.70 | 1.59 | 1.50 | 1.41 | 1.33 | 1.26 | 1.19 | 1.13 |
| n-Undecylcyclopentane | $C_{16}H_{32}$ | 2.90 | 2.65 | 2.44 | 2.25 | 2.09 | 1.94 | 1.81 | 1.70 | 1.60 | 1.50 | 1.42 | 1.33 | 1.26 |
| n-Dodecylcyclopentane | $C_{17}H_{34}$ | 3.36 | 3.06 | 2.80 | 2.57 | 2.38 | 2.21 | 2.05 | 1.92 | 1.80 | 1.69 | 1.59 | 1.49 | 1.40 |
| n-Tridecylcyclopentane | $C_{18}H_{36}$ | 3.87 | 3.51 | 3.20 | 2.93 | 2.70 | 2.49 | 2.31 | 2.16 | 2.02 | 1.88 | 1.77 | 1.65 | 1.55 |
| n-Tetradecylcyclopentane | $C_{19}H_{38}$ | 4.42 | 3.99 | 3.63 | 3.31 | 3.04 | 2.80 | 2.59 | 2.41 | 2.24 | 2.09 | 1.96 | 1.83 | 1.71 |
| n-Pentadecylcyclopentane | $C_{20}H_{40}$ | 5.03 | 4.52 | 4.09 | 3.72 | 3.41 | 3.13 | 2.89 | 2.68 | 2.49 | 2.32 | 2.16 | 2.01 | 1.88 |
| n-Hexadecylcyclopentane | $C_{21}H_{42}$ | 5.68 | 5.10 | 4.60 | 4.17 | 3.80 | 3.49 | 3.21 | 2.97 | 2.75 | 2.55 | 2.38 | 2.21 | 2.06 |

[a] See footnote a of Table 1c-K

[b] For the liquid above the normal boiling point, at saturation pressure.

TABLE 23c-K (PART 1), Page 1 – NORMAL ALKYL CYCLOHEXANES, $C_6$ TO $C_{22}$
KINEMATIC VISCOSITY
For the Normal Liquid Range at Atmospheric Pressure
December 31, 1948

| Compound (liquid) | Formula | Temperature in °C |||||||||||||||| 
|---|---|---|---|---|---|---|---|---|---|---|---|---|---|---|---|---|---|
| | | -25 | -20 | -15 | -10 | -5 | 0 | 5 | 10 | 15 | 20 | 25 | 30 | 35 | 40 | 45 | 50 |
| | | Kinematic viscosity in centistokes [a] |||||||||||||||
| Cyclohexane | $C_6H_{12}$ | | | | | | | 1.641[b] | 1.498 | 1.370 | 1.258 | 1.160 | 1.074 | 0.996 | 0.926 | 0.864 | 0.808 |
| Methylcyclohexane | $C_7H_{14}$ | 1.92 | 1.75 | 1.60 | 1.477 | 1.363 | 1.262 | 1.172 | 1.092 | 1.019 | 0.954 | 0.896 | 0.843 | 0.794 | 0.750 | 0.710 | 0.672 |
| Ethylcyclohexane | $C_8H_{16}$ | 2.19 | 1.99 | 1.82 | 1.670 | 1.538 | 1.421 | 1.317 | 1.226 | 1.142 | 1.069 | 1.004 | 0.945 | 0.892 | 0.843 | 0.800 | 0.760 |
| n-Propylcyclohexane | $C_9H_{18}$ | 2.84 | 2.55 | 2.30 | 2.09 | 1.90 | 1.741 | 1.599 | 1.475 | 1.364 | 1.268 | 1.182 | 1.107 | 1.038 | 0.976 | 0.922 | 0.872 |
| n-Butylcyclohexane | $C_{10}H_{20}$ | | 3.55 | 3.17 | 2.86 | 2.58 | 2.34 | 2.13 | 1.95 | 1.787 | 1.644 | 1.519 | 1.406 | 1.306 | 1.217 | 1.139 | 1.069 |
| n-Pentylcyclohexane | $C_{11}H_{22}$ | | | | 4.03 | 3.60 | 3.23 | 2.90 | 2.61 | 2.36 | 2.14 | 1.95 | 1.779 | 1.632 | 1.508 | 1.403 | 1.311 |
| n-Hexylcyclohexane | $C_{12}H_{24}$ | | | | 5.41 | 4.80 | 4.27 | 3.81 | 3.40 | 3.05 | 2.74 | 2.48 | 2.25 | 2.04 | 1.88 | 1.734 | 1.611 |
| n-Heptylcyclohexane | $C_{13}H_{26}$ | | | | 7.13 | 6.28 | 5.55 | 4.90 | 4.35 | 3.88 | 3.46 | 3.11 | 2.79 | 2.52 | 2.29 | 2.11 | 1.95 |
| n-Octylcyclohexane | $C_{14}H_{28}$ | | | | 9.24 | 8.08 | 7.09 | 6.21 | 5.49 | 4.86 | 4.30 | 3.83 | 3.42 | 3.07 | 2.79 | 2.54 | 2.34 |
| n-Nonylcyclohexane | $C_{15}H_{30}$ | | | | 11.80 | 10.25 | 8.93 | 7.79 | 6.82 | 6.00 | 5.28 | 4.67 | 4.15 | 3.70 | 3.34 | 3.03 | 2.76 |
| n-Decylcyclohexane | $C_{16}H_{32}$ | | | | | 12.82[b] | 11.11 | 9.63 | 8.38 | 7.32 | 6.41 | 5.63 | 4.98 | 4.41 | 3.96 | 3.57 | 3.24 |
| n-Undecylcyclohexane | $C_{17}H_{34}$ | | | | | | | 11.78[b] | 10.18 | 8.85 | 7.71 | 6.72 | 5.90 | 5.21 | 4.65 | 4.18 | 3.77 |
| n-Dodecylcyclohexane | $C_{18}H_{36}$ | | | | | | | | 12.27[b] | 10.59 | 9.15 | 7.95 | 6.95 | 6.10 | 5.40 | 4.84 | 4.35 |
| n-Tridecylcyclohexane | $C_{19}H_{38}$ | | | | | | | | | 10.59 | 10.81 | 9.33 | 8.11 | 7.08 | 6.26 | 5.57 | 4.99 |
| n-Tetradecylcyclohexane | $C_{20}H_{40}$ | | | | | | | | | | | 10.88 | 9.40 | 8.17 | 7.19 | 6.38 | 5.69 |
| n-Pentadecylcyclohexane | $C_{21}H_{42}$ | | | | | | | | | | | | 10.84 | 9.38 | 8.21 | 7.25 | 6.44 |
| n-Hexadecylcyclohexane | $C_{22}H_{44}$ | | | | | | | | | | | | | 10.70 | 9.33 | 8.20 | 7.76 |

a See footnote a of Table 1c-K    b For the undercooled liquid below the normal freezing point.

TABLE 23c-K (PART 1), Page 2 – NORMAL ALKYL CYCLOHEXANES, $C_6$ TO $C_{22}$

KINEMATIC VISCOSITY

For the Normal Liquid Range at Atmospheric Pressure

December 31, 1948 (Corrected)

| Compound (liquid) | Formula | Temperature in °C — Kinematic viscosity in centistokes [a] | | | | | | | | | | | | |
|---|---|---|---|---|---|---|---|---|---|---|---|---|---|---|
| | | 50 | 55 | 60 | 65 | 70 | 75 | 80 | 85 | 90 | 95 | 100 | 105 | 110 |
| Cyclohexane | $C_6H_{12}$ | 0.808 | 0.758 | 0.714 | 0.672 | 0.634 | 0.600 | 0.569 | | | | | | |
| Methylcyclohexane | $C_7H_{14}$ | 0.672 | 0.639 | 0.608 | 0.578 | 0.552 | 0.526 | 0.50 | 0.48 | 0.46 | 0.44 | 0.43 | | |
| Ethylcyclohexane | $C_8H_{16}$ | 0.760 | 0.724 | 0.692 | 0.661 | 0.634 | 0.61 | 0.59 | 0.57 | 0.55 | 0.53 | 0.51 | 0.49 | 0.48 |
| n-Propylcyclohexane | $C_9H_{18}$ | 0.872 | 0.827 | 0.787 | 0.750 | 0.717 | 0.69 | 0.66 | 0.64 | 0.61 | 0.59 | 0.57 | 0.56 | 0.54 |
| n-Butylcyclohexane | $C_{10}H_{20}$ | 1.069 | 1.007 | 0.954 | 0.904 | 0.863 | 0.83 | 0.79 | 0.76 | 0.73 | 0.71 | 0.69 | 0.66 | 0.64 |
| n-Pentylcyclohexane | $C_{11}H_{22}$ | 1.311 | 1.229 | 1.158 | 1.092 | 1.034 | 0.98 | 0.93 | 0.88 | 0.84 | 0.80 | 0.76 | 0.73 | 0.69 |
| n-Hexylcyclohexane | $C_{12}H_{24}$ | 1.611 | 1.502 | 1.406 | 1.317 | 1.240 | 1.17 | 1.10 | 1.04 | 0.98 | 0.93 | 0.88 | 0.84 | 0.80 |
| n-Heptylcyclohexane | $C_{13}H_{26}$ | 1.95 | 1.81 | 1.683 | 1.570 | 1.468 | 1.37 | 1.29 | 1.21 | 1.14 | 1.07 | 1.01 | 0.96 | 0.91 |
| n-Octylcyclohexane | $C_{14}H_{28}$ | 2.34 | 2.15 | 1.99 | 1.85 | 1.72 | 1.60 | 1.50 | 1.40 | 1.31 | 1.23 | 1.15 | 1.09 | 1.02 |
| n-Nonylcyclohexane | $C_{15}H_{30}$ | 2.76 | 2.54 | 2.34 | 2.16 | 2.00 | 1.85 | 1.72 | 1.60 | 1.49 | 1.39 | 1.30 | 1.22 | 1.15 |
| n-Decylcyclohexane | $C_{16}H_{32}$ | 3.24 | 2.96 | 2.72 | 2.49 | 2.30 | 2.12 | 1.96 | 1.82 | 1.69 | 1.57 | 1.46 | 1.37 | 1.28 |
| n-Undecylcyclohexane | $C_{17}H_{34}$ | 3.77 | 3.42 | 3.13 | 2.86 | 2.63 | 2.41 | 2.23 | 2.06 | 1.90 | 1.76 | 1.63 | 1.52 | 1.41 |
| n-Dodecylcyclohexane | $C_{18}H_{36}$ | 4.35 | 3.94 | 3.58 | 3.27 | 2.98 | 2.73 | 2.50 | 2.31 | 2.12 | 1.96 | 1.81 | 1.68 | 1.56 |
| n-Tridecylcyclohexane | $C_{19}H_{38}$ | 4.99 | 4.50 | 4.07 | 3.69 | 3.37 | 3.07 | 2.80 | 2.57 | 2.36 | 2.17 | 2.00 | 1.85 | 1.71 |
| n-Tetradecylcyclohexane | $C_{20}H_{40}$ | 5.69 | 5.10 | 4.60 | 4.16 | 3.78 | 3.43 | 3.13 | 2.86 | 2.61 | 2.40 | 2.20 | 2.02 | 1.87 |
| n-Pentadecylcyclohexane | $C_{21}H_{42}$ | 6.44 | 5.76 | 5.18 | 4.66 | 4.22 | 3.82 | 3.47 | 3.16 | 2.88 | 2.63 | 2.41 | 2.21 | 2.03 |
| n-Hexadecylcyclohexane | $C_{22}H_{44}$ | 7.26 | 6.46 | 5.80 | 5.19 | 4.69 | 4.23 | 3.83 | 3.48 | 3.16 | 2.88 | 2.63 | 2.40 | 2.20 |

[a] See footnote a of Table 1c-K

TABLE 24c-K, Page 1 – NORMAL MONOOLEFINS (1-ALKENES), $C_2$ TO $C_{20}$

KINEMATIC VISCOSITY

For the Normal Liquid Range at Atmospheric Pressure

August 31, 1949 (Corrected)

Temperature in °C

Kinematic viscosity in centistokes[a]

| Compound (liquid) | Formula | -185 | -180 | -175 | -170 | -165 | -160 | -155 | -150 | -145 | -140 | -135 | -130 | -125 | -120 | -115 | -110 |
|---|---|---|---|---|---|---|---|---|---|---|---|---|---|---|---|---|---|
| Ethene (Ethylene) | $C_2H_4$ | | | | 1.06[b] | 0.91 | 0.79 | 0.70 | 0.62 | 0.56 | 0.51 | 0.46 | 0.42 | 0.39 | 0.36 | 0.34 | 0.31 |
| Propene (Propylene) | $C_3H_6$ | 19.5 | 11.2 | 7.00 | 4.71 | 3.42 | 2.66 | 2.15 | 1.77 | 1.47 | 1.27 | 1.10 | 0.97 | 0.86 | 0.77 | 0.70 | 0.64 |
| 1-Butene | $C_4H_8$ | | | | | | | | | | | | | | | 1.18 | 1.07 |
| 1-Pentene | $C_5H_{10}$ | | | | | | | | | | | | | | | | |
| 1-Hexene | $C_6H_{12}$ | | | | | | | | | | | | | | | | |
| 1-Heptene | $C_7H_{14}$ | | | | | | | | | | | | | | | | |
| 1-Octene | $C_8H_{16}$ | | | | | | | | | | | | | | | | |
| 1-Nonene | $C_9H_{18}$ | | | | | | | | | | | | | | | | |
| 1-Decene | $C_{10}H_{20}$ | | | | | | | | | | | | | | | | |
| 1-Undecene | $C_{11}H_{22}$ | | | | | | | | | | | | | | | | |
| 1-Dodecene | $C_{12}H_{24}$ | | | | | | | | | | | | | | | | |
| 1-Tridecene | $C_{13}H_{26}$ | | | | | | | | | | | | | | | | |
| 1-Tetradecene | $C_{14}H_{28}$ | | | | | | | | | | | | | | | | |
| 1-Pentadecene | $C_{15}H_{30}$ | | | | | | | | | | | | | | | | |
| 1-Hexadecene | $C_{16}H_{32}$ | | | | | | | | | | | | | | | | |
| 1-Heptadecene | $C_{17}H_{34}$ | | | | | | | | | | | | | | | | |
| 1-Octadecene | $C_{18}H_{36}$ | | | | | | | | | | | | | | | | |
| 1-Nonadecene | $C_{19}H_{38}$ | | | | | | | | | | | | | | | | |
| 1-Eicosene | $C_{20}H_{40}$ | | | | | | | | | | | | | | | | |

a See footnote a of Table 1c-K.

b For the undercooled liquid below the normal freezing point.

TABLE 24c-K, Page 2 — NORMAL MONOOLEFINS (1-ALKENES), $C_2$ TO $C_{20}$

KINEMATIC VISCOSITY

For the Normal Liquid Range at Atmospheric Pressure

August 31, 1949 (Corrected)

| Compound (liquid) | Formula | Temperature in °C | | | | | | | | | | | | | | | |
|---|---|---|---|---|---|---|---|---|---|---|---|---|---|---|---|---|---|
| | | -110 | -105 | -100 | -95 | -90 | -85 | -80 | -75 | -70 | -65 | -60 | -55 | -50 | -45 | -40 | -35 |
| | | Kinematic viscosity in centistokes [a] | | | | | | | | | | | | | | | |
| Ethene (Ethylene) | $C_2H_4$ | 0.31 | 0.29 | 0.27[b] | | | | | | | | | | | | | |
| Propene (Propylene) | $C_3H_6$ | 0.64 | 0.59 | 0.55 | 0.52 | | | | | | | | | | | | |
| 1-Butene | $C_4H_8$ | 1.07 | 0.96 | 0.87 | 0.80 | 0.74 | 0.68 | 0.63 | 0.59 | 0.55 | 0.52 | 0.49 | 0.46 | 0.44 | 0.42 | 0.40 | 0.38 |
| 1-Pentene | $C_5H_{10}$ | | | | | 1.13 | 1.03 | 0.94 | 0.87 | 0.80 | 0.74 | 0.69 | 0.64 | 0.60 | 0.57 | 0.54 | 0.51 |
| 1-Hexene | $C_6H_{12}$ | | | | | | | | | | | | 0.93 | 0.86 | 0.80 | 0.75 | 0.70 |
| 1-Heptene | $C_7H_{14}$ | | | | | | | | | | | | | | | | |
| 1-Octene | $C_8H_{16}$ | | | | | | | | | | | | | | | | |
| 1-Nonene | $C_9H_{18}$ | | | | | | | | | | | | | | | | |
| 1-Decene | $C_{10}H_{20}$ | | | | | | | | | | | | | | | | |
| 1-Undecene | $C_{11}H_{22}$ | | | | | | | | | | | | | | | | |
| 1-Dodecene | $C_{12}H_{24}$ | | | | | | | | | | | | | | | | |
| 1-Tridecene | $C_{13}H_{26}$ | | | | | | | | | | | | | | | | |
| 1-Tetradecene | $C_{14}H_{28}$ | | | | | | | | | | | | | | | | |
| 1-Pentadecene | $C_{15}H_{30}$ | | | | | | | | | | | | | | | | |
| 1-Hexadecene | $C_{16}H_{32}$ | | | | | | | | | | | | | | | | |
| 1-Heptadecene | $C_{17}H_{34}$ | | | | | | | | | | | | | | | | |
| 1-Octadecene | $C_{18}H_{36}$ | | | | | | | | | | | | | | | | |
| 1-Nonadecene | $C_{19}H_{38}$ | | | | | | | | | | | | | | | | |
| 1-Eicosene | $C_{20}H_{40}$ | | | | | | | | | | | | | | | | |

[a] See footnote a of Table 1c-K.

[b] For the liquid above the normal boiling point, at saturation pressure.

TABLE 24c-K, Page 3 – NORMAL MONOOLEFINS (1-ALKENES), $C_2$ TO $C_{20}$

KINEMATIC VISCOSITY

For the Normal Liquid Range at Atmospheric Pressure

August 31, 1949

Kinematic viscosity in centistokes [a]

| Compound (liquid) | Formula | Temperature in °C | | | | | | | | | | | | | | | |
|---|---|---|---|---|---|---|---|---|---|---|---|---|---|---|---|---|---|
| | | -35 | -30 | -25 | -20 | -15 | -10 | -5 | 0 | 5 | 10 | 15 | 20 | 25 | 30 | 35 | 40 |
| Ethene (Ethylene) | $C_2H_4$ | | | | | | | | | | | | | | | | |
| Propene (Propylene) | $C_3H_6$ | | | | | | | | | | | | | | | | |
| 1-Butene | $C_4H_8$ | 0.38 | | | | | | | | | | | | | | | |
| 1-Pentene | $C_5H_{10}$ | 0.51 | 0.48 | 0.46 | 0.44 | 0.42 | 0.40 | 0.38 | 0.37 | | | | | | | | |
| 1-Hexene | $C_6H_{12}$ | 0.70 | 0.65 | 0.61 | 0.58 | 0.55 | 0.52 | 0.50 | 0.47 | 0.45 | 0.43 | 0.41 | 0.39 | 0.37 | 0.36 | 0.35 | 0.34 |
| 1-Heptene | $C_7H_{14}$ | | | | | | | | 0.61 | 0.58 | 0.55 | 0.52 | 0.50 | 0.48 | 0.47 | 0.45 | 0.43 |
| 1-Octene | $C_8H_{16}$ | | | | | | | | 0.837 | 0.785 | 0.736 | 0.692 | 0.656 | 0.629 | 0.599 | 0.573 | 0.548 |
| 1-Nonene | $C_9H_{18}$ | | | | | | | | 1.127 | 1.045 | 0.972 | 0.904 | 0.851 | 0.807 | 0.766 | 0.727 | 0.690 |
| 1-Decene | $C_{10}H_{20}$ | | | | | | | | 1.49 | 1.37 | 1.262 | 1.167 | 1.091 | 1.025 | 0.965 | 0.909 | 0.858 |
| 1-Undecene | $C_{11}H_{22}$ | | | | | | | | 1.96 | 1.78 | 1.62 | 1.49 | 1.38 | 1.287 | 1.204 | 1.127 | 1.057 |
| 1-Dodecene | $C_{12}H_{24}$ | | | | | | | | 2.54 | 2.28 | 2.06 | 1.87 | 1.72 | 1.60 | 1.49 | 1.39 | 1.290 |
| 1-Tridecene | $C_{13}H_{26}$ | | | | | | | | 3.25 | 2.89 | 2.59 | 2.34 | 2.14 | 1.97 | 1.82 | 1.68 | 1.56 |
| 1-Tetradecene | $C_{14}H_{28}$ | | | | | | | | 4.12 | 3.65 | 3.23 | 2.88 | 2.61 | 2.39 | 2.20 | 2.02 | 1.86 |
| 1-Pentadecene | $C_{15}H_{30}$ | | | | | | | | 5.17 | 4.53 | 3.99 | 3.55 | 3.19 | 2.90 | 2.65 | 2.42 | 2.22 |
| 1-Hexadecene | $C_{16}H_{32}$ | | | | | | | | | 5.60 | 4.86 | 4.28 | 3.83 | 3.47 | 3.16 | 2.88 | 2.63 |
| 1-Heptadecene | $C_{17}H_{34}$ | | | | | | | | | | 5.93[b] | 5.18 | 4.60 | 4.15 | 3.75 | 3.40 | 3.09 |
| 1-Octadecene | $C_{18}H_{36}$ | | | | | | | | | | | | 5.47 | 4.91 | 4.42 | 3.99 | 3.60 |
| 1-Nonadecene | $C_{19}H_{38}$ | | | | | | | | | | | | | 5.79 | 5.19 | 4.65 | 4.18 |
| 1-Eicosene | $C_{20}H_{40}$ | | | | | | | | | | | | | | 6.04[b] | 5.38 | 4.82 |

[a] See footnote a of Table 1c-K.      [b] For the undercooled liquid below the normal freezing point.

TABLE 24c-K, Page 4 — NORMAL MONOOLEFINS (1-ALKENES), $C_2$ TO $C_{20}$

KINEMATIC VISCOSITY

For the Normal Liquid Range at Atmospheric Pressure

August 31, 1949

| Compound (liquid) | Formula | Temperature in °C | | | | | | | | | | | | | | | |
|---|---|---|---|---|---|---|---|---|---|---|---|---|---|---|---|---|---|
| | | 40 | 45 | 50 | 55 | 60 | 65 | 70 | 75 | 80 | 85 | 90 | 95 | 100 | 105 | 110 | 115 |
| | | Kinematic viscosity in centistokes [a] | | | | | | | | | | | | | | | |
| Ethene (Ethylene) | $C_2H_4$ | | | | | | | | | | | | | | | | |
| Propene (Propylene) | $C_3H_6$ | | | | | | | | | | | | | | | | |
| 1-Butene | $C_4H_8$ | | | | | | | | | | | | | | | | |
| 1-Pentene | $C_5H_{10}$ | | | | | | | | | | | | | | | | |
| 1-Hexene | $C_6H_{12}$ | 0.34 | 0.33 | 0.32 | 0.31 | 0.30 | 0.29 | | | | | | | | | | |
| 1-Heptene | $C_7H_{14}$ | 0.43 | 0.41 | 0.40 | 0.39 | 0.38 | 0.36 | 0.35 | 0.34 | 0.34 | 0.33 | 0.32 | 0.31[b] | | | | |
| 1-Octene | $C_8H_{16}$ | 0.548 | 0.525 | 0.503 | 0.483 | 0.465 | 0.448 | 0.433 | 0.420 | 0.408 | 0.395 | 0.383 | 0.373 | 0.363 | 0.35 | 0.34 | 0.34 |
| 1-Nonene | $C_9H_{18}$ | 0.690 | 0.656 | 0.625 | 0.596 | 0.570 | 0.547 | 0.527 | 0.507 | 0.489 | 0.472 | 0.456 | 0.441 | 0.427 | 0.41 | 0.40 | 0.39 |
| 1-Decene | $C_{10}H_{20}$ | 0.858 | 0.811 | 0.768 | 0.729 | 0.694 | 0.662 | 0.634 | 0.609 | 0.585 | 0.562 | 0.541 | 0.521 | 0.502 | 0.48 | 0.47 | 0.45 |
| 1-Undecene | $C_{11}H_{22}$ | 1.057 | 0.993 | 0.935 | 0.883 | 0.838 | 0.795 | 0.759 | 0.725 | 0.693 | 0.663 | 0.635 | 0.610 | 0.587 | 0.56 | 0.54 | 0.52 |
| 1-Dodecene | $C_{12}H_{24}$ | 1.290 | 1.204 | 1.128 | 1.059 | 0.998 | 0.944 | 0.896 | 0.853 | 0.813 | 0.775 | 0.740 | 0.708 | 0.678 | 0.65 | 0.62 | 0.60 |
| 1-Tridecene | $C_{13}H_{26}$ | 1.56 | 1.45 | 1.35 | 1.265 | 1.188 | 1.118 | 1.055 | 0.999 | 0.948 | 0.901 | 0.858 | 0.819 | 0.782 | 0.75 | 0.72 | 0.68 |
| 1-Tetradecene | $C_{14}H_{28}$ | 1.86 | 1.72 | 1.60 | 1.50 | 1.40 | 1.31 | 1.230 | 1.162 | 1.100 | 1.042 | 0.988 | 0.939 | 0.894 | 0.85 | 0.81 | 0.78 |
| 1-Pentadecene | $C_{15}H_{30}$ | 2.22 | 2.05 | 1.89 | 1.76 | 1.64 | 1.53 | 1.43 | 1.35 | 1.269 | 1.197 | 1.132 | 1.073 | 1.019 | 0.97 | 0.92 | 0.88 |
| 1-Hexadecene | $C_{16}H_{32}$ | 2.63 | 2.41 | 2.22 | 2.05 | 1.90 | 1.77 | 1.65 | 1.55 | 1.46 | 1.37 | 1.288 | 1.218 | 1.152 | 1.09 | 1.04 | 0.98 |
| 1-Heptadecene | $C_{17}H_{34}$ | 3.09 | 2.82 | 2.58 | 2.37 | 2.19 | 2.03 | 1.89 | 1.77 | 1.66 | 1.56 | 1.47 | 1.38 | 1.30 | 1.23 | 1.16 | 1.10 |
| 1-Octadecene | $C_{18}H_{36}$ | 3.60 | 3.27 | 2.99 | 2.74 | 2.52 | 2.33 | 2.17 | 2.02 | 1.88 | 1.76 | 1.65 | 1.55 | 1.46 | 1.38 | 1.30 | 1.23 |
| 1-Nonadecene | $C_{19}H_{38}$ | 4.18 | 3.78 | 3.44 | 3.14 | 2.88 | 2.65 | 2.46 | 2.29 | 2.13 | 1.98 | 1.86 | 1.74 | 1.63 | 1.53 | 1.44 | 1.36 |
| 1-Eicosene | $C_{20}H_{40}$ | 4.82 | 4.34 | 3.92 | 3.59 | 3.28 | 3.01 | 2.78 | 2.58 | 2.39 | 2.22 | 2.07 | 1.94 | 1.82 | 1.71 | 1.60 | 1.50 |

[a] See footnote a of Table 1c-K.

[b] For the liquid above the normal boiling point, at saturation pressure.

TABLE 21c-K (PART 1), Page 1 - NORMAL ALKYL BENZENES, $C_6$ TO $C_{22}$

KINEMATIC VISCOSITY

For the Normal Liquid Range at Atmospheric Pressure

October 31, 1948

Temperature in °C

Kinematic viscosity in centistokes[a]

| Compound (liquid) | Formula | -25 | -20 | -15 | -10 | -5 | 0 | 5 | 10 | 15 | 20 | 25 | 30 | 35 | 40 | 45 | 50 |
|---|---|---|---|---|---|---|---|---|---|---|---|---|---|---|---|---|---|
| Benzene | $C_6H_6$ | | | | | | | 0.9929[b] | 0.8538 | 0.7919 | 0.7379 | 0.6899 | 0.6472 | 0.6084 | 0.5739 | 0.5431 | 0.5149 |
| Methylbenzene (Toluene) | $C_7H_8$ | 1.29 | 1.18 | 1.090 | 1.010 | 0.938 | 0.873 | .8156 | .7645 | .7178 | .6767 | .6397 | .6066 | .5758 | .5481 | .5228 | .4991 |
| Ethylbenzene | $C_8H_{10}$ | 1.49 | 1.37 | 1.261 | 1.169 | 1.085 | 1.011 | .9441 | .8848 | .8304 | .7823 | .7389 | .6996 | .6634 | .6305 | .6006 | .5725 |
| n-Propylbenzene | $C_9H_{12}$ | 2.13 | 1.92 | 1.745 | 1.597 | 1.463 | 1.345 | 1.240 | 1.149 | 1.066 | .9944 | .9309 | .8745 | .8231 | .7770 | .7358 | .6979 |
| n-Butylbenzene | $C_{10}H_{14}$ | 2.79 | 2.50 | 2.24 | 2.02 | 1.857 | 1.673 | 1.530 | 1.406 | 1.298 | 1.203 | 1.121 | 1.049 | .984 | .925 | .872 | .818 |
| n-Pentylbenzene | $C_{11}H_{16}$ | | 4.30 | 3.53 | 3.00 | 2.60 | 2.29 | 2.05 | 1.856 | 1.692 | 1.553 | 1.433 | 1.330 | 1.239 | 1.157 | 1.086 | 1.021 |
| n-Hexylbenzene | $C_{12}H_{18}$ | | 5.82 | 4.73 | 4.15 | 3.41 | 2.98 | 2.64 | 2.37 | 2.14 | 1.953 | 1.789 | 1.650 | 1.528 | 1.419 | 1.325 | 1.239 |
| n-Heptylbenzene | $C_{13}H_{20}$ | | 7.81 | 6.27 | 5.20 | 4.42 | 3.83 | 3.37 | 2.99 | 2.69 | 2.43 | 2.21 | 2.03 | 1.864 | 1.722 | 1.599 | 1.488 |
| n-Octylbenzene | $C_{14}H_{22}$ | | 10.42 | 8.25 | 6.76 | 5.69 | 4.87 | 4.25 | 3.75 | 3.33 | 2.99 | 2.71 | 2.46 | 2.25 | 2.07 | 1.913 | 1.771 |
| n-Nonylbenzene | $C_{15}H_{24}$ | | 13.79 | 10.77 | 8.73 | 7.26 | 6.16 | 5.32 | 4.65 | 4.11 | 3.66 | 3.28 | 2.97 | 2.70 | 2.47 | 2.27 | 2.09 |
| n-Decylbenzene | $C_{16}H_{26}$ | | 18.1[b] | 13.97 | 11.18 | 9.20 | 7.72 | 6.61 | 5.72 | 5.02 | 4.44 | 3.96 | 3.56 | 3.22 | 2.92 | 2.66 | 2.39 |
| n-Undecylbenzene | $C_{17}H_{28}$ | | | 18.0[b] | 14.22 | 11.57 | 9.61 | 8.15 | 7.00 | 6.08 | 5.34 | 4.73 | 4.23 | 3.80 | 3.43 | 3.12 | 2.85 |
| n-Dodecylbenzene | $C_{18}H_{30}$ | | | | | 14.45[b] | 11.88 | 9.98 | 8.50 | 7.33 | 6.39 | 5.62 | 4.99 | 4.46 | 4.00 | 3.62 | 3.29 |
| n-Tridecylbenzene | $C_{19}H_{32}$ | | | | | | 14.60[b] | 12.15 | 10.25 | 8.77 | 7.60 | 6.63 | 5.85 | 5.20 | 4.65 | 4.18 | 3.78 |
| n-Tetradecylbenzene | $C_{20}H_{34}$ | | | | | | | | 12.30[b] | 10.44 | 8.98 | 7.79 | 6.83 | 6.03 | 5.36 | 4.81 | 4.32 |
| n-Pentadecylbenzene | $C_{21}H_{36}$ | | | | | | | | | 12.35[b] | 10.54 | 9.09 | 7.92 | 6.96 | 6.15 | 5.49 | 4.92 |
| n-Hexadecylbenzene | $C_{22}H_{38}$ | | | | | | | | | | | 10.56[b] | 9.15 | 7.99 | 7.03 | 6.24 | 5.57 |

a See footnote a of Table 1c-K

b Extrapolated value for the undercooled liquid below the normal freezing point.

TABLE 21c-K (PART 1), Page 2 – NORMAL ALKYL BENZENES, $C_6$ TO $C_{22}$
KINEMATIC VISCOSITY
For the Normal Liquid Range at Atmospheric Pressure
October 31, 1948

Temperature in °C — Kinematic viscosity in centistokes[a]

| Compound (liquid) | Formula | 50 | 55 | 60 | 65 | 70 | 75 | 80 | 85 | 90 | 95 | 100 | 105 | 110 | 115 | 120 | 125 |
|---|---|---|---|---|---|---|---|---|---|---|---|---|---|---|---|---|---|
| Benzene | $C_6H_6$ | 0.5149 | 0.489 | 0.467 | 0.445 | 0.425 | 0.407 | 0.390 | 0.374[b] | | | | | | | | |
| Methylbenzene (Toluene) | $C_7H_8$ | .4991 | .478 | .458 | .439 | .422 | .406 | .391 | .376 | .363 | .351 | .339 | .328 | .318 | | | |
| Ethylbenzene | $C_8H_{10}$ | .5725 | .548 | .525 | .503 | .483 | .464 | .447 | .431 | .416 | .401 | .388 | .375 | .363 | .352 | .341 | 0.331 |
| n-Propylbenzene | $C_9H_{12}$ | .6979 | .664 | .633 | .603 | .577 | .552 | .529 | .508 | .488 | .469 | .452 | .435 | .421 | .406 | .393 | .381 |
| n-Butylbenzene | $C_{10}H_{14}$ | .818 | .781 | .741 | .704 | .671 | .639 | .611 | .584 | .560 | .537 | .516 | .50 | .48 | .46 | .44 | .43 |
| n-Pentylbenzene | $C_{11}H_{16}$ | 1.021 | .963 | .913 | .863 | .822 | .779 | .741 | .707 | .675 | .645 | .617 | .59 | .57 | .54 | .52 | .50 |
| n-Hexylbenzene | $C_{12}H_{18}$ | 1.239 | 1.163 | 1.098 | 1.031 | .980 | .924 | .876 | .833 | .792 | .754 | .720 | .69 | .66 | .63 | .60 | .58 |
| n-Heptylbenzene | $C_{13}H_{20}$ | 1.488 | 1.391 | 1.305 | 1.223 | 1.157 | 1.086 | 1.025 | .971 | .920 | .874 | .831 | .79 | .75 | .72 | .69 | .66 |
| n-Octylbenzene | $C_{14}H_{22}$ | 1.771 | 1.646 | 1.539 | 1.436 | 1.353 | 1.265 | 1.190 | 1.123 | 1.062 | 1.004 | .952 | .90 | .86 | .82 | .78 | .74 |
| n-Nonylbenzene | $C_{15}H_{24}$ | 2.09 | 1.934 | 1.800 | 1.671 | 1.570 | 1.461 | 1.370 | 1.289 | 1.213 | 1.144 | 1.082 | 1.02 | .97 | .92 | .88 | .83 |
| n-Decylbenzene | $C_{16}H_{26}$ | 2.39 | 2.25 | 2.09 | 1.932 | 1.809 | 1.676 | 1.566 | 1.468 | 1.377 | 1.296 | 1.222 | 1.15 | 1.09 | 1.03 | .98 | .93 |
| n-Undecylbenzene | $C_{17}H_{28}$ | 2.85 | 2.61 | 2.41 | 2.22 | 2.07 | 1.911 | 1.779 | 1.663 | 1.555 | 1.458 | 1.371 | 1.29 | 1.22 | 1.15 | 1.09 | 1.03 |
| n-Dodecylbenzene | $C_{18}H_{30}$ | 3.29 | 3.00 | 2.76 | 2.53 | 2.36 | 2.17 | 2.01 | 1.873 | 1.746 | 1.633 | 1.531 | 1.44 | 1.35 | 1.27 | 1.20 | 1.14 |
| n-Tridecylbenzene | $C_{19}H_{32}$ | 3.78 | 3.44 | 3.15 | 2.88 | 2.67 | 2.44 | 2.26 | 2.10 | 1.950 | 1.819 | 1.701 | 1.59 | 1.50 | 1.41 | 1.32 | 1.25 |
| n-Tetradecylbenzene | $C_{20}H_{34}$ | 4.32 | 3.91 | 3.57 | 3.25 | 3.00 | 2.80 | 2.53 | 2.34 | 2.17 | 2.02 | 1.881 | 1.76 | 1.65 | 1.54 | 1.45 | 1.37 |
| n-Pentadecylbenzene | $C_{21}H_{36}$ | 4.92 | 4.43 | 4.02 | 3.65 | 3.36 | 3.06 | 2.81 | 2.60 | 2.40 | 2.23 | 2.07 | 1.93 | 1.80 | 1.69 | 1.59 | 1.49 |
| n-Hexadecylbenzene | $C_{22}H_{38}$ | 5.57 | 5.00 | 4.52 | 4.09 | 3.75 | 3.40 | 3.12 | 2.87 | 2.65 | 2.45 | 2.27 | 2.11 | 1.97 | 1.84 | 1.72 | 1.62 |

a See footnote a of Table 1c-K    b For the liquid above the boiling point, at saturation pressure.

TABLE 21c-K (PART 1), Page 3 - NORMAL ALKYL BENZENES, C$_6$ TO C$_{22}$

KINEMATIC VISCOSITY

For the Normal Liquid Range at Atmospheric Pressure

October 31, 1948

| Compound (liquid) | Formula | Temperature in °C | | | | | |
|---|---|---|---|---|---|---|---|
| | | Kinematic viscosity in centistokes[a] | | | | | |
| | | 125 | 130 | 135 | 140 | 145 | 150 |
| Benzene | C$_6$H$_6$ | | | | | | |
| Methylbenzene (Toluene) | C$_7$H$_8$ | | | | | | |
| Ethylbenzene | C$_8$H$_{10}$ | 0.331 | 0.321 | 0.312 | 0.304[b] | | |
| n-Propylbenzene | C$_9$H$_{12}$ | .381 | .368 | .36 | .35 | 0.34 | 0.33 |
| n-Butylbenzene | C$_{10}$H$_{14}$ | .429 | .41 | .40 | .39 | .38 | .37 |
| n-Pentylbenzene | C$_{11}$H$_{16}$ | .50 | .48 | .47 | .45 | .43 | .42 |
| n-Hexylbenzene | C$_{12}$H$_{18}$ | .58 | .55 | .53 | .51 | .49 | .47 |
| n-Heptylbenzene | C$_{13}$H$_{20}$ | .66 | .63 | .60 | .58 | .56 | .53 |
| n-Octylbenzene | C$_{14}$H$_{22}$ | .74 | .71 | .68 | .65 | .62 | .59 |
| n-Nonylbenzene | C$_{15}$H$_{24}$ | .83 | .79 | .76 | .72 | .69 | .66 |
| n-Decylbenzene | C$_{16}$H$_{26}$ | .93 | .88 | .84 | .80 | .76 | .73 |
| n-Undecylbenzene | C$_{17}$H$_{28}$ | 1.03 | .98 | .93 | .88 | .84 | .80 |
| n-Dodecylbenzene | C$_{18}$H$_{30}$ | 1.14 | 1.08 | 1.02 | .97 | .92 | .87 |
| n-Tridecylbenzene | C$_{19}$H$_{32}$ | 1.25 | 1.18 | 1.12 | 1.06 | 1.00 | .95 |
| n-Tetradecylbenzene | C$_{20}$H$_{34}$ | 1.37 | 1.29 | 1.22 | 1.15 | 1.09 | 1.03 |
| n-Pentadecylbenzene | C$_{21}$H$_{36}$ | 1.49 | 1.40 | 1.32 | 1.25 | 1.18 | 1.11 |
| n-Hexadecylbenzene | C$_{22}$H$_{38}$ | 1.62 | 1.52 | 1.43 | 1.35 | 1.27 | 1.19 |

[a] See footnote a of Table 1c-K    [b] For the liquid above the boiling point, at saturation pressure.

TABLE 5c-K, Page 1 – ALKYL BENZENES, $C_6$ TO $C_9$

KINEMATIC VISCOSITY

For the Normal Liquid Range at Atmospheric Pressure

November 30, 1949

| Compound (liquid) | Formula | Temperature in °C — Kinematic viscosity in centistokes [a] | | | | | | | | | | | | | | | |
|---|---|---|---|---|---|---|---|---|---|---|---|---|---|---|---|---|---|
| | | -25 | -20 | -15 | -10 | -5 | 0 | 5 | 10 | 15 | 20 | 25 | 30 | 35 | 40 | 45 | 50 |
| Benzene | $C_6H_6$ | | | | | | | 0.9229[b] | 0.8538 | 0.7919 | 0.7379 | 0.6899 | 0.6472 | 0.6084 | 0.5739 | 0.5431 | 0.5149 |
| Methylbenzene (Toluene) | $C_7H_8$ | 1.29 | 1.18 | 1.090 | 1.010 | 0.938 | 0.873 | 0.8156 | 0.7645 | 0.7178 | 0.6767 | 0.6397 | 0.6066 | 0.5758 | 0.5481 | 0.5228 | 0.4991 |
| Ethylbenzene | $C_8H_{10}$ | 1.49 | 1.37 | 1.261 | 1.169 | 1.085 | 1.011 | 0.9441 | 0.8848 | 0.8304 | 0.7823 | 0.7389 | 0.6996 | 0.6634 | 0.6305 | 0.6006 | 0.5725 |
| 1,2-Dimethylbenzene (o-Xylene) | " | | | | | 1.348 | 1.236 | 1.139 | 1.057 | 0.983 | 0.919 | 0.862 | 0.812 | 0.765 | 0.724 | 0.686 | 0.652 |
| 1,3-Dimethylbenzene (m-Xylene) | " | | | | | | 0.917 | 0.857 | 0.805 | 0.756 | 0.714 | 0.676 | 0.641 | 0.610 | 0.581 | 0.555 | 0.531 |
| 1,4-Dimethylbenzene (p-Xylene) | " | | | | | | | | | 0.794 | 0.748 | 0.706 | 0.668 | 0.634 | 0.602 | 0.574 | 0.548 |
| n-Propylbenzene | $C_9H_{12}$ | 2.13 | 1.92 | 1.745 | 1.597 | 1.463 | 1.345 | 1.240 | 1.149 | 1.066 | 0.9944 | 0.9309 | 0.8745 | 0.8231 | 0.7770 | 0.7358 | 0.6979 |
| Isopropylbenzene | " | | | | | | 1.224 | 1.133 | 1.054 | 0.982 | 0.918 | 0.862 | 0.812 | 0.766 | 0.724 | 0.686 | 0.651 |
| 1-Methyl-2-ethylbenzene | " | | | | | | | | | | | | | | | | |
| 1-Methyl-3-ethylbenzene | " | | | | | | | | | | | | | | | | |
| 1-Methyl-4-ethylbenzene | " | | | | | | | | 0.930 | 0.871 | 0.819 | 0.772 | 0.730 | 0.692 | 0.658 | 0.627 | 0.596 |
| 1,2,3-Trimethylbenzene | " | | | | | | | | | | | | | | | | |
| 1,2,4-Trimethylbenzene | " | | | | | | | | | | 1.154 | 1.058 | 0.936 | | | | |
| 1,3,5-Trimethylbenzene | " | | | | | | | | | | | | | | | | |

[a] See footnote a of Table 1c-K.   [b] For the undercooled liquid below the normal freezing point.

TABLE 5c-K, Page 2 – ALKYL BENZENES, C$_6$ TO C$_9$

KINEMATIC VISCOSITY

For the Normal Liquid Range at Atmospheric Pressure

November 30, 1949

| Compound (liquid) | Formula | Temperature in °C | | | | | | | | | | | | | | | |
|---|---|---|---|---|---|---|---|---|---|---|---|---|---|---|---|---|---|
| | | 50 | 55 | 60 | 65 | 70 | 75 | 80 | 85 | 90 | 95 | 100 | 105 | 110 | 115 | 120 | 125 |
| | | Kinematic viscosity in centistokes [a] | | | | | | | | | | | | | | | |
| Benzene | C$_6$H$_6$ | 0.5149 | 0.489 | 0.467 | 0.445 | 0.425 | 0.407 | 0.390 | 0.374[b] | | | | | | | | |
| Methylbenzene (Toluene) | C$_7$H$_9$ | 0.4991 | 0.478 | 0.458 | 0.439 | 0.422 | 0.406 | 0.391 | 0.376 | 0.363 | 0.351 | 0.339 | 0.328 | 0.318 | | | |
| Ethylbenzene | C$_8$H$_{10}$ | 0.5725 | 0.548 | 0.525 | 0.503 | 0.483 | 0.464 | 0.447 | 0.431 | 0.416 | 0.401 | 0.388 | 0.375 | 0.363 | 0.352 | 0.341 | 0.331 |
| 1,2-Dimethylbenzene (o-Xylene) | " | 0.652 | 0.620 | 0.592 | 0.565 | 0.541 | 0.518 | 0.497 | 0.477 | 0.459 | 0.441 | 0.425 | 0.410 | 0.396 | 0.382 | 0.370 | 0.358 |
| 1,3-Dimethylbenzene (m-Xylene) | " | 0.531 | 0.509 | 0.488 | 0.469 | 0.451 | 0.434 | 0.419 | 0.404 | 0.390 | 0.377 | 0.365 | 0.353 | 0.342 | 0.332 | 0.322 | 0.313 |
| 1,4-Dimethylbenzene (p-Xylene) | " | 0.548 | 0.524 | 0.502 | 0.481 | 0.462 | 0.444 | 0.428 | 0.412 | 0.397 | 0.383 | 0.370 | 0.358 | 0.346 | 0.335 | 0.325 | 0.315 |
| n-Propylbenzene | C$_9$H$_{12}$ | 0.6979 | 0.664 | 0.633 | 0.603 | 0.577 | 0.552 | 0.529 | 0.508 | 0.488 | 0.469 | 0.452 | 0.435 | 0.421 | 0.406 | 0.393 | 0.381 |
| Isopropylbenzene | " | 0.651 | 0.620 | 0.591 | | | | | | | | | | | | | |
| 1-Methyl-2-ethylbenzene | " | | | | | | | | | | | | | | | | |
| 1-Methyl-3-ethylbenzene | " | | | | | | | | | | | | | | | | |
| 1-Methyl-4-ethylbenzene | " | 0.598 | 0.572 | 0.548 | 0.526 | 0.506 | 0.488 | 0.470 | | | | | | | | | |
| 1,2,3-Trimethylbenzene | " | | | | | | | | | | | | | | | | |
| 1,2,4-Trimethylbenzene | " | | | | | | | | | | | | | | | | |
| 1,3,5-Trimethylbenzene | " | | | | | | | | | | | | | | | | |

a See footnote a of Table 1c-K.

b For the liquid above the normal boiling point, at saturation pressure.

TABLE 5c-K, Page 3 - ALKYL BENZENES, $C_6$ TO $C_9$

KINEMATIC VISCOSITY

For the Normal Liquid Range at Atmospheric Pressure

November 30, 1949

| Compound (liquid) | Formula | Temperature in °C | | | | | |
|---|---|---|---|---|---|---|---|
| | | Kinematic viscosity in centistokes [a] | | | | | |
| | | 125 | 130 | 135 | 140 | 145 | 150 |
| Benzene | $C_6H_6$ | | | | | | |
| Methylbenzene (Toluene) | $C_7H_8$ | | | | | | |
| Ethylbenzene | $C_8H_{10}$ | 0.331 | 0.321 | 0.312 | 0.304[b] | | |
| 1,2-Dimethylbenzene (o-Xylene) | " | 0.358 | 0.347 | 0.337 | 0.327 | 0.318[b] | |
| 1,3-Dimethylbenzene (m-Xylene) | " | 0.313 | 0.304 | 0.296 | 0.288[b] | | |
| 1,4-Dimethylbenzene (p-Xylene) | " | 0.315 | 0.305 | 0.297 | 0.288[b] | | |
| n-Propylbenzene | $C_9H_{12}$ | 0.381 | 0.368 | 0.36 | 0.35 | 0.34 | 0.33 |
| Isopropylbenzene | " | | | | | | |
| 1-Methyl-2-ethylbenzene | " | | | | | | |
| 1-Methyl-3-ethylbenzene | " | | | | | | |
| 1-Methyl-4-ethylbenzene | " | | | | | | |
| 1,2,3-Trimethylbenzene | " | | | | | | |
| 1,2,4-Trimethylbenzene | " | | | | | | |
| 1,3,5-Trimethylbenzene | " | | | | | | |

a See footnote a of Table 1c-K.    b For the liquid above the normal boiling point, at saturation pressure.

TABLE 20d (PART 1), Page 1 — NORMAL PARAFFINS, $C_1$ TO $C_{20}$

DENSITY

For the Normal Liquid Range at Atmospheric Pressure

June 30, 1949; October 31, 1952

Temperature in °C — Density in g/ml[a]

| Compound (liquid) | Formula | -190 | -180 | -170 | -160 | -150 | -140 | -130 | -120 | -110 | -100 | -90 | -80 | -70 | -60 | -50 | -40 |
|---|---|---|---|---|---|---|---|---|---|---|---|---|---|---|---|---|---|
| Methane | $CH_4$ | | 0.4497 | 0.4362 | 0.4218[c] | | | | | | | | | | | | |
| Ethane | $C_2H_6$ | | 0.653 | 0.642 | 0.631 | 0.620 | 0.6086 | 0.5972 | 0.5856 | 0.5737 | 0.5613 | 0.5482 | | | | | |
| Propane | $C_3H_8$ | 0.732[b] | 0.723 | 0.714 | 0.705 | 0.696 | 0.686 | 0.676 | 0.666 | 0.656 | 0.646 | 0.635 | 0.6241 | 0.6130 | 0.6017 | 0.5900 | 0.5784[c] |
| n-Butane | $C_4H_{10}$ | | | | | | 0.739[b] | 0.731 | 0.722 | 0.712 | 0.7008 | 0.6899 | 0.6801 | 0.6703 | 0.6605 | 0.6512 | 0.6416 |
| n-Pentane | $C_5H_{12}$ | | | | | | | 0.762[b] | 0.753 | 0.744 | 0.7350 | 0.7258 | 0.7171 | 0.7084 | 0.6996 | 0.6908 | 0.6820 |
| n-Hexane | $C_6H_{14}$ | | | | | | | | | | 0.7618[b] | 0.7533 | 0.7451 | 0.7368 | 0.7285 | 0.7201 | 0.7117 |
| n-Heptane | $C_7H_{16}$ | | | | | | | | | | | 0.7739 | 0.7660 | 0.7581 | 0.7501 | 0.7420 | 0.7339 |
| n-Octane | $C_8H_{18}$ | | | | | | | | | | | | | | 0.7668[b] | 0.7590 | 0.7511 |

Temperature in °C — Density in g/ml[a]

| Compound (liquid) | Formula | -30 | -20 | -10 | 0 | 10 | 20 | 30 | 40 | 50 | 60 | 70 | 80 | 90 | 100 | 110 | 120 |
|---|---|---|---|---|---|---|---|---|---|---|---|---|---|---|---|---|---|
| Methane | $CH_4$ | | | | | | | | | | | | | | | | |
| Ethane | $C_2H_6$ | | | | | | | | | | | | | | | | |
| Propane | $C_3H_8$ | 0.5664[c] | 0.5541[c] | 0.5414[c] | 0.5282[c] | 0.5146[c] | 0.5005[c] | | | | | | | | | | |
| n-Butane | $C_4H_{10}$ | 0.6318 | 0.6218 | 0.6115 | 0.6011[c] | 0.5907[c] | 0.5788[c] | | | | | | | | | | |
| n-Pentane | $C_5H_{12}$ | 0.6731 | 0.6640 | 0.6546 | 0.6452 | 0.6357 | 0.6262 | 0.6159 | 0.6053[c] | | | | | | | | |
| n-Hexane | $C_6H_{14}$ | 0.7032 | 0.6946 | 0.6858 | 0.6769 | 0.6679 | 0.6594 | 0.6502 | 0.6411 | 0.6316 | 0.6214 | 0.6102[c] | | | | | |
| n-Heptane | $C_7H_{16}$ | 0.7258 | 0.7175 | 0.7091 | 0.7006 | 0.6920 | 0.6838 | 0.6753 | 0.6669 | 0.6583 | 0.6493 | 0.6398 | 0.6303 | 0.6207 | 0.6110[c] | | |
| n-Octane | $C_8H_{18}$ | 0.7432 | 0.7352 | 0.7271 | 0.7189 | 0.7106 | 0.7025 | 0.6945 | 0.6866 | 0.6784 | 0.6701 | 0.6614 | 0.6528 | 0.6442 | 0.6352 | 0.6261 | 0.6166 |

a See footnote a of Table 1d.    b For the undercooled liquid below the normal freezing point.    c At saturation pressure.

TABLE 20j (PART 1), Page 2 – NORMAL PARAFFINS, $C_1$ TO $C_{20}$

DENSITY

For the Normal Liquid Range at Atmospheric Pressure

June 30, 1949; October 31, 1952

| Compound (liquid) | Formula | Temperature in °C | | | | | | | | | | | | | | | |
|---|---|---|---|---|---|---|---|---|---|---|---|---|---|---|---|---|---|
| | | -50 | -40 | -30 | -20 | -10 | 0 | 10 | 20 | 30 | 40 | 50 | 60 | 70 | 80 | 90 | 100 |
| | | Density in g/ml [a] | | | | | | | | | | | | | | | |
| n-Nonane | $C_9H_{20}$ | 0.7724 | 0.7648 | 0.7571 | 0.7493 | 0.7414 | 0.7335 | 0.7254 | 0.7176 | 0.7099 | 0.7022 | 0.6944 | 0.6864 | 0.6781 | 0.6701 | 0.6620 | 0.6536 |
| n-Decane | $C_{10}H_{22}$ | | | 0.7684[b] | 0.7608 | 0.7531 | 0.7454 | 0.7376 | 0.7300 | 0.7224 | 0.7149 | 0.7073 | 0.6996 | 0.6917 | 0.6840 | 0.6761 | 0.6681 |
| n-Undecane | $C_{11}H_{24}$ | | | 0.7778[b] | 0.7703 | 0.7628 | 0.7553 | 0.7477 | 0.7402 | 0.7328 | 0.7254 | 0.7180 | 0.7106 | 0.7029 | 0.6954 | 0.6878 | 0.6800 |
| n-Dodecane | $C_{12}H_{26}$ | | | | | 0.7711[b] | 0.7637 | 0.7562 | 0.7487 | 0.7416 | 0.7344 | 0.7271 | 0.7198 | 0.7123 | 0.7048 | 0.6976 | 0.6900 |
| n-Tridecane | $C_{13}H_{28}$ | | | | | 0.7781[b] | 0.7708 | 0.7635 | 0.7564 | 0.7492 | 0.7421 | 0.7349 | 0.7277 | 0.7204 | 0.7132 | 0.7059 | 0.6985 |
| n-Tetradecane | $C_{14}H_{30}$ | | | | | | | 0.7698 | 0.7628 | 0.7557 | 0.7487 | 0.7417 | 0.7346 | 0.7274 | 0.7203 | 0.7132 | 0.7059 |
| n-Pentadecane | $C_{15}H_{32}$ | | | | | | | 0.7754 | 0.7685 | 0.7615 | 0.7545 | 0.7476 | 0.7406 | 0.7335 | 0.7265 | 0.7195 | 0.7123 |
| n-Hexadecane | $C_{16}H_{34}$ | | | | | | | | 0.7734 | 0.7665 | 0.7597 | 0.7528 | 0.7459 | 0.7389 | 0.7320 | 0.7251 | 0.7180 |
| n-Heptadecane | $C_{17}H_{36}$ | | | | | | | | 0.7780[b] | 0.7710 | 0.7643 | 0.7575 | 0.7506 | 0.7438 | 0.7369 | 0.7300 | 0.7230 |
| n-Octadecane | $C_{18}H_{38}$ | | | | | | | | 0.7819[b] | 0.7751 | 0.7684 | 0.7616 | 0.7548 | 0.7481 | 0.7413 | 0.7345 | 0.7276 |
| n-Nonadecane | $C_{19}H_{40}$ | | | | | | | | 0.7855[b] | 0.7787[b] | 0.7720 | 0.7654 | 0.7587 | 0.7520 | 0.7452 | 0.7385 | 0.7317 |
| n-Eicosane | $C_{20}H_{42}$ | | | | | | | | 0.7887[b] | 0.7821[b] | 0.7754 | 0.7688 | 0.7622 | 0.7554 | 0.7488 | 0.7421 | 0.7354 |

| Compound (liquid) | Formula | Temperature in °C | | | | | | | | | | | | | | | |
|---|---|---|---|---|---|---|---|---|---|---|---|---|---|---|---|---|---|
| | | 110 | 120 | 130 | 140 | 150 | 160 | 170 | 180 | 190 | 200 | 210 | 220 | 230 | 240 | 250 | 260 |
| | | Density in g/ml [a] | | | | | | | | | | | | | | | |
| n-Nonane | $C_9H_{20}$ | 0.6451 | 0.6363 | 0.6270 | 0.6180 | 0.6090 | | | | | | | | | | | |
| n-Decane | $C_{10}H_{22}$ | 0.6600 | 0.6517 | 0.6432 | 0.6348 | 0.6260 | 0.6169 | 0.6074 | | | | | | | | | |
| n-Undecane | $C_{11}H_{24}$ | 0.6722 | 0.6641 | 0.6560 | 0.6479 | 0.6396 | 0.6311 | 0.6223 | 0.6133 | | | | | | | | |
| n-Dodecane | $C_{12}H_{26}$ | 0.6824 | 0.6745 | 0.6667 | 0.6589 | 0.6509 | 0.6427 | 0.6344 | 0.6260 | 0.6173 | 0.6082 | 0.5985 | 0.5878[c] | | | | |
| n-Tridecane | $C_{13}H_{28}$ | 0.6911 | 0.6834 | 0.6757 | 0.6681 | 0.6604 | 0.6525 | 0.6446 | 0.6365 | 0.6283 | 0.6200 | 0.6107 | 0.6010 | 0.5910 | 0.5807[c] | | |
| n-Tetradecane | $C_{14}H_{30}$ | 0.6984 | 0.6911 | 0.6836 | 0.6761 | 0.6685 | 0.6609 | 0.6532 | 0.6454 | 0.6375 | 0.6295 | 0.6209 | 0.6119 | 0.6026 | 0.5933 | 0.5839 | |
| n-Pentadecane | $C_{15}H_{32}$ | 0.7051 | 0.6977 | 0.6904 | 0.6830 | 0.6756 | 0.6682 | 0.6606 | 0.6531 | 0.6454 | 0.6378 | 0.6296 | 0.6211 | 0.6124 | 0.6036 | 0.5949 | 0.5858 |
| n-Hexadecane | $C_{16}H_{34}$ | 0.7109 | 0.7036 | 0.6963 | 0.6891 | 0.6819 | 0.6745 | 0.6672 | 0.6598 | 0.6523 | 0.6447 | 0.6370 | 0.6289 | 0.6206 | 0.6124 | 0.6041 | 0.5955 |
| n-Heptadecane | $C_{17}H_{36}$ | 0.7160 | 0.7089 | 0.7017 | 0.6945 | 0.6874 | 0.6802 | 0.6730 | 0.6657 | 0.6584 | 0.6510 | 0.6435 | 0.6357 | 0.6278 | 0.6199 | 0.6119 | 0.6037 |
| n-Octadecane | $C_{18}H_{38}$ | 0.7206 | 0.7136 | 0.7065 | 0.6994 | 0.6924 | 0.6853 | 0.6781 | 0.6710 | 0.6638 | 0.6566 | 0.6492 | 0.6416 | 0.6340 | 0.6264 | 0.6187 | 0.6108 |
| n-Nonadecane | $C_{19}H_{40}$ | 0.7248 | 0.7178 | 0.7108 | 0.7038 | 0.6968 | 0.6898 | 0.6828 | 0.6757 | 0.6687 | 0.6617 | 0.6543 | 0.6469 | 0.6395 | 0.6321 | 0.6246 | 0.6170 |
| n-Eicosane | $C_{20}H_{42}$ | 0.7286 | 0.7217 | 0.7147 | 0.7078 | 0.7009 | 0.6939 | 0.6870 | 0.6800 | 0.6730 | 0.6661 | 0.6589 | 0.6517 | 0.6444 | 0.6372 | 0.6299 | 0.6224 |

a See footnote a of Table 1d.   b For the undercooled liquid below the normal freezing point.   c At saturation pressure.

TABLE 20d (PART 1), Page 3 — NORMAL PARAFFINS, $C_1$ TO $C_{20}$
DENSITY
For the Normal Liquid Range at Atmospheric Pressure
June 30, 1949; October 31, 1952

Temperature in °C

Density in g/ml [a]

| Compound (liquid) | Formula | 270 | 280 | 290 | 300 | 310 | 320 | 330 | 340 |
|---|---|---|---|---|---|---|---|---|---|
| n-Nonane | $C_9H_{20}$ | | | | | | | | |
| n-Decane | $C_{10}H_{22}$ | | | | | | | | |
| n-Undecane | $C_{11}H_{24}$ | | | | | | | | |
| n-Dodecane | $C_{12}H_{26}$ | | | | | | | | |
| n-Tridecane | $C_{13}H_{28}$ | | | | | | | | |
| n-Tetradecane | $C_{14}H_{30}$ | | | | | | | | |
| n-Pentadecane | $C_{15}H_{32}$ | 0.5766 | | | | | | | |
| n-Hexadecane | $C_{16}H_{34}$ | 0.5868 | 0.5779 | 0.5686[b] | | | | | |
| n-Heptadecane | $C_{17}H_{36}$ | 0.5954 | 0.5870 | 0.5781 | 0.5686 | | | | |
| n-Octadecane | $C_{18}H_{38}$ | 0.6028 | 0.5947 | 0.5862 | 0.5770 | 0.5671 | 0.5567[b] | | |
| n-Nonadecane | $C_{19}H_{40}$ | 0.6092 | 0.6013 | 0.5932 | 0.5845 | 0.5751 | 0.5655 | 0.5555[b] | |
| n-Eicosane | $C_{20}H_{42}$ | 0.6149 | 0.6072 | 0.5992 | 0.5908 | 0.5821 | 0.5731 | 0.5638 | 0.5538 |

a See footnote a of Table 1d.

b At saturation pressure.

## TABLE 1d – PARAFFINS, $C_1$ TO $C_5$

### DENSITY

For the Normal Liquid Range at Atmospheric Pressure

October 31, 1950; October 31, 1952

| Compound (liquid) | Formula | Temperature in °C — Density in g/ml[a] | | | | | | | | | | | | | | | |
|---|---|---|---|---|---|---|---|---|---|---|---|---|---|---|---|---|---|
| | | -190 | -180 | -170 | -160 | -150 | -140 | -130 | -120 | -110 | -100 | -90 | -80 | -70 | -60 | -50 | -40 |
| Methane | $CH_4$ | | 0.4497 | 0.4362 | 0.4218c | | | | | | | | | | | | |
| Ethane | $C_2H_6$ | | 0.653 | 0.642 | 0.631 | 0.620 | 0.6086 | 0.5972 | 0.5856 | 0.5737 | 0.5613 | 0.5482 | | | | | |
| Propane | $C_3H_8$ | 0.732b | 0.723 | 0.714 | 0.705 | 0.696 | 0.686 | 0.676 | 0.666 | 0.656 | 0.646 | 0.635 | 0.6241 | 0.6130 | 0.6017 | 0.5900 | 0.5784c |
| n-Butane | $C_4H_{10}$ | | | | | | 0.739b | 0.731 | 0.722 | 0.712 | 0.7008 | 0.6899 | 0.6801 | 0.6703 | 0.6605 | 0.6512 | 0.6416 |
| 2-Methylpropane (Isobutane) | " | | | | | | | | | | | | 0.664 | 0.654 | 0.644 | 0.634 | 0.6242 |
| n-Pentane | $C_5H_{12}$ | | | | | | | 0.762b | 0.753 | 0.744 | 0.7350 | 0.7258 | 0.7171 | 0.7084 | 0.6996 | 0.6908 | 0.6820 |
| 2-Methylbutane (Isopentane) | " | | | | | | | | | | | | | | | 0.6865 | 0.6772 |
| 2,2-Dimethylpropane (Neopentane) | " | | | | | | | | | | | | | | | | |

| Compound (liquid) | Formula | Temperature in °C — Density in g/ml[a] | | | | | | | |
|---|---|---|---|---|---|---|---|---|---|
| | | 40 | 30 | 20 | 10 | 0 | -10 | -20 | -30 |
| Methane | $CH_4$ | | | | | | | | |
| Ethane | $C_2H_6$ | | | | | | | | |
| Propane | $C_3H_8$ | | | 0.5005c | 0.5146c | 0.5282c | 0.5414c | 0.5541c | 0.5664c |
| n-Butane | $C_4H_{10}$ | | | 0.5788c | 0.5907c | 0.6011c | 0.6115 | 0.6218 | 0.6318 |
| 2-Methylpropane (Isobutane) | " | | | 0.5572c | 0.5694c | 0.5812c | 0.5926c | 0.6036 | 0.6140 |
| n-Pentane | $C_5H_{12}$ | 0.6053c | 0.6159 | 0.6262 | 0.6357 | 0.6452 | 0.6546 | 0.6640 | 0.6731 |
| 2-Methylbutane (Isopentane) | " | | 0.6146c | 0.6197 | 0.6296 | 0.6394 | 0.6490 | 0.6585 | 0.6679 |
| 2,2-Dimethylpropane (Neopentane) | " | | | 0.5910c | 0.6025 | 0.6138 | 0.6247 | 0.6349b | |

a For the air-saturated liquid at one atmosphere.  b For the undercooled liquid below the normal freezing point.  c At saturation pressure.

TABLE 2d (PART 1) – PARAFFINS, C₆

DENSITY

For the Normal Liquid Range at Atmospheric Pressure

October 31, 1950; October 31, 1952

| Compound (liquid) | Formula | Temperature in °C — Density in g/ml [a] | | | | | | | | | | | | | | | |
|---|---|---|---|---|---|---|---|---|---|---|---|---|---|---|---|---|---|
| | | -100 | -90 | -80 | -70 | -60 | -50 | -40 | -30 | -20 | -10 | 0 | 10 | 20 | 30 | 40 | 50 |
| n-Hexane | C₆H₁₄ | 0.7618[b] | 0.7533 | 0.7451 | 0.7368 | 0.7285 | 0.7201 | 0.7117 | 0.7032 | 0.6946 | 0.6858 | 0.6769 | 0.6679 | 0.6594 | 0.6502 | 0.6411 | 0.6316 |
| 2-Methylpentane | " | | | | | | | | | | 0.6798 | 0.6710 | 0.6622 | 0.6532 | 0.6439 | 0.6345 | 0.6250 |
| 3-Methylpentane | " | | | | | | | | | | 0.6911 | 0.6823 | 0.6734 | 0.6643 | 0.6551 | 0.6456 | 0.6360 |
| 2,2-Dimethylbutane | " | | | | | | | | | | | 0.6672 | 0.6582 | 0.6492 | 0.6397 | | |
| 2,3-Dimethylbutane | " | | | | | | | | | | 0.6882 | 0.6796 | 0.6707 | 0.6616 | 0.6525 | 0.6432 | 0.6338 |

| Compound (liquid) | Formula | Temperature in °C — Density in g/ml [a] | |
|---|---|---|---|
| | | 60 | 70 |
| n-Hexane | C₆H₁₄ | 0.6214 | 0.6102[c] |
| 2-Methylpentane | " | 0.6152 | |
| 3-Methylpentane | " | 0.6263 | |
| 2,2-Dimethylbutane | " | | |
| 2,3-Dimethylbutane | " | 0.6243[c] | |

a See footnote a of Table 1d.    b For the undercooled liquid below the normal freezing point.    c At saturation pressure.

TABLE 2d (PART 2) — PARAFFINS, $C_7$

DENSITY

For the Normal Liquid Range at Atmospheric Pressure

October 31, 1950; October 31, 1952

| Compound (liquid) | Formula | Temperature in °C — Density in g/ml[a] | | | | | | | | | | | | | | | |
|---|---|---|---|---|---|---|---|---|---|---|---|---|---|---|---|---|---|
| | | -120 | -110 | -100 | -90 | -80 | -70 | -60 | -50 | -40 | -30 | -20 | -10 | 0 | 10 | 20 | 30 |
| n-Heptane | $C_7H_{16}$ | | | | 0.7739 | 0.7660 | 0.7581 | 0.7501 | 0.7420 | 0.7339 | 0.7258 | 0.7175 | 0.7091 | 0.7006 | 0.6920 | 0.6838 | 0.6753 |
| 2-Methylhexane | " | | | | | | | | | | | | | 0.6958 | 0.6872 | 0.6786 | 0.6700 |
| 3-Methylhexane | " | | | | | | | | | | | | | | 0.6958 | 0.6871 | 0.6785 |
| 3-Ethylpentane | " | 0.8151b | 0.8069 | 0.7998 | 0.7906 | 0.7824 | 0.7742 | 0.7660 | 0.7577 | 0.7493 | 0.7410 | 0.7325 | 0.7240 | 0.7155 | 0.7069 | 0.6982 | 0.6895 |
| 2,2-Dimethylpentane | " | 0.7926 | 0.7841 | 0.7756 | 0.7672 | 0.7587 | 0.7502 | 0.7418 | 0.7333 | 0.7248 | 0.7163 | 0.7079 | 0.6994 | 0.6909 | 0.6824 | 0.6738 | 0.6651 |
| 2,3-Dimethylpentane | " | | | | | | | | | | | | | 0.7123 | 0.7037 | 0.6951 | 0.6865 |
| 2,4-Dimethylpentane | " | | | | | | | | | | | | | 0.6905 | 0.6816 | 0.6727 | 0.6638 |
| 3,3-Dimethylpentane | " | | | | | | | | | | | | 0.7155 | 0.7102 | 0.7017 | 0.6933 | 0.6848 |
| 2,2,3-Trimethylbutane | " | | | | | | | | | | | | | 0.7070 | 0.6986 | 0.6901 | 0.6815 |

| Compound (liquid) | Formula | Temperature in °C — Density in g/ml[a] | | | | | | |
|---|---|---|---|---|---|---|---|---|
| | | 40 | 50 | 60 | 70 | 80 | 90 | 100 |
| n-Heptane | $C_7H_{16}$ | 0.6669 | 0.6583 | 0.6493 | 0.6398 | 0.6303 | 0.6208 | 0.6110c |
| 2-Methylhexane | " | 0.6615 | 0.6529 | 0.6443 | | | | |
| 3-Methylhexane | " | 0.6700 | | | | | | |
| 3-Ethylpentane | " | 0.6807 | 0.6718 | 0.6627 | 0.6534 | 0.6436 | 0.6333 | |
| 2,2-Dimethylpentane | " | 0.6565 | 0.6478 | 0.6390 | 0.6302 | 0.6215c | | |
| 2,3-Dimethylpentane | " | 0.6780 | 0.6694 | | | | | |
| 2,4-Dimethylpentane | " | 0.6550 | 0.6461 | | | | | |
| 3,3-Dimethylpentane | " | 0.6764 | 0.6679 | | | | | |
| 2,2,3-Trimethylbutane | " | 0.6731 | 0.6646 | | | | | |

a See footnote a of Table 1d.   b For the undercooled liquid below the normal freezing point.   c At saturation pressure.

292

## TABLE 3d, Page 1 - PARAFFINS, C$_8$

### DENSITY

For the Normal Liquid Range at Atmospheric Pressure

October 31, 1950; October 31, 1952

Density in g/ml [a]

| Compound (liquid) | Formula [a] | Temperature in °C | | | | | | | | | | | | | | | |
|---|---|---|---|---|---|---|---|---|---|---|---|---|---|---|---|---|---|
| | | -110 | -100 | -90 | -80 | -70 | -60 | -50 | -40 | -30 | -20 | -10 | 0 | 10 | 20 | 30 | 40 |
| n-Octane | C$_8$H$_{18}$ | | | | | | 0.7668[b] | 0.7590 | 0.7511 | 0.7432 | 0.7352 | 0.7271 | 0.7189 | 0.7106 | 0.7025 | 0.6945 | 0.6866 |
| 2-Methylheptane | " | | | | | | | | | | | | 0.7139 | 0.7059 | 0.6979 | 0.6899 | 0.6819 |
| 3-Methylheptane | " | | | | | | | | | | | | 0.7221 | 0.7140 | 0.7058 | 0.6977 | 0.6896 |
| 4-Methylheptane | " | | | | | | | | | | | 0.7291 | 0.7210 | 0.7128 | 0.7046 | 0.6965 | 0.6883 |
| 3-Ethylhexane | " | | | | | | | | | | | | 0.7300 | 0.7218 | 0.7136 | 0.7054 | 0.6972 |
| 2,2-Dimethylhexane | " | | | | | | | | | | | | 0.7119 | 0.7036 | 0.6953 | 0.6870 | 0.6786 |
| 2,3-Dimethylhexane | " | | | | | | | | | | | | 0.7283 | 0.7202 | 0.7121 | 0.7040 | 0.6959 |
| 2,4-Dimethylhexane | " | | | | | | | | | | | | 0.7170 | 0.7087 | 0.7004 | 0.6920 | 0.6837 |
| 2,5-Dimethylhexane | " | | | | | | | | | | 0.7271 | 0.7187 | 0.7103 | 0.7019 | 0.6935 | 0.6851 | 0.6767 |
| 3,3-Dimethylhexane | " | | | | | | | | | | | | 0.7262 | 0.7181 | 0.7100 | 0.7019 | 0.6938 |
| 3,4-Dimethylhexane | " | | | | | | | | | | | | 0.7355 | 0.7274 | 0.7192 | 0.7111 | 0.7030 |
| 2-Methyl-3-ethylpentane | " | | | | | | | | | | | 0.7437 | 0.7355 | 0.7274 | 0.7193 | 0.7112 | 0.7031 |
| 3-Methyl-3-ethylpentane | " | | | | | | | | | | | | 0.7429 | 0.7352 | 0.7274 | 0.7197 | 0.7119 |
| 2,2,3-Trimethylpentane | " | | | | | | | | | | | | 0.7318 | 0.7239 | 0.7160 | 0.7081 | 0.7002 |
| 2,2,4-Trimethylpentane | " | 0.7975[b] | 0.7895 | 0.7814 | 0.7733 | 0.7651 | 0.7570 | 0.7489 | 0.7407 | 0.7326 | 0.7245 | 0.7164 | 0.7083 | 0.7001 | 0.6919 | 0.6836 | 0.6754 |
| 2,3,3-Trimethylpentane | " | | | | | | | | | | | | 0.7417 | 0.7339 | 0.7262 | 0.7184 | 0.7107 |
| 2,3,4-Trimethylpentane | " | | | | | | | | | | | | 0.7352 | 0.7271 | 0.7191 | 0.7110 | 0.7029 |
| 2,2,3,3-Tetramethylbutane | " | | | | | | | | | | | | | | | | |

a See footnote a of Table 1d.  b For the undercooled liquid below the normal freezing point.

TABLE 3d, Page 2 — PARAFFINS, C$_8$

DENSITY

For the Normal Liquid Range at Atmospheric Pressure

October 31, 1950; October 31, 1952

| Compound (liquid) | Formula | Temperature in °C | | | | | | | |
|---|---|---|---|---|---|---|---|---|---|
| | | Density in g/ml[a] | | | | | | | |
| | | 50 | 60 | 70 | 80 | 90 | 100 | 110 | 120 |
| n-Octane | C$_8$H$_{18}$ | 0.6784 | 0.6701 | 0.6614 | 0.6528 | 0.6442 | 0.6352 | 0.6261 | 0.6166 |
| 2-Methylheptane | " | 0.6739 | 0.6659 | | | | | | |
| 3-Methylheptane | " | 0.6814 | 0.6733 | | | | | | |
| 4-Methylheptane | " | 0.6802 | 0.6720 | | | | | | |
| 3-Ethylhexane | " | 0.6890 | 0.6808 | | | | | | |
| 2,2-Dimethylhexane | " | 0.6703 | | | | | | | |
| 2,3-Dimethylhexane | " | 0.6878 | | | | | | | |
| 2,4-Dimethylhexane | " | 0.6754 | | | | | | | |
| 2,5-Dimethylhexane | " | 0.6682 | 0.6595 | 0.6508 | 0.6420 | 0.6331 | 0.6241 | 0.6148[c] | |
| 3,3-Dimethylhexane | " | 0.6858 | 0.6867 | | | | | | |
| 3,4-Dimethylhexane | " | 0.6948 | | | | | | | |
| 2-Methyl-3-ethylpentane | " | 0.6949 | | | | | | | |
| 3-Methyl-3-ethylpentane | " | 0.7041 | | | | | | | |
| 2,2,3-Trimethylpentane | " | 0.6923 | | | | | | | |
| 2,2,4-Trimethylpentane | " | 0.6670 | 0.6585 | 0.6498 | 0.6408 | 0.6314 | 0.6219[c] | | |
| 2,3,3-Trimethylpentane | " | 0.7030 | | | | | | | |
| 2,3,4-Trimethylpentane | " | 0.6949 | | | | | | | |
| 2,2,3,3-Tetramethylbutane | " | | | | | | 0.6574[b] | 0.6485[c] | |

a See footnote a of Table 1d.  b For the undercooled liquid below the normal freezing point.  c At saturation pressure.

TABLE 24d (PART 1), Page 1 – NORMAL MONOOLEFINS, $C_2$ TO $C_{20}$
DENSITY
For the Normal Liquid Range at Atmospheric Pressure
October 31, 1952

| Compound (liquid) | Formula[a] | Temperature in °C / Density in g/ml[a] | | | | | | | | | | | | | | | |
|---|---|---|---|---|---|---|---|---|---|---|---|---|---|---|---|---|---|
| | | -190 | -180 | -170 | -160 | -150 | -140 | -130 | -120 | -110 | -100 | -90 | -80 | -70 | -60 | -50 | -40 |
| Ethene (Ethylene) | $C_2H_4$ | | | 0.6590[b] | 0.6454 | 0.6318 | 0.6182 | 0.6046 | 0.5910 | 0.5774 | 0.5638[c] | | | | | | |
| Propene (Propylene) | $C_3H_6$ | 0.776[b] | 0.764 | 0.753 | 0.741 | 0.729 | 0.718 | 0.706 | 0.694 | 0.682 | 0.671 | 0.659 | 0.647 | 0.6358 | 0.6237 | 0.6116 | 0.5995[c] |
| 1-Butene | $C_4H_8$ | | | | | | | | | 0.740 | 0.729 | 0.718 | 0.707 | 0.6962 | 0.6854 | 0.6746 | 0.6638 |
| 1-Pentene | $C_5H_{10}$ | | | | | | | | | | | 0.754 | 0.744 | 0.734 | 0.723 | 0.713 | 0.702 |
| 1-Hexene | $C_6H_{12}$ | | | | | | | | | | | | | | 0.749 | 0.739 | 0.730 |
| 1-Heptene | $C_7H_{14}$ | | | | | | | | | | | | | | | | |
| 1-Octene | $C_8H_{16}$ | | | | | | | | | | | | | | | | |
| 1-Nonene | $C_9H_{18}$ | | | | | | | | | | | | | | | | |
| 1-Decene | $C_{10}H_{20}$ | | | | | | | | | | | | | | | | |

| Compound (liquid) | Formula[a] | Temperature in °C / Density in g/ml[a] | | | | | | | | | | | | | | | |
|---|---|---|---|---|---|---|---|---|---|---|---|---|---|---|---|---|---|
| | | -30 | -20 | -10 | 0 | 10 | 20 | 30 | 40 | 50 | 60 | 70 | 80 | 90 | 100 | 110 | 120 |
| Ethene (Ethylene) | $C_2H_4$ | | | | | | | | | | | | | | | | |
| Propene (Propylene) | $C_3H_6$ | 0.5868[c] | 0.5736[c] | 0.5598[c] | 0.5454[c] | 0.5302[c] | 0.5139[c] | | | | | | | | | | |
| 1-Butene | $C_4H_8$ | 0.6529 | 0.6419 | 0.6306 | 0.6190[c] | 0.6072[c] | 0.5951[c] | | | | | | | | | | |
| 1-Pentene | $C_5H_{10}$ | 0.692 | 0.688 | 0.672 | 0.6612 | 0.6508 | 0.6405 | | | | | | | | | | |
| 1-Hexene | $C_6H_{12}$ | 0.720 | 0.711 | 0.702 | 0.6920 | 0.6826 | 0.6732 | 0.6637 | 0.6543 | 0.6449 | 0.6354 | | | | | | |
| 1-Heptene | $C_7H_{14}$ | | | | 0.7146 | 0.7058 | 0.6970 | 0.6882 | 0.6793 | 0.6705 | 0.6617 | 0.6528 | 0.6440 | 0.6352 | | | |
| 1-Octene | $C_8H_{16}$ | | | | 0.7316 | 0.7233 | 0.7149 | 0.7066 | 0.6982 | 0.6899 | 0.6816 | 0.6732 | 0.6649 | 0.6565 | 0.6482 | 0.640 | 0.632 |
| 1-Nonene | $C_9H_{18}$ | | | | 0.7450 | 0.7371 | 0.7292 | 0.7213 | 0.7135 | 0.7056 | 0.6977 | 0.6898 | 0.6819 | 0.6741 | 0.6662 | 0.658 | 0.650 |
| 1-Decene | $C_{10}H_{20}$ | | | | 0.7564 | 0.7486 | 0.7408 | 0.7330 | 0.7253 | 0.7175 | 0.7097 | 0.7020 | 0.6942 | 0.6864 | 0.6786 | 0.671 | 0.663 |

a See footnote a of Table 1d.   b For the undercooled liquid below the normal freezing point.   c At saturation pressure.

TABLE 24d (PART 1), Page 2 – NORMAL MONOOLEFINS, $C_2$ TO $C_{20}$

DENSITY

For the Normal Liquid Range at Atmospheric Pressure

October 31, 1952

| Compound (liquid) | Formula | Temperature in °C — Density in g/ml[a] | | | | | | | | | | | | |
|---|---|---|---|---|---|---|---|---|---|---|---|---|---|---|
| | | 0 | 10 | 20 | 30 | 40 | 50 | 60 | 70 | 80 | 90 | 100 | 110 | 120 |
| 1-Undecene | $C_{11}H_{22}$ | 0.7654 | 0.7579 | 0.7503 | 0.7428 | 0.7352 | 0.7276 | 0.7201 | 0.7125 | 0.7050 | 0.6974 | 0.6898 | 0.682 | 0.675 |
| 1-Dodecane | $C_{12}H_{24}$ | 0.7730 | 0.7657 | 0.7584 | 0.7510 | 0.7437 | 0.7364 | 0.7290 | 0.7217 | 0.7144 | 0.7070 | 0.6997 | 0.692 | 0.685 |
| 1-Tridecene | $C_{13}H_{26}$ | 0.7798 | 0.7726 | 0.7653 | 0.7580 | 0.7508 | 0.7436 | 0.7363 | 0.7290 | 0.7218 | 0.7146 | 0.7073 | 0.700 | 0.693 |
| 1-Tetradecene | $C_{14}H_{28}$ | 0.7856 | 0.7785 | 0.7713 | 0.7641 | 0.7570 | 0.7498 | 0.7427 | 0.7355 | 0.7283 | 0.7212 | 0.7140 | 0.707 | 0.700 |
| 1-Pentadecene | $C_{15}H_{30}$ | 0.7907 | 0.7836 | 0.7765 | 0.7694 | 0.7623 | 0.7552 | 0.7481 | 0.7410 | 0.7340 | 0.7269 | 0.7198 | 0.713 | 0.706 |
| 1-Hexadecene | $C_{16}H_{32}$ | 0.7952b | 0.7882 | 0.7811 | 0.7741 | 0.7671 | 0.7600 | 0.7530 | 0.7460 | 0.7389 | 0.7319 | 0.7249 | 0.718 | 0.711 |
| 1-Heptadecene | $C_{17}H_{34}$ | | 0.7922b | 0.7852 | 0.7782 | 0.7712 | 0.7642 | 0.7572 | 0.7502 | 0.7433 | 0.7363 | 0.7293 | 0.722 | 0.715 |
| 1-Octadecene | $C_{18}H_{36}$ | | | 0.7888 | 0.7818 | 0.7749 | 0.7679 | 0.7610 | 0.7540 | 0.7470 | 0.7401 | 0.7331 | 0.726 | 0.719 |
| 1-Nonadecene | $C_{19}H_{38}$ | | | 0.7920b | 0.7851 | 0.7781 | 0.7712 | 0.7643 | 0.7574 | 0.7504 | 0.7435 | 0.7366 | 0.730 | 0.723 |
| 1-Eicosene | $C_{20}H_{40}$ | | | 0.7950b | 0.7881 | 0.7812 | 0.7743 | 0.7674 | 0.7605 | 0.7536 | 0.7467 | 0.7398 | 0.733 | 0.726 |

a See footnote a of Table 1d.

b For the undercooled liquid below the normal freezing point.

TABLE 5d, Page 1 - ALKYL BENZENES, $C_6$ TO $C_9$

DENSITY

For the Normal Liquid Range at Atmospheric Pressure

November 30, 1949; October 31, 1952

| Compound (liquid) | Formula | Temperature in °C — Density in g/ml [a] | | | | | | | | | | | | | | | |
|---|---|---|---|---|---|---|---|---|---|---|---|---|---|---|---|---|---|
| | | 50 | 40 | 30 | 20 | 10 | 0 | -10 | -20 | -30 | -40 | -50 | -60 | -70 | -80 | -90 | -100 |
| Benzene | $C_6H_6$ | 0.8462 | 0.8577 | 0.8685 | 0.8790 | 0.8895 | | | | | | | | | | | |
| Methylbenzene (Toluene) | $C_7H_8$ | 0.8392 | 0.8485 | 0.8577 | 0.8669 | 0.8762 | 0.8854 | 0.8946 | 0.9038 | 0.9131 | 0.9223 | 0.9315 | 0.9408 | 0.9500 | 0.9592 | 0.9684 | |
| Ethylbenzene | $C_8H_{10}$ | 0.8405 | 0.8495 | 0.8583 | 0.8670 | 0.8758 | 0.8845 | 0.8932 | 0.9019 | 0.9107 | 0.9195 | 0.9283 | 0.9371 | 0.9460 | 0.9548 | 0.9637 | |
| 1,2-Dimethylbenzene (o-Xylene) | " | 0.8549 | 0.8634 | 0.8719 | 0.8802 | 0.8886 | 0.8969 | 0.9052 | 0.9135 | 0.9218[b] | | | | | | | |
| 1,3-Dimethylbenzene (m-Xylene) | " | 0.8384 | 0.8470 | 0.8556 | 0.8642 | 0.8726 | 0.8811 | 0.8895 | 0.8979 | 0.9063 | 0.9147 | 0.9230[b] | | | | | |
| 1,4-Dimethylbenzene (p-Xylene) | " | 0.8350 | 0.8437 | 0.8525 | 0.8610 | 0.8697[b] | | | | | | | | | | | |
| n-Propylbenzene | $C_9H_{12}$ | 0.8371 | 0.8454 | 0.8537 | 0.8620 | 0.8703 | 0.8786 | 0.8869 | 0.8952 | 0.9035 | 0.9118 | 0.9200 | 0.9283 | 0.9366 | 0.9449 | 0.9532 | 0.9615[b] |
| Isopropylbenzene | " | 0.8366 | 0.8450 | 0.8534 | 0.8618 | 0.8702 | 0.8786 | | | | | | | | | | |
| 1-Methyl-2-ethylbenzene | " | | 0.8643 | 0.8725 | 0.8807 | 0.8888 | | | | | | | | | | | |
| 1-Methyl-3-ethylbenzene | " | | 0.8482 | 0.8563 | 0.8645 | 0.8728 | | | | | | | | | | | |
| 1-Methyl-4-ethylbenzene | " | 0.8364 | 0.8447 | 0.8530 | 0.8612 | 0.8694 | 0.8776 | | | | | | | | | | |
| 1,2,3-Trimethylbenzene | " | | 0.8786 | 0.8865 | 0.8944 | 0.9023 | 0.9102 | | | | | | | | | | |
| 1,2,4-Trimethylbenzene | " | 0.8516 | 0.8597 | 0.8678 | 0.8758 | 0.8838 | 0.8917 | | | | | | | | | | |
| 1,3,5-Trimethylbenzene | " | 0.8405 | 0.8488 | 0.8571 | 0.8652 | 0.8732 | 0.8813 | | | | | | | | | | |

a See footnote a of Table 1d.

b For the undercooled liquid below the normal freezing point.

298

TABLE 5d, Page 2 - ALKYL BENZENES, C₆ TO C₉

DENSITY

For the Normal Liquid Range at Atmospheric Pressure

November 30, 1949; October 31, 1952

| Compound (liquid) | Formula[a] | Temperature in °C — Density in g/ml[a] | | | | | | | | | | | |
|---|---|---|---|---|---|---|---|---|---|---|---|---|---|
| | | 50 | 60 | 70 | 80 | 90 | 100 | 110 | 120 | 130 | 140 | 150 | 160 |
| Benzene | $C_6H_6$ | 0.8469 | 0.8359 | 0.8247 | 0.8134 | | | | | | | | |
| Methylbenzene (Toluene) | $C_7H_8$ | 0.8392 | 0.8300 | 0.8208 | 0.8115 | 0.8023 | 0.7931 | 0.7838 | | | | | |
| Ethylbenzene | $C_8H_{10}$ | 0.8405 | 0.8315 | 0.8224 | 0.8133 | 0.8041 | 0.7948 | 0.7854 | 0.7759 | 0.7663 | 0.7567[b] | | |
| 1,2-Dimethylbenzene (o-Xylene) | " | 0.8549 | 0.8464 | 0.8378 | 0.8292 | 0.8204 | 0.8116 | 0.8026 | 0.7935 | 0.7844 | 0.7753 | | |
| 1,3-Dimethylbenzene (m-Xylene) | " | 0.8384 | 0.8297 | 0.8210 | 0.8122 | 0.8033 | 0.7944 | 0.7855 | 0.7765 | 0.7676 | 0.7586[b] | | |
| 1,4-Dimethylbenzene (p-Xylene) | " | 0.8350 | 0.8262 | 0.8173 | 0.8083 | 0.7993 | 0.7902 | 0.7810 | 0.7718 | 0.7625 | 0.7531[b] | | |
| n-Propylbenzene | $C_9H_{12}$ | 0.8371 | 0.8287 | 0.8202 | 0.8116 | 0.8028 | 0.7938 | 0.7848 | 0.7755 | 0.7661 | 0.7566 | 0.747 | 0.737[b] |
| Isopropylbenzene | " | 0.8366 | 0.8283 | 0.8199 | 0.8115 | 0.8031 | | | | | | | |
| 1-Methyl-2-ethylbenzene | " | | | | | | | | | | | | |
| 1-Methyl-3-ethylbenzene | " | | | | | | | | | | | | |
| 1-Methyl-4-ethylbenzene | " | 0.8364 | 0.8281 | 0.8197 | 0.8114 | 0.8030 | 0.7945 | | | | | | |
| 1,2,3-Trimethylbenzene | " | | | | | | | | | | | | |
| 1,2,4-Trimethylbenzene | " | 0.8516 | 0.8434 | 0.8351 | 0.8268 | 0.8184 | 0.8099 | | | | | | |
| 1,3,5-Trimethylbenzene | " | 0.8405 | 0.8321 | 0.8237 | 0.8151 | 0.8065 | 0.7978 | | | | | | |

a See footnote a of Table 1d.

b At saturation pressure.

TABLE 20d-E (PART 1), Page 1 – NORMAL PARAFFINS, $C_1$ TO $C_{20}$

DENSITY

For the Normal Liquid Range at Atmospheric Pressure

June 30, 1949; October 31, 1952

Temperature in °F — Density in lb/ft$^3$ [a]

| Compound (liquid) | Formula | -310 | -300 | -290 | -280 | -270 | -260 | -250 | -240 | -230 | -220 | -210 | -200 | -190 | -180 | -170 | -160 |
|---|---|---|---|---|---|---|---|---|---|---|---|---|---|---|---|---|---|
| Methane | $CH_4$ | | 28.45b | 27.98 | 27.51 | 27.03 | 26.53 | 26.03c | | | | | | | | | |
| Ethane | $C_2H_6$ | | 41.1b | 40.7 | 40.3 | 40.0 | 39.5 | 39.1 | 38.8 | 38.4 | 37.99 | 37.60 | 37.20 | 36.80 | 36.39 | 35.98 | 35.56 |
| Propane | $C_3H_8$ | 45.7b | 45.4 | 45.1 | 44.8 | 44.4 | 44.1 | 43.8 | 43.5 | 43.2 | 42.8 | 42.5 | 42.1 | 41.8 | 41.5 | 41.1 | 40.8 |
| n–Butane | $C_4H_{10}$ | | | | | | | | | | 46.1b | 45.9 | 45.6 | 45.3 | 44.9 | 44.6 | 44.21 |
| n–Pentane | $C_5H_{12}$ | | | | | | | | | | | | 47.5 | 47.2 | 46.9 | 46.6 | 46.26 |
| n–Hexane | $C_6H_{14}$ | | | | | | | | | | | | | | | | |
| n–Heptane | $C_7H_{16}$ | | | | | | | | | | | | | | | | |
| n–Octane | $C_8H_{18}$ | | | | | | | | | | | | | | | | |

Temperature in °F — Density in lb/ft$^3$ [a]

| Compound (liquid) | Formula | -150 | -140 | -130 | -120 | -110 | -100 | -90 | -80 | -70 | -60 | -50 | -40 | -30 | -20 | -10 | 0 |
|---|---|---|---|---|---|---|---|---|---|---|---|---|---|---|---|---|---|
| Methane | $CH_4$ | 35.13 | 34.68 | 34.22 | 33.77c | | | | | | | | | | | | |
| Ethane | $C_2H_6$ | 40.4 | 40.0 | 39.6 | 39.26 | 38.89 | 38.50 | 38.11 | 37.72 | 37.32 | 36.91 | 36.51 | 36.10c | 35.69c | 35.27c | 34.85c | 34.42c |
| Propane | $C_3H_8$ | 43.82 | 43.45 | 43.07 | 42.73 | 42.39 | 42.05 | 41.71 | 41.37 | 41.04 | 40.72 | 40.39 | 40.05 | 39.71 | 39.37 | 39.02 | 38.67 |
| n–Butane | $C_4H_{10}$ | 45.95 | 45.63 | 45.31 | 45.01 | 44.71 | 44.40 | 44.10 | 43.80 | 43.49 | 43.19 | 42.88 | 42.57 | 42.27 | 41.96 | 41.64 | 41.32 |
| n–Pentane | $C_5H_{12}$ | | 47.32b | 47.03 | 46.74 | 46.46 | 46.17 | 45.88 | 45.59 | 45.30 | 45.01 | 44.72 | 44.43 | 44.13 | 43.84 | 43.54 | 43.24 |
| n–Hexane | $C_6H_{14}$ | | | 48.31 | 48.04 | 47.76 | 47.48 | 47.21 | 46.94 | 46.66 | 46.38 | 46.10 | 45.81 | 45.53 | 45.25 | 44.96 | 44.67 |
| n–Heptane | $C_7H_{16}$ | | | | | | | | | 47.71 | 47.44 | 47.16 | 46.89 | 46.61 | 46.34 | 46.06 | 45.78 |
| n–Octane | $C_8H_{18}$ | | | | | | | | | | | | | | | | |

a See footnote a of Table 1d-E.　　b For the undercooled liquid below the normal freezing point.　　c At saturation pressure.

TABLE 20d-E (PART 1), Page 2 – NORMAL PARAFFINS, $C_1$ TO $C_{20}$

DENSITY

For the Normal Liquid Range at Atmospheric Pressure

June 30, 1949; October 31, 1952

| Compound (liquid) | Formula | Temperature in °F — Density in lb/ft³ [a] | | | | | | | | | | | | | | | |
|---|---|---|---|---|---|---|---|---|---|---|---|---|---|---|---|---|---|
| | | 10 | 20 | 30 | 40 | 50 | 60 | 70 | 80 | 90 | 100 | 110 | 120 | 130 | 140 | 150 | 160 |
| Methane | $CH_4$ | | | | | | | | | | | | | | | | |
| Ethane | $C_2H_6$ | | | | | | | | | | | | | | | | |
| Propane | $C_3H_8$ | 33.97b | 33.52b | 33.07b | 32.60b | 32.12b | 31.64b | 31.15b | | | | | | | | | |
| n-Butane | $C_4H_{10}$ | 38.32 | 37.96 | 37.60 | 37.24b | 36.88b | 36.46b | 36.05b | | | | | | | | | |
| n-Pentane | $C_5H_{12}$ | 40.99 | 40.67 | 40.34 | 40.01 | 39.68 | 39.35 | 39.02 | 38.66 | 38.30 | 37.93b | | | | | | |
| n-Hexane | $C_6H_{14}$ | 42.93 | 42.63 | 42.32 | 42.01 | 41.69 | 41.41 | 41.10 | 40.78 | 40.46 | 40.15 | 39.82 | 39.49 | 39.15 | 38.79 | 38.40 | 38.02b |
| n-Heptane | $C_7H_{16}$ | 44.38 | 44.09 | 43.79 | 43.50 | 43.20 | 42.92 | 42.63 | 42.33 | 42.04 | 41.75 | 41.45 | 41.16 | 40.85 | 40.53 | 40.20 | 39.87 |
| n-Octane | $C_8H_{18}$ | 45.50 | 45.22 | 44.94 | 44.65 | 44.36 | 44.08 | 43.80 | 43.52 | 43.25 | 42.97 | 42.69 | 42.41 | 42.12 | 41.83 | 41.53 | 41.23 |

| Compound (liquid) | Formula | Temperature in °F — Density in lb/ft³ [a] | | | | | | | | | |
|---|---|---|---|---|---|---|---|---|---|---|---|
| | | 170 | 180 | 190 | 200 | 210 | 220 | 230 | 240 | 250 | 260 |
| Methane | $CH_4$ | | | | | | | | | | |
| Ethane | $C_2H_6$ | | | | | | | | | | |
| Propane | $C_3H_8$ | | | | | | | | | | |
| n-Butane | $C_4H_{10}$ | | | | | | | | | | |
| n-Pentane | $C_5H_{12}$ | | | | | | | | | | |
| n-Hexane | $C_6H_{14}$ | | | | | | | | | | |
| n-Heptane | $C_7H_{16}$ | 39.55 | 39.22 | 38.89 | 38.55 | 38.21b | | | | | |
| n-Octane | $C_8H_{18}$ | 40.93 | 40.63 | 40.33 | 40.03 | 39.72 | 39.40 | 39.09 | 38.76 | 38.43 | 38.10b |

a See footnote a of Table 1d-E.

b At saturation pressure.

## TABLE 20d-E (PART 1), Page 3 — NORMAL PARAFFINS, $C_1$ TO $C_{20}$

### DENSITY

For the Normal Liquid Range at Atmospheric Pressure

June 30, 1949; October 31, 1952

Temperature in °F

Density in lb/ft$^3$ [a]

| Compound (liquid) | Formula | 90 | 80 | 70 | 60 | 50 | 40 | 30 | 20 | 10 | 0 | -10 | -20 | -30 | -40 | -50 | -60 |
|---|---|---|---|---|---|---|---|---|---|---|---|---|---|---|---|---|---|
| n-Nonane | $C_9H_{20}$ | 44.21 | 44.48 | 44.74 | 45.01 | 45.28 | 45.57 | 45.84 | 46.12 | 46.39 | 46.67 | 46.94 | 47.21 | 47.48 | 47.74 | 48.01 | 48.27 |
| n-Decane | $C_{10}H_{22}$ | 44.99 | 45.25 | 45.52 | 45.79 | 46.05 | 46.32 | 46.59 | 46.85 | 47.12 | 47.39 | 47.65 | 47.92 | | | | |
| n-Undecane | $C_{11}H_{24}$ | 45.64 | 45.90 | 46.16 | 46.42 | 46.68 | 46.94 | 47.20 | 47.46 | 47.72 | 47.98 | 48.24 | | | | | |
| n-Dodecane | $C_{12}H_{26}$ | 46.20 | 46.44 | 46.69 | 46.95 | 47.21 | 47.47 | 47.73 | 47.98 | 48.24[b] | | | | | | | |
| n-Tridecane | $C_{13}H_{28}$ | 46.67 | 46.92 | 47.17 | 47.42 | 47.66 | 47.92 | 48.17 | 48.42[b] | | | | | | | | |
| n-Tetradecane | $C_{14}H_{30}$ | 47.08 | 47.32 | 47.57 | 47.82 | 48.06 | 48.30[b] | | | | | | | | | | |
| n-Pentadecane | $C_{15}H_{32}$ | 47.44 | 47.68 | 47.93 | 48.17 | 48.41 | | | | | | | | | | | |
| n-Hexadecane | $C_{16}H_{34}$ | 47.76 | 47.99 | 48.23 | 48.47[b] | | | | | | | | | | | | |
| n-Heptadecane | $C_{17}H_{36}$ | 48.04 | 48.28 | 48.52[b] | 48.76[b] | | | | | | | | | | | | |
| n-Octadecane | $C_{18}H_{38}$ | 48.29 | 48.54[b] | 48.77[b] | 49.00[b] | | | | | | | | | | | | |
| n-Nonadecane | $C_{19}H_{40}$ | 48.52 | 48.75[b] | 48.99[b] | 49.23[b] | | | | | | | | | | | | |
| n-Eicosane | $C_{20}H_{42}$ | 48.73[b] | 48.96[b] | 49.19[b] | 49.42[b] | | | | | | | | | | | | |

Temperature in °F

Density in lb/ft$^3$ [a]

| Compound (liquid) | Formula | 100 | 110 | 120 | 130 | 140 | 150 | 160 | 170 | 180 | 190 | 200 | 210 | 220 | 230 | 240 | 250 |
|---|---|---|---|---|---|---|---|---|---|---|---|---|---|---|---|---|---|
| n-Nonane | $C_9H_{20}$ | 43.94 | 43.67 | 43.40 | 43.13 | 42.85 | 42.56 | 42.28 | 42.00 | 41.72 | 41.44 | 41.15 | 40.86 | 40.57 | 40.27 | 39.97 | 39.66 |
| n-Decane | $C_{10}H_{22}$ | 44.73 | 44.47 | 44.21 | 43.94 | 43.67 | 43.40 | 43.13 | 42.86 | 42.59 | 42.32 | 42.04 | 41.76 | 41.48 | 41.20 | 40.91 | 40.62 |
| n-Undecane | $C_{11}H_{24}$ | 45.39 | 45.13 | 44.87 | 44.62 | 44.36 | 44.09 | 43.83 | 43.57 | 43.31 | 43.04 | 42.77 | 42.50 | 42.23 | 41.96 | 41.68 | 41.40 |
| n-Dodecane | $C_{12}H_{26}$ | 45.95 | 45.69 | 45.44 | 45.19 | 44.93 | 44.67 | 44.41 | 44.15 | 43.90 | 43.65 | 43.39 | 43.13 | 42.87 | 42.60 | 42.33 | 42.05 |
| n-Tridecane | $C_{13}H_{28}$ | 46.43 | 46.18 | 45.93 | 45.68 | 45.43 | 45.17 | 44.92 | 44.67 | 44.42 | 44.17 | 43.91 | 43.66 | 43.40 | 43.14 | 42.88 | 42.61 |
| n-Tetradecane | $C_{14}H_{30}$ | 46.84 | 46.59 | 46.35 | 46.10 | 45.86 | 45.61 | 45.36 | 45.11 | 44.87 | 44.62 | 44.37 | 44.12 | 43.86 | 43.60 | 43.35 | 43.09 |
| n-Pentadecane | $C_{15}H_{32}$ | 47.20 | 46.96 | 46.72 | 46.48 | 46.23 | 45.99 | 45.74 | 45.50 | 45.26 | 45.01 | 44.77 | 44.52 | 44.27 | 44.02 | 43.76 | 43.50 |
| n-Hexadecane | $C_{16}H_{34}$ | 47.52 | 47.28 | 47.04 | 46.80 | 46.56 | 46.32 | 46.08 | 45.84 | 45.60 | 45.36 | 45.12 | 44.87 | 44.63 | 44.38 | 44.13 | 43.87 |
| n-Heptadecane | $C_{17}H_{36}$ | 47.81 | 47.57 | 47.34 | 47.10 | 46.86 | 46.62 | 46.38 | 46.15 | 45.91 | 45.67 | 45.43 | 45.18 | 44.94 | 44.70 | 44.45 | 44.20 |
| n-Octadecane | $C_{18}H_{38}$ | 48.06 | 47.83 | 47.59 | 47.36 | 47.13 | 46.89 | 46.65 | 46.42 | 46.18 | 45.95 | 45.71 | 45.47 | 45.23 | 44.98 | 44.74 | 44.50 |
| n-Nonadecane | $C_{19}H_{40}$ | 48.29 | 48.06 | 47.83 | 47.60 | 47.36 | 47.13 | 46.90 | 46.66 | 46.43 | 46.20 | 45.96 | 45.72 | 45.49 | 45.25 | 45.00 | 44.76 |
| n-Eicosane | $C_{20}H_{42}$ | 48.50 | 48.27 | 48.04 | 47.81 | 47.58 | 47.35 | 47.11 | 46.88 | 46.65 | 46.42 | 46.19 | 45.95 | 45.72 | 45.48 | 45.24 | 45.00 |

a See footnote a of Table 1d-E.   b For the undercooled liquid below the normal freezing point.

TABLE 20d-E (PART 1), Page 4 – NORMAL PARAFFINS, $C_1$ TO $C_{20}$

DENSITY

For the Normal Liquid Range at Atmospheric Pressure

June 30, 1949; October 31, 1952

Temperature in °F

Density in lb/ft³ [a]

| Compound (liquid) | Formula | 260 | 270 | 280 | 290 | 300 | 310 | 320 | 330 | 340 | 350 | 360 | 370 | 380 | 390 | 400 | 410 |
|---|---|---|---|---|---|---|---|---|---|---|---|---|---|---|---|---|---|
| n-Nonane | $C_9H_{20}$ | 39.33 | 39.02 | 38.70 | 38.39 | 38.08 | | | | | | | | | | | |
| n-Decane | $C_{10}H_{22}$ | 40.33 | 40.04 | 39.75 | 39.45 | 39.14 | 38.83 | 38.51 | 38.18 | 37.85 | 37.52 | | | | | | |
| n-Undecane | $C_{11}H_{24}$ | 41.12 | 40.84 | 40.56 | 40.27 | 39.99 | 39.69 | 39.40 | 39.09 | 38.79 | 38.47 | 38.16 | 37.83 | 37.51 | | | |
| n-Dodecane | $C_{12}H_{26}$ | 41.78 | 41.51 | 41.24 | 40.97 | 40.69 | 40.41 | 40.12 | 39.83 | 39.55 | 39.25 | 38.96 | 38.66 | 38.35 | 38.03 | 37.70 | 37.36 |
| n-Tridecane | $C_{13}H_{28}$ | 42.34 | 42.08 | 41.81 | 41.54 | 41.28 | 41.01 | 40.73 | 40.46 | 40.18 | 39.90 | 39.62 | 39.34 | 39.05 | 38.76 | 38.45 | 38.12 |
| n-Tetradecane | $C_{14}H_{30}$ | 42.83 | 42.57 | 42.31 | 42.05 | 41.78 | 41.52 | 41.25 | 40.99 | 40.72 | 40.45 | 40.18 | 39.91 | 39.63 | 39.35 | 39.06 | 38.76 |
| n-Pentadecane | $C_{15}H_{32}$ | 43.25 | 43.00 | 42.74 | 42.48 | 42.23 | 41.97 | 41.71 | 41.45 | 41.19 | 40.93 | 40.66 | 40.40 | 40.13 | 39.87 | 39.59 | 39.30 |
| n-Hexadecane | $C_{16}H_{34}$ | 43.62 | 43.37 | 43.12 | 42.87 | 42.62 | 42.36 | 42.11 | 41.85 | 41.60 | 41.34 | 41.08 | 40.83 | 40.56 | 40.30 | 40.03 | 39.77 |
| n-Heptadecane | $C_{17}H_{36}$ | 43.95 | 43.70 | 43.46 | 43.21 | 42.96 | 42.71 | 42.46 | 42.21 | 41.96 | 41.71 | 41.46 | 41.20 | 40.95 | 40.69 | 40.43 | 40.17 |
| n-Octadecane | $C_{18}H_{38}$ | 44.25 | 44.01 | 43.76 | 43.52 | 43.27 | 43.03 | 42.78 | 42.53 | 42.28 | 42.04 | 41.79 | 41.54 | 41.29 | 41.04 | 40.78 | 40.53 |
| n-Nonadecane | $C_{19}H_{40}$ | 44.52 | 44.28 | 44.03 | 43.79 | 43.55 | 43.30 | 43.06 | 42.82 | 42.58 | 42.33 | 42.08 | 41.84 | 41.60 | 41.36 | 41.10 | 40.85 |
| n-Eicosane | $C_{20}H_{42}$ | 44.76 | 44.52 | 44.28 | 44.04 | 43.80 | 43.56 | 43.32 | 43.08 | 42.84 | 42.60 | 42.35 | 42.11 | 41.87 | 41.63 | 41.38 | 41.13 |

Temperature in °F

Density in lb/ft³ [a]

| Compound (liquid) | Formula | 420 | 430 | 440 | 450 | 460 | 470 | 480 | 490 | 500 | 510 | 520 | 530 | 540 | 550 | 560 | 570 |
|---|---|---|---|---|---|---|---|---|---|---|---|---|---|---|---|---|---|
| n-Nonane | $C_9H_{20}$ | | | | | | | | | | | | | | | | |
| n-Decane | $C_{10}H_{22}$ | | | | | | | | | | | | | | | | |
| n-Undecane | $C_{11}H_{24}$ | | | | | | | | | | | | | | | | |
| n-Dodecane | $C_{12}H_{26}$ | 36.99 | | | | | | | | | | | | | | | |
| n-Tridecane | $C_{13}H_{28}$ | 37.79 | 37.45 | 37.10 | 36.75 | 36.39 | | | | | | | | | | | |
| n-Tetradecane | $C_{14}H_{30}$ | 38.45 | 38.13 | 37.81 | 37.49 | 37.17 | 36.84 | 36.52 | 36.19 | | | | | | | | |
| n-Pentadecane | $C_{15}H_{32}$ | 39.01 | 38.71 | 38.41 | 38.11 | 37.80 | 37.50 | 37.20 | 36.89 | 36.57 | 36.25 | 35.93 | | | | | |
| n-Hexadecane | $C_{16}H_{34}$ | 39.48 | 39.20 | 38.91 | 38.63 | 38.34 | 38.06 | 37.77 | 37.47 | 37.18 | 36.87 | 36.57 | 36.26 | 35.95 | 35.62 | | |
| n-Heptadecane | $C_{17}H_{36}$ | 39.90 | 39.63 | 39.36 | 39.08 | 38.81 | 38.53 | 38.25 | 37.97 | 37.69 | 37.40 | 37.11 | 36.82 | 36.52 | 36.21 | 35.89 | 35.56 |
| n-Octadecane | $C_{18}H_{38}$ | 40.26 | 40.00 | 39.74 | 39.47 | 39.21 | 38.94 | 38.68 | 38.40 | 38.13 | 37.85 | 37.58 | 37.29 | 37.01 | 36.71 | 36.40 | 36.08 |
| n-Nonadecane | $C_{19}H_{40}$ | 40.59 | 40.33 | 40.08 | 39.82 | 39.56 | 39.30 | 39.04 | 38.78 | 38.52 | 38.25 | 37.98 | 37.70 | 37.42 | 37.14 | 36.85 | 36.55 |
| n-Eicosane | $C_{20}H_{42}$ | 40.88 | 40.63 | 40.38 | 40.13 | 39.88 | 39.63 | 39.37 | 39.11 | 38.85 | 38.59 | 38.33 | 38.07 | 37.79 | 37.52 | 37.23 | 36.94 |

[a] See footnote a of Table 1d-E.

TABLE 20d-E (PART 1), Page 5 – NORMAL PARAFFINS, $C_1$ TO $C_{20}$

DENSITY

For the Normal Liquid Range at Atmospheric Pressure

June 30, 1949; October 31, 1952

| Compound (liquid) | Formula[a] | Temperature in °F | | | | | | | |
|---|---|---|---|---|---|---|---|---|---|
| | | Density in lb/ft$^3$ [a] | | | | | | | |
| | | 580 | 590 | 600 | 610 | 620 | 630 | 640 | 650 |
| n-Nonane | $C_9H_{20}$ | | | | | | | | |
| n-**Decane** | $C_{10}H_{22}$ | | | | | | | | |
| n-Undecane | $C_{11}H_{24}$ | | | | | | | | |
| n-Dodecane | $C_{12}H_{26}$ | | | | | | | | |
| n-Tridecane | $C_{13}H_{28}$ | | | | | | | | |
| n-Tetradecane | $C_{14}H_{30}$ | | | | | | | | |
| n-Pentadecane | $C_{15}H_{32}$ | | | | | | | | |
| n-Hexadecane | $C_{16}H_{34}$ | | | | | | | | |
| n-Heptadecane | $C_{17}H_{36}$ | 35.23 | | | | | | | |
| n-Octadecane | $C_{18}H_{38}$ | 35.75 | 35.40 | 35.04 | | | | | |
| n-Nonadecane | $C_{19}H_{40}$ | 36.23 | 35.90 | 35.57 | 35.23 | 34.89 | 34.54 | | |
| n-Eicosane | $C_{20}H_{42}$ | 36.64 | 36.34 | 36.03 | 35.71 | 35.39 | 35.06 | 34.71 | 34.36 |

a See footnote a of Table 1d-E.

TABLE 1d-E, Page 1 – PARAFFINS, C₁ TO C₅

DENSITY

For the Normal Liquid Range at Atmospheric Pressure

October 31, 1950; October 31, 1952

Temperature in °F — Density in lb/ft³ [a]

| Compound (liquid) | Formula | -310 | -300 | -290 | -280 | -270 | -260 | -250 | -240 | -230 | -220 | -210 | -200 | -190 | -180 | -170 | -160 |
|---|---|---|---|---|---|---|---|---|---|---|---|---|---|---|---|---|---|
| Methane | $CH_4$ | | 28.45[b] | 27.98 | 27.51 | 27.03 | 26.53 | 26.03[c] | | | | | | | | | |
| Ethane | $C_2H_6$ | | 41.1[b] | 40.7 | 40.3 | 40.0 | 39.5 | 39.1 | 38.8 | 38.4 | 37.99 | 37.60 | 37.20 | 36.80 | 36.39 | 35.98 | 35.56 |
| Propane | $C_3H_8$ | 45.7[b] | 45.4 | 45.1 | 44.8 | 44.4 | 44.1 | 43.8 | 43.5 | 43.2 | 42.8 | 42.5 | 42.1 | 41.8 | 41.5 | 41.1 | 40.8 |
| n-Butane | $C_4H_{10}$ | | | | | | | | | | 46.1[b] | 45.9 | 45.6 | 45.3 | 44.9 | 44.6 | 44.21 |
| 2-Methylpropane (Isobutane) | " | | | | | | | | | | | | | | | | |
| n-Pentane | $C_5H_{12}$ | | | | | | | | | | | | 47.5 | 47.2 | 46.9 | 46.6 | 46.26 |
| 2-Methylbutane (Isopentane) | " | | | | | | | | | | | | | | | | |
| 2,2-Dimethylpropane (Neopentane) | " | | | | | | | | | | | | | | | | |

Temperature in °F — Density in lb/ft³ [a]

| Compound (liquid) | Formula | -150 | -140 | -130 | -120 | -110 | -100 | -90 | -80 | -70 | -60 | -50 | -40 | -30 | -20 | -10 | 0 |
|---|---|---|---|---|---|---|---|---|---|---|---|---|---|---|---|---|---|
| Methane | $CH_4$ | | | | | | | | | | | | | | | | |
| Ethane | $C_2H_6$ | 35.13 | 34.68 | 34.22 | 33.77[c] | | | | | | | | | | | | |
| Propane | $C_3H_8$ | 40.4 | 40.0 | 39.6 | 39.26 | 38.89 | 38.50 | 38.11 | 37.72 | 37.32 | 36.91 | 36.51 | 36.10[c] | 35.69[c] | 35.27[c] | 34.85[c] | 34.42[c] |
| n-Butane | $C_4H_{10}$ | 43.82 | 43.45 | 43.07 | 42.73 | 42.39 | 42.05 | 41.71 | 41.37 | 41.04 | 40.72 | 40.39 | 40.05 | 39.71 | 39.37 | 39.02 | 38.67 |
| 2-Methylpropane (Isobutane) | " | | | | | 41.4 | 41.0 | 40.7 | 40.4 | 40.0 | 39.6 | 39.3 | 38.97 | 38.62 | 38.26 | 37.90 | 37.53 |
| n-Pentane | $C_5H_{12}$ | 45.95 | 45.63 | 45.31 | 45.01 | 44.71 | 44.40 | 44.10 | 43.80 | 43.49 | 43.19 | 42.88 | 42.57 | 42.27 | 41.96 | 41.64 | 41.32 |
| 2-Methylbutane (Isopentane) | " | | | | | | | | | | 42.92 | 42.60 | 42.28 | 41.96 | 41.63 | 41.30 | 40.98 |
| 2,2-Dimethylpropane (Neopentane) | " | | | | | | | | | | | | | | | | 39.49[b] |

[a] For the air-saturated liquid at one atmosphere.　[b] For the undercooled liquid below the normal freezing point.　[c] At saturation pressure.

## TABLE 1d-E, Page 2 – PARAFFINS, $C_1$ TO $C_5$
### DENSITY
For the Normal Liquid Range at Atmospheric Pressure
October 31, 1950; October 31, 1952

| Compound (liquid) | Formula | Temperature in °F — Density in lb/ft³ [a] | | | | | | | | | |
|---|---|---|---|---|---|---|---|---|---|---|---|
| | | 10 | 20 | 30 | 40 | 50 | 60 | 70 | 80 | 90 | 100 |
| Methane | $CH_4$ | | | | | | | | | | |
| Ethane | $C_2H_6$ | | | | | | | | | | |
| Propane | $C_3H_8$ | 33.97[b] | 33.52[b] | 33.07[b] | 32.60[b] | 32.12[b] | 31.64[b] | 31.15[b] | | | |
| n-Butane | $C_4H_{10}$ | 38.32 | 37.96 | 37.60 | 37.24[b] | 36.88[b] | 36.46[b] | 36.05[b] | | | |
| 2-Methylpropane (Isobutane) | " | 37.15 | 36.76[b] | 36.36[b] | 35.96[b] | 35.55[b] | 35.12[b] | 34.70[b] | | | |
| n-Pentane | $C_5H_{12}$ | 40.99 | 40.67 | 40.34 | 40.01 | 39.68 | 39.35 | 39.02 | 38.66 | 38.30 | 37.93[b] |
| 2-Methylbutane (Isopentane) | " | 40.64 | 40.32 | 39.98 | 39.65 | 39.31 | 38.96 | 38.61 | 38.26 | 37.91[b] | |
| 2,2-Dimethylpropane (Neopentane) | " | 39.14 | 38.77 | 38.39 | 38.00 | 37.61[b] | 37.21[b] | 36.81[b] | | | |

[a] See footnote a of Table 1d-E.　　　[b] At saturation pressure.

306

TABLE 2d-E (PART 1) – PARAFFINS, C$_6$

DENSITY

For the Normal Liquid Range at Atmospheric Pressure

October 31, 1950; October 31, 1952

Temperature in °F

Density in lb/ft3 [a]

| Compound (liquid) | Formula | -140 | -130 | -120 | -110 | -100 | -90 | -80 | -70 | -60 | -50 | -40 | -30 | -20 | -10 | 0 | 10 |
|---|---|---|---|---|---|---|---|---|---|---|---|---|---|---|---|---|---|
| n-Hexane | C$_6$H$_{14}$ | 47.32[b] | 47.03 | 46.74 | 46.46 | 46.17 | 45.88 | 45.59 | 45.30 | 45.01 | 44.72 | 44.43 | 44.13 | 43.84 | 43.54 | 43.24 | 42.93 |
| 2-Methylpentane | " | | | | | | | | | | | | | | | | |
| 3-Methylpentane | " | | | | | | | | | | | | | | | | |
| 2,2-Dimethylbutane | " | | | | | | | | | | | | | | | | |
| 2,3-Dimethylbutane | " | | | | | | | | | | | | | | | | |

Temperature in °F

Density in lb/ft3 [a]

| Compound (liquid) | Formula | 20 | 30 | 40 | 50 | 60 | 70 | 80 | 90 | 100 | 110 | 120 | 130 | 140 | 150 | 160 |
|---|---|---|---|---|---|---|---|---|---|---|---|---|---|---|---|---|
| n-Hexane | C$_6$H$_{14}$ | 42.63 | 42.32 | 42.01 | 41.69 | 41.41 | 41.10 | 40.78 | 40.46 | 40.15 | 39.82 | 39.49 | 39.15 | 38.79 | 38.40 | 38.02[c] |
| 2-Methylpentane | " | 42.26 | 41.95 | 41.65 | 41.34 | 41.03 | 40.71 | 40.39 | 40.07 | 39.74 | 39.41 | 39.08 | 38.75 | 38.41 | | |
| 3-Methylpentane | " | 42.96 | 42.66 | 42.35 | 42.04 | 41.72 | 41.41 | 41.09 | 40.76 | 40.44 | 40.11 | 39.77 | 39.44 | 39.10 | 38.75[c] | |
| 2,2-Dimethylbutane | " | | 41.72 | 41.40 | 41.09 | 40.79 | 40.46 | 40.13 | 39.80 | | | | | | | |
| 2,3-Dimethylbutane | " | 42.79 | 42.48 | 42.18 | 41.87 | 41.56 | 41.24 | 40.92 | 40.60 | 40.28 | 39.96 | 39.63 | 39.30 | 38.97[c] | | |

a See footnote a of Table 1d-E.  b For the undercooled liquid below the normal freezing point.  c At saturation pressure.

TABLE 2d-E (PART 2), Page 1 - PARAFFINS, C$_7$

DENSITY

For the Normal Liquid Range at Atmospheric Pressure

October 31, 1950; October 31, 1952

Temperature in °F

Density in lb/ft³ [a]

| Compound (liquid) | Formula | -190 | -180 | -170 | -160 | -150 | -140 | -130 | -120 | -110 | -100 | -90 | -80 | -70 | -60 | -50 | -40 |
|---|---|---|---|---|---|---|---|---|---|---|---|---|---|---|---|---|---|
| n-Heptane | C$_7$H$_{16}$ | | | | | | | 48.31 | 48.04 | 47.76 | 47.48 | 47.21 | 46.94 | 46.66 | 46.38 | 46.10 | 45.81 |
| 2-Methylhexane | " | | | | | | | | | | | | | | | | |
| 3-Methylhexane | " | | | | | | | | | | | | | | | | |
| 3-Ethylpentane | " | | 50.77 | 50.49 | 50.20 | 49.92 | 49.64 | 49.36 | 49.07 | 48.79 | 48.50 | 48.22 | 47.93 | 47.64 | 47.36 | 47.07 | 46.78 |
| 2,2-Dimethylpentane | " | 49.64 | 49.36 | 49.07 | 48.77 | 48.48 | 48.19 | 47.89 | 47.60 | 47.30 | 47.01 | 46.72 | 46.42 | 46.13 | 45.83 | 45.54 | 45.25 |
| 2,3-Dimethylpentane | " | | | | | | | | | | | | | | | | |
| 2,4-Dimethylpentane | " | | | | | | | | | | | | | | | | |
| 3,3-Dimethylpentane | " | | | | | | | | | | | | | | | | |
| 2,2,3-Trimethylbutane | " | | | | | | | | | | | | | | | | |

Temperature in °F

Density in lb/ft³ [a]

| Compound (liquid) | Formula | -30 | -20 | -10 | 0 | 10 | 20 | 30 | 40 | 50 | 60 | 70 | 80 | 90 | 100 | 110 | 120 |
|---|---|---|---|---|---|---|---|---|---|---|---|---|---|---|---|---|---|
| n-Heptane | C$_7$H$_{16}$ | 45.53 | 45.25 | 44.96 | 44.67 | 44.38 | 44.09 | 43.79 | 43.50 | 43.20 | 42.92 | 42.63 | 42.33 | 42.04 | 41.75 | 41.45 | 41.16 |
| 2-Methylhexane | " | | | | | | | 43.49 | 43.20 | 42.90 | 42.60 | 42.30 | 42.01 | 41.71 | 41.41 | 41.11 | 40.82 |
| 3-Methylhexane | " | | | | | | | | | 43.44 | 43.14 | 42.84 | 42.54 | 42.24 | 41.94 | 41.64 | |
| 3-Ethylpentane | " | 46.49 | 46.20 | 45.91 | 45.61 | 45.32 | 45.02 | 44.73 | 44.43 | 44.13 | 43.83 | 43.53 | 43.22 | 42.92 | 42.62 | 42.31 | 42.00 |
| 2,2-Dimethylpentane | " | 44.95 | 44.66 | 44.37 | 44.07 | 43.78 | 43.48 | 43.19 | 42.89 | 42.60 | 42.30 | 42.00 | 41.70 | 41.40 | 41.10 | 40.80 | 40.50 |
| 2,3-Dimethylpentane | " | | | | | | | 44.52 | 44.23 | 43.93 | 43.63 | 43.33 | 43.04 | 42.74 | 42.44 | 42.14 | 41.85 |
| 2,4-Dimethylpentane | " | | | | | | | 43.16 | 42.86 | 42.55 | 42.24 | 41.93 | 41.63 | 41.32 | 41.01 | 40.70 | 40.40 |
| 3,3-Dimethylpentane | " | | | | | 44.78 | 44.49 | 44.39 | 44.10 | 43.81 | 43.51 | 43.22 | 42.93 | 42.63 | 42.34 | 42.05 | 41.75 |
| 2,2,3-Trimethylbutane | " | | | | | | | 44.20 | 43.90 | 43.61 | 43.32 | 43.02 | 42.73 | 42.43 | 42.14 | 41.84 | 41.55 |

a See footnote a of Table 1d-E.

TABLE 2d-E (PART 2), Page 2 — PARAFFINS, C7

DENSITY

For the Normal Liquid Range at Atmospheric Pressure

October 31, 1950; October 31, 1952

| Compound (liquid) | Formula | Temperature in °F | | | | | | | | |
|---|---|---|---|---|---|---|---|---|---|---|
| | | Density in lb/ft³ a | | | | | | | | |
| | | 130 | 140 | 150 | 160 | 170 | 180 | 190 | 200 | 210 |
| n-Heptane | $C_7H_{16}$ | 40.85 | 40.53 | 40.20 | 39.87 | 39.55 | 39.22 | 38.89 | 38.55 | 38.21b |
| 2-Methylhexane | " | 40.52 | 40.22 | | | | | | | |
| 3-Methylhexane | " | | | | | | | | | |
| 3-Ethylpentane | " | 41.69 | 41.37 | 41.05 | 40.72 | 40.38 | 40.03 | 39.68 | 39.30 | |
| 2,2-Dimethylpentane | " | 40.19 | 39.89 | 39.59 | 39.28 | 38.98 | | | | |
| 2,3-Dimethylpentane | " | 41.55 | | | | | | | | |
| 2,4-Dimethylpentane | " | 40.09 | | | | | | | | |
| 3,3-Dimethylpentane | " | 41.46 | | | | | | | | |
| 2,2,3-Trimethylbutane | " | 41.26 | | | | | | | | |

a See footnote a of Table 1d-E.　　　b At saturation pressure.

TABLE 3d-E, Page 1 — PARAFFINS, C$_8$
DENSITY
For the Normal Liquid Range at Atmospheric Pressure
October 31, 1950; October 31, 1952

| Compound (liquid) | Formula | Temperature in °F — Density in lb/ft$^3$ [a] | | | | | | | | | | | | | | | |
|---|---|---|---|---|---|---|---|---|---|---|---|---|---|---|---|---|---|
| | | -160 | -150 | -140 | -130 | -120 | -110 | -100 | -90 | -80 | -70 | -60 | -50 | -40 | -30 | -20 | -10 |
| n-Octane | C$_8$H$_{18}$ | | | | | | | | | | 47.71 | 47.44 | 47.16 | 46.89 | 46.61 | 46.34 | 46.06 |
| 2-Methylheptane | " | | | | | | | | | | | | | | | | |
| 3-Methylheptane | " | | | | | | | | | | | | | | | | |
| 4-Methylheptane | " | | | | | | | | | | | | | | | | |
| 3-Ethylhexane | " | | | | | | | | | | | | | | | | |
| 2,2-Dimethylhexane | " | | | | | | | | | | | | | | | | |
| 2,3-Dimethylhexane | " | | | | | | | | | | | | | | | | |
| 2,4-Dimethylhexane | " | | | | | | | | | | | | | | | | |
| 2,5-Dimethylhexane | " | | | | | | | | | | | | | | | | |
| 3,3-Dimethylhexane | " | | | | | | | | | | | | | | | | |
| 3,4-Dimethylhexane | " | | | | | | | | | | | | | | | | |
| 2-Methyl-3-ethylpentane | " | | | | | | | | | | | | | | | | |
| 3-Methyl-3-ethylpentane | " | | | | | | | | | | | | | | | | |
| 2,2,3-Trimethylpentane | " | | | | | | | | | | | | | | | | |
| 2,2,4-Trimethylpentane | " | 49.63 | 49.35 | 49.06 | 48.78 | 48.50 | 48.22 | 47.93 | 47.65 | 47.37 | 47.09 | 46.81 | 46.53 | 46.24 | 45.96 | 45.68 | 45.40 |
| 2,3,3-Trimethylpentane | " | | | | | | | | | | | | | | | | |
| 2,3,4-Trimethylpentane | " | | | | | | | | | | | | | | | | |
| 2,2,3,3-Tetramethylbutane | " | | | | | | | | | | | | | | | | |

a See footnote a of Table 1d-E.

309

TABLE 3a-E, Page 2 – PARAFFINS, C₈

DENSITY

For the Normal Liquid Range at Atmospheric Pressure

October 31, 1950; October 31, 1952

Temperature in °F

Density in lb/ft³ [a]

| Compound (liquid) | Formula | 0 | 10 | 20 | 30 | 40 | 50 | 60 | 70 | 80 | 90 | 100 | 110 | 120 | 130 | 140 | 150 |
|---|---|---|---|---|---|---|---|---|---|---|---|---|---|---|---|---|---|
| n-Octane | C₈H₁₈ | 45.78 | 45.50 | 45.22 | 44.94 | 44.65 | 44.36 | 44.08 | 43.80 | 43.52 | 43.25 | 42.97 | 42.69 | 42.41 | 42.12 | 41.83 | 41.53 |
| 2-Methylheptane | " | | | | 44.62 | 44.35 | 44.07 | 43.79 | 43.51 | 43.24 | 42.96 | 42.68 | 42.40 | 42.13 | 41.85 | 41.57 | |
| 3-Methylheptane | " | | 45.63 | 45.35 | 45.13 | 44.85 | 44.57 | 44.29 | 44.01 | 43.72 | 43.44 | 43.16 | 42.88 | 42.59 | 42.31 | 42.03 | |
| 4-Methylheptane | " | | | | 45.06 | 44.78 | 44.50 | 44.22 | 43.93 | 43.65 | 43.36 | 43.08 | 42.80 | 42.52 | 42.23 | 41.95 | |
| 3-Ethylhexane | " | | | | 45.63 | 45.34 | 45.06 | 44.77 | 44.49 | 44.20 | 43.92 | 43.64 | 43.35 | 43.07 | 42.78 | 42.50 | |
| 2,2-Dimethylhexane | " | | | | 44.50 | 44.21 | 43.92 | 43.64 | 43.35 | 43.06 | 42.77 | 42.48 | 42.19 | 41.90 | 41.61 | | |
| 2,3-Dimethylhexane | " | | | | 45.52 | 45.24 | 44.96 | 44.69 | 44.40 | 44.12 | 43.84 | 43.56 | 43.28 | 43.00 | 42.71 | | |
| 2,4-Dimethylhexane | " | | | | 44.82 | 44.53 | 44.24 | 43.95 | 43.66 | 43.38 | 43.09 | 42.80 | 42.51 | 42.22 | 41.93 | | |
| 2,5-Dimethylhexane | " | 45.28 | 44.99 | 44.69 | 44.40 | 44.11 | 43.82 | 43.53 | 43.24 | 42.95 | 42.65 | 42.36 | 42.07 | 41.77 | 41.47 | 41.17 | 40.87 |
| 3,3-Dimethylhexane | " | | | | 45.39 | 45.11 | 44.83 | 44.55 | 44.27 | 43.99 | 43.71 | 43.43 | 43.15 | 42.87 | 42.59 | | |
| 3,4-Dimethylhexane | " | | | | 45.97 | 45.69 | 45.41 | 45.13 | 44.84 | 44.56 | 44.28 | 44.00 | 43.71 | 43.43 | 43.15 | 42.87 | |
| 2-Methyl-3-ethylpentane | " | | 46.54 | 46.25 | 45.97 | 45.69 | 45.41 | 45.13 | 44.85 | 44.56 | 44.28 | 44.00 | 43.72 | 43.44 | 43.16 | | |
| 3-Methyl-3-ethylpentane | " | | | | 46.43 | 46.16 | 45.89 | 45.62 | 45.36 | 45.09 | 44.82 | 44.55 | 44.28 | 44.01 | 43.74 | | |
| 2,2,3-Trimethylpentane | " | | | | 45.74 | 45.47 | 45.19 | 44.92 | 44.64 | 44.37 | 44.10 | 43.82 | 43.55 | 43.27 | 43.00 | | |
| 2,2,4-Trimethylpentane | " | 45.12 | 44.84 | 44.55 | 44.27 | 43.99 | 43.71 | 43.42 | 43.14 | 42.85 | 42.56 | 42.28 | 41.99 | 41.70 | 41.40 | 41.11 | 40.81 |
| 2,3,3-Trimethylpentane | " | | | | 46.35 | 46.09 | 45.82 | 45.55 | 45.28 | 45.01 | 44.74 | 44.48 | 44.21 | 43.94 | 43.67 | | |
| 2,3,4-Trimethylpentane | " | | | | 45.95 | 45.67 | 45.39 | 45.11 | 44.83 | 44.55 | 44.27 | 43.99 | 43.71 | 43.44 | 43.16 | | |
| 2,2,3,3-Tetramethylbutane | " | | | | | | | | | | | | | | | | |

a See footnote a of Table 1d-E.

TABLE 3d-E, Page 3 – PARAFFINS, C$_8$

DENSITY

For the Normal Liquid Range at Atmospheric Pressure

October 31, 1950; October 31, 1952

| Compound (liquid) | Formula | Temperature in °F | | | | | | | | | | |
|---|---|---|---|---|---|---|---|---|---|---|---|---|
| | | 160 | 170 | 180 | 190 | 200 | 210 | 220 | 230 | 240 | |
| | | Density in lb/ft$^3$ [a] | | | | | | | | | |
| n-Octane | C$_8$H$_{18}$ | 41.23 | 40.93 | 40.63 | 40.33 | 40.03 | 39.72 | 39.40 | 39.09 | 38.76 | |
| 2-Methylheptane | = | | | | | | | | | | |
| 3-Methylheptane | = | | | | | | | | | | |
| 4-Methylheptane | = | | | | | | | | | | |
| 3-Ethylhexane | = | | | | | | | | | | |
| 2,2-Dimethylhexane | = | | | | | | | | | | |
| 2,3-Dimethylhexane | = | | | | | | | | | | |
| 2,4-Dimethylhexane | = | 40.57 | 40.26 | 39.96 | 39.65 | 39.34 | 39.02 | 38.70 | 38.38[c] | | |
| 2,5-Dimethylhexane | = | | | | | | | | | | |
| 3,3-Dimethylhexane | = | | | | | | | | | | |
| 3,4-Dimethylhexane | = | | | | | | | | | | |
| 2-Methyl-3-ethylpentane | = | | | | | | | | | | |
| 3-Methyl-3-ethylpentane | = | | | | | | | | | | |
| 2,2,3-Trimethylpentane | = | 40.50 | 40.19 | 39.87 | 39.55 | 39.22 | 38.89 | 38.56 | | | |
| 2,2,4-Trimethylpentane | = | | | | | | | | | | |
| 2,3,3-Trimethylpentane | = | | | | | | | | | | |
| 2,3,4-Trimethylpentane | = | | | | | | 41.10[b] | 40.79 | | | |
| 2,2,3,3-Tetramethylbutane | = | | | | | | | | | | |

a See footnote a of Table 1d-E.    b For the undercooled liquid below the normal freezing point.    c At saturation pressure.

TABLE 24d-E (PART 1), Page 1 - NORMAL MONOOLEFINS, $C_2$ TO $C_{20}$

DENSITY

For the Normal Liquid Range at Atmospheric Pressure

October 31, 1952

Temperature in °F

Density in lb/ft³ [a]

| Compound (liquid) | Formula | -300 | -290 | -280 | -270 | -260 | -250 | -240 | -230 | -220 | -210 | -200 | -190 | -180 | -170 | -160 | -150 |
|---|---|---|---|---|---|---|---|---|---|---|---|---|---|---|---|---|---|
| Ethene (Ethylene) | $C_2H_4$ | | | | 40.97 | 40.48 | 40.01 | 39.53 | 39.07 | 38.59 | 38.12 | 37.65 | 37.18 | 36.74 | 36.24 | 35.76 | 35.29[b] |
| Propene (Propylene) | $C_3H_6$ | 48.0 | 47.7 | 47.2 | 46.8 | 46.4 | 46.0 | 45.6 | 45.2 | 44.8 | 44.3 | 44.0 | 43.6 | 43.2 | 42.7 | 42.3 | 42.0 |
| 1-Butene | $C_4H_8$ | | | | | | | | | | | | | | 46.3 | 46.0 | 45.6 |
| 1-Pentene | $C_5H_{10}$ | | | | | | | | | | | | | | | | |
| 1-Hexene | $C_6H_{12}$ | | | | | | | | | | | | | | | | |
| 1-Heptene | $C_7H_{14}$ | | | | | | | | | | | | | | | | |
| 1-Octene | $C_8H_{16}$ | | | | | | | | | | | | | | | | |
| 1-Nonene | $C_9H_{18}$ | | | | | | | | | | | | | | | | |
| 1-Decene | $C_{10}H_{20}$ | | | | | | | | | | | | | | | | |

Temperature in °F

Density in lb/ft³ [a]

| Compound (liquid) | Formula | -140 | -130 | -120 | -110 | -100 | -90 | -80 | -70 | -60 | -50 | -40 | -30 | -20 | -10 | 0 | 10 |
|---|---|---|---|---|---|---|---|---|---|---|---|---|---|---|---|---|---|
| Ethene (Ethylene) | $C_2H_4$ | 41.6 | 41.1 | 40.7 | 40.3 | 39.92 | 39.52 | 39.10 | 38.69 | 38.26 | 37.84[b] | 37.42[b] | 36.98[b] | 36.54[b] | 36.08[b] | 35.61[b] | 35.14[b] |
| Propene (Propylene) | $C_3H_6$ | 45.2 | 44.8 | 44.4 | 44.1 | 43.7 | 43.31 | 42.94 | 42.56 | 42.19 | 41.81 | 41.44 | 41.06 | 40.68 | 40.30 | 39.92 | 39.52 |
| 1-Butene | $C_4H_8$ | | 47.1 | 46.7 | 46.4 | 46.0 | 45.7 | 45.3 | 44.9 | 44.6 | 44.2 | 43.8 | 43.6 | 43.2 | 43.0 | 42.7 | 42.2 |
| 1-Pentene | $C_5H_{10}$ | | | | | | | 46.9 | 46.5 | 46.2 | 45.9 | 45.6 | 45.2 | 44.9 | 44.6 | 44.3 | 43.9 |
| 1-Hexene | $C_6H_{12}$ | | | | | | | | | | | | | | | | |
| 1-Heptene | $C_7H_{14}$ | | | | | | | | | | | | | | | | |
| 1-Octene | $C_8H_{16}$ | | | | | | | | | | | | | | | | |
| 1-Nonene | $C_9H_{18}$ | | | | | | | | | | | | | | | | |
| 1-Decene | $C_{10}H_{20}$ | | | | | | | | | | | | | | | | |

a See footnote a of Table 1d-E.  b At saturation pressure.

TABLE 24d-E (PART 1), Page 2 - NORMAL MONOOLEFINS, C$_2$ TO C$_{20}$

DENSITY

For the Normal Liquid Range at Atmospheric Pressure

October 31, 1952

Temperature in °F

Density in lb/ft³ [a]

| Compound (liquid) | Formula | 20 | 30 | 40 | 50 | 60 | 70 | 80 | 90 | 100 | 110 | 120 | 130 | 140 | 150 | 160 | 170 |
|---|---|---|---|---|---|---|---|---|---|---|---|---|---|---|---|---|---|
| Ethene (Ethylene) | C$_2$H$_4$ | | | | | | | | | | | | | | | | |
| Propene (Propylene) | C$_3$H$_6$ | 34.65b | 34.15b | 33.63b | 33.10b | 32.56b | | | | | | | | | | | |
| 1-Butene | C$_4$H$_8$ | 39.12 | 38.72b | 38.32b | 37.91b | 37.50b | | | | | | | | | | | |
| 1-Pentene | C$_5$H$_{10}$ | 41.73 | 41.35 | 40.99 | 40.63 | 40.27 | 39.92 | | | | | | | | | | |
| 1-Hexene | C$_6$H$_{12}$ | 43.62 | 43.27 | 42.94 | 42.61 | 42.28 | 41.96 | 41.63 | 41.30 | 40.98 | 40.65 | 40.32 | 40.00 | 39.67 | 39.34b | | |
| 1-Heptene | C$_7$H$_{14}$ | | 44.67 | 44.37 | 44.06 | 43.75 | 43.45 | 43.14 | 42.84 | 42.53 | 42.23 | 41.92 | 41.61 | 41.31 | 41.00 | 40.69 | 40.38 |
| 1-Octene | C$_8$H$_{16}$ | | 45.73 | 45.44 | 45.15 | 44.86 | 44.57 | 44.29 | 43.99 | 43.70 | 43.41 | 43.12 | 42.84 | 42.55 | 42.26 | 41.97 | 41.68 |
| 1-Nonene | C$_9$H$_{18}$ | | 46.56 | 46.29 | 46.01 | 45.74 | 45.47 | 45.19 | 44.92 | 44.65 | 44.38 | 44.10 | 43.83 | 43.56 | 43.28 | 43.01 | 42.73 |
| 1-Decene | C$_{10}$H$_{20}$ | | 47.28 | 47.00 | 46.73 | 46.46 | 46.19 | 45.92 | 45.65 | 45.38 | 45.12 | 44.85 | 44.57 | 44.30 | 44.04 | 43.77 | 43.50 |

Temperature in °F

Density in lb/ft³ [a]

| Compound (liquid) | Formula | 180 | 190 | 200 | 210 | 220 | 230 | 240 |
|---|---|---|---|---|---|---|---|---|
| Ethene (Ethylene) | C$_2$H$_4$ | | | | | | | |
| Propene (Propylene) | C$_3$H$_6$ | | | | | | | |
| 1-Butene | C$_4$H$_8$ | | | | | | | |
| 1-Pentene | C$_5$H$_{10}$ | | | | | | | |
| 1-Hexene | C$_6$H$_{12}$ | | | | | | | |
| 1-Heptene | C$_7$H$_{14}$ | 40.08 | 39.78 | | | | | |
| 1-Octene | C$_8$H$_{16}$ | 41.39 | 41.10 | 40.81 | 40.52 | 40.2 | 40.0 | 39.7 |
| 1-Nonene | C$_9$H$_{18}$ | 42.46 | 42.19 | 41.92 | 41.64 | 41.4 | 41.1 | 40.8 |
| 1-Decene | C$_{10}$H$_{20}$ | 43.23 | 42.96 | 42.69 | 42.42 | 42.2 | 41.9 | 41.6 |

a See footnote a of Table 1d-E.      b At saturation pressure.

TABLE 24d-E (PART 1), Page 3 - NORMAL MONOOLEFINS, $C_2$ TO $C_{20}$

DENSITY

For the Normal Liquid Range at Atmospheric Pressure

October 31, 1952

Temperature in °F

Density in lb/ft³ ᵃ

| Compound (liquid) | Formula | 30 | 40 | 50 | 60 | 70 | 80 | 90 | 100 | 110 | 120 | 130 | 140 | 150 | 160 | 170 | 180 |
|---|---|---|---|---|---|---|---|---|---|---|---|---|---|---|---|---|---|
| 1-Undecene | $C_{11}H_{22}$ | 47.83 | 47.58 | 47.31 | 47.05 | 46.79 | 46.53 | 46.26 | 46.00 | 45.74 | 45.47 | 45.22 | 44.95 | 44.69 | 44.43 | 44.17 | 43.90 |
| 1-Dodecene | $C_{12}H_{24}$ | 48.31 | 48.06 | 47.80 | 47.54 | 47.29 | 47.04 | 46.78 | 46.53 | 46.28 | 46.02 | 45.76 | 45.51 | 45.25 | 45.00 | 44.75 | 44.50 |
| 1-Tridecene | $C_{13}H_{26}$ | 48.73 | 48.48 | 48.23 | 47.98 | 47.73 | 47.47 | 47.22 | 46.97 | 46.72 | 46.47 | 46.21 | 45.96 | 45.71 | 45.46 | 45.21 | 44.96 |
| 1-Tetradecene | $C_{14}H_{28}$ | 49.09 | 48.84 | 48.60 | 48.35 | 48.10 | 47.85 | 47.60 | 47.36 | 47.11 | 46.87 | 46.61 | 46.36 | 46.11 | 45.86 | 45.62 | 45.37 |
| 1-Pentadecene | $C_{15}H_{30}$ | 49.41 | 49.16 | 48.92 | 48.67 | 48.42 | 48.18 | 47.93 | 47.69 | 47.44 | 47.19 | 46.94 | 46.70 | 46.46 | 46.21 | 45.96 | 45.72 |
| 1-Hexadecene | $C_{16}H_{32}$ | 49.69ᵇ | 49.45 | 49.20 | 48.96 | 48.71 | 48.47 | 48.22 | 47.99 | 47.74 | 47.49 | 47.25 | 47.01 | 46.78 | 46.52 | 46.28 | 46.03 |
| 1-Heptadecene | $C_{17}H_{34}$ | | | 49.45ᵇ | 49.21 | 48.97 | 48.72 | 48.48 | 48.24 | 48.00 | 47.76 | 47.51 | 47.27 | 47.03 | 46.78 | 46.55 | 46.30 |
| 1-Octadecene | $C_{18}H_{36}$ | | | | 49.43ᵇ | 49.19 | 48.95 | 48.71 | 48.47 | 48.23 | 47.99 | 47.74 | 47.51 | 47.26 | 47.02 | 46.78 | 46.54 |
| 1-Nonadecene | $C_{19}H_{38}$ | | | | 49.64ᵇ | 49.39ᵇ | 49.15 | 48.91 | 48.67 | 48.43 | 48.19 | 47.95 | 47.71 | 47.48 | 47.23 | 46.99 | 46.75 |
| 1-Eicosene | $C_{20}H_{40}$ | | | | 49.82ᵇ | 49.58ᵇ | 49.34ᵇ | 49.10 | 48.86 | 48.62 | 48.39 | 48.14 | 47.91 | 47.67 | 47.43 | 47.19 | 46.95 |

Temperature in °F

Density in lb/ft³ ᵃ

| Compound (liquid) | Formula | 190 | 200 | 210 | 220 | 230 | 240 | 250 |
|---|---|---|---|---|---|---|---|---|
| 1-Undecene | $C_{11}H_{22}$ | 43.64 | 43.38 | 43.11 | 42.8 | 42.6 | 42.3 | 42.1 |
| 1-Dodecene | $C_{12}H_{24}$ | 44.24 | 43.99 | 43.73 | 43.5 | 43.2 | 43.0 | 42.7 |
| 1-Tridecene | $C_{13}H_{26}$ | 44.71 | 44.46 | 44.20 | 44.0 | 43.7 | 43.5 | 43.2 |
| 1-Tetradecene | $C_{14}H_{28}$ | 45.12 | 44.87 | 44.62 | 44.4 | 44.1 | 43.9 | 43.6 |
| 1-Pentadecene | $C_{15}H_{30}$ | 45.48 | 45.23 | 44.98 | 44.7 | 44.5 | 44.3 | 44.0 |
| 1-Hexadecene | $C_{16}H_{32}$ | 45.79 | 45.55 | 45.30 | 45.1 | 44.8 | 44.6 | 44.3 |
| 1-Heptadecene | $C_{17}H_{34}$ | 46.06 | 45.82 | 45.58 | 45.3 | 45.1 | 44.8 | 44.6 |
| 1-Octadecene | $C_{18}H_{36}$ | 46.30 | 46.06 | 45.81 | 45.6 | 45.3 | 45.1 | 44.8 |
| 1-Nonadecene | $C_{19}H_{38}$ | 46.51 | 46.27 | 46.03 | 45.8 | 45.6 | 45.3 | 45.1 |
| 1-Eicosene | $C_{20}H_{40}$ | 46.71 | 46.47 | 46.23 | 46.0 | 45.8 | 45.5 | 45.3 |

ᵃ See footnote a of Table 1d-E.

ᵇ For the undercooled liquid below the normal freezing point.

TABLE 5d-E, Page 1 – ALKYL BENZENES, $C_6$ TO $C_9$

DENSITY

For the Normal Liquid Range at Atmospheric Pressure

November 30, 1949; October 31, 1952

Temperature in °F

Density in lb/ft3 [a]

| Compound (liquid) | Formula | 0 | -10 | -20 | -30 | -40 | -50 | -60 | -70 | -80 | -90 | -100 | -110 | -120 | -130 | -140 | -150 |
|---|---|---|---|---|---|---|---|---|---|---|---|---|---|---|---|---|---|
| Benzene | $C_6H_6$ | | | | | | | | | | | | | | | | |
| Methylbenzene (Toluene) | $C_7H_8$ | 56.30 | 56.62 | 56.94 | 57.26 | 57.58 | 57.90 | 58.22 | 58.54 | 58.86 | 59.18 | 59.50 | 59.82 | 60.14 | 60.46 | 60.78[b] | |
| Ethylbenzene | $C_8H_{10}$ | 56.18 | 56.49 | 56.79 | 57.10 | 57.40 | 57.70 | 58.01 | 58.32 | 58.62 | 58.93 | 59.24 | 59.54 | 59.85 | 60.16 | 60.46[b] | |
| 1,2-Dimethylbenzene (o-Xylene) | " | 56.91 | 57.20 | | | | | | | | | | | | | | |
| 1,3-Dimethylbenzene (m-Xylene) | " | 55.94 | 56.23 | 56.52 | 56.81 | 57.10 | 57.39 | | | | | | | | | | |
| 1,4-Dimethylbenzene (p-Xylene) | " | | | | | | | | | | | | | | | | |
| n-Propylbenzene | $C_9H_{12}$ | 55.77 | 56.06 | 56.34 | 56.63 | 56.92 | 57.21 | 57.49 | 57.78 | 58.07 | 58.36 | 58.64 | 58.93 | 59.22 | 59.51 | 59.79 | 60.08[b] |
| Isopropylbenzene | " | | | | | | | | | | | | | | | | |
| 1-Methyl-2-ethylbenzene | " | | | | | | | | | | | | | | | | |
| 1-Methyl-3-ethylbenzene | " | | | | | | | | | | | | | | | | |
| 1-Methyl-4-ethylbenzene | " | | | | | | | | | | | | | | | | |
| 1,2,3-Trimethylbenzene | " | | | | | | | | | | | | | | | | |
| 1,2,4-Trimethylbenzene | " | | | | | | | | | | | | | | | | |
| 1,3,5-Trimethylbenzene | " | | | | | | | | | | | | | | | | |

a See footnote a of Table 1d-E.    b For the undercooled liquid below the normal freezing point.

TABLE 5d-E, Page 2 - ALKYL BENZENES, $C_6$ TO $C_9$

DENSITY

For the Normal Liquid Range at Atmospheric Pressure

November 30, 1949; October 31, 1952

| Compound (liquid) | Formula | Temperature in °F — Density in lb/ft$^3$[a] | | | | | | | | | | | | | | | |
|---|---|---|---|---|---|---|---|---|---|---|---|---|---|---|---|---|---|
| | | 10 | 20 | 30 | 40 | 50 | 60 | 70 | 80 | 90 | 100 | 110 | 120 | 130 | 140 | 150 | 160 |
| Benzene | $C_6H_6$ | | | | 55.89[b] | 55.53 | 55.16 | 54.80 | 54.44 | 54.07 | 53.70 | 53.32 | 52.94 | 52.56 | 52.18 | 51.80 | 51.41 |
| Methylbenzene (Toluene) | $C_7H_8$ | 55.98 | 55.66 | 55.34 | 55.02 | 54.70 | 54.37 | 54.06 | 53.74 | 53.42 | 53.09 | 52.77 | 52.45 | 52.13 | 51.81 | 51.49 | 51.17 |
| Ethylbenzene | $C_8H_{10}$ | 55.88 | 55.58 | 55.27 | 54.97 | 54.67 | 54.37 | 54.07 | 53.76 | 53.46 | 53.15 | 52.84 | 52.53 | 52.22 | 51.91 | 51.59 | 51.28 |
| 1,2-Dimethylbenzene (o-Xylene) | " | 56.62 | 56.34 | 56.05 | 55.76 | 55.47 | 55.18 | 54.89 | 54.60 | 54.31 | 54.01 | 53.72 | 53.43 | 53.13 | 52.84 | 52.54 | 52.24 |
| 1,3-Dimethylbenzene (m-Xylene) | " | 55.64 | 55.35 | 55.06 | 54.77 | 54.48 | 54.18 | 53.89 | 53.59 | 53.30 | 53.00 | 52.70 | 52.40 | 52.10 | 51.80 | 51.49 | 51.19 |
| 1,4-Dimethylbenzene (p-Xylene) | " | | | | | | 53.99 | 53.69 | 53.39 | 53.09 | 52.79 | 52.49 | 52.19 | 51.88 | 51.58 | 51.27 | 50.96 |
| n-Propylbenzene | $C_9H_{12}$ | 55.48 | 55.19 | 54.90 | 54.62 | 54.33 | 54.04 | 53.76 | 53.47 | 53.18 | 52.89 | 52.60 | 52.31 | 52.02 | 51.73 | 51.44 | 51.14 |
| Isopropylbenzene | " | | | 54.91 | 54.62 | 54.32 | 54.03 | 53.74 | 53.45 | 53.16 | 52.86 | 52.58 | 52.29 | 52.00 | 51.71 | 51.42 | 51.13 |
| 1-Methyl-2-ethylbenzene | " | | | | | 55.49 | 55.20 | 54.92 | 54.64 | 54.35 | 54.07 | | | | | | |
| 1-Methyl-3-ethylbenzene | " | | | | 54.56 | 54.48 | 54.20 | 53.92 | 53.63 | 53.34 | 53.06 | | | | | | |
| 1-Methyl-4-ethylbenzene | " | | | 54.84 | 54.56 | 54.27 | 53.99 | 53.70 | 53.42 | 53.13 | 52.84 | 52.56 | 52.27 | 51.98 | 51.69 | 51.40 | 51.12 |
| 1,2,3-Trimethylbenzene | " | | | 56.87 | 56.60 | 56.33 | 56.05 | 55.78 | 55.51 | 55.23 | 54.96 | | | | | | |
| 1,2,4-Trimethylbenzene | " | | | 55.72 | 55.44 | 55.18 | 54.90 | 54.62 | 54.34 | 54.06 | 53.78 | 53.50 | 53.22 | 52.94 | 52.65 | 52.36 | 52.08 |
| 1,3,5-Trimethylbenzene | " | | | 55.07 | 54.79 | 54.51 | 54.23 | 53.95 | 53.67 | 53.39 | 53.10 | 52.82 | 52.53 | 52.24 | 51.95 | 51.65 | 51.36 |

a See footnote a of Table 1d-E.  b For the undercooled liquid below the normal freezing point.

TABLE 5d-E, Page 3 – ALKYL BENZENES, C$_6$ TO C$_9$

DENSITY

For the Normal Liquid Range at Atmospheric Pressure

November 30, 1949; October 31, 1952

Temperature in °F

Density in lb/ft$^3$ [a]

| Compound (liquid) | Formula | 170 | 180 | 190 | 200 | 210 | 220 | 230 | 240 | 250 | 260 | 270 | 280 | 290 | 300 | 310 | 320 |
|---|---|---|---|---|---|---|---|---|---|---|---|---|---|---|---|---|---|
| Benzene | C$_6$H$_6$ | 51.02 | 50.62[b] | | | | | | | | | | | | | | |
| Methyl benzene (Toluene) | C$_7$H$_8$ | 50.85 | 50.53 | 50.21 | 49.89 | 49.57 | 49.25 | 48.93 | | | | | | | | | |
| Ethyl benzene | C$_8$H$_{10}$ | 50.96 | 50.64 | 50.32 | 50.00 | 49.68 | 49.36 | 49.03 | 48.70 | 48.37 | 48.04 | 47.71 | 47.37[b] | | | | |
| 1,2-Dimethyl benzene (o-Xylene) | " | 51.94 | 51.64 | 51.34 | 51.03 | 50.72 | 50.41 | 50.10 | 49.79 | 49.47 | 49.16 | 48.84 | 48.53 | 48.21 | | | |
| 1,3-Dimethyl benzene (m-Xylene) | " | 50.88 | 50.58 | 50.27 | 49.96 | 49.65 | 49.34 | 49.03 | 48.72 | 48.41 | 48.10 | 47.79 | 47.48 | | | | |
| 1,4-Dimethyl benzene (p-Xylene) | " | 50.65 | 50.34 | 50.02 | 49.71 | 49.39 | 49.08 | 48.76 | 48.44 | 48.11 | 47.79 | 47.14 | | | | | |
| n-Propyl benzene | C$_9$H$_{12}$ | 50.84 | 50.54 | 50.24 | 49.93 | 49.62 | 49.31 | 48.99 | 48.67 | 48.35 | 48.02 | 47.70 | 47.36 | 47.0 | 46.7 | 46.4 | 46.0[b] |
| Isopropyl benzene | " | 50.84 | 50.54 | 50.25 | 49.96 | | | | | | | | | | | | |
| 1-Methyl-2-ethyl benzene | " | | | | | | | | | | | | | | | | |
| 1-Methyl-3-ethyl benzene | " | | | | | | | | | | | | | | | | |
| 1-Methyl-4-ethyl benzene | " | 50.83 | 50.54 | 50.24 | 49.95 | 49.66 | | | | | | | | | | | |
| 1,2,3-Trimethyl benzene | " | 51.79 | 51.50 | 51.20 | 50.91 | 50.62 | | | | | | | | | | | |
| 1,2,4-Trimethyl benzene | " | 51.06 | 50.76 | 50.47 | 50.17 | 49.86 | | | | | | | | | | | |
| 1,3,5-Trimethyl benzene | " | | | | | | | | | | | | | | | | |

a  See footnote a of Table 1d-E.  b  At saturation pressure.

TABLE 20e (PART 1), Page 1 – NORMAL PARAFFINS, $C_1$ TO $C_{20}$

SURFACE TENSION

For the Normal Liquid Range at Atmospheric Pressure

October 31, 1952

| Compound (liquid) | Formula | Temperature in °C — Surface Tension in dyne/cm[a] | | | | | | | | | | | | | | | |
|---|---|---|---|---|---|---|---|---|---|---|---|---|---|---|---|---|---|
| | | -180 | -170 | -160 | -150 | -140 | -130 | -120 | -110 | -100 | -90 | -80 | -70 | -60 | -50 | -40 | -30 |
| Methane | $CH_4$ | 18.0 | 15.8 | 13.7b | | | | | | | | | | | | | |
| Ethane | $C_2H_6$ | | | 28.08 | 26.34 | 24.62 | 22.91 | 21.23 | 19.57 | 17.93 | 16.31 | | | | | | |
| Propane | $C_3H_8$ | | | | | | 27.8 | 26.3 | 24.9 | 23.4 | 22.0 | 20.6 | 19.2 | 17.85 | 16.49 | 15.15b | |
| n-Butane | $C_4H_{10}$ | | | | | | | | | 27.2 | 25.9 | 24.6 | 23.4 | 22.1 | 20.88 | 19.65 | 18.43 |
| n-Pentane | $C_5H_{12}$ | | | | | | | | | | | | | | | | |
| n-Hexane | $C_6H_{14}$ | | | | | | | | | | | | | | 25.8 | 24.7 | 23.64 |
| n-Heptane | $C_7H_{16}$ | | | | | | | | | | | | | | | | 25.3 |
| n-Octane | $C_8H_{18}$ | | | | | | | | | | | | | | | 27.5 | 26.52 |

| Compound (liquid) | Formula | Temperature in °C — Surface Tension in dyne/cm[a] | | | | | | | | | | | | | | | |
|---|---|---|---|---|---|---|---|---|---|---|---|---|---|---|---|---|---|
| | | -20 | -10 | 0 | 10 | 20 | 25 | 30 | 40 | 50 | 60 | 70 | 80 | 90 | 100 | 110 | 120 |
| Methane | $CH_4$ | | | | | | | | | | | | | | | | |
| Ethane | $C_2H_6$ | | | | | | | | | | | | | | | | |
| Propane | $C_3H_8$ | | | | | | | | | | | | | | | | |
| n-Butane | $C_4H_{10}$ | 17.22 | 16.02 | 14.84b | | | | | | | | | | | | | |
| n-Pentane | $C_5H_{12}$ | 20.5 | 19.3 | 18.2 | 17.1 | 16.00 | 15.48 | 14.95 | 13.8b | | | | | | | | |
| n-Hexane | $C_6H_{14}$ | 22.57 | 21.51 | 20.46 | 19.42 | 18.42 | 17.90 | 17.38 | 16.36 | 15.36 | 14.33 | | | | | | |
| n-Heptane | $C_7H_{16}$ | 24.30 | 23.29 | 22.28 | 21.28 | 20.30 | 19.80 | 19.30 | 18.32 | 17.37 | 16.43 | 15.43 | 14.5 | 13.6 | | | |
| n-Octane | $C_8H_{18}$ | 25.55 | 24.59 | 23.70 | 22.73 | 21.76 | 21.26 | 20.77 | 19.80 | 18.86 | 17.94 | 17.0 | 16.1 | 15.2 | 14.4 | 13.5 | 12.6 |

a See footnote a of Table 1e.    b At saturation pressure.

TABLE 20e (PART 1), Page 2 – NORMAL PARAFFINS, $C_1$ TO $C_{20}$

SURFACE TENSION

For the Normal Liquid Range at Atmospheric Pressure

October 31, 1952

|  |  | Temperature in °C |  |  |  |  |  |  |  |  |  |  |  |  |  |  |  |
|---|---|---|---|---|---|---|---|---|---|---|---|---|---|---|---|---|---|
| Compound (liquid) | Formula | Surface Tension in dyne/cm[a] |  |  |  |  |  |  |  |  |  |  |  |  |  |  |  |
|  |  | 110 | 100 | 90 | 80 | 70 | 60 | 50 | 40 | 30 | 25 | 20 | 10 | 0 | -10 | -20 | -30 |
| n-Nonane | $C_9H_{20}$ | 14.9 | 15.8 | 16.5 | 17.38 | 18.24 | 19.16 | 20.08 | 21.00 | 21.95 | 22.44 | 22.92 | 23.93 | 25.02 | 26.1 | 27.2 | 28.4 |
| n-Decane | $C_{10}H_{22}$ | 15.9 | 16.8 | 17.6 | 18.43 | 19.29 | 20.18 | 21.09 | 22.02 | 22.96 | 23.44 | 23.92 | 24.93 | 26.02 | 27.1 | 28.2 |  |
| n-Undecane | $C_{11}H_{24}$ | 16.8 | 17.6 | 18.5 | 19.31 | 20.16 | 21.07 | 21.96 | 22.88 | 23.80 | 24.27 | 24.74 | 25.76 | 26.82 | 27.9 | 29.0 |  |
| n-Dodecane | $C_{12}H_{26}$ | 17.7 | 18.5 | 19.3 | 20.1 | 20.95 | 21.83 | 22.70 | 23.60 | 24.51 | 24.98 | 25.44 | 26.47 | 27.54 |  |  |  |
| n-Tridecane | $C_{13}H_{28}$ | 18.5 | 19.3 | 20.1 | 20.9 | 21.7 | 22.5 | 23.4 | 24.3 | 25.2 | 25.6 | 26.1 | 27.05 | 28.1 |  |  |  |
| n-Tetradecane | $C_{14}H_{30}$ | 19.2 | 19.9 | 20.7 | 21.5 | 22.3 | 23.1 | 24.0 | 24.8 | 25.7 | 26.2 | 26.6 | 27.6 |  |  |  |  |
| n-Pentadecane | $C_{15}H_{32}$ | 19.8 | 20.5 | 21.3 | 22.1 | 22.9 | 23.7 | 24.5 | 25.3 | 26.2 | 26.7 | 27.1 | 28.1 |  |  |  |  |
| n-Hexadecane | $C_{16}H_{34}$ | 20.2 | 21.0 | 21.8 | 22.6 | 23.3 | 24.2 | 25.0 | 25.8 | 26.7 | 27.1 | 27.6 |  |  |  |  |  |
| n-Heptadecane | $C_{17}H_{36}$ |  | 21.6 | 22.3 | 23.0 | 23.7 | 24.5 | 25.2 | 26.2 | 27.1 | 27.5 | 28.0[b] |  |  |  |  |  |
| n-Octadecane | $C_{18}H_{38}$ |  | 22.2 | 22.9 | 23.6 | 24.3 | 25.0 | 25.8 | 26.6 | 27.5 | 28.0[b] | 28.4[b] |  |  |  |  |  |
| n-Nonadecane | $C_{19}H_{40}$ |  | 22.5 | 23.2 | 23.9 | 24.6 | 25.3 | 26.0 | 26.9 | 27.8[b] | 28.2[b] | 28.7[b] |  |  |  |  |  |
| n-Eicosane | $C_{20}H_{42}$ |  | 23.0 | 23.7 | 24.3 | 25.0 | 25.7 | 26.4 | 27.2 | 28.1[b] | 28.6[b] | 29.0[b] |  |  |  |  |  |

|  |  | Temperature in °C |  |  |  |
|---|---|---|---|---|---|
| Compound (liquid) | Formula | Surface Tension in dyne/cm[a] |  |  |  |
|  |  | 150 | 140 | 130 | 120 |
| n-Nonane | $C_9H_{20}$ | 11.6 | 12.4 | 13.2 | 14.0 |
| n-Decane | $C_{10}H_{22}$ | 12.8 | 13.6 | 14.3 | 15.1 |
| n-Undecane | $C_{11}H_{24}$ | 13.7 | 14.5 | 15.2 | 16.0 |
| n-Dodecane | $C_{12}H_{26}$ | 14.7 | 15.4 | 16.2 | 16.9 |
| n-Tridecane | $C_{13}H_{28}$ | 15.6 | 16.3 | 17.0 | 17.8 |
| n-Tetradecane | $C_{14}H_{30}$ | 16.2 | 17.0 | 17.7 | 18.4 |
| n-Pentadecane | $C_{15}H_{32}$ | 16.9 | 17.8 | 18.3 | 19.0 |
| n-Hexadecane | $C_{16}H_{34}$ | 17.4 | 18.0 | 18.8 | 19.5 |
| n-Heptadecane | $C_{17}H_{36}$ |  |  |  |  |
| n-Octadecane | $C_{18}H_{38}$ |  |  |  |  |
| n-Nonadecane | $C_{19}H_{40}$ |  |  |  |  |
| n-Eicosane | $C_{20}H_{42}$ |  |  |  |  |

a See footnote a of Table 1e.

b For the undercooled liquid below the normal freezing point.

TABLE 1e - PARAFFINS, $C_1$ TO $C_5$

SURFACE TENSION

For the Normal Liquid Range at Atmospheric Pressure

October 31, 1952

| Compound (liquid) | Formula | Temperature in °C — Surface Tension in dyne/cm$^a$ | | | | | | | | | | | | | | | |
|---|---|---|---|---|---|---|---|---|---|---|---|---|---|---|---|---|---|
| | | -180 | -170 | -160 | -150 | -140 | -130 | -120 | -110 | -100 | -90 | -80 | -70 | -60 | -50 | -40 | -30 |
| Methane | $CH_4$ | 18.0 | 15.8 | 13.7$^b$ | | | | | | | | | | | | | |
| Ethane | $C_2H_6$ | | | 28.08 | 26.34 | 24.62 | 22.91 | 21.23 | 19.57 | 17.93 | 16.31 | | | | | | |
| Propane | $C_3H_8$ | | | | | | 27.8 | 26.3 | 24.9 | 23.4 | 22.0 | 20.6 | 19.2 | 17.85 | 16.49 | 15.15$^b$ | |
| n-Butane | $C_4H_{10}$ | | | | | | | | | 27.2 | 25.9 | 24.6 | 23.4 | 22.1 | 20.88 | 19.65 | 18.43 |
| 2-Methylpropane (Isobutane) | " | | | | | | | | | 25.2 | 23.9 | 22.6 | 21.4 | 20.14 | 18.90 | 17.68 | 16.48 |
| n-Pentane | $C_5H_{12}$ | | | | | | | | | | | | | | | | |
| 2-Methylbutane (Isopentane) | " | | | | | | | | | | | | | | | | |
| 2,2-Dimethylpropane (Neopentane) | " | | | | | | | | | | | | | | | | |

| Compound (liquid) | Formula | Temperature in °C — Surface Tension in dyne/cm$^a$ | | | | | | | |
|---|---|---|---|---|---|---|---|---|---|
| | | -20 | -10 | 0 | 10 | 20 | 25 | 30 | 40 |
| Methane | $CH_4$ | | | | | | | | |
| Ethane | $C_2H_6$ | | | | | | | | |
| Propane | $C_3H_8$ | | | | | | | | |
| n-Butane | $C_4H_{10}$ | 17.22 | 16.02 | 14.84$^b$ | | | | | |
| 2-Methylpropane (Isobutane) | " | 15.28 | 14.1$^b$ | | | | | | |
| n-Pentane | $C_5H_{12}$ | 20.5 | 19.3 | 18.2 | 17.1 | 16.00 | 15.48 | 14.95 | 13.8$^b$ |
| 2-Methylbutane (Isopentane) | " | 19.4 | 18.27 | 17.17 | 16.08 | 15.00 | 14.46 | 13.93$^b$ | |
| 2,2-Dimethylpropane (Neopentane) | " | | | | | | | | |

$^a$ For the air-saturated liquid at one atmosphere.  $^b$ At saturation pressure.

TABLE 2e (PART 1) – PARAFFINS, $C_6$

SURFACE TENSION

For the Normal Liquid Range at Atmospheric Pressure

October 31, 1952

| Compound (liquid) | Formula | Temperature in °C | | | | | | | | | | | | |
|---|---|---|---|---|---|---|---|---|---|---|---|---|---|---|
| | | -50 | -40 | -30 | -20 | -10 | 0 | 10 | 20 | 25 | 30 | 40 | 50 | 60 |
| | | Surface Tension in dyne/cm[a] | | | | | | | | | | | | |
| n-Hexane | $C_6H_{14}$ | 25.8 | 24.7 | 23.64 | 22.57 | 21.51 | 20.46 | 19.42 | 18.42 | 17.90 | 17.38 | 16.36 | 15.36 | 14.33 |
| 2-Methylpentane | " | | | | | | 19.4 | 18.4 | 17.38 | 16.87 | 16.37 | 15.36 | 14.4 | 13.4 |
| 3-Methylpentane | " | | | | | | 20.2 | 19.2 | 18.12 | 17.60 | 17.08 | 16.03 | 15.0 | 13.9 |
| 2,2-Dimethylbutane | " | | | | | | 18.2 | 17.3 | 16.30 | 15.81 | 15.31 | 14.33 | | |
| 2,3-Dimethylbutane | " | | | | | | 19.4 | 18.4 | 17.37 | 16.87 | 16.37 | 15.37 | 14.4 | |

a See footnote a of Table 1e.

TABLE 2e (PART 2) – PARAFFINS, $C_7$

SURFACE TENSION

For the Normal Liquid Range at Atmospheric Pressure

October 31, 1952

| Compound (liquid) | Formula | Temperature in °C | | | | | | | | | | | | | |
|---|---|---|---|---|---|---|---|---|---|---|---|---|---|---|---|
| | | -30 | -20 | -10 | 0 | 10 | 20 | 25 | 30 | 40 | 50 | 60 | 70 | 80 | 90 |
| | | Surface Tension in dyne/cm[a] | | | | | | | | | | | | | |
| n-Heptane | $C_7H_{16}$ | 25.3 | 24.30 | 23.29 | 22.28 | 21.28 | 20.30 | 19.80 | 19.30 | 18.32 | 17.37 | 16.43 | 15.43 | 14.5 | 13.6 |
| 2-Methylhexane | " | 24.2 | 23.2 | 22.2 | 21.25 | 20.26 | 19.29 | 18.80 | 18.32 | 17.36 | 16.41 | 15.5 | 14.5 | 13.6 | 12.7 |
| 3-Methylhexane | " | 24.8 | 23.8 | 22.8 | 21.76 | 20.77 | 19.79 | 19.30 | 18.81 | 17.85 | 16.89 | 15.9 | 15.0 | 14.1 | 13.1 |
| 3-Ethylpentane | " | 25.5 | 24.5 | 23.4 | 22.43 | 21.43 | 20.44 | 19.94 | 19.45 | 18.47 | 17.50 | 16.5 | 15.6 | 14.6 | 13.7 |
| 2,2-Dimethylpentane | " | 22.9 | 21.9 | 20.9 | 19.94 | 18.98 | 18.02 | 17.55 | 17.08 | 16.14 | 15.21 | 14.3 | 13.4 | | |
| 2,3-Dimethylpentane | " | 25.0 | 23.9 | 22.9 | 21.93 | 20.94 | 19.96 | 19.47 | 18.98 | 18.02 | 17.06 | 16.1 | 15.2 | 14.2 | |
| 2,4-Dimethylpentane | " | 23.0 | 22.0 | 21.0 | 20.06 | 19.09 | 18.15 | 17.66 | 17.17 | 16.23 | 15.29 | 14.4 | 13.4 | 12.5 | |
| 3,3-Dimethylpentane | " | 24.5 | 23.5 | 22.5 | 21.54 | 20.56 | 19.59 | 19.10 | 18.62 | 17.67 | 16.72 | 15.8 | 14.9 | 13.9 | |
| 2,2,3-Trimethylbutane | " | | 22.6 | 21.6 | 20.66 | 19.70 | 18.76 | 18.26 | 17.77 | 16.81 | 15.89 | 15.0 | 14.1 | 13.2 | |

a See footnote a of Table 1e.

TABLE 3e, Page 1 – PARAFFINS, C$_8$

SURFACE TENSION

For the Normal Liquid Range at Atmospheric Pressure

October 31, 1952

Temperature in °C

| Compound (liquid) | Formula | -40 | -30 | -20 | -10 | 0 | 10 | 20 | 25 | 30 | 40 | 50 | 60 | 70 | 80 | 90 | 100 |
|---|---|---|---|---|---|---|---|---|---|---|---|---|---|---|---|---|---|
| | | | | | | Surface Tension in dyne/cm$^a$ | | | | | | | | | | | |
| n-Octane | C$_8$H$_{18}$ | 27.5 | 26.52 | 25.55 | 24.59 | 23.70 | 22.73 | 21.76 | 21.26 | 20.77 | 19.80 | 18.86 | 17.94 | 17.0 | 16.1 | 15.2 | 14.4 |
| 2-Methylheptane | " | | | | | 22.56 | 21.53 | 20.60 | 20.14 | 19.68 | 18.77 | 17.87 | 16.97 | 16.1 | 15.2 | 14.3 | 13.5 |
| 3-Methylheptane | " | | | | | 23.06 | 22.11 | 21.17 | 20.70 | 20.24 | 19.32 | 18.40 | 17.49 | 16.6 | 15.7 | 14.8 | 13.0 |
| 4-Methylheptane | " | | | | | 22.89 | 21.94 | 21.00 | 20.54 | 20.07 | 19.15 | 18.23 | 17.33 | 16.4 | 15.5 | 14.6 | 13.8 |
| 3-Ethylhexane | " | | | | | 23.41 | 22.46 | 21.51 | 21.04 | 20.58 | 19.64 | 18.72 | 17.80 | 16.9 | 16.0 | 15.1 | 14.2 |
| 2,2-Dimethylhexane | " | | | | | 21.43 | 20.51 | 19.60 | 19.14 | 18.69 | 17.80 | 16.91 | 16.02 | 15.2 | 14.3 | 13.4 | 12.6 |
| 2,3-Dimethylhexane | " | | | | | 22.85 | 21.91 | 20.99 | 20.53 | 20.07 | 19.16 | 18.25 | 17.35 | 16.5 | 15.6 | 14.7 | 13.8 |
| 2,4-Dimethylhexane | " | | | | | 21.90 | 20.97 | 20.05 | 19.59 | 19.13 | 18.22 | 17.32 | 16.43 | 15.6 | 14.7 | 13.8 | 12.9 |
| 2,5-Dimethylhexane | " | | | | | 21.58 | 20.65 | 19.73 | 19.28 | 18.82 | 17.92 | 17.02 | 16.13 | 15.3 | 14.4 | 13.5 | 12.7 |
| 3,3-Dimethylhexane | " | | | | | 22.47 | 21.54 | 20.63 | 20.18 | 19.72 | 18.81 | 17.92 | 17.03 | 16.2 | 15.3 | 14.4 | 13.6 |
| 3,4-Dimethylhexane | " | | | | | 23.53 | 22.58 | 21.64 | 21.18 | 20.71 | 19.79 | 18.87 | 17.96 | 17.1 | 16.2 | 15.3 | 14.4 |
| 2-Methyl-3-ethylpentane | " | | | | | 23.41 | 22.46 | 21.52 | 21.05 | 20.58 | 19.65 | 18.73 | 17.82 | 16.9 | 16.0 | 15.1 | 14.2 |
| 3-Methyl-3-ethylpentane | " | | | | | 23.85 | 22.92 | 21.99 | 21.53 | 21.07 | 20.15 | 19.24 | 18.34 | 17.4 | 16.6 | 15.7 | 14.8 |
| 2,2,3-Trimethylpentane | " | | | | | 22.50 | 21.58 | 20.67 | 20.22 | 19.77 | 18.87 | 17.99 | 17.10 | 16.2 | 15.4 | 14.5 | 13.7 |
| 2,2,4-Trimethylpentane | " | | | | | 20.58 | 19.67 | 18.77 | 18.32 | 17.88 | 16.99 | 16.11 | 15.24 | 14.4 | 13.5 | 12.7 | |
| 2,3,3-Trimethylpentane | " | | | | | 23.41 | 22.48 | 21.56 | 21.10 | 20.65 | 19.75 | 18.85 | 17.96 | 17.1 | 16.2 | 15.3 | 14.5 |
| 2,3,4-Trimethylpentane | " | | | | | 23.00 | 22.07 | 21.14 | 20.68 | 20.22 | 19.31 | 18.41 | 17.51 | 16.6 | 15.7 | 14.9 | 14.0 |
| 2,2,3,3-Tetramethylbutane | " | | | | | | | | | | | | | | | | |

a See footnote a of Table 1e.

TABLE 3e, Page 2 — PARAFFINS, C$_8$

SURFACE TENSION

For the Normal Liquid Range at Atmospheric Pressure

October 31, 1952

| Compound (liquid) | Formula | Temperature in °C | |
|---|---|---|---|
| | | Surface Tension in dyne/cm[a] | |
| | | 110 | 120 |
| n-Octane | C$_8$H$_{18}$ | 13.5 | 12.6 |
| 2-Methylheptane | " | | |
| 3-Methylheptane | " | | |
| 4-Methylheptane | " | | |
| 3-Ethylhexane | " | | |
| 2,2-Dimethylhexane | " | | |
| 2,3-Dimethylhexane | " | | |
| 2,4-Dimethylhexane | " | | |
| 2,5-Dimethylhexane | " | | |
| 3,3-Dimethylhexane | " | | |
| 3,4-Dimethylhexane | " | | |
| 2-Methyl-3-ethylpentane | " | | |
| 3-Methyl-3-ethylpentane | " | | |
| 2,2,3-Trimethylpentane | " | | |
| 2,2,4-Trimethylpentane | " | | |
| 2,3,3-Trimethylpentane | " | | |
| 2,3,4-Trimethylpentane | " | | |
| 2,2,3,3-Tetramethylbutane | " | | |

a See footnote a of Table 1e.

TABLE 5e – ALKYL BENZENES, $C_6$ TO $C_9$
SURFACE TENSION
For the Normal Liquid Range at Atmospheric Pressure
October 31, 1952

| Compound (liquid) | Formula | Temperature in °C — Surface Tension in dyne/cm[a] | | | | | | | | | | | |
|---|---|---|---|---|---|---|---|---|---|---|---|---|---|
| | | 0 | 10 | 20 | 25 | 30 | 40 | 50 | 60 | 70 | 80 | 90 | 100 |
| Benzene | $C_6H_6$ | 30.92 | 30.24 | 28.88 | 28.18 | 27.49 | 26.14 | 24.88 | 23.66 | 22.4 | 21.2 | | |
| Methylbenzene (Toluene) | $C_7H_8$ | 30.92 | 29.70 | 28.53 | 27.92 | 27.32 | 26.15 | 25.04 | 23.94 | 22.9 | 21.8 | 20.7 | 19.6 |
| Ethylbenzene | $C_8H_{10}$ | 31.38 | 30.18 | 29.04 | 28.48 | 27.93 | 26.79 | 25.74 | 24.74 | 23.7 | 22.7 | 21.7 | 20.7 |
| 1,2-Dimethylbenzene (o-Xylene) | " | 32.28 | 31.16 | 30.03 | 29.48 | 28.93 | 27.84 | 26.76 | 25.70 | 24.7 | 23.6 | 22.6 | 21.5 |
| 1,3-Dimethylbenzene (m-Xylene) | " | 30.92 | 29.78 | 28.63 | 28.08 | 27.54 | 26.44 | 25.36 | 24.26 | 23.2 | 22.2 | 21.1 | 20.1 |
| 1,4-Dimethylbenzene (p-Xylene) | " | | | 28.31 | 27.76 | 27.22 | 26.13 | 25.06 | 24.02 | 23.0 | 22.0 | 21.0 | 20.1 |
| n-Propylbenzene | $C_9H_{12}$ | 31.12 | 30.04 | 28.99 | 28.45 | 27.91 | 26.81 | 25.80 | 24.76 | 23.7 | 22.7 | 21.7 | 20.8 |
| Isopropylbenzene | " | | | 28.20 | 27.68 | 27.17 | 26.09 | 25.08 | 24.07 | 23.1 | 22.2 | 21.2 | |
| 1-Methyl-2-ethylbenzene | " | | | 30.20 | 29.66 | 29.13 | 28.11 | | | | | | |
| 1-Methyl-3-ethylbenzene | " | | | 29.07 | 28.52 | 27.97 | 26.89 | | | | | | |
| 1-Methyl-4-ethylbenzene | " | | 29.96 | 28.84 | 28.28 | 27.73 | 26.69 | 25.56 | 24.54 | 23.5 | 22.5 | 21.5 | 20.6 |
| 1,2,3-Trimethylbenzene | " | | | 31.27 | 30.76 | 30.25 | 29.20 | | | | | | |
| 1,2,4-Trimethylbenzene | " | | | 29.71 | 29.19 | 28.67 | 27.66 | 26.63 | 25.60 | 24.6 | 23.6 | 22.7 | 21.7 |
| 1,3,5-Trimethylbenzene | " | 31.04 | 29.92 | 28.83 | 28.31 | 27.79 | 26.75 | 25.74 | 24.74 | 23.8 | 22.8 | 21.8 | 20.8 |

a See footnote a of Table 1e.

TABLE 20i – NORMAL PARAFFINS, $C_1$ TO $C_{20}$

CRITICAL TEMPERATURE, PRESSURE, DENSITY, VOLUME, AND COMPRESSIBILITY FACTOR

June 30, 1949

| Compound | Formula | Critical Temperature | | | | Critical Pressure | | Critical Density | | Critical Volume | | Critical $PV/RT$ |
|---|---|---|---|---|---|---|---|---|---|---|---|---|
| | | °K | °C | °R | °F | atm | lb/in² | g/ml | lb/ft³ | liter/mole | ft³/lb mole | |
| Methane | $CH_4$ | 190.7 | -82.5 | 343.3 | -116.5 | 45.80 | 673.1 | 0.162 | 10.1 | 0.099 | 1.59 | 0.290 |
| Ethane | $C_2H_6$ | 305.43 | +32.27 | 549.77 | +90.09 | 48.20 | 708.3 | 0.203 | 12.7 | 0.148 | 2.37 | 0.288 |
| Propane | $C_3H_8$ | 369.97 | 96.81 | 665.95 | 206.26 | 42.01 | 617.4 | 0.220 | 13.7 | 0.200 | 3.21 | 0.278 |
| n-Butane | $C_4H_{10}$ | 425.17 | 152.01 | 765.31 | 305.62 | 37.47 | 550.7 | 0.228 | 14.2 | 0.255 | 4.08 | 0.274 |
| n-Pentane | $C_5H_{12}$ | 469.78 | 196.62 | 845.60 | 385.92 | 33.31 | 489.5 | 0.232 | 14.5 | 0.311 | 4.98 | 0.268 |
| n-Hexane | $C_6H_{14}$ | 507.9 | 234.7 | 914.1 | 454.5 | 29.92 | 439.7 | 0.234 | 14.6 | 0.368 | 5.90 | 0.264 |
| n-Heptane | $C_7H_{16}$ | 540.16 | 267.01 | 972.31 | 512.62 | 27.01 | 396.9 | 0.235 | 14.7 | 0.426 | 6.82 | 0.260 |
| n-Octane | $C_8H_{18}$ | 569.4 | 296.2 | 1024.9 | 565.2 | 24.64 | 362.1 | 0.235 | 14.7 | 0.486 | 7.77 | 0.256 |
| n-Nonane | $C_9H_{20}$ | 595. | 322. | 1071. | 611. | 22.5 | 331. | 0.236 | 14.7 | 0.543 | 8.72 | 0.250 |
| n-Decane | $C_{10}H_{22}$ | 619. | 346. | 1114. | 654. | 20.8 | 306. | 0.236 | 14.7 | 0.602 | 9.68 | 0.246 |
| n-Undecane | $C_{11}H_{24}$ | 640. | 367. | 1152. | 692. | 19.2 | 282. | 0.237 | 14.8 | 0.660 | 10.6 | 0.242 |
| n-Dodecane | $C_{12}H_{26}$ | 659. | 386. | 1186. | 726. | 17.9 | 263. | 0.237 | 14.8 | 0.718 | 11.5 | 0.237 |
| n-Tridecane | $C_{13}H_{28}$ | 677. | 404. | 1219. | 759. | 17. | 250. | 0.24 | 15. | 0.78 | 12. | 0.23 |
| n-Tetradecane | $C_{14}H_{30}$ | 695. | 422. | 1251. | 791. | 16. | 230. | 0.24 | 15. | 0.83 | 13. | 0.23 |
| n-Pentadecane | $C_{15}H_{32}$ | 710. | 437. | 1278. | 818. | 15. | 220. | 0.24 | 15. | 0.89 | 14. | 0.23 |
| n-Hexadecane | $C_{16}H_{34}$ | 725. | 452. | 1305. | 845. | 14. | 200 | 0.24 | 15. | 0.95 | 15. | 0.22 |
| n-Heptadecane | $C_{17}H_{36}$ | 735. | 462. | 1323. | 863. | 13. | 190. | 0.24 | 15. | 1.0 | 16. | 0.22 |
| n-Octadecane | $C_{18}H_{38}$ | 750. | 477. | 1350. | 890. | 13. | 180. | 0.24 | 15. | 1.1 | 17. | 0.22 |
| n-Nonadecane | $C_{19}H_{40}$ | 760. | 487. | 1368. | 908. | 12. | 170. | 0.24 | 15. | 1.1 | 18. | 0.22 |
| n-Eicosane | $C_{20}H_{42}$ | 775. | 502. | 1395. | 935. | 11. | 160. | 0.24 | 15. | 1.2 | 19. | 0.21 |

## TABLE 1i – PARAFFINS, $C_1$ TO $C_5$
### CRITICAL TEMPERATURE, PRESSURE, DENSITY, VOLUME, AND COMPRESSIBILITY FACTOR
October 31, 1948

| Compound | Formula | Critical Temperature | | | | Critical Pressure | | Critical Density | | Critical Volume | | Critical $pv/RT$ |
|---|---|---|---|---|---|---|---|---|---|---|---|---|
| | | °K | °C | °R | °F | atm | lb/in² | g/ml | lb/ft³ | liter/mole | ft³/lb mole | |
| Methane | $CH_4$ | 190.7 | −82.5 | 343.3 | −116.5 | 45.80 | 673.1 | 0.162 | 10.1 | 0.099 | 1.59 | 0.290 |
| Ethane | $C_2H_6$ | 305.43 | +32.27 | 549.77 | +90.09 | 48.20 | 708.3 | 0.203 | 12.7 | 0.148 | 2.37 | 0.288 |
| Propane | $C_3H_8$ | 369.97 | 96.81 | 665.95 | 206.26 | 42.01 | 617.4 | 0.220 | 13.7 | 0.200 | 3.21 | 0.278 |
| n–Butane | $C_4H_{10}$ | 425.17 | 152.01 | 765.31 | 305.62 | 37.47 | 550.7 | 0.228 | 14.2 | 0.255 | 4.08 | 0.274 |
| 2–Methylpropane (Isobutane) | " | 408.14 | 134.98 | 734.65 | 274.96 | 36.00 | 529.1 | .221 | 13.8 | .263 | 4.21 | .283 |
| n–Pentane | $C_5H_{12}$ | 469.78 | 196.62 | 845.60 | 385.92 | 33.31 | 489.5 | 0.232 | 14.5 | 0.311 | 4.98 | 0.268 |
| 2–Methylbutane (Isopentane) | " | 461.0 | 187.8 | 829.8 | 370.0 | 32.9 | 483. | .234 | 14.6 | .308 | 4.94 | .269 |
| 2,2–Dimethylpropane (Neopentane) | " | 433.76 | 160.60 | 780.77 | 321.08 | 31.57 | 464.0 | .238 | 14.9 | .303 | 4.86 | .269 |

328

TABLE 2i (PART 1) — PARAFFINS, $C_6$
CRITICAL TEMPERATURE, PRESSURE, DENSITY, VOLUME, AND COMPRESSIBILITY FACTOR
October 31, 1948

| Compound | Formula | Critical Temperature | | | | Critical Pressure | | Critical Density | | Critical Volume | | Critical $pv/RT$ |
|---|---|---|---|---|---|---|---|---|---|---|---|---|
| | | °K | °C | °R | °F | atm | lb/in² | g/ml | lb/ft³ | liter/mole | ft³/lb mole | |
| n-Hexane | $C_6H_{14}$ | 507.9 | 234.7 | 914.1 | 454.5 | 29.92 | 439.7 | 0.234 | 14.6 | 0.368 | 5.90 | 0.264 |
| 2-Methylpentane | " | 498.1 | 224.9 | 896.5 | 436.8 | 29.95 | 440.1 | .235 | 14.7 | .367 | 5.87 | .269 |
| 3-Methylpentane | " | 504.4 | 231.2 | 907.8 | 448.2 | 30.83 | 453.1 | .235 | 14.7 | .367 | 5.87 | .273 |
| 2,2-Dimethylbutane | " | 489.4 | 216.2 | 880.9 | 421.2 | 30.67 | 450.5 | .240 | 15.0 | .359 | 5.75 | .274 |
| 2,3-Dimethylbutane | " | 500.3 | 227.1 | 900.5 | 440.8 | 30.99 | 455.4 | .241 | 15.0 | .358 | 5.73 | .270 |

## TABLE 2i (PART 2) — PARAFFINS, C$_7$
### CRITICAL TEMPERATURE, PRESSURE, DENSITY, VOLUME, AND COMPRESSIBILITY FACTOR
October 31, 1948

| Compound | Formula | Critical Temperature | | | | Critical Pressure | | Critical Density | | Critical Volume | | Critical $pv/RT$ |
|---|---|---|---|---|---|---|---|---|---|---|---|---|
| | | °K | °C | °R | °F | atm | lb/in² | g/ml | lb/ft³ | liter/mole | ft³/lb mole | |
| n-Heptane | C$_7$H$_{16}$ | 540.16 | 267.01 | 972.31 | 512.62 | 27.01 | 396.9 | 0.235 | 14.7 | 0.426 | 6.82 | 0.260 |
| 2-Methylhexane | " | 531.1 | 257.9 | 955.9 | 496.2 | 27.2 | 400. | .234 | 14.6 | .428 | 6.86 | .267 |
| 3-Methylhexane | " | 535.6 | 262.4 | 964.0 | 504.3 | 28.1 | 413. | .240 | 15.0 | .418 | 6.70 | .267 |
| 3-Ethylpentane | " | 540.8 | 267.6 | 973.4 | 513.7 | 28.6 | 420. | .241 | 15.0 | .416 | 6.66 | .268 |
| 2,2-Dimethylpentane | " | 520.9 | 247.7 | 937.6 | 477.9 | 28.4 | 417. | .248 | 15.5 | .404 | 6.47 | .268 |
| 2,3-Dimethylpentane | " | 537.8 | 264.6 | 968.0 | 508.3 | 29.2 | 429. | .247 | 15.4 | .405 | 6.49 | .268 |
| 2,4-Dimethylpentane | " | 520.3 | 247.1 | 936.5 | 476.8 | 27.4 | 403. | .239 | 14.9 | .420 | 6.73 | .270 |
| 3,3-Dimethylpentane | " | 536. | 263. | 965. | 505. | 30. | 440. | | | | | |
| 2,2,3-Trimethylbutane | " | 531.5 | 258.3 | 956.6 | 496.9 | 29.75 | 437.2 | .254 | 15.9 | .394 | 6.31 | .269 |

TABLE 3i - PARAFFINS, $C_8$

CRITICAL TEMPERATURE, PRESSURE, DENSITY, VOLUME, AND COMPRESSIBILITY FACTOR

February 28, 1949

| Compound | Formula | Critical Temperature | | | | Critical Pressure | | Critical Density | | Critical Volume | | Critical $PV/RT$ |
|---|---|---|---|---|---|---|---|---|---|---|---|---|
| | | °K | °C | °R | °F | atm | lb/in² | g/ml | lb/ft³ | liter/mole | ft³/lb mole | |
| n-Octane | $C_8H_{18}$ | 569.4 | 296.2 | 1024.9 | 565.2 | 24.64 | 362.1 | 0.235 | 14.7 | 0.486 | 7.77 | 0.256 |
| 2-Methylheptane | " | 561. | 288. | 1010. | 550. | 24.8 | 364. | .234 | 14.6 | .489 | 7.82 | .263 |
| 3-Methylheptane | " | 565. | 292. | 1017. | 557. | 25.6 | 376. | .239 | 14.9 | .478 | 7.67 | .264 |
| 4-Methylheptane | " | 563. | 290. | 1013. | 553. | 25.6 | 376. | .240 | 15.0 | .476 | 7.61 | .264 |
| 3-Ethylhexane | " | 567. | 294. | 1021. | 561. | 26.4 | 388. | .245 | 15.3 | .466 | 7.46 | .264 |
| 2,2-Dimethylhexane | " | 552. | 279. | 994. | 534. | 25.6 | 376. | .245 | 15.3 | .467 | 7.47 | .264 |
| 2,3-Dimethylhexane | " | 566. | 293. | 1019. | 559. | 26.6 | 391. | .248 | 15.5 | .461 | 7.37 | .264 |
| 2,4-Dimethylhexane | " | 555. | 282. | 999. | 539. | 25.8 | 379. | .245 | 15.3 | .466 | 7.47 | .264 |
| 2,5-Dimethylhexane | " | 552. | 279. | 994. | 534. | 25.0 | 367. | .239 | 14.9 | .478 | 7.67 | .264 |
| 3,3-Dimethylhexane | " | 564. | 291. | 1015. | 555. | 27.2 | 400. | .254 | 15.9 | .450 | 7.18 | .264 |
| 3,4-Dimethylhexane | " | 571. | 298. | 1028. | 568. | 27.4 | 403. | .253 | 15.8 | .452 | 7.23 | .264 |
| 2-Methyl-3-ethylpentane | " | 568. | 295. | 1022. | 562. | 27.4 | 403. | .254 | 15.9 | .450 | 7.18 | .264 |
| 3-Methyl-3-ethylpentane | " | 578. | 305. | 1040. | 580. | 28.9 | 425. | .263 | 16.4 | .435 | 6.96 | .265 |
| 2,2,3-Trimethylpentane | " | 567. | 294. | 1021. | 561. | 28.2 | 414. | .261 | 16.3 | .437 | 7.01 | .265 |
| 2,2,4-Trimethylpentane | " | 544.31 | 271.15 | 979.76 | 520.07 | 25.50 | 374.7 | .237 | 14.8 | .482 | 7.72 | .275 |
| 2,3,3-Trimethylpentane | " | 576. | 303. | 1037. | 577. | 29.0 | 426. | .264 | 16.5 | .433 | 6.92 | .266 |
| 2,3,4-Trimethylpentane | " | 568. | 295. | 1022. | 562. | 27.6 | 406. | .256 | 16.0 | .447 | 7.14 | .265 |
| 2,2,3,3-Tetramethylbutane | " | 544.0 | 270.8 | 979.1 | 519.4 | 24.5 | 360. | .238 | 14.9 | .480 | 7.67 | .263 |

2

331

## TABLE 6i - ALKYL CYCLOPENTANES, C$_5$ TO C$_7$
### CRITICAL TEMPERATURE, PRESSURE, DENSITY, VOLUME, AND COMPRESSIBILITY FACTOR
August 31, 1949

| Compound | Formula | Critical Temperature | | | | Critical Pressure | | Critical Density | | Critical Volume | | Critical $PV/RT$ |
|---|---|---|---|---|---|---|---|---|---|---|---|---|
| | | °K | °C | °R | °F | atm | lb/in² | g/ml | lb/ft³ | liter/mole | ft³/lb mole | |
| Cyclopentane | C$_5$H$_{10}$ | 511.76 | 238.60 | 921.17 | 461.48 | 44.55 | 654.7 | 0.270 | 16.9 | 0.260 | 4.15 | 0.276 |
| Methylcyclopentane | C$_6$H$_{12}$ | 532.77 | 259.61 | 958.99 | 499.30 | 37.36 | 549.0 | 0.264 | 16.5 | 0.319 | 5.10 | 0.273 |
| Ethylcyclopentane | C$_7$H$_{14}$ | 569.46 | 296.30 | 1025.03 | 565.34 | 33.53 | 492.8 | 0.262 | 16.4 | 0.375 | 5.99 | 0.269 |
| 1,1-Dimethylcyclopentane | " | 550. | 277. | 990. | 530. | 35. | 510. | .28 | 18. | .35 | 5.6 | .27 |
| 1,cis-2-Dimethylcyclopentane | " | 565. | 292. | 1017. | 557. | 34. | 500. | .27 | 17. | .37 | 5.9 | .27 |
| 1,trans-2-Dimethylcyclopentane | " | 555. | 282. | 999. | 539. | 34. | 500. | .27 | 17. | .36 | 5.8 | .27 |
| 1,cis-3-Dimethylcyclopentane | " | 555. | 282. | 999. | 539. | 34. | 500. | .27 | 17. | .36 | 5.8 | .27 |
| 1,trans-3-Dimethylcyclopentane | " | 555. | 282. | 999. | 539. | 35. | 510. | .28 | 18. | .35 | 5.6 | .27 |

## TABLE 8i (PART 1) — MONOOLEFINS, $C_2$ TO $C_5$
### CRITICAL TEMPERATURE, PRESSURE, DENSITY, VOLUME, AND COMPRESSIBILITY FACTOR
October 31, 1948

| Compound | Formula | Critical Temperature | | | | Critical Pressure | | Critical Density | | Critical Volume | | Critical $PV/RT$ |
|---|---|---|---|---|---|---|---|---|---|---|---|---|
| | | °K | °C | °R | °F | atm | lb/in² | g/ml | lb/ft³ | liter/mole | ft³/lb mole | |
| Ethene (Ethylene) | $C_2H_4$ | 283.06 | 9.90 | 509.51 | 49.82 | 50.50 | 742.1 | 0.227 | 14.2 | 0.124 | 1.98 | 0.269 |
| Propene (Propylene) | $C_3H_6$ | 365.1 | 91.9 | 657.2 | 197.4 | 45.4 | 667. | 0.233 | 14.5 | 0.181 | 2.90 | 0.274 |
| 1-Butene | $C_4H_8$ | 419.6 | 146.4 | 755.3 | 295.6 | 39.7 | 583. | 0.233 | 14.5 | 0.241 | 3.87 | 0.277 |
| cis-2-Butene | " | 428. | 155. | 770. | 311. | 41. | 600. | .238 | 14.9 | .236 | 2.82 | .276 |
| trans-2-Butene | " | | | | | | | | | | | |
| 2-Methylpropene | " | 417.89 | 144.73 | 752.20 | 292.51 | 39.45 | 579.8 | .234 | 14.6 | .240 | 2.88 | .276 |
| 1-Pentene | $C_5H_{10}$ | 474. | 201. | 853. | 394. | 39.9 | 586. | | | | | |
| cis-2-Pentene | " | | | | | | | | | | | |
| trans-2-Pentene | " | | | | | | | | | | | |
| 2-Methyl-1-butene | " | | | | | | | | | | | |
| 3-Methyl-1-butene | " | | | | | | | | | | | |
| 2-Methyl-2-butene | " | | | | | | | | | | | |

## TABLE 11i (PART 1) – DIOLEFINS, $C_3$ TO $C_5$
### CRITICAL TEMPERATURE, PRESSURE, DENSITY, VOLUME, AND COMPRESSIBILITY FACTOR
October 31, 1948

| Compound | Formula | Critical Temperature | | | | Critical Pressure | | Critical Density | | Critical Volume | | Critical $PV/RT$ |
|---|---|---|---|---|---|---|---|---|---|---|---|---|
| | | °K | °C | °R | °F | atm | lb/in² | g/ml | lb/ft³ | liter/mole | ft3/lb mole | |
| Propadiene (Allene) | $C_3H_4$ | 393. | 120. | 707. | 248. | | | | | | | |
| 1,2-Butadiene | $C_4H_6$ | | | | | | | | | | | |
| 1,3-Butadiene | " | 425. | 152. | 765. | 306. | 42.7 | 628. | 0.245 | 15.29 | 0.221 | 3.54 | 0.271 |
| 1,2-Pentadiene | $C_5H_8$ | | | | | | | | | | | |
| 1-*cis*-3-Pentadiene | " | | | | | | | | | | | |
| 1-*trans*-3-Pentadiene | " | | | | | | | | | | | |
| 1,4-Pentadiene | " | | | | | | | | | | | |
| 2,3-Pentadiene | " | | | | | | | | | | | |
| 3-Methyl-1,2-butadiene | " | | | | | | | | | | | |
| 2-Methyl-1,3-butadiene (Isoprene) | " | | | | | | | | | | | |

TABLE 12i – ACETYLENES, $C_2$ TO $C_5$
CRITICAL TEMPERATURE, PRESSURE, DENSITY, VOLUME, AND COMPRESSIBILITY FACTOR
October 31, 1948

| Compound | Formula | Critical Temperature | | | | Critical Pressure | | Critical Density | | Critical Volume | | Critical $PV/RT$ |
|---|---|---|---|---|---|---|---|---|---|---|---|---|
| | | °K | °C | °R | °F | atm | lb/in² | g/ml | lb/ft³ | liter/mole | ft³/lb mole | |
| Ethyne (Acetylene) | $C_2H_2$ | 309.5 | 36.3 | 557.1 | 97.4 | 61.6 | 905. | 0.231 | 14.4 | 0.113 | 1.81 | 0.274 |
| Propyne (Methylacetylene) | $C_3H_4$ | 394.8 | 121.6 | 710.6 | 251.0 | | | | | | | |
| 1-Butyne (Ethylacetylene) | $C_4H_6$ | 463.7. | 190.5 | 834.7 | 375.0 | | | | | | | |
| 2-Butyne (Dimethylacetylene) | " | 488. | 215. | 879. | 419. | | | | | | | |
| 1-Pentyne | $C_5H_8$ | 493. | 220. | 888. | 428. | | | | | | | |
| 2-Pentyne | " | | | | | | | | | | | |
| 3-Methyl-1-butyne | " | | | | | | | | | | | |

TABLE 5i - ALKYL BENZENES, C$_6$ TO C$_9$
CRITICAL TEMPERATURE, PRESSURE, DENSITY, VOLUME, AND COMPRESSIBILITY FACTOR
April 30, 1949

| Compound | Formula | Critical Temperature | | | | Critical Pressure | | Critical Density | | Critical Volume | | Critical $PV/RT$ |
|---|---|---|---|---|---|---|---|---|---|---|---|---|
| | | °K | °C | °R | °F | atm | lb/in² | g/ml | lb/ft³ | liter/mole | ft³/lb mole | |
| Benzene | C$_6$H$_6$ | 562.61 | 289.45 | 1012.70 | 553.01 | 48.6 | 714. | 0.300 | 18.7 | 0.260 | 4.18 | 0.274 |
| Methylbenzene (Toluene) | C$_7$H$_8$ | 594.0 | 320.8 | 1069.2 | 609.51 | 40. | 590. | 0.29 | 18. | 0.32 | 5.2 | 0.26 |
| Ethylbenzene | C$_8$H$_{10}$ | 619.7 | 346.4 | 1115.5 | 655.8 | 37. | 540. | 0.29 | 18. | 0.36 | 5.9 | 0.26 |
| 1,2-Dimethylbenzene (o-xylene) | " | 632.2 | 359.0 | 1138.0 | 678.3 | 36. | 530. | .28 | 17. | .38 | 6.2 | .26 |
| 1,3-Dimethylbenzene (m-xylene) | " | 619.2 | 346.0 | 1114.6 | 654.9 | 35. | 510. | .27 | 17. | .39 | 6.2 | .27 |
| 1,4-Dimethylbenzene (p-xylene) | " | 618.2 | 345.0 | 1112.8 | 653.1 | 34. | 500. | .29 | 18. | .37 | 5.9 | .25 |
| n-Propylbenzene | C$_9$H$_{12}$ | 638. | 365. | 1148. | 688. | 31. | 460. | 0.28 | 17. | 0.44 | 7.1 | 0.26 |
| Isopropylbenzene | " | 636. | 363. | 1145. | 685. | 31. | 460. | .28 | 17. | .44 | 7.1 | .26 |
| 1-Methyl-2-ethylbenzene | " | 653. | 380. | 1175. | 715. | 31. | 460. | .28 | 17. | .44 | 7.1 | .26 |
| 1-Methyl-3-ethylbenzene | " | 636. | 363. | 1145. | 685. | 31. | 460. | .28 | 17. | .44 | 7.1 | .26 |
| 1-Methyl-4-ethylbenzene | " | 636. | 363. | 1145. | 685. | 31. | 460. | .28 | 17. | .44 | 7.1 | .26 |
| 1,2,3-Trimethylbenzene | " | 668. | 395. | 1202. | 742. | 31. | 460. | .28 | 17. | .44 | 7.1 | .26 |
| 1,2,4-Trimethylbenzene | " | 654.7 | 381.5 | 1178.5 | 718.8 | 32. | 470. | .28 | 17. | .44 | 7.1 | .26 |
| 1,3,5-Trimethylbenzene | " | 642. | 369. | 1156. | 696. | 32. | 470. | .28 | 17. | .43 | 7.1 | .26 |

TABLE 20k (PART 1), Page 1 — NORMAL PARAFFINS, $C_1$ TO $C_{20}$
VAPOR PRESSURES AND BOILING POINTS, AT 10 TO 1500 mm Hg
February 28, 1949; December 31, 1952

| Pressure | Methane | Ethane | Propane | n–Butane | n–Pentane | n–Hexane | n–Heptane | n–Octane | n–Nonane |
|---|---|---|---|---|---|---|---|---|---|
| mm Hg | Temperature in °C | | | | | | | | |
| 10 | –195.51 | –142.88 | –108.51 | –77.76 | –50.1 | –25.1 | –2.1 | 19.2 | 39.12 |
| 20 | –191.77 | –136.69 | –100.91 | –68.93 | –40.2 | –14.3 | +9.49 | 31.5 | 51.98 |
| 30 | –189.41 | –132.74 | –96.07 | –63.30 | –33.93 | –7.4 | 16.84 | 39.28 | 60.16 |
| 40 | –187.66 (solid) | –129.78 | –92.44 | –59.08 | –29.22 | –2.3 | 22.352 | 45.12 | 66.30 |
| 50 | –186.25 | –127.39 | –89.51 | –55.66 | –25.41 | +1.85 | 26.808 | 49.847 | 71.255 |
| 60 | –185.06 | –125.36 | –87.02 | –52.77 | –22.18 | 5.36 | 30.573 | 53.838 | 75.445 |
| 80 | –183.12[a] | –122.03 | –82.94 | –48.02 | –16.89 | 11.13 | 36.758 | 60.392 | 82.324 |
| 100 | –181.45 | –119.33 | –79.63 | –44.17 | –12.59 | 15.81 | 41.772 | 65.704 | 87.899 |
| 150 | –178.09 | –114.12 | –73.26 | –36.76 | –4.33 | 24.807 | 51.410 | 75.912 | 98.612 |
| 200 | –175.55 | –110.19 | –68.43 | –31.16 | +1.92 | 31.609 | 58.695 | 83.626 | 106.706 |
| 250 | –173.47 | –106.98 | –64.51 | –26.59 | 7.01 | 37.147 | 64.624 | 89.903 | 113.292 |
| 300 | –171.69 | –104.25 | –61.17 | –22.71 | 11.34 | 41.852 | 69.662 | 95.235 | 118.885 |
| 400 | –168.76 | –99.74 | –55.65 | –16.29 | 18.49 | 49.631 | 77.987 | 104.045 | 128.127 |
| 500 | –166.35 | –96.05 | –51.14 | –11.04 | 24.337 | 55.985 | 84.786 | 111.238 | 135.670 |
| 600 | –164.29 | –92.90 | –47.29 | –6.57 | 29.319 | 61.400 | 90.578 | 117.364 | 142.095 |
| 700 | –162.48 | –90.14 | –43.92 | –2.65 | 33.685 | 66.144 | 95.651 | 122.730 | 147.721 |
| 710 | –162.31 | –89.88 | –43.60 | –2.28 | 34.094 | 66.589 | 96.127 | 123.232 | 148.248 |
| 720 | –162.14 | –89.63 | –43.29 | –1.92 | 34.499 | 67.028 | 96.596 | 123.729 | 148.769 |
| 730 | –161.98 | –89.37 | –42.98 | –1.56 | 34.899 | 67.463 | 97.061 | 124.221 | 149.284 |
| 740 | –161.81 | –89.12 | –42.67 | –1.20 | 35.295 | 67.893 | 97.521 | 124.707 | 149.794 |
| 750 | –161.65 | –88.88 | –42.37 | –0.85 | 35.687 | 68.319 | 97.977 | 125.189 | 150.299 |
| 760 | –161.49 | –88.63 | –42.07 | –0.50 | 36.074 | 68.740 | 98.427 | 125.665 | 150.798 |
| 770 | –161.33 | –88.39 | –41.77 | –0.16 | 36.458 | 69.157 | 98.873 | 126.136 | 151.292 |
| 780 | –161.17 | –88.15 | –41.48 | +0.19 | 36.838 | 69.570 | 99.314 | 126.603 | 151.781 |
| 790 | –161.02 | –87.91 | –41.19 | 0.52 | 37.214 | 69.979 | 99.751 | 127.065 | 152.266 |
| 800 | –160.86 | –87.67 | –40.90 | 0.86 | 37.587 | 70.383 | 100.183 | 127.522 | 152.745 |
| 900 | –159.39 | –85.44 | –38.17 | 4.04 | 41.12 | 74.23 | 104.29 | 131.87 | 157.30 |
| 1000 | –158.04 | –83.38 | –35.66 | 6.95 | 44.37 | 77.75 | 108.06 | 135.85 | 161.47 |
| 1200 | –155.6 | –79.71 | –31.2 | 12.2 | 50.17 | 84.05 | 114.79 | 142.96 | 168.93 |
| 1500 | –152.5 | –75.00 | –25.4 | 18.9 | 57.6 | 92.1 | 123.41 | 152.1 | 178.48 |

The values above are calculated from the constants below and the Antoine equation:

$$\log_{10} P = A - B/(C + t); \quad t = B/(A - \log_{10} P) - C$$

(P in mm Hg; $t$ in °C)

Constants of the Antoine Equation

| | Methane | Ethane | Propane | n–Butane | n–Pentane | n–Hexane | n–Heptane | n–Octane | n–Nonane |
|---|---|---|---|---|---|---|---|---|---|
| A | 6.61184 / 7.69540[b] | 6.80266 | 6.82973 | 6.83029 | 6.85221 | 6.87776 | 6.90240 | 6.92377 | 6.93513 |
| B | 389.93 / 532.20[b] | 656.40 | 813.20 | 945.90 | 1064.63 | 1171.530 | 1268.115 | 1355.126 | 1428.811 |
| C | 266.00 / 275.00[b] | 256.00 | 248.00 | 240.00 | 232.000 | 224.366 | 216.900 | 209.517 | 201.619 |

[a] At the triple point, –182.48°C, the pressure is 87.7 mm Hg.　　[b] For the solid–vapor equilibrium.

# TABLE 20k (PART 1), Page 2 — NORMAL PARAFFINS, $C_1$ TO $C_{20}$
## VAPOR PRESSURES AND BOILING POINTS, AT 10 TO 1500 mm Hg
### February 28, 1949; December 31, 1952

| Pressure | n–Decane | n–Undecane | n–Dodecane | n–Tridecane | n–Tetradecane | n–Pentadecane | n–Hexadecane | n–Heptadecane | n–Octadecane |
|---|---|---|---|---|---|---|---|---|---|
| mm Hg | Temperature in °C | | | | | | | | |
| 10 | 57.7 | 75.1 | 91.6 | 107. | 122. | 136. | 149.2 | 162. | 174. |
| 20 | 71.6 | 89.0 | 106.0 | 122. | 137. | 152. | 165.1 | 178. | 190. |
| 30 | 79.65 | 97.90 | 115.13 | 131. | 147. | 162. | 175.24 | 188. | 201. |
| 40 | 86.05 | 104.55 | 121.99 | 139. | 154. | 169. | 182.83 | 196. | 209. |
| 50 | 91.220 | 109.921 | 127.536 | 144. | 160. | 175. | 188.964 | 202. | 215. |
| 60 | 95.591 | 114.459 | 132.221 | 149. | 165. | 180. | 194.142 | 208. | 220. |
| 80 | 102.767 | 121.908 | 139.911 | 157. | 173. | 188. | 202.638 | 216. | 229. |
| 100 | 108.582 | 127.943 | 146.142 | 163.3 | 179.6 | 195.0 | 209.519 | 223.2 | 236. |
| 150 | 119.752 | 139.533 | 158.107 | 175.6 | 192.3 | 207.9 | 222.725 | 236.6 | 249.8 |
| 200 | 128.190 | 148.286 | 167.142 | 184.9 | 201.8 | 217.7 | 232.691 | 246.8 | 260.1 |
| 250 | 135.054 | 155.404 | 174.490 | 192.5 | 209.5 | 225.6 | 240.791 | 255.0 | 268.5 |
| 300 | 140.883 | 161.447 | 180.728 | 198.9 | 216.1 | 232.3 | 247.666 | 262.0 | 275.6 |
| 400 | 150.511 | 171.428 | 191.030 | 209.5 | 227.0 | 243.4 | 259.013 | 273.5 | 287.4 |
| 500 | 158.369 | 179.571 | 199.435 | 218.1 | 235.8 | 252.5 | 268.265 | 283.0 | 296.9 |
| 600 | 165.060 | 186.503 | 206.590 | 225.5 | 243.4 | 260.2 | 276.138 | 291.0 | 305.1 |
| 700 | 170.919 | 192.572 | 212.854 | 231.92 | 249.96 | 266.9 | 283.027 | 298.0 | 312.2 |
| 710 | 171.468 | 193.140 | 213.440 | 232.53 | 250.58 | 267.58 | 283.672 | 298.6 | 312.9 |
| 720 | 172.010 | 193.702 | 214.020 | 233.12 | 251.19 | 268.20 | 284.309 | 299.29 | 313.54 |
| 730 | 172.547 | 194.258 | 214.593 | 233.71 | 251.80 | 268.82 | 284.940 | 299.93 | 314.20 |
| 740 | 173.078 | 194.808 | 215.161 | 234.30 | 252.39 | 269.43 | 285.564 | 300.57 | 314.84 |
| 750 | 173.603 | 195.352 | 215.723 | 234.87 | 252.99 | 270.03 | 286.182 | 301.20 | 315.49 |
| 760 | 174.123 | 195.890 | 216.278 | 235.44 | 253.57 | 270.63 | 286.793 | 301.82 | 316.12 |
| 770 | 174.638 | 196.423 | 216.828 | 236.01 | 254.15 | 271.22 | 287.397 | 302.44 | 316.75 |
| 780 | 175.147 | 196.950 | 217.372 | 236.57 | 254.72 | 271.81 | 287.995 | 303.05 | 317.37 |
| 790 | 175.652 | 197.473 | 217.912 | 237.12 | 255.29 | 272.39 | 288.589 | 303.6 | 318.0 |
| 800 | 176.150 | 197.990 | 218.445 | 237.67 | 255.85 | 273.0 | 289.175 | 304.2 | 318.6 |
| 900 | 180.89 | 202.90 | 223.51 | 242.9 | 261.2 | 278.4 | 294.74 | 309.9 | 324.4 |
| 1000 | 185.24 | 207.40 | 228.15 | 247.6 | 266.1 | 283.4 | 299.84 | 315.1 | 329.6 |
| 1200 | 193.00 | 215.43 | 236.44 | 256. | 275. | 292. | 308.95 | 324. | 339. |
| 1500 | 202.9 | 225.7 | 247.1 | 267. | 286. | 304. | 320.6 | 336. | 351. |

The values above are calculated from the constants below and the Antoine equation:

$$\log_{10} P = A - B/(C + t); \quad t = B/(A - \log_{10} P) - C$$

(P in mm Hg; t in °C)

### Constants of the Antoine Equation

| | n–Decane | n–Undecane | n–Dodecane | n–Tridecane | n–Tetradecane | n–Pentadecane | n–Hexadecane | n–Heptadecane | n–Octadecane |
|---|---|---|---|---|---|---|---|---|---|
| A | 6.95367 | 6.97674 | 6.98059 | 6.9887 | 6.9957 | 7.0017 | 7.03044 | 7.0115 | 7.0156 |
| B | 1501.268 | 1572.477 | 1625.928 | 1677.43 | 1725.46 | 1768.82 | 1831.317 | 1847.82 | 1883.73 |
| C | 194.480 | 188.022 | 180.311 | 172.90 | 165.75 | 158.60 | 154.528 | 145.52 | 139.46 |

338

| Pressure | $n-$ Nonadecane | $n-$ Eicosane | | | | | | | |
|---|---|---|---|---|---|---|---|---|---|
| mm Hg | Temperature in °C | | | | | | | | |
| 10 | 185. | 196. | | | | | | | |
| 20 | 202. | 213. | | | | | | | |
| 30 | 212. | 224. | | | | | | | |
| 40 | 220. | 232. | | | | | | | |
| 50 | 227. | 238. | | | | | | | |
| 60 | 232. | 244. | | | | | | | |
| 80 | 241. | 253. | | | | | | | |
| 100 | 248. | 260. | | | | | | | |
| 150 | 262. | 274. | | | | | | | |
| 200 | 273. | 285. | | | | | | | |
| 250 | 281.3 | 293.6 | | | | | | | |
| 300 | 288.6 | 300.9 | | | | | | | |
| 400 | 300.5 | 313.0 | | | | | | | |
| 500 | 310.2 | 322.9 | | | | | | | |
| 600 | 318.5 | 331.3 | | | | | | | |
| 700 | 325.8 | 338.7 | | | | | | | |
| 710 | 326.4 | 339.4 | | | | | | | |
| 720 | 327.1 | 340.1 | | | | | | | |
| 730 | 328.2 | 340.7 | | | | | | | |
| 740 | 328.4 | 341.4 | | | | | | | |
| 750 | 329.1 | 342.1 | | | | | | | |
| 760 | 329.7 | 342.7 | | | | | | | |
| 770 | 330.4 | 343.4 | | | | | | | |
| 780 | 331.0 | 344.0 | | | | | | | |
| 790 | 331.6 | 344.6 | | | | | | | |
| 800 | 332.2 | 345.3 | | | | | | | |
| 900 | 338. | 351. | | | | | | | |
| 1000 | 343. | 357. | | | | | | | |
| 1200 | 353. | 366. | | | | | | | |
| 1500 | 365. | 379. | | | | | | | |

The values above are calculated from the constants below and the Antoine equation:

$$\log_{10} P = A - B/(C + t); \quad t = B/(A - \log_{10} P) - C$$

(P in mm Hg; t in °C)

Constants of the Antoine Equation

| | | | | | | | | | |
|---|---|---|---|---|---|---|---|---|---|
| A | 7.0192 | 7.0225 | | | | | | | |
| B | 1917.0 | 1948.7 | | | | | | | |
| C | 133.5 | 127.8 | | | | | | | |

TABLE 20k (PART 1), Page 3 – NORMAL PARAFFINS, $C_1$ TO $C_{20}$
VAPOR PRESSURES AND BOILING POINTS, AT 10 TO 1500 mm Hg
February 28, 1949; December 31, 1952

## TABLE 1k – PARAFFINS, $C_1$ to $C_5$
### VAPOR PRESSURES AND BOILING POINTS, AT 10 TO 1500 mm Hg
June 30, 1944; December 31, 1952

| Pressure | Methane | Ethane | Propane | n–Butane | 2–Methyl-propane (Isobutane) | n–Pentane | 2–Methyl-butane (Isopentane) | 2,2–Dimethyl-propane (Neopentane) | |
|---|---|---|---|---|---|---|---|---|---|
| mm Hg | Temperature in °C | | | | | | | | |
| 10 | −195.51 | −142.88 | −108.51 | −77.76 | −86.42 | −50.1 | −56.9 | | |
| 20 | −191.77 | −136.69 | −100.91 | −68.93 | −77.93 | −40.2 | −47.3 | | |
| 30 | −189.41 (solid) | −132.74 | − 96.07 | −63.30 | −72.52 | −33.93 | −41.10 | | |
| 40 | −187.66 | −129.78 | − 92.44 | −59.08 | −68.45 | −29.22 | −36.47 | | |
| 50 | −186.25 | −127.39 | − 89.51 | −55.66 | −65.16 | −25.41 | −32.73 | | |
| 60 | −185.06 | −125.36 | − 87.02 | −52.77 | −62.37 | −22.18 | −29.56 | | |
| 80 | −183.12 a | −122.03 | − 82.94 | −48.02 | −57.79 | −16.89 | −24.36 | | |
| 100 | −181.45 | −119.33 | − 79.63 | −44.17 | −54.07 | −12.59 | −20.14 | | |
| 150 | −178.09 | −114.12 | − 73.26 | −36.76 | −46.91 | − 4.33 | −12.01 | | |
| 200 | −175.55 | −110.19 | − 68.43 | −31.16 | −41.49 | + 1.92 | − 5.85 | | |
| 250 | −173.47 | −106.98 | − 64.51 | −26.59 | −37.06 | 7.01 | − 0.84 | b | |
| 300 | −171.69 | −104.25 | − 61.17 | −22.71 | −33.30 | 11.34 | + 3.42 | −13.85 | |
| 400 | −168.76 | − 99.74 | − 55.65 | −16.29 | −27.07 | 18.49 | 10.48 | − 7.11 | |
| 500 | −166.35 | − 96.05 | − 51.14 | −11.04 | −21.98 | 24.337 | 16.25 | − 1.59 | |
| 600 | −164.29 | − 92.90 | − 47.29 | − 6.57 | −17.63 | 29.319 | 21.174 | + 3.11 | |
| 700 | −162.48 | − 90.14 | − 43.92 | − 2.65 | −13.81 | 33.685 | 25.489 | 7.24 | |
| 710 | −162.31 | − 89.88 | − 43.60 | − 2.28 | −13.46 | 34.094 | 25.894 | 7.63 | |
| 720 | −162.14 | − 89.63 | − 43.29 | − 1.92 | −13.10 | 34.499 | 26.294 | 8.01 | |
| 730 | −161.98 | − 89.37 | − 42.98 | − 1.56 | −12.75 | 34.899 | 26.689 | 8.39 | |
| 740 | −161.81 | − 89.12 | − 42.67 | − 1.20 | −12.41 | 35.295 | 27.082 | 8.77 | |
| 750 | −161.65 | − 88.88 | − 42.37 | − 0.85 | −12.06 | 35.687 | 27.468 | 9.14 | |
| 760 | −161.49 | − 88.63 | − 42.07 | − 0.50 | −11.73 | 36.074 | 27.852 | 9.503 | |
| 770 | −161.33 | − 88.39 | − 41.77 | − 0.16 | −11.39 | 36.458 | 28.231 | 9.87 | |
| 780 | −161.17 | − 88.15 | − 41.48 | + 0.19 | −11.06 | 36.838 | 28.607 | 10.23 | |
| 790 | −161.02 | − 87.91 | − 41.19 | 0.52 | −10.73 | 37.214 | 28.979 | 10.58 | |
| 800 | −160.86 | − 87.67 | − 40.90 | 0.86 | −10.40 | 37.587 | 29.348 | 10.94 | |
| 900 | −159.39 | − 85.44 | − 38.17 | 4.04 | − 7.31 | 41.12 | 32.85 | 14.29 | |
| 1000 | −158.04 | − 83.38 | − 35.66 | 6.95 | − 4.47 | 44.37 | 36.06 | 17.36 | |
| 1200 | −155.6 | − 79.71 | − 31.2 | 12.2 | + 0.6 | 50.17 | 41.80 | 22.9 | |
| 1500 | −152.5 | − 75.00 | − 25.4 | 18.9 | 7.1 | 57.6 | 49.2 | 29.9 | |

The values above are calculated from the constants below and the Antoine equation:

$$\log_{10} P = A - B/(C + t); \quad t = B/(A - \log_{10} P) - C$$

(P in mm Hg; t in °C)

### Constants of the Antoine Equation

| | | (solid) | | | | | | | | |
|---|---|---|---|---|---|---|---|---|---|---|
| A | 6.61184 | 7.69540 | 6.80266 | 6.82973 | 6.83029 | 6.74808 | 6.85221 | 6.78967 | 6.73812 | |
| B | 389.93 | 532.20 | 656.40 | 813.20 | 945.90 | 882.80 | 1064.63 | 1020.012 | 950.84 | |
| C | 266.00 | 275.00 | 256.00 | 248.00 | 240.00 | 240.00 | 232.000 | 233.097 | 237.00 | |

a At the triple point, − 182.48°C, the pressure is 87.7 mm Hg.

b At the triple point, − 16.6°C, the pressure is 265.4 mm Hg.

## TABLE 2k (PART 1) — PARAFFINS, $C_6$
### VAPOR PRESSURES AND BOILING POINTS, AT 10 TO 1500 mm Hg
March 31, 1944; December 31, 1952

| Pressure | n—Hexane | 2-Methyl-pentane | 3-Methyl-pentane | 2,2-Dimethyl-butane | 2,3-Dimethyl-butane | | | |
|---|---|---|---|---|---|---|---|---|
| mm Hg | | | | | Temperature in °C | | | |
| 10 | −25.1 | −32.1 | −30.1 | −41.5 | −34.9 | | | |
| 20 | −14.3 | −21.6 | −19.4 | −31.1 | −24.3 | | | |
| 30 | − 7.4 | −14.8 | −12.6 | −24.5 | −17.5 | | | |
| 40 | − 2.3 | − 9.8 | − 7.5 | −19.5 | −12.5 | | | |
| 50 | + 1.85 | − 5.7 | − 3.4 | −15.5 | − 8.4 | | | |
| 60 | 5.36 | − 2.2 | + 0.13 | −12.1 | − 4.9 | | | |
| 80 | 11.13 | + 3.45 | 5.87 | − 6.5 | + 0.82 | | | |
| 100 | 15.81 | 8.06 | 10.53 | − 2.0 | 5.45 | | | |
| 150 | 24.807 | 16.92 | 19.48 | + 6.79 | 14.36 | | | |
| 200 | 31.609 | 23.624 | 26.259 | 13.41 | 21.097 | | | |
| 250 | 37.147 | 29.084 | 31.776 | 18.81 | 26.588 | | | |
| 300 | 41.852 | 33.724 | 36.465 | 23.403 | 31.257 | | | |
| 400 | 49.631 | 41.400 | 44.220 | 31.008 | 38.982 | | | |
| 500 | 55.985 | 47.672 | 50.557 | 37.228 | 45.297 | | | |
| 600 | 61.400 | 53.020 | 55.958 | 42.536 | 50.682 | | | |
| 700 | 66.144 | 57.706 | 60.692 | 47.192 | 55.404 | | | |
| 710 | 66.589 | 58.145 | 61.135 | 47.628 | 55.846 | | | |
| 720 | 67.028 | 58.579 | 61.574 | 48.059 | 56.283 | | | |
| 730 | 67.463 | 59.009 | 62.008 | 48.486 | 56.716 | | | |
| 740 | 67.893 | 59.434 | 62.437 | 48.909 | 57.145 | | | |
| 750 | 68.319 | 59.855 | 62.862 | 49.327 | 57.568 | | | |
| 760 | 68.740 | 60.271 | 63.282 | 49.741 | 57.988 | | | |
| 770 | 69.157 | 60.683 | 63.698 | 50.151 | 58.403 | | | |
| 780 | 69.570 | 61.091 | 64.110 | 50.556 | 58.814 | | | |
| 790 | 69.979 | 61.495 | 64.518 | 50.958 | 59.221 | | | |
| 800 | 70.383 | 61.895 | 64.922 | 51.355 | 59.624 | | | |
| 900 | 74.23 | 65.69 | 68.76 | 55.13 | 63.45 | | | |
| 1000 | 77.75 | 69.18 | 72.28 | 58.60 | 66.96 | | | |
| 1200 | 84.05 | 75.40 | 78.56 | 64.80 | 73.24 | | | |
| 1500 | 92.1 | 83.4 | 86.6 | 72.8 | 81.3 | | | |

The values above are calculated from the constants below and the Antoine equation:

$$\log_{10} P = A - B/(C + t); \quad t = B/(A - \log_{10} P) - C$$

(P in mm Hg; $t$ in °C)

### Constants of the Antoine Equation

| | | | | | | | | |
|---|---|---|---|---|---|---|---|---|
| A | 6.87776 | 6.83910 | 6.84887 | 6.75483 | 6.80983 | | | |
| B | 1171.530 | 1135.410 | 1152.368 | 1081.176 | 1127.187 | | | |
| C | 224.366 | 226.572 | 227.129 | 229.343 | 228.900 | | | |

# TABLE 2k (PART 2) — PARAFFINS, $C_7$
## VAPOR PRESSURES AND BOILING POINTS, AT 10 TO 1500 mm Hg
### May 31, 1944; December 31, 1948; December 31, 1952

| Pressure | n–Heptane | 2–Methyl–hexane | 3–Methyl–hexane | 3–Ethyl–pentane | 2,2–Dimethyl–pentane | 2,3–Dimethyl–pentane | 2,4–Dimethyl–pentane | 3,3–Dimethyl–pentane | 2,2,3–Trimethyl–butane |
|---|---|---|---|---|---|---|---|---|---|
| mm Hg | | | | | Temperature in °C | | | | |
| 10 | −2.1 | −9.1 | −7.9 | −6.8 | −18.6 | −10.3 | −17.0 | −14.4 | −18.8 |
| 20 | +9.49 | +2.28 | +3.57 | +4.67 | −7.47 | +1.13 | −5.89 | −2.96 | −7.42 |
| 30 | 16.84 | 9.52 | 10.85 | 12.00 | −0.35 | 8.43 | +1.22 | +4.36 | −0.18 |
| 40 | 22.352 | 14.945 | 16.306 | 17.490 | +4.990 | 13.911 | 6.545 | 9.852 | +5.262 |
| 50 | 26.808 | 19.337 | 20.722 | 21.934 | 9.315 | 18.342 | 10.858 | 14.297 | 9.663 |
| 60 | 30.573 | 23.049 | 24.455 | 25.690 | 12.972 | 22.089 | 14.504 | 18.055 | 13.385 |
| 80 | 36.758 | 29.148 | 30.587 | 31.860 | 18.982 | 28.245 | 20.497 | 24.231 | 19.504 |
| 100 | 41.772 | 34.093 | 35.561 | 36.864 | 23.858 | 33.237 | 25.359 | 29.241 | 24.469 |
| 150 | 51.410 | 43.602 | 45.124 | 46.485 | 33.241 | 42.839 | 34.712 | 38.880 | 34.025 |
| 200 | 58.695 | 50.793 | 52.356 | 53.760 | 40.342 | 50.102 | 41.790 | 46.173 | 41.260 |
| 250 | 64.624 | 56.647 | 58.244 | 59.682 | 46.127 | 56.016 | 47.555 | 52.114 | 47.155 |
| 300 | 69.662 | 61.622 | 63.248 | 64.715 | 51.045 | 61.042 | 52.456 | 57.164 | 52.169 |
| 400 | 77.987 | 69.847 | 71.522 | 73.035 | 59.181 | 69.355 | 60.563 | 65.519 | 60.464 |
| 500 | 84.786 | 76.565 | 78.281 | 79.832 | 65.833 | 76.146 | 67.189 | 72.347 | 67.247 |
| 600 | 90.578 | 82.291 | 84.041 | 85.624 | 71.504 | 81.935 | 72.838 | 78.168 | 73.033 |
| 700 | 95.651 | 87.307 | 89.089 | 90.698 | 76.476 | 87.008 | 77.790 | 83.272 | 78.106 |
| 710 | 96.127 | 87.777 | 89.562 | 91.174 | 76.942 | 87.483 | 78.254 | 83.750 | 78.581 |
| 720 | 96.596 | 88.242 | 90.029 | 91.644 | 77.403 | 87.953 | 78.713 | 84.222 | 79.051 |
| 730 | 97.061 | 88.702 | 90.492 | 92.109 | 77.858 | 88.418 | 79.167 | 84.690 | 79.516 |
| 740 | 97.521 | 89.157 | 90.949 | 92.569 | 78.309 | 88.878 | 79.616 | 85.153 | 79.976 |
| 750 | 97.977 | 89.607 | 91.402 | 93.024 | 78.756 | 89.333 | 80.061 | 85.611 | 80.432 |
| 760 | 98.427 | 90.052 | 91.850 | 93.475 | 79.197 | 89.784 | 80.500 | 86.064 | 80.882 |
| 770 | 98.873 | 90.493 | 92.294 | 93.921 | 79.635 | 90.230 | 80.936 | 86.513 | 81.329 |
| 780 | 99.314 | 90.929 | 92.733 | 94.362 | 80.067 | 90.671 | 81.367 | 86.957 | 81.770 |
| 790 | 99.751 | 91.362 | 93.168 | 94.800 | 80.496 | 91.109 | 81.794 | 87.397 | 82.208 |
| 800 | 100.183 | 91.790 | 93.598 | 95.232 | 80.920 | 91.541 | 82.216 | 87.832 | 82.641 |
| 900 | 104.29 | 95.85 | 97.69 | 99.34 | 84.95 | 95.65 | 86.23 | 91.97 | 86.75 |
| 1000 | 108.06 | 99.58 | 101.44 | 103.11 | 88.65 | 99.42 | 89.91 | 95.76 | 90.53 |
| 1200 | 114.79 | 106.24 | 108.14 | 109.85 | 95.26 | 106.16 | 96.50 | 102.55 | 97.28 |
| 1500 | 123.41 | 114.78 | 116.73 | 118.49 | 103.75 | 114.80 | 104.94 | 111.25 | 105.94 |

The values above are calculated from the constants below and the Antoine equation:

$$\log_{10} P = A - B/(C + t); \quad t = B/(A - \log_{10} P) - C$$

(P in mm Hg; t in °C)

### Constants of the Antoine Equation

| | | | | | | | | | |
|---|---|---|---|---|---|---|---|---|---|
| A | 6.90240 | 6.87318 | 6.86764 | 6.87564 | 6.81480 | 6.85382 | 6.82621 | 6.82667 | 6.79230 |
| B | 1268.115 | 1236.026 | 1240.196 | 1251.827 | 1190.033 | 1238.017 | 1192.041 | 1228.663 | 1200.563 |
| C | 216.900 | 219.545 | 219.223 | 219.887 | 223.303 | 221.823 | 221.634 | 225.316 | 226.050 |

TABLE 3k, Page 1 – PARAFFINS, $C_8$
VAPOR PRESSURES AND BOILING POINTS, AT 10 TO 1500 mm Hg
April 30, 1944; December 31, 1952

| Pressure | n– Octane | 2–Methyl– heptane | 3–Methyl– heptane | 4–Methyl– heptane | 3–Ethyl– hexane | 2,2– Dimethyl– hexane | 2,3– Dimethyl– hexane | 2,4– Dimethyl– hexane | 2,5– Dimethyl– hexane |
|---|---|---|---|---|---|---|---|---|---|
| mm Hg | | | | | Temperature in °C | | | | |
| 10 | 19.2 | 12.3 | 13.3 | 12.4 | 12.8 | 3.1 | 9.9 | 5.2 | 5.3 |
| 20 | 31.5 | 24.4 | 25.4 | 24.5 | 25.0 | 15.0 | 22.1 | 17.2 | 17.2 |
| 30 | 39.28 | 32.15 | 33.15 | 32.23 | 32.68 | 22.54 | 29.77 | 24.77 | 24.74 |
| 40 | 45.12 | 37.93 | 38.94 | 38.00 | 38.47 | 28.21 | 35.56 | 30.47 | 30.42 |
| 50 | 49.847 | 42.606 | 43.626 | 42.669 | 43.160 | 32.797 | 40.240 | 35.085 | 35.018 |
| 60 | 53.838 | 46.555 | 47.585 | 46.614 | 47.121 | 36.676 | 44.196 | 38.984 | 38.904 |
| 80 | 60.392 | 53.040 | 54.087 | 53.094 | 53.627 | 43.051 | 50.694 | 45.389 | 45.289 |
| 100 | 65.704 | 58.297 | 59.358 | 58.347 | 58.902 | 48.222 | 55.965 | 50.585 | 50.468 |
| 150 | 75.912 | 68.398 | 69.490 | 68.445 | 69.041 | 58.169 | 66.098 | 60.576 | 60.426 |
| 200 | 83.626 | 76.033 | 77.149 | 76.078 | 76.707 | 65.695 | 73.762 | 68.134 | 67.959 |
| 250 | 89.903 | 82.246 | 83.383 | 82.290 | 82.947 | 71.825 | 80.001 | 74.288 | 74.092 |
| 300 | 95.235 | 87.523 | 88.679 | 87.568 | 88.249 | 77.035 | 85.303 | 79.519 | 79.304 |
| 400 | 104.045 | 96.244 | 97.433 | 96.292 | 97.013 | 85.652 | 94.069 | 88.169 | 87.923 |
| 500 | 111.238 | 103.364 | 104.581 | 103.415 | 104.170 | 92.695 | 101.230 | 95.237 | 94.964 |
| 600 | 117.364 | 109.429 | 110.672 | 109.484 | 110.269 | 98.698 | 107.333 | 101.261 | 100.966 |
| 700 | 122.730 | 114.742 | 116.007 | 114.801 | 115.611 | 103.961 | 112.681 | 106.540 | 106.225 |
| 710 | 123.233 | 115.239 | 116.507 | 115.299 | 116.112 | 104.454 | 113.182 | 107.035 | 106.718 |
| 720 | 123.729 | 115.731 | 117.001 | 115.791 | 116.607 | 104.941 | 113.677 | 107.524 | 107.205 |
| 730 | 124.221 | 116.218 | 117.489 | 116.278 | 117.096 | 105.423 | 114.167 | 108.008 | 107.687 |
| 740 | 124.707 | 116.699 | 117.973 | 116.760 | 117.581 | 105.901 | 114.652 | 108.487 | 108.164 |
| 750 | 125.189 | 117.176 | 118.452 | 117.237 | 118.060 | 106.373 | 115.132 | 108.960 | 108.636 |
| 760 | 125.665 | 117.647 | 118.925 | 117.709 | 118.534 | 106.840 | 115.607 | 109.429 | 109.103 |
| 770 | 126.136 | 118.114 | 119.394 | 118.176 | 119.004 | 107.303 | 116.077 | 109.893 | 109.565 |
| 780 | 126.602 | 118.576 | 119.858 | 118.638 | 119.468 | 107.761 | 116.542 | 110.352 | 110.022 |
| 790 | 127.065 | 119.034 | 120.318 | 119.097 | 119.929 | 108.215 | 117.003 | 110.808 | 110.476 |
| 800 | 127.522 | 119.486 | 120.773 | 119.550 | 120.384 | 108.663 | 117.459 | 111.258 | 110.924 |
| 900 | 131.86 | 123.79 | 125.09 | 123.85 | 124.71 | 112.93 | 121.79 | 115.54 | 115.18 |
| 1000 | 135.85 | 127.73 | 129.05 | 127.80 | 128.68 | 116.84 | 125.76 | 119.46 | 119.09 |
| 1200 | 142.96 | 134.77 | 136.13 | 134.85 | 135.77 | 123.83 | 132.86 | 126.47 | 126.08 |
| 1500 | 152.1 | 143.8 | 145.2 | 143.9 | 144.9 | 132.8 | 142.0 | 135.5 | 135.0 |

The values above are calculated from the constants below and the Antoine equation:

$$\log_{10} P = A - B/(C + t); \quad t = B/(A - \log_{10} P) - C$$

(P in mm Hg; t in °C)

Constants of the Antoine Equation

| | | | | | | | | | |
|---|---|---|---|---|---|---|---|---|---|
| A | 6.92377 | 6.91735 | 6.89944 | 6.90065 | 6.89098 | 6.83715 | 6.87004 | 6.85305 | 6.85984 |
| B | 1355.126 | 1337.468 | 1331.530 | 1327.661 | 1327.884 | 1273.594 | 1315.503 | 1287.876 | 1287.274 |
| C | 209.517 | 213.693 | 212.414 | 212.568 | 212.595 | 215.072 | 214.157 | 214.790 | 214.412 |

TABLE 3k, Page 2 — PARAFFINS, $C_8$
VAPOR PRESSURES AND BOILING POINTS, AT 10 TO 1500 mm Hg
April 30, 1944; December 31, 1952

| Pressure | 3,3-Dimethyl-hexane | 3,4-Dimethyl-hexane | 2-Methyl-3-ethyl-pentane | 3-Methyl-3-ethyl-pentane | 2,2,3-Trimethyl-pentane | 2,2,4-Trimethyl-pentane | 2,3,3-Trimethyl-pentane | 2,3,4-Trimethyl-pentane | 2,2,3,3-Tetramethyl-butane |
|---|---|---|---|---|---|---|---|---|---|
| mm Hg | | | | Temperature in °C | | | | | |
| 10 | 6.1 | 11.3 | 9.5 | 9.9 | 3.9 | −4.3 | 6.9 | 7.1 | 13.18 |
| 20 | 18.2 | 23.5 | 21.7 | 22.3 | 16.0 | +7.5 | 19.2 | 19.3 | 24.32 |
| 30 | 25.93 | 31.31 | 29.40 | 30.25 | 23.69 | 15.05 | 27.10 | 27.06 | 31.33 |
| 40 | 31.72 | 37.14 | 35.21 | 36.18 | 29.48 | 20.70 | 33.00 | 32.88 | 36.55 |
| 50 | 36.408 | 41.856 | 39.916 | 40.982 | 34.165 | 25.277 | 37.771 | 37.583 | 40.75 |
| 60 | 40.370 | 45.841 | 43.889 | 45.037 | 38.128 | 29.147 | 41.806 | 41.563 | 44.28 |
| 80 | 46.880 | 52.386 | 50.418 | 51.700 | 44.639 | 35.507 | 48.436 | 48.101 | 50.05 |
| 100 | 52.160 | 57.693 | 55.712 | 57.103 | 49.922 | 40.667 | 53.815 | 53.404 | 54.70 |
| 150 | 62.315 | 67.896 | 65.894 | 67.493 | 60.085 | 50.597 | 64.159 | 63.603 | 63.55 (solid) |
| 200 | 69.996 | 75.612 | 73.594 | 75.350 | 67.776 | 58.112 | 71.985 | 71.317 | 70.19 |
| 250 | 76.251 | 81.893 | 79.863 | 81.748 | 74.041 | 64.234 | 78.358 | 77.599 | 75.55 |
| 300 | 81.568 | 87.230 | 85.191 | 87.184 | 79.366 | 69.440 | 83.776 | 82.938 | 80.07 |
| 400 | 90.360 | 96.053 | 94.001 | 96.173 | 88.175 | 78.051 | 92.735 | 91.767 | 87.50 |
| 500 | 97.543 | 103.259 | 101.199 | 103.516 | 95.376 | 85.092 | 100.056 | 98.981 | 93.51 |
| 600 | 103.667 | 109.401 | 107.333 | 109.775 | 101.515 | 91.095 | 106.297 | 105.130 | 98.60 a |
| 700 | 109.033 | 114.781 | 112.709 | 115.258 | 106.896 | 96.358 | 111.767 | 110.518 | 103.52 |
| 710 | 109.536 | 115.285 | 113.212 | 115.772 | 107.400 | 96.851 | 112.279 | 111.023 | 104.03 |
| 720 | 110.033 | 115.783 | 113.710 | 116.280 | 107.899 | 97.338 | 112.786 | 111.522 | 104.52 |
| 730 | 110.524 | 116.276 | 114.203 | 116.783 | 108.392 | 97.821 | 113.287 | 112.016 | 105.02 |
| 740 | 111.011 | 116.764 | 114.690 | 117.280 | 108.880 | 98.298 | 113.783 | 112.505 | 105.51 |
| 750 | 111.493 | 117.247 | 115.172 | 117.772 | 109.363 | 98.771 | 114.274 | 112.988 | 105.99 |
| 760 | 111.969 | 117.725 | 115.650 | 118.259 | 109.841 | 99.238 | 114.760 | 113.467 | 106.47 |
| 770 | 112.441 | 118.198 | 116.122 | 118.741 | 110.314 | 99.701 | 115.241 | 113.941 | 106.94 |
| 780 | 112.908 | 118.666 | 116.590 | 119.218 | 110.782 | 100.159 | 115.717 | 114.409 | 107.41 |
| 790 | 113.371 | 119.130 | 117.053 | 119.691 | 111.247 | 100.613 | 116.189 | 114.874 | 107.88 |
| 800 | 113.828 | 119.588 | 117.511 | 120.158 | 111.706 | 101.062 | 116.655 | 115.333 | 108.33 |
| 900 | 118.18 | 123.95 | 121.87 | 124.60 | 116.07 | 105.33 | 121.09 | 119.70 | 112.70 |
| 1000 | 122.16 | 127.94 | 125.86 | 128.67 | 120.07 | 109.24 | 125.15 | 123.70 | 116.70 |
| 1200 | 129.29 | 135.08 | 133.00 | 135.96 | 127.22 | 116.24 | 132.42 | 130.86 | 123.9 |
| 1500 | 138.4 | 144.2 | 142.2 | 145.3 | 136.4 | 125.22 | 141.7 | 140.0 | 133.0 |

The values above are calculated from the constants below and the Antoine equation:

$$\log_{10} P = A - B/(C + t); \quad t = B/(A - \log_{10} P) - C$$

(P in mm Hg; t in °C)

Constants of the Antoine Equation

| | 3,3-Dimethyl-hexane | 3,4-Dimethyl-hexane | 2-Methyl-3-ethyl-pentane | 3-Methyl-3-ethyl-pentane | 2,2,3-Trimethyl-pentane | 2,2,4-Trimethyl-pentane | 2,3,3-Trimethyl-pentane | 2,3,4-Trimethyl-pentane | 2,2,3,3-Tetramethyl-butane |
|---|---|---|---|---|---|---|---|---|---|
| $A$ | 6.85121 | 6.87986 | 6.86358 | 6.86731 | 6.82546 | 6.81189 | 6.84353 | 6.85396 | 6.87665 / 7.73092 (Solid) |
| $B$ | 1307.882 | 1330.035 | 1318.120 | 1347.209 | 1294.875 | 1257.840 | 1328.046 | 1315.084 | 1329.93 / 1601.54 |
| $C$ | 217.439 | 214.863 | 215.306 | 219.684 | 218.420 | 220.735 | 220.375 | 217.526 | 226.36 / 224.76 |

a At the triple point, 100.81°C, the pressure is 648.24 mm Hg.

TABLE 4k, Page 1 - PARAFFINS, C<sub>9</sub>

## VAPOR PRESSURES AND BOILING POINTS, AT 10 TO 1500 mm Hg
### November 30, 1949

| Pressure | n-Nonane | 2-Methyl-octane | 3-Methyl-octane | 4-Methyl-octane | 3-Ethyl-heptane | 4-Ethyl-heptane | 2,2-Dimethyl-heptane | 2,3-Dimethyl-heptane | 2,4-Dimethyl-heptane |
|---|---|---|---|---|---|---|---|---|---|
| mm Hg | Temperature in °C | | | | | | | | |
| 10 | 39.12 | 32. | 33. | 32. | 32. | 31. | 23. | 29. | 24. |
| 20 | 51.98 | 45. | 46. | 44. | 45. | 43. | 36. | 42. | 36. |
| 30 | 60.16 | 53. | 54. | 53. | 53. | 51. | 44. | 50. | 44. |
| 40 | 66.30 | 59. | 60. | 59. | 59. | 57. | 50. | 56. | 50. |
| 50 | 71.255 | 64. | 65. | 64. | 64. | 62. | 55. | 61. | 55. |
| 60 | 75.445 | 68. | 69. | 68. | 68. | 66. | 59. | 65. | 59. |
| 80 | 82.324 | 75. | 76. | 75. | 75. | 73. | 65. | 72. | 66. |
| 100 | 87.899 | 81. | 81. | 80. | 80. | 79. | 71. | 78. | 71. |
| 150 | 98.612 | 91. | 92. | 91. | 91. | 89. | 81. | 88. | 82. |
| 200 | 106.706 | 99. | 100. | 99. | 99. | 97. | 89. | 97. | 90. |
| 250 | 113.292 | 106. | 107. | 105. | 106. | 104. | 96. | 103. | 96. |
| 300 | 118.885 | 112. | 112. | 111. | 111. | 109. | 101. | 109. | 102. |
| 400 | 128.127 | 120.7 | 121.5 | 120.0 | 120.4 | 118.7 | 110.4 | 117.9 | 111. |
| 500 | 135.670 | 128.2 | 129.1 | 127.5 | 127.9 | 126.1 | 117.8 | 125.4 | 118. |
| 600 | 142.095 | 134.6 | 135.5 | 133.8 | 134.3 | 132.5 | 124.1 | 131.8 | 124. |
| 700 | 147.721 | 140.20 | 141.10 | 139.42 | 139.9 | 138.1 | 129.66 | 137.4 | 130. |
| 710 | 148.248 | 140.73 | 141.63 | 139.95 | 140.4 | 138.6 | 130.18 | 137.9 | 130. |
| 720 | 148.769 | 141.24 | 142.15 | 140.46 | 140.9 | 139.1 | 130.69 | 138.4 | 131. |
| 730 | 149.284 | 141.75 | 142.66 | 140.97 | 141.4 | 139.6 | 131.20 | 138.9 | 131. |
| 740 | 149.794 | 142.26 | 143.17 | 141.48 | 142.0 | 140.1 | 131.70 | 139.4 | 132. |
| 750 | 150.299 | 142.77 | 143.68 | 141.99 | 142.5 | 140.6 | 132.20 | 140.0 | 133. |
| 760 | 150.798 | 143.26 | 144.18 | 142.48 | 143.0 | 141.2 | 132.69 | 140.5 | 133. |
| 770 | 151.292 | 143.75 | 144.67 | 142.97 | 143.5 | 141.7 | 133.18 | 141.0 | 134. |
| 780 | 151.781 | 144.24 | 145.16 | 143.46 | 144.0 | 142.1 | 133.66 | 141.4 | 134. |
| 790 | 152.266 | 144.72 | 145.64 | 143.93 | 144.5 | 142.6 | 134.14 | 142.0 | 134. |
| 800 | 152.745 | 145.20 | 146.12 | 144.41 | 144.9 | 143.1 | 134.61 | 142.4 | 135. |
| 900 | 157.298 | 149.73 | 150.67 | 148.93 | 149.5 | 147.6 | 139.10 | 146.9 | 139. |
| 1000 | 161.47 | 153.9 | 154.9 | 153.1 | 153.7 | 151.7 | 143.2 | 151.1 | 144. |
| 1200 | 168.93 | 161.3 | 162.3 | 160.5 | 161.1 | 159.1 | 150.6 | 158.5 | 151. |
| 1500 | 178.5 | 171. | 172. | 170. | 171. | 169. | 160. | 168. | 160. |

The values above are calculated from the constants below and the Antoine equation:

$$\log_{10} P = A - B/(C + t); \quad t = B/(A - \log_{10} P) - C$$

(P in mm Hg; t in °C)

### Constants of the Antoine Equation

| | n-Nonane | 2-Methyl-octane | 3-Methyl-octane | 4-Methyl-octane | 3-Ethyl-heptane | 4-Ethyl-heptane | 2,2-Dimethyl-heptane | 2,3-Dimethyl-heptane | 2,4-Dimethyl-heptane |
|---|---|---|---|---|---|---|---|---|---|
| A | 6.93513 | 6.9179 | 6.9102 | 6.9155 | 6.901 | 6.905 | 6.8580 | 6.887 | 6.869 |
| B | 1428.811 | 1410.0 | 1411.0 | 1406.0 | 1403. | 1397. | 1355.0 | 1392. | 1360. |
| C | 201.619 | 206.00 | 206.00 | 206.00 | 206.0 | 206.0 | 208.00 | 207.0 | 208. |

345

TABLE 4k, Page 2 — PARAFFINS, C₉
VAPOR PRESSURES AND BOILING POINTS, AT 10 TO 1500 mm Hg
November 30, 1949

| Pressure | 2,5-Dimethyl-heptane | 2,6-Dimethyl-heptane | 3,3-Dimethyl-heptane | 3,4-Dimethyl-heptane | 3,5-Dimethyl-heptane | 4,4-Dimethyl-heptane | 2-Methyl-3-ethylhexane | 2-Methyl-4-ethylhexane | 3-Methyl-3-ethylhexane |
|---|---|---|---|---|---|---|---|---|---|
| mm Hg | | | | Temperature in °C | | | | | |
| 10 | 26. | 26. | 26. | 29. | 26. | 24. | 27. | 24. | 27. |
| 20 | 39. | 38. | 39. | 42. | 39. | 37. | 40. | 36. | 40. |
| 30 | 47. | 46. | 47. | 50. | 47. | 45. | 48. | 44. | 49. |
| 40 | 53. | 52. | 53. | 56. | 53. | 51. | 54. | 50. | 55. |
| 50 | 58. | 57. | 58. | 61. | 57. | 56. | 59. | 55. | 60. |
| 60 | 62. | 61. | 62. | 65. | 62. | 60. | 63. | 59. | 64. |
| 80 | 69. | 68. | 69. | 72. | 68. | 67. | 70. | 66. | 71. |
| 100 | 74. | 73. | 74. | 78. | 74. | 73. | 75. | 72. | 77. |
| 150 | 85. | 84. | 85. | 89. | 84. | 83. | 86. | 82. | 88. |
| 200 | 93. | 92. | 93. | 97. | 92. | 91. | 94. | 90. | 96. |
| 250 | 99. | 98. | 100. | 103. | 99. | 98. | 101. | 97. | 102. |
| 300 | 105. | 104. | 105. | 109. | 104. | 103. | 106. | 102. | 108. |
| 400 | 114. | 112.9 | 114.6 | 118.0 | 113.6 | 112.6 | 115.4 | 111.3 | 117.5 |
| 500 | 121. | 120.3 | 122.1 | 125.5 | 121.0 | 120.1 | 122.9 | 118.8 | 125.2 |
| 600 | 127. | 126.64 | 128.5 | 131.9 | 127.4 | 126.5 | 129.3 | 125.2 | 131.7 |
| 700 | 133. | 132.18 | 134.2 | 137.5 | 132.9 | 132.1 | 134.9 | 130.7 | 137.4 |
| 710 | 133. | 132.70 | 134.7 | 138.0 | 133.4 | 132.6 | 135.4 | 131.2 | 138.0 |
| 720 | 134. | 133.21 | 135.2 | 138.5 | 134.0 | 133.2 | 136.0 | 131.8 | 138.5 |
| 730 | 134. | 133.72 | 135.7 | 139.0 | 134.5 | 133.7 | 136.5 | 132.3 | 139.0 |
| 740 | 135. | 134.22 | 136.2 | 139.6 | 135.0 | 134.2 | 137.0 | 132.8 | 139.5 |
| 750 | 135. | 134.72 | 136.8 | 140.1 | 135.5 | 134.7 | 137.5 | 133.3 | 140.1 |
| 760 | 136. | 135.21 | 137.3 | 140.6 | 136.0 | 135.2 | 138.0 | 133.8 | 140.6 |
| 770 | 137. | 135.70 | 137.8 | 141.1 | 136.4 | 135.8 | 138.6 | 134.3 | 141.1 |
| 780 | 137. | 136.18 | 138.3 | 141.6 | 137.0 | 136.2 | 139.0 | 134.8 | 141.6 |
| 790 | 137. | 136.66 | 138.8 | 142.1 | 137.5 | 136.7 | 139.5 | 135.3 | 142.1 |
| 800 | 138. | 137.13 | 139.2 | 142.5 | 137.9 | 137.2 | 139.9 | 135.7 | 142.5 |
| 900 | 142. | 141.62 | 143.8 | 147.1 | 142.4 | 141.7 | 144.5 | 140.2 | 147.2 |
| 1000 | 147. | 145.7 | 148.0 | 151.3 | 146.6 | 145.9 | 148.7 | 144.4 | 151.4 |
| 1200 | 154. | 153.1 | 155.4 | 158.7 | 153.9 | 153.3 | 156.1 | 151.8 | 159.0 |
| 1500 | 163. | 163. | 165. | 168. | 163. | 163.0 | 165.6 | 161. | 169. |

The values above are calculated from the constants below and the Antoine equation:

$$\log_{10} P = A - B/(C + t); \quad t = B/(A - \log_{10} P) - C$$
(P in mm Hg; t in °C)

Constants of the Antoine Equation

| | 2,5-Dimethyl-heptane | 2,6-Dimethyl-heptane | 3,3-Dimethyl-heptane | 3,4-Dimethyl-heptane | 3,5-Dimethyl-heptane | 4,4-Dimethyl-heptane | 2-Methyl-3-ethylhexane | 2-Methyl-4-ethylhexane | 3-Methyl-3-ethylhexane |
|---|---|---|---|---|---|---|---|---|---|
| A | 6.881 | 6.8725 | 6.869 | 6.897 | 6.878 | 6.858 | 6.872 | 6.854 | 6.863 |
| B | 1372. | 1366.0 | 1385. | 1400. | 1375. | 1373. | 1381. | 1362. | 1404. |
| C | 207. | 207.00 | 210.0 | 208.0 | 208.0 | 210.0 | 208.0 | 209.0 | 212.0 |

TABLE 4k, Page 3 — PARAFFINS, C$_9$
VAPOR PRESSURES AND BOILING POINTS, AT 10 TO 1500 mm Hg
November 30, 1949 (Corrected)

| Pressure | 3-Methyl-4-ethylhexane | 2,2,3-Tri-methylhexane | 2,2,4-Tri-methylhexane | 2,2,5-Tri-methylhexane | 2,3,3-Tri-methylhexane | 2,3,4-Tri-methylhexane | 2,3,5-Tri-methylhexane | 2,4,4-Tri-methylhexane | 3,3,4-Tri-methylhexane |
|---|---|---|---|---|---|---|---|---|---|
| mm Hg | | | | | Temperature in °C | | | | |
| 10 | 29. | 23. | 17. | 16.17 | 25. | 27. | 21. | 19.86 | 27. |
| 20 | 42. | 35. | 30. | 28.51 | 38. | 40. | 34. | 32.54 | 40. |
| 30 | 50. | 43. | 38. | 36.37 | 46. | 48. | 42. | 40.62 | 48. |
| 40 | 56. | 50. | 44. | 42.27 | 52. | 54. | 48. | 46.68 | 55. |
| 50 | 61. | 54. | 48. | 47.044 | 57. | 59. | 53. | 51.587 | 60. |
| 60 | 65. | 59. | 53. | 51.080 | 61. | 63. | 57. | 55.733 | 64. |
| 80 | 72. | 65. | 59. | 57.712 | 68. | 70. | 64. | 62.544 | 71. |
| 100 | 77. | 71. | 65. | 63.092 | 74. | 76. | 69. | 68.069 | 77. |
| 150 | 88. | 82. | 75. | 73.441 | 85. | 86. | 80. | 78.694 | 87. |
| 200 | 96. | 90. | 83. | 81.272 | 93. | 95. | 88. | 86.732 | 96. |
| 250 | 103. | 96. | 90. | 87.649 | 100. | 101. | 94. | 93.276 | 102. |
| 300 | 108. | 102. | 95. | 93.070 | 105. | 107. | 100. | 98.839 | 108. |
| 400 | 117.6 | 111.0 | 104.2 | 102.037 | 114.7 | 116.1 | 108.9 | 108.038 | 117.4 |
| 500 | 125.2 | 118.5 | 111.6 | 109.365 | 122.3 | 123.7 | 116.4 | 115.555 | 125.0 |
| 600 | 131.6 | 124.9 | 118.0 | 115.612 | 128.8 | 130.2 | 122.7 | 121.961 | 131.6 |
| 700 | 137.3 | 130.53 | 123.51 | 121.087 | 134.55 | 135.8 | 128.29 | 127.576 | 137.32 |
| 710 | 137.8 | 131.06 | 124.03 | 121.600 | 135.09 | 136.4 | 128.82 | 128.102 | 137.86 |
| 720 | 138.3 | 131.57 | 124.54 | 122.108 | 135.61 | 136.9 | 129.33 | 128.622 | 138.39 |
| 730 | 138.8 | 132.09 | 125.05 | 122.610 | 136.14 | 137.4 | 129.84 | 129.137 | 138.92 |
| 740 | 139.4 | 132.60 | 125.55 | 123.106 | 136.66 | 137.9 | 130.35 | 129.646 | 139.44 |
| 750 | 139.9 | 133.11 | 126.05 | 123.598 | 137.18 | 138.4 | 130.85 | 130.150 | 139.96 |
| 760 | 140.4 | 133.60 | 126.54 | 124.084 | 137.68 | 139.0 | 131.34 | 130.648 | 140.46 |
| 770 | 140.9 | 134.10 | 127.03 | 124.565 | 138.18 | 139.5 | 131.84 | 131.142 | 140.97 |
| 780 | 141.4 | 134.59 | 127.51 | 125.042 | 138.68 | 139.9 | 132.32 | 131.630 | 141.47 |
| 790 | 141.9 | 135.07 | 127.99 | 125.514 | 139.17 | 140.5 | 132.80 | 132.115 | 141.96 |
| 800 | 142.3 | 135.55 | 128.46 | 125.981 | 139.66 | 140.9 | 133.28 | 132.593 | 142.45 |
| 900 | 146.9 | 140.10 | 132.96 | 130.419 | 144.29 | 145.5 | 137.79 | 137.143 | 147.09 |
| 1000 | 151.1 | 144.3 | 137.1 | 134.49 | 148.5 | 149.7 | 141.9 | 141.32 | 151.4 |
| 1200 | 158.6 | 151.8 | 144.5 | 141.77 | 156.1 | 157.3 | 149.4 | 148.77 | 159.0 |
| 1500 | 168. | 161. | 154. | 151.1 | 166. | 167. | 159. | 158.3 | 169. |

The values above are calculated from the constants below and the Antoine equation:

$$\log_{10} P = A - B/(C + t); \quad t = B/(A - \log_{10} P) - C$$

(P in mm Hg; t in °C)

Constants of the Antoine Equation

| | 3-Methyl-4-ethylhexane | 2,2,3-Tri-methylhexane | 2,2,4-Tri-methylhexane | 2,2,5-Tri-methylhexane | 2,3,3-Tri-methylhexane | 2,3,4-Tri-methylhexane | 2,3,5-Tri-methylhexane | 2,4,4-Tri-methylhexane | 3,3,4-Tri-methylhexane |
|---|---|---|---|---|---|---|---|---|---|
| A | 6.885 | 6.8448 | 6.8391 | 6.83531 | 6.8474 | 6.867 | 6.8505 | 6.85163 | 6.8557 |
| B | 1399. | 1366.0 | 1344.0 | 1324.049 | 1391.0 | 1395. | 1359.0 | 1368.723 | 1401.0 |
| C | 209.0 | 211.00 | 213.00 | 210.737 | 213.00 | 211.0 | 211.00 | 214.047 | 212.00 |

| Pressure | 3,3–Diethyl–pentane | 2,2–Dimethyl–3–ethyl–pentane | 2,3–Dimethyl–3–ethyl–pentane | 2,4–Dimethyl–3–ethyl–pentane | 2,2,3,3–Tetramethyl–pentane | 2,2,3,4–Tetramethyl–pentane | 2,2,4,4–Tetramethyl–pentane | 2,3,3,4–Tetramethyl–pentane | |
|---|---|---|---|---|---|---|---|---|---|
| mm Hg | Temperature in °C |||||||||

**TABLE 4k, Page 4 – PARAFFINS, C9**
**VAPOR PRESSURES AND BOILING POINTS, AT 10 TO 1500 mm Hg**
November 30, 1949 (Corrected)

| Pressure mm Hg | 3,3–Diethyl–pentane | 2,2–Dimethyl–3–ethyl–pentane | 2,3–Dimethyl–3–ethyl–pentane | 2,4–Dimethyl–3–ethyl–pentane | 2,2,3,3–Tetramethyl–pentane | 2,2,3,4–Tetramethyl–pentane | 2,2,4,4–Tetramethyl–pentane | 2,3,3,4–Tetramethyl–pentane | |
|---|---|---|---|---|---|---|---|---|---|
| | | | | Temperature in °C | | | | | |
| 10 | 30.71 | 22. | 28. | 24. | 26.05 | 20.85 | 12.50 | 27.20 | |
| 20 | 43.97 | 35. | 41. | 37. | 39.11 | 33.68 | 25.02 | 40.30 | |
| 30 | 52.40 | 43. | 49. | 45. | 47.43 | 41.85 | 33.00 | 48.64 | |
| 40 | 58.73 | 49. | 55. | 52. | 53.67 | 47.98 | 38.99 | 54.90 | |
| 50 | 63.852 | 54. | 60. | 57. | 58.722 | 52.938 | 43.842 | 59.965 | |
| 60 | 68.178 | 58. | 65. | 61. | 62.993 | 57.133 | 47.943 | 64.245 | |
| 80 | 75.283 | 65. | 72. | 68. | 70.011 | 64.025 | 54.684 | 71.276 | |
| 100 | 81.044 | 71. | 77. | 73. | 75.705 | 69.617 | 60.154 | 76.980 | |
| 150 | 92.118 | 82. | 88. | 84. | 86.659 | 80.373 | 70.680 | 87.946 | |
| 200 | 100.491 | 90. | 97. | 92. | 94.947 | 88.512 | 78.650 | 96.241 | |
| 250 | 107.306 | 96. | 103. | 99. | 101.698 | 95.140 | 85.142 | 102.995 | |
| 300 | 113.096 | 102. | 109. | 104. | 107.436 | 100.775 | 90.664 | 108.735 | |
| 400 | 122.666 | 111.1 | 119. | 113.8 | 116.929 | 110.096 | 99.800 | 118.227 | |
| 500 | 130.483 | 118.6 | 126. | 121.4 | 124.688 | 117.714 | 107.270 | 125.981 | |
| 600 | 137.142 | 125.1 | 133. | 127.9 | 131.303 | 124.208 | 113.641 | 132.591 | |
| 700 | 142.977 | 130.73 | 139. | 133.62 | 137.101 | 129.901 | 119.227 | 138.382 | |
| 710 | 143.523 | 131.27 | 139. | 134.16 | 137.644 | 130.434 | 119.750 | 138.925 | |
| 720 | 144.063 | 131.78 | 140. | 134.68 | 138.181 | 130.961 | 120.267 | 139.461 | |
| 730 | 144.598 | 132.30 | 140. | 135.20 | 138.713 | 131.483 | 120.780 | 139.992 | |
| 740 | 145.127 | 132.82 | 141. | 135.72 | 139.239 | 131.999 | 121.287 | 140.518 | |
| 750 | 145.650 | 133.33 | 141. | 136.23 | 139.759 | 132.510 | 121.788 | 141.037 | |
| 760 | 146.168 | 133.83 | 142. | 136.73 | 140.274 | 133.016 | 122.284 | 141.551 | |
| 770 | 146.681 | 134.33 | 143. | 137.24 | 140.784 | 133.516 | 122.776 | 142.061 | |
| 780 | 147.188 | 134.82 | 143. | 137.73 | 141.288 | 134.011 | 123.262 | 142.564 | |
| 790 | 147.691 | 135.30 | 144. | 138.22 | 141.788 | 134.503 | 123.744 | 143.064 | |
| 800 | 148.188 | 135.79 | 144. | 138.71 | 142.283 | 134.988 | 124.220 | 143.558 | |
| 900 | 152.913 | 140.36 | 149. | 143.32 | 146.982 | 139.602 | 128.750 | 148.250 | |
| 1000 | 157.24 | 144.6 | 153. | 147.6 | 151.29 | 143.83 | 132.91 | 152.55 | |
| 1200 | 164.99 | 152.1 | 161. | 155.1 | 159.0 | 151.40 | 140.34 | 160.24 | |
| 1500 | 174.9 | 162. | 171. | 165. | 168.9 | 161.1 | 149.9 | 170.1 | |

The values above are calculated from the constants below and the Antoine equation:

$$\log_{10} P = A - B/(C + t); \quad t = B/(A - \log_{10} P) - C$$

(P in mm Hg; t in °C)

Constants of the Antoine Equation

| | | | | | | | | | |
|---|---|---|---|---|---|---|---|---|---|
| A | 6.89262 | 6.8482 | 6.853 | 6.8524 | 6.82876 | 6.83173 | 6.79710 | 6.85961 | |
| B | 1451.245 | 1376.0 | 1414. | 1389.0 | 1397.483 | 1374.042 | 1325.183 | 1417.473 | |
| C | 215.575 | 213.00 | 214. | 213.00 | 213.703 | 214.762 | 216.093 | 214.705 | |

TABLE 22-k (PART 1) — NORMAL ALKYL CYCLOPENTANES, $C_5$ TO $C_{21}$
VAPOR PRESSURES AND BOILING POINTS, AT 10 TO 1500 mm Hg
October 31, 1950 (Corrected)

| Pressure | Cyclopentane | Methyl-cyclopentane | Ethyl-cyclopentane | n-Propyl-cyclopentane | n-Butyl-cyclopentane | n-Pentyl-cyclopentane | n-Hexyl-cyclopentane | n-Heptyl-cyclopentane | n-Octyl-cyclopentane |
|---|---|---|---|---|---|---|---|---|---|
| mm Hg | Temperature in °C | | | | | | | | |
| 10 | −40.4 | −23.7 | − 0.09 | 21.3 | 42. | 60. | 79. | 96. | 111. |
| 20 | −30.1 | −12.8 | +11.80 | 33.9 | 55. | 74. | 93. | 110. | 126. |
| 30 | −23.6 | − 5.3 | 19.36 | 41.94 | 63. | 83. | 102. | 120. | 136. |
| 40 | −18.6 | − 0.6 | 25.038 | 47.95 | 70. | 89. | 109. | 127. | 143. |
| 50 | −14.7 | + 3.64 | 29.627 | 52.82 | 75. | 95. | 115. | 133. | 149. |
| 60 | −11.3 | 7.22 | 33.507 | 56.925 | 79. | 99. | 119. | 137. | 154. |
| 80 | − 5.8 | 13.10 | 39.878 | 63.672 | 86. | 107. | 127. | 145. | 162. |
| 100 | − 1.3 | 17.86 | 45.045 | 69.143 | 91.8 | 113. | 133. | 152. | 169. |
| 150 | + 7.28 | 27.025 | 54.978 | 79.657 | 102.8 | 124. | 145. | 164. | 181. |
| 200 | 13.78 | 33.956 | 62.487 | 87.606 | 111.2 | 133. | 154. | 173. | 191. |
| 250 | 19.08 | 39.599 | 68.600 | 94.074 | 117.9 | 140. | 161. | 181. | 199. |
| 300 | 23.572 | 44.395 | 73.794 | 99.569 | 123.7 | 146. | 168. | 187. | 205. |
| 400 | 31.005 | 52.325 | 82.380 | 108.652 | 133.21 | 156. | 178. | 198. | 216. |
| 500 | 37.077 | 58.804 | 89.392 | 116.069 | 140.98 | 164. | 186. | 207. | 225. |
| 600 | 42.250 | 64.326 | 95.367 | 122.387 | 147.59 | 171. | 193. | 214. | 233. |
| 700 | 46.783 | 69.164 | 100.602 | 127.922 | 153.39 | 177. | 200. | 220. | 239. |
| 710 | 47.207 | 69.618 | 101.092 | 128.440 | 153.93 | 177. | 200. | 221. | 240. |
| 720 | 47.627 | 70.066 | 101.577 | 128.953 | 154.46 | 178. | 201. | 222. | 241. |
| 730 | 48.042 | 70.509 | 102.057 | 129.460 | 155.00 | 178. | 201. | 222. | 241. |
| 740 | 48.453 | 70.948 | 102.532 | 129.962 | 155.52 | 179. | 202. | 223. | 242. |
| 750 | 48.860 | 71.382 | 103.001 | 130.458 | 156.05 | 179. | 202. | 223. | 242. |
| 760 | 49.262 | 71.812 | 103.466 | 130.949 | 156.56 | 180. | 203. | 224. | 243. |
| 770 | 49.661 | 72.237 | 103.926 | 131.436 | 157.07 | 180. | 204. | 225. | 244. |
| 780 | 50.054 | 72.658 | 104.381 | 131.917 | 157.57 | 181. | 204. | 225. | 244. |
| 790 | 50.445 | 73.075 | 104.832 | 132.294 | 155.07 | 182. | 205. | 226. | 245. |
| 800 | 50.832 | 73.488 | 105.278 | 132.866 | 158.56 | 182. | 205. | 226. | 245. |
| 900 | 54.50 | 77.41 | 109.52 | 137.35 | 163.25 | 187. | 210. | 231. | 251. |
| 1000 | 57.87 | 81.00 | 113.40 | 141.46 | 167.6 | 191. | 215. | 236. | 256. |
| 1200 | 63.88 | 87.43 | 120.35 | 148.80 | 175.2 | 199. | 223. | 245. | 264. |
| 1500 | 71.6 | 95.7 | 129.3 | 158.2 | 185. | 210. | 234. | 256. | 276. |

The values above are calculated from the constants below and the Antoine equation:

$$\log_{10} P = A - B/(C + t); \quad t = B/(A - \log_{10} P) - C$$

(P in mm Hg; $t$ in °C)

Constants of the Antoine Equation

| | Cyclopentane | Methyl-cyclopentane | Ethyl-cyclopentane | n-Propyl-cyclopentane | n-Butyl-cyclopentane | n-Pentyl-cyclopentane | n-Hexyl-cyclopentane | n-Heptyl-cyclopentane | n-Octyl-cyclopentane |
|---|---|---|---|---|---|---|---|---|---|
| A | 6.88676 | 6.86283 | 6.88709 | 6.90392 | 6.9189 | 6.929 | 6.934 | 6.942 | 6.957 |
| B | 1124.162 | 1186.059 | 1298.599 | 1384.386 | 1460.0 | 1526. | 1589. | 1649. | 1704. |
| C | 231.361 | 226.042 | 220.675 | 213.159 | 205.00 | 197. | 189. | 182. | 175. |

TABLE 22k (PART 2) – NORMAL ALKYL CYCLOPENTANES, $C_5$ TO $C_{21}$
VAPOR PRESSURES AND BOILING POINTS, AT 10 TO 1500 mm Hg
October 31, 1950

| Pressure | n-Nonyl-cyclopentane | n-Decyl-cyclopentane | n-Undecyl-cyclopentane | n-Dodecyl-cyclopentane | n-Tridecyl-cyclopentane | n-Tetradecyl-cyclopentane | n-Pentadecyl-cyclopentane | n-Hexadecyl-cyclopentane | |
|---|---|---|---|---|---|---|---|---|---|
| mm Hg | Temperature in °C | | | | | | | | |
| 10 | 126. | 140.7 | 153. | 166. | 179. | 190. | 201. | 212. | |
| 20 | 142. | 156.7 | 170. | 183. | 196. | 207. | 219. | 230. | |
| 30 | 152. | 166.9 | 180. | 194. | 207. | 219. | 231. | 241. | |
| 40 | 159. | 174.5 | 188. | 202. | 215. | 227. | 239. | 250. | |
| 50 | 166. | 180.6 | 194. | 208. | 221. | 234. | 246. | 257. | |
| 60 | 171. | 185.8 | 200. | 214. | 227. | 239. | 252. | 263. | |
| 80 0 | 179. | 194.4 | 209. | 223. | 236. | 249. | 261. | 272. | |
| 100 | 186. | 201.3 | 216. | 230. | 244. | 256. | 269. | 280. | |
| 150 | 199. | 214.6 | 229. | 244. | 258. | 271. | 283. | 295. | |
| 200 | 209. | 224.6 | 240. | 255. | 269. | 282. | 294. | 307. | |
| 250 | 217. | 232.8 | 248. | 263. | 277. | 290. | 304. | 316. | |
| 300 | 223. | 239.7 | 255. | 270. | 285. | 298. | 311. | 324. | |
| 400 | 235. | 251.1 | 267. | 282. | 297. | 310. | 324. | 336. | |
| 500 | 244. | 260.5 | 277. | 292. | 307. | 321. | 334. | 347. | |
| 600 | 251. | 268.4 | 285. | 301. | 315. | 329. | 343. | 356. | |
| 700 | 258. | 275.4 | 292. | 308. | 323. | 337. | 351. | 364. | |
| 710 | 259. | 276.0 | 293. | 309. | 324. | 338. | 352. | 364. | |
| 720 | 259. | 276.6 | 293. | 309. | 324. | 338. | 352. | 365. | |
| 730 | 260. | 277.3 | 294. | 310. | 325. | 339. | 353. | 366. | |
| 740 | 261. | 277.9 | 295. | 311. | 326. | 340. | 354. | 367. | |
| 750 | 261. | 278.6 | 295. | 311. | 326. | 340. | 354. | 367. | |
| 760 | 262. | 279.2 | 296. | 312. | 327. | 341. | 355. | 368. | |
| 770 | 263. | 279.7 | 297. | 313. | 328. | 342. | 356. | 369. | |
| 780 | 263. | 280.4 | 297. | 313. | 328. | 342. | 356. | 369. | |
| 790 | 264. | 281.0 | 298. | 314. | 329. | 343. | 357. | 370. | |
| 800 | 264. | 281.6 | 298. | 314. | 330. | 344. | 358. | 371. | |
| 900 | 270. | 287.2 | 304. | 320. | 336. | 350. | 364. | 377. | |
| 1000 | 275. | 292. | 310. | 326. | 341. | 355. | 370. | 383. | |
| 1200 | 284. | 302. | 319. | 335. | 351. | 365. | 380. | 393. | |
| 1500 | 295. | 313. | 331. | 348. | 364. | 378. | 393. | 406. | |

The values above are calculated from the constants below and the Antoine equation:

$$\log_{10} P = A - B/(C + t); \quad t = B/(A - \log_{10} P) - C$$

$$(P \text{ in mm Hg}; \ t \text{ in } °C)$$

Constants of the Antoine Equation

| | n-Nonyl | n-Decyl | n-Undecyl | n-Dodecyl | n-Tridecyl | n-Tetradecyl | n-Pentadecyl | n-Hexadecyl | |
|---|---|---|---|---|---|---|---|---|---|
| A | 6.967 | 6.971 | 6.974 | 6.985 | 6.993 | 7.003 | 7.013 | 7.021 | |
| B | 1757. | 1798. | 1854. | 1900. | 1945. | 1987. | 2029. | 2070. | |
| C | 168. | 160.4 | 157. | 151. | 146. | 141. | 136. | 132. | |

**TABLE 6k – ALKYL CYCLOPENTANES, $C_5$ TO $C_7$**
**VAPOR PRESSURES AND BOILING POINTS, AT 10 TO 1500 mm Hg**
August 31, 1944; August 31, 1949; December 31, 1952

| Pressure | Cyclo-pentane | Methyl-cyclopentane | Ethyl-cyclopentane | 1,1-Dimethyl-cyclopentane | 1,cis-2-Dimethyl-cyclopentane | 1,trans-2-Dimethyl-cyclopentane | 1,cis-3-Dimethyl-cyclopentane | 1,trans-3-Dimethyl-cyclopentane | |
|---|---|---|---|---|---|---|---|---|---|
| mm Hg | | | | | Temperature in °C | | | | |
| 10 | −40.4 | −23.7 | −0.09 | −12.31 | −3.26 | −9.0 | −9.2 | −10.0 | |
| 20 | −30.1 | −12.8 | +11.80 | −0.88 | +8.50 | +2.5 | +2.3 | +1.5 | |
| 30 | −23.6 | −5.8 | 19.36 | +6.41 | 16.00 | 9.86 | 9.68 | 8.86 | |
| 40 | −18.6 | −0.6 | 25.038 | 11.886 | 21.623 | 15.38 | 15.20 | 14.37 | |
| 50 | −14.7 | +3.64 | 29.627 | 16.313 | 26.173 | 19.85 | 19.67 | 18.83 | |
| 60 | −11.3 | 7.22 | 33.507 | 20.057 | 30.019 | 23.622 | 23.442 | 22.600 | |
| 80 | −5.8 | 13.10 | 39.878 | 26.210 | 36.339 | 29.825 | 29.646 | 28.794 | |
| 100 | −1.3 | 17.86 | 45.045 | 31.202 | 41.465 | 34.856 | 34.679 | 33.818 | |
| 150 | +7.28 | 27.025 | 54.978 | 40.807 | 51.323 | 44.534 | 44.360 | 43.483 | |
| 200 | 13.78 | 33.956 | 62.487 | 48.076 | 58.781 | 51.855 | 51.684 | 50.796 | |
| 250 | 19.08 | 39.599 | 68.600 | 53.997 | 64.854 | 57.817 | 57.649 | 56.751 | |
| 300 | 23.572 | 44.395 | 73.794 | 59.031 | 70.015 | 62.884 | 62.719 | 61.813 | |
| 400 | 31.005 | 52.325 | 82.380 | 67.359 | 78.551 | 71.266 | 71.106 | 70.186 | |
| 500 | 37.077 | 58.804 | 89.392 | 74.167 | 85.526 | 78.114 | 77.959 | 77.029 | |
| 600 | 42.250 | 64.326 | 95.367 | 79.972 | 91.471 | 83.953 | 83.802 | 82.862 | |
| 700 | 46.783 | 69.164 | 100.602 | 85.061 | 96.681 | 89.069 | 88.923 | 87.975 | |
| 710 | 47.207 | 69.618 | 101.092 | 85.538 | 97.170 | 89.549 | 89.402 | 88.454 | |
| 720 | 47.627 | 70.066 | 101.577 | 86.009 | 97.652 | 90.023 | 89.877 | 88.928 | |
| 730 | 48.042 | 70.509 | 102.057 | 86.476 | 98.130 | 90.492 | 90.346 | 89.396 | |
| 740 | 48.453 | 70.948 | 102.532 | 86.937 | 98.602 | 90.956 | 90.811 | 89.860 | |
| 750 | 48.860 | 71.382 | 103.001 | 87.394 | 99.070 | 91.415 | 91.270 | 90.319 | |
| 760 | 49.262 | 71.812 | 103.466 | 87.846 | 99.532 | 91.869 | 91.725 | 90.773 | |
| 770 | 49.661 | 72.237 | 103.926 | 88.294 | 99.991 | 92.319 | 92.175 | 91.223 | |
| 780 | 50.054 | 72.658 | 104.381 | 88.736 | 100.444 | 92.764 | 92.621 | 91.667 | |
| 790 | 50.445 | 73.075 | 104.832 | 89.175 | 100.893 | 93.206 | 93.062 | 92.108 | |
| 800 | 50.832 | 73.488 | 105.278 | 89.609 | 101.337 | 93.642 | 93.499 | 92.544 | |
| 900 | 54.50 | 77.41 | 109.52 | 93.73 | 105.56 | 97.79 | 97.65 | 96.69 | |
| 1000 | 57.87 | 81.00 | 113.40 | 97.52 | 109.43 | 101.59 | 101.46 | 100.49 | |
| 1200 | 63.88 | 87.43 | 120.35 | 104.29 | 116.35 | 108.39 | 108.26 | 107.28 | |
| 1500 | 71.6 | 95.7 | 129.3 | 113.0 | 125.2 | 117.1 | 117.0 | 116.0 | |

The values above are calculated from the constants below and the Antoine equation:
$$\log_{10} P = A - B/(C + t); \quad t = B/(A - \log_{10} P) - C$$
(P in mm Hg; t in °C)

**Constants of the Antoine Equation**

| | | | | | | | | | |
|---|---|---|---|---|---|---|---|---|---|
| A | 6.88676 | 6.86283 | 6.88709 | 6.81724 | 6.85008 | 6.84422 | 6.83817 | 6.83715 | |
| B | 1124.162 | 1186.059 | 1298.599 | 1219.474 | 1269.140 | 1242.748 | 1240.023 | 1237.456 | |
| C | 231.361 | 226.042 | 220.675 | 221.946 | 220.209 | 221.686 | 221.621 | 222.005 | |

TABLE 15k, Page 1 – ALKYL CYCLOPENTANES, C$_8$
VAPOR PRESSURES AND BOILING POINTS, AT 10 TO 1500 mm Hg
August 31, 1949; December 31, 1952

| Pressure | n–Propyl–cyclopentane | Isopropyl–cyclopentane | 1–Methyl–1–ethyl–cyclopentane | 1–Methyl–cis–2–ethyl–cyclopentane | 1–Methyl–trans–2–ethyl–cyclopentane | 1–Methyl–cis–3–ethyl–cyclopentane | 1–Methyl–trans–3–ethyl–cyclopentane | | |
|---|---|---|---|---|---|---|---|---|---|
| mm Hg | Temperature in °C | | | | | | | | |
| 10 | 21.3 | 16.4 | 12.7 | 18.19 | 13. | 13. | 12. | | |
| 20 | 33.9 | 29.0 | 25.2 | 30.82 | 25. | 26. | 25. | | |
| 30 | 41.94 | 37.05 | 33.15 | 38.86 | 33. | 34. | 33. | | |
| 40 | 47.95 | 43.08 | 39.11 | 44.881 | 39. | 39. | 39. | | |
| 50 | 52.82 | 47.96 | 43.93 | 49.754 | 44. | 44. | 43. | | |
| 60 | 56.925 | 52.077 | 47.999 | 53.871 | 48. | 48. | 48. | | |
| 80 | 63.672 | 58.848 | 54.690 | 60.634 | 55. | 55. | 54. | | |
| 100 | 69.143 | 64.338 | 60.116 | 66.116 | 60.1 | 60.3 | 59.7 | | |
| 150 | 79.657 | 74.892 | 70.550 | 76.653 | 70.5 | 70.7 | 70.1 | | |
| 200 | 87.606 | 82.872 | 78.441 | 84.618 | 78.4 | 78.6 | 77.9 | | |
| 250 | 94.074 | 89.368 | 84.864 | 91.100 | 84.7 | 85.0 | 84.3 | | |
| 300 | 99.569 | 94.887 | 90.323 | 96.606 | 90.2 | 90.4 | 89.7 | | |
| 400 | 108.652 | 104.011 | 99.349 | 105.708 | 99.2 | 99.4 | 98.7 | | |
| 500 | 116.069 | 111.463 | 106.721 | 113.140 | 106.5 | 106.7 | 106.1 | | |
| 600 | 122.387 | 117.813 | 113.004 | 119.471 | 112.7 | 112.9 | 112.3 | | |
| 700 | 127.922 | 123.376 | 118.510 | 125.017 | 118.2 | 118.4 | 117.8 | | |
| 710 | 128.440 | 123.897 | 119.026 | 125.536 | 118.7 | 118.9 | 118.3 | | |
| 720 | 128.953 | 124.412 | 119.535 | 126.049 | 119.2 | 119.4 | 118.8 | | |
| 730 | 129.460 | 124.922 | 120.040 | 126.558 | 119.7 | 119.9 | 119.3 | | |
| 740 | 129.962 | 125.426 | 120.539 | 127.061 | 120.2 | 120.4 | 119.8 | | |
| 750 | 130.458 | 125.925 | 121.033 | 127.553 | 120.7 | 120.9 | 120.3 | | |
| 760 | 130.949 | 126.419 | 121.522 | 128.050 | 121.2 | 121.4 | 120.8 | | |
| 770 | 131.436 | 126.908 | 122.006 | 128.538 | 121.7 | 121.9 | 121.3 | | |
| 780 | 131.917 | 127.392 | 122.485 | 129.020 | 122.2 | 122.4 | 121.8 | | |
| 790 | 132.394 | 127.871 | 122.959 | 129.498 | 122.6 | 122.8 | 122.2 | | |
| 800 | 132.866 | 128.345 | 123.429 | 129.970 | 123.1 | 123.3 | 122.7 | | |
| 900 | 137.35 | 132.85 | 127.89 | 134.46 | 127.5 | 127.7 | 127.1 | | |
| 1000 | 141.46 | 136.98 | 131.98 | 138.58 | 131.6 | 131.8 | 131.2 | | |
| 1200 | 148.80 | 144.36 | 139.29 | 145.93 | 139. | 139. | 138. | | |
| 1500 | 158.2 | 153.8 | 148.7 | 155.4 | 148. | 148. | 148. | | |

The values above are calculated from the constants below and the Antoine equation:

$$\log_{10} P = A - B/(C + t); \quad t = B/(A - \log_{10} P) - C$$
(P in mm Hg; t in °C)

Constants of the Antoine Equation

| | | | | | | | | | |
|---|---|---|---|---|---|---|---|---|---|
| A | 6.90392 | 6.88622 | 6.87148 | 6.90561 | 6.8844 | 6.8838 | 6.8743 | | |
| B | 1384.386 | 1379.415 | 1355.287 | 1388.307 | 1356.0 | 1355.0 | 1351.0 | | |
| C | 213.159 | 217.969 | 218.092 | 216.888 | 217.5 | 217.1 | 217.5 | | |

TABLE 15k, Page 2 — ALKYL CYCLOPENTANES, $C_8$
VAPOR PRESSURES AND BOILING POINTS, AT 10 TO 1500 mm Hg
August 31, 1949; December 31, 1952

| Pressure | 1,1,2-Trimethyl-cyclopentane | 1,1,3-Trimethyl-cyclopentane | 1,cis-2,cis-3-Trimethyl-cyclopentane | 1,cis-2,trans-3-Trimethyl-cyclopentane | 1,trans-2,cis-3-Trimethyl-cyclopentane | 1,cis-2,cis-4-Trimethyl-cyclopentane | 1,cis-2,trans-4-Trimethyl-cyclopentane | 1,trans-2,cis-4-Trimethyl-cyclopentane | |
|---|---|---|---|---|---|---|---|---|---|
| mm Hg | | | | Temperature in °C | | | | | |
| 10 | 6.38 | −0.3 | 14. | 10. | 4. | 10. | 8.9 | 3.48 | |
| 20 | 18.65 | +11.7 | 26. | 22. | 16. | 22. | 21.2 | 15.59 | |
| 30 | 26.46 | 19.39 | 34. | 30. | 24. | 30. | 29.10 | 23.31 | |
| 40 | 32.328 | 25.14 | 40. | 36. | 30. | 36. | 35.01 | 29.095 | |
| 50 | 37.074 | 29.78 | 45. | 40. | 34. | 41. | 39.78 | 33.778 | |
| 60 | 41.087 | 33.712 | 49. | 44. | 38. | 45. | 43.815 | 37.737 | |
| 80 | 47.682 | 40.170 | 56. | 51. | 45. | 51. | 50.446 | 44.242 | |
| 100 | 53.032 | 45.410 | 61.2 | 56.5 | 50.0 | 57 | 55.824 | 49.519 | |
| 150 | 63.326 | 55.493 | 71.7 | 66.9 | 60.2 | 67. | 66.166 | 59.666 | |
| 200 | 71.116 | 63.125 | 79.6 | 74.7 | 68.0 | 75. | 73.989 | 67.343 | |
| 250 | 77.461 | 69.343 | 86.1 | 81.1 | 74.2 | 81. | 80.360 | 73.593 | |
| 300 | 82.856 | 74.629 | 91.6 | 86.5 | 79.6 | 87. | 85.774 | 78.906 | |
| 400 | 91.780 | 83.375 | 100.7 | 95.5 | 88.5 | 96. | 94.727 | 87.693 | |
| 500 | 99.074 | 90.525 | 108.1 | 102.8 | 95.7 | 103. | 102.042 | 94.872 | |
| 600 | 105.293 | 96.622 | 114.4 | 109.0 | 101.8 | 109. | 108.277 | 100.992 | |
| 700 | 110.745 | 101.968 | 120.0 | 114.5 | 107.2 | 115. | 113.741 | 106.355 | |
| 710 | 111.256 | 102.468 | 120.5 | 115.0 | 107.7 | 116. | 114.253 | 106.858 | |
| 720 | 111.761 | 102.964 | 121.0 | 115.5 | 108.3 | 116. | 114.759 | 107.354 | |
| 730 | 112.261 | 103.454 | 121.5 | 116.0 | 108.7 | 117. | 115.260 | 107.846 | |
| 740 | 112.755 | 103.939 | 122.0 | 116.5 | 109.2 | 117. | 115.756 | 108.332 | |
| 750 | 113.245 | 104.418 | 122.5 | 117.0 | 109.7 | 117. | 116.246 | 108.814 | |
| 760 | 113.729 | 104.893 | 123.0 | 117.5 | 110.2 | 118. | 116.731 | 109.290 | |
| 770 | 114.208 | 105.363 | 123.5 | 118.0 | 110.7 | 118. | 117.212 | 109.761 | |
| 780 | 114.683 | 105.828 | 124.0 | 118.5 | 111.1 | 119. | 117.687 | 110.228 | |
| 790 | 115.153 | 106.290 | 124.4 | 118.9 | 111.6 | 119. | 118.158 | 110.690 | |
| 800 | 115.618 | 106.746 | 124.9 | 119.4 | 112.1 | 120. | 118.624 | 111.148 | |
| 900 | 120.04 | 111.08 | 129.4 | 123.8 | 116.4 | 124. | 123.05 | 115.49 | |
| 1000 | 124.09 | 115.06 | 133.5 | 127.9 | 120.5 | 128. | 127.11 | 119.48 | |
| 1200 | 131.34 | 122.17 | 141. | 135. | 128. | 136. | 134.37 | 126.60 | |
| 1500 | 140.6 | 131.3 | 150. | 144. | 137. | 145. | 143.7 | 135.7 | |

The values above are calculated from the constants below and the Antoine equation:

$$\log_{10} P = A - B/(C + t); \quad t = B/(A - \log_{10} P) - C$$

(P in mm Hg; t in °C)

Constants of the Antoine Equation

| | | | | | | | | | |
|---|---|---|---|---|---|---|---|---|---|
| A | 6.82205 | 6.80947 | 6.8485 | 6.8480 | 6.8268 | 6.842 | 6.85448 | 6.84970 | |
| B | 1309.618 | 1275.998 | 1349.0 | 1331.0 | 1301.0 | 1335. | 1333.894 | 1306.153 | |
| C | 218.557 | 219.899 | 217.0 | 218.0 | 219.5 | 219. | 218.952 | 219.808 | |

TABLE 7k, Page 1 — ALKYL CYCLOHEXANES, $C_6$ TO $C_8$
VAPOR PRESSURES AND BOILING POINTS, AT 10 TO 1500 mm Hg

August 31, 1944; March 31, 1947; December 31, 1952

| Pressure | Cyclohexane | Methyl–cyclohexane | Ethyl–cyclohexane | 1,1–Dimethyl–cyclohexane | | | | | |
|---|---|---|---|---|---|---|---|---|---|
| mm Hg | Temperature in °C | | | | | | | | |
| 10 | | -3.2 | 20.6 | 10.1 | | | | | |
| 20 | | +8.7 | 33.4 | 22.6 | | | | | |
| 30 | ————a | 16.30 | 41.49 | 30.55 | | | | | |
| 40 | 6.69 | 21.99 | 47.58 | 36.53 | | | | | |
| 50 | 11.01 | 26.592 | 52.503 | 41.361 | | | | | |
| 60 | 14.67 | 30.485 | 56.664 | 45.449 | | | | | |
| 80 | 20.672 | 36.882 | 63.500 | 52.169 | | | | | |
| 100 | 25.543 | 42.072 | 69.044 | 57.622 | | | | | |
| 150 | 34.912 | 52.057 | 79.704 | 68.115 | | | | | |
| 200 | 42.000 | 59.612 | 87.766 | 76.058 | | | | | |
| 250 | 47.772 | 65.766 | 94.329 | 82.530 | | | | | |
| 300 | 52.678 | 70.998 | 99.906 | 88.033 | | | | | |
| 400 | 60.792 | 79.652 | 109.128 | 97.138 | | | | | |
| 500 | 67.422 | 86.725 | 116.661 | 104.582 | | | | | |
| 600 | 73.074 | 92.756 | 123.080 | 110.930 | | | | | |
| 700 | 78.028 | 98.042 | 128.705 | 116.496 | | | | | |
| 710 | 78.492 | 98.537 | 129.232 | 117.018 | | | | | |
| 720 | 78.950 | 99.027 | 129.753 | 117.533 | | | | | |
| 730 | 79.405 | 99.511 | 130.269 | 118.044 | | | | | |
| 740 | 79.854 | 99.990 | 130.779 | 118.549 | | | | | |
| 750 | 80.299 | 100.465 | 131.284 | 119.048 | | | | | |
| 760 | 80.738 | 100.934 | 131.783 | 119.543 | | | | | |
| 770 | 81.174 | 101.400 | 132.278 | 120.032 | | | | | |
| 780 | 81.604 | 101.859 | 132.767 | 120.516 | | | | | |
| 790 | 82.032 | 102.315 | 133.252 | 120.997 | | | | | |
| 800 | 82.454 | 102.766 | 133.731 | 121.472 | | | | | |
| 900 | 86.47 | 107.05 | 138.29 | 125.98 | | | | | |
| 1000 | 90.15 | 110.98 | 142.47 | 130.12 | | | | | |
| 1200 | 96.73 | 118.01 | 149.93 | 137.53 | | | | | |
| 1500 | 105.2 | 127.0 | 159.5 | 147.0 | | | | | |

The values above are calculated from the constants below and the Antoine equation:

$$\log_{10} P = A - B/(C + t); \quad t = B/(A - \log_{10} P) - C$$

(P in mm Hg; t in °C)

Constants of the Antoine Equation

| | | | | | | | | | |
|---|---|---|---|---|---|---|---|---|---|
| A | 6.84498 | 6.82689 | 6.87041 | 6.80225 | | | | | |
| B | 1203.526 | 1272.864 | 1384.036 | 1323.861 | | | | | |
| C | 222.863 | 221.630 | 215.128 | 218.053 | | | | | |

a At the triple point, 6.67°C, the pressure is 39.96 mm Hg.

TABLE 7k, Page 2 — ALKYL CYCLOHEXANES, $C_8$
VAPOR PRESSURES AND BOILING POINTS, AT 10 TO 1500 mm Hg

August 31, 1944; March 31, 1947; December 31, 1952

| Pressure | 1,cis-2-Dimethyl-cyclohexane | 1,trans-2-Dimethyl-cyclohexane | 1,cis-3-Dimethyl-cyclohexane | 1,trans-3-Dimethyl-cyclohexane | 1,cis-4-Dimethyl-cyclohexane | 1,trans-4-Dimethyl-cyclohexane | | | |
|---|---|---|---|---|---|---|---|---|---|
| mm Hg | Temperature in °C | | | | | | | | |
| 10 | 18.4 | 13.0 | 11.2 | 14.9 | 14.5 | 10.1 | | | |
| 20 | 31.1 | 25.6 | 23.6 | 27.4 | 27.1 | 22.6 | | | |
| 30 | 39.25 | 33.66 | 31.57 | 35.42 | 35.10 | 30.54 | | | |
| 40 | 45.34 | 39.70 | 37.53 | 41.41 | 41.10 | 36.51 | | | |
| 50 | 50.266 | 44.580 | 42.347 | 46.258 | 45.958 | 41.341 | | | |
| 60 | 54.430 | 48.711 | 46.421 | 50.355 | 50.063 | 45.425 | | | |
| 80 | 61.273 | 55.498 | 53.116 | 57.087 | 56.810 | 52.136 | | | |
| 100 | 66.824 | 61.005 | 58.547 | 62.549 | 62.283 | 57.581 | | | |
| 150 | 77.500 | 71.596 | 68.992 | 73.054 | 72.810 | 68.057 | | | |
| 200 | 85.577 | 79.609 | 76.895 | 81.002 | 80.775 | 75.985 | | | |
| 250 | 92.155 | 86.136 | 83.330 | 87.474 | 87.262 | 82.442 | | | |
| 300 | 97.746 | 91.683 | 88.800 | 92.976 | 92.776 | 87.932 | | | |
| 400 | 106.993 | 100.859 | 97.847 | 102.077 | 101.897 | 97.014 | | | |
| 500 | 114.550 | 108.357 | 105.240 | 109.513 | 109.350 | 104.437 | | | |
| 600 | 120.992 | 114.750 | 111.542 | 115.853 | 115.704 | 110.766 | | | |
| 700 | 126.638 | 120.353 | 117.066 | 121.410 | 121.274 | 116.315 | | | |
| 710 | 127.167 | 120.878 | 117.583 | 121.931 | 121.795 | 116.835 | | | |
| 720 | 127.690 | 121.396 | 118.094 | 122.445 | 122.311 | 117.349 | | | |
| 730 | 128.208 | 121.910 | 118.601 | 122.954 | 122.822 | 117.857 | | | |
| 740 | 128.720 | 122.419 | 119.102 | 123.459 | 123.327 | 118.360 | | | |
| 750 | 129.227 | 122.921 | 119.598 | 123.957 | 123.827 | 118.859 | | | |
| 760 | 129.728 | 123.419 | 120.088 | 124.450 | 124.321 | 119.351 | | | |
| 770 | 130.224 | 123.912 | 120.574 | 124.939 | 124.811 | 119.839 | | | |
| 780 | 130.715 | 124.399 | 121.054 | 125.422 | 125.295 | 120.321 | | | |
| 790 | 131.202 | 124.882 | 121.530 | 125.901 | 125.776 | 120.800 | | | |
| 800 | 131.683 | 125.360 | 122.001 | 126.375 | 126.250 | 121.273 | | | |
| 900 | 136.26 | 129.90 | 126.48 | 130.88 | 130.77 | 125.77 | | | |
| 1000 | 140.46 | 134.07 | 130.59 | 135.01 | 134.91 | 129.90 | | | |
| 1200 | 147.96 | 141.51 | 137.92 | 142.40 | 142.31 | 137.28 | | | |
| 1500 | 157.6 | 151.1 | 147.3 | 151.9 | 151.8 | 146.7 | | | |

The values above are calculated from the constants below and the Antoine equation:

$$\log_{10} P = A - B/(C + t); \quad t = B/(A - \log_{10} P) - C$$

(P in mm Hg; t in °C)

Constants of the Antoine Equation

| | 1,cis-2- | 1,trans-2- | 1,cis-3- | 1,trans-3- | 1,cis-4- | 1,trans-4- | | | |
|---|---|---|---|---|---|---|---|---|---|
| A | 6.84164 | 6.83722 | 6.84293 | 6.83866 | 6.83699 | 6.82180 | | | |
| B | 1369.525 | 1356.100 | 1340.658 | 1345.859 | 1347.794 | 1332.613 | | | |
| C | 216.040 | 219.342 | 218.281 | 215.598 | 216.360 | 218.791 | | | |

| | | | | | | | | | |
|---|---|---|---|---|---|---|---|---|---|

TABLE 24k (PART 1), Page 1 – NORMAL MONOOLEFINS (1–ALKENES), $C_2$ TO $C_{20}$
VAPOR PRESSURES AND BOILING POINTS, AT 10 TO 1500 mm Hg
September 30, 1951 (Corrected)

| Pressure | Ethene (Ethylene) | Propene (Propylene) | 1–Butene | 1–Pentene | 1–Hexene | 1–Heptene | 1–Octene | 1–Nonene | 1–Decene |
|---|---|---|---|---|---|---|---|---|---|
| mm Hg | Temperature in °C | | | | | | | | |
| 10 | −153.22 | −112.11 | −81.5 | −54.8 | −29.3 | −6.07 | 15.38 | 35.55 | 54.40 |
| 20 | −147.59 | −104.75 | −72.89 | −45.1 | −18.65 | +5.39 | 27.57 | 48.38 | 67.80 |
| 30 | −144.00 | −100.06 | −67.41 | −38.91 | −11.88 | 12.68 | 35.33 | 56.55 | 76.33 |
| 40 | −141.31 | − 96.55 | −63.29 | −34.28 | − 6.81 | 18.15 | 41.15 | 62.67 | 82.71 |
| 50 | −139.13 | − 93.70 | −59.96 | −30.53 | − 2.70 | 22.569 | 45.848 | 67.612 | 87.875 |
| 60 | −137.28 | − 91.29 | −57.15 | −27.36 | + 0.776 | 26.306 | 49.820 | 71.790 | 92.236 |
| 80 | −134.24 | − 87.33 | −52.52 | −22.14 | 6.482 | 32.443 | 56.343 | 78.651 | 99.396 |
| 100 | −131.78 | − 84.12 | −48.77 | −17.92 | 11.109 | 37.418 | 61.630 | 84.210 | 105.198 |
| 150 | −127.03 | − 77.95 | −41.56 | − 9.789 | 20.006 | 46.982 | 71.789 | 94.889 | 116.342 |
| 200 | −123.44 | − 73.27 | −36.10 | − 3.640 | 26.736 | 54.212 | 79.465 | 102.956 | 124.760 |
| 250 | −120.51 | − 69.46 | −31.65 | + 1.368 | 32.215 | 60.096 | 85.710 | 109.518 | 131.607 |
| 300 | −118.01 | − 66.23 | −27.87 | 5.624 | 36.871 | 65.095 | 91.014 | 115.090 | 137.421 |
| 400 | −113.88 | − 60.87 | −21.62 | 12.664 | 44.569 | 73.357 | 99.778 | 124.295 | 147.024 |
| 500 | −110.51 | − 56.50 | −16.52 | 18.416 | 50.859 | 80.104 | 106.932 | 131.808 | 154.861 |
| 600 | −107.62 | − 52.76 | −12.16 | 23.319 | 56.219 | 85.853 | 113.026 | 138.204 | 161.533 |
| 700 | −105.09 | − 49.49 | − 8.35 | 27.616 | 60.915 | 90.888 | 118.362 | 143.805 | 167.376 |
| 710 | −104.86 | − 49.18 | − 7.99 | 28.019 | 61.356 | 91.360 | 118.861 | 144.330 | 167.923 |
| 720 | −104.62 | − 48.88 | − 7.64 | 28.417 | 61.790 | 91.826 | 119.355 | 144.848 | 168.464 |
| 730 | −104.39 | − 48.58 | − 7.29 | 28.811 | 62.221 | 92.287 | 119.844 | 145.361 | 168.999 |
| 740 | −104.16 | − 48.28 | − 6.94 | 29.201 | 62.647 | 92.744 | 120.328 | 145.869 | 169.528 |
| 750 | −103.93 | − 47.99 | − 6.60 | 29.586 | 63.068 | 93.196 | 120.807 | 146.371 | 170.052 |
| 760 | −103.71 | − 47.70 | − 6.26 | 29.968 | 63.485 | 93.643 | 121.280 | 146.868 | 170.570 |
| 770 | −103.49 | − 47.41 | − 5.93 | 30.346 | 63.898 | 94.085 | 121.749 | 147.360 | 171.084 |
| 780 | −103.27 | − 47.13 | − 5.59 | 30.720 | 64.307 | 94.523 | 122.213 | 147.847 | 171.591 |
| 790 | −103.05 | − 46.85 | − 5.26 | 31.090 | 64.712 | 94.957 | 122.672 | 148.329 | 172.094 |
| 800 | −102.83 | − 46.57 | − 4.94 | 31.456 | 65.112 | 95.386 | 123.127 | 148.806 | 172.592 |
| 900 | −100.78 | − 43.91 | − 1.85 | 34.939 | 68.917 | 99.463 | 127.445 | 153.338 | 177.318 |
| 1000 | − 98.90 | − 41.48 | + 0.99 | 38.132 | 72.41 | 103.20 | 131.40 | 157.49 | 181.65 |
| 1200 | − 95.53 | − 37.13 | 6.1 | 43.84 | 78.64 | 109.88 | 138.48 | 164.91 | 189.39 |
| 1500 | − 91.20 | − 31.55 | 12.6 | 51.16 | 86.64 | 118.44 | 147.54 | 174.41 | 199.30 |

The values above are calculated from the constants below and the Antoine equation:
$$\log_{10} P = A - B/(C + t); \quad t = B/(A - \log_{10} P) - C$$
(P in mm Hg; t in °C)

Constants of the Antoine Equation

| | | | | | | | | | |
|---|---|---|---|---|---|---|---|---|---|
| A | 6.74756 | 6.81960 | 6.84290 | 6.84650 | 6.86572 | 6.90069 | 6.93263 | 6.95387 | 6.96034 |
| B | 585.00 | 785.00 | 926.10 | 1044.895 | 1152.971 | 1257.505 | 1353.486 | 1435.359 | 1501.872 |
| C | 255.00 | 247.00 | 240.00 | 233.516 | 225.849 | 219.179 | 212.764 | 205.535 | 197.578 |

TABLE 24k (PART 1), Page 2 — NORMAL MONOOLEFINS (1-ALKENES), $C_2$ TO $C_{20}$
VAPOR PRESSURES AND BOILING POINTS, AT 10 TO 1500 mm Hg
September 30, 1951

| Pressure | 1-Undecene | 1-Dodecene | 1-Tridecene | 1-Tetradecene | 1-Pentadecene | 1-Hexadecene | 1-Heptadecene | 1-Octadecene | 1-Nonadecene |
|---|---|---|---|---|---|---|---|---|---|
| mm Hg | | | | | Temperature in $^{\circ}C$ | | | | |
| 10 | 72.12 | 88.83 | 104.6 | 119.6 | 133.8 | 147.3 | 160. | 172. | 184. |
| 20 | 86.04 | 103.21 | 119.4 | 134.8 | 149.3 | 163.1 | 176. | 189. | 200. |
| 30 | 94.89 | 112.35 | 128.8 | 144.4 | 159.1 | 173.1 | 186. | 199. | 211. |
| 40 | 101.52 | 119.20 | 135.9 | 151.6 | 166.5 | 180.7 | 194. | 207. | 219. |
| 50 | 106.873 | 124.739 | 141.6 | 157.5 | 172.5 | 186.8 | 200.2 | 213. | 225. |
| 60 | 111.400 | 129.416 | 146.4 | 162.4 | 177.5 | 191.9 | 205.4 | 218. | 231. |
| 80 | 118.830 | 137.094 | 154.3 | 170.5 | 185.8 | 200.3 | 214.0 | 227. | 240. |
| 100 | 124.851 | 143.315 | 160.7 | 177.1 | 192.5 | 207.2 | 221.0 | 234.2 | 247. |
| 150 | 136.415 | 155.261 | 173.0 | 189.7 | 205.4 | 220.3 | 234.4 | 247.8 | 260.5 |
| 200 | 145.149 | 164.284 | 182.3 | 199.2 | 215.1 | 230.3 | 244.5 | 258.1 | 271.0 |
| 250 | 152.253 | 171.621 | 189.8 | 206.9 | 223.1 | 238.4 | 252.7 | 266.5 | 279.5 |
| 300 | 158.284 | 177.850 | 196.2 | 213.5 | 229.8 | 245.2 | 259.7 | 273.6 | 286.7 |
| 400 | 168.247 | 188.139 | 206.83 | 224.4 | 240.9 | 256.6 | 271.3 | 285.3 | 298.6 |
| 500 | 176.376 | 196.533 | 215.47 | 233.24 | 250.0 | 265.9 | 280.7 | 294.9 | 308.4 |
| 600 | 183.298 | 203.680 | 222.83 | 240.79 | 257.71 | 273.7 | 288.7 | 303.1 | 316.7 |
| 700 | 189.357 | 209.936 | 229.26 | 247.39 | 264.47 | 280.6 | 295.8 | 310.3 | 324.0 |
| 710 | 189.925 | 210.522 | 229.87 | 248.02 | 265.11 | 281.3 | 296.4 | 310.9 | 324.6 |
| 720 | 190.485 | 211.101 | 230.46 | 248.62 | 265.73 | 281.9 | 297.1 | 311.6 | 325.3 |
| 730 | 191.040 | 211.674 | 231.05 | 249.23 | 266.35 | 282.5 | 297.7 | 312.2 | 326.0 |
| 740 | 191.590 | 212.241 | 231.63 | 249.83 | 266.96 | 283.2 | 298.4 | 312.9 | 326.6 |
| 750 | 192.133 | 212.802 | 232.22 | 250.43 | 267.57 | 283.8 | 299.0 | 313.6 | 327.3 |
| 760 | 192.671 | 213.357 | 232.78 | 251.01 | 268.17 | 284.4 | 299.7 | 314.2 | 328.0 |
| 770 | 193.203 | 213.906 | 233.35 | 251.59 | 268.76 | 285.0 | 300.2 | 314.8 | 328.5 |
| 780 | 193.729 | 214.450 | 233.91 | 252.16 | 269.35 | 285.6 | 300.9 | 315.4 | 329.2 |
| 790 | 194.251 | 214.989 | 234.46 | 252.73 | 269.93 | 286.3 | 301.5 | 316.1 | 329.9 |
| 800 | 194.767 | 215.521 | 235.01 | 253.30 | 270.51 | 286.8 | 302.1 | 316.7 | 330.5 |
| 900 | 199.669 | 220.582 | 240.22 | 258.64 | 276.0 | 292.4 | 307.8 | 322.5 | 336.3 |
| 1000 | 204.16 | 225.22 | 245.00 | 263.5 | 281.0 | 297.5 | 313.0 | 327.8 | 341.8 |
| 1200 | 212.18 | 233.50 | 253.5 | 272.3 | 290.0 | 306.7 | 322. | 337. | 351. |
| 1500 | 222.46 | 244.11 | 264.4 | 283.5 | 301.4 | 318.4 | 334. | 350. | 364. |

The values above are calculated from the constants below and the Antoine equation:
$$\log_{10} P = A - B/(C + t); \quad t = B/(A - \log_{10} P) - C$$
(P in mm Hg; t in $^{\circ}C$)

Constants of the Antoine Equation

| | 1-Undecene | 1-Dodecene | 1-Tridecene | 1-Tetradecene | 1-Pentadecene | 1-Hexadecene | 1-Heptadecene | 1-Octadecene | 1-Nonadecene |
|---|---|---|---|---|---|---|---|---|---|
| A | 6.96662 | 6.97522 | 6.9692 | 6.9615 | 6.9503 | 6.936 | 6.920 | 6.901 | 6.881 |
| B | 1562.469 | 1619.862 | 1662.68 | 1699.76 | 1730.30 | 1755.2 | 1774.6 | 1789.4 | 1800.3 |
| C | 189.743 | 182.271 | 173.90 | 165.53 | 157.02 | 148.4 | 139.7 | 130.9 | 122.1 |

357

TABLE 24k (PART 1), Page 3 — NORMAL MONOOLEFINS (1-ALKENES), $C_2$ TO $C_{20}$

VAPOR PRESSURES AND BOILING POINTS, AT 10 TO 1500 mm Hg

September 30, 1951

| Pressure | 1-Eicosene | | | | | | | | |
|---|---|---|---|---|---|---|---|---|---|
| mm Hg | Temperature in °C | | | | | | | | |
| 10 | 195. | | | | | | | | |
| 20 | 212. | | | | | | | | |
| 30 | 223. | | | | | | | | |
| 40 | 231. | | | | | | | | |
| 50 | 237. | | | | | | | | |
| 60 | 242. | | | | | | | | |
| 80 | 252. | | | | | | | | |
| 100 | 259. | | | | | | | | |
| 150 | 272.8 | | | | | | | | |
| 200 | 283.3 | | | | | | | | |
| 250 | 292.0 | | | | | | | | |
| 300 | 299.3 | | | | | | | | |
| 400 | 311.4 | | | | | | | | |
| 500 | 321.3 | | | | | | | | |
| 600 | 329.7 | | | | | | | | |
| 700 | 337.1 | | | | | | | | |
| 710 | 337.8 | | | | | | | | |
| 720 | 338.4 | | | | | | | | |
| 730 | 339.1 | | | | | | | | |
| 740 | 339.8 | | | | | | | | |
| 750 | 340.5 | | | | | | | | |
| 760 | 341.2 | | | | | | | | |
| 770 | 341.7 | | | | | | | | |
| 780 | 342.4 | | | | | | | | |
| 790 | 343.1 | | | | | | | | |
| 800 | 343.7 | | | | | | | | |
| 900 | 349.7 | | | | | | | | |
| 1000 | 355.2 | | | | | | | | |
| 1200 | 365. | | | | | | | | |
| 1500 | 378. | | | | | | | | |

The values above are calculated from the constants below and the Antoine equation:

$$\log_{10} P = A - B/(C + t); \quad t = B/(A - \log_{10} P) - C$$

(P in mm Hg; t in °C)

Constants of the Antoine Equation

| A | 6.859 |
| B | 1807.9 |
| C | 113.3 |

| Pressure | Ethene (Ethylene) | Propene (Propylene) | 1- Butene | cis-2- Butene | trans-2- Butene | 2-Methyl- propene (Isobutene) | | | |
|---|---|---|---|---|---|---|---|---|---|
| mm Hg | Temperature in °C | | | | | | | | |
| 10 | −153.22 | −112.11 | −81.5 | −73.42 | −76.3 | −81.95 | | | |
| 20 | −147.59 | −104.75 | −72.89 | −64.58 | −67.46 | −73.37 | | | |
| 30 | −144.00 | −100.06 | −67.41 | −58.94 | −61.82 | −67.90 | | | |
| 40 | −141.31 | −96.55 | −63.29 | −54.72 | −57.60 | −63.79 | | | |
| 50 | −139.13 | −93.70 | −59.96 | −51.305 | −54.18 | −60.472 | | | |
| 60 | −137.28 | −91.29 | −57.15 | −48.416 | −51.29 | −57.664 | | | |
| 80 | −134.24 | −87.33 | −52.52 | −43.672 | −46.54 | −53.051 | | | |
| 100 | −131.78 | −84.12 | −48.77 | −39.824 | −42.69 | −49.309 | | | |
| 150 | −127.03 | −77.95 | −41.56 | −32.426 | −35.29 | −42.111 | | | |
| 200 | −123.44 | −73.27 | −36.10 | −26.831 | −29.69 | −36.666 | | | |
| 250 | −120.51 | −69.46 | −31.65 | −22.276 | −25.13 | −32.231 | | | |
| 300 | −118.01 | −66.23 | −27.87 | −18.405 | −21.26 | −28.462 | | | |
| 400 | −113.88 | −60.87 | −21.62 | −12.005 | −14.85 | −22.227 | | | |
| 500 | −110.51 | −56.50 | −16.52 | −6.776 | −9.62 | −17.133 | | | |
| 600 | −107.62 | −52.76 | −12.16 | −2.321 | −5.16 | −12.789 | | | |
| 700 | −105.09 | −49.49 | −8.35 | +1.584 | −1.26 | −8.983 | | | |
| 710 | −104.86 | −49.18 | −7.99 | 1.950 | −0.89 | −8.626 | | | |
| 720 | −104.62 | −48.88 | −7.64 | 2.311 | −0.53 | −8.274 | | | |
| 730 | −104.39 | −48.58 | −7.29 | 2.669 | −0.17 | −7.925 | | | |
| 740 | −104.16 | −48.28 | −6.94 | 3.023 | +0.18 | −7.580 | | | |
| 750 | −103.93 | −47.99 | −6.60 | 3.374 | 0.53 | −7.238 | | | |
| 760 | −103.71 | −47.70 | −6.26 | 3.720 | 0.88 | −6.900 | | | |
| 770 | −103.49 | −47.41 | −5.93 | 4.063 | 1.22 | −6.565 | | | |
| 780 | −103.27 | −47.13 | −5.59 | 4.403 | 1.56 | −6.234 | | | |
| 790 | −103.05 | −46.85 | −5.26 | 4.740 | 1.90 | −5.906 | | | |
| 800 | −102.83 | −46.57 | −4.94 | 5.072 | 2.23 | −5.581 | | | |
| 900 | −100.78 | −43.91 | −1.85 | 8.235 | 5.40 | −2.497 | | | |
| 1000 | −98.90 | −41.48 | +0.99 | 11.135 | 8.30 | +0.333 | | | |
| 1200 | −95.53 | −37.13 | 6.1 | 16.319 | 13.49 | 5.391 | | | |
| 1500 | −91.20 | −31.55 | 12.6 | 22.97 | 20.1 | 11.88 | | | |

The values above are calculated from the constants below and the Antoine equation:

$$\log_{10} P = A - B/(C + t); \quad t = B/(A - \log_{10} P) - C$$

$$(P \text{ in mm Hg}; \ t \text{ in } °C)$$

Constants of the Antoine Equation

| | | | | | | | | | |
|---|---|---|---|---|---|---|---|---|---|
| A | 6.74756 | 6.81960 | 6.84290 | 6.86926 | 6.86952 | 6.84134 | | | |
| B | 585.00 | 785.00 | 926.10 | 960.100 | 960.80 | 923.200 | | | |
| C | 255.00 | 247.00 | 240.00 | 237.000 | 240.00 | 240.000 | | | |

TABLE 8k (PART 1), Page 1 — MONOOLEFINS, $C_2$ TO $C_5$
VAPOR PRESSURES AND BOILING POINTS, AT 10 TO 1500 mm Hg
July 31, 1944; March 31, 1945; December 31, 1952

TABLE 8k (PART 1), Page 2 — MONOOLEFINS, $C_2$ TO $C_5$
VAPOR PRESSURES AND BOILING POINTS, AT 10 TO 1500 mm Hg
October 31, 1950; December 31, 1952

| Pressure | 1-Pentene | cis-2-Pentene | trans-2-Pentene | 2-Methyl-1-butene | 3-Methyl-1-butene | 2-Methyl-2-butene | | | |
|---|---|---|---|---|---|---|---|---|---|
| mm Hg | | | | Temperature in °C | | | | | |
| 10 | -54.8 | -48.7 | -49.4 | -53.4 | -62.9 | -47.7 | | | |
| 20 | -45.1 | -38.9 | -39.6 | -43.7 | -53.4 | -37.8 | | | |
| 30 | -38.91 | -32.66 | -33.28 | -37.5 | -47.3 | -31.48 | | | |
| 40 | -34.28 | -27.96 | -28.58 | -32.87 | -42.8 | -26.75 | | | |
| 50 | -30.53 | -24.17 | -24.78 | -29.13 | -39.2 | -22.92 | | | |
| 60 | -27.36 | -20.96 | -21.56 | -25.96 | -36.05 | -19.68 | | | |
| 80 | -22.14 | -15.69 | -16.28 | -20.76 | -30.96 | -14.37 | | | |
| 100 | -17.92 | -11.42 | -12.00 | -16.54 | -26.82 | -10.06 | | | |
| 150 | -9.789 | -3.199 | -3.776 | -8.44 | -18.87 | -1.788 | | | |
| 200 | -3.640 | +3.015 | +2.443 | -2.308 | -12.85 | +4.468 | | | |
| 250 | +1.368 | 8.074 | 7.504 | +2.683 | -7.95 | 9.559 | | | |
| 300 | 5.624 | 12.373 | 11.803 | 6.924 | -3.783 | 13.883 | | | |
| 400 | 12.664 | 19.461 | 18.909 | 13.936 | +3.109 | 21.029 | | | |
| 500 | 18.416 | 25.287 | 24.711 | 19.665 | 8.743 | 26.864 | | | |
| 600 | 23.319 | 30.235 | 29.654 | 24.546 | 13.546 | 31.834 | | | |
| 700 | 27.616 | 34.571 | 33.984 | 28.823 | 17.757 | 36.187 | | | |
| 710 | 28.019 | 34.977 | 34.390 | 29.224 | 18.151 | 36.595 | | | |
| 720 | 28.417 | 35.378 | 34.791 | 29.620 | 18.541 | 36.998 | | | |
| 730 | 28.811 | 35.775 | 35.187 | 30.012 | 18.927 | 37.397 | | | |
| 740 | 29.201 | 36.169 | 35.580 | 30.400 | 19.309 | 37.791 | | | |
| 750 | 29.586 | 36.558 | 35.968 | 30.784 | 19.687 | 38.182 | | | |
| 760 | 29.968 | 36.942 | 36.353 | 31.163 | 20.061 | 38.568 | | | |
| 770 | 30.346 | 37.324 | 36.733 | 31.539 | 20.431 | 38.951 | | | |
| 780 | 30.720 | 37.701 | 37.109 | 31.911 | 20.797 | 39.329 | | | |
| 790 | 31.090 | 38.074 | 37.483 | 32.280 | 21.161 | 39.704 | | | |
| 800 | 31.456 | 38.444 | 37.852 | 32.644 | 21.520 | 40.075 | | | |
| 900 | 34.939 | 41.956 | 41.357 | 36.109 | 24.932 | 43.599 | | | |
| 1000 | 38.132 | 45.176 | 44.571 | 39.286 | 28.063 | 46.830 | | | |
| 1200 | 43.84 | 50.93 | 50.31 | 44.96 | 33.66 | 52.60 | | | |
| 1500 | 51.16 | 58.31 | 57.68 | 52.24 | 40.84 | 60.00 | | | |

The values above are calculated from the constants below and the Antoine equation:
$$\log_{10} P = A - B/(C + t); \quad t = B/(A - \log_{10} P) - C$$
(P in mm Hg; t in °C)

Constants of the Antoine Equation

| | | | | | | | | | |
|---|---|---|---|---|---|---|---|---|---|
| A | 6.84650 | 6.87274 | 6.90575 | 6.87314 | 6.82618 | 6.91562 | | | |
| B | 1044.895 | 1067.951 | 1083.987 | 1053.780 | 1013.474 | 1095.088 | | | |
| C | 233.516 | 230.585 | 232.965 | 232.788 | 236.816 | 232.842 | | | |

TABLE 11k (PART 1), Page 1 — DIOLEFINS, $C_3$ TO $C_5$

VAPOR PRESSURES AND BOILING POINTS, AT 10 TO 1500 mm Hg

September 30, 1951

| Pressure | Propadiene (Allene) | 1,2-Butadiene | 1,3-Butadiene | | | | | | |
|---|---|---|---|---|---|---|---|---|---|
| mm Hg | Temperature in °C | | | | | | | | |
| 10 | −99. | −69. | −79.89 | | | | | | |
| 20 | −92. | −60. | −71.24 | | | | | | |
| 30 | −88. | −54. | −65.74 | | | | | | |
| 40 | −85. | −49. | −61.61 | | | | | | |
| 50 | −82.3 | −45.8 | −58.26 | | | | | | |
| 60 | −80.0 | −42.8 | −55.44 | | | | | | |
| 80 | −76.2 | −37.8 | −50.80 | | | | | | |
| 100 | −73.0 | −33.8 | −47.035 | | | | | | |
| 150 | −66.9 | −26.2 | −39.796 | | | | | | |
| 200 | −62.1 | −20.4 | −34.321 | | | | | | |
| 250 | −58.2 | −15.7 | −29.863 | | | | | | |
| 300 | −54.8 | −11.7 | −26.074 | | | | | | |
| 400 | −49.2 | −5.2 | −19.809 | | | | | | |
| 500 | −44.3 | +0.2 | −14.691 | | | | | | |
| 600 | −40.2 | 4.7 | −10.328 | | | | | | |
| 700 | −36.5 | 8.68 | −6.505 | | | | | | |
| 710 | −36.2 | 9.05 | −6.147 | | | | | | |
| 720 | −35.8 | 9.42 | −5.793 | | | | | | |
| 730 | −35.5 | 9.78 | −5.442 | | | | | | |
| 740 | −35.2 | 10.14 | −5.096 | | | | | | |
| 750 | −34.8 | 10.50 | −4.753 | | | | | | |
| 760 | −34.5 | 10.85 | −4.413 | | | | | | |
| 770 | −34.2 | 11.20 | −4.077 | | | | | | |
| 780 | −33.8 | 11.54 | −3.745 | | | | | | |
| 790 | −33.5 | 11.88 | −3.415 | | | | | | |
| 800 | −33.2 | 12.22 | −3.089 | | | | | | |
| 900 | −30.1 | 15.4 | +0.001 | | | | | | |
| 1000 | −27.3 | 18.3 | 2.849 | | | | | | |
| 1200 | −22. | 24. | 7.93 | | | | | | |
| 1500 | −15. | 30. | 14.44 | | | | | | |

The values above are calculated from the constants below and the Antoine equation:

$$\log_{10} P = A - B/(C + t); \quad t = B/(A - \log_{10} P) - C$$
(P in mm Hg; t in °C)

Constants of the Antoine Equation

| | | | | | | | | | |
|---|---|---|---|---|---|---|---|---|---|
| A | 5.6457 | 7.1619 | 6.85941 | | | | | | |
| B | 441.0 | 1121.0 | 935.531 | | | | | | |
| C | 194.0 | 251.00 | 239.554 | | | | | | |

## TABLE 11k (PART 1), Page 2 — DIOLEFINS, $C_3$ TO $C_5$
### VAPOR PRESSURES AND BOILING POINTS, AT 10 TO 1500 mm Hg
September 30, 1951; December 31, 1952

| Pressure | 1,2- Pentadiene | 1,cis-3- Pentadiene | 1,trans-3- Pentadiene | 1,4- Pentadiene | 2,3- Pentadiene | 3-Methyl-1,2- butadiene | 2-Methyl-1,3- butadiene (Isoprene) | | |
|---|---|---|---|---|---|---|---|---|---|
| mm Hg | Temperature in °C | | | | | | | | |
| 10 | −42.6 | −43.1 | −45.1 | −57.1 | −38.4 | −46. | −51.6 | | |
| 20 | −32.5 | −33.1 | −35.1 | −47.6 | −28.5 | −36. | −41.7 | | |
| 30 | −26.04 | −26.67 | −28.7 | −41.5 | −22.1 | −30. | −35.5 | | |
| 40 | −21.22 | −21.88 | −23.91 | −37.0 | −17.39 | −25. | −30.8 | | |
| 50 | −17.33 | −18.01 | −20.04 | −33.3 | −13.55 | −21. | −27.0 | | |
| 60 | −14.04 | −14.74 | −16.78 | −30.2 | −10.30 | −18. | −23.75 | | |
| 80 | − 8.65 | − 9.37 | −11.41 | −25.10 | − 4.97 | −13. | −18.48 | | |
| 100 | − 4.27 | − 5.02 | − 7.06 | −20.96 | − 0.64 | − 8. | −14.21 | | |
| 150 | + 4.116 | + 3.34 | + 1.30 | −12.99 | + 7.67 | 0. | − 5.99 | | |
| 200 | 10.449 | 9.662 | 7.61 | − 6.97 | 13.96 | + 6. | + 0.21 | | |
| 250 | 15.598 | 14.802 | 12.751 | − 2.06 | 19.075 | 11. | 5.27 | | |
| 300 | 19.969 | 19.167 | 17.116 | + 2.11 | 23.424 | 16. | 9.558 | | |
| 400 | 27.184 | 26.379 | 24.330 | 9.011 | 30.612 | 23. | 16.652 | | |
| 500 | 33.069 | 32.265 | 30.219 | 14.648 | 36.482 | 28. | 22.444 | | |
| 600 | 38.077 | 37.278 | 35.236 | 19.452 | 41.485 | 33. | 27.380 | | |
| 700 | 42.460 | 41.667 | 39.629 | 23.663 | 45.867 | 38. | 31.703 | | |
| 710 | 42.870 | 42.079 | 40.040 | 24.058 | 46.278 | 38. | 32.108 | | |
| 720 | 43.276 | 42.485 | 40.447 | 24.448 | 46.684 | 38. | 32.508 | | |
| 730 | 43.677 | 42.887 | 40.850 | 24.834 | 47.085 | 39. | 32.904 | | |
| 740 | 44.074 | 43.285 | 41.248 | 25.216 | 47.483 | 39. | 33.296 | | |
| 750 | 44.467 | 43.679 | 41.642 | 25.593 | 47.876 | 40. | 33.684 | | |
| 760 | 44.856 | 44.068 | 42.032 | 25.967 | 48.265 | 40. | 34.067 | | |
| 770 | 45.241 | 44.454 | 42.418 | 26.338 | 48.650 | 40. | 34.447 | | |
| 780 | 45.621 | 44.835 | 42.800 | 26.704 | 49.031 | 41. | 34.823 | | |
| 790 | 45.999 | 45.213 | 43.178 | 27.067 | 49.409 | 41. | 35.196 | | |
| 800 | 46.372 | 45.587 | 43.553 | 27.426 | 49.783 | 41 | 35.564 | | |
| 900 | 49.915 | 49.139 | 47.109 | 30.838 | 53.332 | 45. | 39.064 | | |
| 1000 | 53.16 | 52.40 | 50.37 | 33.97 | 56.59 | 48. | 42.27 | | |
| 1200 | 58.96 | 58.21 | 56.19 | 39.56 | 62.40 | 55. | 48.01 | | |
| 1500 | 66.38 | 65.66 | 63.66 | 46.74 | 69.86 | 61. | 55.36 | | |

The values above are calculated from the constants below and the Antoine equation:

$$\log_{10} P = A - B/(C + t); \quad t = B/(A - \log_{10} P) - C$$

(P in mm Hg; t in °C)

#### Constants of the Antoine Equation

| | 1,2- Pentadiene | 1,cis-3- Pentadiene | 1,trans-3- Pentadiene | 1,4- Pentadiene | 2,3- Pentadiene | 3-Methyl-1,2- butadiene | 2-Methyl-1,3- butadiene | | |
|---|---|---|---|---|---|---|---|---|---|
| A | 7.01100 | 6.94178 | 6.92257 | 6.84880 | 6.88603 | 7.005 | 6.90334 | | |
| B | 1154.420 | 1118.371 | 1108.937 | 1025.016 | 1086.636 | 1130. | 1080.996 | | |
| C | 234.652 | 231.327 | 232.338 | 232.354 | 223.040 | 234. | 234.668 | | |

| | | | | TABLE 5k, Page 1 – ALKYL BENZENES, $C_6$ TO $C_9$ | | | | | |

TABLE 5k, Page 1 – ALKYL BENZENES, $C_6$ TO $C_9$
VAPOR PRESSURES AND BOILING POINTS, AT 10 TO 1500 mm Hg
June 30, 1944; April 30, 1949; December 31, 1952

| Pressure | Benzene | Methyl-benzene (Toluene) | Ethyl-benzene | 1,2-Dimethyl-benzene (o-Xylene) | 1,3-Dimethyl-benzene (m-Xylene) | 1,4-Dimethyl-benzene (p-Xylene) | | | |
|---|---|---|---|---|---|---|---|---|---|
| mm Hg | Temperature in °C | | | | | | | | |
| 10 | −11.6 (solid) | 6.36 | 25.88 | 32.14 | 28.24 | 27.32 | | | |
| 20 | −2.6 | 18.38 | 38.60 | 45.13 | 41.07 | 40.15 | | | |
| 30 | +2.99[a] | 26.03 | 46.69 | 53.38 | 49.23 | 48.31 | | | |
| 40 | 7.55 | 31.76 | 52.75 | 59.56 | 55.33 | 54.42 | | | |
| 50 | 11.80 | 36.394 | 57.657 | 64.558 | 60.269 | 59.363 | | | |
| 60 | 15.39 | 40.308 | 61.798 | 68.778 | 64.437 | 63.535 | | | |
| 80 | 21.293 | 46.733 | 68.596 | 75.704 | 71.277 | 70.383 | | | |
| 100 | 26.075 | 51.940 | 74.105 | 81.314 | 76.818 | 75.931 | | | |
| 150 | 35.266 | 61.942 | 84.687 | 92.085 | 87.454 | 86.583 | | | |
| 200 | 42.214 | 69.498 | 92.680 | 100.217 | 95.483 | 94.626 | | | |
| 250 | 47.868 | 75.644 | 99.182 | 106.829 | 102.011 | 101.167 | | | |
| 300 | 52.672 | 80.863 | 104.703 | 112.441 | 107.551 | 106.719 | | | |
| 400 | 60.611 | 89.484 | 113.823 | 121.708 | 116.699 | 115.887 | | | |
| 500 | 67.093 | 96.512 | 121.266 | 129.267 | 124.159 | 123.366 | | | |
| 600 | 72.616 | 102.511 | 127.603 | 135.700 | 130.508 | 129.732 | | | |
| 700 | 77.454 | 107.757 | 133.152 | 141.332 | 136.065 | 135.304 | | | |
| 710 | 77.907 | 108.248 | 133.672 | 141.859 | 136.586 | 135.826 | | | |
| 720 | 78.354 | 108.733 | 134.185 | 142.380 | 137.100 | 136.341 | | | |
| 730 | 78.798 | 109.214 | 134.693 | 142.896 | 137.609 | 136.852 | | | |
| 740 | 79.236 | 109.689 | 135.196 | 143.407 | 138.112 | 137.357 | | | |
| 750 | 79.670 | 110.160 | 135.694 | 143.912 | 138.610 | 137.856 | | | |
| 760 | 80.100 | 110.625 | 136.186 | 144.411 | 139.103 | 138.351 | | | |
| 770 | 80.525 | 111.086 | 136.674 | 144.906 | 139.591 | 138.840 | | | |
| 780 | 80.945 | 111.542 | 137.156 | 145.395 | 140.073 | 139.324 | | | |
| 790 | 81.362 | 111.994 | 137.634 | 145.880 | 140.552 | 139.804 | | | |
| 800 | 81.774 | 112.440 | 138.106 | 146.359 | 141.025 | 140.278 | | | |
| 900 | 85.691 | 116.684 | 142.595 | 150.912 | 145.517 | -144.787 | | | |
| 1000 | 89.282 | 120.57 | 146.71 | 155.08 | 149.63 | 148.91 | | | |
| 1200 | 95.698 | 127.52 | 154.06 | 162.53 | 156.98 | 156.29 | | | |
| 1500 | 103.92 | 136.42 | 163.47 | 172.07 | 166.39 | 165.73 | | | |

The values above are calculated from the constants below and the Antoine equation:

$$\log_{10} P = A - B/(C + t); \quad t = B/(A - \log_{10} P) - C$$

$$(P \text{ in mm Hg}; \ t \text{ in } °C)$$

Constants of the Antoine Equation

| | Benzene | Methyl-benzene | Ethyl-benzene | 1,2-Dimethyl-benzene | 1,3-Dimethyl-benzene | 1,4-Dimethyl-benzene | | | |
|---|---|---|---|---|---|---|---|---|---|
| $A$ | 6.90565 | 6.95464 | 6.95719 | 6.99891 | 7.00908 | 6.99052 | | | |
| $B$ | 1211.033 | 1344.800 | 1424.255 | 1474.679 | 1462.266 | 1453.430 | | | |
| $C$ | 220.790 | 219.482 | 213.206 | 213.686 | 215.105 | 215.307 | | | |

[a] At the triple point, 5.525°C, the pressure is 35.856 mm Hg.

# TABLE 5k, Page 2 – ALKYL BENZENES, $C_6$ TO $C_9$
## VAPOR PRESSURES AND BOILING POINTS, AT 10 TO 1500 mm Hg
### June 30, 1944; April 30, 1949; December 31, 1952

| Pressure | n-Propyl-benzene | Isopropyl-benzene | 1-Methyl-2-ethyl-benzene | 1-Methyl-3-ethyl-benzene | 1-Methyl-4-ethyl-benzene | 1,2,3-Trimethyl-benzene | 1,2,4-Trimethyl-benzene | 1,3,5-Trimethyl-benzene | |
|---|---|---|---|---|---|---|---|---|---|
| mm Hg | | | | | Temperature in °C | | | | |
| 10 | 43.44 | 38.29 | 48.46 | 45.68 | 45.68 | 56.79 | 51.75 | 48.82 | |
| 20 | 56.79 | 51.43 | 61.96 | 59.07 | 59.14 | 70.62 | 65.39 | 62.30 | |
| 30 | 65.28 | 59.79 | 70.54 | 67.58 | 67.68 | 79.41 | 74.06 | 70.85 | |
| 40 | 71.64 | 66.06 | 76.97 | 73.95 | 74.09 | 86.00 | 80.54 | 77.25 | |
| 50 | 76.784 | 71.123 | 82.165 | 79.102 | 79.265 | 91.313 | 85.787 | 82.424 | |
| 60 | 81.130 | 75.407 | 86.552 | 83.450 | 83.637 | 95.802 | 90.214 | 86.789 | |
| 80 | 88.264 | 82.433 | 93.751 | 90.584 | 90.811 | 103.168 | 97.475 | 93.949 | |
| 100 | 94.046 | 88.130 | 99.582 | 96.363 | 96.623 | 109.132 | 103.355 | 99.746 | |
| 150 | 105.152 | 99.076 | 110.777 | 107.456 | 107.781 | 120.578 | 114.639 | 110.866 | |
| 200 | 113.542 | 107.346 | 119.229 | 115.829 | 116.205 | 129.215 | 123.153 | 119.254 | |
| 250 | 120.367 | 114.074 | 126.100 | 122.635 | 123.054 | 136.234 | 130.072 | 126.068 | |
| 300 | 126.163 | 119.789 | 131.933 | 128.412 | 128.869 | 142.191 | 135.944 | 131.849 | |
| 400 | 135.737 | 129.230 | 141.563 | 137.949 | 138.469 | 152.022 | 145.634 | 141.387 | |
| 500 | 143.551 | 136.937 | 149.418 | 145.727 | 146.300 | 160.037 | 153.534 | 149.161 | |
| 600 | 150.205 | 143.501 | 156.103 | 152.346 | 152.965 | 166.856 | 160.256 | 155.772 | |
| 700 | 156.031 | 149.249 | 161.954 | 158.138 | 158.799 | 172.823 | 166.137 | 161.556 | |
| 710 | 156.577 | 149.787 | 162.502 | 158.681 | 159.346 | 173.382 | 166.687 | 162.097 | |
| 720 | 157.116 | 150.319 | 163.044 | 159.217 | 159.885 | 173.934 | 167.231 | 162.632 | |
| 730 | 157.650 | 150.846 | 163.579 | 159.747 | 160.420 | 174.480 | 167.770 | 163.162 | |
| 740 | 158.178 | 151.367 | 164.110 | 160.272 | 160.948 | 175.020 | 168.302 | 163.686 | |
| 750 | 158.700 | 151.882 | 164.634 | 160.792 | 161.471 | 175.555 | 168.830 | 164.204 | |
| 760 | 159.217 | 152.392 | 165.153 | 161.305 | 161.989 | 176.084 | 169.351 | 164.716 | |
| 770 | 159.729 | 152.897 | 165.667 | 161.814 | 162.501 | 176.608 | 169.867 | 165.224 | |
| 780 | 160.235 | 153.397 | 166.175 | 162.316 | 163.008 | 177.126 | 170.378 | 165.726 | |
| 790 | 160.737 | 153.892 | 166.679 | 162.815 | 163.510 | 177.640 | 170.884 | 166.224 | |
| 800 | 161.233 | 154.382 | 167.177 | 163.308 | 164.007 | 178.147 | 171.384 | 166.716 | |
| 900 | 165.947 | 159.033 | 171.908 | 167.991 | 168.724 | 182.969 | 176.136 | 171.387 | |
| 1000 | 170.27 | 163.30 | 176.24 | 172.28 | 173.05 | 187.39 | 180.49 | 175.67 | |
| 1200 | 177.98 | 170.91 | 183.98 | 179.94 | 180.76 | 195.27 | 188.26 | 183.30 | |
| 1500 | 187.87 | 180.67 | 193.89 | 189.74 | 190.64 | 205.36 | 198.20 | 193.07 | |

The values above are calculated from the constants below and the Antoine equation:

$$\log_{10} P = A - B/(C + t); \quad t = B/(A - \log_{10} P) - C$$

(P in mm Hg; t in °C)

### Constants of the Antoine Equation

| | n-Propyl-benzene | Isopropyl-benzene | 1-Methyl-2-ethyl-benzene | 1-Methyl-3-ethyl-benzene | 1-Methyl-4-ethyl-benzene | 1,2,3-Trimethyl-benzene | 1,2,4-Trimethyl-benzene | 1,3,5-Trimethyl-benzene | |
|---|---|---|---|---|---|---|---|---|---|
| $A$ | 6.95142 | 6.93666 | 7.00314 | 7.01582 | 6.99802 | 7.04082 | 7.04383 | 7.07436 | |
| $B$ | 1491.297 | 1460.793 | 1535.374 | 1529.184 | 1527.113 | 1593.958 | 1573.267 | 1569.622 | |
| $C$ | 207.140 | 207.777 | 207.300 | 208.509 | 208.921 | 207.078 | 208.564 | 209.578 | |

364

## TABLE 14k, Page 1 – ALKYL BENZENES, $C_{10}$
### VAPOR PRESSURES AND BOILING POINTS, AT 10 TO 1500 mm Hg
#### April 30, 1949; December 31, 1952

| Pressure | n–Butyl–benzene | Isobutyl–benzene | sec–Butyl–benzene | tert–Butyl–benzene | 1–Methyl–2–propyl–benzene | 1–Methyl–3–propyl–benzene | 1–Methyl–4–propyl–benzene | | |
|---|---|---|---|---|---|---|---|---|---|
| mm Hg | | | | Temperature in °C | | | | | |
| 10 | 62.36 | 53.22 | 53.71 | 50.80 | 63.6 | 61.5 | 62.0 | | |
| 20 | 76.33 | 66.98 | 67.50 | 64.42 | 77.6 | 75.4 | 76.0 | | |
| 30 | 85.21 | 75.73 | 76.27 | 73.08 | 86.5 | 84.3 | 84.9 | | |
| 40 | 91.86 | 82.30 | 82.84 | 79.57 | 93.2 | 90.9 | 91.6 | | |
| 50 | 97.241 | 87.605 | 88.154 | 84.820 | 98.6 | 96.3 | 97.0 | | |
| 60 | 101.784 | 92.089 | 92.642 | 89.256 | 103.2 | 100.8 | 101.6 | | |
| 80 | 109.240 | 99.452 | 100.012 | 96.542 | 110.6 | 108.2 | 109.1 | | |
| 100 | 115.281 | 105.420 | 105.984 | 102.448 | 116.7 | 114.2 | 115.1 | | |
| 150 | 126.881 | 116.886 | 117.457 | 113.797 | 128.3 | 125.8 | 126.8 | | |
| 200 | 135.640 | 125.551 | 126.123 | 122.374 | 137.1 | 134.5 | 135.5 | | |
| 250 | 142.763 | 132.601 | 133.174 | 129.353 | 144.2 | 141.6 | 142.7 | | |
| 300 | 148.810 | 138.589 | 139.160 | 135.282 | 150.3 | 147.6 | 148.8 | | |
| 400 | 158.797 | 148.484 | 149.051 | 145.078 | 160.3 | 157.5 | 158.8 | | |
| 500 | 166.944 | 156.560 | 157.122 | 153.076 | 168.5 | 165.6 | 166.9 | | |
| 600 | 173.879 | 163.439 | 163.996 | 159.889 | 175.4 | 172.5 | 173.9 | | |
| 700 | 179.951 | 169.464 | 170.014 | 165.856 | 181.48 | 178.50 | 179.97 | | |
| 710 | 180.519 | 170.028 | 170.578 | 166.415 | 182.05 | 179.07 | 180.54 | | |
| 720 | 181.081 | 170.586 | 171.135 | 166.967 | 182.61 | 179.62 | 181.11 | | |
| 730 | 181.637 | 171.138 | 171.686 | 167.514 | 183.15 | 180.18 | 181.66 | | |
| 740 | 182.187 | 171.684 | 172.232 | 168.055 | 183.72 | 180.72 | 182.21 | | |
| 750 | 182.732 | 172.224 | 172.771 | 168.590 | 184.26 | 181.26 | 182.76 | | |
| 760 | 183.270 | 172.759 | 173.305 | 169.119 | 184.80 | 181.80 | 183.30 | | |
| 770 | 183.803 | 173.288 | 173.834 | 169.644 | 185.34 | 182.33 | 183.83 | | |
| 780 | 184.331 | 173.811 | 174.357 | 170.162 | 185.86 | 182.85 | 184.36 | | |
| 790 | 184.854 | 174.331 | 174.876 | 170.677 | 186.39 | 183.37 | 184.89 | | |
| 800 | 185.371 | 174.844 | 175.388 | 171.185 | 186.91 | 183.88 | 185.41 | | |
| 900 | 190.281 | 179.720 | 180.258 | 176.015 | 191.82 | 188.75 | 190.33 | | |
| 1000 | 194.78 | 184.19 | 184.72 | 180.44 | 196.32 | 193.22 | 194.84 | | |
| 1200 | 202.81 | 192.17 | 192.69 | 188.35 | 204.4 | 201.2 | 202.9 | | |
| 1500 | 213.10 | 202.40 | 202.90 | 198.49 | 214.7 | 211.4 | 213.2 | | |

The values above are calculated from the constants below and the Antoine equation:

$$\log_{10} P = A - B/(C + t); \quad t = B/(A - \log_{10} P) - C$$
$$(P \text{ in mm Hg}; \ t \text{ in } °C)$$

### Constants of the Antoine Equation

| | n–Butyl–benzene | Isobutyl–benzene | sec–Butyl–benzene | tert–Butyl–benzene | 1–Methyl–2–propyl–benzene | 1–Methyl–3–propyl–benzene | 1–Methyl–4–propyl–benzene | | |
|---|---|---|---|---|---|---|---|---|---|
| A | 6.98317 | 6.93033 | 6.95097 | 6.92050 | 7.0023 | 7.0160 | 6.9926 | | |
| B | 1577.965 | 1526.384 | 1540.174 | 1504.572 | 1594.00 | 1591.00 | 1589.00 | | |
| C | 201.378 | 204.171 | 205.101 | 203.328 | 201.95 | 202.95 | 203.15 | | |

**TABLE 14k, Page 2 – ALKYL BENZENES, $C_{10}$**

**VAPOR PRESSURES AND BOILING POINTS, AT 10 TO 1500 mm Hg**

April 30, 1949; December 31, 1952

| Pressure | 1-Methyl-2-isopropyl-benzene | 1-Methyl-3-isopropyl-benzene | 1-Methyl-4-isopropyl-benzene | 1,2-Diethyl-benzene | 1,3-Diethyl-benzene | 1,4-Diethyl-benzene | | | |
|---|---|---|---|---|---|---|---|---|---|
| mm Hg | Temperature in °C | | | | | | | | |
| 10 | 57.5 | 55.2 | 56.4 | 62.86 | 61.44 | 62.84 | | | |
| 20 | 71.4 | 69.0 | 70.3 | 76.75 | 75.29 | 76.82 | | | |
| 30 | 80.2 | 77.8 | 79.2 | 85.66 | 84.09 | 85.71 | | | |
| 40 | 86.8 | 84.4 | 85.8 | 92.29 | 90.68 | 92.37 | | | |
| 50 | 92.2 | 89.7 | 91.1 | 97.658 | 96.010 | 97.755 | | | |
| 60 | 96.7 | 94.2 | 95.7 | 102.188 | 100.508 | 102.300 | | | |
| 80 | 104.2 | 101.6 | 103.1 | 109.623 | 107.891 | 109.759 | | | |
| 100 | 110.2 | 107.6 | 109.1 | 115.647 | 113.870 | 115.801 | | | |
| 150 | 121.8 | 119.1 | 120.7 | 127.213 | 125.350 | 127.402 | | | |
| 200 | 130.5 | 127.8 | 129.4 | 135.946 | 134.016 | 136.159 | | | |
| 250 | 137.6 | 134.9 | 136.6 | 143.048 | 141.062 | 143.280 | | | |
| 300 | 143.7 | 140.9 | 142.6 | 149.076 | 147.043 | 149.324 | | | |
| 400 | 153.7 | 150.8 | 152.6 | 159.031 | 156.917 | 159.304 | | | |
| 500 | 161.8 | 158.9 | 160.7 | 167.151 | 164.970 | 167.444 | | | |
| 600 | 168.7 | 165.8 | 167.7 | 174.064 | 171.824 | 174.373 | | | |
| 700 | 174.83 | 171.84 | 173.78 | 180.115 | 177.823 | 180.437 | | | |
| 710 | 175.40 | 172.41 | 174.35 | 180.681 | 178.385 | 181.005 | | | |
| 720 | 175.96 | 172.97 | 174.91 | 181.241 | 178.940 | 181.566 | | | |
| 730 | 176.51 | 173.52 | 175.47 | 181.795 | 179.489 | 182.121 | | | |
| 740 | 177.07 | 174.07 | 176.02 | 182.344 | 180.033 | 182.671 | | | |
| 750 | 177.61 | 174.61 | 176.56 | 182.886 | 180.570 | 183.214 | | | |
| 760 | 178.15 | 175.14 | 177.10 | 183.423 | 181.102 | 183.752 | | | |
| 770 | 178.68 | 175.68 | 177.64 | 183.954 | 181.629 | 184.285 | | | |
| 780 | 179.21 | 176.20 | 178.17 | 184.479 | 182.150 | 184.811 | | | |
| 790 | 179.74 | 176.72 | 178.69 | 185.001 | 182.667 | 185.334 | | | |
| 800 | 180.25 | 177.24 | 179.21 | 185.516 | 183.177 | 185.850 | | | |
| 900 | 185.17 | 182.12 | 184.13 | 190.409 | 188.027 | 190.753 | | | |
| 1000 | 189.68 | 186.61 | 188.65 | 194.89 | 192.47 | 195.25 | | | |
| 1200 | 197.7 | 194.6 | 196.7 | 202.90 | 200.41 | 203.27 | | | |
| 1500 | 208.0 | 204.9 | 207.0 | 213.15 | 210.56 | 213.54 | | | |

The values above are calculated from the constants below and the Antoine equation:

$$\log_{10} P = A - B/(C + t); \quad t = B/(A - \log_{10} P) - C$$

$(P$ in mm Hg; $t$ in °C)

Constants of the Antoine Equation

| | 1-Methyl-2-isopropyl-benzene | 1-Methyl-3-isopropyl-benzene | 1-Methyl-4-isopropyl-benzene | 1,2-Diethyl-benzene | 1,3-Diethyl-benzene | 1,4-Diethyl-benzene | | | |
|---|---|---|---|---|---|---|---|---|---|
| $A$ | 6.9427 | 6.9428 | 6.9260 | 6.99016 | 7.00600 | 7.00054 | | | |
| $B$ | 1549.00 | 1540.00 | 1538.00 | 1577.894 | 1576.261 | 1589.273 | | | |
| $C$ | 203.20 | 203.98 | 203.10 | 200.554 | 201.004 | 202.019 | | | |

## TABLE 14k, Page 3 – ALKYL BENZENES, $C_{10}$
### VAPOR PRESSURES AND BOILING POINTS, AT 10 TO 1500 mm Hg
April 30, 1949; December 31, 1952

| Pressure | 1,2-Dimethyl-3-ethylbenzene | 1,2-Dimethyl-4-ethylbenzene | 1,3-Dimethyl-2-ethylbenzene | 1,3-Dimethyl-4-ethylbenzene | 1,3-Dimethyl-5-ethylbenzene | 1,4-Dimethyl-2-ethylbenzene | 1,2,3,4-Tetramethylbenzene | 1,2,3,5-Tetramethylbenzene | 1,2,4,5-Tetramethylbenzene |
|---|---|---|---|---|---|---|---|---|---|
| mm Hg | | | | | Temperature in °C | | | | |
| 10 | 71.1 | 68.0 | 68.0 | 66.6 | 63.1 | 65.0 | 79.5 | 74.5 | 73.7[a] |
| 20 | 85.4 | 82.1 | 82.2 | 80.7 | 77.1 | 79.1 | 94.1 | 88.9 | 88.0 |
| 30 | 94.4 | 91.1 | 91.2 | 89.7 | 86.0 | 88.1 | 103.4 | 98.0 | 97.1 |
| 40 | 101.2 | 97.8 | 97.9 | 96.4 | 92.7 | 94.8 | 110.3 | 104.8 | 103.9 |
| 50 | 106.7 | 103.2 | 103.3 | 101.8 | 98.0 | 100.2 | 115.9 | 110.3 | 109.4 |
| 60 | 111.3 | 107.8 | 107.9 | 106.4 | 102.6 | 104.8 | 120.6 | 115.0 | 114.0 |
| 80 | 118.9 | 115.3 | 115.5 | 114.0 | 110.0 | 112.4 | 128.4 | 122.6 | 121.6 |
| 100 | 125.0 | 121.4 | 121.6 | 120.0 | 116.1 | 118.5 | 134.6 | 128.8 | 127.8 |
| 150 | 136.8 | 133.1 | 133.3 | 131.7 | 127.6 | 130.2 | 146.7 | 140.6 | 139.6 |
| 200 | 145.7 | 141.9 | 142.1 | 140.6 | 136.4 | 139.0 | 155.8 | 149.6 | 148.5 |
| 250 | 152.9 | 149.1 | 149.3 | 147.7 | 143.5 | 146.2 | 163.2 | 156.8 | 155.7 |
| 300 | 159.0 | 155.2 | 155.4 | 153.8 | 149.5 | 152.2 | 169.4 | 163.0 | 161.9 |
| 400 | 169.2 | 165.2 | 165.4 | 163.8 | 159.4 | 162.3 | 179.8 | 173.2 | 172.0 |
| 500 | 177.4 | 173.4 | 173.6 | 172.0 | 167.5 | 170.5 | 188.17 | 181.4 | 180.3 |
| 600 | 184.4 | 180.3 | 180.6 | 179.0 | 174.4 | 177.5 | 195.34 | 188.5 | 187.3 |
| 700 | 190.56 | 186.42 | 186.68 | 185.08 | 180.45 | 183.57 | 201.61 | 194.64 | 193.44 |
| 710 | 191.13 | 186.99 | 187.25 | 185.65 | 181.02 | 184.14 | 202.20 | 195.21 | 194.02 |
| 720 | 191.70 | 187.56 | 187.81 | 186.21 | 181.58 | 184.71 | 202.78 | 195.78 | 194.58 |
| 730 | 192.26 | 188.11 | 188.37 | 186.77 | 182.13 | 185.27 | 203.35 | 196.35 | 195.15 |
| 740 | 192.82 | 188.66 | 188.92 | 187.32 | 182.68 | 185.82 | 203.92 | 196.90 | 195.70 |
| 750 | 193.36 | 189.21 | 189.47 | 187.87 | 183.22 | 186.37 | 204.48 | 197.46 | 196.25 |
| 760 | 193.91 | 189.75 | 190.01 | 188.41 | 183.75 | 186.91 | 205.04 | 198.00 | 196.80 |
| 770 | 194.45 | 190.28 | 190.54 | 188.94 | 184.28 | 187.45 | 205.59 | 198.54 | 197.34 |
| 780 | 194.98 | 190.81 | 191.07 | 189.47 | 184.80 | 187.98 | 206.13 | 199.08 | 197.87 |
| 790 | 195.51 | 191.34 | 191.60 | 190.00 | 185.32 | 188.50 | 206.67 | 199.61 | 198.40 |
| 800 | 196.03 | 191.86 | 192.12 | 190.52 | 185.84 | 189.02 | 207.21 | 200.13 | 198.92 |
| 900 | 200.99 | 196.78 | 197.05 | 195.44 | 190.71 | 193.95 | 212.27 | 205.11 | 203.88 |
| 1000 | 205.54 | 201.28 | 201.56 | 199.95 | 195.17 | 198.47 | 216.91 | 209.67 | 208.43 |
| 1200 | 213.6 | 209.3 | 209.6 | 208.0 | 203.1 | 206.5 | 225.2 | 217.8 | 216.5 |
| 1500 | 224.0 | 219.6 | 219.9 | 218.3 | 213.3 | 216.9 | 235.8 | 228.2 | 226.9 |

The values above are calculated from the constants below and the Antoine equation:

$$\log_{10} P = A - B/(C + t); \quad t = B/(A - \log_{10} P) - C$$

(P in mm Hg; t in °C)

### Constants of the Antoine Equation

| | 1,2-Dimethyl-3-ethylbenzene | 1,2-Dimethyl-4-ethylbenzene | 1,3-Dimethyl-2-ethylbenzene | 1,3-Dimethyl-4-ethylbenzene | 1,3-Dimethyl-5-ethylbenzene | 1,4-Dimethyl-2-ethylbenzene | 1,2,3,4-Tetramethylbenzene | 1,2,3,5-Tetramethylbenzene | 1,2,4,5-Tetramethylbenzene |
|---|---|---|---|---|---|---|---|---|---|
| A | 7.0488 | 7.0493 | 7.0440 | 7.0427 | 7.0459 | 7.0301 | 7.0584 | 7.0769 | 7.0790 |
| B | 1646.00 | 1633.00 | 1632.00 | 1629.00 | 1615.00 | 1622.00 | 1689.10 | 1674.00 | 1671.00 |
| C | 201.00 | 202.00 | 202.00 | 203.00 | 204.00 | 204.00 | 199.28 | 200.94 | 201.23 |

[a] Extrapolated value for the undercooled liquid below the freezing point, which is near 80°C.

| | | | | | | |
|---|---|---|---|---|---|---|
| TABLE 27k, Page 1 – NAPHTHALENES, $C_{10}$ TO $C_{12}$ <br> VAPOR PRESSURES AND BOILING POINTS, AT 10 TO 1500 mm Hg <br> August 31, 1949; December 31, 1952 | | | | | | |
| Pressure | Naphthalene | 1–Methyl–<br>naphthalene | 2–Methyl–<br>naphthalene | 1–Ethyl–<br>naphthalene | 2–Ethyl–<br>naphthalene | |
| mm Hg | Temperature in °C | | | | | |
| 10 | 87.59 | 107.55 | 104.85 | 120.1 | 119.1 | |
| 20 | 102.51 | 123.48 | 120.68 | 136.1 | 135.2 | |
| 30 | 112.02 | 133.60 | 130.73 | 146.2 | 145.5 | |
| 40 | 119.14 | 141.17 | 138.25 | 153.9 | 153.2 | |
| 50 | 124.914 | 147.287 | 144.329 | 160.0 | 159.4 | |
| 60 | 129.791 | 152.450 | 149.459 | 165.2 | 164.6 | |
| 80 | 137.805 | 160.919 | 157.872 | 173.8 | 173.2 | |
| 100 | 144.305 | 167.776 | 164.684 | 180.7 | 180.1 | |
| 150 | 156.807 | 180.929 | 177.752 | 194.0 | 193.4 | |
| 200 | 166.265 | 190.851 | 187.610 | 204.0 | 203.5 | |
| 250 | 173.967 | 198.913 | 195.619 | 212.2 | 211.6 | |
| 300 | 180.513 | 205.752 | 202.414 | 219.1 | 218.6 | |
| 400 | 191.340 | 217.037 | 213.626 | 230.6 | 230.0 | |
| 500 | 200.187 | 226.235 | 222.764 | 239.9 | 239.3 | |
| 600 | 207.728 | 234.058 | 230.537 | 247.9 | 247.2 | |
| 700 | 214.338 | 240.902 | 237.336 | 254.9 | 254.1 | |
| 710 | 214.957 | 241.542 | 237.973 | 255.5 | 254.8 | |
| 720 | 215.569 | 242.176 | 238.602 | 256.1 | 255.4 | |
| 730 | 216.175 | 242.802 | 239.224 | 256.8 | 256.1 | |
| 740 | 216.775 | 243.422 | 239.840 | 257.4 | 256.7 | |
| 750 | 217.368 | 244.035 | 240.449 | 258.1 | 257.3 | |
| 760 | 217.955 | 244.642 | 241.052 | 258.67 | 257.9 | |
| 770 | 218.536 | 245.242 | 241.649 | 259.3 | 258.5 | |
| 780 | 219.111 | 245.836 | 242.239 | 259.9 | 259.1 | |
| 790 | 219.681 | 246.425 | 242.824 | 260.5 | 259.7 | |
| 800 | 220.244 | 247.008 | 243.402 | 261.1 | 260.3 | |
| 900 | 225.600 | 252.536 | 248.895 | 266.7 | 265.9 | |
| 1000 | 230.51 | 257.60 | 253.93 | 272. | 271. | |
| 1200 | 239.29 | 266.64 | 262.90 | 281. | 280. | |
| 1500 | 250.56 | 278.20 | 274.39 | 293. | 292. | |

The values above are calculated from the constants below and the Antoine equation:

$$\log_{10} P = A - B/(C + t); \quad t = B/(A - \log_{10} P) - C$$

$$(P \text{ in mm Hg}; \; t \text{ in } °C)$$

Constants of the Antoine Equation

| | | | | | | |
|---|---|---|---|---|---|---|
| A | 6.84577 | 7.06899 | 7.06850 | 6.9599 | 7.0819 | |
| B | 1606.529 | 1852.674 | 1840.268 | 1791.4 | 1886. | |
| C | 187.227 | 197.716 | 198.395 | 180.5 | 191.0 | |

TABLE 20K-E, (PART 1), Page 1 - NORMAL PARAFFINS, $C_1$ TO $C_{20}$

VAPOR PRESSURES AND BOILING POINTS, AT 0.2 TO 30 lb/in²

April 30, 1949; December 31, 1952

| Compound | Formula | Constants of the Antoine equation | | | Temperature in °F | | | | | | | | | | | | | |
| | | A | B | C | -320 | -315 | -310 | -305 | -300 | -295 | -290 | -285 | -280 | -275 | -270 | -265 | -260 | -255 |
| | | | | | Vapor pressure in lb/in² | | | | | | | | | | | | | |
| Methane | $CH_4$ | 5.98179a | 957.86a | 463.00a | 0.19a | 0.32a | 0.53a | 0.83a | 1.27a | 1.88b | 2.64 | 3.63 | 4.90 | 6.50 | 8.48 | 10.90 | 13.83 | 17.33 |
| | | 4.89823 | 701.87 | 446.80 | | | | | | | | | | | | | | |
| Ethane | $C_2H_6$ | 5.08905 | 1181.52 | 428.80 | | | | | | | | | | | | | | |
| Propane | $C_3H_8$ | 5.11612 | 1463.76 | 414.40 | | | | | | | | | | | | | | |
| n-Butane | $C_4H_{10}$ | 5.11668 | 1702.62 | 400.00 | | | | | | | | | | | | | | |
| n-Pentane | $C_5H_{12}$ | 5.13860 | 1916.33 | 385.60 | | | | | | | | | | | | | | |
| n-Hexane | $C_6H_{14}$ | 5.16415 | 2108.754 | 371.859 | | | | | | | | | | | | | | |
| n-Heptane | $C_7H_{16}$ | 5.18879 | 2282.607 | 358.420 | | | | | | | | | | | | | | |
| n-Octane | $C_8H_{18}$ | 5.21016 | 2439.227 | 345.131 | | | | | | | | | | | | | | |
| n-Nonane | $C_9H_{20}$ | 5.22152 | 2571.860 | 330.914 | | | | | | | | | | | | | | |
| n-Decane | $C_{10}H_{22}$ | 5.24006 | 2702.282 | 318.064 | | | | | | | | | | | | | | |

| Compound | Formula | Temperature in °F | | | | | | | | | | | | | | | | |
| | | -250 | -245 | -240 | -235 | -230 | -225 | -220 | -215 | -210 | -205 | -200 | -195 | -190 | -185 | -180 | -175 | -170 | -165 |
| | | Vapor pressure in lb/in² | | | | | | | | | | | | | | | | |
| Methane | $CH_4$ | 21.47 | 26.3 | 31.9 | | | | | | | | | | | | | | |
| Ethane | $C_2H_6$ | | | | | | 0.196 | 0.269 | 0.365 | 0.489 | 0.645 | 0.842 | 1.085 | 1.385 | 1.749 | 2.189 | 2.715 | 3.339 | 4.076 |
| Propane | $C_3H_8$ | | | | | | | | | | | | | | | | | | |
| n-Butane | $C_4H_{10}$ | | | | | | | | | | | | | | | | | | |
| n-Pentane | $C_5H_{12}$ | | | | | | | | | | | | | | | | | | |
| n-Hexane | $C_6H_{14}$ | | | | | | | | | | | | | | | | | | |
| n-Heptane | $C_7H_{16}$ | | | | | | | | | | | | | | | | | | |
| n-Octane | $C_8H_{18}$ | | | | | | | | | | | | | | | | | | |
| n-Nonane | $C_9H_{20}$ | | | | | | | | | | | | | | | | | | |
| n-Decane | $C_{10}H_{22}$ | | | | | | | | | | | | | | | | | | |

Values of the vapor pressure are calculated from the constants given and the Antoine equation: $\log_{10} P = A - B/(C + t)$; $t = B/(A - \log_{10}P) - C$; ($P$ in lb/in²; $t$ in °F)

a For the solid-vapor equilibrium.   b At the triple point, -296.45°F, the pressure is 1.70 lb/in².

TABLE 20k-E (PART 1), Page 2 – NORMAL PARAFFINS, $C_1$ TO $C_{20}$

VAPOR PRESSURES AND BOILING POINTS, AT 0.2 TO 30 lb/in²

April 30, 1949; December 31, 1952

Temperature in °F — Vapor pressure in lb/in²

| Compound | Formula | -160 | -155 | -150 | -145 | -140 | -135 | -130 | -125 | -120 | -115 | -110 | -105 | -100 | -95 | -90 | -85 | -80 | -75 |
|---|---|---|---|---|---|---|---|---|---|---|---|---|---|---|---|---|---|---|---|
| Methane | $CH_4$ | | | | | | | | | | | | | | | | | | |
| Ethane | $C_2H_6$ | 4.938 | 5.940 | 7.099 | 8.430 | 9.952 | 11.68 | 13.64 | 15.85 | 18.32 | 21.08 | 24.15 | 27.55 | 31.31 | | | | | |
| Propane | $C_3H_8$ | | | 0.380 | 0.482 | 0.605 | 0.754 | 0.932 | 1.143 | 1.394 | 1.667 | 2.030 | 2.427 | 2.887 | 3.414 | 4.017 | 4.703 | 5.481 | 6.358 |
| n–Butane | $C_4H_{10}$ | | | | | | | | 0.084 | 0.109 | 0.139 | 0.176 | 0.221 | 0.276 | 0.342 | 0.422 | 0.515 | 0.625 | 0.755 |
| n–Pentane | $C_5H_{12}$ | | | | | | | | | | | | | | | | | | |
| n–Hexane | $C_6H_{14}$ | | | | | | | | | | | | | | | | | | |
| n–Heptane | $C_7H_{16}$ | | | | | | | | | | | | | | | | | | |
| n–Octane | $C_8H_{18}$ | | | | | | | | | | | | | | | | | | |
| n–Nonane | $C_9H_{20}$ | | | | | | | | | | | | | | | | | | |
| n–Decane | $C_{10}H_{22}$ | | | | | | | | | | | | | | | | | | |

Temperature in °F — Vapor pressure in lb/in²

| Compound | Formula | -70 | -65 | -60 | -55 | -50 | -45 | -40 | -35 | -30 | -25 | -20 | -15 | -10 | -5 | 0 | 5 | 10 | 15 |
|---|---|---|---|---|---|---|---|---|---|---|---|---|---|---|---|---|---|---|---|
| Methane | $CH_4$ | | | | | | | | | | | | | | | | | | |
| Ethane | $C_2H_6$ | | | | | | | | | | | | | | | | | | |
| Propane | $C_3H_8$ | 7.344 | 8.448 | 9.680 | 11.05 | 12.57 | 14.24 | 16.09 | 18.11 | 20.33 | 22.76 | 25.4 | 28.3 | | | | | | |
| n–Butane | $C_4H_{10}$ | 0.906 | 1.082 | 1.285 | 1.519 | 1.787 | 2.092 | 2.439 | 2.831 | 3.273 | 3.770 | 4.326 | 4.95 | 5.64 | 6.40 | 7.25 | 8.18 | 9.20 | 10.33 |
| n–Pentane | $C_5H_{12}$ | 0.12 | 0.14 | 0.179 | 0.220 | 0.268 | 0.325 | 0.392 | 0.471 | 0.562 | 0.667 | 0.789 | 0.928 | 1.088 | 1.269 | 1.475 | 1.708 | 1.970 | 2.264 |
| n–Hexane | $C_6H_{14}$ | | | | | | 0.05 | 0.06 | 0.08 | 0.10 | 0.12 | 0.15 | 0.180 | 0.217 | 0.261 | 0.311 | 0.370 | 0.438 | 0.517 |
| n–Heptane | $C_7H_{16}$ | | | | | | | | | | | | | | | | | | |
| n–Octane | $C_8H_{18}$ | | | | | | | | | | | | | | | | | | |
| n–Nonane | $C_9H_{20}$ | | | | | | | | | | | | | | | | | | |
| n–Decane | $C_{10}H_{22}$ | | | | | | | | | | | | | | | | | | |

TABLE 20K-E (PART 1), Page 3 – NORMAL PARAFFINS, $C_1$ TO $C_{20}$
VAPOR PRESSURES AND BOILING POINTS, AT 0.2 TO 30 lb/in²
April 30, 1949; December 31, 1952

| Compound | Formula | Temperature in °F — Vapor pressure in lb/in² | | | | | | | | | | | | | | | | | |
|---|---|---|---|---|---|---|---|---|---|---|---|---|---|---|---|---|---|---|---|
| | | 20 | 25 | 30 | 35 | 40 | 45 | 50 | 55 | 60 | 65 | 70 | 75 | 80 | 85 | 90 | 95 | 100 | 105 |
| Methane | $CH_4$ | | | | | | | | | | | | | | | | | | |
| Ethane | $C_2H_6$ | | | | | | | | | | | | | | | | | | |
| Propane | $C_3H_8$ | | | | | | | | | | | | | | | | | | |
| n-Butane | $C_4H_{10}$ | 11.56 | 12.90 | 14.36 | 15.94 | 17.66 | 19.52 | 21.53 | 23.7 | 26.0 | 28.5 | | | | | | | | |
| n-Pentane | $C_5H_{12}$ | 2.594 | 2.961 | 3.370 | 3.823 | 4.325 | 4.878 | 5.487 | 6.155 | 6.887 | 7.687 | 8.559 | 9.508 | 10.538 | 11.655 | 12.862 | 14.165 | 15.570 | 17.08 |
| n-Hexane | $C_6H_{14}$ | 0.606 | 0.709 | 0.825 | 0.958 | 1.107 | 1.275 | 1.464 | 1.675 | 1.911 | 2.173 | 2.464 | 2.787 | 3.143 | 3.535 | 3.966 | 4.439 | 4.956 | 5.520 |
| n-Hentane | $C_7H_{16}$ | | | 0.205 | 0.244 | 0.288 | 0.339 | 0.398 | 0.465 | 0.541 | 0.628 | 0.726 | 0.836 | 0.960 | 1.099 | 1.254 | 1.428 | 1.620 | 1.833 |
| n-Octane | $C_8H_{18}$ | | | | | | | | | | 0.183 | 0.216 | 0.254 | 0.297 | 0.346 | 0.402 | 0.466 | 0.537 | 0.618 |
| n-Nonane | $C_9H_{20}$ | | | | | | | | | | | | | | | | | 0.179 | 0.210 |
| n-Decane | $C_{10}H_{22}$ | | | | | | | | | | | | | | | | | | |

| Compound | Formula | Temperature in °F — Vapor pressure in lb/in² | | | | | | | | | | | | | | | | | |
|---|---|---|---|---|---|---|---|---|---|---|---|---|---|---|---|---|---|---|---|
| | | 110 | 115 | 120 | 125 | 130 | 135 | 140 | 145 | 150 | 155 | 160 | 165 | 170 | 175 | 180 | 185 | 190 | 195 |
| Methane | $CH_4$ | | | | | | | | | | | | | | | | | | |
| Ethane | $C_2H_6$ | | | | | | | | | | | | | | | | | | |
| Propane | $C_3H_8$ | | | | | | | | | | | | | | | | | | |
| n-Butane | $C_4H_{10}$ | | | | | | | | | | | | | | | | | | |
| n-Pentane | $C_5H_{12}$ | 18.7 | 20.4 | 22.3 | 24.3 | 26.4 | 28.7 | | | | | | | | | | | | |
| n-Hexane | $C_6H_{14}$ | 6.136 | 6.805 | 7.531 | 8.317 | 9.168 | 10.086 | 11.075 | 12.140 | 13.283 | 14.509 | 15.823 | 17.23 | 18.73 | 20.32 | 22.03 | 23.84 | 25.8 | 27.8 |
| n-Heptane | $C_7H_{16}$ | 2.069 | 2.330 | 2.616 | 2.931 | 3.276 | 3.653 | 4.065 | 4.514 | 5.002 | 5.532 | 6.106 | 6.727 | 7.398 | 8.121 | 8.899 | 9.735 | 10.633 | 11.594 |
| n-Octane | $C_8H_{18}$ | 0.709 | 0.811 | 0.925 | 1.051 | 1.192 | 1.348 | 1.521 | 1.712 | 1.922 | 2.153 | 2.406 | 2.683 | 2.985 | 3.315 | 3.674 | 4.064 | 4.487 | 4.945 |
| n-Nonane | $C_9H_{20}$ | 0.245 | 0.284 | 0.330 | 0.381 | 0.438 | 0.503 | 0.576 | 0.657 | 0.748 | 0.849 | 0.961 | 1.085 | 1.222 | 1.374 | 1.541 | 1.724 | 1.924 | 2.144 |
| n-Decane | $C_{10}H_{22}$ | | | | | | 0.189 | 0.219 | 0.254 | 0.293 | 0.337 | 0.387 | 0.443 | 0.505 | 0.575 | 0.652 | 0.739 | 0.834 | 0.940 |

TABLE 20k-E (PART 1), Page 4 — NORMAL PARAFFINS, $C_1$ TO $C_{20}$
VAPOR PRESSURES AND BOILING POINTS, AT 0.2 TO 30 lb/in²
April 30, 1949; December 31, 1952

Temperature in °F — Vapor pressure in lb/in²

| Compound | Formula | 200 | 205 | 210 | 215 | 220 | 225 | 230 | 235 | 240 | 245 | 250 | 255 | 260 | 265 | 270 | 275 | 280 | 285 |
|---|---|---|---|---|---|---|---|---|---|---|---|---|---|---|---|---|---|---|---|
| Methane | $CH_4$ | | | | | | | | | | | | | | | | | | |
| Ethane | $C_2H_6$ | | | | | | | | | | | | | | | | | | |
| Propane | $C_3H_8$ | | | | | | | | | | | | | | | | | | |
| n–Butane | $C_4H_{10}$ | | | | | | | | | | | | | | | | | | |
| n–Pentane | $C_5H_{12}$ | | | | | | | | | | | | | | | | | | |
| n–Hexane | $C_6H_{14}$ | 30.0 | | | | | | | | | | | | | | | | | |
| n–Heptane | $C_7H_{16}$ | 12.623 | 13.723 | 14.897 | 16.148 | 17.48 | 18.89 | 20.40 | 21.99 | 23.68 | 25.47 | 27.36 | 29.35 | | | | | | |
| n–Octane | $C_8H_{18}$ | 5.440 | 5.974 | 6.549 | 7.168 | 7.833 | 8.547 | 9.311 | 10.128 | 11.002 | 11.934 | 12.928 | 13.985 | 15.110 | 16.30 | 17.57 | 18.91 | 20.33 | 21.84 |
| n–Nonane | $C_9H_{20}$ | 2.384 | 2.646 | 2.930 | 3.239 | 3.574 | 3.937 | 4.329 | 4.752 | 5.208 | 5.699 | 6.227 | 6.793 | 7.399 | 8.048 | 8.742 | 9.482 | 10.272 | 11.113 |
| n–Decane | $C_{10}H_{22}$ | 1.057 | 1.185 | 1.326 | 1.482 | 1.651 | 1.837 | 2.039 | 2.260 | 2.499 | 2.759 | 3.041 | 3.346 | 3.676 | 4.031 | 4.414 | 4.826 | 5.268 | 5.743 |

Temperature in °F — Vapor pressure in lb/in²

| Compound | Formula | 290 | 295 | 300 | 305 | 310 | 315 | 320 | 325 | 330 | 335 | 340 | 345 | 350 | 355 | 360 | 365 | 370 | 375 |
|---|---|---|---|---|---|---|---|---|---|---|---|---|---|---|---|---|---|---|---|
| Methane | $CH_4$ | | | | | | | | | | | | | | | | | | |
| Ethane | $C_2H_6$ | | | | | | | | | | | | | | | | | | |
| Propane | $C_3H_8$ | | | | | | | | | | | | | | | | | | |
| n–Butane | $C_4H_{10}$ | | | | | | | | | | | | | | | | | | |
| n–Pentane | $C_5H_{12}$ | | | | | | | | | | | | | | | | | | |
| n–Hexane | $C_6H_{14}$ | | | | | | | | | | | | | | | | | | |
| n–Heptane | $C_7H_{16}$ | | | | | | | | | | | | | | | | | | |
| n–Octane | $C_8H_{18}$ | 23.42 | 25.1 | 26.9 | 28.7 | 30.7 | | | | | | | | | | | | | |
| n–Nonane | $C_9H_{20}$ | 12.008 | 12.958 | 13.968 | 15.037 | 16.170 | 17.37 | 18.64 | 19.98 | 21.39 | 22.88 | 24.44 | 26.09 | 27.83 | 29.65 | | | | |
| n–Decane | $C_{10}H_{22}$ | 6.252 | 6.796 | 7.377 | 7.998 | 8.660 | 9.364 | 10.114 | 10.911 | 11.757 | 12.653 | 13.603 | 14.609 | 15.672 | 16.79 | 17.98 | 19.23 | 20.54 | 21.93 |

TABLE 20K-E (PART 1) Page 5 — NORMAL PARAFFINS, $C_1$ TO $C_{20}$
VAPOR PRESSURES AND BOILING POINTS, AT 0.2 TO 30 lb/in²
April 30, 1949; December 31, 1952

Temperature in °F

Vapor pressure in lb/in²

| Compound | Formula | 380 | 385 | 390 | 395 | 400 |
|---|---|---|---|---|---|---|
| Methane | $CH_4$ | | | | | |
| Ethane | $C_2H_6$ | | | | | |
| Propane | $C_3H_8$ | | | | | |
| n-Butane | $C_4H_{10}$ | | | | | |
| n-Pentane | $C_5H_{12}$ | | | | | |
| n-Hexane | $C_6H_{14}$ | | | | | |
| n-Heptane | $C_7H_{16}$ | | | | | |
| n-Octane | $C_8H_{18}$ | | | | | |
| n-Nonane | $C_9H_{20}$ | | | | | |
| n-Decane | $C_{10}H_{22}$ | 23.39 | 24.92 | 26.5 | 28.2 | 30.0 |

TABLE 20k-E (PART 1), Page 6 — NORMAL PARAFFINS, $C_1$ TO $C_{20}$
VAPOR PRESSURES AND BOILING POINTS, AT 0.2 TO 30 lb/in²
April 30, 1949; December 31, 1952

Temperature in °F — Vapor pressure in lb/in²

| Compound | Formula | Constants of the Antoine equation | | | 130 | 135 | 140 | 145 | 150 | 155 | 160 | 165 | 170 | 175 | 180 | 185 | 190 | 195 |
|---|---|---|---|---|---|---|---|---|---|---|---|---|---|---|---|---|---|---|
| | | A | B | C | | | | | | | | | | | | | | |
| n-Undecane | $C_{11}H_{24}$ | 5.26313 | 2830.459 | 306.440 | | | | | | | | 0.182 | 0.210 | 0.242 | 0.278 | 0.319 | 0.364 | 0.415 |
| n-Dodecane | $C_{12}H_{26}$ | 5.26698 | 2926.670 | 292.560 | | | | | | | | | | | | | | 0.184 |
| n-Tridecane | $C_{13}H_{28}$ | 5.2751 | 3019.37 | 279.22 | | | | | | | | | | | | | | |
| n-Tetradecane | $C_{14}H_{30}$ | 5.2821 | 3105.83 | 266.35 | | | | | | | | | | | | | | |
| n-Pentadecane | $C_{15}H_{32}$ | 5.2881 | 3183.88 | 253.48 | | | | | | | | | | | | | | |
| n-Hexadecane | $C_{16}H_{34}$ | 5.31683 | 3296.371 | 246.150 | | | | | | | | | | | | | | |
| n-Heptadecane | $C_{17}H_{36}$ | 5.2979 | 3326.08 | 229.94 | | | | | | | | | | | | | | |
| n-Octadecane | $C_{18}H_{38}$ | 5.3020 | 3390.71 | 219.03 | | | | | | | | | | | | | | |
| n-Nonadecane | $C_{19}H_{40}$ | 5.3056 | 3450.53 | 208.26 | | | | | | | | | | | | | | |
| n-Eicosane | $C_{20}H_{42}$ | 5.3089 | 3507.21 | 197.95 | | | | | | | | | | | | | | |

Temperature in °F — Vapor pressure in lb/in²

| Compound | Formula | 200 | 205 | 210 | 215 | 220 | 225 | 230 | 235 | 240 | 245 | 250 | 255 | 260 | 265 | 270 | 275 | 280 | 285 |
|---|---|---|---|---|---|---|---|---|---|---|---|---|---|---|---|---|---|---|---|
| n-Undecane | $C_{11}H_{24}$ | 0.472 | 0.536 | 0.606 | 0.684 | 0.770 | 0.865 | 0.970 | 1.085 | 1.212 | 1.350 | 1.501 | 1.666 | 1.847 | 2.041 | 2.254 | 2.484 | 2.733 | 3.002 |
| n-Dodecane | $C_{12}H_{26}$ | 0.211 | 0.243 | 0.278 | 0.317 | 0.361 | 0.409 | 0.464 | 0.524 | 0.591 | 0.665 | 0.746 | 0.836 | 0.934 | 1.042 | 1.160 | 1.289 | 1.430 | 1.584 |
| n-Tridecane | $C_{13}H_{28}$ | | | | | | 0.19 | 0.22 | 0.25 | 0.29 | 0.33 | 0.37 | 0.42 | 0.47 | 0.53 | 0.60 | 0.67 | 0.75 | 0.84 |
| n-Tetradecane | $C_{14}H_{30}$ | | | | | | | | | | | 0.18 | 0.21 | 0.24 | 0.27 | 0.31 | 0.35 | 0.40 | 0.45 |
| n-Pentadecane | $C_{15}H_{32}$ | | | | | | | | | | | | | | | | 0.18 | 0.21 | 0.24 |
| n-Hexadecane | $C_{16}H_{34}$ | | | | | | | | | | | | | | | | | | |
| n-Heptadecane | $C_{17}H_{36}$ | | | | | | | | | | | | | | | | | | |
| n-Octadecane | $C_{18}H_{38}$ | | | | | | | | | | | | | | | | | | |
| n-Nonadecane | $C_{19}H_{40}$ | | | | | | | | | | | | | | | | | | |
| n-Eicosane | $C_{20}H_{42}$ | | | | | | | | | | | | | | | | | | |

a Values of the vapor pressure are calculated from the constants given and the Antoine equation: $\log_{10} P = A - B/(C + t)$; $t = B/(A - \log_{10} P) - C$; (P in lb/in²; t in °F)

TABLE 20k-E (PART 1), Page 7 – NORMAL PARAFFINS, $C_1$ TO $C_{20}$

VAPOR PRESSURES AND BOILING POINTS

April 30, 1949; December 31, 1952

Temperature in °F — Vapor pressure in lb/in²

| Compound | Formula | 290 | 295 | 300 | 305 | 310 | 315 | 320 | 325 | 330 | 335 | 340 | 345 | 350 | 355 | 360 | 365 | 370 | 375 |
|---|---|---|---|---|---|---|---|---|---|---|---|---|---|---|---|---|---|---|---|
| n-Undecane | $C_{11}H_{24}$ | 3.293 | 3.606 | 3.943 | 4.305 | 4.694 | 5.110 | 5.557 | 6.034 | 6.543 | 7.087 | 7.667 | 8.283 | 8.939 | 9.636 | 10.375 | 11.159 | 11.989 | 12.867 |
| n-Dodecane | $C_{12}H_{26}$ | 1.750 | 1.932 | 2.128 | 2.340 | 2.570 | 2.818 | 3.085 | 3.372 | 3.681 | 4.012 | 4.368 | 4.748 | 5.156 | 5.590 | 6.054 | 6.549 | 7.076 | 7.636 |
| n-Tridecane | $C_{13}H_{28}$ | 0.93 | 1.04 | 1.15 | 1.28 | 1.41 | 1.56 | 1.72 | 1.90 | 2.08 | 2.29 | 2.51 | 2.74 | 3.00 | 3.27 | 3.56 | 3.87 | 4.21 | 4.57 |
| n-Tetradecane | $C_{14}H_{30}$ | 0.50 | 0.56 | 0.63 | 0.70 | 0.78 | 0.87 | 0.97 | 1.07 | 1.18 | 1.31 | 1.44 | 1.59 | 1.75 | 1.92 | 2.11 | 2.30 | 2.52 | 2.75 |
| n-Pentadecane | $C_{15}H_{32}$ | 0.27 | 0.30 | 0.34 | 0.39 | 0.43 | 0.49 | 0.54 | 0.61 | 0.68 | 0.75 | 0.84 | 0.93 | 1.03 | 1.14 | 1.25 | 1.38 | 1.52 | 1.67 |
| n-Hexadecane | $C_{16}H_{34}$ |  |  | 0.191 | 0.217 | 0.245 | 0.277 | 0.312 | 0.351 | 0.394 | 0.441 | 0.493 | 0.550 | 0.613 | 0.681 | 0.756 | 0.838 | 0.926 | 1.023 |
| n-Heptadecane | $C_{17}H_{36}$ |  |  |  |  |  |  |  | 0.20 | 0.23 | 0.26 | 0.29 | 0.32 | 0.36 | 0.41 | 0.46 | 0.51 | 0.57 | 0.63 |
| n-Octadecane | $C_{18}H_{38}$ |  |  |  |  |  |  |  |  |  |  |  | 0.20 | 0.22 | 0.25 | 0.28 | 0.31 | 0.35 | 0.39 |
| n-Nonadecane | $C_{19}H_{40}$ |  |  |  |  |  |  |  |  |  |  |  |  |  |  |  | 0.19 | 0.22 | 0.25 |
| n-Eicosane | $C_{20}H_{42}$ |  |  |  |  |  |  |  |  |  |  |  |  |  |  |  |  |  |  |

Temperature in °F — Vapor pressure in lb/in²

| Compound | Formula | 380 | 385 | 390 | 395 | 400 | 405 | 410 | 415 | 420 | 425 | 430 | 435 | 440 | 445 | 450 | 455 | 460 | 465 |
|---|---|---|---|---|---|---|---|---|---|---|---|---|---|---|---|---|---|---|---|
| n-Undecane | $C_{11}H_{24}$ | 13.796 | 14.776 | 15.811 | 16.901 | 18.051 | 19.26 | 20.53 | 21.87 | 22.27 | 24.74 | 26.3 | 27.9 | 29.6 |  |  |  |  |  |
| n-Dodecane | $C_{12}H_{26}$ | 8.231 | 8.863 | 9.532 | 10.242 | 10.993 | 11.787 | 12.626 | 13.511 | 14.445 | 15.429 | 16.46 | 17.56 | 18.70 | 19.90 | 21.17 | 22.49 | 23.88 | 25.3 |
| n-Tridecane | $C_{13}H_{28}$ | 4.95 | 5.36 | 5.80 | 6.26 | 6.76 | 7.28 | 7.84 | 8.43 | 9.06 | 9.72 | 10.42 | 11.16 | 11.94 | 12.76 | 13.63 | 14.55 | 15.51 | 16.5 |
| n-Tetradecane | $C_{14}H_{30}$ | 3.00 | 3.26 | 3.55 | 3.85 | 4.18 | 4.53 | 4.90 | 5.29 | 5.71 | 6.16 | 6.64 | 7.14 | 7.68 | 8.24 | 8.84 | 9.47 | 10.14 | 10.85 |
| n-Pentadecane | $C_{15}H_{32}$ | 1.83 | 2.00 | 2.19 | 2.39 | 2.60 | 2.84 | 3.08 | 3.35 | 3.64 | 3.94 | 4.26 | 4.61 | 4.98 | 5.37 | 5.78 | 6.22 | 6.69 | 7.19 |
| n-Hexadecane | $C_{16}H_{34}$ | 1.128 | 1.242 | 1.365 | 1.498 | 1.642 | 1.797 | 1.964 | 2.143 | 2.336 | 2.543 | 2.764 | 3.002 | 3.256 | 3.527 | 3.817 | 4.125 | 4.454 | 4.804 |
| n-Heptadecane | $C_{17}H_{36}$ | 0.70 | 0.77 | 0.86 | 0.94 | 1.04 | 1.15 | 1.26 | 1.38 | 1.51 | 1.66 | 1.81 | 1.98 | 2.15 | 2.34 | 2.55 | 2.77 | 3.00 | 3.25 |
| n-Octadecane | $C_{18}H_{38}$ | 0.44 | 0.49 | 0.54 | 0.60 | 0.67 | 0.74 | 0.82 | 0.90 | 0.99 | 1.09 | 1.20 | 1.31 | 1.44 | 1.57 | 1.71 | 1.87 | 2.03 | 2.21 |
| n-Nonadecane | $C_{19}H_{40}$ | 0.28 | 0.31 | 0.35 | 0.39 | 0.43 | 0.48 | 0.53 | 0.59 | 0.65 | 0.72 | 0.79 | 0.87 | 0.96 | 1.06 | 1.16 | 1.27 | 1.39 | 1.52 |
| n-Eicosane | $C_{20}H_{42}$ |  | 0.20 | 0.22 | 0.25 | 0.28 | 0.31 | 0.35 | 0.39 | 0.43 | 0.48 | 0.53 | 0.59 | 0.65 | 0.71 | 0.79 | 0.87 | 0.95 | 1.04 |

## TABLE 20k-E (PART 1), Page 8 – NORMAL PARAFFINS, $C_1$ TO $C_{20}$
### VAPOR PRESSURES AND BOILING POINTS
April 30, 1949; December 31, 1952

Temperature in °F — Vapor pressure in lb/in²

| Compound | Formula | 470 | 475 | 480 | 485 | 490 | 495 | 500 | 505 | 510 | 515 | 520 | 525 | 530 | 535 | 540 | 545 | 550 | 555 |
|---|---|---|---|---|---|---|---|---|---|---|---|---|---|---|---|---|---|---|---|
| n-Undecane | $C_{11}H_{24}$ | | | | | | | | | | | | | | | | | | |
| n-Dodecane | $C_{12}H_{26}$ | 26.9 | 28.4 | 30.1 | | | | | | | | | | | | | | | |
| n-Tridecane | $C_{13}H_{28}$ | 17.6 | 18.7 | 19.9 | 21.1 | 22.4 | 23.7 | 25.1 | 26.6 | 28.1 | 29.7 | | | | | | | | |
| n-Tetradecane | $C_{14}H_{30}$ | 11.59 | 12.38 | 13.20 | 14.07 | 14.99 | 15.95 | 17.0 | 18.0 | 19.1 | 20.3 | 21.5 | 22.8 | 24.1 | 25.5 | 26.9 | 28.4 | 30.0 | |
| n-Pentadecane | $C_{15}H_{32}$ | 7.71 | 8.27 | 8.86 | 9.48 | 10.13 | 10.82 | 11.55 | 12.31 | 13.12 | 13.96 | 14.85 | 15.8 | 16.8 | 17.8 | 18.9 | 20.0 | 21.2 | 22.4 |
| n-Hexadecane | $C_{16}H_{34}$ | 5.175 | 5.570 | 5.988 | 6.432 | 6.902 | 7.399 | 7.925 | 8.480 | 9.066 | 9.684 | 10.335 | 11.021 | 11.742 | 12.501 | 13.298 | 14.134 | 15.012 | 15.932 |
| n-Heptadecane | $C_{17}H_{36}$ | 3.52 | 3.80 | 4.10 | 4.42 | 4.76 | 5.13 | 5.51 | 5.92 | 6.35 | 6.81 | 7.29 | 7.80 | 8.34 | 8.91 | 9.50 | 10.14 | 10.80 | 11.50 |
| n-Octadecane | $C_{18}H_{38}$ | 2.40 | 2.61 | 2.83 | 3.06 | 3.31 | 3.58 | 3.86 | 4.16 | 4.48 | 4.82 | 5.18 | 5.56 | 5.96 | 6.38 | 6.84 | 7.31 | 7.82 | 8.34 |
| n-Nonadecane | $C_{19}H_{40}$ | 1.65 | 1.80 | 1.96 | 2.13 | 2.31 | 2.51 | 2.72 | 2.94 | 3.18 | 3.43 | 3.70 | 3.98 | 4.28 | 4.61 | 4.95 | 5.31 | 5.69 | 6.09 |
| n-Eicosane | $C_{20}H_{42}$ | 1.14 | 1.25 | 1.37 | 1.49 | 1.62 | 1.77 | 1.92 | 2.09 | 2.26 | 2.45 | 2.65 | 2.87 | 3.09 | 3.34 | 3.60 | 3.87 | 4.16 | 4.47 |

Temperature in °F — Vapor pressure in lb/in²

| Compound | Formula | 560 | 565 | 570 | 575 | 580 | 585 | 590 | 595 | 600 | 605 | 610 | 615 | 620 | 625 | 630 | 635 | 640 | 645 |
|---|---|---|---|---|---|---|---|---|---|---|---|---|---|---|---|---|---|---|---|
| n-Undecane | $C_{11}H_{24}$ | | | | | | | | | | | | | | | | | | |
| n-Dodecane | $C_{12}H_{26}$ | | | | | | | | | | | | | | | | | | |
| n-Tridecane | $C_{13}H_{28}$ | | | | | | | | | | | | | | | | | | |
| n-Tetradecane | $C_{14}H_{30}$ | | | | | | | | | | | | | | | | | | |
| n-Pentadecane | $C_{15}H_{32}$ | 23.7 | 25.0 | 26.4 | 27.9 | 29.4 | | | | | | | | | | | | | |
| n-Hexadecane | $C_{16}H_{34}$ | 16.90 | 17.91 | 18.96 | 20.07 | 21.22 | 22.43 | 23.69 | 25.0 | 26.4 | 27.8 | 29.3 | | | | | | | |
| n-Heptadecane | $C_{17}H_{36}$ | 12.23 | 13.00 | 13.80 | 14.65 | 15.5 | 16.5 | 17.4 | 18.4 | 19.5 | 20.6 | 21.8 | 23.0 | 24.2 | 25.6 | 26.9 | 28.3 | 29.8 | |
| n-Octadecane | $C_{18}H_{38}$ | 8.90 | 9.49 | 10.11 | 10.76 | 11.44 | 12.16 | 12.91 | 13.70 | 14.52 | 15.39 | 16.3 | 17.2 | 18.2 | 19.3 | 20.3 | 21.5 | 22.6 | 23.9 |
| n-Nonadecane | $C_{19}H_{40}$ | 6.52 | 6.97 | 7.45 | 7.95 | 8.48 | 9.03 | 9.62 | 10.23 | 10.88 | 11.56 | 12.27 | 13.01 | 13.79 | 14.61 | 15.47 | 16.4 | 17.3 | 18.3 |
| n-Eicosane | $C_{20}H_{42}$ | 4.80 | 5.15 | 5.52 | 5.90 | 6.31 | 6.75 | 7.20 | 7.68 | 8.19 | 8.72 | 9.28 | 9.87 | 10.49 | 11.14 | 11.82 | 12.53 | 13.27 | 14.06 |

TABLE 20k-E (PART 1), Page 9 - NORMAL PARAFFINS, $C_1$ TO $C_{20}$

VAPOR PRESSURES AND BOILING POINTS, AT 0.2 TO 30 $lb/in^2$

April 30, 1949; December 31, 1952

Temperature in °F

Vapor pressure in $lb/in^2$

| Compound | Formula | 650 | 655 | 660 | 665 | 670 | 675 | 680 | 685 | 690 | 695 | 700 | 705 | 710 | 715 | 720 |
|---|---|---|---|---|---|---|---|---|---|---|---|---|---|---|---|---|
| n-Undecane | $C_{11}H_{24}$ | | | | | | | | | | | | | | | |
| n-Dodecane | $C_{12}H_{26}$ | | | | | | | | | | | | | | | |
| n-Tridecane | $C_{13}H_{28}$ | | | | | | | | | | | | | | | |
| n-Tetradecane | $C_{14}H_{30}$ | | | | | | | | | | | | | | | |
| n-Pentadecane | $C_{15}H_{32}$ | | | | | | | | | | | | | | | |
| n-Hexadecane | $C_{16}H_{34}$ | | | | | | | | | | | | | | | |
| n-Heptadecane | $C_{17}H_{36}$ | | | | | | | | | | | | | | | |
| n-Octadecane | $C_{18}H_{38}$ | 25.1 | 26.5 | 27.8 | 29.3 | 30.8 | | | | | | | | | | |
| n-Nonadecane | $C_{19}H_{40}$ | 19.3 | 20.4 | 21.5 | 22.6 | 23.8 | 25.1 | 26.4 | 27.7 | 29.1 | 30.6 | | | | | |
| n-Eicosane | $C_{20}H_{42}$ | 14.88 | 15.73 | 16.6 | 17.6 | 18.5 | 19.5 | 20.6 | 21.7 | 22.8 | 24.0 | 25.3 | 26.6 | 27.9 | 29.3 | 30.8 |

## TABLE 1k-E, Page 1 – PARAFFINS, $C_1$ TO $C_5$
### VAPOR PRESSURES AND BOILING POINTS, AT 0.2 TO 30 lb/in²

February 28, 1949; December 31, 1952

### Constants of the Antoine equation

| Compound | Formula[a] | A | B | C |
|---|---|---|---|---|
| Methane | $CH_4$ | 5.98179ᵇ | 957.96ᵇ | 463.00ᵇ |
|  |  | 4.89823 | 701.87 | 446.80 |
| Ethane | $C_2H_6$ | 5.08905 | 1181.52 | 428.80 |
| Propane | $C_3H_8$ | 5.11612 | 1463.76 | 414.40 |
| n-Butane | $C_4H_{10}$ | 5.11668 | 1702.62 | 400.00 |
| 2-Methylpropane (Isobutane) | " | 5.03447 | 1589.04 | 400.00 |
| n-Pentane | $C_5H_{12}$ | 5.13960 | 1916.33 | 385.60 |
| 2-Methylbutane (Isopentane) | " | 5.07606 | 1836.02 | 387.57 |
| 2,2-Dimethylpropane (Neopentane) | " | 5.02451 | 1711.51 | 394.60 |

### Temperature in °F — Vapor pressure in lb/in²

| Compound | Formula[a] | -255 | -260 | -265 | -270 | -275 | -280 | -285 | -290 | -295 | -300 | -305 | -310 | -315 | -320 |
|---|---|---|---|---|---|---|---|---|---|---|---|---|---|---|---|
| Methane | $CH_4$ | 17.33 | 13.83 | 10.90 | 8.48 | 6.50 | 4.90 | 3.63 | 2.64 | 1.88ᶜ | 1.27ᵇ | 0.83ᵇ | 0.53ᵇ | 0.32ᵇ | 0.19ᵇ |
| Ethane | $C_2H_6$ |  |  |  |  |  |  |  |  |  |  |  |  |  |  |
| Propane | $C_3H_8$ |  |  |  |  |  |  |  |  |  |  |  |  |  |  |
| n-Butane | $C_4H_{10}$ |  |  |  |  |  |  |  |  |  |  |  |  |  |  |
| 2-Methylpropane (Isobutane) | " |  |  |  |  |  |  |  |  |  |  |  |  |  |  |
| n-Pentane | $C_5H_{12}$ |  |  |  |  |  |  |  |  |  |  |  |  |  |  |
| 2-Methylbutane (Isopentane) | " |  |  |  |  |  |  |  |  |  |  |  |  |  |  |
| 2,2-Dimethylpropane (Neopentane) | " |  |  |  |  |  |  |  |  |  |  |  |  |  |  |

### Temperature in °F — Vapor pressure in lb/in²

| Compound | Formula[a] | -165 | -170 | -175 | -180 | -185 | -190 | -195 | -200 | -205 | -210 | -215 | -220 | -225 | -230 | -235 | -240 | -245 | -250 |
|---|---|---|---|---|---|---|---|---|---|---|---|---|---|---|---|---|---|---|---|
| Methane | $CH_4$ |  |  |  |  |  |  |  |  |  |  |  |  |  |  |  | 31.9 | 26.3 | 21.47 |
| Ethane | $C_2H_6$ | 4.08 | 3.34 | 2.71 | 2.189 | 1.749 | 1.385 | 1.085 | 0.842 | 0.645 | 0.489 | 0.365 | 0.269 | 0.196 |  |  |  |  |  |
| Propane | $C_3H_8$ |  |  |  |  |  |  |  |  |  |  |  |  |  |  |  |  |  |  |
| n-Butane | $C_4H_{10}$ |  |  |  |  |  |  |  |  |  |  |  |  |  |  |  |  |  |  |
| 2-Methylpropane (Isobutane) | " |  |  |  |  |  |  |  |  |  |  |  |  |  |  |  |  |  |  |
| n-Pentane | $C_5H_{12}$ |  |  |  |  |  |  |  |  |  |  |  |  |  |  |  |  |  |  |
| 2-Methylbutane (Isopentane) | " |  |  |  |  |  |  |  |  |  |  |  |  |  |  |  |  |  |  |
| 2,2-Dimethylpropane (Neopentane) | " |  |  |  |  |  |  |  |  |  |  |  |  |  |  |  |  |  |  |

a Values of the vapor pressure are calculated from the constants given and the Antoine equation: $\log_{10} P = A - B/(C + t)$; $t = B/(A - \log_{10}P) - C$; (P in lb/in²; t in °F).

b For the solid-vapor equilibrium.

c At the triple point, -296.46°F, the pressure is 1.70 lb/in².

TABLE 1k-E, Page 2 - PARAFFINS, $C_1$ TO $C_5$
VAPOR PRESSURES AND BOILING POINTS, AT 0.2 TO 30 lb/in²
February 28, 1949; December 31, 1952

Temperature in °F — Vapor pressure in lb/in²

| Compound | Formula | -160 | -155 | -150 | -145 | -140 | -135 | -130 | -125 | -120 | -115 | -110 | -105 | -100 | -95 | -90 | -85 | -80 | -75 |
|---|---|---|---|---|---|---|---|---|---|---|---|---|---|---|---|---|---|---|---|
| Methane | $CH_4$ | | | | | | | | | | | | | | | | | | |
| Ethane | $C_2H_6$ | 4.94 | 5.94 | 7.10 | 8.43 | 9.95 | 11.68 | 13.64 | 15.85 | 18.32 | 21.08 | 24.15 | 27.55 | 31.31 | | | | | |
| Propane | $C_3H_8$ | | | 0.380 | 0.482 | 0.605 | 0.754 | 0.932 | 1.143 | 1.394 | 1.687 | 2.030 | 2.427 | 2.887 | 3.414 | 4.02 | 4.70 | 5.48 | 6.36 |
| n-Butane | $C_4H_{10}$ | | | | | | | | 0.084 | 0.109 | 0.139 | 0.176 | 0.221 | 0.276 | 0.342 | 0.422 | 0.515 | 0.625 | 0.755 |
| 2-Methylpropane (Isobutane) | " | | | | | | | | 0.180 | 0.229 | 0.268 | 0.359 | 0.445 | 0.547 | 0.668 | 0.810 | 0.977 | 1.171 | 1.397 |
| n-Pentane | $C_5H_{12}$ | | | | | | | | | | | | | | | | | | |
| 2-Methylbutane (Isopentane) | " | | | | | | | | | | | | | | | | | | |
| 2,2-Dimethylpropane (Neopentane) | " | | | | | | | | | | | | | | | | | | |

Temperature in °F — Vapor pressure in lb/in²

| Compound | Formula | -70 | -65 | -60 | -55 | -50 | -45 | -40 | -35 | -30 | -25 | -20 | -15 | -10 | -5 | 0 | 5 | 10 | 15 |
|---|---|---|---|---|---|---|---|---|---|---|---|---|---|---|---|---|---|---|---|
| Methane | $CH_4$ | | | | | | | | | | | | | | | | | | |
| Ethane | $C_2H_6$ | | | | | | | | | | | | | | | | | | |
| Propane | $C_3H_8$ | 7.34 | 8.45 | 9.68 | 11.05 | 12.57 | 14.24 | 16.09 | 18.11 | 20.33 | 22.76 | 25.4 | 28.3 | | | | | | |
| n-Butane | $C_4H_{10}$ | 0.906 | 1.082 | 1.285 | 1.519 | 1.787 | 2.092 | 2.439 | 2.831 | 3.273 | 3.770 | 4.326 | 4.95 | 5.64 | 6.40 | 7.25 | 8.18 | 9.20 | 10.33 |
| 2-Methylpropane (Isobutane) | " | 1.657 | 1.955 | 2.295 | 2.683 | 3.121 | 3.617 | 4.17 | 4.80 | 5.49 | 6.27 | 7.12 | 8.07 | 9.12 | 10.27 | 11.53 | 12.91 | 14.41 | 16.05 |
| n-Pentane | $C_5H_{12}$ | 0.12 | 0.14 | 0.179 | 0.220 | 0.268 | 0.325 | 0.392 | 0.471 | 0.562 | 0.667 | 0.789 | 0.928 | 1.088 | 1.269 | 1.475 | 1.708 | 1.970 | 2.264 |
| 2-Methylbutane (Isopentane) | " | 0.197 | 0.242 | 0.296 | 0.359 | 0.434 | 0.521 | 0.622 | 0.739 | 0.874 | 1.028 | 1.205 | 1.406 | 1.634 | 1.892 | 2.182 | 2.507 | 2.870 | 3.276 |
| 2,2-Dimethylpropane (Neopentane) | " | | | | | | | | | | | | | | | | 5.51 | 6.23 | 7.01 |

TABLE 1k-E, Page 3 — PARAFFINS, $C_1$ TO $C_5$
VAPOR PRESSURES AND BOILING POINTS, AT 0.2 TO 30 lb/in²

February 28, 1949; December 31, 1952

Temperature in °F — Vapor pressure in lb/in²

| Compound | Formula | 20 | 25 | 30 | 35 | 40 | 45 | 50 | 55 | 60 | 65 | 70 | 75 | 80 | 85 | 90 | 95 | 100 | 105 |
|---|---|---|---|---|---|---|---|---|---|---|---|---|---|---|---|---|---|---|---|
| Methane | $CH_4$ | | | | | | | | | | | | | | | | | | |
| Ethane | $C_2H_6$ | | | | | | | | | | | | | | | | | | |
| Propane | $C_3H_8$ | | | | | | | | | | | | | | | | | | |
| n-Butane | $C_4H_{10}$ | 11.56 | 12.90 | 14.36 | 15.94 | 17.66 | 19.52 | 21.53 | 23.7 | 26.0 | 28.5 | | | | | | | | |
| 2-Methylpropane (Isobutane) | " | 17.82 | 19.75 | 21.8 | 24.1 | 26.5 | 29.1 | | | | | | | | | | | | |
| n-Pentane | $C_5H_{12}$ | 2.594 | 2.961 | 3.370 | 3.832 | 4.325 | 4.878 | 5.489 | 6.155 | 6.887 | 7.687 | 8.559 | 9.508 | 10.538 | 11.655 | 12.862 | 14.165 | 15.570 | 17.08 |
| 2-Methylbutane (Isopentane) | " | 3.726 | 4.223 | 4.777 | 5.38 | 6.05 | 6.79 | 7.59 | 8.46 | 9.42 | 10.45 | 11.57 | 12.79 | 14.10 | 15.52 | 17.04 | 18.68 | 20.44 | 22.32 |
| 2,2-Dimethylpropane (Neopentane) | " | 7.88 | 8.82 | 9.85 | 10.98 | 12.20 | 13.53 | 14.96 | 16.51 | 18.18 | 20.0 | 21.9 | 24.0 | 26.2 | 28.6 | | | | |

Temperature in °F — Vapor pressure in lb/in²

| Compound | Formula | 110 | 115 | 120 | 125 | 130 | 135 |
|---|---|---|---|---|---|---|---|
| Methane | $CH_4$ | | | | | | |
| Ethane | $C_2H_6$ | | | | | | |
| Propane | $C_3H_8$ | | | | | | |
| n-Butane | $C_4H_{10}$ | | | | | | |
| 2-Methylpropane (Isobutane) | " | | | | | | |
| n-Pentane | $C_5H_{12}$ | 18.7 | 20.4 | 22.3 | 24.3 | 26.4 | 28.7 |
| 2-Methylbutane (Isopentane) | " | 24.3 | 26.5 | 28.8 | | | |
| 2,2-Dimethylpropane (Neopentane) | " | | | | | | |

TABLE 2k-E (PART 1), Page 1 - PARAFFINS, $C_6$

VAPOR PRESSURES AND BOILING POINTS, AT 0.2 TO 30 lb/in²

February 28, 1949; December 31, 1952

| Compound | Formula | Constants of the Antoine equation | | | Temperature in °F | | | | | | | | | | | | | |
| | | A | B | C | -45 | -40 | -35 | -30 | -25 | -20 | -15 | -10 | -5 | 0 | +5 | 10 | 15 | 20 |
| | | | | | Vapor pressure in lb/in² | | | | | | | | | | | | | |
| n-Hexane | $C_6H_{14}$ | 5.16415 | 2108.754 | 371.859 | 0.05 | 0.06 | 0.08 | 0.10 | 0.12 | 0.15 | 0.180 | 0.217 | 0.261 | 0.311 | 0.370 | 0.438 | 0.517 | 0.606 |
| 2-Methylpentane | " | 5.12550 | 2043.738 | 375.830 | 0.09 | 0.11 | 0.13 | 0.164 | 0.200 | 0.241 | 0.289 | 0.346 | 0.411 | 0.487 | 0.574 | 0.674 | 0.788 | 0.917 |
| 3-Methylpentane | " | 5.13526 | 2074.262 | 376.832 | 0.08 | 0.09 | 0.12 | 0.14 | 0.174 | 0.210 | 0.253 | 0.302 | 0.360 | 0.427 | 0.503 | 0.593 | 0.694 | 0.810 |
| 2,2-Dimethylbutane | " | 5.04122 | 1946.117 | 380.817 | 0.18 | 0.21 | 0.26 | 0.31 | 0.37 | 0.44 | 0.53 | 0.62 | 0.73 | 0.85 | 0.99 | 1.15 | 1.33 | 1.53 |
| 2,3-Dimethylbutane | " | 5.09622 | 2028.937 | 380.020 | 0.11 | 0.13 | 0.164 | 0.199 | 0.241 | 0.289 | 0.345 | 0.410 | 0.485 | 0.572 | 0.671 | 0.784 | 0.912 | 1.057 |

| Compound | Formula | Temperature in °F | | | | | | | | | | | | | | | | | |
| | | 25 | 30 | 35 | 40 | 45 | 50 | 55 | 60 | 65 | 70 | 75 | 80 | 85 | 90 | 95 | 100 | 105 | 110 |
| | | Vapor pressure in lb/in² | | | | | | | | | | | | | | | | | |
| n-Hexane | $C_6H_{14}$ | 0.709 | 0.825 | 0.958 | 1.107 | 1.275 | 1.464 | 1.675 | 1.911 | 2.173 | 2.464 | 2.787 | 3.143 | 3.535 | 3.966 | 4.439 | 4.956 | 5.520 | 6.136 |
| 2-Methylpentane | " | 1.063 | 1.229 | 1.415 | 1.624 | 1.856 | 2.119 | 2.409 | 2.730 | 3.086 | 3.478 | 3.910 | 4.385 | 4.904 | 5.472 | 6.092 | 6.767 | 7.500 | 8.295 |
| 3-Methylpentane | " | 0.940 | 1.088 | 1.255 | 1.442 | 1.652 | 1.886 | 2.147 | 2.437 | 2.758 | 3.112 | 3.503 | 3.933 | 4.404 | 4.920 | 5.484 | 6.098 | 6.766 | 7.491 |
| 2,2-Dimethylbutane | " | 1.76 | 2.01 | 2.30 | 2.610 | 2.957 | 3.342 | 3.765 | 4.231 | 4.742 | 5.301 | 5.912 | 6.577 | 7.301 | 8.066 | 8.936 | 9.856 | 10.848 | 11.917 |
| 2,3-Dimethylbutane | " | 1.221 | 1.409 | 1.612 | 1.844 | 2.101 | 2.388 | 2.705 | 3.056 | 3.444 | 3.870 | 4.337 | 4.849 | 5.409 | 6.019 | 6.663 | 7.404 | 8.185 | 9.030 |

Values of the vapor pressure are calculated from the constants given and the Antoine equation: $\log_{10} P = A - B/(C + t)$; $t = B/(A - \log_{10} P) - C$; (P in lb/in²; t in °F).

380

## TABLE 2k-E (PART 1), Page 2 - PARAFFINS, $C_6$
### VAPOR PRESSURES AND BOILING POINTS, AT 0.2 TO 30 lb/in²
February 28, 1949; December 31, 1952

Temperature in °F

Vapor pressure in lb/in²

| Compound | Formula | 115 | 120 | 125 | 130 | 135 | 140 | 145 | 150 | 155 | 160 | 165 | 170 | 175 | 180 | 185 | 190 | 195 | 200 |
|---|---|---|---|---|---|---|---|---|---|---|---|---|---|---|---|---|---|---|---|
| n-Hexane | $C_6H_{14}$ | 6.805 | 7.531 | 8.317 | 9.168 | 10.086 | 11.075 | 12.140 | 13.283 | 14.509 | 15.823 | 17.23 | 18.73 | 20.32 | 22.03 | 23.84 | 25.8 | 27.8 | 30.0 |
| 2-Methylpentane | " | 9.155 | 10.084 | 11.087 | 12.166 | 13.325 | 14.570 | 15.904 | 17.33 | 18.85 | 20.48 | 22.21 | 24.0 | 26.0 | 28.1 | 30.3 | | | |
| 3-Methylpentane | " | 8.276 | 9.126 | 10.043 | 11.032 | 12.096 | 13.239 | 14.464 | 15.777 | 17.18 | 18.68 | 20.28 | 21.98 | 23.79 | 25.71 | 27.8 | 29.9 | | |
| 2,2-Dimethylbutane | " | 13.066 | 14.300 | 15.622 | 17.04 | 18.55 | 20.16 | 21.88 | 23.71 | 25.65 | 27.7 | 29.9 | 32.2 | | | | | | |
| 2,3-Dimethylbutane | " | 9.943 | 10.927 | 11.986 | 13.124 | 14.345 | 15.652 | 17.05 | 18.54 | 20.14 | 21.83 | 23.63 | 25.55 | 27.6 | 29.7 | | | | |

TABLE 2k-E (PART 2), Page 1 – PARAFFINS, $C_7$

VAPOR PRESSURES AND BOILING POINTS, AT 0.2 TO 30 lb/in²

February 28, 1949; December 31, 1952

| Compound | Formula | Constants of the Antoine equation | | | Temperature in °F — Vapor pressure in lb/in² | | | | | | | | | | | | | |
|---|---|---|---|---|---|---|---|---|---|---|---|---|---|---|---|---|---|---|
| | | A | B | C | 0 | 5 | 10 | 15 | 20 | 25 | 30 | 35 | 40 | 45 | 50 | 55 | 60 | 65 |
| n-Heptane | $C_7H_{16}$ | 5.18879 | 2282.607 | 358.420 | | | | | | | 0.205 | 0.244 | 0.288 | 0.339 | 0.398 | 0.465 | 0.541 | 0.628 |
| 2-Methylhexane | " | 5.15957 | 2224.847 | 363.181 | | | | 0.189 | 0.226 | 0.268 | 0.317 | 0.373 | 0.438 | 0.512 | 0.596 | 0.691 | 0.798 | 0.919 |
| 3-Methylhexane | " | 5.15403 | 2232.353 | 362.601 | | | | 0.17 | 0.209 | 0.248 | 0.294 | 0.346 | 0.407 | 0.476 | 0.554 | 0.643 | 0.744 | 0.858 |
| 3-Ethylpentane | " | 5.16203 | 2253.289 | 363.797 | | | | 0.16 | 0.195 | 0.233 | 0.275 | 0.325 | 0.382 | 0.447 | 0.521 | 0.605 | 0.700 | 0.808 |
| 2,2-Dimethylpentane | " | 5.10119 | 2142.059 | 369.945 | 0.205 | 0.244 | 0.291 | 0.344 | 0.405 | 0.476 | 0.556 | 0.648 | 0.751 | 0.869 | 1.001 | 1.149 | 1.315 | 1.501 |
| 2,3-Dimethylpentane | " | 5.14021 | 2228.431 | 367.281 | | | | 0.205 | 0.243 | 0.288 | 0.340 | 0.399 | 0.466 | 0.543 | 0.631 | 0.730 | 0.841 | 0.966 |
| 2,4-Dimethylpentane | " | 5.11260 | 2145.674 | 366.941 | 0.184 | 0.221 | 0.263 | 0.312 | 0.369 | 0.435 | 0.509 | 0.595 | 0.692 | 0.802 | 0.926 | 1.065 | 1.222 | 1.397 |
| 3,3-Dimethylpentane | " | 5.11306 | 2211.593 | 373.569 | 0.16 | 0.187 | 0.222 | 0.264 | 0.312 | 0.367 | 0.430 | 0.501 | 0.583 | 0.675 | 0.779 | 0.897 | 1.028 | 1.176 |
| 2,2,3-Trimethylbutane | " | 5.07869 | 2161.013 | 374.890 | 0.206 | 0.246 | 0.291 | 0.344 | 0.404 | 0.473 | 0.551 | 0.640 | 0.741 | 0.855 | 0.983 | 1.127 | 1.287 | 1.466 |

| Compound | Formula | Temperature in °F — Vapor pressure in lb/in² | | | | | | | | | | | | | | | | | |
|---|---|---|---|---|---|---|---|---|---|---|---|---|---|---|---|---|---|---|---|
| | | 70 | 75 | 80 | 85 | 90 | 95 | 100 | 105 | 110 | 115 | 120 | 125 | 130 | 135 | 140 | 145 | 150 | 155 |
| n-Heptane | $C_7H_{16}$ | 0.726 | 0.836 | 0.960 | 1.099 | 1.254 | 1.428 | 1.620 | 1.833 | 2.069 | 2.330 | 2.616 | 2.931 | 3.276 | 3.653 | 4.065 | 4.514 | 5.002 | 5.532 |
| 2-Methylhexane | " | 1.056 | 1.208 | 1.378 | 1.568 | 1.779 | 2.012 | 2.271 | 2.555 | 2.869 | 3.212 | 3.589 | 4.001 | 4.450 | 4.939 | 5.470 | 6.047 | 6.671 | 7.345 |
| 3-Methylhexane | " | 0.986 | 1.129 | 1.289 | 1.468 | 1.666 | 1.886 | 2.130 | 2.399 | 2.694 | 3.020 | 3.376 | 3.765 | 4.190 | 4.654 | 5.157 | 5.704 | 6.296 | 6.937 |
| 3-Ethylpentane | " | 0.928 | 1.064 | 1.215 | 1.384 | 1.573 | 1.781 | 2.012 | 2.267 | 2.548 | 2.857 | 3.196 | 3.566 | 3.971 | 4.412 | 4.892 | 5.412 | 5.977 | 6.588 |
| 2,2-Dimethylpentane | " | 1.707 | 1.936 | 2.190 | 2.471 | 2.780 | 3.119 | 3.492 | 3.900 | 4.346 | 4.831 | 5.360 | 5.934 | 6.555 | 7.228 | 7.955 | 8.738 | 9.581 | 10.487 |
| 2,3-Dimethylpentane | " | 1.107 | 1.264 | 1.439 | 1.634 | 1.849 | 2.088 | 2.351 | 2.641 | 2.959 | 3.308 | 3.690 | 4.106 | 4.560 | 5.053 | 5.589 | 6.169 | 6.796 | 7.473 |
| 2,4-Dimethylpentane | " | 1.5919 | 1.8092 | 2.0502 | 2.3169 | 2.6113 | 2.936 | 3.292 | 3.682 | 4.110 | 4.576 | 5.084 | 5.636 | 6.235 | 6.884 | 7.586 | 8.344 | 9.160 | 10.038 |
| 3,3-Dimethylpentane | " | 1.340 | 1.523 | 1.726 | 1.951 | 2.199 | 2.473 | 2.773 | 3.103 | 3.464 | 3.858 | 4.288 | 4.755 | 5.263 | 5.813 | 6.408 | 7.051 | 7.744 | 8.491 |
| 2,2,3-Trimethylbutane | " | 1.664 | 1.885 | 2.128 | 2.397 | 2.693 | 3.018 | 3.374 | 3.763 | 4.188 | 4.650 | 5.153 | 5.698 | 6.288 | 6.926 | 7.615 | 8.357 | 9.154 | 10.011 |

Values of the vapor pressure are calculated from the constants given and the Antoine equation: $\log_{10} P = A - B/(C + t)$; $t = B/(A - \log_{10} P) - C$; (P in lb/in²; t in °F)

## TABLE 2k-E (PART 2), Page 2 – PARAFFINS, $C_7$
### VAPOR PRESSURES AND BOILING POINTS, AT 0.2 TO 30 lb/in²

February 28, 1949; December 31, 1952

| Compound | Formula | Temperature in °F — Vapor pressure in lb/in² | | | | | | | | | | | | | | | | | |
|---|---|---|---|---|---|---|---|---|---|---|---|---|---|---|---|---|---|---|---|
| | | 160 | 165 | 170 | 175 | 180 | 185 | 190 | 195 | 200 | 205 | 210 | 215 | 220 | 225 | 230 | 235 | 240 | 245 |
| n-Heptane | $C_7H_{16}$ | 6.106 | 6.727 | 7.398 | 8.121 | 8.899 | 9.735 | 10.633 | 11.594 | 12.623 | 13.723 | 14.897 | 16.148 | 17.48 | 18.89 | 20.40 | 21.99 | 23.68 | 25.47 |
| 2-Methylhexane | " | 8.073 | 8.857 | 9.700 | 10.606 | 11.577 | 12.617 | 13.730 | 14.917 | 16.183 | 17.53 | 18.97 | 20.49 | 22.11 | 23.82 | 25.64 | 27.56 | 29.58 | |
| 3-Methylhexane | " | 7.628 | 8.373 | 9.175 | 10.037 | 10.961 | 11.952 | 13.011 | 14.143 | 15.350 | 16.64 | 18.01 | 19.46 | 21.01 | 22.64 | 24.38 | 26.21 | 28.15 | |
| 3-Ethylpentane | " | 7.248 | 7.960 | 8.726 | 9.549 | 10.433 | 11.380 | 12.395 | 13.478 | 14.635 | 15.868 | 17.18 | 18.58 | 20.06 | 21.63 | 23.30 | 25.06 | 26.93 | 28.90 |
| 2,2-Dimethylpentane | " | 11.459 | 12.501 | 13.615 | 14.805 | 16.075 | 17.43 | 18.87 | 20.40 | 22.02 | 23.74 | 25.56 | 27.49 | 29.53 | 31.68 | | | | |
| 2,3-Dimethylpentane | " | 8.202 | 8.988 | 9.831 | 10.736 | 11.705 | 12.742 | 13.850 | 15.032 | 16.291 | 17.63 | 19.05 | 20.56 | 22.17 | 23.87 | 25.66 | 27.56 | 29.56 | |
| 2,4-Dimethylpentane | " | 10.981 | 11.993 | 13.077 | 14.235 | 15.472 | 16.79 | 18.20 | 19.69 | 21.28 | 22.96 | 24.75 | 26.64 | 28.64 | 30.75 | | | | |
| 3,3-Dimethylpentane | " | 9.293 | 10.155 | 11.077 | 12.064 | 13.119 | 14.245 | 15.445 | 16.72 | 18.08 | 19.52 | 21.05 | 22.67 | 24.39 | 26.20 | 28.11 | | | |
| 2,2,3-Trimethylbutane | " | 10.929 | 11.912 | 12.964 | 14.066 | 15.283 | 16.56 | 17.91 | 19.35 | 20.88 | 22.50 | 24.21 | 26.02 | 27.93 | 29.95 | | | | |

| Compound | Formula | Temperature in °F — Vapor pressure in lb/in² | |
|---|---|---|---|
| | | 250 | 255 |
| n-Heptane | $C_7H_{16}$ | 27.36 | 29.35 |
| 2-Methylhexane | " | | |
| 3-Methylhexane | " | | |
| 3-Ethylpentane | " | | |
| 2,2-Dimethylpentane | " | | |
| 2,3-Dimethylpentane | " | | |
| 2,4-Dimethylpentane | " | | |
| 3,3-Dimethylpentane | " | | |
| 2,2,3-Trimethylbutane | " | | |

TABLE 3k-E, Page 1 – PARAFFINS, C$_8$

VAPOR PRESSURES AND BOILING POINTS, AT 0.2 TO 30 lb/in²

August 31, 1949; December 31, 1952

| Compound | Formula | Constants of the Antoine equation | | | Temperature in °F — Vapor pressure in lb/in² | | | | | | | | | | | | | |
|---|---|---|---|---|---|---|---|---|---|---|---|---|---|---|---|---|---|---|
| | | A | B | C | 25 | 30 | 35 | 40 | 45 | 50 | 55 | 60 | 65 | 70 | 75 | 80 | 85 | 90 |
| n-Octane | C₈H₁₈ | 5.21016 | 2439.227 | 345.131 | | | | | | | | | 0.183 | 0.216 | 0.254 | 0.297 | 0.346 | 0.402 |
| 2-Methylheptane | " | 5.20374 | 2407.442 | 352.647 | | | | | | | 0.199 | 0.234 | 0.275 | 0.322 | 0.375 | 0.496 | 0.505 | 0.582 |
| 3-Methylheptane | " | 5.18583 | 2396.754 | 350.345 | | | | | | | 0.187 | 0.221 | 0.260 | 0.305 | 0.356 | 0.413 | 0.479 | 0.553 |
| 4-Methylheptane | " | 5.18704 | 2389.790 | 350.622 | | | | | | | 0.197 | 0.233 | 0.274 | 0.320 | 0.373 | 0.434 | 0.502 | 0.580 |
| 3-Ethylhexane | " | 5.17737 | 2390.191 | 350.671 | | | | | | | 0.193 | 0.228 | 0.267 | 0.313 | 0.365 | 0.424 | 0.491 | 0.567 |
| 2,2-Dimethylhexane | " | 5.12354 | 2292.469 | 355.130 | | | 0.177 | 0.210 | 0.248 | 0.292 | 0.342 | 0.399 | 0.464 | 0.538 | 0.622 | 0.716 | 0.822 | 0.941 |
| 2,3-Dimethylhexane | " | 5.15643 | 2367.905 | 353.463 | | | | | | 0.194 | 0.229 | 0.269 | 0.315 | 0.367 | 0.427 | 0.494 | 0.570 | 0.656 |
| 2,4-Dimethylhexane | " | 5.13944 | 2318.177 | 354.622 | | | | 0.184 | 0.218 | 0.257 | 0.302 | 0.354 | 0.412 | 0.479 | 0.554 | 0.639 | 0.735 | 0.843 |
| 2,5-Dimethylhexane | " | 5.14623 | 2317.093 | 353.942 | | | | 0.184 | 0.218 | 0.257 | 0.302 | 0.354 | 0.412 | 0.479 | 0.555 | 0.641 | 0.737 | 0.845 |
| 3,3-Dimethylhexane | " | 5.13760 | 2354.188 | 359.390 | | | | 0.175 | 0.207 | 0.244 | 0.286 | 0.334 | 0.389 | 0.452 | 0.552 | 0.602 | 0.692 | 0.792 |
| 3,4-Dimethylhexane | " | 5.16625 | 2394.063 | 354.753 | | | | | | 0.178 | 0.211 | 0.248 | 0.290 | 0.339 | 0.394 | 0.457 | 0.527 | 0.607 |
| 2-Methyl-3-ethylpentane | " | 5.14997 | 2372.616 | 355.551 | | | | | | 0.199 | 0.235 | 0.276 | 0.322 | 0.375 | 0.436 | 0.504 | 0.581 | 0.668 |
| 3-Methyl-3-ethylpentane | " | 5.15370 | 2424.976 | 363.431 | | | | | | 0.194 | 0.228 | 0.267 | 0.312 | 0.362 | 0.419 | 0.484 | 0.557 | 0.639 |
| 2,2,3-Trimethylpentane | " | 5.11185 | 2330.775 | 361.156 | | | | 0.200 | 0.236 | 0.277 | 0.324 | 0.378 | 0.439 | 0.508 | 0.586 | 0.674 | 0.772 | 0.882 |
| 2,2,4-Trimethylpentane | " | 5.09828 | 2264.112 | 365.323 | 0.198 | 0.235 | 0.277 | 0.325 | 0.381 | 0.443 | 0.515 | 0.596 | 0.687 | 0.789 | 0.904 | 1.033 | 1.176 | 1.336 |
| 2,3,3-Trimethylpentane | " | 5.12992 | 2390.483 | 364.675 | | | | | 0.197 | 0.232 | 0.272 | 0.317 | 0.369 | 0.427 | 0.493 | 0.568 | 0.651 | 0.745 |
| 2,3,4-Trimethylpentane | " | 5.14035 | 2367.151 | 359.547 | | | | | 0.195 | 0.229 | 0.269 | 0.315 | 0.367 | 0.426 | 0.493 | 0.569 | 0.654 | 0.749 |
| 2,2,3,3-Tetramethylbutane | " | 5.16304 | 2393.87 | 375.45 | | | | | | | | | | | | | | |
| 2,2,3,3-Tetramethylbutane | " | 6.01731ᵃ | 2882.77ᵃ | 372.57ᵃ | | | | | | 0.19ᵃ | | 0.23ᵃ | 0.27ᵃ | 0.32ᵃ | 0.38ᵃ | 0.44ᵃ | 0.52ᵃ | 0.61ᵃ |

Values of the vapor pressure are calculated from the constants given and the Antoine equation: $\log_{10} P = A - B/(C + t)$; $t = B/(A - \log_{10} P) - C$; (P in lb/in²; t in °F).

ᵃ For the solid-vapor equilibrium.

TABLE 3k-E, Page 2 - PARAFFINS, $C_8$

VAPOR PRESSURES AND BOILING POINTS, AT 0.2 TO 30 lb/in²

August 31, 1949; December 31, 1952

| Compound | Formula | Temperature in °F — Vapor pressure in lb/in² | | | | | | | | | | | | | | | | | |
|---|---|---|---|---|---|---|---|---|---|---|---|---|---|---|---|---|---|---|---|
| | | 95 | 100 | 105 | 110 | 115 | 120 | 125 | 130 | 135 | 140 | 145 | 150 | 155 | 160 | 165 | 170 | 175 | 180 |
| n-Octane | $C_8H_{18}$ | 0.466 | 0.537 | 0.618 | 0.709 | 0.811 | 0.925 | 1.051 | 1.192 | 1.348 | 1.521 | 1.712 | 1.922 | 2.153 | 2.406 | 2.683 | 2.985 | 3.315 | 3.674 |
| 2-Methylheptane | " | 0.670 | 0.768 | 0.878 | 1.000 | 1.137 | 1.289 | 1.457 | 1.643 | 1.849 | 2.075 | 2.323 | 2.595 | 2.893 | 3.218 | 3.573 | 3.958 | 4.377 | 4.830 |
| 3-Methylheptane | " | 0.637 | 0.731 | 0.836 | 0.954 | 1.085 | 1.230 | 1.392 | 1.571 | 1.768 | 1.986 | 2.225 | 2.467 | 2.774 | 3.087 | 3.428 | 3.800 | 4.203 | 4.641 |
| 4-Methylheptane | " | 0.667 | 0.765 | 0.875 | 0.997 | 1.134 | 1.286 | 1.454 | 1.640 | 1.845 | 2.071 | 2.319 | 2.591 | 2.888 | 3.213 | 3.567 | 3.952 | 4.370 | 4.823 |
| 3-Ethylhexane | " | 0.652 | 0.748 | 0.855 | 0.975 | 1.108 | 1.256 | 1.421 | 1.602 | 1.803 | 2.024 | 2.266 | 2.532 | 2.822 | 3.140 | 3.486 | 3.662 | 4.270 | 4.713 |
| 2,2-Dimethylhexane | " | 1.073 | 1.221 | 1.385 | 1.566 | 1.767 | 1.989 | 2.233 | 2.501 | 2.794 | 3.115 | 3.466 | 3.847 | 4.262 | 4.713 | 5.201 | 5.728 | 6.298 | 6.912 |
| 2,3-Dimethylhexane | " | 0.753 | 0.861 | 0.981 | 1.116 | 1.265 | 1.430 | 1.613 | 1.815 | 2.037 | 2.281 | 2.548 | 2.840 | 3.160 | 3.507 | 3.885 | 4.296 | 4.741 | 5.222 |
| 2,4-Dimethylhexane | " | 0.963 | 1.097 | 1.247 | 1.413 | 1.596 | 1.800 | 2.024 | 2.270 | 2.540 | 2.836 | 3.159 | 3.512 | 3.896 | 4.313 | 4.766 | 5.256 | 5.786 | 6.358 |
| 2,5-Dimethylhexane | " | 0.966 | 1.101 | 1.252 | 1.419 | 1.604 | 1.808 | 2.034 | 2.282 | 2.554 | 2.852 | 3.178 | 3.534 | 3.922 | 4.343 | 4.800 | 5.294 | 5.829 | 6.407 |
| 3,3-Dimethylhexane | " | 0.905 | 1.030 | 1.170 | 1.325 | 1.496 | 1.686 | 1.894 | 2.124 | 2.376 | 2.651 | 2.953 | 3.281 | 3.639 | 4.027 | 4.449 | 4.905 | 5.398 | 5.930 |
| 3,4-Dimethylhexane | " | 0.697 | 0.797 | 0.910 | 1.035 | 1.174 | 1.329 | 1.500 | 1.689 | 1.896 | 2.125 | 2.376 | 2.650 | 2.949 | 3.276 | 3.632 | 4.018 | 4.437 | 4.890 |
| 2-Methyl-3-ethylpentane | " | 0.765 | 0.874 | 0.996 | 1.131 | 1.282 | 1.448 | 1.632 | 1.835 | 2.058 | 2.302 | 2.570 | 2.863 | 3.183 | 3.531 | 3.909 | 4.320 | 4.764 | 5.245 |
| 3-Methyl-3-ethylpentane | " | 0.731 | 0.834 | 0.948 | 1.075 | 1.216 | 1.372 | 1.545 | 1.734 | 1.943 | 2.172 | 2.422 | 2.695 | 2.993 | 3.316 | 3.670 | 4.052 | 4.466 | 4.913 |
| 2,2,3-Trimethylpentane | " | 1.005 | 1.142 | 1.294 | 1.462 | 1.648 | 1.852 | 2.078 | 2.325 | 2.595 | 2.891 | 3.214 | 3.565 | 3.946 | 4.360 | 4.809 | 5.293 | 5.816 | 6.380 |
| 2,2,4-Trimethylpentane | " | 1.513 | 1.708 | 1.925 | 2.163 | 2.424 | 2.711 | 3.025 | 3.367 | 3.741 | 4.147 | 4.588 | 5.066 | 5.584 | 6.142 | 6.745 | 7.393 | 8.091 | 8.839 |
| 2,3,3-Trimethylpentane | " | 0.850 | 0.967 | 1.097 | 1.241 | 1.401 | 1.577 | 1.771 | 1.984 | 2.217 | 2.473 | 2.752 | 3.057 | 3.388 | 3.748 | 4.138 | 4.560 | 5.017 | 5.509 |
| 2,3,4-Trimethylpentane | " | 0.856 | 0.976 | 1.108 | 1.256 | 1.419 | 1.600 | 1.799 | 2.018 | 2.259 | 2.522 | 2.811 | 3.124 | 3.467 | 3.839 | 4.242 | 4.680 | 5.153 | 5.663 |
| 2,2,3,3-Tetramethylbutane | " | 0.71[a] | 0.83[a] | 0.96[a] | 1.11[a] | 1.27[a] | 1.462[a] | 1.673[a] | 1.911[a] | 2.177[a] | 2.473[a] | 2.802[a] | 3.168[a] | 3.573[a] | 4.021[a] | 4.516[a] | 5.06[a] | 5.66[a] | 6.31[a] |

a For the solid-vapor equilibrium.

TABLE 3k-E, Page 3 – PARAFFINS, C$_8$

VAPOR PRESSURES AND BOILING POINTS, AT 0.2 TO 30 lb/in$^2$

August 31, 1949; December 31, 1952

| Compound | Formula | Temperature in °F Vapor pressure in lb/in$^2$ | | | | | | | | | | | | | | | | | |
|---|---|---|---|---|---|---|---|---|---|---|---|---|---|---|---|---|---|---|---|
| | | 185 | 190 | 195 | 200 | 205 | 210 | 215 | 220 | 225 | 230 | 235 | 240 | 245 | 250 | 255 | 260 | 265 | 270 |
| n-Octane | C$_8$H$_{18}$ | 4.064 | 4.487 | 4.945 | 5.440 | 5.974 | 6.549 | 7.168 | 7.833 | 8.547 | 9.311 | 10.128 | 11.002 | 11.934 | 12.928 | 13.985 | 15.110 | 16.304 | 17.57 |
| 2-Methylheptane | " | 5.321 | 5.852 | 6.424 | 7.040 | 7.702 | 8.414 | 9.176 | 9.993 | 10.866 | 11.799 | 12.794 | 13.853 | 14.981 | 16.179 | 17.45 | 18.80 | 20.23 | 21.74 |
| 3-Methylheptane | " | 5.115 | 5.627 | 6.179 | 6.774 | 7.414 | 8.101 | 8.839 | 9.628 | 10.473 | 11.375 | 12.338 | 13.363 | 14.455 | 15.615 | 16.85 | 18.15 | 19.54 | 21.00 |
| 4-Methylheptane | " | 5.313 | 5.842 | 6.414 | 7.029 | 7.690 | 8.400 | 9.162 | 9.977 | 10.849 | 11.780 | 12.772 | 13.830 | 14.955 | 16.150 | 17.42 | 18.76 | 20.19 | 21.70 |
| 3-Ethylhexane | " | 5.192 | 5.709 | 6.268 | 6.869 | 7.515 | 8.209 | 8.953 | 9.750 | 10.601 | 11.511 | 12.481 | 13.515 | 14.614 | 15.782 | 17.02 | 18.34 | 19.73 | 21.20 |
| 2,2-Dimethylhexane | " | 7.573 | 8.283 | 9.045 | 9.861 | 10.735 | 11.668 | 12.664 | 13.726 | 14.856 | 16.057 | 17.33 | 18.69 | 20.12 | 21.64 | 23.24 | 24.9 | 26.7 | 28.6 |
| 2,3-Dimethylhexane | " | 5.742 | 6.303 | 6.906 | 7.555 | 8.252 | 8.998 | 9.798 | 10.652 | 11.565 | 12.537 | 13.573 | 14.675 | 15.846 | 17.09 | 18.41 | 19.80 | 21.27 | 22.83 |
| 2,4-Dimethylhexane | " | 6.975 | 7.638 | 8.350 | 9.114 | 9.932 | 10.807 | 11.743 | 12.740 | 13.803 | 14.935 | 16.14 | 17.41 | 18.77 | 20.20 | 21.72 | 23.32 | 25.0 | 26.8 |
| 2,5-Dimethylhexane | " | 7.029 | 7.699 | 8.418 | 9.190 | 10.017 | 10.902 | 11.847 | 12.855 | 13.930 | 15.073 | 16.29 | 17.58 | 18.95 | 20.40 | 21.93 | 23.56 | 25.3 | 27.1 |
| 3,3-Dimethylhexane | " | 6.504 | 7.121 | 7.783 | 8.494 | 9.256 | 10.070 | 10.940 | 11.868 | 12.857 | 13.910 | 15.029 | 16.217 | 17.48 | 18.81 | 20.22 | 21.72 | 23.29 | 25.0 |
| 3,4-Dimethylhexane | " | 5.381 | 5.909 | 6.478 | 7.091 | 7.749 | 8.455 | 9.211 | 10.020 | 10.884 | 11.806 | 12.791 | 13.834 | 14.945 | 16.125 | 17.38 | 18.70 | 20.11 | 21.59 |
| 2-Methyl-3-ethylpentane | " | 5.764 | 6.323 | 6.925 | 7.572 | 8.266 | 9.010 | 9.806 | 10.657 | 11.565 | 12.552 | 13.562 | 14.658 | 15.821 | 17.06 | 18.36 | 19.75 | 21.21 | 22.76 |
| 3-Methyl-3-ethylpentane | " | 5.396 | 5.915 | 6.475 | 7.075 | 7.720 | 8.410 | 9.149 | 9.938 | 10.780 | 11.677 | 12.632 | 13.648 | 14.726 | 15.870 | 17.08 | 18.36 | 19.72 | 21.15 |
| 2,2,3-Trimethylpentane | " | 6.986 | 7.638 | 8.337 | 9.085 | 9.886 | 10.741 | 11.654 | 12.626 | 13.661 | 14.761 | 15.929 | 17.17 | 18.48 | 19.87 | 21.33 | 22.88 | 24.5 | 26.2 |
| 2,2,4-Trimethylpentane | " | 9.641 | 10.500 | 11.417 | 12.396 | 13.440 | 14.551 | 15.733 | 16.99 | 18.32 | 19.73 | 21.22 | 22.80 | 24.47 | 26.23 | 28.08 | 30.03 | 32.08 | |
| 2,3,3-Trimethylpentane | " | 6.040 | 6.610 | 7.223 | 7.880 | 8.584 | 9.337 | 10.141 | 10.999 | 11.913 | 12.886 | 13.920 | 15.017 | 16.181 | 17.41 | 18.72 | 20.10 | 21.55 | 23.09 |
| 2,3,4-Trimethylpentane | " | 6.214 | 6.806 | 7.443 | 8.126 | 8.858 | 9.642 | 10.479 | 11.373 | 12.325 | 13.340 | 14.418 | 15.564 | 16.78 | 18.07 | 19.43 | 20.87 | 22.40 | 24.00 |
| 2,2,3,3-Tetramethylbutane | " | 7.03$^a$ | 7.82$^a$ | 8.67$^a$ | 9.61$^a$ | 10.62$^a$ | 11.72$^a$ | 12.84$^b$ | 13.89 | 15.01 | 16.19 | 17.44 | 18.77 | 20.17 | 21.7 | 23.2 | 24.9 | 26.6 | 28.5 |

a For the solid-vapor equilibrium.   b At the triple point, 213.46°F, the pressure is 12.53 lb/in$^2$.

TABLE 3k-E, Page 4 – PARAFFINS, C$_8$
VAPOR PRESSURES AND BOILING POINTS, AT 0.2 TO 30 lb/in².
August 31, 1949; December 31, 1952

| Compound | Formula | Temperature in °F | | | | | | | |
|---|---|---|---|---|---|---|---|---|---|
| | | 275 | 280 | 285 | 290 | 295 | 300 | 305 | 310 |
| | | Vapor pressure in lb/in² | | | | | | | |
| n-Octane | C$_8$H$_{18}$ | 18.91 | 20.33 | 21.84 | 23.42 | 25.1 | 26.9 | 28.7 | 30.7 |
| 2-Methylheptane | " | 23.34 | 25.0 | 26.8 | 28.7 | 30.7 | | | |
| 3-Methylheptane | " | 22.55 | 24.19 | 25.9 | 27.7 | 29.6 | | | |
| 4-Methylheptane | " | 23.29 | 25.0 | 26.7 | 28.6 | 30.6 | | | |
| 3-Ethylhexane | " | 22.76 | 24.40 | 26.1 | 28.0 | 29.9 | | | |
| 2,2-Dimethylhexane | " | 30.6 | | | | | | | |
| 2,3-Dimethylhexane | " | 24.5 | 26.2 | 28.0 | 30.0 | | | | |
| 2,4-Dimethylhexane | " | 28.7 | 30.7 | | | | | | |
| 2,5-Dimethylhexane | " | 29.0 | | | | | | | |
| 3,3-Dimethylhexane | " | 26.7 | 28.6 | 30.5 | | | | | |
| 3,4-Dimethylhexane | " | 23.16 | 24.81 | 26.6 | 28.4 | 30.3 | | | |
| 2-Methyl-3-ethylpentane | " | 24.39 | 26.1 | 27.9 | 29.8 | | | | |
| 3-Methyl-3-ethylpentane | " | 22.67 | 24.26 | 25.9 | 27.7 | 29.6 | | | |
| 2,2,3-Trimethylpentane | " | 28.1 | 30.0 | | | | | | |
| 2,2,4-Trimethylpentane | " | | | | | | | | |
| 2,3,3-Trimethylpentane | " | 24.7 | 26.4 | 28.2 | 30.1 | | | | |
| 2,3,4-Trimethylpentane | " | 25.7 | 27.5 | 29.4 | | | | | |
| 2,2,3,3-Tetramethylbutane | " | 30.4 | | | | | | | |

**National Bureau of Standards**

TABLE 4k-E, Page 1 - PARAFFINS, $C_9$
VAPOR PRESSURES AND BOILING POINTS, AT 0.2 TO 30 lb/in²
November 30, 1949 (Corrected)

| Compound | Formula | Constants of the Antoine equation | | | Temperature in °F — Vapor pressure in lb/in² | | | | | | | | | | | | | |
|---|---|---|---|---|---|---|---|---|---|---|---|---|---|---|---|---|---|---|
| | | A | B | C | 55 | 60 | 65 | 70 | 75 | 80 | 85 | 90 | 95 | 100 | 105 | 110 | 115 | 120 |
| n-Nonane | $C_9H_{20}$ | 5.22152 | 2571.860 | 330.914 | | | | | | | | | | 0.179 | 0.210 | 0.245 | 0.264 | 0.330 |
| 2-Methyloctane | " | 5.2043 | 2538.0 | 338.80 | | | | | | | | 0.19 | 0.23 | 0.26 | 0.31 | 0.35 | 0.41 | 0.47 |
| 3-Methyloctane | " | 5.1966 | 2539.8 | 338.80 | | | | | | | | 0.18 | 0.22 | 0.26 | 0.30 | 0.35 | 0.40 | 0.46 |
| 4-Methyloctane | " | 5.2019 | 2530.8 | 338.80 | | | | | | | | 0.20 | 0.23 | 0.27 | 0.32 | 0.37 | 0.42 | 0.48 |
| 3-Ethylheptane | " | 5.187 | 2525. | 338.8 | | | | | | | | 0.20 | 0.23 | 0.27 | 0.31 | 0.36 | 0.42 | 0.48 |
| 4-Ethylheptane | " | 5.191 | 2515. | 338.8 | | | | | | | | 0.21 | 0.25 | 0.29 | 0.33 | 0.39 | 0.45 | 0.51 |
| 2,2-Dimethylheptane | " | 5.1444 | 2439.0 | 342.40 | | | | | 0.20 | 0.23 | 0.27 | 0.32 | 0.37 | 0.43 | 0.49 | 0.57 | 0.65 | 0.74 |
| 2,3-Dimethylheptane | " | 5.173 | 2506. | 340.6 | | | | | | | 0.19 | 0.23 | 0.26 | 0.31 | 0.35 | 0.41 | 0.47 | 0.54 |
| 2,4-Dimethylheptane | " | 5.155 | 2448. | 342. | | | | | 0.19 | 0.20 | 0.26 | 0.31 | 0.36 | 0.41 | 0.48 | 0.55 | 0.63 | 0.72 |
| 2,5-Dimethylheptane | " | 5.167 | 2470. | 341. | | | | | | 0.20 | 0.23 | 0.27 | 0.32 | 0.37 | 0.43 | 0.49 | 0.56 | 0.64 |
| 2,6-Dimethylheptane | " | 5.1589 | 2458.8 | 340.60 | | | | | | 0.21 | 0.24 | 0.28 | 0.33 | 0.38 | 0.44 | 0.50 | 0.58 | 0.66 |
| 3,3-Dimethylheptane | " | 5.155 | 2493. | 346.0 | | | | | | 0.20 | 0.23 | 0.27 | 0.32 | 0.37 | 0.42 | 0.49 | 0.56 | 0.64 |
| 3,4-Dimethylheptane | " | 5.1833 | 2520.0 | 342.4 | | | | | | | 0.19 | 0.23 | 0.26 | 0.31 | 0.36 | 0.41 | 0.47 | 0.54 |
| 3,5-Dimethylheptane | " | 5.164 | 2475. | 342.4 | | | | | 0.19 | 0.20 | 0.24 | 0.28 | 0.32 | 0.37 | 0.43 | 0.49 | 0.57 | 0.65 |
| 4,4-Dimethylheptane | " | 5.144 | 2471. | 346.0 | | | | | | 0.22 | 0.26 | 0.30 | 0.35 | 0.40 | 0.46 | 0.53 | 0.61 | 0.69 |
| 2-Methyl-3-ethylhexane | " | 5.158 | 2486. | 342.4 | | | | | | 0.19 | 0.22 | 0.26 | 0.30 | 0.35 | 0.40 | 0.46 | 0.53 | 0.60 |
| 2-Methyl-4-ethylhexane | " | 5.140 | 2452. | 344.2 | | | | | 0.20 | 0.23 | 0.27 | 0.31 | 0.36 | 0.42 | 0.48 | 0.55 | 0.63 | 0.72 |
| 3-Methyl-3-ethylhexane | " | 5.149 | 2527. | 349.6 | | | | | | 0.19 | 0.22 | 0.25 | 0.29 | 0.34 | 0.39 | 0.45 | 0.51 | 0.59 |
| 3-Methyl-4-ethylhexane | " | 5.171 | 2518. | 344.2 | | | | | | | 0.20 | 0.23 | 0.27 | 0.32 | 0.37 | 0.42 | 0.49 | 0.56 |
| 2,2,3-Trimethylhexane | " | 5.1312 | 2458.8 | 347.80 | | | | | 0.21 | 0.24 | 0.28 | 0.33 | 0.38 | 0.44 | 0.50 | 0.58 | 0.66 | 0.75 |
| 2,2,4-Trimethylhexane | " | 5.1255 | 2419.2 | 351.40 | | | 0.21 | 0.24 | 0.28 | 0.33 | 0.38 | 0.44 | 0.51 | 0.58 | 0.67 | 0.76 | 0.87 | 0.99 |
| 2,2,5-Trimethylhexane | " | 5.12170 | 2383.288 | 347.326 | | 0.186 | 0.220 | 0.258 | 0.301 | 0.350 | 0.406 | 0.470 | 0.542 | 0.622 | 0.712 | 0.813 | 0.926 | 1.052 |
| 2,3,3-Trimethylhexane | " | 5.1338 | 2503.8 | 351.40 | | | | | 0.18 | 0.21 | 0.25 | 0.29 | 0.34 | 0.39 | 0.44 | 0.51 | 0.58 | 0.66 |
| 2,3,4-Trimethylhexane | " | 5.153 | 2511. | 347.8 | | | | | | 0.19 | 0.22 | 0.26 | 0.30 | 0.35 | 0.40 | 0.47 | 0.53 | 0.61 |
| 2,3,5-Trimethylhexane | " | 5.1369 | 2446.2 | 347.80 | | | | 0.19 | 0.22 | 0.26 | 0.30 | 0.35 | 0.41 | 0.47 | 0.54 | 0.62 | 0.71 | 0.81 |
| 2,4,4-Trimethylhexane | " | 5.13802 | 2463.701 | 353.285 | | | | 0.208 | 0.243 | 0.283 | 0.329 | 0.380 | 0.439 | 0.504 | 0.578 | 0.661 | 0.753 | 0.856 |
| 3,3,4-Trimethylhexane | " | 5.1421 | 2521.8 | 349.60 | | | | | | 0.19 | 0.22 | 0.25 | 0.30 | 0.34 | 0.39 | 0.45 | 0.52 | 0.59 |
| 3,3-Diethylpentane | " | 5.17901 | 2612.241 | 356.035 | | | | | | | | 0.210 | 0.244 | 0.282 | 0.326 | 0.375 | 0.430 | 0.492 |
| 2,2-Dimethyl-3-ethylpentane | " | 5.1346 | 2476.8 | 351.40 | | | | 0.18 | 0.21 | 0.25 | 0.29 | 0.33 | 0.39 | 0.44 | 0.51 | 0.58 | 0.67 | 0.76 |
| 2,3-Dimethyl-3-ethylpentane | " | 5.139 | 2545. | 353. | | | | | | | 0.21 | 0.25 | 0.29 | 0.33 | 0.38 | 0.44 | 0.50 | 0.58 |
| 2,4-Dimethyl-3-ethylpentane | " | 5.1388 | 2500.2 | 351.40 | | | | | 0.19 | 0.22 | 0.26 | 0.30 | 0.35 | 0.40 | 0.46 | 0.52 | 0.60 | 0.68 |
| 2,2,3,3-Tetramethylpentane | " | 5.11515 | 2515.469 | 352.665 | | | | | | 0.200 | 0.233 | 0.271 | 0.313 | 0.361 | 0.416 | 0.477 | 0.545 | 0.621 |
| 2,2,3,4-Tetramethylpentane | " | 5.11812 | 2473.276 | 354.572 | | | | 0.196 | 0.229 | 0.267 | 0.310 | 0.359 | 0.414 | 0.476 | 0.545 | 0.623 | 0.710 | 0.806 |
| 2,2,4,4-Tetramethylpentane | " | 5.08349 | 2456.329 | 356.967 | 0.197 | 0.231 | 0.270 | 0.314 | 0.364 | 0.421 | 0.486 | 0.558 | 0.639 | 0.730 | 0.832 | 0.945 | 1.070 | 1.209 |
| 2,3,3,4-Tetramethylpentane | " | 5.14600 | 2551.451 | 354.469 | | | | | | 0.187 | 0.219 | 0.254 | 0.295 | 0.340 | 0.392 | 0.450 | 0.514 | 0.587 |

Values of the vapor pressure are calculated from the constants given and the Antoine equation: $\log_{10} P = A - B/(C + t)$; $t = B/(A - \log_{10} P) - C$; (P in lb/in²; t in °F)

TABLE 4k-E, Page 2 – PARAFFINS, C9

VAPOR PRESSURES AND BOILING POINTS, AT 0.2 TO 30 lb/in²

November 30, 1949 (Corrected)

| Compound | Formula | Temperature in °F — Vapor pressure in lb/in² | | | | | | | | | | | | | | | | | |
|---|---|---|---|---|---|---|---|---|---|---|---|---|---|---|---|---|---|---|---|
| | | 125 | 130 | 135 | 140 | 145 | 150 | 155 | 160 | 165 | 170 | 175 | 180 | 185 | 190 | 195 | 200 | 205 | 210 |
| n-Nonane | C9H20 | 0.381 | 0.438 | 0.503 | 0.576 | 0.657 | 0.748 | 0.849 | 0.961 | 1.085 | 1.222 | 1.374 | 1.541 | 1.724 | 1.924 | 2.144 | 2.384 | 2.646 | 2.930 |
| 2-Methyloctane | " | 0.54 | 0.62 | 0.70 | 0.80 | 0.91 | 1.03 | 1.16 | 1.31 | 1.47 | 1.64 | 1.84 | 2.05 | 2.3 | 2.5 | 2.8 | 3.1 | 3.4 | 3.8 |
| 3-Methyloctane | " | 0.53 | 0.60 | 0.69 | 0.78 | 0.88 | 1.00 | 1.13 | 1.27 | 1.43 | 1.60 | 1.79 | 2.00 | 2.2 | 2.5 | 2.7 | 3.0 | 3.4 | 3.7 |
| 4-Methyloctane | " | 0.56 | 0.64 | 0.72 | 0.82 | 0.94 | 1.06 | 1.19 | 1.34 | 1.51 | 1.69 | 1.89 | 2.11 | 2.3 | 2.6 | 2.9 | 3.2 | 3.5 | 3.9 |
| 3-Ethylheptane | " | 0.55 | 0.63 | 0.72 | 0.82 | 0.93 | 1.05 | 1.18 | 1.33 | 1.50 | 1.68 | 1.87 | 2.09 | 2.3 | 2.6 | 2.9 | 3.2 | 3.5 | 3.9 |
| 4-Ethylheptane | " | 0.59 | 0.67 | 0.76 | 0.87 | 0.98 | 1.11 | 1.25 | 1.41 | 1.58 | 1.77 | 1.98 | 2.2 | 2.4 | 2.7 | 3.0 | 3.3 | 3.7 | 4.1 |
| 2,2-Dimethylheptane | " | 0.84 | 0.96 | 1.09 | 1.23 | 1.38 | 1.55 | 1.74 | 1.95 | 2.2 | 2.4 | 2.7 | 3.0 | 3.3 | 3.7 | 4.0 | 4.4 | 4.9 | 5.4 |
| 2,3-Dimethylheptane | " | 0.62 | 0.70 | 0.80 | 0.91 | 1.03 | 1.16 | 1.31 | 1.47 | 1.65 | 1.84 | 2.05 | 2.3 | 2.5 | 2.8 | 3.1 | 3.4 | 3.8 | 4.2 |
| 2,4-Dimethylheptane | " | 0.82 | 0.93 | 1.05 | 1.19 | 1.34 | 1.51 | 1.70 | 1.90 | 2.12 | 2.4 | 2.6 | 2.9 | 3.2 | 3.6 | 3.9 | 4.3 | 4.8 | 5.3 |
| 2,5-Dimethylheptane | " | 0.74 | 0.84 | 0.95 | 1.08 | 1.22 | 1.37 | 1.54 | 1.73 | 1.93 | 2.16 | 2.40 | 2.7 | 3.0 | 3.3 | 3.6 | 4.0 | 4.4 | 4.8 |
| 2,6-Dimethylheptane | " | 0.76 | 0.86 | 0.98 | 1.10 | 1.25 | 1.40 | 1.58 | 1.77 | 1.98 | 2.20 | 2.4 | 2.7 | 3.0 | 3.3 | 3.7 | 4.1 | 4.5 | 4.9 |
| 3,3-Dimethylheptane | " | 0.73 | 0.83 | 0.94 | 1.06 | 1.20 | 1.35 | 1.51 | 1.69 | 1.89 | 2.11 | 2.3 | 2.6 | 2.9 | 3.2 | 3.5 | 3.9 | 4.3 | 4.7 |
| 3,4-Dimethylheptane | " | 0.62 | 0.71 | 0.80 | 0.91 | 1.03 | 1.16 | 1.31 | 1.47 | 1.65 | 1.84 | 2.05 | 2.3 | 2.5 | 2.8 | 3.1 | 3.4 | 3.8 | 4.2 |
| 3,5-Dimethylheptane | " | 0.74 | 0.84 | 0.95 | 1.08 | 1.22 | 1.37 | 1.54 | 1.73 | 1.93 | 2.16 | 2.4 | 2.7 | 3.0 | 3.3 | 3.6 | 4.0 | 4.4 | 4.8 |
| 4,4-Dimethylheptane | " | 0.79 | 0.90 | 1.02 | 1.15 | 1.29 | 1.45 | 1.63 | 1.82 | 2.03 | 2.3 | 2.5 | 2.8 | 3.1 | 3.4 | 3.8 | 4.2 | 4.6 | 5.0 |
| 2-Methyl-3-ethylhexane | " | 0.69 | 0.79 | 0.89 | 1.01 | 1.14 | 1.29 | 1.45 | 1.62 | 1.81 | 2.0 | 2.2 | 2.5 | 2.8 | 3.1 | 3.4 | 3.8 | 4.1 | 4.6 |
| 2-Methyl-4-ethylhexane | " | 0.82 | 0.93 | 1.05 | 1.19 | 1.34 | 1.51 | 1.69 | 1.89 | 2.11 | 2.3 | 2.6 | 2.9 | 3.2 | 3.5 | 3.9 | 4.3 | 4.7 | 5.2 |
| 3-Methyl-3-ethylhexane | " | 0.67 | 0.76 | 0.86 | 0.97 | 1.10 | 1.23 | 1.38 | 1.55 | 1.73 | 1.93 | 2.15 | 2.4 | 2.6 | 2.9 | 3.2 | 3.6 | 3.9 | 4.3 |
| 3-Methyl-4-ethylhexane | " | 0.64 | 0.73 | 0.82 | 0.93 | 1.06 | 1.19 | 1.34 | 1.50 | 1.68 | 1.86 | 2.10 | 2.3 | 2.6 | 2.9 | 3.2 | 3.5 | 3.9 | 4.2 |
| 2,2,3-Trimethylhexane | " | 0.85 | 0.97 | 1.09 | 1.23 | 1.39 | 1.56 | 1.74 | 1.95 | 2.17 | 2.41 | 2.7 | 3.0 | 3.3 | 3.6 | 4.0 | 4.4 | 4.8 | 5.3 |
| 2,2,4-Trimethylhexane | " | 1.12 | 1.26 | 1.42 | 1.59 | 1.79 | 2.00 | 2.23 | 2.48 | 2.76 | 3.06 | 3.4 | 3.7 | 4.1 | 4.5 | 5.0 | 5.5 | 6.0 | 6.6 |
| 2,2,5-Trimethylhexane | " | 1.191 | 1.345 | 1.515 | 1.703 | 1.909 | 2.136 | 2.383 | 2.654 | 2.950 | 3.272 | 3.621 | 4.001 | 4.412 | 4.856 | 5.335 | 5.852 | 6.408 | 7.005 |
| 2,3,3-Trimethylhexane | " | 0.76 | 0.86 | 0.97 | 1.09 | 1.23 | 1.38 | 1.55 | 1.73 | 1.93 | 2.15 | 2.4 | 2.6 | 2.9 | 3.2 | 3.6 | 3.9 | 4.3 | 4.7 |
| 2,3,4-Trimethylhexane | " | 0.70 | 0.79 | 0.90 | 1.01 | 1.14 | 1.28 | 1.44 | 1.61 | 1.80 | 2.01 | 2.2 | 2.5 | 2.8 | 3.1 | 3.4 | 3.7 | 4.1 | 4.5 |
| 2,3,5-Trimethylhexane | " | 0.92 | 1.04 | 1.18 | 1.32 | 1.49 | 1.67 | 1.87 | 2.09 | 2.3 | 2.6 | 2.9 | 3.2 | 3.5 | 3.9 | 4.3 | 4.7 | 5.1 | 5.6 |
| 2,4,4-Trimethylhexane | " | 0.970 | 1.097 | 1.237 | 1.392 | 1.562 | 1.749 | 1.954 | 2.178 | 2.424 | 2.691 | 2.982 | 3.297 | 3.640 | 4.011 | 4.411 | 4.844 | 5.310 | 5.811 |
| 3,3,4-Trimethylhexane | " | 0.67 | 0.77 | 0.87 | 0.98 | 1.11 | 1.24 | 1.39 | 1.56 | 1.74 | 1.94 | 2.16 | 2.4 | 2.7 | 2.9 | 3.2 | 3.6 | 3.9 | 4.3 |
| 3,3-Diethylpentane | " | 0.561 | 0.637 | 0.723 | 0.818 | 0.923 | 1.040 | 1.168 | 1.309 | 1.464 | 1.633 | 1.819 | 2.022 | 2.243 | 2.483 | 2.744 | 3.027 | 3.334 | 3.665 |
| 2,2-Dimethyl-3-ethylpentane | " | 0.85 | 0.98 | 1.10 | 1.24 | 1.40 | 1.57 | 1.75 | 1.96 | 2.18 | 2.4 | 2.7 | 3.0 | 3.3 | 3.6 | 4.0 | 4.4 | 4.8 | 5.3 |
| 2,3-Dimethyl-3-ethylpentane | " | 0.66 | 0.74 | 0.84 | 0.95 | 1.07 | 1.21 | 1.35 | 1.5 | 1.7 | 1.9 | 2.1 | 2.3 | 2.6 | 2.8 | 3.1 | 3.4 | 3.8 | 4.2 |
| 2,4-Dimethyl-3-ethylpentane | " | 0.78 | 0.88 | 1.00 | 1.13 | 1.27 | 1.42 | 1.59 | 1.78 | 1.98 | 2.21 | 2.4 | 2.7 | 3.0 | 3.3 | 3.7 | 4.0 | 4.4 | 4.8 |
| 2,2,3,3-Tetramethylpentane | " | 0.706 | 0.801 | 0.906 | 1.022 | 1.150 | 1.291 | 1.446 | 1.616 | 1.803 | 2.006 | 2.228 | 2.470 | 2.733 | 3.018 | 3.327 | 3.661 | 4.022 | 4.411 |
| 2,2,3,4-Tetramethylpentane | " | 0.914 | 1.033 | 1.165 | 1.310 | 1.470 | 1.646 | 1.839 | 2.050 | 2.280 | 2.531 | 2.804 | 3.101 | 3.423 | 3.771 | 4.147 | 4.553 | 4.991 | 5.462 |
| 2,2,4,4-Tetramethylpentane | " | 1.362 | 1.532 | 1.718 | 1.922 | 2.146 | 2.390 | 2.657 | 2.947 | 3.263 | 3.606 | 3.977 | 4.378 | 4.811 | 5.278 | 5.781 | 6.321 | 6.901 | 7.522 |
| 2,3,3,4-Tetramethylpentane | " | 0.668 | 0.758 | 0.858 | 0.968 | 1.091 | 1.226 | 1.374 | 1.537 | 1.715 | 1.911 | 2.124 | 2.356 | 2.609 | 2.883 | 3.181 | 3.503 | 3.850 | 4.226 |

390

TABLE 4k-E, Page 3 – PARAFFINS, C9

VAPOR PRESSURES AND BOILING POINTS, AT 0.2 TO 30 lb/in2

November 30, 1949 (Corrected)

Temperature in °F

Vapor pressure in lb/in2

| Compound | Formula | 215 | 220 | 225 | 230 | 235 | 240 | 245 | 250 | 255 | 260 | 265 | 270 | 275 | 280 | 285 | 290 | 295 | 300 |
|---|---|---|---|---|---|---|---|---|---|---|---|---|---|---|---|---|---|---|---|
| n-Nonane | $C_9H_{20}$ | 3.239 | 3.574 | 3.937 | 4.329 | 4.752 | 5.208 | 5.699 | 6.227 | 6.793 | 7.399 | 8.048 | 8.742 | 9.482 | 10.272 | 11.113 | 12.008 | 12.958 | 13.968 |
| 2-Methyloctane | " | 4.2 | 4.6 | 5.0 | 5.5 | 6.04 | 6.60 | 7.19 | 7.83 | 8.51 | 9.24 | 10.02 | 10.85 | 11.73 | 12.67 | 13.67 | 14.72 | 15.84 | 17.03 |
| 3-Methyloctane | " | 4.1 | 4.5 | 4.9 | 5.4 | 5.9 | 6.4 | 7.02 | 7.64 | 8.31 | 9.02 | 9.78 | 10.59 | 11.45 | 12.36 | 13.34 | 14.37 | 15.46 | 16.62 |
| 4-Methyloctane | " | 4.3 | 4.7 | 5.2 | 5.7 | 6.2 | 6.75 | 7.36 | 8.01 | 8.71 | 9.45 | 10.24 | 11.09 | 11.99 | 12.94 | 13.96 | 15.03 | 16.18 | 17.38 |
| 3-Ethylheptane | " | 4.2 | 4.7 | 5.1 | 5.6 | 6.1 | 6.68 | 7.28 | 7.92 | 8.61 | 9.34 | 10.12 | 11.0 | 11.8 | 12.8 | 13.8 | 14.8 | 16.0 | 17.2 |
| 4-Ethylheptane | " | 4.5 | 4.9 | 5.4 | 5.9 | 6.4 | 7.01 | 7.64 | 8.31 | 9.03 | 9.80 | 10.61 | 11.5 | 12.4 | 13.4 | 14.4 | 15.5 | 16.7 | 18.0 |
| 2,2-Dimethylheptane | " | 5.9 | 6.4 | 7.01 | 7.64 | 8.32 | 9.05 | 9.82 | 10.65 | 11.53 | 12.46 | 13.46 | 14.51 | 15.63 | 16.81 | 18.07 | 19.4 | 20.8 | 22.3 |
| 2,3-Dimethylheptane | " | 4.6 | 5.0 | 5.5 | 6.0 | 6.60 | 7.19 | 7.83 | 8.51 | 9.24 | 10.01 | 10.8 | 11.7 | 12.6 | 13.6 | 14.7 | 15.8 | 17.0 | 18.2 |
| 2,4-Dimethylheptane | " | 5.8 | 6.3 | 6.9 | 7.5 | 8.2 | 8.9 | 9.7 | 10.5 | 11.3 | 12.3 | 13.3 | 14.3 | 15.4 | 16.6 | 17.8 | 19.1 | 20.5 | 22.0 |
| 2,5-Dimethylheptane | " | 5.3 | 5.8 | 6.4 | 6.9 | 7.6 | 8.2 | 9.0 | 9.7 | 10.5 | 11.4 | 12.3 | 13.3 | 14.4 | 15.5 | 16.6 | 17.9 | 19.2 | 20.6 |
| 2,6-Dimethylheptane | " | 5.4 | 5.9 | 6.5 | 7.08 | 7.71 | 8.39 | 9.12 | 9.90 | 10.73 | 11.61 | 12.55 | 13.55 | 14.61 | 15.74 | 16.93 | 18.2 | 19.5 | 20.9 |
| 3,3-Dimethylheptane | " | 5.1 | 5.6 | 6.1 | 6.71 | 7.32 | 7.96 | 8.65 | 9.38 | 10.16 | 11.0 | 11.9 | 12.8 | 13.8 | 14.8 | 16.0 | 17.2 | 18.4 | 19.8 |
| 3,4-Dimethylheptane | " | 4.6 | 5.0 | 5.5 | 6.0 | 6.59 | 7.18 | 7.82 | 8.50 | 9.22 | 10.00 | 10.8 | 11.7 | 12.6 | 13.6 | 14.7 | 15.8 | 17.0 | 18.2 |
| 3,5-Dimethylheptane | " | 5.3 | 5.8 | 6.3 | 6.92 | 7.54 | 8.21 | 8.92 | 9.69 | 10.50 | 11.4 | 12.3 | 13.3 | 14.3 | 15.4 | 16.6 | 17.8 | 19.1 | 20.5 |
| 4,4-Dimethylheptane | " | 5.5 | 6.0 | 6.5 | 7.15 | 7.78 | 8.46 | 9.18 | 9.95 | 10.8 | 11.7 | 12.6 | 13.6 | 14.6 | 15.7 | 16.9 | 18.2 | 19.5 | 20.8 |
| 2-Methyl-3-ethylhexane | " | 5.0 | 5.5 | 6.0 | 6.5 | 7.12 | 7.75 | 8.43 | 9.15 | 9.92 | 10.7 | 11.6 | 12.5 | 13.5 | 14.6 | 15.7 | 16.9 | 18.1 | 19.4 |
| 2-Methyl-4-ethylhexane | " | 5.7 | 6.2 | 6.8 | 7.41 | 8.06 | 8.77 | 9.51 | 10.31 | 11.2 | 12.1 | 13.0 | 14.0 | 15.1 | 16.3 | 17.5 | 18.8 | 20.1 | 21.6 |
| 3-Methyl-3-ethylhexane | " | 4.7 | 5.2 | 5.6 | 6.1 | 6.70 | 7.29 | 7.93 | 8.60 | 9.32 | 10.09 | 10.9 | 11.8 | 12.7 | 13.7 | 14.7 | 15.8 | 16.9 | 18.1 |
| 3-Methyl-4-ethylhexane | " | 4.7 | 5.1 | 5.6 | 6.1 | 6.66 | 7.26 | 7.90 | 8.58 | 9.31 | 10.08 | 10.9 | 11.8 | 12.7 | 13.7 | 14.8 | 15.9 | 17.0 | 18.3 |
| 2,2,3-Trimethylhexane | " | 5.8 | 6.3 | 6.90 | 7.51 | 8.17 | 8.87 | 9.63 | 10.43 | 11.28 | 12.18 | 13.15 | 14.17 | 15.25 | 16.39 | 17.6 | 18.9 | 20.2 | 21.7 |
| 2,2,4-Trimethylhexane | " | 7.15 | 7.79 | 8.48 | 9.22 | 10.00 | 10.84 | 11.73 | 12.67 | 13.68 | 14.75 | 15.88 | 17.07 | 18.3 | 19.7 | 21.1 | 22.6 | 24.2 | 25.8 |
| 2,2,5-Trimethylhexane | " | 7.646 | 8.333 | 9.068 | 9.853 | 10.690 | 11.583 | 12.534 | 13.545 | 14.618 | 15.757 | 16.963 | 18.240 | 19.59 | 21.02 | 22.52 | 24.11 | 25.8 | 27.5 |
| 2,3,3-Trimethylhexane | " | 5.2 | 5.6 | 6.2 | 6.72 | 7.31 | 7.95 | 8.62 | 9.34 | 10.11 | 10.93 | 11.80 | 12.72 | 13.70 | 14.73 | 15.83 | 16.99 | 18.2 | 19.5 |
| 2,3,4-Trimethylhexane | " | 4.9 | 5.4 | 5.9 | 6.4 | 6.99 | 7.60 | 8.26 | 8.97 | 9.71 | 10.51 | 11.4 | 12.3 | 13.2 | 14.2 | 15.3 | 16.4 | 17.6 | 18.9 |
| 2,3,5-Trimethylhexane | " | 6.2 | 6.7 | 7.35 | 8.00 | 8.70 | 9.45 | 10.24 | 11.09 | 11.99 | 12.95 | 13.96 | 15.04 | 16.19 | 17.40 | 18.7 | 20.0 | 21.4 | 22.9 |
| 2,4,4-Trimethylhexane | " | 6.349 | 6.927 | 7.545 | 8.207 | 8.914 | 9.669 | 10.473 | 11.330 | 12.240 | 13.207 | 14.233 | 15.320 | 16.471 | 17.688 | 18.97 | 20.33 | 21.76 | 23.27 |
| 3,3,4-Trimethylhexane | " | 4.7 | 5.2 | 5.7 | 6.2 | 6.74 | 7.33 | 7.96 | 8.64 | 9.36 | 10.12 | 10.94 | 11.80 | 12.72 | 13.70 | 14.73 | 15.82 | 16.98 | 18.2 |
| 3,3-Diethylpentane | " | 4.022 | 4.407 | 4.821 | 5.267 | 5.744 | 6.256 | 6.604 | 7.390 | 8.015 | 8.682 | 9.392 | 10.147 | 10.950 | 11.802 | 12.705 | 13.662 | 14.675 | 15.745 |
| 2,2-Dimethyl-3-ethylpentane | " | 5.8 | 6.3 | 6.88 | 7.49 | 8.14 | 8.84 | 9.59 | 10.38 | 11.22 | 12.12 | 13.07 | 14.09 | 15.16 | 16.29 | 17.49 | 18.8 | 20.1 | 21.5 |
| 2,3-Dimethyl-3-ethylpentane | " | 4.6 | 5.0 | 5.5 | 6.0 | 6.5 | 7.1 | 7.7 | 8.3 | 9.0 | 9.7 | 10.5 | 11.4 | 12.3 | 13.2 | 14.2 | 15.2 | 16.3 | 17.5 |
| 2,4-Dimethyl-3-ethylpentane | " | 5.3 | 5.8 | 6.3 | 6.89 | 7.50 | 8.15 | 8.84 | 9.58 | 10.37 | 11.21 | 12.10 | 13.04 | 14.04 | 15.10 | 16.22 | 17.41 | 18.7 | 20.0 |
| 2,2,3,3-Tetramethylpentane | " | 4.829 | 5.279 | 5.763 | 6.280 | 6.834 | 7.427 | 8.060 | 8.735 | 9.453 | 10.218 | 11.031 | 11.893 | 12.808 | 13.777 | 14.803 | 15.887 | 17.031 | 18.24 |
| 2,2,3,4-Tetramethylpentane | " | 5.967 | 6.510 | 7.091 | 7.713 | 8.377 | 9.086 | 9.841 | 10.646 | 11.501 | 12.409 | 13.372 | 14.394 | 15.475 | 16.618 | 17.83 | 19.10 | 20.44 | 21.86 |
| 2,2,4,4-Tetramethylpentane | " | 8.187 | 8.897 | 9.655 | 10.463 | 11.324 | 12.239 | 13.211 | 14.242 | 15.335 | 16.492 | 17.715 | 19.01 | 20.37 | 21.81 | 23.33 | 24.9 | 26.6 | 28.4 |
| 2,3,3,4-Tetramethylpentane | " | 4.630 | 5.065 | 5.532 | 6.034 | 6.571 | 7.145 | 7.759 | 8.414 | 9.113 | 9.856 | 10.647 | 11.487 | 12.378 | 13.323 | 14.323 | 15.382 | 16.500 | 17.681 |

TABLE 4k-E, Page 4 - PARAFFINS, $C_9$

VAPOR PRESSURES AND BOILING POINTS, AT 0.2 TO 30 lb/in2

November 30, 1949 (Corrected)

| Compound | Formula | Temperature in °F — Vapor pressure in lb/in2 | | | | | | | | | | |
|---|---|---|---|---|---|---|---|---|---|---|---|---|
| | | 305 | 310 | 315 | 320 | 325 | 330 | 335 | 340 | 345 | 350 | 355 |
| n-Nonane | $C_9H_{20}$ | 15.037 | 16.170 | 17.37 | 18.64 | 19.98 | 21.39 | 22.88 | 24.44 | 26.09 | 27.83 | 29.65 |
| 2-Methyloctane | " | 18.3 | 19.6 | 21.0 | 22.5 | 24.0 | 25.7 | 27.4 | 29.2 | | | |
| 3-Methyloctane | " | 17.85 | 19.1 | 20.5 | 22.0 | 23.5 | 25.1 | 26.7 | 28.5 | | | |
| 4-Methyloctane | " | 18.7 | 20.0 | 21.4 | 22.9 | 24.5 | 26.2 | 27.9 | 29.8 | | | |
| 3-Ethylheptane | " | 18.4 | 19.7 | 21.1 | 22.6 | 24.2 | 25.8 | 27.5 | 29.3 | | | |
| 4-Ethylheptane | " | 19.3 | 20.6 | 22.1 | 23.6 | 25.2 | 27.0 | 28.7 | | | | |
| 2,2-Dimethylheptane | " | 23.8 | 25.5 | 27.2 | 29.0 | | | | | | | |
| 2,3-Dimethylheptane | " | 19.6 | 21.0 | 22.4 | 24.0 | 25.6 | 27.3 | 29.1 | | | | |
| 2,4-Dimethylheptane | " | 23.5 | 25. | 27. | 29. | | | | | | | |
| 2,5-Dimethylheptane | " | 22.1 | 23.6 | 25. | 27. | 29.2 | | | | | | |
| 2,6-Dimethylheptane | " | 22.4 | 24.0 | 25.6 | 27.3 | 29.2 | | | | | | |
| 3,3-Dimethylheptane | " | 21.2 | 22.6 | 24.2 | 25.8 | 27.5 | 29.3 | | | | | |
| 3,4-Dimethylheptane | " | 19.5 | 20.9 | 22.4 | 23.9 | 25.5 | 27.2 | 29.0 | | | | |
| 3,5-Dimethylheptane | " | 21.9 | 23.5 | 25.1 | 26.8 | 28.5 | | | | | | |
| 4,4-Dimethylheptane | " | 22.3 | 23.8 | 25.4 | 27.1 | 28.9 | | | | | | |
| 2-Methyl-3-ethylhexane | " | 20.8 | 22.3 | 23.8 | 25.4 | 27.1 | 28.9 | | | | | |
| 2-Methyl-4-ethylhexane | " | 23.1 | 24.7 | 26.3 | 28.1 | 29.9 | | | | | | |
| 3-Methyl-3-ethylhexane | " | 19.4 | 20.8 | 22.2 | 23.7 | 25.3 | 27.0 | 28.7 | | | | |
| 3-Methyl-4-ethylhexane | " | 19.6 | 21.0 | 22.4 | 24.0 | 25.6 | 27.3 | 29.1 | | | | |
| 2,2,3-Trimethylhexane | " | 23.2 | 24.7 | 26.4 | 28.1 | 30.0 | | | | | | |
| 2,2,4-Trimethylhexane | " | 27.5 | 29.4 | | | | | | | | | |
| 2,2,5-Trimethylhexane | " | 29.4 | 31.3 | | | | | | | | | |
| 2,3,3-Trimethylhexane | " | 20.9 | 22.3 | 23.8 | 25.4 | 27.0 | 28.8 | | | | | |
| 2,3,4-Trimethylhexane | " | 20.3 | 21.7 | 23.1 | 24.7 | 26.4 | 28.1 | | | | | |
| 2,3,5-Trimethylhexane | " | 24.5 | 26.2 | 27.9 | 29.8 | | | | | | | |
| 2,4,4-Trimethylhexane | " | 24.9 | 26.5 | 28.3 | 30.1 | | | | | | | |
| 3,3,4-Trimethylhexane | " | 19.5 | 20.8 | 22.3 | 23.8 | 25.3 | 27.0 | 28.7 | | | | |
| 3,3-Diethylpentane | " | 16.876 | 18.07 | 19.33 | 20.65 | 22.05 | 23.51 | 25.1 | 26.7 | 28.4 | 30.1 | |
| 2,2-Dimethyl-3-ethylpentane | " | 23.0 | 24.5 | 26.2 | 27.9 | 29.7 | | | | | | |
| 2,3-Dimethyl-3-ethylpentane | " | 18.7 | 20.0 | 21.4 | 22.8 | 24.3 | 25.9 | 28. | 30. | | | |
| 2,4-Dimethyl-3-ethylpentane | " | 21.4 | 22.8 | 24.4 | 26.0 | 27.7 | 29.4 | | | | | |
| 2,2,3,3-Tetramethylpentane | " | 19.51 | 20.85 | 22.26 | 23.75 | 25.3 | 26.9 | 28.7 | | | | |
| 2,2,3,4-Tetramethylpentane | " | 23.35 | 24.9 | 26.6 | 28.3 | 30.1 | | | | | | |
| 2,2,4,4-Tetramethylpentane | " | | | | | | | | | | | |
| 2,3,3,4-Tetramethylpentane | " | 18.93 | 20.24 | 21.62 | 23.07 | 24.6 | 26.2 | 27.9 | 29.7 | | | |

## TABLE 22k-E, (PART 1), Page 1 – NORMAL ALKYL CYCLOPENTANES, C$_5$ TO C$_{13}$
### VAPOR PRESSURES AND BOILING POINTS, AT 0.2 TO 30 lb/in²
October 31, 1950 (Corrected)

| Compound | Formula | A | B | C | \-40 | \-35 | \-30 | \-25 | \-20 | \-15 | \-10 | \-5 | 0 | 5 | 10 | 15 | 20 | 25 |
|---|---|---|---|---|---|---|---|---|---|---|---|---|---|---|---|---|---|---|
| | | Constants of the Antoine equation | | | Temperature in °F — Vapor pressure in lb/in² | | | | | | | | | | | | | |
| Cyclopentane | $C_5H_{10}$ | 5.17315 | 2023.492 | 384.450 | 0.20 | 0.24 | 0.29 | 0.35 | 0.42 | 0.50 | 0.59 | 0.69 | 0.81 | 0.95 | 1.10 | 1.28 | 1.48 | 1.70 |
| Methylcyclopentane | $C_6H_{12}$ | 5.14922 | 2134.906 | 374.876 | | | | | | | 0.20 | 0.24 | 0.28 | 0.34 | 0.40 | 0.47 | 0.55 | 0.65 |
| Ethylcyclopentane | $C_7H_{14}$ | 5.17348 | 2337.479 | 365.215 | | | | | | | | | | | | | | |
| n-Propylcyclopentane | $C_8H_{16}$ | 5.19031 | 2491.895 | 351.686 | | | | | | | | | | | | | | |
| n-Butylcyclopentane | $C_9H_{18}$ | 5.2053 | 2628.0 | 337.00 | | | | | | | | | | | | | | |
| n-Pentylcyclopentane | $C_{10}H_{20}$ | 5.215 | 2747. | 323. | | | | | | | | | | | | | | |
| n-Hexylcyclopentane | $C_{11}H_{22}$ | 5.220 | 2860. | 308. | | | | | | | | | | | | | | |
| n-Heptylcyclopentane | $C_{12}H_{24}$ | 5.228 | 2968. | 296. | | | | | | | | | | | | | | |
| n-Octylcyclopentane | $C_{13}H_{26}$ | 5.243 | 3067. | 283. | | | | | | | | | | | | | | |

| Compound | Formula | 30 | 35 | 40 | 45 | 50 | 55 | 60 | 65 | 70 | 75 | 80 | 85 | 90 | 95 | 100 | 105 | 110 | 115 |
|---|---|---|---|---|---|---|---|---|---|---|---|---|---|---|---|---|---|---|---|
| | | Temperature in °F — Vapor pressure in lb/in² | | | | | | | | | | | | | | | | | |
| Cyclopentane | $C_5H_{10}$ | 1.95 | 2.23 | 2.546 | 2.893 | 3.278 | 3.703 | 4.172 | 4.683 | 5.254 | 5.875 | 6.552 | 7.291 | 8.095 | 8.968 | 9.914 | 10.933 | 12.043 | 13.235 |
| Methylcyclopentane | $C_6H_{12}$ | 0.75 | 0.87 | 1.008 | 1.160 | 1.332 | 1.524 | 1.738 | 1.976 | 2.240 | 2.533 | 2.856 | 3.213 | 3.604 | 4.033 | 4.503 | 5.016 | 5.575 | 6.183 |
| Ethylcyclopentane | $C_7H_{14}$ | 0.182 | 0.215 | 0.254 | 0.299 | 0.350 | 0.408 | 0.475 | 0.550 | 0.635 | 0.730 | 0.838 | 0.958 | 1.093 | 1.243 | 1.409 | 1.594 | 1.798 | 2.023 |
| n-Propylcyclopentane | $C_8H_{16}$ | | | | | | | | | 0.19 | 0.22 | 0.26 | 0.30 | 0.35 | 0.41 | 0.47 | 0.54 | 0.62 | 0.71 |
| n-Butylcyclopentane | $C_9H_{18}$ | | | | | | | | | | | | | | | | | 0.21 | 0.25 |
| n-Pentylcyclopentane | $C_{10}H_{20}$ | | | | | | | | | | | | | | | | | | |
| n-Hexylcyclopentane | $C_{11}H_{22}$ | | | | | | | | | | | | | | | | | | |
| n-Heptylcyclopentane | $C_{12}H_{24}$ | | | | | | | | | | | | | | | | | | |
| n-Octylcyclopentane | $C_{13}H_{26}$ | | | | | | | | | | | | | | | | | | |

a Values of the vapor pressure are calculated from the constants given and the Antoine equation: $\log_{10} P = A - B/(C + t)$; $t = B/(A - \log_{10}P) - C$; (P in lb/in²; t in °F)

TABLE 22k-E, (PART 1), Page 2 - NORMAL ALKYL CYCLOPENTANES, C5 TO C13

VAPOR PRESSURES AND BOILING POINTS, AT 0.2 TO 30 lb/in²

October 31, 1950 (Corrected)

Temperature in °F — Vapor pressure in lb/in²

| Compound | Formula | 120 | 125 | 130 | 135 | 140 | 145 | 150 | 155 | 160 | 165 | 170 | 175 | 180 | 185 | 190 | 195 | 200 | 205 |
|---|---|---|---|---|---|---|---|---|---|---|---|---|---|---|---|---|---|---|---|
| Cyclopentane | $C_5H_{10}$ | 14.517 | 15.89 | 17.37 | 18.95 | 20.65 | 22.45 | 24.4 | 26.4 | 28.6 | | | | | | | | | |
| Methylcyclopentane | $C_6H_{12}$ | 6.842 | 7.557 | 8.330 | 9.164 | 10.064 | 11.032 | 12.072 | 13.187 | 14.382 | 15.660 | 17.02 | 18.48 | 20.03 | 21.68 | 23.43 | 25.3 | 27.3 | 29.3 |
| Ethylcyclopentane | $C_7H_{14}$ | 2.270 | 2.542 | 2.840 | 3.166 | 3.522 | 3.910 | 4.331 | 4.788 | 5.284 | 5.820 | 6.399 | 7.023 | 7.695 | 8.417 | 9.193 | 10.024 | 10.912 | 11.863 |
| n-Propylcyclopentane | $C_8H_{16}$ | 0.808 | 0.918 | 1.040 | 1.175 | 1.325 | 1.490 | 1.672 | 1.872 | 2.091 | 2.331 | 2.592 | 2.878 | 3.188 | 3.525 | 3.891 | 4.287 | 4.715 | 5.176 |
| n-Butylcyclopentane | $C_9H_{18}$ | 0.29 | 0.33 | 0.38 | 0.43 | 0.50 | 0.57 | 0.64 | 0.73 | 0.83 | 0.93 | 1.00 | 1.18 | 1.32 | 1.43 | 1.65 | 1.84 | 2.05 | 2.27 |
| n-Pentylcyclopentane | $C_{10}H_{20}$ | | | | | 0.19 | 0.22 | 0.26 | 0.29 | 0.34 | 0.39 | 0.44 | 0.50 | 0.57 | 0.64 | 0.72 | 0.8 | 0.9 | 1.0 |
| n-Hexylcyclopentane | $C_{11}H_{22}$ | | | | | | | | | | | | 0.20 | 0.23 | 0.26 | 0.30 | 0.34 | 0.39 | 0.44 |
| n-Heptylcyclopentane | $C_{12}H_{24}$ | | | | | | | | | | | | | | | | | | 0.20 |
| n-Octylcyclopentane | $C_{13}H_{26}$ | | | | | | | | | | | | | | | | | | |

Temperature in °F — Vapor pressure in lb/in²

| Compound | Formula | 210 | 215 | 220 | 225 | 230 | 235 | 240 | 245 | 250 | 255 | 260 | 265 | 270 | 275 | 280 | 285 | 290 | 295 |
|---|---|---|---|---|---|---|---|---|---|---|---|---|---|---|---|---|---|---|---|
| Cyclopentane | $C_5H_{10}$ | | | | | | | | | | | | | | | | | | |
| Methylcyclopentane | $C_6H_{12}$ | | | | | | | | | | | | | | | | | | |
| Ethylcyclopentane | $C_7H_{14}$ | 12.878 | 13.959 | 15.110 | 16.34 | 17.63 | 19.01 | 20.48 | 22.02 | 23.66 | 25.4 | 27.2 | 29.1 | | | | | | |
| n-Propylcyclopentane | $C_8H_{16}$ | 5.674 | 6.209 | 6.784 | 7.400 | 8.061 | 8.768 | 9.523 | 10.330 | 11.189 | 12.104 | 13.077 | 14.110 | 15.206 | 16.368 | 17.60 | 18.90 | 20.27 | 21.73 |
| n-Butylcyclopentane | $C_9H_{18}$ | 2.52 | 2.76 | 3.07 | 3.38 | 3.72 | 4.08 | 4.47 | 4.90 | 5.35 | 5.84 | 6.36 | 6.92 | 7.51 | 8.15 | 8.83 | 9.55 | 10.33 | 11.15 |
| n-Pentylcyclopentane | $C_{10}H_{20}$ | 1.1 | 1.3 | 1.4 | 1.6 | 1.8 | 2.0 | 2.2 | 2.4 | 2.6 | 2.9 | 3.2 | 3.5 | 3.8 | 4.2 | 4.6 | 5.0 | 5.4 | 5.9 |
| n-Hexylcyclopentane | $C_{11}H_{22}$ | 0.50 | 0.56 | 0.63 | 0.71 | 0.8 | 0.9 | 1.0 | 1.1 | 1.2 | 1.4 | 1.5 | 1.7 | 1.9 | 2.1 | 2.3 | 2.5 | 2.7 | 3.0 |
| n-Heptylcyclopentane | $C_{12}H_{24}$ | 0.23 | 0.26 | 0.30 | 0.34 | 0.39 | 0.44 | 0.49 | 0.55 | 0.62 | 0.7 | 0.8 | 0.9 | 1.0 | 1.1 | 1.2 | 1.3 | 1.5 | 1.6 |
| n-Octylcyclopentane | $C_{13}H_{26}$ | | | | | 0.18 | 0.21 | 0.24 | 0.27 | 0.31 | 0.35 | 0.39 | 0.44 | 0.50 | 0.56 | 0.62 | 0.70 | 0.78 | 0.86 |

TABLE 22k-E, (PART 1), Page 3 – NORMAL ALKYL CYCLOPENTANES, $C_5$ TO $C_{13}$
VAPOR PRESSURES AND BOILING POINTS, AT 0.2 TO 30 lb/in2
October 31, 1950

Temperature in °F — Vapor pressure in lb/in²

| Compound | Formula | 300 | 305 | 310 | 315 | 320 | 325 | 330 | 335 | 340 | 345 | 350 | 355 | 360 | 365 | 370 | 375 | 380 | 385 |
|---|---|---|---|---|---|---|---|---|---|---|---|---|---|---|---|---|---|---|---|
| Cyclopentane | $C_5H_{10}$ | | | | | | | | | | | | | | | | | | |
| Methylcyclopentane | $C_6H_{12}$ | | | | | | | | | | | | | | | | | | |
| Ethylcyclopentane | $C_7H_{14}$ | | | | | | | | | | | | | | | | | | |
| Propylcyclopentane | $C_8H_{16}$ | 23.26 | 24.87 | 26.6 | 28.4 | | | | | | | | | | | | | | |
| n-Butylcyclopentane | $C_9H_{18}$ | 12.02 | 12.94 | 13.91 | 14.95 | 16.04 | 17.20 | 18.4 | 19.7 | 21.1 | 22.5 | 24.0 | 25.6 | 27.2 | 29.0 | | | | |
| n-Pentylcyclopentane | $C_{10}H_{20}$ | 6.4 | 6.9 | 7.5 | 8.1 | 8.8 | 9.5 | 10.2 | 11.0 | 11.8 | 12.6 | 13.6 | 14.6 | 15.6 | 16.7 | 17.8 | 19.1 | 20. | 22. |
| n-Hexylcyclopentane | $C_{11}H_{22}$ | 3.3 | 3.6 | 3.9 | 4.3 | 4.6 | 5.0 | 5.5 | 5.9 | 6.4 | 6.9 | 7.5 | 8.1 | 8.7 | 9.3 | 10.0 | 10.8 | 11.6 | 12.4 |
| n-Heptylcyclopentane | $C_{12}H_{24}$ | 1.8 | 2.0 | 2.1 | 2.3 | 2.6 | 2.8 | 3.1 | 3.3 | 3.6 | 4.0 | 4.3 | 4.7 | 5.1 | 5.5 | 5.9 | 6.4 | 6.9 | 7.4 |
| n-Octylcyclopentane | $C_{13}H_{26}$ | 1.0 | 1.1 | 1.2 | 1.3 | 1.4 | 1.6 | 1.7 | 1.9 | 2.1 | 2.3 | 2.5 | 2.7 | 3.0 | 3.2 | 3.5 | 3.8 | 4.1 | 4.5 |

Temperature in °F — Vapor pressure in lb/in²

| Compound | Formula | 390 | 395 | 400 | 405 | 410 | 415 | 420 | 425 | 430 | 435 | 440 | 445 | 450 | 455 | 460 | 465 | 470 | 475 |
|---|---|---|---|---|---|---|---|---|---|---|---|---|---|---|---|---|---|---|---|
| Cyclopentane | $C_5H_{10}$ | | | | | | | | | | | | | | | | | | |
| Methylcyclopentane | $C_6H_{12}$ | | | | | | | | | | | | | | | | | | |
| Ethylcyclopentane | $C_7H_{14}$ | | | | | | | | | | | | | | | | | | |
| Propylcyclopentane | $C_8H_{16}$ | | | | | | | | | | | | | | | | | | |
| n-butylcyclopentane | $C_9H_{18}$ | | | | | | | | | | | | | | | | | | |
| n-Pentylcyclopentane | $C_{10}H_{20}$ | 23. | 24. | 26. | 28. | 29. | | | | | | | | | | | | | |
| n-Hexylcyclopentane | $C_{11}H_{22}$ | 13.3 | 14.2 | 15.1 | 16.2 | 17.3 | 18.4 | 19.6 | 21. | 22. | 23. | 25. | 26. | 28. | 30. | | | | |
| n-Heptylcyclopentane | $C_{12}H_{24}$ | 8.0 | 8.6 | 9.2 | 9.9 | 10.6 | 11.3 | 12.1 | 12.9 | 13.8 | 14.7 | 15.7 | 16.7 | 17.8 | 18.9 | 20. | 21. | 22. | 24. |
| n-Octylcyclopentane | $C_{13}H_{26}$ | 4.8 | 5.2 | 5.7 | 6.1 | 6.6 | 7.1 | 7.6 | 8.1 | 8.7 | 9.4 | 10.0 | 10.7 | 11.5 | 12.2 | 13.0 | 13.9 | 14.3 | 15.7 |

395

TABLE 22k-E (PART 1), Page 4 – NORMAL ALKYL CYCLOPENTANES, C$_5$ TO C$_{13}$

VAPOR PRESSURES AND BOILING POINTS, AT 0.2 TO 30 lb/in$^2$

October 31, 1950

Temperature in °F — Vapor pressure in lb/in$^2$

| Compound | Formula | 480 | 485 | 490 | 495 | 500 | 505 | 510 | 515 | 520 | 525 | 530 |
|---|---|---|---|---|---|---|---|---|---|---|---|---|
| Cyclopentane | C$_5$H$_{10}$ | | | | | | | | | | | |
| Methylcyclopentane | C$_6$H$_{12}$ | | | | | | | | | | | |
| Ethylcyclopentane | C$_7$H$_{14}$ | | | | | | | | | | | |
| Propylcyclopentane | C$_8$H$_{16}$ | | | | | | | | | | | |
| n-Butylcyclopentane | C$_9$H$_{18}$ | | | | | | | | | | | |
| n-Pentylcyclopentane | C$_{10}$H$_{20}$ | | | | | | | | | | | |
| n-Hexylcyclopentane | C$_{11}$H$_{22}$ | | | | | | | | | | | |
| n-Hentylcyclopentane | C$_{12}$H$_{24}$ | 25. | 27. | 28. | 30. | | | | | | | |
| n-Octylcyclopentane | C$_{13}$H$_{26}$ | 16.7 | 17.8 | 18.9 | 20.0 | 21. | 22. | 24. | 25. | 26. | 28. | 30. |

Temperature in °F — Vapor pressure in lb/in$^2$

| Compound | Formula |
|---|---|
| | |

TABLE 22k-E (PART 2), Page 1 – NORMAL ALKYL CYCLOPENTANES, C$_{14}$ TO C$_{21}$

VAPOR PRESSURES AND BOILING POINTS[a]

October 31, 1950 (Corrected)

| Compound | Formula | Constants of the Antoine equation | | | Temperature in °F — Vapor pressure in lb/in² | | | | | | | | | | | | | |
|---|---|---|---|---|---|---|---|---|---|---|---|---|---|---|---|---|---|---|
| | | A | B | C | 260 | 265 | 270 | 275 | 280 | 285 | 290 | 295 | 300 | 305 | 310 | 315 | 320 | 325 |
| n-Nonylcyclopentane | C$_{14}$H$_{28}$ | 5.253 | 3163. | 270. | 0.19 | 0.22 | 0.25 | 0.28 | 0.32 | 0.36 | 0.40 | 0.45 | 0.51 | 0.56 | 0.63 | 0.7 | 0.8 | 0.9 |
| n-Decylcyclopentane | C$_{15}$H$_{30}$ | 5.257 | 3236. | 256.7 | | | | | | 0.19 | 0.22 | 0.25 | 0.28 | 0.31 | 0.35 | 0.40 | 0.44 | 0.49 |
| n-Undecylcyclopentane | C$_{16}$H$_{32}$ | 5.260 | 3337. | 251. | | | | | | | | | | | 0.21 | 0.23 | 0.26 | 0.29 |
| n-Dodecylcyclopentane | C$_{17}$H$_{34}$ | 5.271 | 3420. | 240. | | | | | | | | | | | | | | |
| n-Tridecylcyclopentane | C$_{18}$H$_{36}$ | 5.279 | 3501. | 231. | | | | | | | | | | | | | | |
| n-Tetradecylcyclopentane | C$_{19}$H$_{38}$ | 5.289 | 3577. | 222. | | | | | | | | | | | | | | |
| n-Pentadecylcyclopentane | C$_{20}$H$_{40}$ | 5.299 | 3652. | 213. | | | | | | | | | | | | | | |
| n-Hexadecylcyclopentane | C$_{21}$H$_{42}$ | 5.307 | 3726. | 206. | | | | | | | | | | | | | | |

| Compound | Formula | Temperature in °F — Vapor pressure in lb/in² | | | | | | | | | | | | | | | | | |
|---|---|---|---|---|---|---|---|---|---|---|---|---|---|---|---|---|---|---|---|
| | | 330 | 335 | 340 | 345 | 350 | 355 | 360 | 365 | 370 | 375 | 380 | 385 | 390 | 395 | 400 | 405 | 410 | 415 |
| n-Nonylcyclopentane | C$_{14}$H$_{28}$ | 1.0 | 1.1 | 1.2 | 1.3 | 1.4 | 1.6 | 1.7 | 1.9 | 2.0 | 2.2 | 2.4 | 2.6 | 2.9 | 3.1 | 3.4 | 3.7 | 4.0 | 4.3 |
| n-Decylcyclopentane | C$_{15}$H$_{30}$ | 0.55 | 0.61 | 0.63 | 0.76 | 0.84 | 0.93 | 1.02 | 1.13 | 1.24 | 1.36 | 1.49 | 1.64 | 1.79 | 1.96 | 2.14 | 2.33 | 2.53 | 2.75 |
| n-Undecylcyclopentane | C$_{16}$H$_{32}$ | 0.33 | 0.37 | 0.41 | 0.46 | 0.51 | 0.57 | 0.63 | 0.70 | 0.8 | 0.8 | 0.9 | 1.0 | 1.1 | 1.2 | 1.4 | 1.5 | 1.6 | 1.8 |
| n-Dodecylcyclopentane | C$_{17}$H$_{34}$ | 0.19 | 0.21 | 0.24 | 0.27 | 0.30 | 0.33 | 0.37 | 0.41 | 0.46 | 0.51 | 0.57 | 0.6 | 0.7 | 0.8 | 0.8 | 0.9 | 1.0 | 1.1 |
| n-Tridecylcyclopentane | C$_{18}$H$_{36}$ | | | | | | 0.2 | 0.2 | 0.2 | 0.3 | 0.3 | 0.4 | 0.4 | 0.4 | 0.5 | 0.5 | 0.6 | 0.7 | 0.7 |
| n-Tetradecylcyclopentane | C$_{19}$H$_{38}$ | | | | | | | | | | 0.2 | 0.2 | 0.2 | 0.3 | 0.3 | 0.3 | 0.4 | 0.4 | 0.5 |
| n-Pentadecylcyclopentane | C$_{20}$H$_{40}$ | | | | | | | | | | | | | | 0.2 | 0.2 | 0.2 | 0.3 | 0.3 |
| n-Hexadecylcyclopentane | C$_{21}$H$_{42}$ | | | | | | | | | | | | | | | | | | 0.2 |

[a] Values of the vapor pressure are calculated from the constants given and the Antoine equation: $\log_{10} P = A - B/(C + t)$; $t = B/(A - \log_{10} P) - C$; (P in lb/in²; t in °F)

TABLE 22k-E (PART 2), Page 2 - NORMAL ALKYL CYCLOPENTANES, $C_{14}$ TO $C_{21}$

VAPOR PRESSURES AND BOILING POINTS

October 31, 1950

Temperature in °F

Vapor pressure in lb/in²

| Compound | Formula | 420 | 425 | 430 | 435 | 440 | 445 | 450 | 455 | 460 | 465 | 470 | 475 | 480 | 485 | 490 | 495 | 500 | 505 |
|---|---|---|---|---|---|---|---|---|---|---|---|---|---|---|---|---|---|---|---|
| n-Nonylcyclopentane | $C_{14}H_{28}$ | 4.7 | 5.0 | 5.4 | 5.8 | 6.3 | 6.7 | 7.2 | 7.8 | 8.3 | 8.9 | 9.5 | 10.2 | 10.9 | 11.6 | 12.3 | 13.1 | 14.0 | 14.9 |
| n-Decylcyclopentane | $C_{15}H_{30}$ | 2.99 | 3.24 | 3.51 | 3.79 | 4.10 | 4.42 | 4.76 | 5.13 | 5.52 | 5.93 | 6.37 | 6.83 | 7.32 | 7.84 | 8.38 | 8.96 | 9.56 | 10.20 |
| n-Undecylcyclopentane | $C_{16}H_{32}$ | 1.9 | 2.1 | 2.3 | 2.5 | 2.7 | 2.9 | 3.2 | 3.4 | 3.7 | 4.0 | 4.3 | 4.6 | 5.0 | 5.3 | 5.7 | 6.1 | 6.6 | 7.0 |
| n-Dodecylcyclopentane | $C_{17}H_{34}$ | 1.2 | 1.3 | 1.5 | 1.6 | 1.8 | 1.9 | 2.1 | 2.2 | 2.4 | 2.6 | 2.8 | 3.1 | 3.3 | 3.6 | 3.9 | 4.2 | 4.5 | 4.8 |
| n-Tridecylcyclopentane | $C_{18}H_{36}$ | 0.8 | 0.9 | 1.0 | 1.1 | 1.2 | 1.3 | 1.4 | 1.5 | 1.6 | 1.8 | 1.9 | 2.1 | 2.3 | 2.4 | 2.6 | 2.9 | 3.1 | 3.3 |
| n-Tetradecylcyclopentane | $C_{19}H_{38}$ | 0.5 | 0.6 | 0.6 | 0.7 | 0.8 | 0.3 | 0.9 | 1.0 | 1.1 | 1.2 | 1.3 | 1.4 | 1.6 | 1.7 | 1.8 | 2.0 | 2.2 | 2.3 |
| n-Pentadecylcyclopentane | $C_{20}H_{40}$ | 0.3 | 0.4 | 0.4 | 0.5 | 0.5 | 0.6 | 0.6 | 0.7 | 0.7 | 0.8 | 0.9 | 1.0 | 1.1 | 1.2 | 1.3 | 1.4 | 1.5 | 1.6 |
| n-Hexadecylcyclopentane | $C_{21}H_{42}$ | 0.2 | 0.2 | 0.3 | 0.3 | 0.4 | 0.4 | 0.4 | 0.5 | 0.5 | 0.6 | 0.6 | 0.7 | 0.7 | 0.8 | 0.9 | 1.0 | 1.1 | 1.2 |

Temperature in °F

Vapor pressure in lb/in²

| Compound | Formula | 510 | 515 | 520 | 525 | 530 | 535 | 540 | 545 | 550 | 555 | 560 | 565 | 570 | 575 | 580 | 585 | 590 | 595 |
|---|---|---|---|---|---|---|---|---|---|---|---|---|---|---|---|---|---|---|---|
| n-Nonylcyclopentane | $C_{14}H_{28}$ | 15.8 | 16.7 | 17.7 | 18.8 | 19.9 | 21. | 22. | 24. | 25. | 26. | 28. | 29. | | | | | | |
| n-Decylcyclopentane | $C_{15}H_{30}$ | 10.37 | 11.58 | 12.32 | 13.10 | 13.9 | 14.8 | 15.7 | 16.6 | 17.6 | 18.6 | 19.7 | 20.8 | 22.0 | 23.3 | 24.5 | 25.3 | 27.2 | 28.7 |
| n-Undecylcyclopentane | $C_{16}H_{32}$ | 7.5 | 8.0 | 8.6 | 9.1 | 9.7 | 10.3 | 11.0 | 11.7 | 12.4 | 13.2 | 14.0 | 14.3 | 15.7 | 16.6 | 17.5 | 18.5 | 19.6 | 21. |
| n-Dodecylcyclopentane | $C_{17}H_{34}$ | 5.1 | 5.5 | 5.9 | 6.3 | 6.8 | 7.2 | 7.7 | 8.2 | 8.7 | 9.3 | 9.9 | 10.5 | 11.2 | 11.9 | 12.6 | 13.4 | 14.2 | 15.0 |
| n-Tridecylcyclopentane | $C_{18}H_{36}$ | 3.6 | 3.9 | 4.1 | 4.4 | 4.8 | 5.1 | 5.5 | 5.9 | 6.3 | 6.7 | 7.1 | 7.6 | 8.1 | 8.6 | 9.2 | 9.8 | 10.4 | 11.0 |
| n-Tetradecylcyclopentane | $C_{19}H_{38}$ | 2.5 | 2.7 | 2.9 | 3.2 | 3.4 | 3.7 | 3.9 | 4.2 | 4.5 | 4.9 | 5.2 | 5.5 | 5.9 | 6.3 | 6.7 | 7.2 | 7.7 | 8.2 |
| n-Pentadecylcyclopentane | $C_{20}H_{40}$ | 1.8 | 1.9 | 2.1 | 2.2 | 2.4 | 2.6 | 2.8 | 3.0 | 3.3 | 3.5 | 3.8 | 4.0 | 4.3 | 4.6 | 4.9 | 5.3 | 5.6 | 6.0 |
| n-Hexadecylcyclopentane | $C_{21}H_{42}$ | 1.3 | 1.4 | 1.5 | 1.6 | 1.8 | 1.9 | 2.0 | 2.2 | 2.4 | 2.6 | 2.8 | 3.0 | 3.2 | 3.4 | 3.7 | 3.9 | 4.2 | 4.5 |

TABLE 22k-E (PART 2), Page 3 – NORMAL ALKYL CYCLOPENTANES, $C_{14}$ TO $C_{21}$
VAPOR PRESSURES AND BOILING POINTS

October 31, 1950

Temperature in °F — Vapor pressure in lb/in²

| Compound | Formula | 600 | 605 | 610 | 615 | 620 | 625 | 630 | 635 | 640 | 645 | 650 | 655 | 660 | 665 | 670 | 675 | 680 | 685 |
|---|---|---|---|---|---|---|---|---|---|---|---|---|---|---|---|---|---|---|---|
| n-Nonylcyclopentane | $C_{14}H_{28}$ | | | | | | | | | | | | | | | | | | |
| n-Decylcyclopentane | $C_{15}H_{30}$ | 30.2 | | | | | | | | | | | | | | | | | |
| n-Undecylcyclopentane | $C_{16}H_{32}$ | 22. | 23. | 24. | 26. | 27. | 28. | 30. | | | | | | | | | | | |
| n-Dodecylcyclopentane | $C_{17}H_{34}$ | 15.8 | 16.7 | 17.7 | 18.7 | 20. | 21. | 22. | 23. | 24. | 26. | 27. | 28. | 30. | | | | | |
| n-Tridecylcyclopentane | $C_{18}H_{36}$ | 11.6 | 12.3 | 13.1 | 13.8 | 14.6 | 15.5 | 16.3 | 17.2 | 18.2 | 19. | 20. | 21. | 22. | 24. | 25. | 26. | 27. | 29. |
| n-Tetradecylcyclopentane | $C_{19}H_{38}$ | 8.7 | 9.2 | 9.8 | 10.4 | 11.0 | 11.6 | 12.3 | 13.0 | 13.8 | 14.6 | 15.4 | 16.2 | 17.1 | 18.0 | 19.0 | 20. | 21. | 22. |
| n-Pentadecylcyclopentane | $C_{20}H_{40}$ | 6.4 | 6.8 | 7.3 | 7.7 | 8.2 | 8.7 | 9.3 | 9.8 | 10.4 | 11.0 | 11.7 | 12.4 | 13.1 | 13.8 | 14.6 | 15.4 | 16.2 | 17.1 |
| n-Hexadecylcyclopentane | $C_{21}H_{42}$ | 4.8 | 5.2 | 5.5 | 5.9 | 6.3 | 6.7 | 7.1 | 7.5 | 8.0 | 8.5 | 9.0 | 9.5 | 10.1 | 10.7 | 11.3 | 12.0 | 12.6 | 13.3 |

Temperature in °F — Vapor pressure in lb/in²

| Compound | Formula | 690 | 695 | 700 | 705 | 710 | 715 | 720 | 725 | 730 | 735 | 740 | 745 | 750 | 755 | 760 | 765 | 770 | 775 |
|---|---|---|---|---|---|---|---|---|---|---|---|---|---|---|---|---|---|---|---|
| n-Nonylcyclopentane | $C_{14}H_{28}$ | | | | | | | | | | | | | | | | | | |
| n-Decylcyclopentane | $C_{15}H_{30}$ | | | | | | | | | | | | | | | | | | |
| n-Undecylcyclopentane | $C_{16}H_{32}$ | | | | | | | | | | | | | | | | | | |
| n-Dodecylcyclopentane | $C_{17}H_{34}$ | | | | | | | | | | | | | | | | | | |
| n-Tridecylcyclopentane | $C_{18}H_{36}$ | 30. | | | | | | | | | | | | | | | | | |
| n-Tetradecylcyclopentane | $C_{19}H_{38}$ | 23. | 24. | 26. | 27. | 28. | 30. | | | | | | | | | | | | |
| n-Pentadecylcyclopentane | $C_{20}H_{40}$ | 18.0 | 18.9 | 20. | 21. | 22. | 23. | 24. | 26. | 27. | 28. | 29. | | | | | | | |
| n-Hexadecylcyclopentane | $C_{21}H_{42}$ | 14.1 | 14.9 | 15.6 | 16.5 | 17.3 | 18.2 | 19. | 20. | 21. | 22. | 23. | 24. | 26. | 27. | 28. | 30. | | |

TABLE 6k-E, Page 1 - ALKYL CYCLOPENTANES, $C_5$ TO $C_7$,
VAPOR PRESSURES AND BOILING POINTS, AT 0.2 TO 30 lb/in2
November 30, 1949; December 31, 1952

Temperature in °F

| Compound | Formula | Constants of the Antoine equation | | | Vapor pressure in lb/in2 | | | | | | | | | | | | | | |
|---|---|---|---|---|---|---|---|---|---|---|---|---|---|---|---|---|---|---|---|
| | | A | B | C | -40 | -35 | -30 | -25 | -20 | -15 | -10 | -5 | 0 | +5 | 10 | 15 | 20 | 25 |
| Cyclopentane | $C_5H_{10}$ | 5.17315 | 2023.492 | 384.450 | 0.199 | 0.241 | 0.291 | 0.350 | 0.418 | 0.50 | 0.59 | 0.69 | 0.81 | 0.95 | 1.10 | 1.28 | 1.48 | 1.70 |
| Methylcyclopentane | $C_6H_{12}$ | 5.14922 | 2134.906 | 374.876 | | | | | | | 0.199 | 0.238 | 0.285 | 0.338 | 0.400 | 0.471 | 0.55 | 0.65 |
| Ethylcyclopentane | $C_7H_{14}$ | 5.17348 | 2337.478 | 365.215 | | | | | | | | | | | | | | |
| 1,1-Dimethylcyclopentane | " | 5.10363 | 2195.053 | 367.503 | | | | | | | | | | | 0.194 | 0.232 | 0.275 | 0.324 |
| 1,cis-2-Dimethylcyclopentane | " | 5.13647 | 2284.452 | 364.376 | | | | | | | | | | | | | | 0.186 |
| 1,trans-2-Dimethylcyclopentane | " | 5.13061 | 2236.946 | 367.035 | | | | | | | | | | | | 0.188 | 0.224 | 0.266 |
| 1,cis-3-Dimethylcyclopentane | " | 5.12456 | 2232.041 | 366.918 | | | | | | | | | | | | 0.191 | 0.227 | 0.269 |
| 1,trans-3-Dimethylcyclopentane | " | 5.12354 | 2227.421 | 367.609 | | | | | | | | | | | | 0.200 | 0.238 | 0.282 |

Values of the vapor pressure are calculated from the constants given and the Antoine equation: $\log_{10} P = A - B/(C + t)$; $t = B/(A - \log_{10}P) - C$; (P in lb/in2; t in °F)

TABLE 6k-E, Page 2 - ALKYL CYCLOPENTANES, C$_5$ TO C$_7$
VAPOR PRESSURES AND BOILING POINTS, AT 0.2 TO 30 lb/in$^2$
November 30, 1949; December 31, 1952

| Compound | Formula | Temperature in °F | | | | | | | | | | | | | | | | | |
| --- | --- | --- | --- | --- | --- | --- | --- | --- | --- | --- | --- | --- | --- | --- | --- | --- | --- | --- | --- |
| | | Vapor pressure in lb/in$^2$ | | | | | | | | | | | | | | | | | |
| | | 30 | 35 | 40 | 45 | 50 | 55 | 60 | 65 | 70 | 75 | 80 | 85 | 90 | 95 | 100 | 105 | 110 | 115 |
| Cyclopentane | C$_5$H$_{10}$ | 1.95 | 2.23 | 2.546 | 2.893 | 3.278 | 3.703 | 4.172 | 4.688 | 5.254 | 5.875 | 6.552 | 7.291 | 8.095 | 8.968 | 9.914 | 10.938 | 12.043 | 13.235 |
| Methylcyclopentane | C$_6$H$_{12}$ | 0.75 | 0.87 | 1.008 | 1.160 | 1.332 | 1.524 | 1.738 | 1.976 | 2.240 | 2.533 | 2.856 | 3.213 | 3.604 | 4.033 | 4.503 | 5.016 | 5.575 | 6.183 |
| Ethylcyclopentane | C$_7$H$_{14}$ | 0.182 | 0.215 | 0.254 | 0.299 | 0.350 | 0.408 | 0.475 | 0.550 | 0.635 | 0.730 | 0.838 | 0.958 | 1.093 | 1.243 | 1.409 | 1.594 | 1.798 | 2.023 |
| 1,1-Dimethylcyclopentane | " | 0.382 | 0.447 | 0.521 | 0.606 | 0.702 | 0.810 | 0.931 | 1.068 | 1.220 | 1.390 | 1.580 | 1.789 | 2.022 | 2.278 | 2.561 | 2.871 | 3.211 | 3.584 |
| 1,cis-2-Dimethylcyclopentane | " | 0.221 | 0.261 | 0.307 | 0.360 | 0.420 | 0.489 | 0.567 | 0.655 | 0.754 | 0.865 | 0.990 | 1.129 | 1.285 | 1.457 | 1.648 | 1.860 | 2.093 | 2.350 |
| 1,trans-2-Dimethylcyclopentane | " | 0.314 | 0.369 | 0.431 | 0.503 | 0.584 | 0.676 | 0.780 | 0.897 | 1.028 | 1.175 | 1.339 | 1.520 | 1.722 | 1.946 | 2.192 | 2.464 | 2.763 | 3.090 |
| 1,cis-3-Dimethylcyclopentane | " | 0.317 | 0.372 | 0.436 | 0.508 | 0.590 | 0.683 | 0.788 | 0.905 | 1.037 | 1.185 | 1.350 | 1.533 | 1.736 | 1.961 | 2.209 | 2.482 | 2.782 | 3.112 |
| 1,trans-3-Dimethylcyclopentane | " | 0.332 | 0.390 | 0.456 | 0.531 | 0.616 | 0.713 | 0.821 | 0.943 | 1.080 | 1.233 | 1.404 | 1.593 | 1.803 | 2.035 | 2.291 | 2.573 | 2.883 | 3.222 |

TABLE 6k-E, Page 3 - ALKYL CYCLOPENTANES, $C_5$ TO $C_7$

VAPOR PRESSURES AND BOILING POINTS, AT 0.2 TO 30 lb/in2

November 30, 1949   December 31, 1952

| Compound | Formula | Temperature in °F / Vapor pressure in lb/in2 | | | | | | | | | | | | | | | | | |
|---|---|---|---|---|---|---|---|---|---|---|---|---|---|---|---|---|---|---|---|
| | | 120 | 125 | 130 | 135 | 140 | 145 | 150 | 155 | 160 | 165 | 170 | 175 | 180 | 185 | 190 | 195 | 200 | 205 |
| Cyclopentane | $C_5H_{10}$ | 14.517 | 15.89 | 17.37 | 18.95 | 20.65 | 22.45 | 24.4 | 26.4 | 28.6 | | | | | | | | | |
| Methylcyclopentane | $C_6H_{12}$ | 6.842 | 7.557 | 8.330 | 9.164 | 10.064 | 11.032 | 12.072 | 13.187 | 14.382 | 15.660 | 17.02 | 18.48 | 20.03 | 21.68 | 23.43 | 25.3 | 27.3 | 29.3 |
| Ethylcyclopentane | $C_7H_{14}$ | 2.270 | 2.542 | 2.840 | 3.166 | 3.522 | 3.910 | 4.331 | 4.788 | 5.284 | 5.820 | 6.399 | 7.023 | 7.695 | 8.417 | 9.193 | 10.024 | 10.912 | 11.863 |
| 1,1-Dimethylcyclopentane | " | 3.990 | 4.433 | 4.915 | 5.437 | 6.004 | 6.617 | 7.278 | 7.991 | 8.758 | 9.583 | 10.467 | 11.415 | 12.429 | 13.512 | 14.667 | 15.898 | 17.21 | 18.60 |
| 1,cis-2-Dimethylcyclopentane | " | 2.631 | 2.940 | 3.278 | 3.646 | 4.048 | 4.484 | 4.958 | 5.470 | 6.025 | 6.624 | 7.269 | 7.964 | 8.710 | 9.510 | 10.368 | 11.286 | 12.266 | 13.313 |
| 1,trans-2-Dimethylcyclopentane | " | 3.448 | 3.840 | 4.266 | 4.730 | 5.234 | 5.779 | 6.370 | 7.008 | 7.695 | 8.435 | 9.231 | 10.085 | 11.000 | 11.979 | 13.026 | 14.143 | 15.333 | 16.60 |
| 1,cis-3-Dimethylcyclopentane | " | 3.472 | 3.865 | 4.293 | 4.759 | 5.265 | 5.813 | 6.406 | 7.046 | 7.736 | 8.479 | 9.277 | 10.134 | 11.052 | 12.034 | 13.083 | 14.203 | 15.396 | 16.67 |
| 1,trans-3-Dimethylcyclopentane | " | 3.593 | 3.998 | 4.439 | 4.918 | 5.438 | 6.002 | 6.611 | 7.268 | 7.976 | 8.739 | 9.557 | 10.436 | 11.376 | 12.382 | 13.457 | 14.603 | 15.824 | 17.12 |

National Bureau of Standards

TABLE 6k-E, Page 4 – ALKYL CYCLOPENTANES, C$_5$ TO C$_7$
VAPOR PRESSURES AND BOILING POINTS, AT 0.2 TO 30 lb/in2
November 30, 1949; December 31, 1952

| Compound | Formula | Temperature in °F | | | | | | | | | | | |
|---|---|---|---|---|---|---|---|---|---|---|---|---|---|
| | | 210 | 215 | 220 | 225 | 230 | 235 | 240 | 245 | 250 | 255 | 260 | 265 |
| | | Vapor pressure in lb/in2 | | | | | | | | | | | |
| Cyclopentane | C$_5$H$_{10}$ | | | | | | | | | | | | |
| Methylcyclopentane | C$_6$H$_{12}$ | | | | | | | | | | | | |
| Ethylcyclopentane | C$_7$H$_{14}$ | 12.878 | 13.959 | 15.110 | 16.334 | 17.63 | 19.01 | 20.48 | 22.02 | 23.66 | 25.4 | 27.2 | 29.1 |
| 1,1-Dimethylcyclopentane | " | 20.08 | 21.64 | 23.30 | 25.06 | 26.9 | 28.9 | 30.9 | | | | | |
| 1,cis-2-Dimethylcyclopentane | " | 14.427 | 15.614 | 16.88 | 18.22 | 19.64 | 21.14 | 22.73 | 24.41 | 26.2 | 28.1 | 30.0 | |
| 1,trans-2-Dimethylcyclopentane | " | 17.95 | 19.38 | 20.89 | 22.50 | 24.20 | 26.0 | 27.9 | 29.9 | | | | |
| 1,cis-3-Dimethylcyclopentane | " | 18.02 | 19.45 | 20.97 | 22.58 | 24.28 | 28.0 | 30.0 | | | | | |
| 1,trans-3-Dimethylcyclopentane | " | 18.50 | 19.97 | 21.52 | 23.17 | 24.91 | 26.7 | 28.7 | | | | | |

TABLE 15k-E, Page 1 – ALKYL CYCLOPENTANES, C$_8$

VAPOR PRESSURES AND BOILING POINTS, AT 0.2 TO 30 lb/in$^2$

October 31 1950   December 31 1952

| Compound | Formula[a] | Constants of the Antoine equation | | | Temperature in °F — Vapor pressure in lb/in$^2$ | | | | | | | | | | | | | |
|---|---|---|---|---|---|---|---|---|---|---|---|---|---|---|---|---|---|---|
| | | A | B | C | 30 | 35 | 40 | 45 | 50 | 55 | 60 | 65 | 70 | 75 | 80 | 85 | 90 | 95 |
| n-Propylcyclopentane | C$_8$H$_{16}$ | 5.19031 | 2491.895 | 351.686 | | | | | | | | | 0.191 | 0.224 | 0.262 | 0.305 | 0.354 | 0.409 |
| Isopropylcyclopentane | " | 5.17261 | 2482.947 | 360.344 | | | | | | | 0.184 | 0.216 | 0.253 | 0.295 | 0.342 | 0.396 | 0.456 | 0.524 |
| 1-Methyl-1-ethylcyclopentane | " | 5.15787 | 2439.617 | 360.566 | | | | | | 0.194 | 0.228 | 0.266 | 0.310 | 0.361 | 0.417 | 0.482 | 0.554 | 0.635 |
| 1-Methyl-cis-2-ethylcyclopentane | " | 5.19200 | 2498.353 | 358.398 | | | | | | | | 0.195 | 0.228 | 0.267 | 0.310 | 0.360 | 0.416 | 0.479 |
| 1-Methyl-trans-2-ethylcyclopentane | " | 5.1706 | 2440.8 | 359.5 | | | | | | 0.19 | 0.23 | 0.26 | 0.31 | 0.36 | 0.41 | 0.48 | 0.55 | 0.63 |
| 1-Methyl-cis-3-ethylcyclopentane | " | 5.1702 | 2439.0 | 358.8 | | | | | | 0.19 | 0.22 | 0.26 | 0.30 | 0.35 | 0.41 | 0.47 | 0.54 | 0.62 |
| 1-Methyl-trans-3-ethylcyclopentane | " | 5.1607 | 2431.8 | 359.5 | | | | | | 0.20 | 0.23 | 0.27 | 0.32 | 0.37 | 0.42 | 0.49 | 0.56 | 0.65 |
| 1,1,2-Trimethylcyclopentane | " | 5.10844 | 2357.312 | 361.403 | | | | 0.203 | 0.239 | 0.280 | 0.327 | 0.380 | 0.441 | 0.509 | 0.586 | 0.673 | 0.770 | 0.878 |
| 1,1,3-Trimethylcyclopentane | " | 5.09586 | 2296.796 | 363.818 | 0.184 | 0.217 | 0.256 | 0.300 | 0.351 | 0.409 | 0.475 | 0.549 | 0.633 | 0.727 | 0.833 | 0.952 | 1.084 | 1.230 |
| 1,cis-2,cis-3-Trimethylcyclopentane | " | 5.1349 | 2428.2 | 358.6 | | | | | | | 0.22 | 0.25 | 0.29 | 0.34 | 0.40 | 0.46 | 0.53 | 0.60 |
| 1,cis-2,trans-3-Trimethylcyclopentane | " | 5.1344 | 2395.8 | 360.4 | | | | | 0.20 | 0.23 | 0.27 | 0.32 | 0.37 | 0.43 | 0.49 | 0.57 | 0.65 | 0.75 |
| 1,trans-2,cis-3-Trimethylcyclopentane | " | 5.1132 | 2341.8 | 363.1 | | | 0.20 | 0.24 | 0.28 | 0.33 | 0.38 | 0.44 | 0.51 | 0.59 | 0.67 | 0.77 | 0.88 | 1.00 |
| 1,cis-2,cis-4-Trimethylcyclopentane | " | 5.128 | 2403. | 362. | | | | | 0.20 | 0.23 | 0.27 | 0.32 | 0.37 | 0.43 | 0.49 | 0.57 | 0.65 | 0.74 |
| 1,cis-2,trans-4-Trimethylcyclopentane | " | 5.14087 | 2401.009 | 362.114 | | | | | 0.206 | 0.242 | 0.284 | 0.331 | 0.384 | 0.445 | 0.513 | 0.590 | 0.676 | 0.773 |
| 1,trans-2,cis-4-Trimethylcyclopentane | " | 5.13609 | 2351.075 | 363.654 | | | 0.205 | 0.241 | 0.283 | 0.331 | 0.386 | 0.448 | 0.518 | 0.598 | 0.687 | 0.787 | 0.899 | 1.023 |

a Values of the vapor pressure are calculated from the constants given and the Antoine equation: $\log_{10} P = A - B/(C + t)$; $t = B/(A - \log_{10} P) - C$; ($P$ in lb/in$^2$; $t$ in °F)

TABLE 15k-E, Page 2 – ALKYL CYCLOPENTANES, $C_8$

VAPOR PRESSURES AND BOILING POINTS, AT 0.2 TO 30 lb/in2

October 31, 1950; December 31, 1952

| Compound | Formula | Temperature in °F | | | | | | | | | | | | | | | | | |
|---|---|---|---|---|---|---|---|---|---|---|---|---|---|---|---|---|---|---|---|
| | | 100 | 105 | 110 | 115 | 120 | 125 | 130 | 135 | 140 | 145 | 150 | 155 | 160 | 165 | 170 | .175 | 180 | 185 |
| | | Vapor pressure in lb/in2 | | | | | | | | | | | | | | | | | |
| n-Propylcyclopentane | $C_8H_{16}$ | 0.471 | 0.542 | 0.621 | 0.709 | 0.808 | 0.918 | 1.040 | 1.175 | 1.325 | 1.490 | 1.672 | 1.872 | 2.091 | 2.331 | 2.592 | 2.878 | 3.188 | 3.525 |
| Isopropylcyclopentane | " | 0.601 | 0.687 | 0.783 | 0.890 | 1.008 | 1.140 | 1.285 | 1.446 | 1.622 | 1.816 | 2.029 | 2.262 | 2.517 | 2.794 | 3.096 | 3.424 | 3.780 | 4.165 |
| 1-Methyl-1-ethylcyclopentane | " | 0.726 | 0.828 | 0.941 | 1.067 | 1.206 | 1.361 | 1.531 | 1.719 | 1.925 | 2.151 | 2.398 | 2.668 | 2.962 | 3.282 | 3.630 | 4.007 | 4.416 | 4.857 |
| 1-Methyl-cis-2-ethylcyclopentane | " | 0.550 | 0.630 | 0.719 | 0.819 | 0.930 | 1.053 | 1.190 | 1.340 | 1.507 | 1.690 | 1.891 | 2.111 | 2.352 | 2.615 | 2.902 | 3.214 | 3.553 | 3.920 |
| 1-Methyl-trans-2-ethylcyclopentane | " | 0.72 | 0.82 | 0.94 | 1.06 | 1.20 | 1.36 | 1.53 | 1.72 | 1.92 | 2.15 | 2.40 | 2.67 | 2.97 | 3.29 | 3.64 | 4.02 | 4.43 | 4.88 |
| 1-Methyl-cis-3-ethylcyclopentane | " | 0.71 | 0.82 | 0.93 | 1.05 | 1.19 | 1.34 | 1.52 | 1.70 | 1.91 | 2.13 | 2.38 | 2.65 | 2.94 | 3.26 | 3.61 | 3.99 | 4.40 | 4.84 |
| 1-Methyl-trans-3-ethylcyclopentane | " | 0.74 | 0.84 | 0.96 | 1.09 | 1.23 | 1.39 | 1.56 | 1.75 | 1.96 | 2.19 | 2.44 | 2.72 | 3.02 | 3.34 | 3.70 | 4.08 | 4.50 | 4.95 |
| 1,1,2-Trimethylcyclopentane | " | 0.999 | 1.133 | 1.282 | 1.446 | 1.628 | 1.828 | 2.048 | 2.289 | 2.553 | 2.841 | 3.155 | 3.496 | 3.867 | 4.269 | 4.704 | 5.173 | 5.680 | 6.226 |
| 1,1,3-Trimethylcyclopentane | " | 1.393 | 1.573 | 1.772 | 1.991 | 2.232 | 2.496 | 2.785 | 3.100 | 3.444 | 3.818 | 4.225 | 4.665 | 5.142 | 5.657 | 6.213 | 6.811 | 7.454 | 8.145 |
| 1,cis-2,cis-3-Trimethylcyclopentane | " | 0.69 | 0.79 | 0.90 | 1.02 | 1.15 | 1.30 | 1.46 | 1.64 | 1.84 | 2.06 | 2.29 | 2.55 | 2.84 | 3.14 | 3.48 | 3.84 | 4.23 | 4.66 |
| 1,cis-2,trans-3-Trimethylcyclopentane | " | 0.85 | 0.97 | 1.10 | 1.24 | 1.40 | 1.58 | 1.77 | 1.99 | 2.22 | 2.48 | 2.76 | 3.06 | 3.39 | 3.75 | 4.14 | 4.57 | 5.02 | 5.52 |
| 1,trans-2,cis-3-Trimethylcyclopentane | " | 1.14 | 1.29 | 1.46 | 1.64 | 1.84 | 2.07 | 2.31 | 2.58 | 2.87 | 3.19 | 3.54 | 3.92 | 4.33 | 4.77 | 5.25 | 5.77 | 6.33 | 6.93 |
| 1,cis-2,cis-4-Trimethylcyclopentane | " | 0.84 | 0.96 | 1.09 | 1.2 | 1.4 | 1.6 | 1.8 | 2.0 | 2.2 | 2.4 | 2.7 | 3.0 | 3.3 | 3.7 | 4.1 | 4.5 | 4.9 | 5.4 |
| 1,cis-2,trans-4-Trimethylcyclopentane | " | 0.881 | 1.002 | 1.136 | 1.284 | 1.448 | 1.629 | 1.828 | 2.046 | 2.286 | 2.548 | 2.834 | 3.146 | 3.485 | 3.854 | 4.253 | 4.685 | 5.151 | 5.654 |
| 1,trans-2,cis-4-Trimethylcyclopentane | " | 1.162 | 1.316 | 1.487 | 1.676 | 1.884 | 2.112 | 2.363 | 2.638 | 2.938 | 3.266 | 3.622 | 4.009 | 4.429 | 4.884 | 5.376 | 5.907 | 6.479 | 7.095 |

TABLE 15k-E , Page 3 – ALKYL CYCLOPENTANES, C$_8$
VAPOR PRESSURES AND BOILING POINTS, AT 0.2 TO 30 lb/in$^2$
October 31, 1950; December 31, 1952

Temperature in °F

Vapor pressure in lb/in$^2$

| Compound | Formula | 190 | 195 | 200 | 205 | 210 | 215 | 220 | 225 | 230 | 235 | 240 | 245 | 250 | 255 | 260 | 265 | 270 | 275 |
|---|---|---|---|---|---|---|---|---|---|---|---|---|---|---|---|---|---|---|---|
| n-Propylcyclopentane | C$_8$H$_{16}$ | 3.891 | 4.287 | 4.715 | 5.176 | 5.674 | 6.209 | 6.784 | 7.400 | 8.061 | 8.768 | 9.523 | 10.330 | 11.189 | 12.104 | 13.077 | 14.110 | 15.206 | 16.368 |
| Isopropylcyclopentane | " | 4.581 | 5.030 | 5.515 | 6.035 | 6.595 | 7.195 | 7.838 | 8.526 | 9.261 | 10.046 | 10.883 | 11.773 | 12.720 | 13.726 | 14.794 | 15.925 | 17.12 | 18.39 |
| 1-Methyl-1-ethylcyclopentane | " | 5.333 | 5.846 | 6.397 | 6.990 | 7.626 | 8.306 | 9.035 | 9.813 | 10.643 | 11.528 | 12.469 | 13.470 | 14.534 | 15.661 | 16.86 | 18.12 | 19.46 | 20.87 |
| 1-Methyl-cis-2-ethylcyclopentane | " | 4.317 | 4.746 | 5.209 | 5.708 | 6.245 | 6.821 | 7.439 | 8.102 | 8.810 | 9.566 | 10.374 | 11.234 | 12.150 | 13.123 | 14.158 | 15.258 | 16.417 | 17.65 |
| 1-Methyl-trans-2-ethylcyclopentane | " | 5.36 | 5.87 | 6.43 | 7.03 | 7.67 | 8.36 | 9.1 | 9.9 | 10.7 | 11.6 | 12.6 | 13.6 | 14.7 | 15.7 | 16.9 | 18.2 | 19.6 | 21.0 |
| 1-Methyl-cis-3-ethylcyclopentane | " | 5.32 | 5.84 | 6.39 | 6.99 | 7.62 | 8.31 | 9.0 | 9.8 | 10.7 | 11.6 | 12.5 | 13.5 | 14.6 | 15.9 | 17.1 | 18.4 | 19.8 | 21.2 |
| 1-Methyl-trans-3-ethylcyclopentane | " | 5.44 | 5.96 | 6.52 | 7.13 | 7.77 | 8.47 | 9.2 | 10.0 | 10.9 | 11.8 | 12.7 | 13.7 | 14.8 | 16.0 | 17.2 | 18.5 | 19.8 | 21.3 |
| 1,1,2-Trimethylcyclopentane | " | 6.613 | 7.443 | 8.119 | 8.842 | 9.615 | 10.441 | 11.322 | 12.260 | 13.258 | 14.318 | 15.444 | 16.64 | 17.90 | 19.24 | 20.65 | 22.14 | 23.71 | 25.37 |
| 1,1,3-Trimethylcyclopentane | " | 8.885 | 9.678 | 10.525 | 11.429 | 12.394 | 13.421 | 14.513 | 15.674 | 16.90 | 18.21 | 19.59 | 21.05 | 22.60 | 24.23 | 25.9 | 27.8 | 29.7 | 31.6 |
| 1,cis-2,cis-3-Trimethylcyclopentane | " | 5.11 | 5.61 | 6.14 | 6.71 | 7.32 | 7.97 | 8.67 | 9.4 | 10.2 | 11.1 | 12.0 | 12.9 | 14.0 | 15.1 | 16.2 | 17.4 | 18.7 | 20.1 |
| 1,cis-2,trans-3-Trimethylcyclopentane | " | 6.05 | 6.62 | 7.23 | 7.89 | 8.6 | 9.3 | 10.2 | 11.0 | 11.9 | 12.9 | 13.9 | 15.0 | 16.2 | 17.4 | 18.7 | 20.1 | 22. | 23. |
| 1,trans-2,cis-3-Trimethylcyclopentane | " | 7.57 | 8.26 | 9.0 | 9.8 | 10.6 | 11.5 | 12.5 | 13.5 | 14.6 | 15.8 | 17.0 | 18.3 | 19.7 | 21.1 | 23. | 24. | 26. | 28. |
| 1,cis-2,cis-4-Trimethylcyclopentane | " | 6.0 | 6.5 | 7.1 | 7.8 | 8.5 | 9.2 | 10.0 | 10.8 | 11.7 | 12.7 | 13.7 | 14.8 | 15.9 | 17.1 | 18.4 | 19.7 | 21.2 | 23. |
| 1,cis-2,trans-4-Trimethylcyclopentane | " | 6.196 | 6.779 | 7.404 | 8.075 | 8.793 | 9.561 | 10.381 | 11.255 | 12.187 | 13.178 | 14.231 | 15.349 | 16.53 | 17.79 | 19.12 | 20.52 | 22.00 | 23.57 |
| 1,trans-2,cis-4-Trimethylcyclopentane | " | 7.756 | 8.465 | 9.225 | 10.038 | 10.906 | 11.833 | 12.820 | 13.871 | 14.988 | 16.174 | 17.43 | 18.77 | 20.18 | 21.67 | 23.24 | 24.90 | 26.7 | 28.5 |

TABLE 15k-E, Page 4 – ALKYL CYCLOPENTANES, C$_8$
VAPOR PRESSURES AND BOILING POINTS, AT 0.2 TO 30 lb/in²
October 31, 1950; December 31, 1952

| Compound | Formula | Temperature in °F | | | | | | | |
| --- | --- | --- | --- | --- | --- | --- | --- | --- | --- |
| | | 280 | 285 | 290 | 295 | 300 | 305 | 310 | 315 |
| | | Vapor pressure in lb/in² | | | | | | | |
| n-Propylcyclopentane | C$_8$H$_{16}$ | 17.60 | 18.90 | 20.27 | 21.73 | 23.26 | 24.87 | 26.6 | 28.4 |
| Isopropylcyclopentane | " | 19.73 | 21.14 | 22.63 | 24.20 | 25.9 | 27.6 | 29.4 | |
| 1-Methyl-1-ethylcyclopentane | " | 22.36 | 23.33 | 25.6 | 27.3 | 29.2 | | | |
| 1-Methyl-cis-2-ethylcyclopentane | " | 18.95 | 20.32 | 21.78 | 25.31 | 24.92 | 26.6 | 28.4 | |
| 1-Methyl-trans-2-ethylcyclopentane | " | 22.6 | 24. | 27. | 28. | 30. | | | |
| 1-Methyl-cis-3-ethylcyclopentane | " | 22.5 | 24. | 26. | 28. | 29. | | | |
| 1-Methyl-trans-3-ethylcyclopentane | " | 22.8 | 24. | 26. | 28. | 30. | | | |
| 1,1,2-Trimethylcyclopentane | " | 27.1 | 28.9 | | | | | | |
| 1,1,3-Trimethylcyclopentane | " | 33.8 | | | | | | | |
| 1,cis-2,cis-3-Trimethylcyclopentane | " | 22. | 23. | 25. | 26. | 28. | | | |
| 1,cis-2,trans-3-Trimethylcyclopentane | " | 25. | 26. | 28. | | | | | |
| 1,trans-2,cis-3-Trimethylcyclopentane | " | 30. | | | | | | | |
| 1,cis-2,cis-4-Trimethylcyclopentane | " | 24. | 26. | 28. | 30. | | | | |
| 1,cis-2,trans-4-Trimethylcyclopentane | " | 25.21 | 26.9 | 28.3 | | | | | |
| 1,trans-2,cis-4-Trimethylcyclopentane | " | 30.4 | | | | | | | |

TABLE 7k-E, Page 1 - ALKYL CYCLOHEXANES, $C_6$ TO $C_8$
VAPOR PRESSURES AND BOILING POINTS. AT 0.2 TO 30 lb/in2
November 30, 1949; December 31, 1952

| Compound | Formula | Constants of the Antoine equation | | | Temperature in °F — Vapor pressure in lb/in2 | | | | | | | | | | | | | |
| --- | --- | --- | --- | --- | --- | --- | --- | --- | --- | --- | --- | --- | --- | --- | --- | --- | --- | --- |
| | | A | B | C | 25 | 30 | 35 | 40 | 45 | 50 | 55 | 60 | 65 | 70 | 75 | 80 | 85 | 90 |
| Cyclohexane | $C_6H_{12}$ | 5.13137 | 2166.347 | 369.153 | 0.185 | | | a | 0.795 | 0.918 | 1.057 | 1.212 | 1.385 | 1.579 | 1.794 | 2.033 | 2.298 | 2.590 |
| Methylcyclohexane | $C_7H_{14}$ | 5.11328 | 2291.155 | 366.934 | | 0.219 | 0.259 | 0.304 | 0.356 | 0.415 | 0.482 | 0.558 | 0.644 | 0.741 | 0.849 | 0.970 | 1.106 | 1.256 |
| Ethylcyclohexane | $C_8H_{16}$ | 5.15680 | 2491.265 | 355.230 | | | | | | | | | | 0.199 | 0.232 | 0.271 | 0.315 | 0.364 |
| 1,1-Dimethylcyclohexane | " | 5.08864 | 2382.950 | 360.495 | | | | | | 0.192 | 0.226 | 0.264 | 0.308 | 0.358 | 0.414 | 0.478 | 0.549 | 0.630 |
| 1,cis-2-Dimethylcyclohexane | " | 5.12803 | 2465.145 | 356.872 | | | | | | | | | 0.193 | 0.226 | 0.263 | 0.306 | 0.354 | 0.409 |
| 1,trans-2-Dimethylcyclohexane | " | 5.12361 | 2440.980 | 362.816 | | | | | | | 0.191 | 0.224 | 0.262 | 0.305 | 0.353 | 0.409 | 0.471 | 0.541 |
| 1,cis-3-Dimethylcyclohexane | " | 5.12932 | 2413.184 | 360.906 | | | | | | 0.181 | 0.212 | 0.249 | 0.291 | 0.338 | 0.392 | 0.453 | 0.522 | 0.599 |
| 1,trans-3-Dimethylcyclohexane | " | 5.12505 | 2422.546 | 356.076 | | | | | | | | 0.201 | 0.235 | 0.275 | 0.320 | 0.371 | 0.429 | 0.495 |
| 1,cis-4-Dimethylcyclohexane | " | 5.12338 | 2426.029 | 357.448 | | | | | | | | 0.205 | 0.240 | 0.280 | 0.326 | 0.378 | 0.437 | 0.503 |
| 1,trans-4-Dimethylcyclohexane | " | 5.10819 | 2398.703 | 361.824 | | | | | | 0.192 | 0.226 | 0.264 | 0.308 | 0.358 | 0.414 | 0.478 | 0.549 | 0.630 |

Values of the vapor pressure are calculated from the constants given and the Antoine equation: $\log_{10} P = A - B/(C + t)$; $t = B/(A - \log_{10} P) - C$; (P in lb/in2; t in °F)

a At the triple point, 44.01°F, the pressure is 0.773 lb/in2.

TABLE 7k-E, Page 2 – ALKYL CYCLOHEXANES, $C_6$ TO $C_8$.
VAPOR PRESSURES AND BOILING POINTS, AT 0.2 TO 30 lb/in2

November 30, 1949; December 31, 1952

Temperature in °F

Vapor pressure in lb/in2

| Compound | Formula | 95 | 100 | 105 | 110 | 115 | 120 | 125 | 130 | 135 | 140 | 145 | 150 | 155 | 160 | 165 | 170 | 175 | 180 |
|---|---|---|---|---|---|---|---|---|---|---|---|---|---|---|---|---|---|---|---|
| Cyclohexane | $C_6H_{12}$ | 2.911 | 3.264 | 3.652 | 4.075 | 4.538 | 5.042 | 5.590 | 6.185 | 6.829 | 7.526 | 8.278 | 9.089 | 9.962 | 10.899 | 11.904 | 12.981 | 14.133 | 15.363 |
| Methylcyclohexane | $C_7H_{14}$ | 1.424 | 1.609 | 1.813 | 2.039 | 2.287 | 2.559 | 2.856 | 3.182 | 3.537 | 3.923 | 4.343 | 4.798 | 5.291 | 5.824 | 6.398 | 7.017 | 7.683 | 8.398 |
| Ethylcyclohexane | $C_8H_{16}$ | 0.420 | 0.483 | 0.554 | 0.634 | 0.723 | 0.821 | 0.931 | 1.054 | 1.188 | 1.338 | 1.502 | 1.682 | 1.880 | 2.097 | 2.334 | 2.592 | 2.873 | 3.179 |
| 1,1-Dimethylcyclohexane | " | 0.720 | 0.820 | 0.932 | 1.056 | 1.194 | 1.347 | 1.515 | 1.700 | 1.903 | 2.125 | 2.369 | 2.635 | 2.924 | 3.239 | 3.581 | 3.951 | 4.352 | 4.784 |
| 1,*cis*-2-Dimethylcyclohexane | " | 0.471 | 0.540 | 0.618 | 0.705 | 0.801 | 0.909 | 1.029 | 1.161 | 1.307 | 1.468 | 1.645 | 1.839 | 2.052 | 2.284 | 2.537 | 2.813 | 3.113 | 3.438 |
| 1,*trans*-2-Dimethylcyclohexane | " | 0.619 | 0.707 | 0.805 | 0.914 | 1.035 | 1.169 | 1.317 | 1.481 | 1.660 | 1.858 | 2.074 | 2.310 | 2.568 | 2.849 | 3.154 | 3.486 | 3.845 | 4.234 |
| 1,*cis*-3-Dimethylcyclohexane | " | 0.686 | 0.783 | 0.891 | 1.011 | 1.144 | 1.292 | 1.455 | 1.635 | 1.833 | 2.050 | 2.287 | 2.547 | 2.830 | 3.138 | 3.473 | 3.836 | 4.230 | 4.655 |
| 1,*trans*-3-Dimethylcyclohexane | " | 0.568 | 0.651 | 0.743 | 0.846 | 0.960 | 1.088 | 1.228 | 1.384 | 1.556 | 1.744 | 1.952 | 2.178 | 2.426 | 2.697 | 2.992 | 3.312 | 3.660 | 4.037 |
| 1,*cis*-4-Dimethylcyclohexane | " | 0.577 | 0.661 | 0.754 | 0.858 | 0.974 | 1.102 | 1.244 | 1.401 | 1.574 | 1.764 | 1.972 | 2.201 | 2.450 | 2.722 | 3.019 | 3.341 | 3.690 | 4.068 |
| 1,*trans*-4-Dimethylcyclohexane | " | 0.720 | 0.821 | 0.933 | 1.058 | 1.196 | 1.348 | 1.517 | 1.702 | 1.906 | 2.129 | 2.373 | 2.640 | 2.931 | 3.247 | 3.590 | 3.962 | 4.364 | 4.798 |

TABLE 7k-E, Page 3 – ALKYL CYCLOHEXANES, $C_6$ TO $C_8$
VAPOR PRESSURES AND BOILING POINTS, AT 0.2 TO 30 lb/in$^2$
November 30, 1949; December 31, 1952

| Compound | Formula | Temperature in °F — Vapor pressure in lb/in$^2$ |||||||||||||||||| |
|---|---|---|---|---|---|---|---|---|---|---|---|---|---|---|---|---|---|---|---|
| | | 185 | 190 | 195 | 200 | 205 | 210 | 215 | 220 | 225 | 230 | 235 | 240 | 245 | 250 | 255 | 260 | 265 | 270 |
| Cyclohexane | $C_6H_{12}$ | 16.68 | 18.07 | 19.56 | 21.14 | 22.82 | 24.6 | 26.5 | 28.5 | 30.6 | | | | | | | | | |
| Methylcyclohexane | $C_7H_{14}$ | 9.165 | 9.986 | 10.865 | 11.802 | 12.803 | 13.868 | 15.002 | 16.206 | 17.49 | 18.84 | 20.28 | 21.79 | 23.40 | 25.1 | 26.9 | 28.8 | 30.7 | |
| Ethylcyclohexane | $C_8H_{16}$ | 3.510 | 3.869 | 4.257 | 4.676 | 5.128 | 5.614 | 6.137 | 6.697 | 7.298 | 7.942 | 8.629 | 9.363 | 10.146 | 10.979 | 11.866 | 12.808 | 13.808 | 14.868 |
| 1,1-Dimethylcyclohexane | " | 5.251 | 5.753 | 6.293 | 6.873 | 7.494 | 8.159 | 8.870 | 9.630 | 10.439 | 11.301 | 12.218 | 13.193 | 14.227 | 15.323 | 16.483 | 17.71 | 19.01 | 20.38 |
| 1,cis-2-Dimethylcyclohexane | " | 3.791 | 4.172 | 4.583 | 5.026 | 5.504 | 6.017 | 6.567 | 7.157 | 7.788 | 8.464 | 9.184 | 9.952 | 10.77 | 11.641 | 12.565 | 13.547 | 14.587 | 15.689 |
| 1,trans-2-Dimethylcyclohexane | " | 4.653 | 5.106 | 5.593 | 6.117 | 6.679 | 7.282 | 7.927 | 8.617 | 9.354 | 10.139 | 10.976 | 11.866 | 12.812 | 13.816 | 14.881 | 16.009 | 17.20 | 18.46 |
| 1,cis-3-Dimethylcyclohexane | " | 5.115 | 5.610 | 6.142 | 6.715 | 7.329 | 7.987 | 8.691 | 9.444 | 10.247 | 11.103 | 12.015 | 12.984 | 14.014 | 15.106 | 16.264 | 17.49 | 18.79 | 20.15 |
| 1,trans-3-Dimethylcyclohexane | " | 4.444 | 4.884 | 5.358 | 5.869 | 6.418 | 7.007 | 7.638 | 8.314 | 9.036 | 9.807 | 10.630 | 11.505 | 12.437 | 13.426 | 14.476 | 15.589 | 16.77 | 18.02 |
| 1,cis-4-Dimethylcyclohexane | " | 4.477 | 4.919 | 5.395 | 5.907 | 6.457 | 7.048 | 7.681 | 8.358 | 9.081 | 9.854 | 10.677 | 11.554 | 12.486 | 13.477 | 14.527 | 15.641 | 16.82 | 18.07 |
| 1,trans-4-Dimethylcyclohexane | " | 5.267 | 5.772 | 6.315 | 6.898 | 7.523 | 8.191 | 8.907 | 9.671 | 10.486 | 11.353 | 12.277 | 13.258 | 14.299 | 15.403 | 16.57 | 17.81 | 19.12 | 20.50 |

## TABLE 7k-E, Page 4 - ALKYL CYCLOHEXANES, $C_6$ TO $C_8$
### VAPOR PRESSURES AND BOILING POINTS, AT 0.2 TO 30 lb/in$^2$
November 30, 1949; December 31, 1952

| Compound | Formula | Temperature in °F — Vapor pressure in lb/in$^2$ | | | | | | | | | |
|---|---|---|---|---|---|---|---|---|---|---|---|
| | | 275 | 280 | 285 | 290 | 295 | 300 | 305 | 310 | 315 | 320 |
| Cyclohexane | $C_6H_{12}$ | | | | | | | | | | |
| Methyl cyclohexane | $C_7H_{14}$ | | | | | | | | | | |
| Ethyl cyclohexane | $C_8H_{16}$ | 15.990 | 17.18 | 18.43 | 19.76 | 21.16 | 22.63 | 24.18 | 25.8 | 27.5 | 29.3 |
| 1,1-Dimethylcyclohexane | " | 21.82 | 23.34 | 24.9 | 26.6 | 28.4 | 30.2 | | | | |
| 1,cis-2-Dimethylcyclohexane | " | 16.85 | 18.09 | 19.39 | 20.76 | 22.20 | 23.72 | 25.3 | 27.0 | 28.8 | |
| 1,trans-2-Dimethylcyclohexane | " | 19.79 | 21.20 | 22.68 | 24.24 | 25.9 | 27.6 | 29.4 | | | |
| 1,cis-3-Dimethylcyclohexane | " | 21.60 | 23.12 | 24.73 | 26.4 | 28.2 | 30.1 | | | | |
| 1,trans-3-Dimethylcyclohexane | " | 19.33 | 20.72 | 22.19 | 23.74 | 25.4 | 27.1 | 28.9 | | | |
| 1,cis-4-Dimethylcyclohexane | " | 19.38 | 20.77 | 22.24 | 23.79 | 25.4 | 27.1 | 28.9 | | | |
| 1,trans-4-Dimethylcyclohexane | " | 21.96 | 23.49 | 25.1 | 26.8 | 28.6 | 30.5 | | | | |

TABLE 24k–E, (PART 1) Page 1 – NORMAL MONOOLEFINS (1-ALKENES), C$_2$ TO C$_{20}$

VAPOR PRESSURES AND BOILING POINTS, AT 0.2 TO 30 lb/in$^2$

April 30, 1952

Temperature in °F — Vapor pressure in lb/in$^2$

| Compound | Formula | Constants of the Antoine equation A | B | C | -245 | -240 | -235 | -230 | -225 | -220 | -215 | -210 | -205 | -200 | -195 | -190 | -185 | -180 |
|---|---|---|---|---|---|---|---|---|---|---|---|---|---|---|---|---|---|---|
| Ethene (Ethylene) | C$_2$H$_4$ | 5.03395 | 1053.00 | 427.00 | 0.177 | 0.253 | 0.354 | 0.488 | 0.662 | 0.885 | 1.167 | 1.519 | 1.953 | 2.484 | 3.127 | 3.899 | 4.816 | 5.899 |
| Propene (Propylene) | C$_3$H$_6$ | 5.10599 | 1413.00 | 412.60 | | | | | | | | | | | | | | |
| 1-Butene | C$_4$H$_8$ | 5.12929 | 1666.98 | 400.00 | | | | | | | | | | | | | | |
| 1-Pentene | C$_5$H$_{10}$ | 5.13289 | 1880.811 | 388.329 | | | | | | | | | | | | | | |
| 1-Hexene | C$_6$H$_{12}$ | 5.15211 | 2075.348 | 374.528 | | | | | | | | | | | | | | |
| 1-Heptene | C$_7$H$_{14}$ | 5.18708 | 2263.509 | 362.522 | | | | | | | | | | | | | | |

Temperature in °F — Vapor pressure in lb/in$^2$

| Compound | Formula | -175 | -170 | -165 | -160 | -155 | -150 | -145 | -140 | -135 | -130 | -125 | -120 | -115 | -110 | -105 | -100 | -95 | -90 |
|---|---|---|---|---|---|---|---|---|---|---|---|---|---|---|---|---|---|---|---|
| Ethene (Ethylene) | C$_2$H$_4$ | 7.168 | 8.64 | 10.35 | 12.31 | 14.54 | 17.08 | 19.95 | 23.17 | 26.78 | 30.8 | | | | | | | | |
| Propene (Propylene) | C$_3$H$_6$ | | 0.191 | 0.251 | 0.325 | 0.418 | 0.531 | 0.669 | 0.837 | 1.037 | 1.276 | 1.559 | 1.892 | 2.280 | 2.732 | 3.254 | 3.853 | 4.539 | 5.32 |
| 1-Butene | C$_4$H$_8$ | | | | | | | | | | | | | 0.191 | 0.240 | 0.301 | 0.374 | 0.461 | 0.565 |
| 1-Pentene | C$_5$H$_{10}$ | | | | | | | | | | | | | | | | | | |
| 1-Hexene | C$_6$H$_{12}$ | | | | | | | | | | | | | | | | | | |
| 1-Heptene | C$_7$H$_{14}$ | | | | | | | | | | | | | | | | | | |

Temperature in °F — Vapor pressure in lb/in$^2$

| Compound | Formula | -85 | -80 | -75 | -70 | -65 | -60 | -55 | -50 | -45 | -40 | -35 | -30 | -25 | -20 | -15 | -10 | -5 | 0 |
|---|---|---|---|---|---|---|---|---|---|---|---|---|---|---|---|---|---|---|---|
| Ethene (Ethylene) | C$_2$H$_4$ | 6.21 | 7.21 | 8.33 | 9.59 | 10.99 | 12.55 | 14.28 | 16.19 | 18.29 | 20.59 | 23.12 | 25.87 | 28.9 | | | | | |
| Propene (Propylene) | C$_3$H$_6$ | 0.688 | 0.832 | 1.000 | 1.196 | 1.423 | 1.684 | 1.984 | 2.325 | 2.714 | 3.153 | 3.649 | 4.207 | 4.831 | 5.527 | 6.30 | 7.16 | 8.11 | 9.16 |
| 1-Butene | C$_4$H$_8$ | | | | | 0.207 | 0.254 | 0.309 | 0.375 | 0.452 | 0.541 | 0.645 | 0.766 | 0.904 | 1.063 | 1.244 | 1.450 | 1.684 | 1.948 |
| 1-Pentene | C$_5$H$_{10}$ | | | | | | | | | | | | | | 0.199 | 0.240 | 0.288 | 0.343 | 0.408 |
| 1-Hexene | C$_6$H$_{12}$ | | | | | | | | | | | | | | | | | | |
| 1-Heptene | C$_7$H$_{14}$ | | | | | | | | | | | | | | | | | | |

a Values of the vapor pressure are calculated from the constants given and the Antoine equation: $\log_{10} P = A - B/(C + t)$; $t = B/(A - \log_{10} P) - C$; (P in lb/in$^2$; t in °F)

TABLE 24k-E, (PART 1), Page 2 – NORMAL MONOOLEFINS (1-ALKENES), $C_2$ TO $C_{20}$

VAPOR PRESSURES AND BOILING POINTS, AT 0.2 TO 30 lb/in2

April 30, 1952 (Corrected)

| Compound | Formula | Temperature in °F | | | | | | | | | | | | | | | | | |
|---|---|---|---|---|---|---|---|---|---|---|---|---|---|---|---|---|---|---|---|
| | | Vapor pressure in lb/in2 | | | | | | | | | | | | | | | | | |
| | | 5 | 10 | 15 | 20 | 25 | 30 | 35 | 40 | 45 | 50 | 55 | 60 | 65 | 70 | 75 | 80 | 85 | 90 |
| Ethene (Ethylene) | $C_2H_4$ | | | | | | | | | | | | | | | | | | |
| Propene (Propylene) | $C_3H_6$ | | | | | | | | | | | | | | | | | | |
| 1-Butene | $C_4H_8$ | 10.31 | 11.57 | 12.96 | 14.46 | 16.11 | 17.89 | 19.82 | 21.91 | 24.17 | 26.60 | 29.2 | | | | | | | |
| 1-Pentene | $C_5H_{10}$ | 2.244 | 2.577 | 2.949 | 3.363 | 3.824 | 4.334 | 4.898 | 5.519 | 6.202 | 6.951 | 7.770 | 8.664 | 9.639 | 10.697 | 11.846 | 13.089 | 14.431 | 15.880 |
| 1-Hexene | $C_6H_{12}$ | 0.483 | 0.569 | 0.667 | 0.779 | 0.907 | 1.052 | 1.215 | 1.398 | 1.604 | 1.834 | 2.091 | 2.377 | 2.694 | 3.044 | 3.431 | 3.856 | 4.324 | 4.836 |
| 1-Heptene | $C_7H_{14}$ | | | | 0.186 | 0.222 | 0.263 | 0.311 | 0.366 | 0.429 | 0.501 | 0.583 | 0.676 | 0.781 | 0.899 | 1.032 | 1.180 | 1.346 | 1.531 |

| Compound | Formula | Temperature in °F | | | | | | | | | | | | | | | | | |
|---|---|---|---|---|---|---|---|---|---|---|---|---|---|---|---|---|---|---|---|
| | | Vapor pressure in lb/in2 | | | | | | | | | | | | | | | | | |
| | | 95 | 100 | 105 | 110 | 115 | 120 | 125 | 130 | 135 | 140 | 145 | 150 | 155 | 160 | 165 | 170 | 175 | 180 |
| Ethene (Ethylene) | $C_2H_4$ | | | | | | | | | | | | | | | | | | |
| Propene (Propylene) | $C_3H_6$ | | | | | | | | | | | | | | | | | | |
| 1-Butene | $C_4H_8$ | | | | | | | | | | | | | | | | | | |
| 1-Pentene | $C_5H_{10}$ | 17.439 | 19.115 | 20.91 | 22.84 | 24.90 | 27.10 | 29.44 | | | | | | | | | | | |
| 1-Hexene | $C_6H_{12}$ | 5.396 | 6.006 | 6.671 | 7.394 | 8.177 | 9.026 | 9.942 | 10.931 | 11.996 | 13.140 | 14.369 | 15.686 | 17.095 | 18.601 | 20.21 | 21.92 | 23.74 | 25.68 |
| 1-Heptene | $C_7H_{14}$ | 1.737 | 1.964 | 2.216 | 2.494 | 2.799 | 3.134 | 3.501 | 3.902 | 4.340 | 4.817 | 5.335 | 5.898 | 6.506 | 7.165 | 7.875 | 8.640 | 9.464 | 10.349 |

| Compound | Formula | Temperature in °F | | | | | | | | | | | | |
|---|---|---|---|---|---|---|---|---|---|---|---|---|---|---|
| | | Vapor pressure in lb/in2 | | | | | | | | | | | | |
| | | 185 | 190 | 195 | 200 | 205 | 210 | 215 | 220 | 225 | 230 | 235 | 240 | 245 |
| Ethene (Ethylene) | $C_2H_4$ | | | | | | | | | | | | | |
| Propene (Propylene) | $C_3H_6$ | | | | | | | | | | | | | |
| 1-Butene | $C_4H_8$ | | | | | | | | | | | | | |
| 1-Pentene | $C_5H_{10}$ | | | | | | | | | | | | | |
| 1-Hexene | $C_6H_{12}$ | 27.73 | 29.91 | | | | | | | | | | | |
| 1-Heptene | $C_7H_{14}$ | 11.297 | 12.314 | 13.401 | 14.562 | 15.800 | 17.120 | 18.524 | 20.02 | 21.60 | 23.28 | 25.06 | 26.94 | 28.92 |

TABLE 24k-E, (PART 1), Page 3 - NORMAL MONOOLEFINS (1-ALKENES), $C_2$ TO $C_{20}$

VAPOR PRESSURES AND BOILING POINTS, AT 0.2 TO 30 lb/in$^2$

April 30, 1952 (Corrected)

**Constants of the Antoine equation and Vapor pressure (lb/in²), Temperature in °F: 60–125**

| Compound | Formula | A | B | C | 60 | 65 | 70 | 75 | 80 | 85 | 90 | 95 | 100 | 105 | 110 | 115 | 120 | 125 |
|---|---|---|---|---|---|---|---|---|---|---|---|---|---|---|---|---|---|---|
| 1-Octene | $C_8H_{16}$ | 5.21902 | 2436.275 | 350.975 | 0.195 | 0.230 | 0.270 | 0.316 | 0.368 | 0.427 | 0.495 | 0.570 | 0.656 | 0.752 | 0.859 | 0.979 | 1.112 | 1.260 |
| 1-Nonene | $C_9H_{18}$ | 5.24026 | 2583.646 | 337.963 | | | | | | | | 0.187 | 0.219 | 0.256 | 0.297 | 0.344 | 0.397 | 0.457 |
| 1-Decene | $C_{10}H_{20}$ | 5.24673 | 2703.370 | 323.640 | | | | | | | | | | | | | | |
| 1-Undecene | $C_{11}H_{22}$ | 5.25301 | 2812.444 | 309.537 | | | | | | | | | | | | | | |
| 1-Dodecene | $C_{12}H_{24}$ | 5.26161 | 2915.752 | 296.088 | | | | | | | | | | | | | | |
| 1-Tridecene | $C_{13}H_{26}$ | 5.2556 | 2992.82 | 281.02 | | | | | | | | | | | | | | |
| 1-Tetradecene | $C_{14}H_{28}$ | 5.2479 | 3059.57 | 265.95 | | | | | | | | | | | | | | |

**Vapor pressure (lb/in²), Temperature in °F: 130–215**

| Compound | Formula | 130 | 135 | 140 | 145 | 150 | 155 | 160 | 165 | 170 | 175 | 180 | 185 | 190 | 195 | 200 | 205 | 210 | 215 |
|---|---|---|---|---|---|---|---|---|---|---|---|---|---|---|---|---|---|---|---|
| 1-Octene | $C_8H_{16}$ | 1.425 | 1.606 | 1.807 | 2.027 | 2.270 | 2.535 | 2.826 | 3.143 | 3.488 | 3.865 | 4.273 | 4.715 | 5.194 | 5.712 | 6.270 | 6.871 | 7.518 | 8.212 |
| 1-Nonene | $C_9H_{18}$ | 0.524 | 0.599 | 0.683 | 0.778 | 0.882 | 0.998 | 1.127 | 1.269 | 1.426 | 1.598 | 1.787 | 1.995 | 2.222 | 2.469 | 2.739 | 3.033 | 3.352 | 3.697 |
| 1-Decene | $C_{10}H_{20}$ | 0.194 | 0.225 | 0.261 | 0.301 | 0.346 | 0.397 | 0.454 | 0.518 | 0.589 | 0.669 | 0.757 | 0.855 | 0.963 | 1.082 | 1.214 | 1.358 | 1.516 | 1.690 |
| 1-Undecene | $C_{11}H_{22}$ | | | | | | | 0.183 | 0.212 | 0.244 | 0.281 | 0.322 | 0.368 | 0.420 | 0.477 | 0.541 | 0.612 | 0.691 | 0.778 |
| 1-Dodecene | $C_{12}H_{24}$ | | | | | | | | | | | | | 0.183 | 0.211 | 0.242 | 0.277 | 0.316 | 0.360 |
| 1-Tridecene | $C_{13}H_{26}$ | | | | | | | | | | | | | | | | | | |
| 1-Tetradecene | $C_{14}H_{28}$ | | | | | | | | | | | | | | | | | | |

**Vapor pressure (lb/in²), Temperature in °F: 220–305**

| Compound | Formula | 220 | 225 | 230 | 235 | 240 | 245 | 250 | 255 | 260 | 265 | 270 | 275 | 280 | 285 | 290 | 295 | 300 | 305 |
|---|---|---|---|---|---|---|---|---|---|---|---|---|---|---|---|---|---|---|---|
| 1-Octene | $C_8H_{16}$ | 8.957 | 9.754 | 10.607 | 11.518 | 12.490 | 13.525 | 14.627 | 15.798 | 17.041 | 18.360 | 19.76 | 21.23 | 22.80 | 24.45 | 26.19 | 28.03 | 29.96 | |
| 1-Nonene | $C_9H_{18}$ | 4.072 | 4.476 | 4.912 | 5.363 | 5.888 | 6.432 | 7.015 | 7.640 | 8.308 | 9.023 | 9.785 | 10.599 | 11.464 | 12.385 | 13.364 | 14.402 | 15.503 | 16.669 |
| 1-Decene | $C_{10}H_{20}$ | 1.879 | 2.086 | 2.311 | 2.556 | 2.821 | 3.109 | 3.420 | 3.757 | 4.119 | 4.510 | 4.930 | 5.381 | 5.865 | 6.384 | 6.938 | 7.531 | 8.164 | 8.838 |
| 1-Undecene | $C_{11}H_{22}$ | 0.875 | 0.981 | 1.097 | 1.225 | 1.365 | 1.518 | 1.685 | 1.867 | 2.065 | 2.280 | 2.512 | 2.764 | 3.037 | 3.331 | 3.647 | 3.988 | 4.354 | 4.748 |
| 1-Dodecene | $C_{12}H_{24}$ | 0.409 | 0.464 | 0.524 | 0.591 | 0.665 | 0.746 | 0.836 | 0.935 | 1.043 | 1.162 | 1.291 | 1.432 | 1.586 | 1.753 | 1.935 | 2.132 | 2.345 | 2.575 |
| 1-Tridecene | $C_{13}H_{26}$ | 0.191 | 0.219 | 0.251 | 0.286 | 0.325 | 0.368 | 0.416 | 0.470 | 0.529 | 0.595 | 0.67 | 0.75 | 0.83 | 0.93 | 1.03 | 1.15 | 1.27 | 1.41 |
| 1-Tetradecene | $C_{14}H_{28}$ | | | | | | 0.182 | 0.208 | 0.237 | 0.270 | 0.306 | 0.346 | 0.391 | 0.440 | 0.495 | 0.555 | 0.62 | 0.69 | 0.77 |

a Values of the vapor pressure are calculated from the constants given and the Antoine equation: $\log_{10} P = A - B/(C + t)$; $t = B/(A - \log_{10} P) - C$; (P in lb/in$^2$; t in °F)

TABLE 24k-E, (PART 1), Page 4 - NORMAL MONOOLEFINS (1-ALKENES), C₂ TO C₂₀

VAPOR PRESSURES AND BOILING POINTS, AT 0.2 TO 30 lb/in²

April 30, 1952 (Corrected)

Temperature in °F — Vapor pressure in lb/in²

| Compound | Formula | 310 | 315 | 320 | 325 | 330 | 335 | 340 | 345 | 350 | 355 | 360 | 365 | 370 | 375 | 380 | 385 | 390 | 395 |
|---|---|---|---|---|---|---|---|---|---|---|---|---|---|---|---|---|---|---|---|
| 1-Octene | $C_8H_{16}$ | | | | | | | | | | | | | | | | | | |
| 1-Nonene | $C_9H_{18}$ | 17.903 | 19.21 | 20.58 | 22.04 | 23.57 | 25.18 | 26.88 | 28.66 | 30.53 | | | | | | | | | |
| 1-Decene | $C_{10}H_{20}$ | 9.557 | 10.321 | 11.133 | 11.994 | 12.908 | 13.876 | 14.900 | 15.982 | 17.126 | 18.332 | 19.60 | 20.94 | 22.35 | 23.84 | 25.40 | 27.03 | 28.75 | 30.55 |
| 1-Undecene | $C_{11}H_{22}$ | 5.169 | 5.620 | 6.103 | 6.618 | 7.168 | 7.754 | 8.377 | 9.040 | 9.744 | 10.491 | 11.283 | 12.122 | 13.009 | 13.947 | 14.937 | 15.982 | 17.083 | 18.244 |
| 1-Dodecene | $C_{12}H_{24}$ | 2.824 | 3.092 | 3.380 | 3.690 | 4.023 | 4.379 | 4.761 | 5.170 | 5.606 | 6.072 | 6.568 | 7.097 | 7.659 | 8.257 | 8.891 | 9.563 | 10.275 | 11.029 |
| 1-Tridecene | $C_{13}H_{26}$ | 1.56 | 1.72 | 1.89 | 2.08 | 2.28 | 2.50 | 2.73 | 2.98 | 3.26 | 3.55 | 3.86 | 4.20 | 4.55 | 4.94 | 5.35 | 5.78 | 6.24 | 6.74 |
| 1-Tetradecene | $C_{14}H_{28}$ | 0.86 | 0.96 | 1.06 | 1.18 | 1.30 | 1.43 | 1.58 | 1.74 | 1.91 | 2.09 | 2.29 | 2.50 | 2.73 | 2.98 | 3.25 | 3.53 | 3.83 | 4.16 |

Temperature in °F — Vapor pressure in lb/in²

| Compound | Formula | 400 | 405 | 410 | 415 | 420 | 425 | 430 | 435 | 440 | 445 | 450 | 455 | 460 | 465 | 470 | 475 | 480 | 485 |
|---|---|---|---|---|---|---|---|---|---|---|---|---|---|---|---|---|---|---|---|
| 1-Octene | $C_8H_{16}$ | | | | | | | | | | | | | | | | | | |
| 1-Nonene | $C_9H_{18}$ | | | | | | | | | | | | | | | | | | |
| 1-Decene | $C_{10}H_{20}$ | | | | | | | | | | | | | | | | | | |
| 1-Undecene | $C_{11}H_{22}$ | 19.46 | 20.75 | 22.10 | 23.51 | 25.00 | 26.55 | 28.19 | 29.89 | | | | | | | | | | |
| 1-Dodecene | $C_{12}H_{24}$ | 11.826 | 12.668 | 13.557 | 14.494 | 15.482 | 16.522 | 17.616 | 18.77 | 19.97 | 21.24 | 22.57 | 23.96 | 25.42 | 26.95 | 28.55 | 30.22 | | |
| 1-Tridecene | $C_{13}H_{26}$ | 7.26 | 7.82 | 8.41 | 9.03 | 9.69 | 10.39 | 11.13 | 11.91 | 12.73 | 13.59 | 14.51 | 15.47 | 16.47 | 17.53 | 18.65 | 19.81 | 21.04 | 22.32 |
| 1-Tetradecene | $C_{14}H_{28}$ | 4.50 | 4.87 | 5.27 | 5.69 | 6.13 | 6.60 | 7.11 | 7.64 | 8.20 | 8.80 | 9.43 | 10.09 | 10.80 | 11.54 | 12.32 | 13.14 | 14.01 | 14.92 |

Temperature in °F — Vapor pressure in lb/in²

| Compound | Formula | 490 | 495 | 500 | 505 | 510 | 515 | 520 | 525 | 530 | 535 | 540 | 545 |
|---|---|---|---|---|---|---|---|---|---|---|---|---|---|
| 1-Octene | $C_8H_{16}$ | | | | | | | | | | | | |
| 1-Nonene | $C_9H_{18}$ | | | | | | | | | | | | |
| 1-Decene | $C_{10}H_{20}$ | | | | | | | | | | | | |
| 1-Undecene | $C_{11}H_{22}$ | | | | | | | | | | | | |
| 1-Dodecene | $C_{12}H_{24}$ | | | | | | | | | | | | |
| 1-Tridecene | $C_{13}H_{26}$ | 23.66 | 25.06 | 26.53 | 28.06 | 29.7 | | | | | | | |
| 1-Tetradecene | $C_{14}H_{28}$ | 15.87 | 16.87 | 17.92 | 19.03 | 20.18 | 21.39 | 22.65 | 23.97 | 25.35 | 26.79 | 28.3 | 29.9 |

TABLE 24k-E, (PART 1), Page 5 – NORMAL MONOOLEFINS (1-ALKENES), C₂ TO C₂₀

VAPOR PRESSURES AND BOILING POINTS, AT 0.2 TO 30 lb/in²

April 30, 1952 (Corrected)

| Compound | Formula | Constants of the Antoine equation | | | Temperature in °F — Vapor pressure in lb/in² | | | | | | | | | | | | | |
|---|---|---|---|---|---|---|---|---|---|---|---|---|---|---|---|---|---|---|
| | | A | B | C | 270 | 275 | 280 | 285 | 290 | 295 | 300 | 305 | 310 | 315 | 320 | 325 | 330 | 335 |
| 1-Pentadecene | C₁₅H₃₀ | 5.2367 | 3114.54 | 250.64 | 0.180 | 0.205 | 0.233 | 0.264 | 0.299 | 0.338 | 0.381 | 0.428 | 0.480 | 0.54 | 0.60 | 0.67 | 0.75 | 0.83 |
| 1-Hexadecene | C₁₆H₃₂ | 5.222 | 3159.4 | 235.1 | | | | | | 0.18 | 0.21 | 0.24 | 0.27 | 0.30 | 0.34 | 0.38 | 0.43 | 0.48 |
| 1-Heptadecene | C₁₇H₃₄ | 5.206 | 3194.3 | 219.5 | | | | | | | | | | | 0.19 | 0.22 | 0.25 | 0.28 |
| 1-Octadecene | C₁₈H₃₆ | 5.187 | 3220.9 | 203.6 | | | | | | | | | | | | | | |
| 1-Nonadecene | C₁₉H₃₈ | 5.167 | 3240.5 | 187.8 | | | | | | | | | | | | | | |
| 1-Eicosene | C₂₀H₄₀ | 5.145 | 3254.2 | 171.9 | | | | | | | | | | | | | | |

| Compound | Formula | Temperature in °F — Vapor pressure in lb/in² | | | | | | | | | | | | | | | | | |
|---|---|---|---|---|---|---|---|---|---|---|---|---|---|---|---|---|---|---|
| | | 340 | 345 | 350 | 355 | 360 | 365 | 370 | 375 | 380 | 385 | 390 | 395 | 400 | 405 | 410 | 415 | 420 | 425 |
| 1-Pentadecene | C₁₅H₃₀ | 0.92 | 1.02 | 1.13 | 1.24 | 1.37 | 1.51 | 1.65 | 1.81 | 1.99 | 2.17 | 2.37 | 2.59 | 2.82 | 3.06 | 3.33 | 3.61 | 3.91 | 4.24 |
| 1-Hexadecene | C₁₆H₃₂ | 0.54 | 0.60 | 0.66 | 0.74 | 0.82 | 0.91 | 1.00 | 1.11 | 1.22 | 1.34 | 1.47 | 1.61 | 1.77 | 1.93 | 2.11 | 2.30 | 2.51 | 2.73 |
| 1-Heptadecene | C₁₇H₃₄ | 0.31 | 0.35 | 0.40 | 0.44 | 0.49 | 0.55 | 0.61 | 0.68 | 0.75 | 0.84 | 0.92 | 1.02 | 1.12 | 1.23 | 1.35 | 1.48 | 1.63 | 1.78 |
| 1-Octadecene | C₁₈H₃₆ | 0.183 | 0.207 | 0.234 | 0.26 | 0.30 | 0.33 | 0.37 | 0.42 | 0.47 | 0.52 | 0.58 | 0.64 | 0.71 | 0.78 | 0.87 | 0.96 | 1.05 | 1.16 |
| 1-Nonadecene | C₁₉H₃₈ | | | | | 0.18 | 0.20 | 0.23 | 0.26 | 0.29 | 0.32 | 0.36 | 0.40 | 0.45 | 0.50 | 0.56 | 0.62 | 0.68 | 0.76 |
| 1-Eicosene | C₂₀H₄₀ | | | | | | | | | 0.177 | 0.200 | 0.226 | 0.25 | 0.28 | 0.32 | 0.36 | 0.40 | 0.44 | 0.49 |

| Compound | Formula | Temperature in °F — Vapor pressure in lb/in² | | | | | | | | | | | | | | | | | |
|---|---|---|---|---|---|---|---|---|---|---|---|---|---|---|---|---|---|---|
| | | 430 | 435 | 440 | 445 | 450 | 455 | 460 | 465 | 470 | 475 | 480 | 485 | 490 | 495 | 500 | 505 | 510 | 515 |
| 1-Pentadecene | C₁₅H₃₀ | 4.58 | 4.94 | 5.33 | 5.75 | 6.19 | 6.65 | 7.14 | 7.67 | 8.22 | 8.80 | 9.42 | 10.07 | 10.75 | 11.47 | 12.23 | 13.03 | 13.87 | 14.75 |
| 1-Hexadecene | C₁₆H₃₂ | 2.96 | 3.22 | 3.48 | 3.77 | 4.08 | 4.40 | 4.75 | 5.12 | 5.51 | 5.93 | 6.37 | 6.83 | 7.32 | 7.85 | 8.40 | 8.98 | 9.59 | 10.23 |
| 1-Heptadecene | C₁₇H₃₄ | 1.94 | 2.12 | 2.30 | 2.51 | 2.72 | 2.95 | 3.20 | 3.46 | 3.74 | 4.04 | 4.36 | 4.70 | 5.06 | 5.44 | 5.84 | 6.27 | 6.72 | 7.20 |
| 1-Octadecene | C₁₈H₃₆ | 1.27 | 1.39 | 1.52 | 1.66 | 1.82 | 1.98 | 2.15 | 2.34 | 2.54 | 2.76 | 2.99 | 3.23 | 3.49 | 3.77 | 4.07 | 4.38 | 4.71 | 5.07 |
| 1-Nonadecene | C₁₉H₃₈ | 0.84 | 0.92 | 1.01 | 1.11 | 1.22 | 1.34 | 1.46 | 1.60 | 1.74 | 1.90 | 2.06 | 2.24 | 2.43 | 2.64 | 2.86 | 3.09 | 3.34 | 3.60 |
| 1-Eicosene | C₂₀H₄₀ | 0.55 | 0.61 | 0.67 | 0.74 | 0.82 | 0.90 | 0.99 | 1.09 | 1.19 | 1.30 | 1.42 | 1.55 | 1.69 | 1.84 | 2.00 | 2.18 | 2.36 | 2.56 |

a Values of the vapor pressure are calculated from the constants given and the Antoine equation: $\log_{10} P = A - B/(C + t)$; $t = B/(A - \log_{10}P) - C$; ($P$ in lb/in²; $t$ in °F)

TABLE 24k-E, (PART 1), Page 6 – NORMAL MONOOLEFINS (1-ALKENES), C₂ TO C₂₀

VAPOR PRESSURES AND BOILING POINTS, AT 0.2 TO 30 lb/in²

April 30, 1952

### Temperature in °F — Vapor pressure in lb/in²

| Compound | Formula | 520 | 525 | 530 | 535 | 540 | 545 | 550 | 555 | 560 | 565 | 570 | 575 | 580 | 585 | 590 | 595 | 600 | 605 |
|---|---|---|---|---|---|---|---|---|---|---|---|---|---|---|---|---|---|---|---|
| 1-Pentadecene | $C_{15}H_{30}$ | 15.67 | 16.64 | 17.66 | 18.72 | 19.84 | 21.00 | 22.21 | 23.48 | 24.81 | 26.2 | 27.6 | 29.1 | 30.7 | | | | | |
| 1-Hexadecene | $C_{16}H_{32}$ | 10.91 | 11.63 | 12.38 | 13.16 | 13.99 | 14.86 | 15.77 | 16.72 | 17.72 | 18.76 | 19.85 | 20.99 | 22.18 | 23.42 | 24.7 | 26.1 | 27.5 | 28.9 |
| 1-Heptadecene | $C_{17}H_{34}$ | 7.70 | 8.23 | 8.79 | 9.38 | 10.00 | 10.66 | 11.35 | 12.1 | 12.8 | 13.6 | 14.5 | 15.3 | 16.2 | 17.2 | 18.2 | 19.2 | 20.3 | 21.5 |
| 1-Octadecene | $C_{18}H_{36}$ | 5.44 | 5.84 | 6.26 | 6.70 | 7.17 | 7.66 | 8.18 | 8.7 | 9.3 | 9.9 | 10.6 | 11.2 | 11.9 | 12.7 | 13.4 | 14.2 | 15.1 | 16.0 |
| 1-Nonadecene | $C_{19}H_{38}$ | 3.88 | 4.18 | 4.49 | 4.83 | 5.18 | 5.56 | 5.96 | 6.37 | 6.8 | 7.3 | 7.8 | 8.3 | 8.8 | 9.4 | 10.0 | 10.7 | 11.3 | 12.0 |
| 1-Eicosene | $C_{20}H_{40}$ | 2.77 | 2.99 | 3.23 | 3.48 | 3.75 | 4.03 | 4.34 | 4.66 | 5.00 | 5.36 | 5.74 | 6.14 | 6.56 | 7.0 | 7.5 | 8.0 | 8.5 | 9.0 |

### Temperature in °F — Vapor pressure in lb/in²

| Compound | Formula | 610 | 615 | 620 | 625 | 630 | 635 | 640 | 645 | 650 | 655 | 660 | 665 | 670 | 675 | 680 | 685 | 690 | 695 |
|---|---|---|---|---|---|---|---|---|---|---|---|---|---|---|---|---|---|---|---|
| 1-Pentadecene | $C_{15}H_{30}$ | 30.4 | | | | | | | | | | | | | | | | | |
| 1-Hexadecene | $C_{16}H_{32}$ | | | | | | | | | | | | | | | | | | |
| 1-Heptadecene | $C_{17}H_{34}$ | 22.7 | 23.9 | 25.2 | 26.5 | 27.9 | 29.4 | 30.9 | | | | | | | | | | | |
| 1-Octadecene | $C_{18}H_{36}$ | 16.9 | 17.9 | 18.9 | 19.9 | 21.0 | 22.2 | 23.4 | 24.6 | 25.9 | 27.3 | 28.7 | 30.1 | | | | | | |
| 1-Nonadecene | $C_{19}H_{38}$ | 12.7 | 13.5 | 14.3 | 15.1 | 16.0 | 16.9 | 17.9 | 18.9 | 19.9 | 21.0 | 22.1 | 23.3 | 24.5 | 25.8 | 27.1 | 28.5 | 29.9 | |
| 1-Eicosene | $C_{20}H_{40}$ | 9.6 | 10.2 | 10.9 | 11.5 | 12.2 | 12.9 | 13.7 | 14.5 | 15.3 | 16.2 | 17.1 | 18.1 | 19.0 | 20.4 | 21.1 | 22.3 | 23.4 | 24.6 |

### Temperature in °F — Vapor pressure in lb/in²

| Compound | Formula | 700 | 705 | 710 | 715 |
|---|---|---|---|---|---|
| 1-Pentadecene | $C_{15}H_{30}$ | | | | |
| 1-Hexadecene | $C_{16}H_{32}$ | | | | |
| 1-Heptadecene | $C_{17}H_{34}$ | | | | |
| 1-Octadecene | $C_{18}H_{36}$ | | | | |
| 1-Nonadecene | $C_{19}H_{38}$ | | | | |
| 1-Eicosene | $C_{20}H_{40}$ | 25.9 | 27.2 | 28.5 | 29.9 |

## TABLE 8k-E, (PART 1), Page 1 - MONOOLEFINS, $C_2$ TO $C_5$
### VAPOR PRESSURES AND BOILING POINTS[a]
April 30, 1952; December 31, 1952

| Compound | Formula | Constants of the Antoine equation | | | Temperature in °F — Vapor pressure in lb/in² | | | | | | | | | | | | | |
| --- | --- | --- | --- | --- | --- | --- | --- | --- | --- | --- | --- | --- | --- | --- | --- | --- | --- | --- |
| | | A | B | C | -245 | -240 | -235 | -230 | -225 | -220 | -215 | -210 | -205 | -200 | -195 | -190 | -185 | -180 |
| Ethene (Ethylene) | $C_2H_4$ | 5.03395 | 1053.00 | 427.00 | 0.177 | 0.253 | 0.354 | 0.488 | 0.662 | 0.885 | 1.167 | 1.519 | 1.953 | 2.484 | 3.127 | 3.899 | 4.816 | 5.899 |
| Propene (Propylene) | $C_3H_6$ | 5.10599 | 1413.00 | 412.60 | | | | | | | | | | | | | | |
| 1-Butene | $C_4H_8$ | 5.12929 | 1666.98 | 400.00 | | | | | | | | | | | | | | |
| cis-2-Butene | " | 5.15565 | 1728.18 | 394.600 | | | | | | | | | | | | | | |
| trans-2-Butene | " | 5.15591 | 1729.44 | 400.00 | | | | | | | | | | | | | | |
| 2-Methylpropene (Isobutene) | " | 5.12773 | 1661.76 | 400.000 | | | | | | | | | | | | | | |

| Compound | Formula | Temperature in °F — Vapor pressure in lb/in² | | | | | | | | | | | | | | | | | |
| --- | --- | --- | --- | --- | --- | --- | --- | --- | --- | --- | --- | --- | --- | --- | --- | --- | --- | --- |
| | | -175 | -170 | -165 | -160 | -155 | -150 | -145 | -140 | -135 | -130 | -125 | -120 | -115 | -110 | -105 | -100 | -95 | -90 |
| Ethene (Ethylene) | $C_2H_4$ | 7.168 | 8.64 | 10.35 | 12.31 | 14.54 | 17.08 | 19.95 | 23.17 | 26.78 | 30.8 | | | | | | | | |
| Propene (Propylene) | $C_3H_6$ | | 0.191 | 0.251 | 0.325 | 0.418 | 0.531 | 0.669 | 0.837 | 1.037 | 1.276 | 1.559 | 1.892 | 2.280 | 2.732 | 3.254 | 3.853 | 4.539 | 5.32 |
| 1-Butene | $C_4H_8$ | | | | | | | | | | | | | 0.191 | 0.240 | 0.301 | 0.374 | 0.461 | 0.565 |
| cis-2-Butene | " | | | | | | | | | | | | | | | | 0.195 | 0.244 | 0.303 |
| trans-2-Butene | " | | | | | | | | | | | | | | | 0.196 | 0.246 | 0.306 | 0.378 |
| 2-Methylpropene (Isobutene) | " | | | | | | | | | | | | | 0.198 | 0.250 | 0.312 | 0.388 | 0.478 | 0.585 |

a Values of the vapor pressure are calculated from the constants given and the Antoine equation: $\log_{10} P = A - B/(C + t)$; $t = B/(A - \log_{10} P) - C$; (P in lb/in²; t in °F)

TABLE 8k-E (PART 1), Page 2 — MONOOLEFINS, $C_2$ TO $C_5$
VAPOR PRESSURES AND BOILING POINTS, AT 0.2 TO 30 lb/in²
April 30, 1952; December 31, 1952

Temperature in °F

Vapor pressure in lb/in²

| Compound | Formula | -85 | -80 | -75 | -70 | -65 | -60 | -55 | -50 | -45 | -40 | -35 | -30 | -25 | -20 | -15 | -10 | -5 | 0 |
|---|---|---|---|---|---|---|---|---|---|---|---|---|---|---|---|---|---|---|---|
| Ethene (Ethylene) | $C_2H_4$ | | | | | | | | | | | | | | | | | | |
| Propene (Propylene) | $C_3H_6$ | 6.21 | 7.21 | 8.33 | 9.59 | 10.99 | 12.55 | 14.28 | 16.19 | 18.29 | 20.59 | 23.12 | 25.87 | 28.9 | | | | | |
| 1-Butene | $C_4H_8$ | 0.688 | 0.832 | 1.000 | 1.196 | 1.423 | 1.684 | 1.984 | 2.325 | 2.714 | 3.153 | 3.649 | 4.207 | 4.831 | 5.527 | 6.30 | 7.16 | 8.11 | 9.16 |
| cis-2-Butene | " | 0.375 | 0.460 | 0.560 | 0.679 | 0.817 | 0.979 | 1.166 | 1.382 | 1.631 | 1.914 | 2.238 | 2.604 | 3.019 | 3.485 | 4.009 | 4.594 | 5.246 | 5.972 |
| trans-2-Butene | " | 0.463 | 0.564 | 0.683 | 0.823 | 0.985 | 1.173 | 1.390 | 1.639 | 1.924 | 2.249 | 2.616 | 3.032 | 3.500 | 4.025 | 4.612 | 5.266 | 5.992 | 6.797 |
| 2-Methylpropene (Isobutene) | " | 0.712 | 0.860 | 1.034 | 1.236 | 1.470 | 1.739 | 2.047 | 2.398 | 2.797 | 3.249 | 3.758 | 4.330 | 4.970 | 5.684 | 6.478 | 7.359 | 8.332 | 9.404 |

Temperature in °F

Vapor pressure in lb/in²

| Compound | Formula | 5 | 10 | 15 | 20 | 25 | 30 | 35 | 40 | 45 | 50 | 55 | 60 | 65 | 70 | 75 |
|---|---|---|---|---|---|---|---|---|---|---|---|---|---|---|---|---|
| Ethene (Ethylene) | $C_2H_4$ | | | | | | | | | | | | | | | |
| Propene (Propylene) | $C_3H_6$ | | | | | | | | | | | | | | | |
| 1-Butene | $C_4H_8$ | 10.31 | 11.57 | 12.96 | 14.46 | 16.11 | 17.89 | 19.82 | 21.91 | 24.17 | 26.60 | 29.2 | | | | |
| cis-2-Butene | " | 6.775 | 7.662 | 8.639 | 9.713 | 10.890 | 12.176 | 13.579 | 15.107 | 16.76 | 18.56 | 20.50 | 22.60 | 24.86 | 27.29 | 29.89 |
| trans-2-Butene | " | 7.686 | 8.665 | 9.740 | 10.919 | 12.21 | 13.61 | 15.14 | 16.80 | 18.60 | 20.55 | 22.64 | 24.90 | 27.33 | 29.94 | |
| 2-Methylpropene (Isobutene) | " | 10.583 | 11.876 | 13.289 | 14.831 | 16.509 | 18.33 | 20.30 | 22.44 | 24.74 | 27.2 | 29.9 | | | | |

TABLE 8k-E (PART 1), Page 3 – MONOOLEFINS, C₂ TO C₅

VAPOR PRESSURES AND BOILING POINTS[a]

October 31, 1950; December 31, 1952

| Compound | Formula | Constants of the Antoine equation | | | Temperature in °F — Vapor pressure in lb/in² | | | | | | | | | | | | | |
|---|---|---|---|---|---|---|---|---|---|---|---|---|---|---|---|---|---|---|
| | | A | B | C | -80 | -75 | -70 | -65 | -60 | -55 | -50 | -45 | -40 | -35 | -30 | -25 | -20 | -15 |
| 1-Pentene | C₅H₁₀ | 5.13289 | 1880.811 | 388.329 | | | | 0.207 | 0.254 | 0.309 | 0.375 | 0.452 | 0.541 | 0.645 | 0.766 | 0.904 | 1.063 | 1.244 |
| cis-2-Pentene | " | 5.15913 | 1922.312 | 388.053 | | | | | | 0.199 | 0.244 | 0.297 | 0.359 | 0.433 | 0.518 | 0.617 | 0.732 | 0.863 |
| trans-2-Pentene | " | 5.19214 | 1951.177 | 387.337 | | | | | | 0.209 | 0.256 | 0.311 | 0.376 | 0.451 | 0.539 | 0.641 | 0.759 | 0.895 |
| 2-Methyl-1-butene | " | 5.15953 | 1896.804 | 387.013 | | | | 0.186 | 0.229 | 0.280 | 0.340 | 0.411 | 0.494 | 0.590 | 0.702 | 0.832 | 0.980 | 1.150 |
| 3-Methyl-1-butene | " | 5.11257 | 1824.253 | 394.269 | 0.203 | 0.250 | 0.307 | 0.374 | 0.452 | 0.544 | 0.651 | 0.775 | 0.919 | 1.084 | 1.272 | 1.487 | 1.731 | 2.008 |
| 2-Methyl-2-butene | " | 5.20201 | 1971.158 | 387.116 | | | | | | 0.185 | 0.226 | 0.276 | 0.334 | 0.402 | 0.481 | 0.574 | 0.680 | 0.802 |

| Compound | Formula | Temperature in °F — Vapor pressure in lb/in² | | | | | | | | | | | | | | | | | |
|---|---|---|---|---|---|---|---|---|---|---|---|---|---|---|---|---|---|---|---|
| | | -10 | -5 | 0 | 5 | 10 | 15 | 20 | 25 | 30 | 35 | 40 | 45 | 50 | 55 | 60 | 65 | 70 | 75 |
| 1-Pentene | C₅H₁₀ | 1.450 | 1.684 | 1.948 | 2.244 | 2.577 | 2.949 | 3.363 | 3.824 | 4.334 | 4.898 | 5.519 | 6.202 | 6.951 | 7.770 | 8.664 | 9.639 | 10.697 | 11.846 |
| cis-2-Pentene | " | 1.014 | 1.187 | 1.383 | 1.605 | 1.855 | 2.137 | 2.453 | 2.807 | 3.200 | 3.638 | 4.123 | 4.659 | 5.250 | 5.900 | 6.612 | 7.392 | 8.244 | 9.171 |
| trans-2-Pentene | " | 1.050 | 1.227 | 1.428 | 1.656 | 1.912 | 2.200 | 2.524 | 2.885 | 3.287 | 3.734 | 4.229 | 4.776 | 5.373 | 6.041 | 6.767 | 7.561 | 8.428 | 9.373 |
| 2-Methyl-1-butene | " | 1.344 | 1.564 | 1.813 | 2.094 | 2.409 | 2.763 | 3.157 | 3.596 | 4.084 | 4.623 | 5.219 | 5.874 | 6.595 | 7.384 | 8.247 | 9.188 | 10.213 | 11.325 |
| 3-Methyl-1-butene | " | 2.319 | 2.663 | 3.060 | 3.496 | 3.982 | 4.521 | 5.117 | 5.775 | 6.499 | 7.293 | 8.163 | 9.113 | 10.148 | 11.274 | 12.496 | 13.820 | 15.250 | 16.793 |
| 2-Methyl-2-butene | " | 0.944 | 1.105 | 1.289 | 1.496 | 1.731 | 1.996 | 2.292 | 2.624 | 2.994 | 3.406 | 3.863 | 4.369 | 4.927 | 5.540 | 6.215 | 6.953 | 7.760 | 8.640 |

a Values of the vapor pressure are calculated from the constants given and the Antoine equation: $\log_{10} P = A - B/(C + t)$; $t = B/(A - \log_{10} P) - C$; ($P$ in lb/in²; $t$ in °F)

TABLE 8k-E (PART 1), Page 4 — MONOOLEFINS, $C_2$ TO $C_5$

VAPOR PRESSURES AND BOILING POINTS, AT 0.2 TO 30 lb/in²

October 31, 1950; December 31, 1952

| Compound | Formula | Temperature in °F | | | | | | | | | | | | |
|---|---|---|---|---|---|---|---|---|---|---|---|---|---|---|
| | | 80 | 85 | 90 | 95 | 100 | 105 | 110 | 115 | 120 | 125 | 130 | 135 | 140 |
| | | Vapor pressure in lb/in² | | | | | | | | | | | | |
| 1-Pentene | $C_5H_{10}$ | 13.089 | 14.431 | 15.880 | 17.439 | 19.115 | 20.91 | 22.84 | 24.90 | 27.10 | 29.44 | | | |
| cis-2-Pentene | " | 10.180 | 11.274 | 12.459 | 13.740 | 15.122 | 16.611 | 18.211 | 19.93 | 21.77 | 23.74 | 25.84 | 28.08 | |
| trans-2-Pentene | " | 10.400 | 11.514 | 12.721 | 14.024 | 15.431 | 16.945 | 18.573 | 20.32 | 22.19 | 24.20 | 26.34 | 28.62 | |
| 2-Methyl-1-butene | " | 12.552 | 13.837 | 15.246 | 16.765 | 18.399 | 20.16 | 22.04 | 24.05 | 26.21 | 28.51 | | | |
| 3-Methyl-1-butene | " | 18.455 | 20.24 | 22.16 | 24.21 | 26.41 | 28.76 | | | | | | | |
| 2-Methyl-2-butene | " | 9.598 | 10.638 | 11.765 | 12.986 | 14.303 | 15.723 | 17.252 | 18.893 | 20.66 | 22.54 | 24.56 | 26.71 | 29.01 |

TABLE 11k-E, (PART 1), Page 1 - DIOLEFINS, C$_3$ TO C$_5$

VAPOR PRESSURES AND BOILING POINTS[a]

April 30, 1952; December 31, 1952

Constants of the Antoine equation; Temperature in °F; Vapor pressure in lb/in²

| Compound | Formula | A | B | C | -150 | -145 | -140 | -135 | -130 | -125 | -120 | -115 | -110 | -105 | -100 | -95 | -90 | -85 |
|---|---|---|---|---|---|---|---|---|---|---|---|---|---|---|---|---|---|---|
| Propadiene (Allene) | C$_3$H$_4$ | 3.9321 | 793.8 | 317.2 | 0.15 | 0.21 | 0.28 | 0.38 | 0.49 | 0.63 | 0.81 | 1.01 | 1.26 | 1.55 | 1.89 | 2.3 | 2.7 | 3.3 |
| 1,2-Butadiene | C$_4$H$_6$ | 5.4483 | 2017.8 | 419.80 | | | | | | | | | | | | 0.17 | 0.21 | 0.26 |
| 1,3-Butadiene | " | 5.14580 | 1683.956 | 399.197 | | | | | | | | 0.166 | 0.210 | 0.264 | 0.329 | 0.407 | 0.501 | 0.611 |
| 1,2-Pentadiene | C$_5$H$_8$ | 5.29739 | 2077.956 | 390.374 | | | | | | | | | | | | | | |
| 1,cis-3-Pentadiene | " | 5.22817 | 2013.068 | 384.389 | | | | | | | | | | | | | | |
| 1,trans-3-Pentadiene | " | 5.20896 | 1996.087 | 386.208 | | | | | | | | | | | | | | |
| 1,4-Pentadiene | " | 5.13519 | 1845.029 | 386.237 | | | | | | | | | | | | | | |
| 2,3-Pentadiene | " | 5.17242 | 1955.945 | 369.472 | | | | | | | | | | | | | | |
| 3-Methyl-1,2-butadiene | " | 5.291 | 2034. | 389. | | | | | | | | | | | | | | |
| 2-Methyl-1,3-butadiene (Isoprene) | " | 5.18973 | 1945.793 | 390.402 | | | | | | | | | | | | | | |

Temperature in °F; Vapor pressure in lb/in²

| Compound | Formula | -80 | -75 | -70 | -65 | -60 | -55 | -50 | -45 | -40 | -35 | -30 | -25 | -20 | -15 | -10 | -5 | 0 | 5 |
|---|---|---|---|---|---|---|---|---|---|---|---|---|---|---|---|---|---|---|---|
| Propadiene (Allene) | C$_3$H$_4$ | 3.9 | 4.5 | 5.3 | 6.1 | 7.0 | 8.0 | 9.1 | 10.4 | 11.7 | 13.2 | 14.7 | 16.4 | 18.2 | 20.2 | 22.3 | 24.5 | 26.9 | 29.4 |
| 1,2-Butadiene | C$_4$H$_6$ | 0.32 | 0.39 | 0.48 | 0.58 | 0.69 | 0.83 | 0.98 | 1.16 | 1.37 | 1.60 | 1.87 | 2.17 | 2.52 | 2.91 | 3.35 | 3.84 | 4.38 | 4.99 |
| 1,3-Butadiene | " | 0.742 | 0.894 | 1.073 | 1.279 | 1.518 | 1.792 | 2.106 | 2.463 | 2.869 | 3.327 | 3.843 | 4.422 | 5.069 | 5.791 | 6.593 | 7.481 | 8.461 | 9.542 |
| 1,2-Pentadiene | C$_5$H$_8$ | | | | | | | | 0.191 | 0.233 | 0.282 | 0.340 | 0.408 | 0.486 | 0.578 | 0.683 | 0.804 | 0.943 | 1.101 |
| 1,cis-3-Pentadiene | " | | | | | | | | 0.198 | 0.241 | 0.293 | 0.353 | 0.423 | 0.505 | 0.600 | 0.710 | 0.836 | 0.980 | 1.144 |
| 1,trans-3-Pentadiene | " | | | | | | | 0.187 | 0.229 | 0.278 | 0.335 | 0.403 | 0.482 | 0.573 | 0.679 | 0.800 | 0.939 | 1.098 | 1.278 |
| 1,4-Pentadiene | " | | | 0.200 | 0.246 | 0.302 | 0.367 | 0.445 | 0.535 | 0.640 | 0.762 | 0.904 | 1.066 | 1.251 | 1.463 | 1.703 | 1.975 | 2.282 | 2.626 |
| 2,3-Pentadiene | " | | | | | | | | | 0.172 | 0.211 | 0.257 | 0.312 | 0.376 | 0.451 | 0.539 | 0.640 | 0.756 | 0.890 |
| 3-Methyl-1,2-butadiene | " | | | | | | | 0.20 | 0.24 | 0.29 | 0.35 | 0.42 | 0.50 | 0.60 | 0.71 | 0.84 | 0.99 | 1.2 | 1.3 |
| 2-Methyl-1,3-butadiene (Isoprene) | " | | | | | 0.200 | 0.245 | 0.298 | 0.360 | 0.433 | 0.519 | 0.618 | 0.732 | 0.864 | 1.015 | 1.188 | 1.384 | 1.606 | 1.856 |

a  Values of the vapor pressure are calculated from the constants given and the Antoine equation: $\log_{10} P = A - B/(C + t)$; $t = B/(A - \log_{10} P) - C$; (P in lb/in²; t in °F)

TABLE 11k-E, (PART 1), Page 2 - DIOLEFINS, C₃ TO C₅

VAPOR PRESSURES AND BOILING POINTS

April 30, 1952; December 31, 1952

Temperature in °F — Vapor pressure in lb/in²

| Compound | Formula | 10 | 15 | 20 | 25 | 30 | 35 | 40 | 45 | 50 | 55 | 60 | 65 | 70 | 75 | 80 | 85 | 90 | 95 |
|---|---|---|---|---|---|---|---|---|---|---|---|---|---|---|---|---|---|---|---|
| Propadiene (Allene) | $C_3H_4$ | | | | | | | | | | | | | | | | | | |
| 1,2-Butadiene | $C_4H_6$ | 5.67 | 6.42 | 7.25 | 8.16 | 9.17 | 10.27 | 11.48 | 12.80 | 14.23 | 15.79 | 17.49 | 19.3 | 21.3 | 23.5 | 25.8 | 28.3 | 30.9 | |
| 1,3-Butadiene | " | 10.728 | 12.028 | 13.449 | 14.999 | 16.684 | 18.513 | 20.49 | 22.64 | 24.95 | 27.43 | 30.10 | | | | | | | |
| 1,2-Pentadiene | $C_5H_8$ | 1.280 | 1.484 | 1.713 | 1.971 | 2.261 | 2.584 | 2.945 | 3.346 | 3.791 | 4.283 | 4.826 | 5.423 | 6.078 | 6.796 | 7.581 | 8.437 | 9.369 | 10.381 |
| 1,cis-3-Pentadiene | " | 1.330 | 1.541 | 1.779 | 2.046 | 2.346 | 2.680 | 3.053 | 3.467 | 3.926 | 4.433 | 4.991 | 5.605 | 6.279 | 7.016 | 7.822 | 8.699 | 9.653 | 10.689 |
| 1,trans-3-Pentadiene | " | 1.482 | 1.713 | 1.972 | 2.263 | 2.589 | 2.951 | 3.354 | 3.801 | 4.295 | 4.840 | 5.439 | 6.097 | 6.817 | 7.603 | 8.461 | 9.394 | 10.407 | 11.505 |
| 1,4-Pentadiene | " | 3.012 | 3.442 | 3.921 | 4.453 | 5.041 | 5.691 | 6.405 | 7.190 | 8.050 | 8.989 | 10.013 | 11.127 | 12.336 | 13.336 | 15.063 | 16.592 | 18.24 | 20.01 |
| 2,3-Pentadiene | " | 1.042 | 1.216 | 1.414 | 1.637 | 1.888 | 2.171 | 2.487 | 2.840 | 3.233 | 3.668 | 4.151 | 4.683 | 5.269 | 5.913 | 6.619 | 7.390 | 8.232 | 9.148 |
| 3-Methyl-1,2-butadiene | " | 1.6 | 1.8 | 2.1 | 2.4 | 2.7 | 3.1 | 3.5 | 4.0 | 4.5 | 5.1 | 5.8 | 6.5 | 7.2 | 8.1 | 9.0 | 10.0 | 11.1 | 12.3 |
| 2-Methyl-1,3-butadiene (Isoprene) | " | 2.139 | 2.455 | 2.809 | 3.203 | 3.642 | 4.128 | 4.665 | 5.257 | 5.909 | 6.624 | 7.406 | 8.261 | 9.193 | 10.206 | 11.305 | 12.497 | 13.784 | 15.174 |

Temperature in °F — Vapor pressure in lb/in²

| Compound | Formula | 100 | 105 | 110 | 115 | 120 | 125 | 130 | 135 | 140 | 145 | 150 | 155 | 160 |
|---|---|---|---|---|---|---|---|---|---|---|---|---|---|---|
| Propadiene (Allene) | $C_3H_4$ | | | | | | | | | | | | | |
| 1,2-Butadiene | $C_4H_6$ | | | | | | | | | | | | | |
| 1,3-Butadiene | " | | | | | | | | | | | | | |
| 1,2-Pentadiene | $C_5H_8$ | 11.479 | 12.667 | 13.950 | 15.335 | 16.825 | 18.43 | 20.15 | 21.99 | 23.96 | 26.07 | 28.31 | 30.71 | |
| 1,cis-3-Pentadiene | " | 11.811 | 13.024 | 14.333 | 15.744 | 17.261 | 18.89 | 20.64 | 22.51 | 24.51 | 26.64 | 28.92 | | |
| 1,trans-3-Pentadiene | " | 12.692 | 13.974 | 15.356 | 16.843 | 18.44 | 20.15 | 21.99 | 23.95 | 26.04 | 28.27 | 30.65 | | |
| 1,4-Pentadiene | " | 21.91 | 23.95 | 26.13 | 28.46 | 30.94 | | | | | | | | |
| 2,3-Pentadiene | " | 10.143 | 11.222 | 12.389 | 13.651 | 15.010 | 16.474 | 18.046 | 19.73 | 21.54 | 23.47 | 25.54 | 27.74 | 30.08 |
| 3-Methyl-1,2-butadiene | " | 13.5 | 14.9 | 16.4 | 18.0 | 19.7 | 21.6 | 23.5 | 25.7 | 27.9 | 30.3 | | | |
| 2-Methyl-1,3-butadiene (Isoprene) | " | 16.672 | 18.28 | 20.01 | 21.86 | 23.85 | 25.97 | 28.23 | 30.64 | | | | | |

TABLE 5k-E, Page 1 - ALKYL BENZENES, $C_6$ TO $C_9$
VAPOR PRESSURES AND BOILING POINTS, AT 0.2 TO 30 $lb/in^2$
November 30, 1949; December 31, 1952

| Compound | Formula | Constants of the Antoine equation | | | Temperature in °F — Vapor pressure in $lb/in^2$ | | | | | | | | | | | | | | |
|---|---|---|---|---|---|---|---|---|---|---|---|---|---|---|---|---|---|---|---|
| | | A | B | C | 10 | 15 | 20 | 25 | 30 | 35 | 40 | 45 | 50 | 55 | 60 | 65 | 70 | 75 |
| Benzene | $C_6H_6$ | 7.4066[a] | 3407.0[a] | 408.39[a] | 0.183[a] | 0.229[a] | 0.284[a] | 0.351[a] | 0.432[a] | 0.528[a] | 0.643[a] | | | | | | | |
| | | 5.19204 | 2179.859 | 365.422 | | | | | | | | 0.760 | 0.880 | 1.016 | 1.170 | 1.341 | 1.534 | 1.748 |
| Methylbenzene (Toluene) | $C_7H_8$ | 5.24103 | 2420.640 | 363.068 | | | | | | | | 0.204 | 0.240 | 0.282 | 0.331 | 0.386 | 0.448 | 0.519 |
| Ethylbenzene | $C_8H_{10}$ | 5.24358 | 2563.659 | 351.771 | | | | | | | | | | | | | | |
| 1,2-Dimethylbenzene (o-Xylene) | " | 5.28530 | 2654.422 | 352.635 | | | | | | | | | | | | | | |
| 1,3-Dimethylbenzene (m-Xylene) | " | 5.29547 | 2632.079 | 355.189 | | | | | | | | | | | | | | |
| 1,4-Dimethylbenzene (p-Xylene) | " | 5.27691 | 2616.174 | 355.553 | | | | | | | | | | | | | | |
| n-Propylbenzene | $C_9H_{12}$ | 5.23781 | 2684.335 | 340.852 | | | | | | | | | | | | | | |
| Isopropylbenzene | " | 5.22305 | 2629.427 | 341.999 | | | | | | | | | | | | | | |
| 1-Methyl-2-ethylbenzene | " | 5.28953 | 2763.673 | 341.140 | | | | | | | | | | | | | | |
| 1-Methyl-3-ethylbenzene | " | 5.30221 | 2752.531 | 343.316 | | | | | | | | | | | | | | |
| 1-Methyl-4-ethylbenzene | " | 5.28441 | 2748.803 | 344.058 | | | | | | | | | | | | | | |
| 1,2,3-Trimethylbenzene | " | 5.32721 | 2869.124 | 340.740 | | | | | | | | | | | | | | |
| 1,2,4-Trimethylbenzene | " | 5.33022 | 2831.881 | 343.415 | | | | | | | | | | | | | | |
| 1,3,5-Trimethylbenzene | " | 5.36075 | 2825.320 | 345.240 | | | | | | | | | | | | | | |

Values of the vapor pressure are calculated from the constants given and the Antoine equation: $\log_{10} P = A - B/(C + t)$; $t = B/(A - \log_{10} P) - C$; (P in $lb/in^2$; t in °F).

[a] For the solid. At the triple point, 41.945°F, the pressure is 0.6933 $lb/in^2$.

TABLE 5k-E, Page 2 - ALKYL BENZENES, C$_6$ TO C$_9$

VAPOR PRESSURES AND BOILING POINTS, AT 0.2 TO 30 lb/in$^2$

November 30, 1949; December 31, 1952

| Compound | Formula | Temperature in °F — Vapor pressure in lb/in$^2$ | | | | | | | | | | | | | | | | | |
|---|---|---|---|---|---|---|---|---|---|---|---|---|---|---|---|---|---|---|---|
| | | 80 | 85 | 90 | 95 | 100 | 105 | 110 | 115 | 120 | 125 | 130 | 135 | 140 | 145 | 150 | 155 | 160 | 165 |
| Benzene | C$_6$H$_6$ | 1.967 | 2.251 | 2.544 | 2.868 | 3.224 | 3.616 | 4.045 | 4.515 | 5.028 | 5.587 | 6.195 | 6.855 | 7.570 | 8.343 | 9.178 | 10.079 | 11.047 | 12.088 |
| Methylbenzene (Toluene) | C$_7$H$_8$ | 0.599 | 0.690 | 0.791 | 0.905 | 1.032 | 1.174 | 1.331 | 1.505 | 1.698 | 1.912 | 2.146 | 2.404 | 2.687 | 2.997 | 3.335 | 3.703 | 4.104 | 4.540 |
| Ethylbenzene | C$_8$H$_{10}$ | 0.202 | 0.237 | 0.276 | 0.320 | 0.371 | 0.428 | 0.492 | 0.564 | 0.645 | 0.735 | 0.836 | 0.948 | 1.073 | 1.210 | 1.363 | 1.530 | 1.715 | 1.917 |
| 1,2-Dimethylbenzene (o-Xylene) | " | | | 0.194 | 0.227 | 0.264 | 0.306 | 0.353 | 0.406 | 0.467 | 0.534 | 0.610 | 0.695 | 0.789 | 0.894 | 1.010 | 1.138 | 1.280 | 1.436 |
| 1,3-Dimethylbenzene (m-Xylene) | " | | 0.207 | 0.242 | 0.281 | 0.326 | 0.377 | 0.434 | 0.498 | 0.571 | 0.652 | 0.742 | 0.843 | 0.955 | 1.080 | 1.217 | 1.369 | 1.536 | 1.720 |
| 1,4-Dimethylbenzene (p-Xylene) | " | 0.186 | 0.218 | 0.254 | 0.295 | 0.342 | 0.395 | 0.454 | 0.521 | 0.596 | 0.680 | 0.774 | 0.879 | 0.994 | 1.123 | 1.265 | 1.421 | 1.594 | 1.783 |
| n-Propylbenzene | C$_9$H$_{12}$ | | | | | | | 0.192 | 0.224 | 0.259 | 0.299 | 0.344 | 0.395 | 0.452 | 0.516 | 0.588 | 0.667 | 0.756 | 0.854 |
| Isopropylbenzene | " | | | | | 0.188 | 0.219 | 0.254 | 0.295 | 0.340 | 0.391 | 0.449 | 0.514 | 0.586 | 0.667 | 0.756 | 0.856 | 0.966 | 1.088 |
| 1-Methyl-2-ethylbenzene | " | | | | | | | | | 0.198 | 0.229 | 0.265 | 0.306 | 0.351 | 0.402 | 0.460 | 0.524 | 0.595 | 0.675 |
| 1-Methyl-3-ethylbenzene | " | | | | | | | | 0.196 | 0.230 | 0.266 | 0.307 | 0.353 | 0.405 | 0.463 | 0.528 | 0.601 | 0.681 | 0.771 |
| 1-Methyl-4-ethylbenzene | " | | | | | | | | 0.198 | 0.230 | 0.266 | 0.306 | 0.352 | 0.403 | 0.461 | 0.526 | 0.598 | 0.678 | 0.767 |
| 1,2,3-Trimethylbenzene | " | | | | | | | | | | | | 0.198 | 0.229 | 0.263 | 0.302 | 0.346 | 0.396 | 0.451 |
| 1,2,4-Trimethylbenzene | " | | | | | | | | | | 0.193 | 0.223 | 0.258 | 0.297 | 0.340 | 0.390 | 0.445 | 0.507 | 0.576 |
| 1,3,5-Trimethylbenzene | " | | | | | | | | | 0.194 | 0.225 | 0.260 | 0.300 | 0.345 | 0.396 | 0.453 | 0.516 | 0.587 | 0.666 |

## TABLE 5k-E, Page 3 - ALKYL BENZENES, $C_6$ TO $C_9$
## VAPOR PRESSURES AND BOILING POINTS, AT 0.2 TO 30 $lb/in^2$
November 30, 1949; December 31, 1952

| Compound | Formula | Temperature in °F — Vapor pressure in $lb/in^2$ | | | | | | | | | | | | | | | | | |
|---|---|---|---|---|---|---|---|---|---|---|---|---|---|---|---|---|---|---|---|
| | | 170 | 175 | 180 | 185 | 190 | 195 | 200 | 205 | 210 | 215 | 220 | 225 | 230 | 235 | 240 | 245 | 250 | 255 |
| Benzene | $C_6H_6$ | 13.205 | 14.402 | 15.681 | 17.049 | 18.508 | 20.062 | 21.715 | 23.47 | 25.34 | 27.32 | 29.41 | | | | | | | |
| Methylbenzene (Toluene) | $C_7H_8$ | 5.013 | 5.524 | 6.077 | 6.674 | 7.316 | 8.008 | 8.750 | 9.547 | 10.400 | 11.313 | 12.288 | 13.328 | 14.437 | 15.617 | 16.872 | 18.20 | 19.62 | 21.11 |
| Ethylbenzene | $C_8H_{10}$ | 2.139 | 2.381 | 2.646 | 2.934 | 3.248 | 3.588 | 3.957 | 4.356 | 4.787 | 5.252 | 5.753 | 6.291 | 6.870 | 7.490 | 8.155 | 8.865 | 9.625 | 10.435 |
| 1,2-Dimethylbenzene (o-Xylene) | " | 1.608 | 1.797 | 2.003 | 2.229 | 2.475 | 2.743 | 3.034 | 3.351 | 3.694 | 4.065 | 4.465 | 4.897 | 5.363 | 5.864 | 6.401 | 6.978 | 7.596 | 8.258 |
| 1,3-Dimethylbenzene (m-Xylene) | " | 1.922 | 2.143 | 2.385 | 2.648 | 2.935 | 3.247 | 3.586 | 3.953 | 4.350 | 4.779 | 5.242 | 5.740 | 6.275 | 6.851 | 7.468 | 8.129 | 8.837 | 9.592 |
| 1,4-Dimethylbenzene (p-Xylene) | " | 1.990 | 2.218 | 2.466 | 2.736 | 3.030 | 3.350 | 3.696 | 4.072 | 4.478 | 4.916 | 5.388 | 5.896 | 6.442 | 7.029 | 7.657 | 8.330 | 9.049 | 9.817 |
| n-Propylbenzene | $C_9H_{12}$ | 0.962 | 1.082 | 1.214 | 1.359 | 1.518 | 1.692 | 1.882 | 2.090 | 2.316 | 2.562 | 2.829 | 3.118 | 3.432 | 3.770 | 4.135 | 4.528 | 4.950 | 5.405 |
| Isopropylbenzene | " | 1.223 | 1.371 | 1.534 | 1.712 | 1.908 | 2.121 | 2.353 | 2.606 | 2.881 | 3.179 | 3.502 | 3.851 | 4.228 | 4.634 | 5.071 | 5.541 | 6.046 | 6.586 |
| 1-Methyl-2-ethylbenzene | " | 0.763 | 0.861 | 0.969 | 1.088 | 1.220 | 1.364 | 1.522 | 1.695 | 1.884 | 2.090 | 2.314 | 2.558 | 2.823 | 3.109 | 3.419 | 3.754 | 4.115 | 4.504 |
| 1-Methyl-3-ethylbenzene | " | 0.871 | 0.981 | 1.103 | 1.236 | 1.384 | 1.545 | 1.722 | 1.915 | 2.126 | 2.356 | 2.606 | 2.877 | 3.171 | 3.489 | 3.832 | 4.203 | 4.602 | 5.032 |
| 1-Methyl-4-ethylbenzene | " | 0.865 | 0.974 | 1.094 | 1.227 | 1.372 | 1.532 | 1.706 | 1.897 | 2.105 | 2.331 | 2.577 | 2.844 | 3.134 | 3.447 | 3.785 | 4.149 | 4.542 | 4.964 |
| 1,2,3-Trimethylbenzene | " | 0.512 | 0.581 | 0.657 | 0.741 | 0.834 | 0.937 | 1.050 | 1.175 | 1.311 | 1.460 | 1.624 | 1.802 | 1.996 | 2.207 | 2.436 | 2.685 | 2.954 | 3.244 |
| 1,2,4-Trimethylbenzene | " | 0.652 | 0.737 | 0.831 | 0.935 | 1.050 | 1.176 | 1.315 | 1.467 | 1.634 | 1.815 | 2.014 | 2.229 | 2.464 | 2.718 | 2.994 | 3.292 | 3.614 | 3.962 |
| 1,3,5-Trimethylbenzene | " | 0.754 | 0.851 | 0.959 | 1.077 | 1.208 | 1.352 | 1.510 | 1.683 | 1.872 | 2.078 | 2.303 | 2.548 | 2.813 | 3.101 | 3.413 | 3.750 | 4.114 | 4.506 |

TABLE 5k-E, Page 4 - ALKYL BENZENES, $C_6$ TO $C_9$
VAPOR PRESSURES AND BOILING POINTS, AT 0.2 TO 30 lb/in²
November 30, 1949; December 31, 1952

| Compound | Formula | Temperature in °F — Vapor pressure in lb/in² | | | | | | | | | | | | | | | | | |
| --- | --- | --- | --- | --- | --- | --- | --- | --- | --- | --- | --- | --- | --- | --- | --- | --- | --- | --- | --- |
| | | 260 | 265 | 270 | 275 | 280 | 285 | 290 | 295 | 300 | 305 | 310 | 315 | 320 | 325 | 330 | 335 | 340 | 345 |
| Benzene | $C_6H_6$ | 22.70 | 24.37 | 26.14 | 28.01 | 29.98 | | | | | | | | | | | | | |
| Methylbenzene (Toluene) | $C_7H_8$ | | | | | | | | | | | | | | | | | | |
| Ethylbenzene | $C_8H_{10}$ | 11.299 | 12.218 | 13.195 | 14.234 | 15.335 | 16.503 | 17.738 | 19.046 | 20.43 | 21.89 | 23.42 | 25.04 | 26.75 | 28.54 | 30.43 | | | |
| 1,2-Dimethylbenzene (o-Xylene) | " | 8.964 | 9.718 | 10.522 | 11.378 | 12.288 | 13.255 | 14.281 | 15.370 | 16.522 | 17.742 | 19.030 | 20.39 | 21.83 | 23.34 | 24.94 | 26.61 | 28.38 | |
| 1,3-Dimethylbenzene (m-Xylene) | " | 10.399 | 11.258 | 12.174 | 13.147 | 14.181 | 15.278 | 16.441 | 17.672 | 18.975 | 20.35 | 21.81 | 23.34 | 24.96 | 26.66 | 28.45 | | | |
| 1,4-Dimethylbenzene (p-Xylene) | " | 10.636 | 11.509 | 12.437 | 13.425 | 14.472 | 15.584 | 16.761 | 18.01 | 19.32 | 20.72 | 22.19 | 23.74 | 25.37 | 27.08 | 28.89 | | | |
| n-Propylbenzene | $C_9H_{12}$ | 5.892 | 6.414 | 6.973 | 7.570 | 8.207 | 8.886 | 9.610 | 10.380 | 11.197 | 12.065 | 12.986 | 13.961 | 14.993 | 16.083 | 17.236 | 18.45 | 19.73 | 21.08 |
| Isopropylbenzene | " | 7.165 | 7.784 | 8.445 | 9.150 | 9.901 | 10.700 | 11.549 | 12.451 | 13.408 | 14.422 | 15.495 | 16.629 | 17.83 | 19.09 | 20.43 | 21.83 | 23.31 | 24.87 |
| 1-Methyl-2-ethylbenzene | " | 4.922 | 5.371 | 5.853 | 6.369 | 6.921 | 7.511 | 8.140 | 8.812 | 9.527 | 10.288 | 11.096 | 11.954 | 12.864 | 13.827 | 14.847 | 15.926 | 17.065 | 18.27 |
| 1-Methyl-3-ethylbenzene | " | 5.494 | 5.989 | 6.520 | 7.088 | 7.696 | 8.344 | 9.036 | 9.773 | 10.557 | 11.391 | 12.276 | 13.214 | 14.209 | 15.262 | 16.375 | 17.55 | 18.79 | 20.10 |
| 1-Methyl-4-ethylbenzene | " | 5.418 | 5.905 | 6.426 | 6.984 | 7.580 | 8.217 | 8.895 | 9.618 | 10.386 | 11.203 | 12.070 | 12.990 | 13.964 | 14.995 | 16.085 | 17.236 | 18.45 | 19.73 |
| 1,2,3-Trimethylbenzene | " | 3.558 | 3.896 | 4.260 | 4.651 | 5.071 | 5.521 | 6.003 | 6.519 | 7.069 | 7.657 | 8.283 | 8.950 | 9.659 | 10.412 | 11.211 | 12.059 | 12.957 | 13.907 |
| 1,2,4-Trimethylbenzene | " | 4.336 | 4.739 | 5.172 | 5.636 | 6.133 | 6.665 | 7.234 | 7.842 | 8.490 | 9.180 | 9.914 | 10.694 | 11.523 | 12.403 | 13.334 | 14.321 | 15.364 | 16.467 |
| 1,3,5-Trimethylbenzene | " | 4.928 | 5.381 | 5.868 | 6.391 | 6.950 | 7.548 | 8.187 | 8.868 | 9.595 | 10.368 | 11.191 | 12.065 | 12.992 | 13.975 | 15.017 | 16.119 | 17.284 | 18.515 |

TABLE 5k-E, Page 5 - ALKYL BENZENES, $C_6$ TO $C_9$
VAPOR PRESSURES AND BOILING POINTS, AT 0.2 TO 30 lb/in$^2$
November 30, 1949; December 31, 1952

| Compound | Formula | Temperature in °F — Vapor pressure in lb/in$^2$ | | | | | | | | | | |
|---|---|---|---|---|---|---|---|---|---|---|---|---|
| | | 350 | 355 | 360 | 365 | 370 | 375 | 380 | 385 | 390 | 395 | 400 |
| Benzene | $C_6H_6$ | | | | | | | | | | | |
| Methylbenzene (Toluene) | $C_7H_8$ | | | | | | | | | | | |
| Ethylbenzene | $C_8H_{10}$ | | | | | | | | | | | |
| 1,2-Dimethylbenzene (o-Xylene) | " | | | | | | | | | | | |
| 1,3-Dimethylbenzene (m-Xylene) | " | | | | | | | | | | | |
| 1,4-Dimethylbenzene (p-Xylene) | " | | | | | | | | | | | |
| n-Propylbenzene | $C_9H_{12}$ | 22.50 | 24.00 | 25.57 | 27.22 | 28.95 | | | | | | |
| Isopropylbenzene | " | 26.50 | 28.22 | 30.02 | | | | | | | | |
| 1-Methyl-2-ethylbenzene | " | 19.54 | 20.87 | 22.28 | 23.76 | 25.31 | 26.94 | 28.65 | | | | |
| 1-Methyl-3-ethylbenzene | " | 21.48 | 22.94 | 24.47 | 26.07 | 27.76 | 29.53 | | | | | |
| 1-Methyl-4-ethylbenzene | " | 21.08 | 22.50 | 24.00 | 25.57 | 27.22 | 28.95 | | | | | |
| 1,2,3-Trimethylbenzene | " | 14.91 | 15.97 | 17.09 | 18.27 | 19.52 | 20.83 | 22.20 | 23.65 | 25.17 | 26.76 | 28.44 |
| 1,2,4-Trimethylbenzene | " | 17.63 | 18.86 | 20.15 | 21.51 | 22.95 | 24.46 | 26.04 | 27.70 | 29.44 | | |
| 1,3,5-Trimethylbenzene | " | 19.81 | 21.18 | 22.62 | 24.14 | 25.74 | 27.42 | 29.18 | | | | |

TABLE 14k-E, Page 1 - ALKYL BENZENES, $C_{10}$

VAPOR PRESSURES AND BOILING POINTS, AT 0.2 TO 30 lb/in²

November 30, 1949; December 31, 1952

| Compound | Formula | Constants of the Antoine equation | | | Temperature in °F — Vapor pressure in lb/in² | | | | | | | | | | | | | |
|---|---|---|---|---|---|---|---|---|---|---|---|---|---|---|---|---|---|---|
| | | A | B | C | 125 | 130 | 135 | 140 | 145 | 150 | 155 | 160 | 165 | 170 | 175 | 180 | 185 | 190 |
| n-Butylbenzene | $C_{10}H_{14}$ | 5.26956 | 2840.337 | 330.480 | | | | | 0.198 | 0.228 | 0.262 | 0.301 | 0.344 | 0.393 | 0.447 | 0.508 | 0.575 | 0.649 |
| Isobutylbenzene | " | 5.21672 | 2747.491 | 335.508 | | 0.206 | 0.238 | 0.274 | 0.315 | 0.361 | 0.412 | 0.470 | 0.534 | 0.605 | 0.684 | 0.771 | 0.867 | 0.974 |
| sec-Butylbenzene | " | 5.23736 | 2772.313 | 337.182 | | 0.201 | 0.232 | 0.268 | 0.308 | 0.352 | 0.402 | 0.458 | 0.521 | 0.590 | 0.668 | 0.753 | 0.848 | 0.952 |
| tert-Butylbenzene | " | 5.20689 | 2708.230 | 333.990 | 0.202 | 0.234 | 0.271 | 0.311 | 0.357 | 0.409 | 0.466 | 0.530 | 0.602 | 0.681 | 0.769 | 0.867 | 0.974 | 1.092 |
| 1-Methyl-2-propylbenzene | " | 5.2887 | 2869.20 | 331.51 | | | | | 0.185 | 0.214 | 0.246 | 0.283 | 0.324 | 0.369 | 0.421 | 0.478 | 0.542 | 0.61 |
| 1-Methyl-3-propylbenzene | " | 5.3024 | 2863.80 | 333.31 | | | | | 0.207 | 0.238 | 0.274 | 0.314 | 0.359 | 0.410 | 0.466 | 0.529 | 0.599 | 0.676 |
| 1-Methyl-4-propylbenzene | " | 5.2790 | 2860.20 | 333.67 | | | | | 0.201 | 0.232 | 0.267 | 0.306 | 0.349 | 0.398 | 0.453 | 0.514 | 0.581 | 0.656 |
| 1-Methyl-2-isopropylbenzene | " | 5.2291 | 2788.20 | 333.76 | | | 0.191 | 0.221 | 0.254 | 0.292 | 0.335 | 0.382 | 0.435 | 0.495 | 0.561 | 0.63 | 0.72 | 0.80 |
| 1-Methyl-3-isopropylbenzene | " | 5.2292 | 2772.00 | 335.16 | | 0.186 | 0.216 | 0.249 | 0.286 | 0.328 | 0.375 | 0.428 | 0.486 | 0.552 | 0.62 | 0.71 | 0.79 | 0.89 |
| 1-Methyl-4-isopropylbenzene | " | 5.2124 | 2768.40 | 333.58 | | | 0.201 | 0.233 | 0.268 | 0.307 | 0.352 | 0.401 | 0.457 | 0.519 | 0.588 | 0.66 | 0.75 | 0.84 |
| 1,2-Diethylbenzene | " | 5.27655 | 2840.209 | 328.997 | | | | | 0.192 | 0.222 | 0.256 | 0.294 | 0.337 | 0.384 | 0.438 | 0.497 | 0.563 | 0.637 |
| 1,3-Diethylbenzene | " | 5.29239 | 2837.270 | 329.807 | | | | | 0.207 | 0.239 | 0.275 | 0.316 | 0.362 | 0.413 | 0.470 | 0.533 | 0.604 | 0.662 |
| 1,4-Diethylbenzene | " | 5.28693 | 2860.691 | 331.634 | | | | | 0.193 | 0.222 | 0.256 | 0.294 | 0.336 | 0.384 | 0.437 | 0.496 | 0.562 | 0.635 |
| 1,2-Dimethyl-3-ethylbenzene | " | 5.3352 | 2962.80 | 329.80 | | | | | | | | 0.193 | 0.222 | 0.255 | 0.292 | 0.334 | 0.380 | 0.432 |
| 1,2-Dimethyl-4-ethylbenzene | " | 5.3357 | 2939.40 | 331.60 | | | | | | | 0.197 | 0.227 | 0.261 | 0.299 | 0.342 | 0.389 | 0.442 | 0.502 |
| 1,3-Dimethyl-2-ethylbenzene | " | 5.3304 | 2937.60 | 331.60 | | | | | | | 0.196 | 0.226 | 0.260 | 0.298 | 0.340 | 0.388 | 0.441 | 0.500 |
| 1,3-Dimethyl-4-ethylbenzene | " | 5.3291 | 2922.20 | 333.40 | | | | | | 0.183 | 0.212 | 0.243 | 0.279 | 0.319 | 0.364 | 0.415 | 0.471 | 0.533 |
| 1,3-Dimethyl-5-ethylbenzene | " | 5.3323 | 2907.00 | 335.20 | | | | | 0.190 | 0.219 | 0.252 | 0.290 | 0.332 | 0.379 | 0.431 | 0.490 | 0.555 | 0.627 |
| 1,4-Dimethyl-2-ethylbenzene | " | 5.3165 | 2919.60 | 335.20 | | | | | | 0.199 | 0.229 | 0.264 | 0.302 | 0.345 | 0.393 | 0.446 | 0.506 | 0.572 |
| 1,2,3,4-Tetramethylbenzene | " | 5.3448 | 3040.38 | 326.70 | | | | | | | | | | | 0.193 | 0.221 | 0.253 | 0.289 |
| 1,2,3,5-Tetramethylbenzene | " | 5.3633 | 3013.20 | 329.69 | | | | | | | | | 0.187 | 0.215 | 0.247 | 0.283 | 0.323 | 0.367 |
| 1,2,4,5-Tetramethylbenzene | " | 5.3654 | 3007.80 | 330.21 | | | | | | | | | 0.196 | 0.225 | 0.258 | 0.295 | 0.337 | 0.383 |

a Values of the vapor pressure are calculated from the constants given and the Antoine equation: $\log_{10} P = A - B/(C + t)$; $t = B/(A - \log_{10}P) - C$; (P in lb/in²; t in °F)

TABLE 14k-E, Page 2 - ALKYL BENZENES, C$_{10}$
VAPOR PRESSURES AND BOILING POINTS, AT 0.2 TO 30 lb/in2
November 30, 1949; December 31, 1952

Temperature in °F

Vapor pressure in lb/in²

| Compound | Formula | 195 | 200 | 205 | 210 | 215 | 220 | 225 | 230 | 235 | 240 | 245 | 250 | 255 | 260 | 265 | 270 | 275 | 280 |
|---|---|---|---|---|---|---|---|---|---|---|---|---|---|---|---|---|---|---|---|
| n-Butylbenzene | C$_{10}$H$_{14}$ | 0.732 | 0.823 | 0.923 | 1.034 | 1.155 | 1.288 | 1.433 | 1.592 | 1.765 | 1.953 | 2.158 | 2.380 | 2.620 | 2.880 | 3.160 | 3.463 | 3.789 | 4.139 |
| Isobutylbenzene | " | 1.091 | 1.219 | 1.360 | 1.514 | 1.682 | 1.866 | 2.065 | 2.282 | 2.517 | 2.771 | 3.047 | 3.344 | 3.664 | 4.009 | 4.380 | 4.778 | 5.204 | 5.662 |
| sec-Butylbenzene | " | 1.067 | 1.193 | 1.331 | 1.482 | 1.647 | 1.827 | 2.023 | 2.236 | 2.467 | 2.718 | 2.988 | 3.281 | 3.596 | 3.936 | 4.301 | 4.693 | 5.114 | 5.565 |
| tert-Butylbenzene | " | 1.223 | 1.365 | 1.521 | 1.692 | 1.878 | 2.081 | 2.302 | 2.541 | 2.800 | 3.081 | 3.384 | 3.710 | 4.063 | 4.441 | 4.848 | 5.284 | 5.752 | 6.252 |
| 1-Methyl-2-propylbenzene | " | 0.69 | 0.78 | 0.87 | 0.98 | 1.09 | 1.22 | 1.36 | 1.51 | 1.67 | 1.85 | 2.05 | 2.26 | 2.49 | 2.74 | 3.01 | 3.30 | 3.61 | 3.95 |
| 1-Methyl-3-propylbenzene | " | 0.76 | 0.86 | 0.96 | 1.08 | 1.20 | 1.34 | 1.49 | 1.65 | 1.83 | 2.03 | 2.24 | 2.47 | 2.72 | 2.99 | 3.28 | 3.59 | 3.93 | 4.30 |
| 1-Methyl-4-propylbenzene | " | 0.74 | 0.83 | 0.93 | 1.04 | 1.16 | 1.30 | 1.44 | 1.60 | 1.77 | 1.96 | 2.17 | 2.39 | 2.63 | 2.89 | 3.17 | 3.48 | 3.80 | 4.15 |
| 1-Methyl-2-isopropylbenzene | " | 0.90 | 1.01 | 1.13 | 1.26 | 1.41 | 1.56 | 1.73 | 1.92 | 2.12 | 2.34 | 2.58 | 2.84 | 3.11 | 3.41 | 3.74 | 4.08 | 4.46 | 4.86 |
| 1-Methyl-3-isopropylbenzene | " | 1.00 | 1.12 | 1.25 | 1.39 | 1.55 | 1.72 | 1.91 | 2.11 | 2.33 | 2.57 | 2.83 | 3.11 | 3.41 | 3.73 | 4.08 | 4.46 | 4.85 | 5.29 |
| 1-Methyl-4-isopropylbenzene | " | 0.94 | 1.06 | 1.18 | 1.32 | 1.47 | 1.63 | 1.80 | 2.00 | 2.21 | 2.43 | 2.68 | 2.94 | 3.23 | 3.54 | 3.87 | 4.22 | 4.61 | 5.02 |
| 1,2-Diethylbenzene | " | 0.718 | 0.808 | 0.907 | 1.016 | 1.136 | 1.268 | 1.412 | 1.569 | 1.741 | 1.927 | 2.130 | 2.350 | 2.589 | 2.847 | 3.126 | 3.427 | 3.751 | 4.100 |
| 1,3-Diethylbenzene | " | 0.769 | 0.865 | 0.971 | 1.087 | 1.215 | 1.355 | 1.508 | 1.675 | 1.858 | 2.056 | 2.272 | 2.506 | 2.759 | 3.033 | 3.329 | 3.648 | 3.992 | 4.362 |
| 1,4-Diethylbenzene | " | 0.716 | 0.805 | 0.904 | 1.012 | 1.132 | 1.262 | 1.405 | 1.561 | 1.731 | 1.917 | 2.118 | 2.336 | 2.573 | 2.829 | 3.106 | 3.405 | 3.726 | 4.072 |
| 1,2-Dimethyl-3-ethylbenzene | " | 0.489 | 0.553 | 0.624 | 0.70 | 0.79 | 0.88 | 0.99 | 1.10 | 1.23 | 1.37 | 1.52 | 1.68 | 1.86 | 2.05 | 2.26 | 2.49 | 2.73 | 3.00 |
| 1,2-Dimethyl-4-ethylbenzene | " | 0.567 | 0.640 | 0.72 | 0.81 | 0.91 | 1.02 | 1.13 | 1.26 | 1.41 | 1.56 | 1.73 | 1.91 | 2.11 | 2.33 | 2.56 | 2.82 | 3.09 | 3.38 |
| 1,3-Dimethyl-2-ethylbenzene | " | 0.565 | 0.637 | 0.72 | 0.81 | 0.90 | 1.01 | 1.13 | 1.26 | 1.40 | 1.55 | 1.72 | 1.90 | 2.10 | 2.32 | 2.55 | 2.80 | 3.07 | 3.37 |
| 1,3-Dimethyl-4-ethylbenzene | " | 0.602 | 0.68 | 0.76 | 0.86 | 0.96 | 1.07 | 1.20 | 1.33 | 1.48 | 1.64 | 1.82 | 2.01 | 2.22 | 2.44 | 2.68 | 2.95 | 3.23 | 3.54 |
| 1,3-Dimethyl-5-ethylbenzene | " | 0.71 | 0.80 | 0.89 | 1.00 | 1.12 | 1.25 | 1.39 | 1.54 | 1.71 | 1.90 | 2.10 | 2.32 | 2.55 | 2.81 | 3.08 | 3.38 | 3.70 | 4.05 |
| 1,4-Dimethyl-2-ethylbenzene | " | 0.65 | 0.73 | 0.82 | 0.92 | 1.02 | 1.14 | 1.27 | 1.42 | 1.57 | 1.74 | 1.92 | 2.12 | 2.34 | 2.58 | 2.83 | 3.11 | 3.40 | 3.72 |
| 1,2,3,4-Tetramethylbenzene | " | 0.329 | 0.374 | 0.423 | 0.478 | 0.540 | 0.607 | 0.68 | 0.76 | 0.86 | 0.95 | 1.06 | 1.18 | 1.31 | 1.45 | 1.61 | 1.78 | 1.96 | 2.16 |
| 1,2,3,5-Tetramethylbenzene | " | 0.417 | 0.473 | 0.534 | 0.603 | 0.68 | 0.76 | 0.85 | 0.95 | 1.06 | 1.19 | 1.32 | 1.46 | 1.62 | 1.79 | 1.98 | 2.18 | 2.40 | 2.64 |
| 1,2,4,5-Tetramethylbenzene | " | 0.435 | 0.493 | 0.557 | 0.627 | 0.71 | 0.79 | 0.89 | 0.99 | 1.11 | 1.23 | 1.37 | 1.52 | 1.68 | 1.86 | 2.05 | 2.26 | 2.49 | 2.73 |

TABLE 14-E, Page 3 - ALKYL BENZENES, C$_{10}$
VAPOR PRESSURES AND BOILING POINTS, AT 0.2 TO 30 lb/in$^2$
November 30, 1949; December 31, 1952

| Compound | Formula | Temperature in °F | | | | | | | | | | | | | | | | | |
|---|---|---|---|---|---|---|---|---|---|---|---|---|---|---|---|---|---|---|---|
| | | Vapor pressure in lb/in$^2$ | | | | | | | | | | | | | | | | | |
| | | 285 | 290 | 295 | 300 | 305 | 310 | 315 | 320 | 325 | 330 | 335 | 340 | 345 | 350 | 355 | 360 | 365 | 370 |
| n-Butylbenzene | C$_{10}$H$_{14}$ | 4.516 | 4.920 | 5.352 | 5.815 | 6.309 | 6.837 | 7.400 | 7.999 | 8.637 | 9.314 | 10.034 | 10.797 | 11.605 | 12.461 | 13.366 | 14.322 | 15.331 | 16.395 |
| Isobutylbenzene | " | 6.150 | 6.673 | 7.230 | 7.824 | 8.456 | 9.128 | 9.843 | 10.601 | 11.404 | 12.255 | 13.155 | 14.106 | 15.112 | 16.172 | 17.289 | 18.47 | 19.70 | 21.01 |
| sec-Butylbenzene | " | 6.047 | 6.563 | 7.113 | 7.700 | 8.324 | 8.989 | 9.695 | 10.444 | 11.239 | 12.081 | 12.972 | 13.914 | 14.910 | 15.960 | 17.068 | 18.235 | 19.46 | 20.76 |
| tert-Butylbenzene | " | 6.787 | 7.357 | 7.965 | 8.613 | 9.302 | 10.035 | 10.812 | 11.636 | 12.509 | 13.433 | 14.410 | 15.441 | 16.530 | 17.678 | 18.89 | 20.16 | 21.50 | 22.90 |
| 1-Methyl-2-nropylbenzene | " | 4.31 | 4.70 | 5.12 | 5.56 | 6.04 | 6.55 | 7.09 | 7.67 | 8.29 | 8.94 | 9.64 | 10.37 | 11.16 | 11.98 | 12.86 | 13.79 | 14.77 | 15.80 |
| 1-Methyl-3-nropylbenzene | " | 4.69 | 5.10 | 5.55 | 6.03 | 6.54 | 7.09 | 7.67 | 8.30 | 8.96 | 9.66 | 10.41 | 11.20 | 12.03 | 12.92 | 13.86 | 14.85 | 15.90 | 17.00 |
| 1-Methyl-4-nropylbenzene | " | 4.53 | 4.93 | 5.36 | 5.82 | 6.32 | 6.85 | 7.41 | 8.01 | 8.64 | 9.32 | 10.04 | 10.80 | 11.60 | 12.46 | 13.36 | 14.31 | 15.32 | 16.38 |
| 1-Methyl-2-isopropylbenzene | " | 5.28 | 5.74 | 6.23 | 6.76 | 7.31 | 7.91 | 8.54 | 9.21 | 9.92 | 10.68 | 11.48 | 12.33 | 13.22 | 14.17 | 15.17 | 16.22 | 17.33 | 18.50 |
| 1-Methyl-3-isopropylbenzene | " | 5.75 | 6.24 | 6.77 | 7.33 | 7.93 | 8.56 | 9.24 | 9.96 | 10.72 | 11.53 | 12.38 | 13.29 | 14.25 | 15.26 | 16.32 | 17.44 | 18.63 | 19.87 |
| 1-Methyl-4-isopropylbenzene | " | 5.46 | 5.93 | 6.43 | 6.97 | 7.54 | 8.14 | 8.79 | 9.48 | 10.20 | 10.98 | 11.79 | 12.66 | 13.57 | 14.54 | 15.56 | 16.63 | 17.76 | 18.94 |
| 1,2-Diethylbenzene | " | 4.475 | 4.877 | 5.308 | 5.769 | 6.262 | 6.788 | 7.350 | 7.948 | 8.584 | 9.261 | 9.980 | 10.742 | 11.550 | 12.405 | 13.310 | 14.266 | 15.276 | 16.341 |
| 1,3-Diethylbenzene | " | 4.759 | 5.185 | 5.641 | 6.129 | 6.651 | 7.208 | 7.802 | 8.435 | 9.108 | 9.823 | 10.582 | 11.388 | 12.241 | 13.145 | 14.100 | 15.109 | 16.175 | 17.299 |
| 1,4-Diethylbenzene | " | 4.444 | 4.842 | 5.269 | 5.728 | 6.215 | 6.737 | 7.294 | 7.887 | 8.518 | 9.189 | 9.901 | 10.657 | 11.458 | 12.306 | 13.203 | 14.151 | 15.152 | 16.209 |
| 1,2-Dimethyl-3-ethylbenzene | " | 3.28 | 3.59 | 3.92 | 4.27 | 4.66 | 5.06 | 5.50 | 5.96 | 6.46 | 6.99 | 7.56 | 8.16 | 8.80 | 9.48 | 10.20 | 10.96 | 11.78 | 12.63 |
| 1,2-Dimethyl-4-ethylbenzene | " | 3.70 | 4.04 | 4.41 | 4.81 | 5.23 | 5.68 | 6.16 | 6.68 | 7.23 | 7.81 | 8.44 | 9.10 | 9.80 | 10.55 | 11.34 | 12.18 | 13.06 | 14.00 |
| 1,3-Dimethyl-2-ethylbenzene | " | 3.68 | 4.02 | 4.39 | 4.78 | 5.20 | 5.65 | 6.13 | 6.64 | 7.18 | 7.77 | 8.39 | 9.04 | 9.74 | 10.48 | 11.27 | 12.10 | 12.98 | 13.91 |
| 1,3-Dimethyl-4-ethylbenzene | " | 3.87 | 4.22 | 4.60 | 5.01 | 5.45 | 5.91 | 6.41 | 6.94 | 7.51 | 8.11 | 8.75 | 9.44 | 10.16 | 10.93 | 11.74 | 12.60 | 13.51 | 14.47 |
| 1,3-Dimethyl-5-ethylbenzene | " | 4.42 | 4.82 | 5.24 | 5.70 | 6.19 | 6.71 | 7.27 | 7.86 | 8.49 | 9.17 | 9.88 | 10.64 | 11.44 | 12.30 | 13.20 | 14.15 | 15.16 | 16.22 |
| 1,4-Dimethyl-2-ethylbenzene | " | 4.06 | 4.43 | 4.83 | 5.25 | 5.70 | 6.19 | 6.70 | 7.25 | 7.84 | 8.46 | 9.12 | 9.83 | 10.57 | 11.37 | 12.20 | 13.09 | 14.02 | 15.01 |
| 1,2,3,4-Tetramethylbenzene | " | 2.37 | 2.60 | 2.85 | 3.12 | 3.40 | 3.71 | 4.04 | 4.40 | 4.78 | 5.19 | 5.62 | 6.09 | 6.58 | 7.11 | 7.67 | 8.27 | 8.90 | 9.57 |
| 1,2,3,5-Tetramethylbenzene | " | 2.89 | 3.17 | 3.47 | 3.79 | 4.13 | 4.50 | 4.89 | 5.31 | 5.77 | 6.25 | 6.76 | 7.31 | 7.89 | 8.51 | 9.17 | 9.87 | 10.61 | 11.40 |
| 1,2,4,5-Tetramethylbenzene | " | 2.99 | 3.28 | 3.59 | 3.91 | 4.27 | 4.65 | 5.05 | 5.49 | 5.95 | 6.45 | 6.98 | 7.54 | 8.14 | 8.78 | 9.46 | 10.18 | 10.94 | 11.74 |

## TABLE 14k-E, Page 4 — ALKYL BENZENES, C$_{10}$
### VAPOR PRESSURES AND BOILING POINTS, AT 0.2 TO 30 lb/in²
November 30, 1949; December 31, 1952

Temperature in °F — Vapor pressure in lb/in²

| Compound | Formula | 375 | 380 | 385 | 390 | 395 | 400 | 405 | 410 | 415 | 420 | 425 | 430 | 435 | 440 | 445 | 450 | 455 |
|---|---|---|---|---|---|---|---|---|---|---|---|---|---|---|---|---|---|---|
| n-Butylbenzene | C$_{10}$H$_{14}$ | 17.517 | 18.70 | 19.94 | 21.25 | 22.62 | 24.06 | 25.57 | 27.15 | 28.81 | | | | | | | | |
| Isobutylbenzene | " | 22.38 | 23.81 | 25.32 | 26.90 | 28.55 | | | | | | | | | | | | |
| sec-Butylbenzene | " | 22.11 | 23.54 | 25.04 | 26.60 | 28.25 | | | | | | | | | | | | |
| tert-Butylbenzene | " | 24.38 | 25.93 | 27.55 | 29.25 | 31.03 | | | | | | | | | | | | |
| 1-Methyl-2-propylbenzene | " | 16.89 | 18.04 | 19.24 | 20.51 | 21.8 | 23.2 | 24.7 | 26.3 | 27.9 | 29.6 | | | | | | | |
| 1-Methyl-3-propylbenzene | " | 18.17 | 19.39 | 20.68 | 22.0 | 23.5 | 25.0 | 26.5 | 28.2 | | | | | | | | | |
| 1-Methyl-4-propylbenzene | " | 17.50 | 18.68 | 19.91 | 21.2 | 22.6 | 24.0 | 25.5 | 27.1 | 28.7 | | | | | | | | |
| 1-Methyl-2-isopropylbenzene | " | 19.73 | 21.03 | 22.4 | 23.5 | 25.3 | 26.9 | 28.5 | | | | | | | | | | |
| 1-Methyl-3-isopropylbenzene | " | 21.2 | 22.6 | 24.0 | 25.5 | 27.1 | 28.7 | | | | | | | | | | | |
| 1-Methyl-4-isopropylbenzene | " | 20.20 | 21.5 | 22.9 | 24.3 | 25.9 | 27.5 | 29.1 | | | | | | | | | | |
| 1,2-Diethylbenzene | " | 17.464 | 18.65 | 19.89 | 21.20 | 22.57 | 24.02 | 25.53 | 27.12 | 28.78 | | | | | | | | |
| 1,3-Diethylbenzene | " | 18.48 | 19.73 | 21.04 | 22.42 | 23.87 | 25.39 | 26.99 | 28.66 | | | | | | | | | |
| 1,4-Diethylbenzene | " | 17.322 | 18.49 | 19.73 | 21.03 | 22.39 | 23.82 | 25.32 | 26.89 | 28.54 | | | | | | | | |
| 1,2-Dimethyl-3-ethylbenzene | " | 13.54 | 14.49 | 15.50 | 16.56 | 17.68 | 18.86 | 20.10 | 21.4 | 22.8 | 24.2 | 25.7 | 27.3 | 28.9 | | | | |
| 1,2-Dimethyl-4-ethylbenzene | " | 14.99 | 16.03 | 17.13 | 18.29 | 19.51 | 20.79 | 22.1 | 23.6 | 25.0 | 26.6 | 28.2 | | | | | | |
| 1,3-Dimethyl-2-ethylbenzene | " | 14.89 | 15.93 | 17.02 | 18.17 | 19.39 | 20.66 | 22.0 | 23.4 | 24.9 | 26.4 | 28.0 | 29.7 | | | | | |
| 1,3-Dimethyl-4-ethylbenzene | " | 15.48 | 16.55 | 17.68 | 18.87 | 20.12 | 21.4 | 22.8 | 24.3 | 25.8 | 27.4 | 29.0 | | | | | | |
| 1,3-Dimethyl-5-ethylbenzene | " | 17.34 | 18.52 | 19.76 | 21.08 | 22.4 | 23.9 | 25.4 | 27.0 | 28.7 | | | | | | | | |
| 1,4-Dimethyl-2-ethylbenzene | " | 16.06 | 17.15 | 18.31 | 19.52 | 20.81 | 22.2 | 23.6 | 25.0 | 26.6 | 28.2 | | | | | | | |
| 1,2,3,4-Tetramethylbenzene | " | 10.28 | 11.03 | 11.82 | 12.66 | 13.55 | 14.49 | 15.47 | 16.51 | 17.60 | 18.75 | 19.96 | 21.2 | 22.6 | 24.0 | 25.4 | 26.9 | 28.5 |
| 1,2,3,5-Tetramethylbenzene | " | 12.23 | 13.11 | 14.03 | 15.01 | 16.05 | 17.13 | 18.28 | 19.49 | 20.75 | 22.1 | 23.5 | 24.9 | 26.5 | 28.1 | 29.8 | | |
| 1,2,4,5-Tetramethylbenzene | " | 12.60 | 13.50 | 14.45 | 15.46 | 16.52 | 17.63 | 18.8 | 20.0 | 21.3 | 22.7 | 24.1 | 25.6 | 27.2 | 28.9 | | | |

TABLE 27k-E, Page 1 - NAPHTHALENES, $C_{10}$ TO $C_{12}$
VAPOR PRESSURES AND BOILING POINTS[a]
October 31, 1950; December 31, 1952

| Compound | Formula | Constants of the Antoine equation | | | Temperature in °F — Vapor pressure in lb/in² | | | | | | | | | | | | | |
|---|---|---|---|---|---|---|---|---|---|---|---|---|---|---|---|---|---|---|
| | | A | B | C | 190 | 195 | 200 | 205 | 210 | 215 | 220 | 225 | 230 | 235 | 240 | 245 | 250 | 255 |
| Naphthalene | $C_{10}H_{10}$ | 5.13216 | 2891.752 | 305.009 | 0.196 | 0.223 | 0.255 | 0.290 | 0.329 | 0.372 | 0.421 | 0.474 | 0.533 | 0.599 | 0.670 | 0.749 | 0.835 | 0.930 |
| 1-Methylnaphthalene | $C_{11}H_{12}$ | 5.35558 | 3334.813 | 323.889 | | | | | | | | 0.190 | 0.216 | 0.245 | 0.276 | 0.311 | 0.350 | 0.393 |
| 2-Methylnaphthalene | " | 5.35489 | 3312.482 | 325.111 | | | | | | | 0.190 | 0.215 | 0.244 | 0.276 | 0.311 | 0.350 | 0.394 | 0.441 |
| 1-Ethylnaphthalene | $C_{12}H_{14}$ | 5.2463 | 3224.5 | 292.9 | | | | | | | | | | | | 0.19 | 0.20 | 0.23 |
| 2-Ethylnaphthalene | " | 5.3683 | 3395. | 311.8 | | | | | | | | | | | | | 0.21 | 0.24 |

| Compound | Formula | Temperature in °F — Vapor pressure in lb/in² | | | | | | | | | | | | | | | | | |
|---|---|---|---|---|---|---|---|---|---|---|---|---|---|---|---|---|---|---|---|
| | | 260 | 265 | 270 | 275 | 280 | 285 | 290 | 295 | 300 | 305 | 310 | 315 | 320 | 325 | 330 | 335 | 340 | 345 |
| Naphthalene | $C_{10}H_{10}$ | 1.033 | 1.145 | 1.268 | 1.401 | 1.546 | 1.702 | 1.871 | 2.054 | 2.252 | 2.464 | 2.693 | 2.938 | 3.202 | 3.485 | 3.787 | 4.110 | 4.455 | 4.824 |
| 1-Methylnaphthalene | $C_{11}H_{12}$ | 0.440 | 0.493 | 0.550 | 0.612 | 0.681 | 0.756 | 0.838 | 0.927 | 1.024 | 1.129 | 1.243 | 1.367 | 1.500 | 1.645 | 1.801 | 1.968 | 2.149 | 2.343 |
| 2-Methylnaphthalene | " | 0.494 | 0.552 | 0.615 | 0.684 | 0.760 | 0.842 | 0.928 | 1.031 | 1.137 | 1.253 | 1.378 | 1.514 | 1.660 | 1.818 | 1.988 | 2.172 | 2.369 | 2.580 |
| 1-Ethylnaphthalene | $C_{12}H_{14}$ | 0.26 | 0.29 | 0.33 | 0.37 | 0.41 | 0.46 | 0.52 | 0.58 | 0.64 | 0.71 | 0.79 | 0.87 | 0.97 | 1.07 | 1.17 | 1.29 | 1.42 | 1.55 |
| 2-Ethylnaphthalene | " | 0.27 | 0.30 | 0.34 | 0.38 | 0.43 | 0.48 | 0.53 | 0.59 | 0.66 | 0.73 | 0.81 | 0.90 | 0.99 | 1.09 | 1.20 | 1.32 | 1.45 | 1.58 |

a Values of the vapor pressure are calculated from the constants given and the Antoine equation: $\log_{10} P = A - B/(C + t)$; $t = B/(A - \log_{10} P) - C$; ($P$ in lb/in²; $t$ in °F)

TABLE 27k-E, Page 2 - NAPHTHALENES, $C_{10}$ TO $C_{12}$
VAPOR PRESSURES AND BOILING POINTS
October 31, 1950; December 31, 1952

Temperature in °F — Vapor pressure in lb/in²

| Compound | Formula | 350 | 355 | 360 | 365 | 370 | 375 | 380 | 385 | 390 | 395 | 400 | 405 | 410 | 415 | 420 | 425 | 430 | 435 |
|---|---|---|---|---|---|---|---|---|---|---|---|---|---|---|---|---|---|---|---|
| Naphthalene | $C_{10}H_{10}$ | 5.216 | 5.633 | 6.077 | 6.549 | 7.049 | 7.579 | 8.141 | 8.735 | 9.363 | 10.026 | 10.726 | 11.464 | 12.241 | 13.058 | 13.918 | 14.822 | 15.771 | 16.766 |
| 1-Methylnaphthalene | $C_{11}H_{12}$ | 2.551 | 2.775 | 3.014 | 3.270 | 3.543 | 3.835 | 4.146 | 4.478 | 4.831 | 5.206 | 5.605 | 6.028 | 6.477 | 6.952 | 7.455 | 7.987 | 8.549 | 9.142 |
| 2-Methylnaphthalene | " | 2.807 | 3.051 | 3.311 | 3.589 | 3.886 | 4.203 | 4.540 | 4.900 | 5.282 | 5.688 | 6.118 | 6.576 | 7.060 | 7.572 | 8.115 | 8.688 | 9.293 | 9.931 |
| 1-Ethylnaphthalene | $C_{12}H_{14}$ | 1.70 | 1.86 | 2.03 | 2.21 | 2.41 | 2.62 | 2.85 | 3.09 | 3.35 | 3.62 | 3.91 | 4.23 | 4.56 | 4.91 | 5.29 | 5.68 | 6.11 | 6.55 |
| 2-Ethylnaphthalene | " | 1.73 | 1.89 | 2.07 | 2.25 | 2.45 | 2.66 | 2.89 | 3.14 | 3.40 | 3.67 | 3.97 | 4.29 | 4.62 | 4.98 | 5.36 | 5.76 | 6.19 | 6.65 |

Temperature in °F — Vapor pressure in lb/in²

| Compound | Formula | 440 | 445 | 450 | 455 | 460 | 465 | 470 | 475 | 480 | 485 | 490 | 495 | 500 | 505 | 510 | 515 | 520 | 525 |
|---|---|---|---|---|---|---|---|---|---|---|---|---|---|---|---|---|---|---|---|
| Naphthalene | $C_{10}H_{10}$ | 17.81 | 18.90 | 20.05 | 21.24 | 22.50 | 23.81 | 25.2 | 26.6 | 28.1 | 29.6 | | | | | | | | |
| 1-Methylnaphthalene | $C_{11}H_{12}$ | 9.768 | 10.428 | 11.123 | 11.854 | 12.624 | 13.432 | 14.282 | 15.173 | 16.108 | 17.09 | 18.20 | 19.19 | 20.31 | 21.48 | 22.71 | 23.99 | 25.3 | 26.7 |
| 2-Methylnaphthalene | " | 10.604 | 11.313 | 12.060 | 12.545 | 13.670 | 14.537 | 15.446 | 16.401 | 17.40 | 18.45 | 19.54 | 20.69 | 21.90 | 23.15 | 24.4 | 25.8 | 27.2 | 28.7 |
| 1-Ethylnaphthalene | $C_{12}H_{14}$ | 7.03 | 7.52 | 8.05 | 8.61 | 9.19 | 9.81 | 10.46 | 11.15 | 11.87 | 12.62 | 13.4 | 14.3 | 15.1 | 16.0 | 17.0 | 18.0 | 19.0 | 20.1 |
| 2-Ethylnaphthalene | " | 7.12 | 7.63 | 8.17 | 8.73 | 9.33 | 9.96 | 10.62 | 11.31 | 12.05 | 12.8 | 13.6 | 14.5 | 15.4 | 16.3 | 17.3 | 18.3 | 19.4 | 20.5 |

## TABLE 27k-E, Page 3 - NAPHTHALENES, $C_{10}$ TO $C_{12}$
### VAPOR PRESSURES AND BOILING POINTS, AT 0.2 TO 30 lb/in²
October 31, 1950; December 31, 1952

| Compound | Formula | Temperature in °F — Vapor pressure in lb/in² | | | | | | |
|---|---|---|---|---|---|---|---|---|
| | | 530 | 535 | 540 | 545 | 550 | 555 | 560 |
| Naphthalene | $C_{10}H_{10}$ | | | | | | | |
| 1-Methylnaphthalene | $C_{11}H_{12}$ | 28.2 | 29.7 | | | | | |
| 2-Methylnaphthalene | " | | | | | | | |
| 1-Ethylnaphthalene | $C_{12}H_{14}$ | 21.3 | 22.5 | 23.7 | 25.0 | 26.4 | 27.8 | 29.2 |
| 2-Ethylnaphthalene | " | 21.7 | 22.9 | 24.1 | 25.5 | 26.9 | 28.3 | 29.8 |

| Compound | Formula | Normal Boiling Point | Heat of Vaporization, $\Delta H v$, at saturation pressure | | | | | | Entropy of Vaporization, $\Delta S v$ at satn. press. |
|---|---|---|---|---|---|---|---|---|---|
| | | At 1 atm. | At 25°C | | | At Normal Boiling Point | | | At Normal Boiling Point |
| | | °C | kcal/mole | cal/g | BTU/lb | kcal/mole | cal/g | BTU/lb | cal/deg mole |
| Methane | $CH_4$ | −161.49 | — | — | — | 1.955 | 121.87 | 219.22 | 17.51 |
| Ethane | $C_2H_6$ | −88.63 | | | | 3.517 | 116.97 | 210.41 | 19.06 |
| Propane | $C_3H_8$ | −42.07 | 3.605 | 81.76 | 147.07 | 4.487 | 101.76 | 183.05 | 19.42 |
| n−Butane | $C_4H_{10}$ | −0.50 | 5.035 | 86.63 | 155.83 | 5.352 | 92.09 | 165.64 | 19.63 |
| n−Pentane | $C_5H_{12}$ | +36.074 | 6.316 | 87.54 | 157.48 | 6.160 | 85.38 | 153.59 | 19.92 |
| n−Hexane | $C_6H_{14}$ | 68.742 | 7.540 | 87.50 | 157.40 | 6.896 | 80.03 | 143.96 | 20.17 |
| n−Heptane | $C_7H_{16}$ | 98.428 | 8.735 | 87.18 | 156.82 | 7.575 | 75.60 | 135.99 | 20.38 |
| n−Octane | $C_8H_{18}$ | 125.665 | 9.915 | 86.80 | 156.14 | 8.214 | 71.91 | 129.35 | 20.59 |
| n−Nonane | $C_9H_{20}$ | 150.794 | 11.099 | 86.54 | 155.67 | 8.82 | 68.8 | 123.7 | 20.80 |
| n−Decane | $C_{10}H_{22}$ | 174.123 | 12.276 | 86.28 | 155.20 | 9.39 | 66.0 | 118.7 | 20.98 |
| n−Undecane | $C_{11}H_{24}$ | 195.88 | 13.464 | 86.14 | 154.95 | 9.92 | 63.5 | 114.2 | 21.1 |
| n−Dodecane | $C_{12}H_{26}$ | 216.278 | 14.647 | 86.0 | 154.7 | 10.44 | 61.3 | 110.2 | 21.3 |
| n−Tridecane | $C_{13}H_{28}$ | 235.47 | 15.83 | 85.9 | 154.5 | 10.9 | 59.1 | 106.3 | 21.5 |
| n−Tetradecane | $C_{14}H_{30}$ | 253.59 | 17.01 | 85.7 | 154.2 | 11.4 | 57.5 | 103.4 | 21.6 |
| n−Pentadecane | $C_{15}H_{32}$ | 270.74 | 18.20 | 85.7 | 154.2 | 11.8 | 55.6 | 100.0 | 21.8 |
| n−Hexadecane | $C_{16}H_{34}$ | 287.05 | 19.38 | 85.6 | 154.0 | 12.3 | 54.3 | 97.7 | 22.0 |
| n−Heptadecane | $C_{17}H_{36}$ | 302.56 | 20.6 | 85.5 | 154. | 12.7 | 52.8 | 95.0 | 22.1 |
| n−Octadecane | $C_{18}H_{38}$ | 317.38 | 21.7[a] | 85.3[a] | 153.[a] | 13.1 | 51.5 | 92.6 | 22.2 |
| n−Nonadecane | $C_{19}H_{40}$ | 331.55 | 22.9[a] | 85.3[a] | 153.[a] | 13.5 | 50.3 | 90.5 | 22.3 |
| n−Eicosane | $C_{20}H_{42}$ | 345.12 | 24.1[a] | 85.3[a] | 153.[a] | 13.8 | 48.8 | 87.8 | 22.3 |

TABLE 20m − NORMAL PARAFFINS, $C_1$ TO $C_{20}$
HEAT AND ENTROPY OF VAPORIZATION, AT 25°C AND AT THE NORMAL BOILING POINT
APRIL 30, 1949

[a] Extrapolated value for the undercooled liquid below the normal freezing point.

TABLE 1m — PARAFFINS, $C_1$ TO $C_5$

HEAT AND ENTROPY OF VAPORIZATION, AT 25°C AND AT THE NORMAL BOILING POINT

March 31, 1944; May 31, 1947

| Compound | Formula | Normal Boiling Point | Heat of Vaporization, $\Delta Hv$, at saturation pressure | | | | | | Entropy of Vaporization, $\Delta Sv$ at satn. press. |
|---|---|---|---|---|---|---|---|---|---|
| | | At 1 atm. | At 25°C | | | At Normal Boiling Point | | | At Normal Boiling Point |
| | | °C | kcal/mole | cal/g | BTU/lb | kcal/mole | cal/g | BTU/lb | cal/deg mole |
| Methane | $CH_4$ | −161.49 | ——— | ——— | ——— | 1.955 | 121.87 | 219.22 | 17.51 |
| Ethane | $C_2H_6$ | − 88.63 | | | | 3.517 | 116.97 | 210.41 | 19.06 |
| Propane | $C_3H_8$ | − 42.07 | 3.605 | 81.76 | 147.07 | 4.487 | 101.76 | 183.05 | 19.42 |
| n−Butane | $C_4H_{10}$ | − 0.50 | 5.035 | 86.63 | 155.83 | 5.352 | 92.09 | 165.64 | 19.63 |
| 2−Methylpropane (Isobutane) | " | − 11.73 | 4.570 | 78.63 | 141.44 | 5.089 | 87.56 | 157.50 | 19.47 |
| n−Pentane | $C_5H_{12}$ | 36.074 | 6.316 | 87.54 | 157.48 | 6.160 | 85.38 | 153.59 | 19.92 |
| 2−Methylbutane (Isopentane) | " | 27.854 | 5.878 | 81.47 | 146.56 | 5.842 | 80.97 | 145.66 | 19.41 |
| 2,2−Dimethylpropane (Neopentane) | " | 9.50 | 5.205 | 72.15 | 129.78 | 5.438 | 75.37 | 135.59 | 19.24 |

TABLE 2m — PARAFFINS, $C_6$ AND $C_7$
## HEAT AND ENTROPY OF VAPORIZATION, AT 25°C AND AT THE NORMAL BOILING POINT
March 31, 1944; May 31, 1947

| Compound | Formula | Normal Boiling Point | Heat of Vaporization, $\Delta Hv$, at saturation pressure | | | | | | Entropy of Vaporization, $\Delta Sv$ at satn. press. |
|---|---|---|---|---|---|---|---|---|---|
| | | At 1 atm. | At 25°C | | | At Normal Boiling Point | | | At Normal Boiling Point |
| | | °C | kcal/mole | cal/g | BTU/lb | kcal/mole | cal/g | BTU/lb | cal/deg mole |
| n–Hexane | $C_6H_{14}$ | 68.742 | 7.540 | 87.50 | 157.40 | 6.896 | 80.03 | 143.96 | 20.17 |
| 2–Methylpentane | " | 60.274 | 7.138 | 82.83 | 149.00 | 6.643 | 77.09 | 138.67 | 19.92 |
| 3–Methylpentane | " | 63.284 | 7.235 | 83.96 | 151.03 | 6.711 | 77.88 | 140.09 | 19.95 |
| 2,2–Dimethylbutane | " | 49.743 | 6.617 | 76.79 | 138.13 | 6.287 | 72.96 | 131.24 | 19.47 |
| 2,3–Dimethylbutane | " | 57.990 | 6.960 | 80.77 | 145.29 | 6.519 | 75.65 | 136.08 | 19.68 |
| n–Heptane | $C_7H_{16}$ | 98.428 | 8.735 | 87.18 | 156.82 | 7.575 | 75.60 | 135.99 | 20.38 |
| 2–Methylhexane | " | 90.05 | 8.318 | 83.02 | 149.33 | 7.329 | 73.14 | 131.56 | 20.18 |
| 3–Methylhexane | " | 91.95 | 8.385 | 83.68 | 150.53 | 7.358 | 73.43 | 132.09 | 20.15 |
| 3–Ethylpentane | " | 93.468 | 8.419 | 84.02 | 151.14 | 7.398 | 73.83 | 132.81 | 20.18 |
| 2,2–Dimethylpentane | " | 79.205 | 7.751 | 77.36 | 139.15 | 6.969 | 69.55 | 125.11 | 19.78 |
| 2,3–Dimethylpentane | " | 89.79 | 8.184 | 81.68 | 146.92 | 7.262 | 72.48 | 130.38 | 20.01 |
| 2,4–Dimethylpentane | " | 80.51 | 7.860 | 78.44 | 141.11 | 7.050 | 70.36 | 126.56 | 19.93 |
| 3,3–Dimethylpentane | " | 86.071 | 7.892 | 78.76 | 141.68 | 7.085 | 70.71 | 127.19 | 19.72 |
| 2,2,3–Trimethylbutane | " | 80.871 | 7.657 | 76.42 | 137.46 | 6.918 | 69.04 | 124.19 | 19.54 |

TABLE 3m – PARAFFINS, $C_8$

HEAT AND ENTROPY OF VAPORIZATION, AT 25°C AND AT THE NORMAL BOILING POINT

March 31, 1944

| Compound | Formula | Normal Boiling Point | Heat of Vaporization, $\Delta Hv$, at saturation pressure | | | | | | Entropy of Vaporization, $\Delta Sv$ at satn. press. |
|---|---|---|---|---|---|---|---|---|---|
| | | At 1 atm. | At 25°C | | | At Normal Boiling Point | | | At Normal Boiling Point |
| | | °C | kcal/mole | cal/g | BTU/lb | kcal/mole | cal/g | BTU/lb | cal/deg mole |
| *n*-Octane | $C_8H_{18}$ | 125.66 | 9.915 | 86.80 | 156.14 | 8.360 | 73.19 | 131.65 | 20.96 |
| 2-Methylheptane | " | 117.64 | 9.483 | 83.02 | 149.34 | 8.03 | 70.3 | 126.5 | 20.55 |
| 3-Methylheptane | " | 118.92 | 9.520 | 83.35 | 149.92 | 8.14 | 71.3 | 128.2 | 20.76 |
| 4-Methylheptane | " | 117.71 | 9.482 | 83.01 | 149.32 | 8.100 | 70.91 | 127.56 | 20.72 |
| 3-Ethylhexane | " | 118.53 | 9.475 | 82.95 | 149.21 | 8.19 | 71.7 | 129.0 | 20.91 |
| 2,2-Dimethylhexane | " | 106.84 | 8.912 | 78.02 | 140.35 | 7.73 | 67.7 | 121.7 | 20.34 |
| 2,3-Dimethylhexane | " | 115.60 | 9.271 | 81.17 | 146.00 | 8.02 | 70.2 | 126.3 | 20.63 |
| 2,4-Dimethylhexane | " | 109.43 | 9.026 | 79.02 | 142.14 | 7.82 | 68.5 | 123.2 | 20.44 |
| 2,5-Dimethylhexane | " | 109.10 | 9.048 | 79.21 | 142.49 | 7.84 | 68.6 | 123.5 | 20.51 |
| 3,3-Dimethylhexane | " | 111.97 | 8.971 | 78.54 | 141.28 | 7.82 | 68.5 | 123.2 | 20.30 |
| 3,4-Dimethylhexane | " | 117.72 | 9.315 | 81.55 | 146.69 | 8.02 | 70.2 | 126.3 | 20.52 |
| 2-Methyl-3-ethylpentane | " | 115.65 | 9.207 | 80.60 | 144.99 | 7.96 | 69.7 | 125.4 | 20.47 |
| 3-Methyl-3-ethylpentane | " | 118.26 | 9.080 | 79.49 | 142.99 | 7.91 | 69.3 | 124.6 | 20.21 |
| 2,2,3-Trimethylpentane | " | 109.84 | 8.823 | 77.24 | 138.95 | 7.69 | 67.3 | 121.1 | 20.08 |
| 2,2,4-Trimethylpentane | " | 99.24 | 8.396 | 73.50 | 132.22 | 7.410 | 64.87 | 116.69 | 19.90 |
| 2,3,3-Trimethylpentane | " | 114.76 | 8.895 | 77.87 | 140.08 | 7.78 | 68.1 | 122.5 | 20.06 |
| 2,3,4-Trimethylpentane | " | 113.47 | 9.012 | 78.90 | 141.92 | 7.810 | 68.37 | 122.99 | 20.20 |
| 2,2,3,3-Tetramethylbutane | " | 106.30 | 10.24[a] | 89.6[a] | 161.3[a] | 7.56 | 66.2 | 119.1 | 19.92 |

[a] Heat of sublimation, for the process, $C_mH_n$ (solid) = $C_mH_n$ (gas), at saturation pressure at the indicated temperature.

439

## TABLE 4m — PARAFFINS, $C_9$
### HEAT AND ENTROPY OF VAPORIZATION, AT 25°C AND AT THE NORMAL BOILING POINT
March 31, 1945

| Compound | Formula | Normal Boiling Point At 1 atm. °C | Heat of Vaporization, $\Delta Hv$, at saturation pressure — At 25°C kcal/mole | At 25°C cal/g | At 25°C BTU/lb | At Normal Boiling Point kcal/mole | At Normal Boiling Point cal/g | At Normal Boiling Point BTU/lb | Entropy of Vaporization, $\Delta Sv$ at satn. press. At Normal Boiling Point cal/deg mole |
|---|---|---|---|---|---|---|---|---|---|
| n–Nonane | $C_9H_{20}$ | 150.80 | 11.099 | 86.54 | 155.67 | 9.030 | 70.41 | 126.65 | 21.30 |
| 2–Methyloctane | " | 143.26 | 10.67 | 83.2 | 149.7 | 8.76 | 68.3 | 122.9 | 21.03 |
| 3–Methyloctane | " | 144.18 | 10.69 | 83.4 | 149.9 | 8.79 | 68.5 | 123.3 | 21.06 |
| 4–Methyloctane | " | 142.48 | 10.69 | 83.4 | 149.9 | 8.75 | 68.2 | 122.7 | 21.06 |
| 3–Ethylheptane | " | 143. | 10.71 | 83.5 | 150.2 | 8.78 | 68.5 | 123.1 | 21.10 |
| 4–Ethylheptane | " | 142. | 10.71 | 83.5 | 150.2 | 8.76 | 68.3 | 122.9 | 21.10 |
| 2,2–Dimethylheptane | " | 130.5 | 10.10 | 78.8 | 141.7 | 8.31 | 64.8 | 116.6 | 20.58 |
| 2,3–Dimethylheptane | " | 140.7 | 10.46 | 81.6 | 146.7 | 8.63 | 67.3 | 121.0 | 20.84 |
| 2,4–Dimethylheptane | " | 133. | 10.25 | 79.9 | 143.8 | 8.45 | 65.9 | 118.5 | 20.80 |
| 2,5–Dimethylheptane | " | 136. | 10.25 | 79.9 | 143.8 | 8.51 | 66.4 | 119.3 | 20.80 |
| 2,6–Dimethylheptane | " | 135.21 | 10.24 | 79.8 | 143.6 | 8.49 | 66.2 | 119.1 | 20.80 |
| 3,3–Dimethylheptane | " | 137.3 | 10.19 | 79.5 | 142.9 | 8.44 | 65.8 | 118.4 | 20.55 |
| 3,4–Dimethylheptane | " | 143. | 10.48 | 81.7 | 147.0 | 8.69 | 67.8 | 121.9 | 20.87 |
| 3,5–Dimethylheptane | " | 136. | 10.27 | 80.1 | 144.0 | 8.52 | 66.4 | 119.5 | 20.83 |
| 4,4–Dimethylheptane | " | 138. | 10.19 | 79.5 | 142.9 | 8.45 | 65.9 | 118.5 | 20.55 |
| 2–Methyl–3–ethylhexane | " | 139. | 10.48 | 81.7 | 147.0 | 8.60 | 67.1 | 120.6 | 20.87 |
| 2–Methyl–4–ethylhexane | " | 136. | 10.27 | 80.1 | 144.0 | 8.52 | 66.4 | 119.5 | 20.83 |
| 3–Methyl–3–ethylhexane | " | 143. | 10.28 | 80.2 | 144.2 | 8.54 | 66.6 | 119.8 | 20.53 |
| 3–Methyl–4–ethylhexane | " | 143. | 10.50 | 81.9 | 147.3 | 8.70 | 67.8 | 122.0 | 20.90 |
| 2,3,3–Trimethylhexane | " | 134. | 10.02 | 78.1 | 140.5 | 8.31 | 64.8 | 116.6 | 20.40 |
| 2,2,4–Trimethylhexane | " | 126.54 | 9.69 | 75.6 | 135.9 | 8.13 | 63.4 | 114.0 | 20.34 |
| 2,2,5–Trimethylhexane | " | 124.09 | 9.601 | 74.86 | 134.66 | 8.07 | 62.9 | 113.2 | 20.31 |
| 2,3,3–Trimethylhexane | " | 138. | 10.09 | 78.7 | 141.5 | 8.36 | 65.2 | 117.3 | 20.34 |
| 2,3,4–Trimethylhexane | " | 140. | 10.26 | 80.0 | 143.9 | 8.53 | 66.5 | 119.6 | 20.64 |
| 2,3,5–Trimethylhexane | " | 131.37 | 9.900 | 77.19 | 138.86 | 8.32 | 64.9 | 116.7 | 20.57 |
| 2,4,4–Trimethylhexane | " | 131. | 9.76 | 76.1 | 136.9 | 8.20 | 63.9 | 115.0 | 20.29 |
| 3,3,4–Trimethylhexane | " | 139. | 10.11 | 78.8 | 141.8 | 8.40 | 65.5 | 117.8 | 20.37 |
| 3,3–Diethylpentane | " | 146.5 | 10.36 | 80.8 | 145.3 | 8.60 | 67.1 | 120.6 | 20.50 |
| 2,2–Dimethyl–3–ethylpentane | " | 133.83 | 10.04 | 78.3 | 140.8 | 8.32 | 64.9 | 116.7 | 20.43 |
| 2,3–Dimethyl–3–ethylpentane | " | 142. | 10.17 | 79.3 | 142.6 | 8.44 | 65.8 | 118.4 | 20.32 |
| 2,4–Dimethyl–3–ethylpentane | " | 136.73 | 10.26 | 80.0 | 143.9 | 8.46 | 66.0 | 118.7 | 20.64 |
| 2,2,3,3–Tetramethylpentane | " | 140.23 | 9.80 | 76.4 | 137.4 | 8.43 | 65.7 | 118.2 | 20.38 |
| 2,2,3,4–Tetramethylpentane | " | 133.01 | 9.80 | 76.4 | 137.4 | 8.19 | 63.9 | 114.9 | 20.17 |
| 2,2,4,4–Tetramethylpentane | " | 122.28 | 9.11 | 71.0 | 127.8 | 7.85 | 61.2 | 110.1 | 19.86 |
| 2,3,3,4–Tetramethylpentane | " | 141.54 | 9.98 | 77.8 | 140.0 | 8.35 | 65.1 | 117.1 | 20.13 |

| | | Normal Boiling Point | Heat of Vaporization, $\Delta H_v$, at saturation pressure | | | | | | Entropy of Vaporization, $\Delta S_v$ at satn. press. |
|---|---|---|---|---|---|---|---|---|---|
| Compound | Formula | At 1 atm. | At 25°C | | | At Normal Boiling Point | | | At Normal Boiling Point |
| | | °C | kcal/mole | cal/g | BTU/lb | kcal/mole | cal/g | BTU/lb | cal/deg mole |
| Cyclopentane | $C_5H_{10}$ | 49.262 | 6.818 | 97.22 | 174.88 | 6.524 | 93.03 | 167.34 | 20.23 |
| Methylcyclopentane | $C_6H_{12}$ | 71.812 | 7.560 | 89.83 | 161.59 | 6.916 | 82.18 | 147.83 | 20.05 |
| Ethylcyclopentane | $C_7H_{14}$ | 103.466 | 8.720 | 88.81 | 159.76 | 7.715 | 78.58 | 141.35 | 20.48 |
| 1,1-Dimethylcyclopentane | " | 87.846 | 8.079 | 82.29 | 148.02 | 7.239 | 73.73 | 132.63 | 20.05 |
| cis-1,2-Dimethylcyclopentane | " | 99.532 | 8.549 | 87.07 | 156.63 | 7.576 | 77.16 | 138.80 | 20.33 |
| trans-1,2-Dimethylcyclopentane | " | 91.869 | 8.259 | 84.12 | 151.32 | 7.375 | 75.12 | 135.12 | 20.20 |
| cis-1,3-Dimethylcyclopentane | " | 91.723 | 8.248 | 84.01 | 151.11 | 7.361 | 74.97 | 134.86 | 20.17 |
| trans-1,3-Dimethylcyclopentane | " | 90.773 | 8.200 | 83.52 | 150.23 | 7.332 | 74.68 | 134.33 | 20.15 |

TABLE 6m – ALKYL CYCLOPENTANES, $C_5$ TO $C_7$
HEAT AND ENTROPY OF VAPORIZATION, AT 25°C AND AT THE NORMAL BOILING POINT
May 31, 1947; October 31, 1948

TABLE 7m — ALKYL CYCLOHEXANES, $C_6$ TO $C_8$
HEAT AND ENTROPY OF VAPORIZATION, AT 25°C AND AT THE NORMAL BOILING POINT

March 31, 1945; March 31, 1947

| Compound | Formula | Normal Boiling Point | Heat of Vaporization, $\Delta Hv$, at saturation pressure | | | | | | Entropy of Vaporization, $\Delta Sv$ at satn. press. |
|---|---|---|---|---|---|---|---|---|---|
| | | At 1 atm. | At 25°C | | | At Normal Boiling Point | | | At Normal Boiling Point |
| | | °C | kcal/mole | cal/g | BTU/lb | kcal/mole | cal/g | BTU/lb | cal/deg mole |
| Cyclohexane | $C_6H_{12}$ | 80.74 | 7.895 | 93.81 | 168.75 | 7.19 | 85.4 | 153.7 | 20.30 |
| Methylcyclohexane | $C_7H_{14}$ | 100.94 | 8.451 | 86.07 | 154.83 | 7.58 | 77.2 | 138.9 | 20.26 |
| Ethylcyclohexane | $C_8H_{16}$ | 131.79 | 9.673 | 86.21 | 155.07 | 8.29 | 73.9 | 132.9 | 20.47 |
| 1,1–Dimethylcyclohexane | " | 119.54 | 9.043 | 80.59 | 144.97 | 7.88 | 70.2 | 126.3 | 20.06 |
| 1,cis–2–Dimethylcyclohexane | " | 129.73 | 9.492 | 84.59 | 152.17 | 8.18 | 72.9 | 131.1 | 20.29 |
| 1,trans–2–Dimethylcyclohexane | " | 123.42 | 9.167 | 81.70 | 146.96 | 7.98 | 71.1 | 127.9 | 20.13 |
| 1,cis–3–Dimethylcyclohexane[a] | " | 120.09 | 9.136 | 81.42 | 146.46 | 7.96 | 70.9 | 127.6 | 20.25 |
| 1,trans–3–Dimethylcyclohexane[b] | " | 124.45 | 9.368 | 83.49 | 150.18 | 8.09 | 72.1 | 129.7 | 20.35 |
| 1,cis–4–Dimethylcyclohexane | " | 124.32 | 9.328 | 83.13 | 149.54 | 8.07 | 71.9 | 129.4 | 20.30 |
| 1,trans–4–Dimethylcyclohexane | " | 119.35 | 9.052 | 80.67 | 145.11 | 7.90 | 70.4 | 126.6 | 20.12 |

[a] Formerly labeled "trans"; see footnote b of Table 7a.    [b] Formerly labeled "cis"; see footnote c of Table 7a.

TABLE 8m (PART 1), Page 1 — MONOOLEFINS, $C_2$ TO $C_4$

## HEAT AND ENTROPY OF VAPORIZATION, AT 25°C AND AT THE NORMAL BOILING POINT

March 31, 1945 (Corrected)

| Compound | Formula | Normal Boiling Point | Heat of Vaporization, $\Delta H v$, at saturation pressure | | | | | | Entropy of Vaporization, $\Delta S v$ at satn. press. |
|---|---|---|---|---|---|---|---|---|---|
| | | At 1 atm. | At 25°C | | | At Normal Boiling Point | | | At Normal Boiling Point |
| | | °C | kcal/mole | cal/g | BTU/lb | kcal/mole | cal/g | BTU/lb | cal/deg mole |
| Ethene (Ethylene) | $C_2H_4$ | −103.71 | —— | —— | —— | 3.237 | 115.39 | 207.56 | 19.10 |
| Propene (Propylene) | $C_3H_6$ | − 47.70 | —— | —— | —— | 4.402 | 104.62 | 188.19 | 19.52 |
| 1-Butene | $C_4H_8$ | − 6.25 | 4.87 | 86.8 | 156.1 | 5.238 | 93.36 | 167.93 | 19.62 |
| cis-2-Butene | " | 3.72 | 5.30 | 94.5 | 169.9 | 5.580 | 99.46 | 178.91 | 20.15 |
| trans-2-Butene | " | 0.88 | 5.15 | 91.8 | 165.1 | 5.439 | 96.94 | 174.37 | 19.85 |
| 2-Methylpropene (Isobutene) | " | − 6.90 | 4.92 | 87.7 | 157.7 | 5.286 | 94.22 | 169.48 | 19.85 |

TABLE 5m – ALKYL BENZENES, $C_6$ TO $C_9$
## HEAT AND ENTROPY OF VAPORIZATION, AT 25°C AND AT THE NORMAL BOILING POINT

June 30, 1944; March 31, 1945

| Compound | Formula | Normal Boiling Point At 1 atm. °C | Heat of Vaporization, $\Delta Hv$, at saturation pressure | | | | | | Entropy of Vaporization, $\Delta Sv$ at satn. press. At Normal Boiling Point cal/deg mole |
|---|---|---|---|---|---|---|---|---|---|
| | | | At 25°C | | | At Normal Boiling Point | | | |
| | | | kcal/mole | cal/g | BTU/lb | kcal/mole | cal/g | BTU/lb | |
| Benzene | $C_6H_6$ | 80.10 | 8.090 | 103.57 | 186.31 | 7.353 | 94.14 | 169.34 | 20.81 |
| Methylbenzene (Toluene) | $C_7H_8$ | 110.62 | 9.080 | 98.55 | 177.28 | 8.00 | 86.8 | 156.2 | 20.85 |
| Ethylbenzene | $C_8H_{10}$ | 136.19 | 10.097 | 95.11 | 171.09 | 8.60 | 81.0 | 145.7 | 21.01 |
| 1,2-Dimethylbenzene (o-Xylene) | " | 144.42 | 10.381 | 97.79 | 175.90 | 8.80 | 82.9 | 149.1 | 21.07 |
| 1,3-Dimethylbenzene (m-Xylene) | " | 139.10 | 10.195 | 96.03 | 172.75 | 8.70 | 82.0 | 147.4 | 21.10 |
| 1,4-Dimethylbenzene (p-Xylene) | " | 138.35 | 10.128 | 95.40 | 171.61 | 8.62 | 81.2 | 146.1 | 20.95 |
| n-Propylbenzene | $C_9H_{12}$ | 159.22 | 11.049 | 91.93 | 165.37 | 9.14 | 76.0 | 136.8 | 21.14 |
| Isopropylbenzene | " | 152.40 | 10.789 | 89.77 | 161.48 | 8.97 | 74.6 | 134.3 | 21.08 |
| 1-Methyl-2-ethylbenzene | " | 165.15 | 11.40 | 94.9 | 170.7 | 9.29 | 77.3 | 139.0 | 21.2 |
| 1-Methyl-3-ethylbenzene | " | 161.30 | 11.21 | 93.3 | 167.8 | 9.21 | 76.6 | 137.8 | 21.2 |
| 1-Methyl-4-ethylbenzene | " | 162.05 | 11.14 | 92.7 | 166.7 | 9.18 | 76.4 | 137.4 | 21.1 |
| 1,2,3-Trimethylbenzene | " | 176.15 | 11.725 | 97.56 | 175.49 | 9.57 | 79.6 | 143.2 | 21.3 |
| 1,2,4-Trimethylbenzene | " | 169.25 | 11.457 | 95.33 | 171.48 | 9.38 | 78.0 | 140.4 | 21.2 |
| 1,3,5-Trimethylbenzene | " | 164.70 | 11.346 | 94.40 | 169.82 | 9.33 | 77.6 | 139.6 | 21.3 |

444

| Compound | Formula | State | Heat of Combustion, $-\Delta Hc^{o}$, at 25°C and constant pressure, to form: | | | | | |
|---|---|---|---|---|---|---|---|---|
| | | | $H_2O$ (liq.) and $CO_2$ (gas) | | | $H_2O$ (gas) and $CO_2$ (gas) | | |
| | | | kcal/mole | cal/g | BTU/lb | kcal/mole | cal/g | BTU/lb |
| Hydrogen | $H_2$ | gas | 68.3174 | 33887.6 | 60957.7 | 57.7979 | 28669.6 | 51571.4 |
| Carbon | C | solid graphite | 94.0518 | 7831.1 | 14086.8 | | | |
| Carbon monoxide | CO | gas | 67.6361 | 2414.7 | 4343.6 | | | |

TABLE On — $H_2$, C, CO
HEAT OF COMBUSTION, AT 25°C
April 30, 1945; May 31, 1945

445

TABLE 20n (PART 1) — NORMAL PARAFFINS, $C_1$ TO $C_{20}$
HEAT OF COMBUSTION, AT 25°C
December 31, 1945; December 31, 1952

| Compound | Formula | State | Heat of Combustion, $-\Delta Hc^0$, at 25°C and constant pressure, to form: | | | | | |
| | | | $H_2O$ (liq.) and $CO_2$ (gas) | | | $H_2O$ (gas) and $CO_2$ (gas) | | |
| | | | kcal/mole | cal/g | BTU/lb | kcal/mole | cal/g | BTU/lb |
|---|---|---|---|---|---|---|---|---|
| Methane | $CH_4$ | gas | 212.80 | 13265. | 23861. | 191.76 | 11954. | 21502. |
| " | " | liquid | | | | | | |
| Ethane | $C_2H_6$ | gas | 372.82 | 12399. | 22304. | 341.26 | 11350. | 20416. |
| " | " | liquid | | | | | | |
| Propane | $C_3H_8$ | gas | 530.60 | 12034. | 21646. | 488.53 | 11079. | 19929. |
| " | " | liquid[a] | 526.78 | 11947. | 21490. | 484.70 | 10992. | 19774. |
| n–Butane | $C_4H_{10}$ | gas | 687.65 | 11832. | 21283. | 635.05 | 10926. | 19655. |
| " | " | liquid[a] | 682.51 | 11743. | 21124. | 629.92 | 10838. | 19496. |
| n–Pentane | $C_5H_{12}$ | gas | 845.16 | 11715. | 21072. | 782.04 | 10840. | 19499. |
| " | " | liquid | 838.80 | 11626. | 20914. | 775.68 | 10752. | 19340. |
| n–Hexane | $C_6H_{14}$ | gas | 1002.57 | 11634. | 20928. | 928.93 | 10780. | 19391. |
| " | " | liquid | 995.01 | 11547. | 20771. | 921.37 | 10692. | 19233. |
| n–Heptane | $C_7H_{16}$ | gas | 1160.01 | 11577. | 20825. | 1075.85 | 10737. | 19314. |
| " | " | liquid | 1151.27 | 11490. | 20668. | 1067.11 | 10650. | 19157. |
| n–Octane | $C_8H_{18}$ | gas | 1317.45 | 11534. | 20747. | 1222.77 | 10705. | 19256. |
| " | " | liquid | 1307.53 | 11447. | 20591. | 1212.85 | 10618. | 19100. |
| n–Nonane | $C_9H_{20}$ | gas | 1474.90 | 11500. | 20687. | 1369.70 | 10680. | 19211. |
| " | " | liquid | 1463.80 | 11414. | 20531. | 1358.60 | 10593. | 19056. |
| n–Decane | $C_{10}H_{22}$ | gas | 1632.34 | 11473. | 20638. | 1516.63 | 10660. | 19175. |
| " | " | liquid | 1620.06 | 11387. | 20483. | 1504.35 | 10573. | 19020. |
| n–Undecane | $C_{11}H_{24}$ | gas | 1789.78 | 11451. | 20598. | 1663.55 | 10643. | 19145. |
| " | " | liquid | 1776.32 | 11365. | 20443. | 1650.09 | 10557. | 18990. |
| n–Dodecane | $C_{12}H_{26}$ | gas | 1947.23 | 11432. | 20564. | 1810.48 | 10629. | 19120. |
| " | " | liquid | 1932.59 | 11346. | 20410. | 1795.84 | 10543. | 18966. |
| n–Tridecane | $C_{13}H_{28}$ | gas | 2104.67 | 11416. | 20536. | 1957.40 | 10618. | 19099. |
| " | " | liquid | 2088.85 | 11331. | 20382. | 1941.58 | 10532. | 18945. |
| n–Tetradecane | $C_{14}H_{30}$ | gas | 2262.11 | 11403. | 20512. | 2104.32 | 10608. | 19081. |
| " | " | liquid | 2245.11 | 11317. | 20358. | 2087.32 | 10522. | 18927. |
| n–Pentadecane | $C_{15}H_{32}$ | gas | 2419.55 | 11391. | 20491. | 2251.24 | 10599. | 19065. |
| " | " | liquid | 2401.37 | 11306. | 20337. | 2233.06 | 10513. | 18911. |
| n–Hexadecane | $C_{16}H_{34}$ | gas | 2577.00 | 11381. | 20472. | 2398.17 | 10591. | 19052. |
| " | " | liquid | 2557.64 | 11295. | 20318. | 2378.81 | 10506. | 18898. |
| n–Heptadecane | $C_{17}H_{36}$ | gas | 2734.44 | 11372. | 20456. | 2545.09 | 10584. | 19039. |
| " | " | liquid | 2713.90 | 11286. | 20302. | 2524.55 | 10499. | 18886. |
| n–Octadecane | $C_{18}H_{38}$ | gas | 2891.88 | 11364. | 20441. | 2692.01 | 10573. | 19028. |
| " | " | liquid | 2870.16 | 11278. | 20288. | 2670.29 | 20493. | 18875. |
| n–Nonadecane | $C_{19}H_{40}$ | gas | 3049.33 | 11356. | 20428. | 2838.94 | 10573. | 19019. |
| " | " | liquid | 3026.43 | 11271. | 20275. | 2816.04 | 10488. | 18865. |
| n–Eicosane | $C_{20}H_{42}$ | gas | 3206.77 | 11350. | 20416. | 2985.86 | 10568. | 19010. |
| " | " | liquid | 3182.69 | 11265. | 20263. | 2961.78 | 10483. | 18857. |

[a] At saturation pressure.

TABLE 1n — PARAFFINS, $C_1$ TO $C_5$
HEAT OF COMBUSTION, AT 25°C
March 31, 1944; April 30, 1945; December 31, 1952

| Compound | Formula | State | Heat of Combustion, $-\Delta H c^0$, at 25°C and constant pressure, to form: | | | | | |
| | | | $H_2O$ (liq.) and $CO_2$ (gas) | | | $H_2O$ (gas) and $CO_2$ (gas) | | |
| | | | kcal/mole | cal/g | BTU/lb | kcal/mole | cal/g | BTU/lb |
|---|---|---|---|---|---|---|---|---|
| Methane | $CH_4$ | gas | 212.80 | 13265. | 23861. | 191.76 | 11954. | 21502. |
| " | " | liquid | | | | | | |
| Ethane | $C_2H_6$ | gas | 372.82 | 12399. | 22304. | 341.26 | 11350. | 20416. |
| " | " | liquid | | | | | | |
| Propane | $C_3H_8$ | gas | 530.60 | 12034. | 21646. | 488.53 | 11079. | 19929. |
| " | " | liquid[a] | 526.78 | 11947. | 21490. | 484.70 | 10992. | 19774. |
| n–Butane | $C_4H_{10}$ | gas | 687.65 | 11832. | 21283. | 635.05 | 10926. | 19655. |
| " | " | liquid[a] | 682.51 | 11743. | 21224. | 629.92 | 10838. | 19496. |
| 2–Methylpropane (Isobutane) | " | gas | 685.65 | 11797. | 21221. | 633.05 | 10892. | 19593. |
| " | " | liquid[a] | 680.93 | 11716. | 21075. | 628.34 | 10811. | 19447. |
| n–Pentane | $C_5H_{12}$ | gas | 845.16 | 11715. | 21072. | 782.04 | 10840. | 19499. |
| " | " | liquid | 838.80 | 11626. | 20914. | 775.68 | 10752. | 19340. |
| 2–Methylbutane (Isopentane) | " | gas | 843.24 | 11688. | 21025. | 780.12 | 10813. | 19451. |
| " | " | liquid | 837.31 | 11606. | 20877. | 774.19 | 10731. | 19303. |
| 2,2–Dimethylpropane (Neopentane) | " | gas | 840.49 | 11650. | 20956. | 777.37 | 10775. | 19382. |
| " | " | liquid[a] | 835.18 | 11576. | 20824. | 772.06 | 10701. | 19250. |

[a] At saturation pressure.

TABLE 2n — PARAFFINS, $C_6$ AND $C_7$
HEAT OF COMBUSTION, AT 25°C
March 31, 1944; April 30, 1945

| Compound | Formula | State | Heat of Combustion, $-\Delta H c^o$, at 25°C and constant pressure, to form: | | | | | |
|---|---|---|---|---|---|---|---|---|
| | | | $H_2O$ (liq.) and $CO_2$ (gas) | | | $H_2O$ (gas) and $CO_2$ (gas) | | |
| | | | kcal/mole | cal/g | BTU/lb | kcal/mole | cal/g | BTU/lb |
| n–Hexane | $C_6H_{14}$ | gas | 1002.57 | 11634.5 | 20928. | 928.93 | 10780.0 | 19391. |
| " | " | liquid | 995.01 | 11546.8 | 20771. | 921.37 | 10692.2 | 19233. |
| 2-Methylpentane | " | gas | 1000.87 | 11614.8 | 20893 | 927.23 | 10760.2 | 19356. |
| " | " | liquid | 993.71 | 11531.7 | 20743. | 920.07 | 10677.1 | 19206. |
| 3-Methylpentane | " | gas | 1001.51 | 11622.2 | 20906. | 927.87 | 10767.6 | 19369. |
| " | " | liquid | 994.25 | 11538.0 | 20755. | 920.61 | 10683.4 | 19218. |
| 2,2-Dimethylbutane | " | gas | 998.17 | 11583.5 | 20837. | 924.53 | 10728.9 | 19299. |
| " | " | liquid | 991.52 | 11506.3 | 20698. | 917.88 | 10651.7 | 19161. |
| 2,3-Dimethylbutane | " | gas | 1000.04 | 11605.2 | 20876. | 926.40 | 10750.6 | 19338. |
| " | " | liquid | 993.05 | 11524.0 | 20730. | 919.41 | 10669.5 | 19192. |
| n–Heptane | $C_7H_{16}$ | gas | 1160.01 | 11577.2 | 20825. | 1075.85 | 10737.2 | 19314. |
| " | " | liquid | 1151.27 | 11489.9 | 20668. | 1067.11 | 10650.0 | 19157. |
| 2-Methylhexane | " | gas | 1158.30 | 11560.1 | 20795. | 1074.14 | 10720.2 | 19284. |
| " | " | liquid | 1149.97 | 11477.0 | 20645. | 1065.81 | 10637.0 | 19134. |
| 3-Methylhexane | " | gas | 1158.94 | 11566.5 | 20806. | 1074.78 | 10726.6 | 19295. |
| " | " | liquid | 1150.55 | 11482.8 | 20655. | 1066.39 | 10642.8 | 19145. |
| 3-Ethylpentane | " | gas | 1159.56 | 11572.7 | 20817. | 1075.40 | 10732.7 | 19306. |
| " | " | liquid | 1151.13 | 11488.6 | 20666. | 1066.97 | 10648.6 | 19155. |
| 2,2-Dimethylpentane | " | gas | 1155.61 | 11533.3 | 20746. | 1071.45 | 10693.3 | 19235. |
| " | " | liquid | 1147.85 | 11455.8 | 20607. | 1063.69 | 10615.9 | 19096. |
| 2,3-Dimethylpentane | " | gas | 1157.28 | 11549.9 | 20776. | 1073.12 | 10710.0 | 19265. |
| " | " | liquid | 1149.09 | 11468.2 | 20629. | 1064.93 | 10628.3 | 19118. |
| 2,4-Dimethylpentane | " | gas | 1156.60 | 11543.1 | 20764. | 1072.44 | 10703.2 | 19253. |
| " | " | liquid | 1148.73 | 11464.6 | 20623. | 1064.57 | 10624.7 | 19112. |
| 3,3-Dimethylpentane | " | gas | 1156.73 | 11544.4 | 20766. | 1072.57 | 10704.5 | 19255. |
| " | " | liquid | 1148.83 | 11465.6 | 20625. | 1064.67 | 10625.7 | 19114. |
| 2,2,3-Trimethylbutane | " | gas | 1155.94 | 11536.6 | 20752. | 1071.78 | 10696.6 | 19241. |
| " | " | liquid | 1148.27 | 11460.0 | 20614. | 1064.11 | 10620.1 | 19104. |

## TABLE 3n – PARAFFINS, $C_8$
## HEAT OF COMBUSTION, AT 25°C
March 31, 1944; April 30, 1945

| Compound | Formula | State | Heat of Combustion, $-\Delta H_c^0$, at 25°C and constant pressure, to form: | | | | | |
| --- | --- | --- | --- | --- | --- | --- | --- | --- |
| | | | $H_2O$ (liq.) and $CO_2$ (gas) | | | $H_2O$ (gas) and $CO_2$ (gas) | | |
| | | | kcal/mole | cal/g | BTU/lb | kcal/mole | cal/g | BTU/lb |
| n-Octane | $C_8H_{18}$ | gas | 1317.45 | 11533.9 | 20747. | 1222.77 | 10705.0 | 19256. |
| " | " | liquid | 1307.53 | 11447.1 | 20591. | 1212.85 | 10618.2 | 19100. |
| 2-Methylheptane | | gas | 1315.76 | 11519.1 | 20721. | 1221.08 | 10690.2 | 19230. |
| " | " | liquid | 1306.28 | 11436.1 | 20572. | 1211.60 | 10607.2 | 19080. |
| 3-Methylheptane | | gas | 1316.44 | 11525.1 | 20732. | 1221.76 | 10696.2 | 19240. |
| " | " | liquid | 1306.92 | 11441.7 | 20582. | 1212.24 | 10612.8 | 19091. |
| 4-Methylheptane | | gas | 1316.57 | 11526.2 | 20734. | 1221.89 | 10697.3 | 19243. |
| " | " | liquid | 1307.09 | 11443.2 | 20584. | 1212.41 | 10614.3 | 19093. |
| 3-Ethylhexane | | gas | 1316.87 | 11528.8 | 20738. | 1222.19 | 10699.9 | 19247. |
| " | " | liquid | 1307.39 | 11445.8 | 20589. | 1212.71 | 10616.9 | 19098. |
| 2,2-Dimethylhexane | | gas | 1313.56 | 11499.9 | 20686. | 1218.88 | 10671.0 | 19195. |
| " | " | liquid | 1304.64 | 11421.8 | 20546. | 1209.96 | 10592.9 | 19055. |
| 2,3-Dimethylhexane | | gas | 1316.13 | 11522.4 | 20727. | 1221.45 | 10693.5 | 19236. |
| " | " | liquid | 1306.86 | 11441.2 | 20581. | 1212.18 | 10612.3 | 19090. |
| 2,4-Dimethylhexane | | gas | 1314.83 | 11511.0 | 20706. | 1220.15 | 10682.1 | 19215. |
| " | " | liquid | 1305.80 | 11431.9 | 20564. | 1211.12 | 10603.0 | 19073. |
| 2,5-Dimethylhexane | | gas | 1314.05 | 11504.2 | 20694. | 1219.37 | 10675.3 | 19203. |
| " | " | liquid | 1305.00 | 11424.9 | 20551. | 1210.32 | 10596.0 | 19060. |
| 3,3-Dimethylhexane | | gas | 1314.65 | 11509.4 | 20703. | 1219.97 | 10680.5 | 19212. |
| " | " | liquid | 1305.68 | 11430.9 | 20562. | 1211.00 | 10602.0 | 19071. |
| 3,4-Dimethylhexane | | gas | 1316.36 | 11524.4 | 20730. | 1221.68 | 10695.5 | 19239. |
| " | " | liquid | 1307.04 | 11442.8 | 20583. | 1212.36 | 10613.9 | 19092. |
| 2-Methyl-3-ethylpentane | | gas | 1316.79 | 11528.1 | 20737. | 1222.11 | 10699.2 | 19246. |
| " | " | liquid | 1307.58 | 11447.5 | 20592. | 1212.90 | 10618.6 | 19101. |
| 3-Methyl-3-ethylpentane | | gas | 1315.88 | 11520.2 | 20723. | 1221.20 | 10691.3 | 19232. |
| " | " | liquid | 1306.80 | 11440.7 | 20580. | 1212.12 | 10611.8 | 19089. |
| 2,2,3-Trimethylpentane | | gas | 1314.66 | 11509.5 | 20703. | 1219.98 | 10680.6 | 19212. |
| " | " | liquid | 1305.83 | 11432.2 | 20564. | 1211.15 | 10603.3 | 19073. |
| 2,2,4-Trimethylpentane | | gas | 1313.69 | 11501.0 | 20688. | 1219.01 | 10672.1 | 19197. |
| " | " | liquid | 1305.29 | 11427.5 | 20556. | 1210.61 | 10598.6 | 19065. |
| 2,3,3-Trimethylpentane | | gas | 1315.54 | 11517.2 | 20717. | 1220.86 | 10688.3 | 19226. |
| " | " | liquid | 1306.64 | 11439.3 | 20577. | 1211.96 | 10610.4 | 19086. |
| 2,3,4-Trimethylpentane | | gas | 1315.29 | 11515.0 | 20713. | 1220.61 | 10686.1 | 19222. |
| " | " | liquid | 1306.28 | 11436.1 | 20572. | 1211.60 | 10607.2 | 19080. |
| 2,2,3,3-Tetramethylbutane | | gas | 1313.27 | 11497.3 | 20682. | 1218.59 | 10668.4 | 19191. |
| " | " | liquid | 1303.03 | 11407.7 | 20520. | 1208.35 | 10578.8 | 19029. |

TABLE 22n (PART 1) – NORMAL ALKYL CYCLOPENTANES, $C_5$ TO $C_{21}$
HEAT OF COMBUSTION, AT 25°C
March 31, 1946

| Compound | Formula | State | Heat of Combustion, $-\Delta Hc^0$, at 25°C and constant pressure, to form: | | | | | |
|---|---|---|---|---|---|---|---|---|
| | | | $H_2O$ (liq.) and $CO_2$ (gas) | | | $H_2O$ (gas) and $CO_2$ (gas) | | |
| | | | kcal/mole | cal/g | BTU/lb | kcal/mole | cal/g | BTU/lb |
| Cyclopentane | $C_5H_{10}$ | gas | 793.39 | 11313.1 | 20350. | 740.79 | 10563.1 | 19001. |
| " | " | liquid | 786.54 | 11215.5 | 20175 | 733.94 | 10465.4 | 18825. |
| Methylcyclopentane | $C_6H_{12}$ | gas | 948.72 | 11273.4 | 20279. | 885.60 | 10523.3 | 18930. |
| " | " | liquid | 941.14 | 11183.3 | 20117. | 878.02 | 10433.2 | 18768. |
| Ethylcyclopentane | $C_7H_{14}$ | gas | 1106.21 | 11266.9 | 20267. | 1032.57 | 10516.9 | 18918. |
| " | " | liquid | 1097.50 | 11178.2 | 20108. | 1023.86 | 10428.2 | 18758. |
| n–Propylcyclopentane | $C_8H_{16}$ | gas | 1263.56 | 11260.9 | 20256. | 1179.40 | 10510.8 | 18907. |
| " | " | liquid | 1253.74 | 11173.4 | 20099. | 1169.58 | 10423.3 | 18750. |
| n–Butylcyclopentane | $C_9H_{18}$ | gas | 1421.10 | 11257.7 | 20250. | 1326.42 | 10507.6 | 18901. |
| " | " | liquid | 1410.10 | 11170.5 | 20094. | 1315.42 | 10420.5 | 18745. |
| n–Pentylcyclopentane | $C_{10}H_{20}$ | gas | 1578.54 | 11254.4 | 20245. | 1473.34 | 10504.4 | 18895. |
| " | " | liquid | | | | | | |
| n–Hexylcyclopentane | $C_{11}H_{22}$ | gas | 1735.99 | 11251.8 | 20240. | 1620.28 | 10501.8 | 18891. |
| " | " | liquid | | | | | | |
| n–Heptylcyclopentane | $C_{12}H_{24}$ | gas | 1893.43 | 11249.5 | 20236. | 1767.20 | 10499.6 | 18887. |
| " | " | liquid | | | | | | |
| n–Octylcyclopentane | $C_{13}H_{26}$ | gas | 2050.87 | 11247.6 | 20232. | 1914.12 | 10497.6 | 18883. |
| " | " | liquid | | | | | | |
| n–Nonylcyclopentane | $C_{14}H_{28}$ | gas | 2208.32 | 11246.0 | 20230. | 2061.05 | 10496.1 | 18880. |
| " | " | liquid | | | | | | |
| n–Decylcyclopentane | $C_{15}H_{30}$ | gas | 2365.76 | 11244.6 | 20227. | 2207.97 | 10494.6 | 18878. |
| " | " | liquid | | | | | | |
| n–Undecylcyclopentane | $C_{16}H_{32}$ | gas | 2523.20 | 11243.4 | 20225. | 2354.89 | 10493.4 | 18876. |
| " | " | liquid | | | | | | |
| n–Dodecylcyclopentane | $C_{17}H_{34}$ | gas | 2680.65 | 11242.4 | 20223. | 2501.82 | 10492.4 | 18874. |
| " | " | liquid | | | | | | |
| n–Tridecylcyclopentane · | $C_{18}H_{36}$ | gas | 2838.09 | 11241.4 | 20221. | 2648.74 | 10491.4 | 18872. |
| " | " | liquid | | | | | | |
| n–Tetradecylcyclopentane | $C_{19}H_{38}$ | gas | 2995.53 | 11240.5 | 20220. | 2795.66 | 10490.5 | 18870. |
| " | " | liquid | | | | | | |
| n–Pentadecylcyclopentane | $C_{20}H_{40}$ | gas | 3152.97 | 11239.7 | 20218. | 2942.58 | 10489.7 | 18869. |
| " | " | liquid· | | | | | | |
| n–Hexadecylcyclopentane | $C_{21}H_{42}$ | gas | 3310.42 | 11239.1 | 20217. | 3089.51 | 10489.1 | 18868. |
| " | " | liquid | | | | | | |

## TABLE 6n — ALKYL CYCLOPENTANES, $C_5$ TO $C_7$
## HEAT OF COMBUSTION, AT 25°C
October 31, 1948

| Compound | Formula | State | Heat of Combustion, $-\Delta Hc^0$, at 25°C and constant pressure, to form: | | | | | |
| | | | $H_2O$ (liq) and $CO_2$ (gas) | | | $H_2O$ (gas) and $CO_2$ (gas) | | |
| | | | kcal/mole | cal/g | BTU/lb | kcal/mole | cal/g | BTU/lb |
|---|---|---|---|---|---|---|---|---|
| Cyclopentane | $C_5H_{10}$ | gas | 793.39 | 11313.1 | 20350. | 740.79 | 10563.1 | 19001. |
| " | " | liq | 786.54 | 11215.5 | 20175. | 733.94 | 10465.4 | 18825. |
| Methylcyclopentane | $C_6H_{12}$ | gas | 948.72 | 11273.4 | 20279. | 885.60 | 10523.3 | 18930. |
| " | " | liq | 941.14 | 11183.3 | 20117. | 878.02 | 10433.2 | 18768. |
| Ethylcyclopentane | $C_7H_{14}$ | gas | 1106.23 | 11267.1 | 20268. | 1032.59 | 10517.1 | 18918. |
| " | " | liq | 1097.50 | 11178.2 | 20108. | 1023.86 | 10428.2 | 18758. |
| 1,1-Dimethylcyclopentane | " | gas | 1103.53 | 11239.6 | 20218. | 1029.89 | 10489.6 | 18869. |
| " | " | liq | 1095.44 | 11157.2 | 20070. | 1021.80 | 10407.2 | 18721. |
| cis-1,2-Dimethylcyclopentane | " | gas | 1105.62 | 11260.9 | 20256. | 1031.98 | 10510.9 | 18907. |
| " | " | liq | 1097.06 | 11173.7 | 20100. | 1023.42 | 10423.7 | 18750. |
| trans-1,2-Dimethylcyclopentane | " | gas | 1103.91 | 11243.5 | 20225. | 1030.27 | 10493.5 | 18876. |
| " | " | liq | 1095.64 | 11159.3 | 20074. | 1022.00 | 10409.2 | 18724. |
| cis-1,3-Dimethylcyclopentane | " | gas | 1104.64 | 11250.9 | 20238. | 1031.00 | 10500.9 | 18889. |
| " | " | liq | 1096.39 | 11166.9 | 20087. | 1022.75 | 10416.9 | 18738. |
| trans-1,3-Dimethylcyclopentane | " | gas | 1104.11 | 11245.5 | 20229. | 1030.47 | 10495.5 | 18880. |
| " | " | liq | 1095.90 | 11161.9 | 20078. | 1022.26 | 10411.9 | 18729. |

451

TABLE 23n (PART 1) — NORMAL ALKYL CYCLOHEXANES, $C_6$ TO $C_{22}$

HEAT OF COMBUSTION, AT 25°C

March 31, 1946

| Compound | Formula | State | Heat of Combustion, $-\Delta Hc^0$, at 25°C and constant pressure, to form: | | | | | |
| | | | $H_2O$ (liq.) and $CO_2$ (gas) | | | $H_2O$ (gas) and $CO_2$ (gas) | | |
| | | | kcal/mole | cal/g | BTU/lb | kcal/mole | cal/g | BTU/lb |
| Cyclohexane | $C_6H_{12}$ | gas | 944.79 | 11226.7 | 20195. | 881.67 | 10476.7 | 18846. |
| " | " | liquid | 936.88 | 11132.7 | 20026. | 873.76 | 10382.7 | 18676. |
| Methylcyclohexane | $C_7H_{14}$ | gas | 1099.59 | 11199.5 | 20146. | 1025.95 | 10449.5 | 18797. |
| " | " | liquid | 1091.13 | 11113.3 | 19991. | 1017.49 | 10363.3 | 18642. |
| Ethylcyclohexane | $C_8H_{16}$ | gas | 1257.90 | 11210.4 | 20166. | 1173.74 | 10460.4 | 18816. |
| " | " | liquid | 1248.23 | 11124.3 | 20011. | 1164.07 | 10374.3 | 18661. |
| n–Propylcyclohexane | $C_9H_{18}$ | gas | 1415.12 | 11210.3 | 20165. | 1320.44 | 10460.3 | 18816. |
| " | " | liquid | 1404.34 | 11124.9 | 20012. | 1309.66 | 10374.9 | 18663. |
| n–Butylcyclohexane | $C_{10}H_{20}$ | gas | 1572.74 | 11213.0 | 20170. | 1467.54 | 10463.0 | 18821. |
| " | " | liquid | 1560.78 | 11127.8 | 20017. | 1455.58 | 10377.8 | 18668. |
| n–Pentylcyclohexane | $C_{11}H_{22}$ | gas | 1730.18 | 11214.1 | 20172. | 1614.47 | 10464.1 | 18823. |
| " | " | liquid | | | | | | |
| n–Hexylcyclohexane | $C_{12}H_{24}$ | gas | 1887.63 | 11215.1 | 20174. | 1761.40 | 10465.1 | 18825. |
| " | " | liquid | | | | | | |
| n–Heptylcyclohexane | $C_{13}H_{26}$ | gas | 2045.07 | 11215.8 | 20175. | 1908.32 | 10465.8 | 18826. |
| " | " | liquid | | | | | | |
| n–Octylcyclohexane | $C_{14}H_{28}$ | gas | 2202.51 | 11216.5 | 20176. | 2055.24 | 10466.5 | 18827. |
| " | " | liquid | | | | | | |
| n–Nonylcyclohexane | $C_{15}H_{30}$ | gas | 2359.96 | 11217.1 | 20178. | 2202.17 | 10467.1 | 18828. |
| " | " | liquid | | | | | | |
| n–Decylcyclohexane | $C_{16}H_{32}$ | gas | 2517.40 | 11217.6 | 20178. | 2349.09 | 10467.6 | 18829. |
| " | " | liquid | | | | | | |
| n–Undecylcyclohexane | $C_{17}H_{34}$ | gas | 2674.84 | 11218.0 | 20179. | 2496.01 | 10468.0 | 18830. |
| " | " | liquid | | | | | | |
| n–Dodecylcyclohexane | $C_{18}H_{36}$ | gas | 2832.28 | 11218.4 | 20180. | 2642.93 | 10468.4 | 18831. |
| " | " | liquid | | | | | | |
| n–Tridecylcyclohexane | $C_{19}H_{38}$ | gas | 2989.73 | 11218.8 | 20181. | 2789.86 | 10468.8 | 18831. |
| " | " | liquid | | | | | | |
| n–Tetradecylcyclohexane | $C_{20}H_{40}$ | gas | 3147.17 | 11219.1 | 20181. | 2936.78 | 10469.1 | 18832. |
| " | " | liquid | | | | | | |
| n–Pentadecylcyclohexane | $C_{21}H_{42}$ | gas | 3304.61 | 11219.3 | 20182. | 3083.70 | 10469.3 | 18832. |
| " | " | liquid | | | | | | |
| n–Hexadecylcyclohexane | $C_{22}H_{44}$ | gas | 3462.06 | 11219.6 | 20182. | 3230.63 | 10469.6 | 18833. |
| " | " | liquid | | | | | | |

TABLE 7n – ALKYL CYCLOHEXANES, $C_6$ TO $C_8$
HEAT OF COMBUSTION, AT 25°C
October 31, 1948

| Compound | Formula | State | Heat of Combustion, $-\Delta Hc^o$, at 25°C and constant pressure, to form: | | | | | |
| | | | $H_2O$ (liq) and $CO_2$ (gas) | | | $H_2O$ (gas) and $CO_2$ (gas) | | |
| | | | kcal/mole | cal/g | BTU/lb | kcal/mole | cal/g | BTU/lb |
|---|---|---|---|---|---|---|---|---|
| Cyclohexane | $C_6H_{12}$ | gas | 944.79 | 11226.7 | 20195. | 881.67 | 10476.7 | 18846. |
| " | " | liq | 936.88 | 11132.7 | 20026. | 873.76 | 10382.7 | 18676. |
| Methylcyclohexane | $C_7H_{14}$ | gas | 1099.59 | 11199.5 | 20146. | 1025.95 | 10449.5 | 18797. |
| " | " | liq | 1091.13 | 11113.3 | 19991. | 1017.49 | 10363.3 | 18642. |
| Ethylcyclohexane | $C_8H_{16}$ | gas | 1257.90 | 11210.4 | 20166. | 1173.74 | 10460.4 | 18816. |
| " | " | liq | 1248.23 | 11124.3 | 20011. | 1164.07 | 10374.3 | 18661. |
| 1,1-Dimethylcyclohexane | " | gas | 1255.69 | 11190.7 | 20130. | 1171.53 | 10440.7 | 18781. |
| " | " | liq | 1246.65 | 11110.2 | 19985. | 1162.49 | 10360.1 | 18636. |
| cis-1,2-Dimethylcyclohexane | " | gas | 1257.80 | 11209.5 | 20164. | 1173.64 | 10459.5 | 18815. |
| " | " | liq | 1248.31 | 11125.0 | 20012. | 1164.15 | 10374.9 | 18663. |
| trans-1,2-Dimethylcyclohexane | " | gas | 1255.93 | 11192.9 | 20134. | 1171.77 | 10442.8 | 18785. |
| " | " | liq | 1246.76 | 11111.2 | 19987. | 1162.60 | 10361.1 | 18638. |
| cis-1,3-Dimethylcyclohexane | " | gas | 1254.79 | 11182.7 | 20116. | 1170.63 | 10432.7 | 18767. |
| " | " | liq | 1245.65 | 11101.2 | 19969. | 1161.49 | 10351.2 | 18620. |
| trans-1,3-Dimethylcyclohexane | " | gas | 1256.75 | 11200.2 | 20147. | 1172.59 | 10450.1 | 18798. |
| " | " | liq | 1247.38 | 11116.7 | 19997. | 1163.22 | 10366.6 | 18648. |
| cis-1,4-Dimethylcyclohexane | " | gas | 1256.73 | 11200.0 | 20147. | 1172.57 | 10450.0 | 18798. |
| " | " | liq | 1247.40 | 11116.8 | 19997. | 1163.24 | 10366.8 | 18648. |
| trans-1,4-Dimethylcyclohexane | " | gas | 1254.83 | 11183.1 | 20116. | 1170.67 | 10433.0 | 18767. |
| " | " | liq | 1245.78 | 11102.4 | 19971. | 1161.62 | 10352.4 | 18622. |

TABLE 24n (PART 1) — NORMAL MONOOLEFINS (1-ALKENES), $C_2$ TO $C_{20}$
HEAT OF COMBUSTION, AT 25°C
December 31, 1945; December 31, 1952

| Compound | Formula | State | Heat of Combustion, $-\Delta Hc^0$, at 25°C and constant pressure, to form: | | | | | |
| | | | $H_2O$ (liq.) and $CO_2$ (gas) | | | $H_2O$ (gas) and $CO_2$ (gas) | | |
| | | | kcal/mole | cal/g | BTU/lb | kcal/mole | cal/g | BTU/lb |
|---|---|---|---|---|---|---|---|---|
| Ethene (Ethylene) | $C_2H_4$ | gas | 337.23 | 12022. | 21625. | 316.20 | 11272. | 20276. |
| " | " | liquid | | | | | | |
| Propene (Propylene) | $C_3H_6$ | gas | 491.99 | 11692. | 21032. | 460.43 | 10942. | 19683. |
| " | " | liquid | | | | | | |
| 1-Butene | $C_4H_8$ | gas | 649.45 | 11577. | 20824. | 607.37 | 10826. | 19475. |
| " | " | liquid | | | | | | |
| 1-Pentene | $C_5H_{10}$ | gas | 806.85 | 11505. | 20696. | 754.25 | 10755. | 19346. |
| " | " | liquid | | | | | | |
| 1-Hexene | $C_6H_{12}$ | gas | 964.26 | 11458. | 20611. | 901.14 | 10708. | 19262. |
| " | " | liquid | | | | | | |
| 1-Heptene | $C_7H_{14}$ | gas | 1121.69 | 11425. | 20551. | 1048.05 | 10675. | 19202. |
| " | " | liquid | | | | | | |
| 1-Octene | $C_8H_{16}$ | gas | 1279.13 | 11400. | 20506. | 1194.97 | 10650. | 19157. |
| " | " | liquid | | | | | | |
| 1-Nonene | $C_9H_{18}$ | gas | 1436.58 | 11380. | 20471. | 1341.90 | 10630. | 19122. |
| " | " | liquid | | | | | | |
| 1-Decene | $C_{10}H_{20}$ | gas | 1594.02 | 11365. | 20443. | 1488.82 | 10615. | 19094. |
| " | " | liquid | | | | | | |
| 1-Undecene | $C_{11}H_{22}$ | gas | 1751.46 | 11352. | 20420. | 1635.75 | 10602. | 19071. |
| " | " | liquid | | | | | | |
| 1-Dodecene | $C_{12}H_{24}$ | gas | 1908.91 | 11342. | 20401. | 1782.68 | 10592. | 19052. |
| " | " | liquid | | | | | | |
| 1-Tridecene | $C_{13}H_{26}$ | gas | 2066.35 | 11332. | 20385. | 1929.60 | 10582. | 19036. |
| " | " | liquid | | | | | | |
| 1-Tetradecene | $C_{14}H_{28}$ | gas | 2223.79 | 11325. | 20371. | 2076.52 | 10575. | 19022. |
| " | " | liquid | | | | | | |
| 1-Pentadecene | $C_{15}H_{30}$ | gas | 2381.23 | 11318. | 20359. | 2223.44 | 10568. | 19010. |
| " | " | liquid | | | | | | |
| 1-Hexadecene | $C_{16}H_{32}$ | gas | 2538.68 | 11312. | 20349. | 2370.37 | 10562. | 19000. |
| " | " | liquid | | | | | | |
| 1-Heptadecene | $C_{17}H_{34}$ | gas | 2696.13 | 11307. | 20340. | 2517.30 | 10557. | 18991. |
| " | " | liquid | | | | | | |
| 1-Octadecene | $C_{18}H_{36}$ | gas | 2853.57 | 11303. | 20332. | 2664.22 | 10553. | 18982. |
| " | " | liquid | | | | | | |
| 1-Nonadecene | $C_{19}H_{38}$ | gas | 3011.01 | 11299. | 20324. | 2811.14 | 10549. | 18975. |
| " | " | liquid | | | | | | |
| 1-Eicosene | $C_{20}H_{40}$ | gas | 3168.45 | 11295. | 20318. | 2958.06 | 10545. | 18968. |

454

TABLE 8n (PART 1) — MONOOLEFINS, $C_2$ TO $C_5$
HEAT OF COMBUSTION, AT 25°C
October 31, 1945; December 31, 1952

| Compound | Formula | State | Heat of Combustion, $-\Delta Hc^0$, at 25°C and constant pressure, to form: | | | | | |
|---|---|---|---|---|---|---|---|---|
| | | | $H_2O$ (liq.) and $CO_2$ (gas) | | | $H_2O$ (gas) and $CO_2$ (gas) | | |
| | | | kcal/mole | cal/g | BTU/lb | kcal/mole | cal/g | BTU/lb |
| Ethene (Ethylene) | $C_2H_4$ | gas | 337.23 | 12022. | 21625. | 316.20 | 11272. | 20276. |
| " | " | liquid | | | | | | |
| Propene (Propylene) | $C_3H_6$ | gas | 491.99 | 11692. | 21032. | 460.43 | 10942. | 19683. |
| " | " | liquid | | | | | | |
| 1-Butene | $C_4H_8$ | gas | 649.45 | 11577. | 20824. | 607.37 | 10826. | 19475. |
| " | " | liquid | | | | | | |
| cis-2-Butene | " | gas | 647.81 | 11547. | 20772. | 605.73 | 10797. | 19422. |
| " | " | liquid | | | | | | |
| trans-2-Butene | " | gas | 646.81 | 11529. | 20738. | 604.73 | 10779. | 19389. |
| " | " | liquid | | | | | | |
| 2-Methylpropene (Isobutene) | " | gas | 645.43 | 11505. | 20695. | 603.36 | 10755. | 19346. |
| " | " | liquid | | | | | | |
| 1-Pentene | $C_5H_{10}$ | gas | 806.85 | 11505. | 20696. | 754.25 | 10755. | 29346. |
| " | " | liquid | | | | | | |
| cis-2-Pentene | " | gas | 805.34 | 11484. | 20657. | 752.74 | 10734. | 19308. |
| " | " | liquid | | | | | | |
| trans-2-Pentene | " | gas | 804.26 | 11468. | 20629. | 751.66 | 10718. | 19280. |
| " | " | liquid | | | | | | |
| 2-Methyl-1-butene | " | gas | 803.17 | 11453. | 20601. | 750.57 | 10703. | 19252. |
| " | " | liquid | | | | | | |
| 3-Methyl-1-butene | " | gas | 804.93 | 11478. | 20646. | 752.33 | 10728. | 19297. |
| " | " | liquid | | | | | | |
| 2-Methyl-2-butene | " | gas | 801.68 | 11431. | 20563. | 749.08 | 10681. | 19214. |
| " | " | liquid | | | | | | |

455

TABLE 8n (PART 2) — MONOOLEFINS, $C_6$
HEAT OF COMBUSTION, AT 25°C
October 31, 1945

| Compound | Formula | State | Heat of Combustion, $-\Delta Hc°$, at 25°C and constant pressure, to form: | | | | | |
|---|---|---|---|---|---|---|---|---|
| | | | $H_2O$ (liq.) and $CO_2$ (gas) | | | $H_2O$ (gas) and $CO_2$ (gas) | | |
| | | | kcal/mole | cal/g | BTU/lb | kcal/mole | cal/g | BTU/lb |
| 1-Hexene | $C_6H_{12}$ | gas | 964.26 | 11458.0 | 20611. | 901.14 | 10708.0 | 19262. |
| " | " | liquid | | | | | | |
| cis-2-Hexene | " | gas | 962.66 | 11439.0 | 20577. | 899.54 | 10689.0 | 19228. |
| " | " | liquid | | | | | | |
| trans-2-Hexene | " | gas | 961.66 | 11427.1 | 20555. | 898.54 | 10677.1 | 19206. |
| " | " | liquid | | | | | | |
| cis-3-Hexene | " | gas | 962.66 | 11439.0 | 20577. | 899.54 | 10689.0 | 19228. |
| " | " | liquid | | | | | | |
| trans-3-Hexene | " | gas | 961.66 | 11427.1 | 20555. | 898.54 | 10677.1 | 19206. |
| " | " | liquid | | | | | | |
| 2-Methyl-1-pentene | " | gas | 960.66 | 11415.2 | 20534. | 897.54 | 10665.2 | 19185. |
| " | " | liquid | | | | | | |
| 3-Methyl-1-pentene | " | gas | 963.20 | 11445.4 | 20588. | 900.08 | 10695.4 | 19239. |
| " | " | liquid | | | | | | |
| 4-Methyl-1-pentene | " | gas | 962.56 | 11437.8 | 20575. | 899.44 | 10687.8 | 19225. |
| " | " | liquid | | | | | | |
| 2-Methyl-2-pentene | " | gas | 959.26 | 11398.6 | 20504. | 896.14 | 10648.6 | 19155. |
| " | " | liquid | | | | | | |
| 3-Methyl-cis-2-pentene | " | gas | 959.90 | 11406.2 | 20518. | 896.78 | 10656.2 | 19169. |
| " | " | liquid | | | | | | |
| 3-Methyl-trans-2-pentene | " | gas | 959.90 | 11406.2 | 20518. | 896.78 | 10656.2 | 19169. |
| " | " | liquid | | | | | | |
| 4-Methyl-cis-2-pentene | " | gas | 960.96 | 11418.8 | 20540. | 897.84 | 10668.8 | 19191. |
| " | " | liquid | | | | | | |
| 4-Methyl-trans-2-pentene | " | gas | 959.96 | 11406.9 | 20519. | 896.84 | 10656.9 | 19170. |
| " | " | liquid | | | | | | |
| 2-Ethyl-1-butene | " | gas | 961.30 | 11422.8 | 20548. | 898.18 | 10672.8 | 19198. |
| " | " | liquid | | | | | | |
| 2,3-Dimethyl-1-butene | " | gas | 959.44 | 11400.7 | 20508. | 896.32 | 10650.7 | 19159. |
| " | " | liquid | | | | | | |
| 3,3-Dimethyl-1-butene | " | gas | 959.97 | 11407.0 | 20519. | 896.85 | 10657.0 | 19170. |
| " | " | liquid | | | | | | |
| 2,3-Dimethyl-2-butene | " | gas | 958.31 | 11387.3 | 20484. | 895.19 | 10637.3 | 19135. |
| " | " | liquid | | | | | | |

TABLE 9n, Page 1 — MONOOLEFINS, $C_7$

HEAT OF COMBUSTION, AT 25°C

October 31, 1945

| Compound | Formula | State | Heat of Combustion, $-\Delta Hc^o$, at 25°C and constant pressure, to form: | | | | | |
| | | | $H_2O$ (liq.) and $CO_2$ (gas) | | | $H_2O$ (gas) and $CO_2$ (gas) | | |
| | | | kcal/mole | cal/g | BTU/lb | kcal/mole | cal/g | BTU/lb |
|---|---|---|---|---|---|---|---|---|
| 1-Heptene | $C_7H_{14}$ | gas | 1121.69 | 11424.6 | 20551. | 1048.05 | 10674.6 | 19202. |
| " | " | liquid | | | | | | |
| cis-2-Heptene | " | gas | 1120.09 | 11408.3 | 20522. | 1046.45 | 10658.3 | 19172. |
| " | " | liquid | | | | | | |
| trans-2-Heptene | " | gas | 1119.09 | 11398.1 | 20503. | 1045.45 | 10648.1 | 19154. |
| " | " | liquid | | | | | | |
| cis-3-Heptene | " | gas | 1120.09 | 11408.3 | 20522. | 1046.45 | 10658.3 | 19172. |
| " | " | liquid | | | | | | |
| trans-3-Heptene | " | gas | 1119.09 | 11398.1 | 20503. | 1045.45 | 10648.1 | 19154. |
| " | " | liquid | | | | | | |
| 2-Methyl-1-hexene | " | gas | 1118.08 | 11387.8 | 20485. | 1044.44 | 10637.8 | 19136. |
| " | " | liquid | | | | | | |
| 3-Methyl-1-hexene | " | gas | 1120.62 | 11413.7 | 20531. | 1046.98 | 10663.7 | 19182. |
| " | " | liquid | | | | | | |
| 4-Methyl-1-hexene | " | gas | 1120.62 | 11413.7 | 20531. | 1046.98 | 10663.7 | 19182. |
| " | " | liquid | | | | | | |
| 5-Methyl-1-hexene | " | gas | 1119.98 | 11407.2 | 20520. | 1046.34 | 10657.2 | 19170. |
| " | " | liquid | | | | | | |
| 2-Methyl-2-hexene | " | gas | 1116.68 | 11373.6 | 20459. | 1043.04 | 10623.6 | 19110. |
| " | " | liquid | | | | | | |
| 3-Methyl-cis-2-hexene | " | gas | 1117.32 | 11380.1 | 20471. | 1043.68 | 10630.1 | 19122. |
| " | " | liquid | | | | | | |
| 3-Methyl-trans-2-hexene | " | gas | 1117.32 | 11380.1 | 20471. | 1043.68 | 10630.1 | 19122. |
| " | " | liquid | | | | | | |
| 4-Methyl-cis-2-hexene | " | gas | 1119.02 | 11397.4 | 20502. | 1045.38 | 10647.4 | 19153. |
| " | " | liquid | | | | | | |
| 4-Methyl-trans-2-hexene | " | gas | 1118.02 | 11387.2 | 20484. | 1044.38 | 10637.2 | 19134. |
| " | " | liquid | | | | | | |
| 5-Methyl-cis-2-hexene | " | gas | 1118.38 | 11390.9 | 20490. | 1044.74 | 10640.9 | 19141. |
| " | " | liquid | | | | | | |
| 5-Methyl-trans-2-hexene | " | gas | 1117.38 | 11380.7 | 20472. | 1043.74 | 10630.7 | 19123. |
| " | " | liquid | | | | | | |
| 2-Methyl-cis-3-hexene | " | gas | 1118.38 | 11390.9 | 20490. | 1044.74 | 10640.9 | 19141. |
| " | " | liquid | | | | | | |
| 2-Methyl-trans-3-hexene | " | gas | 1117.38 | 11380.7 | 20472. | 1043.74 | 10630.7 | 19123. |
| " | " | liquid | | | | | | |
| 3-Methyl-cis-3-hexene | " | gas | 1117.32 | 11380.1 | 20471. | 1043.68 | 10630.1 | 19122. |
| " | " | liquid | | | | | | |
| 3-Methyl-trans-3-hexene | " | gas | 1117.32 | 11380.1 | 20471. | 1043.68 | 10630.1 | 19122. |
| " | " | liquid | | | | | | |

457

TABLE 9n, Page 2 — MONOOLEFINS, $C_7$
HEAT OF COMBUSTION, AT 25°C
October 31, 1945

| Compound | Formula | State | Heat of Combustion, $-\Delta Hc^o$, at 25°C and constant pressure, to form: | | | | | |
| | | | $H_2O$ (liq.) and $CO_2$ (gas) | | | $H_2O$ (gas) and $CO_2$ (gas) | | |
| | | | kcal/mole | cal/g | BTU/lb | kcal/mole | cal/g | BTU/lb |
|---|---|---|---|---|---|---|---|---|
| 2-Ethyl-1-pentene | $C_7H_{14}$ | gas | 1118.72 | 11394.3 | 20496. | 1045.08 | 10644.4 | 19147. |
| " | " | liquid | | | | | | |
| 3-Ethyl-1-pentene | " | gas | 1121.24 | 11420.0 | 20542. | 1047.60 | 10670.0 | 19193. |
| " | " | liquid | | | | | | |
| 2,3-Dimethyl-1-pentene | " | gas | 1117.06 | 11377.4 | 20466. | 1043.42 | 10627.4 | 19117. |
| " | " | liquid | | | | | | |
| 2,4-Dimethyl-1-pentene | " | gas | 1116.38 | 11370.5 | 20454. | 1042.74 | 10620.5 | 19104. |
| " | " | liquid | | | | | | |
| 3,3-Dimethyl-1-pentene | " | gas | 1118.41 | 11391.2 | 20491. | 1044.77 | 10641.2 | 19142. |
| " | " | liquid | | | | | | |
| 3,4-Dimethyl-1-pentene | " | gas | 1118.96 | 11396.8 | 20501. | 1045.32 | 10646.8 | 19152. |
| " | " | liquid | | | | | | |
| 4,4-Dimethyl-1-pentene | " | gas | 1117.29 | 11379.8 | 20470. | 1043.65 | 10629.8 | 19121. |
| " | " | liquid | | | | | | |
| 3-Ethyl-2-pentene | " | gas | 1117.94 | 11386.4 | 20482. | 1044.30 | 10636.4 | 19133. |
| " | " | liquid | | | | | | |
| 2,3-Dimethyl-2-pentene | " | gas | 1115.46 | 11361.1 | 20437. | 1041.82 | 10611.2 | 19088. |
| " | " | liquid | | | | | | |
| 2,4-Dimethyl-2-pentene | " | gas | 1114.98 | 11356.3 | 20428. | 1041.34 | 10606.3 | 19079. |
| " | " | liquid | | | | | | |
| 3,4-Dimethyl-cis-2-pentene | " | gas | 1115.66 | 11363.2 | 20440. | 1042.02 | 10613.2 | 19091. |
| " | " | liquid | | | | | | |
| 3,4-Dimethyl-trans-2-pentene | " | gas | 1115.66 | 11363.2 | 20440. | 1042.02 | 10613.2 | 19091. |
| " | " | liquid | | | | | | |
| 4,4-Dimethyl-cis-2-pentene | " | gas | 1115.69 | 11363.5 | 20441. | 1042.05 | 10613.5 | 19092. |
| " | " | liquid | | | | | | |
| 4,4-Dimethyl-trans-2-pentene | " | gas | 1114.69 | 11353.3 | 20422. | 1041.05 | 10603.3 | 19073. |
| " | " | liquid | | | | | | |
| 3-Methyl-2-ethyl-1-butene | " | gas | 1117.06 | 11377.4 | 20466. | 1043.42 | 10627.4 | 19117. |
| " | " | liquid | | | | | | |
| 2,3,3-Trimethyl-1-butene | " | gas | 1115.72 | 11363.8 | 20441. | 1042.08 | 10613.8 | 19092. |
| " | " | liquid | | | | | | |

TABLE 11n (PART 1) — DIOLEFINS, $C_3$ TO $C_5$
HEAT OF COMBUSTION, AT 25°C
October 31, 1948; December 31, 1952

| Compound | Formula | State | Heat of Combustion, $-\Delta Hc^\circ$, at 25°C and constant pressure, to form: | | | | | |
|---|---|---|---|---|---|---|---|---|
| | | | $H_2O$ (liq.) and $CO_2$ (gas) | | | $H_2O$ (gas) and $CO_2$ (gas) | | |
| | | | kcal/mole | cal/g | BTU/lb | kcal/mole | cal/g | BTU/lb |
| Propadiene (Allene) | $C_3H_4$ | gas | 464.71 | 11600. | 20866. | 443.67 | 11075. | 19921. |
| " | " | liquid | | | | | | |
| 1,2-Butadiene | $C_4H_6$ | gas | 619.93 | 11461. | 20616. | 588.37 | 10878. | 19567. |
| " | " | liquid | | | | | | |
| 1,3-Butadiene | " | gas | 607.49 | 11231. | 20203. | 575.93 | 10648. | 19153. |
| " | " | liquid | 602.37 | 11136. | 20032. | 570.82 | 10553. | 18983. |
| 1,2-Pentadiene | $C_5H_8$ | gas | 778.31 | 11427. | 20554. | 736.25 | 10809. | 19444. |
| " | " | liquid | | | | | | |
| 1-cis-3-Pentadiene | " | gas | 762.21 | 11190. | 20129. | 720.15 | 10573. | 19018. |
| " | " | liquid | | | | | | |
| 1-trans-3-Pentadiene | " | gas | 762.11 | 11189. | 20127. | 720.05 | 10571. | 19016. |
| " | " | liquid | | | | | | |
| 1,4-Pentadiene | " | gas | 768.71 | 11286. | 20301. | 726.65 | 10668. | 19190. |
| " | " | liquid | | | | | | |
| 2,3-Pentadiene | " | gas | 776.61 | 11402. | 20509. | 734.55 | 10784. | 19399. |
| " | " | liquid | | | | | | |
| 3-Methyl-1,2-butadiene | " | gas | 774.51 | 11371. | 20454. | 732.45 | 10753. | 19343. |
| " | " | liquid | | | | | | |
| 2-Methyl-1,3-butadiene (Isoprene) | " | gas | 761.61 | 11181. | 20113. | 719.55 | 10564. | 19003. |
| " | " | liquid | 755.31 | 11069. | 19947. | 713.25 | 10471. | 18836. |

TABLE 25n (PART 1)— NORMAL ACETYLENES (1 – ALKYNES), $C_2$ TO $C_{20}$
HEAT OF COMBUSTION, AT 25°C
March 31, 1946; December 31, 1952

| Compound | Formula | State | Heat of Combustion, $-\Delta H c^o$, at 25°C and constant pressure, to form: | | | | | |
| | | | $H_2O$ (liq.) and $CO_2$ (gas) | | | $H_2O$ (gas) and $CO_2$ (gas) | | |
| | | | kcal/mole | cal/g | BTU/lb | kcal/mole | cal/g | BTU/lb |
|---|---|---|---|---|---|---|---|---|
| Ethyne (Acetylene) | $C_2H_2$ | gas | 310.62 | 11930. | 21460. | 300.10 | 11526. | 20734. |
| " | " | liquid | | | | | | |
| Propyne (Methylacetylene) | $C_3H_4$ | gas | 463.11 | 11560. | 20794. | 442.07 | 11035. | 19849. |
| " | " | liquid | | | | | | |
| 1–Butyne (Ethylacetylene) | $C_4H_6$ | gas | 620.64 | 11474 | 20640. | 589.08 | 10891. | 19590. |
| " | " | liquid | | | | | | |
| 1–Pentyne | $C_5H_8$ | gas | 778.03 | 11422. | 20547. | 735.95 | 10805. | 19436. |
| " | " | liquid | | | | | | |
| 1–Hexyne | $C_6H_{10}$ | gas | 935.45 | 11388. | 20486. | 882.85 | 10748. | 19334. |
| " | " | liquid | | | | | | |
| 1–Heptyne | $C_7H_{12}$ | gas | 1092.89 | 11365. | 20443. | 1029.77 | 10708. | 19262. |
| " | " | liquid | | | | | | |
| 1–Octyne | $C_8H_{14}$ | gas | 1250.34 | 11347. | 20411. | 1176.70 | 10679. | 19209. |
| " | " | liquid | | | | | | |
| 1–Nonyne | $C_9H_{16}$ | gas | 1407.78 | 11333. | 20386. | 1323.62 | 10656. | 19168. |
| " | " | liquid | | | | | | |
| 1–Decyne | $C_{10}H_{18}$ | gas | 1565.22 | 11322. | 20366. | 1470.54 | 10637. | 19134. |
| " | " | liquid | | | | | | |
| 1–Undecyne | $C_{11}H_{20}$ | gas | 1722.67 | 11313. | 20350. | 1617.48 | 10622. | 19108. |
| " | " | liquid | | | | | | |
| 1–Dodecyne | $C_{12}H_{22}$ | gas | 1880.11 | 11306. | 20337. | 1764.40 | 10610. | 19086. |
| " | " | liquid | | | | | | |
| 1–Tridecyne | $C_{13}H_{24}$ | gas | 2037.55 * | 11300. | 20326. | 1911.32 | 10600. | 19066. |
| " | " | liquid | | | | | | |
| 1–Tetradecyne | $C_{14}H_{26}$ | gas | 2194.99 | 11294. | 20316. | 2058.24 | 10590. | 19050. |
| " | " | liquid | | | | | | |
| 1–Pentadecyne | $C_{15}H_{28}$ | gas | 2352.44 | 11290. | 20308. | 2205.17 | 10583. | 19036. |
| " | " | liquid | | | | | | |
| 1–Hexadecyne | $C_{16}H_{30}$ | gas | 2509.98 | 11285. | 20300. | 2352.09 | 10576. | 19024. |
| " | " | liquid | | | | | | |
| 1–Heptadecyne | $C_{17}H_{32}$ | gas | 2667.32 | 11282. | 20294. | 2499.01 | 10570. | 19013. |
| " | " | liquid | | | | | | |
| 1–Octadecyne | $C_{18}H_{34}$ | gas | 2824.77 | 11279. | 20288. | 2645.94 | 10565. | 19004. |
| " | " | liquid | | | | | | |
| 1–Nonadecyne | $C_{19}H_{36}$ | gas | 2982.21 | 11276. | 20283. | 2792.86 | 10560. | 18995. |
| " | " | liquid | | | | | | |
| 1–Eicosyne | $C_{20}H_{38}$ | gas | 3139.65 | 11273. | 20279. | 2939.78 | 10556. | 18988. |
| " | " | liquid | | | | | | |

460

| Compound | Formula | State | Heat of Combustion, $-\Delta H c^{\circ}$ at 25°C and constant pressure, to form: | | | | | |
|---|---|---|---|---|---|---|---|---|
| | | | $H_2O$ (liq.) and $CO_2$ (gas) | | | $H_2O$ (gas) and $CO_2$ (gas) | | |
| | | | kcal/mole | cal/g | BTU/lb | kcal/mole | cal/g | BTU/lb |
| Ethyne (Acetylene) | $C_2H_2$ | gas | 310.62 | 11930. | 21460. | 300.10 | 11526. | 20734. |
| " | " | liquid | | | | | | |
| Propyne (Methylacetylene) | $C_3H_4$ | gas | 463.11 | 11560. | 20794. | 442.07 | 11035. | 19849. |
| " | " | liquid | | | | | | |
| 1-Butyne (Ethylacetylene) | $C_4H_6$ | gas | 620.64 | 11474. | 20640. | 589.08 | 10891. | 19590. |
| " | " | liquid | | | | | | |
| 2-Butyne (Dimethylacetylene) | " | gas | 616.13 | 11391. | 20490. | 584.57 | 10807. | 19440. |
| " | " | liquid | | | | | | |
| 1-Pentyne | $C_5H_8$ | gas | 778.03 | 11422. | 20547. | 735.95 | 10805. | 19436. |
| " | " | liquid | | | | | | |
| 2-Pentyne | " | gas | 774.33 | 11368. | 20449. | 732.25 | 10750. | 19338. |
| " | " | liquid | | | | | | |
| 3-Methyl-1-butyne | " | gas | 776.13 | 11395. | 20497. | 734.05 | 10777. | 19386. |
| " | " | liquid | | | | | | |

TABLE 12n – ACETYLENES, $C_2$ TO $C_5$
HEAT OF COMBUSTION, AT 25°C
March 31, 1946; December 31, 1952

461

## TABLE 21n (PART 1) — NORMAL ALKYL BENZENES, $C_6$ TO $C_{22}$
## HEAT OF COMBUSTION, AT 25°C
### December 31, 1945

| Compound | Formula | State | Heat of Combustion, $-\Delta H_c^o$, at 25°C and constant pressure, to form: | | | | | |
| | | | $H_2O$ (liq.) and $CO_2$ (gas) | | | $H_2O$ (gas) and $CO_2$ (gas) | | |
| | | | kcal/mole | cal/g | BTU/lb | kcal/mole | cal/g | BTU/lb |
|---|---|---|---|---|---|---|---|---|
| Benzene | $C_6H_6$ | gas | 789.08 | 10102.4 | 18172. | 757.52 | 9698.4 | 17446. |
| " | " | liquid | 780.98 | 9998.7 | 17986. | 749.42 | 9594.7 | 17259. |
| Methylbenzene (Toluene) | $C_7H_8$ | gas | 943.58 | 10241.4 | 18422. | 901.50 | 9784.7 | 17601. |
| " | " | liquid | 934.50 | 10142.8 | 18245. | 892.42 | 9686.1 | 17424. |
| Ethylbenzene | $C_8H_{10}$ | gas | 1101.13 | 10372.4 | 18658. | 1048.53 | 9876.9 | 17767. |
| " | " | liquid | 1091.03 | 10277.2 | 18487. | 1038.43 | 9781.7 | 17596. |
| n-Propylbenzene | $C_9H_{12}$ | gas | 1258.24 | 10469.1 | 18832. | 1195.12 | 9943.9 | 17887. |
| " | " | liquid | 1247.19 | 10377.2 | 18667. | 1184.07 | 9852.0 | 17722. |
| n-Butylbenzene | $C_{10}H_{14}$ | gas | 1415.44 | 10546.3 | 18971. | 1341.80 | 9997.6 | 17984. |
| " | " | liquid | 1403.46 | 10457.0 | 18810. | 1329.82 | 9908.4 | 17823. |
| n-Pentylbenzene | $C_{11}H_{16}$ | gas | 1572.88 | 10610.5 | 19086. | 1488.72 | 10042.8 | 18065. |
| " | " | liquid | | | | | | |
| n-Hexylbenzene | $C_{12}H_{18}$ | gas | 1730.33 | 10663.7 | 19182. | 1635.65 | 10080.2 | 18132. |
| " | " | liquid | | | | | | |
| n-Heptylbenzene | $C_{13}H_{20}$ | gas | 1887.77 | 10708.3 | 19262. | 1782.58 | 10111.6 | 18189. |
| " | " | liquid | | | | | | |
| n-Octylbenzene | $C_{14}H_{22}$ | gas | 2045.21 | 10746.4 | 19331. | 1929.50 | 10138.4 | 18237. |
| " | " | liquid | | | | | | |
| n-Nonylbenzene | $C_{15}H_{24}$ | gas | 2202.66 | 10779.3 | 19390. | 2076.43 | 10161.5 | 18279. |
| " | " | liquid | | | | | | |
| n-Decylbenzene | $C_{16}H_{26}$ | gas | 2360.10 | 10807.9 | 19441. | 2223.35 | 10181.7 | 18315. |
| " | " | liquid | | | | | | |
| n-Undecylbenzene | $C_{17}H_{28}$ | gas | 2517.54 | 10833.1 | 19487. | 2370.27 | 10199.4 | 18347. |
| " | " | liquid | | | | | | |
| n-Dodecylbenzene | $C_{18}H_{30}$ | gas | 2674.98 | 10855.4 | 19527. | 2517.19 | 10215.0 | 18375. |
| " | " | liquid | | | | | | |
| n-Tridecylbenzene | $C_{19}H_{32}$ | gas | 2832.43 | 10875.3 | 19563. | 2664.12 | 10229.1 | 18400. |
| " | " | liquid | | | | | | |
| n-Tetradecylbenzene | $C_{20}H_{34}$ | gas | 2989.87 | 10893.2 | 19595. | 2811.04 | 10241.6 | 18423. |
| " | " | liquid | | | | | | |
| n-Pentadecylbenzene | $C_{21}H_{36}$ | gas | 3147.31 | 10909.3 | 19624. | 2957.96 | 10253.0 | 18443. |
| " | " | liquid | | | | | | |
| n-Hexadecylbenzene | $C_{22}H_{38}$ | gas | 3304.76 | 10924.0 | 19650. | 3104.89 | 10263.3 | 18462. |
| " | " | liquid | | | | | | |

TABLE 5n – ALKYL BENZENES, $C_6$ TO $C_9$
HEAT OF COMBUSTION, AT 25°C
March 31, 1945

| Compound | Formula | State | Heat of Combustion, $-\Delta Hc^o$, at 25°C and constant pressure, to form: | | | | | |
|---|---|---|---|---|---|---|---|---|
| | | | $H_2O$ (liq.) and $CO_2$ (gas) | | | $H_2O$ (gas) and $CO_2$ (gas) | | |
| | | | kcal/mole | cal/g | BTU/lb | kcal/mole | cal/g | BTU/lb |
| Benzene | $C_6H_6$ | gas | 789.08 | 10102.4 | 18172. | 757.52 | 9698.4 | 17446. |
| " | " | liquid | 780.98 | 9998.7 | 17986. | 749.42 | 9594.7 | 17259. |
| | $C_7H_8$ | gas | 943.58 | 10241.4 | | | | |
| Methylbenzene (Toluene) | $C_7H_8$ | gas | 943.58 | 10241.4 | 18422. | 901.50 | 9784.7 | 17601. |
| " | " | liquid | 934.50 | 10142.8 | 18245. | 892.42 | 9686.1 | 17424 |
| Ethylbenzene | $C_8H_{10}$ | gas | 1101.13 | 10372.4 | 18658. | 1048.53 | 9876.9 | 17767. |
| " | " | liquid | 1091.03 | 10277.2 | 18487. | 1038.43 | 9781.7 | 17596. |
| 1,2-Dimethylbenzene (o-Xylene) | " | gas | 1098.54 | 10348.0 | 18614. | 1045.94 | 9852.5 | 17723. |
| " | " | liquid | 1088.16 | 10250.2 | 18438. | 1035.56 | 9754.7 | 17547. |
| 1,3-Dimethylbenzene (m-Xylene) | " | gas | 1098.12 | 10344.0 | 18607. | 1045.52 | 9848.5 | 17716. |
| " | " | liquid | 1087.92 | 10247.9 | 18434. | 1035.32 | 9752.4 | 17543. |
| 1,4-Dimethylbenzene (p-Xylene) | " | gas | 1098.29 | 10345.6 | 18610. | 1045.69 | 9850.1 | 17719. |
| " | " | liquid | 1088.16 | 10250.2 | 18438. | 1035.56 | 9754.7 | 17547. |
| n-Propylbenzene | $C_9H_{12}$ | gas | 1258.24 | 10469.1 | 18832. | 1195.12 | 9943.9 | 17887. |
| " | " | liquid | 1247.19 | 10377.2 | 18667. | 1184.07 | 9852.0 | 17722. |
| Isopropylbenzene | " | gas | 1257.31 | 10461.4 | 18818. | 1194.19 | 9936.2 | 17873. |
| " | " | liquid | 1246.52 | 10371.6 | 18657. | 1183.40 | 9846.4 | 17712. |
| 1-Methyl-2-ethylbenzene | " | gas | 1256.66 | 10456.0 | 18808. | 1193.54 | 9930.8 | 17864. |
| " | " | liquid | 1245.26 | 10361.1 | 18638. | 1182.14 | 9835.9 | 17693. |
| 1-Methyl-3-ethylbenzene | " | gas | 1255.92 | 10449.8 | 18797. | 1192.80 | 9924.6 | 17853. |
| " | " | liquid | 1244.71 | 10356.5 | 18630. | 1181.59 | 9831.3 | 17685. |
| 1-Methyl-4-ethylbenzene | " | gas | 1255.59 | 10447.1 | 18792. | 1192.47 | 9921.9 | 17848. |
| " | " | liquid | 1244.45 | 10354.4 | 18626. | 1181.33 | 9829.2 | 17681. |
| 1,2,3-Trimethylbenzene | " | gas | 1254.08 | 10434.5 | 18770. | 1190.96 | 9909.3 | 17825. |
| " | " | liquid | 1242.36 | 10337.0 | 18594. | 1179.24 | 9811.8 | 17650. |
| 1,2,4-Trimethylbenzene | " | gas | 1253.04 | 10425.8 | 18754. | 1189.92 | 9900.7 | 17809. |
| " | " | liquid | 1241.58 | 10330.5 | 18583. | 1178.46 | 9805.3 | 17638. |
| 1,3,5-Trimethylbenzene | " | gas | 1252.53 | 10421.6 | 18747. | 1189.41 | 9896.4 | 17802. |
| " | " | liquid | 1241.19 | 10327.2 | 18577. | 1178.07 | 9802.1 | 17632. |

## TABLE 13n – STYRENES, $C_8$ AND $C_9$
## HEAT OF COMBUSTION, AT 25°C
February 28, 1949

| Compound | Formula | State | Heat of Combustion, $-\Delta Hc^o$, at 25°C and constant pressure, to form: | | | | | |
| --- | --- | --- | --- | --- | --- | --- | --- | --- |
| | | | $H_2O$ (liq) and $CO_2$ (gas) | | | $H_2O$ (gas) and $CO_2$ (gas) | | |
| | | | kcal/mole | cal/g | BTU/lb | kcal/mole | cal/g | BTU/lb |
| Ethenylbenzene (Styrene) | $C_8H_8$ | gas | 1060.90 | 10186.9 | 18324. | 1018.83 | 9782.9 | 17598. |
| " | " | liq | 1050.51 | 10087.1 | 18145. | 1008.44 | 9683.1 | 17418. |
| Isopropenylbenzene | $C_9H_{10}$ | gas | 1215.05 | 10282.2 | 18496. | 1162.46 | 9837.2 | 17695. |
| " | " | liq | | | | | | |
| cis-1-Propenylbenzene | " | gas | 1217.05 | 10299.1 | 18526. | 1164.46 | 9854.1 | 17726. |
| " | " | liq | | | | | | |
| trans-1-Propenylbenzene | " | gas | 1216.05 | 10290.7 | 18511. | 1163.46 | 9845.6 | 17711. |
| " | " | liq | | | | | | |
| 1-Methyl-2-ethenylbenzene | " | gas | 1216.35 | 10293.2 | 18516. | 1163.76 | 9848.2 | 17715. |
| " | " | liq | | | | | | |
| 1-Methyl-3-ethenylbenzene | " | gas | 1215.65 | 10287.3 | 18505. | 1163.06 | 9842.3 | 17704. |
| " | " | liq | | | | | | |
| 1-Methyl-4-ethenylbenzene | " | gas | 1215.45 | 10285.6 | 18502. | 1162.86 | 9840.6 | 17701. |
| " | " | liq | | | | | | |

TABLE Op — $O_2$, $H_2$, $H_2O$, $N_2$, C, CO, $CO_2$

## HEAT OF FORMATION, ENTROPY, AND FREE ENERGY OF FORMATION, AT 25°C

April 30, 1945

| Compound | Formula | State | Heat of Formation $\Delta H_f^0$ At 25°C kcal/mole | Entropy $S^0$ At 25°C cal/deg mole | Free Energy of Formation $\Delta F_f^0$ At 25°C kcal/mole |
|---|---|---|---|---|---|
| Oxygen | $O_2$ | gas | 0 | 49.003 | 0 |
| Hydrogen | $H_2$ | gas | 0 | 31.211 | 0 |
| Water | $H_2O$ | gas | −57.7979 | 45.106 | −54.6351 |
| " | " | liquid | −68.3174 | 16.716 | −56.6899 |
| Nitrogen | $N_2$ | gas | 0 | 45.767 | 0 |
| Carbon | C | solid, graphite | 0 | 1.3609 | 0 |
| Carbon monoxide | CO | gas | −26.4157 | 47.300 | −32.8077 |
| Carbon dioxide | $CO_2$ | gas | −94.0518 | 51.061 | −94.2598 |

465

TABLE 20p (PART 1) — NORMAL PARAFFINS, $C_1$ TO $C_{20}$
HEAT OF FORMATION, ENTROPY, AND FREE ENERGY OF FORMATION, AT 25°C

June 30, 1946; December 31, 1952

| Compound | Formula | State | Heat of Formation $\Delta H_f^0$ At 25°C kcal/mole | Entropy $S^0$ At 25°C cal/deg mole | Free Energy of Formation $\Delta F_f^0$ At 25°C kcal/mole |
|---|---|---|---|---|---|
| Methane | $CH_4$ | gas | −17.889 | 44.50 | −12.140 |
| " | " | liquid | | | |
| Ethane | $C_2H_6$ | gas | −20.236 | 54.85 | −7.860 |
| " | " | liquid | | | |
| Propane | $C_3H_8$ | gas | −24.820 | 64.51 | −5.614 |
| " | " | liquid | −28.643 | | |
| n−Butane | $C_4H_{10}$ | gas | −30.15 | 74.12 | −4.10 |
| " | " | liquid | −35.29 | | |
| n−Pentane | $C_5H_{12}$ | gas | −35.00 | 83.40 | −2.00 |
| " | " | liquid | −41.36 | 62.92 | −2.25 |
| n−Hexane | $C_6H_{14}$ | gas | −39.96 | 92.83 | −0.07 |
| " | " | liquid | −47.52 | 70.72 | −1.03 |
| n−Heptane | $C_7H_{16}$ | gas | −44.89 | 102.24 | +1.94 |
| " | " | liquid | −53.63 | 78.52 | 0.27 |
| n−Octane | $C_8H_{18}$ | gas | −49.82 | 111.55 | 3.95 |
| " | " | liquid | −59.74 | 86.23 | 1.58 |
| n−Nonane | $C_9H_{20}$ | gas | −54.74 | 120.86 | 5.96 |
| " | " | liquid | | | |
| n−Decane | $C_{10}H_{22}$ | gas | −59.67 | 130.17 | 7.97 |
| " | " | liquid | | | |
| n−Undecane | $C_{11}H_{24}$ | gas | −64.60 | 139.48 | 9.98 |
| " | " | liquid | | | |
| n−Dodecane | $C_{12}H_{26}$ | gas | −69.52 | 148.79 | 11.98 |
| " | " | liquid | | | |
| n−Tridecane | $C_{13}H_{28}$ | gas | −74.45 | 158.09 | 13.99 |
| " | " | liquid | | | |
| n−Tetradecane | $C_{14}H_{30}$ | gas | −79.38 | 167.40 | 16.00 |
| " | " | liquid | | | |
| n−Pentadecane | $C_{15}H_{32}$ | gas | −84.31 | 176.71 | 18.01 |
| " | " | liquid | | | |
| n−Hexadecane | $C_{16}H_{34}$ | gas | −89.23 | 186.02 | 20.02 |
| " | " | liquid | | | |
| n−Heptadecane | $C_{17}H_{36}$ | gas | −94.15 | 195.33 | 22.03 |
| " | " | liquid | | | |
| n−Octadecane | $C_{18}H_{38}$ | gas | −99.08 | 204.64 | 24.04 |
| " | " | liquid | | | |
| n−Nonadecane | $C_{19}H_{40}$ | gas | −104.00 | 213.95 | 26.05 |
| " | " | liquid | | | |
| n−Eicosane | $C_{20}H_{42}$ | gas | −108.93 | 223.26 | 28.06 |
| " | " | liquid | | | |

TABLE 1p — PARAFFINS, $C_1$ TO $C_5$

HEAT OF FORMATION, ENTROPY, AND FREE ENERGY OF FORMATION, AT 25°C

April 30, 1944; April 30, 1945; December 31, 1952

| Compound | Formula | State | Heat of Formation $\Delta H f^{\circ}$ At 25°C kcal/mole | Entropy $S^{\circ}$ At 25°C cal/deg mole | Free Energy of Formation $\Delta F f^{\circ}$ At 25°C kcal/mole |
|---|---|---|---|---|---|
| Methane | $CH_4$ | gas | −17.889 | 44.50 | −12.140 |
| " | " | liquid | | | |
| Ethane | $C_2H_6$ | gas | −20.236 | 54.85 | −7.860 |
| " | " | liquid | | | |
| Propane | $C_3H_8$ | gas | −24.820 | 64.51 | −5.614 |
| " | " | liquid[a] | −28.643 | | |
| n-Butane | $C_4H_{10}$ | gas | −30.15 | 74.12 | −4.10 |
| " | " | liquid[a] | −35.29 | | |
| 2-Methylpropane (Isobutane) | " | gas | −32.15 | 70.42 | −5.00 |
| " | " | liquid[a] | −37.87 | | |
| n-Pentane | $C_5H_{12}$ | gas | −35.00 | 83.40 | −2.00 |
| " | " | liquid | −41.36 | 62.92 | −2.25 |
| 2-Methylbutane (Isopentane) | " | gas | −36.92 | 82.12 | −3.50 |
| " | " | liquid | −42.85 | 62.52 | −3.59 |
| 2,2-Dimethylpropane (Neopentane) | " | gas | −39.67 | 73.23 | −3.64 |
| " | " | liquid[a] | −44.98 | | |

[a] At saturation pressure.

467

TABLE 2o (PART 1) — PARAFFINS, $C_6$

HEAT OF FORMATION, ENTROPY, AND FREE ENERGY OF FORMATION, AT 25°C

April 30, 1944; April 30, 1945; November 30, 1946; December 31, 1952

| Compound | Formula | State | Heat of Formation $\Delta H_f^o$ At 25°C kcal/mole | Entropy $S^o$ At 25°C cal/deg mole | Free Energy of Formation $\Delta F_f^o$ At 25°C kcal/mole |
|---|---|---|---|---|---|
| n-Hexane | $C_6H_{14}$ | gas | -39.96 | 92.83 | -0.07 |
| " | " | liquid | -47.52 | 70.72 | -1.03 |
| 2-Methylpentane | " | gas | -41.66 | 90.95 | -1.20 |
| " | " | liquid | -48.82 | 69.51 | -1.97 |
| 3-Methylpentane | " | gas | -41.02 | 90.77 | -0.51 |
| " | " | liquid | -48.28 | 69.22 | -1.34 |
| 2,2-Dimethylbutane | " | gas | -44.35 | 85.62 | -2.37 |
| " | " | liquid | -51.00 | 65.08 | -2.90 |
| 2,3-Dimethylbutane | " | gas | -42.49 | 87.42 | -0.98 |
| " | " | liquid | -49.48 | 66.36 | -1.69 |

468

| Compound | Formula | State | Heat of Formation $\Delta H f^{O}$ At 25°C kcal/mole | Entropy $S^{O}$ At 25°C cal/deg mole | Free Energy of Formation $\Delta F f^{O}$ At 25°C kcal/mole |
|---|---|---|---|---|---|
| *n*-Heptane | $C_7H_{16}$ | gas | -44.89 | 102.24 | 1.94 |
| " | " | liquid | -53.63 | 78.52 | 0.27 |
| 2-Methylhexane | " | gas | -46.60 | 100.35 | 0.77 |
| " | " | liquid | -54.93 | 77.29 | -0.68 |
| 3-Methylhexane | " | gas | -45.96 | 101.37 | 1.10 |
| " | " | liquid | -54.35 | 78.23 | -0.39 |
| 3-Ethylpentane | " | gas | -45.34 | 98.30 | 2.57 |
| " | " | liquid | -53.77 | 75.16 | 1.04 |
| 2,2-Dimethylpentane | " | gas | -49.29 | 93.85 | 0.02 |
| " | " | liquid | -57.05 | 71.65 | -1.15 |
| 2,3-Dimethylpentane | " | gas | -47.62 | 98.96 | 0.16 |
| " | " | liquid | -55.81 | 76.27 | -1.27 |
| 2,4-Dimethylpentane | " | gas | -48.30 | 94.80 | 0.72 |
| " | " | liquid | -56.17 | 72.47 | -0.49 |
| 3,3-Dimethylpentane | " | gas | -48.17 | 95.53 | 0.63 |
| " | " | liquid | -56.07 | 73.44 | -0.69 |
| 2,2,3-Trimethylbutane | " | gas | -48.96 | 91.60 | 1.02 |
| " | " | liquid | -56.63 | 69.87 | -0.17 |

TABLE 2p (PART 2) — PARAFFINS, $C_7$
HEAT OF FORMATION, ENTROPY, AND FREE ENERGY OF FORMATION, AT 25°C
April 30, 1944; April 30, 1945; November 30, 1946; December 31, 1952

TABLE 3p — PARAFFINS, $C_8$

HEAT OF FORMATION, ENTROPY, AND FREE ENERGY OF FORMATION, AT 25°C

April 30, 1944; April 30, 1945; December 31, 1952

| Compound | Formula | State | Heat of Formation $\Delta H f^o$ At 25°C kcal/mole | Entropy $S^o$ At 25°C cal/deg mole | Free Energy of Formation $\Delta F f^o$ At 25°C kcal/mole |
|---|---|---|---|---|---|
| n–Octane | $C_8H_{18}$ | gas | −49.82 | 111.55 | 3.95 |
| " | " | liquid | −59.74 | 86.23 | 1.58 |
| 2–Methylheptane | " | gas | −51.50 | 108.81 | 3.06 |
| " | " | liquid | −60.98 | 84.16 | 0.92 |
| 3–Methylheptane | " | gas | −50.82 | 110.32 | 3.29 |
| " | " | liquid | −60.34 | 85.66 | 1.12 |
| 4–Methylheptane | " | gas | −50.69 | 108.35 | 4.00 |
| " | " | liquid | −60.17 | 83.72 | 1.86 |
| 3–Ethylhexane | " | gas | −50.40 | 109.51 | 3.95 |
| " | " | liquid | −59.88 | 84.95 | 1.80 |
| 2,2–Dimethylhexane | " | gas | −53.71 | 103.06 | 2.56 |
| " | " | liquid | −62.63 | 79.33 | 0.72 |
| 2,3–Dimethylhexane | " | gas | −51.13 | 106.11 | 4.23 |
| " | " | liquid | −60.40 | 81.91 | 2.17 |
| 2,4–Dimethylhexane | " | gas | −52.44 | 106.51 | 2.80 |
| " | " | liquid | −61.47 | 82.62 | 0.89 |
| 2,5–Dimethylhexane | " | gas | −53.21 | 104.93 | 2.50 |
| " | " | liquid | −62.26 | 80.96 | 0.59 |
| 3,3–Dimethylhexane | " | gas | −52.61 | 104.70 | 3.17 |
| " | " | liquid | −61.58 | 81.12 | 1.23 |
| 3,4–Dimethylhexane[a] | " | gas | −50.91 | 107.15 | 4.14 |
| " | " | liquid | −60.23 | 82.97 | 2.03 |
| 2–Methyl–3–ethylpentane | " | gas | −50.48 | 105.43 | 5.08 |
| " | " | liquid | −59.69 | 81.41 | 3.03 |
| 3–Methyl–3–ethylpentane | " | gas | −51.38 | 103.48 | 4.76 |
| " | " | liquid | −60.46 | 79.97 | 2.69 |
| 2,2,3–Trimethylpentane | " | gas | −52.61 | 110.62 | 4.09 |
| " | " | liquid | −61.44 | 78.30 | 2.22 |
| 2,2,4–Trimethylpentane | " | gas | −53.57 | 101.15 | 3.27 |
| " | " | liquid | −61.97 | 78.40 | 1.65 |
| 2,3,3–Trimethylpentane | " | gas | −51.73 | 103.14 | 4.52 |
| " | " | liquid | −60.63 | 79.93 | 2.54 |
| 2,3,4–Trimethylpentane | " | gas | −51.97 | 102.31 | 4.52 |
| " | " | liquid | −60.98 | 78.71 | 2.54 |
| 2,2,3,3–Tetramethylbutane | " | gas | −53.99 | 93.06 | 5.27 |
| " | " | liquid | −64.23 | 65.89 | 3.13 |

[a] See footnotes a and b of Table 3r.

470

TABLE 22p (PART 1) — NORMAL ALKYL CYCLOPENTANES, $C_5$ TO $C_{21}$

HEAT OF FORMATION, ENTROPY, AND FREE ENERGY OF FORMATION, AT 25°C

April 30, 1949; December 31, 1952

| Compound | Formula | State | Heat of Formation $\Delta H_f^o$ At 25°C kcal/mole | Entropy $S^o$ At 25°C cal/deg mole | Free Energy of Formation $\Delta F_f^o$ At 25°C kcal/mole |
|---|---|---|---|---|---|
| Cyclopentane | $C_5H_{10}$ | gas | −18.46 | 70.00 | 9.23 |
| " | " | liquid | −25.30 | 48.82 | 8.70 |
| Methylcyclopentane | $C_6H_{12}$ | gas | −25.50 | 81.24 | 8.55 |
| " | " | liquid | −33.07 | 59.26 | 7.53 |
| Ethylcyclopentane | $C_7H_{14}$ | gas | −30.37 | 90.42 | 10.66 |
| " | " | liquid | −39.10 | 67.00 | 8.91 |
| n−Propylcyclopentane | $C_8H_{16}$ | gas | −35.39 | 99.73 | 12.56 |
| " | " | liquid | −45.21 | 74.98 | 10.12 |
| n−Butylcyclopentane | $C_9H_{18}$ | gas | −40.22 | 109.04 | 14.67 |
| " | " | liquid | −51.22 | | |
| n−Pentylcyclopentane | $C_{10}H_{20}$ | gas | −45.15 | 118.35 | 16.68 |
| " | " | liquid | | | |
| n−Hexylcyclopentane | $C_{11}H_{22}$ | gas | −50.07 | 127.66 | 18.69 |
| " | " | liquid | | | |
| n−Heptylcyclopentane | $C_{12}H_{24}$ | gas | −55.00 | 136.96 | 20.70 |
| " | " | liquid | | | |
| n−Octylcyclopentane | $C_{13}H_{26}$ | gas | −59.92 | 146.27 | 22.71 |
| " | " | liquid | | | |
| n−Nonylcyclopentane | $C_{14}H_{28}$ | gas | −64.85 | 155.58 | 24.72 |
| " | " | liquid | | | |
| n−Decylcyclopentane | $C_{15}H_{30}$ | gas | −69.78 | 164.89 | 26.72 |
| " | " | liquid | | | |
| n−Undecylcyclopentane | $C_{16}H_{32}$ | gas | −74.70 | 174.20 | 28.73 |
| " | " | liquid | | | |
| n−Dodecylcyclopentane | $C_{17}H_{34}$ | gas | −79.63 | 183.51 | 30.74 |
| " | " | liquid | | | |
| n−Tridecylcyclopentane | $C_{18}H_{36}$ | gas | −84.55 | 192.89 | 32.75 |
| " | " | liquid | | | |
| n−Tetradecylcyclopentane | $C_{19}H_{38}$ | gas | −89.48 | 202.13 | 34.76 |
| " | " | liquid | | | |
| n−Pentadecylcyclopentane | $C_{20}H_{40}$ | gas | −94.41 | 211.44 | 36.77 |
| " | " | liquid | | | |
| n−Hexadecylcyclopentane | $C_{21}H_{42}$ | gas | −99.33 | 220.75 | 38.78 |
| " | " | liquid | | | |

TABLE 6p — ALKYL CYCLOPENTANES, $C_5$ TO $C_7$

HEAT OF FORMATION, ENTROPY, AND FREE ENERGY OF FORMATION, AT 25°C

April 30, 1949; December 31, 1952

| Compound | Formula | State | Heat of Formation $\Delta H_f^o$ At 25°C kcal/mole | Entropy $S^o$ At 25°C cal/deg mole | Free Energy of Formation $\Delta F_f^o$ At 25°C kcal/mole |
|---|---|---|---|---|---|
| Cyclopentane | $C_5H_{10}$ | gas | −18.46 | 70.00 | 9.23 |
| " | " | liquid | −25.30 | 48.82 | 8.70 |
| Methylcyclopentane | $C_6H_{12}$ | gas | −25.50 | 81.24 | 8.55 |
| " | " | liquid | −33.07 | 59.26 | 7.53 |
| Ethylcyclopentane | $C_7H_{14}$ | gas | −30.37 | 90.42 | 10.66 |
| " | " | liquid | −39.10 | 67.00 | 8.92 |
| 1,1-Dimethylcyclopentane | " | gas | −33.05 | 85.87 | 9.33 |
| " | " | liquid | −41.14 | 63.34 | 7.96 |
| 1,cis-2-Dimethylcyclopentane | " | gas | −30.96 | 87.51 | 10.93 |
| " | " | liquid | −39.52 | 64.33 | 9.29 |
| 1,trans-2-Dimethylcyclopentane | " | gas | −32.67 | 87.67 | 9.17 |
| " | " | liquid | −40.94 | 64.86 | 7.70 |
| 1,cis-3-Dimethylcyclopentane | " | gas | −31.93 | 87.67 | 9.91 |
| " | " | liquid | −40.19 | 64.88 | 8.45 |
| 1,trans-3-Dimethylcyclopentane | " | gas | −32.47 | 87.67 | 9.37 |
| " | " | liquid | −40.68 | 64.97 | 7.93 |

TABLE 23p (PART 1) — NORMAL ALKYL CYCLOHEXANES, $C_6$ TO $C_{22}$

HEAT OF FORMATION, ENTROPY, AND FREE ENERGY OF FORMATION, AT 25°C

April 30, 1949; December 31, 1952

| Compound | Formula | State | Heat of Formation $\Delta H f^{\circ}$ At 25°C kcal/mole | Entropy $S^{\circ}$ At 25°C cal/deg mole | Free Energy of Formation $\Delta F f^{\circ}$ At 25°C kcal/mole |
|---|---|---|---|---|---|
| Cyclohexane | $C_6H_{12}$ | gas | −29.43 | 71.28 | 7.59 |
| " | " | liquid | −37.34 | 48.85 | 6.37 |
| Methylcyclohexane | $C_7H_{14}$ | gas | −36.99 | 82.06 | 6.52 |
| " | " | liquid | −45.45 | 59.26 | 4.86 |
| Ethylcyclohexane | $C_8H_{16}$ | gas | −41.05 | 91.44 | 9.38 |
| " | " | liquid | −50.72 | 67.12 | 6.96 |
| n−Propylcyclohexane | $C_9H_{18}$ | gas | −46.20 | 100.27 | 11.31 |
| " | " | liquid | −56.98 | 74.48 | 8.22 |
| n−Butylcyclohexane | $C_{10}H_{20}$ | gas | −50.95 | 109.58 | 13.49 |
| " | " | liquid | −62.91 | 82.21 | 9.69 |
| n−Pentylcyclohexane | $C_{11}H_{22}$ | gas | −55.88 | 118.89 | 15.50 |
| " | " | liquid | | | |
| n−Hexylcyclohexane | $C_{12}H_{24}$ | gas | −60.80 | 128.20 | 17.51 |
| " | " | liquid | | | |
| n−Heptylcyclohexane | $C_{13}H_{26}$ | gas | −65.73- | 137.51 | 19.52 |
| " | " | liquid | | | |
| n−Octylcyclohexane | $C_{14}H_{28}$ | gas | −70.65 | 146.82 | 21.53 |
| " | " | liquid | | | |
| n−Nonylcyclohexane | $C_{15}H_{30}$ | gas | −75.58 | 156.12 | 23.54 |
| " | " | liquid | | | |
| n−Decylcyclohexane | $C_{16}H_{32}$ | gas | −80.51 | 165.43 | 25.54 |
| " | " | liquid | | | |
| n−Undecylcyclohexane | $C_{17}H_{34}$ | gas | −85.43 | 174.74 | 27.55 |
| " | " | liquid | | | |
| n−Dodecylcyclohexane | $C_{18}H_{36}$ | gas | −90.36 | 184.05 | 29.56 |
| " | " | liquid | | | |
| n−Tridecylcyclohexane | $C_{19}H_{38}$ | gas | −95.28 | 193.36 | 31.57 |
| " | " | liquid | | | |
| n−Tetradecylcyclohexane | $C_{20}H_{40}$ | gas | −100.21 | 202.67 | 33.58 |
| " | " | liquid | | | |
| n−Pentadecylcyclohexane | $C_{21}H_{42}$ | gas | −105.14 | 211.98 | 35.59 |
| " | " | liquid | | | |
| n−Hexadecylcyclohexane | $C_{22}H_{44}$ | gas | −110.06 | 221.29 | 37.60 |
| " | " | liquid | | | |

| Compound | Formula | State | Heat of Formation $\Delta Hf^{o}$ At 25°C kcal/mole | Entropy $S^{o}$ At 25°C cal/deg mole | Free Energy of Formation $\Delta Ff^{o}$ At 25°C kcal/mole |
|---|---|---|---|---|---|
| Cyclohexane | $C_6H_{12}$ | gas | −29.43 | 71.28 | 7.59 |
| " | " | liq | −37.34 | 48.85 | 6.37 |
| Methylcyclohexane | $C_7H_{14}$ | gas | −36.99 | 82.06 | 6.52 |
| " | " | liq | −45.45 | 59.26 | 4.86 |
| Ethylcyclohexane | $C_8H_{16}$ | gas | −41.05 | 91.44 | 9.38 |
| " | " | liq | −50.72 | 67.12 | 6.96 |
| 1,1-Dimethylcyclohexane | " | gas | −43.26 | 87.24 | 8.42 |
| " | " | liq | −52.31 | 63.89 | 6.34 |
| cis-1,2-Dimethylcyclohexane | " | gas | −41.15 | 89.51 | 9.85 |
| " | " | liq | −50.64 | 65.56 | 7.50 |
| trans-1,2-Dimethylcyclohexane | " | gas | −43.02 | 88.65 | 8.24 |
| " | " | liq | −52.19 | 65.20 | 6.06 |
| cis-1,3-Dimethylcyclohexane | " | gas | −44.16 | 88.54 | 7.13 |
| " | " | liq | −53.30 | 64.98 | 5.02 |
| trans-1,3-Dimethylcyclohexane | " | gas | −42.20 | 89.92 | 8.68 |
| " | " | liq | −51.57 | 65.99 | 6.44 |
| cis-1,4-Dimethylcyclohexane | " | gas | −42.22 | 88.54 | 9.07 |
| " | " | liq | −51.55 | 64.70 | 6.85 |
| trans-1,4-Dimethylcyclohexane | " | gas | −44.12 | 87.19 | 7.58 |
| " | " | liq | −53.18 | 63.80 | 5.50 |

TABLE 7p – ALKYL CYCLOHEXANES, $C_6$ TO $C_8$
HEAT OF FORMATION, ENTROPY, AND FREE ENERGY OF FORMATION, AT 25°C
October 31, 1948

474

| Compound | Formula | State | Heat of Formation $\Delta H_f^\circ$ | Entropy $S^\circ$ | Free Energy of Formation $\Delta F_f^\circ$ |
|---|---|---|---|---|---|
| | | | At 25°C | At 25°C | At 25°C |
| | | | kcal/mole | cal/deg mole | kcal/mole |
| Ethene (Ethylene) | $C_2H_4$ | gas | 12.496 | 52.45 | 16.282 |
| " | " | liquid | | | |
| Propene (Propylene) | $C_3H_6$ | gas | 4.879 | 63.80 | 14.990 |
| " | " | liquid | | | |
| 1-Butene | $C_4H_8$ | gas | -0.03 | 73.04 | 17.09 |
| " | " | liquid | | | |
| 1-Pentene | $C_5H_{10}$ | gas | -5.00 | 82.65 | 18.96 |
| " | " | liquid | | | |
| 1-Hexene | $C_6H_{12}$ | gas | -9.96 | 91.93 | 20.94 |
| " | " | liquid | | | |
| 1-Heptene | $C_7H_{14}$ | gas | -14.89 | 101.24 | 22.95 |
| " | " | liquid | | | |
| 1-Octene | $C_8H_{16}$ | gas | -19.82 | 110.55 | 24.96 |
| " | " | liquid | | | |
| 1-Nonene | $C_9H_{18}$ | gas | -24.74 | 119.86 | 26.97 |
| " | " | liquid | | | |
| 1-Decene | $C_{10}H_{20}$ | gas | -29.67 | 129.17 | 28.98 |
| " | " | liquid | | | |
| 1-Undecene | $C_{11}H_{22}$ | gas | -34.60 | 138.48 | 30.98 |
| " | " | liquid | | | |
| 1-Dodecene | $C_{12}H_{24}$ | gas | -39.52 | 147.78 | 32.99 |
| " | " | liquid | | | |
| 1-Tridecene | $C_{13}H_{26}$ | gas | -44.45 | 157.09 | 35.00 |
| " | " | liquid | | | |
| 1-Tetradecene | $C_{14}H_{28}$ | gas | -49.36 | 166.40 | 37.01 |
| " | " | liquid | | | |
| 1-Pentadecene | $C_{15}H_{30}$ | gas | -54.31 | 175.71 | 39.02 |
| " | " | liquid | | | |
| 1-Hexadecene | $C_{16}H_{32}$ | gas | -59.23 | 185.02 | 41.03 |
| " | " | liquid | | | |
| 1-Heptadecene | $C_{17}H_{34}$ | gas | -64.15 | 194.33 | 43.04 |
| " | " | liquid | | | |
| 1-Octadecene | $C_{18}H_{36}$ | gas | -69.08 | 203.64 | 45.05 |
| " | " | liquid | | | |
| 1-Nonadecene | $C_{19}H_{38}$ | gas | -74.00 | 212.95 | 47.06 |
| " | " | liquid | | | |
| 1-Eicosene | $C_{20}H_{40}$ | gas | -78.93 | 222.26 | 49.07 |
| " | " | solid | | | |

TABLE 24p (PART 1) – NORMAL MONOOLEFINS (1-ALKENES), $C_2$ TO $C_{20}$
HEAT OF FORMATION, ENTROPY, AND FREE ENERGY OF FORMATION, AT 25°C

June 30, 1946; December 31, 1952

TABLE 8p (PART 1) — MONOOLEFINS, $C_2$ TO $C_5$

HEAT OF FORMATION, ENTROPY, AND FREE ENERGY OF FORMATION, AT 25°C

November 30, 1945; May 31, 1947; December 31, 1952

| Compound | Formula | State | Heat of Formation $\Delta Hf^o$ At 25°C kcal/mole | Entropy $S^o$ At 25°C cal/deg mole | Free Energy of Formation $\Delta Ff^o$ At 25°C kcal/mole |
|---|---|---|---|---|---|
| Ethene (Ethylene) | $C_2H_4$ | gas | 12.496 | 52.45 | 16.282 |
| " | " | liquid | | | |
| Propene (Propylene) | $C_3H_6$ | gas | 4.879 | 63.80 | 14.990 |
| " | " | liquid | | | |
| 1-Butene | $C_4H_8$ | gas | -0.03 | 73.04 | 17.09 |
| " | " | liquid | | | |
| cis-2-Butene | " | gas | -1.67 | 71.90 | 15.74 |
| " | " | liquid | | | |
| trans-2-Butene | " | gas | -2.67 | 70.86 | 15.05 |
| " | " | liquid | | | |
| 2-Methylpropene (Isobutene) | " | gas | -4.04 | 70.17 | 13.88 |
| " | " | liquid | | | |
| 1-Pentene | $C_5H_{10}$ | gas | -5.00 | 82.65 | 18.96 |
| " | " | liquid | | | |
| cis-2-Pentene | " | gas | -6.71 | 82.76 | 17.17 |
| " | " | liquid | | | |
| trans-2-Pentene | " | gas | -7.59 | 81.36 | 16.76 |
| " | " | liquid | | | |
| 2-Methyl-1-butene | " | gas | -8.68 | 81.73 | 15.51 |
| " | " | liquid | | | |
| 3-Methyl-1-butene | " | gas | -6.92 | 79.70 | 17.87 |
| " | " | liquid | | | |
| 2-Methyl-2-butene | " | gas | -10.17 | 80.92 | 14.26 |
| " | " | liquid | | | |

| | | | Heat of Formation $\Delta H f^{\circ}$ | Entropy $S^{\circ}$ | Free Energy of Formation $\Delta F f^{\circ}$ |
|---|---|---|---|---|---|
| Compound | Formula | State | At 25°C | At 25°C | At 25°C |
| | | | kcal/mole | cal/deg mole | kcal/mole |
| 1-Hexene | $C_6H_{12}$ | gas | -9.96 | 91.93 | 20.94 |
| " | " | liquid | | | |
| cis-2-Hexene | " | gas | -11.56 | 92.37 | 19.16 |
| " | " | liquid | | | |
| trans-2-Hexene | " | gas | -12.56 | 90.97 | 18.63 |
| " | " | liquid | | | |
| cis-3-Hexene | " | gas | -11.56 | 90.73 | 19.66 |
| " | " | liquid | | | |
| trans-3-Hexene | " | gas | -12.56 | 89.59 | 19.04 |
| " | " | liquid | | | |
| 2-Methyl-1-pentene | " | gas | -13.56 | 91.34 | 17.47 |
| " | " | liquid | | | |
| 3-Methyl-1-pentene | " | gas | -11.02 | 90.06 | 20.40 |
| " | " | liquid | | | |
| 4-Methyl-1-pentene | " | gas | -11.66 | 87.89 | 20.45 |
| " | " | liquid | | | |
| 2-Methyl-2-pentene | " | gas | -14.96 | 90.45 | 16.34 |
| " | " | liquid | | | |
| 3-Methyl-cis-2-pentene | " | gas | -14.32 | 90.45 | 16.98 |
| " | " | liquid | | | |
| 3-Methyl-trans-2-pentene | " | gas | -14.32 | 91.26 | 16.74 |
| " | " | liquid | | | |
| 4-Methyl-cis-2-pentene | " | gas | -13.26 | 89.23 | 18.40 |
| " | " | liquid | | | |
| 4-Methyl-trans-2-pentene | " | gas | -14.26 | 88.02 | 17.77 |
| " | " | liquid | | | |
| 2-Ethyl-1-butene | " | gas | -12.92 | 90.01 | 18.51 |
| " | " | liquid | | | |
| 2,3-Dimethyl-1-butene | " | gas | -14.78 | 87.39 | 17.43 |
| " | " | liquid | | | |
| 3,3-Dimethyl-1-butene | " | gas | -14.25 | 82.16 | 19.53 |
| " | " | liquid | | | |
| 2,3-Dimethyl-2-butene | " | gas | -15.91 | 86.67 | 16.52 |
| " | " | liquid | | | |

TABLE 8p (PART 2) — MONOOLEFINS, $C_6$

HEAT OF FORMATION, ENTROPY, AND FREE ENERGY OF FORMATION, AT 25°C

November 30, 1945; December 31, 1952

| | | | Heat of Formation $\Delta H_f^{\circ}$ | Entropy $S^{\circ}$ | Free Energy of Formation $\Delta F_f^{\circ}$ |
|---|---|---|---|---|---|
| Compound | Formula | State | At 25°C | At 25°C | At 25°C |
| | | | kcal/mole | cal/deg mole | kcal/mole |
| Propadiene (Allene) | $C_3H_4$ | gas | 45.92 | 58.30 | 48.37 |
| " | " | liquid | | | |
| | | | | | |
| 1,2–Butadiene | $C_4H_6$ | gas | 38.77 | 70.03 | 47.43 |
| " | " | liquid | | | |
| 1,3–Butadiene | " | gas | 26.33 | 66.62 | 36.01 |
| " | " | liquid | 21.21 | | |
| | | | | | |
| 1,2–Pentadiene | $C_5H_8$ | gas | 34.80 | 79.7 | 50.29 |
| " | " | liquid | | | |
| 1,cis–3–Pentadiene | " | gas | 18.70 | 77.5 | 34.88 |
| " | " | liquid | | | |
| 1,trans–3–Pentadiene | " | gas | 18.60 | 76.4 | 35.07 |
| " | " | liquid | | | |
| 1,4–Pentadiene | " | gas | 25.20 | 79.7 | 40.69 |
| " | " | liquid | | | |
| 2,3–Pentadiene | " | gas | 33.10 | 77.6 | 49.22 |
| " | " | liquid | | | |
| 3–Methyl–1,2–butadiene | " | gas | 31.00 | 76.4 | 47.47 |
| " | " | liquid | | | |
| 2–Methyl–1,3–butadiene (Isoprene) | " | gas | 18.10 | 75.44 | 34.87 |
| " | " | liquid | 11.80 | | |

**TABLE 11p (PART 1) – DIOLEFINS, $C_3$ TO $C_5$**

**HEAT OF FORMATION, ENTROPY, AND FREE ENERGY OF FORMATION, AT 25°C**

February 28, 1949; December 31, 1952

TABLE 18p – ALKYL CYCLOPENTENES, $C_5$ TO $C_7$

HEAT OF FORMATION, ENTROPY, AND FREE ENERGY OF FORMATION, AT 25°C

December 31, 1952

| Compound | Formula | State | Heat of Formation $\Delta H f^o$ | Entropy $S^o$ | Free Energy of Formation $\Delta F f^o$ |
| --- | --- | --- | --- | --- | --- |
| | | | At 25°C | At 25°C | At 25°C |
| | | | kcal/mole | cal/deg mole | kcal/mole |
| Cyclopentene | $C_5H_8$ | gas | 7.87 | 69.23 | 26.48 |
| " | " | liquid | 1.16 | 48.10 | |
| | | | | | |
| 1–Methylcyclopentene | $C_6H_{10}$ | gas | | 78.0 | |
| " | " | liquid | | | |
| 3–Methylcyclopentene | " | gas | | 79.0 | |
| " | " | liquid | | | |
| 4–Methylcyclopentene | " | gas | | 78.6 | |
| " | " | liquid | | | |
| | | | | | |
| 1–Ethylcyclopentene | $C_7H_{12}$ | gas | | | |
| " | " | liquid | | | |
| 3–Ethylcyclopentene | " | gas | | | |
| " | " | liquid | | | |
| 4–Ethylcyclopentene | " | gas | | | |
| " | " | liquid | | | |
| 1,2–Dimethylcyclopentene | " | gas | | 84.0 | |
| " | " | liquid | | | |
| 1,3–Dimethylcyclopentene | " | gas | | 86.4 | |
| " | " | liquid | | | |
| 1,4–Dimethylcyclopentene | " | gas | | 87.3 | |
| " | " | liquid | | | |
| 1,5–Dimethylcyclopentene | " | gas | | 86.4 | |
| " | " | liquid | | | |
| 3,3–Dimethylcyclopentene | " | gas | | 83.1 | |
| " | " | liquid | | | |
| 3,cis–4–Dimethylcyclopentene | " | gas | | 86.4 | |
| " | " | liquid | | | |
| 3,trans–4–Dimethylcyclopentene | " | gas | | 86.8 | |
| " | " | liquid | | | |
| 3,cis–5–Dimethylcyclopentene | " | gas | | 84.6 | |
| " | " | liquid | | | |
| 3,trans–5–Dimethylcyclopentene | " | gas | | 84.6 | |
| " | " | liquid | | | |
| 4,4–Dimethylcyclopentene | " | gas | | | |
| " | " | liquid | | | |

## TABLE 25p (PART 1) — NORMAL ACETYLENES (1-ALKYNES), $C_2$ TO $C_{20}$
### HEAT OF FORMATION, ENTROPY, AND FREE ENERGY OF FORMATION, AT 25°C
June 30, 1946; December 31, 1952

| Compound | Formula | State | Heat of Formation $\Delta H_f^o$ At 25°C kcal/mole | Entropy $S^o$ At 25°C cal/deg mole | Free Energy of Formation $\Delta F_f^o$ At 25°C kcal/mole |
|---|---|---|---|---|---|
| Ethyne (Acetylene) | $C_2H_2$ | gas | 54.194 | 47.997 | 50.000 |
| " | " | liquid | | | |
| Propyne (Methylacetylene) | $C_3H_4$ | gas | 44.319 | 59.30 | 46.313 |
| " | " | liquid | | | |
| 1–Butyne (Ethylacetylene) | $C_4H_6$ | gas | 39.48 | 69.51 | 48.30 |
| " | " | liquid | | | |
| 1–Pentyne | $C_5H_8$ | gas | 34.50 | 78.82 | 50.16 |
| " | " | liquid | | | |
| 1–Hexyne | $C_6H_{10}$ | gas | 29.55 | 88.13 | 52.17 |
| " | " | liquid | | | |
| 1–Heptyne | $C_7H_{12}$ | gas | 24.62 | 97.44 | 54.18 |
| " | " | liquid | | | |
| 1–Octyne | $C_8H_{14}$ | gas | 19.70 | 106.75 | 56.19 |
| " | " | liquid | | | |
| 1–Nonyne | $C_9H_{16}$ | gas | 14.77 | 116.06 | 58.20 |
| " | " | liquid | | | |
| 1–Decyne | $C_{10}H_{18}$ | gas | 9.85 | 125.36 | 60.20 |
| " | " | liquid | | | |
| 1–Undecyne | $C_{11}H_{20}$ | gas | 4.92 | 134.67 | 62.21 |
| " | " | liquid | | | |
| 1–Dodecyne | $C_{12}H_{22}$ | gas | −0.01 | 143.98 | 64.22 |
| " | " | liquid | | | |
| 1–Tridecyne | $C_{13}H_{24}$ | gas | −4.93 | 153.29 | 66.23 |
| " | " | liquid | | | |
| 1–Tetradecyne | $C_{14}H_{26}$ | gas | −9.86 | 162.60 | 68.24 |
| " | " | liquid | | | |
| 1–Pentadecyne | $C_{15}H_{28}$ | gas | −14.78 | 171.91 | 70.25 |
| " | " | liquid | | | |
| 1–Hexadecyne | $C_{16}H_{30}$ | gas | −19.71 | 181.22 | 72.26 |
| " | " | liquid | | | |
| 1–Heptadecyne | $C_{17}H_{32}$ | gas | −24.64 | 190.53 | 74.27 |
| " | " | liquid | | | |
| 1–Octadecyne | $C_{18}H_{34}$ | gas | −29.56 | 199.84 | 76.28 |
| " | " | liquid | | | |
| 1–Nonadecyne | $C_{19}H_{36}$ | gas | −34.49 | 209.15 | 78.29 |
| " | " | liquid | | | |
| 1–Eicosyne | $C_{20}H_{38}$ | gas | −39.41 | 218.46 | 81.00 |
| " | " | liquid | | | |

TABLE 12p — ACETYLENES, $C_2$ TO $C_5$
HEAT OF FORMATION, ENTROPY, AND FREE ENERGY OF FORMATION, AT 25°C

June 30, 1946; December 31, 1952

| Compound | Formula | State | Heat of Formation $\Delta Hf°$ At 25°C kcal/mole | Entropy $S°$ At 25°C cal/deg mole | Free Energy of Formation $\Delta Ff°$ At 25°C kcal/mole |
|---|---|---|---|---|---|
| Ethyne (Acetylene) | $C_2H_2$ | gas | 54.194 | 47.997 | 50.000 |
| " | " | liquid | | | |
| Propyne (Methylacetylene) | $C_3H_4$ | gas | 44.319 | 59.30 | 46.313 |
| " | " | liquid | | | |
| 1-Butyne (Ethylacetylene) | $C_4H_6$ | gas | 39.48 | 69.51 | 48.30 |
| " | " | liquid | | | |
| 2-Butyne (Dimethylacetylene) | " | gas | 34.97 | 67.71 | 44.32 |
| " | " | liquid | | | |
| 1-Pentyne | $C_5H_8$ | gas | 34.50 | 79.10 | 50.16 |
| " | " | liquid | | | |
| 2-Pentyne | " | gas | 30.80 | 79.30 | 46.41 |
| " | " | liquid | | | |
| 3-Methyl-1-butyne | " | gas | 32.60 | 76.23 | 49.12 |
| " | " | liquid | | | |

481

## TABLE 21p (PART 1) — NORMAL ALKYL BENZENES, $C_6$ TO $C_{22}$
### HEAT OF FORMATION, ENTROPY, AND FREE ENERGY OF FORMATION, AT 25°C
June 30, 1946; December 31, 1952

| Compound | Formula | State | Heat of Formation $\Delta H_f^o$ At 25°C kcal/mole | Entropy $S^o$ At 25°C cal/deg mole | Free Energy of Formation $\Delta F_f^o$ At 25°C kcal/mole |
|---|---|---|---|---|---|
| Benzene | $C_6H_6$ | gas | 19.820 | 64.34 | 30.989 |
| " | " | liquid | | | |
| Methylbenzene (Toluene) | $C_7H_8$ | gas | 11.950 | 76.42 | 29.228 |
| " | " | liquid | | | |
| Ethylbenzene | $C_8H_{10}$ | gas | 7.120 | 86.15 | 31.208 |
| " | " | liquid | | | |
| n-Propylbenzene | $C_9H_{12}$ | gas | 1.870 | 95.76 | 32.805 |
| " | " | liquid | | | |
| n-Butylbenzene | $C_{10}H_{14}$ | gas | -3.30 | 105.04 | 34.58 |
| " | " | liquid | | | |
| n-Pentylbenzene | $C_{11}H_{16}$ | gas | -8.23 | 114.47 | 36.54 |
| " | " | liquid | | | |
| n-Hexylbenzene | $C_{12}H_{18}$ | gas | -13.15 | 123.78 | 38.55 |
| " | " | liquid | | | |
| n-Heptylbenzene | $C_{13}H_{20}$ | gas | -18.08 | 133.09 | 40.56 |
| " | " | liquid | | | |
| n-Octylbenzene | $C_{14}H_{22}$ | gas | -23.00 | 142.40 | 42.57 |
| " | " | liquid | | | |
| n-Nonylbenzene | $C_{15}H_{24}$ | gas | -27.93 | 151.71 | 44.58 |
| " | " | liquid | | | |
| n-Decylbenzene | $C_{16}H_{26}$ | gas | -32.86 | 161.02 | 46.58 |
| " | " | liquid | | | |
| n-Undecylbenzene | $C_{17}H_{28}$ | gas | -37.78 | 170.32 | 48.59 |
| " | " | liquid | | | |
| n-Dodecylbenzene | $C_{18}H_{30}$ | gas | -42.71 | 179.63 | 50.60 |
| " | " | liquid | | | |
| n-Tridecylbenzene | $C_{19}H_{32}$ | gas | -47.63 | 188.94 | 52.61 |
| " | " | liquid | | | |
| n-Tetradecylbenzene | $C_{20}H_{34}$ | gas | -52.56 | 198.25 | 54.62 |
| " | " | liquid | | | |
| n-Pentadecylbenzene | $C_{21}H_{36}$ | gas | -57.49 | 207.56 | 56.63 |
| " | " | liquid | | | |
| n-Hexadecylbenzene | $C_{22}H_{38}$ | gas | -62.41 | 216.87 | 58.64 |
| " | " | liquid | | | |

482

| Compound | Formula | State | Heat of Formation $\Delta H f^o$ At 25°C kcal/mole | Entropy $S^o$ At 25°C cal/deg mole | Free Energy of Formation $\Delta F f^o$ At 25°C kcal/mole |
|---|---|---|---|---|---|
| Benzene | $C_6H_6$ | gas | 19.820 | 64.34 | 30.989 |
| " | " | liquid | 11.718 | 41.30 | 29.756 |
| Methylbenzene (Toluene) | $C_7H_8$ | gas | 11.950 | 76.42 | 29.228 |
| " | " | liquid | 2.867 | 52.48 | 27.282 |
| Ethylbenzene | $C_8H_{10}$ | gas | 7.120 | 86.15 | 31.208 |
| " | " | liquid | -2.977 | 60.99 | 28.614 |
| 1,2-Dimethylbenzene (o-Xylene) | " | gas | 4.540 | 84.31 | 29.177 |
| " | " | liquid | -5.841 | 58.91 | 26.370 |
| 1,3-Dimethylbenzene (m-Xylene) | " | gas | 4.120 | 85.49 | 28.405 |
| " | " | liquid | -6.075 | 60.27 | 25.730 |
| 1,4-Dimethylbenzene (p-Xylene) | " | gas | 4.290 | 84.23 | 28.952 |
| " | " | liquid | -5.838 | 59.12 | 26.310 |
| n-Propylbenzene | $C_9H_{12}$ | gas | 1.870 | 95.74 | 32.810 |
| " | " | liquid | -9.178 | 69.44 | 29.600 |
| Isopropylbenzene | " | gas | 0.940 | 92.87 | 32.738 |
| " | " | liquid | -9.848 | 66.87 | 29.708 |
| 1-Methyl-2-ethylbenzene | " | gas | 0.290 | 95.42 | 31.323 |
| " | " | liquid | -11.110 | 68.42 | 27.973 |
| 1-Methyl-3-ethylbenzene | " | gas | -0.460 | 96.60 | 30.217 |
| " | " | liquid | -11.670 | 69.90 | 26.977 |
| 1-Methyl-4-ethylbenzene | " | gas | -0.780 | 95.34 | 30.281 |
| " | " | liquid | -11.920 | 68.84 | 27.041 |
| 1,2,3-Trimethylbenzene | " | gas | -2.290 | 93.50 | 29.319 |
| " | " | liquid | -14.013 | 66.40 | 25.679 |
| 1,2,4-Trimethylbenzene | " | gas | -3.330 | 94.73 | 27.912 |
| " | " | liquid | -14.785 | 67.93 | 24.462 |
| 1,3,5-Trimethylbenzene | " | gas | -3.840 | 92.15 | 28.172 |
| " | " | liquid | -15.184 | 65.35 | 24.832 |

TABLE 5p — ALKYL BENZENES, $C_6$ TO $C_9$

HEAT OF FORMATION, ENTROPY, AND FREE ENERGY OF FORMATION, AT 25°C

November 30, 1945

483

TABLE 13p – STYRENES, $C_8$ AND $C_9$
HEAT OF FORMATION, ENTROPY, AND FREE ENERGY OF FORMATION, AT 25°C
February 28, 1949

| Compound | Formula | State | Heat of Formation $\Delta H_f^o$ At 25°C kcal/mole | Entropy $S^o$ At 25°C cal/deg mole | Free Energy of Formation $\Delta F_f^o$ At 25°C kcal/mole |
|---|---|---|---|---|---|
| Ethenylbenzene (Styrene) | $C_8H_8$ | gas | 35.22 | 82.48 | 51.10 |
| " | " | liq | 24.83 | | |
| Isopropenylbenzene | $C_9H_{10}$ | gas | 27.00 | 91.7 | 49.84 |
| " | " | liq | | | |
| cis-1-Propenylbenzene | " | gas | 29.00 | 91.7 | 51.84 |
| " | " | liq | | | |
| trans-1-Propenylbenzene | " | gas | 28.00 | 90.9 | 51.08 |
| " | " | liq | | | |
| 1-Methyl-2-ethenylbenzene | " | gas | 28.30 | 91.7 | 51.14 |
| " | " | liq | | | |
| 1-Methyl-3-ethenylbenzene | " | gas | 27.60 | 93.1 | 50.02 |
| " | " | liq | | | |
| 1-Methyl-4-ethenylbenzene | " | gas | 27.40 | 91.7 | 50.24 |
| " | " | liq | | | |

484

| Compound | Formula | Standard Heat[a] of Vaporization $\Delta H v^0$ | Standard Entropy of Vaporization $\Delta S v^0$ | Standard Free Energy of Vaporization $\Delta F v^0$ |
|---|---|---|---|---|
| | | At 25°C | At 25°C | At 25°C |
| | | kcal/mole | cal/deg mole | kcal/mole |
| Methane | $CH_4$ | | | |
| Ethane | $C_2H_6$ | | | |
| Propane | $C_3H_8$ | 3.823[b] | | |
| n–Butane | $C_4H_{10}$ | 5.138[b] | | |
| 2–Methylpropane (Isobutane) | " | 4.717 | | |
| n–Pentane | $C_5H_{12}$ | 6.357 | 20.48 | 0.252 |
| 2–Methylbutane (Isopentane) | " | 5.934 | 19.60 | 0.090 |
| 2,2–Dimethylpropane (Neopentane) | " | 5.311[b] | | |

**TABLE 1q – PARAFFINS, $C_1$ TO $C_5$**
**STANDARD HEAT, ENTROPY, AND FREE ENERGY OF VAPORIZATION, AT 25°C**
May 31, 1944 (Corrected)

[a] For the heat of vaporization at 25°C and saturation pressure see the corresponding "m" table. [b] Liquid at saturation pressure.

| | | Standard Heat[a] of Vaporization $\Delta Hv^o$ | Standard Entropy of Vaporization $\Delta Sv^o$ | Standard Free Energy of Vaporization $\Delta Fv^o$ |
|---|---|---|---|---|
| Compound | Formula | At 25°C | At 25°C | At 25°C |
| | | kcal/mole | cal/deg mole | kcal/mole |
| n–Hexane | $C_6H_{14}$ | 7.555 | 22.11 | 0.963 |
| 2–Methylpentane | " | 7.160 | 21.44 | 0.767 |
| 3–Methylpentane | " | 7.255 | 21.55 | 0.830 |
| 2,2–Dimethylbutane | " | 6.651 | 20.54 | 0.527 |
| 2,3–Dimethylbutane | " | 6.985 | 21.06 | 0.706 |

TABLE 2q (PART 1) – PARAFFINS, $C_6$
STANDARD HEAT, ENTROPY, AND FREE ENERGY OF VAPORIZATION, AT 25°C
May 31, 1944 (Corrected)

[a] For the heat of vaporization at 25°C and saturation pressure see the corresponding "m" table.

TABLE 2q (PART 2) — PARAFFINS, $C_7$
STANDARD HEAT, ENTROPY, AND FREE ENERGY OF VAPORIZATION, AT 25°C

May 31, 1944 (Corrected)

| Compound | Formula | Standard Heat[a] of Vaporization $\Delta H v^0$ At 25°C kcal/mole | Standard Entropy of Vaporization $\Delta S v^0$ At 25°C cal/deg mole | Standard Free Energy of Vaporization $\Delta F v^0$ At 25°C kcal/mole |
|---|---|---|---|---|
| n–Heptane | $C_7H_{16}$ | 8.739 | 23.72 | 1.666 |
| 2–Methylhexane | " | 8.325 | 23.06 | 1.448 |
| 3–Methylhexane | " | 8.391 | 23.14 | 1.491 |
| 3–Ethylpentane | " | 8.425 | 23.14 | 1.525 |
| 2,2–Dimethylpentane | " | 7.764 | 22.10 | 1.174 |
| 2,3–Dimethylpentane | " | 8.191 | 22.69 | 1.426 |
| 2,4–Dimethylpentane | " | 7.872 | 22.33 | 1.214 |
| 3,3–Dimethylpentane | " | 7.901 | 22.09 | 1.316 |
| 2,2,3–Trimethylbutane | " | 7.669 | 21.73 | 1.190 |

[a] For the heat of vaporization at 25°C and saturation pressure see the corresponding "m" table.

## TABLE 3q — PARAFFINS, $C_8$
### STANDARD HEAT, ENTROPY, AND FREE ENERGY OF VAPORIZATION, AT 25°C
#### May 31, 1944 (Corrected)

| Compound | Formula | Standard Heat[a] of Vaporization $\Delta Hv^o$ At 25°C kcal/mole | Standard Entropy of Vaporization $\Delta Sv^o$ At 25°C cal/deg mole | Standard Free Energy of Vaporization $\Delta Fv^o$ At 25°C kcal/mole |
|---|---|---|---|---|
| n–Octane | $C_8H_{18}$ | 9.915 | 25.32 | 2.365 |
| 2–Methylheptane | " | 9.484 | 24.65 | 2.135 |
| 3–Methylheptane | " | 9.521 | 24.66 | 2.167 |
| 4–Methylheptane | " | 9.483 | 24.63 | 2.138 |
| 3–Ethylhexane | " | 9.476 | 24.56 | 2.152 |
| 2,2–Dimethylhexane | " | 8.915 | 23.73 | 1.839 |
| 2,3–Dimethylhexane | " | 9.272 | 24.19 | 2.060 |
| 2,4–Dimethylhexane | " | 9.029 | 23.89 | 1.907 |
| 2,5–Dimethylhexane | " | 9.051 | 23.97 | 1.905 |
| 3,3–Dimethylhexane | " | 8.973 | 23.53 | 1.942 |
| 3,4–Dimethylhexane | " | 9.316 | 24.18 | 2.107 |
| 2–Methyl–3–ethylpentane | " | 9.209 | 24.02 | 2.048 |
| 3–Methyl–3–ethylpentane | " | 9.081 | 23.51 | 2.071 |
| 2,2,3–Trimethylpentane | " | 8.826 | 23.32 | 1.874 |
| 2,2,4–Trimethylpentane | " | 8.402 | 22.75 | 1.620 |
| 2,3,3–Trimethylpentane | " | 8.897 | 23.21 | 1.976 |
| 2,3,4–Trimethylpentane | " | 9.014 | 23.60 | 1.976 |
| 2,2,3,3–Tetramethylbutane | " | 10.24[b] | 27.17[b] | 2.139[b] |

[a] For the heat of vaporization at 25°C and saturation pressure see the corresponding "m" table.

[b] For the process of sublimation, $C_mH_n$ (solid) = $C_mH_n$ (gas), with the solid and the gas in their appropriate standard references states.

## TABLE 6q – ALKYL CYCLOPENTANES, $C_5$ TO $C_7$
### STANDARD HEAT, ENTROPY, AND FREE ENERGY OF VAPORIZATION, AT 25°C
#### October 31, 1948

| Compound | Formula | Standard Heat[a] of Vaporization $\Delta Hv^0$ At 25°C kcal/mole | Standard Entropy of Vaporization $\Delta Sv^0$ At 25°C cal/deg mole | Standard Free Energy of Vaporization $\Delta Fv^0$ At 25°C kcal/mole |
|---|---|---|---|---|
| Cyclopentane | $C_5H_{10}$ | 6.845 | 21.18 | 0.530 |
| Methylcyclopentane | $C_6H_{12}$ | 7.571 | 21.98 | 1.018 |
| Ethylcyclopentane | $C_7H_{14}$ | 8.727 | 23.42 | 1.745 |
| 1,1–Dimethylcyclopentane | " | 8.086 | 22.53 | 1.368 |
| cis–1,2–Dimethylcyclopentane | " | 8.556 | 23.18 | 1.645 |
| trans–1,2–Dimethylcyclopentane | " | 8.266 | 22.81 | 1.466 |
| cis–1,3–Dimethylcyclopentane | " | 8.255 | 22.79 | 1.461 |
| trans–1,3–Dimethylcyclopentane | " | 8.207 | 22.70 | 1.438 |

[a] For the heat of vaporization at 25°C and saturation pressure see the corresponding "m" table.

TABLE 7q – ALKYL CYCLOHEXANES, $C_6$ TO $C_8$
STANDARD HEAT, ENTROPY, AND FREE ENERGY OF VAPORIZATION, AT 25°C
March 31, 1947 (Corrected)

| Compound | Formula | Standard Heat[a] of Vaporization $\Delta H v^0$ At 25°C kcal/mole | Standard Entropy of Vaporization $\Delta S v^0$ At 25°C cal/deg mole | Standard Free Energy of Vaporization $\Delta F v^0$ At 25°C kcal/mole |
|---|---|---|---|---|
| Cyclohexane | $C_6H_{12}$ | 7.908 | 22.43 | 1.219 |
| Methylcyclohexane | $C_7H_{14}$ | 8.458 | 22.80 | 1.659 |
| Ethylcyclohexane | $C_8H_{16}$ | 9.674 | 24.32 | 2.423 |
| 1,1-Dimethylcyclohexane | " | 9.046 | 23.35 | 2.083 |
| 1,cis-2-Dimethylcyclohexane | " | 9.493 | 23.95 | 2.351 |
| 1,trans-2-Dimethylcyclohexane | " | 9.169 | 23.45 | 2.176 |
| 1,cis-3-Dimethylcyclohexane | " | 9.139 | 23.56 | 2.114 |
| 1,trans-3-Dimethylcyclohexane | " | 9.370 | 23.93 | 2.235 |
| 1,cis-4-Dimethylcyclohexane | " | 9.330 | 23.84 | 2.223 |
| 1,trans-4-Dimethylcyclohexane | " | 9.055 | 23.39 | 2.082 |

[a] For the heat of vaporization at 25°C and saturation pressure see the corresponding "m" table.

| | | TABLE 5q — ALKYL BENZENES, $C_6$ TO $C_9$ STANDARD HEAT, ENTROPY, AND FREE ENERGY OF VAPORIZATION, AT 25°C July 31, 1944; March 31, 1945 (Corrected) | | |
|---|---|---|---|---|
| Compound | Formula | Standard Heat[a] of Vaporization $\Delta Hv^o$ At 25°C kcal/mole | Standard Entropy of Vaporization $\Delta Sv^o$ At 25°C cal/deg mole | Standard Free Energy of Vaporization $\Delta Fv^o$ At 25°C kcal/mole |
| Benzene | $C_6H_6$ | 8.102 | 23.04 | 1.233 |
| Methylbenzene (Toluene) | $C_7H_8$ | 9.083 | 23.94 | 1.946 |
| Ethylbenzene | $C_8H_{10}$ | 10.097 | 25.16 | 2.594 |
| 1,2-Dimethylbenzene (o-Xylene) | " | 10.381 | 25.40 | 2.807 |
| 1,3-Dimethylbenzene (m-Xylene) | " | 10.195 | 25.22 | 2.675 |
| 1,4-Dimethylbenzene (p-Xylene) | " | 10.128 | 25.11 | 2.642 |
| n-Propylbenzene | $C_9H_{12}$ | 11.048 | 26.3 | 3.21 |
| Isopropylbenzene | " | 10.788 | 26.0 | 3.03 |
| 1-Methyl-2-ethylbenzene | " | 11.40 | 27.0 | 3.35 |
| 1-Methyl-3-ethylbenzene | " | 11.21 | 26.7 | 3.24 |
| 1-Methyl-4-ethylbenzene | " | 11.14 | 26.5 | 3.24 |
| 1,2,3-Trimethylbenzene | " | 11.723 | 27.1 | 3.64 |
| 1,2,4-Trimethylbenzene | " | 11.455 | 26.8 | 3.45 |
| 1,3,5-Trimethylbenzene | " | 11.344 | 26.8 | 3.34 |

[a] For the heat of vaporization at 25°C and saturation pressure see the corresponding "m" table.

491

Table 00r – O, H, N, C

HEAT CONTENT FUNCTION, $(H^o-H_0^o)/T$, FOR THE IDEAL GAS STATE, AT 0° TO 5000°K

June 30, 1946; August 31, 1949

Temperature in °K — Heat Content Function, $(H^o-H_0^o)/T$, in cal/deg mole

| Compound (gas, monatomic) | Formula | 0 | 298.16 | 300 | 400 | 500 | 600 | 700 | 800 | 900 | 1000 | 1100 | 1200 | 1300 | 1400 | 1500 |
|---|---|---|---|---|---|---|---|---|---|---|---|---|---|---|---|---|
| Oxygen | O | 0 | 5.3910 | 5.3901 | 5.3372 | 5.2907 | 5.2528 | 5.2221 | 5.1970 | 5.1763 | 5.1588 | 5.1440 | 5.1313 | 5.1203 | 5.1107 | 5.1022 |
| Hydrogen | H | 0 | 4.9680 | 4.9680 | 4.9680 | 4.9680 | 4.9680 | 4.9680 | 4.9680 | 4.9680 | 4.9680 | 4.9680 | 4.9680 | 4.9680 | 4.9680 | 4.9680 |
| Nitrogen | N | 0 | 4.9680 | 4.9680 | 4.9680 | 4.9680 | 4.9680 | 4.9680 | 4.9680 | 4.9680 | 4.9680 | 4.9680 | 4.9680 | 4.9680 | 4.9680 | 4.9680 |
| Carbon | C | 0 | 4.2284 | 5.2269 | 5.1644 | 5.1262 | 5.1005 | 5.0819 | 5.0679 | 5.0570 | 5.0482 | 5.0410 | 5.0350 | 5.0301 | 5.0259 | 5.0223 |

Temperature in °K — Heat Content Function, $(H^o-H_0^o)/T$, in cal/deg mole

| Compound (gas, monatomic) | Formula | 1000 | 1250 | 1500 | 1750 | 2000 | 2250 | 2500 | 2750 | 3000 | 3500 | 4000 | 4500 | 5000 |
|---|---|---|---|---|---|---|---|---|---|---|---|---|---|---|
| Oxygen | O | 5.1588 | 5.1256 | 5.1022 | 5.0848 | 5.0714 | 5.0610 | 5.0530 | 5.0470 | 5.0429 | 5.0398 | 5.0430 | 5.0516 | 5.0644 |
| Hydrogen | H | 4.9680 | 4.9680 | 4.9680 | 4.9680 | 4.9680 | 4.9680 | 4.9680 | 4.9680 | 4.9680 | 4.9680 | 4.9680 | 4.9680 | 4.9680 |
| Nitrogen | N | 4.9680 | 4.9680 | 4.9680 | 4.9680 | 4.9681 | 4.9683 | 4.9699 | 4.9702 | 4.9726 | 4.9829 | 5.0033 | 5.0362 | 5.0825 |
| Carbon | C | 5.0482 | 5.0324 | 5.0223 | 5.0163 | 5.0137 | 5.0147 | 5.0190 | 5.0262 | 5.0360 | 5.0616 | 5.0918 | 5.1238 | 5.1552 |

TABLE Or − $O_2$, $H_2$, OH, $H_2O$, $N_2$, NO, C, CO, $CO_2$

HEAT CONTENT FUNCTION, $(H°-H°_0)/T$, AT 0° TO 5000°K

July 31, 1944; August 31, 1946; June 30, 1949

Heat Content Function, $(H°-H°_0)/T$, in cal/deg mole — Temperature in °K

| Compound | Formula | State | 0 | 50 | 100 | 150 | 200 | 250 | 296.16 | 300 | 400 | 500 | 600 | 700 | 800 | 900 | 1000 |
|---|---|---|---|---|---|---|---|---|---|---|---|---|---|---|---|---|---|
| Oxygen | $O_2$ | gas | 0 | | 6.904 | 6.913 | 6.922 | 6.931 | 6.942 | 6.942 | 6.981 | 7.048 | 7.132 | 7.225 | 7.320 | 7.411 | 7.497 |
| Hydrogen | $H_2$ | gas | 0 | 6.5265 | 7.1670 | 6.9233 | 6.8028 | 6.7771 | 6.7877 | 6.7882 | 6.8275 | 6.8590 | 6.8825 | 6.9022 | 6.9218 | 6.9423 | 6.9658 |
| Hydroxyl | OH | gas | 0 | | | | | | 7.064 | 7.064 | 7.074 | 7.070 | 7.068 | 7.067 | 7.073 | 7.086 | 7.106 |
| Water | $H_2O$ | gas | 0 | | | | | | 7.941 | 7.940 | 7.985 | 8.051 | 8.137 | 8.245 | 8.362 | 8.483 | 8.608 |
| Nitrogen | $N_2$ | gas | 0 | | | | 6.9465 | 6.9482 | 6.9502 | 6.9503 | 6.9559 | 6.9701 | 6.9967 | 7.0361 | 7.0857 | 7.1422 | 7.2025 |
| Nitric Oxide | NO | gas | 0 | | 7.427 | 7.481 | 7.453 | 7.411 | 7.359 | 7.356 | 7.302 | 7.288 | 7.302 | 7.338 | 7.387 | 7.445 | 7.506 |
| Carbon | C | solid graphite | 0 | | 0.1445 | 0.2877 | 0.4599 | 0.6499 | 0.8437 | 0.8510 | 1.257 | 1.642 | 1.997 | 2.317 | 2.602 | 2.855 | 3.075 |
| Carbon Monoxide | CO | gas | 0 | | 6.934 | | 6.947 | 6.950 | 6.951 | 6.952 | 6.959 | 6.980 | 7.016 | 7.065 | 7.125 | 7.190 | 7.257 |
| Carbon Dioxide | $CO_2$ | gas | 0 | | | | | | 7.506 | 7.515 | 7.987 | 8.446 | 8.871 | 9.259 | 9.612 | 9.932 | 10.222 |

Heat Content Function, $(H°-H°_0)/T$, in cal/deg mole — Temperature in °K

| Compound | Formula | State | 1100 | 1200 | 1300 | 1400 | 1500 | 1750 | 2000 | 2250 | 2500 | 2750 | 3000 | 3500 | 4000 | 4500 | 5000 |
|---|---|---|---|---|---|---|---|---|---|---|---|---|---|---|---|---|---|
| Oxygen | $O_2$ | gas | 7.578 | 7.653 | 7.724 | 7.789 | 7.851 | 7.989 | 8.109 | 8.219 | 8.320 | 8.415 | 8.505 | 8.669 | 8.816 | 8.949 | 9.064 |
| Hydrogen | $H_2$ | gas | 6.9927 | 7.0230 | 7.0563 | 7.0919 | 7.1295 | 7.2309 | 7.3358 | 7.4395 | 7.5402 | 7.6369 | 7.7286 | 7.8956 | 8.0430 | 8.1733 | 8.2898 |
| Hydroxyl | OH | gas | 7.131 | 7.161 | 7.196 | 7.234 | 7.273 | 7.376 | 7.480 | 7.581 | 7.677 | 7.768 | 7.853 | 8.007 | 8.144 | 8.268 | 8.382 |
| Water | $H_2O$ | gas | 8.733 | 8.858 | 8.984 | 9.109 | 9.232 | 9.533 | 9.815 | 10.074 | 10.308 | 10.52 | 10.72 | 11.05 | 11.34 | 11.57 | 11.77 |
| Nitrogen | $N_2$ | gas | 7.2650 | 7.3273 | 7.3882 | 7.4467 | 7.5024 | 7.6328 | 7.7474 | 7.8477 | 7.9356 | 8.0131 | 8.0818 | 8.199 | 8.294 | 8.375 | 8.444 |
| Nitric Oxide | NO | gas | 7.567 | 7.627 | 7.686 | 7.742 | 7.796 | 7.914 | 8.015 | 8.103 | 8.180 | 8.248 | 8.308 | 8.408 | 8.493 | 8.567 | 8.636 |
| Carbon | C | solid graphite | 3.269 | 3.442 | 3.600 | 3.744 | 3.876 | 4.16 | 4.39 | 4.58 | 4.74 | 4.88 | 5.01 | 5.22 | 5.40 | | |
| Carbon Monoxide | CO | gas | 7.324 | 7.390 | 7.454 | 7.515 | 7.572 | 7.704 | 7.818 | 7.917 | 8.003 | 8.078 | 8.145 | 8.257 | 8.349 | 8.425 | 8.490 |
| Carbon Dioxide | $CO_2$ | gas | 10.486 | 10.728 | 10.949 | 11.151 | 11.336 | 11.74 | 12.07 | 12.35 | 12.59 | 12.80 | 12.98 | 13.29 | 13.54 | 13.75 | 13.93 |

TABLE 20r (PART 1) - NORMAL PARAFFINS, $C_1$ TO $C_{20}$

HEAT CONTENT FUNCTION, $(H^\circ - H^\circ_0)/T$, FOR THE IDEAL GAS STATE, AT 0° TO 1500°K

November 30, 1945; December 31, 1952

| Compound (gas) | Formula | Temperature in °K | | | | | | | | | | | | | | |
|---|---|---|---|---|---|---|---|---|---|---|---|---|---|---|---|---|
| | | 0 | 298.16 | 300 | 400 | 500 | 600 | 700 | 800 | 900 | 1000 | 1100 | 1200 | 1300 | 1400 | 1500 |
| | | Heat Content Function, $(H^\circ - H^\circ_0)/T$, in cal/deg mole | | | | | | | | | | | | | | |
| Methane | $CH_4$ | 0 | 8.039 | 8.042 | 8.307 | 8.730 | 9.249 | 9.816 | 10.401 | 10.985 | 11.56 | 12.11 | 12.65 | 13.15 | 13.63 | 14.09 |
| Ethane | $C_2H_6$ | 0 | 9.578 | 9.596 | 10.74 | 12.02 | 13.36 | 14.68 | 15.95 | 17.15 | 18.28 | 19.35 | 20.35 | 21.29 | 22.17 | 23.00 |
| Propane | $C_3H_8$ | 0 | 11.78 | 11.82 | 13.89 | 16.08 | 18.22 | 20.27 | 22.20 | 24.00 | 25.67 | 27.23 | 28.68 | 30.02 | 31.27 | 32.43 |
| n-Butane | $C_4H_{10}$ | 0 | 15.58 | 15.63 | 18.35 | 21.19 | 23.96 | 26.60 | 29.08 | 31.39 | 33.54 | 35.53 | 37.39 | 39.11 | 40.71 | 42.18 |
| n-Pentane | $C_5H_{12}$ | 0 | 18.88 | 18.94 | 22.38 | 25.94 | 29.38 | 32.64 | 35.71 | 38.55 | 41.19 | 43.63 | 45.91 | 48.01 | 49.96 | 51.75 |
| n-Hexane | $C_6H_{14}$ | 0 | 22.21 | 22.29 | 26.45 | 30.72 | 34.82 | 38.71 | 42.35 | 45.73 | 48.85 | 51.75 | 54.44 | 56.92 | 59.22 | 61.34 |
| n-Heptane | $C_7H_{16}$ | 0 | 25.54 | 25.63 | 30.51 | 35.49 | 40.26 | 44.77 | 49.00 | 52.91 | 56.52 | 59.86 | 62.97 | 65.83 | 68.48 | 70.92 |
| n-Octane | $C_8H_{18}$ | 0 | 28.87 | 28.97 | 34.57 | 40.26 | 45.70 | 50.83 | 55.64 | 60.09 | 64.18 | 67.97 | 71.50 | 74.74 | 77.74 | 80.50 |
| n-Nonane | $C_9H_{20}$ | 0 | 32.20 | 32.32 | 38.64 | 45.04 | 51.14 | 56.89 | 62.29 | 67.26 | 71.85 | 76.08 | 80.03 | 83.65 | 87.00 | 90.08 |
| n-Decane | $C_{10}H_{22}$ | 0 | 35.53 | 35.66 | 42.70 | 49.81 | 56.58 | 62.96 | 68.93 | 74.44 | 79.51 | 84.20 | 88.55 | 92.55 | 96.25 | 99.67 |
| n-Undecane | $C_{11}H_{24}$ | 0 | 38.86 | 39.01 | 46.76 | 54.59 | 62.02 | 69.02 | 75.57 | 81.61 | 87.17 | 92.31 | 97.08 | 101.46 | 105.51 | 109.25 |
| n-Dodecane | $C_{12}H_{26}$ | 0 | 42.19 | 42.35 | 50.83 | 59.36 | 67.46 | 75.08 | 82.22 | 88.79 | 94.84 | 100.42 | 105.61 | 110.37 | 114.77 | 118.83 |
| n-Tridecane | $C_{13}H_{28}$ | 0 | 45.52 | 45.69 | 54.89 | 64.13 | 72.89 | 81.14 | 88.86 | 95.97 | 102.50 | 108.53 | 114.14 | 119.28 | 124.03 | 128.41 |
| n-Tetradecane | $C_{14}H_{30}$ | 0 | 46.85 | 49.04 | 58.95 | 68.91 | 78.33 | 87.20 | 95.50 | 103.14 | 110.16 | 116.64 | 122.67 | 128.19 | 133.29 | 137.99 |
| n-Pentadecane | $C_{15}H_{32}$ | 0 | 52.18 | 52.38 | 63.01 | 73.68 | 83.77 | 93.27 | 102.14 | 110.32 | 117.82 | 124.76 | 131.19 | 137.09 | 142.54 | 147.58 |
| n-Hexadecane | $C_{16}H_{34}$ | 0 | 55.51 | 55.73 | 67.08 | 78.46 | 89.21 | 99.33 | 108.79 | 117.49 | 125.49 | 132.87 | 139.72 | 146.00 | 151.80 | 157.16 |
| n-Heptadecane | $C_{17}H_{36}$ | 0 | 58.84 | 59.07 | 71.14 | 83.23 | 94.65 | 105.39 | 115.43 | 124.67 | 133.15 | 140.98 | 148.25 | 154.91 | 161.06 | 166.74 |
| n-Octadecane | $C_{18}H_{38}$ | 0 | 62.17 | 62.41 | 75.20 | 88.00 | 100.09 | 111.45 | 122.07 | 131.85 | 140.81 | 149.09 | 156.78 | 163.82 | 170.32 | 176.32 |
| n-Nonadecane | $C_{19}H_{40}$ | 0 | 65.50 | 65.76 | 79.27 | 92.78 | 105.53 | 117.51 | 128.72 | 139.02 | 148.48 | 157.20 | 165.31 | 172.73 | 179.58 | 185.90 |
| n-Eicosane | $C_{20}H_{42}$ | 0 | 68.83 | 69.10 | 83.33 | 97.55 | 110.97 | 123.58 | 135.36 | 146.20 | 156.14 | 165.32 | 173.83 | 181.63 | 188.83 | 195.49 |
| Increment per CH2 group, applicable beyond n-Hexane | | 0 | 3.330 | 3.344 | 4.063 | 4.774 | 5.439 | 6.062 | 6.643 | 7.176 | 7.663 | 8.112 | 8.528 | 8.908 | 9.258 | 9.582 |

494

TABLE 1r – PARAFFINS, C₁ TO C₅

HEAT CONTENT FUNCTION, $(H^O-H^O_0)/T$, FOR THE IDEAL GAS STATE, AT 0° TO 1500°K

August 31, 1944; February 28, 1949; December 31, 1952

| Compound (gas) | Formula | Temperature in °K | | | | | | | | | | | | | | |
|---|---|---|---|---|---|---|---|---|---|---|---|---|---|---|---|---|
| | | Heat Content Function, $(H^O-H^O_0)/T$, in cal/deg mole | | | | | | | | | | | | | | |
| | | 0 | 100 | 150 | 200 | 250 | 298.16 | 300 | 350 | 400 | 450 | 500 | 600 | 700 | 800 | 900 |
| Methane | CH₄ | 0 | 7.949 | 7.949 | 7.954 | 7.979 | 8.039 | 8.042 | 8.151 | 8.307 | 8.502 | 8.730 | 9.249 | 9.816 | 10.401 | 10.985 |
| Ethane | C₂H₆ | 0 | 8.11 | 8.39 | 8.72 | 9.12 | 9.578 | 9.596 | 10.13 | 10.74 | 11.36 | 12.02 | 13.36 | 14.68 | 15.95 | 17.15 |
| Propane | C₃H₈ | 0 | 8.14 | 9.22 | 10.03 | 10.89 | 11.78 | 11.82 | 12.83 | 13.89 | 14.98 | 16.08 | 18.22 | 20.27 | 22.20 | 24.00 |
| n-Butane | C₄H₁₀ | 0 | | | 13.16 | 14.37 | 15.58 | 15.63 | 16.96 | 18.35 | 19.77 | 21.19 | 23.96 | 26.60 | 29.08 | 31.39 |
| 2-Methylpropane (Isobutane) | " | 0 | | | 11.52 | 12.94 | 14.34 | 14.39 | 15.90 | 17.41 | 18.97 | 20.50 | 23.45 | 26.20 | 28.76 | 31.13 |
| n-Pentane | C₅H₁₂ | 0 | | | 15.73 | 17.32 | 18.88 | 18.94 | 20.63 | 22.38 | 24.16 | 25.94 | 29.38 | 32.64 | 35.71 | 38.55 |
| 2-Methylbutane (Isopentane) | " | 0 | | | 14.44 | 16.03 | 17.76 | 17.82 | 19.63 | 21.49 | 23.37 | 25.24 | 28.83 | 32.24 | 35.38 | 38.32 |
| 2,2-Dimethylpropane (Neopentane) | " | 0 | | | 12.87 | 14.89 | 16.87 | 16.94 | 18.99 | 21.07 | 23.12 | 25.13 | 28.98 | 32.53 | 35.80 | 38.78 |

| Compound (gas) | Formula | Temperature in °K | | | | | |
|---|---|---|---|---|---|---|---|
| | | Heat Content Function, $(H^O-H^O_0)/T$, in cal/deg mole | | | | | |
| | | 1000 | 1100 | 1200 | 1300 | 1400 | 1500 |
| Methane | CH₄ | 11.56 | 12.11 | 12.65 | 13.15 | 13.63 | 14.09 |
| Ethane | C₂H₆ | 18.28 | 19.35 | 20.35 | 21.29 | 22.17 | 23.00 |
| Propane | C₃H₈ | 25.67 | 27.23 | 28.68 | 30.02 | 31.27 | 32.43 |
| n-Butane | C₄H₁₀ | 33.54 | 35.53 | 37.39 | 39.11 | 40.71 | 42.18 |
| 2-Methylpropane (Isobutane) | " | 33.31 | 35.34 | 37.23 | 38.96 | 40.56 | 42.03 |
| n-Pentane | C₅H₁₂ | 41.19 | 43.63 | 45.91 | 48.01 | 49.96 | 51.75 |
| 2-Methylbutane (Isopentane) | " | 41.01 | 43.53 | 45.86 | 47.99 | 49.99 | 51.83 |
| 2,2-Dimethylpropane (Neopentane) | " | 41.51 | 44.02 | 46.34 | 48.49 | 50.47 | 52.28 |

TABLE 2r (PART 1) — PARAFFINS, $C_6$

HEAT CONTENT FUNCTION, $(H^o - H^o_0)/T$, FOR THE IDEAL GAS STATE, AT $0°$ TO $1500°K$

September 30, 1944; November 30, 1946; December 31, 1952

| Compound (gas) | Formula | Temperature in °K | | | | | | | | | | | | | | |
|---|---|---|---|---|---|---|---|---|---|---|---|---|---|---|---|---|
| | | 0 | 298.16 | 300 | 400 | 500 | 600 | 700 | 800 | 900 | 1000 | 1100 | 1200 | 1300 | 1400 | 1500 |
| | | Heat Content Function, $(H^o - H^o_0)/T$, in cal/deg mole | | | | | | | | | | | | | | |
| n-Hexane | $C_6H_{14}$ | 0 | 22.21 | 22.29 | 26.45 | 30.72 | 34.82 | 38.71 | 42.35 | 45.73 | 48.85 | 51.75 | 54.44 | 56.92 | 59.22 | 61.34 |
| 2-Methylpentane | " | 0 | 20.45 | 20.54 | 25.2 | 29.9 | 34.2 | 38.3 | 42.0 | 45.5 | 48.7 | | | | | |
| 3-Methylpentane | " | 0 | 22.21 | 22.29 | 26.45 | 30.72 | 34.8 | 38.7 | 42.3 | 45.7 | 48.8 | | | | | |
| 2,2-Dimethylbutane | " | 0 | 19.83 | 19.91 | 24.7 | 29.5 | 33.9 | 38.0 | 41.9 | 45.3 | 48.6 | | | | | |
| 2,3-Dimethylbutane | " | 0 | 19.84 | 19.93 | 24.58 | 29.22 | 33.62 | 37.73 | 41.54 | 45.00 | 48.24 | | | | | |

TABLE 2r (PART 2) – PARAFFINS, $C_7$

HEAT CONTENT FUNCTION, $(H°-H°_0)/T$, FOR THE IDEAL GAS STATE, AT 0° TO 1500°K

September 30, 1944; December 31, 1952

| Compound (gas) | Formula | Temperature in °K | | | | | | | | | | | | | | |
|---|---|---|---|---|---|---|---|---|---|---|---|---|---|---|---|---|
| | | 0 | 298.16 | 300 | 400 | 500 | 600 | 700 | 800 | 900 | 1000 | 1100 | 1200 | 1300 | 1400 | 1500 |
| | | Heat Content Function, $(H°-H°_0)/T$, in cal/deg mole | | | | | | | | | | | | | | |
| n-Heptane | $C_7H_{16}$ | 0 | 25.54 | 25.63 | 30.51 | 35.49 | 40.26 | 44.77 | 49.00 | 52.91 | 56.52 | 59.86 | 62.97 | 65.83 | 68.48 | 70.92 |
| 2-Methylhexane | " | 0 | 23.89 | 23.98 | 29.6 | 35.0 | 40.2 | 44.9 | 49.2 | 53.2 | 56.7 | | | | | |
| 3-Methylhexane | " | 0 | 23.32 | 23.41 | 29.0 | 34.5 | 39.7 | 44.5 | 48.8 | 52.8 | 56.4 | | | | | |
| 3-Ethylpentane | " | 0 | 22.52 | 22.61 | 28.3 | 33.8 | 39.0 | 43.8 | 48.2 | 52.2 | 55.8 | | | | | |
| 2,2-Dimethylpentane | " | 0 | 22.35 | 22.44 | 28.4 | 34.1 | 39.5 | 44.5 | 49.0 | 53.0 | 56.7 | | | | | |
| 2,3-Dimethylpentane | " | 0 | 22.21 | 22.30 | 28.2 | 33.8 | 39.2 | 44.1 | 48.5 | 52.5 | 56.1 | | | | | |
| 2,4-Dimethylpentane | " | 0 | 22.25 | 22.34 | 28.3 | 34.1 | 39.5 | 44.5 | 49.0 | 53.0 | 56.6 | | | | | |
| 3,3-Dimethylpentane | " | 0 | 22.48 | 22.57 | 28.5 | 34.2 | 39.7 | 44.7 | 49.2 | 53.2 | 56.9 | | | | | |
| 2,2,3-Trimethylbutane | " | 0 | 22.48 | 22.58 | 28.25 | 33.81 | 39.10 | 43.97 | 48.4 | 52.5 | 56.3 | 59.7 | 62.9 | 65.8 | 68.5 | 71.0 |

497

TABLE 3r – PARAFFINS, $C_8$
HEAT CONTENT FUNCTION, $(H°-H°_0)/T$, FOR THE IDEAL GAS STATE, AT 0° TO 1500°K
October 31, 1944; December 31, 1952

| Compound (gas) | Formula | Temperature in °K — Heat Content Function, $(H°-H°_0)/T$, in cal/deg mole | | | | | | | | | | | | | | |
|---|---|---|---|---|---|---|---|---|---|---|---|---|---|---|---|---|
| | | 0 | 296.16 | 300 | 400 | 500 | 600 | 700 | 800 | 900 | 1000 | 1100 | 1200 | 1300 | 1400 | 1500 |
| n-Octane | $C_8H_{18}$ | 0 | 28.87 | 28.97 | 34.57 | 40.26 | 45.70 | 50.83 | 55.64 | 60.09 | 64.18 | 67.97 | 71.50 | 74.74 | 77.74 | 80.50 |
| 2-Methylheptane | " | 0 | 27.32 | 27.43 | 33.8 | 40.0 | 45.8 | 51.2 | 56.0 | 60.3 | 64.5 | | | | | |
| 3-Methylheptane | " | 0 | 26.99 | 27.10 | 33.5 | 39.7 | 45.6 | 51.0 | 55.8 | 60.2 | 64.4 | | | | | |
| 4-Methylheptane | " | 0 | 26.72 | 26.83 | 33.3 | 39.5 | 45.3 | 50.7 | 55.6 | 60.0 | 64.2 | | | | | |
| 3-Ethylhexane | " | 0 | 25.28 | 25.39 | 31.8 | 38.1 | 44.0 | 49.5 | 54.5 | 59.0 | 63.2 | | | | | |
| 2,2-Dimethylhexane | " | 0 | 25.98 | 26.09 | 32.8 | 39.2 | 45.2 | 50.8 | 55.9 | 60.4 | 64.6 | | | | | |
| 2,3-Dimethylhexane | " | 0 | 26.35 | 26.46 | 33.2 | 39.9 | 46.0 | 51.6 | 56.4 | 60.8 | 64.9 | | | | | |
| 2,4-Dimethylhexane | " | 0 | 25.24 | 25.35 | 32.1 | 38.5 | 44.6 | 50.2 | 55.2 | 59.6 | 63.8 | | | | | |
| 2,5-Dimethylhexane | " | 0 | 25.58 | 25.69 | 32.4 | 38.9 | 45.0 | 50.6 | 55.5 | 59.9 | 64.1 | | | | | |
| 3,3-Dimethylhexane | " | 0 | 25.21 | 25.32 | 32.1 | 38.6 | 44.8 | 50.5 | 55.6 | 60.2 | 64.4 | | | | | |
| 3,4-Dimethylhexane[a,b] | " | 0 | 26.57 | 26.69 | 33.0 | 39.2 | 45.1 | 50.5 | 55.4 | 60.0 | 64.1 | | | | | |
| 2-Methyl-3-ethylpentane | " | 0 | 25.85 | 25.96 | 32.7 | 39.2 | 45.3 | 50.8 | 55.6 | 60.1 | 64.3 | | | | | |
| 3-Methyl-3-ethylpentane | " | 0 | 25.24 | 25.35 | 32.4 | 38.9 | 45.0 | 50.6 | 55.7 | 60.3 | 64.7 | | | | | |
| 2,2,3-Trimethylpentane | " | 0 | 24.77 | 24.88 | 31.9 | 38.6 | 44.8 | 50.5 | 55.5 | 60.1 | 64.4 | | | | | |
| 2,2,4-Trimethylpentane | " | 0 | 24.77 | 24.88 | 31.9 | 38.6 | 44.8 | 50.5 | 55.5 | 60.1 | 64.4 | | | | | |
| 2,3,3-Trimethylpentane | " | 0 | 25.17 | 25.28 | 32.2 | 38.9 | 45.2 | 50.8 | 55.7 | 60.3 | 64.7 | | | | | |
| 2,3,4-Trimethylpentane | " | 0 | 24.74 | 24.85 | 31.9 | 38.8 | 45.1 | 50.7 | 55.6 | 60.0 | 64.4 | | | | | |
| 2,2,3,3-Tetramethylbutane | " | 0 | 25.09 | 25.22 | 32.2 | 39.0 | 45.3 | 51.0 | 56.3 | 61.0 | 65.3 | | | | | |

a The values tabulated are for the equilibrium mixture of the dextro, levo, and meso isomers of 3,4-dimethylhexane. For the temperatures given in this table, the equilibrium amounts of these isomers are very close to the ratios 1:1:2 for dextro, levo, and meso, respectively.

b The values of the heat content function for the separate isomers, and for the racemic (dextro + levo) mixture, are not greatly different from the values tabulated for the equilibrium mixture of the dextro, levo, and meso isomers of 3,4-dimethylhexane.

498

TABLE 22r (PART 1) – NORMAL ALKYL CYCLOPENTANES, $C_5$ TO $C_{21}$
HEAT CONTENT FUNCTION, $(H°-H°_0)/T$, FOR THE IDEAL GAS STATE, AT 0° TO 1500°K
March 31, 1947; December 31, 1952

| Compound (gas) | Formula | Temperature in °K — Heat Content Function, $(H°-H°_0)/T$, in cal/deg mole | | | | | | | | | | | | | | |
|---|---|---|---|---|---|---|---|---|---|---|---|---|---|---|---|---|
| | | 0 | 298.16 | 300 | 400 | 500 | 600 | 700 | 800 | 900 | 1000 | 1100 | 1200 | 1300 | 1400 | 1500 |
| Cyclopentane | $C_5H_{10}$ | 0 | 12.07 | 12.12 | 15.12 | 18.52 | 21.98 | 25.29 | 28.40 | 31.29 | 33.97 | 36.46 | 38.75 | 40.87 | 42.83 | 44.65 |
| Methylcyclopentane | $C_6H_{12}$ | 0 | 16.01 | 16.09 | 19.88 | 24.03 | 28.17 | 32.09 | 35.75 | 39.15 | 42.28 | 45.18 | 47.87 | 50.34 | 52.62 | 54.74 |
| Ethylcyclopentane | $C_7H_{14}$ | 0 | 19.43 | 19.52 | 23.96 | 28.77 | 33.55 | 38.13 | 42.37 | 46.34 | 49.98 | 53.37 | 56.50 | 59.37 | 62.05 | 64.54 |
| n-Propylcyclopentane | $C_8H_{16}$ | 0 | 22.76 | 22.86 | 28.02 | 33.54 | 38.99 | 44.19 | 49.01 | 53.52 | 57.64 | 61.48 | 65.03 | 68.28 | 71.31 | 74.12 |
| n-Butylcyclopentane | $C_9H_{18}$ | 0 | 26.09 | 26.21 | 32.09 | 38.32 | 44.43 | 50.25 | 55.66 | 60.69 | 65.31 | 69.59 | 73.56 | 77.19 | 80.57 | 83.70 |
| n-Pentylcyclopentane | $C_{10}H_{20}$ | 0 | 29.42 | 29.55 | 36.15 | 43.09 | 49.87 | 56.32 | 62.30 | 67.87 | 72.97 | 77.71 | 82.08 | 86.09 | 89.82 | 93.29 |
| n-Hexylcyclopentane | $C_{11}H_{22}$ | 0 | 32.75 | 32.90 | 40.21 | 47.87 | 55.31 | 62.38 | 68.94 | 75.04 | 80.63 | 85.82 | 90.61 | 95.00 | 99.08 | 102.87 |
| n-Heptylcyclopentane | $C_{12}H_{24}$ | 0 | 36.08 | 36.24 | 44.28 | 52.64 | 60.74 | 68.44 | 75.58 | 82.22 | 88.30 | 93.93 | 99.14 | 103.91 | 108.34 | 112.45 |
| n-Octylcyclopentane | $C_{13}H_{26}$ | 0 | 39.41 | 39.58 | 48.34 | 57.41 | 66.18 | 74.50 | 82.23 | 89.40 | 95.96 | 102.04 | 107.67 | 112.82 | 117.60 | 122.03 |
| n-Nonylcyclopentane | $C_{14}H_{28}$ | 0 | 42.74 | 42.93 | 52.40 | 62.19 | 71.62 | 80.56 | 88.87 | 96.57 | 103.62 | 110.15 | 116.20 | 121.73 | 126.86 | 131.61 |
| n-Decylcyclopentane | $C_{15}H_{30}$ | 0 | 46.07 | 46.27 | 56.46 | 66.96 | 77.06 | 86.63 | 95.51 | 103.75 | 111.28 | 118.27 | 124.72 | 130.63 | 136.11 | 141.20 |
| n-Undecylcyclopentane | $C_{16}H_{32}$ | 0 | 49.40 | 49.62 | 60.53 | 71.74 | 82.50 | 92.69 | 102.16 | 110.92 | 118.95 | 126.38 | 133.25 | 139.54 | 145.37 | 150.78 |
| n-Dodecylcyclopentane | $C_{17}H_{34}$ | 0 | 52.73 | 52.96 | 64.59 | 76.51 | 87.94 | 98.75 | 108.80 | 118.10 | 126.61 | 134.49 | 141.78 | 148.45 | 154.63 | 160.36 |
| n-Tridecylcyclopentane | $C_{18}H_{36}$ | 0 | 56.06 | 56.30 | 68.65 | 81.28 | 93.38 | 104.81 | 115.44 | 125.28 | 134.27 | 142.60 | 150.31 | 157.36 | 163.89 | 169.94 |
| n-Tetradecylcyclopentane | $C_{19}H_{38}$ | 0 | 59.39 | 59.65 | 72.72 | 86.06 | 98.82 | 110.87 | 122.09 | 132.45 | 141.93 | 150.71 | 158.84 | 166.27 | 173.15 | 179.52 |
| n-Pentadecylcyclopentane | $C_{20}H_{40}$ | 0 | 62.72 | 62.99 | 76.78 | 90.83 | 104.26 | 116.94 | 128.73 | 139.63 | 149.60 | 158.83 | 167.36 | 175.17 | 182.40 | 189.11 |
| n-Hexadecylcyclopentane | $C_{21}H_{42}$ | 0 | 66.05 | 66.34 | 80.84 | 95.61 | 109.70 | 123.00 | 135.37 | 146.80 | 157.26 | 166.94 | 175.89 | 184.08 | 191.66 | 198.69 |
| Increment per $CH_2$ group, applicable beyond ethylcyclopentane | | 0 | 3.330 | 3.344 | 4.063 | 4.774 | 5.439 | 6.062 | 6.643 | 7.176 | 7.663 | 8.112 | 8.528 | 8.908 | 9.258 | 9.582 |

TABLE 6r – ALKYL CYCLOPENTANES, $C_5$ TO $C_7$

HEAT CONTENT FUNCTION, $(H°-H°_0)/T$, FOR THE IDEAL GAS STATE, AT 0° TO 1500°K

April 30, 1949; December 31, 1952

Temperature in °K

Heat Content Function, $(H°-H°_0)/T$, in cal/deg mole

| Compound (gas) | Formula | 0 | 298.16 | 300 | 400 | 500 | 600 | 700 | 800 | 900 | 1000 | 1100 | 1200 | 1300 | 1400 | 1500 |
|---|---|---|---|---|---|---|---|---|---|---|---|---|---|---|---|---|
| Cyclopentane | $C_5H_{10}$ | 0 | 12.07 | 12.12 | 15.12 | 18.52 | 21.98 | 25.29 | 28.40 | 31.29 | 33.97 | 36.46 | 38.75 | 40.87 | 42.83 | 44.65 |
| Methylcyclopentane | $C_6H_{12}$ | 0 | 16.01 | 16.09 | 19.88 | 24.03 | 28.17 | 32.09 | 35.75 | 39.15 | 42.28 | 45.18 | 47.87 | 50.34 | 52.62 | 54.74 |
| Ethylcyclopentane | $C_7H_{14}$ | 0 | 19.43 | 19.52 | 23.96 | 28.77 | 33.55 | 38.13 | 42.37 | 46.34 | 49.98 | 53.37 | 56.50 | 59.37 | 62.05 | 64.54 |
| 1,1-Dimethylcyclopentane | " | 0 | 18.66 | 18.77 | 23.51 | 28.59 | 33.63 | 38.32 | 42.64 | 46.69 | 50.38 | 53.77 | 56.92 | 59.78 | 62.42 | 64.87 |
| 1,cis-2-Dimethylcyclopentane | " | 0 | 18.86 | 18.95 | 23.63 | 28.71 | 33.71 | 38.38 | 42.70 | 46.69 | 50.36 | 53.73 | 56.86 | 59.72 | 62.36 | 64.79 |
| 1,trans-2-Dimethylcyclopentane | " | 0 | 18.94 | 19.05 | 23.71 | 28.79 | 33.77 | 38.42 | 42.68 | 46.69 | 50.34 | 53.69 | 56.82 | 59.68 | 62.30 | 64.73 |
| 1,cis-3-Dimethylcyclopentane | " | 0 | 18.94 | 19.05 | 23.71 | 28.79 | 33.77 | 38.42 | 42.68 | 46.69 | 50.34 | 53.69 | 56.82 | 59.68 | 62.30 | 64.73 |
| 1,trans-3-Dimethylcyclopentane | " | 0 | 18.94 | 19.05 | 23.71 | 28.79 | 33.77 | 38.42 | 42.68 | 46.69 | 50.34 | 53.69 | 56.82 | 59.68 | 62.30 | 64.73 |

TABLE 23r (PART 1) - NORMAL ALKYL CYCLOHEXANES, C$_6$ TO C$_{22}$

HEAT CONTENT FUNCTION, $(H^O-H^O_0)/T$, FOR THE IDEAL GAS STATE, AT 0° TO 1500°K

March 31, 1947; December 31, 1952

| Compound (gas) | Formula | Temperature in °K |  |  |  |  |  |  |  |  |  |  |  |  |  |  |
|---|---|---|---|---|---|---|---|---|---|---|---|---|---|---|---|---|
|  |  | 0 | 298.16 | 300 | 400 | 500 | 600 | 700 | 800 | 900 | 1000 | 1100 | 1200 | 1300 | 1400 | 1500 |
|  |  | Heat Content Function, $(H^O-H^O_0)/T$, in cal/deg mole |  |  |  |  |  |  |  |  |  |  |  |  |  |  |
| Cyclohexane | C$_6$H$_{12}$ | 0 | 14.21 | 14.26 | 18.38 | 22.85 | 27.34 | 31.64 | 35.67 | 39.40 | 42.85 | 46.0 | 48.9 | 51.6 | 54.0 | 56.3 |
| Methylcyclohexane | C$_7$H$_{14}$ | 0 | 17.55 | 17.66 | 22.84 | 28.26 | 33.53 | 38.53 | 43.16 | 47.42 | 51.33 | 54.9 | 58.2 | 61.2 | 64.0 | 66.5 |
| Ethylcyclohexane | C$_8$H$_{16}$ | 0 | 20.45 | 20.58 | 26.7 | 32.9 | 38.9 | 44.6 | 49.9 | 54.7 | 59.1 | 63.1 | 66.8 | 70.2 | 73.3 | 76.2 |
| n-Propylcyclohexane | C$_9$H$_{18}$ | 0 | 23.14 | 23.30 | 30.4 | 37.6 | 44.3 | 50.7 | 56.5 | 61.9 | 66.8 | 71.2 | 75.3 | 79.1 | 82.6 | 85.8 |
| n-Butylcyclohexane | C$_{10}$H$_{20}$ | 0 | 26.47 | 26.64 | 34.5 | 42.4 | 49.7 | 56.8 | 63.1 | 69.1 | 74.5 | 79.3 | 83.8 | 88.0 | 91.9 | 95.4 |
| n-Pentylcyclohexane | C$_{11}$H$_{22}$ | 0 | 29.80 | 29.99 | 38.5 | 47.1 | 55.2 | 62.8 | 69.8 | 76.3 | 82.1 | 87.4 | 92.4 | 96.9 | 101.1 | 105.0 |
| n-Hexylcyclohexane | C$_{12}$H$_{24}$ | 0 | 33.13 | 33.33 | 42.6 | 51.9 | 60.6 | 68.9 | 76.4 | 83.4 | 89.8 | 95.5 | 100.9 | 105.8 | 110.4 | 114.5 |
| n-Heptylcyclohexane | C$_{13}$H$_{26}$ | 0 | 36.46 | 36.68 | 46.6 | 56.7 | 66.1 | 74.9 | 83.1 | 90.6 | 97.4 | 103.6 | 109.4 | 114.7 | 119.6 | 124.1 |
| n-Octylcyclohexane | C$_{14}$H$_{28}$ | 0 | 39.79 | 40.02 | 50.7 | 61.5 | 71.5 | 81.0 | 89.7 | 97.8 | 105.1 | 111.7 | 117.9 | 123.7 | 128.9 | 133.7 |
| n-Nonylcyclohexane | C$_{15}$H$_{30}$ | 0 | 43.12 | 43.36 | 54.8 | 66.2 | 76.9 | 87.1 | 96.3 | 105.0 | 112.8 | 119.9 | 126.5 | 132.6 | 138.2 | 143.3 |
| n-Decylcyclohexane | C$_{16}$H$_{32}$ | 0 | 46.45 | 46.71 | 58.8 | 71.0 | 82.4 | 93.1 | 103.0 | 112.2 | 120.4 | 128.0 | 135.0 | 141.5 | 147.4 | 152.9 |
| n-Undecylcyclohexane | C$_{17}$H$_{34}$ | 0 | 49.78 | 50.05 | 62.9 | 75.8 | 87.8 | 99.2 | 109.6 | 119.3 | 128.1 | 136.1 | 143.5 | 150.4 | 156.7 | 162.4 |
| n-Dodecylcyclohexane | C$_{18}$H$_{36}$ | 0 | 53.11 | 53.40 | 66.9 | 80.5 | 93.3 | 105.2 | 116.3 | 126.5 | 135.7 | 144.2 | 152.1 | 159.3 | 165.9 | 172.0 |
| n-Tridecylcyclohexane | C$_{19}$H$_{38}$ | 0 | 56.44 | 56.74 | 71.0 | 85.3 | 98.7 | 111.3 | 122.9 | 133.7 | 143.4 | 152.3 | 160.6 | 168.2 | 175.2 | 181.6 |
| n-Tetradecylcyclohexane | C$_{20}$H$_{40}$ | 0 | 59.77 | 60.08 | 75.1 | 90.1 | 104.1 | 117.4 | 129.5 | 140.9 | 151.1 | 160.4 | 169.1 | 177.1 | 184.5 | 191.2 |
| n-Pentadecylcyclohexane | C$_{21}$H$_{42}$ | 0 | 63.10 | 63.43 | 79.1 | 94.8 | 109.6 | 123.4 | 136.2 | 148.1 | 158.7 | 168.5 | 177.7 | 186.0 | 193.7 | 200.8 |
| n-Hexadecylcyclohexane | C$_{22}$H$_{44}$ | 0 | 66.43 | 66.77 | 83.2 | 99.6 | 115.0 | 129.5 | 142.8 | 155.2 | 166.3 | 176.6 | 186.2 | 194.9 | 203.0 | 210.3 |
| Increment per CH$_2$ group, applicable beyond n-propylcyclohexane | | 0 | 3.330 | 3.344 | 4.06 | 4.77 | 5.44 | 6.06 | 6.64 | 7.18 | 7.66 | 8.11 | 8.53 | 8.91 | 9.26 | 9.58 |

## TABLE 7r – ALKYL CYCLOHEXANES, $C_6$ TO $C_8$

HEAT CONTENT FUNCTION, $(H^\circ - H^\circ_0)/T$, FOR THE IDEAL GAS STATE, AT 0° TO 1500°K

April 30, 1947

| Compound (gas) | Formula | Temperature in °K |||||||||||||||
|---|---|---|---|---|---|---|---|---|---|---|---|---|---|---|---|---|
| | | 0 | 298.16 | 300 | 400 | 500 | 600 | 700 | 800 | 900 | 1000 | 1100 | 1200 | 1300 | 1400 | 1500 |
| | | Heat Content Function, $(H^\circ - H^\circ_0)/T$, in cal/deg mole ||||||||||||||
| Cyclohexane | $C_6H_{12}$ | 0 | 14.21 | 14.28 | 18.38 | 22.85 | 27.34 | 31.64 | 35.67 | 39.40 | 42.85 | 46.0 | 48.9 | 51.6 | 54.0 | 56.3 |
| Methylcyclohexane | $C_7H_{14}$ | 0 | 17.55 | 17.66 | 22.84 | 28.26 | 33.53 | 38.53 | 43.16 | 47.42 | 51.33 | 54.9 | 58.2 | 61.2 | 64.0 | 66.5 |
| Ethylcyclohexane | $C_8H_{16}$ | 0 | 20.45 | 20.58 | 26.7 | 32.9 | 38.9 | 44.6 | 49.9 | 54.7 | 59.1 | 63.1 | 66.8 | 70.2 | 73.3 | 76.2 |
| 1,1-Dimethylcyclohexane | " | 0 | 19.72 | 19.85 | 25.9 | 32.1 | 38.2 | 44.0 | 49.4 | 54.4 | 58.9 | 63.0 | 66.8 | 70.3 | 73.5 | 76.4 |
| 1,cis-2-Dimethylcyclohexane | " | 0 | 20.16 | 20.29 | 26.3 | 32.5 | 38.6 | 44.3 | 49.6 | 54.4 | 58.9 | 63.0 | 66.7 | 70.1 | 73.3 | 76.1 |
| 1,trans-2-Dimethylcyclohexane | " | 0 | 20.44 | 20.58 | 26.7 | 33.0 | 39.0 | 44.7 | 50.0 | 54.9 | 59.3 | 63.4 | 67.1 | 70.5 | 73.6 | 76.5 |
| 1,cis-3-Dimethylcyclohexane[a] | " | 0 | 20.35 | 20.48 | 26.5 | 32.7 | 38.8 | 44.5 | 49.8 | 54.7 | 59.1 | 63.2 | 67.0 | 70.5 | 73.6 | 76.5 |
| 1,trans-3-Dimethylcyclohexane[b] | " | 0 | 20.35 | 20.48 | 26.5 | 32.7 | 38.7 | 44.3 | 49.6 | 54.4 | 58.8 | 62.9 | 66.6 | 70.0 | 73.1 | 76.0 |
| 1,cis-4-Dimethylcyclohexane | " | 0 | 20.35 | 20.48 | 26.5 | 32.7 | 38.7 | 44.3 | 49.6 | 54.4 | 58.8 | 62.9 | 66.6 | 70.0 | 73.1 | 76.0 |
| 1,trans-4-Dimethylcyclohexane | " | 0 | 20.38 | 20.51 | 26.6 | 32.8 | 38.9 | 44.7 | 50.0 | 54.8 | 59.3 | 63.4 | 67.1 | 70.5 | 73.6 | 76.5 |

a Formerly labeled "trans"; see footnote b of Table 7a.

b Formerly labeled "cis"; see footnote c of Table 7a.

TABLE 24r (PART 1) – NORMAL MONOOLEFINS (1-ALKENES), $C_2$ TO $C_{20}$
HEAT CONTENT FUNCTION, $(H°-H°_0)/T$, FOR THE IDEAL GAS STATE, AT 0° TO 1500°K

November 30, 1945; April 30, 1946; December 31, 1952

| Compound (gas) | Formula | Temperature in °K | | | | | | | | | | | | | | |
|---|---|---|---|---|---|---|---|---|---|---|---|---|---|---|---|---|
| | | 0 | 298.16 | 300 | 400 | 500 | 600 | 700 | 800 | 900 | 1000 | 1100 | 1200 | 1300 | 1400 | 1500 |
| | | Heat Content Function, $(H°-H°_0)/T$, in cal/deg mole | | | | | | | | | | | | | | |
| Ethene (Ethylene) | $C_2H_4$ | 0 | 8.47 | 8.48 | 9.28 | 10.23 | 11.22 | 12.18 | 13.10 | 13.96 | 14.76 | 15.52 | 16.22 | 16.88 | 17.50 | 18.07 |
| Propene (Propylene) | $C_3H_6$ | 0 | 10.86 | 10.88 | 12.48 | 14.15 | 15.82 | 17.42 | 18.94 | 20.36 | 21.69 | 22.92 | 24.07 | 25.13 | 26.12 | 27.05 |
| 1-Butene | $C_4H_8$ | 0 | 13.79 | 13.83 | 16.21 | 18.68 | 21.08 | 23.35 | 25.46 | 27.43 | 29.25 | 30.95 | 32.51 | 33.96 | 35.31 | 36.56 |
| 1-Pentene | $C_5H_{10}$ | 0 | 17.59 | 17.64 | 20.67 | 23.79 | 26.82 | 29.68 | 32.34 | 34.82 | 37.12 | 39.25 | 41.22 | 43.05 | 44.75 | 46.31 |
| 1-Hexene | $C_6H_{12}$ | 0 | 20.89 | 20.95 | 24.70 | 28.54 | 32.24 | 35.72 | 38.97 | 41.98 | 44.77 | 47.35 | 49.74 | 51.95 | 54.00 | 55.88 |
| 1-Heptene | $C_7H_{14}$ | 0 | 24.22 | 24.29 | 28.76 | 33.31 | 37.68 | 41.78 | 45.61 | 49.16 | 52.43 | 55.46 | 58.27 | 60.86 | 63.26 | 65.46 |
| 1-Octene | $C_8H_{16}$ | 0 | 27.55 | 27.64 | 32.83 | 38.09 | 43.12 | 47.84 | 52.26 | 56.33 | 60.10 | 63.57 | 66.80 | 69.77 | 72.52 | 75.04 |
| 1-Nonene | $C_9H_{18}$ | 0 | 30.88 | 30.98 | 36.89 | 42.86 | 48.56 | 53.91 | 58.90 | 63.51 | 67.76 | 71.69 | 75.32 | 78.67 | 81.77 | 84.63 |
| 1-Decene | $C_{10}H_{20}$ | 0 | 34.21 | 34.33 | 40.95 | 47.64 | 54.00 | 59.97 | 65.54 | 70.68 | 75.42 | 79.80 | 83.85 | 87.58 | 91.03 | 94.21 |
| 1-Undecene | $C_{11}H_{22}$ | 0 | 37.54 | 37.67 | 45.02 | 52.41 | 59.44 | 66.03 | 72.18 | 77.86 | 83.08 | 87.91 | 92.38 | 96.49 | 100.29 | 103.79 |
| 1-Dodecene | $C_{12}H_{24}$ | 0 | 40.87 | 41.01 | 49.08 | 57.18 | 64.87 | 72.09 | 78.83 | 85.04 | 90.75 | 96.02 | 100.91 | 105.40 | 109.55 | 113.37 |
| 1-Tridecene | $C_{13}H_{26}$ | 0 | 44.20 | 44.36 | 53.14 | 61.96 | 70.31 | 78.15 | 85.47 | 92.21 | 98.41 | 104.13 | 109.44 | 114.31 | 118.81 | 122.95 |
| 1-Tetradecene | $C_{14}H_{28}$ | 0 | 47.53 | 47.70 | 57.20 | 66.73 | 75.75 | 84.22 | 92.11 | 99.39 | 106.07 | 112.25 | 117.96 | 123.21 | 128.06 | 132.54 |
| 1-Pentadecene | $C_{15}H_{30}$ | 0 | 50.86 | 51.05 | 61.27 | 71.51 | 81.19 | 90.28 | 98.76 | 106.56 | 113.74 | 120.36 | 126.49 | 132.12 | 137.32 | 142.12 |
| 1-Hexadecene | $C_{16}H_{32}$ | 0 | 54.19 | 54.39 | 65.33 | 76.28 | 86.63 | 96.34 | 105.40 | 113.74 | 121.40 | 128.47 | 135.02 | 141.03 | 146.58 | 151.70 |
| 1-Heptadecene | $C_{17}H_{34}$ | 0 | 57.52 | 57.73 | 69.39 | 81.05 | 92.07 | 102.40 | 112.04 | 120.92 | 129.06 | 136.58 | 143.55 | 149.94 | 155.84 | 161.28 |
| 1-Octadecene | $C_{18}H_{36}$ | 0 | 60.85 | 61.08 | 73.46 | 85.83 | 97.51 | 108.46 | 118.69 | 128.09 | 136.73 | 144.69 | 152.08 | 158.85 | 165.10 | 170.86 |
| 1-Nonadecene | $C_{19}H_{38}$ | 0 | 64.18 | 64.42 | 77.52 | 90.60 | 102.95 | 114.53 | 125.33 | 135.27 | 144.39 | 152.81 | 160.60 | 167.75 | 174.35 | 180.45 |
| 1-Eicosene | $C_{20}H_{40}$ | 0 | 67.51 | 67.77 | 81.58 | 95.38 | 108.39 | 120.59 | 131.97 | 142.44 | 152.05 | 160.92 | 169.13 | 176.66 | 183.61 | 190.03 |
| Increment per $CH_2$ group, applicable beyond 1-hexene | | 0 | 3.330 | 3.344 | 4.063 | 4.774 | 5.439 | 6.062 | 6.643 | 7.176 | 7.663 | 8.112 | 8.528 | 8.908 | 9.258 | 9.582 |

## TABLE 8r (PART 1) – MONOOLEFINS, C$_2$ TO C$_5$

### HEAT CONTENT FUNCTION, $(H°-H°_0)/T$, FOR THE IDEAL GAS STATE, AT 0° TO 1500°K

December 31, 1944; March 31, 1945; October 31, 1945; April 30, 1946; December 31, 1952

| Compound (gas) | Formula | \multicolumn{15}{c}{Temperature in °K} |
|---|---|---|

Heat Content Function, $(H°-H°_0)/T$, in cal/deg mole

| Compound (gas) | Formula | 0 | 298.16 | 300 | 400 | 500 | 600 | 700 | 800 | 900 | 1000 | 1100 | 1200 | 1300 | 1400 | 1500 |
|---|---|---|---|---|---|---|---|---|---|---|---|---|---|---|---|---|
| Ethene (Ethylene) | C$_2$H$_4$ | 0 | 8.47 | 8.48 | 9.28 | 10.23 | 11.22 | 12.18 | 13.10 | 13.96 | 14.76 | 15.52 | 16.22 | 16.88 | 17.50 | 18.07 |
| Propene (Propylene) | C$_3$H$_6$ | 0 | 10.86 | 10.88 | 12.48 | 14.15 | 15.82 | 17.42 | 18.94 | 20.36 | 21.69 | 22.92 | 24.07 | 25.13 | 26.12 | 27.05 |
| 1-Butene | C$_4$H$_8$ | 0 | 13.79 | 13.83 | 16.21 | 18.68 | 21.08 | 23.35 | 25.46 | 27.43 | 29.25 | 30.95 | 32.51 | 33.96 | 35.31 | 36.56 |
| cis-2-Butene | " | 0 | 13.23 | 13.27 | 15.36 | 17.68 | 20.01 | 22.26 | 24.39 | 26.38 | 28.23 | 29.96 | 31.57 | 33.06 | 34.45 | 35.74 |
| trans-2-Butene | " | 0 | 14.05 | 14.10 | 16.46 | 18.84 | 21.16 | 23.37 | 25.43 | 27.38 | 29.19 | 30.87 | 32.43 | 33.88 | 35.22 | 36.47 |
| 2-Methylpropene (Isobutene) | " | 0 | 13.69 | 13.74 | 16.30 | 18.83 | 21.25 | 23.50 | 25.62 | 27.56 | 29.37 | 31.06 | 32.63 | 34.08 | 35.42 | 36.67 |
| 1-Pentene | C$_5$H$_{10}$ | 0 | 17.59 | 17.64 | 20.67 | 23.79 | 26.82 | 29.68 | 32.34 | 34.82 | 37.12 | 39.25 | 41.22 | 43.05 | 44.75 | 46.31 |
| cis-2-Pentene | " | 0 | 16.25 | 16.29 | 19.24 | 22.38 | 25.47 | 28.41 | 31.14 | 33.68 | 36.05 | 38.22 | 40.24 | 42.12 | 43.86 | 45.48 |
| trans-2-Pentene | " | 0 | 16.69 | 16.94 | 20.03 | 23.18 | 26.24 | 29.10 | 31.78 | 34.27 | 36.58 | 38.72 | 40.69 | 42.53 | 44.24 | 45.83 |
| 2-Methyl-1-butene | " | 0 | 16.77 | 16.82 | 20.20 | 23.53 | 26.69 | 29.63 | 32.34 | 34.83 | 37.15 | 39.30 | 41.27 | 43.11 | 44.82 | 46.39 |
| 3-Methyl-1-butene | " | 0 | 17.23 | 17.29 | 20.95 | 24.42 | 27.61 | 30.53 | 33.20 | 35.66 | 37.94 | 40.04 | 41.99 | 43.79 | 45.44 | 46.97 |
| 2-Methyl-2-butene | " | 0 | 16.21 | 16.26 | 19.34 | 22.50 | 25.53 | 28.43 | 31.14 | 33.66 | 36.00 | 38.17 | 40.18 | 42.05 | 43.79 | 45.40 |

TABLE 8r (PART 2) - MONOOLEFINS, C$_6$

HEAT CONTENT FUNCTION, $(H°-H°_0)/T$, FOR THE IDEAL GAS STATE, AT 0° TO 1500°K

April 30, 1945; October 31, 1945; December 31, 1952

Temperature in °K

Heat Content Function, $(H°-H°_0)/T$, in cal/deg mole

| Compound (gas) | Formula | 0 | 298.16 | 300 | 400 | 500 | 600 | 700 | 800 | 900 | 1000 | 1100 | 1200 | 1300 | 1400 | 1500 |
|---|---|---|---|---|---|---|---|---|---|---|---|---|---|---|---|---|
| 1-Hexene | C$_6$H$_{12}$ | 0 | 20.89 | 20.95 | 24.70 | 28.54 | 32.24 | 35.72 | 38.97 | 41.98 | 44.77 | 47.35 | 49.74 | 51.95 | 54.00 | 55.88 |
| cis-2-Hexene | " | 0 | 20.05 | 20.11 | 23.7 | 27.5 | 31.2 | 34.7 | 38.0 | 41.1 | 43.9 | | | | | |
| trans-2-Hexene | " | 0 | 20.69 | 20.75 | 24.5 | 28.3 | 32.0 | 35.4 | 38.7 | 41.6 | 44.4 | | | | | |
| cis-3-Hexene | " | 0 | 19.29 | 19.36 | 23.1 | 27.0 | 30.8 | 34.4 | 37.7 | 40.8 | 45.1 | | | | | |
| trans-3-Hexene | " | 0 | 20.13 | 20.19 | 24.2 | 28.1 | 31.9 | 35.5 | 38.7 | 41.7 | 44.5 | | | | | |
| 2-Methyl-1-pentene | " | 0 | 20.57 | 20.63 | 24.7 | 28.6 | 32.4 | 36.0 | 39.2 | 42.2 | 45.0 | | | | | |
| 3-Methyl-1-pentene | " | 0 | 20.50 | 20.57 | 25.3 | 30.0 | 34.4 | 38.5 | 42.2 | 45.6 | 48.8 | | | | | |
| 4-Methyl-1-pentene | " | 0 | 18.39 | 18.45 | 22.4 | 26.4 | 30.3 | 34.0 | 37.3 | 40.4 | 43.2 | | | | | |
| 2-Methyl-2-pentene | " | 0 | 19.05 | 19.11 | 23.0 | 27.0 | 30.8 | 34.4 | 37.8 | 40.8 | 43.7 | | | | | |
| 3-Methyl-cis-2-pentene | " | 0 | 19.05 | 19.11 | 23.0 | 27.0 | 30.8 | 34.4 | 37.8 | 40.8 | 43.7 | | | | | |
| 3-Methyl-trans-2-pentene | " | 0 | 19.05 | 19.11 | 23.0 | 27.0 | 30.8 | 34.4 | 37.8 | 40.8 | 43.7 | | | | | |
| 4-Methyl-cis-2-pentene | " | 0 | 19.51 | 19.58 | 23.8 | 27.9 | 31.8 | 35.3 | 38.6 | 41.6 | 44.5 | | | | | |
| 4-Methyl-trans-2-pentene | " | 0 | 20.33 | 20.40 | 24.8 | 28.9 | 32.8 | 36.3 | 39.5 | 42.5 | 45.3 | | | | | |
| 2-Ethyl-1-butene | " | 0 | 19.81 | 19.87 | 24.0 | 28.1 | 32.0 | 35.6 | 38.9 | 42.0 | 44.8 | | | | | |
| 2,3-Dimethyl-1-butene | " | 0 | 20.03 | 20.10 | 24.7 | 29.0 | 33.0 | 36.6 | 39.8 | 42.8 | 45.6 | | | | | |
| 3,3-Dimethyl-1-butene | " | 0 | 17.53 | 17.59 | 21.9 | 26.2 | 30.1 | 33.8 | 37.3 | 40.3 | 43.2 | | | | | |
| 2,3-Dimethyl-2-butene | " | 0 | 19.11 | 19.16 | 23.0 | 26.9 | 30.7 | 34.2 | 37.5 | 40.5 | 43.4 | | | | | |

TABLE 11r - (Part 1) - DIOLEFINS, $C_3$ to $C_5$

HEAT CONTENT FUNCTION, $(H^o - H^o_0)/T$, FOR THE IDEAL GAS STATE, AT 0° TO 1500°K

September 30, 1947; April 30, 1948

| Compound (gas) | Formula | Temperature in °K | | | | | | | | | | | | | | |
|---|---|---|---|---|---|---|---|---|---|---|---|---|---|---|---|---|
| | | 0 | 298.16 | 300 | 400 | 500 | 600 | 700 | 800 | 900 | 1000 | 1100 | 1200 | 1300 | 1400 | 1500 |
| | | Heat Content Function , $(H^o - H^o_0)/T$, in cal/deg mole | | | | | | | | | | | | | | |
| Propadiene (Allene) | $C_3H_4$ | 0 | 10.12 | 10.15 | 11.54 | 12.94 | 14.28 | 15.51 | 16.66 | 17.71 | 18.68 | 19.57 | 20.40 | 21.17 | 21.88 | 22.54 |
| 1,2-Butadiene | $C_4H_6$ | 0 | 12.92 | 12.96 | 15.07 | 17.16 | 19.15 | 21.01 | 22.74 | 24.34 | 25.82 | 27.18 | 28.44 | 29.62 | 30.70 | 31.70 |
| 1,3-Butadiene | " | 0 | 12.16 | 12.20 | 14.59 | 16.97 | 19.18 | 21.19 | 23.01 | 24.66 | 26.16 | 27.54 | 28.80 | 29.96 | 31.03 | 32.02 |
| 1,2-Pentadiene | $C_5H_8$ | 0 | 16.2 | 16.3 | 19.3 | 22.3 | 25.0 | 27.6 | 29.9 | 32.0 | 34.0 | 35.8 | 37.4 | 39.0 | 40.4 | 41.7 |
| cis-1,3-Pentadiene (cis-Piperylene) | " | 0 | 14.5 | 14.6 | 17.5 | 20.5 | 23.4 | 26.0 | 28.5 | 30.7 | 32.7 | 34.6 | 36.7 | 37.9 | 39.4 | 40.7 |
| trans-1,3-Pentadiene (trans-Piperylene) | " | 0 | 15.3 | 15.4 | 18.6 | 21.7 | 24.5 | 27.1 | 29.5 | 31.7 | 33.7 | 35.5 | 37.2 | 38.7 | 40.1 | 41.4 |
| 1,4-Pentadiene | " | 0 | 16.5 | 16.6 | 19.6 | 22.4 | 25.2 | 27.7 | 29.9 | 32.0 | 34.0 | 35.8 | 37.4 | 39.0 | 40.4 | 41.7 |
| 2,3-Pentadiene | " | 0 | 15.7 | 15.8 | 18.6 | 21.4 | 24.0 | 26.5 | 28.8 | 31.0 | 33.0 | 34.8 | 36.5 | 38.1 | 39.5 | 40.9 |
| 3-Methyl-1,2-butadiene | " | 0 | 15.8 | 15.8 | 18.9 | 21.8 | 24.6 | 27.1 | 29.4 | 31.5 | 33.5 | 35.3 | 37.0 | 38.6 | 40.0 | 41.3 |
| 2-Methyl-1,3-butadiene (Isoprene) | " | 0 | 15.0 | 15.1 | 18.4 | 21.7 | 24.6 | 27.3 | 29.7 | 31.9 | 33.8 | 35.7 | 37.4 | 38.9 | 40.3 | 41.6 |

TABLE 18r – ALKYL CYCLOPENTENES, $C_5$ TO $C_7$

HEAT CONTENT FUNCTION, $(H^\circ - H^\circ_0)/T$, FOR THE IDEAL GAS STATE, AT $0^\circ$ TO $1500^\circ K$

December 31, 1952

Temperature in °K

Heat Content Function, $(H^\circ - H^\circ_0)/T$, in cal/deg mole

| Compound (gas) | Formula | 0 | 298.16 | 300 | 400 | 500 | 600 | 700 | 800 | 900 | 1000 | 1100 | 1200 | 1300 | 1400 | 1500 |
|---|---|---|---|---|---|---|---|---|---|---|---|---|---|---|---|---|
| Cyclopentene | $C_5H_8$ | 0 | 11.61 | 11.65 | 14.12 | 16.98 | 19.90 | 22.71 | 25.36 | 27.82 | 30.09 | 32.19 | 34.13 | 35.92 | 37.57 | 39.10 |
| 1,-Methylcyclopentene | $C_6H_{10}$ | 0 | 14.9 | 15.0 | 18.3 | 22.0 | 25.6 | 29.0 | 32.2 | 35.2 | 37.9 | 40.5 | 42.8 | 44.9 | 46.9 | 48.8 |
| 3-Methylcyclopentene | " | 0 | 14.6 | 14.7 | 18.1 | 21.8 | 25.5 | 29.0 | 32.2 | 35.2 | 38.0 | 40.5 | 42.8 | 45.0 | 47.0 | 48.8 |
| 4-Methylcyclopentene | " | 0 | 14.5 | 14.6 | 18.0 | 21.7 | 25.4 | 28.9 | 32.1 | 35.1 | 37.9 | 40.5 | 42.8 | 44.9 | 46.9 | 48.7 |
| 1-Ethylcyclopentene | $C_7H_{12}$ | | | | | | | | | | | | | | | |
| 3-Ethylcyclopentene | " | | | | | | | | | | | | | | | |
| 4-Ethylcyclopentene | " | | | | | | | | | | | | | | | |
| 1,2-Dimethylcyclopentene | " | 0 | 18.2 | 18.3 | 22.5 | 27.0 | 31.3 | 35.3 | 39.1 | 42.6 | 45.8 | 48.8 | 51.5 | 54.0 | 56.3 | 58.4 |
| 1,3-Dimethylcyclopentene | " | 0 | 17.9 | 18.0 | 22.3 | 26.8 | 31.2 | 35.3 | 39.1 | 42.6 | 45.8 | 48.8 | 51.6 | 54.1 | 56.4 | 58.5 |
| 1,4-Dimethylcyclopentene | " | 0 | 17.8 | 18.0 | 22.2 | 26.7 | 31.1 | 35.2 | 39.0 | 42.5 | 45.7 | 48.7 | 51.5 | 54.0 | 56.3 | 58.4 |
| 1,5-Dimethylcyclopentene | " | 0 | 17.9 | 18.0 | 22.3 | 26.8 | 31.1 | 35.2 | 39.1 | 42.6 | 45.8 | 48.8 | 51.5 | 54.0 | 56.3 | 58.5 |
| 3,3-Dimethylcyclopentene | " | 0 | 17.0 | 17.1 | 21.5 | 26.2 | 30.7 | 35.0 | 39.0 | 42.7 | 46.0 | 49.1 | 52.0 | 54.6 | 57.0 | 59.1 |
| 3,cis-4-Dimethylcyclopentene | " | 0 | 17.4 | 17.5 | 21.9 | 26.5 | 31.0 | 35.2 | 39.1 | 42.7 | 46.0 | 49.0 | 51.7 | 54.2 | 56.5 | 58.7 |
| 3,trans-4-Dimethylcyclopentene | " | 0 | 17.6 | 17.7 | 22.1 | 26.7 | 31.1 | 35.2 | 39.0 | 42.6 | 45.9 | 48.9 | 51.6 | 54.1 | 56.4 | 58.6 |
| 3,cis-5-Dimethylcyclopentene | " | 0 | 17.6 | 17.7 | 22.1 | 26.7 | 31.1 | 35.2 | 39.0 | 42.6 | 45.9 | 48.9 | 51.6 | 54.1 | 56.4 | 58.6 |
| 3,trans-5-Dimethylcyclopentene | " | 0 | 17.6 | 17.7 | 22.1 | 26.7 | 31.1 | 35.2 | 39.0 | 42.6 | 45.9 | 48.9 | 51.6 | 54.1 | 56.4 | 58.6 |
| 4,4-Dimethylcyclopentene | " | | | | | | | | | | | | | | | |

TABLE 19r – ALKYL CYCLOHEXENES, $C_6$ TO $C_8$

HEAT CONTENT FUNCTION, $(H°-H°_0)/T$, FOR THE IDEAL GAS STATE, AT 0° TO 1500°K

December 31, 1952

| Compound (gas) | Formula | Temperature in °K | | | | | | | | | | | | | | |
| --- | --- | --- | --- | --- | --- | --- | --- | --- | --- | --- | --- | --- | --- | --- | --- | --- |
| | | 0 | 298.16 | 300 | 400 | 500 | 600 | 700 | 800 | 900 | 1000 | 1100 | 1200 | 1300 | 1400 | 1500 |
| | | Heat Content Function, $(H°-H°_0)/T$, in cal/deg mole | | | | | | | | | | | | | | |
| Cyclohexene | $C_6H_{10}$ | 0 | 13.98 | 14.05 | 18.04 | 22.20 | 26.20 | 29.93 | 33.35 | 36.47 | 39.33 | 41.94 | 44.34 | 46.53 | 48.55 | 50.42 |
| 1-Methylcyclohexene | $C_7H_{12}$ | | | | | | | | | | | | | | | |
| 3-Methylcyclohexene | " | | | | | | | | | | | | | | | |
| 4-Methylcyclohexene | " | | | | | | | | | | | | | | | |
| 1-Ethylcyclohexene | $C_8H_{14}$ | | | | | | | | | | | | | | | |
| 3-Ethylcyclohexene | " | | | | | | | | | | | | | | | |
| 4-Ethylcyclohexene | " | | | | | | | | | | | | | | | |
| 1,2-Dimethylcyclohexene | " | | | | | | | | | | | | | | | |
| 1,3-Dimethylcyclohexene | " | | | | | | | | | | | | | | | |
| 1,4-Dimethylcyclohexene | " | | | | | | | | | | | | | | | |
| 1,5-Dimethylcyclohexene | " | | | | | | | | | | | | | | | |
| 1,6-Dimethylcyclohexene | " | | | | | | | | | | | | | | | |
| 3,3-Dimethylcyclohexene | " | | | | | | | | | | | | | | | |
| 3,cis-4-Dimethylcyclohexene | " | | | | | | | | | | | | | | | |
| 3,trans-4-Dimethylcyclohexene | " | | | | | | | | | | | | | | | |
| 3,cis-5-Dimethylcyclohexene | " | | | | | | | | | | | | | | | |
| 3,trans-5-Dimethylcyclohexene | " | | | | | | | | | | | | | | | |
| 3,cis-6-Dimethylcyclohexene | " | | | | | | | | | | | | | | | |
| 3,trans-6-Dimethylcyclohexene | " | | | | | | | | | | | | | | | |
| 4,4-Dimethylcyclohexene | " | | | | | | | | | | | | | | | |
| 4,cis-5-Dimethylcyclohexene | " | | | | | | | | | | | | | | | |
| 4,trans-5-Dimethylcyclohexene | " | | | | | | | | | | | | | | | |

### TABLE 25r (PART 1) — NORMAL ACETYLENES (1-ALKYNES), $C_2$ TO $C_{20}$
### HEAT CONTENT FUNCTION, $(H°-H°_0)/T$, FOR THE IDEAL GAS STATE, AT 0° TO 1500°K

February 28, 1946; December 31, 1952

| Compound (gas) | Formula | Temperature in °K | | | | | | | | | | | | | | |
| --- | --- | --- | --- | --- | --- | --- | --- | --- | --- | --- | --- | --- | --- | --- | --- | --- |
| | | 0 | 298.16 | 300 | 400 | 500 | 600 | 700 | 800 | 900 | 1000 | 1100 | 1200 | 1300 | 1400 | 1500 |
| | | Heat Content Function, $(H°-H°_0)/T$, in cal/deg mole | | | | | | | | | | | | | | |
| Ethyne (Acetylene) | $C_2H_2$ | 0 | 8.021 | 8.036 | 8.853 | 9.582 | 10.212 | 10.762 | 11.249 | 11.689 | 12.090 | 12.460 | 12.802 | 13.119 | 13.416 | 13.694 |
| Propyne (Methylacetylene) | $C_3H_4$ | 0 | 10.41 | 10.44 | 11.82 | 13.17 | 14.44 | 15.62 | 16.72 | 17.73 | 18.67 | 19.54 | 20.35 | 21.10 | 21.80 | 22.45 |
| 1-Butyne (Ethylacetylene) | $C_4H_6$ | 0 | 12.81 | 12.83 | 15.08 | 17.22 | 19.22 | 21.09 | 22.80 | 24.38 | 25.83 | 27.18 | 28.42 | 29.58 | 30.65 | 31.64 |
| 1-Pentyne | $C_5H_8$ | 0 | 16.61 | 16.64 | 19.54 | 22.33 | 24.96 | 27.42 | 29.68 | 31.77 | 33.70 | 35.48 | 37.13 | 38.67 | 40.09 | 41.39 |
| 1-Hexyne | $C_6H_{10}$ | 0 | 19.94 | 19.98 | 23.60 | 27.10 | 30.40 | 33.48 | 36.32 | 38.95 | 41.36 | 43.59 | 45.66 | 47.58 | 49.35 | 50.97 |
| 1-Heptyne | $C_7H_{12}$ | 0 | 23.27 | 23.33 | 27.67 | 31.88 | 35.84 | 39.54 | 42.97 | 46.12 | 49.03 | 51.70 | 54.19 | 56.49 | 58.61 | 60.55 |
| 1-Octyne | $C_8H_{14}$ | 0 | 26.60 | 26.67 | 31.73 | 36.65 | 41.28 | 45.61 | 49.61 | 53.30 | 56.69 | 59.82 | 62.71 | 65.39 | 67.86 | 70.14 |
| 1-Nonyne | $C_9H_{16}$ | 0 | 29.93 | 30.02 | 35.79 | 41.43 | 46.72 | 51.67 | 56.25 | 60.47 | 64.35 | 67.93 | 71.24 | 74.30 | 77.12 | 79.72 |
| 1-Decyne | $C_{10}H_{18}$ | 0 | 33.26 | 33.36 | 39.86 | 46.20 | 52.16 | 57.73 | 62.90 | 67.65 | 72.02 | 76.04 | 79.77 | 83.21 | 86.38 | 89.30 |
| 1-Undecyne | $C_{11}H_{20}$ | 0 | 36.59 | 36.70 | 43.92 | 50.97 | 57.59 | 63.79 | 69.54 | 74.83 | 79.68 | 84.15 | 88.30 | 92.12 | 95.64 | 98.88 |
| 1-Dodecyne | $C_{12}H_{22}$ | 0 | 39.92 | 40.05 | 47.98 | 55.75 | 63.03 | 69.85 | 76.18 | 82.00 | 87.34 | 92.26 | 96.83 | 101.03 | 104.90 | 108.46 |
| 1-Tridecyne | $C_{13}H_{24}$ | 0 | 43.25 | 43.39 | 52.04 | 60.52 | 68.47 | 75.92 | 82.82 | 89.18 | 95.00 | 100.38 | 105.35 | 109.93 | 114.15 | 118.05 |
| 1-Tetradecyne | $C_{14}H_{26}$ | 0 | 46.58 | 46.74 | 56.11 | 65.30 | 73.91 | 81.98 | 89.47 | 96.35 | 102.67 | 108.49 | 113.88 | 118.84 | 123.41 | 127.63 |
| 1-Pentadecyne | $C_{15}H_{28}$ | 0 | 49.91 | 50.08 | 60.17 | 70.07 | 79.35 | 88.04 | 96.11 | 103.53 | 110.33 | 116.60 | 122.41 | 127.75 | 132.67 | 137.21 |
| 1-Hexadecyne | $C_{16}H_{30}$ | 0 | 53.24 | 53.42 | 64.23 | 74.84 | 84.79 | 94.10 | 102.75 | 110.71 | 117.99 | 124.71 | 130.94 | 136.66 | 141.93 | 146.79 |
| 1-Heptadecyne | $C_{17}H_{32}$ | 0 | 56.57 | 56.77 | 68.30 | 79.62 | 90.23 | 100.16 | 109.40 | 117.88 | 125.66 | 132.82 | 139.47 | 145.57 | 151.19 | 156.37 |
| 1-Octadecyne | $C_{18}H_{34}$ | 0 | 59.90 | 60.11 | 72.36 | 84.39 | 95.67 | 106.23 | 116.04 | 125.06 | 133.32 | 140.94 | 147.99 | 154.47 | 160.44 | 165.96 |
| 1-Nonadecyne | $C_{19}H_{36}$ | 0 | 63.23 | 63.46 | 76.42 | 89.17 | 101.11 | 112.29 | 122.68 | 132.23 | 140.98 | 149.05 | 156.52 | 163.38 | 169.70 | 175.54 |
| 1-Eicosyne | $C_{20}H_{38}$ | 0 | 66.56 | 66.80 | 80.48 | 93.94 | 106.55 | 118.35 | 129.32 | 139.41 | 148.64 | 157.16 | 165.05 | 172.29 | 178.96 | 185.12 |
| Increment per $CH_2$ group, applicable beyond 1-pentyne | | 0 | 3.330 | 3.344 | 4.063 | 4.774 | 5.439 | 6.062 | 6.643 | 7.176 | 7.663 | 8.112 | 8.528 | 8.908 | 9.258 | 9.582 |

TABLE 12r – ACETYLENES, $C_2$ TO $C_5$

HEAT CONTENT FUNCTION, $(H°-H°_0)/T$, FOR THE IDEAL GAS STATE, AT 0° TO 1500°K

April 30, 1945

| Compound (gas) | Formula | Temperature in °K | | | | | | | | | | | | | | |
| --- | --- | --- | --- | --- | --- | --- | --- | --- | --- | --- | --- | --- | --- | --- | --- | --- |
| | | 0 | 298.16 | 300 | 400 | 500 | 600 | 700 | 800 | 900 | 1000 | 1100 | 1200 | 1300 | 1400 | 1500 |
| | | Heat Content Function, $(H°-H°_0)/T$, in cal/deg mole | | | | | | | | | | | | | | |
| Ethyne (Acetylene) | $C_2H_2$ | 0 | 8.021 | 8.036 | 8.853 | 9.582 | 10.212 | 10.762 | 11.249 | 11.689 | 12.090 | 12.460 | 12.802 | 13.119 | 13.416 | 13.694 |
| Propyne (Methylacetylene) | $C_3H_4$ | 0 | 10.41 | 10.44 | 11.82 | 13.17 | 14.44 | 15.62 | 16.72 | 17.73 | 18.67 | 19.54 | 20.35 | 21.10 | 21.80 | 22.45 |
| 1-Butyne (Ethylacetylene) | $C_4H_6$ | 0 | 12.81 | 12.83 | 15.08 | 17.22 | 19.22 | 21.09 | 22.80 | 24.38 | 25.83 | 27.18 | 28.42 | 29.58 | 30.65 | 31.64 |
| 2-Butyne (Dimethylacetylene) | " | 0 | 13.28 | 13.32 | 15.15 | 17.03 | 18.86 | 20.62 | 22.28 | 23.84 | 25.29 | 26.64 | 27.90 | 29.06 | 30.15 | 31.16 |
| 1-Pentyne | $C_5H_8$ | 0 | 16.61 | 16.64 | 19.6 | 22.4 | 25.1 | 27.5 | 29.8 | 31.8 | 33.7 | 35.5 | 37.1 | 38.7 | 40.1 | 41.4 |
| 2-Pentyne | " | 0 | 15.68 | 15.72 | 18.4 | 21.1 | 23.6 | 26.1 | 28.4 | 30.5 | 32.4 | 34.3 | 36.0 | 37.5 | 39.0 | 40.4 |
| 3-Methyl-1-butyne | " | 0 | 15.37 | 15.40 | 18.6 | 21.6 | 24.5 | 27.0 | 29.4 | 31.5 | 33.5 | 35.3 | 37.0 | 38.5 | 39.9 | 41.2 |

TABLE 21r (PART 1) – NORMAL ALKYL BENZENES, C6 TO C22

HEAT CONTENT FUNCTION, $(H^o - H^o_0)/T$, FOR THE IDEAL GAS STATE, AT $0^o$ TO $1500^o K$

November 30, 1945; December 31, 1952

| Compound (gas) | Formula | 0 | 298.16 | 300 | 400 | 500 | 600 | 700 | 800 | 900 | 1000 | 1100 | 1200 | 1300 | 1400 | 1500 |
|---|---|---|---|---|---|---|---|---|---|---|---|---|---|---|---|---|
| | | | | | | Heat Content Function, $(H^o - H^o_0)/T$, in cal/deg mole | | | | | | | | | | |
| Benzene | $C_6H_6$ | 0 | 11.41 | 11.46 | 14.41 | 17.50 | 20.48 | 23.24 | 25.76 | 28.07 | 30.16 | 32.07 | 33.82 | 35.42 | 36.89 | 38.24 |
| Methylbenzene (Toluene) | $C_7H_8$ | 0 | 14.44 | 14.51 | 18.17 | 21.94 | 25.56 | 28.92 | 32.03 | 34.86 | 37.45 | 39.82 | 41.99 | 43.98 | 45.81 | 47.50 |
| Ethylbenzene | $C_8H_{10}$ | 0 | 17.89 | 17.97 | 22.44 | 26.99 | 31.33 | 35.35 | 39.03 | 42.38 | 45.45 | 48.25 | 50.82 | 53.18 | 55.34 | 57.35 |
| n-Propylbenzene | $C_9H_{12}$ | 0 | 21.69 | 21.78 | 26.90 | 31.45 | 37.07 | 41.68 | 45.91 | 49.77 | 53.32 | 56.55 | 59.23 | 62.27 | 64.78 | 67.10 |
| n-Butylbenzene | $C_{10}H_{14}$ | 0 | 24.99 | 25.09 | 30.93 | 36.85 | 42.49 | 47.72 | 52.54 | 56.93 | 60.97 | 64.65 | 68.05 | 71.17 | 74.03 | 76.67 |
| n-Pentylbenzene | $C_{11}H_{16}$ | 0 | 28.32 | 28.44 | 35.00 | 41.63 | 47.93 | 53.79 | 59.18 | 64.11 | 68.63 | 72.77 | 76.58 | 80.08 | 83.29 | 86.26 |
| n-Hexylbenzene | $C_{12}H_{18}$ | 0 | 31.65 | 31.78 | 39.06 | 46.40 | 53.37 | 59.85 | 65.82 | 71.29 | 76.29 | 80.88 | 85.11 | 88.99 | 92.55 | 95.84 |
| n-Heptylbenzene | $C_{13}H_{20}$ | 0 | 34.98 | 35.13 | 43.13 | 51.18 | 58.81 | 65.91 | 72.47 | 78.46 | 83.96 | 88.99 | 93.64 | 97.90 | 101.81 | 105.42 |
| n-Octylbenzene | $C_{14}H_{22}$ | 0 | 38.31 | 38.47 | 47.19 | 55.95 | 64.25 | 71.98 | 79.11 | 85.64 | 91.62 | 97.11 | 102.16 | 106.80 | 111.06 | 115.01 |
| n-Nonylbenzene | $C_{15}H_{24}$ | 0 | 41.64 | 41.82 | 51.25 | 60.73 | 69.69 | 78.04 | 85.75 | 92.81 | 99.28 | 105.22 | 110.69 | 115.71 | 120.32 | 124.59 |
| n-Decylbenzene | $C_{16}H_{26}$ | 0 | 44.97 | 45.16 | 55.32 | 65.50 | 75.12 | 84.10 | 92.40 | 99.99 | 106.94 | 113.33 | 119.22 | 124.62 | 129.58 | 134.17 |
| n-Undecylbenzene | $C_{17}H_{28}$ | 0 | 48.30 | 48.50 | 59.38 | 70.27 | 80.56 | 90.16 | 99.04 | 107.17 | 114.61 | 121.44 | 127.75 | 133.53 | 138.84 | 143.75 |
| n-Dodecylbenzene | $C_{18}H_{30}$ | 0 | 51.63 | 51.85 | 63.44 | 75.05 | 86.00 | 96.22 | 105.68 | 114.34 | 122.27 | 129.55 | 136.28 | 142.44 | 148.10 | 153.33 |
| n-Tridecylbenzene | $C_{19}H_{32}$ | 0 | 54.96 | 55.19 | 67.50 | 79.82 | 91.44 | 102.29 | 112.32 | 121.52 | 129.93 | 137.67 | 144.80 | 151.34 | 157.35 | 162.92 |
| n-Tetradecylbenzene | $C_{20}H_{34}$ | 0 | 58.29 | 58.54 | 71.57 | 84.60 | 96.88 | 108.35 | 118.97 | 128.69 | 137.60 | 145.78 | 153.33 | 160.25 | 166.61 | 172.50 |
| n-Pentadecylbenzene | $C_{21}H_{36}$ | 0 | 61.62 | 61.88 | 75.63 | 89.37 | 102.32 | 114.41 | 125.61 | 135.87 | 145.26 | 153.89 | 161.86 | 169.16 | 175.87 | 182.08 |
| n-Hexadecylbenzene | $C_{22}H_{38}$ | 0 | 64.95 | 65.22 | 79.69 | 94.14 | 107.76 | 120.47 | 132.25 | 143.05 | 152.92 | 162.00 | 170.39 | 178.07 | 185.13 | 191.66 |
| Increment per $CH_2$ group, applicable beyond n-pentylbenzene | | 0 | 3.330 | 3.344 | 4.063 | 4.774 | 5.439 | 6.062 | 6.643 | 7.176 | 7.663 | 8.112 | 8.528 | 8.908 | 9.258 | 9.582 |

Temperature in °K

TABLE 5r – ALKYL BENZENES, $C_6$ TO $C_9$

HEAT CONTENT FUNCTION, $(H^o-H^o_0)/T$, FOR THE IDEAL GAS STATE, AT 0° TO 1500°K

November 30, 1945

| Compound (gas) | Formula | Temperature in °K | | | | | | | | | | | | | | |
|---|---|---|---|---|---|---|---|---|---|---|---|---|---|---|---|---|
| | | 0 | 298.16 | 300 | 400 | 500 | 600 | 700 | 800 | 900 | 1000 | 1100 | 1200 | 1300 | 1400 | 1500 |
| | | Heat Content Function, $(H^o-H^o_0)/T$, in cal/deg.mole | | | | | | | | | | | | | | |
| Benzene | $C_6H_6$ | 0 | 11.41 | 11.46 | 14.41 | 17.50 | 20.48 | 23.24 | 25.76 | 28.07 | 30.16 | 32.07 | 33.82 | 35.42 | 36.89 | 38.24 |
| Methylbenzene (Toluene) | $C_7H_8$ | 0 | 14.44 | 14.51 | 18.17 | 21.94 | 25.56 | 28.92 | 32.03 | 34.86 | 37.45 | 39.82 | 41.99 | 43.98 | 45.81 | 47.50 |
| Ethylbenzene | $C_8H_{10}$ | 0 | 17.89 | 17.97 | 22.44 | 26.99 | 31.33 | 35.35 | 39.03 | 42.38 | 45.45 | 48.25 | 50.82 | 53.18 | 55.34 | 57.35 |
| 1,2-Dimethylbenzene (o-Xylene) | " | 0 | 18.70 | 18.78 | 23.23 | 27.61 | 31.78 | 35.66 | 39.23 | 42.52 | 45.53 | 48.30 | 50.84 | 53.17 | 55.32 | 57.31 |
| 1,3-Dimethylbenzene (m-Xylene) | " | 0 | 17.86 | 17.94 | 22.31 | 26.72 | 30.94 | 34.88 | 38.52 | 41.86 | 44.93 | 47.74 | 50.32 | 52.69 | 54.87 | 56.88 |
| 1,4-Dimethylbenzene (n-Xylene) | " | 0 | 17.97 | 18.04 | 22.32 | 26.66 | 30.83 | 34.74 | 38.36 | 41.69 | 44.76 | 47.56 | 50.14 | 52.52 | 54.70 | 56.72 |
| n-Propylbenzene | $C_9H_{12}$ | 0 | 21.69 | 21.78 | 27.0 | 32.2 | 37.2 | 41.8 | 46.0 | 49.8 | 53.4 | 56.6 | 59.5 | 62.3 | 64.8 | 67.1 |
| Isopropylbenzene | " | 0 | 20.45 | 20.54 | 26.0 | 31.4 | 36.6 | 41.3 | 45.6 | 49.5 | 53.1 | 56.4 | 59.4 | 62.1 | 64.6 | 67.0 |
| 1-Methyl-2-ethylbenzene | " | 0 | 22.15 | 22.25 | 27.5 | 32.7 | 37.6 | 42.1 | 46.2 | 50.0 | 53.5 | 56.7 | 59.7 | 62.4 | 64.9 | 67.2 |
| 1-Methyl-3-ethylbenzene | " | 0 | 21.31 | 21.40 | 26.6 | 31.8 | 36.7 | 41.3 | 45.5 | 49.4 | 52.9 | 56.2 | 59.2 | 61.9 | 64.4 | 66.7 |
| 1-Methyl-4-ethylbenzene | " | 0 | 21.42 | 21.51 | 26.6 | 31.7 | 36.6 | 41.2 | 45.4 | 49.2 | 52.8 | 56.0 | 59.0 | 61.7 | 64.2 | 66.6 |
| 1,2,3-Trimethylbenzene | " | 0 | 22.10 | 22.19 | 27.0 | 32.0 | 36.6 | 41.1 | 45.2 | 48.9 | 52.4 | 55.6 | 58.6 | 61.3 | 63.9 | 66.2 |
| 1,2,4-Trimethylbenzene | " | 0 | 22.17 | 22.26 | 27.1 | 32.1 | 36.8 | 41.2 | 45.3 | 49.1 | 52.6 | 55.8 | 58.7 | 61.5 | 64.0 | 66.3 |
| 1,3,5-Trimethylbenzene | " | 0 | 21.22 | 21.31 | 26.21 | 31.23 | 36.04 | 40.55 | 44.74 | 48.59 | 52.13 | 55.39 | 58.39 | 61.15 | 63.70 | 66.05 |

TABLE 13r — STYRENES, $C_8$ and $C_9$

HEAT CONTENT FUNCTION, $(H^o - H_0^o)/T$, FOR THE IDEAL GAS STATE, AT $0^o$ TO $1500^o K$

September 30, 1947

| Compound (gas) | Formula | Temperature in $^oK$ | | | | | | | | | | | | | | |
|---|---|---|---|---|---|---|---|---|---|---|---|---|---|---|---|---|
| | | 0 | 298.16 | 300 | 400 | 500 | 600 | 700 | 800 | 900 | 1000 | 1100 | 1200 | 1300 | 1400 | 1500 |
| | | Heat Content Function, $(H^o - H_0^o)/T$, in cal/deg mole | | | | | | | | | | | | | | |
| Ethenylbenzene (Styrene; Vinylbenzene; Phenylethylene) | $C_8H_8$ | 0 | 16.72 | 16.79 | 21.07 | 25.32 | 29.28 | 32.92 | 36.22 | 39.22 | 41.95 | 44.44 | 46.70 | 48.77 | 50.67 | 52.42 |
| Isopropenylbenzene ($\alpha$-Methylstyrene; Phenylethylene) | $C_9H_{10}$ | 0 | 20.3 | 20.3 | 25.2 | 30.0 | 34.6 | 38.8 | 42.6 | 46.1 | 49.3 | 52.2 | 54.9 | 57.3 | 59.6 | 61.6 |
| cis-1-Propenylbenzene (cis-$\beta$-Methylstyrene; cis-1-Phenyl-1-propene) | " | 0 | 20.3 | 20.3 | 25.2 | 30.0 | 34.6 | 38.8 | 42.6 | 46.1 | 49.3 | 52.2 | 54.9 | 57.3 | 59.6 | 61.6 |
| trans-1-Propenylbenzene (trans-$\beta$-Methylstyrene; trans-1-Phenyl-1-propene) | " | 0 | 19.9 | 20.0 | 25.1 | 30.0 | 34.6 | 38.9 | 42.7 | 46.2 | 49.5 | 52.4 | 55.1 | 57.5 | 59.8 | 61.8 |
| 1-Methyl-2-ethenylbenzene (o-Methylstyrene) | " | 0 | 20.3 | 20.3 | 25.2 | 30.0 | 34.6 | 38.8 | 42.6 | 46.1 | 49.3 | 52.2 | 54.9 | 57.3 | 59.6 | 61.6 |
| 1-Methyl-3-ethenylbenzene (m-Methylstyrene) | " | 0 | 20.3 | 20.3 | 25.2 | 30.0 | 34.6 | 38.8 | 42.6 | 46.1 | 49.3 | 52.2 | 54.9 | 57.3 | 59.6 | 61.6 |
| 1-Methyl-4-ethenylbenzene (p-Methylstyrene) | " | 0 | 20.3 | 20.3 | 25.2 | 30.0 | 34.6 | 38.8 | 42.6 | 46.1 | 49.3 | 52.2 | 54.9 | 57.3 | 59.6 | 61.6 |

512

Table 00s — O, H, N, C

FREE ENERGY FUNCTION, $(F^\circ-H^\circ_0)/T$, FOR THE IDEAL GAS STATE. AT 0° TO 5000°K

June 30, 1946; August 31, 1949

Free Energy Function, $(F^\circ-H^\circ_0)/T$, in cal/deg mole

| Compound (gas, monatomic) | Formula | Temperature in °K | | | | | | | | | | | | | | |
|---|---|---|---|---|---|---|---|---|---|---|---|---|---|---|---|---|
| | | 0 | 298.16 | 300 | 400 | 500 | 600 | 700 | 800 | 900 | 1000 | 1100 | 1200 | 1300 | 1400 | 1500 |
| Oxygen | O | 0 | -33.0779 | -33.1109 | -34.6543 | -35.8401 | -36.8012 | -37.6086 | -38.3041 | -38.9151 | -39.4595 | -39.9504 | -40.3974 | -40.8078 | -41.1869 | -41.5391 |
| Hydrogen | H | 0 | -22.4247 | -22.4552 | -23.8844 | -24.9930 | -25.8987 | -26.6646 | -27.3279 | -27.9131 | -28.4365 | -28.9100 | -29.3422 | -29.7399 | -30.1081 | -30.4508 |
| Nitrogen | N | 0 | -31.6467 | -31.6772 | -33.1064 | -34.2150 | -35.1208 | -35.8867 | -36.5500 | -37.1352 | -37.6586 | -38.1321 | -38.5643 | -38.9620 | -39.3302 | -39.6729 |
| Carbon | C | 0 | -32.5327 | -32.5648 | -34.0591 | -35.2071 | -36.1303 | -36.9241 | -37.6017 | -38.1980 | -38.7303 | -39.2111 | -39.6494 | -40.0523 | -40.4249 | -40.7715 |

Free Energy Function, $(F^\circ-H^\circ_0)/T$, in cal/deg mole

| Compound (gas, monatomic) | Formula | Temperature in °K | | | | | | | | | | | | |
|---|---|---|---|---|---|---|---|---|---|---|---|---|---|---|
| | | 1000 | 1250 | 1500 | 1750 | 2000 | 2250 | 2500 | 2750 | 3000 | 3500 | 4000 | 4500 | 5000 |
| Oxygen | O | -39.4595 | -40.6068 | -41.5391 | -42.3246 | -43.0027 | -43.6025 | -44.1322 | -44.6135 | -45.0524 | -45.8295 | -46.5026 | -47.0970 | -47.6299 |
| Hydrogen | H | -28.4365 | -29.8042 | -30.4508 | -31.2170 | -31.8803 | -32.4655 | -32.9889 | -33.4624 | -33.8947 | -34.6605 | -35.3229 | -35.9090 | -36.4325 |
| Nitrogen | N | -37.6586 | -38.7672 | -39.6729 | -40.4387 | -41.1021 | -41.6708 | -42.2108 | -42.6844 | -43.1170 | -43.8841 | -44.5507 | -45.1418 | -45.6747 |
| Carbon | C | -38.7303 | -39.8550 | -40.7715 | -41.5455 | -42.2151 | -42.8057 | -43.3342 | -43.8129 | -44.2506 | -45.0288 | -45.7066 | -46.3082 | -46.8496 |

TABLE Os – O₂, H₂, OH, H₂O, N₂, NO, C, CO, CO₂

FREE ENERGY FUNCTION, $(F°-H°_0)/T$, AT 0° TO 5000°K

July 31, 1944; August 31, 1946; June 30, 1949

Temperature in °K

Free Energy Function, $(F°-H°_0)/T$, in cal/deg mole

| Compound | Formula | State | 0 | 50 | 100 | 150 | 200 | 250 | 298.16 | 300 | 400 | 500 | 600 | 700 | 800 | 900 | 1000 |
|---|---|---|---|---|---|---|---|---|---|---|---|---|---|---|---|---|---|
| Oxygen | $O_2$ | gas | 0 | | -34.486 | -37.297 | -39.292 | -40.835 | -42.061 | -42.106 | -44.112 | -45.675 | -46.968 | -48.071 | -49.044 | -49.911 | -50.697 |
| Hydrogen | $H_2$ | gas | 0 | | | | | -23.331 | -24.423 | -24.465 | -26.422 | -27.950 | -29.203 | -30.265 | -31.186 | -32.004 | -32.738 |
| Hydroxyl | $OH$ | gas | 0 | | | | | | -36.824 | -36.859 | -38.904 | -40.483 | -41.772 | -42.860 | -43.804 | -44.637 | -45.385 |
| Water | $H_2O$ | gas | 0 | | | | | | -37.165 | -37.214 | -39.505 | -41.293 | -42.766 | -44.024 | -45.128 | -46.116 | -47.010 |
| Nitrogen | $N_2$ | gas | 0 | | | | -36.044 | -37.595 | -38.817 | -38.859 | -40.861 | -42.415 | -43.688 | -44.769 | -45.711 | -46.550 | -47.306 |
| Nitric Oxide | $NO$ | gas | 0 | | -34.844 | -37.864 | -40.012 | -41.667 | -42.980 | -43.028 | -45.134 | -46.760 | -48.090 | -49.219 | -50.202 | -51.075 | -51.864 |
| Carbon | $C$ | solid graphite | 0 | | -0.0739 | -0.1582 | -0.2639 | -0.3866 | -0.5172 | -0.5227 | -0.824 | -1.146 | -1.477 | -1.810 | -2.138 | -2.459 | -2.771 |
| Carbon Monoxide | $CO$ | gas | 0 | | -32.762 | | -37.574 | -39.124 | -40.350 | -40.391 | -42.393 | -43.947 | -45.222 | -46.308 | -47.254 | -48.097 | -48.860 |
| Carbon Dioxide | $CO_2$ | gas | 0 | | | | | | -43.555 | -43.601 | -45.828 | -47.667 | -49.238 | -50.635 | -51.895 | -53.047 | -54.109 |

Temperature in °K

Free Energy Function, $(F°-H°_0)/T$, in cal/deg mole

| Compound | Formula | State | 1100 | 1200 | 1300 | 1400 | 1500 | 1750 | 2000 | 2250 | 2500 | 2750 | 3000 | 3500 | 4000 | 4500 | 5000 |
|---|---|---|---|---|---|---|---|---|---|---|---|---|---|---|---|---|---|
| Oxygen | $O_2$ | gas | -51.415 | -52.077 | -52.695 | -53.272 | -53.808 | -55.028 | -56.104 | -57.065 | -57.937 | -58.735 | -59.471 | -60.795 | -61.963 | -63.008 | -63.958 |
| Hydrogen | $H_2$ | gas | -33.402 | -34.010 | -34.573 | -35.098 | -35.590 | -36.697 | -37.669 | -38.538 | -39.328 | -40.051 | -40.719 | -41.922 | -42.987 | -43.942 | -44.809 |
| Hydroxyl | $OH$ | gas | -46.063 | -46.686 | -47.261 | -47.795 | -48.295 | -49.422 | -50.414 | -51.300 | -52.104 | -52.840 | -53.521 | -54.744 | -55.822 | -56.789 | -57.666 |
| Water | $H_2O$ | gas | -47.831 | -48.593 | -49.303 | -49.969 | -50.598 | -52.038 | -53.322 | -54.488 | -55.555 | -56.55 | -57.47 | -59.17 | -60.70 | -62.06 | -63.31 |
| Nitrogen | $N_2$ | gas | -47.994 | -48.629 | -49.218 | -49.768 | -50.284 | -51.452 | -52.478 | -53.397 | -54.228 | -54.987 | -55.687 | -56.941 | -58.043 | -59.025 | -59.910 |
| Nitric Oxide | $NO$ | gas | -52.583 | -53.245 | -53.858 | -54.428 | -54.964 | -56.174 | -57.237 | -58.187 | -59.045 | -59.829 | -60.549 | -61.839 | -62.966 | -63.968 | -64.868 |
| Carbon | $C$ | solid graphite | -3.073 | -3.365 | -3.647 | -3.919 | -4.181 | -4.80 | -5.37 | -5.90 | -6.39 | -6.85 | -7.28 | -8.07 | -8.78 | | |
| Carbon Monoxide | $CO$ | gas | -49.554 | -50.194 | -50.789 | -51.345 | -51.864 | -53.041 | -54.078 | -55.004 | -55.842 | -56.608 | -57.314 | -58.578 | -59.688 | -60.676 | -61.566 |
| Carbon Dioxide | $CO_2$ | gas | -55.096 | -56.019 | -56.887 | -57.706 | -58.481 | -60.26 | -61.85 | -63.29 | -64.61 | -65.82 | -66.94 | -68.98 | -70.78 | -72.40 | -73.87 |

TABLE 20s (PART 1) – NORMAL PARAFFINS, $C_1$ TO $C_{20}$

FREE ENERGY FUNCTION, $(F°-H°_0)/T$, FOR THE IDEAL GAS STATE, AT 0° TO 1500°K

November 30, 1945; December 31, 1952

Free Energy Function, $(F°-H°_0)/T$, in cal/deg mole

| Compound (gas) | Formula | 0 | 298.16 | 300 | 400 | 500 | 600 | 700 | 800 | 900 | 1000 | 1100 | 1200 | 1300 | 1400 | 1500 |
|---|---|---|---|---|---|---|---|---|---|---|---|---|---|---|---|---|
| Methane | $CH_4$ | 0 | -36.46 | -36.51 | -38.86 | -40.75 | -42.39 | -43.86 | -45.21 | -46.47 | -47.65 | -48.78 | -49.86 | -50.89 | -51.88 | -52.84 |
| Ethane | $C_2H_6$ | 0 | -45.27 | -45.33 | -48.24 | -50.77 | -53.08 | -55.25 | -57.29 | -59.24 | -61.11 | -62.90 | -64.63 | -66.30 | -67.91 | -69.46 |
| Propane | $C_3H_8$ | 0 | -52.73 | -52.80 | -56.48 | -59.81 | -62.93 | -65.90 | -68.74 | -71.47 | -74.10 | -76.63 | -79.07 | -81.43 | -83.70 | -85.86 |
| n-Butane | $C_4H_{10}$ | 0 | -58.54 | -58.65 | -63.51 | -67.91 | -72.01 | -75.91 | -79.63 | -83.18 | -86.60 | -89.90 | -93.08 | -96.14 | -99.09 | -101.95 |
| n-Pentane | $C_5H_{12}$ | 0 | -64.52 | -64.65 | -70.57 | -75.94 | -80.96 | -85.74 | -90.31 | -94.67 | -98.87 | -102.92 | -106.83 | -110.58 | -114.21 | -117.72 |
| n-Hexane | $C_6H_{14}$ | 0 | -70.62 | -70.77 | -77.75 | -84.11 | -90.06 | -95.73 | -101.14 | -106.32 | -111.31 | -116.10 | -120.74 | -125.19 | -129.49 | -133.64 |
| n-Heptane | $C_7H_{16}$ | 0 | -76.70 | -76.86 | -84.91 | -92.25 | -99.13 | -105.68 | -111.95 | -117.93 | -123.70 | -129.25 | -134.62 | -139.76 | -144.74 | -149.54 |
| n-Octane | $C_8H_{18}$ | 0 | -82.68 | -82.86 | -91.97 | -100.29 | -108.10 | -115.54 | -122.66 | -129.45 | -136.00 | -142.30 | -148.40 | -154.24 | -159.89 | -165.34 |
| n-Nonane | $C_9H_{20}$ | 0 | -88.66 | -88.86 | -99.03 | -108.34 | -117.07 | -125.39 | -133.36 | -140.96 | -148.30 | -155.36 | -162.18 | -168.71 | -175.04 | -181.14 |
| n-Decane | $C_{10}H_{22}$ | 0 | -94.64 | -94.86 | -106.09 | -116.38 | -126.04 | -135.25 | -144.06 | -152.48 | -160.60 | -168.41 | -175.96 | -183.19 | -190.19 | -196.93 |
| n-Undecane | $C_{11}H_{24}$ | 0 | -100.62 | -100.86 | -113.15 | -124.42 | -135.01 | -145.10 | -154.77 | -163.99 | -172.90 | -181.46 | -189.74 | -197.67 | -205.34 | -212.73 |
| n-Dodecane | $C_{12}H_{26}$ | 0 | -106.60 | -106.85 | -120.22 | -132.46 | -143.98 | -154.96 | -165.48 | -175.51 | -185.20 | -194.51 | -203.52 | -212.14 | -220.50 | -228.53 |
| n-Tridecane | $C_{13}H_{28}$ | 0 | -112.57 | -112.85 | -127.28 | -140.51 | -152.95 | -164.62 | -176.18 | -187.03 | -197.49 | -207.57 | -217.31 | -226.62 | -235.65 | -244.33 |
| n-Tetradecane | $C_{14}H_{30}$ | 0 | -118.55 | -118.85 | -134.34 | -148.55 | -161.92 | -174.67 | -186.88 | -198.54 | -209.79 | -220.62 | -231.09 | -241.10 | -250.80 | -260.13 |
| n-Pentadecane | $C_{15}H_{32}$ | 0 | -124.53 | -124.85 | -141.40 | -156.59 | -170.89 | -184.53 | -197.59 | -210.06 | -222.09 | -233.67 | -244.87 | -255.58 | -265.95 | -275.92 |
| n-Hexadecane | $C_{16}H_{34}$ | 0 | -130.51 | -130.85 | -148.46 | -164.64 | -179.86 | -194.38 | -208.30 | -221.57 | -234.39 | -246.73 | -258.65 | -270.05 | -281.10 | -291.72 |
| n-Heptadecane | $C_{17}H_{36}$ | 0 | -136.49 | -136.85 | -155.52 | -172.68 | -188.83 | -204.24 | -219.00 | -233.09 | -246.69 | -259.78 | -272.43 | -284.53 | -296.25 | -307.52 |
| n-Octadecane | $C_{18}H_{38}$ | 0 | -142.47 | -142.85 | -162.58 | -180.72 | -197.80 | -214.10 | -229.70 | -244.61 | -258.99 | -272.83 | -286.21 | -299.01 | -311.40 | -323.32 |
| n-Nonadecane | $C_{19}H_{40}$ | 0 | -148.45 | -148.85 | -169.64 | -188.77 | -206.77 | -223.95 | -240.41 | -256.12 | -271.29 | -285.89 | -299.99 | -313.48 | -326.55 | -339.12 |
| n-Eicosane | $C_{20}H_{42}$ | 0 | -154.43 | -154.85 | -176.70 | -196.81 | -215.74 | -233.81 | -251.12 | -267.64 | -283.59 | -298.94 | -313.77 | -327.96 | -341.70 | -354.91 |
| Increment per $CH_2$ group, applicable beyond n-heptane | | 0 | -5.979 | -5.999 | -7.061 | -8.043 | -8.970 | -9.856 | -10.705 | -11.516 | -12.299 | -13.053 | -13.781 | -14.477 | -15.151 | -15.798 |

Temperature in °K

## TABLE 1s – PARAFFINS, C₁ TO C₅

### FREE ENERGY FUNCTION, $(F^\circ - H^\circ_0)/T$, FOR THE IDEAL GAS STATE, AT 0° TO 1500°K

August 31, 1944; February 28, 1949; December 31, 1952

| Compound (gas) | Formula | Temperature in °K | | | | | | | | | | | | | | |
|---|---|---|---|---|---|---|---|---|---|---|---|---|---|---|---|---|
| | | Free Energy Function, $(F^\circ - H^\circ_0)/T$, in cal/deg mole | | | | | | | | | | | | | | |
| | | 0 | 100 | 150 | 200 | 250 | 298.16 | 300 | 350 | 400 | 450 | 500 | 600 | 700 | 800 | 900 |
| Methane | CH₄ | 0 | -27.77 | -30.99 | -33.28 | -35.05 | -36.46 | -36.51 | -37.76 | -38.86 | -39.85 | -40.75 | -42.39 | -43.86 | -45.21 | -46.47 |
| Ethane | C₂H₆ | 0 | -35.83 | -39.17 | -41.63 | -43.62 | -45.27 | -45.33 | -46.85 | -48.24 | -49.54 | -50.77 | -53.08 | -55.25 | -57.29 | -59.24 |
| Propane | C₃H₈ | 0 | -42.08 | -45.65 | -48.41 | -50.75 | -52.73 | -52.80 | -54.71 | -56.48 | -58.19 | -59.81 | -62.93 | -65.90 | -68.74 | -71.47 |
| n-Butane | C₄H₁₀ | 0 | | | -52.83 | -55.93 | -58.54 | -58.65 | -61.15 | -63.51 | -65.76 | -67.91 | -72.01 | -75.91 | -79.63 | -83.18 |
| 2-Methylpropane (Isobutane) | " | 0 | | | -50.98 | -53.69 | -56.08 | -56.16 | -58.50 | -60.72 | -62.87 | -64.95 | -68.95 | -72.78 | -76.45 | -79.98 |
| n-Pentane | C₅H₁₂ | 0 | | | -57.66 | -61.34 | -64.52 | -64.65 | -67.69 | -70.57 | -73.31 | -75.94 | -80.96 | -85.74 | -90.31 | -94.67 |
| 2-Methylbutane (Isopentane) | " | 0 | | | -58.06 | -61.47 | -64.36 | -64.47 | -67.32 | -70.07 | -72.72 | -75.28 | -80.21 | -84.92 | -89.44 | -93.77 |
| 2,2-Dimethylpropane (Neopentane) | " | 0 | | | -50.48 | -53.56 | -56.36 | -56.46 | -59.24 | -61.93 | -64.50 | -67.04 | -71.96 | -76.70 | -81.27 | -85.67 |

| Compound (gas) | Formula | Temperature in °K | | | | | |
|---|---|---|---|---|---|---|---|
| | | Free Energy Function, $(F^\circ - H^\circ_0)/T$, in cal/deg mole | | | | | |
| | | 1000 | 1100 | 1200 | 1300 | 1400 | 1500 |
| Methane | CH₄ | -47.65 | -48.78 | -49.86 | -50.89 | -51.88 | -52.84 |
| Ethane | C₂H₆ | -61.11 | -62.90 | -64.63 | -66.30 | -67.91 | -69.46 |
| Propane | C₃H₈ | -74.10 | -76.63 | -79.07 | -81.43 | -83.70 | -85.86 |
| n-Butane | C₄H₁₀ | -86.60 | -89.90 | -93.08 | -96.14 | -99.09 | -101.95 |
| 2-Methylpropane (Isobutane) | " | -83.38 | -86.65 | -89.80 | -92.86 | -95.81 | -98.64 |
| n-Pentane | C₅H₁₂ | -98.87 | -102.92 | -106.83 | -110.58 | -114.21 | -117.72 |
| 2-Methylbutane (Isopentane) | " | -97.96 | -101.98 | -105.87 | -109.65 | -113.28 | -116.78 |
| 2,2-Dimethylpropane (Neopentane) | " | -89.90 | -93.98 | -97.92 | -101.71 | -105.37 | -108.91 |

TABLE 2s (PART 1) – PARAFFINS, $C_6$

FREE ENERGY FUNCTION, $(F^O-H^O_0)/T$, FOR THE IDEAL GAS STATE, AT $0^O$ TO $1500^O K$
September 30, 1944; November 30, 1946; December 31, 1952

| Compound (gas) | Formula | Temperature in $^O K$ | | | | | | | | | | | | | | | |
|---|---|---|---|---|---|---|---|---|---|---|---|---|---|---|---|---|---|
| | | 0 | 298.16 | 300 | 400 | 500 | 600 | 700 | 800 | 900 | 1000 | 1100 | 1200 | 1300 | 1400 | 1500 |
| | | | Free Energy Function, $(F^O-H^O_0)/T$, in cal/deg mole | | | | | | | | | | | | | | |
| n-Hexane | $C_6H_{14}$ | 0 | -70.62 | -70.77 | -77.75 | -84.11 | -90.06 | -95.73 | -101.14 | -106.32 | -111.31 | -116.10 | -120.74 | -125.19 | -129.49 | -133.64 |
| 2-Methylpentane | " | 0 | -70.50 | -70.64 | -77.2 | -83.3 | -89.1 | -94.7 | -100.1 | -105.3 | -110.3 | -115.0 | -119.6 | -124.1 | -128.4 | -132.5 |
| 3-Methylpentane | " | 0 | -68.56 | -68.71 | -75.69 | -82.05 | -88.00 | -93.67 | -99.08 | -104.3 | -109.3 | -114.0 | -118.7 | -123.1 | -127.4 | -131.6 |
| 2,2-Dimethylbutane | " | 0 | -65.79 | -65.91 | -72.3 | -78.3 | -84.1 | -89.6 | -95.0 | -100.2 | -105.1 | -109.9 | -114.5 | -119.0 | -123.2 | -127.4 |
| 2,3-Dimethylbutane | " | 0 | -67.58 | -67.70 | -74.06 | -80.05 | -85.77 | -91.27 | -96.54 | -101.67 | -106.57 | -111.33 | -115.88 | -120.29 | -124.57 | -128.70 |

TABLE 2s (PART 2) — PARAFFINS, C$_7$

FREE ENERGY FUNCTION, $(F°-H°_0)/T$, FOR THE IDEAL GAS STATE, AT 0° TO 1500°K

September 30, 1944; December 31, 1952

| Compound (gas) | Formula | Temperature in °K | | | | | | | | | | | | | | |
|---|---|---|---|---|---|---|---|---|---|---|---|---|---|---|---|---|
| | | 0 | 298.16 | 300 | 400 | 500 | 600 | 700 | 800 | 900 | 1000 | 1100 | 1200 | 1300 | 1400 | 1500 |
| | | Free Energy Function, $(F°-H°_0)/T$, in cal/deg mole | | | | | | | | | | | | | | |
| n-Heptane | C$_7$H$_{16}$ | 0 | -76.70 | -76.87 | -84.91 | -92.25 | -99.13 | -105.68 | -111.95 | -117.93 | -123.70 | -129.25 | -134.62 | -139.76 | -144.74 | -149.54 |
| 2-Methylhexane | " | 0 | -76.46 | -76.61 | -84.4 | -91.6 | -98.4 | -104.9 | -111.1 | -117.2 | -123.0 | | | | | |
| 3-Methylhexane | " | 0 | -78.05 | -78.19 | -85.8 | -92.9 | -99.6 | -106.0 | -112.2 | -118.2 | -124.0 | | | | | |
| 3-Ethylpentane | " | 0 | -76.02 | -76.26 | -83.7 | -90.6 | -97.1 | -103.3 | -109.4 | -115.3 | -121.1 | | | | | |
| 2,2-Dimethylpentane | " | 0 | -71.50 | -71.64 | -79.0 | -86.0 | -92.6 | -98.8 | -105.0 | -111.0 | -117.0 | | | | | |
| 2,3-Dimethylpentane | " | 0 | -76.75 | -76.89 | -84.4 | -91.2 | -97.8 | -104.0 | -110.1 | -116.1 | -121.8 | | | | | |
| 2,4-Dimethylpentane | " | 0 | -72.55 | -72.69 | -80.2 | -87.1 | -93.7 | -100.0 | -106.1 | -112.2 | -118.0 | | | | | |
| 3,3-Dimethylpentane | " | 0 | -73.05 | -73.19 | -80.8 | -87.7 | -94.4 | -100.7 | -106.9 | -113.0 | -118.8 | | | | | |
| 2,2,3-Trimethylbutane | " | 0 | -69.12 | -69.26 | -76.56 | -83.45 | -90.07 | -96.47 | -102.7 | -108.6 | -114.3 | -119.9 | -125.2 | -130.4 | -135.4 | -140.2 |

TABLE 3s – PARAFFINS, $C_8$
FREE ENERGY FUNCTION, $(F^o - H_0^o)/T$, FOR THE IDEAL GAS STATE, AT 0° TO 1500°K
October 31, 1944; December 31, 1952

| Compound (gas) | Formula | 0 | 298.16 | 300 | 400 | 500 | 600 | 700 | 800 | 900 | 1000 | 1100 | 1200 | 1300 | 1400 | 1500 |
|---|---|---|---|---|---|---|---|---|---|---|---|---|---|---|---|---|
| | | | | | | Free Energy Function, $(F^o - H_0^o)/T$, in cal/deg mole | | | | | | | | | | |
| n-Octane | $C_8H_{18}$ | 0 | -82.68 | -82.86 | -91.97 | -100.29 | -108.10 | -115.54 | -122.66 | -129.45 | -136.00 | -142.30 | -148.40 | -154.24 | -159.89 | -165.34 |
| 2-Methylheptane | " | 0 | -81.49 | -81.66 | -90.5 | -98.7 | -106.5 | -113.9 | -121.1 | -128.1 | -134.6 | | | | | |
| 3-Methylheptane | " | 0 | -83.33 | -83.50 | -92.3 | -100.4 | -108.1 | -115.5 | -122.7 | -129.6 | -136.1 | | | | | |
| 4-Methylheptane | " | 0 | -81.63 | -81.79 | -90.5 | -98.6 | -106.2 | -113.6 | -120.7 | -127.6 | -134.1 | | | | | |
| 3-Ethylhexane | " | 0 | -84.23 | -84.39 | -92.8 | -100.5 | -107.8 | -114.9 | -121.9 | -128.7 | -135.1 | | | | | |
| 2,2-Dimethylhexane | " | 0 | -77.08 | -77.24 | -85.9 | -93.9 | -101.4 | -108.7 | -115.9 | -122.8 | -129.3 | | | | | |
| 2,3-Dimethylhexane | " | 0 | -79.76 | -79.92 | -88.7 | -96.9 | -104.6 | -112.0 | -119.2 | -126.2 | -132.8 | | | | | |
| 2,4-Dimethylhexane | " | 0 | -81.27 | -81.43 | -89.9 | -97.8 | -105.3 | -112.5 | -119.6 | -126.4 | -133.0 | | | | | |
| 2,5-Dimethylhexane | " | 0 | -79.35 | -79.51 | -88.1 | -96.0 | -103.5 | -110.7 | -117.8 | -124.6 | -131.2 | | | | | |
| 3,3-Dimethylhexane | " | 0 | -79.49 | -79.65 | -88.1 | -95.9 | -103.4 | -110.6 | -117.7 | -124.6 | -131.2 | | | | | |
| 3,4-Dimethylhexane[a,b] | " | 0 | -80.58 | -80.77 | -89.3 | -97.3 | -105.0 | -112.4 | -119.5 | -126.2 | -132.8 | | | | | |
| 2-Methyl-3-ethylpentane | " | 0 | -79.58 | -79.74 | -88.3 | -96.3 | -103.9 | -111.3 | -118.4 | -125.3 | -131.8 | | | | | |
| 3-Methyl-3-ethylpentane | " | 0 | -78.24 | -78.40 | -86.9 | -94.8 | -102.2 | -109.5 | -116.6 | -123.6 | -130.1 | | | | | |
| 2,2,3-Trimethylpentane | " | 0 | -76.85 | -77.00 | -85.4 | -93.2 | -100.6 | -107.8 | -114.9 | -121.8 | -128.4 | | | | | |
| 2,2,4-Trimethylpentane | " | 0 | -76.38 | -76.53 | -84.9 | -92.7 | -100.1 | -107.3 | -114.4 | -121.3 | -127.9 | | | | | |
| 2,3,3-Trimethylpentane | " | 0 | -77.97 | -78.12 | -86.7 | -94.5 | -102.0 | -109.3 | -116.4 | -123.3 | -129.9 | | | | | |
| 2,3,4-Trimethylpentane | " | 0 | -77.57 | -77.72 | -86.2 | -94.0 | -101.5 | -108.7 | -115.8 | -122.6 | -129.2 | | | | | |
| 2,2,3,3-Tetramethylbutane | " | 0 | -67.97 | -68.12 | -76.3 | -84.3 | -91.9 | -99.4 | -106.5 | -113.4 | -120.1 | | | | | |

Temperature in °K

a See footnote d of Table 3r.
b The values of the free energy function for the racemic (dextro + levo) mixture are, algebraically, about 1.2 cal/deg mole higher, and those for the meso form about 1.5 cal/deg mole higher than the values tabulated for the equilibrium mixture of the dextro, levo, and meso isomers of 3,4-dimethylhexane.

TABLE 22s (PART 1) – NORMAL ALKYL CYCLOPENTANES, $C_5$ TO $C_{21}$

FREE ENERGY FUNCTION, $(F°-H°_0)/T$, FOR THE IDEAL GAS STATE, AT 0° TO 1500°K

March 31, 1947; December 31, 1952

Temperature in °K

Free Energy Function, $(F°-H°_0)/T$, in cal/deg mole

| Compound (gas) | Formula | 0 | 298.16 | 300 | 400 | 500 | 600 | 700 | 800 | 900 | 1000 | 1100 | 1200 | 1300 | 1400 | 1500 |
|---|---|---|---|---|---|---|---|---|---|---|---|---|---|---|---|---|
| Cyclopentane | $C_5H_{10}$ | 0 | -57.93 | -58.00 | -61.88 | -65.62 | -69.30 | -72.95 | -76.52 | -80.04 | -83.48 | -86.84 | -90.13 | -93.31 | -96.40 | -99.42 |
| Methylcyclopentane | $C_6H_{12}$ | 0 | -65.23 | -65.33 | -70.45 | -75.33 | -80.07 | -84.72 | -89.26 | -93.68 | -97.97 | -102.13 | -106.18 | -110.08 | -113.89 | -117.63 |
| Ethylcyclopentane | $C_7H_{14}$ | 0 | -70.99 | -71.12 | -77.44 | -83.41 | -89.14 | -94.72 | -100.16 | -105.37 | -110.44 | -115.33 | -120.09 | -124.72 | -129.12 | -133.45 |
| n-Propylcyclopentane | $C_8H_{16}$ | 0 | -76.97 | -77.12 | -84.50 | -91.45 | -98.11 | -104.58 | -110.86 | -116.89 | -122.74 | -128.38 | -133.87 | -139.20 | -144.27 | -149.25 |
| n-Butylcyclopentane | $C_9H_{18}$ | 0 | -82.95 | -83.12 | -91.56 | -99.50 | -107.08 | -114.43 | -121.57 | -128.40 | -135.04 | -141.44 | -147.65 | -153.67 | -159.42 | -165.05 |
| n-Pentylcyclopentane | $C_{10}H_{20}$ | 0 | -88.93 | -89.12 | -98.62 | -107.54 | -116.05 | -124.29 | -132.28 | -139.92 | -147.34 | -154.49 | -161.43 | -168.15 | -174.57 | -180.84 |
| n-Hexylcyclopentane | $C_{11}H_{22}$ | 0 | -94.91 | -95.12 | -105.68 | -115.58 | -125.02 | -134.14 | -142.98 | -151.43 | -159.64 | -167.54 | -175.21 | -182.63 | -189.72 | -196.64 |
| n-Heptylcyclopentane | $C_{12}H_{24}$ | 0 | -100.88 | -101.12 | -112.74 | -123.62 | -133.99 | -144.00 | -153.68 | -162.95 | -171.94 | -180.60 | -189.00 | -197.10 | -204.88 | -212.44 |
| n-Octylcyclopentane | $C_{13}H_{26}$ | 0 | -106.86 | -107.11 | -119.81 | -131.67 | -142.96 | -153.86 | -164.39 | -174.47 | -184.23 | -193.65 | -202.78 | -211.58 | -220.03 | -228.24 |
| n-Nonylcyclopentane | $C_{14}H_{28}$ | 0 | -112.84 | -113.11 | -126.87 | -139.71 | -151.93 | -163.71 | -175.10 | -185.98 | -196.53 | -206.70 | -216.56 | -226.06 | -235.18 | -244.04 |
| n-Decylcyclopentane | $C_{15}H_{30}$ | 0 | -118.82 | -119.11 | -133.93 | -147.75 | -160.90 | -173.57 | -185.80 | -197.50 | -208.83 | -219.75 | -230.34 | -240.54 | -250.33 | -259.83 |
| n-Undecylcyclopentane | $C_{16}H_{32}$ | 0 | -124.80 | -125.11 | -140.99 | -155.80 | -169.87 | -183.42 | -196.50 | -209.01 | -221.13 | -232.81 | -244.12 | -255.01 | -265.48 | -275.63 |
| n-Dodecylcyclopentane | $C_{17}H_{34}$ | 0 | -130.78 | -131.11 | -148.05 | -163.84 | -178.64 | -193.28 | -207.21 | -220.53 | -233.45 | -245.86 | -257.90 | -269.49 | -280.63 | -291.43 |
| n-Tridecylcyclopentane | $C_{18}H_{36}$ | 0 | -136.76 | -137.11 | -155.11 | -171.88 | -187.81 | -203.14 | -217.92 | -232.05 | -245.73 | -258.91 | -271.68 | -283.97 | -295.78 | -307.23 |
| n-Tetradecylcyclopentane | $C_{19}H_{38}$ | 0 | -142.74 | -143.11 | -162.17 | -179.93 | -196.78 | -212.99 | -228.62 | -243.56 | -258.03 | -271.97 | -285.46 | -298.44 | -310.93 | -323.03 |
| n-Pentadecylcyclopentane | $C_{20}H_{40}$ | 0 | -148.72 | -149.11 | -169.23 | -187.97 | -205.75 | -222.85 | -239.32 | -255.08 | -270.33 | -285.02 | -299.24 | -312.92 | -326.08 | -338.82 |
| n-Hexadecylcyclopentane | $C_{21}H_{42}$ | 0 | -154.70 | -155.11 | -176.29 | -196.01 | -214.72 | -232.70 | -250.03 | -266.59 | -282.63 | -298.07 | -313.02 | -327.40 | -341.23 | -354.62 |
| Increment per $CH_2$ group, applicable beyond ethylcyclopentane | | 0 | -5.979 | -5.999 | -7.061 | -8.043 | -8.970 | -9.856 | -10.705 | -11.516 | -12.299 | -13.053 | -13.781 | -14.477 | -15.151 | -15.798 |

TABLE 6s - ALKYL CYCLOPENTANES, $C_5$ TO $C_7$

FREE ENERGY FUNCTION, $(F°-H°_0)/T$, FOR THE IDEAL GAS STATE, AT 0° TO 1500°K

April 30, 1949; December 31, 1952

Temperature in °K

Free Energy Function, $(F°-H°_0)/T$, in cal/deg mole

| Compound (gas) | Formula | 0 | 298.16 | 300 | 400 | 500 | 600 | 700 | 800 | 900 | 1000 | 1100 | 1200 | 1300 | 1400 | 1500 |
|---|---|---|---|---|---|---|---|---|---|---|---|---|---|---|---|---|
| Cyclopentane | $C_5H_{10}$ | 0 | -57.93 | -58.00 | -61.88 | -65.62 | -69.30 | -72.95 | -76.52 | -80.04 | -83.48 | -86.84 | -90.13 | -93.31 | -96.40 | -99.42 |
| Methylcyclopentane | $C_6H_{12}$ | 0 | -65.23 | -65.33 | -70.45 | -75.33 | -80.07 | -84.72 | -89.26 | -93.68 | -97.97 | -102.13 | -106.18 | -110.08 | -113.89 | -117.63 |
| Ethylcyclopentane | $C_7H_{14}$ | 0 | -70.99 | -71.12 | -77.44 | -83.41 | -89.14 | -94.72 | -100.16 | -105.37 | -110.44 | -115.33 | -120.09 | -124.72 | -129.12 | -133.45 |
| 1,1-Dimethylcyclopentane | " | 0 | -67.21 | -67.36 | -73.36 | -79.14 | -84.72 | -90.28 | -95.75 | -101.02 | -106.13 | -111.05 | -115.87 | -120.51 | -125.04 | -129.51 |
| 1,cis-2-Dimethylcyclopentane | " | 0 | -68.65 | -68.81 | -74.91 | -80.71 | -86.35 | -91.91 | -97.36 | -102.65 | -107.76 | -112.70 | -117.50 | -122.12 | -126.63 | -131.10 |
| 1,trans-2-Dimethylcyclopentane | " | 0 | -68.73 | -68.87 | -75.01 | -80.81 | -86.43 | -92.03 | -97.54 | -102.79 | -107.90 | -112.84 | -117.64 | -122.26 | -126.77 | -131.24 |
| 1,cis-3-Dimethylcyclopentane | " | 0 | -68.73 | -68.87 | -75.01 | -80.81 | -86.45 | -92.03 | -97.54 | -102.79 | -107.90 | -112.84 | -117.64 | -122.26 | -126.77 | -131.24 |
| 1-trans-3-Dimethylcyclopentane | " | 0 | -68.73 | -68.87 | -75.01 | -80.81 | -86.45 | -92.03 | -97.54 | -102.79 | -107.90 | -112.84 | -117.64 | -122.26 | -126.77 | -131.24 |

TABLE 23s (PART 1) – NORMAL ALKYL CYCLOHEXANES, $C_6$ TO $C_{22}$

FREE ENERGY FUNCTION, $(F^0-H^0_0)/T$, FOR THE IDEAL GAS STATE, AT 0° TO 1500°K

March 31, 1947; December 31, 1952

| Compound (gas) | Formula | Temperature in °K | | | | | | | | | | | | | | |
|---|---|---|---|---|---|---|---|---|---|---|---|---|---|---|---|---|
| | | 0 | 298.16 | 300 | 400 | 500 | 600 | 700 | 800 | 900 | 1000 | 1100 | 1200 | 1300 | 1400 | 1500 |
| | | Free Energy Function, $(F^0-H^0_0)/T$, in cal/deg mole | | | | | | | | | | | | | | |
| Cyclohexane | $C_6H_{12}$ | 0 | -57.07 | -57.16 | -61.80 | -66.39 | -70.96 | -75.50 | -79.98 | -84.40 | -88.74 | -93.0 | -97.1 | -101.1 | -105.0 | -108.8 |
| Methylcyclohexane | $C_7H_{14}$ | 0 | -64.51 | -64.62 | -70.38 | -76.06 | -81.68 | -87.24 | -92.70 | -98.04 | -103.24 | -106.3 | -113.2 | -118.0 | -122.6 | -127.1 |
| Ethylcyclohexane | $C_8H_{16}$ | 0 | -70.99 | -71.12 | -77.8 | -84.5 | -91.0 | -97.4 | -103.7 | -109.9 | -115.9 | -121.7 | -127.3 | -132.8 | -138.1 | -143.3 |
| n-Propylcyclohexane | $C_9H_{18}$ | 0 | -77.13 | -77.29 | -84.9 | -92.5 | -99.9 | -107.2 | -114.4 | -121.4 | -128.2 | -134.7 | -141.0 | -147.2 | -153.2 | -159.0 |
| n-Butylcyclohexane | $C_{10}H_{20}$ | 0 | -83.11 | -83.29 | -92.0 | -100.5 | -108.9 | -117.1 | -125.1 | -132.9 | -140.5 | -147.7 | -154.8 | -161.7 | -168.4 | -174.8 |
| n-Pentylcyclohexane | $C_{11}H_{22}$ | 0 | -89.09 | -89.29 | -99.0 | -108.6 | -117.8 | -126.9 | -135.8 | -144.4 | -152.8 | -160.8 | -168.6 | -176.2 | -183.5 | -190.6 |
| n-Hexylcyclohexane | $C_{12}H_{24}$ | 0 | -95.07 | -95.29 | -106.1 | -116.6 | -126.8 | -136.8 | -146.5 | -156.0 | -165.1 | -173.9 | -182.3 | -190.6 | -198.6 | -206.4 |
| n-Heptylcyclohexane | $C_{13}H_{26}$ | 0 | -101.05 | -101.29 | -113.1 | -124.7 | -135.8 | -146.6 | -157.2 | -167.5 | -177.4 | -186.9 | -196.1 | -205.1 | -213.8 | -222.2 |
| n-Octylcyclohexane | $C_{14}H_{28}$ | 0 | -107.02 | -107.28 | -120.2 | -132.7 | -144.7 | -156.5 | -167.9 | -179.0 | -189.7 | -199.9 | -209.9 | -219.6 | -229.0 | -238.0 |
| n-Nonylcyclohexane | $C_{15}H_{30}$ | 0 | -113.00 | -113.28 | -127.3 | -140.7 | -153.7 | -166.4 | -178.6 | -190.5 | -202.0 | -213.0 | -223.7 | -234.1 | -244.1 | -253.8 |
| n-Decylcyclohexane | $C_{16}H_{32}$ | 0 | -118.98 | -119.28 | -134.3 | -148.8 | -162.7 | -176.2 | -189.3 | -202.0 | -214.3 | -226.1 | -237.5 | -248.6 | -259.2 | -269.6 |
| n-Undecylcyclohexane | $C_{17}H_{34}$ | 0 | -124.96 | -125.28 | -141.4 | -156.8 | -171.7 | -186.1 | -200.0 | -213.6 | -226.6 | -239.1 | -251.2 | -263.0 | -274.4 | -285.4 |
| n-Dodecylcyclohexane | $C_{18}H_{36}$ | 0 | -130.94 | -131.28 | -148.4 | -164.9 | -180.6 | -195.9 | -210.7 | -225.1 | -238.9 | -252.1 | -265.0 | -277.5 | -289.6 | -301.2 |
| n-Tridecylcyclohexane | $C_{19}H_{38}$ | 0 | -136.92 | -137.28 | -155.5 | -172.9 | -189.6 | -205.8 | -221.4 | -236.6 | -251.2 | -265.2 | -278.8 | -292.0 | -304.7 | -317.0 |
| n-Tetradecylcyclohexane | $C_{20}H_{40}$ | 0 | -142.90 | -143.28 | -162.6 | -180.9 | -198.6 | -215.7 | -232.1 | -248.1 | -263.5 | -278.3 | -292.6 | -306.5 | -319.8 | -332.8 |
| n-Pentadecylcyclohexane | $C_{21}H_{42}$ | 0 | -148.88 | -149.28 | -169.6 | -189.0 | -207.5 | -225.5 | -242.8 | -259.6 | -275.8 | -291.3 | -306.4 | -321.0 | -335.0 | -348.6 |
| n-Hexadecylcyclohexane | $C_{22}H_{44}$ | 0 | -154.86 | -155.28 | -176.7 | -197.0 | -216.5 | -235.4 | -253.5 | -271.2 | -288.1 | -304.3 | -320.1 | -335.4 | -350.2 | -364.4 |
| Increment per CH2 group, applicable beyond n-propylcyclohexane | | 0 | -5.979 | -5.999 | -7.06 | -8.04 | -8.97 | -9.86 | -10.70 | -11.52 | -12.30 | -13.05 | -13.78 | -14.48 | -15.15 | -15.80 |

TABLE 7s - ALKYL CYCLOHEXANES, $C_6$ TO $C_8$

FREE ENERGY FUNCTION, $(F^o-H^o_0)/T$, FOR THE IDEAL GAS STATE, AT 0° TO 1500°K

April 30, 1947

| Compound (gas) | Formula | Temperature in °K | | | | | | | | | | | | | | |
|---|---|---|---|---|---|---|---|---|---|---|---|---|---|---|---|---|
| | | 0 | 298.16 | 300 | 400 | 500 | 600 | 700 | 800 | 900 | 1000 | 1100 | 1200 | 1300 | 1400 | 1500 |
| | | Free Energy Function, $(F^o-H^o_0)/T$, in cal/deg mole | | | | | | | | | | | | | | |
| Cyclohexane | $C_6H_{12}$ | 0 | -57.07 | -57.16 | -61.80 | -66.39 | -70.96 | -75.50 | -79.98 | -84.40 | -88.74 | -93.0 | -97.1 | -101.1 | -105.0 | -108.8 |
| Methylcyclohexane | $C_7H_{14}$ | 0 | -64.51 | -64.62 | -70.38 | -76.06 | -81.68 | -87.24 | -92.70 | -98.04 | -103.24 | -108.3 | -113.2 | -118.0 | -122.6 | -127.1 |
| Ethylcyclohexane | $C_8H_{16}$ | 0 | -70.99 | -71.12 | -77.8 | -84.5 | -91.0 | -97.4 | -103.7 | -109.9 | -115.9 | -121.7 | -127.3 | -132.8 | -138.1 | -143.3 |
| 1,1-Dimethylcyclohexane | " | 0 | -67.52 | -67.67 | -74.1 | -80.6 | -87.0 | -93.3 | -99.6 | -105.7 | -111.7 | -117.5 | -123.1 | -128.5 | -133.8 | -139.1 |
| 1,cis-2-Dimethylcyclohexane | " | 0 | -69.35 | -69.49 | -76.1 | -82.6 | -89.1 | -95.5 | -101.8 | -107.9 | -113.9 | -119.7 | -125.3 | -130.7 | -136.0 | -141.3 |
| 1,trans-2-Dimethylcyclohexane[a] | " | 0 | -68.21 | -68.36 | -75.1 | -81.7 | -88.3 | -94.7 | -101.1 | -107.3 | -113.3 | -119.1 | -124.8 | -130.2 | -135.6 | -140.8 |
| 1,cis-3-Dimethylcyclohexane[a] | " | 0 | -68.19 | -68.34 | -75.0 | -81.6 | -88.1 | -94.5 | -100.8 | -107.0 | -113.0 | -118.8 | -124.4 | -129.9 | -135.2 | -140.4 |
| 1,trans-3-Dimethylcyclohexane[b] | " | 0 | -69.57 | -69.72 | -76.4 | -83.0 | -89.4 | -95.8 | -102.1 | -108.3 | -114.2 | -120.0 | -125.6 | -131.0 | -136.3 | -141.5 |
| 1,cis-4-Dimethylcyclohexane | " | 0 | -68.19 | -68.34 | -75.0 | -81.6 | -88.1 | -94.5 | -100.8 | -106.9 | -112.8 | -118.6 | -124.2 | -129.6 | -134.9 | -140.1 |
| 1,trans-4-Dimethylcyclohexane | " | 0 | -66.81 | -66.96 | -73.6 | -80.2 | -86.7 | -93.2 | -99.6 | -105.7 | -111.8 | -117.6 | -123.2 | -128.7 | -134.0 | -139.3 |

a Formerly labeled "trans"; see footnote b of Table 7a.

b Formerly labeled "cis"; see footnote c of Table 7a.

TABLE 24s (PART 1) - NORMAL MONOOLEFINS (1-ALKENES), $C_2$ TO $C_{20}$

FREE ENERGY FUNCTION, $(F^o - H_0^o)/T$, FOR THE IDEAL GAS STATE, AT $0^o$ TO $1500^oK$

November 30, 1945; April 30, 1946; December 31 1952

| Compound (gas) | Formula | Temperature in °K | | | | | | | | | | | | | | |
|---|---|---|---|---|---|---|---|---|---|---|---|---|---|---|---|---|
| | | 0 | 298.16 | 300 | 400 | 500 | 600 | 700 | 800 | 900 | 1000 | 1100 | 1200 | 1300 | 1400 | 1500 |
| | | | Free Energy Function, $(F^o - H_0^o)/T$, in cal/deg mole | | | | | | | | | | | | | |
| Ethene (Ethylene) | $C_2H_4$ | 0 | -43.98 | -44.03 | -46.61 | -48.74 | -50.70 | -52.50 | -54.19 | -55.78 | -57.29 | -58.74 | -60.12 | -61.44 | -62.71 | -63.94 |
| Propene (Propylene) | $C_3H_6$ | 0 | -52.95 | -53.02 | -56.39 | -59.32 | -62.05 | -64.61 | -67.04 | -69.36 | -71.57 | -73.69 | -75.73 | -77.70 | -79.60 | -81.43 |
| 1-Butene | $C_4H_8$ | 0 | -59.25 | -59.34 | -63.64 | -67.52 | -71.14 | -74.56 | -77.82 | -80.94 | -83.93 | -86.79 | -89.55 | -92.22 | -94.79 | -97.27 |
| 1-Pentene | $C_5H_{10}$ | 0 | -65.06 | -65.19 | -70.67 | -75.62 | -80.22 | -84.57 | -88.71 | -92.65 | -96.43 | -100.06 | -103.56 | -106.93 | -110.18 | -113.36 |
| 1-Hexene | $C_6H_{12}$ | 0 | -71.04 | -71.19 | -77.73 | -83.65 | -89.17 | -94.40 | -99.39 | -104.14 | -108.70 | -113.08 | -117.31 | -121.37 | -125.30 | -129.13 |
| 1-Heptene | $C_7H_{14}$ | 0 | -77.02 | -77.19 | -84.79 | -91.69 | -98.08 | -104.26 | -110.10 | -115.66 | -121.00 | -126.13 | -131.09 | -135.85 | -140.45 | -144.93 |
| 1-Octene | $C_8H_{16}$ | 0 | -83.00 | -83.19 | -91.85 | -99.74 | -106.98 | -114.11 | -120.80 | -127.17 | -133.30 | -139.19 | -144.87 | -150.32 | -155.60 | -160.73 |
| 1-Nonene | $C_9H_{18}$ | 0 | -88.98 | -89.19 | -98.91 | -107.78 | -115.89 | -123.97 | -131.50 | -138.69 | -145.60 | -152.24 | -158.65 | -164.80 | -170.75 | -176.52 |
| 1-Decene | $C_{10}H_{20}$ | 0 | -94.96 | -95.19 | -105.97 | -115.82 | -124.80 | -133.82 | -142.21 | -150.20 | -157.90 | -165.29 | -172.43 | -179.28 | -185.90 | -192.32 |
| 1-Undecene | $C_{11}H_{22}$ | 0 | -100.94 | -101.18 | -113.04 | -123.86 | -133.70 | -143.68 | -152.92 | -161.72 | -170.20 | -178.34 | -186.22 | -193.76 | -201.06 | -208.12 |
| 1-Dodecene | $C_{12}H_{24}$ | 0 | -106.91 | -107.18 | -120.10 | -131.91 | -142.61 | -153.54 | -163.62 | -173.24 | -182.49 | -191.40 | -200.00 | -208.23 | -216.21 | -223.92 |
| 1-Tridecene | $C_{13}H_{26}$ | 0 | -112.89 | -113.18 | -127.16 | -139.95 | -151.52 | -163.39 | -174.32 | -184.75 | -194.79 | -204.45 | -213.78 | -222.71 | -231.36 | -239.72 |
| 1-Tetradecene | $C_{14}H_{28}$ | 0 | -118.87 | -119.18 | -134.22 | -147.99 | -160.43 | -173.25 | -185.03 | -196.27 | -207.09 | -217.50 | -227.56 | -237.19 | -246.51 | -255.51 |
| 1-Pentadecene | $C_{15}H_{30}$ | 0 | -124.85 | -125.18 | -141.28 | -156.04 | -169.33 | -183.10 | -195.74 | -207.78 | -219.39 | -230.56 | -241.34 | -251.66 | -261.66 | -271.31 |
| 1-Hexadecene | $C_{16}H_{32}$ | 0 | -130.83 | -131.18 | -148.34 | -164.08 | -178.24 | -192.96 | -206.44 | -219.30 | -231.69 | -243.61 | -255.12 | -266.14 | -276.81 | -287.11 |
| 1-Heptadecene | $C_{17}H_{34}$ | 0 | -136.81 | -137.18 | -155.40 | -172.12 | -187.15 | -202.82 | -217.14 | -230.82 | -243.99 | -256.66 | -269.72 | -282.68 | -280.62 / -291.96 | -302.91 |
| 1-Octadecene | $C_{18}H_{36}$ | 0 | -142.79 | -143.18 | -162.46 | -180.17 | -196.05 | -212.67 | -227.85 | -242.33 | -256.29 | -269.72 | -282.68 | -295.09 | -307.11 | -318.71 |
| 1-Nonadecene | $C_{19}H_{38}$ | 0 | -148.77 | -149.18 | -169.52 | -188.21 | -204.96 | -222.53 | -238.56 | -253.85 | -268.59 | -282.77 | -296.46 | -309.57 | -322.26 | -334.50 |
| 1-Eicosene | $C_{20}H_{40}$ | 0 | -154.75 | -155.18 | -176.58 | 196.25 | -213.87 | -232.38 | -249.26 | -265.36 | -280.89 | -295.82 | -310.24 | -324.05 | -337.41 | -350.30 |
| Increment per CH₂ group, applicable beyond 1-hexene | | 0 | -5.979 | -5.999 | -7.061 | -8.043 | -8.907 | -9.856 | -10.705 | -11.516 | -12.229 | -13.052 | -13.781 | -14.477 | -15.151 | -15.798 |

TABLE 8s (PART 1) — MONOOLEFINS, $C_2$ TO $C_5$

FREE ENERGY FUNCTION, $(F^o-H^o_0)/T$, FOR THE IDEAL GAS STATE, AT 0° TO 1500°K.

December 31, 1944; March 31, 1945; October 31, 1945; April 30, 1946; December 31, 1952

| Compound (gas) | Formula | Temperature in °K |||||||||||||||
|---|---|---|---|---|---|---|---|---|---|---|---|---|---|---|---|---|
| | | 0 | 298.16 | 300 | 400 | 500 | 600 | 700 | 800 | 900 | 1000 | 1100 | 1200 | 1300 | 1400 | 1500 |
| | | Free Energy Function, $(F^o-H^o_0)/T$, in cal/deg mole ||||||||||||||
| Ethene (Ethylene) | $C_2H_4$ | 0 | -43.98 | -44.03 | -46.61 | -48.74 | -50.70 | -52.50 | -54.19 | -55.78 | -57.29 | -58.74 | -60.12 | -61.44 | -62.71 | -63.94 |
| Propene (Propylene) | $C_3H_6$ | 0 | -52.95 | -53.02 | -56.39 | -59.32 | -62.05 | -64.61 | -67.04 | -69.36 | -71.57 | -73.69 | -75.73 | -77.70 | -79.60 | -81.43 |
| 1-Butene | $C_4H_8$ | 0 | -59.25 | -59.34 | -63.64 | -67.52 | -71.14 | -74.56 | -77.82 | -80.94 | -83.93 | -86.79 | -89.55 | -92.22 | -94.79 | -97.27 |
| cis-2-Butene | " | 0 | -58.67 | -58.75 | -62.89 | -66.51 | -69.94 | -73.19 | -76.30 | -79.29 | -82.17 | -84.95 | -87.62 | -90.20 | -92.70 | -95.12 |
| trans-2-Butene | " | 0 | -56.80 | -56.89 | -61.31 | -65.19 | -68.84 | -72.27 | -75.53 | -78.64 | -81.62 | -84.47 | -87.22 | -89.87 | -92.44 | -94.91 |
| 2-Methylpropene (Isobutene) | " | 0 | -56.47 | -56.56 | -60.90 | -64.77 | -68.42 | -71.88 | -75.15 | -78.29 | -81.29 | -84.17 | -86.94 | -89.60 | -92.17 | -94.66 |
| 1-Pentene | $C_5H_{10}$ | 0 | -65.06 | -65.19 | -70.67 | -75.62 | -80.22 | -84.57 | -88.71 | -92.65 | -96.43 | -100.06 | -103.56 | -106.93 | -110.18 | -113.36 |
| cis-2-Pentene | " | 0 | -66.51 | -66.60 | -71.73 | -76.30 | -80.64 | -84.80 | -88.76 | -92.59 | -96.27 | -99.82 | -102.22 | -106.52 | -109.70 | -112.81 |
| trans-2-Pentene | " | 0 | -64.47 | -64.58 | -69.90 | -74.69 | -79.18 | -83.45 | -87.52 | -91.50 | -95.14 | -98.72 | -102.18 | -105.52 | -108.73 | -111.84 |
| 2-Methyl-1-butene | " | 0 | -64.96 | -65.06 | -70.41 | -75.23 | -79.80 | -84.14 | -88.27 | -92.24 | -96.04 | -99.69 | -103.18 | -106.55 | -109.80 | -112.96 |
| 3-Methyl-1-butene | " | 0 | -62.47 | -62.57 | -67.99 | -73.12 | -77.87 | -82.34 | -86.59 | -90.65 | -94.51 | -98.23 | -101.77 | -105.20 | -108.51 | -111.73 |
| 2-Methyl-2-butene | " | 0 | -64.71 | -64.79 | -69.87 | -74.53 | -78.89 | -83.06 | -87.03 | -90.85 | -94.52 | -98.06 | -101.46 | -104.75 | -107.91 | -110.99 |

TABLE 8s (PART 2) — MONOOLEFINS, C$_6$

FREE ENERGY FUNCTION, $(F°-H°_0)/T$, FOR THE IDEAL GAS STATE, AT 0° TO 1500°K

April 30, 1945; October 31, 1945; December 31, 1952

| Compound (gas) | Formula | Temperature in °K | | | | | | | | | | | | | | |
|---|---|---|---|---|---|---|---|---|---|---|---|---|---|---|---|---|
| | | 0 | 298.16 | 300 | 400 | 500 | 600 | 700 | 800 | 900 | 1000 | 1100 | 1200 | 1300 | 1400 | 1500 |
| | | Free Energy Function, $(F°-H°_0)/T$, in cal/deg mole | | | | | | | | | | | | | | |
| 1-Hexene | C$_6$H$_{12}$ | 0 | -71.04 | -71.19 | -77.73 | -83.65 | -89.17 | -94.40 | -99.39 | -104.14 | -108.70 | -113.08 | -117.31 | -121.37 | -125.30 | -129.13 |
| cis-2-Hexene | " | 0 | -72.32 | -72.45 | -78.8 | -84.4 | -89.7 | -94.8 | -99.6 | -104.3 | -108.8 | | | | | |
| trans-2-Hexene | " | 0 | -70.28 | -70.43 | -77.0 | -82.8 | -88.3 | -93.5 | -98.4 | -103.1 | -107.7 | | | | | |
| cis-3-Hexene | " | 0 | -71.44 | -71.54 | -77.7 | -83.6 | -88.4 | -93.4 | -98.2 | -102.9 | -107.3 | | | | | |
| trans-3-Hexene | " | 0 | -69.46 | -69.59 | -76.0 | -81.8 | -87.2 | -92.4 | -97.4 | -102.1 | -106.7 | | | | | |
| 2-Methyl-1-pentene | " | 0 | -70.77 | -70.91 | -77.4 | -83.3 | -88.9 | -94.2 | -99.2 | -104.0 | -108.5 | | | | | |
| 3-Methyl-1-pentene | " | 0 | -69.56 | -69.68 | -76.4 | -82.8 | -88.9 | -94.6 | -100.1 | -105.3 | -110.4 | | | | | |
| 4-Methyl-1-pentene | " | 0 | -69.50 | -69.63 | -75.9 | -81.6 | -87.1 | -92.2 | -97.1 | -102.6 | -106.4 | | | | | |
| 2-Methyl-2-pentene | " | 0 | -71.40 | -71.51 | -77.6 | -83.1 | -88.3 | -93.4 | -98.2 | -102.8 | -107.3 | | | | | |
| 3-Methyl-cis-2-pentene | " | 0 | -71.40 | -71.51 | -77.6 | -83.1 | -88.3 | -93.4 | -98.2 | -102.8 | -107.3 | | | | | |
| 3-Methyl-trans-2-pentene | " | 0 | -72.21 | -72.32 | -78.4 | -83.9 | -89.2 | -94.2 | -99.0 | -103.6 | -108.1 | | | | | |
| 4-Methyl-cis-2-pentene | " | 0 | -69.72 | -69.83 | -76.0 | -81.8 | -87.2 | -92.4 | -97.3 | -102.1 | -106.6 | | | | | |
| 4-Methyl-trans-2-pentene | " | 0 | -67.69 | -67.81 | -74.3 | -80.3 | -85.9 | -91.2 | -96.3 | -101.1 | -105.7 | | | | | |
| 2-Ethyl-1-butene | " | 0 | -70.20 | -70.31 | -76.7 | -82.4 | -87.9 | -93.1 | -98.1 | -102.8 | -107.4 | | | | | |
| 2,3-Dimethyl-1-butene | " | 0 | -67.36 | -67.48 | -73.9 | -79.9 | -85.6 | -90.9 | -96.0 | -100.9 | -105.5 | | | | | |
| 3,3-Dimethyl-1-butene | " | 0 | -64.63 | -64.75 | -70.8 | -76.4 | -81.8 | -86.9 | -91.9 | -96.7 | -101.2 | | | | | |
| 2,3-Dimethyl-2-butene | " | 0 | -67.56 | -67.68 | -73.8 | -79.3 | -84.5 | -89.5 | -94.3 | -98.9 | -103.3 | | | | | |

TABLE 11s (PART 1) – DIOLEFINS, $C_3$ TO $C_5$

FREE ENERGY FUNCTION, $(F°-H°_0)/T$, FOR THE IDEAL GAS STATE, AT 0° TO 1500°K

September 30, 1947; April 30, 1948

Temperature in °K

Free Energy Function, $(F°-H°_0)/T$, in cal/deg mole

| Compound (gas) | Formula | 0 | 298.16 | 300 | 400 | 500 | 600 | 700 | 800 | 900 | 1000 | 1100 | 1200 | 1300 | 1400 | 1500 |
|---|---|---|---|---|---|---|---|---|---|---|---|---|---|---|---|---|
| Propadiene (Allene) | $C_3H_4$ | 0 | -48.18 | -48.24 | -51.35 | -54.08 | -56.55 | -58.85 | -61.00 | -63.02 | -64.94 | -66.76 | -68.50 | -70.16 | -71.76 | -73.29 |
| 1,2-Butadiene | $C_4H_6$ | 0 | -57.11 | -57.19 | -61.21 | -64.79 | -68.10 | -71.19 | -74.11 | -76.88 | -79.52 | -82.04 | -84.47 | -86.80 | -89.02 | -91.18 |
| 1,3-Butadiene | " | 0 | -54.46 | -54.54 | -58.38 | -61.89 | -65.18 | -68.29 | -71.24 | -74.05 | -76.72 | -79.28 | -81.73 | -84.09 | -86.35 | -88.52 |
| 1,2-Pentadiene | $C_5H_8$ | 0 | -63.5 | -63.6 | -68.7 | -73.3 | -77.6 | -81.7 | -85.5 | -89.1 | -92.6 | -95.9 | -99.1 | -102.2 | -105.1 | -108.0 |
| 1,cis-3-Pentadiene | " | 0 | -62.9 | -63.0 | -67.6 | -71.8 | -75.8 | -79.6 | -83.3 | -86.7 | -90.1 | -93.3 | -96.4 | -99.3 | -102.2 | -105.0 |
| 1,trans-3-Pentadiene | " | 0 | -61.1 | -61.2 | -66.1 | -70.5 | -74.7 | -78.7 | -82.5 | -86.1 | -89.5 | -92.8 | -96.0 | -99.0 | -101.9 | -104.8 |
| 1,4-Pentadiene | " | 0 | -63.2 | -63.3 | -68.5 | -73.1 | -77.4 | -81.5 | -85.4 | -89.0 | -92.5 | -95.8 | -99.0 | -102.0 | -105.0 | -107.8 |
| 2,3-Pentadiene | " | 0 | -61.9 | -62.0 | -66.9 | -71.4 | -75.5 | -79.4 | -83.1 | -86.6 | -90.0 | -93.2 | -96.3 | -99.3 | -102.2 | -104.9 |
| 3-Methyl-1,2-butadiene | " | 0 | -60.6 | -60.7 | -65.7 | -70.2 | -74.5 | -78.5 | -82.2 | -85.8 | -89.2 | -92.5 | -95.7 | -98.7 | -101.6 | -104.4 |
| 2-Methyl-1,3-butadiene (Isoprene) | " | 0 | -60.4 | -60.5 | -65.3 | -69.8 | -74.0 | -78.0 | -81.8 | -85.4 | -88.9 | -92.2 | -95.4 | -98.4 | -101.4 | -104.2 |

528

TABLE 18s — ALKYL CYCLOPENTENES, $C_5$ TO $C_7$
FREE ENERGY FUNCTION, $(F^0 - H^0_0)/T$, FOR THE IDEAL GAS STATE, AT $0^0$ TO $1500^0K$
December 31, 1952

Free Energy Function, $(F^0 - H^0_0)/T$, in cal/deg mole

| Compound (gas) | Formula | 0 | 298.16 | 300 | 400 | 500 | 600 | 700 | 800 | 900 | 1000 | 1100 | 1200 | 1300 | 1400 | 1500 |
|---|---|---|---|---|---|---|---|---|---|---|---|---|---|---|---|---|
| Cyclopentene | $C_5H_8$ | 0 | -57.62 | -57.69 | -61.37 | -64.82 | -68.18 | -71.46 | -74.67 | -77.80 | -80.85 | -83.81 | -86.70 | -89.50 | -92.23 | -94.87 |
| 1-Methylcyclopentene | $C_6H_{10}$ | 0 | -63.1 | -63.2 | -67.9 | -72.4 | -76.7 | -80.9 | -85.0 | -89.0 | -92.8 | -96.6 | -100.2 | -103.7 | -107.1 | -110.4 |
| 3-Methylcyclopentene | " | 0 | -64.4 | -64.5 | -69.2 | -73.6 | -77.9 | -82.1 | -86.2 | -90.2 | -94.0 | -97.7 | -101.4 | -104.9 | -108.3 | -111.6 |
| 4-Methylcyclopentene | " | 0 | -64.1 | -64.2 | -68.8 | -73.2 | -77.5 | -81.7 | -85.8 | -89.8 | -93.6 | -97.3 | -100.9 | -104.4 | -107.8 | -111.1 |
| 1-Ethylcyclopentene | $C_7H_{12}$ | | | | | | | | | | | | | | | |
| 3-Ethylcyclopentene | " | | | | | | | | | | | | | | | |
| 4-Ethylcyclopentene | " | | | | | | | | | | | | | | | |
| 1,2-Dimethylcyclopentene | " | 0 | -65.8 | -65.9 | -71.8 | -77.3 | -82.6 | -87.7 | -92.7 | -97.5 | -102.1 | -106.6 | -110.9 | -115.1 | -119.2 | -123.2 |
| 1,3-Dimethylcyclopentene | " | 0 | -68.5 | -68.6 | -74.3 | -79.8 | -85.1 | -90.2 | -95.2 | -100.0 | -104.6 | -109.1 | -113.5 | -117.7 | -121.8 | -125.8 |
| 1,4-Dimethylcyclopentene | " | 0 | -69.5 | -69.7 | -75.4 | -80.8 | -86.1 | -91.2 | -96.2 | -101.0 | -105.6 | -110.1 | -114.4 | -118.6 | -122.7 | -126.7 |
| 1,5-Dimethylcyclopentene | " | 0 | -68.5 | -68.6 | -74.3 | -79.8 | -85.1 | -90.2 | -95.2 | -100.0 | -104.6 | -109.1 | -113.4 | -117.6 | -121.7 | -125.7 |
| 3,3-Dimethylcyclopentene | " | 0 | -66.1 | -66.2 | -71.7 | -77.0 | -82.2 | -87.3 | -92.3 | -97.1 | -101.7 | -106.2 | -110.6 | -114.9 | -119.0 | -123.0 |
| 3,cis-4-Dimethylcyclopentene | " | 0 | -69.0 | -69.1 | -74.7 | -80.1 | -85.4 | -90.5 | -95.5 | -100.3 | -104.9 | -109.4 | -113.8 | -118.0 | -122.1 | -126.1 |
| 3,trans-4-Dimethylcyclopentene | " | 0 | -69.2 | -69.4 | -75.0 | -80.4 | -85.7 | -90.8 | -95.8 | -100.6 | -105.2 | -109.7 | -114.1 | -118.3 | -122.4 | -126.4 |
| 3,cis-5-Dimethylcyclopentene | " | 0 | -67.0 | -67.1 | -72.8 | -78.2 | -83.5 | -88.6 | -93.6 | -98.4 | -103.0 | -107.5 | -111.9 | -116.1 | -120.2 | -124.2 |
| 3,trans-5-Dimethylcyclopentene | " | 0 | -67.0 | -67.1 | -72.8 | -78.2 | -83.5 | -88.6 | -93.6 | -98.4 | -103.0 | -107.5 | -111.9 | -116.1 | -120.2 | -124.2 |
| 4,4-Dimethylcyclopentene | " | | | | | | | | | | | | | | | |

Temperature in $^0K$

TABLE 19s – ALKYL CYCLOHEXENES, $C_6$ TO $C_8$

FREE ENERGY FUNCTION, $(F°-H°_0)/T$, FOR THE IDEAL GAS STATE, AT 0° TO 1500°K

December 31, 1952

| Compound (gas) | Formula | Temperature in °K | | | | | | | | | | | | | | |
|---|---|---|---|---|---|---|---|---|---|---|---|---|---|---|---|---|
| | | 0 | 298.16 | 300 | 400 | 500 | 600 | 700 | 800 | 900 | 1000 | 1100 | 1200 | 1300 | 1400 | 1500 |
| | | Free Energy Function, $(F°-H°_0)/T$, in cal/deg mole | | | | | | | | | | | | | | |
| Cyclohexene | $C_6H_{10}$ | 0 | -60.29 | -60.38 | -64.96 | -69.43 | -73.84 | -78.16 | -82.38 | -86.49 | -90.48 | -94.36 | -98.12 | -101.75 | -105.27 | -108.68 |
| 1-Methylcyclohexene | $C_7H_{12}$ | | | | | | | | | | | | | | | |
| 3-Methylcyclohexene | " | | | | | | | | | | | | | | | |
| 4-Methylcyclohexene | " | | | | | | | | | | | | | | | |
| 1-Ethylcyclohexene | $C_8H_{14}$ | | | | | | | | | | | | | | | |
| 3-Ethylcyclohexene | " | | | | | | | | | | | | | | | |
| 4-Ethylcyclohexene | " | | | | | | | | | | | | | | | |
| 1,2-Dimethylcyclohexene | " | | | | | | | | | | | | | | | |
| 1,3-Dimethylcyclohexene | " | | | | | | | | | | | | | | | |
| 1,4-Dimethylcyclohexene | " | | | | | | | | | | | | | | | |
| 1,5-Dimethylcyclohexene | " | | | | | | | | | | | | | | | |
| 1,6-Dimethylcyclohexene | " | | | | | | | | | | | | | | | |
| 3,3-Dimethylcyclohexene | " | | | | | | | | | | | | | | | |
| 3,cis-4-Dimethylcyclohexene | " | | | | | | | | | | | | | | | |
| 3,trans-4-Dimethylcyclohexene | " | | | | | | | | | | | | | | | |
| 3,cis-5-Dimethylcyclohexene | " | | | | | | | | | | | | | | | |
| 3,trans-5-Dimethylcyclohexene | " | | | | | | | | | | | | | | | |
| 3,cis-6-Dimethylcyclohexene | " | | | | | | | | | | | | | | | |
| 3,trans-6-Dimethylcyclohexene | " | | | | | | | | | | | | | | | |
| 4,4-Dimethylcyclohexene | " | | | | | | | | | | | | | | | |
| 4,cis-5-Dimethylcyclohexene | " | | | | | | | | | | | | | | | |
| 4,trans-5-Dimethylcyclohexene | " | | | | | | | | | | | | | | | |

TABLE 25s (PART 1) — NORMAL ACETYLENES (1-ALKYNES), C₂ TO C₂₀

FREE ENERGY FUNCTION, $(F°-H°_0)/T$, FOR THE IDEAL GAS STATE, AT 0° TO 1500°K

February 28, 1946; December 31, 1952

| Compound (gas) | Formula | Temperature in °K | | | | | | | | | | | | | | |
|---|---|---|---|---|---|---|---|---|---|---|---|---|---|---|---|---|
| | | 0 | 298.16 | 300 | 400 | 500 | 600 | 700 | 800 | 900 | 1000 | 1100 | 1200 | 1300 | 1400 | 1500 |
| | | Free Energy Function, $(F°-H°_0)/T$, in cal/deg mole | | | | | | | | | | | | | | |
| Ethyne (Acetylene) | C₂H₂ | 0 | -39.976 | -40.025 | -42.451 | -44.508 | -46.313 | -47.930 | -49.400 | -50.752 | -52.005 | -53.175 | -54.275 | -55.313 | -56.296 | -57.231 |
| Propyne (Methylacetylene) | C₃H₄ | 0 | -48.89 | -48.95 | -52.14 | -54.92 | -57.44 | -59.76 | -61.91 | -63.94 | -65.86 | -67.68 | -69.42 | -71.07 | -72.66 | -74.19 |
| 1-Butyne (Ethylacetylene) | C₄H₆ | 0 | -56.70 | -56.78 | -60.78 | -64.38 | -67.70 | -70.81 | -73.74 | -76.51 | -79.16 | -81.69 | -84.11 | -86.43 | -88.66 | -90.81 |
| 1-Pentyne | C₅H₈ | 0 | -62.51 | -62.63 | -67.81 | -72.48 | -76.78 | -80.82 | -84.63 | -88.22 | -91.66 | -94.96 | -98.12 | -101.14 | -104.05 | -106.90 |
| 1-Hexyne | C₆H₁₀ | 0 | -68.49 | -68.63 | -74.87 | -80.52 | -85.75 | -90.68 | -95.34 | -99.74 | -103.96 | -108.01 | -111.90 | -115.62 | -119.20 | -122.70 |
| 1-Heptyne | C₇H₁₂ | 0 | -74.47 | -74.63 | -81.93 | -88.57 | -94.72 | -100.53 | -106.04 | -111.25 | -116.26 | -121.07 | -125.68 | -130.09 | -134.35 | -138.50 |
| 1-Octyne | C₈H₁₄ | 0 | -80.45 | -80.63 | -88.99 | -96.61 | -103.69 | -110.39 | -116.74 | -122.77 | -128.56 | -134.12 | -139.46 | -144.57 | -149.50 | -154.29 |
| 1-Nonyne | C₉H₁₆ | 0 | -86.43 | -86.63 | -96.05 | -104.65 | -112.66 | -120.24 | -127.45 | -134.28 | -140.86 | -147.17 | -153.24 | -159.05 | -164.65 | -170.09 |
| 1-Decyne | C₁₀H₁₈ | 0 | -92.40 | -92.62 | -103.12 | -112.70 | -121.63 | -130.10 | -138.16 | -145.80 | -153.16 | -160.22 | -167.02 | -173.52 | -179.80 | -185.89 |
| 1-Undecyne | C₁₁H₂₀ | 0 | -98.38 | -98.62 | -110.18 | -120.74 | -130.60 | -139.96 | -148.86 | -157.32 | -165.45 | -173.28 | -180.81 | -188.00 | -194.96 | -201.69 |
| 1-Dodecyne | C₁₂H₂₂ | 0 | -104.36 | -104.62 | -117.24 | -128.78 | -139.57 | -149.81 | -159.56 | -168.83 | -177.75 | -186.33 | -194.59 | -202.48 | -210.11 | -217.49 |
| 1-Tridecyne | C₁₃H₂₄ | 0 | -110.34 | -110.62 | -124.30 | -136.82 | -148.54 | -159.67 | -170.27 | -180.35 | -190.05 | -199.38 | -208.37 | -216.96 | -225.26 | -233.28 |
| 1-Tetradecyne | C₁₄H₂₆ | 0 | -116.32 | -116.62 | -131.36 | -144.87 | -157.51 | -169.52 | -180.98 | -191.86 | -202.35 | -212.44 | -222.15 | -231.43 | -240.41 | -249.08 |
| 1-Pentadecyne | C₁₅H₂₈ | 0 | -122.30 | -122.62 | -138.42 | -152.91 | -166.48 | -179.38 | -191.68 | -203.38 | -214.65 | -225.49 | -235.93 | -245.91 | -255.56 | -264.88 |
| 1-Hexadecyne | C₁₆H₃₀ | 0 | -128.28 | -128.62 | -145.48 | -160.95 | -175.45 | -189.24 | -202.38 | -214.90 | -226.95 | -238.54 | -249.71 | -260.39 | -270.71 | -280.68 |
| 1-Heptadecyne | C₁₇H₃₂ | 0 | -134.26 | -134.62 | -152.54 | -169.00 | -184.42 | -199.09 | -213.09 | -226.41 | -239.25 | -251.60 | -263.49 | -274.86 | -285.86 | -296.48 |
| 1-Octadecyne | C₁₈H₃₄ | 0 | -140.24 | -140.62 | -159.60 | -177.04 | -193.39 | -208.95 | -223.80 | -237.93 | -251.55 | -264.65 | -277.27 | -289.34 | -301.01 | -312.27 |
| 1-Nonadecyne | C₁₉H₃₆ | 0 | -146.22 | -146.62 | -166.66 | -185.08 | -202.36 | -218.80 | -234.50 | -249.44 | -263.85 | -277.70 | -291.05 | -303.82 | -316.16 | -328.07 |
| 1-Eicosyne | C₂₀H₃₈ | 0 | -152.20 | -152.62 | -173.72 | -193.12 | -211.33 | -228.66 | -245.20 | -260.96 | -276.14 | -290.76 | -304.84 | -318.30 | -331.32 | -343.87 |
| Increment per CH₂ group, applicable beyond 1-pentyne | | 0 | -5.979 | -5.999 | -7.061 | -8.043 | -8.970 | -9.856 | -10.705 | -11.516 | -12.299 | -13.053 | -13.781 | -14.477 | -15.151 | -15.798 |

TABLE 12s – ACETYLENES, $C_2$ TO $C_5$

FREE ENERGY FUNCTION, $(F^o-H^o{}_0)/T$, FOR THE IDEAL GAS STATE, AT 0° TO 1500°K

April 30, 1945

| Compound (gas) | Formula | Temperature in °K | | | | | | | | | | | | | | |
|---|---|---|---|---|---|---|---|---|---|---|---|---|---|---|---|---|
| | | 0 | 298.16 | 300 | 400 | 500 | 600 | 700 | 800 | 900 | 1000 | 1100 | 1200 | 1300 | 1400 | 1500 |
| | | Free Energy Function, $(F^o-H^o{}_0)/T$, in cal/deg mole | | | | | | | | | | | | | | |
| Ethyne (Acetylene) | $C_2H_2$ | 0 | -39.976 | -40.025 | -42.451 | -44.508 | -46.313 | -47.930 | -49.400 | -50.752 | -52.005 | -53.175 | -54.275 | -55.313 | -56.296 | -57.231 |
| Propyne (Methylacetylene) | $C_3H_4$ | 0 | -48.89 | -48.95 | -52.14 | -54.92 | -57.44 | -59.76 | -61.91 | -63.94 | -65.86 | -67.68 | -69.42 | -71.07 | -72.66 | -74.19 |
| 1-Butyne (Ethylacetylene) | $C_4H_6$ | 0 | -56.70 | -56.78 | -60.78 | -64.38 | -67.70 | -70.81 | -73.74 | -76.51 | -79.16 | -81.69 | -84.11 | -86.43 | -88.66 | -90.81 |
| 2-Butyne (Dimethylacetylene) | " | 0 | -54.43 | -54.51 | -58.59 | -62.18 | -65.44 | -68.46 | -71.35 | -74.06 | -76.65 | -79.12 | -81.50 | -83.78 | -85.97 | -88.09 |
| 1-Pentyne | $C_5H_8$ | 0 | -62.49 | -62.60 | -67.8 | -72.5 | -76.8 | -80.9 | -84.7 | -88.3 | -91.8 | -95.1 | -98.2 | -101.2 | -104.2 | -107.0 |
| 2-Pentyne | " | 0 | -63.62 | -63.72 | -68.6 | -73.0 | -77.1 | -80.9 | -84.5 | -88.0 | -91.3 | -94.5 | -97.6 | -100.5 | -103.3 | -106.1 |
| 3-Methyl-1-butyne | " | 0 | -60.86 | -60.95 | -65.8 | -70.3 | -74.5 | -78.5 | -82.2 | -85.8 | -89.2 | -92.5 | -95.6 | -98.7 | -101.6 | -104.4 |

TABLE 21s (PART 1) - NORMAL ALKYL BENZENES, C₆ TO C₂₂

FREE ENERGY FUNCTION, $(F°-H°_0)/T$, FOR THE IDEAL GAS STATE, AT 0° TO 1500°K

November 30, 1945; December 31, 1952

| Compound (gas) | Formula | Temperature in °K | | | | | | | | | | | | | | |
| --- | --- | --- | --- | --- | --- | --- | --- | --- | --- | --- | --- | --- | --- | --- | --- | --- |
| | | 0 | 298.16 | 300 | 400 | 500 | 600 | 700 | 800 | 900 | 1000 | 1100 | 1200 | 1300 | 1400 | 1500 |
| | | Free Energy Function, $(F°-H°_0)/T$, in cal/deg mole | | | | | | | | | | | | | | |
| Benzene | C₆H₆ | 0 | -52.93 | -53.00 | -56.69 | -60.24 | -63.70 | -67.06 | -70.34 | -73.50 | -76.57 | -79.54 | -82.40 | -85.18 | -87.85 | -90.45 |
| Methylbenzene (Toluene) | C₇H₈ | 0 | -61.98 | -62.07 | -66.74 | -71.20 | -75.52 | -79.72 | -83.79 | -87.72 | -91.53 | -95.21 | -98.77 | -102.21 | -105.53 | -108.75 |
| Ethylbenzene | C₈H₁₀ | 0 | -68.26 | -68.37 | -74.14 | -79.64 | -84.94 | -90.08 | -95.05 | -99.84 | -104.47 | -108.94 | -113.25 | -117.42 | -121.44 | -125.32 |
| n-Pronylbenzene | C₉H₁₂ | 0 | -74.07 | -74.22 | -81.17 | -87.74 | -94.02 | -100.09 | -105.94 | -111.55 | -116.97 | -122.21 | -127.26 | -132.13 | -136.83 | -141.41 |
| n-Butylbenzene | C₁₀H₁₄ | 0 | -80.05 | -80.22 | -88.23 | -95.77 | -102.97 | -109.92 | -116.62 | -123.04 | -129.24 | -135.23 | -141.01 | -146.57 | -151.95 | -157.18 |
| n-Pentylbenzene | C₁₁H₁₆ | 0 | -86.15 | -86.34 | -95.41 | -103.94 | -112.07 | -119.91 | -127.45 | -134.69 | -141.68 | -148.41 | -154.92 | -161.18 | -167.23 | -173.10 |
| n-Hexylbenzene | C₁₂H₁₈ | 0 | -92.13 | -92.34 | -102.47 | -111.98 | -121.04 | -129.77 | -138.16 | -146.21 | -153.98 | -161.46 | -168.70 | -175.66 | -182.38 | -188.90 |
| n-Heptylbenzene | C₁₃H₂₀ | 0 | -98.11 | -98.34 | -109.53 | -120.05 | -130.01 | -139.62 | -148.86 | -157.72 | -166.28 | -174.52 | -182.48 | -190.13 | -197.53 | -204.70 |
| n-Octylbenzene | C₁₄H₂₂ | 0 | -104.09 | -104.34 | -116.59 | -128.07 | -138.98 | -149.48 | -159.56 | -169.24 | -178.58 | -187.57 | -196.26 | -204.61 | -212.68 | -220.49 |
| n-Nonylbenzene | C₁₅H₂₄ | 0 | -110.07 | -110.34 | -123.65 | -136.11 | -147.95 | -159.33 | -170.27 | -180.75 | -190.88 | -200.62 | -210.04 | -219.09 | -227.83 | -236.29 |
| n-Decylbenzene | C₁₆H₂₆ | 0 | -116.04 | -116.34 | -130.72 | -144.16 | -156.92 | -169.19 | -180.98 | -192.27 | -203.18 | -213.68 | -223.82 | -233.56 | -242.98 | -252.09 |
| n-Undecylbenzene | C₁₇H₂₈ | 0 | -122.02 | -122.33 | -137.78 | -152.20 | -165.89 | -179.05 | -191.68 | -203.79 | -215.47 | -226.73 | -237.61 | -248.04 | -258.14 | -267.89 |
| n-Dodecylbenzene | C₁₈H₃₀ | 0 | -128.00 | -128.33 | -144.84 | -160.24 | -174.86 | -188.90 | -202.38 | -215.30 | -227.77 | -239.76 | -251.39 | -262.52 | -273.29 | -283.69 |
| n-Tridecylbenzene | C₁₉H₃₂ | 0 | -133.98 | -134.33 | -151.90 | -168.28 | -183.83 | -198.76 | -213.09 | -226.82 | -240.07 | -252.83 | -265.17 | -277.00 | -288.44 | -299.48 |
| n-Tetradecylbenzene | C₂₀H₃₄ | 0 | -139.96 | -140.33 | -158.96 | -176.33 | -192.80 | -208.61 | -223.80 | -238.33 | -252.37 | -265.89 | -278.95 | -291.47 | -303.59 | -315.28 |
| n-Pentadecylbenzene | C₂₁H₃₆ | 0 | -145.94 | -146.33 | -166.02 | -184.37 | -201.77 | -218.47 | -234.50 | -249.85 | -264.67 | -278.94 | -292.73 | -305.95 | -318.74 | -331.08 |
| n-Hexadecylbenzene | C₂₂H₃₈ | 0 | -151.92 | -152.33 | -173.08 | -192.41 | -210.74 | -228.33 | -245.20 | -261.37 | -276.97 | -291.99 | -306.51 | -320.43 | -332.89 | -346.88 |
| Increment per CH₂ group, applicable beyond n-pentylbenzene | | 0 | -5.979 | -5.999 | -7.061 | -8.043 | -8.970 | -9.856 | -10.705 | -11.516 | -12.299 | -13.053 | -13.781 | -14.477 | -15.151 | -15.798 |

TABLE 5s — ALKYL BENZENES, $C_6$ TO $C_9$

FREE ENERGY FUNCTION, $(F^\circ - H^\circ_0)/T$, FOR THE IDEAL GAS STATE, AT 0° TO 1500°K

November 30, 1945

Free Energy Function, $(F^\circ - H^\circ_0)/T$, in cal/deg mole

| Compound (gas) | Formula | Temperature in °K | | | | | | | | | | | | | | |
|---|---|---|---|---|---|---|---|---|---|---|---|---|---|---|---|---|
| | | 0 | 298.16 | 300 | 400 | 500 | 600 | 700 | 800 | 900 | 1000 | 1100 | 1200 | 1300 | 1400 | 1500 |
| Benzene | $C_6H_6$ | 0 | -52.93 | -53.00 | -56.69 | -60.24 | -63.70 | -67.06 | -70.34 | -73.50 | -76.57 | -79.54 | -82.40 | -85.18 | -87.85 | -90.45 |
| Methylbenzene (Toluene) | $C_7H_8$ | 0 | -61.98 | -62.07 | -66.74 | -71.20 | -75.52 | -79.72 | -83.79 | -87.72 | -91.53 | -95.21 | -98.77 | -102.21 | -105.53 | -108.75 |
| Ethylbenzene | $C_8H_{10}$ | 0 | -68.26 | -68.37 | -74.14 | -79.64 | -84.94 | -90.08 | -95.05 | -99.84 | -104.47 | -108.94 | -113.25 | -117.42 | -121.44 | -125.32 |
| 1,2-Dimethylbenzene (o-Xylene) | " | 0 | -65.61 | -65.73 | -71.74 | -77.40 | -82.81 | -88.01 | -93.01 | -97.82 | -102.46 | -106.93 | -111.24 | -115.39 | -119.42 | -123.30 |
| 1,3-Dimethylbenzene (m-Xylene) | " | 0 | -67.63 | -67.74 | -73.50 | -78.95 | -84.20 | -89.28 | -94.18 | -98.91 | -103.48 | -107.89 | -112.15 | -116.27 | -120.25 | -124.11 |
| 1,4-Dimethylbenzene (p-Xylene) | " | 0 | -66.26 | -66.37 | -72.15 | -77.59 | -82.83 | -87.89 | -92.76 | -97.48 | -102.02 | -106.42 | -110.66 | -114.77 | -118.74 | -122.59 |
| n-Propylbenzene | $C_9H_{12}$ | 0 | -74.05 | -74.19 | -81.2 | -87.8 | -94.1 | -100.1 | -106.0 | -111.6 | -117.1 | -122.3 | -127.4 | -132.2 | -136.9 | -141.5 |
| Isopropylbenzene | " | 0 | -72.42 | -72.54 | -79.2 | -85.6 | -91.8 | -97.8 | -103.6 | -109.2 | -114.6 | -119.8 | -124.8 | -129.6 | -134.4 | -138.9 |
| 1-Methyl-2-ethylbenzene | " | 0 | -73.27 | -73.41 | -80.5 | -87.2 | -93.6 | -99.8 | -105.6 | -111.3 | -116.8 | -122.0 | -127.1 | -132.0 | -136.7 | -141.2 |
| 1-Methyl-3-ethylbenzene | " | 0 | -75.29 | -75.42 | -82.3 | -88.8 | -95.0 | -101.0 | -106.8 | -112.4 | -117.8 | -123.0 | -128.0 | -132.9 | -137.5 | -142.1 |
| 1-Methyl-4-ethylbenzene | " | 0 | -73.92 | -74.05 | -80.9 | -87.4 | -93.6 | -99.6 | -105.4 | -111.0 | -116.3 | -121.5 | -126.5 | -131.4 | -136.0 | -140.5 |
| 1,2,3-Trimethylbenzene | " | 0 | -71.40 | -71.53 | -78.4 | -84.9 | -91.2 | -97.2 | -102.9 | -108.5 | -113.8 | -119.0 | -123.9 | -128.7 | -133.4 | -137.8 |
| 1,2,4-Trimethylbenzene | " | 0 | -72.57 | -72.70 | -79.6 | -86.2 | -92.4 | -98.4 | -104.2 | -109.8 | -115.1 | -120.3 | -125.3 | -130.1 | -134.7 | -139.2 |
| 1,3,5-Trimethylbenzene | " | 0 | -70.93 | -71.06 | -77.66 | -84.04 | -90.18 | -96.08 | -101.77 | -107.26 | -112.56 | -117.68 | -122.62 | -127.40 | -132.03 | -136.50 |

TABLE 13s - STYRENES, $C_8$ and $C_9$

FREE ENERGY FUNCTION, $(F^0-H_0^0)/T$, FOR THE IDEAL GAS STATE, AT $0^0$ TO $1500^0$K

September 30, 1947

| Compound (gas) | Formula | Temperature in °K |||||||||||||||
| --- | --- | --- | --- | --- | --- | --- | --- | --- | --- | --- | --- | --- | --- | --- | --- | --- |
| | | Free Energy Function , $(F^0-H_0^0)/T$, in cal/deg mole |||||||||||||||
| | | 0 | 298.16 | 300 | 400 | 500 | 600 | 700 | 800 | 900 | 1000 | 1100 | 1200 | 1300 | 1400 | 1500 |
| Ethenylbenzene (Styrene; Vinylbenzene; Phenylethylene) | $C_8H_8$ | 0 | -65.76 | -65.86 | -71.28 | -76.44 | -81.42 | -86.21 | -90.82 | -95.26 | -99.54 | -103.66 | -107.61 | -111.44 | -115.13 | -118.68 |
| Isopropenylbenzene (α-Methylstyrene; 2-Phenyl-1-propene) | $C_9H_{10}$ | 0 | -71.4 | -71.5 | -78.1 | -84.2 | -90.1 | -95.8 | -101.2 | -106.4 | -111.4 | -116.3 | -120.9 | -125.4 | -129.7 | -133.9 |
| cis-1-Propenylbenzene (cis-β-Methylstyrene; cis-1-Phenyl-1-propene) | " | 0 | -71.4 | -71.5 | -78.1 | -84.2 | -90.1 | -95.8 | -101.2 | -106.4 | -111.4 | -116.3 | -120.9 | -125.4 | -129.7 | -133.9 |
| trans-1-Propenylbenzene (trans-β-Methylstyrene; trans-1-Phenyl-1-propene) | " | 0 | -71.0 | -71.1 | -77.6 | -83.7 | -89.6 | -95.3 | -100.7 | -105.9 | -111.0 | -115.8 | -120.5 | -125.0 | -129.4 | -133.5 |
| 1-Methyl-2-ethenylbenzene (o-Methylstyrene) | " | 0 | -71.4 | -71.5 | -78.1 | -84.2 | -90.1 | -95.8 | -101.2 | -106.4 | -111.4 | -116.3 | -120.9 | -125.4 | -129.7 | -133.9 |
| 1-Methyl-3-ethenylbenzene (m-Methylstyrene) | " | 0 | -72.8 | -72.9 | -79.5 | -85.6 | -91.5 | -97.2 | -102.6 | -107.8 | -112.8 | -117.7 | -122.3 | -126.8 | -131.1 | -135.3 |
| 1-Methyl-4-ethenylbenzene (p-Methylstyrene) | " | 0 | -71.4 | -71.5 | -78.1 | -84.2 | -90.1 | -95.8 | -101.2 | -106.4 | -111.4 | -116.3 | -120.9 | -125.4 | -129.7 | -133.9 |

534

Table 00t — O, H, N, C,

ENTROPY, S°, FOR THE IDEAL GAS STATE, AT 0° TO 5000°K

June 30, 1946; August 31, 1949

Temperature in °K

Entropy, $S^o$, in cal/deg mole

| Compound (gas, monatomic) | Formula | 0 | 298.16 | 300 | 400 | 500 | 600 | 700 | 800 | 900 | 1000 | 1100 | 1200 | 1300 | 1400 | 1500 |
|---|---|---|---|---|---|---|---|---|---|---|---|---|---|---|---|---|
| Oxygen | O | 0 | 38.4689 | 38.5010 | 39.9915 | 41.1308 | 42.0540 | 42.8307 | 43.5011 | 44.0914 | 44.6183 | 45.0944 | 45.5287 | 45.9281 | 46.2976 | 46.6413 |
| Hydrogen | H | 0 | 27.3927 | 27.4232 | 28.8524 | 29.9610 | 30.8667 | 31.6326 | 32.2959 | 32.8811 | 33.4045 | 33.8780 | 34.3102 | 34.7079 | 35.0761 | 35.4188 |
| Nitrogen | N | 0 | 36.6147 | 36.6452 | 38.0744 | 39.1830 | 40.0888 | 40.8547 | 41.5180 | 42.1032 | 42.6266 | 43.1001 | 43.5323 | 43.9300 | 44.2982 | 44.6409 |
| Carbon | C | 0 | 37.7611 | 37.7917 | 39.2235 | 40.3333 | 41.2308 | 42.0060 | 42.6696 | 43.2550 | 43.7785 | 44.2521 | 44.6844 | 45.0824 | 45.4508 | 45.7938 |

Temperature in °K

Entropy, $S^o$, in cal/deg mole

| Compound (gas, monatomic) | Formula | 1000 | 1250 | 1500 | 1750 | 2000 | 2250 | 2500 | 2750 | 3000 | 3500 | 4000 | 4500 | 5000 |
|---|---|---|---|---|---|---|---|---|---|---|---|---|---|---|
| Oxygen | O | 44.6183 | 45.7324 | 46.6413 | 47.4094 | 48.0741 | 48.6635 | 49.1852 | 49.6605 | 50.0953 | 50.8693 | 51.5456 | 52.1486 | 52.6943 |
| Hydrogen | H | 33.4045 | 34.7722 | 35.4188 | 36.1850 | 36.8483 | 37.4335 | 37.9569 | 38.4304 | 38.8627 | 39.6285 | 40.2919 | 40.8770 | 41.4005 |
| Nitrogen | N | 42.6266 | 43.7352 | 44.6409 | 45.4067 | 46.0702 | 46.4070 | 47.1797 | 47.6546 | 48.0896 | 48.8670 | 49.5540 | 50.1780 | 50.7572 |
| Carbon | C | 43.7785 | 44.8874 | 45.7938 | 46.5618 | 47.2288 | 47.8204 | 48.3532 | 48.8391 | 49.2866 | 50.0904 | 50.7984 | 51.4320 | 52.0048 |

TABLE 0t – O₂, H₂, OH, H₂O, N₂, NO, C, CO, CO₂

ENTROPY, $S^o$, at 0° TO 5000°K

July 31, 1944; August 31, 1946; June 30, 1949

Entropy, $S^o$, in cal/deg mole

| Compound | Formula | State | Temperature in °K | | | | | | | | | | | | | | |
|---|---|---|---|---|---|---|---|---|---|---|---|---|---|---|---|---|---|
| | | | 0 | 50 | 100 | 150 | 200 | 250 | 298.16 | 300 | 400 | 500 | 600 | 700 | 800 | 900 | 1000 |
| Oxygen | O₂ | gas | 0 | | 41.390 | 44.210 | 46.214 | 47.766 | 49.003 | 49.048 | 51.093 | 52.723 | 54.100 | 55.296 | 56.364 | 57.322 | 58.194 |
| Hydrogen | H₂ | gas | 0 | | | | | 30.108 | 31.211 | 31.253 | 33.250 | 34.809 | 36.085 | 37.167 | 38.108 | 38.946 | 39.704 |
| Hydroxyl | OH | gas | 0 | | | | | | 43.888 | 43.923 | 45.978 | 47.553 | 48.840 | 49.927 | 50.877 | 51.723 | 52.491 |
| Water | H₂O | gas | 0 | | | | 42.990 | 44.543 | 45.106 | 45.154 | 47.490 | 49.344 | 50.903 | 52.269 | 53.490 | 54.599 | 55.618 |
| Nitrogen | N₂ | gas | 0 | | | | | | 45.767 | 45.809 | 47.818 | 49.385 | 50.685 | 51.805 | 52.797 | 53.692 | 54.509 |
| Nitric Oxide | NO | gas | 0 | | 42.271 | 45.345 | 47.465 | 49.078 | 50.339 | 50.384 | 52.436 | 54.048 | 55.392 | 56.557 | 57.589 | 58.520 | 59.370 |
| Carbon | C | solid graphite | 0 | | 0.2184 | 0.4459 | 0.7238 | 1.0365 | 1.3609 | 1.3737 | 2.081 | 2.788 | 3.474 | 4.127 | 4.740 | 5.314 | 5.846 |
| Carbon Monoxide | CO | gas | 0 | | 39.696 | | 44.521 | 46.074 | 47.301 | 47.343 | 49.352 | 50.927 | 52.238 | 53.373 | 54.379 | 55.287 | 56.117 |
| Carbon Dioxide | CO₂ | gas | 0 | | | | | | 51.061 | 51.116 | 53.815 | 56.113 | 58.109 | 59.894 | 61.507 | 62.979 | 64.331 |

Entropy, $S^o$, in cal/deg mole

| Compound | Formula | State | Temperature in °K | | | | | | | | | | | | | | |
|---|---|---|---|---|---|---|---|---|---|---|---|---|---|---|---|---|---|
| | | | 1100 | 1200 | 1300 | 1400 | 1500 | 1750 | 2000 | 2250 | 2500 | 2750 | 3000 | 3500 | 4000 | 4500 | 5000 |
| Oxygen | O₂ | gas | 58.993 | 59.730 | 60.419 | 61.061 | 61.659 | 63.017 | 64.213 | 65.284 | 66.257 | 67.150 | 67.976 | 69.464 | 70.779 | 71.957 | 73.022 |
| Hydrogen | H₂ | gas | 40.395 | 41.033 | 41.629 | 42.190 | 42.720 | 43.928 | 45.005 | 45.978 | 46.868 | 47.688 | 48.448 | 49.818 | 51.090 | 52.115 | 53.099 |
| Hydroxyl | OH | gas | 53.194 | 53.847 | 54.457 | 55.029 | 55.568 | 56.798 | 57.894 | 58.881 | 59.781 | 60.608 | 61.374 | 62.751 | 63.966 | 65.057 | 66.048 |
| Water | H₂O | gas | 56.564 | 57.451 | 58.287 | 59.078 | 59.830 | 61.571 | 63.137 | 64.562 | 65.863 | 67.07 | 68.19 | 70.22 | 72.04 | 73.63 | 75.08 |
| Nitrogen | N₂ | gas | 55.259 | 55.955 | 56.606 | 57.215 | 57.786 | 59.085 | 60.225 | 61.245 | 62.164 | 63.000 | 63.769 | 65.140 | 66.337 | 67.400 | 68.354 |
| Nitric Oxide | NO | gas | 60.150 | 60.872 | 61.544 | 62.170 | 62.760 | 64.088 | 65.252 | 66.290 | 67.225 | 68.077 | 68.857 | 70.247 | 71.459 | 72.535 | 73.504 |
| Carbon | C | solid graphite | 6.342 | 6.807 | 7.247 | 7.663 | 8.057 | 8.96 | 9.76 | 10.48 | 11.13 | 11.73 | 12.29 | 13.29 | 14.18 | | |
| Carbon Monoxide | CO | gas | 56.878 | 57.584 | 58.243 | 58.860 | 59.436 | 60.745 | 61.896 | 62.921 | 63.845 | 64.686 | 65.459 | 66.835 | 68.037 | 69.101 | 70.056 |
| Carbon Dioxide | CO₂ | gas | 65.582 | 66.747 | 67.836 | 68.857 | 69.817 | 72.00 | 73.92 | 75.64 | 77.20 | 78.62 | 79.92 | 82.27 | 84.32 | 86.15 | 87.80 |

TABLE 20t (PART 1) – NORMAL PARAFFINS, $C_1$ TO $C_{20}$
ENTROPY, $S^o$, FOR THE IDEAL GAS STATE, AT 0° TO 1500°K
November 30, 1945; December 31, 1952

| Compound (gas) | Formula | Temperature in °K — Entropy, $S^o$, in cal/deg mole | | | | | | | | | | | | | | |
|---|---|---|---|---|---|---|---|---|---|---|---|---|---|---|---|---|
| | | 0 | 298.16 | 300 | 400 | 500 | 600 | 700 | 800 | 900 | 1000 | 1100 | 1200 | 1300 | 1400 | 1500 |
| Methane | $CH_4$ | 0 | 44.50 | 44.55 | 47.17 | 49.48 | 51.64 | 53.68 | 55.61 | 57.45 | 59.21 | 60.89 | 62.50 | 64.04 | 65.51 | 66.93 |
| Ethane | $C_2H_6$ | 0 | 54.85 | 54.93 | 58.98 | 62.79 | 66.44 | 69.93 | 73.24 | 76.39 | 79.39 | 82.25 | 84.98 | 87.59 | 90.08 | 92.46 |
| Propane | $C_3H_8$ | 0 | 64.51 | 64.62 | 70.37 | 75.89 | 81.15 | 86.17 | 90.94 | 95.47 | 99.77 | 103.86 | 107.75 | 111.45 | 114.97 | 118.29 |
| n-Butane | $C_4H_{10}$ | 0 | 74.12 | 74.28 | 81.86 | 89.10 | 95.97 | 102.51 | 108.71 | 114.57 | 120.14 | 125.43 | 130.47 | 135.25 | 139.80 | 144.13 |
| n-Pentane | $C_5H_{12}$ | 0 | 83.40 | 83.59 | 92.95 | 101.88 | 110.34 | 118.38 | 126.02 | 133.22 | 140.06 | 146.55 | 152.74 | 158.59 | 164.17 | 169.47 |
| n-Hexane | $C_6H_{14}$ | 0 | 92.83 | 93.06 | 104.20 | 114.83 | 124.88 | 134.44 | 143.49 | 152.05 | 160.16 | 167.85 | 175.18 | 182.11 | 188.71 | 194.98 |
| n-Heptane | $C_7H_{16}$ | 0 | 102.24 | 102.50 | 115.42 | 127.74 | 139.39 | 150.45 | 160.95 | 170.84 | 180.22 | 189.11 | 197.59 | 205.59 | 213.20 | 220.46 |
| n-Octane | $C_8H_{18}$ | 0 | 111.55 | 111.84 | 126.54 | 140.56 | 153.80 | 166.37 | 178.30 | 189.53 | 200.18 | 210.28 | 219.90 | 228.98 | 237.61 | 245.84 |
| n-Nonane | $C_9H_{20}$ | 0 | 120.86 | 121.19 | 137.67 | 153.37 | 168.21 | 182.29 | 195.65 | 208.22 | 220.14 | 231.44 | 242.21 | 252.36 | 262.02 | 271.22 |
| n-Decane | $C_{10}H_{22}$ | 0 | 130.17 | 130.53 | 148.79 | 166.19 | 182.62 | 198.20 | 212.99 | 226.92 | 240.11 | 252.60 | 264.52 | 275.74 | 286.43 | 296.60 |
| n-Undecane | $C_{11}H_{24}$ | 0 | 139.48 | 139.87 | 159.92 | 179.01 | 197.03 | 214.12 | 230.34 | 245.61 | 260.07 | 273.77 | 286.83 | 299.13 | 310.84 | 321.98 |
| n-Dodecane | $C_{12}H_{26}$ | 0 | 148.78 | 149.22 | 171.04 | 191.82 | 211.44 | 230.04 | 247.69 | 264.30 | 280.03 | 294.94 | 309.14 | 322.52 | 335.24 | 347.36 |
| n-Tridecane | $C_{13}H_{28}$ | 0 | 158.09 | 158.56 | 182.16 | 204.64 | 225.84 | 245.96 | 265.04 | 282.99 | 299.99 | 316.10 | 331.44 | 345.90 | 359.65 | 372.74 |
| n-Tetradecane | $C_{14}H_{30}$ | 0 | 167.40 | 167.90 | 193.29 | 217.46 | 240.25 | 261.88 | 282.39 | 301.68 | 319.95 | 337.26 | 353.75 | 369.28 | 384.06 | 398.12 |
| n-Pentadecane | $C_{15}H_{32}$ | 0 | 176.71 | 177.24 | 204.41 | 230.28 | 254.66 | 277.79 | 299.73 | 320.38 | 339.92 | 358.43 | 376.06 | 392.67 | 408.47 | 423.50 |
| n-Hexadecane | $C_{16}H_{34}$ | 0 | 186.02 | 186.59 | 215.54 | 243.09 | 269.07 | 293.71 | 317.08 | 339.07 | 359.88 | 379.60 | 398.37 | 416.06 | 432.88 | 448.98 |
| n-Heptadecane | $C_{17}H_{36}$ | 0 | 195.33 | 195.93 | 226.66 | 255.91 | 283.48 | 309.63 | 334.43 | 357.76 | 379.84 | 400.76 | 420.68 | 439.44 | 457.29 | 474.26 |
| n-Octadecane | $C_{18}H_{38}$ | 0 | 204.64 | 205.27 | 237.78 | 268.73 | 297.89 | 325.54 | 351.78 | 376.45 | 399.80 | 421.92 | 442.99 | 462.82 | 481.70 | 499.64 |
| n-Nonadecane | $C_{19}H_{40}$ | 0 | 213.95 | 214.62 | 248.91 | 281.54 | 312.30 | 341.47 | 369.13 | 395.14 | 419.76 | 443.09 | 465.30 | 486.21 | 506.11 | 525.02 |
| n-Eicosane | $C_{20}H_{42}$ | 0 | 223.26 | 223.96 | 260.03 | 294.36 | 326.71 | 357.38 | 386.47 | 413.84 | 439.73 | 464.26 | 487.61 | 509.60 | 530.52 | 550.40 |
| Increment per $CH_2$ group, applicable beyond n-heptane | | 0 | 9.309 | 9.343 | 11.124 | 12.817 | 14.409 | 15.918 | 17.348 | 18.692 | 19.962 | 21.165 | 22.309 | 23.385 | 24.409 | 25.380 |

TABLE 1t – PARAFFINS, C$_1$ TO C$_5$

ENTROPY, S°, FOR THE IDEAL GAS STATE, AT 0° TO 1500°K

August 31, 1944; February 28, 1949; December 31, 1952

Entropy, $S^o$, in cal/deg mole — Temperature in °K

| Compound (gas) | Formula | 0 | 100 | 150 | 200 | 250 | 298.16 | 300 | 350 | 400 | 450 | 500 | 600 | 700 | 800 | 900 |
|---|---|---|---|---|---|---|---|---|---|---|---|---|---|---|---|---|
| Methane | CH$_4$ | 0 | 35.72 | 38.94 | 41.23 | 43.03 | 44.50 | 44.55 | 45.91 | 47.17 | 48.35 | 49.48 | 51.64 | 53.68 | 55.61 | 57.45 |
| Ethane | C$_2$H$_6$ | 0 | 43.94 | 47.56 | 50.35 | 52.74 | 54.85 | 54.93 | 56.98 | 58.98 | 60.90 | 62.79 | 66.44 | 69.93 | 73.24 | 76.39 |
| Propane | C$_3$H$_8$ | 0 | 50.52 | 54.87 | 58.44 | 61.64 | 64.51 | 64.62 | 67.54 | 70.37 | 73.17 | 75.89 | 81.15 | 86.17 | 90.94 | 95.47 |
| n-Butane | C$_4$H$_{10}$ | 0 |  |  | 65.99 | 70.30 | 74.12 | 74.28 | 78.11 | 81.86 | 85.53 | 89.10 | 95.97 | 102.51 | 108.71 | 114.57 |
| 2-Methylpropane (Isobutane) | " | 0 |  |  | 62.50 | 66.63 | 70.42 | 70.55 | 74.40 | 78.13 | 81.84 | 85.45 | 92.40 | 98.98 | 105.21 | 111.11 |
| n-Pentane | C$_5$H$_{12}$ | 0 |  |  | 73.39 | 78.66 | 83.40 | 83.59 | 88.32 | 92.95 | 97.47 | 101.88 | 110.34 | 118.38 | 126.02 | 133.22 |
| 2-Methylbutane (Isopentane) | ' | 0 |  |  | 72.50 | 77.50 | 82.12 | 82.29 | 86.95 | 91.56 | 96.09 | 100.52 | 109.04 | 117.16 | 124.82 | 132.09 |
| 2,2-Dimethylpropane (Neopentane) | " | 0 |  |  | 63.35 | 68.45 | 73.23 | 73.40 | 78.23 | 83.00 | 87.62 | 92.17 | 100.94 | 109.23 | 117.07 | 124.45 |

| Compound (gas) | Formula | 1000 | 1100 | 1200 | 1300 | 1400 | 1500 |
|---|---|---|---|---|---|---|---|
| Methane | CH$_4$ | 59.21 | 60.89 | 62.50 | 64.04 | 65.51 | 66.93 |
| Ethane | C$_2$H$_6$ | 79.39 | 82.25 | 84.98 | 87.59 | 90.08 | 92.46 |
| Propane | C$_3$H$_8$ | 99.77 | 103.86 | 107.75 | 111.45 | 114.97 | 118.29 |
| n-Butane | C$_4$H$_{10}$ | 120.14 | 125.43 | 130.47 | 135.25 | 139.80 | 144.13 |
| 2-Methylpropane (Isobutane) | " | 116.69 | 121.99 | 127.03 | 131.82 | 136.37 | 140.67 |
| n-Pentane | C$_5$H$_{12}$ | 140.06 | 146.55 | 152.74 | 158.59 | 164.17 | 169.47 |
| 2-Methylbutane (Isopentane) | ' | 138.97 | 145.51 | 151.73 | 157.64 | 163.27 | 168.61 |
| 2,2-Dimethylpropane (Neopentane) | " | 131.41 | 138.00 | 144.26 | 150.20 | 155.84 | 161.19 |

538

TABLE 2t (PART 1) — PARAFFINS. C$_6$

ENTROPY, S°, FOR THE IDEAL GAS STATE, AT 0° TO 1500°K

September 30, 1944; November 30, 1946; December 31, 1952

Temperature in °K

Entropy, S°, in cal/deg mole

| Compound (gas) | Formula | 0 | 298.16 | 300 | 400 | 500 | 600 | 700 | 800 | 900 | 1000 | 1100 | 1200 | 1300 | 1400 | 1500 |
|---|---|---|---|---|---|---|---|---|---|---|---|---|---|---|---|---|
| n-Hexane | C$_6$H$_{14}$ | 0 | 92.83 | 93.06 | 104.20 | 114.83 | 124.88 | 134.44 | 143.49 | 152.05 | 160.16 | 167.85 | 175.18 | 182.11 | 188.71 | 194.98 |
| 2-Methylpentane | " | 0 | 90.95 | 91.18 | 102.4 | 113.2 | 123.3 | 133.0 | 142.1 | 150.8 | 159.0 | | | | | |
| 3-Methylpentane | " | 0 | 90.77 | 91.00 | 102.1 | 112.8 | 122.8 | 132.4 | 141.4 | 150.0 | 158.1 | | | | | |
| 2,2-Dimethylbutane | " | 0 | 85.62 | 85.82 | 97.0 | 107.8 | 118.0 | 127.6 | 136.9 | 145.5 | 153.7 | | | | | |
| 2,3-Dimethylbutane | " | 0 | 87.42 | 87.63 | 98.64 | 109.27 | 119.39 | 129.00 | 138.08 | 146.67 | 154.81 | | | | | |

TABLE 2t (PART 2) – PARAFFINS, C$_7$

ENTROPY, S°, FOR THE IDEAL GAS STATE, AT 0° TO 1500°K

September 30, 1944; December 31, 1952

| Compound (gas) | Formula | Temperature in °K | | | | | | | | | | | | | | | | |
|---|---|---|---|---|---|---|---|---|---|---|---|---|---|---|---|---|---|---|
| | | 0 | 298.16 | 300 | 400 | 500 | 600 | 700 | 800 | 900 | 1000 | 1100 | 1200 | 1300 | 1400 | 1500 |
| | | | Entropy, S°, in cal/deg mole | | | | | | | | | | | | | |
| n-Heptane | C$_7$H$_{16}$ | 0 | 102.24 | 102.50 | 115.42 | 127.74 | 139.39 | 150.45 | 160.95 | 170.84 | 180.22 | 189.11 | 197.59 | 205.59 | 213.20 | 220.46 |
| 2-Methylhexane | " | 0. | 100.35 | 100.59 | 114.0 | 126.6 | 138.6 | 149.8 | 160.3 | 170.4 | 179.7 | | | | | |
| 3-Methylhexane | " | 0 | 101.37 | 101.60 | 114.8 | 127.4 | 139.3 | 150.5 | 161.0 | 171.0 | 180.4 | | | | | |
| 3-Ethylpentane | " | 0 | 98.30 | 98.53 | 111.6 | 124.0 | 135.7 | 146.7 | 157.2 | 167.1 | 176.5 | | | | | |
| 2,2-Dimethylpentane | " | 0 | 93.85 | 94.08 | 107.4 | 120.0 | 132.0 | 143.4 | 154.0 | 164.0 | 173.6 | | | | | |
| 2,3-Dimethylpentane | " | 0 | 98.96 | 99.19 | 112.6 | 125.0 | 137.0 | 148.1 | 158.6 | 168.6 | 177.9 | | | | | |
| 2,4-Dimethylpentane | " | 0 | 94.80 | 95.03 | 108.5 | 121.2 | 133.2 | 144.5 | 155.1 | 165.2 | 174.6 | | | | | |
| 3,3-Dimethylpentane | " | 0. | 95.53 | 95.76 | 109.3 | 121.9 | 134.1 | 145.4 | 156.1 | 166.2 | 175.7 | | | | | |
| 2,2,3-Trimethylbutane | " | 0 | 91.60 | 91.84 | 104.81 | 117.26 | 129.17 | 140.44 | 151.1 | 161.1 | 170.6 | 179.6 | 188.1 | 196.2 | 203.9 | 211.2 |

TABLE 3t - PARAFFINS, $C_8$

ENTROPY, $S^O$, FOR THE IDEAL GAS STATE, AT 0° TO 1500°K

October 31, 1944; December 31, 1952

| Compound (gas) | Formula | Temperature in °K | | | | | | | | | | | | | | |
|---|---|---|---|---|---|---|---|---|---|---|---|---|---|---|---|---|
| | | | | | | | | Entropy, $S^O$, in cal/deg mole | | | | | | | | |
| | | 0 | 298.16 | 300 | 400 | 500 | 600 | 700 | 800 | 900 | 1000 | 1100 | 1200 | 1300 | 1400 | 1500 |
| n-Octane | $C_8H_{18}$ | 0 | 111.55 | 111.84 | 126.54 | 140.56 | 153.80 | 166.37 | 178.30 | 189.53 | 200.18 | 210.28 | 219.90 | 228.98 | 237.61 | 245.84 |
| 2-Methylheptane | " | 0 | 108.81 | 109.09 | 124.3 | 138.7 | 152.3 | 165.1 | 177.1 | 188.4 | 199.1 | | | | | |
| 3-Methylheptane | " | 0 | 110.32 | 110.60 | 125.8 | 140.1 | 153.7 | 166.5 | 178.5 | 189.8 | 200.5 | | | | | |
| 4-Methylheptane | " | 0 | 108.35 | 108.62 | 123.8 | 138.1 | 151.5 | 164.8 | 176.3 | 187.6 | 198.3 | | | | | |
| 3-Ethylhexane | " | 0 | 109.51 | 109.78 | 124.6 | 138.6 | 151.8 | 164.4 | 176.4 | 187.7 | 198.3 | | | | | |
| 2,2-Dimethylhexane | " | 0 | 103.06 | 103.33 | 118.7 | 133.1 | 146.6 | 159.5 | 171.8 | 183.2 | 193.9 | | | | | |
| 2,3-Dimethylhexane | " | 0 | 106.11 | 106.38 | 121.9 | 136.8 | 150.6 | 163.6 | 175.6 | 187.0 | 197.7 | | | | | |
| 2,4-Dimethylhexane | " | 0 | 106.51 | 106.78 | 122.0 | 136.3 | 149.9 | 162.7 | 174.8 | 186.0 | 196.8 | | | | | |
| 2,5-Dimethylhexane | " | 0 | 104.93 | 105.20 | 120.5 | 134.9 | 148.5 | 161.3 | 173.3 | 184.5 | 195.3 | | | | | |
| 3,3-Dimethylhexane | " | 0 | 104.70 | 104.97 | 120.2 | 134.5 | 148.2 | 161.1 | 173.3 | 184.8 | 195.6 | | | | | |
| 3,4-Dimethylhexane[a,b] | " | 0 | 107.15 | 107.46 | 122.3 | 136.6 | 150.1 | 162.8 | 174.9 | 186.2 | 196.9 | | | | | |
| 2-Methyl-3-ethylpentane | " | 0 | 105.43 | 105.70 | 121.0 | 135.5 | 149.2 | 162.1 | 174.0 | 185.4 | 196.1 | | | | | |
| 3-Methyl-3-ethylpentane | " | 0 | 103.48 | 103.75 | 119.3 | 133.7 | 147.2 | 160.1 | 172.3 | 183.9 | 194.8 | | | | | |
| 2,2,3-Trimethylpentane | " | 0 | 101.62 | 101.88 | 117.3 | 131.8 | 145.4 | 158.3 | 170.4 | 181.9 | 192.8 | | | | | |
| 2,2,4-Trimethylpentane | " | 0 | 101.15 | 101.41 | 116.8 | 131.3 | 144.9 | 157.8 | 169.9 | 181.4 | 192.3 | | | | | |
| 2,3,3-Trimethylpentane | " | 0 | 103.14 | 103.40 | 118.9 | 133.4 | 147.2 | 160.1 | 172.1 | 183.6 | 194.6 | | | | | |
| 2,3,4-Trimethylpentane | " | 0 | 102.31 | 102.57 | 118.1 | 132.8 | 146.6 | 159.4 | 171.4 | 182.6 | 193.6 | | | | | |
| 2,2,3,3-Tetramethylbutane | " | 0 | 93.06 | 93.34 | 108.5 | 123.2 | 137.2 | 150.4 | 162.8 | 174.4 | 185.4 | | | | | |

a See footnote d of Table 3r.

b The values of the entropy for the racemic (dextro + levo) mixture are, algebraically, about 1.2 cal/deg mole lower, and those for the meso form about 1.5 cal/deg mole lower, than the values tabulated for the equilibrium mixture of the dextro, levo, and meso isomers of 3,4-dimethylhexane.

TABLE 22t (PART 1) – NORMAL ALKYL CYCLOPENTANES, C5 TO C21
ENTROPY, S°, FOR THE IDEAL GAS STATE, AT 0° TO 1500°K
March 31, 1947; December 31, 1952

| Compound (gas) | Formula | Temperature in °K |  |  |  |  |  |  |  |  |  |  |  |  |  |  |
|---|---|---|---|---|---|---|---|---|---|---|---|---|---|---|---|---|
|  |  |  |  |  |  |  | Entropy, S°, in cal/deg mole |  |  |  |  |  |  |  |  |  |
|  |  | 0 | 298.16 | 300 | 400 | 500 | 600 | 700 | 800 | 900 | 1000 | 1100 | 1200 | 1300 | 1400 | 1500 |
| Cyclopentane | $C_5H_{10}$ | 0 | 70.00 | 70.12 | 77.00 | 84.14 | 91.28 | 98.24 | 104.92 | 111.33 | 117.45 | 123.30 | 128.88 | 134.18 | 139.23 | 144.07 |
| Methylcyclopentane | $C_6H_{12}$ | 0 | 81.24 | 81.42 | 90.33 | 99.36 | 108.24 | 116.81 | 125.01 | 132.83 | 140.25 | 147.31 | 154.05 | 160.42 | 166.51 | 172.37 |
| Ethylcyclopentane | $C_7H_{14}$ | 0 | 90.42 | 90.64 | 101.40 | 112.18 | 122.69 | 132.85 | 142.53 | 151.71 | 160.42 | 168.70 | 176.59 | 184.09 | 191.17 | 197.99 |
| n-Propylcyclopentane | $C_8H_{16}$ | 0 | 99.73 | 99.98 | 112.52 | 125.00 | 137.10 | 148.77 | 159.88 | 170.40 | 180.38 | 189.87 | 198.90 | 207.47 | 215.58 | 223.37 |
| n-Butylcyclopentane | $C_9H_{18}$ | 0 | 109.04 | 109.33 | 123.65 | 137.81 | 151.51 | 164.69 | 177.23 | 189.09 | 200.34 | 211.03 | 221.21 | 230.86 | 239.99 | 248.75 |
| n-Pentylcyclopentane | $C_{10}H_{20}$ | 0 | 118.35 | 118.67 | 134.77 | 150.63 | 165.92 | 180.60 | 194.57 | 207.79 | 220.31 | 232.19 | 243.52 | 254.25 | 264.40 | 274.13 |
| n-Hexylcyclopentane | $C_{11}H_{22}$ | 0 | 127.66 | 128.01 | 145.90 | 163.45 | 180.33 | 196.52 | 211.92 | 226.48 | 240.27 | 253.36 | 265.83 | 277.63 | 288.81 | 299.51 |
| n-Heptylcyclopentane | $C_{12}H_{24}$ | 0 | 136.96 | 137.36 | 157.02 | 176.27 | 194.73 | 212.44 | 229.27 | 245.17 | 260.23 | 274.53 | 288.14 | 301.01 | 313.22 | 324.89 |
| n-Octylcyclopentane | $C_{13}H_{26}$ | 0 | 146.27 | 146.70 | 168.14 | 189.08 | 209.14 | 228.36 | 246.62 | 263.86 | 280.19 | 295.69 | 310.44 | 324.40 | 337.62 | 350.27 |
| n-Nonylcyclopentane | $C_{14}H_{28}$ | 0 | 155.58 | 156.04 | 179.27 | 201.90 | 223.55 | 244.28 | 263.97 | 282.55 | 300.15 | 316.85 | 332.75 | 347.79 | 362.03 | 375.65 |
| n-Decylcyclopentane | $C_{15}H_{30}$ | 0 | 164.89 | 165.38 | 190.39 | 214.72 | 237.96 | 260.19 | 281.31 | 301.25 | 320.12 | 338.02 | 355.06 | 371.17 | 386.44 | 401.03 |
| n-Undecylcyclopentane | $C_{16}H_{32}$ | 0 | 174.20 | 174.73 | 201.52 | 227.53 | 252.37 | 276.11 | 298.66 | 319.94 | 340.08 | 359.19 | 377.37 | 394.55 | 410.85 | 426.41 |
| n-Dodecylcyclopentane | $C_{17}H_{34}$ | 0 | 183.51 | 184.07 | 212.64 | 240.35 | 266.78 | 292.03 | 316.01 | 338.63 | 360.04 | 380.35 | 399.68 | 417.94 | 435.26 | 451.79 |
| n-Tridecylcyclopentane | $C_{18}H_{36}$ | 0 | 192.82 | 193.41 | 223.76 | 253.17 | 281.19 | 307.95 | 333.36 | 357.32 | 380.00 | 401.51 | 421.99 | 441.33 | 459.67 | 477.17 |
| n-Tetradecylcyclopentane | $C_{19}H_{38}$ | 0 | 202.13 | 203.76 | 234.89 | 265.98 | 295.60 | 323.87 | 350.71 | 376.01 | 399.96 | 422.68 | 444.30 | 464.71 | 484.08 | 502.55 |
| n-Pentadecylcyclopentane | $C_{20}H_{40}$ | 0 | 211.44 | 212.10 | 246.01 | 278.80 | 310.01 | 339.78 | 368.05 | 394.71 | 419.93 | 443.85 | 466.61 | 488.09 | 508.49 | 527.93 |
| n-Hexadecylcyclopentane | $C_{21}H_{42}$ | 0 | 220.75 | 221.44 | 257.14 | 291.62 | 324.42 | 355.70 | 385.40 | 413.40 | 439.89 | 465.01 | 488.92 | 511.48 | 532.90 | 553.31 |
| Increment per CH2 group, applicable beyond ethylcyclopentane |  | 0 | 9.309 | 9.343 | 11.124 | 12.817 | 14.409 | 15.918 | 17.348 | 18.692 | 19.962 | 21.165 | 22.309 | 23.385 | 24.409 | 25.380 |

## TABLE 6t – ALKYL CYCLOPENTANES, $C_5$ TO $C_7$
### ENTROPY, $S^0$, FOR THE IDEAL GAS STATE, AT 0° TO 1500°K
April 30, 1949; December 31, 1952

Temperature in °K

Entropy, $S^0$, in cal/deg mole

| Compound (gas) | Formula | 0 | 298.16 | 300 | 400 | 500 | 600 | 700 | 800 | 900 | 1000 | 1100 | 1200 | 1300 | 1400 | 1500 |
|---|---|---|---|---|---|---|---|---|---|---|---|---|---|---|---|---|
| Cyclopentane | $C_5H_{10}$ | 0 | 70.00 | 70.12 | 77.00 | 84.14 | 91.28 | 98.24 | 104.92 | 111.33 | 117.45 | 123.30 | 128.88 | 134.18 | 139.23 | 144.07 |
| Methylcyclopentane | $C_6H_{12}$ | 0 | 81.24 | 81.42 | 90.33 | 99.36 | 108.24 | 116.81 | 125.01 | 132.83 | 140.25 | 147.31 | 154.05 | 160.42 | 166.51 | 172.37 |
| Ethylcyclopentane | $C_7H_{14}$ | 0 | 90.42 | 90.64 | 101.40 | 112.18 | 122.69 | 132.85 | 142.53 | 151.71 | 160.42 | 168.70 | 176.59 | 184.09 | 191.17 | 197.99 |
| 1,1-Dimethylcyclopentane | " | 0 | 85.87 | 86.13 | 96.87 | 107.73 | 118.35 | 128.60 | 138.39 | 147.71 | 156.51 | 164.82 | 172.79 | 180.29 | 187.46 | 194.38 |
| 1,cis-2-Dimethylcyclopentane | " | 0 | 87.51 | 87.76 | 98.54 | 109.42 | 120.06 | 130.29 | 140.06 | 149.34 | 158.12 | 166.43 | 174.36 | 181.84 | 188.99 | 195.89 |
| 1,trans-2-Dimethylcyclopentane | " | 0 | 87.67 | 87.92 | 98.72 | 109.60 | 120.22 | 130.45 | 140.22 | 149.48 | 158.24 | 166.53 | 174.46 | 181.94 | 189.07 | 195.97 |
| 1,cis-3-Dimethylcyclopentane | " | 0 | 87.67 | 87.92 | 98.72 | 109.60 | 120.22 | 130.45 | 140.22 | 149.48 | 158.24 | 166.53 | 174.46 | 181.94 | 189.07 | 195.97 |
| 1,trans-3-Dimethylcyclopentane | " | 0 | 87.67 | 87.92 | 98.72 | 109.60 | 120.22 | 130.45 | 140.22 | 149.48 | 158.24 | 166.53 | 174.46 | 181.94 | 189.07 | 195.97 |

TABLE 23t (PART 1) — NORMAL ALKYL CYCLOHEXANES, C6 TO C22
ENTROPY, S°, FOR THE IDEAL GAS STATE, AT 0° TO 1500°K
March 31, 1947; December 31, 1952

| Compound (gas) | Formula | Temperature in °K | | | | | | | | | | | | | | |
|---|---|---|---|---|---|---|---|---|---|---|---|---|---|---|---|---|
| | | 0 | 298.16 | 300 | 400 | 500 | 600 | 700 | 800 | 900 | 1000 | 1100 | 1200 | 1300 | 1400 | 1500 |
| | | Entropy, $S^o$, in cal/deg mole | | | | | | | | | | | | | | |
| Cyclohexane | $C_6H_{12}$ | 0 | 71.28 | 71.44 | 80.18 | 89.24 | 98.30 | 107.14 | 115.65 | 123.80 | 131.59 | 139.0 | 146.0 | 152.7 | 159.0 | 165.1 |
| Methylcyclohexane | $C_7H_{14}$ | 0 | 82.06 | 82.28 | 93.22 | 104.32 | 115.21 | 125.77 | 135.86 | 145.46 | 154.57 | 163.2 | 171.4 | 179.2 | 186.6 | 193.7 |
| Ethylcyclohexane | $C_8H_{16}$ | 0 | 91.44 | 91.70 | 104.5 | 117.3 | 129.9 | 142.0 | 153.6 | 164.5 | 174.9 | 184.8 | 194.2 | 203.0 | 211.4 | 219.5 |
| n-Propylcyclohexane | $C_9H_{18}$ | 0 | 100.27 | 100.59 | 115.3 | 130.1 | 144.2 | 157.9 | 170.9 | 183.3 | 195.0 | 205.9 | 216.3 | 226.3 | 235.8 | 244.8 |
| n-Butylcyclohexane | $C_{10}H_{20}$ | 0 | 109.58 | 109.93 | 126.4 | 142.9 | 158.6 | 173.8 | 188.3 | 202.0 | 215.0 | 227.1 | 238.6 | 249.7 | 260.2 | 270.2 |
| n-Pentylcyclohexane | $C_{11}H_{22}$ | 0 | 118.89 | 119.28 | 137.5 | 155.7 | 173.0 | 189.7 | 205.6 | 220.7 | 234.9 | 248.2 | 260.9 | 273.1 | 284.6 | 295.6 |
| n-Hexylcyclohexane | $C_{12}H_{24}$ | 0 | 128.20 | 128.62 | 148.7 | 168.6 | 187.4 | 205.7 | 222.9 | 239.4 | 254.9 | 269.4 | 283.2 | 296.4 | 309.0 | 320.9 |
| n-Heptylcyclohexane | $C_{13}H_{26}$ | 0 | 137.51 | 137.96 | 159.8 | 181.4 | 201.8 | 221.6 | 240.3 | 258.1 | 274.8 | 290.5 | 305.5 | 319.8 | 333.4 | 346.3 |
| n-Octylcyclohexane | $C_{14}H_{28}$ | 0 | 146.82 | 147.30 | 170.9 | 194.2 | 216.3 | 237.5 | 257.7 | 276.8 | 294.8 | 311.7 | 327.8 | 343.2 | 357.8 | 371.7 |
| n-Nonylcyclohexane | $C_{15}H_{30}$ | 0 | 156.12 | 156.65 | 182.0 | 207.0 | 230.7 | 253.4 | 275.0 | 295.4 | 314.8 | 332.9 | 350.2 | 366.6 | 382.3 | 397.1 |
| n-Decylcyclohexane | $C_{16}H_{32}$ | 0 | 165.43 | 165.99 | 193.1 | 219.8 | 245.1 | 269.3 | 292.3 | 314.1 | 334.7 | 354.0 | 372.5 | 390.0 | 406.7 | 422.5 |
| n-Undecylcyclohexane | $C_{17}H_{34}$ | 0 | 174.74 | 175.33 | 204.3 | 232.7 | 259.5 | 285.3 | 309.7 | 332.8 | 354.7 | 375.2 | 394.8 | 413.3 | 431.1 | 447.8 |
| n-Dodecylcyclohexane | $C_{18}H_{36}$ | 0 | 184.05 | 184.68 | 215.4 | 245.5 | 273.9 | 301.2 | 327.1 | 351.5 | 374.6 | 396.3 | 417.1 | 436.7 | 455.5 | 473.2 |
| n-Tridecylcyclohexane | $C_{19}H_{38}$ | 0 | 193.36 | 194.02 | 226.5 | 258.3 | 288.3 | 317.1 | 344.4 | 370.2 | 394.6 | 417.5 | 439.4 | 460.1 | 479.9 | 498.6 |
| n-Tetradecylcyclohexane | $C_{20}H_{40}$ | 0 | 202.67 | 203.36 | 237.6 | 271.1 | 302.7 | 333.0 | 361.7 | 388.9 | 414.6 | 438.7 | 461.7 | 483.5 | 504.3 | 524.0 |
| n-Pentadecylcyclohexane | $C_{21}H_{42}$ | 0 | 211.98 | 212.71 | 248.7 | 283.9 | 317.1 | 348.9 | 379.1 | 407.6 | 434.5 | 459.8 | 484.0 | 506.9 | 528.7 | 549.4 |
| n-Hexadecylcyclohexane | $C_{22}H_{44}$ | 0 | 221.29 | 222.05 | 259.9 | 296.8 | 331.5 | 364.9 | 396.5 | 426.3 | 454.5 | 481.0 | 506.3 | 530.2 | 553.1 | 574.7 |
| Increment per CH2 group, applicable beyond n-propylcyclohexane | | 0 | 9.309 | 9.343 | 11.12 | 12.82 | 14.41 | 15.92 | 17.35 | 18.69 | 19.96 | 21.16 | 22.31 | 23.38 | 24.41 | 25.38 |

TABLE 7t - ALKYL CYCLOHEXANES, $C_6$ TO $C_8$
ENTROPY, $S°$, FOR THE IDEAL GAS STATE, AT 0° TO 1500°K

April 30, 1947

| Compound (gas) | Formula | Temperature in °K | | | | | | | | | | | | | | |
|---|---|---|---|---|---|---|---|---|---|---|---|---|---|---|---|---|
| | | 0 | 298.16 | 300 | 400 | 500 | 600 | 700 | 800 | 900 | 1000 | 1100 | 1200 | 1300 | 1400 | 1500 |
| | | | Entropy, $S°$, in cal/deg mole | | | | | | | | | | | | | |
| Cyclohexane | $C_6H_{12}$ | 0 | 71.28 | 71.44 | 80.18 | 89.24 | 98.30 | 107.14 | 115.65 | 123.80 | 131.59 | 139.0 | 146.0 | 152.7 | 159.0 | 165.1 |
| Methylcyclohexane | $C_7H_{14}$ | 0 | 82.06 | 82.28 | 93.22 | 104.32 | 115.21 | 125.77 | 135.86 | 145.46 | 154.57 | 163.2 | 171.4 | 179.2 | 186.6 | 193.7 |
| Ethylcyclohexane | $C_8H_{16}$ | 0 | 91.44 | 91.70 | 104.5 | 117.3 | 129.9 | 142.0 | 153.6 | 164.5 | 174.9 | 184.8 | 194.2 | 203.0 | 211.4 | 219.5 |
| 1,1-Dimethylcyclohexane | " | 0 | 87.24 | 87.52 | 100.0 | 112.7 | 125.2 | 137.4 | 149.0 | 160.1 | 170.6 | 180.5 | 189.9 | 198.8 | 207.3 | 215.5 |
| 1,cis-2-Dimethylcyclohexane | " | 0 | 89.51 | 89.79 | 102.4 | 115.2 | 127.7 | 139.8 | 151.4 | 162.4 | 172.8 | 182.7 | 192.0 | 200.8 | 209.3 | 217.4 |
| 1,trans-2-Dimethylcyclohexane | " | 0 | 88.65 | 88.94 | 101.7 | 114.7 | 127.3 | 139.5 | 151.1 | 162.2 | 172.6 | 182.5 | 191.9 | 200.8 | 209.2 | 217.3 |
| 1,cis-3-Dimethylcyclohexane a | " | 0 | 88.54 | 88.82 | 101.5 | 114.3 | 126.8 | 139.0 | 150.6 | 161.6 | 172.1 | 182.0 | 191.4 | 200.3 | 208.8 | 216.9 |
| 1,trans-3-Dimethylcyclohexane b | " | 0 | 89.92 | 90.20 | 102.8 | 115.6 | 128.1 | 140.2 | 151.7 | 162.6 | 173.0 | 182.9 | 192.2 | 201.0 | 209.4 | 217.5 |
| 1,cis-4-Dimethylcyclohexane | " | 0 | 88.54 | 88.82 | 101.5 | 114.2 | 126.7 | 138.8 | 150.3 | 161.2 | 171.6 | 181.5 | 190.8 | 199.6 | 208.0 | 216.1 |
| 1,trans-4-Dimethylcyclohexane | " | 0 | 87.19 | 87.47 | 100.2 | 113.1 | 125.7 | 137.9 | 149.5 | 160.6 | 171.1 | 181.0 | 190.3 | 199.2 | 207.7 | 215.8 |

a Formerly labeled "trans"; see footnote b of Table 7a.    b Formerly labeled "cis"; see footnote c of Table 7a.

TABLE 24t (PART 1) – NORMAL MONOOLEFINS (1-ALKENES), $C_2$ TO $C_{20}$
ENTROPY, $S^o$, FOR THE IDEAL GAS STATE, AT 0° TO 1500°K
November 30, 1945; April 30, 1946; December 31, 1952

| Compound (gas) | Formula | Temperature in °K | | | | | | | | | | | | | | |
| | | Entropy, $S^o$, in cal/deg mole | | | | | | | | | | | | | | |
| | | 0 | 298.16 | 300 | 400 | 500 | 600 | 700 | 800 | 900 | 1000 | 1100 | 1200 | 1300 | 1400 | 1500 |
|---|---|---|---|---|---|---|---|---|---|---|---|---|---|---|---|---|
| Ethene (Ethylene) | $C_2H_4$ | 0 | 52.45 | 52.51 | 55.89 | 58.98 | 61.92 | 64.68 | 67.28 | 69.74 | 72.06 | 74.26 | 76.34 | 78.32 | 80.21 | 82.01 |
| Propene (Propylene) | $C_3H_6$ | 0 | 63.80 | 63.90 | 68.86 | 73.47 | 77.87 | 82.04 | 85.98 | 89.72 | 93.26 | 96.61 | 99.80 | 102.84 | 105.72 | 108.48 |
| 1-Butene | $C_4H_8$ | 0 | 73.04 | 73.17 | 79.85 | 86.20 | 92.22 | 97.91 | 103.28 | 108.37 | 113.18 | 117.74 | 122.06 | 126.18 | 130.10 | 133.83 |
| 1-Pentene | $C_5H_{10}$ | 0 | 82.65 | 82.83 | 91.34 | 99.41 | 107.04 | 114.25 | 121.05 | 127.47 | 133.55 | 139.31 | 144.78 | 149.98 | 154.93 | 159.67 |
| 1-Hexene | $C_6H_{12}$ | 0 | 91.93 | 92.14 | 102.43 | 112.19 | 121.41 | 130.12 | 138.36 | 146.12 | 153.47 | 160.43 | 167.05 | 173.32 | 179.30 | 185.01 |
| 1-Heptene | $C_7H_{14}$ | 0 | 101.24 | 101.48 | 113.55 | 125.01 | 135.82 | 146.04 | 155.71 | 164.81 | 173.43 | 181.60 | 189.36 | 196.70 | 203.71 | 210.39 |
| 1-Octene | $C_8H_{16}$ | 0 | 110.55 | 110.83 | 124.68 | 137.82 | 150.23 | 161.96 | 173.06 | 183.50 | 193.39 | 202.76 | 211.67 | 220.09 | 228.12 | 235.77 |
| 1-Nonene | $C_9H_{18}$ | 0 | 119.86 | 120.17 | 135.80 | 150.64 | 164.64 | 177.87 | 190.40 | 202.20 | 213.36 | 223.92 | 233.98 | 243.48 | 252.53 | 261.15 |
| 1-Decene | $C_{10}H_{20}$ | 0 | 129.17 | 129.51 | 146.93 | 163.46 | 179.05 | 193.79 | 207.75 | 220.89 | 233.32 | 245.09 | 256.29 | 266.86 | 276.94 | 286.53 |
| 1-Undecene | $C_{11}H_{22}$ | 0 | 138.48 | 138.85 | 158.05 | 176.28 | 193.46 | 209.71 | 225.10 | 239.58 | 253.28 | 266.26 | 278.60 | 290.24 | 301.34 | 311.91 |
| 1-Dodecene | $C_{12}H_{24}$ | 0 | 147.78 | 148.20 | 169.17 | 189.09 | 207.86 | 225.63 | 242.45 | 258.27 | 273.24 | 287.42 | 300.90 | 313.63 | 325.75 | 337.29 |
| 1-Tridecene | $C_{13}H_{26}$ | 0 | 157.09 | 157.54 | 180.30 | 201.91 | 222.27 | 241.55 | 259.80 | 276.96 | 293.20 | 308.58 | 323.21 | 337.02 | 350.16 | 362.67 |
| 1-Tetradecene | $C_{14}H_{28}$ | 0 | 166.40 | 166.88 | 191.42 | 214.73 | 236.68 | 257.46 | 277.14 | 295.66 | 313.17 | 329.75 | 345.52 | 360.40 | 374.57 | 388.05 |
| 1-Pentadecene | $C_{15}H_{30}$ | 0 | 175.71 | 176.23 | 202.55 | 227.54 | 251.09 | 273.38 | 294.49 | 314.35 | 333.13 | 350.92 | 367.83 | 383.78 | 398.98 | 413.43 |
| 1-Hexadecene | $C_{16}H_{32}$ | 0 | 185.02 | 185.57 | 213.67 | 240.36 | 265.50 | 289.30 | 311.84 | 333.04 | 353.09 | 372.08 | 390.14 | 407.17 | 423.39 | 438.81 |
| 1-Heptadecene | $C_{17}H_{34}$ | 0 | 194.33 | 194.91 | 224.79 | 253.18 | 279.91 | 305.22 | 329.19 | 351.73 | 373.05 | 393.24 | 412.45 | 430.56 | 447.80 | 464.19 |
| 1-Octadecene | $C_{18}H_{36}$ | 0 | 203.64 | 204.26 | 235.92 | 265.99 | 294.32 | 321.14 | 346.54 | 370.42 | 393.01 | 414.41 | 434.76 | 453.94 | 472.21 | 489.57 |
| 1-Nonadecene | $C_{19}H_{38}$ | 0 | 212.95 | 213.60 | 247.04 | 278.81 | 308.73 | 337.05 | 363.88 | 389.12 | 412.98 | 435.58 | 457.07 | 477.32 | 496.62 | 514.95 |
| 1-Eicosene | $C_{20}H_{40}$ | 0 | 222.26 | 222.94 | 258.17 | 291.63 | 323.14 | 352.97 | 381.23 | 407.81 | 432.94 | 456.74 | 479.38 | 500.71 | 521.03 | 540.33 |
| Increment per CH₂ group, applicable beyond 1-hexene | | 0 | 9.309 | 9.343 | 11.124 | 12.817 | 14.409 | 15.918 | 17.348 | 18.692 | 19.962 | 21.165 | 22.309 | 23.385 | 24.409 | 25.380 |

TABLE 8t (PART 1) — MONOOLEFINS, $C_2$ TO $C_5$

ENTROPY, $S^o$, FOR THE IDEAL GAS STATE, AT 0° TO 1500°K

December 31, 1944; March 31, 1945; October 31, 1945; April 30, 1946; December 31, 1952

| Compound (gas) | Formula | Temperature in °K |||||||||||||||
| | | Entropy, $s^o$, in cal/deg mole ||||||||||||||| 
| | | 0 | 298.16 | 300 | 400 | 500 | 600 | 700 | 800 | 900 | 1000 | 1100 | 1200 | 1300 | 1400 | 1500 |
|---|---|---|---|---|---|---|---|---|---|---|---|---|---|---|---|---|
| Ethene (Ethylene) | $C_2H_4$ | 0 | 52.45 | 52.51 | 55.89 | 58.98 | 61.92 | 64.68 | 67.28 | 69.74 | 72.06 | 74.26 | 76.34 | 78.32 | 80.21 | 82.01 |
| Propene (Propylene) | $C_3H_6$ | 0 | 63.80 | 63.90 | 68.86 | 73.47 | 77.87 | 82.04 | 85.98 | 89.72 | 93.26 | 96.61 | 99.80 | 102.84 | 105.72 | 108.48 |
| 1-Butene | $C_4H_8$ | 0 | 73.04 | 73.16 | 79.85 | 86.20 | 92.22 | 97.91 | 103.28 | 108.37 | 113.18 | 117.74 | 122.06 | 126.18 | 130.10 | 133.83 |
| cis-2-Butene | " | 0 | 71.90 | 72.02 | 78.25 | 84.19 | 89.95 | 95.46 | 100.69 | 105.67 | 110.40 | 114.91 | 119.19 | 123.26 | 127.15 | 130.86 |
| trans-2-Butene | " | 0 | 70.86 | 70.98 | 77.76 | 84.04 | 90.00 | 95.64 | 100.97 | 106.02 | 110.81 | 115.34 | 119.65 | 123.75 | 127.66 | 131.38 |
| 2-Methylpropene (Isobutene) | " | 0 | 70.17 | 70.30 | 77.21 | 83.60 | 89.67 | 95.38 | 100.77 | 105.85 | 110.66 | 115.23 | 119.56 | 123.68 | 127.59 | 131.33 |
| 1-Pentene | $C_5H_{10}$ | 0 | 82.65 | 82.83 | 91.34 | 99.41 | 107.04 | 114.25 | 121.05 | 127.47 | 133.55 | 139.31 | 144.78 | 149.98 | 154.93 | 159.67 |
| cis-2-Pentene | " | 0 | 82.76 | 82.89 | 90.97 | 98.68 | 106.11 | 113.21 | 119.90 | 126.27 | 132.32 | 138.04 | 143.46 | 148.64 | 153.56 | 158.29 |
| trans-2-Pentene | " | 0 | 81.36 | 81.52 | 89.93 | 97.87 | 105.42 | 112.55 | 119.30 | 125.67 | 131.72 | 137.44 | 142.87 | 148.05 | 152.97 | 157.67 |
| 2-Methyl-1-butene | " | 0 | 81.73 | 81.88 | 90.61 | 98.76 | 106.49 | 113.77 | 120.61 | 127.07 | 133.19 | 138.99 | 144.45 | 149.66 | 154.62 | 159.35 |
| 3-Methyl-1-butene | " | 0 | 79.70 | 79.86 | 88.94 | 97.54 | 105.48 | 112.87 | 119.79 | 126.31 | 132.45 | 136.27 | 143.76 | 148.99 | 153.95 | 158.70 |
| 2-Methyl-2-butene | " | 0 | 80.92 | 81.05 | 89.21 | 97.03 | 104.42 | 111.49 | 118.17 | 124.51 | 130.52 | 136.23 | 141.64 | 146.80 | 151.70 | 156.39 |

TABLE 8t (PART 2) - MONOOLEFINS, C$_6$

ENTROPY, S°, FOR THE IDEAL GAS STATE, AT 0° TO 1500°K

April 30, 1945; October 31, 1945; December 31, 1952

| Compound (gas) | Formula | Temperature in °K — Entropy, S°, in cal/deg mole | | | | | | | | | | | | | |
|---|---|---|---|---|---|---|---|---|---|---|---|---|---|---|---|
| | | 0 | 298.16 | 300 | 400 | 500 | 600 | 700 | 800 | 900 | 1000 | 1100 | 1200 | 1300 | 1400 | 1500 |
| 1-Hexene | C$_6$H$_{12}$ | 0 | 91.93 | 92.14 | 102.43 | 112.19 | 121.41 | 130.12 | 138.36 | 146.12 | 153.47 | 160.43 | 167.05 | 173.32 | 179.30 | 185.01 |
| cis-2-Hexene | " | 0 | 92.37 | 92.56 | 102.5 | 111.9 | 120.9 | 129.5 | 137.6 | 145.4 | 152.7 | | | | | |
| trans-2-Hexene | " | 0 | 90.97 | 91.18 | 101.5 | 111.1 | 120.3 | 128.9 | 137.1 | 144.7 | 152.1 | | | | | |
| cis-3-Hexene | " | 0 | 90.73 | 91.78 | 100.7 | 110.6 | 119.2 | 126.8 | 136.0 | 143.7 | 151.0 | | | | | |
| trans-3-Hexene | " | 0 | 89.59 | 89.78 | 100.2 | 109.9 | 119.0 | 127.9 | 136.1 | 143.8 | 151.2 | | | | | |
| 2-Methyl-1-pentene | " | 0 | 91.34 | 91.54 | 102.1 | 111.9 | 121.3 | 130.2 | 138.4 | 146.2 | 153.5 | | | | | |
| 3-Methyl-1-pentene | " | 0 | 90.06 | 90.25 | 101.7 | 112.8 | 123.3 | 133.1 | 142.3 | 150.9 | 159.2 | | | | | |
| 4-Methyl-1-pentene | " | 0 | 87.89 | 88.08 | 98.3 | 108.0 | 117.0 | 126.2 | 133.4 | 143.0 | 149.6 | | | | | |
| 2-Methyl-2-pentene | " | 0 | 90.45 | 90.62 | 100.6 | 110.1 | 119.2 | 127.8 | 135.9 | 143.6 | 151.0 | | | | | |
| 3-Methyl-cis-2-pentene | " | 0 | 90.45 | 90.62 | 100.6 | 110.1 | 119.2 | 127.8 | 135.9 | 143.6 | 151.0 | | | | | |
| 3-Methyl-trans-2-pentene | " | 0 | 91.26 | 91.43 | 101.4 | 110.9 | 120.0 | 128.6 | 136.8 | 144.5 | 151.8 | | | | | |
| 4-Methyl-cis-2-pentene | " | 0 | 89.23 | 89.41 | 99.8 | 109.7 | 119.0 | 127.7 | 135.9 | 143.7 | 151.0 | | | | | |
| 4-Methyl-trans-2-pentene | " | 0 | 88.02 | 88.21 | 99.1 | 109.2 | 118.7 | 127.5 | 135.8 | 143.6 | 151.0 | | | | | |
| 2-Ethyl-1-butene | " | 0 | 90.01 | 90.18 | 100.7 | 110.5 | 119.9 | 128.7 | 137.0 | 144.8 | 152.2 | | | | | |
| 2,3-Dimethyl-1-butene | " | 0 | 87.39 | 87.58 | 98.6 | 108.9 | 118.6 | 127.5 | 135.8 | 143.7 | 151.1 | | | | | |
| 3,3-Dimethyl-1-butene | " | 0 | 82.16 | 82.34 | 92.7 | 102.6 | 111.9 | 120.7 | 129.2 | 137.0 | 144.4 | | | | | |
| 2,3-Dimethyl-2-butene | " | 0 | 86.67 | 86.84 | 96.8 | 106.2 | 115.2 | 123.7 | 131.8 | 139.4 | 146.7 | | | | | |

## TABLE 11t (PART 1) – DIOLEFINS, $C_3$ TO $C_5$
## ENTROPY, $S°$, FOR THE IDEAL GAS STATE, AT 0° TO 1500°K

September 30, 1947; April 30, 1948

Temperature in °K

Entropy, $S°$, in cal/deg mole

| Compound (gas) | Formula | 0 | 298.16 | 300 | 400 | 500 | 600 | 700 | 800 | 900 | 1000 | 1100 | 1200 | 1300 | 1400 | 1500 |
|---|---|---|---|---|---|---|---|---|---|---|---|---|---|---|---|---|
| Propadiene (Allene) | $C_3H_4$ | 0 | 58.30 | 58.39 | 62.89 | 67.02 | 70.83 | 74.36 | 77.65 | 80.73 | 83.61 | 86.33 | 88.90 | 91.33 | 93.64 | 95.83 |
| 1,2-Butadiene | $C_4H_6$ | 0 | 70.03 | 70.15 | 76.28 | 81.95 | 87.25 | 92.20 | 96.85 | 101.22 | 105.34 | 109.22 | 112.91 | 116.42 | 119.72 | 122.88 |
| 1,3-Butadiene | " | 0 | 66.62 | 66.74 | 72.97 | 78.86 | 84.36 | 89.48 | 94.25 | 98.71 | 102.88 | 106.82 | 110.53 | 114.05 | 117.38 | 120.54 |
| 1,2-Pentadiene | $C_5H_8$ | 0 | 79.7 | 79.9 | 88.0 | 95.6 | 102.6 | 109.3 | 115.4 | 121.1 | 126.6 | 131.7 | 136.5 | 141.2 | 145.5 | 149.7 |
| 1,cis-3-Pentadiene | " | 0 | 77.5 | 77.6 | 85.1 | 92.3 | 99.2 | 105.7 | 111.7 | 117.4 | 122.18 | 127.9 | 132.7 | 137.2 | 141.6 | 145.7 |
| 1,trans-3-Pentadiene | " | 0 | 76.4 | 76.6 | 84.6 | 92.2 | 99.2 | 105.8 | 112.0 | 117.8 | 123.2 | 128.3 | 133.1 | 137.7 | 142.1 | 146.2 |
| 1,4-Pentadiene | " | 0 | 79.7 | 79.9 | 88.1 | 95.5 | 102.6 | 109.2 | 115.3 | 121.0 | 126.5 | 131.6 | 136.4 | 144.0 | 145.3 | 149.5 |
| 2,3-Pentadiene | " | 0 | 77.6 | 77.8 | 85.5 | 92.8 | 99.5 | 105.9 | 111.9 | 117.6 | 123.0 | 128.0 | 132.8 | 137.4 | 141.7 | 145.8 |
| 3-Methyl-1,2-butadiene | " | 0 | 76.4 | 76.5 | 84.6 | 92.0 | 99.1 | 105.6 | 111.6 | 117.3 | 122.7 | 127.8 | 132.7 | 137.3 | 141.6 | 145.7 |
| 2-Methyl-1,3-butadiene (Isoprene) | " | 0 | 75.44 | 75.59 | 83.7 | 91.4 | 98.6 | 105.3 | 111.5 | 117.3 | 122.7 | 127.9 | 132.7 | 137.3 | 141.7 | 145.8 |

TABLE 18t — ALKYL CYCLOPENTENES, C₅ TO C₇

ENTROPY, $S^\circ$, FOR THE IDEAL GAS STATE, AT 0° TO 1500°K

December 31, 1952

| Compound (gas) | Formula | Temperature in °K | | | | | | | | | | | | | | |
|---|---|---|---|---|---|---|---|---|---|---|---|---|---|---|---|---|
| | | 0 | 298.16 | 300 | 400 | 500 | 600 | 700 | 800 | 900 | 1000 | 1100 | 1200 | 1300 | 1400 | 1500 |
| | | Entropy, $S^\circ$, in cal/deg mole | | | | | | | | | | | | | | |
| Cyclopentene | C6H8 | 0 | 69.23 | 69.34 | 75.49 | 81.80 | 88.08 | 94.17 | 100.03 | 105.62 | 110.94 | 116.00 | 120.83 | 125.42 | 129.80 | 133.97 |
| 1-Methylcyclopentene | C6H10 | 0 | 78.0 | 78.2 | 86.2 | 94.4 | 102.3 | 109.9 | 117.2 | 124.2 | 130.7 | 137.1 | 143.0 | 148.6 | 154.0 | 159.2 |
| 3-Methylcyclopentene | " | 0 | 79.0 | 79.2 | 87.3 | 95.4 | 103.4 | 111.1 | 118.4 | 125.4 | 132.0 | 138.2 | 144.2 | 149.9 | 155.3 | 160.4 |
| 4-Methylcyclopentene | " | 0 | 78.6 | 78.8 | 86.8 | 94.9 | 102.9 | 110.6 | 117.9 | 124.9 | 131.5 | 137.8 | 143.7 | 149.3 | 154.7 | 159.8 |
| 1-Ethylcyclopentene | C7H12 | | | | | | | | | | | | | | | |
| 3-Ethylcyclopentene | " | | | | | | | | | | | | | | | |
| 4-Ethylcyclopentene | " | | | | | | | | | | | | | | | |
| 1,2-Dimethylcyclopentene | " | 0 | 84.0 | 84.2 | 94.3 | 104.3 | 113.9 | 123.0 | 131.8 | 140.1 | 147.9 | 155.4 | 162.4 | 169.1 | 175.5 | 181.6 |
| 1,3-Dimethylcyclopentene | " | 0 | 86.4 | 86.6 | 96.6 | 106.6 | 116.3 | 125.5 | 134.3 | 142.6 | 150.4 | 157.9 | 165.1 | 171.8 | 178.2 | 184.3 |
| 1,4-Dimethylcyclopentene | " | 0 | 87.3 | 87.7 | 97.6 | 107.5 | 117.2 | 126.4 | 135.2 | 143.5 | 151.3 | 158.8 | 165.9 | 172.6 | 179.0 | 185.1 |
| 1,5-Dimethylcyclopentene | " | 0 | 86.4 | 86.6 | 96.6 | 106.6 | 116.2 | 125.4 | 134.3 | 142.6 | 150.4 | 157.9 | 164.9 | 171.6 | 178.0 | 184.2 |
| 3,3-Dimethylcyclopentene | " | 0 | 83.1 | 83.3 | 93.2 | 103.2 | 112.9 | 122.3 | 131.3 | 139.8 | 147.7 | 155.3 | 162.6 | 169.5 | 176.0 | 182.1 |
| 3,cis-4-Dimethylcyclopentene | " | 0 | 86.4 | 86.6 | 96.6 | 106.6 | 116.4 | 125.7 | 134.6 | 143.0 | 150.9 | 158.4 | 165.5 | 172.2 | 178.6 | 184.8 |
| 3,trans-4-Dimethylcyclopentene | " | 0 | 86.8 | 87.1 | 97.1 | 107.1 | 116.8 | 126.0 | 134.8 | 143:2 | 151.1 | 158.6 | 165.7 | 172.4 | 178.8 | 185.0 |
| 3,cis-5-Dimethylcyclopentene | " | 0 | 84.6 | 84.8 | 94.9 | 104.9 | 114.6 | 123.8 | 132.6 | 141.0 | 148.9 | 156.4 | 163.5 | 170.2 | 176.6 | 182.8 |
| 3,trans-5-Dimethylcyclopentene | " | 0 | 84.6 | 84.8 | 94.9 | 104.9 | 114.6 | 123.8 | 132.6 | 141.0 | 148.9 | 156.4 | 163.5 | 170.2 | 176.6 | 182.8 |
| 4,4-Dimethylcyclopentene | " | | | | | | | | | | | | | | | |

TABLE 19t – ALKYL CYCLOHEXENES, $C_6$ TO $C_8$

ENTROPY, $S^o$, FOR THE IDEAL GAS STATE, AT 0° TO 1500°K

December 31, 1952

| Compound (gas) | Formula | Temperature in °K | | | | | | | | | | | | | | |
|---|---|---|---|---|---|---|---|---|---|---|---|---|---|---|---|---|
| | | 0 | 298.16 | 300 | 400 | 500 | 600 | 700 | 800 | 900 | 1000 | 1100 | 1200 | 1300 | 1400 | 1500 |
| | | | | | | Entropy, $S^o$, in cal/deg mole | | | | | | | | | | |
| Cyclohexene | $C_6H_{10}$ | 0 | 74.27 | 74.43 | 83.00 | 91.63 | 100.04 | 108.09 | 115.73 | 122.96 | 129.81 | 136.30 | 142.46 | 148.28 | 153.82 | 159.10 |
| 1-Methylcyclohexene | $C_7H_{12}$ | | | | | | | | | | | | | | | |
| 3-Methylcyclohexene | " | | | | | | | | | | | | | | | |
| 4-Methylcyclohexene | " | | | | | | | | | | | | | | | |
| 1-Ethylcyclohexene | $C_8H_{14}$ | | | | | | | | | | | | | | | |
| 3-Ethylcyclohexene | " | | | | | | | | | | | | | | | |
| 4-Ethylcyclohexene | " | | | | | | | | | | | | | | | |
| 1,2-Dimethylcyclohexene | " | | | | | | | | | | | | | | | |
| 1,3-Dimethylcyclohexene | " | | | | | | | | | | | | | | | |
| 1,4-Dimethylcyclohexene | " | | | | | | | | | | | | | | | |
| 1,5-Dimethylcyclohexene | " | | | | | | | | | | | | | | | |
| 1,6-Dimethylcyclohexene | " | | | | | | | | | | | | | | | |
| 3,3-Dimethylcyclohexene | " | | | | | | | | | | | | | | | |
| 3,cis-4-Dimethylcyclohexene | " | | | | | | | | | | | | | | | |
| 3,trans-4-Dimethylcyclohexene | " | | | | | | | | | | | | | | | |
| 3,cis-5-Dimethylcyclohexene | " | | | | | | | | | | | | | | | |
| 3,trans-5-Dimethylcyclohexene | " | | | | | | | | | | | | | | | |
| 3,cis-6-Dimethylcyclohexene | " | | | | | | | | | | | | | | | |
| 3,trans-6-Dimethylcyclohexene | " | | | | | | | | | | | | | | | |
| 4,4-Dimethylcyclohexene | " | | | | | | | | | | | | | | | |
| 4,cis-5-Dimethylcyclohexene | " | | | | | | | | | | | | | | | |
| 4,trans-5-Dimethylcyclohexene | " | | | | | | | | | | | | | | | |

TABLE 25t (PART 1) – NORMAL ACETYLENES (1-ALKYNES), C$_2$ TO C$_{20}$
ENTROPY, S°, FOR THE IDEAL GAS STATE, AT 0° TO 1500°K
February 28, 1946; December 31, 1952

| Compound (gas) | Formula | Temperature in °K | | | | | | | | | | | | | | |
| | | 0 | 298.16 | 300 | 400 | 500 | 600 | 700 | 800 | 900 | 1000 | 1100 | 1200 | 1300 | 1400 | 1500 |
| | | | Entropy, S°, in cal/deg mole | | | | | | | | | | | | | |
| Ethyne (Acetylene) | C$_2$H$_2$ | 0 | 47.997 | 48.061 | 51.304 | 54.090 | 56.525 | 58.692 | 60.649 | 62.441 | 64.095 | 65.635 | 67.077 | 68.432 | 69.712 | 70.925 |
| Propyne (Methylacetylene) | C$_3$H$_4$ | 0 | 59.30 | 59.39 | 63.96 | 68.09 | 71.88 | 75.38 | 78.63 | 81.67 | 84.53 | 87.22 | 89.77 | 92.17 | 94.46 | 96.64 |
| 1-Butyne (Ethylacetylene) | C$_4$H$_6$ | 0 | 69.51 | 69.61 | 75.86 | 81.60 | 86.92 | 91.90 | 96.54 | 100.89 | 104.99 | 108.87 | 112.53 | 116.01 | 119.31 | 122.45 |
| 1-Pentyne | C$_5$H$_8$ | 0 | 78.82 | 78.95 | 86.98 | 94.42 | 101.33 | 107.82 | 113.89 | 119.58 | 124.95 | 130.04 | 134.84 | 139.40 | 143.62 | 147.83 |
| 1-Hexyne | C$_6$H$_{10}$ | 0 | 88.13 | 88.29 | 98.10 | 107.24 | 115.74 | 123.74 | 131.24 | 138.27 | 144.91 | 151.20 | 157.15 | 162.78 | 168.03 | 173.21 |
| 1-Heptyne | C$_7$H$_{12}$ | 0 | 97.44 | 97.64 | 109.23 | 120.05 | 130.15 | 139.66 | 148.59 | 156.76 | 164.87 | 172.37 | 179.46 | 186.17 | 192.44 | 198.59 |
| 1-Octyne | C$_8$H$_{14}$ | 0 | 106.75 | 106.98 | 120.35 | 132.87 | 144.56 | 155.57 | 165.93 | 175.66 | 184.84 | 193.54 | 201.77 | 209.56 | 216.85 | 223.97 |
| 1-Nonyne | C$_9$H$_{16}$ | 0 | 116.06 | 116.32 | 131.48 | 145.69 | 158.97 | 171.49 | 183.28 | 194.35 | 204.80 | 214.70 | 224.08 | 232.94 | 241.26 | 249.35 |
| 1-Decyne | C$_{10}$H$_{18}$ | 0 | 125.36 | 125.67 | 142.60 | 158.50 | 173.38 | 187.41 | 200.63 | 213.04 | 224.76 | 235.86 | 246.38 | 256.32 | 265.67 | 274.73 |
| 1-Undecyne | C$_{11}$H$_{20}$ | 0 | 134.67 | 135.01 | 153.72 | 171.32 | 187.78 | 203.33 | 217.98 | 231.73 | 244.72 | 257.03 | 268.69 | 279.71 | 290.07 | 300.11 |
| 1-Dodecyne | C$_{12}$H$_{22}$ | 0 | 143.98 | 144.35 | 164.85 | 184.14 | 202.19 | 219.25 | 235.33 | 250.42 | 264.68 | 278.20 | 291.00 | 303.10 | 314.48 | 325.49 |
| 1-Tridecyne | C$_{13}$H$_{24}$ | 0 | 153.29 | 153.69 | 175.97 | 196.96 | 216.60 | 235.16 | 252.67 | 269.12 | 284.65 | 299.36 | 313.31 | 326.48 | 338.89 | 350.87 |
| 1-Tetradecyne | C$_{14}$H$_{26}$ | 0 | 162.60 | 163.04 | 187.10 | 209.77 | 231.01 | 251.08 | 270.02 | 287.81 | 304.61 | 320.52 | 335.62 | 349.86 | 363.30 | 376.25 |
| 1-Pentadecyne | C$_{15}$H$_{28}$ | 0 | 171.91 | 172.38 | 198.22 | 222.59 | 245.42 | 267.00 | 287.37 | 306.50 | 324.57 | 341.69 | 357.93 | 373.25 | 387.71 | 401.63 |
| 1-Hexadecyne | C$_{16}$H$_{30}$ | 0 | 181.22 | 181.72 | 209.34 | 235.41 | 259.83 | 282.92 | 304.72 | 325.19 | 344.53 | 362.86 | 380.24 | 396.64 | 412.12 | 427.01 |
| 1-Heptadecyne | C$_{17}$H$_{32}$ | 0 | 190.53 | 191.07 | 220.47 | 248.22 | 274.24 | 298.84 | 322.07 | 343.88 | 364.49 | 384.02 | 402.55 | 420.02 | 436.53 | 452.39 |
| 1-Octadecyne | C$_{18}$H$_{34}$ | 0 | 199.84 | 200.41 | 231.59 | 261.04 | 288.65 | 314.75 | 339.41 | 362.58 | 384.46 | 405.18 | 424.86 | 443.40 | 460.94 | 477.77 |
| 1-Nonadecyne | C$_{19}$H$_{36}$ | 0 | 209.15 | 209.75 | 242.72 | 273.86 | 303.06 | 330.67 | 356.76 | 381.27 | 404.42 | 426.35 | 447.17 | 466.79 | 485.35 | 503.15 |
| 1-Eicocyne | C$_{20}$H$_{38}$ | 0 | 218.46 | 219.10 | 253.84 | 286.68 | 317.46 | 346.59 | 374.11 | 399.96 | 424.38 | 447.52 | 469.48 | 490.18 | 509.76 | 528.53 |
| Increment per CH$_2$ group, applicable beyond 1-pentyne | | 0 | 9.309 | 9.343 | 11.124 | 12.817 | 14.409 | 15.918 | 17.348 | 18.692 | 19.962 | 21.165 | 22.309 | 23.385 | 24.409 | 25.380 |

TABLE 12t – ACETYLENES, $C_2$ TO $C_5$

ENTROPY, $S^o$, FOR THE IDEAL GAS STATE, AT 0° TO 1500°K

April 30, 1945

| Compound (gas) | Formula | Temperature in °K | | | | | | | | | | | | | | |
|---|---|---|---|---|---|---|---|---|---|---|---|---|---|---|---|---|
| | | 0 | 298.16 | 300 | 400 | 500 | 600 | 700 | 800 | 900 | 1000 | 1100 | 1200 | 1300 | 1400 | 1500 |
| | | Entropy, $S^o$, in cal/deg mole | | | | | | | | | | | | | | |
| Ethyne (Acetylene) | $C_2H_2$ | 0 | 47.997 | 48.061 | 51.304 | 54.090 | 56.525 | 58.692 | 60.649 | 62.441 | 64.095 | 65.635 | 67.077 | 68.432 | 69.712 | 70.925 |
| Propyne (Methylacetylene) | $C_3H_4$ | 0 | 59.30 | 59.39 | 63.96 | 68.09 | 71.88 | 75.38 | 78.63 | 81.67 | 84.53 | 87.22 | 89.77 | 92.17 | 94.46 | 96.64 |
| 1-Butyne (Ethylacetylene) | $C_4H_6$ | 0 | 69.51 | 69.61 | 75.86 | 81.60 | 86.92 | 91.90 | 96.54 | 100.89 | 104.99 | 108.87 | 112.53 | 116.01 | 119.31 | 122.45 |
| 2-Butyne (Dimethylacetylene) | " | 0 | 67.71 | 67.83 | 73.74 | 79.21 | 84.30 | 89.10 | 93.63 | 97.90 | 101.94 | 105.76 | 109.40 | 112.84 | 116.12 | 119.25 |
| 1-Pentyne | $C_5H_8$ | 0 | 79.10 | 79.24 | 87.4 | 94.9 | 101.9 | 108.4 | 114.5 | 120.1 | 125.5 | 130.6 | 135.3 | 139.9 | 144.3 | 148.4 |
| 2-Pentyne | " | 0 | 79.30 | 79.44 | 87.0 | 94.1 | 100.7 | 107.0 | 112.9 | 118.5 | 123.7 | 128.8 | 133.6 | 138.0 | 142.3 | 146.5 |
| 3-Methyl-1-butyne | " | 0 | 76.23 | 76.35 | 84.4 | 91.9 | 99.0 | 105.5 | 111.6 | 117.3 | 122.7 | 127.8 | 132.6 | 137.2 | 141.5 | 145.6 |

TABLE 21t (PART 1) – NORMAL ALKYL BENZENES, $C_6$ TO $C_{22}$,
ENTROPY, $S^o$, FOR THE IDEAL GAS STATE, AT 0° TO 1500°K
November 30, 1945; December 31, 1952

| Compound (gas) | Formula | Temperature in °K — Entropy, $S^o$, in cal/deg mole | | | | | | | | | | | | | |
|---|---|---|---|---|---|---|---|---|---|---|---|---|---|---|---|
| | | 0 | 298.16 | 300 | 400 | 500 | 600 | 700 | 800 | 900 | 1000 | 1100 | 1200 | 1300 | 1400 | 1500 |
| Benzene | $C_6H_6$ | 0 | 64.34 | 64.46 | 71.10 | 77.74 | 84.17 | 90.30 | 96.10 | 101.57 | 106.73 | 111.61 | 116.22 | 120.59 | 124.74 | 128.68 |
| Methylbenzene (Toluene) | $C_7H_8$ | 0 | 76.42 | 76.57 | 84.91 | 93.13 | 101.08 | 108.64 | 115.81 | 122.58 | 128.98 | 135.03 | 140.76 | 146.19 | 151.34 | 156.25 |
| Ethylbenzene | $C_8H_{10}$ | 0 | 86.15 | 86.34 | 96.59 | 106.63 | 116.28 | 125.43 | 134.08 | 142.23 | 149.92 | 157.19 | 164.07 | 170.59 | 176.79 | 182.67 |
| n-Propylbenzene | $C_9H_{12}$ | 0 | 95.76 | 96.00 | 108.07 | 119.19 | 131.09 | 141.77 | 151.85 | 161.32 | 170.29 | 178.76 | 186.79 | 194.40 | 201.61 | 208.51 |
| n-Butylbenzene | $C_{10}H_{14}$ | 0 | 105.04 | 105.31 | 119.16 | 132.62 | 145.46 | 157.64 | 169.16 | 179.97 | 190.21 | 199.88 | 209.06 | 217.74 | 225.98 | 233.85 |
| n-Pentylbenzene | $C_{11}H_{16}$ | 0 | 114.47 | 114.78 | 130.41 | 145.57 | 160.00 | 173.70 | 186.63 | 198.80 | 210.31 | 221.18 | 231.50 | 241.26 | 250.52 | 259.36 |
| n-Hexylbenzene | $C_{12}H_{18}$ | 0 | 123.78 | 124.12 | 141.53 | 158.39 | 174.41 | 189.62 | 203.98 | 217.49 | 230.27 | 242.34 | 253.81 | 264.64 | 274.93 | 284.74 |
| n-Heptylbenzene | $C_{13}H_{20}$ | 0 | 133.09 | 133.47 | 152.66 | 171.20 | 188.82 | 205.54 | 221.33 | 236.18 | 250.23 | 263.51 | 276.12 | 288.03 | 299.34 | 310.12 |
| n-Octylbenzene | $C_{14}H_{22}$ | 0 | 142.40 | 142.81 | 163.78 | 184.02 | 203.23 | 221.45 | 238.67 | 254.88 | 270.20 | 284.68 | 298.43 | 311.42 | 323.75 | 335.50 |
| n-Nonylbenzene | $C_{15}H_{24}$ | 0 | 151.71 | 152.15 | 174.91 | 196.84 | 217.64 | 237.37 | 256.02 | 273.57 | 290.16 | 305.84 | 320.74 | 334.80 | 348.16 | 360.88 |
| n-Decylbenzene | $C_{16}H_{26}$ | 0 | 161.02 | 161.50 | 186.03 | 209.66 | 232.04 | 253.29 | 273.37 | 292.26 | 310.12 | 327.00 | 343.04 | 358.18 | 372.56 | 386.26 |
| n-Undecylbenzene | $C_{17}H_{28}$ | 0 | 170.32 | 170.84 | 197.15 | 222.47 | 246.45 | 269.21 | 290.72 | 310.95 | 330.08 | 348.17 | 365.35 | 381.57 | 396.97 | 411.64 |
| n-Dodecylbenzene | $C_{18}H_{30}$ | 0 | 179.63 | 180.18 | 208.28 | 235.29 | 260.86 | 285.13 | 308.07 | 329.64 | 350.04 | 369.34 | 387.66 | 404.96 | 421.38 | 437.02 |
| n-Tridecylbenzene | $C_{19}H_{32}$ | 0 | 188.94 | 189.52 | 219.40 | 248.11 | 275.27 | 301.04 | 325.41 | 348.34 | 370.01 | 390.50 | 409.97 | 428.34 | 445.79 | 462.40 |
| n-Tetradecylbenzene | $C_{20}H_{34}$ | 0 | 198.25 | 198.87 | 230.53 | 260.92 | 289.68 | 316.96 | 342.76 | 367.03 | 389.97 | 411.66 | 432.28 | 451.72 | 470.20 | 487.78 |
| n-Pentadecylbenzene | $C_{21}H_{36}$ | 0 | 207.56 | 208.21 | 241.65 | 273.74 | 304.09 | 332.88 | 360.11 | 385.72 | 409.93 | 432.83 | 454.59 | 475.11 | 494.61 | 513.16 |
| n-Hexadecylbenzene | $C_{22}H_{38}$ | 0 | 216.87 | 217.55 | 252.77 | 286.56 | 318.50 | 348.80 | 377.46 | 404.41 | 429.89 | 454.00 | 476.90 | 498.50 | 519.02 | 538.54 |
| Increment per $CH_2$ group, applicable beyond n-pentylbenzene | | 0 | 9.309 | 9.343 | 11.124 | 12.817 | 14.409 | 15.918 | 17.348 | 18.692 | 19.962 | 21.165 | 22.309 | 23.385 | 24.409 | 25.380 |

TABLE 5t – ALKYL BENZENES, C$_6$ TO C$_9$

ENTROPY, S°, FOR THE IDEAL GAS STATE, AT 0° TO 1500°K

November 30, 1945

| Compound (gas) | Formula | Temperature in °K | | | | | | | | | | | | | | |
|---|---|---|---|---|---|---|---|---|---|---|---|---|---|---|---|---|
| | | 0 | 298.16 | 300 | 400 | 500 | 600 | 700 | 800 | 900 | 1000 | 1100 | 1200 | 1300 | 1400 | 1500 |
| | | Entropy, S°, in cal/deg mole | | | | | | | | | | | | | | |
| Benzene | C$_6$H$_6$ | 0 | 64.34 | 64.46 | 71.10 | 77.74 | 84.17 | 90.30 | 96.10 | 101.57 | 106.73 | 111.61 | 116.22 | 120.59 | 124.74 | 128.68 |
| Methylbenzene (Toluene) | C$_7$H$_8$ | 0 | 76.42 | 76.57 | 84.91 | 93.13 | 101.08 | 108.64 | 115.81 | 122.58 | 128.98 | 135.03 | 140.76 | 146.19 | 151.34 | 156.25 |
| Ethylbenzene | C$_8$H$_{10}$ | 0 | 86.15 | 86.34 | 96.59 | 106.63 | 116.28 | 125.43 | 134.08 | 142.23 | 149.92 | 157.19 | 164.07 | 170.59 | 176.79 | 182.67 |
| 1,2-Dimethylbenzene (o-Xylene) | " | 0 | 84.31 | 84.51 | 94.96 | 105.01 | 114.60 | 123.67 | 132.24 | 140.34 | 147.99 | 155.22 | 162.07 | 168.56 | 174.73 | 180.61 |
| 1,3-Dimethylbenzene (m-Xylene) | " | 0 | 85.49 | 85.68 | 95.81 | 105.67 | 115.14 | 124.16 | 132.70 | 140.78 | 148.41 | 155.63 | 162.47 | 168.96 | 175.12 | 181.00 |
| 1,4-Dimethylbenzene (p-Xylene) | " | 0 | 84.23 | 84.41 | 94.47 | 104.25 | 113.66 | 122.63 | 131.13 | 139.17 | 146.78 | 153.98 | 160.81 | 167.29 | 173.44 | 179.31 |
| n-Propylbenzene | C$_9$H$_{12}$ | 0 | 95.74 | 95.97 | 108.1 | 119.9 | 131.2 | 141.9 | 152.0 | 161.5 | 170.5 | 178.9 | 186.9 | 194.5 | 201.7 | 208.6 |
| Isopropylbenzene | " | 0 | 92.87 | 93.08 | 105.2 | 117.0 | 128.3 | 139.0 | 149.2 | 158.7 | 167.6 | 176.1 | 184.2 | 191.8 | 199.0 | 205.9 |
| 1-Methyl-2-ethylbenzene | " | 0 | 95.42 | 95.66 | 108.0 | 119.9 | 131.2 | 141.8 | 151.9 | 161.4 | 170.3 | 178.8 | 186.8 | 194.3 | 201.6 | 208.4 |
| 1-Methyl-3-ethylbenzene | " | 0 | 96.60 | 96.83 | 108.9 | 120.5 | 131.7 | 142.3 | 152.3 | 161.8 | 170.7 | 179.2 | 187.2 | 194.7 | 201.9 | 208.8 |
| 1-Methyl-4-ethylbenzene | " | 0 | 95.34 | 95.56 | 107.5 | 119.1 | 130.2 | 140.8 | 150.8 | 160.2 | 169.1 | 177.5 | 185.5 | 193.1 | 200.3 | 207.1 |
| 1,2,3-Trimethylbenzene | " | 0 | 93.50 | 93.73 | 105.4 | 116.9 | 127.8 | 138.3 | 148.1 | 157.4 | 166.2 | 174.6 | 182.5 | 190.1 | 197.2 | 204.0 |
| 1,2,4-Trimethylbenzene | " | 0 | 94.73 | 94.96 | 106.7 | 118.2 | 129.2 | 139.6 | 149.5 | 158.8 | 167.7 | 176.0 | 184.0 | 191.5 | 198.7 | 205.5 |
| 1,3,5-Trimethylbenzene | " | 0 | 92.15 | 92.37 | 103.87 | 115.28 | 126.22 | 136.64 | 146.51 | 155.85 | 164.69 | 173.07 | 181.01 | 188.56 | 195.73 | 202.55 |

## TABLE 13t - STYRENES, C$_8$ and C$_9$

### ENTROPY, S$^0$, FOR THE IDEAL GAS STATE, AT 0$^0$ TO 1500$^0$K

September 30, 1947

Temperature in $^0$K

Entropy, S$^0$, in cal/deg mole

| Compound (gas) | Formula | 0 | 298.16 | 300 | 400 | 500 | 600 | 700 | 800 | 900 | 1000 | 1100 | 1200 | 1300 | 1400 | 1500 |
|---|---|---|---|---|---|---|---|---|---|---|---|---|---|---|---|---|
| Ethenylbenzene (Styrene; Vinylbenzene; Phenylethylene) | C$_8$H$_8$ | 0 | 82.48 | 82.65 | 92.35 | 101.76 | 110.70 | 119.13 | 127.04 | 134.48 | 141.49 | 148.10 | 154.31 | 160.21 | 165.80 | 171.10 |
| Isopropenylbenzene (α-Methylstyrene; 2-Phenyl-1-propene) | C$_9$H$_{10}$ | 0 | 91.7 | 91.8 | 103.3 | 114.2 | 124.7 | 134.6 | 143.8 | 152.5 | 160.7 | 168.5 | 175.8 | 182.7 | 189.3 | 195.5 |
| cis-1-Propenylbenzene (cis-β-Methylstyrene; cis-1-Phenyl-1-propene) | " | 0 | 91.7 | 91.8 | 103.3 | 114.2 | 124.7 | 134.6 | 143.8 | 152.5 | 160.7 | 168.5 | 175.8 | 182.7 | 189.3 | 195.5 |
| trans-1-Propenylbenzene (trans-β-Methylstyrene; trans-1-Phenyl-1-propene) | " | 0 | 90.9 | 91.1 | 102.7 | 113.7 | 124.2 | 134.2 | 143.4 | 152.1 | 160.5 | 168.2 | 175.6 | 182.5 | 189.2 | 195.3 |
| 1-Methyl-2-ethenylbenzene (o-Methylstyrene) | " | 0 | 91.7 | 91.8 | 103.3 | 114.2 | 124.7 | 134.6 | 143.8 | 152.5 | 160.7 | 168.5 | 175.8 | 182.7 | 189.3 | 195.5 |
| 1-Methyl-3-ethenylbenzene (m-Methylstyrene) | " | 0 | 93.1 | 93.2 | 104.7 | 115.6 | 126.1 | 136.0 | 145.2 | 153.9 | 162.1 | 169.9 | 177.2 | 184.1 | 190.7 | 196.7 |
| 1-Methyl-4-ethenylbenzene (p-Methylstyrene) | " | 0 | 91.7 | 91.8 | 103.3 | 114.2 | 124.7 | 134.6 | 143.8 | 152.5 | 160.7 | 168.5 | 175.8 | 182.7 | 189.3 | 195.5 |

Table 00u – O, H, N, C

HEAT CONTENT (ENTHALPY), $(H^o-H^o_0)$, FOR THE IDEAL GAS STATE, AT 0° TO 5000°K

June 30, 1946; August 31, 1949

Heat Content (Enthalpy), $(H^o-H^o_0)$, in cal/mole

| Compound (gas monatomic) | Formula | Temperature in °K | | | | | | | | | | | | | | |
|---|---|---|---|---|---|---|---|---|---|---|---|---|---|---|---|---|
| | | 0 | 298.16 | 300 | 400 | 500 | 600 | 700 | 800 | 900 | 1000 | 1100 | 1200 | 1300 | 1400 | 1500 |
| Oxygen | O | 0 | 1607.4 | 1617.0 | 2134.9 | 2645.4 | 3151.7 | 3655.5 | 4157.6 | 4658.7 | 5158.8 | 5658.4 | 6157.6 | 6656.4 | 7155.0 | 7653.3 |
| Hydrogen | H | 0 | 1481.2 | 1490.4 | 1987.2 | 2484.0 | 2980.8 | 3477.6 | 3974.4 | 4471.2 | 4968.0 | 5464.7 | 5961.5 | 6458.3 | 6955.1 | 7451.9 |
| Nitrogen | N | 0 | 1481.2 | 1490.4 | 1987.2 | 2484.0 | 2980.8 | 3477.6 | 3974.4 | 4471.2 | 4968.0 | 5464.7 | 5961.5 | 6458.3 | 6955.1 | 7451.9 |
| Carbon | C | 0 | 1558.9 | 1568.1 | 2065.8 | 2563.1 | 3060.3 | 3557.3 | 4054.3 | 4551.3 | 5048.2 | 5545.1 | 6042.0 | 6539.1 | 7036.3 | 7533.4 |

Heat Content (Enthalpy), $(H^o-H^o_0)$, in cal/mole

| Compound (gas monatomic) | Formula | Temperature in °K | | | | | | | | | | | | |
|---|---|---|---|---|---|---|---|---|---|---|---|---|---|---|
| | | 1000 | 1250 | 1500 | 1750 | 2000 | 2250 | 2500 | 2750 | 3000 | 3500 | 4000 | 4500 | 5000 |
| Oxygen | O | 5158.8 | 6407.0 | 7653.3 | 8898.4 | 10142.8 | 11387.2 | 12632.5 | 13879.3 | 15128.7 | 17639.3 | 20172.0 | 22732.2 | 25322.0 |
| Hydrogen | H | 4968.0 | 6210.0 | 7451.9 | 8694.0 | 9936.0 | 11178.0 | 12420.0 | 13662.0 | 14904.0 | 17388.0 | 19872.0 | 22356.0 | 24840.0 |
| Nitrogen | N | 4968.0 | 6210.0 | 7451.9 | 8694.0 | 9936.2 | 11178.7 | 12422.3 | 13668.1 | 14917.8 | 17440.2 | 20013.2 | 22662.9 | 25412.5 |
| Carbon | C | 5048.2 | 6290.5 | 7533.4 | 8778.5 | 10027.6 | 11283.1 | 12547.5 | 13822.1 | 15108.0 | 17715.6 | 20367.2 | 23057.1 | 25776.0 |

TABLE 0u – O₂, H₂, OH, H₂O, N₂, NO, C, CO, CO₂

HEAT CONTENT (ENTHALPY), $(H^\circ - H^\circ_0)$, AT 0° TO 5000°K

July 31, 1944; August 31, 1946; June 30, 1949

Heat Content (Enthalpy), $(H^\circ - H^\circ_0)$, in cal/mole

| Compound | Formula | State | Temperature in °K |||||||||||||||
|---|---|---|---|---|---|---|---|---|---|---|---|---|---|---|---|---|---|
| | | | 0 | 50 | 100 | 150 | 200 | 250 | 298.16 | 300 | 400 | 500 | 600 | 700 | 800 | 900 | 1000 |
| Oxygen | $O_2$ | gas | 0 | | 690.4 | 1037.0 | 1384.4 | 1732.5 | 2069.8 | 2082.6 | 2792.4 | 3524.0 | 4279.2 | 5057.5 | 5856.0 | 6669.9 | 7497.0 |
| Hydrogen | $H_2$ | gas | 0 | 326.3 | 716.7 | 1038.5 | 1360.6 | 1694.3 | 2023.6 | 2036.5 | 2731.0 | 3429.5 | 4129.5 | 4831.5 | 5537.4 | 6248.0 | 6965.8 |
| Hydroxyl | OH | gas | 0 | | | | | | 2106.2 | 2119.2 | 2829.6 | 3535.0 | 4240.8 | 4946.9 | 5658.4 | 6377.4 | 7106.0 |
| Water | $H_2O$ | gas | 0 | | | | | | 2367.7 | 2382.4 | 3194.0 | 4025.5 | 4882.2 | 5771.5 | 6689.6 | 7634.7 | 8608.0 |
| Nitrogen | $N_2$ | gas | 0 | | | | 1389.30 | 1737.1 | 2072.27 | 2085.09 | 2782.4 | 3485.0 | 4198.0 | 4925.3 | 5668.6 | 6428.0 | 7202.5 |
| Nitric Oxide | NO | gas | 0 | | 742.7 | 1122.2 | 1490.6 | 1852.8 | 2194.2 | 2206.8 | 2920.8 | 3644.0 | 4381.2 | 5136.6 | 5909.6 | 6700.5 | 7506.0 |
| Carbon | C | solid graphite | 0 | | 14.451 | 43.155 | 91.980 | 162.475 | 251.56 | 255.30 | 502.8 | 821.0 | 1198.2 | 1621.9 | 2081.6 | 2569.5 | 3075.0 |
| Carbon Monoxide | CO | gas | 0 | | 693.4 | | 1389.4 | 1737.5 | 2072.6 | 2085.6 | 2783.6 | 3490.0 | 4209.6 | 4945.5 | 5700.0 | 6471.0 | 7257.0 |
| Carbon Dioxide | $CO_2$ | gas | 0 | | | | | | 2238.1 | 2254.0 | 3194.8 | 4223.0 | 5322.6 | 6481.3 | 7689.6 | 8938.8 | 10222.0 |

Heat Content (Enthalpy), $(H^\circ - H^\circ_0)$, in cal/mole

| Compound | Formula | State | Temperature in °K |||||||||||||||
|---|---|---|---|---|---|---|---|---|---|---|---|---|---|---|---|---|---|
| | | | 1100 | 1200 | 1300 | 1400 | 1500 | 1750 | 2000 | 2250 | 2500 | 2750 | 3000 | 3500 | 4000 | 4500 | 5000 |
| Oxygen | $O_2$ | gas | 8335.8 | 9183.6 | 10041.2 | 10904.6 | 11776.5 | 13981. | 16218. | 18493. | 20800. | 23141. | 25515. | 30342. | 35264. | 40271. | 45320. |
| Hydrogen | $H_2$ | gas | 7692.0 | 8427.5 | 9173.2 | 9928.7 | 10694.2 | 12654.1 | 14671.6 | 16738.9 | 18850.5 | 21001.5 | 23185.8 | 27635. | 32172. | 36780. | 41449. |
| Hydroxyl | OH | gas | 7844.1 | 8593.2 | 9354.8 | 10127.6 | 10909.5 | 12908. | 14960. | 17057. | 19193. | 21362. | 23559. | 28025. | 32576. | 37206. | 41910. |
| Water | $H_2O$ | gas | 9606.3 | 10630. | 11679. | 12753. | 13848. | 16683. | 19630. | 22666. | 25770. | 28930. | 32160. | 38675. | 45360. | 52065. | 58880. |
| Nitrogen | $N_2$ | gas | 7991.5 | 8792.8 | 9604.7 | 10425.4 | 11253.6 | 13357.4 | 15494.8 | 17659.8 | 19839.0 | 22036.0 | 24245.4 | 28697. | 33176. | 37688. | 42220. |
| Nitric Oxide | NO | gas | 8323.7 | 9152.4 | 9991.8 | 10838.8 | 11694.0 | 13850. | 16030. | 18232. | 20450. | 22682. | 24924. | 29428. | 33972. | 38552. | 43180. |
| Carbon | C | solid graphite | 3596. | 4130. | 4680. | 5242. | 5814. | 7280. | 8780. | 10305. | 11850. | 13420. | 15030. | 18270. | 21600. | | |
| Carbon Monoxide | CO | gas | 8056.4 | 8868.0 | 9690.2 | 10521.0 | 11358.0 | 13482. | 15636. | 17813. | 20008. | 22214. | 24435. | 28900. | 33396. | 37912. | 42450. |
| Carbon Dioxide | $CO_2$ | gas | 11535. | 12874. | 14234. | 15611. | 17004. | 20545. | 24140. | 27788. | 31480. | 35200. | 38940. | 46520. | 54160. | 61880. | 69650. |

TABLE 20u (PART 1) - NORMAL PARAFFINS, C₁ TO C₂₀

HEAT CONTENT (ENTHALPY), $(H° - H°_0)$, FOR THE IDEAL GAS STATE , AT 0° TO 1500°K

November 30, 1949; December 31, 1952

Heat Content (Enthalpy), $(H° - H°_0)$, in cal/mole

| Compound (gas) | Formula | Temperature in °K |  |  |  |  |  |  |  |  |  |  |  |  |  |  |
|---|---|---|---|---|---|---|---|---|---|---|---|---|---|---|---|---|
| | | 0 | 298.16 | 300 | 400 | 500 | 600 | 700 | 800 | 900 | 1000 | 1100 | 1200 | 1300 | 1400 | 1500 |
| Methane | $CH_4$ | 0 | 2397. | 2413. | 3323. | 4365. | 5549. | 6871. | 8321. | 9887. | 11560. | 13320. | 15170. | 17100. | 19090. | 21130. |
| Ethane | $C_2H_6$ | 0 | 2856. | 2879. | 4296. | 6010. | 8016. | 10280. | 12760. | 15440. | 18280. | 21290. | 24420. | 27680. | 31040. | 34500. |
| Propane | $C_3H_8$ | 0 | 3512. | 3546. | 5556. | 8040. | 10930. | 14190. | 17760. | 21600. | 25670. | 29950. | 34420. | 39030. | 43780. | 48650. |
| n-Butane | $C_4H_{10}$ | 0 | 4645. | 4689. | 7340. | 10595. | 14376. | 18620. | 23264. | 28251. | 33540. | 39083. | 44868. | 50843. | 56994. | 63270. |
| n-Pentane | $C_5H_{12}$ | 0 | 5629. | 5682. | 8952. | 12970. | 17628. | 22848. | 28568. | 34695. | 41190. | 47993. | 55092. | 62413. | 69944. | 77625. |
| n-Hexane | $C_6H_{14}$ | 0 | 6622. | 6687. | 10580. | 15360. | 20892. | 27097. | 33880. | 41157. | 48850. | 56925. | 65328. | 73996. | 82908. | 92010. |
| n-Heptane | $C_7H_{16}$ | 0 | 7615. | 7689. | 12204. | 17745. | 24156. | 31339. | 39200. | 47619. | 56520. | 65850. | 75560. | 85580. | 95870. | 106380. |
| n-Octane | $C_8H_{18}$ | 0 | 8608. | 8691. | 13828. | 20130. | 27420. | 35581. | 44512. | 54081. | 64180. | 74770. | 85800. | 97160. | 108840. | 120750. |
| n-Nonane | $C_9H_{20}$ | 0 | 9601. | 9696. | 15456. | 22520. | 30684. | 39823. | 49832. | 60534. | 71850. | 83690. | 96040. | 108740. | 121800. | 135120. |
| n-Decane | $C_{10}H_{22}$ | 0 | 10594. | 10698. | 17080. | 24905. | 33948. | 44072. | 55144. | 66996. | 79510. | 92620. | 106260. | 120320. | 134750. | 149500. |
| n-Undecane | $C_{11}H_{24}$ | 0 | 11587. | 11703. | 18704. | 27295. | 37212. | 48314. | 60456. | 73449. | 87170. | 101540. | 116560. | 131900. | 147710. | 163880. |
| n-Dodecane | $C_{12}H_{26}$ | 0 | 12579. | 12705. | 20332. | 29680. | 40476. | 52556. | 65776. | 79911. | 94840. | 110460. | 126730. | 143480. | 160680. | 178240. |
| n-Tridecane | $C_{13}H_{28}$ | 0 | 13572. | 13707. | 21956. | 32065. | 43734. | 56798. | 71088. | 86373. | 102500. | 119980. | 136970. | 155060. | 173640. | 192620. |
| n-Tetradecane | $C_{14}H_{30}$ | 0 | 14565. | 14712. | 23580. | 34455. | 46998. | 61040. | 76400. | 92826. | 110160. | 128300. | 147200. | 166650. | 186610. | 206980. |
| n-Pentadecane | $C_{15}H_{32}$ | 0 | 15558. | 15714. | 25204. | 36840. | 50262. | 65289. | 81712. | 99288. | 117820. | 137240. | 157430. | 178220. | 199560. | 221370. |
| n-Hexadecane | $C_{16}H_{34}$ | 0 | 16551. | 16719. | 26832. | 39230. | 53526. | 69531. | 87032. | 105741. | 125490. | 146160. | 167660. | 189800. | 212520. | 235740. |
| n-Heptadecane | $C_{17}H_{36}$ | 0 | 17543. | 17721. | 28456. | 41615. | 56790. | 73773. | 92344. | 112203. | 133150. | 155080. | 177900. | 201380. | 225480. | 250110. |
| n-Octadecane | $C_{18}H_{38}$ | 0 | 18537. | 18723. | 30080. | 44000. | 60054. | 78015. | 97656. | 118665. | 140810. | 164000. | 188140. | 212970. | 238450. | 264480. |
| n-Nonadecane | $C_{19}H_{40}$ | 0 | 19529. | 19728. | 31708. | 46390. | 63318. | 82257. | 102976. | 125118. | 148480. | 172920. | 198370. | 224550. | 251410. | 278850. |
| n-Eicosane | $C_{20}H_{42}$ | 0 | 20522. | 20730. | 33332. | 48775. | 66582. | 86506. | 108288. | 131580. | 156140. | 181850. | 208600. | 235220. | 264360. | 293240. |
| Increment per CH₂ group, applicable beyond n-hexane | | 0 | 992.9 | 1003.2 | 1625.2 | 2387.0 | 3262.4 | 4243.4 | 5314.4 | 6458.4 | 7663. | 8923. | 10234. | 11580. | 12961. | 14373. |

TABLE 1u – PARAFFINS, $C_1$ TO $C_5$

HEAT CONTENT (ENTHALPY), $(H^\circ - H^\circ_0)$, FOR THE IDEAL GAS STATE, AT 0° TO 1500°K

August 31, 1944; February 28, 1949; December 31, 1952

Heat Content (Enthalpy), $(H^\circ - H^\circ_0)$, in cal/mole

| Compound (gas) | Formula | Temperature in °K | | | | | | | | | | | | | | |
|---|---|---|---|---|---|---|---|---|---|---|---|---|---|---|---|---|
| | | 0 | 100 | 150 | 200 | 250 | 298.16 | 300 | 350 | 400 | 450 | 500 | 600 | 700 | 800 | 900 |
| Methane | $CH_4$ | 0 | 794.9 | 1192. | 1591. | 1995. | 2397. | 2413. | 2853. | 3323. | 3826. | 4365. | 5549. | 6871. | 8321. | 9887. |
| Ethane | $C_2H_6$ | 0 | 811.0 | 1258. | 1744. | 2280. | 2856. | 2879. | 3546. | 4296. | 5112. | 6010. | 8016. | 10280. | 12760. | 15440. |
| Propane | $C_3H_8$ | 0 | 844.0 | 1383. | 2006. | 2722. | 3512. | 3546. | 4490. | 5556. | 6741. | 8040. | 10930. | 14190. | 17760. | 21600. |
| n-Butane | $C_4H_{10}$ | 0 | | | 2632. | 3592. | 4645. | 4689. | 5996. | 7340. | 8896. | 10595. | 14376. | 18620. | 23264. | 28251. |
| 2-Methylpropane (Isobutane) | " | 0 | | | 2304. | 3235. | 4276. | 4317. | 5565. | 6964. | 8536. | 10250. | 14070. | 18340. | 23010. | 28020. |
| n-Pentane | $C_5H_{12}$ | 0 | | | 3146. | 4330. | 5629. | 5682. | 7220. | 8952. | 10872. | 12970. | 17628. | 22848. | 28568. | 34695. |
| 2-Methylbutane (Isopentane) | " | 0 | | | 2888. | 4008. | 5295. | 5346. | 6870. | 8596. | 10516. | 12620. | 17300. | 22570. | 28300. | 34490. |
| 2,2-Dimethylpropane (Neopentane) | " | 0 | | | 2574. | 3722. | 5030. | 5082. | 6646. | 8428. | 10400. | 12570. | 17390. | 22770. | 28640. | 34900. |

Heat Content (Enthalpy), $(H^\circ - H^\circ_0)$, in cal/mole

| Compound (gas) | Formula | Temperature in °K | | | | | |
|---|---|---|---|---|---|---|---|
| | | 1000 | 1100 | 1200 | 1300 | 1400 | 1500 |
| Methane | $CH_4$ | 11560. | 13320. | 15170. | 17100. | 19090. | 21130. |
| Ethane | $C_2H_6$ | 18280. | 21290. | 24420. | 27680. | 31040. | 34500. |
| Propane | $C_3H_8$ | 25670. | 29950. | 34420. | 39030. | 43780. | 48650. |
| n-Butane | $C_4H_{10}$ | 33540. | 39033. | 44868. | 50843. | 56994. | 63270. |
| 2-Methylpropane (Isobutane) | " | 33310. | 38870. | 44680. | 50650. | 56780. | 63050. |
| n-Pentane | $C_5H_{12}$ | 41190. | 47993. | 55092. | 62413. | 69944. | 77625. |
| 2-Methylbutane (Isopentane) | " | 41010. | 47880. | 55030. | 62390. | 69990. | 77740. |
| 2,2-Dimethylpropane (Neopentane) | " | 41510. | 48420. | 55610. | 63040. | 70660. | 78420. |

## TABLE 2u (PART 1) — PARAFFINS, $C_6$
### HEAT CONTENT (ENTHALPY), $(H^\circ - H^\circ_0)$, FOR THE IDEAL GAS STATE, AT 0° TO 1500°K
September 30, 1944; November 30, 1944; December 31, 1952

Temperature in °K

Heat Content (Enthalpy), $(H^\circ - H^\circ_0)$, in cal/mole

| Compound (gas) | Formula | 0 | 298.16 | 300 | 400 | 500 | 600 | 700 | 800 | 900 | 1000 | 1100 | 1200 | 1300 | 1400 | 1500 |
|---|---|---|---|---|---|---|---|---|---|---|---|---|---|---|---|---|
| n-Hexane | $C_6H_{14}$ | 0 | 6622. | 6687. | 10580. | 15360. | 20892. | 27097. | 33880. | 41157. | 48850 | 56925. | 65328. | 73996. | 82908. | 92010. |
| 2-Methylpentane | " | 0 | 6097. | 6162. | 10080. | 14950. | 20520. | 26810. | 33600. | 40950. | 48700. | | | | | |
| 3-Methylpentane | " | 0 | 6622. | 6687. | 10580. | 15360. | 20880. | 27090. | 33840. | 41130. | 48800. | | | | | |
| 2,2-Dimethylbutane | " | 0 | 5912. | 5973. | 9880. | 14750. | 20340. | 26600. | 33520. | 40770. | 48600. | | | | | |
| 2,3-Dimethylbutane | " | 0 | 5916. | 5978. | 9833. | 14610. | 20170. | 26410. | 33230. | 40500. | 48240. | | | | | |

562

TABLE 2u (PART 2) - PARAFFINS, $C_7$
HEAT CONTENT (ENTHALPY), $(H^o - H^o_0)$, FOR THE IDEAL GAS STATE , AT 0° TO 1500°K
September 30, 1944; December 31, 1952

| Compound (gas) | Formula | Temperature in °K | | | | | | | | | | | | | | |
|---|---|---|---|---|---|---|---|---|---|---|---|---|---|---|---|---|
| | | 0 | 298.16 | 300 | 400 | 500 | 600 | 700 | 800 | 900 | 1000 | 1100 | 1200 | 1300 | 1400 | 1500 |
| | | Heat Content (Enthalpy), $(H^o - H^o_0)$, in cal/mole | | | | | | | | | | | | | | |
| n-Heptane | $C_7H_{16}$ | 0 | 7615. | 7689. | 12204. | 17745. | 24156. | 31339. | 39200. | 47619. | 56520. | 65850. | 75560. | 85580. | 95870. | 106380. |
| 2-Methylhexane | " | 0 | 7123. | 7194. | 11840. | 17510. | 24100. | 31450. | 39400. | 47800. | 56700. | | | | | |
| 3-Methylhexane | " | 0 | 6953. | 7023. | 11620. | 17240. | 23800. | 31130. | 39100. | 47500. | 56400. | | | | | |
| 3-Ethylpentane | " | 0 | 6715. | 6783. | 11320. | 16890. | 23390. | 30680. | 38600. | 47000. | 55800. | | | | | |
| 2,2-Dimethylpentane | " | 0 | 6664. | 6732. | 11350. | 17050. | 23690. | 31140. | 39200. | 47700. | 56700. | | | | | |
| 2,3-Dimethylpentane | " | 0 | 6622. | 6690. | 11270. | 16910. | 23500. | 30860. | 38800. | 47300. | 56100. | | | | | |
| 2,4-Dimethylpentane | " | 0 | 6634. | 6702. | 11330. | 17040. | 23690. | 31140. | 39200. | 47700. | 56600. | | | | | |
| 3,3-Dimethylpentane | " | 0 | 6703. | 6771. | 11410. | 17120. | 23800. | 31260. | 39300. | 47900. | 56900. | | | | | |
| 2,2,3-Trimethylbutane | " | 0 | 6703. | 6774. | 11300. | 16905. | 23460. | 30779. | 38720. | 47250. | 56300. | 65700. | 75500. | 85500. | 95900. | 106500. |

## TABLE 3u – PARAFFINS, C8
### HEAT CONTENT (ENTHALPY), $(H° - H°_0)$, FOR THE IDEAL GAS STATE, AT 0° TO 1500°K
October 31, 1944; December 31, 1852

Temperature in °K

Heat Content (Enthalpy), $(H° - H°_0)$, in cal/mole

| Compound (gas) | Formula a | 0 | 298.16 | 300 | 400 | 500 | 600 | 700 | 800 | 900 | 1000 | 1100 | 1200 | 1300 | 1400 | 1500 |
|---|---|---|---|---|---|---|---|---|---|---|---|---|---|---|---|---|
| n-Octane | C8H18 | 0 | 8608. | 8691. | 13828. | 20130. | 27420. | 35581. | 44512. | 54081. | 64180. | 74767. | 85800. | 97162. | 108836. | 120750. |
| 2-Methylheptane | " | 0 | 8146. | 8229. | 13530. | 19990. | 27490. | 35840. | 44800. | 54300. | 64500. | | | | | |
| 3-Methylheptane | " | 0 | 8047. | 8130. | 13400. | 19850. | 27350. | 35700. | 44600. | 54200. | 64400. | | | | | |
| 4-Methylheptane | " | 0 | 7967. | 8049. | 13300. | 19740. | 27200. | 35500. | 44400. | 54000. | 64200. | | | | | |
| 3-Ethylhexane | " | 0 | 7537. | 7617. | 12720. | 19050. | 26410. | 34640. | 43600. | 53100. | 63200. | | | | | |
| 2,2-Dimethylhexane | " | 0 | 7746. | 7827. | 13110. | 19600. | 27120. | 35530. | 44700. | 54400. | 64600. | | | | | |
| 2,3-Dimethylhexane | " | 0 | 7857. | 7938. | 13280. | 19940. | 27620. | 36110. | 45200. | 54700. | 64900. | | | | | |
| 2,4-Dimethylhexane | " | 0 | 7526. | 7605. | 12840. | 19260. | 26760. | 35140. | 44100. | 53700. | 63800. | | | | | |
| 2,5-Dimethylhexane | " | 0 | 7627. | 7707. | 12970. | 19470. | 27020. | 35410. | 44400. | 53900. | 64100. | | | | | |
| 3,3-Dimethylhexane | " | 0 | 7517. | 7596. | 12850. | 19310. | 26860. | 35320. | 44500. | 54200. | 64400. | | | | | |
| 3,4-Dimethylhexane a | " | 0 | 7922. | 8007. | 13210. | 19620. | 27060. | 35320. | 44300. | 54000. | 64100. | | | | | |
| 2-Methyl-3-ethylpentane | " | 0 | 7707. | 7788. | 13100. | 19630. | 27180. | 35550. | 44500. | 54000. | 64300. | | | | | |
| 3-Methyl-3-ethylpentane | " | 0 | 7526. | 7605. | 12960. | 19470. | 27000. | 35400. | 44500. | 54300. | 64700. | | | | | |
| 2,2,3-Trimethylpentane | " | 0 | 7385. | 7464. | 12750. | 19290. | 26880. | 35340. | 44400. | 54100. | 64400. | | | | | |
| 2,2,4-Trimethylpentane | " | 0 | 7385. | 7464. | 12750. | 19290. | 26880. | 35340. | 44400. | 54100. | 64400. | | | | | |
| 2,3,3-Trimethylpentane | " | 0 | 7505. | 7584. | 12890. | 19470. | 27090. | 35540. | 44600. | 54200. | 64700. | | | | | |
| 2,3,4-Trimethylpentane | " | 0 | 7376. | 7455. | 12750. | 19380. | 27030. | 35470. | 44400. | 54000. | 64400. | | | | | |
| 2,2,3,3-Tetramethylbutane | " | 0 | 7482. | 7565. | 12880. | 19480. | 27170. | 35730. | 45000. | 54900. | 65300. | | | | | |

a See footnotes a and b of Table 3r.

## TABLE 22u (PART 1) – NORMAL ALKYL CYCLOPENTANES, $C_5$ TO $C_{21}$
### HEAT CONTENT (ENTHALPY), $(H°-H°_0)$, FOR THE IDEAL GAS STATE, AT 0° TO 1500°K
March 31, 1947; December 31, 1952

Heat Content (Enthalpy), $(H°-H°_0)$, in cal/mole

| Compound (gas) | Formula | \*Temperature in °K\* 0 | 298.16 | 300 | 400 | 500 | 600 | 700 | 800 | 900 | 1000 | 1100 | 1200 | 1300 | 1400 | 1500 |
|---|---|---|---|---|---|---|---|---|---|---|---|---|---|---|---|---|
| Cyclopentane | $C_5H_{10}$ | 0 | 3599. | 3636. | 6048. | 9260. | 13188. | 17703. | 22720. | 28161. | 33970. | 40110. | 46500. | 53130. | 59960. | 66880. |
| Methylcyclopentane | $C_6H_{12}$ | 0 | 4774. | 4827. | 7952. | 12015. | 16902. | 22463. | 28600. | 35235. | 42280. | 49700. | 57440. | 65440. | 73670. | 82110. |
| Ethylcyclopentane | $C_7H_{14}$ | 0 | 5793. | 5856. | 9584. | 14385. | 20130. | 26691. | 33896. | 41706. | 49980. | 58710. | 67800. | 77180. | 86870. | 96810. |
| n-Propylcyclopentane | $C_8H_{16}$ | 0 | 6786. | 6858. | 11208. | 16770. | 23394. | 30933. | 39208. | 48168. | 57640. | 67630. | 78040. | 88760. | 99830. | 111180. |
| n-Butylcyclopentane | $C_9H_{18}$ | 0 | 7779. | 7863. | 12836. | 19160. | 26658. | 35175. | 44528. | 54621. | 65310. | 76550. | 88270. | 100350. | 112800. | 125550. |
| n-Pentylcyclopentane | $C_{10}H_{20}$ | 0 | 8772. | 8865. | 14460. | 21545. | 29922. | 39424. | 49840. | 61083. | 72970. | 85480. | 98500. | 111920. | 125750. | 139940. |
| n-Hexylcyclopentane | $C_{11}H_{22}$ | 0 | 9765. | 9870. | 16084. | 23935. | 33186. | 43666. | 55152. | 67536. | 80630. | 94400. | 108730. | 123500. | 138710. | 154300. |
| n-Heptylcyclopentane | $C_{12}H_{24}$ | 0 | 10758. | 10872. | 17712. | 26320. | 36444. | 47908. | 60464. | 73998. | 88300. | 103320. | 118970. | 135080. | 151680. | 168680. |
| n-Octylcyclopentane | $C_{13}H_{26}$ | 0 | 11750. | 11874. | 19336. | 28705. | 39708. | 52150. | 65784. | 80460. | 95960. | 112240. | 129200. | 146670. | 164640. | 183040. |
| n-Nonylcyclopentane | $C_{14}H_{28}$ | 0 | 12743. | 12879. | 20960. | 31095. | 42972. | 56392. | 71096. | 86913. | 103620. | 121160. | 139440. | 158250. | 177600. | 197420. |
| n-Decylcyclopentane | $C_{15}H_{30}$ | 0 | 13736. | 13881. | 22584. | 33480. | 46236. | 60641. | 76408. | 93375. | 111280. | 130100. | 149660. | 169820. | 190550. | 211800. |
| n-Undecylcyclopentane | $C_{16}H_{32}$ | 0 | 14729. | 14886. | 24212. | 35870. | 49500. | 64883. | 81728. | 99828. | 118950. | 139020. | 159900. | 181400. | 203520. | 226170. |
| n-Dodecylcyclopentane | $C_{17}H_{34}$ | 0 | 15722. | 15888. | 25836. | 38255. | 52764. | 69125. | 87040. | 106290. | 126610. | 147940. | 170140. | 192980. | 216480. | 240540. |
| n-Tridecylcyclopentane | $C_{18}H_{36}$ | 0 | 16715. | 16890. | 27460. | 40640. | 56028. | 73367. | 92352. | 112752. | 134270. | 156660. | 180370. | 204570. | 229450. | 254910. |
| n-Tetradecylcyclopentane | $C_{19}H_{38}$ | 0 | 17708. | 17895. | 29088. | 43030. | 59292. | 77609. | 97672. | 119205. | 141930. | 165780. | 190610. | 216150. | 242410. | 269280. |
| n-Pentadecylcyclopentane | $C_{20}H_{40}$ | 0 | 16700. | 18897. | 30712. | 45415. | 62556. | 81856. | 102984. | 125667. | 149600. | 174710. | 200830. | 227720. | 255360. | 283660. |
| n-Hexadecylcyclopentane | $C_{21}H_{42}$ | 0 | 19693. | 19902. | 32336. | 47805. | 65820. | 86100. | 108296. | 132120. | 157260. | 183630. | 211070. | 239300. | 268320. | 298040 |
| Increment per $CH_2$ group, applicable beyond ethylcyclopentane | | 0 | 992.9 | 1003.2 | 1625.2 | 2387.0 | 3263.4 | 4243.4 | 5314.4 | 6458.4 | 7663. | 8923. | 10234. | 11580. | 12961. | 14373. |

## TABLE 6u – ALKYL CYCLOPENTANES, $C_5$ TO $C_7$
### HEAT CONTENT (ENTHALPY), $(H°-H°_0)$, FOR THE IDEAL GAS STATE, AT 0° TO 1500°K
April 30, 1949; December 31, 1952

Temperature in °K

Heat Content (Enthalpy), $(H°-H°_0)$, in cal/mole

| Compound (gas) | Formula | 0 | 298.16 | 300 | 400 | 500 | 600 | 700 | 800 | 900 | 1000 | 1100 | 1200 | 1300 | 1400 | 1500 |
|---|---|---|---|---|---|---|---|---|---|---|---|---|---|---|---|---|
| Cyclopentane | $C_5H_{10}$ | 0 | 3599. | 3636. | 6048. | 9260. | 13188. | 17703. | 22720. | 28161. | 33970. | 40110. | 46500. | 53130. | 59960. | 66980. |
| Methylcyclopentane | $C_6H_{12}$ | 0 | 4774. | 4827. | 7952. | 12015. | 16902. | 22463. | 28600. | 35235. | 42280. | 49700. | 57440. | 65440. | 73670. | 82110 |
| Ethylcyclopentane | $C_7H_{14}$ | 0 | 5793. | 5856. | 9584. | 14385. | 20130. | 26691. | 33896. | 41706. | 49980. | 58710. | 67800. | 77180. | 86870. | 96810. |
| 1,1-Dimethylcyclopentane | " | 0 | 5564. | 5631. | 9404. | 14300. | 20180. | 26820. | 34110. | 42020. | 50380. | 59150. | 68300. | 77710. | 87390. | 97300. |
| 1,cis-2-Dimethylcyclopentane | " | 0 | 5623. | 5685. | 9452. | 14360. | 20230. | 26870. | 34160. | 42020. | 50360. | 59100. | 68230. | 77640. | 87300. | 97180. |
| 1,trans-2-Dimethylcyclopentane | " | 0 | 5647. | 5715. | 9484. | 14400. | 20260. | 26890. | 34140. | 42020. | 50340. | 59060. | 68180. | 77580. | 87220. | 97100. |
| 1,cis-3-Dimethylcyclopentane | " | 0 | 5647. | 5715. | 9484. | 14400. | 20260. | 26890. | 34140. | 42020. | 50340. | 59060. | 68180. | 77580. | 89220. | 97100. |
| 1,trans-3-Dimethylcyclopentane | " | 0 | 5647. | 5715. | 9484. | 14400. | 20260. | 26890. | 34140. | 42020. | 50340. | 59060. | 68180. | 77580. | 87220. | 97100. |

TABLE 23u (PART 1) – NORMAL ALKYL CYCLOHEXANES, C6 TO C22

HEAT CONTENT (ENTHALPY), $(H^0 - H^0_0)$, FOR THE IDEAL GAS STATE   AT 0° TO 1500°K

March 31, 1947; December 31, 1952

| Compound (gas) | Formula | \multicolumn{15}{c}{Temperature in °K} |  |  |  |  |  |  |  |  |  |  |  |  |  |
|---|---|---|---|---|---|---|---|---|---|---|---|---|---|---|---|---|
|  |  | 0 | 298.16 | 300 | 400 | 500 | 600 | 700 | 800 | 900 | 1000 | 1100 | 1200 | 1300 | 1400 | 1500 |
|  |  | \multicolumn{16}{c}{Heat Content (Enthalpy), $(H^0 - H^0_0)$, in cal/mole} |
| Cyclohexane | $C_6H_{12}$ | 0 | 4237. | 4284. | 7352. | 11425. | 16404. | 22148. | 28536. | 33460. | 42850. | 50600. | 58680. | 67080. | 75600. | 84450. |
| Methylcyclohexane | $C_7H_{14}$ | 0 | 5233. | 5298. | 9136. | 14130. | 20118. | 26971. | 34528. | 42678. | 51330. | 60390. | 69840. | 79560. | 89600. | 99750. |
| Ethylcyclohexane | $C_8H_{16}$ | 0 | 6097. | 6174. | 10680. | 16450. | 23340. | 31220. | 39920. | 49230. | 59100. | 69400. | 80200. | 91300. | 102600. | 114300. |
| n-Propylcyclohexane | $C_9H_{18}$ | 0 | 6899. | 6990. | 12160. | 18800. | 26580. | 35490. | 45200. | 55710. | 66800. | 78300. | 90400. | 102800. | 115600. | 128700. |
| n-Butylcyclohexane | $C_{10}H_{20}$ | 0 | 7892. | 7992. | 13800. | 21200. | 29820. | 39760. | 50480. | 62190. | 74500. | 87200. | 100600. | 114400. | 128700. | 143100. |
| n-Pentylcyclohexane | $C_{11}H_{22}$ | 0 | 8885. | 8997. | 15400. | 23550. | 33120. | 43960. | 55840. | 68670. | 82100. | 96100. | 110900. | 126000. | 141500. | 157500. |
| n-Hexylcyclohexane | $C_{12}H_{24}$ | 0 | 9878. | 9999. | 17040. | 25950. | 36360. | 48230. | 61120. | 75060. | 89800. | 105000. | 121100. | 137500. | 154600. | 171800. |
| n-Heptylcyclohexane | $C_{13}H_{26}$ | 0 | 10871. | 11004. | 18640. | 28350. | 39660. | 52430. | 66180. | 81540. | 97400. | 114000. | 131300. | 149100. | 167400. | 186200. |
| n-Octylcyclohexane | $C_{14}H_{28}$ | 0 | 11864. | 12006. | 20280. | 30750. | 42900. | 56700. | 71760. | 88020. | 105100. | 122000. | 141500. | 160800. | 180500. | 200600. |
| n-Nonylcyclohexane | $C_{15}H_{30}$ | 0 | 12857. | 13008. | 21920. | 33100. | 46140. | 60970. | 77040. | 94500. | 112800. | 131900. | 151800. | 172400. | 193500. | 215000. |
| n-Decylcyclohexane | $C_{16}H_{32}$ | 0 | 13849. | 14013. | 23520. | 35500. | 49440. | 65170. | 82400. | 100980. | 120400. | 140800. | 162000. | 184000. | 206400. | 229400. |
| n-Undecylcyclohexane | $C_{17}H_{34}$ | 0 | 14842. | 15015. | 25160. | 37900. | 52680. | 69440. | 87680. | 107370. | 128100. | 149700. | 172200. | 195500. | 219400. | 243600. |
| n-Dodecylcyclohexane | $C_{18}H_{36}$ | 0 | 15835. | 16020. | 26760. | 40250. | 55980. | 73640. | 93040. | 113850. | 135700. | 158600. | 182500. | 207100. | 232300. | 258000. |
| n-Tridecylcyclohexane | $C_{19}H_{38}$ | 0 | 16828. | 17022. | 28400. | 42650. | 59220. | 77910. | 98320. | 120330. | 143400. | 167500. | 192700. | 218700. | 245300. | 272400. |
| n-Tetradecylcyclohexane | $C_{20}H_{40}$ | 0 | 17821. | 18024. | 30040. | 45050. | 62460. | 82180. | 103600. | 126810. | 151100. | 176400. | 202900. | 230200. | 258300. | 286800. |
| n-Pentadecylcyclohexane | $C_{21}H_{42}$ | 0 | 18814. | 19029. | 31640. | 47400. | 65760. | 86380. | 108960. | 133290. | 158700. | 185400. | 213200. | 241800. | 271200. | 301200. |
| n-Hexadecylcyclohexane | $C_{22}H_{44}$ | 0 | 19807. | 20031. | 33280. | 49600. | 69000. | 90650. | 114240. | 139680. | 166300. | 194300. | 223400. | 253400. | 284200. | 315400. |
| Increment per $CH_2$ group, applicable beyond n-propylcyclohexane |  | 0 | 992.9 | 1003.2 | 1625. | 2387. | 3263. | 4243. | 5314. | 6458. | 7560. | 8920. | 10230. | 11580. | 12960. | 14370. |

TABLE 7u – ALKYL CYCLOHEXANES, C$_6$ TO C$_8$

HEAT CONTENT (ENTHALPY), $(H^o-H^o_0)$, FOR THE IDEAL GAS STATE , AT 0° TO 1500°K

April 30, 1947

| Compound (gas) | Formula | Temperature in °K | | | | | | | | | | | | | | |
|---|---|---|---|---|---|---|---|---|---|---|---|---|---|---|---|---|
| | | 0 | 298.16 | 300 | 400 | 500 | 600 | 700 | 800 | 900 | 1000 | 1100 | 1200 | 1300 | 1400 | 1500 |
| | | Heat Content (Enthalpy), $(H^o-H^o_0)$, in cal/mole | | | | | | | | | | | | | | |
| Cyclohexane | C$_6$H$_{12}$ | 0 | 4237. | 4284. | 7352. | 11425. | 16404. | 22148. | 28536. | 35460. | 42850. | 50600. | 58680. | 67080. | 75600. | 84450. |
| Methylcyclohexane | C$_7$H$_{14}$ | 0 | 5233. | 5298. | 9136. | 14130. | 20118. | 26971. | 34528. | 42678. | 51330. | 60390. | 69840. | 79560. | 89600. | 99750. |
| Ethylcyclohexane | C$_8$H$_{16}$ | 0 | 6097. | 6174. | 10680. | 16450. | 23340. | 31220. | 39920. | 49230. | 59100. | 69400. | 80200. | 91300. | 102600. | 114300. |
| 1,1-Dimethylcyclohexane | " | 0 | 5880. | 5955. | 10360. | 16050. | 22920. | 30800. | 39520. | 48960. | 58900. | 69300. | 80200. | 91400. | 102900. | 114600. |
| 1,cis-2-Dimethylcyclohexane | " | 0 | 6011. | 6087. | 10520. | 16250. | 23160. | 31010. | 39680. | 48960. | 58900. | 69300. | 80000. | 91100. | 102600. | 114200. |
| 1,trans-2-Dimethylcyclohexane | " | 0 | 6094. | 6174. | 10680. | 16500. | 23400. | 31290. | 40000. | 49410. | 59300. | 69700. | 80500. | 91700. | 103000. | 114800. |
| 1,cis-3-Dimethylcyclohexane[a] | " | 0 | 6068. | 6144. | 10600. | 16350. | 23280. | 31150. | 39840. | 49230. | 59100. | 69500. | 80400. | 91700. | 103000. | 114800. |
| 1,trans-3-Dimethylcyclohexane[b] | " | 0 | 6068. | 6144. | 10600. | 16350. | 23220. | 31010. | 39680. | 48960. | 58800. | 69200. | 79900. | 91000. | 102300. | 114000. |
| 1,cis-4-Dimethylcyclohexane | " | 0 | 6068. | 6144. | 10600. | 16350. | 23220. | 31010. | 39680. | 48960. | 58800. | 69200. | 79900. | 91000. | 102300. | 114000. |
| 1,trans-4-Dimethylcyclohexane | " | 0 | 6076. | 6153. | 10640. | 16400. | 23340. | 31290. | 40000. | 49320. | 59300. | 69700. | 80500. | 91700. | 103000. | 114800. |

[a] Formerly labeled "trans"; see footnote b of Table 7a.   [b] Formerly labeled "cis"; see footnote c of Table 7a.

TABLE 24u (PART 1) - NORMAL MONOOLEFINS (1-ALKENES), C₂ TO C₂₀
HEAT CONTENT (ENTHALPY), $(H^o-H^o_0)$, FOR THE IDEAL GAS STATE , AT 0° TO 1500°K

November 30, 1945; April 30, 1946; December 31, 1952

Heat Content (Enthalpy), $(H^o-H^o_0)$, in cal/mole — Temperature in °K

| Compound (gas) | Formula | 0 | 298.16 | 300 | 400 | 500 | 600 | 700 | 800 | 900 | 1000 | 1100 | 1200 | 1300 | 1400 | 1500 |
|---|---|---|---|---|---|---|---|---|---|---|---|---|---|---|---|---|
| Ethene (Ethylene) | $C_2H_4$ | 0 | 2525. | 2544. | 3711. | 5117. | 6732. | 8527. | 10480. | 12560. | 14760. | 17070. | 19470. | 21950. | 24490. | 27100. |
| Propene (Propylene) | $C_3H_6$ | 0 | 3237. | 3265. | 4990. | 7076. | 9492. | 12200. | 15150. | 18320. | 21690. | 25210. | 28880. | 32670. | 36570. | 40570. |
| 1-Butene | $C_4H_8$ | 0 | 4112. | 4149. | 6484. | 9350. | 12650. | 16340. | 20370. | 24690. | 29250. | 34040. | 39010. | 44150. | 49430. | 54840. |
| 1-Pentene | $C_5H_{10}$ | 0 | 5246. | 5292. | 8269. | 11906. | 16100. | 20770. | 25870. | 31340. | 37120. | 43170. | 49460. | 55960. | 62640. | 69470. |
| 1-Hexene | $C_6H_{12}$ | 0 | 6228. | 6285. | 9881. | 14281. | 19350. | 25000. | 31170. | 37780. | 44770. | 52080. | 59690. | 67530. | 75590. | 83820. |
| 1-Heptene | $C_7H_{14}$ | 0 | 7221. | 7288. | 11506. | 16668. | 22610. | 29240. | 36480. | 44240. | 52430. | 61000. | 69920. | 79110. | 88550. | 98190. |
| 1-Octene | $C_8H_{16}$ | 0 | 8214. | 8291. | 13131. | 19055. | 25880. | 33490. | 41800. | 50700. | 60100. | 69930. | 80160. | 90690. | 101510. | 112570. |
| 1-Nonene | $C_9H_{18}$ | 0 | 9207. | 9295. | 14757. | 21442. | 29140. | 37730. | 47110. | 57150. | 67760. | 78850. | 90390. | 102270. | 114470. | 126940. |
| 1-Decene | $C_{10}H_{20}$ | 0 | 10200. | 10298. | 16382. | 23829. | 32400. | 41970. | 52430. | 63610. | 75420. | 87770. | 100630. | 113850. | 127430. | 141310. |
| 1-Undecene | $C_{11}H_{22}$ | 0 | 11192. | 11301. | 18007. | 26216. | 35660. | 46220. | 57740. | 70070. | 83080. | 96700. | 110860. | 125430. | 140400. | 155680. |
| 1-Dodecene | $C_{12}H_{24}$ | 0 | 12185. | 12304. | 19632. | 28603. | 38930. | 50460. | 63050. | 76530. | 90750. | 105620. | 121090. | 137010. | 153360. | 170060. |
| 1-Tridecene | $C_{13}H_{26}$ | 0 | 13178. | 13307. | 21257. | 30990. | 42190. | 54700. | 68370. | 82990. | 98410. | 114540. | 131330. | 148590. | 166320. | 184430. |
| 1-Tetradecene | $C_{14}H_{28}$ | 0 | 14171. | 14311. | 22883. | 33377. | 45450. | 58940. | 73680. | 89440. | 106070. | 123460. | 141560. | 160170. | 179280. | 198800. |
| 1-Pentadecene | $C_{15}H_{30}$ | 0 | 15164. | 15314. | 24508. | 35764. | 48720. | 63190. | 79000. | 95900. | 113740. | 132390. | 151800. | 171750. | 192240. | 213180. |
| 1-Hexadecene | $C_{16}H_{32}$ | 0 | 16157. | 16317. | 26133. | 38151. | 51980. | 67430. | 84310. | 102360. | 121400. | 141310. | 162030. | 183330. | 205200. | 227550. |
| 1-Heptadecene | $C_{17}H_{34}$ | 0 | 17150. | 17320. | 27758. | 40538. | 55240. | 71670. | 89620. | 108820. | 129060. | 150230. | 172260. | 194910. | 218160. | 241920. |
| 1-Octadecene | $C_{18}H_{36}$ | 0 | 18143. | 18323. | 29383. | 42925. | 58510. | 75920. | 94940. | 115280. | 136730. | 159160. | 182500. | 206490. | 231120. | 256300. |
| 1-Nonadecene | $C_{19}H_{38}$ | 0 | 19136. | 19327. | 31009. | 45312. | 61770. | 80160. | 100250. | 121730. | 144390. | 168080. | 192730. | 218070. | 244080. | 270670. |
| 1-Eicosene | $C_{20}H_{40}$ | 0. | 20129. | 20330. | 32634. | 47699. | 65030. | 84400. | 105570. | 128190. | 152050. | 177000. | 202970. | 229650. | 257040. | 285040. |
| Increment per CH₂ group, applicable beyond 1-hexene | | 0 | 992.9 | 1003.2 | 1625.2 | 2387.0 | 3263. | 4243. | 5314. | 6458. | 7663. | 8923. | 10234. | 11580. | 12961. | 14373. |

TABLE 8u (PART 1) – MONOOLEFINS, $C_2$ TO $C_5$

HEAT CONTENT (ENTHALPY), $(H°-H°_0)$, FOR THE IDEAL GAS STATE, AT 0° TO 1500°K

December 31, 1944; March 31, 1945; October 31, 1945; April 30, 1946; December 31, 1952

Heat Content (Enthalpy), $(H°-H°_0)$, in cal/mole

| Compound (gas) | Formula | 0 | 298.16 | 300 | 400 | 500 | 600 | 700 | 800 | 900 | 1000 | 1100 | 1200 | 1300 | 1400 | 1500 |
|---|---|---|---|---|---|---|---|---|---|---|---|---|---|---|---|---|
| Ethene (Ethylene) | $C_2H_4$ | 0 | 2525. | 2544. | 3711. | 5117. | 6732. | 8727. | 10480. | 12560. | 14760. | 17070. | 19470. | 21950. | 24490. | 27100. |
| Propene (Propylene) | $C_3H_6$ | 0 | 3237. | 3265. | 4990. | 7076. | 9492. | 12200. | 15150. | 18320. | 21690. | 25210. | 28880. | 32670. | 36570. | 40570. |
| 1-Butene | $C_4H_8$ | 0 | 4112. | 4149. | 6484. | 9350. | 12650. | 16340. | 20370. | 24690. | 29250. | 34040. | 39010. | 44150. | 49430. | 54840. |
| cis-2-Butene | " | 0 | 3981. | 3981. | 6144. | 8839. | 12010. | 15530. | 19510. | 23740. | 28230. | 32960. | 37880. | 42980. | 48230. | 53620. |
| trans-2-Butene | " | 0 | 4190. | 4228. | 6582. | 9422. | 12690. | 16360. | 20350. | 24640. | 29190. | 33960. | 38920. | 44040. | 49310. | 54710. |
| 2-Methylpropene (Isobutene) | " | 0 | 4082. | 4121. | 6522. | 9414. | 12750. | 16450. | 20490. | 24800. | 29370. | 34170. | 39150. | 44300. | 49590. | 55000. |
| 1-Pentene | $C_5H_{10}$ | 0 | 5246. | 5292. | 8269. | 11906. | 16100. | 20770. | 25870. | 31340. | 37120. | 43170. | 49460. | 55960. | 62640. | 69470. |
| cis-2-Pentene | " | 0 | 4845. | 4887. | 7696. | 11190. | 15280. | 19890. | 24910. | 30310. | 36050. | 47040. | 48290. | 54760. | 61400. | 56220. |
| trans-2-Pentene | " | 0 | 5037. | 5042. | 8013. | 11600. | 15750. | 20370. | 25420. | 30840. | 36580. | 42590. | 48830. | 55290. | 61930. | 68750. |
| 2-Methyl-1-butene | " | 0 | 5000. | 5046. | 8080. | 11770. | 16010. | 20740. | 25870. | 31350. | 37150. | 43230. | 49520. | 56040. | 62750. | 69590. |
| 3-Methyl-1-butene | " | 0 | 5137. | 5187. | 8380. | 12210. | 16570. | 21370. | 26560. | 32090. | 37940. | 44040. | 50390. | 56930. | 63620. | 70460. |
| 2-Methyl-2-butene | " | 0 | 4833. | 4878. | 7736. | 11250. | 15320. | 19900. | 24910. | 30290. | 36000. | 41990. | 48220. | 54670. | 61310. | 68100. |

TABLE 8u (PART 2) - MONOOLEFINS, C$_6$

HEAT CONTENT (ENTHALPY), $(H^o-H_0^o)$, FOR THE IDEAL GAS STATE , AT 0° TO 1500°K

April 30, 1945; October 31, 1945; December 31, 1952

Heat Content (Enthalpy), $(H^o-H_0^o)$, in cal/mole

Temperature in °K

| Compound (gas) | Formula | 0 | 298.16 | 300 | 400 | 500 | 600 | 700 | 800 | 900 | 1000 | 1100 | 1200 | 1300 | 1400 | 1500 |
|---|---|---|---|---|---|---|---|---|---|---|---|---|---|---|---|---|
| 1-Hexene | C$_6$H$_{12}$ | 0 | 6228. | 6285. | 9881. | 14281. | 19350. | 25000. | 31170. | 37780. | 44770. | 52080. | 59690. | 67530. | 75590. | 83820. |
| cis-2-Hexene | " | 0 | 5978. | 6033. | 9480. | 13750. | 18700. | 24300. | 30400. | 37000. | 43900. | | | | | |
| trans-2-Hexene | " | 0 | 6170. | 6225. | 9800. | 14170. | 19200. | 24800. | 31000. | 37400. | 44400. | | | | | |
| cis-3-Hexene | " | 0 | 5752. | 5808. | 9220. | 13490. | 18500. | 24100. | 30200. | 36700. | 43700. | | | | | |
| trans-3-Hexene | " | 0 | 6003. | 6057. | 9660. | 14080. | 19100. | 24800. | 31000. | 37600. | 44500. | | | | | |
| 2-Methyl-1-pentene | " | 0 | 6133. | 6189. | 9880. | 14300. | 19400. | 25200. | 31400. | 38000. | 45000. | | | | | |
| 3-Methyl-1-pentene | " | 0 | 6112. | 6171. | 10120. | 15000. | 20600. | 27000. | 33800. | 41000. | 48800. | | | | | |
| 4-Methyl-1-pentene | " | 0 | 5484. | 5535. | 8960. | 13220. | 18200. | 23800. | 29800. | 36400. | 43200. | | | | | |
| 2-Methyl-2-pentene | " | 0 | 5680. | 5733. | 9210. | 13500. | 18500. | 24100. | 30200. | 36700. | 43700. | | | | | |
| 3-Methyl-cis-2-pentene | " | 0 | 5680. | 5733. | 9210. | 13500. | 18500. | 24100. | 30200. | 36700. | 43700. | | | | | |
| 3-Methyl-trans-2-pentene | " | 0 | 5680. | 5733. | 9210. | 13500. | 13500. | 24100. | 30200. | 36700. | 43700. | | | | | |
| 4-Methyl-cis-2-pentene | " | 0 | 5817. | 5874. | 9510. | 13950. | 19050. | 24700. | 30900. | 37500. | 44500. | | | | | |
| 4-Methyl-trans-2-pentene | " | 0 | 6062. | 6120. | 9910. | 14460. | 19700. | 25400. | 31600. | 38300. | 45300. | | | | | |
| 2-Ethyl-1-butene | " | 0 | 5907. | 5961. | 9610. | 14070. | 19200. | 24900. | 31100. | 37800. | 44800. | | | | | |
| 2,3-Dimethyl-1-butene | " | 0 | 5972. | 6030. | 9890. | 14520. | 19800. | 25600. | 31900. | 38500. | 45600. | | | | | |
| 3,3-Dimethyl-1-butene | " | 0 | 5277. | 5277. | 8760. | 13100. | 18100. | 23700. | 29800. | 36300. | 43200. | | | | | |
| 2,3-Dimethyl-2-butene | " | 0 | 5698. | 5748. | 9210. | 13450. | 18400. | 23900. | 30000. | 36500. | 43400. | | | | | |

## TABLE 11u (PART 1) – DIOLEFINS $C_3$ TO $C_5$

### HEAT CONTENT (ENTHALPY), $(H^o - H^o_0)$, FOR THE IDEAL GAS STATE, AT 0° TO 1500°K

October 31, 1947; April 30, 1948

| Compound (gas) | Formula | \multicolumn{15}{c}{Temperature in °K} |
|---|---|---|---|---|---|---|---|---|---|---|---|---|---|---|---|---|
| | | 0 | 298.16 | 300 | 400 | 500 | 600 | 700 | 800 | 900 | 1000 | 1100 | 1200 | 1300 | 1400 | 1500 |
| | | \multicolumn{15}{c}{Heat Content (Enthalpy), $(H^o - H^o_0)$, in cal/mole} |
| Propadiene (Allene) | $C_3H_4$ | 0 | 3017.4 | 3045.0 | 4616.0 | 6470.0 | 8568.0 | 10857.0 | 13328.0 | 15939.0 | 18660.0 | 21527.0 | 24480.0 | 27521.0 | 30632.0 | 33810.0 |
| 1,2-Butadiene | $C_4H_6$ | 0 | 3852.2 | 3888.0 | 6028.0 | 8580.0 | 11490.0 | 14707.0 | 18192.0 | 21906.0 | 25820.0 | 29898.0 | 34128.0 | 38506.0 | 42980.0 | 47550.0 |
| 1,3-Butadiene | " | 0 | 3625.6 | 3660.0 | 5856.0 | 8485.0 | 11508.0 | 14833.0 | 18408.0 | 22194.0 | 26160.0 | 30294.0 | 34560.0 | 38948.0 | 43442.0 | 48030.0 |
| 1,2-Pentadiene | $C_5H_8$ | 0 | 4830. | 4890. | 7720. | 11150. | 15000. | 19920. | 23920. | 28800. | 34000. | 39380. | 44880. | 50700. | 56560. | 62550. |
| 1,cis-3-Pentadiene | " | 0 | 4323. | 4380. | 7000. | 10250. | 14040. | 18200. | 22800. | 27630. | 32700. | 38060. | 43560. | 49270. | 55160. | 61050. |
| 1,trans-3-Pentadiene | " | 0 | 4562. | 4620. | 7440. | 10850. | 14700. | 18970. | 23600. | 28530. | 33700. | 39050. | 44640. | 50310. | 56140. | 62100. |
| 1,4-Pentadiene | " | 0 | 4920. | 4980. | 7840. | 11200. | 15120. | 19390. | 23920. | 28800. | 34000. | 39380. | 44880. | 50700. | 56560. | 62550. |
| 2,3-Pentadiene | " | 0 | 4681. | 4740. | 7440. | 10700. | 14400. | 18550. | 23040. | 27900. | 33000. | 38280. | 43800. | 49530. | 55300. | 61350. |
| 3-Methyl-1,2-butadiene | " | 0 | 4711. | 4740. | 7560. | 10900. | 14760. | 18970. | 23520. | 28850. | 33500. | 38830. | 44400. | 50180. | 56000. | 61950. |
| 2-Methyl-1,3-butadiene (Isoprene) | " | 0 | 4472. | 4530. | 7360. | 10850. | 14760. | 19110. | 23760. | 28710. | 33800. | 39270. | 44880. | 50570. | 56420. | 62400. |

TABLE 18u – ALKYL CYCLOPENTENES, $C_5$ TO $C_7$
HEAT CONTENT (ENTHALPY), $(H^o-H^o_0)$, FOR THE IDEAL GAS STATE, AT 0° TO 1500°K
December 31, 1952

| Compound (gas) | Formula | Temperature in °K | | | | | | | | | | | | | | |
|---|---|---|---|---|---|---|---|---|---|---|---|---|---|---|---|---|
| | | 0 | 298.16 | 300 | 400 | 500 | 600 | 700 | 800 | 900 | 1000 | 1100 | 1200 | 1300 | 1400 | 1500 |
| | | Heat Content (Enthalpy), $(H^o-H^o_0)$, in cal/mole | | | | | | | | | | | | | | |
| Cyclopentene | $C_5H_8$ | 0 | 3462. | 3495. | 5648. | 8490. | 11940. | 15897. | 20288. | 25038. | 30090. | 35409. | 40956. | 46696. | 52598. | 58650. |
| 1-Methylcyclopentene | $C_6H_{10}$ | 0 | 4443 | 4500 | 7320 | 11000 | 15360 | 20300 | 25760 | 31680 | 37900 | 44550 | 51360 | 58370 | 65660 | 73200 |
| 3-Methylcyclopentene | " | 0 | 4353 | 4410 | 7240 | 10900 | 15300 | 20300 | 25760 | 31680 | 38000 | 44550 | 51360 | 58500 | 65800 | 73200 |
| 4-Methylcyclopentene | " | 0 | 4323 | 4380 | 7200 | 10850 | 15240 | 20230 | 25680 | 31590 | 37900 | 44550 | 51360 | 58370 | 65660 | 73050 |
| 1-Ethylcyclopentene | $C_7H_{12}$ | | | | | | | | | | | | | | | |
| 3-Ethylcyclopentene | " | | | | | | | | | | | | | | | |
| 4-Ethylcyclopentene | " | | | | | | | | | | | | | | | |
| 1,2-Dimethylcyclopentene | " | 0 | 5427 | 5490 | 9000 | 13500 | 18780 | 24710 | 31280 | 38340 | 45800 | 53680 | 61800 | 70200 | 78820 | 87600 |
| 1,3-Dimethylcyclopentene | " | 0 | 5337 | 5400 | 8920 | 13400 | 18720 | 24710 | 31280 | 38340 | 45800 | 53680 | 61920 | 70330 | 78960 | 87750 |
| 1,4-Dimethylcyclopentene | " | 0 | 5307 | 5400 | 8880 | 13350 | 18660 | 24640 | 31200 | 38250 | 45700 | 53570 | 61800 | 70200 | 78820 | 87600 |
| 1,5-Dimethylcyclopentene | " | 0 | 5337 | 5400 | 8920 | 13400 | 18660 | 24640 | 31280 | 38340 | 45800 | 53680 | 61800 | 70200 | 78820 | 87750 |
| 3,3-Dimethylcyclopentene | " | 0 | 5069 | 5130 | 8600 | 13100 | 18420 | 24500 | 31200 | 38430 | 46000 | 54010 | 62400 | 70980 | 79800 | 88650 |
| 3,cis-4-Dimethylcyclopentene | " | 0 | 5188 | 5250 | 8760 | 13250 | 18600 | 24640 | 31280 | 38430 | 46000 | 53900 | 62040 | 70460 | 79100 | 88050 |
| 3,trans-4-Dimethylcyclopentene | " | 0 | 5248 | 5310 | 8840 | 13350 | 18660 | 24640 | 31200 | 38340 | 45900 | 53790 | 61920 | 70330 | 78960 | 87900 |
| 3,cis-5-Dimethylcyclopentene | " | 0 | 5248 | 5310 | 8840 | 13350 | 18660 | 24640 | 31200 | 38340 | 45900 | 53790 | 61920 | 70330 | 78960 | 87900 |
| 3,trans-5-Dimethylcyclopentene | " | 0 | 5248 | 5310 | 8840 | 13350 | 18660 | 24640 | 31200 | 38340 | 45900 | 53790 | 61920 | 70330 | 78960 | 87900 |
| 4,4-Dimethylcyclopentene | " | 0 | | | | | | | | | | | | | | |

TABLE 19u – ALKYL CYCLOHEXENES, $C_6$ TO $C_8$

HEAT CONTENT (ENTHALPY), $(H^\circ - H^\circ_0)$, FOR THE IDEAL GAS STATE , AT 0° TO 1500°K

December 31, 1952

Temperature in °K

Heat Content (Enthalpy), $(H^\circ - H^\circ_0)$, in cal/mole

| Compound (gas) | Formula | 0 | 298.16 | 300 | 400 | 500 | 600 | 700 | 800 | 900 | 1000 | 1100 | 1200 | 1300 | 1400 | 1500 |
|---|---|---|---|---|---|---|---|---|---|---|---|---|---|---|---|---|
| Cyclohexene | $C_6H_{10}$ | 0 | 4168. | 4215. | 7216. | 11100. | 15720. | 20950. | 26680. | 32820. | 39330. | 46130. | 53210. | 60490. | 67970. | 75630. |
| 1-Methylcyclohexene | $C_7H_{12}$ | | | | | | | | | | | | | | | |
| 3-Methylcyclohexene | " | | | | | | | | | | | | | | | |
| 4-Methylcyclohexene | " | | | | | | | | | | | | | | | |
| 1-Ethylcyclohexene | $C_8H_{14}$ | | | | | | | | | | | | | | | |
| 3-Ethylcyclohexene | " | | | | | | | | | | | | | | | |
| 4-Ethylcyclohexene | " | | | | | | | | | | | | | | | |
| 1,2-Dimethylcyclohexene | " | | | | | | | | | | | | | | | |
| 1,3-Dimethylcyclohexene | " | | | | | | | | | | | | | | | |
| 1,4-Dimethylcyclohexene | " | | | | | | | | | | | | | | | |
| 1,5-Dimethylcyclohexene | " | | | | | | | | | | | | | | | |
| 1,6-Dimethylcyclohexene | " | | | | | | | | | | | | | | | |
| 3,3-Dimethylcyclohexene | " | | | | | | | | | | | | | | | |
| 3,cis-4-Dimethylcyclohexene | " | | | | | | | | | | | | | | | |
| 3,trans-4-Dimethylcyclohexene | " | | | | | | | | | | | | | | | |
| 3,cis-5-Dimethylcyclohexene | " | | | | | | | | | | | | | | | |
| 3,trans-5-Dimethylcyclohexene | " | | | | | | | | | | | | | | | |
| 3,cis-6-Dimethylcyclohexene | " | | | | | | | | | | | | | | | |
| 3,trans-6-Dimethylcyclohexene | " | | | | | | | | | | | | | | | |
| 4,4-Dimethylcyclohexene | " | | | | | | | | | | | | | | | |
| 4,cis-5-Dimethylcyclohexene | " | | | | | | | | | | | | | | | |
| 4,trans-5-Dimethylcyclohexene | " | | | | | | | | | | | | | | | |

TABLE 25u (PART 1) — NORMAL ACETYLENES (1-ALKYNES), $C_2$ TO $C_{20}$
HEAT CONTENT (ENTHALPY), $(H^o - H^o_0)$, FOR THE IDEAL GAS STATE, AT 0° TO 1500°K
February 28, 1946; December 31, 1952

Heat Content (Enthalpy), $(H^o - H^o_0)$, in cal/mole

Temperature in °K

| Compound (gas) | Formula | 0 | 298.16 | 300 | 400 | 500 | 600 | 700 | 800 | 900 | 1000 | 1100 | 1200 | 1300 | 1400 | 1500 |
|---|---|---|---|---|---|---|---|---|---|---|---|---|---|---|---|---|
| Ethyne (Acetylene) | $C_2H_2$ | 0 | 2391.5 | 2410.8 | 3541.2 | 4791.0 | 6127. | 7533. | 8999. | 10520. | 12090. | 13706. | 15362. | 17055. | 18782. | 20541. |
| Propyne (Methylacetylene) | $C_3H_4$ | 0 | 3104. | 3131. | 4728. | 6584. | 8663. | 10935. | 13372. | 15956. | 18670. | 21490. | 24420. | 27430. | 30520. | 33670. |
| 1-Butyne (Ethylacetylene) | $C_4H_6$ | 0 | 3820. | 3850. | 6031. | 8610. | 11540. | 14760. | 18240. | 21940. | 25830. | 29890. | 34110. | 38450. | 42910. | 47460. |
| 1-Pentyne | $C_5H_8$ | 0 | 4952. | 4992. | 7816. | 11165. | 14976. | 19194. | 23744. | 28593. | 33700. | 39030. | 44560. | 50270. | 56130. | 62080. |
| 1-Hexyne | $C_6H_{10}$ | 0 | 5945. | 5994. | 9440. | 13550. | 18240. | 23436. | 29056. | 35055. | 41360. | 47950. | 54790. | 61850. | 69090. | 76460. |
| 1-Heptyne | $C_7H_{12}$ | 0 | 6938. | 6999. | 11068. | 15940. | 21504. | 27678. | 34376. | 41508. | 49030. | 56870. | 65030. | 73440. | 82050. | 90820. |
| 1-Octyne | $C_8H_{14}$ | 0 | 7931. | 8001. | 12692. | 18325. | 24768. | 31927. | 39688. | 47970. | 56690. | 65800. | 75250. | 85010. | 95000. | 105210. |
| 1-Nonyne | $C_9H_{16}$ | 0 | 8924. | 9006. | 14316. | 20715. | 28032. | 36169. | 45000. | 54423. | 64350. | 74720. | 85490. | 96590. | 107970. | 119580. |
| 1-Decyne | $C_{10}H_{18}$ | 0 | 9917. | 10008. | 15944. | 23100. | 31296. | 40411. | 50320. | 60885. | 72020. | 83640. | 95720. | 108170. | 120930. | 133950. |
| 1-Undecyne | $C_{11}H_{20}$ | 0 | 10910. | 11010. | 17568. | 25485. | 34554. | 44653. | 55632. | 67347. | 79680. | 92560. | 105960. | 119760. | 133900. | 148320. |
| 1-Dodecyne | $C_{12}H_{22}$ | 0 | 11902. | 12015. | 19192. | 27875. | 37818. | 48895. | 60944. | 73800. | 87340. | 101490. | 116200. | 131340. | 146860. | 162690. |
| 1-Tridecyne | $C_{13}H_{24}$ | 0 | 12895. | 13017. | 20816. | 30260. | 41082. | 53144. | 66256. | 80262. | 95000. | 110420. | 126420. | 142910. | 159810. | 177080. |
| 1-Tetradecyne | $C_{14}H_{26}$ | 0 | 13888. | 14022. | 22444. | 32650. | 44346. | 57386. | 71576. | 86715. | 102670. | 119340. | 136660. | 154490. | 172770. | 191440. |
| 1-Pentadecyne | $C_{15}H_{28}$ | 0 | 14881. | 15024. | 24068. | 35035. | 47610. | 61628. | 76888. | 93177. | 110330. | 128260. | 146890. | 166080. | 185740. | 205820. |
| 1-Hexadecyne | $C_{16}H_{30}$ | 0 | 15874. | 16026. | 25692. | 37420. | 50874. | 65870. | 82200. | 99639. | 117990. | 137180. | 157130. | 177660. | 198700. | 220180. |
| 1-Heptadecyne | $C_{17}H_{32}$ | 0 | 16867. | 17031. | 27320. | 39810. | 54138. | 70112. | 87520. | 106092. | 125660. | 146100. | 167360. | 189240. | 211670. | 234560. |
| 1-Octadecyne | $C_{18}H_{34}$ | 0 | 17860. | 18033. | 28944. | 42195. | 57402. | 74361. | 92832. | 112554. | 133320. | 155030. | 177590. | 200810. | 224620. | 248940. |
| 1-Nonadecyne | $C_{19}H_{36}$ | 0 | 18853. | 19038. | 30568. | 44585. | 60666. | 78603. | 98144. | 119007. | 140980. | 163960. | 187820. | 212390. | 237580. | 263310. |
| 1-Eicosyne | $C_{20}H_{38}$ | 0 | 19846. | 20040. | 32192. | 46970. | 63930. | 82845. | 103456. | 125469. | 148640. | 172880. | 198060. | 223980. | 250540. | 277680. |
| Increment per $CH_2$ group, applicable beyond 1-pentyne | | 0 | 992.9 | 1003.2 | 1625.2 | 2387.0 | 3263.4 | 4243.4 | 5314.4 | 6458.4 | 7663. | 8923. | 10234. | 11580. | 12961. | 14373. |

TABLE 12u — ACETYLENES, $C_2$ TO $C_5$

HEAT CONTENT (ENTHALPY), $(H^o - H^o_0)$, FOR THE IDEAL GAS STATE , AT 0° TO 1500°K

April 30, 1945

Heat Content (Enthalpy), $(H^o - H^o_0)$, in cal/mole

| Compound (gas) | Formula | Temperature in °K | | | | | | | | | | | | | | |
|---|---|---|---|---|---|---|---|---|---|---|---|---|---|---|---|---|
| | | 0 | 298.16 | 300 | 400 | 500 | 600 | 700 | 800 | 900 | 1000 | 1100 | 1200 | 1300 | 1400 | 1500 |
| Ethyne (Acetylene) | $C_2H_2$ | 0 | 2391.5 | 2410.8 | 3541.2 | 4791.0 | 6127. | 7533. | 8999. | 10520. | 12090. | 13706. | 15362. | 17055. | 18782. | 20541. |
| Propyne (Methylacetylene) | $C_3H_4$ | 0 | 3104. | 3131. | 4728. | 6584. | 8663. | 10935. | 13372. | 15956. | 18670. | 21490. | 24420. | 27430. | 30520. | 33670. |
| 1-Butyne (Ethylacetylene) | $C_4H_6$ | 0 | 3820. | 3850. | 6031. | 8610. | 11540. | 14760. | 18240. | 21940. | 25830. | 29990. | 34110. | 38450. | 42910. | 47460. |
| 2-Butyne (Dimethylacetylene) | " | 0 | 3961. | 3995. | 6060. | 8513. | 11320. | 14440. | 17880. | 21450. | 25290. | 29300. | 33480. | 37780. | 42210. | 46740. |
| 1-Pentyne | $C_5H_8$ | 0 | 4952. | 4992. | 7840. | 11210. | 15000. | 19300. | 23800. | 28700. | 33700. | 39100. | 44600. | 50300. | 56100. | 62100. |
| 2-Pentyne | " | 0 | 4675. | 4716. | 7360. | 10540. | 14200. | 18000. | 22700. | 27400. | 32500. | 37700. | 43200. | 48800. | 54600. | 60500. |
| 3-Methyl-1-butyne | " | 0 | 4583. | 4620. | 7440. | 10820. | 14700. | 18900. | 23500. | 28400. | 33500. | 38800. | 44400. | 50100. | 55900. | 61900. |

TABLE 21u (PART 1) – NORMAL ALKYL BENZENES, $C_6$ TO $C_{22}$

HEAT CONTENT (ENTHALPY), $(H°-H°_0)$, FOR THE IDEAL GAS STATE, AT 0° TO 1500°K

November 30, 1945; December 31, 1952

| Compound (gas) | Formula | Temperature in °K — Heat Content (Enthalpy), $(H°-H°_0)$, in cal/mole | | | | | | | | | | | | | | |
|---|---|---|---|---|---|---|---|---|---|---|---|---|---|---|---|---|
| | | 0 | 298.16 | 300 | 400 | 500 | 600 | 700 | 800 | 900 | 1000 | 1100 | 1200 | 1300 | 1400 | 1500 |
| Benzene | $C_6H_6$ | 0 | 3401. | 3437. | 5762. | 8750. | 12285. | 16267. | 20612. | 25260. | 30163. | 35280. | 40590. | 46040. | 51640. | 57350. |
| Methylbenzene (Toluene) | $C_7H_8$ | 0 | 4306. | 4352. | 7269. | 10969. | 15334. | 20247. | 25621. | 31373. | 37449. | 43800. | 50390. | 57180. | 64130. | 71250. |
| Ethylbenzene | $C_8H_{10}$ | 0 | 5335. | 5391. | 8976. | 13496. | 18799. | 24746. | 31222. | 38144. | 45448. | 53080. | 60980. | 69130. | 77480. | 86020. |
| n-Propylbenzene | $C_9H_{12}$ | 0 | 6467. | 6534. | 10760. | 15725. | 22242. | 29176. | 36728. | 44793. | 53320. | 62200. | 71080. | 80950. | 90690. | 100650. |
| n-Butylbenzene | $C_{10}H_{14}$ | 0 | 7451. | 7527. | 12372. | 18425. | 25494. | 33404. | 42032. | 51237. | 60970. | 71120. | 81660. | 92520. | 103640. | 115000. |
| n-Pentylbenzene | $C_{11}H_{16}$ | 0 | 8444. | 8532. | 14000. | 20815. | 28758. | 37653. | 47344. | 57699. | 68630. | 80050. | 91900. | 104100. | 116610. | 129390. |
| n-Hexylbenzene | $C_{12}H_{18}$ | 0 | 9437. | 9534. | 15624. | 23200. | 32022. | 41895. | 52656. | 64161. | 76290. | 88970. | 102130. | 115690. | 129570. | 143760. |
| n-Heptylbenzene | $C_{13}H_{20}$ | 0 | 10430. | 10559. | 17252. | 25590. | 35286. | 46137. | 57976. | 70614. | 83960. | 97890. | 112370. | 127270. | 142530. | 158130. |
| n-Octylbenzene | $C_{14}H_{22}$ | 0 | 11422. | 11541. | 18876. | 27975. | 38550. | 50386. | 63298. | 77076. | 91620. | 106620. | 122590. | 138840. | 155480. | 172520. |
| n-Nonylbenzene | $C_{15}H_{24}$ | 0 | 12415. | 12546. | 20500. | 30365. | 41814. | 54628. | 68600. | 83529. | 99280. | 115740. | 132830. | 150420. | 168450. | 186880. |
| n-Decylbenzene | $C_{16}H_{26}$ | 0 | 13408. | 13548. | 22128. | 32750. | 45072. | 58870. | 73920. | 89991. | 106940. | 124660. | 143060. | 162010. | 181410. | 201260. |
| n-Undecylbenzene | $C_{17}H_{28}$ | 0 | 14401. | 14550. | 23752. | 35135. | 48336. | 63112. | 79232. | 96453. | 114610. | 133580. | 153300. | 173590. | 194380. | 215620. |
| n-Dodecylbenzene | $C_{18}H_{30}$ | 0 | 15394. | 15555. | 25376. | 37525. | 51600. | 67354. | 84544. | 102906. | 122270. | 142500. | 163540. | 185170. | 207340. | 230000. |
| n-Tridecylbenzene | $C_{19}H_{32}$ | 0 | 16387. | 16557. | 27000. | 39910. | 54864. | 71603. | 89856. | 109368. | 129990. | 151440. | 173760. | 196740. | 220290. | 244380. |
| n-Tetradecylbenzene | $C_{20}H_{34}$ | 0 | 17380. | 17562. | 28628. | 42300. | 58128. | 75845. | 95176. | 115821. | 137600. | 160360. | 184000. | 208320. | 233250. | 258750. |
| n-Pentadecylbenzene | $C_{21}H_{36}$ | 0 | 18373. | 18564. | 30252. | 44685. | 61392. | 80087. | 100488. | 122283. | 145260. | 169280. | 194230. | 219910. | 246220. | 273120. |
| n-Hexadecylbenzene | $C_{22}H_{38}$ | 0 | 19965. | 19566. | 31876. | 47070. | 64656. | 84329. | 105800. | 128745. | 152920. | 178200. | 204470. | 231490. | 259180. | 287490. |
| Increment per $CH_2$ group, applicable beyond n-pentylbenzene | | 0 | 992.9 | 1003.2 | 1625.2 | 2387.0 | 3263.4 | 4243.4 | 5314.4 | 6458.4 | 7663. | 8923. | 10234. | 11580. | 12961. | 14373. |

TABLE 5u – ALKYL BENZENES, $C_6$ TO $C_9$

HEAT CONTENT (ENTHALPY), $(H^o - H^o_0)$, FOR THE IDEAL GAS STATE, AT 0° TO 1500°K

November 30, 1945

Temperature in °K

Heat Content (Enthalpy), $(H^o - H^o_0)$, in cal/mole

| Compound (gas) | Formula | 0 | 298.16 | 300 | 400 | 500 | 600 | 700 | 800 | 900 | 1000 | 1100 | 1200 | 1300 | 1400 | 1500 |
|---|---|---|---|---|---|---|---|---|---|---|---|---|---|---|---|---|
| Benzene | $C_6H_6$ | 0 | 3401. | 3437. | 5762. | 8750. | 12285. | 16267. | 20612. | 25260. | 30163. | 35280. | 40590. | 46040. | 51640. | 57350. |
| Methylbenzene (Toluene) | $C_7H_8$ | 0 | 4306. | 4352. | 7269. | 10969. | 15534. | 20247. | 25621. | 31373. | 37449. | 43800. | 50390. | 57180. | 64130. | 71250. |
| Ethylbenzene | $C_8H_{10}$ | 0 | 5335. | 5391. | 8976. | 13496. | 18799. | 24746. | 31222. | 38144. | 45448. | 53080. | 60980. | 69130. | 77480. | 86020. |
| 1,2-Dimethylbenzene (o-Xylene) | " | 0 | 5576. | 5635. | 9291. | 13806. | 19070. | 24962. | 31386. | 38265. | 45531. | 53130. | 61000. | 69120. | 77450. | 85960. |
| 1,3-Dimethylbenzene (m-Xylene) | " | 0 | 5325. | 5382. | 8925. | 13359. | 18563. | 24415. | 30817. | 37678. | 44933. | 52520. | 60390. | 68500. | 76820. | 85330. |
| 1,4-Dimethylbenzene (p-Xylene) | " | 0 | 5358. | 5414. | 8929. | 13330. | 18499. | 24319. | 30690. | 37525. | 44755. | 52320. | 60170. | 68270. | 76580. | 85080. |
| n-Propylbenzene | $C_9H_{12}$ | 0 | 6467. | 6534. | 10790. | 16090. | 22300. | 29250. | 36810. | 44860. | 53360. | 62200. | 71400. | 81000. | 90700. | 100600. |
| Isopropylbenzene | " | 0 | 6097. | 6162. | 10380. | 15700. | 21940. | 28900. | 36470. | 44560. | 53090. | 62000. | 71200. | 80800. | 90500. | 100400. |
| 1-Methyl-2-ethylbenzene | " | 0 | 6604. | 6674. | 11000. | 16330. | 22530. | 29460. | 36990. | 45040. | 53530. | 62400. | 71600. | 81100. | 90800. | 100700. |
| 1-Methyl-3-ethylbenzene | " | 0 | 6354. | 6421. | 10630. | 15890. | 22030. | 28910. | 36420. | 44450. | 52930. | 61800. | 71000. | 80500. | 90200. | 100100. |
| 1-Methyl-4-ethylbenzene | " | 0 | 6386. | 6453. | 10640. | 15860. | 21960. | 28820. | 36290. | 44300. | 52750. | 61600. | 70800. | 80200. | 89900. | 99900. |
| 1,2,3-Trimethylbenzene | " | 0 | 6590. | 6658. | 10810. | 15980. | 21990. | 28750. | 36130. | 44050. | 52430. | 61200. | 70300. | 79700. | 89400. | 99300. |
| 1,2,4-Trimethylbenzene | " | 0 | 6609. | 6677. | 10860. | 16030. | 22060. | 28830. | 36230. | 44160. | 52550. | 61300. | 70500. | 79900. | 89600. | 99500. |
| 1,3,5-Trimethylbenzene | " | 0 | 6326. | 6392. | 10486. | 15616. | 21623. | 28386. | 35789. | 43728. | 52131. | 60930. | 70070. | 79500. | 89180. | 99080. |

## TABLE 13u - STYRENES, C$_8$ and C$_9$

### HEAT CONTENT, $(H^o - H^o_0)$, FOR THE IDEAL GAS STATE, AT 0° TO 1500°K

September 30, 1947

Heat Content, $(H^o - H^o_0)$, in cal/mole

| Compound (gas) | Formula | Temperature in °K | | | | | | | | | | | | | | |
|---|---|---|---|---|---|---|---|---|---|---|---|---|---|---|---|---|
| | | 0 | 298.16 | 300 | 400 | 500 | 600 | 700 | 800 | 900 | 1000 | 1100 | 1200 | 1300 | 1400 | 1500 |
| Ethenylbenzene (Styrene; Vinylbenzene; Phenylethylene) | C$_8$H$_8$ | 0 | 4985. | 5037. | 8428. | 12660. | 17568. | 23044. | 28976. | 35298. | 41950. | 48880. | 56040. | 63400. | 70940. | 78630 |
| Isopropenylbenzene (α-Methylstyrene; 2-Phenyl-1-propene) | C$_9$H$_{10}$ | 0 | 6050. | 6090. | 10080. | 15000. | 20760. | 27160. | 34080. | 41490. | 49300. | 57400. | 65900. | 74500. | 83400. | 92400. |
| cis-1-Propenylbenzene (cis-β-Methylstyrene; cis-1-Phenyl-1-propene) | " | 0 | 6050. | 6090. | 10080. | 15000. | 20760. | 27160. | 34080. | 41490. | 49300. | 57400. | 65900. | 74500. | 83400. | 92400. |
| trans-1-Propenylbenzene (trans-β-Methylstyrene; trans-1-Phenyl-1-propene) | " | 0 | 5930. | 6000. | 10040. | 15000. | 20760. | 27230. | 34160. | 41580. | 49500. | 57600. | 66100. | 74800. | 83700. | 92700. |
| 1-Methyl-2-ethenylbenzene (o-Methylstyrene) | " | 0 | 6050. | 6090. | 10080. | 15000. | 20760. | 27160. | 34080. | 41490. | 49300. | 57400. | 65900. | 74500. | 83400. | 92400. |
| 1-Methyl-3-ethenylbenzene (m-Methylstyrene) | " | 0 | 6050. | 6090. | 10080. | 15000. | 20760. | 27160. | 34080. | 41490. | 49300. | 57400. | 65900. | 74500 | 83400. | 92400. |
| 1-Methyl-4-ethenylbenzene (p-Methylstyrene) | " | 0 | 6050. | 6090. | 10080. | 15000. | 20760. | 27160. | 34080. | 41490. | 49300. | 57400. | 65900. | 74500. | 83400. | 92400. |

TABLE Ou-E – $O_2$, $H_2$, OH, $H_2O$, $N_2$, NO, C, CO, $CO_2$

HEAT CONTENT (ENTHALPY), $(H°-H°_0)$, AT $-459.69°$ TO $2200°F$

November 30, 1944; August 31, 1946; June 30, 1949

Heat Content (Enthalpy), $(H°-H°_0)$, in BTU/lb

| Compound | Formula | State | Temperature in °F | | | | | | | | | | | | | |
|---|---|---|---|---|---|---|---|---|---|---|---|---|---|---|---|---|
| | | | -459.69 | 0 | 32 | 60 | 68 | 77 | 100 | 200 | 300 | 400 | 500 | 600 | 700 | 800 |
| Oxygen | $O_2$ | gas | 0 | 99.64 | 106.56 | 112.64 | 114.38 | 116.35 | 121.38 | 143.47 | 165.93 | 188.77 | 212.03 | 235.69 | 259.77 | 284.22 |
| Hydrogen | $H_2$ | gas | 0 | 1542.4 | 1651.7 | 1747.5 | 1774.9 | 1805.8 | 1884.7 | 2228.6 | 2574.0 | 2920.3 | 3267.0 | 3614.1 | 3961.6 | 4309.9 |
| Hydroxyl | OH | gas | 0 | 190.29 | 203.80 | 215.60 | 218.96 | 222.76 | 232.39 | 274.18 | 315.71 | 357.16 | 398.62 | 440.10 | 481.55 | 523.07 |
| Water | $H_2O$ | gas | 0 | 202.14 | 216.33 | 228.78 | 232.35 | 236.41 | 246.62 | 291.55 | 337.03 | 383.14 | 429.98 | 477.67 | 526.40 | 576.10 |
| Nitrogen | $N_2$ | gas | 0 | 113.94 | 121.88 | 128.84 | 130.82 | 133.05 | 138.77 | 163.63 | 188.56 | 213.61 | 238.86 | 264.33 | 290.10 | 316.16 |
| Nitric Oxide | NO | gas | 0 | 113.29 | 120.85 | 127.48 | 129.37 | 131.53 | 136.95 | 160.70 | 184.59 | 208.67 | 232.99 | 257.59 | 282.54 | 307.83 |
| Carbon | C | solid graphite | 0 | 25.58 | 30.32 | 34.80 | 36.13 | 37.68 | 41.72 | 61.62 | 84.97 | 111.46 | 140.81 | 172.70 | 206.79 | 242.81 |
| Carbon Monoxide | CO | gas | 0 | 114.03 | 121.96 | 128.90 | 130.89 | 133.10 | 138.83 | 163.70 | 188.71 | 213.91 | 239.35 | 265.08 | 291.13 | 317.52 |
| Carbon Dioxide | $CO_2$ | gas | 0 | 76.30 | 82.50 | 88.04 | 89.64 | 91.48 | 96.14 | 117.27 | 139.56 | 162.92 | 187.21 | 212.35 | 238.24 | 264.83 |

Heat Content (Enthalpy), $(H°-H°_0)$, in BTU/lb

| Compound | Formula | State | Temperature in °F | | | | | | | | | | | | | |
|---|---|---|---|---|---|---|---|---|---|---|---|---|---|---|---|---|
| | | | 900 | 1000 | 1100 | 1200 | 1300 | 1400 | 1500 | 1600 | 1700 | 1800 | 1900 | 2000 | 2100 | 2200 |
| Oxygen | $O_2$ | gas | 309.03 | 334.15 | 359.52 | 385.13 | 410.96 | 437.00 | 463.23 | 489.62 | 516.16 | 542.88 | 569.73 | 596.68 | 623.74 | 650.97 |
| Hydrogen | $H_2$ | gas | 4659.4 | 5010.0 | 5361.9 | 5715.5 | 6071.3 | 6429.4 | 6789.8 | 7152.8 | 7518.5 | 7887.0 | 8258.3 | 8632.2 | 9008.9 | 9388.4 |
| Hydroxyl | OH | gas | 564.79 | 606.73 | 648.91 | 691.40 | 734.21 | 777.32 | 820.75 | 864.54 | 908.71 | 953.30 | 998.28 | 1043.6 | 1089.3 | 1135.2 |
| Water | $H_2O$ | gas | 626.68 | 678.12 | 730.37 | 783.49 | 837.48 | 892.25 | 947.76 | 1004.1 | 1061.2 | 1119.1 | 1177.7 | 1237.2 | 1297.3 | 1358.0 |
| Nitrogen | $N_2$ | gas | 342.54 | 369.25 | 396.27 | 423.60 | 451.23 | 479.15 | 507.35 | 535.80 | 564.47 | 593.35 | 622.43 | 651.67 | 681.07 | 710.61 |
| Nitric Oxide | NO | gas | 333.44 | 359.39 | 385.67 | 412.24 | 439.06 | 466.12 | 493.40 | 520.87 | 548.55 | 576.44 | 604.49 | 632.66 | 660.99 | 689.47 |
| Carbon | C | solid graphite | 280.46 | 319.59 | 360.00 | 401.33 | 443.39 | 486.20 | 529.7 | 573.7 | 618.4 | 663.9 | 710.1 | 756.7 | 803.9 | 851.5 |
| Carbon Monoxide | CO | gas | 344.30 | 371.42 | 398.87 | 426.62 | 454.67 | 482.98 | 511.55 | 540.37 | 569.42 | 598.68 | 628.12 | 657.74 | 687.49 | 717.35 |
| Carbon Dioxide | $CO_2$ | gas | 292.03 | 319.81 | 348.08 | 376.81 | 405.94 | 435.5 | 465.4 | 495.6 | 526.1 | 556.9 | 587.9 | 619.1 | 650.6 | 682.2 |

TABLE 20u-E (PART 1) Page 1 - NORMAL PARAFFINS, C$_1$ TO C$_{20}$

HEAT CONTENT (ENTHALPY), $(H^{\circ}-H^{\circ}_0)$, FOR THE IDEAL GAS STATE, AT -459.69° TO 2200°F

December 31, 1945; December 31, 1952

Heat Content (Enthalpy), $(H^{\circ}-H^{\circ}_0)$, in BTU/lb

| Compound (gas) | Formula | -459.69 | 0 | 32 | 60 | 68 | 77 | 100 | 200 | 300 | 400 | 500 | 600 | 700 | 800 |
|---|---|---|---|---|---|---|---|---|---|---|---|---|---|---|---|
| Methane | CH$_4$ | 0 | 229.5 | 245.6 | 259.9 | 264.1 | 268.8 | 281.1 | 336.8 | 397.1 | 461.9 | 531.7 | 606.5 | 686.0 | 770.2 |
| Ethane | C$_2$H$_6$ | 0 | 140.22 | 152.55 | 163.80 | 167.10 | 170.86 | 180.64 | 226.6 | 278.1 | 335.1 | 397.5 | 465.2 | 537.8 | 614.8 |
| Propane | C$_3$H$_8$ | 0 | 115.04 | 126.30 | 136.74 | 139.83 | 143.27 | 152.60 | 196.89 | 247.4 | 303.8 | 365.3 | 431.8 | 503.1 | 578.6 |
| n-Butane | C$_4$H$_{10}$ | 0 | 114.20 | 126.12 | 136.98 | 140.17 | 143.76 | 153.11 | 197.46 | 247.88 | 303.87 | 365.03 | 430.98 | 501.46 | 576.04 |
| n-Pentane | C$_5$H$_{12}$ | 0 | 111.05 | 122.82 | 133.59 | 136.76 | 140.35 | 149.60 | 193.68 | 243.77 | 299.47 | 360.23 | 425.68 | 495.50 | 569.45 |
| n-Hexane | C$_6$H$_{14}$ | 0 | 110.05 | 121.28 | 131.70 | 134.77 | 138.23 | 147.48 | 191.42 | 241.35 | 296.82 | 357.27 | 422.36 | 491.85 | 565.41 |
| n-Heptane | C$_7$H$_{16}$ | 0 | 105.52 | 116.44 | 126.55 | 129.54 | 132.90 | 141.86 | 184.46 | 232.87 | 286.62 | 345.20 | 408.25 | 475.52 | 546.72 |
| n-Octane | C$_8$H$_{18}$ | 0 | 107.42 | 118.63 | 129.00 | 132.08 | 135.56 | 144.74 | 188.47 | 238.18 | 293.32 | 353.45 | 418.15 | 487.12 | 560.10 |
| n-Nonane | C$_9$H$_{20}$ | 0 | 106.60 | 117.79 | 128.15 | 131.21 | 134.66 | 143.85 | 187.53 | 237.16 | 292.23 | 352.20 | 416.74 | 485.52 | 558.33 |
| n-Decane | C$_{10}$H$_{22}$ | 0 | 105.89 | 117.08 | 127.42 | 130.48 | 133.94 | 143.11 | 186.74 | 236.29 | 291.29 | 351.16 | 415.59 | 484.30 | 556.98 |

Temperature in °F

Heat Content (Enthalpy), $(H^{\circ}-H^{\circ}_0)$, in BTU/lb

| Compound (gas) | Formula | 900 | 1000 | 1100 | 1200 | 1300 | 1400 | 1500 | 1600 | 1700 | 1800 | 1900 | 2000 | 2100 | 2200 |
|---|---|---|---|---|---|---|---|---|---|---|---|---|---|---|---|
| Methane | CH$_4$ | 858.8 | 951.6 | 1048.4 | 1149.1 | 1253.3 | 1361. | 1471. | 1584. | 1701. | 1820. | 1942. | 2065. | 2191. | 2318. |
| Ethane | C$_2$H$_6$ | 695.6 | 780.4 | 868.8 | 960.3 | 1054.7 | 1152. | 1253. | 1356. | 1461. | 1568. | 1678. | 1789. | 1902. | 2017. |
| Propane | C$_3$H$_8$ | 658.1 | 741.2 | 827.6 | 917.0 | 1009.3 | 1104. | 1202. | 1302. | 1404. | 1508. | 1613. | 1721. | 1829. | 1940. |
| n-Butane | C$_4$H$_{10}$ | 654.47 | 736.43 | 821.54 | 909.72 | 1000.7 | 1094.1 | 1189.9 | 1288.0 | 1388.4 | 1490.4 | 1594.2 | 1699.7 | 1806.2 | 1914.5 |
| n-Pentane | C$_5$H$_{12}$ | 647.26 | 728.52 | 812.82 | 900.04 | 990.0 | 1082.4 | 1177.1 | 1274.2 | 1373.3 | 1474.0 | 1576.5 | 1680.5 | 1785.9 | 1892.3 |
| n-Hexane | C$_6$H$_{14}$ | 642.69 | 723.37 | 807.21 | 893.84 | 983.1 | 1074.8 | 1168.9 | 1265.2 | 1363.4 | 1463.3 | 1564.8 | 1667.8 | 1772.3 | 1877.9 |
| n-Heptane | C$_7$H$_{16}$ | 621.60 | 699.77 | 780.85 | 864.64 | 950.9 | 1039.6 | 1130.5 | 1223.5 | 1318.5 | 1415.0 | 1513.0 | 1612.6 | 1713.4 | 1815.3 |
| n-Octane | C$_8$H$_{18}$ | 636.86 | 717.02 | 800.17 | 886.06 | 974.4 | 1065.2 | 1158.3 | 1253.6 | 1350.9 | 1449.7 | 1550.0 | 1651.9 | 1755.1 | 1859.3 |
| n-Nonane | C$_9$H$_{20}$ | 634.95 | 714.90 | 797.74 | 883.35 | 971.5 | 1062.0 | 1154.7 | 1249.7 | 1346.7 | 1445.1 | 1545.1 | 1646.5 | 1749.3 | 1853.1 |
| n-Decane | C$_{10}$H$_{22}$ | 633.40 | 713.14 | 795.83 | 881.24 | 969.1 | 1059.4 | 1152.0 | 1246.6 | 1343.2 | 1441.3 | 1540.9 | 1642.0 | 1744.5 | 1848.1 |

Temperature in °F

TABLE 20u-E (PART 1), Page 2 — NORMAL PARAFFINS, $C_1$ TO $C_{20}$

HEAT CONTENT (ENTHALPY), $(H°-H°_0)$, FOR THE IDEAL GAS STATE, AT -459.69° TO 2200°F

December 31, 1945; December 31, 1952

| Compound (gas) | Formula | Temperature in °F — Heat Content (Enthalpy), $(H°-H°_0)$, in BTU/lb | | | | | | | | | | | | |
| | | -459.69 | 0 | 32 | 60 | 68 | 77 | 100 | 200 | 300 | 400 | 500 | 600 | 700 | 800 |
|---|---|---|---|---|---|---|---|---|---|---|---|---|---|---|---|
| n-Undecane | $C_{11}H_{24}$ | 0 | 105.44 | 116.56 | 126.87 | 129.92 | 133.35 | 142.51 | 186.07 | 235.59 | 290.55 | 350.36 | 414.67 | 483.23 | 555.80 |
| n-Dodecane | $C_{12}H_{26}$ | 0 | 104.86 | 116.02 | 126.35 | 129.40 | 132.84 | 142.01 | 185.56 | 235.03 | 289.91 | 349.65 | 413.88 | 482.36 | 554.81 |
| n-Tridecane | $C_{13}H_{28}$ | 0 | 104.45 | 115.61 | 125.93 | 128.97 | 132.43 | 141.57 | 185.10 | 234.53 | 289.36 | 349.02 | 413.17 | 481.59 | 553.97 |
| n-Tetradecane | $C_{14}H_{30}$ | 0 | 104.20 | 115.31 | 125.60 | 128.64 | 132.07 | 141.22 | 184.69 | 234.10 | 288.91 | 348.54 | 412.61 | 480.94 | 553.26 |
| n-Pentadecane | $C_{15}H_{32}$ | 0 | 103.89 | 114.99 | 125.29 | 128.32 | 131.76 | 140.89 | 184.34 | 233.72 | 288.50 | 348.08 | 412.12 | 480.43 | 552.69 |
| n-Hexadecane | $C_{16}H_{34}$ | 0 | 103.64 | 114.74 | 125.02 | 128.07 | 131.48 | 140.63 | 184.07 | 233.42 | 288.18 | 347.72 | 411.70 | 479.94 | 552.14 |
| n-Heptadecane | $C_{17}H_{36}$ | 0 | 103.39 | 114.49 | 124.78 | 127.82 | 131.24 | 140.38 | 183.80 | 233.13 | 287.85 | 347.36 | 411.32 | 479.51 | 551.65 |
| n-Octadecane | $C_{18}H_{38}$ | 0 | 103.16 | 114.27 | 124.55 | 127.59 | 131.03 | 140.15 | 183.56 | 232.86 | 287.56 | 347.05 | 410.98 | 479.13 | 551.22 |
| n-Nonadecane | $C_{19}H_{40}$ | 0 | 102.99 | 114.10 | 124.38 | 127.41 | 130.83 | 139.97 | 183.36 | 232.66 | 287.33 | 346.79 | 410.68 | 478.78 | 550.83 |
| n-Eicosane | $C_{20}H_{42}$ | 0 | 102.82 | 113.91 | 124.20 | 127.23 | 130.66 | 139.78 | 183.16 | 232.45 | 287.10 | 346.54 | 410.41 | 478.50 | 550.53 |

| Compound (gas) | Formula | Temperature in °F — Heat Content (Enthalpy), $(H°-H°_0)$, in BTU/lb | | | | | | | | | | | | |
| | | 900 | 1000 | 1100 | 1200 | 1300 | 1400 | 1500 | 1600 | 1700 | 1800 | 1900 | 2000 | 2100 | 2200 |
|---|---|---|---|---|---|---|---|---|---|---|---|---|---|---|---|
| n-Undecane | $C_{11}H_{24}$ | 632.08 | 711.67 | 794.18 | 879.43 | 967.2 | 1057.3 | 1149.6 | 1244.1 | 1340.4 | 1438.3 | 1537.6 | 1638.5 | 1740.7 | 1844.0 |
| n-Dodecane | $C_{12}H_{26}$ | 631.02 | 710.54 | 792.91 | 878.01 | 965.6 | 1055.5 | 1147.6 | 1241.9 | 1338.1 | 1436.8 | 1534.9 | 1635.6 | 1737.5 | 1840.6 |
| n-Tridecane | $C_{13}H_{28}$ | 630.09 | 709.50 | 791.82 | 876.80 | 964.2 | 1054.0 | 1145.9 | 1240.1 | 1336.2 | 1433.6 | 1532.6 | 1633.1 | 1734.8 | 1837.7 |
| n-Tetradecane | $C_{14}H_{30}$ | 629.29 | 708.61 | 790.81 | 875.69 | 963.0 | 1052.6 | 1144.5 | 1238.6 | 1334.5 | 1431.8 | 1530.7 | 1631.0 | 1732.5 | 1835.2 |
| n-Pentadecane | $C_{15}H_{32}$ | 628.61 | 707.84 | 790.00 | 874.78 | 962.0 | 1051.5 | 1143.3 | 1237.2 | 1332.9 | 1430.1 | 1528.8 | 1629.0 | 1730.4 | 1833.0 |
| n-Hexadecane | $C_{16}H_{34}$ | 628.04 | 707.22 | 789.24 | 873.95 | 961.1 | 1050.6 | 1142.2 | 1236.0 | 1331.7 | 1428.8 | 1527.3 | 1627.4 | 1728.7 | 1831.1 |
| n-Heptadecane | $C_{17}H_{36}$ | 627.50 | 706.62 | 788.61 | 873.25 | 960.3 | 1049.7 | 1141.2 | 1235.0 | 1330.5 | 1427.5 | 1526.0 | 1625.9 | 1727.1 | 1829.5 |
| n-Octadecane | $C_{18}H_{38}$ | 627.01 | 706.09 | 788.05 | 872.64 | 959.6 | 1048.9 | 1140.4 | 1234.0 | 1329.5 | 1426.4 | 1524.8 | 1624.6 | 1725.7 | 1828.0 |
| n-Nonadecane | $C_{19}H_{40}$ | 626.62 | 705.65 | 787.52 | 872.04 | 959.0 | 1048.2 | 1139.6 | 1233.2 | 1328.6 | 1425.5 | 1523.8 | 1623.5 | 1724.5 | 1826.6 |
| n-Eicosane | $C_{20}H_{42}$ | 626.24 | 705.22 | 787.04 | 871.54 | 958.4 | 1047.6 | 1139.0 | 1232.5 | 1327.8 | 1424.5 | 1522.8 | 1622.4 | 1723.3 | 1825.4 |

TABLE 1u-E, Page 1 - PARAFFINS, $C_1$ TO $C_5$

HEAT CONTENT (ENTHALPY), $(H^\circ - H^\circ_0)$, FOR THE IDEAL GAS STATE, AT $-459.69^\circ$ TO $2200^\circ$F

November 30, 1944; February 28, 1949; December 31, 1952

| Compound (gas) | Formula | Temperature in °F |  |  |  |  |  |  |  |  |  |  |  |  |  |
|---|---|---|---|---|---|---|---|---|---|---|---|---|---|---|---|
|  |  | −459.69 | −300 | −250 | −200 | −150 | −100 | −50 | 0 | 32 | 50 | 60 | 68 | 77 | 100 |
|  |  | Heat Content (Enthalpy), $(H^\circ - H^\circ_0)$, in BTU/lb |  |  |  |  |  |  |  |  |  |  |  |  |  |
| Methane | $CH_4$ | 0 | 79.08 | 103.8 | 128.6 | 153.4 | 178.2 | 203.2 | 228.6 | 245.1 | 254.5 | 259.8 | 264.0 | 268.8 | 281.1 |
| Ethane | $C_2H_6$ | 0 |  | 57.09 | 72.05 | 88.71 | 104.23 | 121.66 | 140.13 | 152.54 | 159.74 | 163.81 | 167.10 | 170.85 | 180.66 |
| Propane | $C_3H_8$ | 0 |  | 41.34 | 53.76 | 68.01 | 81.74 | 97.47 | 114.48 | 126.07 | 132.84 | 136.68 | 139.79 | 143.28 | 152.69 |
| n-Butane | $C_4H_{10}$ | 0 |  |  |  |  | 81.59 | 97.22 | 114.47 | 126.25 | 133.13 | 137.03 | 140.19 | 143.76 | 153.20 |
| 2-Methylpropane (Isobutane) | " | 0 |  |  |  |  | 71.43 | 86.55 | 103.40 | 114.97 | 121.75 | 125.60 | 128.73 | 132.33 | 141.61 |
| n-Pentane | $C_5H_{12}$ | 0 |  |  |  |  | 78.56 | 94.08 | 111.22 | 122.92 | 129.75 | 133.63 | 136.77 | 140.35 | 149.69 |
| 2-Methylbutane (Isopentane) | " | 0 |  |  |  |  | 72.13 | 86.92 | 103.48 | 114.89 | 121.58 | 125.38 | 128.47 | 132.02 | 141.20 |
| 2,2-Dimethylpropane (Neopentane) | " | 0 |  |  |  |  | 64.30 | 79.28 | 96.16 | 107.83 | 114.68 | 118.59 | 121.75 | 125.41 | 134.84 |

| Compound (gas) | Formula | Temperature in °F |  |  |  |  |  |  |  |  |  |  |  |  |  |
|---|---|---|---|---|---|---|---|---|---|---|---|---|---|---|---|
|  |  | 150 | 200 | 250 | 300 | 350 | 400 | 500 | 600 | 700 | 800 | 900 | 1000 | 1100 | 1200 |
|  |  | Heat Content (Enthalpy), $(H^\circ - H^\circ_0)$, in BTU/lb |  |  |  |  |  |  |  |  |  |  |  |  |  |
| Methane | $CH_4$ | 308.6 | 337.0 | 366.4 | 397.1 | 428.9 | 461.9 | 531.7 | 606.5 | 686.0 | 770.2 | 858.8 | 951.6 | 1048.4 | 1149.1 |
| Ethane | $C_2H_6$ | 203.00 | 226.7 | 251.7 | 278.1 | 305.9 | 335.1 | 397.5 | 465.2 | 537.8 | 614.8 | 695.6 | 780.4 | 868.8 | 960.3 |
| Propane | $C_3H_8$ | 174.13 | 197.04 | 221.4 | 247.4 | 274.9 | 303.8 | 365.3 | 431.8 | 503.1 | 578.6 | 658.1 | 741.2 | 827.6 | 917.0 |
| n-Butane | $C_4H_{10}$ | 174.74 | 197.46 | 221.97 | 247.88 | 275.18 | 303.87 | 365.03 | 430.98 | 501.46 | 576.04 | 654.47 | 736.43 | 821.54 | 909.72 |
| 2-Methylpropane (Isobutane) | " | 163.00 | 185.90 | 210.3 | 236.4 | 263.9 | 292.9 | 354.7 | 421.4 | 492.4 | 567.4 | 646.3 | 728.7 | 814.2 | 902.6 |
| n-Pentane | $C_5H_{12}$ | 171.07 | 193.68 | 218.04 | 243.77 | 270.95 | 299.47 | 360.23 | 425.68 | 495.50 | 569.45 | 647.26 | 728.52 | 812.82 | 900.04 |
| 2-Methylbutane (Isopentane) | " | 162.19 | 184.88 | 209.1 | 234.9 | 262.1 | 290.7 | 351.6 | 417.4 | 487.9 | 562.5 | 640.4 | 722.0 | 807.2 | 895.1 |
| 2,2-Dimethylpropane (Neopentane) | " | 156.60 | 179.93 | 204.8 | 231.3 | 259.2 | 288.7 | 351.5 | 419.3 | 491.4 | 567.5 | 647.4 | 730.7 | 816.8 | 905.8 |

TABLE 1u-E, Page 2 – PARAFFINS, $C_1$ TO $C_5$

HEAT CONTENT (ENTHALPY), $(H^\circ - H^\circ_0)$, FOR THE IDEAL GAS STATE, AT $-459.69^\circ$ TO $2200^\circ F$

November 30, 1944; February 28, 1949; December 31, 1952

Heat Content (Enthalpy), $(H^\circ - H^\circ_0)$, in BTU/lb

| Compound (gas) | Formula | Temperature in °F | | | | | | | | | |
|---|---|---|---|---|---|---|---|---|---|---|---|
| | | 1300 | 1400 | 1500 | 1600 | 1700 | 1800 | 1900 | 2000 | 2100 | 2200 |
| Methane | $CH_4$ | 1253.3 | 1361. | 1471. | 1584. | 1701. | 1820. | 1942. | 2065. | 2191. | 2318. |
| Ethane | $C_2H_6$ | 1054.7 | 1152. | 1253. | 1356. | 1461. | 1568. | 1678. | 1789. | 1902. | 2017. |
| Propane | $C_3H_8$ | 1009.3 | 1104. | 1202. | 1302. | 1404. | 1508. | 1613. | 1721. | 1829. | 1940. |
| n-Butane | $C_4H_{10}$ | 1000.68 | 1094.1 | 1189.9 | 1288.0 | 1388.4 | 1490.4 | 1594.2 | 1699.7 | 1806.2 | 1914.5 |
| 2-Methylpropane (Isobutane) | " | 993.5 | 1087. | 1183. | 1282. | 1383. | 1485. | 1588. | 1693. | 1800. | 1908. |
| n-Pentane | $C_5H_{12}$ | 989.99 | 1082.4 | 1177.1 | 1274.2 | 1373.3 | 1474.0 | 1576.5 | 1680.5 | 1785.9 | 1892.3 |
| 2-Methylbutane (Isopentane) | " | 985.4 | 1078. | 1174. | 1272. | 1372. | 1473. | 1576. | 1681. | 1787. | 1895. |
| 2,2-Dimethylpropane (Neopentane) | " | 997.4 | 1091. | 1187. | 1286. | 1386. | 1488. | 1592. | 1698. | 1804. | 1912. |

TABLE 2u-E (PART 1) – PARAFFINS, C$_6$

HEAT CONTENT (ENTHALPY), $(H^o - H^o_0)$, FOR THE IDEAL GAS STATE, AT −459.69° TO 2200°F

December 31, 1944; November 30, 1946; December 31, 1952

Temperature in °F

Heat Content (Enthalpy), $(H^o - H^o_0)$, in BTU/lb

| Compound (gas) | Formula | −459.69 | 0 | 32 | 60 | 68 | 77 | 100 | 200 | 300 | 400 | 500 | 600 | 700 | 800 |
|---|---|---|---|---|---|---|---|---|---|---|---|---|---|---|---|
| n-Hexane | C$_6$H$_{14}$ | 0 | 110.05 | 121.28 | 131.70 | 134.77 | 138.23 | 147.48 | 191.42 | 241.35 | 296.82 | 357.27 | 422.36 | 491.85 | 565.41 |
| 2-Methylpentane | " | 0 | 99.93 | 110.74 | 120.88 | 123.90 | 127.28 | 136.45 | 180.54 | 231.3 | 287.9 | 349.0 | 414.5 | 484.9 | 559.4 |
| 3-Methylpentane | " | 0 | 110.11 | 121.32 | 131.72 | 134.79 | 138.23 | 147.48 | 191.40 | 241.4 | 296.8 | 357.2 | 422.1 | 491.7 | 565.3 |
| 2,2-Dimethylbutane | " | 0 | 96.11 | 106.88 | 116.96 | 119.97 | 123.41 | 132.47 | 176.43 | 227.1 | 283.6 | 345.0 | 410.7 | 480.7 | 555.0 |
| 2,3-Dimethylbutane | " | 0 | 95.86 | 106.84 | 117.04 | 120.07 | 123.50 | 132.56 | 176.02 | 225.7 | 281.1 | 341.8 | 407.2 | 477.1 | 551.1 |

Temperature in °F

Heat Content (Enthalpy), $(H^o - H^o_0)$, in BTU/lb

| Compound (gas) | Formula | 900 | 1000 | 1100 | 1200 | 1300 | 1400 | 1500 | 1600 | 1700 | 1800 | 1900 | 2000 | 2100 | 2200 |
|---|---|---|---|---|---|---|---|---|---|---|---|---|---|---|---|
| n-Hexane | C$_6$H$_{14}$ | 642.69 | 723.37 | 807.21 | 893.84 | 983.1 | 1074.8 | 1168.9 | 1265.2 | 1363.4 | 1463.3 | 1564.8 | 1667.8 | 1772.3 | 1877.9 |
| 2-Methylpentane | " | 636.8 | 717.7 | 802.3 | 889.9 | 979.8 | | | | | | | | | |
| 3-Methylpentane | " | 642.2 | 722.6 | 806.5 | 893.3 | 982.3 | | | | | | | | | |
| 2,2-Dimethylbutane | " | 634.0 | 715.8 | 799.3 | 885.9 | 976.6 | | | | | | | | | |
| 2,3-Dimethylbutane | " | 628.8 | 709.8 | 793.5 | 880.2 | 969.9 | | | | | | | | | |

## TABLE 2u-E (PART 2) — PARAFFINS, C₇
### HEAT CONTENT (ENTHALPY), $(H°-H°_0)$, FOR THE IDEAL GAS STATE, AT −459.69° TO 2200°F
December 31, 1944; December 31, 1952

Temperature in °F — Heat Content (Enthalpy), $(H°-H°_0)$, in BTU/lb

| Compound (gas) | Formula | −459.69 | 0 | 32 | 60 | 68 | 77 | 100 | 200 | 300 | 400 | 500 | 600 | 700 | 800 |
|---|---|---|---|---|---|---|---|---|---|---|---|---|---|---|---|
| n-Heptane | C7H16 | 0 | 105.52 | 116.44 | 126.55 | 129.54 | 132.90 | 141.86 | 184.46 | 232.87 | 286.62 | 345.20 | 408.25 | 475.52 | 546.72 |
| 2-Methylhexane | " | 0 | 98.36 | 110.13 | 120.98 | 124.17 | 127.88 | 137.32 | 182.47 | 233.5 | 290.1 | 351.9 | 418.6 | 489.6 | 564.4 |
| 3-Methylhexane | " | 0 | 95.58 | 107.25 | 117.99 | 121.15 | 124.82 | 134.17 | 178.84 | 229.3 | 285.4 | 346.8 | 413.2 | 484.0 | 558.6 |
| 3-Ethylpentane | " | 0 | 91.90 | 103.30 | 113.83 | 116.93 | 120.55 | 129.72 | 173.77 | 223.7 | 279.3 | 340.2 | 406.0 | 476.3 | 550.6 |
| 2,2-Dimethylpentane | " | 0 | 90.80 | 102.24 | 112.83 | 115.96 | 119.64 | 128.90 | 173.69 | 224.8 | 281.6 | 343.9 | 411.1 | 482.9 | 558.8 |
| 2,3-Dimethylpentane | " | 0 | 90.08 | 101.53 | 112.11 | 115.23 | 118.88 | 128.11 | 172.56 | 223.1 | 279.3 | 341.1 | 407.8 | 478.9 | 553.8 |
| 2,4-Dimethylpentane | " | 0 | 90.18 | 101.65 | 112.27 | 115.41 | 119.10 | 128.38 | 173.27 | 224.4 | 281.4 | 343.8 | 411.1 | 482.9 | 558.8 |
| 3,3-Dimethylpentane | " | 0 | 91.08 | 102.71 | 113.45 | 116.61 | | 129.68 | 174.70 | 225.9 | 282.8 | 345.4 | 413.0 | 485.0 | 561.0 |
| 2,2,3-Trimethylbutane | " | 0 | 92.22 | 103.40 | 113.76 | 116.82 | 120.34 | 129.48 | 173.36 | 223.47 | 279.39 | 340.79 | 407.14 | 477.80 | 552.33 |

Temperature in °F — Heat Content (Enthalpy), $(H°-H°_0)$, in BTU/lb

| Compound (gas) | Formula | 900 | 1000 | 1100 | 1200 | 1300 | 1400 | 1500 | 1600 | 1700 | 1800 | 1900 | 2000 | 2100 | 2200 |
|---|---|---|---|---|---|---|---|---|---|---|---|---|---|---|---|
| n-Heptane | C7H16 | 621.60 | 699.77 | 780.85 | 864.64 | 950.9 | 1039.6 | 1130.5 | 1223.5 | 1318.5 | 1415.0 | 1513.0 | 1612.6 | 1713.4 | 1815.3 |
| 2-Methylhexane | " | 642.5 | 723.4 | 806.7 | 892.6 | 981.3 | | | | | | | | | |
| 3-Methylhexane | " | 636.9 | 718.0 | 801.3 | 887.2 | 975.9 | | | | | | | | | |
| 3-Ethylpentane | " | 628.3 | 709.1 | 792.4 | 878.0 | 965.8 | | | | | | | | | |
| 2,2-Dimethylpentane | " | 638.0 | 720.0 | 804.3 | 891.2 | 980.9 | | | | | | | | | |
| 2,3-Dimethylpentane | " | 631.7 | 712.8 | 797.2 | 883.7 | 971.5 | | | | | | | | | |
| 2,4-Dimethylpentane | " | 638.0 | 720.1 | 804.4 | 891.0 | 979.7 | | | | | | | | | |
| 3,3-Dimethylpentane | " | 639.9 | 722.0 | 807.3 | 895.0 | 984.8 | | | | | | | | | |
| 2,2,3-Trimethylbutane | " | 630.18 | 711.38 | 795.85 | 883.39 | 973.7 | 1066.0 | 1160.1 | 1256.7 | 1355.1 | 1454.2 | 1555.1 | 1658.5 | 1763.4 | 1869.2 |

TABLE 3u-E, Page 1 - PARAFFINS, C$_8$

HEAT CONTENT (ENTHALPY), $(H^o-H^o_0)$, FOR THE IDEAL GAS STATE, AT -459.69° TO 2200°F

December 31, 1944; December 31, 1952

| Compound (gas) | Formula | Temperature in °F | | | | | | | | | | | | | |
|---|---|---|---|---|---|---|---|---|---|---|---|---|---|---|---|
| | | -459.69 | 0 | 32 | 60 | 68 | 77 | 100 | 200 | 300 | 400 | 500 | 600 | 700 | 800 |
| | | Heat Content (Enthalpy), $(H^o-H^o_0)$, in BTU/lb | | | | | | | | | | | | | |
| n-Octane | C$_8$H$_{18}$ | 0 | 107.42 | 118.63 | 129.00 | 132.08 | 135.56 | 144.74 | 188.47 | 238.18 | 293.32 | 353.45 | 418.15 | 487.12 | 560.10 |
| 2-Methylheptane | " | 0 | 98.73 | 110.53 | 121.40 | 124.60 | 128.28 | 137.78 | 182.97 | 234.0 | 290.5 | 352.3 | 418.9 | 489.7 | 564.2 |
| 3-Methylheptane | " | 0 | 97.54 | 109.18 | 119.92 | 123.09 | 126.73 | 136.14 | 181.04 | 231.9 | 288.3 | 350.1 | 416.6 | 487.6 | 562.0 |
| 4-Methylheptane | " | 0 | 96.60 | 108.09 | 118.72 | 121.85 | 125.47 | 134.81 | 179.52 | 230.3 | 286.7 | 348.2 | 414.4 | 484.8 | 558.8 |
| 3-Ethylhexane | " | 0 | 91.15 | 102.07 | 112.24 | 115.24 | 118.69 | 127.71 | 171.08 | 220.8 | 276.2 | 336.8 | 402.1 | 471.7 | 545.3 |
| 2,2-Dimethylhexane | " | 0 | 93.01 | 104.52 | 115.19 | 118.34 | 121.99 | 131.35 | 176.32 | 227.5 | 284.3 | 346.2 | 413.0 | 484.1 | 559.3 |
| 2,3-Dimethylhexane | " | 0 | 95.40 | 106.56 | 117.03 | 120.13 | 123.73 | 133.06 | 178.40 | 230.6 | 289.0 | 352.5 | 420.6 | 492.8 | 568.4 |
| 2,4-Dimethylhexane | " | 0 | 89.44 | 101.03 | 111.71 | 114.85 | 118.52 | 127.82 | 172.42 | 223.0 | 279.1 | 340.7 | 407.3 | 478.4 | 553.2 |
| 2,5-Dimethylhexane | " | 0 | 91.45 | 102.82 | 113.37 | 116.49 | 120.11 | 129.40 | 174.17 | 225.2 | 282.2 | 344.4 | 411.4 | 482.6 | 557.4 |

| Compound (gas) | Formula | Temperature in °F | | | | | | | | | | | | | |
|---|---|---|---|---|---|---|---|---|---|---|---|---|---|---|---|
| | | 900 | 1000 | 1100 | 1200 | 1300 | 1400 | 1500 | 1600 | 1700 | 1800 | 1900 | 2000 | 2100 | 2200 |
| | | Heat Content (Enthalpy), $(H^o-H^o_0)$, in BTU/lb | | | | | | | | | | | | | |
| n-Octane | C$_8$H$_{18}$ | 636.86 | 717.02 | 800.17 | 886.06 | 974.4 | 1065.2 | 1158.3 | 1253.6 | 1350.9 | 1449.7 | 1550.0 | 1651.9 | 1755.1 | 1859.3 |
| 2-Methylheptane | " | 641.4 | 721.4 | 803.9 | 889.5 | 978.7 | | | | | | | | | |
| 3-Methylheptane | " | 638.6 | 718.4 | 801.8 | 888.2 | 977.5 | | | | | | | | | |
| 4-Methylheptane | " | 635.4 | 715.2 | 798.6 | 885.1 | 974.3 | | | | | | | | | |
| 3-Ethylpentane | " | 622.4 | 702.6 | 785.1 | 870.4 | 958.8 | | | | | | | | | |
| 2,2-Dimethylhexane | " | 638.3 | 720.3 | 804.6 | 891.5 | 980.7 | | | | | | | | | |
| 2,3-Dimethylhexane | " | 647.0 | 727.8 | 810.3 | 895.7 | 984.9 | | | | | | | | | |
| 2,4-Dimethylhexane | " | 630.4 | 710.6 | 794.0 | 880.2 | 968.6 | | | | | | | | | |
| 2,5-Dimethylhexane | " | 635.0 | 715.1 | 797.6 | 883.2 | 972.4 | | | | | | | | | |

TABLE 3u-E, Page 2 — PARAFFINS, C$_8$

HEAT CONTENT (ENTHALPY), ($H^o-H^o_0$), FOR THE IDEAL GAS STATE, AT -459.69° TO 2200°F

December 31, 1944; December 31, 1952

| Compound (gas) | Formula | Temperature in °F | | | | | | | | | | | | | |
|---|---|---|---|---|---|---|---|---|---|---|---|---|---|---|---|
| | | -459.69 | 0 | 32 | 60 | 68 | 77 | 100 | 200 | 300 | 400 | 500 | 600 | 700 | 800 |
| | | Heat Content (Enthalpy), ($H^o-H^o_0$), in BTU/lb | | | | | | | | | | | | | |
| 3,3-Dimethylhexane | C$_8$H$_{18}$ | 0 | 89.31 | 100.88 | 111.56 | 114.71 | 118.38 | 127.69 | 172.43 | 223.2 | 279.8 | 341.8 | 408.8 | 480.4 | 556.0 |
| 3,4-Dimethylhexane[a] | " | 0 | 96.40 | 107.70 | 118.16 | 121.26 | 124.76 | 134.05 | 178.32 | 228.8 | 284.9 | 346.2 | 412.2 | 482.2 | 556.0 |
| 2-Methyl-3-ethylpentane | " | 0 | 92.33 | 103.86 | 114.55 | 117.71 | 121.37 | 130.77 | 175.98 | 227.4 | 284.6 | 346.9 | 413.9 | 485.0 | 559.6 |
| 3-Methyl-3-ethylpentane | " | 0 | 88.57 | 100.50 | 111.48 | 114.72 | 118.52 | 128.04 | 173.71 | 225.2 | 282.2 | 344.3 | 411.1 | 482.2 | 557.3 |
| 2,2,3-Trimethylpentane | " | 0 | 87.62 | 98.98 | 109.53 | 112.65 | 116.30 | 125.59 | 170.54 | 221.9 | 279.2 | 341.7 | 409.1 | 480.9 | 556.3 |
| 2,2,4-Trimethylpentane | " | 0 | 87.62 | 98.98 | 109.53 | 112.65 | 116.30 | 125.59 | 170.54 | 221.9 | 279.2 | 341.7 | 409.1 | 480.9 | 556.3 |
| 2,3,3-Trimethylpentane | " | 0 | 89.59 | 100.90 | 111.43 | 114.55 | 118.19 | 127.48 | 172.58 | 224.2 | 281.8 | 344.8 | 412.4 | 484.1 | 559.4 |
| 2,3,4-Trimethylpentane | " | 0 | 88.29 | 99.24 | 109.53 | 112.59 | 116.16 | 125.35 | 170.26 | 222.2 | 280.2 | 343.6 | 411.4 | 483.3 | 558.4 |
| 2,2,3,3-Tetramethylbutane | " | 0 | 89.12 | 100.50 | 111.09 | 114.22 | 117.83 | 127.21 | 172.38 | 224.1 | 281.9 | 345.2 | 413.5 | 486.0 | 562.4 |

| Compound (gas) | Formula | Temperature in °F | | | | | | | | | | | | | |
|---|---|---|---|---|---|---|---|---|---|---|---|---|---|---|---|
| | | 900 | 1000 | 1100 | 1200 | 1300 | 1400 | 1500 | 1600 | 1700 | 1800 | 1900 | 2000 | 2100 | 2200 |
| | | Heat Content (Enthalpy), ($H^o-H^o_0$), in BTU/lb | | | | | | | | | | | | | |
| 3,3-Dimethylhexane | C$_8$H$_{18}$ | 635.1 | 717.1 | 801.5 | 888.3 | 977.5 | | | | | | | | | |
| 3,4-Dimethylhexane[a] | " | 633.1 | 713.9 | 798.3 | 885.1 | 973.6 | | | | | | | | | |
| 2-Methyl-3-ethylpentane | " | 636.8 | 716.7 | 799.1 | 885.0 | 975.0 | | | | | | | | | |
| 3-Methyl-3-ethylpentane | " | 635.5 | 717.2 | 802.3 | 890.5 | 981.5 | | | | | | | | | |
| 2,2,3-Trimethylpentane | " | 634.4 | 715.5 | 799.7 | 887.0 | 977.1 | | | | | | | | | |
| 2,2,4-Trimethylpentane | " | 634.4 | 715.5 | 799.7 | 887.0 | 977.1 | | | | | | | | | |
| 2,3,3-Trimethylpentane | " | 637.6 | 718.4 | 801.6 | 888.6 | 980.4 | | | | | | | | | |
| 2,3,4-Trimethylpentane | " | 635.4 | 715.2 | 798.4 | 885.4 | 976.3 | | | | | | | | | |
| 2,2,3,3-Tetramethylbutane | " | 642.2 | 725.3 | 811.4 | 900.1 | 991.1 | | | | | | | | | |

a See footnotes a and b of Table 3r.

TABLE 22u-E (PART 1), Page 1 - NORMAL ALKYL CYCLOPENTANES, C₅ TO C₂₁
HEAT CONTENT (ENTHALPY), $(H^o - H^o_0)$, FOR THE IDEAL GAS STATE, AT -459.69°F TO 2200°F
October 31, 1947; December 31, 1952

Temperature in °F

Heat Content (Enthalpy), $(H^o - H^o_0)$, in BTU/lb

| Compound (gas) | Formula | -459.69 | 0 | 32 | 60 | 63 | 77 | 100 | 200 | 300 | 400 | 500 | 600 | 700 | 800 |
|---|---|---|---|---|---|---|---|---|---|---|---|---|---|---|---|
| Cyclopentane | C₅H₁₀ | 0 | 72.84 | 80.43 | 87.66 | 89.83 | 92.31 | 98.96 | 132.00 | 171.60 | 217.39 | 269.06 | 326.1 | 387.8 | 453.9 |
| Methylcyclopentane | C₆H₁₂ | 0 | 80.48 | 88.97 | 97.01 | 99.40 | 102.04 | 109.43 | 145.24 | 187.48 | 235.74 | 289.67 | 348.7 | 412.3 | 479.9 |
| Ethylcyclopentane | C₇H₁₄ | 0 | 83.78 | 92.61 | 100.91 | 103.41 | 106.14 | 113.74 | 150.40 | 193.38 | 242.26 | 296.66 | 356.1 | 420.4 | 488.8 |
| n-Propylcyclopentane | C₈H₁₆ | 0 | 85.73 | 94.84 | 103.40 | 105.95 | 108.79 | 116.55 | 154.03 | 197.76 | 247.31 | 302.28 | 362.3 | 426.9 | 495.7 |
| n-Butylcyclopentane | C₉H₁₈ | 0 | 87.29 | 96.63 | 105.36 | 107.97 | 110.85 | 118.79 | 156.89 | 201.22 | 251.30 | 306.72 | 367.0 | 432.0 | 501.0 |
| n-Pentylcyclopentane | C₁₀H₂₀ | 0 | 88.50 | 98.01 | 106.91 | 109.55 | 112.50 | 120.53 | 159.14 | 203.93 | 254.43 | 310.21 | 370.9 | 436.1 | 505.4 |
| n-Hexylcyclopentane | C₁₁H₂₂ | 0 | 89.63 | 99.23 | 108.22 | 110.89 | 113.85 | 121.99 | 160.99 | 206.17 | 257.05 | 313.11 | 374.0 | 439.4 | 508.9 |
| n-Heptylcyclopentane | C₁₂H₂₄ | 0 | 90.38 | 100.13 | 109.25 | 111.95 | 114.98 | 123.18 | 162.63 | 208.05 | 259.18 | 315.47 | 376.5 | 442.1 | 511.8 |
| n-Octylcyclopentane | C₁₃H₂₆ | 0 | 91.08 | 100.99 | 110.14 | 112.86 | 115.92 | 124.19 | 163.86 | 209.62 | 260.99 | 317.49 | 378.7 | 444.5 | 514.3 |

Temperature in °F

Heat Content (Enthalpy), $(H^o - H^o_0)$, in BTU/lb

| Compound (gas) | Formula | 900 | 1000 | 1100 | 1200 | 1300 | 1400 | 1500 | 1600 | 1700 | 1800 | 1900 | 2000 | 2100 | 2200 |
|---|---|---|---|---|---|---|---|---|---|---|---|---|---|---|---|
| Cyclopentane | C₅H₁₀ | 523.9 | 597.5 | 674.4 | 754.4 | 837.2 | 922.6 | 1010.5 | 1100.5 | 1192.4 | 1286.2 | 1381.7 | 1478.7 | 1577.2 | 1677.2 |
| Methylcyclopentane | C₆H₁₂ | 551.4 | 626.3 | 704.6 | 785.6 | 869.3 | 955.5 | 1044.0 | 1134.8 | 1227.6 | 1321.9 | 1417.8 | 1515.2 | 1614.0 | 1714.3 |
| Ethylcyclopentane | C₇H₁₄ | 560.7 | 636.2 | 715.1 | 796.8 | 881.0 | 967.9 | 1057.2 | 1148.6 | 1241.9 | 1336.7 | 1433.2 | 1531.5 | 1631.4 | 1732.6 |
| n-Propylcyclopentane | C₈H₁₆ | 568.0 | 643.8 | 723.0 | 805.0 | 889.3 | 976.3 | 1065.8 | 1157.3 | 1250.8 | 1345.6 | 1442.1 | 1540.4 | 1640.2 | 1741.3 |
| n-Butylcyclopentane | C₉H₁₈ | 573.7 | 649.8 | 729.1 | 811.2 | 895.8 | 983.0 | 1072.4 | 1164.0 | 1257.5 | 1352.5 | 1449.1 | 1547.4 | 1647.1 | 1748.1 |
| n-Pentylcyclopentane | C₁₀H₂₀ | 578.2 | 654.5 | 734.0 | 816.3 | 901.0 | 988.2 | 1077.8 | 1169.5 | 1263.0 | 1357.9 | 1454.5 | 1552.8 | 1652.5 | 1753.6 |
| n-Hexylcyclopentane | C₁₁H₂₂ | 581.9 | 658.3 | 738.0 | 820.4 | 905.2 | 992.5 | 1082.1 | 1173.9 | 1267.4 | 1362.4 | 1459.0 | 1557.3 | 1656.9 | 1757.9 |
| n-Heptylcyclopentane | C₁₂H₂₄ | 585.0 | 661.6 | 741.4 | 823.9 | 908.8 | 996.1 | 1085.8 | 1177.6 | 1271.2 | 1366.2 | 1462.8 | 1561.1 | 1660.8 | 1761.7 |
| n-Octylcyclopentane | C₁₃H₂₆ | 587.6 | 664.4 | 744.2 | 826.8 | 911.7 | 999.1 | 1088.8 | 1180.6 | 1274.3 | 1369.4 | 1466.1 | 1564.3 | 1663.9 | 1764.8 |

TABLE 22u-E (PART 1), Page 2 — NORMAL ALKYL CYCLOPENTANES, $C_5$ TO $C_{21}$

HEAT CONTENT (ENTHALPY), $(H^\circ - H^\circ_0)$, FOR THE IDEAL GAS STATE, AT $-459.69^\circ$ TO $2200^\circ$F

October 31, 1947; December 31, 1952

Temperature in °F

Heat Content (Enthalpy), $(H^\circ - H^\circ_0)$, in BTU/lb

| Compound (gas) | Formula | -459.69 | 0 | 32 | 60 | 68 | 77 | 100 | 200 | 300 | 400 | 500 | 600 | 700 | 800 |
|---|---|---|---|---|---|---|---|---|---|---|---|---|---|---|---|
| n-Nonylcyclopentane | $C_{14}H_{28}$ | 0 | 91.77 | 101.68 | 110.94 | 113.67 | 116.73 | 125.07 | 164.97 | 210.96 | 262.57 | 319.25 | 380.6 | 446.5 | 516.4 |
| n-Decylcyclopentane | $C_{15}H_{30}$ | 0 | 92.28 | 102.27 | 111.59 | 114.35 | 117.44 | 125.82 | 165.93 | 212.12 | 263.90 | 320.74 | 382.3 | 448.2 | 518.3 |
| n-Undecylcyclopentane | $C_{16}H_{32}$ | 0 | 92.76 | 102.81 | 112.19 | 114.96 | 118.06 | 126.49 | 166.80 | 213.17 | 265.12 | 322.08 | 383.7 | 449.8 | 519.8 |
| n-Dodecylcyclopentane | $C_{17}H_{34}$ | 0 | 93.15 | 103.26 | 112.69 | 115.48 | 118.61 | 127.07 | 167.54 | 214.06 | 266.14 | 323.23 | 385.0 | 451.1 | 521.3 |
| n-Tridecylcyclopentane | $C_{18}H_{36}$ | 0 | 93.49 | 103.66 | 113.14 | 115.94 | 119.09 | 127.59 | 168.21 | 214.86 | 267.06 | 324.26 | 386.1 | 452.3 | 522.5 |
| n-Tetradecylcyclopentane | $C_{19}H_{38}$ | 0 | 93.83 | 104.04 | 113.55 | 116.38 | 119.53 | 128.06 | 168.82 | 215.60 | 267.91 | 325.20 | 387.1 | 453.4 | 523.6 |
| n-Pentadecylcyclopentane | $C_{20}H_{40}$ | 0 | 94.11 | 104.36 | 113.92 | 116.75 | 119.91 | 128.47 | 169.35 | 216.24 | 268.64 | 326.02 | 388.0 | 454.4 | 524.7 |
| n-Hexadecylcyclopentane | $C_{21}H_{42}$ | 0 | 94.43 | 104.70 | 114.27 | 117.10 | 120.27 | 128.85 | 169.82 | 216.82 | 269.34 | 326.79 | 388.8 | 455.2 | 525.6 |

Temperature in °F

Heat Content (Enthalpy), $(H^\circ - H^\circ_0)$, in BTU/lb

| Compound (gas) | Formula | 900 | 1000 | 1100 | 1200 | 1300 | 1400 | 1500 | 1600 | 1700 | 1800 | 1900 | 2000 | 2100 | 2200 |
|---|---|---|---|---|---|---|---|---|---|---|---|---|---|---|---|
| n-Nonylcyclopentane | $C_{14}H_{28}$ | 589.8 | 666.7 | 746.6 | 829.2 | 914.3 | 1001.7 | 1091.4 | 1183.3 | 1277.1 | 1372.2 | 1468.8 | 1567.0 | 1666.6 | 1767.5 |
| n-Decylcyclopentane | $C_{15}H_{30}$ | 591.8 | 668.7 | 748.7 | 831.4 | 916.5 | 1004.0 | 1093.8 | 1185.7 | 1279.3 | 1374.4 | 1471.1 | 1569.3 | 1668.9 | 1769.8 |
| n-Undecylcyclopentane | $C_{16}H_{32}$ | 593.5 | 670.5 | 750.6 | 833.3 | 918.4 | 1006.0 | 1095.8 | 1187.7 | 1281.4 | 1376.5 | 1473.2 | 1571.4 | 1671.0 | 1771.9 |
| n-Dodecylcyclopentane | $C_{17}H_{34}$ | 595.0 | 672.1 | 752.2 | 835.0 | 920.1 | 1007.7 | 1097.6 | 1189.5 | 1283.3 | 1378.4 | 1475.0 | 1573.2 | 1672.8 | 1773.7 |
| n-Tridecylcyclopentane | $C_{18}H_{36}$ | 596.3 | 673.5 | 753.7 | 836.5 | 921.7 | 1009.2 | 1099.1 | 1191.1 | 1284.8 | 1380.0 | 1476.7 | 1574.9 | 1674.5 | 1775.3 |
| n-Tetradecylcyclopentane | $C_{19}H_{38}$ | 597.5 | 674.7 | 754.9 | 837.8 | 923.0 | 1010.6 | 1100.5 | 1192.5 | 1286.3 | 1381.5 | 1478.2 | 1576.4 | 1675.9 | 1776.7 |
| n-Pentadecylcyclopentane | $C_{20}H_{40}$ | 598.6 | 675.8 | 756.1 | 839.0 | 924.3 | 1011.9 | 1101.8 | 1193.8 | 1287.5 | 1382.7 | 1479.4 | 1577.6 | 1677.2 | 1778.0 |
| n-Hexadecylcyclopentane | $C_{21}H_{42}$ | 599.6 | 676.8 | 757.1 | 840.0 | 925.3 | 1013.0 | 1102.9 | 1194.9 | 1288.7 | 1383.9 | 1480.6 | 1578.8 | 1678.3 | 1779.2 |

TABLE 6u-E — ALKYL CYCLOPENTANES, $C_5$ TO $C_7$

HEAT CONTENT (ENTHALPY), $(H^o-H^o_0)$, FOR THE IDEAL GAS STATE, AT $-459.69°$ TO $2200°F$

April 30, 1949; December 31, 1952

Heat Content (Enthalpy), $(H^o-H^o_0)$, in BTU/lb

| Compound (gas) | Formula | Temperature in °F | | | | | | | | | | | | | |
|---|---|---|---|---|---|---|---|---|---|---|---|---|---|---|---|
| | | -459.69 | 0 | 32 | 60 | 68 | 77 | 100 | 200 | 300 | 400 | 500 | 600 | 700 | 800 |
| Cyclopentane | $C_5H_{10}$ | 0 | 72.84 | 80.43 | 87.66 | 89.83 | 92.31 | 98.96 | 132.00 | 171.60 | 217.39 | 269.06 | 326.1 | 387.8 | 453.9 |
| Methylcyclopentane | $C_6H_{12}$ | 0 | 80.48 | 88.97 | 97.01 | 99.40 | 102.04 | 109.43 | 145.24 | 187.48 | 235.74 | 289.67 | 348.7 | 412.3 | 479.9 |
| Ethylcyclopentane | $C_7H_{14}$ | 0 | 83.78 | 92.61 | 100.91 | 103.41 | 106.14 | 113.74 | 150.40 | 193.38 | 242.26 | 296.66 | 356.1 | 420.4 | 488.8 |
| 1,1-Dimethylcyclopentane | " | 0 | 79.63 | 88.44 | 96.77 | 99.26 | 101.94 | 109.65 | 146.71 | 190.4 | 240.2 | 295.9 | 357. | 422. | 491. |
| 1,cis-2-Dimethylcyclopentane | " | 0 | 80.97 | 89.61 | 97.83 | 100.28 | 103.02 | 110.59 | 147.56 | 191.32 | 241.3 | 297.0 | 358. | 423. | 492. |
| 1,trans-2-Dimethylcyclopentane | " | 0 | 81.66 | 90.23 | 98.40 | 100.84 | 103.46 | 111.12 | 148.10 | 191.94 | 242.0 | 297.7 | 358. | 423. | 492. |
| 1,cis-3-Dimethylcyclopentane | " | 0 | 81.66 | 90.23 | 98.40 | 100.84 | 103.46 | 111.12 | 148.10 | 191.94 | 242.0 | 297.7 | 358. | 423. | 492. |
| 1,trans-3-Dimethylcyclopentane | " | 0 | 81.66 | 90.23 | 98.40 | 100.84 | 103.46 | 111.12 | 148.10 | 191.94 | 242.0 | 297.7 | 358. | 423. | 492. |

Heat Content (Enthalpy), $(H^o-H^o_0)$, in BTU/lb

| Compound (gas) | Formula | Temperature in °F | | | | | | | | | | | | | |
|---|---|---|---|---|---|---|---|---|---|---|---|---|---|---|---|
| | | 900 | 1000 | 1100 | 1200 | 1300 | 1400 | 1500 | 1600 | 1700 | 1800 | 1900 | 2000 | 2100 | 2200 |
| Cyclopentane | $C_5H_{10}$ | 523.9 | 597.5 | 674.4 | 754.4 | 837.2 | 922.6 | 1010.5 | 1100.5 | 1192.4 | 1286.2 | 1381.7 | 1478.7 | 1577.2 | 1677.2 |
| Methylcyclopentane | $C_6H_{12}$ | 551.4 | 626.3 | 704.6 | 785.6 | 869.3 | 955.5 | 1044.0 | 1134.8 | 1227.6 | 1321.9 | 1417.8 | 1515.2 | 1614.0 | 1714.3 |
| Ethylcyclopentane | $C_7H_{14}$ | 560.7 | 636.2 | 715.1 | 796.8 | 881.0 | 967.9 | 1057.2 | 1148.6 | 1241.9 | 1336.7 | 1433.2 | 1531.5 | 1631.4 | 1732.6 |
| 1,1-Dimethylcyclopentane | " | 564. | 640. | 720. | 803. | 888. | 976. | 1065. | 1157. | 1251. | 1346. | 1443. | 1541. | 1641. | 1742. |
| 1,cis-2-Dimethylcyclopentane | " | 565. | 641. | 721. | 803. | 888. | 975. | 1064. | 1156. | 1250. | 1345. | 1442. | 1540. | 1639. | 1740. |
| 1,trans-2-Dimethylcyclopentane | " | 565. | 641. | 720. | 803. | 887. | 974. | 1064. | 1155. | 1249. | 1344. | 1440. | 1538. | 1638. | 1738. |
| 1,cis-3-Dimethylcyclopentane | " | 565. | 641. | 720. | 803. | 887. | 974. | 1064. | 1155. | 1249. | 1344. | 1440. | 1538. | 1638. | 1738. |
| 1,trans-3-Dimethylcyclopentane | " | 565. | 641. | 720. | 803. | 887. | 974. | 1064. | 1155. | 1249. | 1344. | 1440. | 1538. | 1638. | 1738. |

TABLE 23u-E (PART 1), Page 1 - NORMAL ALKYL CYCLOHEXANES, C6 TO C22

HEAT CONTENT (ENTHALPY), $(H°-H°_0)$, FOR THE IDEAL GAS STATE, AT -459.69° TO 2200°F

November 30, 1947; December 31, 1952

Heat Content (Enthalpy), $(H°-H°_0)$, in BTU/lb

| Compound (gas) | Formula | Temperature in °F |  |  |  |  |  |  |  |  |  |  |  |  |  |
|---|---|---|---|---|---|---|---|---|---|---|---|---|---|---|---|
|  |  | -459.69 | 0 | 32 | 60 | 68 | 77 | 100 | 200 | 300 | 400 | 500 | 600 | 700 | 800 |
| Cyclohexane | C6H12 | 0 | 69.80 | 77.90 | 85.61 | 87.92 | 90.56 | 97.63 | 132.68 | 174.57 | 222.96 | 277.5 | 337.7 | 403.1 | 473.2 |
| Methylcyclohexane | C7H14 | 0 | 73.31 | 82.18 | 90.59 | 93.11 | 95.88 | 103.63 | 141.31 | 185.84 | 236.69 | 293.4 | 355.4 | 422.4 | 493.9 |
| Ethylcyclohexane | C8H16 | 0 | 73.89 | 83.33 | 92.20 | 94.84 | 97.74 | 105.82 | 144.64 | 189.9 | 241.3 | 298.5 | 360.9 | 428.3 | 500.3 |
| n-Propylcyclohexane | C9H18 | 0 | 74.73 | 84.00 | 92.81 | 95.45 | 98.31 | 106.50 | 146.03 | 192.5 | 245.1 | 302.9 | 365.4 | 433.3 | 505.5 |
| n-Butylcyclohexane | C10H20 | 0 | 77.10 | 86.59 | 95.58 | 98.26 | 102.50 | 109.50 | 149.51 | 196.3 | 249.1 | 306.8 | 369.1 | 437.2 | 509.7 |
| n-Pentylcyclohexane | C11H22 | 0 | 79.16 | 88.82 | 97.92 | 100.63 | 103.59 | 111.95 | 152.08 | 198.9 | 251.7 | 309.8 | 372.8 | 440.4 | 512.3 |
| n-Hexylcyclohexane | C12H24 | 0 | 80.78 | 90.58 | 99.80 | 102.55 | 105.57 | 114.00 | 154.48 | 201.5 | 254.5 | 312.5 | 375.3 | 443.1 | 515.2 |
| n-Heptylcyclohexane | C13H26 | 0 | 82.78 | 92.42 | 101.54 | 104.28 | 107.25 | 115.66 | 156.14 | 203.4 | 256.7 | 315.0 | 377.9 | 445.4 | 517.0 |
| n-Octylcyclohexane | C14H28 | 0 | 83.90 | 93.67 | 102.90 | 105.65 | 108.68 | 117.15 | 157.90 | 205.4 | 258.7 | 316.9 | 379.7 | 447.3 | 519.2 |

Heat Content (Enthalpy), $(H°-H°_0)$, in BTU/lb

| Compound (gas) | Formula | Temperature in °F |  |  |  |  |  |  |  |  |  |  |  |  |  |
|---|---|---|---|---|---|---|---|---|---|---|---|---|---|---|---|
|  |  | 900 | 1000 | 1100 | 1200 | 1300 | 1400 | 1500 | 1600 | 1700 | 1800 | 1900 | 2000 | 2100 | 2200 |
| Cyclohexane | C6H12 | 547.5 | 625.6 | 707.2 | 792.0 | 879.8 | 970.0 | 1062.5 | 1157.2 | 1254.0 | 1353.1 | 1453.5 | 1554.4 | 1656.9 | 1761.9 |
| Methylcyclohexane | C7H14 | 569.4 | 648.4 | 730.8 | 816.1 | 904.2 | 994.7 | 1087.3 | 1182.3 | 1279.2 | 1377.5 | 1477.5 | 1579.5 | 1682.6 | 1785.9 |
| Ethylcyclohexane | C8H16 | 576.3 | 655.8 | 738.2 | 823.4 | 911. | 1001. | 1094. | 1188. | 1285. | 1383. | 1485. | 1584. | 1686. | 1790. |
| n-Propylcyclohexane | C9H18 | 581.0 | 660.0 | 742.6 | 828.1 | 916. | 1006. | 1097. | 1191. | 1287. | 1385. | 1485. | 1586. | 1689. | 1792. |
| n-Butylcyclohexane | C10H20 | 584.6 | 663.3 | 746.2 | 831.8 | 920. | 1009. | 1100. | 1194. | 1289. | 1387. | 1487. | 1588. | 1691. | 1794. |
| n-Pentylcyclohexane | C11H22 | 587.8 | 666.9 | 749.5 | 834.5 | 922. | 1011. | 1102. | 1196. | 1292. | 1390. | 1488. | 1589. | 1691. | 1794. |
| n-Hexylcyclohexane | C12H24 | 590.4 | 669.0 | 751.2 | 836.3 | 924. | 1013. | 1104. | 1198. | 1294. | 1391. | 1490. | 1590. | 1692. | 1794. |
| n-Heptylcyclohexane | C13H26 | 592.6 | 671.7 | 753.7 | 838.3 | 925. | 1014. | 1105. | 1199. | 1295. | 1392. | 1491. | 1591. | 1692. | 1795. |
| n-Octylcyclohexane | C14H28 | 594.4 | 673.2 | 755.4 | 840.2 | 927. | 1016. | 1107. | 1200. | 1296. | 1394. | 1493. | 1592. | 1693. | 1796. |

TABLE 23u-E (PART 1), Page 2 - NORMAL ALKYL CYCLOHEXANES, $C_6$ TO $C_{22}$
HEAT CONTENT (ENTHALPY), $(H^°-H^°_0)$, FOR THE IDEAL GAS STATE, AT -459.69° TO 2200°F
November 30, 1947; December 31, 1952

Temperature in °F

Heat Content (Enthalpy), $(H^°-H^°_0)$, in BTU/lb

| Compound (gas) | Formula | -459.69 | 0 | 32 | 60 | 68 | 77 | 100 | 200 | 300 | 400 | 500 | 600 | 700 | 800 |
|---|---|---|---|---|---|---|---|---|---|---|---|---|---|---|---|
| n-Nonylcyclohexane | $C_{15}H_{30}$ | 0 | 84.40 | 94.51 | 103.99 | 106.81 | 109.93 | 118.50 | 159.55 | 207.0 | 260.1 | 318.2 | 381.1 | 449.0 | 521.1 |
| n-Decylcyclohexane | $C_{16}H_{32}$ | 0 | 85.80 | 95.77 | 105.15 | 107.94 | 111.01 | 119.57 | 160.58 | 209.1 | 261.5 | 319.9 | 382.9 | 450.5 | 522.2 |
| n-Undecylcyclohexane | $C_{17}H_{34}$ | 0 | 86.55 | 96.60 | 106.06 | 108.86 | 111.97 | 120.56 | 161.78 | 209.5 | 262.9 | 321.2 | 384.1 | 451.8 | 523.6 |
| n-Dodecylcyclohexane | $C_{18}H_{36}$ | 0 | 87.27 | 97.40 | 106.90 | 109.72 | 112.82 | 121.44 | 162.66 | 210.3 | 263.7 | 322.3 | 385.5 | 452.9 | 524.5 |
| n-Tridecylcyclohexane | $C_{19}H_{38}$ | 0 | 87.86 | 98.06 | 107.62 | 110.45 | 113.59 | 122.24 | 163.62 | 211.4 | 264.8 | 323.3 | 386.4 | 454.0 | 525.7 |
| n-Tetradecylcyclohexane | $C_{20}H_{40}$ | 0 | 88.40 | 98.66 | 108.26 | 111.11 | 114.28 | 122.95 | 164.49 | 212.3 | 265.8 | 324.2 | 387.2 | 454.9 | 526.7 |
| n-Pentadecylcyclohexane | $C_{21}H_{42}$ | 0 | 88.94 | 99.25 | 108.88 | 111.73 | 114.90 | 123.60 | 165.11 | 212.9 | 266.4 | 325.0 | 388.2 | 455.8 | 527.3 |
| n-Hexadecylcyclohexane | $C_{22}H_{44}$ | 0 | 89.37 | 99.73 | 109.40 | 112.27 | 115.46 | 124.19 | 165.83 | 213.7 | 267.3 | 325.8 | 388.9 | 456.5 | 528.2 |

Temperature in °F

Heat Content (Enthalpy), $(H^°-H^°_0)$, in BTU/lb

| Compound (gas) | Formula | 900 | 1000 | 1100 | 1200 | 1300 | 1400 | 1500 | 1600 | 1700 | 1800 | 1900 | 2000 | 2100 | 2200 |
|---|---|---|---|---|---|---|---|---|---|---|---|---|---|---|---|
| n-Nonylcyclohexane | $C_{15}H_{30}$ | 596.0 | 674.5 | 756.9 | 841.9 | 929. | 1018. | 1109. | 1202. | 1298. | 1395. | 1493. | 1593. | 1694. | 1796. |
| n-Decylcyclohexane | $C_{16}H_{32}$ | 597.5 | 676.3 | 758.6 | 843.1 | 930. | 1018. | 1110. | 1203. | 1298. | 1395. | 1494. | 1593. | 1694. | 1797. |
| n-Undecylcyclohexane | $C_{17}H_{34}$ | 598.7 | 677.2 | 759.2 | 843.9 | 931. | 1020. | 1111. | 1204. | 1299. | 1396. | 1494. | 1594. | 1695. | 1797. |
| n-Dodecylcyclohexane | $C_{18}H_{36}$ | 599.8 | 678.7 | 760.5 | 844.0 | 931. | 1020. | 1111. | 1205. | 1300. | 1397. | 1495. | 1594. | 1695. | 1797. |
| n-Tridecylcyclohexane | $C_{19}H_{38}$ | 600.8 | 679.4 | 761.5 | 845.9 | 932. | 1021. | 1112. | 1205. | 1300. | 1397. | 1495. | 1595. | 1696. | 1797. |
| n-Tetradecylcyclohexane | $C_{20}H_{40}$ | 601.7 | 680.1 | 762.3 | 846.9 | 933. | 1022. | 1113. | 1206. | 1301. | 1398. | 1496. | 1596. | 1696. | 1798. |
| n-Pentadecylcyclohexane | $C_{21}H_{42}$ | 602.5 | 681.2 | 763.3 | 847.6 | 934. | 1022. | 1113. | 1207. | 1302. | 1398. | 1496. | 1596. | 1696. | 1798. |
| n-Hexadecylcyclohexane | $C_{22}H_{44}$ | 603.2 | 681.7 | 763.6 | 847.9 | 934. | 1023. | 1114. | 1207. | 1302. | 1399. | 1496. | 1596. | 1697. | 1798. |

## TABLE 7u-E – ALKYL CYCLOHEXANES, $C_6$ to $C_8$

### HEAT CONTENT, $(H^o - H'^o_0)$, FOR THE IDEAL GAS STATE, AT $-459.69^\circ$ TO $2200^\circ F$

November 30, 1947

| Compound (gas) | Formula | Temperature in °F Heat Content, $(H^o - H'^o_0)$, in BTU/lb | | | | | | | | | | | | | |
| --- | --- | --- | --- | --- | --- | --- | --- | --- | --- | --- | --- | --- | --- | --- | --- |
| | | -459.69 | 0 | 32 | 60 | 68 | 77 | 100 | 200 | 300 | 400 | 500 | 600 | 700 | 800 |
| Cyclohexane | $C_6H_{12}$ | 0 | 69.80 | 77.90 | 85.61 | 87.92 | 90.56 | 97.63 | 132.68 | 174.57 | 222.96 | 277.5 | 337.7 | 403.1 | 473.2 |
| Methylcyclohexane | $C_7H_{14}$ | 0 | 73.31 | 82.18 | 90.59 | 93.11 | 95.88 | 103.63 | 141.31 | 185.84 | 236.69 | 293.4 | 355.4 | 422.4 | 493.9 |
| Ethylcyclohexane | $C_8H_{16}$ | 0 | 73.89 | 83.33 | 92.20 | 94.84 | 97.74 | 105.82 | 144.64 | 189.9 | 241.3 | 299.5 | 360.9 | 428.3 | 500.3 |
| 1,1-Dimethylcyclohexane | " | 0 | 71.05 | 80.23 | 88.86 | 91.43 | 94.26 | 102.13 | 140.04 | 184.5 | 235.2 | 291.9 | 354.1 | 421.5 | 493.5 |
| cis-1,2-Dimethylcyclohexane | " | 0 | 73.07 | 82.29 | 90.95 | 93.53 | 96.36 | 104.28 | 142.43 | 186.2 | 238.2 | 295.3 | 358.0 | 425.3 | 496.9 |
| trans-1,2-Dimethylcyclohexane | " | 0 | 74.53 | 83.66 | 92.31 | 94.90 | 97.70 | 105.74 | 144.47 | 190.1 | 242.0 | 299.3 | 361.8 | 429.3 | 501.4 |
| cis-1,3-Dimethylcyclohexane | " | 0 | 73.80 | 83.09 | 91.82 | 94.41 | 97.27 | 105.24 | 143.59 | 188.5 | 239.8 | 297.0 | 359.8 | 427.3 | 499.1 |
| trans-1,3-Dimethylcyclohexane | " | 0 | 74.05 | 83.21 | 91.86 | 94.44 | 97.27 | 105.21 | 143.54 | 194.2 | 239.8 | 296.8 | 359.0 | 425.8 | 496.9 |
| cis-1,4-Dimethylcyclohexane | " | 0 | 74.05 | 83.21 | 91.86 | 94.44 | 97.27 | 105 21 | 143.54 | 194.2 | 239.8 | 296.8 | 359.0 | 425.8 | 496.9 |
| trans-1,4-Dimethylcyclohexane | " | 0 | 73.52 | 83.00 | 91.87 | 94.50 | 97.41 | 105.47 | 144.12 | 189.2 | 240.5 | 297.8 | 360.7 | 428.8 | 501.4 |

| Compound (gas) | Formula | Temperature in °F Heat Content, $(H^o - H'^o_0)$, in BTU/lb | | | | | | | | | | | | | |
| --- | --- | --- | --- | --- | --- | --- | --- | --- | --- | --- | --- | --- | --- | --- | --- |
| | | 900 | 1000 | 1100 | 1200 | 1300 | 1400 | 1500 | 1600 | 1700 | 1800 | 1900 | 2000 | 2100 | 2200 |
| Cyclohexane | $C_6H_{12}$ | 547.5 | 625.6 | 707.2 | 792.0 | 879.8 | 970.0 | 1062.5 | 1157.2 | 1254.0 | 1353.1 | 1453.5 | 1554.4 | 1656.9 | 1761.9 |
| Methylcyclohexane | $C_7H_{14}$ | 569.4 | 648.4 | 730.8 | 816.1 | 904.2 | 994.7 | 1087.3 | 1182.3 | 1279.2 | 1377.5 | 1477.5 | 1579.5 | 1682.6 | 1785.9 |
| Ethylcyclohexane | $C_8H_{16}$ | 576.3 | 655.8 | 738.2 | 823.4 | 911. | 1001. | 1094. | 1188. | 1285. | 1383. | 1483. | 1584. | 1686. | 1790. |
| 1,1-Dimethylcyclohexane | " | 569.6 | 649.6 | 733.1 | 819.4 | 908. | 999. | 1092. | 1187. | 1285. | 1384. | 1485. | 1587. | 1691. | 1795. |
| cis-1,2-Dimethylcyclohexane | " | 572.7 | 651.9 | 733.9 | 819.2 | 908. | 999. | 1092. | 1186. | 1283. | 1381. | 1481. | 1583. | 1686. | 1789. |
| trans-1,2-Dimethylcyclohexane | " | 577.4 | 657.3 | 740.5 | 826.4 | 914. | 1005. | 1099. | 1194. | 1291. | 1389. | 1489. | 1590. | 1693. | 1797. |
| cis-1,3-Dimethylcyclohexane | " | 575.0 | 654.7 | 737.7 | 823.4 | 911. | 1002. | 1095. | 1191. | 1289. | 1388. | 1489. | 1590. | 1693. | 1797. |
| trans-1,3-Dimethylcyclohexane | " | 572.6 | 651.9 | 734.0 | 818.9 | 907. | 997. | 1090. | 1185. | 1281. | 1379. | 1479. | 1579. | 1681. | 1785. |
| cis-1,4-Dimethylcyclohexane | " | 572.6 | 651.9 | 734.0 | 818.9 | 907. | 997. | 1090. | 1185. | 1281. | 1379. | 1479. | 1579. | 1681. | 1785. |
| trans-1,4-Dimethylcyclohexane | " | 577.6 | 657.1 | 739.5 | 825.1 | 914. | 1005. | 1099. | 1194. | 1291. | 1389. | 1489. | 1590. | 1693. | 1797. |

TABLE 24u-E (PART 1), Page 1 — NORMAL MONOOLEFINS (1-ALKENES), C2 TO C20
HEAT CONTENT (ENTHALPY), $(H°-H°_0)$, FOR THE IDEAL GAS STATE, AT -459.69° TO 2200°F
March 31, 1946; December 31, 1952

Heat Content (Enthalpy), $(H°-H°_0)$, in BTU/lb — Temperature in °F

| Compound (gas) | Formula | -459.69 | 0 | 32 | 60 | 68 | 77 | 100 | 200 | 300 | 400 | 500 | 600 | 700 | 800 |
|---|---|---|---|---|---|---|---|---|---|---|---|---|---|---|---|
| Ethene (Ethylene) | C2H4 | 0 | 135.2 | 145.9 | 155.7 | 158.6 | 161.9 | 170.5 | 211.1 | 256.6 | 306.7 | 361.1 | 419.4 | 481.3 | 546.6 |
| Propene (Propylene) | C3H6 | 0 | 112.0 | 122.6 | 132.3 | 135.1 | 138.4 | 146.8 | 186.8 | 231.7 | 281.2 | 335.3 | 399.5 | 455.6 | 521.3 |
| 1-Butene | C4H8 | 0 | 105.9 | 116.2 | 125.8 | 128.6 | 131.8 | 140.3 | 180.8 | 226.8 | 277.9 | 333.4 | 399.0 | 456.5 | 523.7 |
| 1-Pentene | C5H10 | 0 | 107.8 | 118.5 | 128.3 | 131.2 | 134.6 | 143.2 | 184.5 | 231.3 | 283.1 | 339.6 | 400.2 | 464.6 | 532.5 |
| 1-Hexene | C6H12 | 0 | 106.3 | 117.0 | 126.9 | 129.8 | 133.1 | 141.8 | 183.4 | 230.6 | 282.9 | 339.7 | 400.7 | 465.6 | 534.2 |
| 1-Heptene | C7H14 | 0 | 105.4 | 116.1 | 126.0 | 128.9 | 132.3 | 141.0 | 182.8 | 230.3 | 282.8 | 340.0 | 401.3 | 466.6 | 535.5 |
| 1-Octene | C8H16 | 0 | 104.7 | 115.4 | 125.4 | 128.3 | 131.7 | 140.5 | 182.4 | 230.0 | 282.8 | 340.2 | 401.9 | 467.4 | 536.7 |
| 1-Nonene | C9H18 | 0 | 104.1 | 114.9 | 124.9 | 127.8 | 131.2 | 140.0 | 182.1 | 229.9 | 282.8 | 340.4 | 402.2 | 468.0 | 537.4 |
| 1-Decene | C10H20 | 0 | 103.7 | 114.5 | 124.5 | 127.4 | 130.8 | 139.7 | 181.9 | 229.8 | 282.9 | 340.5 | 402.5 | 468.4 | 538.0 |
| 1-Undecene | C11H22 | 0 | 103.3 | 114.2 | 124.2 | 127.1 | 130.5 | 139.4 | 181.6 | 229.6 | 282.9 | 340.6 | 402.7 | 468.8 | 538.7 |

Heat Content (Enthalpy), $(H°-H°_0)$, in BTU/lb — Temperature in °F

| Compound (gas) | Formula | 900 | 1000 | 1100 | 1200 | 1300 | 1400 | 1500 | 1600 | 1700 | 1800 | 1900 | 2000 | 2100 | 2200 |
|---|---|---|---|---|---|---|---|---|---|---|---|---|---|---|---|
| Ethene (Ethylene) | C2H4 | 615.0 | 686.2 | 759.8 | 835.9 | 914.2 | 994.9 | 1078. | 1162. | 1248. | 1336. | 1425. | 1515. | 1607. | 1700. |
| Propene (Propylene) | C3H6 | 590.2 | 662.0 | 736.8 | 814.3 | 894.3 | 976.4 | 1060. | 1146. | 1234. | 1324. | 1415. | 1507. | 1601. | 1696. |
| 1-Butene | C4H8 | 594.2 | 667.8 | 744.3 | 823.2 | 904.4 | 988.0 | 1074. | 1161. | 1250. | 1341. | 1434. | 1528. | 1623. | 1719. |
| 1-Pentene | C5H10 | 603.9 | 678.5 | 755.9 | 835.9 | 918.3 | 1002.9 | 1089. | 1178. | 1268. | 1360. | 1454. | 1549. | 1645. | 1742. |
| 1-Hexene | C6H12 | 606.1 | 681.3 | 759.2 | 839.8 | 922.9 | 1008.0 | 1095. | 1185. | 1276. | 1368. | 1462. | 1558. | 1654. | 1752. |
| 1-Heptene | C7H14 | 607.9 | 683.5 | 761.9 | 843.0 | 926.3 | 1011.9 | 1100. | 1189. | 1281. | 1374. | 1468. | 1564. | 1661. | 1759. |
| 1-Octene | C8H16 | 609.4 | 685.3 | 764.0 | 845.4 | 929.1 | 1015.0 | 1103. | 1193. | 1285. | 1378. | 1473. | 1569. | 1666. | 1765. |
| 1-Nonene | C9H18 | 610.4 | 686.5 | 765.5 | 847.1 | 931.1 | 1017.2 | 1105. | 1196. | 1288. | 1381. | 1476. | 1572. | 1670. | 1769. |
| 1-Decene | C10H20 | 611.3 | 687.7 | 766.8 | 848.5 | 932.7 | 1019.0 | 1107. | 1198. | 1290. | 1384. | 1479. | 1575. | 1673. | 1772. |
| 1-Undecene | C11H22 | 612.0 | 688.5 | 767.8 | 849.7 | 934.0 | 1020.5 | 1109. | 1200. | 1292. | 1386. | 1481. | 1578. | 1676. | 1775. |

TABLE 24u-E (PART 1), Page 2 — NORMAL MONOOLEFINS (1-ALKENES), $C_2'$ TO $C_{20}$
HEAT CONTENT (ENTHALPY), $(H^o - H^o_0)$, FOR THE IDEAL GAS STATE, AT $-459.69°$ TO $2200°F$
March 31, 1946; December 31, 1952

Heat Content (Enthalpy), $(H^o - H^o_0)$, in BTU/lb

| Compound (gas) | Formula | \-459.69 | 0 | 32 | 60 | 68 | 77 | 100 | 200 | 300 | 400 | 500 | 600 | 700 | 800 |
|---|---|---|---|---|---|---|---|---|---|---|---|---|---|---|---|
| 1-Dodecene | $C_{12}H_{24}$ | 0 | 103.0 | 113.9 | 123.9 | 126.9 | 130.2 | 139.1 | 181.5 | 229.6 | 282.9 | 340.8 | 402.9 | 469.1 | 539.1 |
| 1-Tridecene | $C_{13}H_{26}$ | 0 | 102.8 | 113.6 | 123.7 | 126.6 | 130.0 | 138.9 | 181.3 | 229.5 | 282.8 | 340.8 | 403.1 | 469.4 | 539.4 |
| 1-Tetradecene | $C_{14}H_{28}$ | 0 | 102.6 | 113.4 | 123.5 | 126.5 | 129.8 | 138.7 | 181.2 | 229.4 | 282.9 | 340.9 | 403.2 | 469.5 | 539.7 |
| 1-Pentadecene | $C_{15}H_{30}$ | 0 | 102.4 | 113.2 | 123.3 | 126.3 | 129.7 | 138.6 | 181.1 | 229.4 | 282.8 | 341.0 | 403.4 | 469.8 | 540.0 |
| 1-Hexadecene | $C_{16}H_{32}$ | 0 | 102.2 | 113.1 | 123.2 | 126.1 | 129.5 | 138.4 | 181.0 | 229.3 | 282.9 | 341.0 | 403.5 | 470.0 | 540.3 |
| 1-Heptadecene | $C_{17}H_{34}$ | 0 | 102.1 | 112.9 | 123.0 | 126.0 | 129.4 | 138.3 | 180.9 | 229.3 | 282.9 | 341.1 | 403.6 | 470.1 | 540.5 |
| 1-Octadecene | $C_{18}H_{36}$ | 0 | 101.9 | 112.8 | 122.9 | 125.9 | 129.3 | 138.2 | 180.8 | 229.2 | 282.9 | 341.1 | 403.7 | 470.3 | 540.7 |
| 1-Nonadecene | $C_{19}H_{38}$ | 0 | 101.8 | 112.7 | 122.8 | 125.8 | 129.2 | 138.1 | 180.8 | 229.2 | 282.9 | 341.2 | 403.7 | 470.4 | 540.8 |
| 1-Eicosene | $C_{20}H_{40}$ | 0 | 101.7 | 112.6 | 122.7 | 125.7 | 129.1 | 138.0 | 180.7 | 229.2 | 282.9 | 341.2 | 403.8 | 470.5 | 541.0 |

Temperature in °F

Heat Content (Enthalpy), $(H^o - H^o_0)$, in BTU/lb

| Compound (gas) | Formula | 900 | 1000 | 1100 | 1200 | 1300 | 1400 | 1500 | 1600 | 1700 | 1800 | 1900 | 2000 | 2100 | 2200 |
|---|---|---|---|---|---|---|---|---|---|---|---|---|---|---|---|
| 1-Dodecene | $C_{12}H_{24}$ | 612.5 | 689.2 | 768.7 | 850.8 | 935.2 | 1021.8 | 1110. | 1201. | 1294. | 1388. | 1483. | 1580. | 1678. | 1777. |
| 1-Tridecene | $C_{13}H_{26}$ | 613.0 | 689.8 | 769.4 | 851.6 | 936.1 | 1022.9 | 1112. | 1203. | 1295. | 1389. | 1485. | 1582. | 1680. | 1779. |
| 1-Tetradecene | $C_{14}H_{28}$ | 613.4 | 690.3 | 770.0 | 852.3 | 936.9 | 1023.8 | 1113. | 1204. | 1296. | 1391. | 1486. | 1583. | 1681. | 1781. |
| 1-Pentadecene | $C_{15}H_{30}$ | 613.9 | 690.8 | 770.6 | 852.9 | 937.7 | 1024.6 | 1114. | 1205. | 1298. | 1392. | 1487. | 1584. | 1683. | 1782. |
| 1-Hexadecene | $C_{16}H_{32}$ | 614.1 | 691.2 | 771.0 | 853.5 | 938.3 | 1025.3 | 1114. | 1206. | 1298. | 1393. | 1488. | 1586. | 1684. | 1784. |
| 1-Heptadecene | $C_{17}H_{34}$ | 614.4 | 691.5 | 771.5 | 854.0 | 938.8 | 1025.8 | 1115. | 1206. | 1299. | 1394. | 1489. | 1587. | 1685. | 1785. |
| 1-Octadecene | $C_{18}H_{36}$ | 614.7 | 691.9 | 771.9 | 854.4 | 939.3 | 1026.4 | 1116. | 1207. | 1300. | 1394. | 1490. | 1587. | 1686. | 1786. |
| 1-Nonadecene | $C_{19}H_{38}$ | 614.9 | 692.1 | 772.1 | 854.7 | 939.7 | 1026.9 | 1116. | 1208. | 1301. | 1395. | 1491. | 1588. | 1687. | 1786. |
| 1-Eicosene | $C_{20}H_{40}$ | 615.1 | 692.4 | 772.5 | 855.1 | 940.1 | 1027.3 | 1117. | 1208. | 1301. | 1396. | 1492. | 1589. | 1688. | 1787. |

Temperature in °F

TABLE 8u-E (PART 1) - MONOOLEFINS, C2 TO C5

HEAT CONTENT (ENTHALPY), $(H^o-H^o_0)$, FOR THE IDEAL GAS STATE, AT -459.69° TO 2200°F

May 31, 1946; December 31, 1952

Heat Content (Enthalpy), $(H^o-H^o_0)$, in BTU/lb — Temperature in °F

| Compound (gas) | Formula | -459.69 | 0 | 32 | 60 | 68 | 77 | 100 | 200 | 300 | 400 | 500 | 600 | 700 | 800 |
|---|---|---|---|---|---|---|---|---|---|---|---|---|---|---|---|
| Ethene (Ethylene) | C2H4 | 0 | 135.2 | 145.9 | 155.7 | 158.6 | 161.9 | 170.5 | 211.1 | 256.6 | 306.7 | 361.1 | 419.4 | 481.3 | 546.6 |
| Propene (Propylene) | C3H6 | 0 | 112.0 | 122.6 | 132.3 | 135.1 | 138.4 | 146.8 | 186.8 | 231.7 | 281.2 | 335.3 | 393.5 | 455.6 | 521.3 |
| 1-Butene | C4H8 | 0 | 105.9 | 116.2 | 125.8 | 128.6 | 131.8 | 140.3 | 180.8 | 226.8 | 277.9 | 333.4 | 393.0 | 456.5 | 523.7 |
| cis-2-Butene | " | 0 | 102.7 | 112.2 | 121.0 | 123.6 | 126.5 | 134.3 | 171.8 | 214.6 | 262.7 | 315.5 | 372.9 | 434.2 | 499.3 |
| trans-2-Butene | " | 0 | 107.4 | 118.1 | 128.1 | 131.0 | 134.3 | 143.0 | 183.9 | 229.8 | 280.4 | 335.4 | 394.4 | 457.5 | 524.3 |
| 2-Methylpropene (Isobutene) | " | 0 | 103.3 | 114.3 | 124.5 | 127.5 | 130.9 | 139.7 | 181.5 | 228.2 | 279.8 | 335.8 | 396.1 | 459.9 | 527.2 |
| 1-Pentene | C5H10 | 0 | 107.8 | 118.5 | 128.3 | 131.2 | 134.6 | 143.2 | 184.5 | 231.3 | 283.1 | 339.6 | 400.2 | 464.6 | 532.5 |
| cis-2-Pentene | " | 0 | 99.5 | 109.3 | 118.4 | 121.1 | 124.3 | 132.3 | 171.2 | 215.7 | 265.6 | 320.2 | 379.4 | 442.8 | 510.0 |
| trans-2-Pentene | " | 0 | 102.9 | 113.3 | 123.0 | 125.9 | 129.2 | 137.7 | 178.3 | 224.5 | 275.6 | 331.3 | 391.3 | 455.0 | 522.3 |
| 2-Methyl-1-butene | " | 0 | 100.8 | 111.8 | 121.8 | 124.8 | 128.2 | 137.0 | 179.2 | 226.8 | 279.4 | 336.5 | 397.7 | 463.0 | 531.8 |
| 3-Methyl-1-butene | " | 0 | 102.5 | 114.2 | 125.0 | 128.1 | 131.8 | 141.1 | 185.6 | 235.3 | 289.9 | 348.9 | 411.8 | 478.2 | 547.9 |
| 2-Methyl-2-butene | " | 0 | 98.5 | 108.6 | 118.0 | 120.8 | 124.0 | 132.2 | 171.8 | 217.0 | 267.0 | 321.6 | 380.5 | 443.5 | 510.2 |

Heat Content (Enthalpy), $(H^o-H^o_0)$, in BTU/lb — Temperature in °F

| Compound (gas) | Formula | 900 | 1000 | 1100 | 1200 | 1300 | 1400 | 1500 | 1600 | 1700 | 1800 | 1900 | 2000 | 2100 | 2200 |
|---|---|---|---|---|---|---|---|---|---|---|---|---|---|---|---|
| Ethene (Ethylene) | C2H4 | 615.0 | 686.2 | 759.8 | 835.9 | 914.2 | 994.9 | 1078. | 1162. | 1248. | 1336. | 1425. | 1515. | 1607. | 1700. |
| Propene (Propylene) | C3H6 | 590.2 | 662.0 | 736.8 | 814.3 | 894.3 | 976.4 | 1060. | 1146. | 1234. | 1324. | 1415. | 1507. | 1601. | 1696. |
| 1-Butene | C4H8 | 594.2 | 667.8 | 744.3 | 823.2 | 904.4 | 988.0 | 1074. | 1161. | 1250. | 1341. | 1434. | 1528. | 1623. | 1719. |
| cis-2-Butene | " | 568.0 | 639.9 | 714.7 | 792.2 | 872.4 | 954.6 | 1039. | 1126. | 1214. | 1304. | 1396. | 1489. | 1584. | 1680. |
| trans-2-Butene | " | 594.1 | 667.0 | 743.0 | 821.5 | 902.6 | 985.9 | 1071. | 1159. | 1248. | 1338. | 1430. | 1524. | 1619. | 1715. |
| 2-Methylpropene (Isobutene) | " | 598.0 | 671.6 | 747.9 | 826.8 | 908.2 | 992.0 | 1078. | 1166. | 1255. | 1346. | 1439. | 1533. | 1628. | 1724. |
| 1-Pentene | C5H10 | 603.9 | 678.5 | 755.9 | 835.9 | 918.3 | 1002.9 | 1089. | 1178. | 1268. | 1360. | 1454. | 1549. | 1645. | 1742. |
| cis-2-Pentene | " | 580.2 | 653.6 | 730.1 | 809.2 | 891.0 | 975. | 1061. | 1149. | 1238. | 1330. | 1423. | 1517. | 1613. | 1710. |
| trans-2-Pentene | " | 593.0 | 666.8 | 743.5 | 822.8 | 904.6 | 989. | 1075. | 1163. | 1257. | 1344. | 1437. | 1531. | 1627. | 1724. |
| 2-Methyl-1-butene | " | 603.7 | 678.5 | 756.1 | 836.3 | 918.9 | 1004. | 1091. | 1180. | 1270. | 1362. | 1457. | 1551. | 1648. | 1745. |
| 3-Methyl-1-butene | " | 620.7 | 696.4 | 774.6 | 855.6 | 938.9 | 1024. | 1112. | 1201. | 1292. | 1385. | 1479. | 1574. | 1670. | 1768. |
| 2-Methyl-2-butene | " | 580.3 | 653.6 | 729.7 | 808.5 | 889.9 | 974. | 1059. | 1147. | 1237. | 1328. | 1421. | 1515. | 1611. | 1707. |

TABLE 8u-E (PART 2), Page 1 – MONOOLEFINS, C₆

HEAT CONTENT (ENTHALPY), $(H°-H°_0)$, FOR THE IDEAL GAS STATE, AT -459.69° TO 2200°F

May 31, 1946; December 31, 1952

| Compound (gas) | Formula | Temperature in °F — Heat Content (Enthalpy), $(H°-H°_0)$, in BTU/lb | | | | | | | | | | | | | |
|---|---|---|---|---|---|---|---|---|---|---|---|---|---|---|---|
| | | -459.69 | 0 | 32 | 60 | 68 | 77 | 100 | 200 | 300 | 400 | 500 | 600 | 700 | 800 |
| 1-Hexene | C₆H₁₂ | 0 | 106.3 | 117.0 | 126.9 | 129.8 | 133.1 | 141.8 | 183.4 | 230.6 | 282.9 | 339.7 | 400.7 | 465.6 | 534.2 |
| cis-2-Hexene | " | 0 | 102.4 | 112.5 | 121.9 | 124.6 | 127.8 | 136.1 | 175.8 | 221.3 | 272.1 | 327.6 | 387.5 | 451.3 | 519. |
| trans-2-Hexene | " | 0 | 105.2 | 115.8 | 125.6 | 128.5 | 131.9 | 140.5 | 181.8 | 228.7 | 280.6 | 337.1 | 397.6 | 461.8 | 530. |
| cis-3-Hexene | " | 0 | 98.2 | 108.0 | 117.2 | 119.9 | 123.0 | 131.2 | 170.5 | 215.7 | 266.4 | 322.3 | 382.7 | 447.0 | 515. |
| trans-3-Hexene | " | 0 | 102.0 | 112.4 | 122.1 | 125.0 | 128.3 | 136.9 | 178.5 | 226.0 | 278.5 | 335.0 | 395.5 | 460.6 | 530. |
| 2-Methyl-1-pentene | " | 0 | 102.2 | 113.8 | 124.4 | 127.5 | 131.1 | 140.2 | 183.0 | 230.7 | 283.2 | 340.5 | 402.4 | 468.7 | 538. |
| 3-Methyl-1-pentene | " | 0 | 101.6 | 113.1 | 123.8 | 126.9 | 130.6 | 140.0 | 185.6 | 237.7 | 295.7 | 358.9 | 426.8 | 499.3 | 576. |
| 4-Methyl-1-pentene | " | 0 | 92.0 | 102.0 | 111.3 | 114.0 | 117.2 | 125.4 | 164.9 | 210.2 | 260.8 | 316.3 | 376.3 | 440.7 | 508. |
| 2-Methyl-2-pentene | " | 0 | 95.6 | 105.8 | 115.3 | 118.2 | 121.4 | 129.8 | 169.9 | 215.8 | 266.6 | 322.4 | 382.7 | 447.0 | 515. |

| Compound (gas) | Formula | Temperature in °F — Heat Content (Enthalpy), $(H°-H°_0)$, in BTU/lb | | | | | | | | | | | | | |
|---|---|---|---|---|---|---|---|---|---|---|---|---|---|---|---|
| | | 900 | 1000 | 1100 | 1200 | 1300 | 1400 | 1500 | 1600 | 1700 | 1800 | 1900 | 2000 | 2100 | 2200 |
| 1-Hexene | C₆H₁₂ | 606.1 | 681.3 | 759.2 | 839.8 | 922.9 | 1008.0 | 1095. | 1185. | 1276. | 1368. | 1462. | 1558. | 1654. | 1752. |
| cis-2-Hexene | " | 590. | 665. | 743. | 823. | 905. | | | | | | | | | |
| trans-2-Hexene | " | 602. | 677. | 753. | 831. | 914. | | | | | | | | | |
| cis-3-Hexene | " | 586. | 660. | 737. | 816. | 900. | | | | | | | | | |
| trans-3-Hexene | " | 602. | 678. | 756. | 836. | 918. | | | | | | | | | |
| 2-Methyl-1-pentene | " | 610. | 685. | 763. | 844. | 928. | | | | | | | | | |
| 3-Methyl-1-pentene | " | 655. | 738. | 824. | 913. | 1005. | | | | | | | | | |
| 4-Methyl-1-pentene | " | 578. | 652. | 730. | 810. | 891. | | | | | | | | | |
| 2-Methyl-2-pentene | " | 586. | 660. | 737. | 816. | 900. | | | | | | | | | |

TABLE 8u-E (PART 2), Page 2 — MONOOLEFINS, C₆

HEAT CONTENT (ENTHALPY), $(H°-H°_0)$, FOR THE IDEAL GAS STATE, AT -459.69° TO 2200°F

May 31, 1946; December 31, 1952

Heat Content (Enthalpy), $(H°-H°_0)$, in BTU/lb

| Compound (gas) | Formula | Temperature in °F | | | | | | | | | | | | | |
|---|---|---|---|---|---|---|---|---|---|---|---|---|---|---|---|
| | | -459.69 | 0 | 32 | 60 | 68 | 77 | 100 | 200 | 300 | 400 | 500 | 600 | 700 | 800 |
| 3-Methyl-cis-2-nentene | C6H12 | 0 | 95.6 | 105.8 | 115.3 | 118.2 | 121.4 | 129.8 | 169.9 | 215.8 | 266.6 | 322.4 | 382.7 | 447.0 | 515. |
| 3-Methyl-trans-2-nentene | " | 0 | 95.6 | 105.8 | 115.3 | 118.2 | 121.4 | 129.8 | 169.9 | 215.8 | 266.6 | 322.4 | 382.7 | 447.0 | 515. |
| 4-Methyl-cis-2-nentene | " | 0 | 97.2 | 108.0 | 118.0 | 121.0 | 124.3 | 133.1 | 175.2 | 222.8 | 275.6 | 332.9 | 394.3 | 459.2 | 528. |
| 4-Methyl-trans-2-nentene | " | 0 | 100.3 | 112.0 | 122.8 | 125.9 | 129.6 | 138.8 | 182.8 | 231.9 | 286.0 | 344.8 | 407.9 | 473.8 | 543. |
| 2-Ethyl-1-butene | " | 0 | 99.0 | 109.8 | 119.8 | 122.8 | 126.3 | 135.0 | 177.2 | 225.0 | 278.0 | 335.6 | 397.4 | 462.9 | 532. |
| 2,3-Dimethyl-1-butene | " | 0 | 98.1 | 109.9 | 120.7 | 123.9 | 127.6 | 137.0 | 181.8 | 231.9 | 286.9 | 346.4 | 409.9 | 476.8 | 547. |
| 3,3-Dimethyl-1-butene | " | 0 | 86.8 | 96.6 | 105.8 | 108.5 | 111.7 | 119.9 | 160.0 | 206.3 | 257.9 | 313.7 | 373.4 | 437.4 | 506. |
| 2,3-Dimethyl-2-butene | " | 0 | 95.6 | 106.0 | 115.6 | 118.4 | 121.8 | 130.1 | 170.1 | 215.5 | 265.8 | 321.1 | 380.7 | 443.8 | 511. |

Heat Content (Enthalpy), $(H°-H°_0)$, in BTU/lb

| Compound (gas) | Formula | Temperature in °F | | | | | | | | | | | | | |
|---|---|---|---|---|---|---|---|---|---|---|---|---|---|---|---|
| | | 900 | 1000 | 1100 | 1200 | 1300 | 1400 | 1500 | 1600 | 1700 | 1800 | 1900 | 2000 | 2100 | 2200 |
| 3-Methyl-cis-2-nentene | C6H12 | 586. | 660. | 737. | 816. | 900. | | | | | | | | | |
| 3-Methyl-trans-2-nentene | " | 586. | 660. | 737. | 816. | 900. | | | | | | | | | |
| 4-Methyl-cis-2-nentene | " | 600. | 676. | 753. | 834. | 917. | | | | | | | | | |
| 4-Methyl-trans-2-nentene | " | 615. | 691. | 770. | 851. | 934. | | | | | | | | | |
| 2-Ethyl-1-butene | " | 604. | 680. | 759. | 841. | 924. | | | | | | | | | |
| 2,3-Dimethyl-1-butene | " | 621. | 697. | 775. | 855. | 940. | | | | | | | | | |
| 3,3-Dimethyl-1-butene | " | 578. | 653. | 728. | 807. | 889. | | | | | | | | | |
| 2,3-Dimethyl-2-butene | " | 582. | 656. | 733. | 812. | 894. | | | | | | | | | |

## TABLE 11n-E (Part 1) - DIOLEFINS, C$_3$ TO C$_5$

HEAT CONTENT, (H°- H°$_0$), FOR THE IDEAL GAS STATE, AT -459.69° TO 2200 °F

October 31, 1947; April 30, 1948 (Corrected)

Temperature in °F — Heat Content, (H°- H°$_0$) in BTU/lb

| Compound (gas) | Formula | -459.69 | 0 | 32 | 60 | 68 | 77 | 100 | 200 | 300 | 400 | 500 | 600 | 700 | 800 |
|---|---|---|---|---|---|---|---|---|---|---|---|---|---|---|---|
| Propadiene (Allene) | C$_3$H$_4$ | 0 | 109.81 | 120.18 | 129.64 | 132.41 | 135.48 | 143.77 | 182.12 | 224.59 | 270.85 | 320.65 | 373.61 | 429.18 | 487.30 |
| 1,2-Butadiene | C$_4$H$_6$ | 0 | 102.44 | 112.76 | 122.21 | 124.98 | 128.11 | 136.37 | 175.01 | 218.08 | 265.24 | 316.20 | 370.66 | 428.31 | 488.92 |
| 1,3-Butadiene | " | 0 | 95.37 | 105.40 | 114.69 | 117.43 | 120.58 | 128.77 | 167.92 | 212.28 | 261.26 | 314.26 | 370.83 | 430.54 | 493.11 |
| 1,2-Pentadiene | C$_5$H$_8$ | 0 | 102.16 | 112.39 | 121.91 | 124.73 | 127.56 | 136.4 | 176.8 | 222.7 | 273.0 | 326.9 | 384.1 | 445.4 | 510.0 |
| cis-1,3-Pentadiene (cis-Piperylene) | " | 0 | 90.79 | 100.24 | 109.01 | 111.61 | 114.17 | 122.4 | 159.7 | 202.4 | 250.1 | 302.5 | 358.9 | 418.1 | 480.4 |
| trans-1,3-Pentadiene (trans-Piperylene) | " | 0 | 94.85 | 105.18 | 114.76 | 117.58 | 120.48 | 129.3 | 169.6 | 215.1 | 265.2 | 319.0 | 376.2 | 436.9 | 500.8 |
| 1,4-Pentadiene | " | 0 | 101.66 | 113.29 | 123.75 | 126.79 | 129.93 | 139.2 | 180.3 | 225.4 | 274.7 | 328.7 | 387.1 | 448.2 | 511.9 |
| 2,3-Pentadiene | " | 0 | 98.97 | 108.96 | 118.20 | 120.92 | 123.62 | 132.2 | 170.8 | 214.3 | 262.2 | 313.7 | 268.7 | 427.5 | 489.7 |
| 3-Methyl-1,2-Butadiene | " | 0 | 96.38 | 107.53 | 117.64 | 120.59 | 124.41 | 132.7 | 173.2 | 217.9 | 266.9 | 320.4 | 377.7 | 437.9 | 500.8 |
| 2-Methyl-1,3-Butadiene (Isoprene) | " | 0 | 93.58 | 103.36 | 112.57 | 115.32 | 118.10 | 126.8 | 167.1 | 213.4 | 264.7 | 319.5 | 377.6 | 439.4 | 504.5 |

Temperature in °F — Heat Content, (H°- H°$_0$) in BTU/lb

| Compound (gas) | Formula | 900 | 1000 | 1100 | 1200 | 1300 | 1400 | 1500 | 1600 | 1700 | 1800 | 1900 | 2000 | 2100 | 2200 |
|---|---|---|---|---|---|---|---|---|---|---|---|---|---|---|---|
| Propadiene (Allene) | C$_3$H$_4$ | 548.05 | 610.97 | 675.72 | 742.35 | 810.73 | 880.61 | 951.92 | 1024.74 | 1098.9 | 1174.4 | 1250.9 | 1328.3 | 1406.6 | 1485.9 |
| 1,2-Butadiene | C$_4$H$_6$ | 562.28 | 618.17 | 686.36 | 756.71 | 829.03 | 903.09 | 978.76 | 1055.99 | 1134.8 | 1215.1 | 1296.7 | 1379.2 | 1462.6 | 1547.1 |
| 1,3-Butadiene | " | 568.21 | 625.65 | 695.21 | 766.70 | 839.97 | 915.04 | 991.74 | 1069.79 | 1149.1 | 1229.7 | 1311.5 | 1394.3 | 1478.2 | 1562.9 |
| 1,2-Pentadiene | C$_5$H$_8$ | 576.6 | 645.4 | 716.5 | 790.3 | 866.6 | 944.6 | 1023.8 | 1103.6 | 1185.0 | 1269.8 | 1355.8 | 1441.6 | 1528.2 | 1616.0 |
| cis-1,3-Pentadiene (cis-Piperylene) | " | 546.8 | 615.8 | 686.4 | 758.6 | 833.0 | 909.9 | 988.9 | 1068.9 | 1150.1 | 1233.2 | 1318.0 | 1404.4 | 1491.2 | 1577.7 |
| trans-1,3-Pentadiene (trans-Piperylene) | " | 567.6 | 637.1 | 709.0 | 783.1 | 858.9 | 936.2 | 1015.0 | 1096.1 | 1178.6 | 1261.4 | 1345.3 | 1430.6 | 1517.0 | 1604.5 |
| 1,4-Pentadiene | " | 577.3 | 645.4 | 716.4 | 790.3 | 866.6 | 944.6 | 1023.8 | 1103.6 | 1185.0 | 1269.8 | 1355.8 | 1441.6 | 1528.2 | 1616.0 |
| 2,3-Pentadiene | " | 554.4 | 622.1 | 692.9 | 766.0 | 840.9 | 917.1 | 994.9 | 1074.7 | 1166.5 | 1240.1 | 1324.5 | 1408.8 | 1494.8 | 1583.4 |
| 3-Methyl-1,2-Butadiene | " | 566.5 | 634.7 | 705.1 | 778.1 | 853.7 | 930.8 | 1008.3 | 1089.8 | 1172.3 | 1256.7 | 1341.9 | 1427.1 | 1513.2 | 1600.4 |
| 2-Methyl-1,3-Butadiene (Isoprene) | " | 571.7 | 641.5 | 713.8 | 787.3 | 861.9 | 939.7 | 1020.5 | 1102.3 | 1185.0 | 1268.1 | 1353.2 | 1437.8 | 1524.6 | 1612.3 |

TABLE 18u-E, Page 1 - ALKYL CYCLOPENTENES, $C_5$ TO $C_7$

HEAT CONTENT (ENTHALPY), $(H°-H°_0)$, FOR THE IDEAL GAS STATE, AT -459.69° TO 2200°F

December 31, 1952

| Compound (gas) | Formula | Temperature in °F Heat Content (Enthalpy), $(H°-H°_0)$, in BTU/lb | | | | | | | | | | | | | |
|---|---|---|---|---|---|---|---|---|---|---|---|---|---|---|---|
| | | -459.69 | 0 | 32 | 60 | 68 | 77 | 100 | 200 | 300 | 400 | 500 | 600 | 700 | 800 |
| Cyclopentene | $C_5H_8$ | 0 | 72.54 | 80.01 | 86.98 | 89.05 | 91.43 | 97.66 | 128.13 | 164.22 | 205.93 | 252.79 | 304.31 | 360.06 | 419.64 |
| 1-Methylcyclopentene | $C_6H_{10}$ | 0 | 78.1 | 85.7 | 92.9 | 95.1 | 97.3 | 104.3 | 137.3 | 176.6 | 221.4 | 271.0 | 324.9 | 382.8 | 444.4 |
| 3-Methylcyclopentene | " | 0 | 75.3 | 83.3 | 90.8 | 93.0 | 95.4 | 102.4 | 135.7 | 174.7 | 219.3 | 269.0 | 323.5 | 382.1 | 444.3 |
| 4-Methylcyclopentene | " | 0 | 74.7 | 82.7 | 90.2 | 92.4 | 94.7 | 101.7 | 134.8 | 173.8 | 218.2 | 267.8 | 322.2 | 380.7 | 442.8 |

| Compound (gas) | Formula | Temperature in °F Heat Content (Enthalpy), $(H°-H°_0)$, in BTU/lb | | | | | | | | | | | | | |
|---|---|---|---|---|---|---|---|---|---|---|---|---|---|---|---|
| | | 900 | 1000 | 1100 | 1200 | 1300 | 1400 | 1500 | 1600 | 1700 | 1800 | 1900 | 2000 | 2100 | 2200 |
| Cyclopentene | $C_5H_8$ | 482.76 | 549.07 | 618.23 | 689.99 | 764.12 | 840.49 | 918.95 | 999.29 | 1081.34 | 1164.98 | 1250.04 | 1336.37 | 1423.97 | 1512.76 |
| 1-Methylcyclopentene | $C_6H_{10}$ | 509.4 | 577.9 | 649.4 | 723.1 | 798.8 | 877.5 | 958.9 | 1041.2 | 1124.5 | 1209.1 | 1295.4 | 1383.8 | 1473.9 | 1565.6 |
| 3-Methylcyclopentene | " | 509.5 | 577.8 | 649.3 | 723.7 | 800.6 | 879.2 | 959.2 | 1040.9 | 1124.5 | 1210.7 | 1298.5 | 1387.1 | 1476.6 | 1566.6 |
| 4-Methylcyclopentene | " | 507.9 | 576.1 | 647.4 | 721.6 | 798.3 | 877.6 | 958.9 | 1041.2 | 1124.5 | 1209.1 | 1295.5 | 1384.0 | 1473.6 | 1563.5 |

TABLE 18II-E, Page 2 – ALKYL CYCLOPENTENES, $C_5$ TO $C_7$

HEAT CONTENT (ENTHALPY), $(H°-H°_0)$, FOR THE IDEAL GAS STATE, AT −459.69° TO 2200°F
December 31, 1952

**Temperature in °F — Heat Content (Enthalpy), $(H°-H°_0)$, in BTU/lb**

| Compound (gas) | Formula | -459.69 | 0 | 32 | 60 | 68 | 77 | 100 | 200 | 300 | 400 | 500 | 600 | 700 | 800 |
|---|---|---|---|---|---|---|---|---|---|---|---|---|---|---|---|
| 1-Ethylcyclopentene | C7H10 | | | | | | | | | | | | | | |
| 3-Ethylcyclopentene | " | | | | | | | | | | | | | | |
| 4-Ethylcyclopentene | " | | | | | | | | | | | | | | |
| 1,2-Dimethylcyclopentene | " | 0 | 80.4 | 88.7 | 96.6 | 99.0 | 101.5 | 108.8 | 144.1 | 185.4 | 232.3 | 283.8 | 339.5 | 396.9 | 462.0 |
| 1,3-Dimethylcyclopentene | " | 0 | 78.0 | 86.7 | 94.8 | 97.2 | 99.8 | 107.2 | 142.7 | 183.9 | 230.4 | 282.0 | 338.2 | 398.3 | 462.0 |
| 1,4-Dimethylcyclopentene | " | 0 | 78.7 | 87.0 | 94.9 | 97.3 | 99.3 | 107.1 | 142.1 | 183.0 | 229.5 | 281.1 | 337.1 | 397.0 | 460.7 |
| 1,5-Dimethylcyclopentene | " | 0 | 78.3 | 86.8 | 94.8 | 97.2 | 99.8 | 107.2 | 142.6 | 183.9 | 230.5 | 281.7 | 337.2 | 397.1 | 460.7 |
| 3,3-Dimethylcyclopentene | " | 0 | 74.2 | 82.3 | 90.0 | 92.3 | 94.8 | 102.0 | 136.8 | 177.9 | 224.7 | 276.4 | 332.6 | 393.3 | 458.1 |
| 3,cis-4-Dimethylcyclopentene | " | 0 | 75.4 | 84.0 | 92.0 | 94.4 | 97.0 | 104.4 | 139.7 | 180.9 | 227.6 | 279.4 | 335.9 | 396.4 | 460.7 |
| 3,trans-4-Dimethylcyclopentene | " | 0 | 76.6 | 85.1 | 93.2 | 95.6 | 98.2 | 105.6 | 141.0 | 182.5 | 229.4 | 281.1 | 337.2 | 397.1 | 460.7 |
| 3,cis-5-Dimethylcyclopentene | " | 0 | 76.6 | 85.1 | 93.2 | 95.6 | 98.2 | 105.6 | 141.0 | 182.5 | 229.4 | 281.1 | 337.2 | 397.1 | 460.7 |
| 3,trans-5-Dimethylcyclopentene | " | 0 | 76.6 | 85.1 | 93.2 | 95.6 | 98.2 | 105.6 | 141.0 | 182.5 | 229.4 | 281.1 | 337.2 | 397.1 | 460.7 |
| 4,4-Dimethylcyclopentene | " | 0 | 76.6 | 85.1 | 93.2 | 95.6 | 98.2 | 105.6 | 141.0 | 182.5 | 229.4 | 281.1 | 337.2 | 397.1 | 460.7 |

**Temperature in °F — Heat Content (Enthalpy), $(H°-H°_0)$, in BTU/lb**

| Compound (gas) | Formula | 900 | 1000 | 1100 | 1200 | 1300 | 1400 | 1500 | 1600 | 1700 | 1800 | 1900 | 2000 | 2100 | 2200 |
|---|---|---|---|---|---|---|---|---|---|---|---|---|---|---|---|
| 1-Ethylcyclopentene | C7H12 | | | | | | | | | | | | | | |
| 3-Ethylcyclopentene | " | | | | | | | | | | | | | | |
| 4-Ethylcyclopentene | " | | | | | | | | | | | | | | |
| 1,2-Dimethylcyclopentene | " | 529.0 | 599.1 | 672.0 | 747.3 | 824.8 | 904.9 | 987.2 | 1070.8 | 1155.7 | 1242.4 | 1330.6 | 1419.9 | 1510.3 | 1601.6 |
| 1,3-Dimethylcyclopentene | " | 529.0 | 599.1 | 672.0 | 747.3 | 824.8 | 904.8 | 987.1 | 1071.7 | 1158.0 | 1244.9 | 1333.0 | 1422.5 | 1513.0 | 1604.4 |
| 1,4-Dimethylcyclopentene | " | 527.6 | 597.6 | 670.4 | 745.6 | 823.0 | 902.8 | 985.1 | 1069.6 | 1155.7 | 1242.6 | 1330.6 | 1419.9 | 1510.3 | 1601.6 |
| 1,5-Dimethylcyclopentene | " | 528.4 | 599.2 | 672.1 | 747.3 | 824.8 | 904.9 | 987.2 | 1070.8 | 1155.7 | 1242.4 | 1330.5 | 1419.8 | 1510.6 | 1603.4 |
| 3,3-Dimethylcyclopentene | " | 526.4 | 598.0 | 672.6 | 749.4 | 828.1 | 909.3 | 993.0 | 1079.1 | 1166.9 | 1255.6 | 1345.6 | 1437.2 | 1529.3 | 1621.3 |
| 3,cis-4-Dimethylcyclopentene | " | 528.4 | 599.3 | 673.1 | 749.4 | 828.1 | 908.8 | 991.3 | 1075.0 | 1160.2 | 1247.1 | 1335.4 | 1424.9 | 1516.0 | 1608.9 |
| 3,trans-4-Dimethylcyclopentene | " | 527.5 | 597.7 | 671.4 | 747.7 | 826.3 | 906.9 | 989.2 | 1072.9 | 1158.0 | 1244.8 | 1333.0 | 1422.3 | 1513.3 | 1606.2 |
| 3,cis-5-Dimethylcyclopentene | " | 527.5 | 597.7 | 671.4 | 747.7 | 826.3 | 906.9 | 989.2 | 1072.9 | 1158.0 | 1244.8 | 1333.0 | 1422.3 | 1513.3 | 1606.2 |
| 3,trans-5-Dimethylcyclopentene | " | 527.5 | 597.7 | 671.4 | 747.7 | 826.3 | 906.9 | 989.2 | 1072.9 | 1158.0 | 1244.8 | 1333.0 | 1422.3 | 1513.3 | 1606.2 |
| 4,4-Dimethylcyclopentene | " | 527.5 | 597.7 | 671.4 | 747.7 | 826.3 | 906.9 | 989.2 | 1072.9 | 1158.0 | 1244.8 | 1333.0 | 1422.3 | 1513.3 | 1606.2 |

TABLE 25u-E (PART 1), Page 1 - NORMAL ACETYLENES (1-ALKYNES), $C_2$ TO $C_{20}$
HEAT CONTENT (ENTHALPY), $(H°-H°_0)$, FOR THE IDEAL GAS STATE, AT -459.69° TO 2200°F
February 28, 1946; December 31, 1952

| Compound (gas) | Formula | Temperature in °F | | | | | | | | | | | | | |
|---|---|---|---|---|---|---|---|---|---|---|---|---|---|---|---|
| | | -459.69 | 0 | 32 | 60 | 68 | 77 | 100 | 200 | 300 | 400 | 500 | 600 | 700 | 800 |
| | | Heat Content (Enthalpy), $(H°-H°_0)$, in BTU/lb | | | | | | | | | | | | | |
| Ethyne (Acetylene) | C2H2 | 0 | 135.0 | 147.3 | 158.4 | 161.6 | 165.2 | 174.6 | 217.5 | 263.1 | 311.1 | 361.0 | 412.6 | 465.8 | 520.3 |
| Propyne (Methylacetylene) | C3H4 | 0 | 112.8 | 123.5 | 133.3 | 136.2 | 139.4 | 147.8 | 186.9 | 229.7 | 276.0 | 325.5 | 378.0 | 433.1 | 490.8 |
| 1-Butyne (Ethylacetylene) | C4H6 | 0 | 100.4 | 111.0 | 120.8 | 123.6 | 127.0 | 135.3 | 174.7 | 218.4 | 266.1 | 317.5 | 372.3 | 430.1 | 490.7 |
| 1-Pentyne | C5H8 | 0 | 103.5 | 114.4 | 124.4 | 127.3 | 130.8 | 139.3 | 179.8 | 224.8 | 273.9 | 326.9 | 383.6 | 443.6 | 506.7 |
| 1-Hexyne | C6H10 | 0 | 102.8 | 113.7 | 123.8 | 126.7 | 130.2 | 138.8 | 179.7 | 225.4 | 275.4 | 329.5 | 387.3 | 448.6 | 513.0 |
| 1-Heptyne | C7H12 | 0 | 101.4 | 113.3 | 123.4 | 126.3 | 129.8 | 138.5 | 179.8 | 225.9 | 276.6 | 331.3 | 389.9 | 452.0 | 517.5 |
| 1-Octyne | C8H14 | 0 | 102.0 | 113.0 | 123.0 | 126.0 | 129.5 | 138.2 | 179.7 | 226.2 | 277.3 | 332.6 | 391.8 | 454.7 | 521.0 |
| 1-Nonyne | C9H16 | 0 | 101.8 | 112.8 | 122.8 | 125.8 | 129.2 | 138.0 | 179.7 | 226.5 | 278.0 | 333.7 | 393.4 | 456.8 | 525.6 |
| 1-Decyne | C10H18 | 0 | 101.5 | 112.5 | 122.6 | 125.6 | 129.0 | 137.8 | 179.7 | 226.7 | 278.5 | 334.5 | 394.6 | 458.3 | 525.6 |
| 1-Undecyne | C11H20 | 0 | 101.3 | 112.3 | 122.4 | 125.4 | 128.9 | 137.7 | 179.7 | 226.9 | 278.8 | 335.2 | 395.5 | 459.6 | 527.3 |

| Compound (gas) | Formula | Temperature in °F | | | | | | | | | | | | | |
|---|---|---|---|---|---|---|---|---|---|---|---|---|---|---|---|
| | | 900 | 1000 | 1100 | 1200 | 1300 | 1400 | 1500 | 1600 | 1700 | 1800 | 1900 | 2000 | 2100 | 2200 |
| | | Heat Content (Enthalpy), $(H°-H°_0)$, in BTU/lb | | | | | | | | | | | | | |
| Ethyne (Acetylene) | C2H2 | 576.1 | 633.1 | 691.0 | 750.4 | 810.7 | 872.0 | 934.2 | 997.2 | 1061. | 1126. | 1191. | 1257. | 1324. | 1392. |
| Propyne (Methylacetylene) | C3H4 | 550.7 | 612.8 | 676.9 | 742.8 | 810.5 | 879.7 | 950.4 | 1023. | 1096. | 1171. | 1247. | 1324. | 1401. | 1480. |
| 1-Butyne (Ethylacetylene) | C4H6 | 554.0 | 619.8 | 687.7 | 757.7 | 829.5 | 903.2 | 978.5 | 1056. | 1134. | 1214. | 1295. | 1377. | 1460. | 1544. |
| 1-Pentyne | C5H8 | 572.4 | 640.7 | 711.4 | 784.3 | 859.2 | 936.0 | 1014.6 | 1095. | 1177. | 1260. | 1344. | 1430. | 1517. | 1604. |
| 1-Hexyne | C6H10 | 580.3 | 650.3 | 722.8 | 797.6 | 874.3 | 953.0 | 1033.5 | 1116. | 1200. | 1285. | 1372. | 1460. | 1548. | 1638. |
| 1-Heptyne | C7H12 | 586.0 | 657.2 | 730.9 | 806.9 | 885.0 | 965.1 | 1046.9 | 1131. | 1216. | 1303. | 1391. | 1480. | 1571. | 1662. |
| 1-Octyne | C8H14 | 590.2 | 662.3 | 736.9 | 813.9 | 893.0 | 974.1 | 1057.1 | 1142. | 1228. | 1316. | 1405. | 1496. | 1587. | 1680. |
| 1-Nonyne | C9H16 | 593.4 | 666.2 | 741.5 | 819.2 | 899.1 | 981.0 | 1064.8 | 1150. | 1238. | 1326. | 1417. | 1508. | 1600. | 1694. |
| 1-Decyne | C10H18 | 596.1 | 669.4 | 745.3 | 823.6 | 904.1 | 986.6 | 1071.0 | 1157. | 1245. | 1335. | 1425. | 1517. | 1611. | 1705. |
| 1-Undecyne | C11H20 | 598.2 | 672.0 | 748.3 | 827.1 | 908.1 | 991.0 | 1076.0 | 1163. | 1251. | 1341. | 1433. | 1525. | 1619. | 1714. |

TABLE 25u-E (PART 1), Page 2 – NORMAL ACETYLENES (1-ALKYNES), $C_2$ TO $C_{20}$

HEAT CONTENT (ENTHALPY), $(H^\circ - H^\circ_0)$, FOR THE IDEAL GAS STATE, AT −459.69° TO 2200°F

February 28, 1946; December 31, 1952

Temperature in °F

Heat Content (Enthalpy), $(H^\circ - H^\circ_0)$, in BTU/lb

| Compound (gas) | Formula | −459.69 | 0 | 32 | 60 | 68 | 77 | 100 | 200 | 300 | 400 | 500 | 600 | 700 | 800 |
|---|---|---|---|---|---|---|---|---|---|---|---|---|---|---|---|
| 1-Dodecyne | $C_{12}H_{22}$ | 0 | 101.3 | 112.2 | 122.4 | 125.3 | 128.7 | 137.6 | 179.6 | 227.0 | 279.2 | 335.8 | 396.3 | 460.7 | 528.7 |
| 1-Tridecyne | $C_{13}H_{24}$ | 0 | 101.1 | 112.1 | 122.2 | 125.2 | 128.6 | 137.5 | 179.6 | 227.1 | 279.5 | 336.2 | 397.0 | 461.7 | 529.9 |
| 1-Tetradecyne | $C_{14}H_{26}$ | 0 | 101.0 | 112.0 | 122.1 | 125.1 | 128.5 | 137.4 | 179.6 | 227.2 | 279.7 | 336.6 | 397.6 | 462.5 | 530.9 |
| 1-Pentadecyne | $C_{15}H_{28}$ | 0 | 100.9 | 111.9 | 122.0 | 125.0 | 128.5 | 137.3 | 179.6 | 227.3 | 279.9 | 337.0 | 398.1 | 463.1 | 531.8 |
| 1-Hexadecyne | $C_{16}H_{30}$ | 0 | 100.8 | 111.8 | 122.0 | 125.0 | 128.4 | 137.3 | 179.6 | 227.4 | 280.1 | 337.3 | 398.5 | 463.7 | 532.6 |
| 1-Heptadecyne | $C_{17}H_{32}$ | 0 | 100.8 | 111.8 | 121.9 | 124.9 | 128.3 | 137.2 | 179.6 | 227.4 | 280.3 | 337.6 | 398.9 | 464.3 | 533.2 |
| 1-Octadecyne | $C_{18}H_{34}$ | 0 | 100.7 | 111.7 | 121.9 | 124.8 | 128.3 | 137.2 | 179.6 | 227.5 | 280.4 | 337.8 | 399.3 | 464.8 | 533.9 |
| 1-Nonadecyne | $C_{19}H_{36}$ | 0 | 100.7 | 111.7 | 121.8 | 124.8 | 128.2 | 137.2 | 179.6 | 227.6 | 280.6 | 338.0 | 399.6 | 465.2 | 534.4 |
| 1-Eicosyne | $C_{20}H_{38}$ | 0 | 100.6 | 111.6 | 121.8 | 124.8 | 128.2 | 137.1 | 179.6 | 227.6 | 280.7 | 338.2 | 399.9 | 465.5 | 534.9 |

Temperature in °F

Heat Content (Enthalpy), $(H^\circ - H^\circ_0)$, in BTU/lb

| Compound (gas) | Formula | 900 | 1000 | 1100 | 1200 | 1300 | 1400 | 1500 | 1600 | 1700 | 1800 | 1900 | 2000 | 2100 | 2200 |
|---|---|---|---|---|---|---|---|---|---|---|---|---|---|---|---|
| 1-Dodecyne | $C_{12}H_{22}$ | 599.9 | 674.0 | 750.8 | 830.0 | 911.4 | 994.8 | 1080.2 | 1168. | 1257. | 1347. | 1439. | 1532. | 1626. | 1721. |
| 1-Tridecyne | $C_{13}H_{24}$ | 601.4 | 675.8 | 753.0 | 832.5 | 914.1 | 998.0 | 1083.8 | 1172. | 1261. | 1352. | 1444. | 1537. | 1632. | 1728. |
| 1-Tetradecyne | $C_{14}H_{26}$ | 602.7 | 677.4 | 754.8 | 834.5 | 916.6 | 1000.7 | 1086.8 | 1175. | 1265. | 1356. | 1448. | 1542. | 1637. | 1733. |
| 1-Pentadecyne | $C_{15}H_{28}$ | 603.8 | 678.7 | 756.4 | 836.4 | 918.7 | 1003.1 | 1089.4 | 1178. | 1268. | 1359. | 1452. | 1546. | 1641. | 1738. |
| 1-Hexadecyne | $C_{16}H_{30}$ | 604.7 | 679.9 | 757.7 | 838.0 | 920.5 | 1005.1 | 1091.7 | 1180. | 1271. | 1362. | 1455. | 1550. | 1645. | 1742. |
| 1-Hentadecyne | $C_{17}H_{32}$ | 605.6 | 680.9 | 758.9 | 839.4 | 922.1 | 1006.9 | 1093.7 | 1183. | 1273. | 1365. | 1458. | 1553. | 1649. | 1745. |
| 1-Octadecyne | $C_{18}H_{34}$ | 606.3 | 681.8 | 760.0 | 840.7 | 923.5 | 1008.5 | 1095.6 | 1185. | 1275. | 1367. | 1461. | 1556. | 1652. | 1749. |
| 1-Nonadecyne | $C_{19}H_{36}$ | 607.0 | 682.6 | 761.0 | 841.7 | 924.8 | 1010.0 | 1097.2 | 1186. | 1277. | 1369. | 1463. | 1558. | 1654. | 1751. |
| 1-Eicosyne | $C_{20}H_{38}$ | 607.6 | 683.3 | 761.8 | 842.8 | 925.9 | 1011.2 | 1098.6 | 1188. | 1279. | 1371. | 1465. | 1560. | 1657. | 1754. |

TABLE 12u-E - ACETYLENES, C₂ TO C₅

HEAT CONTENT (ENTHALPY), $(H^\circ-H^\circ_0)$, FOR THE IDEAL GAS STATE, AT -459.69° TO 2200°F

January 31, 1946

Heat Content (Enthalpy), $(H^\circ-H^\circ_0)$, in BTU/lb

| Compound (gas) | Formula | \-459.69 | 0 | 32 | 60 | 68 | 77 | 100 | 200 | 300 | 400 | 500 | 600 | 700 | 800 |
|---|---|---|---|---|---|---|---|---|---|---|---|---|---|---|---|
| | | | | | | | | | Temperature in °F | | | | | | |
| Ethyne (Acetylene) | $C_2H_2$ | 0 | 135.0 | 147.3 | 158.4 | 161.6 | 165.2 | 174.6 | 217.5 | 263.1 | 311.1 | 361.0 | 412.6 | 465.8 | 520.3 |
| Propyne (Methylacetylene) | $C_3H_4$ | 0 | 112.8 | 123.5 | 133.3 | 136.2 | 139.4 | 147.8 | 186.9 | 229.7 | 276.0 | 325.5 | 378.0 | 433.1 | 490.8 |
| 1-Butyne (Ethylacetylene) | $C_4H_6$ | 0 | 100.4 | 111.0 | 120.8 | 123.6 | 127.0 | 135.3 | 174.7 | 218.4 | 266.1 | 317.5 | 372.3 | 430.1 | 490.7 |
| 2-Butyne (Dimethylacetylene) | " | 0 | 106.7 | 116.8 | 126.0 | 128.7 | 131.7 | 139.7 | 177.0 | 218.5 | 263.8 | 312.8 | 365.4 | 421.2 | 480.0 |
| 1-Pentyne | $C_5H_8$ | 0 | 102.8 | 114.0 | 124.2 | 127.2 | 130.8 | 139.4 | 180.4 | 225.6 | 274.9 | 328. | 385. | 445. | 509. |
| 2-Pentyne | " | 0 | 98.2 | 108.3 | 117.6 | 120.3 | 123.5 | 131.5 | 169.4 | 211.8 | 258.4 | 309. | 363. | 421. | 482. |
| 3-Methyl-1-butyne | " | 0 | 94.1 | 104.8 | 114.6 | 117.5 | 121.0 | 129.4 | 169.8 | 215.0 | 264.6 | 318. | 376. | 436. | 499. |

Heat Content (Enthalpy), $(H^\circ-H^\circ_0)$, in BTU/lb

| Compound (gas) | Formula | 900 | 1000 | 1100 | 1200 | 1300 | 1400 | 1500 | 1600 | 1700 | 1800 | 1900 | 2000 | 2100 | 2200 |
|---|---|---|---|---|---|---|---|---|---|---|---|---|---|---|---|
| | | | | | | | Temperature in °F | | | | | | | | |
| Ethyne (Acetylene) | $C_2H_2$ | 576.1 | 633.1 | 691.2 | 750.4 | 810.7 | 872.0 | 934.2 | 997.2 | 1061. | 1126. | 1191. | 1257. | 1324. | 1392. |
| Propyne (Methylacetylene) | $C_3H_4$ | 550.7 | 612.8 | 676.9 | 742.8 | 810.5 | 879.7 | 950.4 | 1023. | 1096. | 1171. | 1247. | 1324. | 1401. | 1480. |
| 1-Butyne (Ethylacetylene) | $C_4H_6$ | 554.0 | 619.8 | 687.7 | 757.7 | 829.5 | 903.2 | 978.6 | 1056. | 1134. | 1214. | 1295. | 1377. | 1460. | 1544. |
| 2-Butyne (Dimethylacetylene) | " | 541.7 | 605.8 | 672.2 | 741.0 | 811.9 | 884.7 | 959.1 | 1035. | 1113. | 1192. | 1272. | 1354. | 1437. | 1520. |
| 1-Pentyne | $C_5H_8$ | 574. | 643. | 713. | 786. | 860. | 937. | 1015. | 1095. | 1177. | 1260. | 1345. | 1430. | 1517. | 1604. |
| 2-Pentyne | " | 546. | 613. | 682. | 753. | 827. | 902. | 980. | 1059. | 1140. | 1222. | 1305. | 1390. | 1476. | 1563. |
| 3-Methyl-1-butyne | " | 565. | 634. | 705. | 778. | 853. | 930. | 1009. | 1089. | 1171. | 1255. | 1339. | 1425. | 1511. | 1598. |

TABLE 21u-E (PART 1), Page 1 – NORMAL ALKYL BENZENES, C6 TO C22

HEAT CONTENT (ENTHALPY), $(H°-H°_0)$, FOR THE IDEAL GAS STATE, AT -459.69° TO 2200°F

January 31, 1946; December 31, 1952

| Compound (gas) | Formula | Temperature in °F | | | | | | | | | | | | | |
|---|---|---|---|---|---|---|---|---|---|---|---|---|---|---|---|
| | | Heat Content (Enthalpy), $(H°-H°_0)$, in BTU/lb | | | | | | | | | | | | | |
| | | -459.69 | 0 | 32 | 60 | 68 | 77 | 100 | 200 | 300 | 400 | 500 | 600 | 700 | 800 |
| Benzene | C6H6 | 0 | 60.63 | 67.60 | 74.19 | 76.12 | 78.33 | 84.20 | 112.94 | 146.66 | 184.9 | 227.2 | 273.2 | 322.4 | 374.5 |
| Methylbenzene (Toluene) | C7H8 | 0 | 64.85 | 72.46 | 79.60 | 81.69 | 84.07 | 90.38 | 121.01 | 156.61 | 196.8 | 241.1 | 289.2 | 340.6 | 395.1 |
| Ethylbenzene | C8H10 | 0 | 69.66 | 77.89 | 85.60 | 87.84 | 90.39 | 97.15 | 129.86 | 167.71 | 210.3 | 257.1 | 307.8 | 361.9 | 419.1 |
| n-Propylbenzene | C9H12 | 0 | 69.94 | 81.14 | 90.82 | 93.57 | 96.79 | 104.54 | 139.22 | 176.06 | 217.1 | 266.0 | 321.3 | 377.9 | 436.5 |
| n-Butylbenzene | C10H14 | 0 | 77.82 | 86.54 | 94.69 | 97.10 | 99.86 | 107.12 | 142.12 | 182.41 | 227.5 | 277.0 | 330.4 | 387.3 | 447.5 |
| n-Pentylbenzene | C11H16 | 0 | 79.89 | 88.85 | 97.19 | 99.66 | 102.47 | 109.92 | 145.70 | 186.81 | 232.8 | 283.1 | 337.5 | 395.4 | 456.7 |
| n-Hexylbenzene | C12H18 | 0 | 81.58 | 90.72 | 99.23 | 101.75 | 104.62 | 112.19 | 148.62 | 190.40 | 237.1 | 288.2 | 343.3 | 402.1 | 464.2 |
| n-Heptylbenzene | C13H20 | 0 | 83.04 | 92.32 | 100.97 | 103.53 | 106.43 | 114.14 | 151.10 | 193.46 | 240.8 | 292.5 | 348.3 | 407.7 | 470.6 |
| n-Octylbenzene | C14H22 | 0 | 84.24 | 93.67 | 102.43 | 105.02 | 107.96 | 115.77 | 153.18 | 196.04 | 243.8 | 296.1 | 352.5 | 412.5 | 476.0 |

| Compound (gas) | Formula | Temperature in °F | | | | | | | | | | | | | |
|---|---|---|---|---|---|---|---|---|---|---|---|---|---|---|---|
| | | Heat Content (Enthalpy), $(H°-H°_0)$, in BTU/lb | | | | | | | | | | | | | |
| | | 900 | 1000 | 1100 | 1200 | 1300 | 1400 | 1500 | 1600 | 1700 | 1800 | 1900 | 2000 | 2100 | 2200 |
| Benzene | C6H6 | 429.1 | 486.1 | 545.2 | 606.2 | 668.9 | 733.2 | 799.0 | 866.1 | 934.5 | 1004. | 1074. | 1146. | 1218. | 1291. |
| Methylbenzene (Toluene) | C7H8 | 452.4 | 512.2 | 574.1 | 638.2 | 704.1 | 771.7 | 840.9 | 911.6 | 983.6 | 1057. | 1131. | 1206. | 1283. | 1360. |
| Ethylbenzene | C8H10 | 479.1 | 541.5 | 606.2 | 673.1 | 741.9 | 812.4 | 884.5 | 958.1 | 1033. | 1109. | 1187. | 1265. | 1345. | 1425. |
| n-Propylbenzene | C9H12 | 498.2 | 562.6 | 629.2 | 698.0 | 768.9 | 841.8 | 915.8 | 988.9 | 1064. | 1145. | 1228. | 1308. | 1390. | 1472. |
| n-Butylbenzene | C10H14 | 510.7 | 576.5 | 644.6 | 714.9 | 787.4 | 861.7 | 937.6 | 1015.2 | 1094. | 1175. | 1256. | 1339. | 1422. | 1507. |
| n-Pentylbenzene | C11H16 | 520.9 | 587.9 | 657.2 | 728.8 | 802.5 | 878.1 | 955.5 | 1034.4 | 1115. | 1197. | 1280. | 1364. | 1449. | 1535. |
| n-Hexylbenzene | C12H18 | 529.4 | 597.3 | 667.7 | 740.4 | 815.1 | 891.7 | 970.2 | 1050.3 | 1132. | 1215. | 1299. | 1384. | 1471. | 1558. |
| n-Heptylbenzene | C13H20 | 536.6 | 605.3 | 676.5 | 750.0 | 825.7 | 903.2 | 982.5 | 1034.5 | 1146. | 1230. | 1315. | 1402. | 1489. | 1578. |
| n-Octylbenzene | C14H22 | 542.6 | 612.0 | 684.0 | 758.2 | 834.6 | 913.0 | 993.1 | 1075.0 | 1158. | 1243. | 1329. | 1416. | 1505. | 1594. |

TABLE 21u-E (PART 1), Page 2 - NORMAL ALKYL BENZENES, $C_6$ TO $C_{22}$

HEAT CONTENT (ENTHALPY), $(H^o-H^o_0)$, FOR THE IDEAL GAS STATE, AT $-459.69^o$ TO $2200^o$F

January 31, 1946; December 31, 1952

Heat Content (Enthalpy), $(H^o-H^o_0)$, in BTU/lb

| Compound (gas) | Formula | Temperature in °F | | | | | | | | | | | | | |
|---|---|---|---|---|---|---|---|---|---|---|---|---|---|---|---|
| | | -459.69 | 0 | 32 | 60 | 68 | 77 | 100 | 200 | 300 | 400 | 500 | 600 | 700 | 800 |
| n-Nonylbenzene | $C_{15}H_{24}$ | 0 | 85.39 | 94.88 | 103.73 | 106.34 | 109.29 | 117.19 | 154.99 | 198.26 | 246.5 | 299.3 | 356.1 | 416.7 | 480.7 |
| n-Decylbenzene | $C_{16}H_{26}$ | 0 | 86.24 | 95.86 | 104.81 | 107.45 | 110.45 | 118.43 | 156.59 | 200.23 | 248.9 | 302.0 | 359.2 | 420.2 | 484.7 |
| n-Undecylbenzene | $C_{17}H_{28}$ | 0 | 87.02 | 96.74 | 105.77 | 108.44 | 111.47 | 119.50 | 157.97 | 201.92 | 250.9 | 304.4 | 362.0 | 423.4 | 488.3 |
| n-Dodecylbenzene | $C_{18}H_{30}$ | 0 | 87.82 | 97.58 | 106.66 | 109.34 | 112.37 | 120.48 | 159.18 | 203.44 | 252.7 | 306.5 | 364.4 | 426.2 | 491.5 |
| n-Tridecylbenzene | $C_{19}H_{32}$ | 0 | 88.44 | 98.27 | 107.41 | 110.12 | 113.18 | 121.32 | 160.27 | 204.78 | 254.3 | 308.4 | 366.6 | 428.7 | 494.3 |
| n-Tetradecylbenzene | $C_{20}H_{34}$ | 0 | 89.03 | 98.92 | 108.12 | 110.84 | 113.90 | 122.11 | 161.27 | 206.01 | 255.8 | 310.1 | 368.6 | 430.9 | 496.9 |
| n-Pentadecylbenzene | $C_{21}H_{36}$ | 0 | 89.53 | 99.48 | 108.73 | 111.46 | 114.56 | 122.80 | 162.15 | 207.10 | 257.1 | 311.7 | 370.4 | 433.0 | 499.1 |
| n-Hexadecylbenzene | $C_{22}H_{38}$ | 0 | 89.98 | 99.99 | 109.29 | 112.04 | 115.14 | 123.42 | 162.95 | 208.09 | 258.3 | 313.1 | 372.0 | 434.8 | 501.2 |

Heat Content (Enthalpy), $(H^o-H^o_0)$, in BTU/lb

| Compound (gas) | Formula | Temperature in °F | | | | | | | | | | | | | |
|---|---|---|---|---|---|---|---|---|---|---|---|---|---|---|---|
| | | 900 | 1000 | 1100 | 1200 | 1300 | 1400 | 1500 | 1600 | 1700 | 1800 | 1900 | 2000 | 2100 | 2200 |
| n-Nonylbenzene | $C_{15}H_{24}$ | 547.9 | 617.9 | 690.4 | 765.3 | 842.3 | 921.3 | 1002.2 | 1084.8 | 1169. | 1255. | 1341. | 1429. | 1518. | 1608. |
| n-Decylbenzene | $C_{16}H_{26}$ | 552.4 | 623.0 | 696.1 | 771.5 | 849.1 | 928.7 | 1010.1 | 1093.4 | 1178. | 1264. | 1352. | 1440. | 1530. | 1621. |
| n-Undecylbenzene | $C_{17}H_{28}$ | 556.4 | 627.5 | 701.0 | 777.0 | 855.1 | 935.1 | 1017.1 | 1100.9 | 1186. | 1273. | 1361. | 1450. | 1541. | 1632. |
| n-Dodecylbenzene | $C_{18}H_{30}$ | 560.0 | 631.4 | 705.4 | 781.8 | 860.3 | 940.8 | 1023.3 | 1107.6 | 1194. | 1281. | 1369. | 1459. | 1550. | 1642. |
| n-Tridecylbenzene | $C_{19}H_{32}$ | 563.2 | 635.0 | 709.3 | 786.1 | 865.0 | 946.0 | 1028.9 | 1113.6 | 1200. | 1287. | 1376. | 1467. | 1558. | 1650. |
| n-Tetradecylbenzene | $C_{20}H_{34}$ | 566.1 | 638.2 | 712.8 | 789.9 | 869.2 | 950.6 | 1033.8 | 1118.9 | 1206. | 1294. | 1383. | 1473. | 1565. | 1658. |
| n-Pentadecylbenzene | $C_{21}H_{36}$ | 568.6 | 641.0 | 716.0 | 793.4 | 873.0 | 954.7 | 1038.3 | 1123.7 | 1211. | 1299. | 1389. | 1480. | 1572. | 1665. |
| n-Hexadecylbenzene | $C_{22}H_{38}$ | 570.9 | 643.6 | 718.9 | 796.6 | 876.5 | 958.4 | 1042.3 | 1128.1 | 1216. | 1304. | 1394. | 1486. | 1578. | 1671. |

TABLE 5u-E, Page 1 – ALKYL BENZENES, $C_6$ TO $C_8$

HEAT CONTENT (ENTHALPY), $(H°-H°_0)$, FOR THE IDEAL GAS STATE, AT $-459.69°$ TO $2200°F$

December 31, 1945

| Compound (gas) | Formula | Temperature in °F — Heat Content (Enthalpy), $(H°-H°_0)$, in BTU/lb | | | | | | | | | | | | | |
|---|---|---|---|---|---|---|---|---|---|---|---|---|---|---|---|
| | | -459.69 | 0 | 32 | 60 | 68 | 77 | 100 | 200 | 300 | 400 | 500 | 600 | 700 | 800 |
| Benzene | $C_6H_6$ | 0 | 60.63 | 67.60 | 74.19 | 76.12 | 78.33 | 84.20 | 112.94 | 146.66 | 184.9 | 227.2 | 273.2 | 322.4 | 374.5 |
| Methylbenzene (Toluene) | $C_7H_8$ | 0 | 64.85 | 72.46 | 79.60 | 81.69 | 84.07 | 90.38 | 121.01 | 156.61 | 196.8 | 241.1 | 289.2 | 340.6 | 395.1 |
| Ethylbenzene | $C_8H_{10}$ | 0 | 69.66 | 77.89 | 85.60 | 87.84 | 90.39 | 97.15 | 129.86 | 167.71 | 210.3 | 257.1 | 307.8 | 361.9 | 419.1 |
| 1,2-Dimethylbenzene (o-Xylene) | " | 0 | 72.82 | 81.46 | 89.48 | 91.82 | 94.48 | 101.48 | 134.95 | 173.11 | 215.6 | 262.2 | 312.5 | 366.1 | 422.8 |
| 1,3-Dimethylbenzene (m-Xylene) | " | 0 | 69.59 | 77.80 | 85.45 | 87.69 | 90.24 | 96.96 | 129.33 | 166.57 | 208.3 | 254.3 | 304.0 | 357.2 | 413.5 |
| 1,4-Dimethylbenzene (p-Xylene) | " | 0 | 70.20 | 78.40 | 86.03 | 88.25 | 90.78 | 97.45 | 129.57 | 166.52 | 208.0 | 253.6 | 303.0- | 355.8 | 411.9 |

| Compound (gas) | Formula | Temperature in °F — Heat Content (Enthalpy), $(H°-H°_0)$, in BTU/lb | | | | | | | | | | | | | |
|---|---|---|---|---|---|---|---|---|---|---|---|---|---|---|---|
| | | 900 | 1000 | 1100 | 1200 | 1300 | 1400 | 1500 | 1600 | 1700 | 1800 | 1900 | 2000 | 2100 | 2200 |
| Benzene | $C_6H_6$ | 429.1 | 486.1 | 545.2 | 606.2 | 668.9 | 733.2 | 799.0 | 866.1 | 934.5 | 1004. | 1074. | 1146. | 1218. | 1291. |
| Methylbenzene (Toluene) | $C_7H_8$ | 452.4 | 512.2 | 574.1 | 638.2 | 704.1 | 771.7 | 840.9 | 911.6 | 983.6 | 1057. | 1131. | 1206. | 1283. | 1360. |
| Ethylbenzene | $C_8H_{10}$ | 479.1 | 541.5 | 606.2 | 673.1 | 741.9 | 812.4 | 884.5 | 958.1 | 1033. | 1109. | 1187. | 1265. | 1345. | 1425. |
| 1,2-Dimethylbenzene (o-Xylene) | " | 482.2 | 544.2 | 608.5 | 675.0 | 743.4 | 813.6 | 885.4 | 958.7 | 1033. | 1109. | 1186. | 1265. | 1344. | 1424. |
| 1,3-Dimethylbenzene (m-Xylene) | " | 472.7 | 534.5 | 598.7 | 665.0 | 733.3 | 803.4 | 875.2 | 948.4 | 1023. | 1099. | 1176. | 1254. | 1333. | 1413. |
| 1,4-Dimethylbenzene (p-Xylene) | " | 470.8 | 532.3 | 596.2 | 662.3 | 730.4 | 800.3 | 871.8 | 944.9 | 1019. | 1095. | 1172. | 1250. | 1329. | 1409. |

TABLE 5u-E, Page 2 - ALKYL BENZENES, $C_9$

HEAT CONTENT (ENTHALPY), $(H^o - H^o_0)$, FOR THE IDEAL GAS STATE, AT $-459.69^o$ TO $2200^o$F

December 31, 1945

Heat Content (Enthalpy), $(H^o - H^o_0)$, in BTU/lb

| Compound (gas) | Formula | Temperature in °F | | | | | | | | | | | | | |
|---|---|---|---|---|---|---|---|---|---|---|---|---|---|---|---|
| | | -459.69 | 0 | 32 | 60 | 68 | 77 | 100 | 200 | 300 | 400 | 500 | 600 | 700 | 800 |
| n-Propylbenzene | $C_9H_{12}$ | 0 | 74.73 | 83.51 | 91.68 | 94.06 | 96.79 | 103.9 | 138.3 | 177.7 | 221.8 | 270.3 | 322.7 | 378.6 | 437.6 |
| Isopropylbenzene | " | 0 | 69.71 | 78.25 | 86.25 | 88.58 | 91.26 | 98.2 | 132.3 | 171.7 | 215.9 | 264.6 | 317.2 | 373.2 | 432.3 |
| 1-Methyl-2-ethylbenzene | " | 0 | 76.13 | 85.21 | 93.63 | 96.07 | 98.85 | 106.2 | 141.1 | 181.0 | 225.4 | 273.9 | 326.2 | 381.9 | 440.8 |
| 1-Methyl-3-ethylbenzene | " | 0 | 73.28 | 81.97 | 90.07 | 92.42 | 95.10 | 102.2 | 136.2 | 175.2 | 218.9 | 266.9 | 318.7 | 374.1 | 432.6 |
| 1-Methyl-4-ethylbenzene | " | 0 | 73.82 | 82.50 | 90.58 | 92.92 | 95.58 | 102.6 | 136.4 | 175.2 | 218.6 | 266.3 | 317.8 | 372.9 | 431.1 |
| 1,2,3-Trimethylbenzene | " | 0 | 75.99 | 85.14 | 93.67 | 96.00 | 98.63 | 105.6 | 139.2 | 177.7 | 220.6 | 267.6 | 318.4 | 372.6 | 430.1 |
| 1,2,4-Trimethylbenzene | " | 0 | 76.09 | 85.32 | 93.92 | 96.26 | 98.91 | 106.0 | 139.7 | 178.4 | 221.4 | 268.6 | 319.5 | 373.8 | 431.4 |
| 1,3,5-Trimethylbenzene | " | 0 | 72.70 | 81.56 | 89.84 | 92.11 | 94.68 | 101.55 | 134.56 | 172.62 | 215.3 | 262.2 | 312.9 | 367.2 | 424.7 |

Heat Content (Enthalpy), $(H^o - H^o_0)$, in BTU/lb

| Compound (gas) | Formula | Temperature in °F | | | | | | | | | | | | | |
|---|---|---|---|---|---|---|---|---|---|---|---|---|---|---|---|
| | | 900 | 1000 | 1100 | 1200 | 1300 | 1400 | 1500 | 1600 | 1700 | 1800 | 1900 | 2000 | 2100 | 2200 |
| n-Propylbenzene | $C_9H_{12}$ | 499.4 | 563.7 | 630.2 | 698.9 | 769.6 | 842. | 916. | 992. | 1069. | 1148. | 1228. | 1308. | 1390. | 1473. |
| Isopropylbenzene | " | 494.2 | 558.8 | 625.6 | 694.5 | 765.5 | 838. | 913. | 989. | 1066. | 1145. | 1224. | 1305. | 1387. | 1469. |
| 1-Methyl-2-ethylbenzene | " | 502.3 | 566.4 | 632.9 | 701.5 | 772.2 | 845. | 919. | 994. | 1071. | 1150. | 1229. | 1310. | 1391. | 1474. |
| 1-Methyl-3-ethylbenzene | " | 493.9 | 557.8 | 624.2 | 692.7 | 763.3 | 836. | 910. | 985. | 1062. | 1140. | 1220. | 1300. | 1382. | 1465. |
| 1-Methyl-4-ethylbenzene | " | 492.2 | 555.9 | 622.0 | 690.3 | 760.6 | 833. | 907. | 982. | 1059. | 1137. | 1216. | 1297. | 1378. | 1461. |
| 1,2,3-Trimethylbenzene | " | 490.4 | 553.4 | 618.7 | 686.4 | 756.0 | 828. | 901. | 976. | 1052. | 1130. | 1209. | 1289. | 1371. | 1453. |
| 1,2,4-Trimethylbenzene | " | 491.8 | 554.9 | 620.4 | 688.1 | 757.9 | 830. | 903. | 978. | 1055. | 1132. | 1212. | 1292. | 1373. | 1455. |
| 1,3,5-Trimethylbenzene | " | 485.1 | 548.3 | 613.8 | 681.6 | 751.5 | 823.3 | 896.8 | 971.9 | 1048. | 1126. | 1206. | 1286. | 1367. | 1449. |

## TABLE 13u-E — STYRENES, $C_8$ and $C_9$

HEAT CONTENT, $(H^o - H^o_0)$, FOR THE IDEAL GAS STATE, AT $-459.69^o$ to $2200^o$F

September 30, 1947

| Compound (gas) | Formula | Temperature in °F | | | | | | | | | | | | | |
|---|---|---|---|---|---|---|---|---|---|---|---|---|---|---|---|
| | | -459.69 | 0 | 32 | 60 | 68 | 77 | 100 | 200 | 300 | 400 | 500 | 600 | 700 | 800 |
| | | Heat Content, $(H^o-H^o_0)$, in BTU/lb | | | | | | | | | | | | | |
| Ethenylbenzene(Styrene;Vinylbenzene;Phenylethylene) | $C_8H_8$ | 0 | 66.30 | 74.12 | 81.43 | 83.60 | 86.11 | 92.61 | 124.19 | 160.54 | 201.19 | 245.59 | 293.35 | 344.22 | 397.85 |
| Isopropenylbenzene (α-Methylstyrene; 2-Phenyl-1-propene) | $C_9H_{10}$ | 0 | 70.5 | 79.0 | 86.8 | 89.1 | 92.1 | 98.6 | 131.4 | 168.8 | 210.4 | 256.2 | 305.6 | 358.1 | 413.3 |
| cis-1-Propenylbenzene (cis-β-Methylstyrene; cis-1-Phenyl-1-propene) | " | 0 | 70.5 | 79.0 | 86.8 | 89.1 | 92.1 | 98.6 | 131.4 | 168.8 | 210.4 | 256.2 | 305.6 | 358.1 | 413.3 |
| trans-1-Propenylbenzene (trans-β-Methylstyrene; trans-1-Phenyl-1-propene) | " | 0 | 68.9 | 77.4 | 85.4 | 87.7 | 90.3 | 97.3 | 130.6 | 168.4 | 210.3 | 256.1 | 305.6 | 358.5 | 414.3 |
| 1-Methyl-2-ethenylbenzene (o-Methylstyrene) | " | 0 | 70.5 | 79.0 | 86.8 | 89.1 | 92.1 | 98.6 | 131.4 | 168.8 | 210.4 | 256.2 | 305.6 | 358.1 | 413.3 |
| 1-Methyl-3-ethenylbenzene (m-Methylstyrene) | " | 0 | 70.5 | 79.0 | 86.8 | 89.1 | 92.1 | 98.6 | 131.4 | 168.8 | 210.4 | 256.2 | 305.6 | 358.1 | 413.3 |
| 1-Methyl-4-ethenylbenzene (p-Methylstyrene) | " | 0 | 70.5 | 79.0 | 86.8 | 89.1 | 92.1 | 98.6 | 131.4 | 168.8 | 210.4 | 256.2 | 305.6 | 358.1 | 413.3 |

| Compound (gas) | Formula | Temperature in °F | | | | | | | | | | | | | |
|---|---|---|---|---|---|---|---|---|---|---|---|---|---|---|---|
| | | 900 | 1000 | 1100 | 1200 | 1300 | 1400 | 1500 | 1600 | 1700 | 1800 | 1900 | 2000 | 2100 | 2200 |
| | | Heat Content, $(H^o-H^o_0)$, in BTU/lb | | | | | | | | | | | | | |
| Ethenylbenzene(Styrene;Vinylbenzene;Phenylethylene) | $C_8H_8$ | 453.87 | 512.13 | 572.41 | 634.55 | 698.39 | 763.80 | 830.6 | 898.6 | 967.7 | 1038.0 | 1131.3 | 1181.3 | 1254.3 | 1328.2 |
| Isopropenylbenzene (α-Methylstyrene; 2-Phenyl-1-propene) | $C_9H_{10}$ | 470.8 | 530.8 | 593.0 | 657.3 | 723.4 | 790.9 | 860. | 931. | 1003. | 1075. | 1149. | 1224. | 1300. | 1376. |
| cis-1-Propenylbenzene (cis-β-Methylstyrene; cis-1-Phenyl-1-propene) | " | 470.8 | 530.8 | 593.0 | 657.3 | 723.4 | 790.9 | 860. | 931. | 1003. | 1075. | 1149. | 1224. | 1300. | 1376. |
| trans-1-Propenylbenzene (trans-β-Methylstyrene; trans-1-Phenyl-1-propene) | " | 472.0 | 532.0 | 594.3 | 659.0 | 726.1 | 794.1 | 863. | 934. | 1006. | 1079. | 1153. | 1228. | 1305. | 1381. |
| 1-Methyl-2-ethenylbenzene (o-Methylstyrene) | " | 470.8 | 530.8 | 593.0 | 657.3 | 723.4 | 790.9 | 860. | 931. | 1003. | 1075. | 1149. | 1224. | 1300. | 1376. |
| 1-Methyl-3-ethenylbenzene (m-Methylstyrene) | " | 470.8 | 530.8 | 593.0 | 657.3 | 723.4 | 790.9 | 860. | 931. | 1003. | 1075. | 1149. | 1224. | 1300. | 1376. |
| 1-Methyl-4-ethenylbenzene (p-Methylstyrene) | " | 470.8 | 530.8 | 593.0 | 657.3 | 723.4 | 790.9 | 860. | 931. | 1003. | 1075. | 1149. | 1224. | 1300. | 1376. |

610

TABLE Ou-G — $O_2$, $H_2$, OH, $H_2O$, $N_2$, NO, C, CO, $CO_2$
HEAT CONTENT (ENTHALPY), $(H°-H°_0)$, AT -273.16° TO 1200°C
November 30, 1944; August 31, 1946; June 30, 1949

Heat Content (Enthalpy), $(H°-H°_0)$, in cal/g

| Compound | Formula | State | Temperature in °C | | | | | | | | | | | | | | |
|---|---|---|---|---|---|---|---|---|---|---|---|---|---|---|---|---|---|
| | | | -273.16 | 0 | 25 | 100 | 200 | 300 | 400 | 500 | 600 | 700 | 800 | 900 | 1000 | 1100 | 1200 |
| Oxygen | $O_2$ | gas | 0 | 59.236 | 64.681 | 81.244 | 103.919 | 127.319 | 151.453 | 176.249 | 201.56 | 227.31 | 253.43 | 279.85 | 306.57 | 333.50 | 360.67 |
| Hydrogen | $H_2$ | gas | 0 | 918.20 | 1003.87 | 1261.95 | 1608.02 | 1955.08 | 2302.97 | 2652.53 | 3004.3 | 3359.3 | 3718.4 | 4081.9 | 4450.4 | 4823.9 | 5202.3 |
| Hydroxyl | OH | gas | 0 | 113.30 | 123.84 | 155.20 | 196.71 | 238.20 | 279.70 | 321.42 | 363.57 | 406.25 | 449.49 | 493.36 | 537.92 | 583.21 | 629.05 |
| Water | $H_2O$ | gas | 0 | 120.26 | 131.42 | 165.10 | 210.93 | 258.07 | 306.94 | 357.49 | 409.54 | 463.15 | 518.20 | 574.64 | 632.49 | 691.75 | 752.24 |
| Nitrogen | $N_2$ | gas | 0 | 67.757 | 73.967 | 92.623 | 117.633 | 142.968 | 168.782 | 195.157 | 222.11 | 249.61 | 277.64 | 306.13 | 335.02 | 364.23 | 393.73 |
| Nitric Oxide | NO | gas | 0 | 67.185 | 73.120 | 90.924 | 114.93 | 139.35 | 164.36 | 189.96 | 216.16 | 242.89 | 270.23 | 297.55 | 325.43 | 353.60 | 282.12 |
| Carbon | C | solid graphite | 0 | 16.853 | 20.946 | 35.72 | 60.73 | 90.91 | 125.25 | 162.79 | 202.86 | 244.6 | 287.7 | 331.8 | 377.3 | 423.8 | 471.2 |
| Carbon Monoxide | CO | gas | 0 | 67.799 | 73.995 | 92.668 | 117.790 | 143.341 | 169.448 | 196.208 | 223.58 | 251.50 | 279.92 | 308.78 | 338.04 | 367.63 | 397.46 |
| Carbon Dioxide | $CO_2$ | gas | 0 | 45.863 | 50.854 | 66.645 | 89.510 | 114.091 | 140.082 | 167.256 | 195.41 | 224.37 | 254.03 | 284.31 | 315.09 | 346.28 | 377.84 |

TABLE 20u – G (PART 1) – NORMAL PARAFFINS, $C_1$ TO $C_{20}$

HEAT CONTENT (ENTHALPY), $(H°-H°_0)$, FOR THE IDEAL GAS STATE, AT $-273.16°$ TO $1200°C$

December 31, 1945; December 31, 1952

| Compound (gas) | Formula | Temperature in °C | | | | | | | | | | | | | | |
|---|---|---|---|---|---|---|---|---|---|---|---|---|---|---|---|---|
| | | -273.16 | 0 | 25 | 100 | 200 | 300 | 400 | 500 | 600 | 700 | 800 | 900 | 1000 | 1100 | 1200 |
| | | Heat Content (Enthalpy), $(H°-H°_0)$, in cal/g | | | | | | | | | | | | | | |
| Methane | $CH_4$ | 0 | 136.51 | 149.42 | 191.14 | 253.82 | 325.24 | 405.39 | 493.70 | 589.44 | 692.0 | 800.3 | 914.2 | 1033.2 | 1156.4 | 1282.8 |
| Ethane | $C_2H_6$ | 0 | 84.80 | 94.98 | 129.25 | 183.62 | 247.80 | 320.92 | 401.56 | 488.99 | 582.0 | 680.7 | 783.8 | 891.1 | 1002.0 | 1116.2 |
| Propane | $C_3H_8$ | 0 | 70.21 | 79.65 | 112.65 | 166.25 | 229.43 | .22 | 380.41 | 465.94 | 556.9 | 652.7 | 753.0 | 856.8 | 963.7 | 1073.4 |
| n-Butane | $C_4H_{10}$ | 0 | 70.11 | 79.92 | 112.97 | 166.31 | 229.06 | 300.05 | 378.22 | 462.51 | 552.20 | 646.44 | 744.90 | 846.88 | 951.97 | 1059.46 |
| n-Pentane | $C_5H_{12}$ | 0 | 68.28 | 78.02 | 110.83 | 163.89 | 226.19 | 296.55 | 374.09 | 457.58 | 546.30 | 639.50 | 736.86 | 837.56 | 941.21 | 1047.20 |
| n-Hexane | $C_6H_{14}$ | 0 | 67.42 | 76.84 | 109.57 | 162.44 | 224.41 | 294.42 | 371.43 | 454.44 | 542.47 | 635.04 | 731.60 | 831.41 | 934.11 | 1039.20 |
| n-Heptane | $C_7H_{16}$ | 0 | 66.59 | 76.00 | 108.63 | 161.34 | 223.11 | 292.83 | 369.57 | 452.19 | 539.8 | 631.8 | 727.8 | 827.0 | 929.0 | 1033.4 |
| n-Octane | $C_8H_{18}$ | 0 | 65.95 | 75.36 | 107.93 | 160.51 | 222.13 | 291.63 | 368.11 | 450.48 | 537.7 | 629.3 | 724.9 | 823.6 | 925.2 | 1029.0 |
| n-Nonane | $C_9H_{20}$ | 0 | 65.48 | 74.86 | 107.40 | 159.91 | 221.38 | 290.68 | 367.02 | 449.11 | 536.1 | 627.4 | 722.6 | 821.0 | 922.2 | 1025.5 |
| n-Decane | $C_{10}H_{22}$ | 0 | 65.08 | 74.46 | 106.95 | 159.38 | 220.76 | 289.97 | 366.11 | 448.04 | 534.8 | 625.9 | 720.8 | 818.9 | 919.6 | 1022.8 |
| n-Undecane | $C_{11}H_{24}$ | 0 | 64.80 | 74.13 | 106.58 | 158.97 | 220.26 | 289.35 | 365.36 | 447.12 | 533.7 | 624.6 | 719.3 | 817.2 | 917.7 | 1020.5 |
| n-Dodecane | $C_{12}H_{26}$ | 0 | 64.50 | 73.85 | 106.29 | 158.62 | 219.84 | 288.83 | 364.75 | 446.40 | 532.9 | 623.5 | 718.1 | 815.7 | 916.0 | 1018.6 |
| n-Tridecane | $C_{13}H_{28}$ | 0 | 64.27 | 73.62 | 106.03 | 158.32 | 219.46 | 288.38 | 364.22 | 445.78 | 532.1 | 622.6 | 717.0 | 814.5 | 914.6 | 1017.0 |
| n-Tetradecane | $C_{14}H_{30}$ | 0 | 64.10 | 73.42 | 105.80 | 158.07 | 219.16 | 288.00 | 363.76 | 445.22 | 531.4 | 621.8 | 716.1 | 813.5 | 913.4 | 1015.6 |
| n-Pentadecane | $C_{15}H_{32}$ | 0 | 63.92 | 73.25 | 105.60 | 157.84 | 218.89 | 287.70 | 363.36 | 444.75 | 530.8 | 621.2 | 715.3 | 812.5 | 912.3 | 1014.4 |
| n-Hexadecane | $C_{16}H_{34}$ | 0 | 63.78 | 73.09 | 105.45 | 157.66 | 218.67 | 287.42 | 363.04 | 444.33 | 530.4 | 620.6 | 714.7 | 811.7 | 911.4 | 1013.3 |
| n-Heptadecane | $C_{17}H_{36}$ | 0 | 63.65 | 72.96 | 105.30 | 157.48 | 218.46 | 287.16 | 362.73 | 443.98 | 529.9 | 620.1 | 714.0 | 811.0 | 910.6 | 1012.5 |
| n-Octadecane | $C_{18}H_{38}$ | 0 | 63.52 | 72.84 | 105.16 | 157.32 | 218.28 | 286.93 | 362.45 | 443.66 | 529.5 | 619.6 | 713.5 | 810.4 | 909.9 | 1011.6 |
| n-Nonadecane | $C_{19}H_{40}$ | 0 | 63.43 | 72.73 | 105.05 | 157.20 | 218.12 | 286.73 | 362.22 | 443.36 | 529.2 | 619.2 | 713.0 | 809.9 | 909.2 | 1010.9 |
| n-Eicosane | $C_{20}H_{42}$ | 0 | 63.33 | 72.63 | 104.94 | 157.07 | 217.97 | 286.56 | 362.00 | 443.11 | 528.9 | 618.8 | 712.6 | 809.3 | 908.6 | 1010.2 |

TABLE 1u-G – PARAFFINS, $C_1$ TO $C_5$

HEAT CONTENT (ENTHALPY), $(H^o - H^o_0)$, FOR THE IDEAL GAS STATE, AT -273.16° TO 1200°C

November 30, 1944; February 28, 1949; December 31, 1952

| Compound (gas) | Formula | Temperature in °C — Heat Content (Enthalpy), $(H^o - H^o_0)$, in cal/g | | | | | | | | | | | | | | |
|---|---|---|---|---|---|---|---|---|---|---|---|---|---|---|---|---|
| | | -273.16 | -200 | -150 | -100 | -50 | 0 | 25 | 50 | 100 | 150 | 200 | 300 | 400 | 500 | 600 |
| Methane | $CH_4$ | 0 | 36.25 | 61.03 | 85.81 | 110.74 | 136.26 | 149.42 | 162.94 | 191.21 | 221.42 | 253.82 | 325.24 | 405.39 | 493.70 | 589.44 |
| Ethane | $C_2H_6$ | 0 | | 33.70 | 49.13 | 66.05 | 84.80 | 94.98 | 105.81 | 129.28 | 155.21 | 183.62 | 247.80 | 320.92 | 401.56 | 488.99 |
| Propane | $C_3H_8$ | 0 | | 24.59 | 37.67 | 52.74 | 70.09 | 79.65 | 90.02 | 112.72 | 138.15 | 166.25 | 229.43 | 301.22 | 380.41 | 465.94 |
| n-Butane | $C_4H_{10}$ | 0 | | | | 52.58 | 70.18 | 79.92 | 90.33 | 112.97 | 138.92 | 166.31 | 229.06 | 300.05 | 378.22 | 462.51 |
| 2-Methylpropane (Isobutane) | " | 0 | | | | 46.70 | 63.91 | 73.57 | 83.85 | 106.52 | 132.00 | 160.21 | 223.62 | 295.13 | 373.73 | 458.45 |
| n-Pentane | $C_5H_{12}$ | 0 | | | | 50.85 | 68.33 | 78.02 | 89.34 | 110.83 | 137.54 | 163.89 | 226.19 | 296.55 | 374.09 | 479.58 |
| 2-Methylbutane (Isopentane) | " | 0 | | | | 46.93 | 63.87 | 73.39 | 83.56 | 105.94 | 131.16 | 159.00 | 221.54 | 292.53 | 370.32 | 454.51 |
| 2,2-Dimethylpropane (Neopentane) | " | 0 | | | | 42.66 | 59.94 | 69.72 | 80.17 | 103.27 | 129.18 | 157.83 | 222.28 | 294.89 | 374.55 | 459.96 |

| Compound (gas) | Formula | Temperature in °C — Heat Content (Enthalpy), $(H^o - H^o_0)$, in cal/g | | | | | |
|---|---|---|---|---|---|---|---|
| | | 700 | 800 | 900 | 1000 | 1100 | 1200 |
| Methane | $CH_4$ | 692.0 | 800.3 | 914.2 | 1033.2 | 1156.4 | 1282.8 |
| Ethane | $C_2H_6$ | 582.0 | 680.7 | 783.8 | 891.1 | 1002.0 | 1116.2 |
| Propane | $C_3H_8$ | 556.9 | 652.7 | 753.0 | 856.8 | 963.7 | 1073.4 |
| n-Butane | $C_4H_{10}$ | 552.20 | 646.44 | 744.90 | 846.88 | 951.97 | 1059.46 |
| 2-Methylpropane | " | 548.2 | 642.7 | 741.6 | 843.6 | 948.4 | 1055.7 |
| n-Pentane | $C_5H_{12}$ | 546.30 | 639.50 | 736.86 | 837.56 | 941.21 | 1047.20 |
| 2-Methylbutane (Isopentane) | " | 543.7 | 637.7 | 735.8 | 837.1 | 941.6 | 1048.6 |
| 2,2-Dimethylpropane (Neopentane) | " | 550.3 | 645.0 | 743.7 | 845.9 | 950.8 | 1057.9 |

TABLE 2u-G (PART 1) – PARAFFINS, C$_6$

HEAT CONTENT (ENTHALPY), $(H^o-H^o_0)$, FOR THE IDEAL GAS STATE, AT -273.16° TO 1200°C

November 30, 1944; November 30, 1946; December 31, 1952

Heat Content (Enthalpy), $(H^o-H^o_0)$, in cal/g

| Compound (gas) | Formula | Temperature in °C | | | | | | | | | | | | | | |
|---|---|---|---|---|---|---|---|---|---|---|---|---|---|---|---|---|
| | | -273.16 | 0 | 25 | 100 | 200 | 300 | 400 | 500 | 600 | 700 | 800 | 900 | 1000 | 1100 | 1200 |
| n-Hexane | C$_6$H$_{14}$ | 0 | 67.42 | 76.84 | 109.57 | 162.44 | 224.41 | 294.42 | 371.43 | 454.44 | 542.47 | 635.04 | 731.60 | 831.41 | 934.11 | 1039.20 |
| 2-Methylpentane | " | 0 | 61.56 | 70.76 | 103.57 | 157.40 | 219.97 | 290.85 | 369.2 | 451.8 | 540.7 | | | | | |
| 3-Methylpentane | " | 0 | 67.45 | 76.85 | 109.57 | 162.44 | 224.31 | 294.34 | 371.1 | 454.1 | 542.1 | | | | | |
| 2,2-Dimethylbutane | " | 0 | 59.42 | 68.61 | 101.27 | 155.06 | 217.84 | 288.44 | 366.9 | 450.0 | 538.8 | | | | | |
| 2,3-Dimethylbutane | " | 0 | 59.39 | 68.65 | 100.98 | 153.70 | 215.93 | 286.33 | 363.8 | 446.8 | 535.2 | | | | | |

TABLE 2u-G (PART 2) – PARAFFINS, $C_7$

HEAT CONTENT (ENTHALPY), $(H^0-H^0_0)$, FOR THE IDEAL GAS STATE, AT -273.16° TO 1200°C

November 30, 1944; December 31, 1952

| Compound (aas) | Formula | Temperature in °C | | | | | | | | | | | | | | |
| --- | --- | --- | --- | --- | --- | --- | --- | --- | --- | --- | --- | --- | --- | --- | --- | --- |
| | | -273.16 | 0 | 25 | 100 | 200 | 300 | 400 | 500 | 600 | 700 | 800 | 900 | 1000 | 1100 | 1200 |
| | | Heat Content (Enthalpy), $(H^0-H^0_0)$, in cal/a | | | | | | | | | | | | | | |
| n-Heptane | $C_7H_{16}$ | 0 | 66.59 | 76.00 | 108.63 | 161.34 | 223.11 | 292.83 | 369.57 | 452.19 | 539.8 | 631.8 | 727.8 | 827.0 | 929.0 | 1033.4 |
| 2-Methylhexane | " | 0 | 61.23 | 71.09 | 104.67 | 158.62 | 222.06 | 293.54 | 371.4 | 454.1 | 541.5 | | | | | |
| 3-Methylhexane | " | 0 | 59.62 | 69.39 | 102.62 | 156.05 | 219.14 | 290.37 | 368.4 | 451.1 | 538.5 | | | | | |
| 3-Ethylpentane | " | 0 | 57.43 | 67.02 | 99.77 | 152.69 | 215.19 | 285.98 | 363.5 | 446.1 | 533.0 | | | | | |
| 2,2-Dimethylpentane | " | 0 | 56.84 | 66.51 | 99.79 | 153.91 | 217.80 | 290.15 | 369.1 | 452.8 | 541.3 | | | | | |
| 2,3-Dimethylpentane | " | 0 | 56.44 | 66.09 | 99.12 | 152.68 | 216.05 | 287.63 | 365.4 | 448.9 | 536.2 | | | | | |
| 2,4-Dimethylpentane | " | 0 | 56.51 | 66.21 | 99.56 | 153.79 | 217.78 | 290.16 | 369.1 | 452.9 | 540.7 | | | | | |
| 3,3-Dimethylpentane | " | 0 | 57.10 | 66.90 | 100.36 | 154.57 | 218.80 | 291.34 | 370.1 | 454.6 | 543.5 | | | | | |
| 2,2,3-Trimethylbutane | " | 0 | 57.48 | 66.90 | 99.54 | 152.72 | 215.75 | 286.91 | 364.57 | 448.18 | 537.2 | 630.2 | 727.0 | 825.2 | 929.0 | 1034.4 |

TABLE 3u-G - PARAFFINS, $C_8$

HEAT CONTENT (ENTHALPY), $(H^o-H^o_0)$, FOR THE IDEAL GAS STATE, AT -273.16° TO 1200°C

December 31, 1944; December 31, 1952

| Compound (gas) | Formula | Temperature in °C |  |  |  |  |  |  |  |  |  |  |  |  |  |  |
|---|---|---|---|---|---|---|---|---|---|---|---|---|---|---|---|---|
|  |  | -273.16 | 0 | 25 | 100 | 200 | 300 | 400 | 500 | 600 | 700 | 800 | 900 | 1000 | 1100 | 1200 |
|  |  | Heat Content (Enthalpy), $(H^o-H^o_0)$, in cal/g |  |  |  |  |  |  |  |  |  |  |  |  |  |  |
| n-Octane | $C_8H_{18}$ | 0 | 65.95 | 75.36 | 107.93 | 160.51 | 222.13 | 291.63 | 368.11 | 450.48 | 537.7 | 629.3 | 724.9 | 823.6 | 925.2 | 1029.0 |
| 2-Methylheptane | " | 0 | 61.45 | 71.32 | 104.96 | 158.89 | 222.2 | 293.5 | 370.7 | 452.5 | 540.0 |  |  |  |  |  |
| 3-Methylheptane | " | 0 | 60.70 | 70.45 | 103.87 | 157.68 | 221.0 | 292.3 | 369.0 | 451.4 | 539.4 |  |  |  |  |  |
| 4-Methylheptane | " | 0 | 60.09 | 69.75 | 103.02 | 156.75 | 219.8 | 290.7 | 367.2 | 449.6 | 537.6 |  |  |  |  |  |
| 3-Ethylhexane | " | 0 | 56.74 | 65.98 | 98.24 | 150.95 | 213.1 | 283.2 | 360.1 | 442.1 | 529.0 |  |  |  |  |  |
| 2,2-Dimethylhexane | " | 0 | 58.11 | 67.81 | 101.26 | 155.39 | 218.9 | 290.6 | 369.2 | 453.0 | 541.2 |  |  |  |  |  |
| 2,3-Dimethylhexane | " | 0 | 59.24 | 68.79 | 102.47 | 157.93 | 223.0 | 295.6 | 373.9 | 456.1 | 543.5 |  |  |  |  |  |
| 2,4-Dimethylhexane | " | 0 | 56.16 | 65.89 | 99.05 | 152.56 | 215.8 | 287.3 | 364.5 | 447.1 | 534.5 |  |  |  |  |  |
| 2,5-Dimethylhexane | " | 0 | 57.16 | 66.77 | 100.05 | 154.21 | 218.0 | 289.7 | 367.1 | 449.0 | 536.5 |  |  |  |  |  |
| 3,3-Dimethylhexane | " | 0 | 56.08 | 65.81 | 99.07 | 152.90 | 216.6 | 288.7 | 367.5 | 451.3 | 539.4 |  |  |  |  |  |
| 3,4-Dimethylhexane a | " | 0 | 59.87 | 69.35 | 102.33 | 155.76 | 218.6 | 289.2 | 366.1 | 449.5 | 537.3 |  |  |  |  |  |
| 2-Methyl-3-ethylpentane | " | 0 | 57.74 | 67.47 | 101.09 | 155.56 | 219.4 | 291.0 | 368.1 | 449.8 | 537.9 |  |  |  |  |  |
| 3-Methyl-3-ethylpentane | " | 0 | 55.87 | 65.89 | 99.84 | 154.23 | 217.9 | 289.5 | 367.6 | 451.8 | 541.5 |  |  |  |  |  |
| 2,2,3-Trimethylpentane | " | 0 | 55.02 | 64.65 | 98.05 | 152.53 | 216.7 | 288.9 | 366.9 | 450.3 | 539.1 |  |  |  |  |  |
| 2,2,4-Trimethylpentane | " | 0 | 55.02 | 64.65 | 98.05 | 152.53 | 216.7 | 288.9 | 366.9 | 450.3 | 539.1 |  |  |  |  |  |
| 2,3,3-Trimethylpentane | " | 0 | 56.09 | 65.70 | 99.20 | 154.01 | 218.5 | 290.7 | 368.7 | 451.3 | 540.8 |  |  |  |  |  |
| 2,3,4-Trimethylpentane | " | 0 | 55.17 | 64.57 | 97.92 | 153.10 | 217.9 | 290.2 | 367.2 | 449.6 | 538.6 |  |  |  |  |  |
| 2,2,3,3-Tetramethylbutane | " | 0 | 55.37 | 65.50 | 99.09 | 154.02 | 219.0 | 292.0 | 371.6 | 456.9 | 546.9 |  |  |  |  |  |

a See footnotes a and b of Table 3r.

TABLE 22u—G (PART 1) — NORMAL ALKYL CYCLOPENTANES, $C_5$ TO $C_{21}$

HEAT CONTENT (ENTHALPY), $(H°-H°_0)$, FOR THE IDEAL GAS STATE, AT −273.16° TO 1200°C

October 31, 1947; December 31, 1952

| Compound (gas) | Formula | Temperature in °C | | | | | | | | | | | | | | |
|---|---|---|---|---|---|---|---|---|---|---|---|---|---|---|---|---|
| | | −273.16 | 0 | 25 | 100 | 200 | 300 | 400 | 500 | 600 | 700 | 800 | 900 | 1000 | 1100 | 1200 |
| | | Heat Content (Enthalpy), $(H°-H°_0)$, in cal/g | | | | | | | | | | | | | | |
| Cyclopentane | $C_5H_{10}$ | 0 | 44.71 | 51.32 | 75.84 | 118.70 | 172.12 | 234.4 | 304.1 | 380.2 | 461.7 | 548.0 | 638.2 | 731.9 | 828.6 | 927.9 |
| Methylcyclopentane | $C_6H_{12}$ | 0 | 49.46 | 56.73 | 83.37 | 128.80 | 184.39 | 248.5 | 319.7 | 397.0 | 479.5 | 566.5 | 657.6 | 751.8 | 848.9 | 948.5 |
| Ethylcyclopentane | $C_7H_{14}$ | 0 | 51.49 | 59.00 | 86.30 | 132.39 | 188.45 | 253.2 | 324.9 | 402.9 | 486.0 | 573.7 | 665.4 | 760.1 | 858.0 | 958.6 |
| n-Propylcyclopentane | $C_8H_{16}$ | 0 | 52.72 | 60.48 | 88.36 | 135.17 | 191.79 | 256.9 | 329.0 | 407.3 | 490.6 | 578.4 | 670.3 | 765.1 | 862.9 | 963.5 |
| n-Butylcyclopentane | $C_9H_{18}$ | 0 | 53.72 | 61.62 | 90.00 | 137.36 | 194.39 | 259.8 | 332.2 | 410.7 | 494.2 | 582.1 | 674.0 | 769.0 | 866.9 | 967.3 |
| n-Pentylcyclopentane | $C_{10}H_{20}$ | 0 | 54.48 | 62.54 | 91.29 | 139.08 | 196.46 | 262.2 | 334.8 | 413.5 | 497.1 | 585.1 | 677.0 | 772.0 | 869.8 | 970.3 |
| n-Hexylcyclopentane | $C_{11}H_{22}$ | 0 | 55.17 | 63.29 | 92.34 | 140.53 | 198.18 | 264.1 | 336.9 | 415.7 | 499.4 | 587.5 | 679.5 | 774.5 | 872.4 | 972.8 |
| n-Heptylcyclopentane | $C_{12}H_{24}$ | 0 | 55.86 | 63.92 | 93.23 | 141.70 | 199.56 | 265.7 | 338.6 | 417.6 | 501.4 | 589.5 | 681.6 | 776.6 | 874.5 | 974.9 |
| n-Octylcyclopentane | $C_{13}H_{26}$ | 0 | 56.11 | 64.44 | 93.97 | 142.70 | 200.75 | 267.0 | 340.1 | 419.2 | 503.0 | 591.2 | 683.5 | 778.4 | 876.2 | 976.6 |
| n-Nonylcyclopentane | $C_{14}H_{28}$ | 0 | 56.53 | 64.89 | 94.60 | 143.56 | 201.79 | 268.1 | 341.4 | 420.5 | 504.4 | 592.7 | 684.8 | 779.9 | 877.7 | 978.1 |
| n-Decylcyclopentane | $C_{15}H_{30}$ | 0 | 56.85 | 65.29 | 95.15 | 144.30 | 202.68 | 269.2 | 342.5 | 421.7 | 505.7 | 594.0 | 686.1 | 781.2 | 879.0 | 979.4 |
| n-Undecylcyclopentane | $C_{16}H_{32}$ | 0 | 57.15 | 65.63 | 95.65 | 144.96 | 203.47 | 270.0 | 343.4 | 422.7 | 506.7 | 595.1 | 687.2 | 782.3 | 880.2 | 980.5 |
| n-Dodecylcyclopentane | $C_{17}H_{34}$ | 0 | 57.40 | 65.94 | 96.07 | 145.53 | 204.15 | 270.8 | 344.3 | 423.6 | 507.7 | 596.1 | 688.3 | 783.4 | 881.2 | 981.5 |
| n-Tridecylcyclopentane | $C_{18}H_{36}$ | 0 | 57.63 | 66.21 | 96.45 | 146.03 | 204.76 | 271.5 | 345.0 | 424.4 | 508.5 | 596.9 | 689.1 | 784.3 | 882.1 | 982.4 |
| n-Tetradecylcyclopentane | $C_{19}H_{38}$ | 0 | 57.84 | 66.45 | 96.80 | 146.50 | 205.31 | 272.1 | 345.7 | 425.1 | 509.3 | 597.7 | 689.9 | 785.1 | 882.9 | 983.2 |
| n-Pentadecylcyclopentane | $C_{20}H_{40}$ | 0 | 58.02 | 66.66 | 97.10 | 146.91 | 205.80 | 272.7 | 346.3 | 425.8 | 510.0 | 598.4 | 690.6 | 785.8 | 883.6 | 983.9 |
| n-Hexadecylcyclopentane | $C_{21}H_{42}$ | 0 | 58.20 | 66.86 | 97.37 | 147.29 | 206.25 | 273.1 | 346.9 | 426.4 | 510.6 | 599.0 | 691.3 | 786.5 | 884.3 | 984.6 |

TABLE 6u-G — ALKYL CYCLOPENTANES, $C_5$ TO $C_7$

HEAT CONTENT (ENTHALPY), $(H^o-H^o_0)$, FOR THE IDEAL GAS STATE, AT $-273.16^o$ TO $1200^oC$

April 30, 1949; December 31. 1952

| Compound (gas) | Formula | Temperature in °C | | | | | | | | | | | | | | |
|---|---|---|---|---|---|---|---|---|---|---|---|---|---|---|---|---|
| | | -273.16 | 0 | 25 | 100 | 200 | 300 | 400 | 500 | 600 | 700 | 800 | 900 | 1000 | 1100 | 1200 |
| | | Heat Content (Enthalpy), $(H^o-H^o_0)$, in cal/a | | | | | | | | | | | | | | |
| Cyclopentane | $C_5H_{10}$ | 0 | 44.71 | 51.32 | 75.84 | 118.70 | 172.12 | 234.4 | 304.1 | 380.2 | 461.7 | 548.0 | 638.2 | 731.9 | 828.6 | 927.9 |
| Methylcyclopentane | $C_6H_{12}$ | 0 | 49.46 | 56.73 | 83.37 | 128.80 | 184.39 | 248.5 | 319.7 | 397.0 | 479.5 | 566.5 | 657.6 | 751.8 | 848.9 | 948.5 |
| Ethylcyclopentane | $C_7H_{14}$ | 0 | 51.49 | 59.00 | 86.30 | 132.39 | 188.45 | 253.2 | 324.9 | 402.9 | 486.0 | 573.7 | 665.4 | 760.1 | 858.0 | 958.6 |
| 1,1-Dimethylcyclopentane | " | 0 | 49.17 | 56.67 | 85.28 | 131.2 | 188.6 | 254. | 327. | 406. | 490. | 578. | 670. | 765. | 863. | 964. |
| 1,cis-2-Dimethylcyclopentane | " | 0 | 49.82 | 57.27 | 84.76 | 131.8 | 189.1 | 255. | 327. | 406. | 490. | 578. | 670. | 765. | 863. | 963. |
| 1,trans-2-Dimethylcyclopentane | " | 0 | 50.16 | 57.52 | 85.06 | 132.2 | 189.5 | 255. | 327. | 406. | 490. | 577. | 669. | 764. | 862. | 962. |
| 1,cis-3-Dimethylcyclopentane | " | 0 | 50.16 | 57.52 | 85.06 | 132.2 | 189.5 | 255. | 327. | 406. | 490. | 577. | 669. | 764. | 862. | 962. |
| 1,trans-3-Dimethylcyclopentane | " | 0 | 50.16 | 57.52 | 85.06 | 132.2 | 189.5 | 255. | 327. | 406. | 490. | 577. | 669. | 764. | 862. | 962. |

TABLE 23u-G (PART 1).- NORMAL ALKYL CYCLOHEXANES, C$_6$ TO C$_{22}$

HEAT CONTENT (ENTHALPY), $(H°-H°_0)$, FOR THE IDEAL GAS STATE, AT -273.16° TO 1200°C

November 30, 1947; December 31, 1952

| Compound (gas) | Formula | Temperature in °C | | | | | | | | | | | | | | |
|---|---|---|---|---|---|---|---|---|---|---|---|---|---|---|---|---|
| | | -273.16 | 0 | 25 | 100 | 200 | 300 | 400 | 500 | 600 | 700 | 800 | 900 | 1000 | 1100 | 1200 |
| | | Heat Content (Enthalpy), $(H°-H°_0)$, in cal/g | | | | | | | | | | | | | | |
| Cyclohexane | C$_6$H$_{12}$ | 0 | 43.30 | 50.35 | 76.36 | 121.66 | 178.08 | 244.05 | 318.0 | 398.7 | 485.1 | 576.1 | 671.1 | 770.1 | 870.9 | 974.7 |
| Methylcyclohexane | C$_7$H$_{14}$ | 0 | 45.69 | 53.30 | 81.34 | 129.20 | 187.62 | 255.20 | 330.4 | 411.9 | 498.7 | 589.9 | 685.2 | 783.5 | 884.9 | 988.2 |
| Ethylcyclohexane | C$_8$H$_{16}$ | 0 | 46.33 | 54.34 | 83.24 | 131.77 | 190.6 | 258.6 | 334.3 | 416. | 503. | 594. | 688. | 786. | 887. | 990. |
| n-Propylcyclohexane | C$_9$H$_{18}$ | 0 | 46.70 | 54.65 | 84.08 | 133.8 | 193.1 | 261.5 | 336.8 | 418. | 505. | 596. | 690. | 788. | 889. | 992. |
| n-Butylcyclohexane | C$_{10}$H$_{20}$ | 0 | 48.14 | 56.98 | 86.05 | 136.0 | 195.2 | 263.7 | 338.8 | 420. | 507. | 597. | 691. | 789. | 890. | 993. |
| n-Pentylcyclohexane | C$_{11}$H$_{22}$ | 0 | 49.38 | 57.59 | 87.47 | 137.5 | 197.2 | 265.3 | 341.6 | 422. | 508. | 598. | 693. | 790. | 890. | 993. |
| n-Hexylcyclohexane | C$_{12}$H$_{24}$ | 0 | 50.35 | 58.69 | 88.83 | 139.0 | 198.6 | 266.9 | 342.0 | 423. | 510. | 599. | 693. | 791. | 891. | 993. |
| n-Heptylcyclohexane | C$_{13}$H$_{26}$ | 0 | 51.38 | 59.62 | 89.76 | 140.2 | 200.0 | 268.0 | 343.3 | 424. | 510. | 600. | 694. | 791. | 891. | 993. |
| n-Octylcyclohexane | C$_{14}$H$_{28}$ | 0 | 52.07 | 60.42 | 90.76 | 141.3 | 201.0 | 269.2 | 344.2 | 425. | 512. | 601. | 695. | 792. | 892. | 994. |
| n-Nonylcyclohexane | C$_{15}$H$_{30}$ | 0 | 52.54 | 61.11 | 91.68 | 142.1 | 201.8 | 270.2 | 345.0 | 426. | 512. | 602. | 696. | 793. | 892. | 994. |
| n-Decylcyclohexane | C$_{16}$H$_{32}$ | 0 | 53.24 | 61.71 | 92.26 | 142.9 | 202.8 | 270.3 | 346.0 | 427. | 513. | 603. | 696. | 793. | 893. | 994. |
| n-Undecylcyclohexane | C$_{17}$H$_{34}$ | 0 | 53.70 | 62.25 | 92.93 | 143.7 | 203.5 | 271.7 | 346.6 | 428. | 514. | 603. | 697. | 793. | 893. | 994. |
| n-Dodecylcyclohexane | C$_{18}$H$_{36}$ | 0 | 54.15 | 62.72 | 93.42 | 144.1 | 204.2 | 272.2 | 347.3 | 428. | 514. | 604. | 697. | 794. | 893. | 994. |
| n-Tridecylcyclohexane | C$_{19}$H$_{38}$ | 0 | 54.52 | 63.15 | 93.96 | 144.8 | 204.7 | 272.8 | 347.8 | 429. | 514. | 604. | 697. | 794. | 893. | 995. |
| n-Tetradecylcyclohexane | C$_{20}$H$_{40}$ | 0 | 54.84 | 63.53 | 94.45 | 145.3 | 205.2 | 273.4 | 348.2 | 429. | 515. | 604. | 698. | 794. | 894. | 995. |
| n-Pentadecylcyclohexane | C$_{21}$H$_{42}$ | 0 | 55.17 | 63.88 | 94.80 | 145.6 | 205.7 | 273.8 | 348.7 | 430. | 515. | 604. | 698. | 795. | 894. | 995. |
| n-Hexadecylcyclohexane | C$_{22}$H$_{44}$ | 0 | 55.44 | 64.19 | 95.21 | 146.1 | 206.1 | 274.2 | 349.1 | 430. | 515. | 605. | 698. | 795. | 894. | 995. |

TABLE 7u-G – ALKYL CYCLOHEXANES, $C_6$ TO $C_8$

HEAT CONTENT (ENTHALPY), $(H°-H°_0)$, FOR THE IDEAL GAS STATE, AT $-273.16°$ TO $1200°C$

November 30, 1947

| Compound (aas) | Formula | Temperature in °C | | | | | | | | | | | | | | |
|---|---|---|---|---|---|---|---|---|---|---|---|---|---|---|---|---|
| | | Heat Content (Enthalpy), $(H°-H°_0)$, in cal/a | | | | | | | | | | | | | | |
| | | -273.16 | 0 | 25 | 100 | 200 | 300 | 400 | 500 | 600 | 700 | 800 | 900 | 1000 | 1100 | 1200 |
| Cyclohexane | $C_6H_{12}$ | 0 | 43.30 | 50.35 | 76.36 | 121.66 | 178.08 | 244.05 | 318.0 | 398.7 | 485.1 | 576.1 | 671.1 | 770.1 | 870.9 | 974.7 |
| Methylcyclohexane | $C_7H_{14}$ | 0 | 45.69 | 53.30 | 81.34 | 129.20 | 187.62 | 255.20 | 330.4 | 411.9 | 498.7 | 589.9 | 685.2 | 783.5 | 884.9 | 988.2 |
| Ethylcyclohexane | $C_8H_{16}$ | 0 | 46.33 | 54.34 | 83.24 | 131.77 | 190.6 | 258.6 | 334.3 | 416. | 503. | 594. | 688. | 786. | 887. | 990. |
| 1,1-Dimethylcyclohexane | " | 0 | 44.60 | 52.40 | 80.63 | 128.36 | 186.9 | 254.8 | 330.7 | 413. | 501. | 592. | 688. | 787. | 889. | 993. |
| 1,cis-2-Dimethylcyclohexane | " | 0 | 45.74 | 53.57 | 81.97 | 130.04 | 189.0 | 256.8 | 332.3 | 414. | 501. | 592. | 687. | 785. | 887. | 990. |
| 1,trans-2-Dimethylcyclohexane | " | 0 | 46.51 | 54.31 | 83.17 | 132.10 | 191.1 | 259.2 | 335.0 | 417. | 504. | 596. | 692. | 790. | 891. | 994. |
| 1,cis-3-Dimethylcyclohexane | " | 0 | 46.19 | 54.07 | 82.63 | 130.88 | 190.0 | 258.0 | 333.6 | 416. | 503. | 594. | 690. | 790. | 891. | 994. |
| 1,trans-3-Dimethylcyclohexane | " | 0 | 46.26 | 54.07 | 82.61 | 130.91 | 189.6 | 256.9 | 332.3 | 414. | 500. | 591. | 686. | 734. | 885. | 988. |
| 1,cis-4-Dimethylcyclohexane | " | 0 | 46.26 | 54.07 | 82.61 | 130.91 | 189.6 | 256.9 | 332.3 | 414. | 500. | 591. | 686. | 784. | 885. | 988. |
| 1,trans-4-Dimethylcyclohexane | " | 0 | 46.14 | 54.15 | 82.94 | 131.31 | 190.5 | 259.1 | 335.1 | 417. | 504. | 596. | 692. | 790. | 891. | 994. |

TABLE 24u-G (PART 1) — NORMAL MONOOLEFINS (1-ALKENES), C2 TO C20
HEAT CONTENT (ENTHALPY), $(H^\circ-H^\circ_0)$, FOR THE IDEAL GAS STATE, AT −273.16° TO 1200°C
March 31, 1946; December 31, 1952

Heat Content (Enthalpy), $(H^\circ-H^\circ_0)$, in cal/g

| Compound (aas) | Formula | Temperature in °C | | | | | | | | | | | | | | |
|---|---|---|---|---|---|---|---|---|---|---|---|---|---|---|---|---|
| | | −273.16 | 0 | 25 | 100 | 200 | 300 | 400 | 500 | 600 | 700 | 800 | 900 | 1000 | 1100 | 1200 |
| Ethene (Ethylene) | C2H4 | 0 | 81.11 | 90.01 | 120.2 | 168.2 | 223.9 | 286.2 | 354.4 | 427.4 | 504.7 | 586.1 | 670.8 | 758.5 | 848.5 | 940.8 |
| Propene (Propylene) | C3H6 | 0 | 68.14 | 76.93 | 166.7 | 154.1 | 209.4 | 272.0 | 340.7 | 414.7 | 493.6 | 576.3 | 662.6 | 752.0 | 844.0 | 938.4 |
| 1-Butene | C4H8 | 0 | 64.61 | 73.29 | 103.4 | 152.1 | 209.0 | 273.0 | 343.3 | 419.0 | 499.1 | 583.5 | 671.2 | 762.1 | 855.6 | 951.4 |
| 1-Pentene | C5H10 | 0 | 65.86 | 74.80 | 105.5 | 155.0 | 212.8 | 277.7 | 348.8 | 425.5 | 506.8 | 592.1 | 680.9 | 772.8 | 867.4 | 964.3 |
| 1-Hexene | C6H12 | 0 | 65.05 | 74.01 | 104.9 | 154.8 | 213.0 | 278.4 | 350.1 | 427.4 | 509.3 | 595.2 | 684.7 | 777.2 | 872.3 | 969.6 |
| 1-Heptene | C7H14 | 0 | 64.55 | 73.55 | 104.6 | 154.8 | 213.3 | 279.0 | 351.2 | 428.9 | 511.2 | 597.5 | 687.5 | 780.4 | 875.9 | 973.6 |
| 1-Octene | C8H16 | 0 | 64.17 | 73.20 | 104.4 | 154.8 | 213.6 | 279.6 | 352.1 | 430.1 | 512.7 | 599.3 | 689.6 | 782.8 | 878.5 | 976.6 |
| 1-Nonene | C9H18 | 0 | 63.88 | 72.94 | 104.3 | 154.8 | 213.7 | 280.0 | 352.7 | 430.9 | 513.8 | 600.7 | 691.2 | 784.6 | 880.6 | 978.9 |
| 1-Decene | C10H20 | 0 | 63.65 | 72.72 | 104.1 | 154.8 | 213.9 | 280.3 | 353.2 | 431.7 | 514.7 | 601.8 | 692.6 | 786.2 | 882.3 | 980.7 |
| 1-Undecene | C11H22 | 0 | 63.46 | 72.54 | 104.0 | 154.8 | 214.0 | 280.6 | 353.6 | 432.2 | 515.4 | 602.7 | 693.6 | 787.4 | 883.7 | 982.3 |
| 1-Dodecene | C12H24 | 0 | 63.30 | 72.40 | 103.9 | 154.8 | 214.1 | 280.8 | 354.0 | 432.7 | 516.1 | 603.5 | 694.5 | 788.4 | 884.9 | 983.6 |
| 1-Tridecene | C13H26 | 0 | 63.16 | 72.27 | 103.8 | 154.8 | 214.2 | 280.9 | 354.3 | 433.2 | 516.6 | 604.1 | 695.2 | 789.3 | 885.8 | 984.6 |
| 1-Tetradecene | C14H28 | 0 | 63.05 | 72.17 | 103.8 | 154.8 | 214.2 | 281.1 | 354.5 | 433.5 | 517.0 | 604.6 | 695.9 | 790.0 | 886.7 | 985.5 |
| 1-Pentadecene | C15H30 | 0 | 62.95 | 72.08 | 103.7 | 154.8 | 214.3 | 281.2 | 354.8 | 433.8 | 517.5 | 605.1 | 696.5 | 790.6 | 887.4 | 986.4 |
| 1-Hexadecene | C16H32 | 0 | 62.86 | 72.00 | 103.7 | 154.8 | 214.3 | 281.3 | 354.9 | 434.1 | 517.8 | 605.5 | 696.9 | 791.2 | 888.0 | 987.0 |
| 1-Heptadecene | C17H34 | 0 | 62.79 | 71.93 | 103.6 | 154.8 | 214.4 | 281.4 | 355.1 | 434.3 | 518.1 | 605.9 | 697.3 | 791.7 | 888.5 | 987.7 |
| 1-Octadecene | C18H36 | 0 | 62.71 | 71.86 | 103.6 | 154.8 | 214.4 | 281.5 | 355.3 | 434.5 | 518.4 | 606.2 | 697.8 | 792.1 | 889.0 | 988.2 |
| 1-Nonadecene | C19H38 | 0 | 62.66 | 71.81 | 103.6 | 154.8 | 214.5 | 281.6 | 355.4 | 434.7 | 518.6 | 606.5 | 698.1 | 792.5 | 889.5 | 988.7 |
| 1-Eicosene | C20H40 | 0 | 62.60 | 71.76 | 103.5 | 154.8 | 214.5 | 281.7 | 355.5 | 434.9 | 518.8 | 606.7 | 698.4 | 792.9 | 889.9 | 989.1 |

TABLE 8u-G (PART 1) – MONOOLEFINS, C$_2$ TO C$_5$

HEAT CONTENT (ENTHALPY), $(H°-H°_0)$, FOR THE IDEAL GAS STATE, AT −273.16° TO 1200°C

April 30, 1946; December 31, 1952

| Compound (gas) | Formula | Temperature in °C | | | | | | | | | | | | | | |
|---|---|---|---|---|---|---|---|---|---|---|---|---|---|---|---|---|
| | | −273.16 | 0 | 25 | 100 | 200 | 300 | 400 | 500 | 600 | 700 | 800 | 900 | 1000 | 1100 | 1200 |
| | | Heat Content (Enthalpy), $(H°-H°_0)$, in cal/g | | | | | | | | | | | | | | |
| Ethene (Ethylene) | C$_2$H$_4$ | 0 | 81.11 | 90.01 | 120.2 | 168.2 | 223.9 | 286.2 | 354.4 | 427.4 | 504.7 | 586.1 | 670.8 | 758.5 | 848.5 | 940.8 |
| Propene (Propylene) | C$_3$H$_6$ | 0 | 68.14 | 76.93 | 106.7 | 154.1 | 209.4 | 272.0 | 340.7 | 414.7 | 493.6 | 576.3 | 662.6 | 752.0 | 844.0 | 938.4 |
| 1-Butene | C$_4$H$_8$ | 0 | 64.61 | 73.29 | 103.4 | 152.1 | 209.0 | 273.0 | 334.3 | 419.0 | 499.1 | 583.5 | 671.2 | 762.1 | 855.6 | 951.4 |
| cis-2-Butene | " | 0 | 62.35 | 70.33 | 98.2 | 143.8 | 198.2 | 260.0 | 328.4 | 402.4 | 481.2 | 564.5 | 651.3 | 741.4 | 834.3 | 929.7 |
| trans-2-Butene | " | 0 | 65.71 | 74.68 | 105.2 | 153.6 | 209.8 | 273.4 | 343.1 | 418.2 | 498.1 | 582.1 | 669.7 | 760.2 | 853.4 | 949.1 |
| 2-Methylpropene (Isobutene) | " | 0 | 63.56 | 72.76 | 103.9 | 153.2 | 210.6 | 274.9 | 345.4 | 421.0 | 501.2 | 585.7 | 673.7 | 764.7 | 858.4 | 954.2 |
| 1-Pentene | C$_5$H$_{10}$ | 0 | 65.86 | 74.80 | 105.5 | 155.0 | 212.8 | 277.7 | 348.8 | 425.5 | 506.8 | 592.1 | 680.9 | 772.8 | 867.4 | 964.3 |
| cis-2-Pentene | " | 0 | 60.76 | 69.09 | 98.0 | 145.3 | 201.4 | 265.3 | 335.4 | 411.0 | 491.7 | 576.2 | 664.3 | 755.8 | 849.9 | 946.4 |
| trans-2-Pentene | " | 0 | 63.01 | 71.82 | 102.1 | 150.8 | 208.0 | 272.2 | 342.6 | 418.5 | 499.2 | 564.0 | 672.1 | 763.4 | 857.4 | 954.0 |
| 2-Methyl-1-butene | " | 0 | 62.13 | 71.30 | 102.6 | 152.9 | 211.3 | 277.0 | 348.7 | 425.6 | 507.1 | 592.8 | 681.7 | 773.8 | 868.9 | 966.0 |
| 3-Methyl-1-butene | " | 0 | 63.48 | 73.25 | 106.3 | 158.6 | 218.9 | 285.8 | 358.4 | 436.0 | 518.2 | 604.3 | 693.9 | 786.5 | 881.4 | 978.3 |
| 2-Methyl-2-butene | " | 0 | 60.39 | 68.92 | 98.4 | 146.1 | 202.1 | 265.6 | 335.5 | 410.8 | 491.1 | 575.5 | 663.4 | 754.6 | 848.6 | 944.9 |

TABLE 8u-G (PART 2) – MONOOLEFINS, C$_6$

HEAT CONTENT (ENTHALPY), $(H^o - H^o_0)$, FOR THE IDEAL GAS STATE, AT −273.16° TO 1200°C

May 31, 1946; December 31, 1952

| Compound (Gas) | Formula | Temperature in °C |  |  |  |  |  |  |  |  |  |  |  |  |  |  |
|---|---|---|---|---|---|---|---|---|---|---|---|---|---|---|---|---|
|  |  | −273.16 | 0 | 25 | 100 | 200 | 300 | 400 | 500 | 600 | 700 | 800 | 900 | 1000 | 1100 | 1200 |
|  |  | Heat Content (Enthalpy), $(H^o - H^o_0)$, in cal/a |  |  |  |  |  |  |  |  |  |  |  |  |  |  |  |
| 1-Hexene | C$_6$H$_{12}$ | 0 | 65.05 | 74.01 | 104.9 | 154.8 | 213.0 | 278.4 | 350.1 | 427.4 | 509.3 | 595.2 | 684.7 | 777.2 | 872.3 | 969.6 |
| cis-2-Hexene | " | 0 | 62.55 | 71.03 | 100.6 | 148.9 | 205.8 | 270.2 | 341.2 | 418.1 | 499. |  |  |  |  |  |
| trans-2-Hexene | " | 0 | 64.38 | 73.32 | 104.1 | 153.6 | 211.4 | 276.1 | 348.2 | 423.5 | 504. |  |  |  |  |  |
| cis-3-Hexene | " | 0 | 60.05 | 68.35 | 97.6 | 145.8 | 203.1 | 267.9 | 338.9 | 414.8 | 496. |  |  |  |  |  |
| trans-3-Hexene | " | 0 | 62.47 | 71.33 | 102.2 | 152.4 | 210.2 | 275.8 | 348.1 | 425.3 | 506. |  |  |  |  |  |
| 2-Methyl-1-pentene | " | 0 | 63.26 | 72.88 | 104.8 | 155.0 | 213.8 | 280.5 | 352.5 | 429.7 | 512. |  |  |  |  |  |
| 3-Methyl-1-pentene | " | 0 | 62.88 | 72.63 | 106.5 | 161.7 | 226.4 | 299.4 | 378.9 | 463.9 | 555. |  |  |  |  |  |
| 4-Methyl-1-pentene | " | 0 | 56.72 | 65.16 | 94.5 | 142.6 | 199.6 | 264.4 | 334.4 | 411.0 | 492. |  |  |  |  |  |
| 2-Methyl-2-pentene | " | 0 | 58.84 | 67.49 | 97.4 | 145.9 | 203.1 | 267.9 | 338.9 | 414.8 | 496. |  |  |  |  |  |
| 3-Methyl-cis-2-pentene | " | 0 | 58.84 | 67.49 | 97.4 | 145.9 | 203.1 | 267.9 | 338.9 | 414.8 | 496. |  |  |  |  |  |
| 3-Methyl-trans-2-pentene | " | 0 | 58.84 | 67.49 | 97.4 | 145.9 | 203.1 | 267.9 | 338.9 | 414.8 | 496. |  |  |  |  |  |
| 4-Methyl-cis-2-pentene | " | 0 | 60.05 | 69.12 | 100.4 | 150.8 | 209.4 | 274.8 | 346.9 | 424.1 | 506. |  |  |  |  |  |
| 4-Methyl-trans-2-pentene | " | 0 | 62.28 | 72.03 | 104.8 | 156.5 | 216.7 | 283.1 | 355.1 | 433.3 | 516. |  |  |  |  |  |
| 2-Ethyl-1-butene | " | 0 | 61.05 | 70.19 | 101.5 | 152.1 | 211.1 | 277.1 | 349.2 | 427.3 | 510. |  |  |  |  |  |
| 2,3-Dimethyl-1-butene | " | 0 | 61.08 | 70.96 | 104.2 | 157.0 | 217.8 | 285.1 | 358.5 | 436.0 | 518. |  |  |  |  |  |
| 3,3-Dimethyl-1-butene | " | 0 | 53.70 | 62.11 | 91.9 | 141.0 | 198.0 | 262.6 | 334.4 | 410.0 | 490. |  |  |  |  |  |
| 2,3-Dimethyl-2-butene | " | 0 | 58.94 | 67.71 | 97.5 | 145.4 | 202.1 | 265.8 | 336.5 | 412.5 | 493. |  |  |  |  |  |

TABLE 11u-G (PART 1) – DIOLEFINS, C₃ TO C₅

HEAT CONTENT (ENTHALPY), ($H^o-H^o_0$), FOR THE IDEAL GAS STATE, AT -273.16° TO 1200°C

October 31, 1947; April 30, 1948

Temperature in °C

Heat Content (Enthalpy), ($H^o-H^o_0$), in cal/a

| Compound (gas) | Formula | -273.16 | 0 | 25 | 100 | 200 | 300 | 400 | 500 | 600 | 700 | 800 | 900 | 1000 | 1100 | 1200 |
|---|---|---|---|---|---|---|---|---|---|---|---|---|---|---|---|---|
| Propadiene (Allene) | $C_3H_4$ | 0 | 66.809 | 75.118 | 103.96 | 148.44 | 199.29 | 255.21 | 315.74 | 380.04 | 447.63 | 518.01 | 591.03 | 666.40 | 743.60 | 822.49 |
| 1,2-Butadiene | $C_4H_6$ | 0 | 62.688 | 71.221 | 100.04 | 145.28 | 197.40 | 255.43 | 318.60 | 386.19 | 457.62 | 532.24 | 609.71 | 689.98 | 772.26 | 856.27 |
| 1,3-Butadiene | " | 0 | 58.593 | 67.032 | 96.17 | 142.97 | 197.16 | 257.25 | 322.18 | 391.19 | 463.66 | 539.31 | 617.56 | 698.11 | 780.69 | 865.07 |
| 1,2-Pentadiene | $C_5H_8$ | 0 | 62.48 | 70.91 | 101.2 | 149.5 | 204.4 | 266.1 | 332.6 | 403.2 | 478.3 | 556.7 | 636.7 | 721.2 | 807.1 | 894.4 |
| 1,cis-3-Pentadiene | " | 0 | 55.72 | 63.47 | 91.5 | 136.8 | 190.6 | 250.2 | 316.1 | 386.3 | 459.7 | 537.4 | 617.6 | 700.6 | 786.5 | 873.2 |
| 1,trans-3-Pentadiene | " | 0 | 58.47 | 66.98 | 97.2 | 145.1 | 200.0 | 261.1 | 327.8 | 399.0 | 474.1 | 551.9 | 633.2 | 716.1 | 801.0 | 888.1 |
| 1,4-Pentadiene | " | 0 | 62.98 | 72.23 | 103.1 | 150.4 | 205.9 | 267.4 | 332.9 | 403.1 | 478.3 | 556.7 | 636.9 | 721.2 | 807.1 | 894.4 |
| 2,3-Pentadiene | " | 0 | 60.58 | 68.72 | 97.7 | 143.5 | 196.2 | 255.4 | 326.0 | 390.0 | 464.1 | 540.9 | 621.0 | 704.4 | 788.9 | 876.3 |
| 3-Methyl-1,2-butadiene | " | 0 | 59.78 | 69.16 | 99.1 | 146.1 | 200.9 | 261.4 | 326.9 | 396.7 | 471.2 | 548.8 | 629.6 | 713.8 | 799.1 | 885.8 |
| 2-Methyl-1,3-butadiene (Isoprene) | " | 0 | 57.46 | 65.65 | 95.8 | 144.8 | 200.7 | 262.9 | 330.1 | 401.7 | 475.8 | 554.6 | 636.6 | 719.8 | 805.1 | 892.4 |

TABLE 18u-G – ALKYL CYCLOPENTENES, $C_5$ TO $C_7$

HEAT CONTENT (ENTHALPY), $(H^o - H_0^o)$, FOR THE IDEAL GAS STATE, AT $-273.16^o$ TO $1200^oC$

December 31, 1952

| Compound (nas) | Formula | Temperature in °C | | | | | | | | | | | | | | |
|---|---|---|---|---|---|---|---|---|---|---|---|---|---|---|---|---|
| | | -273.16 | 0 | 25 | 100 | 200 | 300 | 400 | 500 | 600 | 700 | 800 | 900 | 1000 | 1100 | 1200 |
| | | | | | | Heat Content (Enthalpy), $(H^o - H_0^o)$, in cal/a | | | | | | | | | | |
| Cyclopentene | $C_5H_8$ | 0 | 44.48 | 50.83 | 73.46 | 112.52 | 160.91 | 217.12 | 279.99 | 348.40 | 421.44 | 498.53 | 579.13 | 662.68 | 748.73 | 837.01 |
| 1-Methylcyclopentene | $C_6H_{10}$ | 0 | 47.6 | 54.1 | 78.8 | 121.0 | 172.0 | 230.3 | 295.2 | 365.9 | 440.6 | 520.3 | 602.8 | 687.4 | 775.2 | 866.2 |
| 3-Methylcyclopentene | " | 0 | 46.3 | 53.0 | 77.8 | 119.8 | 171.1 | 230.2 | 295.2 | 365.8 | 441.6 | 520.7 | 602.7 | 688.6 | 777.1 | 866.9 |
| 4-Methylcyclopentene | " | 0 | 46.0 | 52.6 | 77.4 | 119.2 | 170.4 | 229.4 | 294.3 | 364.8 | 440.3 | 520.4 | 602.8 | 687.4 | 775.3 | 865.2 |
| 1-Ethylcyclopentene | $C_7H_{12}$ | | | | | | | | | | | | | | | |
| 3-Ethylcyclopentene | " | | | | | | | | | | | | | | | |
| 4-Ethylcyclopentene | " | | | | | | | | | | | | | | | |
| 1,2-Dimethylcyclopentene | " | 0 | 49.3 | 56.4 | 82.7 | 126.9 | 179.8 | 239.7 | 306.4 | 378.5 | 455.0 | 535.9 | 619.7 | 706.3 | 795.4 | 886.3 |
| 1,3-Dimethylcyclopentene | " | 0 | 48.2 | 55.5 | 81.9 | 125.9 | 179.0 | 239.6 | 306.4 | 378.5 | 455.0 | 535.8 | 620.6 | 707.7 | 796.8 | 887.8 |
| 1,4-Dimethylcyclopentene | " | 0 | 48.4 | 55.2 | 81.5 | 125.4 | 178.5 | 238.9 | 305.6 | 377.6 | 454.0 | 534.7 | 619.4 | 706.3 | 795.4 | 886.3 |
| 1,5-Dimethylcyclopentene | " | 0 | 48.3 | 55.5 | 81.9 | 126.0 | 178.6 | 238.8 | 306.2 | 378.6 | 455.0 | 535.9 | 619.7 | 706.3 | 795.3 | 887.2 |
| 3,3-Dimethylcyclopentene | " | 0 | 45.8 | 52.7 | 78.6 | 122.7 | 175.9 | 237.1 | 305.2 | 379.0 | 456.8 | 538.9 | 625.2 | 713.9 | 805.1 | 897.2 |
| 3,cis-4-Dimethylcyclopentene | " | 0 | 46.7 | 53.9 | 80.2 | 124.3 | 177.7 | 238.7 | 306.2 | 379.2 | 456.8 | 538.2 | 622.1 | 708.9 | 798.1 | 890.2 |
| 3,trans-4-Dimethylcyclopentene | " | 0 | 47.3 | 54.6 | 81.0 | 125.3 | 178.5 | 238.9 | 305.5 | 378.3 | 455.8 | 537.0 | 620.9 | 707.6 | 796.7 | 888.7 |
| 3,cis-5-Dimethylcyclopentene | " | 0 | 47.3 | 54.6 | 81.0 | 125.3 | 178.5 | 238.9 | 305.5 | 378.3 | 455.8 | 537.0 | 620.9 | 707.6 | 796.7 | 888.7 |
| 3,trans-5-Dimethylcyclopentene | " | 0 | 47.3 | 54.6 | 81.0 | 125.3 | 178.5 | 238.9 | 305.5 | 378.3 | 455.8 | 537.0 | 620.9 | 707.6 | 796.7 | 888.7 |
| 4,4-Dimethylcyclopentene | " | | | | | | | | | | | | | | | |

TABLE 25u-G (PART 1) - NORMAL ACETYLENES (1-ALKYNES), $C_2$ TO $C_{20}$
HEAT CONTENT (ENTHALPY), $(H°-H°_0)$, FOR THE IDEAL GAS STATE, AT -273.16° TO 1200°C
February 28, 1946; December 31, 1952

Temperature in °C

Heat Content (Enthalpy), $(H°-H°_0)$, in cal/g

| Compound (gas) | Formula | -273.16 | 0 | 25 | 100 | 200 | 300 | 400 | 500 | 600 | 700 | 800 | 900 | 1000 | 1100 | 1200 |
|---|---|---|---|---|---|---|---|---|---|---|---|---|---|---|---|---|
| Ethyne (Acetylene) | $C_2H_2$ | 0 | 81.89 | 91.85 | 123.9 | 170.8 | 221.3 | 274.6 | 330.3 | 388.2 | 448.0 | 509.6 | 572.8 | 637.5 | 703.4 | 770.7 |
| Propyne (Methylacetylene) | $C_3H_4$ | 0 | 68.67 | 77.48 | 106.6 | 151.3 | 201.8 | 257.3 | 317.1 | 380.6 | 447.5 | 517.2 | 589.7 | 664.3 | 741.0 | 819.2 |
| 1-Butyne (Ethylacetylene) | $C_4H_6$ | 0 | 61.72 | 70.63 | 99.9 | 145.7 | 198.2 | 256.4 | 319.5 | 386.9 | 457.9 | 532.2 | 609.4 | 689.1 | 771.0 | 854.8 |
| 1-Pentyne | $C_5H_8$ | 0 | 63.58 | 72.70 | 102.8 | 150.0 | 204.2 | 264.6 | 330.2 | 400.2 | 474.3 | 551.7 | 632.1 | 715.3 | 800.8 | 887.9 |
| 1-Hexyne | $C_6H_{10}$ | 0 | 63.22 | 72.38 | 102.8 | 150.8 | 206.1 | 267.8 | 334.9 | 406.8 | 482.6 | 561.9 | 644.4 | 729.7 | 817.3 | 906.6 |
| 1-Heptyne | $C_7H_{12}$ | 0 | 63.00 | 72.15 | 102.9 | 151.4 | 207.4 | 270.0 | 338.3 | 411.3 | 486.5 | 569.2 | 653.2 | 740.0 | 829.0 | 919.8 |
| 1-Octyne | $C_8H_{14}$ | 0 | 62.79 | 71.97 | 102.9 | 151.8 | 208.4 | 271.7 | 340.8 | 414.7 | 492.9 | 574.6 | 659.6 | 747.5 | 837.6 | 929.7 |
| 1-Nonyne | $C_9H_{16}$ | 0 | 62.70 | 71.84 | 102.9 | 152.2 | 209.2 | 273.0 | 342.7 | 417.3 | 496.2 | 578.8 | 664.7 | 753.4 | 844.4 | 937.4 |
| 1-Decyne | $C_{10}H_{18}$ | 0 | 62.54 | 71.74 | 102.9 | 152.4 | 209.8 | 274.0 | 344.2 | 419.5 | 499.0 | 582.1 | 668.7 | 758.0 | 849.8 | 943.5 |
| 1-Undecyne | $C_{11}H_{20}$ | 0 | 62.44 | 71.65 | 102.9 | 152.6 | 210.2 | 274.8 | 345.5 | 421.2 | 501.2 | 584.8 | 672.0 | 761.9 | 854.2 | 948.5 |
| 1-Dodecyne | $C_{12}H_{22}$ | 0 | 62.40 | 71.57 | 102.9 | 152.8 | 210.7 | 275.5 | 346.5 | 422.6 | 503.0 | 587.1 | 674.7 | 765.1 | 857.9 | 952.6 |
| 1-Tridecyne | $C_{13}H_{24}$ | 0 | 62.32 | 71.51 | 102.9 | 152.9 | 211.0 | 276.2 | 347.4 | 423.8 | 504.5 | 589.1 | 677.0 | 767.7 | 860.9 | 956.1 |
| 1-Tetradecyne | $C_{14}H_{26}$ | 0 | 62.27 | 71.46 | 102.9 | 153.1 | 211.3 | 276.6 | 348.2 | 424.8 | 505.9 | 590.7 | 679.0 | 770.1 | 863.5 | 959.1 |
| 1-Pentadecyne | $C_{15}H_{28}$ | 0 | 62.22 | 71.42 | 102.9 | 153.2 | 211.6 | 277.1 | 348.8 | 425.7 | 507.0 | 592.1 | 680.6 | 772.1 | 865.8 | 961.7 |
| 1-Hexadecyne | $C_{16}H_{30}$ | 0 | 62.17 | 71.38 | 102.9 | 153.3 | 211.8 | 277.4 | 349.4 | 426.5 | 508.0 | 593.3 | 682.2 | 773.8 | 867.8 | 963.9 |
| 1-Heptadecyne | $C_{17}H_{32}$ | 0 | 62.14 | 71.34 | 102.9 | 153.4 | 212.0 | 277.8 | 349.9 | 427.2 | 508.9 | 594.4 | 683.4 | 775.3 | 869.6 | 966.0 |
| 1-Octadecyne | $C_{18}H_{34}$ | 0 | 62.10 | 71.31 | 102.9 | 153.4 | 212.2 | 278.1 | 350.3 | 427.8 | 509.7 | 595.4 | 684.6 | 776.7 | 871.1 | 967.7 |
| 1-Nonadecyne | $C_{19}H_{36}$ | 0 | 62.09 | 71.28 | 102.9 | 153.5 | 212.3 | 278.4 | 350.7 | 428.4 | 510.4 | 596.3 | 685.6 | 777.9 | 872.5 | 969.3 |
| 1-Eicosyne | $C_{20}H_{38}$ | 0 | 62.05 | 71.26 | 102.9 | 153.6 | 212.5 | 278.6 | 351.1 | 428.9 | 511.0 | 597.0 | 686.6 | 779.0 | 873.8 | 970.7 |

TABLE 12u-G – ACETYLENES, $C_2$ TO $C_5$

HEAT CONTENT (ENTHALPY), $(H^\circ - H_0^\circ)$, FOR THE IDEAL GAS STATE, AT $-273.16^\circ$ TO $1200^\circ C$

January 31, 1946

| Compound (gas) | Formula | Temperature in °C | | | | | | | | | | | | | | |
|---|---|---|---|---|---|---|---|---|---|---|---|---|---|---|---|---|
| | | -273.16 | 0 | 25 | 100 | 200 | 300 | 400 | 500 | 600 | 700 | 800 | 900 | 1000 | 1100 | 1200 |
| | | Heat Content (Enthalpy), $(H^\circ - H_0^\circ)$, in cal/g | | | | | | | | | | | | | | |
| Ethyne (Acetylene) | $C_2H_2$ | 0 | 81.89 | 91.85 | 123.9 | 170.8 | 221.3 | 274.6 | 330.3 | 388.2 | 448.0 | 509.6 | 572.8 | 637.5 | 703.4 | 770.7 |
| Propyne (Methylacetylene) | $C_3H_4$ | 0 | 68.67 | 77.48 | 106.6 | 151.3 | 201.8 | 257.3 | 317.1 | 380.6 | 447.5 | 517.2 | 589.7 | 664.3 | 741.0 | 819.2 |
| 1-Butyne (Ethylacetylene) | $C_4H_6$ | 0 | 61.72 | 70.63 | 99.9 | 145.7 | 198.2 | 256.4 | 319.5 | 386.9 | 457.9 | 532.2 | 609.4 | 689.1 | 771.0 | 854.8 |
| 2-Butyne (Dimethylacetylene) | " | 0 | 64.92 | 73.23 | 101.1 | 144.6 | 194.8 | 251.0 | 312.4 | 378.2 | 448.2 | 521.5 | 598.0 | 676.9 | 758.2 | 841.5 |
| 1-Pentyne | $C_5H_8$ | 0 | 63.39 | 72.70 | 103.2 | 150.6 | 205. | 266. | 331. | 401. | 475. | 552. | 632. | 715. | 801. | 888. |
| 2-Pentyne | " | 0 | 60.22 | 68.64 | 96.9 | 141.5 | 193. | 251. | 315. | 384. | 456. | 533. | 612. | 694. | 779. | 865. |
| 3-Methyl-1-butyne | " | 0 | 58.27 | 67.28 | 97.3 | 144.8 | 200. | 260. | 326. | 397. | 471. | 549. | 629. | 712. | 798. | 885. |

## TABLE 21u-G (PART 1) - NORMAL ALKYL BENZENES, $C_6$ TO $C_{22}$

HEAT CONTENT (ENTHALPY), $(H° - H°_0)$, FOR THE IDEAL GAS STATE, AT $-273.16°$ TO $1200°C$

January 31, 1946; December 31, 1952

| Compound (gas) | Formula | Temperature in °C | | | | | | | | | | | | | | |
|---|---|---|---|---|---|---|---|---|---|---|---|---|---|---|---|---|
| | | Heat Content (Enthalpy), $(H° - H°_0)$, in cal/g | | | | | | | | | | | | | | |
| | | −273.16 | 0 | 25 | 100 | 200 | 300 | 400 | 500 | 600 | 700 | 800 | 900 | 1000 | 1100 | 1200 |
| Benzene | $C_6H_6$ | 0 | 37.58 | 43.54 | 64.89 | 101.00 | 144.52 | 194.1 | 248.5 | 307.1 | 369.0 | 433.9 | 501.2 | 570.6 | 641.8 | 714.6 |
| Methylbenzene (Toluene) | $C_7H_8$ | 0 | 40.28 | 46.74 | 69.51 | 107.51 | 153.08 | 204.9 | 262.0 | 323.4 | 388.4 | 456.6 | 527.5 | 600.6 | 675.7 | 752.4 |
| Ethylbenzene | $C_8H_{10}$ | 0 | 43.30 | 50.25 | 74.57 | 114.92 | 163.02 | 217.5 | 277.3 | 341.4 | 409.3 | 480.4 | 554.2 | 630.4 | 708.6 | 788.5 |
| n-Propylbenzene | $C_9H_{12}$ | 0 | 45.10 | 53.81 | 79.78 | 118.77 | 169.78 | 226.8 | 288.3 | 354.3 | 424.3 | 497.6 | 571.1 | 651.2 | 732.8 | 814.9 |
| n-Butylbenzene | $C_{10}H_{14}$ | 0 | 48.11 | 55.52 | 81.55 | 124.38 | 175.15 | 232.5 | 295.5 | 362.9 | 434.5 | 509.3 | 587.1 | 667.4 | 749.8 | 834.0 |
| n-Pentylbenzene | $C_{11}H_{16}$ | 0 | 49.39 | 56.96 | 83.59 | 127.27 | 178.94 | 237.3 | 301.4 | 370.1 | 442.8 | 519.0 | 598.2 | 679.9 | 763.8 | 849.6 |
| n-Hexylbenzene | $C_{12}H_{18}$ | 0 | 50.43 | 58.16 | 85.26 | 129.63 | 182.07 | 241.3 | 306.2 | 376.0 | 449.7 | 527.0 | 607.4 | 690.3 | 775.4 | 862.3 |
| n-Heptylbenzene | $C_{13}H_{20}$ | 0 | 51.32 | 59.16 | 86.68 | 131.65 | 184.71 | 244.6 | 310.4 | 380.9 | 455.6 | 533.8 | 615.1 | 699.0 | 785.1 | 873.1 |
| n-Octylbenzene | $C_{14}H_{22}$ | 0 | 52.07 | 60.02 | 87.86 | 133.34 | 186.95 | 247.5 | 313.9 | 385.1 | 460.5 | 539.5 | 621.6 | 706.4 | 793.3 | 882.3 |
| n-Nonylbenzene | $C_{15}H_{24}$ | 0 | 52.74 | 60.76 | 88.89 | 134.81 | 188.89 | 249.9 | 316.9 | 388.7 | 464.8 | 544.5 | 627.3 | 712.8 | 800.5 | 890.2 |
| n-Decylbenzene | $C_{16}H_{26}$ | 0 | 53.29 | 61.40 | 89.80 | 136.09 | 190.55 | 252.0 | 319.5 | 391.9 | 468.5 | 548.8 | 632.2 | 718.4 | 806.7 | 897.1 |
| n-Undecylbenzene | $C_{17}H_{28}$ | 0 | 53.78 | 61.97 | 90.59 | 137.21 | 192.04 | 253.9 | 321.8 | 394.7 | 471.8 | 552.6 | 636.6 | 723.3 | 812.2 | 903.1 |
| n-Dodecylbenzene | $C_{18}H_{30}$ | 0 | 54.24 | 62.47 | 91.29 | 138.21 | 193.36 | 255.6 | 323.9 | 397.2 | 474.7 | 555.9 | 640.5 | 727.7 | 817.1 | 908.5 |
| n-Tridecylbenzene | $C_{19}H_{32}$ | 0 | 54.63 | 62.92 | 91.91 | 139.10 | 194.53 | 257.1 | 325.7 | 399.4 | 477.3 | 559.0 | 643.9 | 731.5 | 821.3 | 913.3 |
| n-Tetradecylbenzene | $C_{20}H_{34}$ | 0 | 54.99 | 63.32 | 92.48 | 139.90 | 195.59 | 258.4 | 327.3 | 401.4 | 479.7 | 561.7 | 647.0 | 735.0 | 825.2 | 917.6 |
| n-Pentadecylbenzene | $C_{21}H_{36}$ | 0 | 55.30 | 63.68 | 92.98 | 140.62 | 196.54 | 259.6 | 328.8 | 403.2 | 481.8 | 564.1 | 649.8 | 738.1 | 828.8 | 921.5 |
| n-Hexadecylbenzene | $C_{22}H_{38}$ | 0 | 55.59 | 64.01 | 93.44 | 141.27 | 197.40 | 260.7 | 330.2 | 404.8 | 483.7 | 566.3 | 652.3 | 741.0 | 832.0 | 925.0 |

TABLE 5u-G – ALKYL BENZENES, C$_6$ TO C$_9$

HEAT CONTENT (ENTHALPY), ($H^o-H^o_0$), FOR THE IDEAL GAS STATE, AT $-273.16^\circ$ TO $1200^\circ$C

December 31, 1945

| Compound (gas) | Formula | Temperature in °C | | | | | | | | | | | | | | |
|---|---|---|---|---|---|---|---|---|---|---|---|---|---|---|---|---|
| | | -273.16 | 0 | 25 | 100 | 200 | 300 | 400 | 500 | 600 | 700 | 800 | 900 | 1000 | 1100 | 1200 |
| | | Heat Content (Enthalpy), ($H^o-H^o_0$), in cal/g | | | | | | | | | | | | | | |
| Benzene | C$_6$H$_6$ | 0 | 37.58 | 43.54 | 64.89 | 101.00 | 144.52 | 194.1 | 248.5 | 307.1 | 369.0 | 433.9 | 501.2 | 570.6 | 641.8 | 714.6 |
| Methylbenzene (Toluene) | C$_7$H$_8$ | 0 | 40.28 | 46.74 | 69.51 | 107.51 | 153.08 | 204.9 | 262.0 | 323.4 | 388.4 | 456.6 | 527.5 | 600.6 | 675.7 | 752.4 |
| Ethylbenzene | C$_8$H$_{10}$ | 0 | 43.30 | 50.25 | 74.57 | 114.92 | 163.02 | 217.5 | 277.3 | 341.4 | 409.3 | 480.4 | 554.2 | 630.4 | 708.6 | 788.5 |
| 1,2-Dimethylbenzene (o-Xylene) | " | 0 | 45.29 | 52.52 | 77.43 | 117.90 | 165.70 | 219.7 | 279.0 | 342.7 | 410.2 | 480.9 | 554.5 | 630.4 | 708.3 | 788.1 |
| 1,3-Dimethylbenzene (m-Xylene) | " | 0 | 43.25 | 50.16 | 74.24 | 113.87 | 161.06 | 214.6 | 273.6 | 337.2 | 404.6 | 475.3 | 548.7 | 624.5 | 702.4 | 782.1 |
| 1,4-Dimethylbenzene (p-Xylene) | " | 0 | 43.58 | 50.47 | 74.36 | 113.68 | 160.54 | 213.8 | 272.5 | 335.8 | 403.0 | 473.4 | 546.7 | 622.4 | 700.2 | 779.8 |
| n-Propylbenzene | C$_9$H$_{12}$ | 0 | 46.43 | 53.81 | 79.36 | 121.2 | 171.0 | 227.3 | 288.9 | 354.9 | 424.7 | 498. | 574. | 652. | 733. | 815. |
| Isopropylbenzene | " | 0 | 43.50 | 50.73 | 76.01 | 118.0 | 167.9 | 224.3 | 286.1 | 352.3 | 422.4 | 496. | 572. | 650. | 731. | 813. |
| 1-Methyl-2-ethylbenzene | " | 0 | 47.37 | 54.95 | 80.98 | 123.2 | 173.0 | 229.1 | 290.5 | 356.4 | 426.1 | 499. | 575. | 653. | 734. | 816. |
| 1-Methyl-3-ethylbenzene | " | 0 | 45.57 | 52.87 | 78.16 | 119.7 | 168.9 | 224.7 | 285.8 | 351.5 | 421.1 | 494. | 570. | 648. | 728. | 811. |
| 1-Methyl-4-ethylbenzene | " | 0 | 45.86 | 53.14 | 78.26 | 119.5 | 168.4 | 223.9 | 284.8 | 350.3 | 419.7 | 492. | 568. | 646. | 726. | 808. |
| 1,2,3-Trimethylbenzene | " | 0 | 47.33 | 54.83 | 79.82 | 120.7 | 168.9 | 223.5 | 283.7 | 348.4 | 417.2 | 489. | 565. | 642. | 722. | 804. |
| 1,2,4-Trimethylbenzene | " | 0 | 47.43 | 54.99 | 80.12 | 121.1 | 169.5 | 224.2 | 284.5 | 349.3 | 418.2 | 490. | 566. | 644. | 724. | 805. |
| 1,3,5-Trimethylbenzene | " | 0 | 45.34 | 52.64 | 77.20 | 117.70 | 165.84 | 220.5 | 280.8 | 345.7 | 414.6 | 487.0 | 562.3 | 640.2 | 720.2 | 802.1 |

TABLE 13u-G — STYRENES, C8 and C9

HEAT CONTENT, $(H°-H°_0)$, FOR THE IDEAL GAS STATE, AT -273.16° to 1200 °C

September 30, 1947

| Compound (gas) | Formula | Temperature in °C | | | | | | | | | | | | | | |
|---|---|---|---|---|---|---|---|---|---|---|---|---|---|---|---|---|
| | | -273.16 | 0 | 25 | 100 | 200 | 300 | 400 | 500 | 600 | 700 | 800 | 900 | 1000 | 1100 | 1200 |
| | | Heat Content, $(H°-H°_0)$, in cal/g | | | | | | | | | | | | | | |
| Ethenylbenzene (Styrene; Vinylbenzene; Phenylethylene) | $C_8H_8$ | 0 | 41.20 | 47.87 | 71.33 | 109.95 | 155.46 | 206.68 | 262.55 | 322.30 | 385.38 | 451.3 | 519.5 | 589.6 | 661.6 | 735.0 |
| Isopropenylbenzene (α-Methylstyrene; 2-Phenyl-1-propene) | $C_9H_{10}$ | 0 | 43.9 | 51.2 | 75.4 | 115.0 | 162.0 | 214.8 | 272.3 | 353.9 | 399.2 | 467. | 538. | 611. | 686. | 762. |
| cis-1-Propenylbenzene (cis-β-Methylstyrene; cis-1-Phenyl-1-propene) | " | 0 | 43.9 | 51.2 | 75.4 | 115.0 | 162.0 | 214.8 | 272.3 | 333.9 | 399.2 | 467. | 538. | 611. | 686. | 762. |
| trans-1-Propenylbenzene (trans-β-Methylstyrene; trans-1-Phenyl-1-propene) | " | 0 | 43.1 | 50.2 | 75.0 | 115.0 | 162.0 | 215.3 | 272.9 | 334.6 | 400.6 | 469. | 540. | 613. | 688. | 764. |
| 1-Methyl-2-ethenylbenzene (o-Methylstyrene) | " | 0 | 43.9 | 51.2 | 75.4 | 115.0 | 162.0 | 214.8 | 272.3 | 333.9 | 399.2 | 467. | 538. | 611. | 686. | 762. |
| 1-Methyl-3-ethenylbenzene (m-Methylstyrene) | " | 0 | 43.9 | 51.2 | 75.4 | 115.0 | 162.0 | 214.8 | 272.3 | 333.9 | 399.2 | 467. | 538. | 611. | 686. | 762. |
| 1-Methyl-4-ethenylbenzene (p-Methylstyrene) | " | 0 | 43.9 | 51.2 | 75.4 | 115.0 | 162.0 | 214.8 | 272.3 | 333.9 | 399.2 | 467. | 538. | 611. | 686. | 762. |

Table 00v – O, H, N, C

HEAT CAPACITY, $C_p^o$, FOR THE IDEAL GAS STATE, AT 0° TO 5000°K

June 30, 1946; August 31, 1949

Temperature in °K

Heat Capacity, $C_p^o$, in cal/deg mole

| Compound (gas, monatomic) | Formula | 0 | 298.16 | 300 | 400 | 500 | 600 | 700 | 800 | 900 | 1000 | 1100 | 1200 | 1300 | 1400 | 1500 |
|---|---|---|---|---|---|---|---|---|---|---|---|---|---|---|---|---|
| Oxygen | O | 0 | 5.2364 | 5.2338 | 5.1341 | 5.0802 | 5.0486 | 5.0284 | 5.0150 | 5.0055 | 4.9988 | 4.9936 | 4.9894 | 4.9964 | 4.9838 | 4.9819 |
| Hydrogen | H | 0 | 4.9680 | 4.9680 | 4.9680 | 4.9680 | 4.9680 | 4.9680 | 4.9680 | 4.9680 | 4.9680 | 4.9680 | 4.9680 | 4.9680 | 4.9680 | 4.9680 |
| Nitrogen | N | 0 | 4.9680 | 4.9680 | 4.9680 | 4.9680 | 4.9680 | 4.9680 | 4.9680 | 4.9680 | 4.9680 | 4.9680 | 4.9680 | 4.9680 | 4.9680 | 4.9680 |
| Carbon | C | 0 | 4.9803 | 4.9801 | 4.9747 | 4.9723 | 4.9709 | 4.9701 | 4.9697 | 4.9693 | 4.9691 | 4.9691 | 4.9697 | 4.9605 | 4.9725 | 4.9747 |

Temperature in °K

Heat Capacity, $C_p^o$, in cal/deg mole

| Compound (gas, monatomic) | Formula | 1000 | 1250 | 1500 | 1750 | 2000 | 2250 | 2500 | 2750 | 3000 | 3500 | 4000 | 4500 | 5000 |
|---|---|---|---|---|---|---|---|---|---|---|---|---|---|---|
| Oxygen | O | 4.9936 | 4.9878 | 4.9819 | 4.9788 | 4.9776 | 4.9164 | 4.9834 | 4.9917 | 5.0041 | 5.0411 | 5.0914 | 5.1495 | 5.2102 |
| Hydrogen | H | 4.9680 | 4.9680 | 4.9680 | 4.9680 | 4.9680 | 4.9680 | 4.9680 | 4.9680 | 4.9680 | 4.9680 | 4.9680 | 4.9680 | 4.9680 |
| Nitrogen | N | 4.9680 | 4.9680 | 4.9680 | 4.9682 | 4.9690 | 4.9715 | 4.9777 | 4.9900 | 5.0108 | 5.0866 | 5.2143 | 5.3927 | 5.6109 |
| Carbon | C | 4.9691 | 4.9700 | 4.9747 | 4.9865 | 5.0075 | 5.0384 | 5.0769 | 5.1208 | 5.1677 | 5.2610 | 5.3442 | 5.4115 | 5.9351 |

TABLE Ov - $O_2$, $H_2$, OH, $H_2O$, $N_2$, NO, C, CO, $CO_2$

HEAT CAPACITY, $C_p^o$, AT 0° TO 5000°K

July 31, 1944; August 31, 1946; June 30, 1949

Temperature in °K

Heat Capacity, $C_p^o$, in cal/deg mole

| Compound | Formula | State | 0 | 50 | 100 | 150 | 200 | 250 | 296.16 | 300 | 400 | 500 | 600 | 700 | 800 | 900 | 1000 |
|---|---|---|---|---|---|---|---|---|---|---|---|---|---|---|---|---|---|
| Oxygen | $O_2$ | gas | 0 | | 6.958 | 6.958 | 6.961 | 6.979 | 7.017 | 7.019 | 7.194 | 7.429 | 7.670 | 7.885 | 8.064 | 8.212 | 8.335 |
| Hydrogen | $H_2$ | gas | 0 | 9.072 | 6.729 | 6.348 | 6.561 | 6.769 | 6.892 | 6.895 | 6.974 | 6.993 | 7.008 | 7.035 | 7.078 | 7.139 | 7.217 |
| Hydroxyl | OH | gas | 0 | | | | | | 7.141 | 7.139 | 7.074 | 7.048 | 7.053 | 7.087 | 7.150 | 7.234 | 7.333 |
| Water | $H_2O$ | gas | 0 | | | | | | 8.025 | 8.026 | 8.185 | 8.415 | 8.677 | 8.959 | 9.254 | 9.559 | 9.861 |
| Nitrogen | $N_2$ | gas | 0 | | | | 6.957 | 6.959 | 6.960 | 6.961 | 6.991 | 7.070 | 7.197 | 7.351 | 7.512 | 7.671 | 7.816 |
| Nitric Oxide | NO | gas | 0 | 7.562 | 7.714 | 7.451 | 7.278 | 7.183 | 7.137 | 7.134 | 7.162 | 7.289 | 7.468 | 7.657 | 7.833 | 7.990 | 8.126 |
| Carbon | C | solid graphite | 0 | | 0.394 | 0.767 | 1.190 | 1.632 | 2.066 | 2.083 | 2.851 | 3.496 | 4.03 | 4.43 | 4.75 | 4.98 | 5.14 |
| Carbon Monoxide | CO | gas | 0 | 6.955 | 6.955 | 6.955 | 6.956 | 6.958 | 6.965 | 6.965 | 7.013 | 7.120 | 7.276 | 7.451 | 7.624 | 7.787 | 7.932 |
| Carbon Dioxide | $CO_2$ | gas | 0 | | | | | | 8.874 | 8.894 | 9.871 | 10.662 | 11.311 | 11.849 | 12.300 | 12.678 | 12.995 |

Temperature in °K

Heat Capacity, $C_p^o$, in cal/deg mole

| Compound | Formula | State | 1100 | 1200 | 1300 | 1400 | 1500 | 1750 | 2000 | 2250 | 2500 | 2750 | 3000 | 3500 | 4000 | 4500 | 5000 |
|---|---|---|---|---|---|---|---|---|---|---|---|---|---|---|---|---|---|
| Oxygen | $O_2$ | gas | 8.440 | 8.530 | 8.608 | 8.676 | 8.739 | 8.888 | 9.030 | 9.168 | 9.302 | 9.431 | 9.552 | 9.763 | 9.933 | 10.063 | 10.157 |
| Hydrogen | $H_2$ | gas | 7.308 | 7.404 | 7.505 | 7.610 | 7.713 | 7.958 | 8.175 | 8.364 | 8.526 | 8.667 | 8.791 | 8.993 | 9.151 | 9.282 | 9.389 |
| Hydroxyl | OH | gas | 7.440 | 7.551 | 7.663 | 7.772 | 7.875 | 8.110 | 8.308 | 8.474 | 8.614 | 8.733 | 8.838 | 9.015 | 9.162 | 9.290 | 9.406 |
| Water | $H_2O$ | gas | 10.145 | 10.413 | 10.668 | 10.909 | 11.134 | 11.62 | 12.01 | 12.32 | 12.56 | 12.8 | 12.9 | 13.2 | 13.3 | 13.4 | 13.5 |
| Nitrogen | $N_2$ | gas | 7.947 | 8.063 | 8.165 | 8.253 | 8.330 | 8.486 | 8.602 | 8.690 | 8.759 | 8.815 | 8.861 | 8.934 | 8.989 | 9.035 | 9.076 |
| Nitric Oxide | NO | gas | 8.243 | 8.342 | 8.426 | 8.498 | 8.560 | 8.682 | 8.771 | 8.840 | 8.895 | 8.941 | 8.981 | 9.049 | 9.107 | 9.158 | 9.208 |
| Carbon | C | solid graphite | 5.27 | 5.42 | 5.57 | 5.67 | 5.76 | 5.93 | 6.05 | 6.16 | 6.26 | 6.34 | 6.42 | 6.57 | 6.72 | | |
| Carbon Monoxide | CO | gas | 8.058 | 8.168 | 8.265 | 8.349 | 8.419 | 8.561 | 8.665 | 8.744 | 8.806 | 8.856 | 8.898 | 8.963 | 9.015 | 9.059 | 9.096 |
| Carbon Dioxide | $CO_2$ | gas | 13.26 | 13.49 | 13.68 | 13.85 | 13.99 | 14.3 | 14.5 | 14.6 | 14.8 | 14.9 | 15.0 | 15.2 | 15.3 | 15.5 | 15.6 |

## TABLE 20v (PART 1) - NORMAL PARAFFINS, C₁ TO C₂₀

### HEAT CAPACITY, $C_p^o$, FOR THE IDEAL GAS STATE, AT 0° TO 1500°K

November 30, 1945; December 31, 1952

| Compound (gas) | Formula | Temperature in °K — Heat Capacity, $C_p^o$, in cal/deg mole | | | | | | | | | | | | | | |
|---|---|---|---|---|---|---|---|---|---|---|---|---|---|---|---|---|
| | | 0 | 298.16 | 300 | 400 | 500 | 600 | 700 | 800 | 900 | 1000 | 1100 | 1200 | 1300 | 1400 | 1500 |
| Methane | $CH_4$ | 0 | 8.536 | 8.552 | 9.736 | 11.133 | 12.546 | 13.88 | 15.10 | 16.21 | 17.21 | 18.09 | 18.88 | 19.57 | 20.18 | 20.71 |
| Ethane | $C_2H_6$ | 0 | 12.585 | 12.648 | 15.68 | 18.66 | 21.35 | 23.72 | 25.83 | 27.69 | 29.33 | 30.77 | 32.02 | 33.11 | 34.07 | 34.90 |
| Propane | $C_3H_8$ | 0 | 17.57 | 17.66 | 22.54 | 27.04 | 30.88 | 34.20 | 37.08 | 39.61 | 41.83 | 43.75 | 45.42 | 46.89 | 48.16 | 49.26 |
| n-Butane | $C_4H_{10}$ | 0 | 23.29 | 23.40 | 29.60 | 35.34 | 40.30 | 44.55 | 48.23 | 51.44 | 54.22 | 56.64 | 58.74 | 60.58 | 62.17 | 63.57 |
| n-Pentane | $C_5H_{12}$ | 0 | 28.73 | 28.87 | 36.53 | 43.58 | 49.64 | 54.83 | 59.30 | 63.18 | 66.55 | 69.48 | 72.02 | 74.24 | 76.16 | 77.83 |
| n-Hexane | $C_6H_{14}$ | 0 | 34.20 | 34.37 | 43.47 | 51.83 | 58.99 | 65.10 | 70.36 | 74.93 | 78.89 | 82.32 | 85.30 | 87.89 | 90.14 | 92.10 |
| n-Heptane | $C_7H_{16}$ | 0 | 39.67 | 39.86 | 50.42 | 60.07 | 68.33 | 75.38 | 81.43 | 86.68 | 91.21 | 95.2 | 98.6 | 101.6 | 104.1 | 106.4 |
| n-Octane | $C_8H_{18}$ | 0 | 45.14 | 45.35 | 57.36 | 68.32 | 77.67 | 85.66 | 92.50 | 98.43 | 103.6 | 108.0 | 111.8 | 115.2 | 118.1 | 120.6 |
| n-Nonane | $C_9H_{20}$ | 0 | 50.60 | 50.85 | 64.30 | 76.56 | 87.01 | 95.93 | 103.56 | 110.17 | 115.9 | 120.8 | 125.1 | 128.9 | 132.1 | 134.9 |
| n-Decane | $C_{10}H_{22}$ | 0 | 56.07 | 56.34 | 71.24 | 84.81 | 96.36 | 106.21 | 114.63 | 121.92 | 128.2 | 133.7 | 138.4 | 142.5 | 146.1 | 149.2 |
| n-Undecane | $C_{11}H_{24}$ | 0 | 61.53 | 61.84 | 78.18 | 93.05 | 105.70 | 116.48 | 125.69 | 133.66 | 140.6 | 146.5 | 151.7 | 156.2 | 160.0 | 163.4 |
| n-Dodecane | $C_{12}H_{26}$ | 0 | 67.00 | 67.33 | 85.13 | 101.30 | 115.04 | 126.76 | 136.76 | 145.41 | 152.9 | 159.4 | 165.0 | 169.8 | 174.0 | 177.7 |
| n-Tridecane | $C_{13}H_{28}$ | 0 | 72.47 | 72.82 | 92.07 | 109.55 | 124.38 | 137.03 | 147.82 | 157.16 | 165.2 | 172.2 | 178.2 | 183.5 | 188.0 | 192.0 |
| n-Tetradecane | $C_{14}H_{30}$ | 0 | 77.93 | 78.32 | 99.01 | 117.79 | 133.72 | 147.31 | 158.89 | 168.90 | 177.6 | 185.0 | 191.5 | 197.2 | 202.0 | 206.2 |
| n-Pentadecane | $C_{15}H_{32}$ | 0 | 83.40 | 83.81 | 105.95 | 126.04 | 143.07 | 157.59 | 169.95 | 180.65 | 189.9 | 197.9 | 204.8 | 210.8 | 216.0 | 220.5 |
| n-Hexadecane | $C_{16}H_{34}$ | 0 | 88.86 | 89.31 | 112.89 | 134.28 | 152.41 | 167.86 | 181.02 | 192.39 | 202.2 | 210.7 | 218.0 | 224.5 | 230.0 | 234.8 |
| n-Heptadecane | $C_{17}H_{36}$ | 0 | 94.33 | 94.80 | 119.83 | 142.53 | 161.75 | 178.14 | 192.08 | 204.14 | 214.6 | 223.5 | 231.3 | 238.1 | 244.0 | 249.1 |
| n-Octadecane | $C_{18}H_{38}$ | 0 | 99.80 | 100.29 | 126.77 | 150.78 | 171.09 | 188.42 | 203.15 | 215.89 | 226.9 | 236.4 | 244.6 | 251.8 | 257.9 | 263.3 |
| n-Nonadecane | $C_{19}H_{40}$ | 0 | 105.26 | 105.79 | 133.71 | 159.02 | 180.43 | 198.69 | 214.21 | 227.63 | 239.2 | 249.2 | 257.9 | 265.4 | 271.9 | 277.6 |
| n-Eicosane | $C_{20}H_{42}$ | 0 | 110.73 | 111.28 | 140.65 | 167.27 | 189.78 | 208.97 | 225.28 | 239.38 | 251.6 | 262.0 | 271.2 | 279.1 | 285.9 | 291.9 |
| Increment per $CH_2$ group, applicable beyond n-hexane | | 0 | 5.466 | 5.494 | 6.941 | 8.246 | 9.342 | 10.276 | 11.065 | 11.746 | 12.33 | 12.84 | 13.28 | 13.66 | 13.98 | 14.27 |

TABLE 1v – PARAFFINS, $C_1$ TO $C_5$

HEAT CAPACITY, $C_p^o$, FOR THE IDEAL GAS STATE, AT 0° TO 1500°K

August 31, 1944; February 28, 1949; December 31, 1952

| Compound (gas) | Formula | Temperature in °K — Heat Capacity, $C_p^o$, in cal/deg mole | | | | | | | | | | | | | | |
|---|---|---|---|---|---|---|---|---|---|---|---|---|---|---|---|---|
| | | 0 | 100 | 150 | 200 | 250 | 298.16 | 300 | 350 | 400 | 450 | 500 | 600 | 700 | 800 | 900 |
| Methane | $CH_4$ | 0 | 7.949 | 7.953 | 8.002 | 8.185 | 8.536 | 8.552 | 9.082 | 9.721 | 10.42 | 11.13 | 12.55 | 13.88 | 15.10 | 16.21 |
| Ethane | $C_2H_6$ | 0 | 8.59 | 9.32 | 10.17 | 11.28 | 12.58 | 12.64 | 14.13 | 15.68 | 17.19 | 18.66 | 21.35 | 23.72 | 25.83 | 27.69 |
| Propane | $C_3H_8$ | 0 | 9.84 | 11.61 | 13.25 | 15.37 | 17.57 | 17.66 | 20.11 | 22.54 | 24.84 | 27.02 | 30.88 | 34.20 | 37.08 | 39.61 |
| n-Butane | $C_4H_{10}$ | 0 | | | | 20.51 | 23.29 | 23.40 | 26.54 | 29.60 | 32.55 | 35.34 | 40.30 | 44.55 | 48.23 | 51.44 |
| 2-Methylpropane (Isobutane) | " | 0 | | | 17.15 | 20.10 | 23.14 | 23.25 | 26.54 | 29.77 | 32.81 | 35.62 | 40.62 | 44.85 | 48.49 | 51.65 |
| n-Pentane | $C_5H_{12}$ | 0 | | | | 25.29 | 28.73 | 28.87 | 32.75 | 36.53 | 40.16 | 43.58 | 49.64 | 54.83 | 59.30 | 63.18 |
| 2-Methylbutane (Isopentane) | " | 0 | | | | 24.52 | 28.39 | 28.54 | 32.59 | 36.49 | 40.21 | 43.71 | 49.89 | 55.19 | 59.71 | 63.66 |
| 2,2-Dimethylpropane (Neopentane) | " | 0 | | | 21.03 | 25.03 | 29.07 | 29.21 | 33.45 | 37.55 | 41.44 | 45.00 | 51.21 | 56.40 | 60.78 | 64.55 |

| Compound (gas) | Formula | Temperature in °K — Heat Capacity, $C_p^o$, in cal/deg mole | | | | | |
|---|---|---|---|---|---|---|---|
| | | 1000 | 1100 | 1200 | 1300 | 1400 | 1500 |
| Methane | $CH_4$ | 17.21 | 18.09 | 18.88 | 19.57 | 20.18 | 20.71 |
| Ethane | $C_2H_6$ | 29.33 | 30.77 | 32.02 | 33.11 | 34.07 | 34.90 |
| Propane | $C_3H_8$ | 41.83 | 43.75 | 45.42 | 46.89 | 48.16 | 49.26 |
| n-Butane | $C_4H_{10}$ | 54.22 | 56.64 | 58.74 | 60.58 | 62.17 | 63.57 |
| 2-Methylpropane (Isobutane) | " | 54.40 | 56.81 | 58.89 | 60.71 | 62.29 | 63.67 |
| n-Pentane | $C_5H_{12}$ | 66.55 | 69.48 | 72.02 | 74.24 | 76.16 | 77.83 |
| 2-Methylbutane (Isopentane) | " | 67.12 | 70.10 | 72.68 | 74.94 | 76.88 | 78.55 |
| 2,2-Dimethylpropane (Neopentane) | " | 67.80 | 70.62 | 73.04 | 75.15 | 76.99 | 78.60 |

TABLE 2v (PART 1) – PARAFFINS, C$_6$

HEAT CAPACITY, $c_p^o$, FOR THE IDEAL GAS STATE, AT 0° TO 1500°K

September 30, 1944; November 30, 1946; December 31, 1952

| Compound (gas) | Formula | 0 | 298.16 | 300 | 400 | 500 | 600 | 700 | 800 | 900 | 1000 | 1100 | 1200 | 1300 | 1400 | 1500 |
|---|---|---|---|---|---|---|---|---|---|---|---|---|---|---|---|---|
| | | | | | | | | | Temperature in °K | | | | | | | |
| | | | | | | Heat Capacity, $c_p^o$, in cal/deg mole | | | | | | | | | | |
| n-Hexane | C$_6$H$_{14}$ | 0 | 34.20 | 34.37 | 43.47 | 51.83 | 58.99 | 65.10 | 70.36 | 74.93 | 78.89 | 82.32 | 85.30 | 87.89 | 90.14 | 92.10 |
| 2-Methylpentane | " | 0 | 34.46 | 34.63 | 44.0 | 52.5 | 59.6 | 65.7 | 70.8 | 75.3 | 79.2 | | | | | |
| 3-Methylpentane | " | 0 | 34.20 | 34.37 | 43.47 | 51.83 | 59.0 | 65.1 | 70.4 | 74.9 | 78.9 | | | | | |
| 2,2-Dimethylbutane | " | 0 | 33.91 | 34.09 | 43.7 | 52.5 | 60.0 | 66.1 | 71.4 | 75.6 | 79.7 | | | | | |
| 2,3-Dimethylbutane | " | 0 | 33.59 | 33.76 | 43.3 | 51.9 | 59.2 | 65.4 | 70.7 | 75.2 | 79.1 | | | | | |

TABLE 2v (PART 2) — PARAFFINS, $C_7$

HEAT CAPACITY, $C_p^o$, FOR THE IDEAL GAS STATE, AT 0° TO 1500°K

September 30, 1944; December 31, 1952

| Compound (gas) | Formula | Temperature in °K | | | | | | | | | | | | | | |
|---|---|---|---|---|---|---|---|---|---|---|---|---|---|---|---|---|
| | | 0 | 298.16 | 300 | 400 | 500 | 600 | 700 | 800 | 900 | 1000 | 1100 | 1200 | 1300 | 1400 | 1500 |
| | | Heat Capacity, $C_p^o$, in cal/deg mole | | | | | | | | | | | | | | |
| n-Heptane | $C_7H_{16}$ | 0 | 39.67 | 39.86 | 50.42 | 60.07 | 68.33 | 75.38 | 81.43 | 86.68 | 91.2 | 95.2 | 98.6 | 101.6 | 104.1 | 106.4 |
| 2-Methylhexane | " | 0 | a | a | a | a | a | a | a | a | a | | | | | |
| 3-Methylhexane | " | 0 | a | a | a | a | a | a | a | a | a | | | | | |
| 3-Ethylpentane | " | 0 | a | a | a | a | a | a | a | a | a | | | | | |
| 2,2-Dimethylpentane | " | 0 | a | a | a | a | a | a | a | a | a | | | | | |
| 2,3-Dimethylpentane | " | 0 | a | a | a | a | a | a | a | a | a | | | | | |
| 2,4-Dimethylpentane | " | 0 | a | a | a | a | a | a | a | a | a | | | | | |
| 3,3-Dimethylpentane | " | 0 | a | a | a | a | a | a | a | a | a | | | | | |
| 2,2,3-Trimethylbutane | " | 0 | 39.33 | 39.54 | 50.83 | 61.04 | 69.61 | 76.74 | 82.73 | 87.88 | 92.32 | 96.16 | 99.48 | 102.4 | 104.8 | 107.0 |

a Until more data become available, the heat capacity of any branched-chain heptane may be taken as equal to that of the normal heptane. The meager data now available indicate that the difference in heat capacity between normal heptane and any of its isomers is not likely to exceed 3 percent.

TABLE 3v — PARAFFINS, $C_8$

HEAT CAPACITY, $C_p°$, FOR THE IDEAL GAS STATE, AT 0° TO 1500°K

October 31, 1944; December 31, 1952

| Compound (gas) | Formula | Temperature in °K | | | | | | | | | | | | | | |
|---|---|---|---|---|---|---|---|---|---|---|---|---|---|---|---|---|
| | | 0 | 298.16 | 300 | 400 | 500 | 600 | 700 | 800 | 900 | 1000 | 1100 | 1200 | 1300 | 1400 | 1500 |
| | | | | | Heat Capacity, $C_p°$, in cal/deg mole | | | | | | | | | | | |
| n-Octane | $C_8H_{18}$ | 0 | 45.14 | 45.56 | 57.36 | 68.32 | 77.67 | 85.66 | 92.50 | 98.43 | 103.6 | 108.0 | 111.8 | 115.2 | 118.1 | 120.6 |
| 2-Methylheptane | " | 0 | a | a | a | a | a | a | a | a | a | | | | | |
| 3-Methylheptane | " | 0 | a | a | a | a | a | a | a | a | a | | | | | |
| 4-Methylheptane | " | 0 | a | a | a | a | a | a | a | a | a | | | | | |
| 3-Ethylhexane | " | 0 | a | a | a | a | a | a | a | a | a | | | | | |
| 2,2-Dimethylhexane | " | 0 | a | a | a | a | a | a | a | a | a | | | | | |
| 2,3-Dimethylhexane | " | 0 | a | a | a | a | a | a | a | a | a | | | | | |
| 2,4-Dimethylhexane | " | 0 | a | a | a | a | a | a | a | a | a | | | | | |
| 2,5-Dimethylhexane | " | 0 | a | a | a | a | a | a | a | a | a | | | | | |
| 3,3-Dimethylhexane | " | 0 | a | a | a | a | a | a | a | a | a | | | | | |
| 3,4-Dimethylhexane | " | 0 | a | a | a | a | a | a | a | a | a | | | | | |
| 2-Methyl-3-ethylpentane | " | 0 | a | a | a | a | a | a | a | a | a | | | | | |
| 3-Methyl-3-ethylpentane | " | 0 | a | a | a | a | a | a | a | a | a | | | | | |
| 2,2,3-Trimethylpentane | " | 0 | a | a | a | a | a | a | a | a | a | | | | | |
| 2,2,4-Trimethylpentane | " | 0 | a | a | a | a | a | a | a | a | a | | | | | |
| 2,3,3-Trimethylpentane | " | 0 | a | a | a | a | a | a | a | a | a | | | | | |
| 2,3,4-Trimethylpentane | " | 0 | a | a | a | a | a | a | a | a | a | | | | | |
| 2,2,3,3-Tetramethylbutane | " | 0 | 46.03 | 46.29 | 59.88 | 71.76 | 81.52 | 89.52 | 96.18 | 101.8 | 106.6 | | | | | |

a Until more data become available, the heat capacity of any branched-chain octane may be taken as equal to that of normal octane. The meager data now available indicate that the difference in heat capacity between normal octane and any of its isomers is not likely to exceed 3 percent.

## TABLE 22v (PART 1) – NORMAL ALKYL CYCLOPENTANES, C5 TO C21
### HEAT CAPACITY, $C_p^o$, FOR THE IDEAL GAS STATE, AT 0° TO 1500°K
March 31, 1947; December 31, 1952

| Compound (gas) | Formula | Temperature in °K / Heat Capacity, $C_p^o$, in cal/deg mole | | | | | | | | | | | | | |
|---|---|---|---|---|---|---|---|---|---|---|---|---|---|---|---|
| | | 0 | 298.16 | 300 | 400 | 500 | 600 | 700 | 800 | 900 | 1000 | 1100 | 1200 | 1300 | 1400 | 1500 |
| Cyclopentane | $C_5H_{10}$ | 0 | 19.82 | 19.98 | 28.24 | 35.86 | 42.36 | 47.81 | 52.44 | 56.37 | 59.75 | 62.68 | 65.18 | 67.36 | 69.24 | 70.89 |
| Methylcyclopentane | $C_6H_{12}$ | 0 | 26.24 | 26.46 | 36.11 | 44.94 | 52.43 | 58.68 | 64.00 | 68.53 | 72.44 | 75.82 | 78.72 | 81.24 | 83.43 | 85.35 |
| Ethylcyclopentane | $C_7H_{14}$ | 0 | 31.49 | 31.75 | 43.89 | 53.03 | 61.70 | 69.02 | 75.22 | 80.54 | 85.16 | 89.11 | 92.51 | 95.47 | 98.02 | 100.23 |
| n-Propylcyclopentane | $C_8H_{16}$ | 0 | 36.96 | 37.24 | 50.83 | 61.28 | 71.04 | 79.30 | 86.28 | 92.29 | 97.5 | 102.0 | 105.8 | 109.1 | 112.0 | 114.5 |
| n-Butylcyclopentane | $C_9H_{18}$ | 0 | 42.42 | 42.74 | 57.77 | 69.52 | 80.38 | 89.57 | 97.35 | 104.03 | 109.8 | 114.8 | 119.1 | 122.8 | 126.0 | 128.8 |
| n-Pentylcyclopentane | $C_{10}H_{20}$ | 0 | 47.89 | 48.23 | 64.71 | 77.77 | 89.73 | 99.85 | 108.42 | 115.78 | 122.2 | 127.6 | 132.3 | 136.4 | 140.0 | 143.0 |
| n-Hexylcyclopentane | $C_{11}H_{22}$ | 0 | 53.35 | 53.73 | 71.65 | 86.01 | 99.07 | 110.12 | 119.48 | 127.52 | 134.5 | 140.5 | 145.6 | 150.1 | 154.0 | 157.3 |
| n-Heptylcyclopentane | $C_{12}H_{24}$ | 0 | 58.82 | 59.22 | 78.60 | 94.26 | 108.41 | 120.40 | 130.54 | 139.27 | 146.8 | 153.3 | 158.9 | 163.8 | 167.9 | 171.6 |
| n-Octylcyclopentane | $C_{13}H_{26}$ | 0 | 64.29 | 64.71 | 85.54 | 102.51 | 117.75 | 130.68 | 141.61 | 151.02 | 159.2 | 166.1 | 172.2 | 177.4 | 181.9 | 185.8 |
| n-Nonylcyclopentane | $C_{14}H_{28}$ | 0 | 69.75 | 70.21 | 92.48 | 110.75 | 127.09 | 140.95 | 152.68 | 162.76 | 171.5 | 179.0 | 185.4 | 191.1 | 195.9 | 200.1 |
| n-Decylcyclopentane | $C_{15}H_{30}$ | 0 | 75.22 | 75.70 | 99.42 | 119.00 | 136.44 | 151.23 | 163.74 | 174.51 | 183.8 | 191.8 | 198.7 | 204.7 | 209.9 | 214.4 |
| n-Undecylcyclopentane | $C_{16}H_{32}$ | 0 | 80.68 | 81.20 | 106.36 | 127.24 | 145.78 | 161.50 | 174.80 | 186.25 | 196.2 | 204.6 | 212.0 | 218.4 | 223.9 | 228.6 |
| n-Dodecylcyclopentane | $C_{17}H_{34}$ | 0 | 86.15 | 86.69 | 113.30 | 135.49 | 155.12 | 171.78 | 185.87 | 198.00 | 208.5 | 217.5 | 225.3 | 232.0 | 237.8 | 242.9 |
| n-Tridecylcyclopentane | $C_{18}H_{36}$ | 0 | 91.62 | 92.18 | 120.24 | 143.74 | 164.46 | 182.06 | 196.94 | 209.75 | 220.8 | 230.3 | 238.6 | 245.7 | 251.8 | 257.2 |
| n-Tetradecylcyclopentane | $C_{19}H_{38}$ | 0 | 97.08 | 97.68 | 127.18 | 151.98 | 173.80 | 192.33 | 208.00 | 221.49 | 233.2 | 243.2 | 251.8 | 259.4 | 265.8 | 271.5 |
| n-Pentadecylcyclopentane | $C_{20}H_{40}$ | 0 | 102.55 | 103.17 | 134.12 | 160.23 | 183.15 | 202.61 | 219.06 | 233.24 | 245.5 | 256.0 | 265.1 | 273.0 | 279.8 | 285.7 |
| n-Hexadecylcyclopentane | $C_{21}H_{42}$ | 0 | 108.01 | 108.67 | 141.06 | 168.47 | 192.49 | 212.88 | 230.13 | 244.98 | 257.8 | 266.8 | 278.4 | 286.7 | 293.8 | 300.0 |
| Increment per CH2 group, applicable beyond ethylcyclopentane | | 0 | 5.466 | 5.494 | 6.941 | 8.246 | 9.342 | 10.276 | 11.065 | 11.746 | 12.33 | 12.84 | 13.28 | 13.66 | 13.98 | 14.27 |

TABLE 6v – ALKYL CYCLOPENTANES, $C_5$ TO $C_7$

HEAT CAPACITY, $C_p^o$, FOR THE IDEAL GAS STATE, AT 0° TO 1500°K

April 30, 1949; December 31, 1952

Temperature in °K

Heat Capacity, $C_p^o$, in cal/deg mole

| Compound (gas) | Formula | 0 | 298.16 | 300 | 400 | 500 | 600 | 700 | 800 | 900 | 1000 | 1100 | 1200 | 1300 | 1400 | 1500 |
|---|---|---|---|---|---|---|---|---|---|---|---|---|---|---|---|---|
| Cyclopentane | $C_5H_{10}$ | 0 | 19.82 | 19.98 | 28.24 | 38.86 | 42.36 | 47.81 | 52.44 | 56.37 | 59.75 | 62.63 | 65.18 | 67.36 | 69.24 | 70.89 |
| Methylcyclopentane | $C_6H_{12}$ | 0 | 26.24 | 26.46 | 36.11 | 44.94 | 52.43 | 58.68 | 64.00 | 68.53 | 72.44 | 75.82 | 78.72 | 81.24 | 83.43 | 85.35 |
| Ethylcyclopentane | $C_7H_{14}$ | 0 | 31.49 | 31.75 | 43.89 | 53.03 | 61.70 | 69.02 | 75.22 | 80.54 | 85.16 | 89.11 | 92.51 | 95.47 | 98.02 | 100.23 |
| 1,1-Dimethylcyclopentane | " | 0 | 31.86 | 32.16 | 43.55 | 54.01 | 62.78 | 70.08 | 76.18 | 81.38 | 85.83 | 89.62 | 92.89 | 95.75 | 98.19 | 100.31 |
| 1,cis-2-Dimethylcyclopentane | " | 0 | 32.06 | 32.34 | 43.67 | 54.03 | 62.72 | 69.92 | 75.98 | 81.14 | 85.57 | 89.38 | 92.65 | 95.51 | 97.97 | 100.11 |
| 1,trans-2-Dimethylcyclopentane | " | 0 | 32.14 | 32.44 | 43.71 | 54.03 | 62.66 | 69.88 | 75.84 | 80.98 | 85.43 | 89.24 | 92.51 | 95.39 | 97.85 | 100.01 |
| 1,cis-3-Dimethylcyclopentane | " | 0 | 32.14 | 32.44 | 43.71 | 54.03 | 62.66 | 69.88 | 75.84 | 80.98 | 85.43 | 89.24 | 92.51 | 95.39 | 97.85 | 100.01 |
| 1,trans-3-Dimethylcyclopentane | " | 0 | 32.14 | 32.44 | 43.71 | 54.03 | 62.66 | 69.88 | 75.84 | 80.98 | 85.43 | 89.24 | 92.51 | 95.39 | 97.85 | 100.01 |

TABLE 23v (PART 1) — NORMAL ALKYL CYCLOHEXANES, $C_6$ TO $C_{22}$

HEAT CAPACITY, $C_p^\circ$, FOR THE IDEAL GAS STATE, AT 0° TO 1500°K

March 31, 1947; December 31, 1952

| Compound (gas) | Formula | Temperature in °K — Heat Capacity, $C_p^\circ$, in cal/deg mole | | | | | | | | | | | | | |
|---|---|---|---|---|---|---|---|---|---|---|---|---|---|---|---|
| | | 0 | 298.16 | 300 | 400 | 500 | 600 | 700 | 800 | 900 | 1000 | 1100 | 1200 | 1300 | 1400 | 1500 |
| Cyclohexane | $C_6H_{12}$ | 0 | 25.40 | 25.58 | 35.82 | 45.47 | 53.83 | 60.87 | 66.76 | 71.68 | 75.80 | 79.3 | 82.2 | 84.7 | 86.8 | 88.6 |
| Methylcyclohexane | $C_7H_{14}$ | 0 | 32.27 | 32.51 | 44.35 | 55.21 | 64.46 | 72.23 | 78.74 | 84.20 | 88.79 | 92.7 | 96.0 | 98.8 | 101.2 | 103.2 |
| Ethylcyclohexane | $C_8H_{16}$ | 0 | 37.96 | 38.23 | 51.6 | 63.8 | 74.1 | 82.8 | 90.1 | 96.2 | 101.3 | 105.7 | 109.4 | 112.5 | 115.3 | 117.6 |
| n-Propylcyclohexane | $C_9H_{18}$ | 0 | 44.03 | 44.32 | 59.1 | 72.6 | 83.8 | 93.3 | 101.2 | 107.8 | 113.4 | 118.5 | 122.7 | 126.2 | 129.3 | 131.9 |
| n-Butylcyclohexane | $C_{10}H_{20}$ | 0 | 49.50 | 49.81 | 66.0 | 80.8 | 93.1 | 103.6 | 112.3 | 119.6 | 125.7 | 131.3 | 136.0 | 139.9 | 143.3 | 146.2 |
| n-Pentylcyclohexane | $C_{11}H_{22}$ | 0 | 54.96 | 55.31 | 73.0 | 89.1 | 102.5 | 113.9 | 123.3 | 131.3 | 138.1 | 144.2 | 149.3 | 153.5 | 157.3 | 160.4 |
| n-Hexylcyclohexane | $C_{12}H_{24}$ | 0 | 60.43 | 60.80 | 79.9 | 97.4 | 111.8 | 124.1 | 134.4 | 143.0 | 150.4 | 157.0 | 162.5 | 167.2 | 171.2 | 174.7 |
| n-Hentylcyclohexane | $C_{13}H_{26}$ | 0 | 65.89 | 66.30 | 86.9 | 105.6 | 121.2 | 134.4 | 145.4 | 154.8 | 162.7 | 169.9 | 175.8 | 180.8 | 185.2 | 189.0 |
| n-Octylcyclohexane | $C_{14}H_{28}$ | 0 | 71.36 | 71.79 | 93.8 | 113.8 | 130.5 | 144.7 | 156.5 | 166.6 | 175.0 | 182.7 | 189.1 | 194.5 | 199.2 | 203.2 |
| n-Nonylcyclohexane | $C_{15}H_{30}$ | 0 | 76.83 | 77.28 | 100.7 | 122.1 | 139.8 | 155.0 | 167.6 | 178.3 | 187.4 | 195.5 | 202.4 | 208.2 | 213.2 | 217.5 |
| n-Decylcyclohexane | $C_{16}H_{32}$ | 0 | 82.29 | 82.78 | 107.7 | 130.4 | 149.2 | 165.3 | 178.6 | 190.0 | 199.7 | 208.4 | 215.7 | 221.8 | 227.2 | 231.8 |
| n-Undecylcyclohexane | $C_{17}H_{34}$ | 0 | 87.76 | 88.27 | 114.6 | 138.6 | 158.5 | 175.5 | 189.7 | 201.8 | 212.0 | 221.3 | 228.9 | 235.5 | 241.1 | 246.1 |
| n-Dodecylcyclohexane | $C_{18}H_{36}$ | 0 | 93.22 | 93.77 | 121.6 | 146.8 | 167.9 | 185.8 | 200.7 | 213.6 | 224.4 | 234.1 | 242.2 | 249.1 | 255.1 | 260.3 |
| n-Tridecylcyclohexane | $C_{19}H_{38}$ | 0 | 98.69 | 99.26 | 128.5 | 155.1 | 177.2 | 196.1 | 211.8 | 225.3 | 236.7 | 246.9 | 255.5 | 262.8 | 269.1 | 274.6 |
| n-Tetradecylcyclohexane | $C_{20}H_{40}$ | 0 | 104.16 | 104.75 | 135.4 | 163.4 | 186.5 | 206.4 | 222.9 | 237.0 | 249.0 | 259.7 | 268.8 | 276.5 | 283.1 | 288.9 |
| n-Pentadecylcyclohexane | $C_{21}H_{42}$ | 0 | 109.62 | 110.25 | 142.4 | 171.6 | 195.9 | 216.7 | 233.9 | 248.8 | 261.4 | 272.6 | 282.1 | 290.1 | 297.1 | 303.1 |
| n-Hexadecylcyclohexane | $C_{22}H_{44}$ | 0 | 115.09 | 115.74 | 149.3 | 179.8 | 205.2 | 226.9 | 245.0 | 260.6 | 273.7 | 285.4 | 295.3 | 303.8 | 311.0 | 317.4 |
| Increment per $CH_2$ group, applicable beyond n-propylcyclohexane | | 0 | 5.466 | 5.494 | 6.94 | 8.25 | 9.34 | 10.28 | 11.06 | 11.75 | 12.33 | 12.84 | 13.28 | 13.66 | 13.98 | 14.27 |

TABLE 7v – ALKYL CYCLOHEXANES, $C_6$ TO $C_8$

HEAT CAPACITY, $C_p^o$, FOR THE IDEAL GAS STATE, AT 0° TO 1500°K

April 30, 1947 (Corrected)

| Compound (gas) | Formula | Temperature in °K | | | | | | | | | | | | | | |
|---|---|---|---|---|---|---|---|---|---|---|---|---|---|---|---|---|
| | | 0 | 298.16 | 300 | 400 | 500 | 600 | 700 | 800 | 900 | 1000 | 1100 | 1200 | 1300 | 1400 | 1500 |
| | | Heat Capacity, $C_p^o$, in cal/deg mole | | | | | | | | | | | | | | |
| Cyclohexane | $C_6H_{12}$ | 0 | 25.40 | 25.58 | 35.82 | 45.47 | 53.83 | 60.87 | 66.76 | 71.68 | 75.80 | 79.3 | 82.2 | 84.7 | 86.8 | 88.6 |
| Methylcyclohexane | $C_7H_{14}$ | 0 | 32.27 | 32.51 | 44.35 | 55.21 | 64.46 | 72.23 | 78.74 | 84.20 | 88.79 | 92.7 | 96.0 | 98.8 | 101.2 | 103.2 |
| Ethylcyclohexane | $C_8H_{16}$ | 0 | 37.96 | 38.23 | 51.6 | 63.8 | 74.1 | 82.8 | 90.1 | 96.2 | 101.3 | 105.7 | 109.4 | 112.5 | 115.3 | 117.6 |
| 1,1-Dimethylcyclohexane | " | 0 | 36.9 | 37.2 | 50.7 | 63.3 | 74.1 | 83.2 | 90.7 | 97.0 | 102.2 | 106.6 | 110.3 | 113.5 | 116.2 | 118.4 |
| 1,cis-2-Dimethylcyclohexane | " | 0 | 37.4 | 37.7 | 51.1 | 63.5 | 74.0 | 82.8 | 90.1 | 96.3 | 101.4 | 105.8 | 109.5 | 112.7 | 115.4 | 117.7 |
| 1,trans-2-Dimethylcyclohexane | " | 0 | 38.0 | 38.3 | 51.9 | 64.2 | 74.6 | 83.3 | 90.5 | 96.6 | 101.7 | 106.0 | 109.7 | 112.8 | 115.5 | 117.8 |
| 1,cis-3-Dimethylcyclohexane[a] | " | 0 | 37.6 | 37.9 | 51.2 | 63.6 | 74.2 | 83.1 | 90.5 | 96.7 | 102.0 | 106.4 | 110.1 | 113.3 | 116.0 | 118.3 |
| 1,trans-3-Dimethylcyclohexane[b] | " | 0 | 37.6 | 37.9 | 51.1 | 63.4 | 73.8 | 82.5 | 89.8 | 95.9 | 101.1 | 105.5 | 109.2 | 112.4 | 115.2 | 117.5 |
| 1,cis-4-Dimethylcyclohexane | " | 0 | 37.6 | 37.9 | 51.1 | 63.4 | 73.8 | 82.5 | 89.8 | 95.9 | 101.1 | 105.5 | 109.2 | 112.4 | 115.2 | 117.5 |
| 1,trans-4-Dimethylcyclohexane | " | 0 | 37.7 | 38.0 | 51.6 | 64.0 | 74.6 | 83.3 | 90.6 | 96.8 | 101.9 | 106.2 | 109.9 | 113.0 | 115.7 | 118.0 |

[a] Formerly labeled "trans"; see footnote b of Table 7a.

[b] Formerly labeled "cis"; See footnote c of Table 7a.

TABLE 24v (PART 1) – NORMAL MONOOLEFINS (1-ALKENES), $C_2$ TO $C_{20}$
HEAT CAPACITY, $C_p^o$, FOR THE IDEAL GAS STATE, AT 0° TO 1500°K
November 30, 1945; April 30, 1946; December 31, 1952

| Compound (gas) | Formula | Temperature in °K |||||||||||||||
|---|---|---|---|---|---|---|---|---|---|---|---|---|---|---|---|---|
| | | 0 | 298.16 | 300 | 400 | 500 | 600 | 700 | 800 | 900 | 1000 | 1100 | 1200 | 1300 | 1400 | 1500 |
| | | Heat Capacity, $C_p^o$, in cal/deg mole ||||||||||||||||
| Ethene (Ethylene) | $C_2H_4$ | 0 | 10.41 | 10.45 | 12.90 | 15.16 | 17.10 | 18.76 | 20.20 | 21.46 | 22.57 | 23.54 | 24.39 | 25.14 | 25.79 | 26.36 |
| Propene (Propylene) | $C_3H_6$ | 0 | 15.27 | 15.34 | 19.10 | 22.62 | 25.70 | 28.37 | 30.68 | 32.70 | 34.46 | 35.99 | 37.32 | 38.49 | 39.51 | 40.39 |
| 1-Butene | $C_4H_8$ | 0 | 20.47 | 20.57 | 26.04 | 30.93 | 35.14 | 38.71 | 41.80 | 44.49 | 46.82 | 48.85 | 50.62 | 52.16 | 53.50 | 54.67 |
| 1-Pentene | $C_5H_{10}$ | 0 | 26.19 | 26.31 | 33.10 | 39.23 | 44.56 | 49.06 | 52.95 | 56.32 | 59.21 | 61.74 | 63.94 | 65.85 | 67.51 | 68.98 |
| 1-Hexene | $C_6H_{12}$ | 0 | 31.63 | 31.78 | 40.03 | 47.47 | 53.90 | 59.34 | 64.02 | 68.06 | 71.54 | 74.58 | 77.22 | 79.51 | 81.50 | 83.24 |
| 1-Heptene | $C_7H_{14}$ | 0 | 37.10 | 37.27 | 46.97 | 55.72 | 63.24 | 69.62 | 75.08 | 79.81 | 83.9 | 87.4 | 90.5 | 93.2 | 95.5 | 97.5 |
| 1-Octene | $C_8H_{16}$ | 0 | 42.56 | 42.77 | 53.91 | 63.96 | 72.58 | 79.89 | 86.15 | 91.55 | 96.2 | 100.3 | 103.8 | 106.8 | 109.5 | 111.8 |
| 1-Nonene | $C_9H_{18}$ | 0 | 48.03 | 48.26 | 60.85 | 72.21 | 81.93 | 90.17 | 97.22 | 103.30 | 108.5 | 113.1 | 117.1 | 120.5 | 123.4 | 126.0 |
| 1-Decene | $C_{10}H_{20}$ | 0 | 53.49 | 53.76 | 67.79 | 80.45 | 91.27 | 100.44 | 108.28 | 115.04 | 120.9 | 125.9 | 130.3 | 134.2 | 137.4 | 140.3 |
| 1-Undecene | $C_{11}H_{22}$ | 0 | 58.96 | 59.25 | 74.74 | 88.70 | 100.61 | 110.72 | 119.34 | 126.79 | 133.2 | 138.8 | 143.6 | 147.8 | 151.4 | 154.6 |
| 1-Dodecene | $C_{12}H_{24}$ | 0 | 64.43 | 64.74 | 81.68 | 96.95 | 109.95 | 121.00 | 130.41 | 138.54 | 145.5 | 151.6 | 156.9 | 161.5 | 165.4 | 168.9 |
| 1-Tridecene | $C_{13}H_{26}$ | 0 | 69.89 | 70.24 | 88.62 | 105.19 | 119.29 | 131.27 | 141.48 | 150.28 | 157.8 | 164.5 | 170.2 | 175.1 | 179.4 | 183.1 |
| 1-Tetradecene | $C_{14}H_{28}$ | 0 | 75.36 | 75.73 | 95.56 | 113.44 | 128.64 | 141.55 | 152.54 | 162.03 | 170.2 | 177.3 | 183.5 | 188.8 | 193.3 | 197.4 |
| 1-Pentadecene | $C_{15}H_{30}$ | 0 | 80.82 | 81.23 | 102.50 | 121.68 | 137.98 | 151.82 | 163.60 | 173.77 | 182.5 | 190.1 | 196.7 | 202.4 | 207.3 | 211.7 |
| 1-Hexadecene | $C_{16}H_{32}$ | 0 | 86.29 | 86.72 | 109.44 | 129.93 | 147.32 | 162.10 | 174.67 | 185.52 | 194.8 | 203.0 | 210.0 | 216.1 | 221.3 | 225.9 |
| 1-Heptadecene | $C_{17}H_{34}$ | 0 | 91.76 | 92.21 | 116.38 | 138.18 | 156.66 | 172.38 | 185.74 | 197.27 | 207.2 | 215.8 | 223.3 | 229.8 | 235.3 | 240.2 |
| 1-Octadecene | $C_{18}H_{36}$ | 0 | 97.22 | 97.71 | 123.32 | 146.42 | 166.00 | 182.65 | 196.80 | 209.01 | 219.5 | 228.7 | 236.6 | 243.4 | 249.3 | 254.5 |
| 1-Nonadecene | $C_{19}H_{38}$ | 0 | 102.69 | 103.20 | 130.26 | 154.67 | 175.35 | 192.93 | 207.86 | 220.76 | 231.8 | 241.5 | 249.9 | 257.1 | 263.2 | 268.8 |
| 1-Eicosene | $C_{20}H_{40}$ | 0 | 108.15 | 108.70 | 137.20 | 162.91 | 184.69 | 203.20 | 218.93 | 232.50 | 244.2 | 254.3 | 263.1 | 270.8 | 277.2 | 283.0 |
| Increment per $CH_2$ group, applicable beyond 1-hexene | | 0 | 5.466 | 5.494 | 6.941 | 8.246 | 9.342 | 10.276 | 11.065 | 11.746 | 12.33 | 12.84 | 13.28 | 13.66 | 13.98 | 14.27 |

TABLE 8v (PART 1) – MONOOLEFINS, C2 TO C5

HEAT CAPACITY, $C_p^o$, FOR THE IDEAL GAS STATE, AT 0° TO 1500°K

December 31, 1944; March 31, 1945; October 31, 1945; April 30, 1946; December 31, 1952

| Compound (gas) | Formula | Temperature in °K | | | | | | | | | | | | | | |
|---|---|---|---|---|---|---|---|---|---|---|---|---|---|---|---|---|
| | | 0 | 298.16 | 300 | 400 | 500 | 600 | 700 | 800 | 900 | 1000 | 1100 | 1200 | 1300 | 1400 | 1500 |
| | | Heat Capacity, $C_p^o$, in cal/deg mole | | | | | | | | | | | | | | |
| Ethene (Ethylene) | $C_2H_4$ | 0 | 10.41 | 10.45 | 12.90 | 15.16 | 17.10 | 18.76 | 20.20 | 21.46 | 22.57 | 23.54 | 24.39 | 25.14 | 25.79 | 26.36 |
| Propene (Propylene) | $C_3H_6$ | 0 | 15.27 | 15.34 | 19.10 | 22.62 | 25.70 | 28.37 | 30.68 | 32.70 | 34.46 | 35.99 | 37.32 | 38.49 | 39.51 | 40.39 |
| 1-Butene | $C_4H_8$ | 0 | 20.47 | 20.57 | 26.04 | 30.93 | 35.14 | 38.71 | 41.80 | 44.49 | 46.82 | 48.85 | 50.62 | 52.16 | 53.50 | 54.67 |
| cis-2-Butene | " | 0 | 18.86 | 18.96 | 24.33 | 29.39 | 33.80 | 37.60 | 40.87 | 43.70 | 46.15 | 48.28 | 50.13 | 51.74 | 53.13 | 54.35 |
| trans-2-Butene | " | 0 | 20.99 | 21.08 | 26.02 | 30.68 | 34.80 | 38.38 | 41.50 | 44.20 | 46.58 | 48.65 | 50.44 | 52.00 | 53.36 | 54.55 |
| 2-Methylpropene (Isobutene) | " | 0 | 21.30 | 21.39 | 26.57 | 31.24 | 35.30 | 38.31 | 41.86 | 44.53 | 46.85 | 48.88 | 50.63 | 52.17 | 53.51 | 54.68 |
| 1-Pentene | $C_5H_{10}$ | 0 | 26.19 | 26.31 | 33.10 | 39.23 | 44.56 | 49.06 | 52.95 | 56.32 | 59.21 | 61.74 | 63.94 | 65.85 | 67.51 | 68.98 |
| cis-2-Pentene | " | 0 | 24.32 | 24.45 | 31.57 | 38.05 | 43.62 | 48.25 | 52.29 | 55.76 | 58.78 | 61.38 | 63.66 | 65.61 | 67.32 | 68.81 |
| trans-2-Pentene | " | 0 | 25.92 | 26.04 | 32.67 | 38.75 | 44.02 | 48.54 | 52.45 | 55.85 | 58.81 | 61.37 | 63.62 | 65.56 | 67.25 | 68.72 |
| 2-Methyl-1-butene | " | 0 | 26.69 | 26.82 | 33.71 | 39.81 | 44.97 | 49.40 | 53.23 | 56.54 | 59.44 | 61.93 | 64.13 | 66.02 | 67.68 | 69.12 |
| 3-Methyl-1-butene | " | 0 | 28.35 | 28.47 | 35.26 | 40.97 | 45.90 | 50.15 | 53.85 | 57.03 | 59.83 | 62.28 | 64.42 | 66.28 | 67.89 | 69.32 |
| 2-Methyl-2-butene | " | 0 | 25.10 | 25.22 | 31.93 | 38.07 | 43.42 | 48.04 | 52.05 | 55.52 | 58.55 | 61.16 | 63.45 | 65.42 | 67.14 | 68.63 |

643

TABLE 8v (PART 2) - MONOOLEFINS, $C_6$

HEAT CAPACITY, $C_p^\circ$, FOR THE IDEAL GAS STATE, AT 0° TO 1500°K

April 30, 1945; October 31, 1945; December 31, 1952

| Compound (gas) | Formula | Temperature in °K |  |  |  |  |  |  |  |  |  |  |  |  |  |  |
|---|---|---|---|---|---|---|---|---|---|---|---|---|---|---|---|---|
|  |  | 0 | 298.16 | 300 | 400 | 500 | 600 | 700 | 800 | 900 | 1000 | 1100 | 1200 | 1300 | 1400 | 1500 |
|  |  | Heat Capacity, $C_p^\circ$, in cal/deg mole |  |  |  |  |  |  |  |  |  |  |  |  |  |  |
| 1-Hexene | $C_6H_{12}$ | 0 | 31.63 | 31.78 | 40.03 | 47.47 | 53.90 | 59.34 | 64.02 | 68.06 | 71.54 | 74.58 | 77.22 | 79.51 | 81.50 | 83.24 |
| cis-2-Hexene | " | 0 | 30.04 | 30.19 | 38.6 | 46.4 | 53.0 | 58.6 | 63.4 | 67.6 | 71.2 |  |  |  |  |  |
| trans-2-Hexene | " | 0 | 31.64 | 31.78 | 39.7 | 47.1 | 53.4 | 58.9 | 63.6 | 67.6 | 71.2 |  |  |  |  |  |
| cis-3-Hexene | " | 0 | 29.55 | 29.71 | 38.5 | 46.4 | 53.2 | 58.7 | 63.5 | 67.6 | 71.2 |  |  |  |  |  |
| trans-3-Hexene | " | 0 | 31.75 | 31.90 | 40.2 | 47.6 | 53.9 | 59.2 | 63.9 | 67.8 | 71.4 |  |  |  |  |  |
| 2-Methyl-1-pentene | " | 0 | 32.41 | 32.56 | 40.8 | 48.1 | 54.4 | 59.8 | 64.4 | 68.4 | 71.8 |  |  |  |  |  |
| 3-Methyl-1-pentene | " | 0 | 34.64 | 34.82 | 44.4 | 52.6 | 59.7 | 65.7 | 70.9 | 75.4 | 79.3 |  |  |  |  |  |
| 4-Methyl-1-pentene | " | 0 | 30.23 | 30.44 | 38.9 | 46.4 | 52.9 | 58.4 | 63.1 | 67.1 | 70.7 |  |  |  |  |  |
| 2-Methyl-2-pentene | " | 0 | 30.26 | 30.42 | 39.0 | 46.6 | 53.2 | 58.6 | 63.4 | 67.5 | 71.1 |  |  |  |  |  |
| 3-Methyl-cis-2-pentene | " | 0 | 30.26 | 30.42 | 39.0 | 46.6 | 53.2 | 58.6 | 63.4 | 67.5 | 71.1 |  |  |  |  |  |
| 3-Methyl-trans-2-pentene | " | 0 | 30.26 | 30.42 | 39.0 | 46.6 | 53.2 | 58.6 | 63.4 | 67.5 | 71.1 |  |  |  |  |  |
| 4-Methyl-cis-2-pentene | " | 0 | 31.92 | 32.07 | 40.5 | 47.8 | 54.1 | 59.4 | 64.0 | 68.0 | 71.5 |  |  |  |  |  |
| 4-Methyl-trans-2-pentene | " | 0 | 33.80 | 33.94 | 41.9 | 48.8 | 54.8 | 60.0 | 64.5 | 68.4 | 71.8 |  |  |  |  |  |
| 2-Ethyl-1-butene | " | 0 | 31.92 | 32.08 | 40.7 | 48.2 | 54.5 | 59.8 | 64.4 | 68.4 | 71.9 |  |  |  |  |  |
| 2,3-Dimethyl-1-butene | " | 0 | 34.29 | 34.44 | 42.6 | 49.5 | 55.4 | 60.5 | 65.0 | 68.8 | 72.2 |  |  |  |  |  |
| 3,3-Dimethyl-1-butene | " | 0 | 30.23 | 30.39 | 38.9 | 46.7 | 53.4 | 58.9 | 63.6 | 67.3 | 71.0 |  |  |  |  |  |
| 2,3-Dimethyl-2-butene | " | 0 | 30.48 | 30.63 | 38.6 | 46.1 | 52.5 | 58.0 | 62.9 | 67.0 | 70.7 |  |  |  |  |  |

TABLE 11v (PART 1) – DIOLEFINS, $C_3$ TO $C_5$

HEAT CAPACITY, $C_p^o$, FOR THE IDEAL GAS STATE, AT 0° TO 1500°K

October 31, 1947; April 30, 1948

| Compound (gas) | Formula | Temperature in °K — Heat Capacity, $C_p^o$, in cal/deg mole | | | | | | | | | | | | | | |
|---|---|---|---|---|---|---|---|---|---|---|---|---|---|---|---|---|
| | | 0 | 298.16 | 300 | 400 | 500 | 600 | 700 | 800 | 900 | 1000 | 1100 | 1200 | 1300 | 1400 | 1500 |
| Propadiene (Allene) | $C_3H_4$ | 0 | 14.10 | 14.16 | 17.21 | 19.82 | 22.00 | 23.84 | 25.42 | 26.80 | 28.00 | 29.04 | 29.96 | 30.75 | 31.45 | 32.06 |
| 1,2-Butadiene | $C_4H_6$ | 0 | 19.15 | 19.23 | 23.54 | 27.39 | 30.72 | 33.54 | 36.01 | 38.16 | 40.02 | 41.62 | 43.02 | 44.23 | 45.29 | 46.20 |
| 1,3-Butadiene | " | 0 | 19.01 | 19.11 | 24.29 | 28.52 | 31.84 | 34.55 | 36.84 | 38.81 | 40.52 | 42.02 | 43.32 | 44.47 | 45.47 | 46.34 |
| 1,2-Pentadiene | $C_5H_8$ | 0 | 25.2 | 25.3 | 31.4 | 36.5 | 40.8 | 44.5 | 47.7 | 50.4 | 52.8 | 54.9 | 56.7 | 58.2 | 59.6 | 60.7 |
| 1,cis-3-Pentadiene | " | 0 | 22.6 | 22.7 | 29.5 | 35.3 | 39.9 | 43.8 | 47.0 | 49.8 | 52.2 | 54.3 | 56.1 | 57.7 | 59.1 | 60.3 |
| 1,trans-3-Pentadiene | " | 0 | 24.7 | 24.9 | 31.2 | 36.6 | 40.9 | 44.6 | 47.7 | 50.3 | 52.6 | 54.7 | 56.4 | 58.0 | 59.3 | 60.5 |
| 1,4-Pentadiene | " | 0 | 25.1 | 25.2 | 31.3 | 36.5 | 40.8 | 44.4 | 47.6 | 50.3 | 52.7 | 54.7 | 56.5 | 58.1 | 59.4 | 60.6 |
| 2,3-Pentadiene | " | 0 | 24.2 | 24.3 | 29.9 | 35.0 | 39.4 | 43.2 | 46.6 | 49.5 | 52.0 | 54.2 | 56.1 | 57.7 | 59.1 | 60.3 |
| 3-Methyl-1,2-butadiene | " | 0 | 25.2 | 25.3 | 31.0 | 36.0 | 40.3 | 44.0 | 47.2 | 50.0 | 52.4 | 54.5 | 56.3 | 57.9 | 59.3 | 60.5 |
| 2-Methyl-1,3-butadiene (Isoprene) | " | 0 | 25.0 | 25.2 | 31.8 | 37.1 | 41.4 | 45.0 | 48.0 | 50.6 | 52.9 | 54.9 | 56.6 | 58.2 | 59.5 | 60.6 |

TABLE 16v – ALKYL CYCLOPENTENES, $C_5$ TO $C_7$

HEAT CAPACITY, $C_p^o$, FOR THE IDEAL GAS STATE, AT 0° TO 1500°K

December 31, 1952

Temperature in °K

Heat Capacity, $C_p^o$, in cal/deg mole

| Compound (gas) | Formula | 0 | 298.16 | 300 | 400 | 500 | 600 | 700 | 800 | 900 | 1000 | 1100 | 1200 | 1300 | 1400 | 1500 |
|---|---|---|---|---|---|---|---|---|---|---|---|---|---|---|---|---|
| Cyclopentene | $C_5H_8$ | 0 | 17.95 | 18.08 | 25.08 | 31.62 | 37.19 | 41.86 | 45.78 | 49.11 | 51.94 | 54.37 | 56.45 | 58.24 | 59.79 | 61.13 |
| 1-Methylcyclopentene | $C_6H_{10}$ | 0 | 24.1 | 24.3 | 32.5 | 40.2 | 46.8 | 52.3 | 57.0 | 60.9 | 64.3 | 67.2 | 69.7 | 71.9 | 73.8 | 75.4 |
| 3-Methylcyclopentene | " | 0 | 23.9 | 24.1 | 32.6 | 40.5 | 47.1 | 52.6 | 57.2 | 61.1 | 64.5 | 67.4 | 69.9 | 72.0 | 73.9 | 75.5 |
| 4-Methylcyclopentene | " | 0 | 23.9 | 24.1 | 32.6 | 40.4 | 47.0 | 52.5 | 57.1 | 61.1 | 64.4 | 67.3 | 69.8 | 71.9 | 73.8 | 75.4 |
| 1-Ethylcyclonentene | $C_7H_{12}$ | | | | | | | | | | | | | | | |
| 3-Ethylcyclopentene | " | | | | | | | | | | | | | | | |
| 4-Ethylcyclonentene | " | 0 | 30.3 | 30.5 | 40.0 | 48.9 | 56.4 | 62.7 | 68.1 | 72.7 | 76.7 | 80.1 | 83.1 | 85.6 | 87.9 | 89.7 |
| 1,2-Dimethylcyclopentene | " | 0 | 30.1 | 30.3 | 40.1 | 49.1 | 56.7 | 63.0 | 68.4 | 73.0 | 76.9 | 80.3 | 83.2 | 85.7 | 87.9 | 89.8 |
| 1,3-Dimethylcyclopentene | " | 0 | 30.0 | 30.3 | 40.0 | 49.0 | 56.6 | 62.9 | 68.3 | 72.9 | 76.8 | 80.2 | 83.1 | 85.6 | 87.8 | 89.7 |
| 1,4-Dimethylcyclonentene | " | 0 | 30.1 | 30.3 | 40.1 | 49.1 | 56.6 | 63.0 | 68.4 | 72.9 | 76.8 | 80.2 | 83.2 | 85.7 | 87.9 | 89.8 |
| 1,5-Dimethylcyclonentene | " | 0 | 29.4 | 29.6 | 39.8 | 49.4 | 57.4 | 64.1 | 69.7 | 74.3 | 78.3 | 81.6 | 84.5 | 86.9 | 89.0 | 90.9 |
| 3,3-Dimethylcyclopentene | " | 0 | 29.8 | 30.0 | 40.2 | 49.5 | 57.2 | 63.6 | 69.0 | 73.5 | 77.4 | 80.7 | 83.6 | 86.1 | 88.2 | 90.1 |
| 3,cis-4-Dimethylcyclopentene | " | 0 | 30.0 | 30.2 | 40.2 | 49.4 | 57.0 | 63.3 | 68.6 | 73.2 | 77.1 | 80.4 | 83.3 | 85.8 | 88.0 | 89.8 |
| 3,trans-4-Dimethylcyclopentene | " | 0 | 30.0 | 30.2 | 40.2 | 49.4 | 57.0 | 63.3 | 68.6 | 73.2 | 77.1 | 80.4 | 83.3 | 85.8 | 88.0 | 89.8 |
| 3,cis-5-Dimethylcyclopentene | " | 0 | 30.0 | 30.2 | 40.2 | 49.4 | 57.0 | 63.3 | 68.6 | 73.2 | 77.1 | 80.4 | 83.3 | 85.8 | 88.0 | 89.8 |
| 3,trans-5-Dimethylcyclonentene | " | 0 | 30.0 | 30.2 | 40.2 | 49.4 | 57.0 | 63.3 | 68.6 | | | | | | | |
| 4,4-Dimethylcyclonentene | " | | | | | | | | | | | | | | | |

TABLE 19v – ALKYL CYCLOHEXENES, $C_6$ TO $C_8$

HEAT CAPACITY, $C_p^o$, FOR THE IDEAL GAS STATE, AT 0° TO 1500°K

December 31, 1952

Heat Capacity, $C_p^o$, in cal/deg mole

| Compound (gas) | Formula | Temperature in °K | | | | | | | | | | | | | | |
|---|---|---|---|---|---|---|---|---|---|---|---|---|---|---|---|---|
| | | 0 | 298.16 | 300 | 400 | 500 | 600 | 700 | 800 | 900 | 1000 | 1100 | 1200 | 1300 | 1400 | 1500 |
| Cyclohexene | $C_6H_{10}$ | 0 | 25.10 | 25.28 | 34.64 | 42.78 | 49.45 | 54.92 | 59.49 | 63.34 | 66.62 | 69.43 | 71.85 | 73.92 | 75.72 | 77.27 |
| 1-Methylcyclohexene | $C_7H_{12}$ | | | | | | | | | | | | | | | |
| 3-Methylcyclohexene | " | | | | | | | | | | | | | | | |
| 4-Methylcyclohexene | " | | | | | | | | | | | | | | | |
| 1-Ethylcyclohexene | $C_8H_{14}$ | | | | | | | | | | | | | | | |
| 3-Ethylcyclohexene | " | | | | | | | | | | | | | | | |
| 4-Ethylcyclohexene | " | | | | | | | | | | | | | | | |
| 1,2-Dimethylcyclohexene | " | | | | | | | | | | | | | | | |
| 1,3-Dimethylcyclohexene | " | | | | | | | | | | | | | | | |
| 1,4-Dimethylcyclohexene | " | | | | | | | | | | | | | | | |
| 1,5-Dimethylcyclohexene | " | | | | | | | | | | | | | | | |
| 1,6-Dimethylcyclohexene | " | | | | | | | | | | | | | | | |
| 3,3-Dimethylcyclohexene | " | | | | | | | | | | | | | | | |
| 3,cis-4-Dimethylcyclohexene | " | | | | | | | | | | | | | | | |
| 3,trans-4-Dimethylcyclohexene | " | | | | | | | | | | | | | | | |
| 3,cis-5-Dimethylcyclohexene | " | | | | | | | | | | | | | | | |
| 3,trans-5-Dimethylcyclohexene | " | | | | | | | | | | | | | | | |
| 3,cis-6-Dimethylcyclohexene | " | | | | | | | | | | | | | | | |
| 3,trans-6-Dimethylcyclohexene | " | | | | | | | | | | | | | | | |
| 4,4-Dimethylcyclohexene | " | | | | | | | | | | | | | | | |
| 4,cis-5-Dimethylcyclohexene | " | | | | | | | | | | | | | | | |
| 4,trans-5-Dimethylcyclohexene | " | | | | | | | | | | | | | | | |

TABLE 25v (PART 1) - NORMAL ACETYLENES (1-ALKYNES), $C_2$ TO $C_{20}$
HEAT CAPACITY, $C_p°$, FOR THE IDEAL GAS STATE, AT 0° TO 1500°K
February 28, 1946; December 31, 1952

Temperature in °K

Heat Capacity, $C_p°$, in cal/deg mole

| Compound (gas) | Formula | 0 | 298.16 | 300 | 400 | 500 | 600 | 700 | 800 | 900 | 1000 | 1100 | 1200 | 1300 | 1400 | 1500 |
|---|---|---|---|---|---|---|---|---|---|---|---|---|---|---|---|---|
| Ethyne (Acetylene) | $C_2H_2$ | 0 | 10.199 | 10.532 | 11.973 | 12.967 | 13.728 | 14.366 | 14.933 | 15.449 | 15.922 | 16.353 | 16.744 | 17.099 | 17.418 | 17.704 |
| Propyne (Methylacetylene) | $C_3H_4$ | 0 | 14.50 | 14.55 | 17.33 | 19.74 | 21.80 | 23.58 | 25.14 | 26.51 | 27.71 | 28.77 | 29.69 | 30.50 | 31.21 | 31.84 |
| 1-Butyne (Ethylacetylene) | $C_4H_6$ | 0 | 19.46 | 19.54 | 23.87 | 27.63 | 30.83 | 33.57 | 35.95 | 38.02 | 39.84 | 41.42 | 42.80 | 44.01 | 45.06 | 45.98 |
| 1-Pentyne | $C_5H_8$ | 0 | 25.18 | 25.28 | 30.93 | 35.93 | 40.25 | 43.92 | 47.10 | 49.85 | 52.23 | 54.31 | 56.12 | 57.70 | 59.07 | 60.29 |
| 1-Hexyne | $C_6H_{10}$ | 0 | 30.65 | 30.77 | 37.87 | 44.18 | 49.59 | 54.20 | 58.16 | 61.60 | 64.56 | 67.15 | 69.40 | 71.36 | 73.05 | 74.56 |
| 1-Heptyne | $C_7H_{12}$ | 0 | 36.11 | 36.27 | 44.81 | 52.42 | 58.93 | 64.47 | 69.23 | 73.34 | 76.9 | 80.0 | 82.7 | 85.0 | 87.04 | 88.83 |
| 1-Octyne | $C_8H_{14}$ | 0 | 41.58 | 41.76 | 51.75 | 60.67 | 68.28 | 74.75 | 80.30 | 85.09 | 89.2 | 92.8 | 96.0 | 98.7 | 101.0 | 103.1 |
| 1-Nonyne | $C_9H_{16}$ | 0 | 47.04 | 47.26 | 58.69 | 68.91 | 77.62 | 85.02 | 91.36 | 96.83 | 101.6 | 105.7 | 109.2 | 112.3 | 115.0 | 117.4 |
| 1-Decyne | $C_{10}H_{18}$ | 0 | 52.51 | 52.75 | 65.64 | 77.16 | 86.96 | 95.30 | 102.42 | 108.58 | 113.9 | 118.5 | 122.5 | 126.0 | 129.0 | 131.6 |
| 1-Undecyne | $C_{11}H_{20}$ | 0 | 57.98 | 58.24 | 72.58 | 85.41 | 96.30 | 105.58 | 113.49 | 120.33 | 126.2 | 131.3 | 135.8 | 139.6 | 143.0 | 145.9 |
| 1-Dodecyne | $C_{12}H_{22}$ | 0 | 63.44 | 63.74 | 79.52 | 92.65 | 105.64 | 115.85 | 124.56 | 132.07 | 138.6 | 144.2 | 149.0 | 153.3 | 157.0 | 160.2 |
| 1-Tridecyne | $C_{13}H_{24}$ | 0 | 68.91 | 69.23 | 86.46 | 101.90 | 114.99 | 126.13 | 135.62 | 143.82 | 150.9 | 157.0 | 162.3 | 167.0 | 170.9 | 174.4 |
| 1-Tetradecyne | $C_{14}H_{26}$ | 0 | 74.37 | 74.73 | 93.40 | 110.14 | 124.33 | 136.40 | 146.68 | 155.56 | 163.2 | 169.8 | 175.6 | 180.6 | 184.9 | 188.7 |
| 1-Pentadecyne | $C_{15}H_{28}$ | 0 | 79.84 | 80.22 | 100.34 | 118.39 | 133.67 | 146.68 | 157.75 | 167.31 | 175.6 | 182.7 | 188.9 | 194.3 | 198.9 | 203.0 |
| 1-Hexadecyne | $C_{16}H_{30}$ | 0 | 85.31 | 85.71 | 107.28 | 126.64 | 143.01 | 156.96 | 168.82 | 179.06 | 187.9 | 195.5 | 202.2 | 207.9 | 212.9 | 217.2 |
| 1-Heptadecyne | $C_{17}H_{32}$ | 0 | 90.77 | 91.21 | 114.22 | 134.88 | 152.35 | 167.23 | 179.88 | 190.80 | 200.2 | 208.4 | 215.4 | 221.6 | 226.9 | 231.5 |
| 1-Octadecyne | $C_{18}H_{34}$ | 0 | 96.24 | 96.70 | 121.16 | 143.13 | 161.70 | 177.51 | 190.94 | 202.55 | 212.6 | 221.2 | 228.7 | 235.2 | 240.8 | 245.8 |
| 1-Nonadecyne | $C_{19}H_{36}$ | 0 | 101.70 | 102.20 | 128.10 | 151.37 | 171.04 | 187.78 | 202.01 | 214.29 | 224.9 | 234.0 | 242.0 | 248.9 | 254.8 | 260.1 |
| 1-Eicosyne | $C_{20}H_{38}$ | 0 | 107.17 | 107.69 | 135.04 | 159.62 | 180.38 | 198.06 | 213.08 | 226.04 | 237.2 | 246.9 | 255.3 | 262.6 | 268.8 | 274.3 |
| Increment per CH2 group, applicable beyond 1-pentyne | | 0 | 5.466 | 5.494 | 6.941 | 8.246 | 9.342 | 10.276 | 11.065 | 11.746 | 12.33 | 12.84 | 13.28 | 13.66 | 13.98 | 14.27 |

## TABLE 12v – ACETYLENES, $C_2$ TO $C_5$
## HEAT CAPACITY, $C_p^o$, FOR THE IDEAL GAS STATE, AT 0° TO 1500°K

April 30, 1945

Heat Capacity, $C_p^o$, in cal/deg mole

| Compound (gas) | Formula | Temperature in °K | | | | | | | | | | | | | | |
|---|---|---|---|---|---|---|---|---|---|---|---|---|---|---|---|---|
| | | 0 | 298.16 | 300 | 400 | 500 | 600 | 700 | 800 | 900 | 1000 | 1100 | 1200 | 1300 | 1400 | 1500 |
| Ethyne (Acetylene) | $C_2H_2$ | 0 | 10.499 | 10.532 | 11.973 | 12.967 | 13.728 | 14.366 | 14.933 | 15.449 | 15.922 | 16.353 | 16.744 | 17.099 | 17.418 | 17.704 |
| Propyne (Methylacetylene) | $C_3H_4$ | 0 | 14.50 | 14.55 | 17.33 | 19.74 | 21.80 | 23.58 | 25.14 | 26.51 | 27.71 | 28.77 | 29.69 | 30.50 | 31.21 | 31.84 |
| 1-Butyne (Ethylacetylene) | $C_4H_6$ | 0 | 19.46 | 19.54 | 23.87 | 27.63 | 30.83 | 33.57 | 35.95 | 38.02 | 39.84 | 41.42 | 42.80 | 44.01 | 45.06 | 45.98 |
| 2-Butyne (Dimethylacetylene) | " | 0 | 18.63 | 18.70 | 22.62 | 26.36 | 29.68 | 32.59 | 35.14 | 37.36 | 39.29 | 40.98 | 42.44 | 43.71 | 44.82 | 45.78 |
| 1-Pentyne | $C_5H_8$ | 0 | 25.50 | 25.65 | 31.1 | 36.1 | 40.4 | 44.0 | 47.1 | 49.8 | 52.2 | 54.3 | 56.1 | 57.7 | 59.1 | 60.2 |
| 2-Pentyne | " | 0 | 23.59 | 23.69 | 29.2 | 34.3 | 38.7 | 42.6 | 45.9 | 48.9 | 51.4 | 53.6 | 55.6 | 57.2 | 58.7 | 59.9 |
| 3-Methyl-1-butyne | " | 0 | 25.02 | 25.13 | 31.1 | 36.2 | 40.6 | 44.2 | 47.4 | 50.1 | 52.4 | 54.5 | 56.3 | 57.8 | 59.2 | 60.4 |

## TABLE 21v (PART 1) - NORMAL ALKYL BENZENES, $C_6$ TO $C_{22}$
### HEAT CAPACITY, $C_p^o$, FOR THE IDEAL GAS STATE, AT 0° TO 1500°K
November 30, 1945; December 31, 1952

| Compound (gas) | Formula | Temperature in °K — Heat Capacity, $C_p^o$, in cal/deg mole | | | | | | | | | | | | | |
|---|---|---|---|---|---|---|---|---|---|---|---|---|---|---|---|
| | | 0 | 298.16 | 300 | 400 | 500 | 600 | 700 | 800 | 900 | 1000 | 1100 | 1200 | 1300 | 1400 | 1500 |
| Benzene | $C_6H_6$ | 0 | 19.52 | 19.65 | 26.74 | 32.80 | 37.74 | 41.75 | 45.06 | 47.83 | 50.16 | 52.16 | 53.86 | 55.32 | 56.58 | 57.67 |
| Methylbenzene (Toluene) | $C_7H_8$ | 0 | 24.80 | 24.95 | 33.25 | 40.54 | 46.58 | 51.57 | 55.72 | 59.22 | 62.19 | 64.73 | 66.90 | 68.77 | 70.38 | 71.78 |
| Ethylbenzene | $C_8H_{10}$ | 0 | 30.69 | 30.88 | 40.76 | 49.35 | 56.44 | 62.28 | 67.15 | 71.27 | 74.77 | 77.77 | 80.35 | 82.57 | 84.49 | 86.16 |
| n-Propylbenzene | $C_9H_{12}$ | 0 | 36.41 | 36.62 | 47.82 | 57.65 | 65.86 | 72.63 | 78.30 | 83.10 | 87.16 | 90.66 | 93.67 | 96.26 | 98.50 | 100.47 |
| n-Butylbenzene | $C_{10}H_{14}$ | 0 | 41.85 | 42.09 | 54.75 | 65.89 | 75.20 | 82.91 | 89.37 | 94.84 | 99.49 | 103.50 | 106.95 | 109.92 | 112.49 | 114.73 |
| n-Pentylbenzene | $C_{11}H_{16}$ | 0 | 47.32 | 47.59 | 61.69 | 74.14 | 84.55 | 93.18 | 100.43 | 106.59 | 111.83 | 116.34 | 120.23 | 123.57 | 126.47 | 129.00 |
| n-Hexylbenzene | $C_{12}H_{18}$ | 0 | 52.79 | 53.08 | 68.63 | 82.39 | 93.89 | 103.46 | 111.50 | 118.34 | 124.2 | 129.2 | 133.5 | 137.2 | 140.4 | 143.3 |
| n-Heptylbenzene | $C_{13}H_{20}$ | 0 | 58.25 | 58.58 | 75.57 | 90.63 | 103.23 | 113.73 | 122.56 | 130.08 | 136.5 | 142.0 | 146.8 | 150.9 | 154.4 | 157.5 |
| n-Octylbenzene | $C_{14}H_{22}$ | 0 | 63.72 | 64.07 | 82.51 | 98.88 | 112.58 | 124.01 | 133.62 | 141.83 | 148.8 | 154.8 | 160.1 | 164.5 | 168.4 | 171.8 |
| n-Nonylbenzene | $C_{15}H_{24}$ | 0 | 69.18 | 69.57 | 89.45 | 107.12 | 121.92 | 134.28 | 144.69 | 153.57 | 161.2 | 167.7 | 173.3 | 178.2 | 182.4 | 186.1 |
| n-Decylbenzene | $C_{16}H_{26}$ | 0 | 74.65 | 75.06 | 96.40 | 115.37 | 131.26 | 144.56 | 155.76 | 165.32 | 173.5 | 180.5 | 186.6 | 191.9 | 196.4 | 200.3 |
| n-Undecylbenzene | $C_{17}H_{28}$ | 0 | 80.12 | 80.55 | 103.34 | 123.62 | 140.60 | 154.84 | 166.82 | 177.07 | 185.8 | 193.4 | 199.9 | 205.5 | 210.4 | 214.6 |
| n-Dodecylbenzene | $C_{18}H_{30}$ | 0 | 85.58 | 86.05 | 110.28 | 131.86 | 149.94 | 165.11 | 177.88 | 188.81 | 198.2 | 206.2 | 213.2 | 219.2 | 224.4 | 228.9 |
| n-Tridecylbenzene | $C_{19}H_{32}$ | 0 | 91.05 | 91.54 | 117.22 | 140.11 | 159.29 | 175.39 | 188.95 | 200.56 | 210.5 | 219.0 | 226.4 | 232.8 | 238.3 | 243.2 |
| n-Tetradecylbenzene | $C_{20}H_{34}$ | 0 | 96.51 | 97.04 | 124.16 | 148.35 | 168.63 | 185.66 | 200.02 | 212.30 | 222.8 | 231.9 | 239.7 | 246.5 | 252.3 | 257.4 |
| n-Pentadecylbenzene | $C_{21}H_{36}$ | 0 | 101.98 | 102.53 | 131.10 | 156.60 | 177.97 | 195.94 | 211.08 | 224.05 | 235.2 | 244.7 | 253.0 | 260.1 | 266.3 | 271.7 |
| n-Hexadecylbenzene | $C_{22}H_{38}$ | 0 | 107.45 | 108.02 | 138.04 | 164.85 | 187.31 | 206.22 | 222.14 | 235.80 | 247.5 | 257.6 | 266.3 | 273.8 | 280.3 | 286.0 |
| Increment per $CH_2$ group, applicable beyond n-pentylbenzene | | 0 | 5.466 | 5.494 | 6.941 | 8.246 | 9.342 | 10.276 | 11.065 | 11.746 | 12.33 | 12.84 | 13.28 | 13.66 | 13.98 | 14.27 |

TABLE 5v – ALKYL-BENZENES, $C_6$ TO $C_9$

HEAT CAPACITY, $C_p^o$, FOR THE IDEAL GAS STATE, AT 0° TO 1500°K

November 30, 1945

| Compound (gas) | Formula | Temperature in °K — Heat Capacity, $C_p^o$, in cal/deg mole | | | | | | | | | | | | | |
|---|---|---|---|---|---|---|---|---|---|---|---|---|---|---|---|
| | | 0 | 298.16 | 300 | 400 | 500 | 600 | 700 | 800 | 900 | 1000 | 1100 | 1200 | 1300 | 1400 | 1500 |
| Benzene | $C_6H_6$ | 0 | 19.52 | 19.65 | 26.74 | 32.80 | 37.74 | 41.75 | 45.06 | 47.83 | 50.16 | 52.16 | 53.86 | 55.32 | 56.58 | 57.67 |
| Methylbenzene (Toluene) | $C_7H_8$ | 0 | 24.80 | 24.95 | 33.25 | 40.54 | 46.58 | 51.57 | 55.72 | 59.22 | 62.19 | 64.73 | 66.90 | 68.77 | 70.38 | 71.78 |
| Ethylbenzene | $C_8H_{10}$ | 0 | 30.69 | 30.88 | 40.76 | 49.35 | 56.44 | 62.28 | 67.15 | 71.27 | 74.77 | 77.77 | 80.35 | 82.57 | 84.49 | 86.16 |
| 1,2-Dimethylbenzene (o-Xylene) | " | 0 | 31.85 | 32.02 | 41.03 | 49.11 | 55.98 | 61.76 | 66.64 | 70.80 | 74.35 | 77.40 | 80.02 | 82.28 | 84.24 | 85.93 |
| 1,3-Dimethylbenzene (m-Xylene) | " | 0 | 30.49 | 30.66 | 40.03 | 48.43 | 55.51 | 61.43 | 66.41 | 70.63 | 74.23 | 77.31 | 79.95 | 82.22 | 84.19 | 85.89 |
| 1,4-Dimethylbenzene (p-Xylene) | " | 0 | 30.32 | 30.49 | 39.70 | 48.06 | 55.16 | 61.12 | 66.14 | 70.39 | 74.02 | 77.13 | 79.80 | 82.09 | 84.07 | 85.79 |
| n-Propylbenzene | $C_9H_{12}$ | 0 | 36.73 | 36.99 | 48.0 | 57.8 | 66.0 | 72.7 | 78.3 | 83.1 | 87.1 | 90.6 | 93.6 | 96.2 | 98.5 | 100.4 |
| Isopropylbenzene | " | 0 | 36.26 | 36.47 | 48.0 | 57.9 | 66.2 | 72.9 | 78.6 | 83.3 | 87.3 | 90.8 | 93.8 | 96.4 | 98.6 | 100.6 |
| 1-Methyl-2-ethylbenzene | " | 0 | 37.74 | 37.94 | 48.5 | 57.9 | 65.8 | 72.5 | 78.1 | 82.8 | 86.9 | 90.4 | 93.5 | 96.1 | 98.3 | 100.3 |
| 1-Methyl-3-ethylbenzene | " | 0 | 36.38 | 36.59 | 47.5 | 57.2 | 65.4 | 72.1 | 77.8 | 82.7 | 86.8 | 90.4 | 93.4 | 96.0 | 98.3 | 100.3 |
| 1-Methyl-4-ethylbenzene | " | 0 | 36.22 | 36.42 | 47.2 | 56.9 | 65.0 | 71.8 | 77.6 | 82.4 | 86.6 | 90.2 | 93.2 | 95.9 | 98.2 | 100.2 |
| 1,2,3-Trimethylbenzene | " | 0 | 36.85 | 37.04 | 46.9 | 56.1 | 64.0 | 70.9 | 76.7 | 81.6 | 85.9 | 89.5 | 92.7 | 95.4 | 97.8 | 99.8 |
| 1,2,4-Trimethylbenzene | " | 0 | 37.10 | 37.28 | 47.1 | 56.2 | 64.2 | 71.0 | 76.8 | 81.7 | 86.0 | 89.6 | 92.8 | 95.5 | 97.3 | 99.8 |
| 1,3,5-Trimethylbenzene | " | 0 | 35.91 | 36.10 | 46.41 | 55.92 | 64.08 | 70.99 | 76.84 | 81.81 | 86.07 | 89.72 | 92.86 | 95.56 | 97.89 | 99.91 |

## TABLE 13v - STYRENES, C$_8$ and C$_9$

### HEAT CAPACITY, $C_p^o$, FOR THE IDEAL GAS STATE, AT 0° TO 1500°K

September 30, 1947

| Compound (gas) | Formula | Temperature in °K — Heat Capacity, $C_p^o$, in cal/deg mole | | | | | | | | | | | | | | |
|---|---|---|---|---|---|---|---|---|---|---|---|---|---|---|---|---|
| | | 0 | 298.16 | 300 | 400 | 500 | 600 | 700 | 800 | 900 | 1000 | 1100 | 1200 | 1300 | 1400 | 1500 |
| Ethenylbenzene (Styrene; Vinylbenzene; Phenylethylene) | C$_8$H$_8$ | 0 | 29.18 | 29.35 | 38.32 | 45.94 | 52.14 | 57.21 | 61.40 | 64.93 | 67.92 | 70.48 | 72.66 | 74.54 | 76.16 | 77.57 |
| Isopropenylbenzene (α-Methylstyrene; 2-Phenyl-1-propene) | C$_9$H$_{10}$ | 0 | 34.7 | 34.9 | 44.8 | 53.5 | 60.7 | 66.8 | 71.8 | 76.1 | 79.8 | 82.9 | 85.6 | 87.9 | 89.9 | 91.6 |
| cis-1-Propenylbenzene (cis-β-Methylstyrene; cis-1-Phenyl-1-propene) | " | 0 | 34.7 | 34.9 | 44.8 | 53.5 | 60.7 | 66.8 | 71.8 | 76.1 | 79.8 | 82.9 | 85.6 | 87.9 | 89.9 | 91.6 |
| trans-1-Propenylbenzene (trans-β-Methylstyrene; trans-1-Phenyl-1-propene) | " | 0 | 34.9 | 35.1 | 45.2 | 54.0 | 61.2 | 67.2 | 72.2 | 76.4 | 80.0 | 83.1 | 85.8 | 88.1 | 90.0 | 91.7 |
| 1-Methyl-2-ethenylbenzene (o-Methylstyrene) | " | 0 | 34.7 | 34.9 | 44.8 | 53.5 | 60.7 | 66.8 | 71.8 | 76.1 | 79.8 | 82.9 | 85.6 | 87.9 | 89.9 | 91.6 |
| 1-Methyl-3-ethenylbenzene (m-Methylstyrene) | " | 0 | 34.7 | 34.9 | 44.8 | 53.5 | 60.7 | 66.8 | 71.8 | 76.1 | 79.8 | 82.9 | 85.6 | 87.9 | 89.9 | 91.6 |
| 1-Methyl-4-ethenylbenzene (p-Methylstyrene) | " | 0 | 34.7 | 34.9 | 44.8 | 53.5 | 60.7 | 66.8 | 71.8 | 76.1 | 79.8 | 82.9 | 85.6 | 87.9 | 89.9 | 91.6 |

652

TABLE 0v-E — $O_2$, $H_2$, OH, $H_2O$, $N_2$, NO, C, CO, $CO_2$

HEAT CAPACITY, $C_p^o$, AT -459.69° TO 2200°F

November 30, 1944; August 31, 1946; June 30, 1949

| Compound | Formula | State | Temperature in °F — Heat Capacity, $C_p^o$, in BTU/lb deg F | | | | | | | | | | | | | |
|---|---|---|---|---|---|---|---|---|---|---|---|---|---|---|---|---|
| | | | -459.69 | 0 | 32 | 60 | 68 | 77 | 100 | 200 | 300 | 400 | 500 | 600 | 700 | 800 |
| Oxygen | $O_2$ | gas | 0 | 0.2178 | 0.2182 | 0.2188 | 0.2189 | 0.2191 | 0.2197 | 0.2225 | 0.2260 | 0.2303 | 0.2345 | 0.2387 | 0.2426 | 0.2462 |
| Hydrogen | $H_2$ | gas | 0 | 3.364 | 3.390 | 3.408 | 3.412 | 3.416 | 3.425 | 3.449 | 3.461 | 3.466 | 3.469 | 3.473 | 3.479 | 3.487 |
| Hydroxyl | OH | gas | 0 | 0.4220 | 0.4209 | 0.4201 | 0.4198 | 0.4196 | 0.4189 | 0.4166 | 0.4151 | 0.4143 | 0.4140 | 0.4143 | 0.4151 | 0.4164 |
| Water | $H_2O$ | gas | 0 | 0.4431 | 0.4438 | 0.4446 | 0.4448 | 0.4452 | 0.4459 | 0.4505 | 0.4566 | 0.4637 | 0.4714 | 0.4796 | 0.4881 | 0.4969 |
| Nitrogen | $N_2$ | gas | 0 | 0.2481 | 0.2482 | 0.2482 | 0.2483 | 0.2483 | 0.2483 | 0.2488 | 0.2498 | 0.2514 | 0.2535 | 0.2561 | 0.2591 | 0.2622 |
| Nitric Oxide | NO | gas | 0 | 0.2386 | 0.2381 | 0.2378 | 0.2377 | 0.2377 | 0.2375 | 0.2378 | 0.2392 | 0.2416 | 0.2446 | 0.2480 | 0.2515 | 0.2550 |
| Carbon | C | solid graphite | 0 | 0.1398 | 0.1531 | 0.1648 | 0.1681 | 0.1719 | 0.1809 | 0.2170 | 0.2499 | 0.2797 | 0.3068 | 0.331 | 0.351 | 0.369 |
| Carbon Monoxide | CO | gas | 0 | 0.2482 | 0.2483 | 0.2484 | 0.2484 | 0.2485 | 0.2486 | 0.2494 | 0.2509 | 0.2530 | 0.2557 | 0.2589 | 0.2623 | 0.2658 |
| Carbon Dioxide | $CO_2$ | gas | 0 | 0.1904 | 0.1952 | 0.1991 | 0.2003 | 0.2015 | 0.2046 | 0.2172 | 0.2284 | 0.2384 | 0.2473 | 0.2553 | 0.2625 | 0.2690 |

| Compound | Formula | State | Temperature in °F — Heat Capacity, $C_p^o$, in BTU/lb deg F | | | | | | | | | | | | | |
|---|---|---|---|---|---|---|---|---|---|---|---|---|---|---|---|---|
| | | | 900 | 1000 | 1100 | 1200 | 1300 | 1400 | 1500 | 1600 | 1700 | 1800 | 1900 | 2000 | 2100 | 2200 |
| Oxygen | $O_2$ | gas | 0.2495 | 0.2524 | 0.2550 | 0.2574 | 0.2595 | 0.2614 | 0.2632 | 0.2649 | 0.2664 | 0.2678 | 0.2691 | 0.2703 | 0.2714 | 0.2725 |
| Hydrogen | $H_2$ | gas | 3.498 | 3.512 | 3.528 | 3.547 | 3.568 | 3.592 | 3.617 | 3.643 | 3.670 | 3.698 | 3.726 | 3.755 | 3.784 | 3.812 |
| Hydroxyl | OH | gas | 0.4183 | 0.4206 | 0.4233 | 0.4263 | 0.4295 | 0.4329 | 0.4364 | 0.4400 | 0.4437 | 0.4473 | 0.4510 | 0.4546 | 0.4580 | 0.4614 |
| Water | $H_2O$ | gas | 0.5059 | 0.5152 | 0.5246 | 0.5340 | 0.5433 | 0.5523 | 0.5610 | 0.5694 | 0.5776 | 0.5855 | 0.5933 | 0.6007 | 0.6080 | 0.6149 |
| Nitrogen | $N_2$ | gas | 0.2654 | 0.2686 | 0.2718 | 0.2748 | 0.2777 | 0.2804 | 0.2830 | 0.2854 | 0.2876 | 0.2897 | 0.2916 | 0.2934 | 0.2950 | 0.2966 |
| Nitric Oxide | NO | gas | 0.2583 | 0.2615 | 0.2644 | 0.2671 | 0.2697 | 0.2720 | 0.2741 | 0.2760 | 0.2778 | 0.2794 | 0.2809 | 0.2822 | 0.2835 | 0.2846 |
| Carbon | C | solid graphite | 0.384 | 0.398 | 0.409 | 0.418 | 0.425 | 0.431 | 0.437 | 0.444 | 0.451 | 0.458 | 0.465 | 0.469 | 0.473 | 0.478 |
| Carbon Monoxide | CO | gas | 0.2693 | 0.2727 | 0.2759 | 0.2790 | 0.2819 | 0.2846 | 0.2870 | 0.2893 | 0.2914 | 0.2934 | 0.2952 | 0.2969 | 0.2985 | 0.2999 |
| Carbon Dioxide | $CO_2$ | gas | 0.2750 | 0.2803 | 0.2852 | 0.2896 | 0.2936 | 0.2972 | 0.3005 | 0.3035 | 0.3063 | 0.3088 | 0.3111 | 0.3133 | 0.3153 | 0.3170 |

TABLE 20 v-E (PART 1), Page 1 – NORMAL PARAFFINS, $C_1$ TO $C_{20}$

HEAT CAPACITY, $c_p^o$, FOR THE IDEAL GAS STATE, AT $-459.69^\circ$ TO $2200^\circ F$

December 31, 1945; December 31, 1952

Temperature in °F

Heat Capacity, $c_p^o$, in BTU/lb deg F

| Compound (gas) | Formula | -459.69 | 0 | 32 | 60 | 68 | 77 | 100 | 200 | 300 | 400 | 500 | 600 | 700 | 800 |
|---|---|---|---|---|---|---|---|---|---|---|---|---|---|---|---|
| Methane | $CH_4$ | 0 | 0.5074 | 0.5168 | 0.5258 | 0.5285 | 0.5318 | 0.5398 | 0.5797 | 0.6250 | 0.6735 | 0.7229 | 0.7718 | 0.8191 | 0.8645 |
| Ethane | $C_2H_6$ | 0 | 0.3769 | 0.3940 | 0.4092 | 0.4136 | 0.4183 | 0.4312 | 0.4872 | 0.5434 | 0.5986 | 0.6510 | 0.7000 | 0.7457 | 0.7882 |
| Propane | $C_3H_8$ | 0 | 0.3498 | 0.3699 | 0.3875 | 0.3925 | 0.3982 | 0.4126 | 0.4744 | 0.5343 | 0.5911 | 0.6432 | 0.6907 | 0.7345 | 0.7750 |
| n-Butane | $C_4H_{10}$ | 0 | 0.3537 | 0.3731 | 0.3900 | 0.3950 | 0.4004 | 0.4142 | 0.4739 | 0.5316 | 0.5865 | 0.6374 | 0.6840 | 0.7266 | 0.7658 |
| n-Pentane | $C_5H_{12}$ | 0 | 0.3513 | 0.3707 | 0.3876 | 0.3924 | 0.3980 | 0.4117 | 0.4711 | 0.5284 | 0.5827 | 0.6329 | 0.6787 | 0.7208 | 0.7594 |
| n-Hexane | $C_6H_{14}$ | 0 | 0.3501 | 0.3695 | 0.3864 | 0.3912 | 0.3966 | 0.4104 | 0.4694 | 0.5264 | 0.5803 | 0.6301 | 0.6754 | 0.7168 | 0.7548 |
| n-Heptane | $C_7H_{16}$ | 0 | 0.3489 | 0.3683 | 0.3853 | 0.3902 | 0.3956 | 0.4093 | 0.4684 | 0.5250 | 0.5786 | 0.6278 | 0.6728 | 0.7140 | 0.7517 |
| n-Octane | $C_8H_{18}$ | 0 | 0.3482 | 0.3676 | 0.3845 | 0.3893 | 0.3949 | 0.4086 | 0.4674 | 0.5240 | 0.5772 | 0.6263 | 0.6710 | 0.7118 | 0.7494 |
| n-Nonane | $C_9H_{20}$ | 0 | 0.3478 | 0.3672 | 0.3840 | 0.3888 | 0.3943 | 0.4080 | 0.4668 | 0.5231 | 0.5762 | 0.6250 | 0.6694 | 0.7101 | 0.7474 |
| n-Decane | $C_{10}H_{22}$ | 0 | 0.3473 | 0.3666 | 0.3835 | 0.3884 | 0.3938 | 0.4075 | 0.4661 | 0.5224 | 0.5754 | 0.6241 | 0.6683 | 0.7088 | 0.7459 |

Temperature in °F

Heat Capacity, $c_p^o$, in BTU/lb deg F

| Compound (gas) | Formula | 900 | 1000 | 1100 | 1200 | 1300 | 1400 | 1500 | 1600 | 1700 | 1800 | 1900 | 2000 | 2100 | 2200 |
|---|---|---|---|---|---|---|---|---|---|---|---|---|---|---|---|
| Methane | $CH_4$ | 0.9076 | 0.9486 | 0.9874 | 1.024 | 1.059 | 1.091 | 1.121 | 1.149 | 1.176 | 1.201 | 1.224 | 1.245 | 1.265 | 1.283 |
| Ethane | $C_2H_6$ | 0.8282 | 0.8656 | 0.9005 | 0.9329 | 0.9632 | 0.9914 | 1.018 | 1.042 | 1.064 | 1.085 | 1.104 | 1.122 | 1.139 | 1.154 |
| Propane | $C_3H_8$ | 0.8124 | 0.8470 | 0.8793 | 0.9094 | 0.9374 | 0.9632 | 0.9869 | 1.009 | 1.029 | 1.048 | 1.066 | 1.082 | 1.097 | 1.111 |
| n-Butane | $C_4H_{10}$ | 0.8021 | 0.8356 | 0.8668 | 0.8960 | 0.9221 | 0.9467 | 0.9694 | 0.9904 | 1.0100 | 1.0280 | 1.0447 | 1.0602 | 1.0745 | 1.0879 |
| n-Pentane | $C_5H_{12}$ | 0.7949 | 0.8276 | 0.8589 | 0.8860 | 0.9120 | 0.9360 | 0.9581 | 0.9786 | 0.9976 | 1.0152 | 1.0314 | 1.0465 | 1.0603 | 1.0732 |
| n-Hexane | $C_6H_{14}$ | 0.7899 | 0.8221 | 0.8520 | 0.8796 | 0.9052 | 0.9287 | 0.9505 | 0.9706 | 0.9892 | 1.0064 | 1.0223 | 1.0370 | 1.0507 | 1.0632 |
| n-Heptane | $C_7H_{16}$ | 0.7863 | 0.8182 | 0.8478 | 0.8751 | 0.900 | 0.924 | 0.945 | 0.965 | 0.983 | 1.000 | 1.016 | 1.030 | 1.044 | 1.056 |
| n-Octane | $C_8H_{18}$ | 0.7836 | 0.8153 | 0.8446 | 0.8716 | 0.896 | 0.920 | 0.941 | 0.960 | 0.978 | 0.995 | 1.011 | 1.025 | 1.038 | 1.051 |
| n-Nonane | $C_9H_{20}$ | 0.7815 | 0.8130 | 0.8420 | 0.8688 | 0.894 | 0.916 | 0.933 | 0.957 | 0.975 | 0.992 | 1.007 | 1.021 | 1.034 | 1.047 |
| n-Decane | $C_{10}H_{22}$ | 0.7799 | 0.8111 | 0.8400 | 0.8667 | 0.891 | 0.914 | 0.935 | 0.954 | 0.972 | 0.989 | 1.004 | 1.018 | 1.031 | 1.043 |

TABLE 20v-E (PART 1), Page 2 - NORMAL MONOOLEFINS, $C_1$ TO $C_{20}$
HEAT CAPACITY, $c_p^o$, FOR THE IDEAL GAS STATE, AT -459.69° TO 2200°F
December 31, 1945; December 31, 1952

Temperature in °F

Heat Capacity, $c_p^o$, in BTU/lb deg F

| Compound (gas) | Formula | -459.69 | 0 | 32 | 60 | 68 | 77 | 100 | 200 | 300 | 400 | 500 | 600 | 700 | 800 |
|---|---|---|---|---|---|---|---|---|---|---|---|---|---|---|---|
| n-Undecane | $C_{11}H_{24}$ | 0 | 0.3470 | 0.3664 | 0.3832 | 0.3880 | 0.3934 | 0.4072 | 0.4656 | 0.5218 | 0.5747 | 0.6232 | 0.6673 | 0.7076 | 0.7446 |
| n-Dodecane | $C_{12}H_{26}$ | 0 | 0.3466 | 0.3660 | 0.3828 | 0.3876 | 0.3931 | 0.4068 | 0.4653 | 0.5214 | 0.5742 | 0.6225 | 0.6665 | 0.7068 | 0.7436 |
| n-Tridecane | $C_{13}H_{28}$ | 0 | 0.3463 | 0.3657 | 0.3826 | 0.3874 | 0.3928 | 0.4064 | 0.4649 | 0.5210 | 0.5737 | 0.6220 | 0.6658 | 0.7060 | 0.7427 |
| n-Tetradecane | $C_{14}H_{30}$ | 0 | 0.3462 | 0.3655 | 0.3824 | 0.3872 | 0.3926 | 0.4063 | 0.4647 | 0.5206 | 0.5733 | 0.6214 | 0.6652 | 0.7052 | 0.7420 |
| n-Pentadecane | $C_{15}H_{32}$ | 0 | 0.3460 | 0.3653 | 0.3822 | 0.3869 | 0.3924 | 0.4060 | 0.4644 | 0.5203 | 0.5729 | 0.6210 | 0.6647 | 0.7047 | 0.7413 |
| n-Hexadecane | $C_{16}H_{34}$ | 0 | 0.3458 | 0.3652 | 0.3820 | 0.3868 | 0.3922 | 0.4059 | 0.4642 | 0.5200 | 0.5726 | 0.6206 | 0.6643 | 0.7042 | 0.7408 |
| n-Heptadecane | $C_{17}H_{36}$ | 0 | 0.3457 | 0.3650 | 0.3818 | 0.3866 | 0.3920 | 0.4057 | 0.4640 | 0.5198 | 0.5723 | 0.6203 | 0.6638 | 0.7037 | 0.7402 |
| n-Octadecane | $C_{18}H_{38}$ | 0 | 0.3456 | 0.3649 | 0.3817 | 0.3865 | 0.3919 | 0.4055 | 0.4638 | 0.5196 | 0.5721 | 0.6200 | 0.6635 | 0.7034 | 0.7398 |
| n-Nonadecane | $C_{19}H_{40}$ | 0 | 0.3455 | 0.3648 | 0.3816 | 0.3864 | 0.3918 | 0.4054 | 0.4637 | 0.5194 | 0.5718 | 0.6197 | 0.6632 | 0.7030 | 0.7394 |
| n-Eicosane | $C_{20}H_{42}$ | 0 | 0.3454 | 0.3647 | 0.3815 | 0.3862 | 0.3916 | 0.4053 | 0.4635 | 0.5192 | 0.5716 | 0.6195 | 0.6629 | 0.7027 | 0.7390 |

Temperature in °F

Heat Capacity, $c_p^o$, in BTU/lb deg F

| Compound (gas) | Formula | 900 | 1000 | 1100 | 1200 | 1300 | 1400 | 1500 | 1600 | 1700 | 1800 | 1900 | 2000 | 2100 | 2200 |
|---|---|---|---|---|---|---|---|---|---|---|---|---|---|---|---|
| n-Undecane | $C_{11}H_{24}$ | 0.7784 | 0.8096 | 0.8383 | 0.8649 | 0.889 | 0.912 | 0.933 | 0.952 | 0.970 | 0.986 | 1.001 | 1.015 | 1.028 | 1.040 |
| n-Dodecane | $C_{12}H_{26}$ | 0.7773 | 0.8083 | 0.8370 | 0.8634 | 0.888 | 0.910 | 0.931 | 0.950 | 0.968 | 0.984 | 0.999 | 1.013 | 1.026 | 1.038 |
| n-Tridecane | $C_{13}H_{28}$ | 0.7763 | 0.8072 | 0.8358 | 0.8621 | 0.886 | 0.909 | 0.929 | 0.948 | 0.966 | 0.982 | 0.998 | 1.011 | 1.024 | 1.036 |
| n-Tetradecane | $C_{14}H_{30}$ | 0.7755 | 0.8063 | 0.8348 | 0.8610 | 0.885 | 0.908 | 0.928 | 0.947 | 0.965 | 0.981 | 0.996 | 1.010 | 1.022 | 1.034 |
| n-Pentadecane | $C_{15}H_{32}$ | 0.7748 | 0.8055 | 0.8339 | 0.8600 | 0.884 | 0.906 | 0.927 | 0.946 | 0.963 | 0.980 | 0.995 | 1.008 | 1.021 | 1.033 |
| n-Hexadecane | $C_{16}H_{34}$ | 0.7741 | 0.8048 | 0.8331 | 0.8592 | 0.884 | 0.906 | 0.926 | 0.945 | 0.962 | 0.978 | 0.994 | 1.007 | 1.020 | 1.032 |
| n-Heptadecane | $C_{17}H_{36}$ | 0.7736 | 0.8041 | 0.8324 | 0.8585 | 0.883 | 0.905 | 0.925 | 0.944 | 0.961 | 0.978 | 0.992 | 1.006 | 1.019 | 1.031 |
| n-Octadecane | $C_{18}H_{38}$ | 0.7730 | 0.8036 | 0.8318 | 0.8578 | 0.882 | 0.904 | 0.924 | 0.943 | 0.960 | 0.977 | 0.992 | 1.005 | 1.018 | 1.030 |
| n-Nonadecane | $C_{19}H_{40}$ | 0.7726 | 0.8031 | 0.8313 | 0.8572 | 0.881 | 0.903 | 0.924 | 0.942 | 0.960 | 0.976 | 0.991 | 1.004 | 1.017 | 1.029 |
| n-Eicosane | $C_{20}H_{42}$ | 0.7722 | 0.8026 | 0.8308 | 0.8567 | 0.881 | 0.903 | 0.923 | 0.942 | 0.959 | 0.975 | 0.990 | 1.004 | 1.016 | 1.028 |

TABLE 1v-E, Page 1 - PARAFFINS, $C_1$ TO $C_5$

HEAT CAPACITY, $c_p^o$, FOR THE IDEAL GAS STATE, AT $-459.69°$ TO $2200°F$

November 30, 1944; February 28, 1949; December 31, 1952

Heat Capacity, $c_p^o$, in BTU/lb deg F — Temperature in °F

| Compound (gas) | Formula | -459.69 | -300 | -250 | -200 | -150 | -100 | -50 | 0 | 32 | 50 | 60 | 68 | 77 | 100 |
|---|---|---|---|---|---|---|---|---|---|---|---|---|---|---|---|
| Methane | $CH_4$ | 0 | 0.4952 | 0.4952 | 0.4952 | 0.4961 | 0.4984 | 0.5045 | 0.5132 | 0.5201 | 0.5245 | 0.5271 | 0.5293 | 0.5318 | 0.5393 |
| Ethane | $C_2H_6$ | 0 | | 0.2917 | 0.3044 | 0.3208 | 0.3379 | 0.3582 | 0.3805 | 0.3958 | 0.4047 | 0.4097 | 0.4138 | 0.4181 | 0.4306 |
| Propane | $C_3H_8$ | 0 | | 0.2347 | 0.2557 | 0.2797 | 0.3024 | 0.3279 | 0.3548 | 0.3725 | 0.3828 | 0.3885 | 0.3931 | 0.3982 | 0.4121 |
| n-Butane | $C_4H_{10}$ | 0 | | | | | 0.2951 | | 0.3578 | 0.3751 | 0.3851 | 0.3908 | 0.3953 | 0.4004 | 0.4142 |
| 2-Methylpropane (Isobutane) | " | 0 | | | | | | 0.3220. | 0.3510 | 0.3701 | 0.3811 | 0.3872 | 0.3922 | 0.3979 | 0.4120 |
| n-Pentane | $C_5H_{12}$ | 0 | | | | | | | 0.3554 | 0.3727 | 0.3827 | 0.3883 | 0.3929 | 0.3980 | 0.4117 |
| 2-Methylbutane (Isopentane) | " | 0 | | | | | | | 0.3456 | 0.3654 | 0.3765 | 0.3827 | 0.3877 | 0.3932 | 0.4078 |
| 2,2-Dimethylpropane (Neopentane) | " | 0 | | | | | 0.2915 | 0.3215 | 0.3529 | 0.3734 | 0.3850 | 0.3914 | 0.3966 | 0.4027 | 0.4174 |

Heat Capacity, $c_p^o$, in BTU/lb deg F — Temperature in °F

| Compound (gas) | Formula | 150 | 200 | 250 | 300 | 350 | 400 | 500 | 600 | 700 | 800 | 900 | 1000 | 1100 | 1200 |
|---|---|---|---|---|---|---|---|---|---|---|---|---|---|---|---|
| Methane | $CH_4$ | 0.5577 | 0.5783 | 0.6008 | 0.6241 | 0.6483 | 0.6731 | 0.7229 | 0.7720 | 0.8193 | 0.8645 | 0.9076 | 0.9486 | 0.9874 | 1.024 |
| Ethane | $C_2H_6$ | 0.4581 | 0.4865 | 0.5152 | 0.5434 | 0.5712 | 0.5986 | 0.6510 | 0.7000 | 0.7457 | 0.7882 | 0.8282 | 0.8656 | 0.9005 | 0.9329 |
| Propane | $C_3H_8$ | 0.4427 | 0.4737 | 0.5045 | 0.5342 | 0.5629 | 0.5907 | 0.6429 | 0.6906 | 0.7346 | 0.7750 | 0.8124 | 0.8470 | 0.8793 | 0.9094 |
| n-Butane | $C_4H_{10}$ | 0.4441 | 0.4739 | 0.5029 | 0.5316 | 0.5595 | 0.5865 | 0.6374 | 0.6840 | 0.7266 | 0.7658 | 0.8021 | 0.8356 | 0.8668 | 0.8960 |
| 2-Methylpropane (Isobutane) | " | 0.4434 | 0.4747 | 0.5056 | 0.5352 | 0.5636 | 0.5911 | 0.6425 | 0.6894 | 0.7321 | 0.7711 | 0.8070 | 0.8401 | 0.8707 | 0.8991 |
| n-Pentane | $C_5H_{12}$ | 0.4416 | 0.4711 | 0.5000 | 0.5284 | 0.5560 | 0.5827 | 0.6329 | 0.6787 | 0.7208 | 0.7594 | 0.7949 | 0.8276 | 0.8589 | 0.8860 |
| 2-Methylbutane (Isopentane) | " | 0.4388 | 0.4694 | 0.4994 | 0.5286 | 0.5568 | 0.5841 | 0.6354 | 0.6820 | 0.7250 | 0.7643 | 0.8004 | 0.8334 | 0.8643 | 0.8929 |
| 2,2-Dimethylpropane (Neopentane) | " | 0.4499 | 0.4821 | 0.5137 | 0.5441 | 0.5734 | 0.6015 | 0.6536 | 0.7004 | 0.7427 | 0.7811 | 0.8161 | 0.8480 | 0.8775 | 0.9046 |

TABLE 1v-E, Page 2 — PARAFFINS, $C_1$ TO $C_5$

HEAT CAPACITY, $c_p^o$, FOR THE IDEAL GAS STATE, AT $-459.69^o$ TO $2200^o$F

November 30, 1944; February 28, 1949; December 31, 1952

| Compound (gas) | Formula | Temperature in °F Heat Capacity, $c_p^o$, in BTU/lb deg F | | | | | | | | | |
|---|---|---|---|---|---|---|---|---|---|---|---|
| | | 1300 | 1400 | 1500 | 1600 | 1700 | 1800 | 1900 | 2000 | 2100 | 2200 |
| Methane | $CH_4$ | 1.059 | 1.091 | 1.121 | 1.149 | 1.176 | 1.201 | 1.224 | 1.245 | 1.265 | 1.283 |
| Ethane | $C_2H_6$ | 0.9632 | 0.9914 | 1.018 | 1.042 | 1.064 | 1.085 | 1.104 | 1.122 | 1.139 | 1.154 |
| Propane | $C_3H_8$ | 0.9374 | 0.9632 | 0.9969 | 1.009 | 1.029 | 1.048 | 1.066 | 1.082 | 1.097 | 1.111 |
| n-Butane | $C_4H_{10}$ | 0.9221 | 0.9467 | 0.9694 | 0.9904 | 1.0100 | 1.0280 | 1.0447 | 1.0602 | 1.0745 | 1.0879 |
| 2-Methylpropane (Isobutane) | " | 0.9253 | 0.9498 | 0.9724 | 0.9933 | 1.013 | 1.030 | 1.047 | 1.062 | 1.077 | 1.090 |
| n-Pentane | $C_5H_{12}$ | 0.9120 | 0.9360 | 0.9581 | 0.9786 | 0.9976 | 1.0152 | 1.0314 | 1.0465 | 1.0603 | 1.0732 |
| 2-Methylbutane (Isopentane) | " | 0.9196 | 0.9441 | 0.9666 | 0.9875 | 1.007 | 1.025 | 1.041 | 1.056 | 1.070 | 1.083 |
| 2,2-Dimethylpropane (Neopentane) | " | 0.9296 | 0.9527 | 0.9741 | 0.9937 | 1.012 | 1.028 | 1.044 | 1.058 | 1.072 | 1.084 |

**National Bureau of Standards**

TABLE 2v-E (PART 1) – PARAFFINS, C$_6$

HEAT CAPACITY, $c_p^o$, FOR THE IDEAL GAS STATE, AT −459.69° TO 2200°F

December 31, 1944; November 30, 1946; December 31, 1952

| Compound (gas) | Formula | Temperature in °F | | | | | | | | | | | | | |
|---|---|---|---|---|---|---|---|---|---|---|---|---|---|---|
| | | −459.69 | 0 | 32 | 60 | 68 | 77 | 100 | 200 | 300 | 400 | 500 | 600 | 700 | 800 |
| | | Heat Capacity, $c_p^o$, in BTU/lb deg F | | | | | | | | | | | | | |
| n-Hexane | C$_6$H$_{14}$ | 0 | 0.3501 | 0.3695 | 0.3864 | 0.3912 | 0.3966 | 0.4104 | 0.4694 | 0.5264 | 0.5803 | 0.6301 | 0.6754 | 0.7168 | 0.7548 |
| 2-Methylpentane | " | 0 | 0.3515 | 0.3716 | 0.389 | 0.394 | 0.400 | 0.414 | 0.475 | 0.533 | 0.588 | 0.638 | 0.663 | 0.724 | 0.762 |
| 3-Methylpentane | " | 0 | 0.3501 | 0.3695 | 0.386 | 0.391 | 0.397 | 0.410 | 0.469 | 0.526 | 0.580 | 0.630 | 0.676 | 0.717 | 0.755 |
| 2,2-Dimethylpentane | " | 0 | 0.3441 | 0.3646 | 0.382 | 0.388 | 0.393 | 0.408 | 0.470 | 0.530 | 0.587 | 0.639 | 0.687 | 0.729 | 0.766 |
| 2,3-Dimethylpentane | " | 0 | 0.3397 | 0.3604 | 0.378 | 0.384 | 0.390 | 0.404 | 0.466 | 0.525 | 0.581 | 0.631 | 0.678 | 0.720 | 0.758 |

| Compound (gas) | Formula | Temperature in °F | | | | | | | | | | | | | |
|---|---|---|---|---|---|---|---|---|---|---|---|---|---|---|
| | | 900 | 1000 | 1100 | 1200 | 1300 | 1400 | 1500 | 1600 | 1700 | 1800 | 1900 | 2000 | 2100 | 2200 |
| | | Heat Capacity, $c_p^o$, in BTU/lb deg F | | | | | | | | | | | | | |
| n-Hexane | C$_6$H$_{14}$ | 0.7899 | 0.8221 | 0.8520 | 0.8796 | 0.9052 | 0.9287 | 0.9505 | 0.9706 | 0.9892 | 1.0064 | 1.0223 | 1.0370 | 1.0507 | 1.0632 |
| 2-Methylpentane | " | 0.796 | 0.827 | 0.857 | 0.884 | 0.909 | | | | | | | | | |
| 3-Methylpentane | " | 0.790 | 0.822 | 0.852 | 0.879 | 0.905 | | | | | | | | | |
| 2,2-Dimethylpentane | " | 0.802 | 0.834 | 0.861 | 0.887 | 0.913 | | | | | | | | | |
| 2,3-Dimethylpentane | " | 0.793 | 0.826 | 0.856 | 0.683 | 0.908 | | | | | | | | | |

TABLE 2v-E (PART 2) - PARAFFINS, $C_7$

HEAT CAPACITY, $C_p^o$, FOR THE IDEAL GAS STATE, AT -459.69° TO 2200°F

December 31, 1944; December 31, 1952

| Compound (gas) | Formula | Temperature in °F | | | | | | | | | | | | | |
|---|---|---|---|---|---|---|---|---|---|---|---|---|---|---|---|
| | | -459.69 | 0 | 32 | 60 | 68 | 77 | 100 | 200 | 300 | 400 | 500 | 600 | 700 | 800 |
| | | Heat Capacity, $C_p^o$, in BTU/lb deg F | | | | | | | | | | | | | |
| n-Heptane | $C_7H_{16}$ | 0 | 0.3489 | 0.3663 | 0.3853 | 0.3902 | 0.3956 | 0.4093 | 0.4684 | 0.5250 | 0.5786 | 0.6278 | 0.6728 | 0.7140 | 0.7517 |
| 2-Methylhexane | " | 0 | a | a | a | a | a | a | a | a | a | a | a | a | a |
| 3-Methylhexane | " | 0 | a | a | a | a | a | a | a | a | a | a | a | a | a |
| 3-Ethylpentane | " | 0 | a | a | a | a | a | a | a | a | a | a | a | a | a |
| 2,2-Dimethylpentane | " | 0 | a | a | a | a | a | a | a | a | a | a | a | a | a |
| 2,3-Dimethylpentane | " | 0 | a | a | a | a | a | a | a | a | a | a | a | a | a |
| 2,4-Dimethylpentane | " | 0 | a | a | a | a | a | a | a | a | a | a | a | a | a |
| 3,3-Dimethylpentane | " | 0 | a | a | a | a | a | a | a | a | a | a | a | a | a |
| 2,2,3-Trimethylbutane | " | 0 | 0.3421 | 0.3630 | 0.3812 | 0.3882 | 0.3923 | 0.4070 | 0.4702 | 0.5305 | 0.5872 | 0.6388 | 0.6854 | 0.7274 | 0.7653 |

| Compound (gas) | Formula | Temperature in °F | | | | | | | | | | | | | |
|---|---|---|---|---|---|---|---|---|---|---|---|---|---|---|---|
| | | 900 | 1000 | 1100 | 1200 | 1300 | 1400 | 1500 | 1600 | 1700 | 1800 | 1900 | 2000 | 2100 | 2200 |
| | | Heat Capacity, $C_p^o$, in BTU/lb deg F | | | | | | | | | | | | | |
| n-Heptane | $C_7H_{16}$ | 0.7863 | 0.8182 | 0.8478 | 0.8751 | 0.900 | 0.924 | 0.945 | 0.965 | 0.983 | 1.000 | 1.016 | 1.030 | 1.044 | 1.056 |
| 2-Methylhexane | " | a | a | a | a | a | a | a | a | | | | | | |
| 3-Methylhexane | " | a | a | a | a | a | a | a | a | | | | | | |
| 3-Ethylpentane | " | a | a | a | a | a | a | a | a | | | | | | |
| 2,2-Dimethylpentane | " | a | a | a | a | a | a | a | a | | | | | | |
| 2,3-Dimethylpentane | " | a | a | a | a | a | a | a | a | | | | | | |
| 2,4-Dimethylpentane | " | a | a | a | a | a | a | a | a | | | | | | |
| 3,3-Dimethylpentane | " | a | a | a | a | a | | | | | | | | | |
| 2,2,3-Trimethylbutane | " | 0.7997 | 0.8311 | 0.8601 | 0.8869 | 0.911 | 0.934 | 0.955 | 0.974 | 0.992 | 1.009 | 1.024 | 1.038 | 1.050 | 1.062 |

a Until more data become available, the heat capacity of any branched-chain heptane may be taken as equal to that of the normal heptane. The meager data now available indicate that the difference in heat capacity between normal heptane and any of its isomers is not likely to exceed 3 percent.

TABLE 3v-E, Page 1 - PARAFFINS, C$_8$

HEAT CAPACITY, $c_p^o$, FOR THE IDEAL GAS STATE, AT -459.69° TO 2200°F

December 31, 1944; December 31, 1952

| Compound (gas) | Formula | Temperature in °F | | | | | | | | | | | | | |
|---|---|---|---|---|---|---|---|---|---|---|---|---|---|---|---|
| | | Heat Capacity, $c_p^o$, in BTU/lb deg F | | | | | | | | | | | | | |
| | | -459.69 | 0 | 32 | 60 | 68 | 77 | 100 | 200 | 300 | 400 | 500 | 600 | 700 | 800 |
| n-Octane | C$_8$H$_{18}$ | 0 | 0.3482 | 0.3676 | 0.3845 | 0.3893 | 0.3949 | 0.4086 | 0.4674 | 0.5240 | 0.5772 | 0.6263 | 0.6710 | 0.7118 | 0.7494 |
| 2-Methylheptane | " | 0 | a | a | a | a | a | a | a | a | a | a | a | a | a |
| 3-Methylheptane | " | 0 | a | a | a | a | a | a | a | a | a | a | a | a | a |
| 4-Methylheptane | " | 0 | a | a | a | a | a | a | a | a | a | a | a | a | a |
| 3-Ethylhexane | " | 0 | a | a | a | a | a | a | a | a | a | a | a | a | a |
| 2,2-Dimethylhexane | " | 0 | a | a | a | a | a | a | a | a | a | a | a | a | a |
| 2,3-Dimethylhexane | " | 0 | a | a | a | a | a | a | a | a | a | a | a | a | a |
| 2,4-Dimethylhexane | " | 0 | a | a | a | a | a | a | a | a | a | a | a | a | a |
| 2,5-Dimethylhexane | " | 0 | a | a | a | a | a | a | a | a | a | a | a | a | a |

| Compound (gas) | Formula | Temperature in °F | | | | | | | | | | | | | |
|---|---|---|---|---|---|---|---|---|---|---|---|---|---|---|---|
| | | Heat Capacity, $c_p^o$, in BTU/lb deg F | | | | | | | | | | | | | |
| | | 900 | 1000 | 1100 | 1200 | 1300 | 1400 | 1500 | 1600 | 1700 | 1800 | 1900 | 2000 | 2100 | 2200 |
| n-Octane | C$_8$H$_{18}$ | 0.7836 | 0.8153 | 0.8446 | 0.8716 | 0.896 | 0.920 | 0.941 | 0.960 | 0.978 | 0.995 | 1.011 | 1.025 | 1.038 | 1.051 |
| 2-Methylheptane | " | a | a | a | a | a | | | | | | | | | |
| 3-Methylheptane | " | a | a | a | a | a | | | | | | | | | |
| 4-Methylheptane | " | a | a | a | a | a | | | | | | | | | |
| 3-Ethylhexane | " | a | a | a | a | a | | | | | | | | | |
| 2,2-Dimethylhexane | " | a | a | a | a | a | | | | | | | | | |
| 2,3-Dimethylhexane | " | a | a | a | a | a | | | | | | | | | |
| 2,4-Dimethylhexane | " | a | a | a | a | a | | | | | | | | | |
| 2,5-Dimethylhexane | " | a | a | a | a | a | | | | | | | | | |

a Until more data become available, the heat capacity of any branched-chain octane may be taken as equal to that of normal octane. The meager data now available indicate that the difference in heat capacity between normal octane and any of its isomers is not likely to exceed 3 percent.

TABLE 3v-E, Page 2 - PARAFFINS, C8

HEAT CAPACITY, $C_p^o$, FOR THE IDEAL GAS STATE, AT -459.69° TO 2200°F

December 31, 1944; December 31, 1952

Temperature in °F

Heat Capacity, $C_p^o$, in BTU/lb deg F

| Compound (gas) | Formula | -459.69 | 0 | 32 | 60 | 68 | 77 | 100 | 200 | 300 | 400 | 500 | 600 | 700 | 800 |
|---|---|---|---|---|---|---|---|---|---|---|---|---|---|---|---|
| 3,3-Dimethylhexane | $C_8H_{18}$ | 0 | a | a | a | a | a | a | a | a | a | a | a | a | a |
| 3,4-Dimethylhexane | " | 0 | a | a | a | a | a | a | a | a | a | a | a | a | a |
| 2-Methyl-3-ethylpentane | " | 0 | a | a | a | a | a | a | a | a | a | a | a | a | a |
| 3-Methyl-3-ethylpentane | " | 0 | a | a | a | a | a | a | a | a | a | a | a | a | a |
| 2,2,3-Trimethylpentane | " | 0 | a | a | a | a | a | a | a | a | a | a | a | a | a |
| 2,2,4-Trimethylpentane | " | 0 | a | a | a | a | a | a | a | a | a | a | a | a | a |
| 2,3,3-Trimethylpentane | " | 0 | a | a | a | a | a | a | a | a | a | a | a | a | a |
| 2,3,4-Trimethylpentane | " | 0 | a | a | a | a | a | a | a | a | a | a | a | a | a |
| 2,2,3,3-Tetramethylbutane | " | 0 | 0.3480 | 0.3710 | 0.3908 | 0.3964 | 0.4027 | 0.4186 | 0.4856 | 0.5482 | 0.6060 | 0.6580 | 0.7044 | 0.7459 | 0.7831 |

Temperature in °F

Heat Capacity, $C_p^o$, in BTU/lb deg F

| Compound (gas) | Formula | 900 | 1000 | 1100 | 1200 | 1300 | 1400 | 1500 | 1600 | 1700 | 1800 | 1900 | 2000 | 2100 | 2200 |
|---|---|---|---|---|---|---|---|---|---|---|---|---|---|---|---|
| 3,3-Dimethylhexane | $C_8H_{18}$ | a | a | a | a | a | | | | | | | | | |
| 3,4-Dimethylhexane | " | a | a | a | a | a | | | | | | | | | |
| 2-Methyl-3-ethylpentane | " | a | a | a | a | a | | | | | | | | | |
| 3-Methyl-3-ethylpentane | " | a | a | a | a | a | | | | | | | | | |
| 2,2,3-Trimethylpentane | " | a | a | a | a | a | | | | | | | | | |
| 2,2,4-Trimethylpentane | " | a | a | a | a | a | | | | | | | | | |
| 2,3,3-Trimethylpentane | " | a | a | a | a | a | | | | | | | | | |
| 2,3,4-Trimethylpentane | " | a | a | a | a | a | | | | | | | | | |
| 2,2,3,3-Tetramethylbutane | " | 0.817 | 0.847 | 0.875 | 0.900 | 0.924 | | | | | | | | | |

a Until more data become available, the heat capacity of any branched-chain octane may be taken as equal to that of normal octane. The meager data now available indicate that the difference in heat capacity between normal octane and any of its isomers is not likely to exceed 3 percent.

TABLE 22v-E (PART 1), Page 1 — NORMAL ALKYL CYCLOPENTANES, $C_5$ TO $C_{21}$
HEAT CAPACITY, $c_p^o$, FOR THE IDEAL GAS STATE, AT −459.69° TO 2200°F
October 31, 1947; December 31, 1952

Temperature in °F

Heat Capacity, $c_p^o$, in BTU/lb deg F

| Compound (gas) | Formula | -459.69 | 0 | 32 | 60 | 68 | 77 | 100 | 200 | 300 | 400 | 500 | 600 | 700 | 800 |
|---|---|---|---|---|---|---|---|---|---|---|---|---|---|---|---|
| Cyclopentane | $C_5H_{10}$ | 0 | 0.2311 | 0.2525 | 0.2712 | 0.2765 | 0.2824 | 0.2978 | 0.3637 | 0.4274 | 0.4878 | 0.5434 | 0.5939 | 0.6397 | 0.6812 |
| Methylcyclopentane | $C_6H_{12}$ | 0 | 0.2616 | 0.2826 | 0.3010 | 0.3062 | 0.3116 | 0.3270 | 0.3912 | 0.4530 | 0.5113 | 0.5649 | 0.6133 | 0.6571 | 0.6967 |
| Ethylcyclopentane | $C_7H_{14}$ | 0 | 0.2514 | 0.2815 | 0.3062 | 0.3130 | 0.3205 | 0.3389 | 0.4100 | 0.4689 | 0.5202 | 0.5700 | 0.6185 | 0.6625 | 0.7024 |
| n-Propylcyclopentane | $C_8H_{16}$ | 0 | 0.2629 | 0.2916 | 0.3153 | 0.3218 | 0.3292 | 0.3469 | 0.4164 | 0.4749 | 0.5263 | 0.5756 | 0.6234 | 0.6668 | 0.7062 |
| n-Butylcyclopentane | $C_9H_{18}$ | 0 | 0.2719 | 0.2996 | 0.3224 | 0.3288 | 0.3358 | 0.3532 | 0.4213 | 0.4794 | 0.5308 | 0.5800 | 0.6272 | 0.6701 | 0.7090 |
| n-Pentylcyclopentane | $C_{10}H_{20}$ | 0 | 0.2790 | 0.3059 | 0.3281 | 0.3343 | 0.3412 | 0.3582 | 0.4252 | 0.4831 | 0.5345 | 0.5835 | 0.6303 | 0.6727 | 0.7113 |
| n-Hexylcyclopentane | $C_{11}H_{22}$ | 0 | 0.2849 | 0.3110 | 0.3328 | 0.3389 | 0.3456 | 0.3623 | 0.4285 | 0.4860 | 0.5376 | 0.5863 | 0.6327 | 0.6749 | 0.7131 |
| n-Heptylcyclopentane | $C_{12}H_{24}$ | 0 | 0.2897 | 0.3153 | 0.3366 | 0.3426 | 0.3492 | 0.3657 | 0.4312 | 0.4886 | 0.5401 | 0.5887 | 0.6348 | 0.6767 | 0.7148 |
| n-Octylcyclopentane | $C_{13}H_{26}$ | 0 | 0.2938 | 0.3189 | 0.3399 | 0.3457 | 0.3524 | 0.3685 | 0.4335 | 0.4907 | 0.5423 | 0.5907 | 0.6365 | 0.6782 | 0.7161 |

Temperature in °F

Heat Capacity, $c_p^o$, in BTU/lb deg F

| Compound (gas) | Formula | 900 | 1000 | 1100 | 1200 | 1300 | 1400 | 1500 | 1600 | 1700 | 1800 | 1900 | 2000 | 2100 | 2200 |
|---|---|---|---|---|---|---|---|---|---|---|---|---|---|---|---|
| Cyclopentane | $C_5H_{10}$ | 0.7192 | 0.7538 | 0.7855 | 0.8145 | 0.8413 | 0.8660 | 0.8888 | 0.9096 | 0.9288 | 0.9466 | 0.9630 | 0.9781 | 0.9921 | 1.0051 |
| Methylcyclopentane | $C_6H_{12}$ | 0.7331 | 0.7663 | 0.7967 | 0.8246 | 0.8504 | 0.8742 | 0.8961 | 0.9162 | 0.9347 | 0.9519 | 0.9677 | 0.9824 | 0.9960 | 1.0087 |
| Ethylcyclopentane | $C_7H_{14}$ | 0.7388 | 0.7719 | 0.8025 | 0.8308 | 0.8568 | 0.8808 | 0.9027 | 0.9230 | 0.9415 | 0.9588 | 0.9748 | 0.9895 | 1.0029 | 1.0154 |
| n-Propylcyclopentane | $C_8H_{16}$ | 0.7419 | 0.7747 | 0.8048 | 0.8327 | 0.858 | 0.882 | 0.904 | 0.924 | 0.942 | 0.959 | 0.975 | 0.989 | 1.003 | 1.015 |
| n-Butylcyclopentane | $C_9H_{18}$ | 0.7444 | 0.7768 | 0.8067 | 0.8342 | 0.860 | 0.883 | 0.905 | 0.924 | 0.942 | 0.959 | 0.975 | 0.989 | 1.003 | 1.015 |
| n-Pentylcyclopentane | $C_{10}H_{20}$ | 0.7465 | 0.7786 | 0.8082 | 0.8355 | 0.861 | 0.884 | 0.905 | 0.925 | 0.943 | 0.960 | 0.975 | 0.989 | 1.002 | 1.015 |
| n-Hexylcyclopentane | $C_{11}H_{22}$ | 0.7481 | 0.7800 | 0.8094 | 0.8365 | 0.862 | 0.885 | 0.906 | 0.925 | 0.943 | 0.960 | 0.975 | 0.989 | 1.002 | 1.014 |
| n-Heptylcyclopentane | $C_{12}H_{24}$ | 0.7494 | 0.7811 | 0.8104 | 0.8374 | 0.862 | 0.885 | 0.906 | 0.925 | 0.943 | 0.960 | 0.975 | 0.989 | 1.002 | 1.014 |
| n-Octylcyclopentane | $C_{13}H_{26}$ | 0.7506 | 0.7822 | 0.8113 | 0.8381 | 0.863 | 0.886 | 0.907 | 0.926 | 0.944 | 0.960 | 0.975 | 0.989 | 1.002 | 1.014 |

TABLE 22v-E (PART 1), Page 2 – NORMAL ALKYL CYCLOPENTANES, $C_5$ TO $C_{21}$
HEAT CAPACITY, $c_p^o$, FOR THE IDEAL GAS STATE, AT $-459.69°$ TO $2200°F$
October 31, 1947; December 31, 1952

Temperature in °F

Heat Capacity, $c_p^o$, in BTU/lb deg F

| Compound (gas) | Formula | -459.69 | 0 | 32 | 60 | 68 | 77 | 100 | 200 | 300 | 400 | 500 | 600 | 700 | 800 |
|---|---|---|---|---|---|---|---|---|---|---|---|---|---|---|---|
| n-Nonylcyclopentane | $C_{14}H_{28}$ | 0 | 0.2974 | 0.3221 | 0.3428 | 0.3490 | 0.3550 | 0.3710 | 0.4355 | 0.4926 | 0.5440 | 0.5924 | 0.6385 | 0.6795 | 0.7172 |
| n-Decylcyclopentane | $C_{15}H_{30}$ | 0 | 0.3004 | 0.3248 | 0.3452 | 0.3509 | 0.3573 | 0.3732 | 0.4371 | 0.4941 | 0.5456 | 0.5940 | 0.6393 | 0.6806 | 0.7182 |
| n-Undecylcyclopentane | $C_{16}H_{32}$ | 0 | 0.3032 | 0.3272 | 0.3473 | 0.3530 | 0.3593 | 0.3750 | 0.4386 | 0.4955 | 0.5470 | 0.5952 | 0.6404 | 0.6816 | 0.7191 |
| n-Dodecylcyclopentane | $C_{17}H_{34}$ | 0 | 0.3055 | 0.3293 | 0.3492 | 0.3548 | 0.3611 | 0.3767 | 0.4400 | 0.4967 | 0.5482 | 0.5964 | 0.6414 | 0.6825 | 0.7198 |
| n-Tridecylcyclopentane | $C_{18}H_{36}$ | 0 | 0.3076 | 0.3311 | 0.3509 | 0.3564 | 0.3627 | 0.3781 | 0.4411 | 0.4978 | 0.5493 | 0.5975 | 0.6423 | 0.6832 | 0.7205 |
| n-Tetradecylcyclopentane | $C_{19}H_{38}$ | 0 | 0.3096 | 0.3328 | 0.3524 | 0.3579 | 0.3640 | 0.3795 | 0.4421 | 0.4988 | 0.5503 | 0.5984 | 0.6431 | 0.6839 | 0.7211 |
| n-Pentadecylcyclopentane | $C_{20}H_{40}$ | 0 | 0.3112 | 0.3343 | 0.3537 | 0.3592 | 0.3653 | 0.3806 | 0.4431 | 0.4996 | 0.5512 | 0.5992 | 0.6438 | 0.6846 | 0.7217 |
| n-Hexadecylcyclopentane | $C_{21}H_{42}$ | 0 | 0.3128 | 0.3356 | 0.3550 | 0.3604 | 0.3665 | 0.3817 | 0.4439 | 0.5004 | 0.5520 | 0.5999 | 0.6445 | 0.6852 | 0.7222 |

Temperature in °F

Heat Capacity, $c_p^o$, in BTU/lb deg F

| Compound (gas) | Formula | 900 | 1000 | 1100 | 1200 | 1300 | 1400 | 1500 | 1600 | 1700 | 1800 | 1900 | 2000 | 2100 | 2200 |
|---|---|---|---|---|---|---|---|---|---|---|---|---|---|---|---|
| n-Nonylcyclopentane | $C_{14}H_{28}$ | 0.7516 | 0.7830 | 0.8120 | 0.8387 | 0.863 | 0.886 | 0.907 | 0.926 | 0.944 | 0.960 | 0.975 | 0.989 | 1.002 | 1.014 |
| n-Decylcyclopentane | $C_{15}H_{30}$ | 0.7524 | 0.7838 | 0.8126 | 0.8392 | 0.864 | 0.886 | 0.907 | 0.926 | 0.944 | 0.960 | 0.975 | 0.989 | 1.002 | 1.014 |
| n-Undecylcyclopentane | $C_{16}H_{32}$ | 0.7532 | 0.7844 | 0.8131 | 0.8397 | 0.864 | 0.887 | 0.907 | 0.926 | 0.944 | 0.960 | 0.975 | 0.989 | 1.002 | 1.014 |
| n-Dodecylcyclopentane | $C_{17}H_{34}$ | 0.7538 | 0.7850 | 0.8136 | 0.8401 | 0.865 | 0.887 | 0.908 | 0.927 | 0.944 | 0.960 | 0.976 | 0.989 | 1.002 | 1.014 |
| n-Tridecylcyclopentane | $C_{18}H_{36}$ | 0.7544 | 0.7855 | 0.8141 | 0.8405 | 0.865 | 0.887 | 0.908 | 0.927 | 0.944 | 0.960 | 0.975 | 0.989 | 1.002 | 1.013 |
| n-Tetradecylcyclopentane | $C_{19}H_{38}$ | 0.7550 | 0.7859 | 0.8145 | 0.8408 | 0.865 | 0.887 | 0.908 | 0.927 | 0.944 | 0.960 | 0.975 | 0.989 | 1.002 | 1.013 |
| n-Pentadecylcyclopentane | $C_{20}H_{40}$ | 0.7554 | 0.7863 | 0.8148 | 0.8411 | 0.865 | 0.888 | 0.908 | 0.927 | 0.944 | 0.961 | 0.975 | 0.989 | 1.002 | 1.013 |
| n-Hexadecylcyclopentane | $C_{21}H_{42}$ | 0.7558 | 0.7867 | 0.8151 | 0.8414 | 0.866 | 0.888 | 0.908 | 0.927 | 0.944 | 0.961 | 0.975 | 0.989 | 1.002 | 1.013 |

## TABLE 6v-E – ALKYL CYCLOPENTANES, $C_5$ TO $C_7$

HEAT CAPACITY, $c_p^o$, FOR THE IDEAL GAS STATE, AT $-459.69°$ TO $2200°F$

April 30, 1949; December 31, 1952

Temperature in °F

Heat Capacity, $c_p^o$, in BTU/lb deg F

| Compound (gas) | Formula | -459.69 | 0 | 32 | 60 | 68 | 77 | 100 | 200 | 300 | 400 | 500 | 600 | 700 | 800 |
|---|---|---|---|---|---|---|---|---|---|---|---|---|---|---|---|
| Cyclopentane | $C_5H_{10}$ | 0 | 0.2311 | 0.2525 | 0.2712 | 0.2765 | 0.2824 | 0.2978 | 0.3637 | 0.4274 | 0.4878 | 0.5434 | 0.5939 | 0.6397 | 0.6812 |
| Methylcyclopentane | $C_6H_{12}$ | 0 | 0.2616 | 0.2826 | 0.3010 | 0.3062 | 0.3116 | 0.3270 | 0.3912 | 0.4530 | 0.5113 | 0.5649 | 0.6133 | 0.6571 | 0.6967 |
| Ethylcyclopentane | $C_7H_{14}$ | 0 | 0.2514 | 0.2815 | 0.3062 | 0.3130 | 0.3205 | 0.3389 | 0.4100 | 0.4689 | 0.5202 | 0.5700 | 0.6185 | 0.6625 | 0.7024 |
| 1,1-Dimethylcyclopentane | " | 0 | 0.2746 | 0.2956 | 0.3140 | 0.3193 | 0.3243 | 0.3402 | 0.4051 | 0.4678 | 0.5271 | 0.5811 | 0.6297 | 0.6736 | 0.7132 |
| 1,cis-2-Dimethylcyclopentane | " | 0 | 0.2764 | 0.2975 | 0.3159 | 0.3211 | 0.3263 | 0.3420 | 0.4066 | 0.4688 | 0.5276 | 0.5811 | 0.6292 | 0.6725 | 0.7116 |
| 1,trans-2-Dimethylcyclopentane | " | 0 | 0.2779 | 0.2987 | 0.3170 | 0.3222 | 0.3271 | 0.3430 | 0.4072 | 0.4692 | 0.5276 | 0.5808 | 0.6283 | 0.6720 | 0.7116 |
| 1,cis-3-Dimethylcyclopentane | " | 0 | 0.2779 | 0.2987 | 0.3170 | 0.3222 | 0.3271 | 0.3430 | 0.4072 | 0.4692 | 0.5276 | 0.5808 | 0.6283 | 0.6720 | 0.7116 |
| 1,trans-3-Dimethylcyclopentane | " | 0 | 0.2779 | 0.2987 | 0.3170 | 0.3222 | 0.3271 | 0.3430 | 0.4072 | 0.4692 | 0.5276 | 0.5808 | 0.6283 | 0.6720 | 0.7116 |

Temperature in °F

Heat Capacity, $c_p^o$, in BTU/lb deg F

| Compound (gas) | Formula | 900 | 1000 | 1100 | 1200 | 1300 | 1400 | 1500 | 1600 | 1700 | 1800 | 1900 | 2000 | 2100 | 2200 |
|---|---|---|---|---|---|---|---|---|---|---|---|---|---|---|---|
| Cyclopentane | $C_5H_{10}$ | 0.7192 | 0.7538 | 0.7855 | 0.8145 | 0.8413 | 0.8660 | 0.8888 | 0.9096 | 0.9288 | 0.9466 | 0.9630 | 0.9781 | 0.9921 | 1.0051 |
| Methylcyclopentane | $C_6H_{12}$ | 0.7331 | 0.7663 | 0.7967 | 0.8246 | 0.8504 | 0.8742 | 0.8961 | 0.9162 | 0.9347 | 0.9519 | 0.9677 | 0.9824 | 0.9960 | 1.0087 |
| Ethylcyclopentane | $C_7H_{14}$ | 0.7388 | 0.7719 | 0.8025 | 0.8308 | 0.8568 | 0.8808 | 0.9027 | 0.9230 | 0.9415 | 0.9588 | 0.9748 | 0.9895 | 1.0029 | 1.0154 |
| 1,1-Dimethylcyclopentane | " | 0.7490 | 0.7816 | 0.8115 | 0.8389 | 0.8641 | 0.8871 | 0.9081 | 0.9275 | 0.9454 | 0.9621 | 0.9775 | 0.9915 | 1.0044 | 1.0164 |
| 1,cis-2-Dimethylcyclopentane | " | 0.7471 | 0.7795 | 0.8092 | 0.8364 | 0.8615 | 0.8845 | 0.9057 | 0.9251 | 0.9430 | 0.9597 | 0.9751 | 0.9892 | 1.0022 | 1.0143 |
| 1,trans-2-Dimethylcyclopentane | " | 0.7462 | 0.7780 | 0.8076 | 0.8348 | 0.8600 | 0.8831 | 0.9042 | 0.9236 | 0.9416 | 0.9584 | 0.9739 | 0.9880 | 1.0010 | 1.0132 |
| 1,cis-3-Dimethylcyclopentane | " | 0.7462 | 0.7780 | 0.8076 | 0.8348 | 0.8600 | 0.8831 | 0.9042 | 0.9236 | 0.9416 | 0.9584 | 0.9739 | 0.9880 | 1.0010 | 1.0132 |
| 1,trans-3-Dimethylcyclopentane | " | 0.7462 | 0.7780 | 0.8076 | 0.8348 | 0.8600 | 0.8831 | 0.9042 | 0.9236 | 0.9416 | 0.9584 | 0.9739 | 0.9880 | 1.0010 | 1.0132 |

TABLE 23v-E (PART 1), Page 1 — NORMAL ALKYL CYCLOHEXANES, $C_6$ TO $C_{22}$
HEAT CAPACITY, $C_p^0$, FOR THE IDEAL GAS STATE, AT $-459.69°$ TO $2200°F$
November 30, 1947; December 31, 1952

Temperature in °F

Heat Capacity, $C_p^0$, in BTU/lb deg F

| Compound (gas) | Formula | -459.69 | 0 | 32 | 60 | 68 | 77 | 100 | 200 | 300 | 400 | 500 | 600 | 700 | 800 |
|---|---|---|---|---|---|---|---|---|---|---|---|---|---|---|---|
| Cyclohexane | $C_6H_{12}$ | 0 | 0.2494 | 0.2710 | 0.2900 | 0.2954 | 0.3016 | 0.3171 | 0.3850 | 0.4515 | 0.5153 | 0.5746 | 0.6288 | 0.6780 | 0.7227 |
| Methylcyclohexane | $C_7H_{14}$ | 0 | 0.2756 | 0.2977 | 0.3170 | 0.3224 | 0.3285 | 0.3444 | 0.4118 | 0.4769 | 0.5384 | 0.5949 | 0.6463 | 0.6928 | 0.7351 |
| Ethylcyclohexane | $C_8H_{16}$ | 0 | 0.2857 | 0.3076 | 0.3267 | 0.3321 | 0.3381 | 0.3538 | 0.421 | 0.485 | 0.545 | 0.600 | 0.650 | 0.696 | 0.737 |
| n-Propylcyclohexane | $C_9H_{18}$ | 0 | 0.2975 | 0.3188 | 0.3374 | 0.3427 | 0.3486 | 0.3642 | 0.429 | 0.492 | 0.552 | 0.606 | 0.654 | 0.698 | 0.739 |
| n-Butylcyclohexane | $C_{10}H_{20}$ | 0 | 0.3023 | 0.3233 | 0.3416 | 0.3468 | 0.3527 | 0.3676 | 0.432 | 0.494 | 0.554 | 0.606 | 0.654 | 0.698 | 0.738 |
| n-Pentylcyclohexane | $C_{11}H_{22}$ | 0 | 0.3057 | 0.3266 | 0.3450 | 0.3502 | 0.3560 | 0.3711 | 0.435 | 0.497 | 0.555 | 0.608 | 0.655 | 0.698 | 0.738 |
| n-Hexylcyclohexane | $C_{12}H_{24}$ | 0 | 0.3097 | 0.3301 | 0.3480 | 0.3531 | 0.3588 | 0.3735 | 0.437 | 0.498 | 0.556 | 0.609 | 0.655 | 0.698 | 0.737 |
| n-Heptylcyclohexane | $C_{13}H_{26}$ | 0 | 0.3114 | 0.3321 | 0.3503 | 0.3554 | 0.3611 | 0.3760 | 0.439 | 0.500 | 0.557 | 0.609 | 0.655 | 0.698 | 0.737 |
| n-Octylcyclohexane | $C_{14}H_{28}$ | 0 | 0.3138 | 0.3344 | 0.3524 | 0.3575 | 0.3632 | 0.3776 | 0.441 | 0.501 | 0.558 | 0.609 | 0.655 | 0.698 | 0.736 |

Temperature in °F

Heat Capacity, $C_p^0$, in BTU/lb deg F

| Compound (gas) | Formula | 900 | 1000 | 1100 | 1200 | 1300 | 1400 | 1500 | 1600 | 1700 | 1800 | 1900 | 2000 | 2100 | 2200 |
|---|---|---|---|---|---|---|---|---|---|---|---|---|---|---|---|
| Cyclohexane | $C_6H_{12}$ | 0.7631 | 0.7997 | 0.8328 | 0.8627 | 0.8899 | 0.9147 | 0.937 | 0.953 | 0.976 | 0.993 | 1.009 | 1.023 | 1.036 | 1.048 |
| Methylcyclohexane | $C_7H_{14}$ | 0.7733 | 0.8080 | 0.8395 | 0.8680 | 0.8940 | 0.9177 | 0.939 | 0.959 | 0.977 | 0.993 | 1.008 | 1.022 | 1.035 | 1.046 |
| Ethylcyclohexane | $C_8H_{16}$ | 0.775 | 0.809 | 0.840 | 0.867 | 0.893 | 0.916 | 0.957 | 0.957 | 0.974 | 0.990 | 1.005 | 1.019 | 1.032 | 1.043 |
| n-Propylcyclohexane | $C_9H_{18}$ | 0.775 | 0.808 | 0.837 | 0.864 | 0.888 | 0.912 | 0.934 | 0.954 | 0.971 | 0.987 | 1.002 | 1.016 | 1.028 | 1.040 |
| n-Butylcyclohexane | $C_{10}H_{20}$ | 0.774 | 0.807 | 0.836 | 0.862 | 0.886 | 0.909 | 0.931 | 0.951 | 0.969 | 0.985 | 1.000 | 1.013 | 1.026 | 1.037 |
| n-Pentylcyclohexane | $C_{11}H_{22}$ | 0.773 | 0.805 | 0.834 | 0.861 | 0.885 | 0.908 | 0.930 | 0.950 | 0.967 | 0.983 | 0.997 | 1.011 | 1.023 | 1.035 |
| n-Hexylcyclohexane | $C_{12}H_{24}$ | 0.772 | 0.804 | 0.833 | 0.859 | 0.883 | 0.907 | 0.928 | 0.948 | 0.965 | 0.981 | 0.996 | 1.009 | 1.021 | 1.033 |
| n-Heptylcyclohexane | $C_{13}H_{26}$ | 0.771 | 0.803 | 0.833 | 0.858 | 0.882 | 0.905 | 0.927 | 0.947 | 0.964 | 0.979 | 0.994 | 1.007 | 1.020 | 1.031 |
| n-Octylcyclohexane | $C_{14}H_{28}$ | 0.771 | 0.803 | 0.832 | 0.858 | 0.881 | 0.904 | 0.926 | 0.945 | 0.962 | 0.978 | 0.992 | 1.006 | 1.018 | 1.030 |

TABLE 23v-E (PART 1), Page 2 — NORMAL ALKYL CYCLOHEXANES, $C_6$ TO $C_{22}$
HEAT CAPACITY, $C_p^o$, FOR THE IDEAL GAS STATE, AT $-459.69^o$ TO $2200^o$F
November 30, 1947; December 31, 1952

| Compound (gas) | Formula | Temperature in °F | | | | | | | | | | | | | |
|---|---|---|---|---|---|---|---|---|---|---|---|---|---|---|---|
| | | Heat Capacity, $C_p^o$, in BTU/lb deg F | | | | | | | | | | | | | |
| | | -459.69 | 0 | 32 | 60 | 68 | 77 | 100 | 200 | 300 | 400 | 500 | 600 | 700 | 800 |
| n-Nonylcyclohexane | $C_{15}H_{30}$ | 0 | 0.3164 | 0.3366 | 0.3543 | 0.3593 | 0.3649 | 0.3795 | 0.442 | 0.502 | 0.559 | 0.609 | 0.655 | 0.697 | 0.736 |
| n-Decylcyclohexane | $C_{16}H_{32}$ | 0 | 0.3179 | 0.3381 | 0.3558 | 0.3609 | 0.3664 | 0.3812 | 0.443 | 0.503 | 0.559 | 0.610 | 0.656 | 0.698 | 0.736 |
| n-Undecylcyclohexane | $C_{17}H_{34}$ | 0 | 0.3195 | 0.3396 | 0.3572 | 0.3622 | 0.3678 | 0.3822 | 0.444 | 0.503 | 0.560 | 0.610 | 0.656 | 0.697 | 0.736 |
| n-Dodecylcyclohexane | $C_{18}H_{36}$ | 0 | 0.3202 | 0.3406 | 0.3583 | 0.3634 | 0.3690 | 0.3836 | 0.445 | 0.504 | 0.560 | 0.610 | 0.656 | 0.697 | 0.735 |
| n-Tridecylcyclohexane | $C_{19}H_{38}$ | 0 | 0.3219 | 0.3420 | 0.3595 | 0.3645 | 0.3701 | 0.3844 | 0.446 | 0.505 | 0.561 | 0.611 | 0.656 | 0.698 | 0.735 |
| n-Tetradecylcyclohexane | $C_{20}H_{40}$ | 0 | 0.3235 | 0.3433 | 0.3606 | 0.3655 | 0.3711 | 0.3855 | 0.446 | 0.506 | 0.561 | 0.611 | 0.656 | 0.697 | 0.735 |
| n-Pentadecylcyclohexane | $C_{21}H_{42}$ | 0 | 0.3239 | 0.3439 | 0.3614 | 0.3664 | 0.3719 | 0.3861 | 0.447 | 0.506 | 0.561 | 0.611 | 0.656 | 0.697 | 0.735 |
| n-Hexadecylcyclohexane | $C_{22}H_{44}$ | 0 | 0.3249 | 0.3448 | 0.3622 | 0.3672 | 0.3727 | 0.3870 | 0.448 | 0.507 | 0.561 | 0.611 | 0.656 | 0.697 | 0.735 |

| Compound (gas) | Formula | Temperature in °F | | | | | | | | | | | | | |
|---|---|---|---|---|---|---|---|---|---|---|---|---|---|---|---|
| | | Heat Capacity, $C_p^o$, in BTU/lb deg F | | | | | | | | | | | | | |
| | | 900 | 1000 | 1100 | 1200 | 1300 | 1400 | 1500 | 1600 | 1700 | 1800 | 1900 | 2000 | 2100 | 2200 |
| n-Nonylcyclohexane | $C_{15}H_{30}$ | 0.770 | 0.802 | 0.831 | 0.857 | 0.881 | 0.903 | 0.925 | 0.944 | 0.961 | 0.977 | 0.992 | 1.005 | 1.017 | 1.029 |
| n-Decylcyclohexane | $C_{16}H_{32}$ | 0.770 | 0.801 | 0.830 | 0.856 | 0.880 | 0.903 | 0.924 | 0.943 | 0.961 | 0.976 | 0.990 | 1.004 | 1.017 | 1.028 |
| n-Undecylcyclohexane | $C_{17}H_{34}$ | 0.770 | 0.801 | 0.830 | 0.856 | 0.879 | 0.902 | 0.923 | 0.942 | 0.959 | 0.975 | 0.990 | 1.003 | 1.015 | 1.027 |
| n-Dodecylcyclohexane | $C_{18}H_{36}$ | 0.769 | 0.800 | 0.829 | 0.855 | 0.879 | 0.902 | 0.923 | 0.942 | 0.959 | 0.974 | 0.989 | 1.002 | 1.015 | 1.026 |
| n-Tridecylcyclohexane | $C_{19}H_{38}$ | 0.769 | 0.800 | 0.829 | 0.855 | 0.879 | 0.901 | 0.922 | 0.941 | 0.958 | 0.974 | 0.988 | 1.002 | 1.014 | 1.025 |
| n-Tetradecylcyclohexane | $C_{20}H_{40}$ | 0.769 | 0.800 | 0.828 | 0.854 | 0.878 | 0.900 | 0.921 | 0.940 | 0.958 | 0.973 | 0.988 | 1.001 | 1.013 | 1.025 |
| n-Pentadecylcyclohexane | $C_{21}H_{42}$ | 0.769 | 0.799 | 0.828 | 0.854 | 0.878 | 0.900 | 0.921 | 0.940 | 0.957 | 0.973 | 0.987 | 1.001 | 1.013 | 1.024 |
| n-Hexadecylcyclohexane | $C_{22}H_{44}$ | 0.769 | 0.799 | 0.828 | 0.854 | 0.877 | 0.900 | 0.920 | 0.939 | 0.956 | 0.972 | 0.986 | 1.000 | 1.012 | 1.023 |

## TABLE 7v-E - ALKYL CYCLOHEXANES, $C_6$ to $C_8$

HEAT CAPACITY, $C_p^o$, FOR THE IDEAL GAS STATE, AT $-459.69^o$ TO $2200^o$F

November 30, 1947

| Compound (gas) | Formula | Temperature in °F | | | | | | | | | | | | | |
|---|---|---|---|---|---|---|---|---|---|---|---|---|---|---|---|
| | | -459.69 | 0 | 32 | 60 | 68 | 77 | 100 | 200 | 300 | 400 | 500 | 600 | 700 | 800 |
| | | Heat Capacity , $C_p^o$, in BTU/lb deg F | | | | | | | | | | | | | |
| Cyclohexane | $C_6H_{12}$ | 0 | 0.2494 | 0.2710 | 0.2900 | 0.2954 | 0.3016 | 0.3171 | 0.3850 | 0.4515 | 0.5153 | 0.5746 | 0.6288 | 0.6780 | 0.7227 |
| Methylcyclohexane | $C_7H_{14}$ | 0 | 0.2756 | 0.2977 | 0.3170 | 0.3224 | 0.3285 | 0.3444 | 0.4118 | 0.4769 | 0.5384 | 0.5949 | 0.6463 | 0.6928 | 0.7351 |
| Ethylcyclohexane | $C_8H_{16}$ | 0 | 0.2857 | 0.3076 | 0.3267 | 0.3321 | 0.3381 | 0.3538 | 0.421 | 0.485 | 0.545 | 0.600 | 0.650 | 0.696 | 0.737 |
| 1,1-Dimethylcyclohexane | " | 0 | 0.277 | 0.299 | 0.318 | 0.323 | 0.329 | 0.345 | 0.412 | 0.477 | 0.540 | 0.597 | 0.650 | 0.698 | 0.741 |
| cis-1,2-Dimethylcyclohexane | " | 0 | 0.282 | 0.303 | 0.322 | 0.327 | 0.333 | 0.349 | 0.416 | 0.481 | 0.542 | 0.598 | 0.649 | 0.696 | 0.737 |
| trans-1,2-Dimethylcyclohexane | " | 0 | 0.285 | 0.307 | 0.327 | 0.333 | 0.338 | 0.355 | 0.423 | 0.488 | 0.549 | 0.604 | 0.655 | 0.700 | 0.742 |
| cis-1,3-Dimethylcyclohexane | " | 0 | 0.284 | 0.305 | 0.324 | 0.329 | 0.335 | 0.351 | 0.417 | 0.481 | 0.543 | 0.599 | 0.651 | 0.698 | 0.740 |
| trans-1,3-Dimethylcyclohexane | " | 0 | 0.285 | 0.306 | 0.324 | 0.329 | 0.335 | 0.351 | 0.416 | 0.480 | 0.541 | 0.597 | 0.648 | 0.693 | 0.735 |
| cis-1,4-Dimethylcyclohexane | " | 0 | 0.285 | 0.306 | 0.324 | 0.329 | 0.335 | 0.351 | 0.416 | 0.480 | 0.541 | 0.597 | 0.648 | 0.693 | 0.735 |
| trans-1,4-Dimethylcyclohexane | " | 0 | 0.282 | 0.305 | 0.324 | 0.330 | 0.336 | 0.352 | 0.420 | 0.485 | 0.546 | 0.603 | 0.655 | 0.701 | 0.742 |

| Compound (gas) | Formula | Temperature in °F | | | | | | | | | | | | | |
|---|---|---|---|---|---|---|---|---|---|---|---|---|---|---|---|
| | | 900 | 1000 | 1100 | 1200 | 1300 | 1400 | 1500 | 1600 | 1700 | 1800 | 1900 | 2000 | 2100 | 2200 |
| | | Heat Capacity, $C_p^o$, in BTU/lb deg F | | | | | | | | | | | | | |
| Cyclohexane | $C_6H_{12}$ | 0.7631 | 0.7997 | 0.8328 | 0.8627 | 0.8899 | 0.9147 | 0.937 | 0.958 | 0.976 | 0.993 | 1.009 | 1.023 | 1.036 | 1.048 |
| Methylcyclohexane | $C_7H_{14}$ | 0.7733 | 0.8080 | 0.8395 | 0.8680 | 0.8940 | 0.9177 | 0.939 | 0.959 | 0.977 | 0.993 | 1.008 | 1.022 | 1.035 | 1.046 |
| Ethylcyclohexane | $C_8H_{16}$ | 0.775 | 0.809 | 0.840 | 0.867 | 0.893 | 0.916 | 0.937 | 0.957 | 0.974 | 0.990 | 1.005 | 1.019 | 1.032 | 1.043 |
| 1,1-Dimethylcyclohexane | " | 0.780 | 0.814 | 0.846 | 0.875 | 0.901 | 0.924 | 0.945 | 0.965 | 0.982 | 0.999 | 1.014 | 1.027 | 1.040 | 1.050 |
| cis-1,2-Dimethylcyclohexane | " | 0.775 | 0.809 | 0.840 | 0.868 | 0.894 | 0.917 | 0.938 | 0.958 | 0.975 | 0.992 | 1.007 | 1.020 | 1.033 | 1.044 |
| trans-1,2-Dimethylcyclohexane | " | 0.779 | 0.812 | 0.843 | 0.871 | 0.896 | 0.919 | 0.940 | 0.959 | 0.977 | 0.993 | 1.007 | 1.021 | 1.033 | 1.045 |
| cis-1,3-Dimethylcyclohexane | " | 0.778 | 0.813 | 0.844 | 0.872 | 0.899 | 0.922 | 0.944 | 0.963 | 0.981 | 0.997 | 1.012 | 1.026 | 1.038 | 1.049 |
| trans-1,3-Dimethylcyclohexane | " | 0.772 | 0.806 | 0.837 | 0.865 | 0.891 | 0.914 | 0.936 | 0.955 | 0.972 | 0.989 | 1.004 | 1.018 | 1.031 | 1.042 |
| cis-1,4-Dimethylcyclohexane | " | 0.772 | 0.806 | 0.837 | 0.865 | 0.891 | 0.914 | 0.936 | 0.955 | 0.972 | 0.989 | 1.004 | 1.018 | 1.031 | 1.042 |
| trans-1,4-Dimethylcyclohexane | " | 0.779 | 0.813 | 0.845 | 0.873 | 0.898 | 0.921 | 0.942 | 0.961 | 0.979 | 0.995 | 1.009 | 1.023 | 1.036 | 1.047 |

TABLE 24v-E (PART 1), Page 1-- NORMAL MONOOLEFINS (1-ALKENES), $C_2$ TO $C_{20}$

HEAT CAPACITY, $c_p^o$, FOR THE IDEAL GAS STATE, AT -459.69° TO 2200°F

March 31, 1946; December 31, 1952

| Compound (gas) | Formula | Temperature in °F |||||||||||||| |
|---|---|---|---|---|---|---|---|---|---|---|---|---|---|---|---|
| | | -459.69 | 0 | 32 | 60 | 68 | 77 | 100 | 200 | 300 | 400 | 500 | 600 | 700 | 800 |
| | | Heat Capacity, $c_p^o$, in BTU/lb deg F ||||||||||||| |
| Ethene (Ethylene) | $C_2H_4$ | 0 | 0.3324 | 0.3483 | 0.3622 | 0.3662 | 0.3708 | 0.3820 | 0.4208 | 0.4780 | 0.5229 | 0.5642 | 0.6019 | 0.6365 | 0.6682 |
| Propene (Propylene) | $C_3H_6$ | 0 | 0.3239 | 0.3400 | 0.3341 | 0.3581 | 0.3627 | 0.3742 | 0.4241 | 0.4727 | 0.5192 | 0.5626 | 0.6026 | 0.6396 | 0.6737 |
| 1-Butene | $C_4H_8$ | 0 | 0.3201 | 0.3388 | 0.3548 | 0.3595 | 0.3646 | 0.3774 | 0.4323 | 0.4840 | 0.5324 | 0.5771 | 0.6181 | 0.6553 | 0.6893 |
| 1-Pentene | $C_5H_{10}$ | 0 | 0.3292 | 0.3476 | 0.3635 | 0.3681 | 0.3732 | 0.3859 | 0.4402 | 0.4918 | 0.5404 | 0.5855 | 0.6270 | 0.6646 | 0.6990 |
| 1-Hexene | $C_6H_{12}$ | 0 | 0.3312 | 0.3497 | 0.3659 | 0.3704 | 0.3756 | 0.3885 | 0.4435 | 0.4958 | 0.5448 | 0.5903 | 0.6320 | 0.6700 | 0.7045 |
| 1-Heptene | $C_7H_{14}$ | 0 | 0.3329 | 0.3516 | 0.3677 | 0.3723 | 0.3776 | 0.3905 | 0.4459 | 0.4986 | 0.5482 | 0.5939 | 0.6356 | 0.6737 | 0.7085 |
| 1-Octene | $C_8H_{16}$ | 0 | 0.3343 | 0.3530 | 0.3693 | 0.3739 | 0.3790 | 0.3921 | 0.4478 | 0.5008 | 0.5506 | 0.5964 | 0.6384 | 0.6765 | 0.7114 |
| 1-Nonene | $C_9H_{18}$ | 0 | 0.3353 | 0.3540 | 0.3703 | 0.3749 | 0.3802 | 0.3933 | 0.4493 | 0.5025 | 0.5525 | 0.5986 | 0.6405 | 0.6788 | 0.7138 |
| 1-Decene | $C_{10}H_{20}$ | 0 | 0.3362 | 0.3550 | 0.3713 | 0.3759 | 0.3811 | 0.3944 | 0.4504 | 0.5039 | 0.5540 | 0.6001 | 0.6422 | 0.6805 | 0.7156 |
| 1-Undecene | $C_{11}H_{22}$ | 0 | 0.3367 | 0.3556 | 0.3720 | 0.3767 | 0.3819 | 0.3951 | 0.4514 | 0.5050 | 0.5553 | 0.6015 | 0.6436 | 0.6820 | 0.7170 |

| Compound (gas) | Formula | Temperature in °F |||||||||||||| |
|---|---|---|---|---|---|---|---|---|---|---|---|---|---|---|---|
| | | 900 | 1000 | 1100 | 1200 | 1300 | 1400 | 1500 | 1600 | 1700 | 1800 | 1900 | 2000 | 2100 | 2200 |
| | | Heat Capacity, $c_p^o$, in BTU/lb deg F ||||||||||||| |
| Ethene (Ethylene) | $C_2H_4$ | 0.6976 | 0.7248 | 0.7501 | 0.7737 | 0.7956 | 0.8160 | 0.8349 | 0.8525 | 0.8688 | 0.8841 | 0.8983 | 0.9114 | 0.9235 | 0.9347 |
| Propene (Propylene) | $C_3H_6$ | 0.7051 | 0.7342 | 0.7613 | 0.7863 | 0.8096 | 0.8310 | 0.8509 | 0.8693 | 0.8863 | 0.9022 | 0.9170 | 0.9306 | 0.9432 | 0.9549 |
| 1-Butene | $C_4H_8$ | 0.7210 | 0.7501 | 0.7772 | 0.8021 | 0.8252 | 0.8464 | 0.8662 | 0.8846 | 0.9017 | 0.9173 | 0.9319 | 0.9453 | 0.9578 | 0.9694 |
| 1-Pentene | $C_5H_{10}$ | 0.7307 | 0.7601 | 0.7873 | 0.8121 | 0.8350 | 0.8563 | 0.8759 | 0.8942 | 0.9111 | 0.9267 | 0.9411 | 0.9545 | 0.9669 | 0.9784 |
| 1-Hexene | $C_6H_{12}$ | 0.7365 | 0.7658 | 0.7929 | 0.8178 | 0.8407 | 0.8620 | 0.8818 | 0.9001 | 0.9170 | 0.9325 | 0.9469 | 0.9602 | 0.9726 | 0.9841 |
| 1-Heptene | $C_7H_{14}$ | 0.7405 | 0.7698 | 0.7970 | 0.8221 | 0.845 | 0.866 | 0.86 | 0.904 | 0.921 | 0.936 | 0.952 | 0.965 | 0.977 | 0.988 |
| 1-Octene | $C_8H_{16}$ | 0.7434 | 0.7729 | 0.8000 | 0.8250 | 0.848 | 0.869 | 0.890 | 0.908 | 0.924 | 0.940 | 0.954 | 0.967 | 0.980 | 0.991 |
| 1-Nonene | $C_9H_{18}$ | 0.7458 | 0.7753 | 0.8025 | 0.8274 | 0.850 | 0.872 | 0.891 | 0.910 | 0.927 | 0.943 | 0.956 | 0.970 | 0.982 | 0.993 |
| 1-Decene | $C_{10}H_{20}$ | 0.7476 | 0.7771 | 0.8043 | 0.8294 | 0.853 | 0.874 | 0.893 | 0.911 | 0.928 | 0.944 | 0.959 | 0.972 | 0.984 | 0.995 |
| 1-Undecene | $C_{11}H_{22}$ | 0.7492 | 0.7786 | 0.8059 | 0.8309 | 0.854 | 0.875 | 0.895 | 0.913 | 0.930 | 0.946 | 0.960 | 0.973 | 0.985 | 0.997 |

TABLE 24v-E (PART 1), Page 2— NORMAL MONOOLEFINS (1-ALKENES), $C_2$ TO $C'_{20}$
HEAT CAPACITY, $c_p^o$, FOR THE IDEAL GAS STATE, AT -459.69° TO 2200°F

March 31, 1946; December 31, 1952

Temperature in °F

Heat Capacity, $c_p^o$, in BTU/lb deg F

| Compound (gas) | Formula | -459.69 | 0 | 32 | 60 | 68 | 77 | 100 | 200 | 300 | 400 | 500 | 600 | 700 | 800 |
|---|---|---|---|---|---|---|---|---|---|---|---|---|---|---|---|
| 1-Dodecene | $C_{12}H_{24}$ | 0 | 0.3372 | 0.3562 | 0.3726 | 0.3773 | 0.3826 | 0.3958 | 0.4522 | 0.5059 | 0.5564 | 0.6026 | 0.6447 | 0.6832 | 0.7183 |
| 1-Tridecene | $C_{13}H_{26}$ | 0 | 0.3378 | 0.3567 | 0.3731 | 0.3778 | 0.3830 | 0.3964 | 0.4529 | 0.5067 | 0.5572 | 0.6035 | 0.6457 | 0.6842 | 0.7193 |
| 1-Tetradecene | $C_{14}H_{28}$ | 0 | 0.3382 | 0.3571 | 0.3736 | 0.3782 | 0.3835 | 0.3968 | 0.4535 | 0.5074 | 0.5580 | 0.6044 | 0.6466 | 0.6851 | 0.7203 |
| 1-Pentadecene | $C_{15}H_{30}$ | 0 | 0.3385 | 0.3575 | 0.3740 | 0.3787 | 0.3839 | 0.3972 | 0.4540 | 0.5080 | 0.5586 | 0.6051 | 0.6473 | 0.6858 | 0.7210 |
| 1-Hexadecene | $C_{16}H_{32}$ | 0 | 0.3388 | 0.3578 | 0.3743 | 0.3790 | 0.3843 | 0.3976 | 0.4543 | 0.5085 | 0.5592 | 0.6057 | 0.6479 | 0.6865 | 0.7218 |
| 1-Heptadecene | $C_{17}H_{34}$ | 0 | 0.3391 | 0.3581 | 0.3746 | 0.3793 | 0.3846 | 0.3979 | 0.4547 | 0.5089 | 0.5597 | 0.6062 | 0.6485 | 0.6871 | 0.7224 |
| 1-Octadecene | $C_{18}H_{36}$ | 0 | 0.3394 | 0.3584 | 0.3749 | 0.3796 | 0.3848 | 0.3982 | 0.4551 | 0.5093 | 0.5602 | 0.6067 | 0.6490 | 0.6876 | 0.7229 |
| 1-Nonadecene | $C_{19}H_{38}$ | 0 | 0.3396 | 0.3586 | 0.3751 | 0.3798 | 0.3851 | 0.3985 | 0.4554 | 0.5097 | 0.5606 | 0.6072 | 0.6494 | 0.6881 | 0.7234 |
| 1-Eicosene | $C_{20}H_{40}$ | 0 | 0.3398 | 0.3588 | 0.3753 | 0.3800 | 0.3853 | 0.3987 | 0.4556 | 0.5100 | 0.5609 | 0.6075 | 0.6498 | 0.6885 | 0.7238 |

Temperature in °F

Heat Capacity, $c_p^o$, in BTU/lb deg F

| Compound (gas) | Formula | 900 | 1000 | 1100 | 1200 | 1300 | 1400 | 1500 | 1600 | 1700 | 1800 | 1900 | 2000 | 2100 | 2200 |
|---|---|---|---|---|---|---|---|---|---|---|---|---|---|---|---|
| 1-Dodecene | $C_{12}H_{24}$ | 0.7504 | 0.7799 | 0.8072 | 0.8322 | 0.855 | 0.876 | 0.897 | 0.914 | 0.932 | 0.947 | 0.962 | 0.975 | 0.987 | 0.998 |
| 1-Tridecene | $C_{13}H_{26}$ | 0.7515 | 0.7811 | 0.8083 | 0.8332 | 0.856 | 0.877 | 0.898 | 0.916 | 0.933 | 0.948 | 0.962 | 0.976 | 0.988 | 0.999 |
| 1-Tetradecene | $C_{14}H_{28}$ | 0.7524 | 0.7820 | 0.8092 | 0.8343 | 0.857 | 0.879 | 0.898 | 0.917 | 0.934 | 0.949 | 0.963 | 0.977 | 0.988 | 1.000 |
| 1-Pentadecene | $C_{15}H_{30}$ | 0.7532 | 0.7827 | 0.8100 | 0.8351 | 0.858 | 0.879 | 0.899 | 0.917 | 0.934 | 0.950 | 0.964 | 0.977 | 0.989 | 1.001 |
| 1-Hexadecene | $C_{16}H_{32}$ | 0.7539 | 0.7835 | 0.8108 | 0.8358 | 0.859 | 0.880 | 0.900 | 0.918 | 0.935 | 0.951 | 0.965 | 0.978 | 0.990 | 1.002 |
| 1-Heptadecene | $C_{17}H_{34}$ | 0.7546 | 0.7841 | 0.8114 | 0.8365 | 0.860 | 0.881 | 0.901 | 0.919 | 0.936 | 0.951 | 0.966 | 0.979 | 0.991 | 1.002 |
| 1-Octadecene | $C_{18}H_{36}$ | 0.7551 | 0.7847 | 0.8119 | 0.8370 | 0.860 | 0.882 | 0.901 | 0.920 | 0.937 | 0.952 | 0.966 | 0.979 | 0.992 | 1.003 |
| 1-Nonadecene | $C_{19}H_{38}$ | 0.7556 | 0.7851 | 0.8124 | 0.8375 | 0.860 | 0.882 | 0.902 | 0.920 | 0.937 | 0.952 | 0.967 | 0.979 | 0.992 | 1.003 |
| 1-Eicosene | $C_{20}H_{40}$ | 0.7560 | 0.7856 | 0.8129 | 0.8380 | 0.861 | 0.882 | 0.902 | 0.920 | 0.937 | 0.953 | 0.968 | 0.980 | 0.992 | 1.004 |

## TABLE 8v-E (PART 1) – MONOOLEFINS, $C_2$ TO $C_5$

### HEAT CAPACITY, $C_p^o$, FOR THE IDEAL GAS STATE, AT -459.69° TO 2200°F

May 31, 1946; December 31, 1952

**Temperature in °F**

Heat Capacity, $C_p^o$, in BTU/lb deg F

| Compound (gas) | Formula | -459.69 | 0 | 32 | 60 | 68 | 77 | 100 | 200 | 300 | 400 | 500 | 600 | 700 | 800 |
|---|---|---|---|---|---|---|---|---|---|---|---|---|---|---|---|
| Ethene (Ethylene) | $C_2H_4$ | 0 | 0.3324 | 0.3483 | 0.3622 | 0.3662 | 0.3708 | 0.3820 | 0.4308 | 0.4780 | 0.5229 | 0.5642 | 0.6019 | 0.6365 | 0.6682 |
| Propene (Propylene) | $C_3H_6$ | 0 | 0.3239 | 0.3400 | 0.3541 | 0.3581 | 0.3627 | 0.3742 | 0.4241 | 0.4727 | 0.5192 | 0.5626 | 0.6026 | 0.6396 | 0.6737 |
| 1-Butene | $C_4H_8$ | 0 | 0.3201 | 0.3388 | 0.3548 | 0.3595 | 0.3646 | 0.3774 | 0.4323 | 0.4840 | 0.5324 | 0.5771 | 0.6181 | 0.6553 | 0.6893 |
| cis-2-Butene | " | 0 | 0.2948 | 0.3119 | 0.3269 | 0.3311 | 0.3359 | 0.3483 | 0.4016 | 0.4539 | 0.5041 | 0.5508 | 0.5938 | 0.6333 | 0.6696 |
| trans-2-Butene | " | 0 | 0.3358 | 0.3516 | 0.3654 | 0.3694 | 0.3739 | 0.3852 | 0.4343 | 0.4824 | 0.5286 | 0.5719 | 0.6121 | 0.6492 | 0.6835 |
| 2-Methylpropene (Isobutene) | " | 0 | 0.3374 | 0.3549 | 0.3701 | 0.3744 | 0.3794 | 0.3915 | 0.4433 | 0.4925 | 0.5387 | 0.5816 | 0.6211 | 0.6576 | 0.6912 |
| 1-Pentene | $C_5H_{10}$ | 0 | 0.3292 | 0.3476 | 0.3635 | 0.3681 | 0.3732 | 0.3859 | 0.4402 | 0.4918 | 0.5404 | 0.5855 | 0.6270 | 0.6646 | 0.6990 |
| cis-2-Pentene | " | 0 | 0.3012 | 0.3201 | 0.3366 | 0.3412 | 0.3466 | 0.3598 | 0.4167 | 0.4711 | 0.5225 | 0.5700 | 0.6133 | 0.6522 | 0.6875 |
| trans-2-Pentene | " | 0 | 0.3273 | 0.3448 | 0.3601 | 0.3644 | 0.3694 | 0.3816 | 0.4346 | 0.4855 | 0.5337 | 0.5783 | 0.6193 | 0.6571 | 0.6915 |
| 2-Methyl-1-butene | " | 0 | 0.3353 | 0.3542 | 0.3705 | 0.3751 | 0.3803 | 0.3934 | 0.4486 | 0.5006 | 0.5489 | 0.5930 | 0.6331 | 0.6699 | 0.7038 |
| 3-Methyl-1-butene | " | 0 | 0.3564 | 0.3766 | 0.3936 | 0.3984 | 0.4040 | 0.4172 | 0.4720 | 0.5216 | 0.5667 | 0.6083 | 0.6467 | 0.6820 | 0.7145 |
| 2-Methyl-2-butene | " | 0 | 0.3149 | 0.3327 | 0.3483 | 0.3527 | 0.3577 | 0.3701 | 0.4236 | 0.4751 | 0.5238 | 0.5690 | 0.6106 | 0.6491 | 0.6844 |

**Temperature in °F**

Heat Capacity, $C_p^o$, in BTU/lb deg F

| Compound (gas) | Formula | 900 | 1000 | 1100 | 1200 | 1300 | 1400 | 1500 | 1600 | 1700 | 1800 | 1900 | 2000 | 2100 | 2200 |
|---|---|---|---|---|---|---|---|---|---|---|---|---|---|---|---|
| Ethene (Ethylene) | $C_2H_4$ | 0.6976 | 0.7248 | 0.7501 | 0.7737 | 0.7956 | 0.8160 | 0.8349 | 0.8525 | 0.8688 | 0.8841 | 0.8983 | 0.9114 | 0.9235 | 0.9347 |
| Propene (Propylene) | $C_3H_6$ | 0.7051 | 0.7342 | 0.7613 | 0.7863 | 0.8096 | 0.8310 | 0.8509 | 0.8693 | 0.8863 | 0.9022 | 0.9170 | 0.9306 | 0.9432 | 0.9549 |
| 1-Butene | $C_4H_8$ | 0.7210 | 0.7501 | 0.7772 | 0.8021 | 0.8252 | 0.8464 | 0.8662 | 0.8846 | 0.9017 | 0.9173 | 0.9319 | 0.9453 | 0.9578 | 0.9694 |
| cis-2-Butene | " | 0.7031 | 0.7339 | 0.7623 | 0.7886 | 0.8128 | 0.8352 | 0.8560 | 0.8751 | 0.8929 | 0.9093 | 0.9245 | 0.9385 | 0.9514 | 0.9634 |
| trans-2-Butene | " | 0.7154 | 0.7448 | 0.7719 | 0.7971 | 0.8207 | 0.8425 | 0.8627 | 0.8812 | 0.8984 | 0.9143 | 0.9291 | 0.9427 | 0.9554 | 0.9672 |
| 2-Methylpropene (Isobutene) | " | 0.7223 | 0.7512 | 0.7780 | 0.8028 | 0.8257 | 0.8471 | 0.8668 | 0.8850 | 0.9018 | 0.9175 | 0.9320 | 0.9455 | 0.9580 | 0.9695 |
| 1-Pentene | $C_5H_{10}$ | 0.7307 | 0.7601 | 0.7873 | 0.8121 | 0.8350 | 0.8563 | 0.8759 | 0.8942 | 0.9111 | 0.9267 | 0.9411 | 0.9545 | 0.9669 | 0.9784 |
| cis-2-Pentene | " | 0.7205 | 0.7509 | 0.7788 | 0.8046 | 0.8285 | 0.8505 | 0.8707 | 0.8896 | 0.9071 | 0.9230 | 0.9378 | 0.9515 | 0.9642 | 0.9760 |
| trans-2-Pentene | " | 0.7235 | 0.7531 | 0.7803 | 0.8057 | 0.8291 | 0.8507 | 0.8707 | 0.8892 | 0.9066 | 0.9224 | 0.9371 | 0.9506 | 0.9632 | 0.9748 |
| 2-Methyl-1-butene | " | 0.7352 | 0.7640 | 0.7906 | 0.8153 | 0.8383 | 0.8593 | 0.8787 | 0.8969 | 0.9138 | 0.9292 | 0.9435 | 0.9569 | 0.9692 | 0.9806 |
| 3-Methyl-1-butene | " | 0.7448 | 0.7726 | 0.7982 | 0.8219 | 0.8441 | 0.8647 | 0.8838 | 0.9015 | 0.9179 | 0.9331 | 0.9472 | 0.9601 | 0.9721 | 0.9834 |
| 2-Methyl-2-butene | " | 0.7172 | 0.7474 | 0.7753 | 0.8013 | 0.8252 | 0.8473 | 0.8675 | 0.8865 | 0.9042 | 0.9202 | 0.9351 | 0.9489 | 0.9617 | 0.9736 |

National Bureau of Standards

TABLE 8v-E (PART 2), Page 1 - MONOOLEFINS, C$_6$

HEAT CAPACITY, $c_p^o$, FOR THE IDEAL GAS STATE, AT -459.69° TO 2200°F

May 31, 1946; December 31, 1952

Heat Capacity, $c_p^o$, in BTU/lb deg F

| Compound (gas) | Formula | Temperature in °F | | | | | | | | | | | | | |
|---|---|---|---|---|---|---|---|---|---|---|---|---|---|---|---|
| | | -459.69 | 0 | 32 | 60 | 68 | 77 | 100 | 200 | 300 | 400 | 500 | 600 | 700 | 800 |
| 1-Hexene | C$_6$H$_{12}$ | 0 | 0.3312 | 0.3497 | 0.3659 | 0.3704 | 0.3756 | 0.3885 | 0.4435 | 0.4958 | 0.5448 | 0.5903 | 0.6320 | 0.6700 | 0.7045 |
| cis-2-Hexene | " | 0 | 0.3135 | 0.3313 | 0.3471 | 0.3516 | 0.3567 | 0.3695 | 0.4254 | 0.480 | 0.531 | 0.578 | 0.621 | 0.660 | 0.696 |
| trans-2-Hexene | " | 0 | 0.3352 | 0.3520 | 0.3667 | 0.3709 | 0.3757 | 0.3877 | 0.4403 | 0.492 | 0.541 | 0.585 | 0.626 | 0.664 | 0.699 |
| cis-3-Hexene | " | 0 | 0.3035 | 0.3231 | 0.3405 | 0.3454 | 0.3509 | 0.3646 | 0.4233 | 0.479 | 0.531 | 0.579 | 0.623 | 0.662 | 0.697 |
| trans-3-Hexene | " | 0 | 0.3320 | 0.3508 | 0.3672 | 0.3717 | 0.3770 | 0.3901 | 0.4454 | 0.498 | 0.547 | 0.591 | 0.632 | 0.669 | 0.703 |
| 2-Methyl-1-pentene | " | 0 | 0.3396 | 0.3586 | 0.3749 | 0.3795 | 0.3849 | 0.3979 | 0.4529 | 0.505 | 0.553 | 0.597 | 0.638 | 0.676 | 0.710 |
| 3-Methyl-1-pentene | " | 0 | 0.3566 | 0.3798 | 0.3995 | 0.4050 | 0.4113 | 0.4268 | 0.4911 | 0.550 | 0.604 | 0.654 | 0.700 | 0.742 | 0.780 |
| 4-Methyl-1-pentene | " | 0 | 0.3131 | 0.3326 | 0.3495 | 0.3542 | 0.3590 | 0.3730 | 0.4295 | 0.483 | 0.532 | 0.578 | 0.620 | 0.658 | 0.693 |
| 2-Methyl-2-pentene | " | 0 | 0.3121 | 0.3319 | 0.3490 | 0.3538 | 0.3593 | 0.3729 | 0.4303 | 0.484 | 0.534 | 0.581 | 0.624 | 0.661 | 0.696 |

Heat Capacity, $c_p^o$, in BTU/lb deg F

| Compound (gas) | Formula | Temperature in °F | | | | | | | | | | | | | |
|---|---|---|---|---|---|---|---|---|---|---|---|---|---|---|---|
| | | 900 | 1000 | 1100 | 1200 | 1300 | 1400 | 1500 | 1600 | 1700 | 1800 | 1900 | 2000 | 2100 | 2200 |
| 1-Hexene | C$_6$H$_{12}$ | 0.7365 | 0.7658 | 0.7929 | 0.8178 | 0.8407 | 0.8620 | 0.8818 | 0.9001 | 0.9170 | 0.9325 | 0.9469 | 0.9602 | 0.9726 | 0.9841 |
| cis-2-Hexene | " | 0.728 | 0.759 | 0.787 | 0.813 | 0.837 | | | | | | | | | |
| trans-2-Hexene | " | 0.731 | 0.761 | 0.788 | 0.812 | 0.836 | | | | | | | | | |
| cis-3-Hexene | " | 0.730 | 0.760 | 0.787 | 0.813 | 0.836 | | | | | | | | | |
| trans-3-Hexene | " | 0.735 | 0.764 | 0.790 | 0.815 | 0.838 | | | | | | | | | |
| 2-Methyl-1-pentene | " | 0.741 | 0.770 | 0.797 | 0.822 | 0.844 | | | | | | | | | |
| 3-Methyl-1-pentene | " | 0.815 | 0.848 | 0.878 | 0.906 | 0.932 | | | | | | | | | |
| 4-Methyl-1-pentene | " | 0.726 | 0.755 | 0.782 | 0.807 | 0.830 | | | | | | | | | |
| 2-Methyl-2-pentene | " | 0.728 | 0.759 | 0.786 | 0.811 | 0.835 | | | | | | | | | |

TABLE 8v-E (PART 2), Page 2 - MONOOLEFINS, $C_6$

HEAT CAPACITY, $c_p^o$, FOR THE IDEAL GAS STATE, AT $-459.69^o$ TO $2200^o F$

May 31, 1946; December 31, 1952

| Compound (gas) | Formula | Temperature in °F — Heat Capacity, $c_p^o$, in BTU/lb deg F | | | | | | | | | | | | |
|---|---|---|---|---|---|---|---|---|---|---|---|---|---|---|
| | | -459.69 | 0 | 32 | 60 | 68 | 77 | 100 | 200 | 300 | 400 | 500 | 600 | 700 | 800 |
| 3-Methyl-cis-2-pentene | $C_6H_{12}$ | 0 | 0.3121 | 0.3319 | 0.3490 | 0.3538 | 0.3593 | 0.3729 | 0.4303 | 0.484 | 0.534 | 0.581 | 0.624 | 0.661 | 0.696 |
| 3-Methyl-trans-2-pentene | " | 0 | 0.3121 | 0.3319 | 0.3490 | 0.3538 | 0.3593 | 0.3729 | 0.4303 | 0.484 | 0.534 | 0.581 | 0.624 | 0.661 | 0.696 |
| 4-Methyl-cis-2-pentene | " | 0 | 0.3314 | 0.3515 | 0.3686 | 0.3734 | 0.3790 | 0.3925 | 0.4490 | 0.501 | 0.549 | 0.594 | 0.635 | 0.672 | 0.705 |
| 4-Methyl-trans-2-pentene | " | 0 | 0.3563 | 0.3753 | 0.3915 | 0.3961 | 0.4014 | 0.4140 | 0.4674 | 0.517 | 0.562 | 0.604 | 0.643 | 0.679 | 0.712 |
| 2-Ethyl-1-butene | " | 0 | 0.3312 | 0.3513 | 0.3686 | 0.3735 | 0.3790 | 0.3928 | 0.4504 | 0.504 | 0.554 | 0.599 | 0.639 | 0.676 | 0.710 |
| 2,3-Dimethyl-1-butene | " | 0 | 0.3601 | 0.3800 | 0.3970 | 0.4017 | 0.4072 | 0.4204 | 0.4752 | 0.525 | 0.571 | 0.612 | 0.650 | 0.686 | 0.718 |
| 3,3-Dimethyl-1-butene | " | 0 | 0.3143 | 0.3330 | 0.3491 | 0.3538 | 0.3590 | 0.3722 | 0.4288 | 0.483 | 0.535 | 0.582 | 0.626 | 0.664 | 0.699 |
| 2,3-Dimethyl-2-butene | " | 0 | 0.3217 | 0.3383 | 0.3530 | 0.3572 | 0.3620 | 0.3741 | 0.4269 | 0.479 | 0.528 | 0.574 | 0.616 | 0.654 | 0.689 |

| Compound (gas) | Formula | Temperature in °F — Heat Capacity, $c_p^o$, in BTU/lb deg F | | | | | | | | | | | | |
|---|---|---|---|---|---|---|---|---|---|---|---|---|---|---|
| | | 900 | 1000 | 1100 | 1200 | 1300 | 1400 | 1500 | 1600 | 1700 | 1800 | 1900 | 2000 | 2100 | 2200 |
| 3-Methyl-cis-2-pentene | $C_6H_{12}$ | 0.728 | 0.759 | 0.786 | 0.811 | 0.835 | | | | | | | | | |
| 3-Methyl-trans-2-pentene | " | 0.728 | 0.759 | 0.786 | 0.811 | 0.835 | | | | | | | | | |
| 4-Methyl-cis-2-pentene | " | 0.737 | 0.766 | 0.792 | 0.817 | 0.840 | | | | | | | | | |
| 4-Methyl-trans-2-pentene | " | 0.743 | 0.771 | 0.797 | 0.822 | 0.844 | | | | | | | | | |
| 2-Ethyl-1-butene | " | 0.741 | 0.770 | 0.797 | 0.822 | 0.845 | | | | | | | | | |
| 2,3-Dimethyl-1-butene | " | 0.749 | 0.777 | 0.803 | 0.826 | 0.849 | | | | | | | | | |
| 3,3-Dimethyl-1-butene | " | 0.732 | 0.760 | 0.785 | 0.808 | 0.833 | | | | | | | | | |
| 2,3-Dimethyl-2-butene | " | 0.722 | 0.753 | 0.780 | 0.806 | 0.830 | | | | | | | | | |

TABLE 11v-E (Part 1) - DIOLEFINS, C₃ to C₅

HEAT CAPACITY, $C_p^o$, FOR THE IDEAL GAS STATE, AT -459.69° TO 2200°F

October 31, 1947; April 30, 1948

Temperature in °F

Heat Capacity, $C_p^o$, in BTU/lb deg F

| Compound (gas) | Formula | -459.69 | 0 | 32 | 60 | 68 | 77 | 100 | 200 | 300 | 400 | 500 | 600 | 700 | 800 |
|---|---|---|---|---|---|---|---|---|---|---|---|---|---|---|---|
| Propadiene (Allene) | C₃H₄ | 0 | 0.3157 | 0.3309 | 0.3439 | 0.3476 | 0.3517 | 0.3621 | 0.4051 | 0.4446 | 0.4808 | 0.5135 | 0.5431 | 0.5700 | 0.5946 |
| 1,2-Butadiene | C₄H₆ | 0 | 0.3173 | 0.3326 | 0.3458 | 0.3496 | 0.3538 | 0.3644 | 0.4091 | 0.4514 | 0.4909 | 0.5275 | 0.5611 | 0.5916 | 0.6196 |
| 1,3-Butadiene | " | 0 | 0.3045 | 0.3243 | 0.3412 | 0.3459 | 0.3512 | 0.3644 | 0.4187 | 0.4675 | 0.5109 | 0.5489 | 0.5820 | 0.6116 | 0.6383 |
| 1,2-Pentadiene | C₅H₈ | 0 | 0.336 | 0.344 | 0.360 | 0.364 | 0.370 | 0.382 | 0.432 | 0.478 | 0.520 | 0.558 | 0.592 | 0.624 | 0.653 |
| cis-1,3-Pentadiene (cis-Piperylene) | " | 0 | 0.285 | 0.304 | 0.321 | 0.326 | 0.332 | 0.345 | 0.401 | 0.453 | 0.500 | 0.542 | 0.578 | 0.612 | 0.643 |
| trans-1,3-Pentadiene (trans-Piperylene) | " | 0 | 0.321 | 0.339 | 0.354 | 0.359 | 0.362 | 0.376 | 0.428 | 0.476 | 0.521 | 0.559 | 0.594 | 0.625 | 0.654 |
| 1,4-Pentadiene | " | 0 | 0.326 | 0.343 | 0.359 | 0.363 | 0.368 | 0.380 | 0.431 | 0.477 | 0.520 | 0.558 | 0.592 | 0.623 | 0.651 |
| 2,3-Pentadiene | " | 0 | 0.318 | 0.334 | 0.347 | 0.351 | 0.355 | 0.366 | 0.412 | 0.456 | 0.498 | 0.536 | 0.571 | 0.604 | 0.634 |
| 3-Methyl-1,2-Butadiene | " | 0 | 0.331 | 0.347 | 0.361 | 0.365 | 0.370 | 0.381 | 0.428 | 0.472 | 0.513 | 0.550 | 0.585 | 0.616 | 0.645 |
| 2-Methyl-1,3-Butadiene (Isoprene) | " | 0 | 0.319 | 0.340 | 0.357 | 0.362 | 0.367 | 0.381 | 0.436 | 0.485 | 0.528 | 0.567 | 0.601 | 0.632 | 0.660 |

Temperature in °F

Heat Capacity, $C_p^o$, in BTU/lb deg F

| Compound (gas) | Formula | 900 | 1000 | 1100 | 1200 | 1300 | 1400 | 1500 | 1600 | 1700 | 1800 | 1900 | 2000 | 2100 | 2200 |
|---|---|---|---|---|---|---|---|---|---|---|---|---|---|---|---|
| Propadiene (Allene) | C₃H₄ | 0.6172 | 0.6381 | 0.6575 | 0.6755 | 0.6921 | 0.7075 | 0.7216 | 0.7350 | 0.7473 | 0.7586 | 0.7691 | 0.7789 | 0.7881 | 0.7965 |
| 1,2-Butadiene | C₄H₆ | 0.6457 | 0.6700 | 0.6924 | 0.7131 | 0.7322 | 0.7497 | 0.7659 | 0.7809 | 0.7948 | 0.8076 | 0.8195 | 0.8305 | 0.8407 | 0.8501 |
| 1,3-Butadiene | " | 0.6626 | 0.6849 | 0.7055 | 0.7244 | 0.7420 | 0.7583 | 0.7734 | 0.7874 | 0.8004 | 0.8125 | 0.8238 | 0.8342 | 0.8438 | 0.8528 |
| 1,2-Pentadiene | C₅H₈ | 0.680 | 0.704 | 0.727 | 0.748 | 0.767 | 0.785 | 0.802 | 0.818 | 0.832 | 0.844 | 0.856 | 0.868 | 0.878 | 0.887 |
| cis-1,3-Pentadiene (cis-Piperylene) | " | 0.670 | 0.694 | 0.718 | 0.739 | 0.758 | 0.777 | 0.793 | 0.809 | 0.823 | 0.836 | 0.849 | 0.861 | 0.871 | 0.881 |
| trans-1,3-Pentadiene (trans-Piperylene) | " | 0.681 | 0.704 | 0.726 | 0.746 | 0.764 | 0.782 | 0.799 | 0.814 | 0.827 | 0.841 | 0.853 | 0.864 | 0.874 | 0.884 |
| 1,4-Pentadiene | " | 0.678 | 0.703 | 0.725 | 0.746 | 0.766 | 0.783 | 0.799 | 0.815 | 0.829 | 0.842 | 0.855 | 0.865 | 0.875 | 0.885 |
| 2,3-Pentadiene | " | 0.662 | 0.689 | 0.713 | 0.735 | 0.755 | 0.774 | 0.792 | 0.808 | 0.823 | 0.837 | 0.849 | 0.861 | 0.871 | 0.881 |
| 3-Methyl-1,2-Butadiene | " | 0.672 | 0.697 | 0.720 | 0.742 | 0.761 | 0.780 | 0.796 | 0.812 | 0.826 | 0.839 | 0.852 | 0.863 | 0.874 | 0.884 |
| 2-Methyl-1,3-Butadiene (Isoprene) | " | 0.686 | 0.709 | 0.730 | 0.750 | 0.769 | 0.786 | 0.802 | 0.817 | 0.830 | 0.844 | 0.856 | 0.867 | 0.877 | 0.886 |

TABLE 18v-E, Page 1 - ALKYL CYCLOPENTENES, $C_5$ TO $C_7$

HEAT CAPACITY, $c_p^o$, FOR THE IDEAL GAS STATE, AT -459.69° TO 2200°F

December 31, 1952

| Compound (gas) | Formula | Temperature in °F | | | | | | | | | | | | | |
|---|---|---|---|---|---|---|---|---|---|---|---|---|---|---|---|
| | | -459.69 | 0 | 32 | 60 | 68 | 77 | 100 | 200 | 300 | 400 | 500 | 600 | 700 | 800 |
| | | Heat Capacity, $c_p^o$, in BTU/lb deg F | | | | | | | | | | | | | |
| Cyclopentene | $C_5H_8$ | 0 | 0.2239 | 0.2398 | 0.2544 | 0.2586 | 0.2634 | 0.2761 | 0.3331 | 0.3900 | 0.4434 | 0.4925 | 0.5371 | 0.5775 | 0.6140 |
| 1-Methylcyclopentene | $C_6H_{10}$ | 0 | 0.251 | 0.269 | 0.285 | 0.288 | 0.293 | 0.306 | 0.362 | 0.417 | 0.468 | 0.517 | 0.561 | 0.601 | 0.636 |
| 2-Methylcyclopentene | " | 0 | 0.247 | 0.265 | 0.281 | 0.286 | 0.291 | 0.304 | 0.362 | 0.418 | 0.472 | 0.521 | 0.564 | 0.605 | 0.640 |
| 3-Methylcyclopentene | " | 0 | 0.246 | 0.265 | 0.281 | 0.286 | 0.291 | 0.304 | 0.362 | 0.418 | 0.471 | 0.520 | 0.563 | 0.603 | 0.639 |

| Compound (gas) | Formula | Temperature in °F | | | | | | | | | | | | | |
|---|---|---|---|---|---|---|---|---|---|---|---|---|---|---|---|
| | | 900 | 1000 | 1100 | 1200 | 1300 | 1400 | 1500 | 1600 | 1700 | 1800 | 1900 | 2000 | 2100 | 2200 |
| | | Heat Capacity, $c_p^o$, in BTU/lb deg F | | | | | | | | | | | | | |
| Cyclopentene | $C_5H_8$ | 0.6472 | 0.6774 | 0.7050 | 0.7303 | 0.7533 | 0.7745 | 0.7999 | 0.8118 | 0.8282 | 0.8432 | 0.8571 | 0.8700 | 0.8818 | 0.8927 |
| 1-Methylcyclopentene | $C_6H_{10}$ | 0.669 | 0.700 | 0.726 | 0.751 | 0.774 | 0.794 | 0.814 | 0.832 | 0.848 | 0.861 | 0.877 | 0.892 | 0.903 | 0.914 |
| 2-Methylcyclopentene | " | 0.672 | 0.702 | 0.729 | 0.753 | 0.776 | 0.797 | 0.816 | 0.835 | 0.850 | 0.865 | 0.878 | 0.892 | 0.904 | 0.915 |
| 3-Methylcyclopentene | " | 0.670 | 0.701 | 0.728 | 0.753 | 0.775 | 0.796 | 0.815 | 0.833 | 0.849 | 0.864 | 0.877 | 0.890 | 0.903 | 0.914 |

TABLE 18v-E, Page 2 – ALKYL CYCLOPENTENES, $C_5$ TO $C_7$

HEAT CAPACITY, $C_p^o$, FOR THE IDEAL GAS STATE, AT -459.69° TO 2200°F

December 31, 1952

| Compound (gas) | Formula | Temperature in °F | | | | | | | | | | | | | |
|---|---|---|---|---|---|---|---|---|---|---|---|---|---|---|---|
| | | -459.69 | 0 | 32 | 60 | 68 | 77 | 100 | 200 | 300 | 400 | 500 | 600 | 700 | 800 |
| | | Heat Capacity, $C_p^o$, in BTU/lb deg F | | | | | | | | | | | | | |
| 1-Ethylcyclopentene | $C_7H_{12}$ | | | | | | | | | | | | | | |
| 3-Ethylcyclopentene | " | | | | | | | | | | | | | | |
| 4-Ethylcyclopentene | " | 0 | 0.273 | 0.291 | 0.306 | 0.310 | 0.315 | 0.327 | 0.382 | 0.436 | 0.488 | 0.535 | 0.578 | 0.616 | 0.652 |
| 1,2-Dimethylcyclopentene | " | 0 | 0.268 | 0.267 | 0.303 | 0.308 | 0.313 | 0.326 | 0.383 | 0.438 | 0.490 | 0.538 | 0.581 | 0.619 | 0.655 |
| 1,3-Dimethylcyclopentene | " | 0 | 0.269 | 0.288 | 0.303 | 0.308 | 0.312 | 0.326 | 0.382 | 0.437 | 0.489 | 0.537 | 0.580 | 0.618 | 0.654 |
| 1,4-Dimethylcyclopentene | " | 0 | 0.268 | 0.287 | 0.303 | 0.308 | 0.313 | 0.326 | 0.383 | 0.438 | 0.490 | 0.537 | 0.580 | 0.619 | 0.655 |
| 1,5-Dimethylcyclopentene | " | 0 | 0.261 | 0.280 | 0.295 | 0.300 | 0.306 | 0.319 | 0.378 | 0.436 | 0.492 | 0.542 | 0.588 | 0.629 | 0.666 |
| 3,3-Dimethylcyclopentene | " | 0 | 0.263 | 0.283 | 0.299 | 0.304 | 0.310 | 0.323 | 0.382 | 0.441 | 0.494 | 0.542 | 0.586 | 0.626 | 0.661 |
| 3,cis-4-Dimethylcyclopentene | " | 0 | 0.267 | 0.286 | 0.301 | 0.306 | 0.312 | 0.325 | 0.383 | 0.440 | 0.494 | 0.541 | 0.584 | 0.622 | 0.658 |
| 3,trans-4-Dimethylcyclopentene | " | 0 | 0.267 | 0.286 | 0.301 | 0.306 | 0.312 | 0.325 | 0.383 | 0.440 | 0.494 | 0.541 | 0.584 | 0.622 | 0.658 |
| 3,cis-5-Dimethylcyclopentene | " | 0 | 0.267 | 0.286 | 0.301 | 0.306 | 0.312 | 0.325 | 0.383 | 0.440 | 0.494 | 0.541 | 0.584 | 0.622 | 0.658 |
| 3,trans-5-Dimethylcyclopentene | " | | | | | | | | | | | | | | |
| 4,4-Dimethylcyclopentene | " | | | | | | | | | | | | | | |

| Compound (gas) | Formula | Temperature in °F | | | | | | | | | | | | | |
|---|---|---|---|---|---|---|---|---|---|---|---|---|---|---|---|
| | | 900 | 1000 | 1100 | 1200 | 1300 | 1400 | 1500 | 1600 | 1700 | 1800 | 1900 | 2000 | 2100 | 2200 |
| | | Heat Capacity, $C_p^o$, in BTU/lb deg F | | | | | | | | | | | | | |
| 1-Ethylcyclopentene | $C_7H_{12}$ | | | | | | | | | | | | | | |
| 3-Ethylcyclopentene | " | | | | | | | | | | | | | | |
| 4-Ethylcyclopentene | " | 0.684 | 0.713 | 0.740 | 0.765 | 0.789 | 0.810 | 0.828 | 0.847 | 0.864 | 0.878 | 0.893 | 0.906 | 0.919 | 0.929 |
| 1,2-Dimethylcyclopentene | " | 0.687 | 0.716 | 0.743 | 0.768 | 0.791 | 0.812 | 0.830 | 0.848 | 0.865 | 0.879 | 0.894 | 0.906 | 0.918 | 0.929 |
| 1,3-Dimethylcyclopentene | " | 0.686 | 0.715 | 0.742 | 0.767 | 0.790 | 0.810 | 0.829 | 0.848 | 0.864 | 0.878 | 0.893 | 0.905 | 0.916 | 0.928 |
| 1,4-Dimethylcyclopentene | " | 0.687 | 0.716 | 0.743 | 0.767 | 0.790 | 0.810 | 0.829 | 0.848 | 0.865 | 0.879 | 0.894 | 0.906 | 0.918 | 0.929 |
| 1,5-Dimethylcyclopentene | " | 0.699 | 0.730 | 0.756 | 0.781 | 0.805 | 0.826 | 0.845 | 0.861 | 0.878 | 0.893 | 0.905 | 0.918 | 0.929 | 0.940 |
| 3,3-Dimethylcyclopentene | " | 0.693 | 0.722 | 0.749 | 0.773 | 0.796 | 0.817 | 0.836 | 0.852 | 0.869 | 0.883 | 0.897 | 0.909 | 0.921 | 0.932 |
| 3,cis-4-Dimethylcyclopentene | " | 0.689 | 0.718 | 0.745 | 0.770 | 0.793 | 0.814 | 0.832 | 0.849 | 0.866 | 0.880 | 0.895 | 0.907 | 0.919 | 0.929 |
| 3,trans-4-Dimethylcyclopentene | " | 0.689 | 0.718 | 0.745 | 0.770 | 0.793 | 0.814 | 0.832 | 0.849 | 0.866 | 0.880 | 0.895 | 0.907 | 0.919 | 0.929 |
| 3,cis-5-Dimethylcyclopentene | " | 0.689 | 0.718 | 0.745 | 0.770 | 0.793 | 0.814 | 0.832 | 0.849 | 0.866 | 0.880 | 0.895 | 0.907 | 0.919 | 0.929 |
| 3,trans-5-Dimethylcyclopentene | " | | | | | | | | | | | | | | |
| 4,4-Dimethylcyclopentene | " | | | | | | | | | | | | | | |

TABLE 25v-E (PART 1), Page 1 - NORMAL ACETYLENES (1-ALKYNES), $C_2$ TO $C_{20}$

HEAT CAPACITY, $c_p^o$, FOR THE IDEAL GAS STATE, AT $-459.69°$ TO $2200°F$

February 28, 1946; December 31, 1952

Temperature in °F

Heat Capacity, $c_p^o$, in BTU/lb deg F

| Compound (gas) | Formula | -459.69 | 0 | 32 | 60 | 68 | 77 | 100 | 200 | 300 | 400 | 500 | 600 | 700 | 800 |
|---|---|---|---|---|---|---|---|---|---|---|---|---|---|---|---|
| Ethyne (Acetylene) | $C_2H_2$ | 0 | 0.3719 | 0.3854 | 0.3966 | 0.3996 | 0.4030 | 0.4114 | 0.4434 | 0.4692 | 0.4902 | 0.5082 | 0.5239 | 0.5382 | 0.5514 |
| Propyne (Methylacetylene) | $C_3H_4$ | 0 | 0.3290 | 0.3427 | 0.3545 | 0.3578 | 0.3616 | 0.3710 | 0.4100 | 0.4462 | 0.4797 | 0.5103 | 0.5384 | 0.5642 | 0.5882 |
| 1-Butyne (Ethylacteylene) | $C_4H_6$ | 0 | 0.3218 | 0.3377 | 0.3513 | 0.3552 | 0.3595 | 0.3703 | 0.4155 | 0.4573 | 0.4959 | 0.5311 | 0.5633 | 0.5929 | 0.6202 |
| 1-Pentyne | $C_5H_8$ | 0 | 0.3310 | 0.3471 | 0.3609 | 0.3649 | 0.3694 | 0.3804 | 0.4271 | 0.4708 | 0.5116 | 0.5493 | 0.5839 | 0.6155 | 0.6442 |
| 1-Hexyne | $C_6H_{10}$ | 0 | 0.3331 | 0.3497 | 0.3640 | 0.3682 | 0.3729 | 0.3842 | 0.4328 | 0.4785 | 0.5212 | 0.5605 | 0.5964 | 0.6292 | 0.6593 |
| 1-Heptyne | $C_7H_{12}$ | 0 | 0.3346 | 0.3517 | 0.3664 | 0.3706 | 0.3752 | 0.3870 | 0.4369 | 0.4840 | 0.5280 | 0.5683 | 0.6053 | 0.6390 | 0.6699 |
| 1-Octyne | $C_8H_{14}$ | 0 | 0.3357 | 0.3531 | 0.3680 | 0.3722 | 0.3771 | 0.3891 | 0.4399 | 0.4881 | 0.5331 | 0.5743 | 0.6120 | 0.6464 | 0.6778 |
| 1-Nonyne | $C_9H_{16}$ | 0 | 0.3367 | 0.3541 | 0.3694 | 0.3736 | 0.3784 | 0.3907 | 0.4423 | 0.4912 | 0.5369 | 0.5789 | 0.6171 | 0.6520 | 0.6839 |
| 1-Decyne | $C_{10}H_{18}$ | 0 | 0.3372 | 0.3549 | 0.3703 | 0.3747 | 0.3796 | 0.3919 | 0.4443 | 0.4938 | 0.5401 | 0.5826 | 0.6212 | 0.6565 | 0.6888 |
| 1-Undecyne | $C_{11}H_{20}$ | 0 | 0.3378 | 0.3556 | 0.3711 | 0.3755 | 0.3805 | 0.3929 | 0.4458 | 0.4958 | 0.5427 | 0.5855 | 0.6245 | 0.6602 | 0.6929 |

Temperature in °F

Heat Capacity, $c_p^o$, in BTU/lb deg F

| Compound (gas) | Formula | 900 | 1000 | 1100 | 1200 | 1300 | 1400 | 1500 | 1600 | 1700 | 1800 | 1900 | 2000 | 2100 | 2200 |
|---|---|---|---|---|---|---|---|---|---|---|---|---|---|---|---|
| Ethyne (Acetylene) | $C_2H_2$ | 0.5638 | 0.5754 | 0.5865 | 0.5971 | 0.6072 | 0.6168 | 0.6259 | 0.6345 | 0.6426 | 0.6504 | 0.6577 | 0.6646 | 0.6711 | 0.6772 |
| Propyne (Methylacetylene) | $C_3H_4$ | 0.6104 | 0.6310 | 0.6503 | 0.6682 | 0.6849 | 0.7004 | 0.7148 | 0.7282 | 0.7407 | 0.7522 | 0.7630 | 0.7730 | 0.7822 | 0.7908 |
| 1-Butyne (Ethylacetylene) | $C_4H_6$ | 0.6453 | 0.6686 | 0.6902 | 0.7103 | 0.7289 | 0.7462 | 0.7622 | 0.7770 | 0.7908 | 0.8035 | 0.8153 | 0.8263 | 0.8364 | 0.8459 |
| 1-Pentyne | $C_5H_8$ | 0.6711 | 0.6957 | 0.7185 | 0.7394 | 0.7590 | 0.7769 | 0.7936 | 0.8090 | 0.8234 | 0.8366 | 0.8489 | 0.8602 | 0.8708 | 0.8807 |
| 1-Hexyne | $C_6H_{10}$ | 0.6870 | 0.7125 | 0.7361 | 0.7578 | 0.7778 | 0.7964 | 0.8137 | 0.8295 | 0.8443 | 0.8580 | 0.8706 | 0.8822 | 0.8930 | 0.9031 |
| 1-Heptyne | $C_7H_{12}$ | 0.6982 | 0.7244 | 0.7485 | 0.7708 | 0.791 | 0.810 | 0.828 | 0.844 | 0.859 | 0.873 | 0.886 | 0.898 | 0.909 | 0.919 |
| 1-Octyne | $C_8H_{14}$ | 0.7068 | 0.7333 | 0.7578 | 0.7805 | 0.801 | 0.821 | 0.838 | 0.855 | 0.870 | 0.884 | 0.897 | 0.909 | 0.921 | 0.931 |
| 1-Nonyne | $C_9H_{16}$ | 0.7132 | 0.7401 | 0.7650 | 0.7879 | 0.809 | 0.828 | 0.847 | 0.863 | 0.879 | 0.893 | 0.906 | 0.918 | 0.930 | 0.940 |
| 1-Decyne | $C_{10}H_{18}$ | 0.7184 | 0.7456 | 0.7707 | 0.7939 | 0.815 | 0.835 | 0.853 | 0.870 | 0.885 | 0.900 | 0.913 | 0.925 | 0.937 | 0.947 |
| 1-Undecyne | $C_{11}H_{20}$ | 0.7226 | 0.7501 | 0.7754 | 0.7988 | 0.820 | 0.840 | 0.858 | 0.875 | 0.891 | 0.906 | 0.919 | 0.931 | 0.943 | 0.953 |

TABLE 25v-E (PART 1), Page 2 - NORMAL ACETYLENES (1-ALKYNES),$C_{12}$ TO $C_{20}$
HEAT CAPACITY, $C_p^o$, FOR THE IDEAL GAS STATE, AT -459.69° TO 2200°F
February 28, 1946; December 31. 1952

Heat Capacity, $C_p^o$, in BTU/lb deg F

| Compound (gas) | Formula | Temperature in °F | | | | | | | | | | | | | |
|---|---|---|---|---|---|---|---|---|---|---|---|---|---|---|---|
| | | -459.69 | 0 | 32 | 60 | 68 | 77 | 100 | 200 | 300 | 400 | 500 | 600 | 700 | 800 |
| 1-Dodecyne | $C_{12}H_{22}$ | 0 | 0.3383 | 0.3563 | 0.3719 | 0.3762 | 0.3812 | 0.3938 | 0.4470 | 0.4975 | 0.5448 | 0.5880 | 0.6273 | 0.6632 | 0.6961 |
| 1-Tridecyne | $C_{13}H_{24}$ | 0 | 0.3387 | 0.3567 | 0.3724 | 0.3769 | 0.3819 | 0.3945 | 0.4481 | 0.4990 | 0.5466 | 0.5901 | 0.6297 | 0.6658 | 0.6989 |
| 1-Tetradecyne | $C_{14}H_{26}$ | 0 | 0.3391 | 0.3572 | 0.3730 | 0.3774 | 0.3824 | 0.3952 | 0.4490 | 0.5002 | 0.5481 | 0.5919 | 0.6316 | 0.6680 | 0.7013 |
| 1-Pentadecyne | $C_{15}H_{28}$ | 0 | 0.3394 | 0.3576 | 0.3734 | 0.3779 | 0.3829 | 0.3957 | 0.4498 | 0.5013 | 0.5494 | 0.5934 | 0.6334 | 0.6699 | 0.7034 |
| 1-Hexadecyne | $C_{16}H_{30}$ | 0 | 0.3396 | 0.3579 | 0.3737 | 0.3782 | 0.3833 | 0.3961 | 0.4505 | 0.5022 | 0.5506 | 0.5948 | 0.6349 | 0.6716 | 0.7052 |
| 1-Heptadecyne | $C_{17}H_{32}$ | 0 | 0.3399 | 0.3582 | 0.3741 | 0.3786 | 0.3837 | 0.3966 | 0.4511 | 0.5030 | 0.5516 | 0.5960 | 0.6362 | 0.6731 | 0.7068 |
| 1-Octadecyne | $C_{18}H_{34}$ | 0 | 0.3400 | 0.3584 | 0.3744 | 0.3789 | 0.3840 | 0.3969 | 0.4517 | 0.5038 | 0.5525 | 0.5970 | 0.6374 | 0.6744 | 0.7082 |
| 1-Nonadecyne | $C_{19}H_{36}$ | 0 | 0.3403 | 0.3587 | 0.3746 | 0.3792 | 0.3843 | 0.3972 | 0.4522 | 0.5044 | 0.5533 | 0.5980 | 0.6385 | 0.6756 | 0.7094 |
| 1-Eicosyne | $C_{20}H_{38}$ | 0 | 0.3404 | 0.3589 | 0.3749 | 0.3794 | 0.3846 | 0.3975 | 0.4526 | 0.5050 | 0.5541 | 0.5988 | 0.6395 | 0.6766 | 0.7106 |

Heat Capacity, $C_p^o$, in BTU/lb deg F

| Compound (gas) | Formula | Temperature in °F | | | | | | | | | | | | | |
|---|---|---|---|---|---|---|---|---|---|---|---|---|---|---|---|
| | | 900 | 1000 | 1100 | 1200 | 1300 | 1400 | 1500 | 1600 | 1700 | 1800 | 1900 | 2000 | 2100 | 2200 |
| 1-Dodecyne | $C_{12}H_{22}$ | 0.7262 | 0.7538 | 0.7793 | 0.8027 | 0.824 | 0.844 | 0.863 | 0.880 | 0.896 | 0.910 | 0.924 | 0.936 | 0.948 | 0.958 |
| 1-Tridecyne | $C_{13}H_{24}$ | 0.7292 | 0.7569 | 0.7826 | 0.8062 | 0.828 | 0.848 | 0.866 | 0.884 | 0.900 | 0.914 | 0.928 | 0.940 | 0.952 | 0.963 |
| 1-Tetradecyne | $C_{14}H_{26}$ | 0.7317 | 0.7596 | 0.7853 | 0.8091 | 0.831 | 0.851 | 0.870 | 0.887 | 0.903 | 0.918 | 0.931 | 0.944 | 0.955 | 0.966 |
| 1-Pentadecyne | $C_{15}H_{28}$ | 0.7339 | 0.7619 | 0.7878 | 0.8117 | 0.834 | 0.854 | 0.873 | 0.890 | 0.906 | 0.921 | 0.934 | 0.947 | 0.958 | 0.969 |
| 1-Hexadecyne | $C_{16}H_{30}$ | 0.7358 | 0.7640 | 0.7900 | 0.8139 | 0.836 | 0.856 | 0.875 | 0.892 | 0.908 | 0.923 | 0.937 | 0.949 | 0.961 | 0.972 |
| 1-Heptadecyne | $C_{17}H_{32}$ | 0.7375 | 0.7657 | 0.7918 | 0.8158 | 0.838 | 0.858 | 0.877 | 0.894 | 0.911 | 0.925 | 0.939 | 0.952 | 0.963 | 0.974 |
| 1-Octadecyne | $C_{18}H_{34}$ | 0.7390 | 0.7673 | 0.7934 | 0.8175 | 0.840 | 0.860 | 0.879 | 0.896 | 0.913 | 0.927 | 0.941 | 0.954 | 0.966 | 0.977 |
| 1-Nonadecyne | $C_{19}H_{36}$ | 0.7404 | 0.7687 | 0.7949 | 0.8190 | 0.841 | 0.862 | 0.881 | 0.898 | 0.914 | 0.929 | 0.943 | 0.956 | 0.967 | 0.978 |
| 1-Eicosyne | $C_{20}H_{38}$ | 0.7416 | 0.7700 | 0.7963 | 0.8205 | 0.843 | 0.863 | 0.882 | 0.900 | 0.916 | 0.931 | 0.945 | 0.957 | 0.969 | 0.980 |

TABLE 12v-E – ACETYLENES, C₂ TO C₅

HEAT CAPACITY, $C_p^o$, FOR THE IDEAL GAS STATE, AT -459.69° TO 2200°F

January 31, 1946

| Compound (gas) | Formula | Temperature in °F |  |  |  |  |  |  |  |  |  |  |  |  |  |
|---|---|---|---|---|---|---|---|---|---|---|---|---|---|---|---|
|  |  | -459.69 | 0 | 32 | 60 | 68 | 77 | 100 | 200 | 300 | 400 | 500 | 600 | 700 | 800 |
|  |  | Heat Capacity, $C_p^o$, in BTU/lb deg F |  |  |  |  |  |  |  |  |  |  |  |  |  |  |
| Ethyne (Acetylene) | C₂H₂ | 0 | 0.3719 | 0.3854 | 0.3966 | 0.3996 | 0.4030 | 0.4114 | 0.4434 | 0.4692 | 0.4902 | 0.5082 | 0.5239 | 0.5382 | 0.5514 |
| Propyne (Methylacetylene) | C₃H₄ | 0 | 0.3290 | 0.3427 | 0.3545 | 0.3578 | 0.3616 | 0.3710 | 0.4100 | 0.4462 | 0.4797 | 0.5103 | 0.5384 | 0.5642 | 0.5882 |
| 1-Butyne (Ethylacetylene) | C₄H₆ | 0 | 0.3218 | 0.3377 | 0.3513 | 0.3552 | 0.3595 | 0.3703 | 0.4155 | 0.4573 | 0.4959 | 0.5311 | 0.5633 | 0.5929 | 0.6202 |
| 2-Butyne (Dimethylacetylene) | " | 0 | 0.3130 | 0.3259 | 0.3372 | 0.3404 | 0.3441 | 0.3534 | 0.3939 | 0.4337 | 0.4721 | 0.5082 | 0.5419 | 0.5731 | 0.6021 |
| 1-Pentyne | C₅H₈ | 0 | 0.3393 | 0.3541 | 0.3670 | 0.3707 | 0.3741 | 0.385 | 0.430 | 0.474 | 0.514 | 0.552 | 0.586 | 0.617 | 0.645 |
| 2-Pentyne | " | 0 | 0.3107 | 0.3254 | 0.3383 | 0.3419 | 0.3461 | 0.357 | 0.402 | 0.445 | 0.486 | 0.525 | 0.561 | 0.594 | 0.625 |
| 3-Methyl-1-butyne | " | 0 | 0.3251 | 0.3428 | 0.3579 | 0.3622 | 0.3671 | 0.379 | 0.428 | 0.474 | 0.515 | 0.554 | 0.589 | 0.620 | 0.649 |

| Compound (gas) | Formula | Temperature in °F |  |  |  |  |  |  |  |  |  |  |  |  |  |
|---|---|---|---|---|---|---|---|---|---|---|---|---|---|---|---|
|  |  | 900 | 1000 | 1100 | 1200 | 1300 | 1400 | 1500 | 1600 | 1700 | 1800 | 1900 | 2000 | 2100 | 2200 |
|  |  | Heat Capacity, $C_p^o$, in BTU/lb deg F |  |  |  |  |  |  |  |  |  |  |  |  |  |  |
| Ethyne (Acetylene) | C₂H₂ | 0.5638 | 0.5754 | 0.5865 | 0.5971 | 0.6072 | 0.6168 | 0.6259 | 0.6345 | 0.6426 | 0.6504 | 0.6577 | 0.6646 | 0.6711 | 0.6772 |
| Propyne (Methylacetylene) | C₃H₄ | 0.6104 | 0.6310 | 0.6503 | 0.6682 | 0.6849 | 0.7004 | 0.7148 | 0.7282 | 0.7407 | 0.7522 | 0.7630 | 0.7730 | 0.7822 | 0.7908 |
| 1-Butyne (Ethylacetylene) | C₄H₆ | 0.6453 | 0.6686 | 0.6902 | 0.7103 | 0.7289 | 0.7462 | 0.7622 | 0.7770 | 0.7908 | 0.8035 | 0.8153 | 0.8263 | 0.8364 | 0.8459 |
| 2-Butyne (Dimethylacetylene) | " | 0.6290 | 0.6540 | 0.6771 | 0.6985 | 0.7184 | 0.7368 | 0.7538 | 0.7695 | 0.7841 | 0.7975 | 0.8100 | 0.8215 | 0.8321 | 0.8420 |
| 1-Pentyne | C₅H₈ | 0.671 | 0.696 | 0.718 | 0.739 | 0.759 | 0.776 | 0.793 | 0.809 | 0.823 | 0.836 | 0.848 | 0.860 | 0.870 | 0.880 |
| 2-Pentyne | " | 0.653 | 0.679 | 0.703 | 0.726 | 0.746 | 0.766 | 0.783 | 0.800 | 0.815 | 0.829 | 0.842 | 0.854 | 0.865 | 0.875 |
| 3-Methyl-1-butyne | " | 0.675 | 0.699 | 0.722 | 0.742 | 0.761 | 0.779 | 0.796 | 0.811 | 0.826 | 0.839 | 0.851 | 0.862 | 0.873 | 0.882 |

TABLE 21v-E (PART 1), Page 1 - NORMAL ALKYL BENZENES, $C_6$ TO $C_{22}$.
HEAT CAPACITY, $c_p^o$, FOR THE IDEAL GAS STATE, AT -459.69° TO 2200°F
January 31, 1946 ; December 31, 1952

| Compound (gas) | Formula | Temperature in °F | | | | | | | | | | | | | |
|---|---|---|---|---|---|---|---|---|---|---|---|---|---|---|---|
| | | -459.69 | 0 | 32 | 60 | 68 | 77 | 100 | 200 | 300 | 400 | 500 | 600 | 700 | 800 |
| | | Heat Capacity, $c_p^o$, in BTU/lb deg F | | | | | | | | | | | | | |
| Benzene | $C_6H_6$ | 0 | 0.2101 | 0.2265 | 0.2404 | 0.2448 | 0.2497 | 0.2619 | 0.3131 | 0.3604 | 0.4035 | 0.4421 | 0.4764 | 0.5068 | 0.5341 |
| Methylbenzene (Toluene) | $C_7H_8$ | 0 | 0.2300 | 0.2461 | 0.2599 | 0.2641 | 0.2690 | 0.2809 | 0.3316 | 0.3791 | 0.4231 | 0.4628 | 0.4984 | 0.5304 | 0.5592 |
| Ethylbenzene | $C_8H_{10}$ | 0 | 0.2487 | 0.2654 | 0.2795 | 0.2839 | 0.2889 | 0.3014 | 0.3538 | 0.4026 | 0.4476 | 0.4882 | 0.5244 | 0.5569 | 0.5862 |
| n-Propylbenzene | $C_9H_{12}$ | 0 | 0.2598 | 0.2778 | 0.2934 | 0.2978 | 0.3028 | 0.3151 | 0.3676 | 0.4167 | 0.4622 | 0.5034 | 0.5406 | 0.5738 | 0.6038 |
| n-Butylbenzene | $C_{10}H_{14}$ | 0 | 0.2683 | 0.2864 | 0.3022 | 0.3066 | 0.3116 | 0.3242 | 0.3772 | 0.4270 | 0.4731 | 0.5150 | 0.5527 | 0.5867 | 0.6173 |
| n-Pentylbenzene | $C_{11}H_{16}$ | 0 | 0.2755 | 0.2937 | 0.3095 | 0.3140 | 0.3190 | 0.3317 | 0.3851 | 0.4354 | 0.4822 | 0.5246 | 0.5627 | 0.5971 | 0.6281 |
| n-Hexylbenzene | $C_{12}H_{18}$ | 0 | 0.2814 | 0.2997 | 0.3155 | 0.3200 | 0.3251 | 0.3378 | 0.3917 | 0.4424 | 0.4896 | 0.5324 | 0.5709 | 0.6056 | 0.6371 |
| n-Heptylbenzene | $C_{13}H_{20}$ | 0 | 0.2864 | 0.3048 | 0.3206 | 0.3252 | 0.3302 | 0.3431 | 0.3972 | 0.4483 | 0.4957 | 0.5389 | 0.5778 | 0.6128 | 0.6446 |
| n-Octylbenzene | $C_{14}H_{22}$ | 0 | 0.2905 | 0.3090 | 0.3250 | 0.3295 | 0.3346 | 0.3475 | 0.4019 | 0.4533 | 0.5010 | 0.5445 | 0.5837 | 0.6190 | 0.6511 |

| Compound (gas) | Formula | Temperature in °F | | | | | | | | | | | | | |
|---|---|---|---|---|---|---|---|---|---|---|---|---|---|---|---|
| | | 900 | 1000 | 1100 | 1200 | 1300 | 1400 | 1500 | 1600 | 1700 | 1800 | 1900 | 2000 | 2100 | 2200 |
| | | Heat Capacity, $c_p^o$, in BTU/lb deg F | | | | | | | | | | | | | |
| Benzene | $C_6H_6$ | 0.5566 | 0.5807 | 0.6008 | 0.6190 | 0.6356 | 0.6507 | 0.6646 | 0.6774 | 0.6890 | 0.6998 | 0.7096 | 0.7187 | 0.7271 | 0.7348 |
| Methylbenzene (Toluene) | $C_7H_8$ | 0.5853 | 0.6089 | 0.6304 | 0.6499 | 0.6678 | 0.6842 | 0.6992 | 0.7130 | 0.7256 | 0.7373 | 0.7480 | 0.7578 | 0.7669 | 0.7754 |
| Ethylbenzene | $C_8H_{10}$ | 0.6126 | 0.6366 | 0.6586 | 0.6786 | 0.6969 | 0.7137 | 0.7291 | 0.7433 | 0.7563 | 0.7683 | 0.7794 | 0.7896 | 0.7990 | 0.8077 |
| n-Propylbenzene | $C_9H_{12}$ | 0.6310 | 0.6558 | 0.6783 | 0.6989 | 0.7177 | 0.7349 | 0.7508 | 0.7654 | 0.7789 | 0.7912 | 0.8026 | 0.8130 | 0.8228 | 0.8319 |
| n-Butylbenzene | $C_{10}H_{14}$ | 0.6450 | 0.6702 | 0.6933 | 0.7143 | 0.7335 | 0.7512 | 0.7675 | 0.7825 | 0.7963 | 0.8090 | 0.8207 | 0.8315 | 0.8415 | 0.8507 |
| n-Pentylbenzene | $C_{11}H_{16}$ | 0.6563 | 0.6819 | 0.7054 | 0.7269 | 0.7465 | 0.7645 | 0.7811 | 0.7964 | 0.8105 | 0.8234 | 0.8353 | 0.8463 | 0.8566 | 0.8660 |
| n-Hexylbenzene | $C_{12}H_{18}$ | 0.6656 | 0.6916 | 0.7155 | 0.7372 | 0.757 | 0.775 | 0.792 | 0.808 | 0.822 | 0.835 | 0.847 | 0.859 | 0.869 | 0.879 |
| n-Heptylbenzene | $C_{13}H_{20}$ | 0.6734 | 0.6998 | 0.7238 | 0.7459 | 0.766 | 0.785 | 0.802 | 0.818 | 0.832 | 0.845 | 0.858 | 0.869 | 0.880 | 0.889 |
| n-Octylbenzene | $C_{14}H_{22}$ | 0.6802 | 0.7067 | 0.7310 | 0.7534 | 0.774 | 0.793 | 0.810 | 0.826 | 0.840 | 0.854 | 0.866 | 0.878 | 0.889 | 0.898 |

TABLE 21v-E (PART 1), Page 2 - NORMAL ALKYL BENZENES, C₆ TO C₂₂

HEAT CAPACITY, $c_p^o$, FOR THE IDEAL GAS STATE, AT -459.69° TO 2200°F

January 31, 1946: December 31, 1952

Temperature in °F

Heat Capacity, $c_p^o$, in BTU/lb deg F

| Compound (gas) | Formula | -459.69 | 0 | 32 | 60 | 68 | 77 | 100 | 200 | 300 | 400 | 500 | 600 | 700 | 800 |
|---|---|---|---|---|---|---|---|---|---|---|---|---|---|---|---|
| n-Nonyl benzene | $C_{15}H_{24}$ | 0 | 0.2942 | 0.3127 | 0.3287 | 0.3333 | 0.3383 | 0.3513 | 0.4059 | 0.4576 | 0.5056 | 0.5493 | 0.5887 | 0.6243 | 0.6566 |
| n-Decyl bensene | $C_{16}H_{26}$ | 0 | 0.2973 | 0.3159 | 0.3319 | 0.3365 | 0.3416 | 0.3546 | 0.4095 | 0.4614 | 0.5096 | 0.5536 | 0.5932 | 0.6290 | 0.6615 |
| n-Undecyl benzene | $C_{17}H_{28}$ | 0 | 0.3001 | 0.3187 | 0.3348 | 0.3394 | 0.3445 | 0.3575 | 0.4126 | 0.4647 | 0.5132 | 0.5573 | 0.5970 | 0.6330 | 0.6658 |
| n-Dodecyl benzene | $C_{18}H_{30}$ | 0 | 0.3026 | 0.3212 | 0.3374 | 0.3420 | 0.3471 | 0.3601 | 0.4153 | 0.4676 | 0.5163 | 0.5605 | 0.6004 | 0.6366 | 0.6695 |
| n-Tridecyl benzene | $C_{19}H_{32}$ | 0 | 0.3047 | 0.3234 | 0.3396 | 0.3442 | 0.3494 | 0.3624 | 0.4178 | 0.4702 | 0.5190 | 0.5635 | 0.6035 | 0.6399 | 0.6729 |
| n-Tetradecyl benzene | $C_{20}H_{34}$ | 0 | 0.3068 | 0.3255 | 0.3417 | 0.3463 | 0.3514 | 0.3645 | 0.4200 | 0.4725 | 0.5215 | 0.5661 | 0.6063 | 0.6428 | 0.6759 |
| n-Pentadecyl benzene | $C_{21}H_{36}$ | 0 | 0.3085 | 0.3273 | 0.3435 | 0.3481 | 0.3532 | 0.3664 | 0.4220 | 0.4746 | 0.5238 | 0.5685 | 0.6088 | 0.6454 | 0.6786 |
| n-Hexadecyl benzene | $C_{22}H_{38}$ | 0 | 0.3102 | 0.3289 | 0.3451 | 0.3498 | 0.3550 | 0.3681 | 0.4238 | 0.4766 | 0.5258 | 0.5706 | 0.6110 | 0.6478 | 0.6811 |

Temperature in °F

Heat Capacity, $c_p^o$, in BTU/lb deg F

| Compound (gas) | Formula | 900 | 1000 | 1100 | 1200 | 1300 | 1400 | 1500 | 1600 | 1700 | 1800 | 1900 | 2000 | 2100 | 2200 |
|---|---|---|---|---|---|---|---|---|---|---|---|---|---|---|---|
| n-Nonyl benzene | $C_{15}H_{24}$ | 0.6860 | 0.7127 | 0.7372 | 0.7598 | 0.780 | 0.799 | 0.817 | 0.833 | 0.848 | 0.861 | 0.874 | 0.885 | 0.896 | 0.906 |
| n-Decyl benzene | $C_{16}H_{26}$ | 0.6910 | 0.7180 | 0.7427 | 0.7653 | 0.786 | 0.805 | 0.823 | 0.839 | 0.854 | 0.868 | 0.880 | 0.892 | 0.903 | 0.913 |
| n-Undecyl benzene | $C_{17}H_{28}$ | 0.6954 | 0.7225 | 0.7474 | 0.7703 | 0.791 | 0.810 | 0.828 | 0.844 | 0.860 | 0.873 | 0.886 | 0.898 | 0.909 | 0.919 |
| n-Dodecyl benzene | $C_{18}H_{30}$ | 0.6993 | 0.7266 | 0.7516 | 0.7746 | 0.796 | 0.815 | 0.833 | 0.849 | 0.864 | 0.878 | 0.891 | 0.903 | 0.914 | 0.924 |
| n-Tridecyl benzene | $C_{19}H_{32}$ | 0.7029 | 0.7302 | 0.7554 | 0.7785 | 0.800 | 0.819 | 0.837 | 0.854 | 0.869 | 0.883 | 0.896 | 0.908 | 0.919 | 0.929 |
| n-Tetradecyl benzene | $C_{20}H_{34}$ | 0.7060 | 0.7335 | 0.7588 | 0.7819 | 0.803 | 0.823 | 0.841 | 0.857 | 0.873 | 0.887 | 0.900 | 0.912 | 0.923 | 0.933 |
| n-Pentadecyl benzene | $C_{21}H_{36}$ | 0.7088 | 0.7364 | 0.7618 | 0.7851 | 0.806 | 0.826 | 0.844 | 0.861 | 0.876 | 0.891 | 0.904 | 0.916 | 0.927 | 0.937 |
| n-Hexadecyl benzene | $C_{22}H_{38}$ | 0.7114 | 0.7391 | 0.7646 | 0.7880 | 0.809 | 0.829 | 0.847 | 0.864 | 0.880 | 0.894 | 0.907 | 0.919 | 0.930 | 0.941 |

TABLE 5v-E, Page 1 - ALKYL BENZENES, C$_6$ TO C$_8$

HEAT CAPACITY, $c_p^o$, FOR THE IDEAL GAS STATE, AT -459.69° TO 2200°F

December 31, 1945

| Compound (gas) | Formula | Temperature in °F — Heat Capacity, $c_p^o$, in BTU/lb deg F | | | | | | | | | | | | |
|---|---|---|---|---|---|---|---|---|---|---|---|---|---|---|
| | | -459.69 | 0 | 32 | 60 | 68 | 77 | 100 | 200 | 300 | 400 | 500 | 600 | 700 | 800 |
| Benzene | C$_6$H$_6$ | 0 | 0.2101 | 0.2265 | 0.2404 | 0.2448 | 0.2497 | 0.2619 | 0.3131 | 0.3604 | 0.4035 | 0.4421 | 0.4764 | 0.5068 | 0.5341 |
| Methylbenzene (Toluene) | C$_7$H$_8$ | 0 | 0.2300 | 0.2461 | 0.2599 | 0.2641 | 0.2690 | 0.2809 | 0.3316 | 0.3791 | 0.4231 | 0.4628 | 0.4984 | 0.5304 | 0.5592 |
| Ethylbenzene | C$_8$H$_{10}$ | 0 | 0.2487 | 0.2654 | 0.2795 | 0.2839 | 0.2889 | 0.3014 | 0.3538 | 0.4026 | 0.4476 | 0.4882 | 0.5244 | 0.5569 | 0.5862 |
| 1,2-Dimethylbenzene (o-Xylene) | " | 0 | 0.2628 | 0.2781 | 0.2914 | 0.2953 | 0.2998 | 0.3110 | 0.3587 | 0.4039 | 0.4462 | 0.4850 | 0.5202 | 0.5522 | 0.5813 |
| 1,3-Dimethylbenzene (m-Xylene) | " | 0 | 0.2491 | 0.2647 | 0.2782 | 0.2823 | 0.2870 | 0.2986 | 0.3482 | 0.3952 | 0.4392 | 0.4793 | 0.5156 | 0.5485 | 0.5782 |
| 1,4-Dimethylbenzene (p-Xylene) | " | 0 | 0.2488 | 0.2639 | 0.2769 | 0.2809 | 0.2855 | 0.2968 | 0.3454 | 0.3919 | 0.4357 | 0.4758 | 0.5123 | 0.5453 | 0.5753 |

| Compound (gas) | Formula | Temperature in °F — Heat Capacity, $c_p^o$, in BTU/lb deg F | | | | | | | | | | | | |
|---|---|---|---|---|---|---|---|---|---|---|---|---|---|---|
| | | 900 | 1000 | 1100 | 1200 | 1300 | 1400 | 1500 | 1600 | 1700 | 1800 | 1900 | 2000 | 2100 | 2200 |
| Benzene | C$_6$H$_6$ | 0.5586 | 0.5807 | 0.6008 | 0.6190 | 0.6356 | 0.6507 | 0.6646 | 0.6774 | 0.6890 | 0.6998 | 0.7096 | 0.7187 | 0.7271 | 0.7348 |
| Methylbenzene (Toluene) | C$_7$H$_8$ | 0.5853 | 0.6089 | 0.6304 | 0.6499 | 0.6678 | 0.6842 | 0.6992 | 0.7130 | 0.7256 | 0.7373 | 0.7480 | 0.7578 | 0.7669 | 0.7754 |
| Ethylbenzene | C$_8$H$_{10}$ | 0.6126 | 0.6366 | 0.6586 | 0.6786 | 0.6969 | 0.7137 | 0.7291 | 0.7433 | 0.7563 | 0.7683 | 0.7794 | 0.7896 | 0.7990 | 0.8077 |
| 1,2-Dimethylbenzene (o-Xylene) | " | 0.6078 | 0.6319 | 0.6540 | 0.6743 | 0.6929 | 0.7099 | 0.7256 | 0.7400 | 0.7533 | 0.7655 | 0.7767 | 0.7871 | 0.7967 | 0.8055 |
| 1,3-Dimethylbenzene (m-Xylene) | " | 0.6052 | 0.6298 | 0.6523 | 0.6728 | 0.6916 | 0.7089 | 0.7247 | 0.7392 | 0.7526 | 0.7649 | 0.7762 | 0.7866 | 0.7962 | 0.8051 |
| 1,4-Dimethylbenzene (p-Xylene) | " | 0.6025 | 0.6273 | 0.6500 | 0.6707 | 0.6896 | 0.7070 | 0.7230 | 0.7377 | 0.7512 | 0.7636 | 0.7750 | 0.7855 | 0.7952 | 0.8042 |

TABLE 5v-E, Page 2 – ALKYL BENZENES, C9

HEAT CAPACITY, $c_p^o$, FOR THE IDEAL GAS STATE, AT -459.69° TO 2200°F

December 31, 1945

Heat Capacity, $c_p^o$, in BTU/lb deg F

| Compound (gas) | Formula | Temperature in °F |||||||||||||| 
|---|---|---|---|---|---|---|---|---|---|---|---|---|---|---|---|
| | | -459.69 | 0 | 32 | 60 | 68 | 77 | 100 | 200 | 300 | 400 | 500 | 600 | 700 | 800 |
| n-Propylbenzene | C9H12 | 0 | 0.2671 | 0.2830 | 0.2968 | 0.3010 | 0.3054 | 0.3180 | 0.369 | 0.418 | 0.464 | 0.505 | 0.542 | 0.575 | 0.604 |
| Isopropylbenzene | " | 0 | 0.2591 | 0.2767 | 0.2917 | 0.2962 | 0.3015 | 0.3143 | 0.368 | 0.418 | 0.464 | 0.506 | 0.543 | 0.576 | 0.606 |
| 1-Methyl-2-ethylbenzene | " | 0 | 0.2755 | 0.2914 | 0.3050 | 0.3091 | 0.3138 | 0.3256 | 0.375 | 0.422 | 0.465 | 0.505 | 0.541 | 0.573 | 0.602 |
| 1-Methyl-3-ethylbenzene | " | 0 | 0.2634 | 0.2796 | 0.2934 | 0.2977 | 0.3025 | 0.3146 | 0.366 | 0.414 | 0.459 | 0.500 | 0.537 | 0.570 | 0.600 |
| 1-Methyl-4-ethylbenzene | " | 0 | 0.2632 | 0.2788 | 0.2923 | 0.2964 | 0.3012 | 0.3130 | 0.363 | 0.411 | 0.456 | 0.497 | 0.534 | 0.567 | 0.597 |
| 1,2,3-Trimethylbenzene | " | 0 | 0.2710 | 0.2857 | 0.2986 | 0.3023 | 0.3064 | 0.3171 | 0.363 | 0.407 | 0.450 | 0.489 | 0.526 | 0.559 | 0.589 |
| 1,2,4-Trimethylbenzene | " | 0 | 0.2735 | 0.2880 | 0.3007 | 0.3044 | 0.3085 | 0.3190 | 0.365 | 0.409 | 0.451 | 0.491 | 0.527 | 0.560 | 0.590 |
| 1,3,5-Trimethylbenzene | " | 0 | 0.2616 | 0.2769 | 0.2903 | 0.2942 | 0.2986 | 0.3097 | 0.3577 | 0.4040 | 0.4481 | 0.4887 | 0.5257 | 0.5595 | 0.5902 |

Heat Capacity, $c_p^o$, in BTU/lb deg F

| Compound (gas) | Formula | Temperature in °F |||||||||||||| 
|---|---|---|---|---|---|---|---|---|---|---|---|---|---|---|---|
| | | 900 | 1000 | 1100 | 1200 | 1300 | 1400 | 1500 | 1600 | 1700 | 1800 | 1900 | 2000 | 2100 | 2200 |
| n-Propylbenzene | C9H12 | 0.631 | 0.656 | 0.678 | 0.699 | 0.717 | 0.735 | 0.750 | 0.765 | 0.779 | 0.791 | 0.802 | 0.813 | 0.823 | 0.832 |
| Isopropylbenzene | " | 0.633 | 0.658 | 0.680 | 0.701 | 0.719 | 0.736 | 0.752 | 0.767 | 0.780 | 0.792 | 0.804 | 0.814 | 0.824 | 0.833 |
| 1-Methyl-2-ethylbenzene | " | 0.629 | 0.654 | 0.676 | 0.697 | 0.716 | 0.733 | 0.749 | 0.764 | 0.777 | 0.790 | 0.801 | 0.812 | 0.822 | 0.831 |
| 1-Methyl-3-ethylbenzene | " | 0.627 | 0.652 | 0.675 | 0.695 | 0.715 | 0.732 | 0.748 | 0.763 | 0.777 | 0.789 | 0.801 | 0.811 | 0.821 | 0.830 |
| 1-Methyl-4-ethylbenzene | " | 0.625 | 0.650 | 0.673 | 0.694 | 0.713 | 0.730 | 0.747 | 0.762 | 0.775 | 0.788 | 0.800 | 0.810 | 0.820 | 0.829 |
| 1,2,3-Trimethylbenzene | " | 0.617 | 0.642 | 0.666 | 0.687 | 0.707 | 0.725 | 0.741 | 0.757 | 0.771 | 0.784 | 0.796 | 0.807 | 0.817 | 0.826 |
| 1,2,4-Trimethylbenzene | " | 0.618 | 0.643 | 0.667 | 0.688 | 0.708 | 0.726 | 0.742 | 0.757 | 0.771 | 0.784 | 0.796 | 0.807 | 0.817 | 0.827 |
| 1,3,5-Trimethylbenzene | " | 0.6182 | 0.5438 | 0.6671 | 0.6886 | 0.7082 | 0.7262 | 0.7428 | 0.7581 | 0.7721 | 0.7850 | 0.7968 | 0.8078 | 0.8179 | 0.8272 |

682

TABLE 13v-E – STYRENES, C8 and C9

HEAT CAPACITY, $C_p^o$, FOR THE IDEAL GAS STATE, AT −459.69 to 2200°F

September 30, 1947

Heat Capacity, $C_p^o$, in BTU/lb deg F — Temperature in °F

| Compound (gas) | Formula | −459.69 | 0 | 32 | 60 | 68 | 77 | 100 | 200 | 300 | 400 | 500 | 600 | 700 | 800 |
|---|---|---|---|---|---|---|---|---|---|---|---|---|---|---|---|
| Ethenylbenzene(Styrene;Vinylbenzene;Phenylethylene) | $C_8H_8$ | 0 | 0.2392 | 0.2564 | 0.2711 | 0.2753 | 0.2800 | 0.2917 | 0.3403 | 0.3850 | 0.4256 | 0.4619 | 0.4942 | 0.5231 | 0.5489 |
| Isopropenylbenzene (α-Methylstyrene; 2-Phenyl-1-propene) | $C_9H_{10}$ | 0 | 0.255 | 0.271 | 0.285 | 0.289 | 0.293 | 0.305 | 0.352 | 0.396 | 0.437 | 0.474 | 0.507 | 0.537 | 0.565 |
| cis-1-Propenylbenzene (cis-β-Methylstyrene; cis-1-Phenyl-1-propene) | " | 0 | 0.255 | 0.271 | 0.285 | 0.289 | 0.293 | 0.305 | 0.352 | 0.396 | 0.437 | 0.474 | 0.507 | 0.537 | 0.565 |
| trans-1-Propenylbenzene (trans-β-Methylstyrene; trans-1-Phenyl-1-propene) | " | 0 | 0.256 | 0.272 | 0.287 | 0.291 | 0.295 | 0.307 | 0.355 | 0.400 | 0.441 | 0.478 | 0.511 | 0.541 | 0.568 |
| 1-Methyl-2-ethenylbenzene (o-Methylstyrene) | " | 0 | 0.255 | 0.271 | 0.285 | 0.289 | 0.293 | 0.305 | 0.352 | 0.396 | 0.437 | 0.474 | 0.507 | 0.537 | 0.565 |
| 1-Methyl-3-ethenylbenzene (m-Methylstyrene) | " | 0 | 0.255 | 0.271 | 0.285 | 0.289 | 0.293 | 0.305 | 0.352 | 0.396 | 0.437 | 0.474 | 0.507 | 0.537 | 0.565 |
| 1-Methyl-4-ethenylbenzene (p-Methylstyrene) | " | 0 | 0.255 | 0.271 | 0.285 | 0.289 | 0.293 | 0.305 | 0.352 | 0.396 | 0.437 | 0.474 | 0.507 | 0.537 | 0.565 |

Heat Capacity, $C_p^o$, in BTU/lb deg F — Temperature in °F

| Compound (gas) | Formula | 900 | 1000 | 1100 | 1200 | 1300 | 1400 | 1500 | 1600 | 1700 | 1800 | 1900 | 2000 | 2100 | 2200 |
|---|---|---|---|---|---|---|---|---|---|---|---|---|---|---|---|
| Ethenylbenzene(Styrene;Vinylbenzene;Phenylethylene) | $C_8H_8$ | 0.5722 | 0.5932 | 0.6123 | 0.6298 | 0.6457 | 0.6603 | 0.6737 | 0.6860 | 0.6972 | 0.7076 | 0.7171 | 0.7258 | 0.7340 | 0.7415 |
| Isopropenylbenzene (α-Methylstyrene; 2-Phenyl-1-propene) | $C_9H_{10}$ | 0.589 | 0.611 | 0.632 | 0.651 | 0.668 | 0.684 | 0.698 | 0.712 | 0.724 | 0.735 | 0.745 | 0.755 | 0.764 | 0.772 |
| cis-1-Propenylbenzene (cis-β-Methylstyrene; cis-1-Phenyl-1-propene) | " | 0.589 | 0.611 | 0.632 | 0.651 | 0.668 | 0.684 | 0.698 | 0.712 | 0.724 | 0.735 | 0.745 | 0.755 | 0.764 | 0.772 |
| trans-1-Propenylbenzene (trans-β-Methylstyrene; trans-1-Phenyl-1-propene) | " | 0.593 | 0.615 | 0.635 | 0.653 | 0.670 | 0.686 | 0.700 | 0.713 | 0.726 | 0.737 | 0.747 | 0.756 | 0.764 | 0.772 |
| 1-Methyl-2-ethenylbenzene (o-Methylstyrene) | " | 0.589 | 0.611 | 0.632 | 0.651 | 0.668 | 0.684 | 0.698 | 0.712 | 0.724 | 0.735 | 0.745 | 0.755 | 0.764 | 0.772 |
| 1-Methyl-3-ethenylbenzene (m-Methylstyrene) | " | 0.589 | 0.611 | 0.632 | 0.651 | 0.668 | 0.684 | 0.698 | 0.712 | 0.724 | 0.735 | 0.745 | 0.755 | 0.764 | 0.772 |
| 1-Methyl-4-ethenylbenzene (p-Methylstyrene) | " | 0.589 | 0.611 | 0.632 | 0.651 | 0.668 | 0.684 | 0.698 | 0.712 | 0.724 | 0.735 | 0.745 | 0.755 | 0.764 | 0.772 |

TABLE Ov-G – $O_2$, $H_2$, OH, $H_2O$, $N_2$, NO, C, CO, $CO_2$

HEAT CAPACITY, $C_p^o$, AT −273.16° TO 1200°C

November 30, 1944; August 31, 1946; June 30, 1949

| Compound | Formula | State | Temperature in °C | | | | | | | | | | | | | | |
| --- | --- | --- | --- | --- | --- | --- | --- | --- | --- | --- | --- | --- | --- | --- | --- | --- | --- |
| | | | −273.16 | 0 | 25 | 100 | 200 | 300 | 400 | 500 | 600 | 700 | 800 | 900 | 1000 | 1100 | 1200 |
| | | | Heat Capacity, $C_p^o$, in cal/g deg C | | | | | | | | | | | | | | |
| Oxygen | $O_2$ | gas | 0 | 0.2184 | 0.2193 | 0.2231 | 0.2301 | 0.2377 | 0.2447 | 0.2506 | 0.2555 | 0.2595 | 0.2619 | 0.2658 | 0.2684 | 0.2706 | 0.2726 |
| Hydrogen | $H_2$ | gas | 0 | 3.392 | 3.1419 | 3.453 | 3.468 | 3.474 | 3.485 | 3.504 | 3.532 | 3.569 | 3.613 | 3.660 | 3.709 | 3.761 | 3.812 |
| Hydroxyl | OH | gas | 0 | 0.4212 | 0.4199 | 0.4167 | 0.4146 | 0.4144 | 0.4160 | 0.4193 | 0.4239 | 0.4295 | 0.4357 | 0.4422 | 0.4488 | 0.4553 | 0.4614 |
| Water | $H_2O$ | gas | 0 | 0.4441 | 0.4454 | 0.4515 | 0.4634 | 0.4776 | 0.4930 | 0.5092 | 0.5260 | 0.5429 | 0.5590 | 0.5741 | 0.5884 | 0.6020 | 0.6147 |
| Nitrogen | $N_2$ | gas | 0 | 0.2484 | 0.2484 | 0.2491 | 0.2514 | 0.2555 | 0.2609 | 0.2666 | 0.2723 | 0.2776 | 0.2825 | 0.2867 | 0.2905 | 0.2938 | 0.2966 |
| Nitric Oxide | NO | gas | 0 | 0.2382 | 0.2378 | 0.2380 | 0.2415 | 0.2472 | 0.2535 | 0.2595 | 0.2649 | 0.2696 | 0.2737 | 0.2772 | 0.2801 | 0.2826 | 0.2847 |
| Carbon | C | solid graphite | 0 | 0.1532 | 0.1720 | 0.2213 | 0.2776 | 0.325 | 0.361 | 0.389 | 0.410 | 0.425 | 0.436 | 0.448 | 0.461 | 0.470 | 0.478 |
| Carbon Monoxide | CO | gas | 0 | 0.2485 | 0.2487 | 0.2497 | 0.2530 | 0.2582 | 0.2643 | 0.2706 | 0.2765 | 0.2819 | 0.2865 | 0.2906 | 0.2942 | 0.2973 | 0.2999 |
| Carbon Dioxide | $CO_2$ | gas | 0 | 0.1953 | 0.2016 | 0.2188 | 0.2378 | 0.2533 | 0.2662 | 0.2769 | 0.2859 | 0.2935 | 0.2998 | 0.3052 | 0.3097 | 0.3137 | 0.3171 |

TABLE 20v-G (PART 1) – NORMAL PARAFFINS, $C_1$ TO $C_{20}$

HEAT CAPACITY, $c_p^o$, FOR THE IDEAL GAS STATE, AT $-273.16°$ TO $1200°C$

December 31, 1945; October 31, 1952; December 31, 1952

Temperature in °C

Heat Capacity, $c_p^o$, in cal/g deg C

| Compound (gas) | Formula | -273.16 | 0 | 25 | 100 | 200 | 300 | 400 | 500 | 600 | 700 | 800 | 900 | 1000 | 1100 | 1200 |
|---|---|---|---|---|---|---|---|---|---|---|---|---|---|---|---|---|
| Methane | $CH_4$ | 0 | 0.5171 | 0.5321 | 0.5853 | 0.6700 | 0.7587 | 0.8435 | 0.9216 | 0.9926 | 1.057 | 1.114 | 1.164 | 1.209 | 1.248 | 1.283 |
| Ethane | $C_2H_6$ | 0 | 0.3943 | 0.4186 | 0.4993 | 0.5946 | 0.6870 | 0.7687 | 0.8411 | 0.9051 | 0.961 | 1.011 | 1.054 | 1.092 | 1.125 | 1.154 |
| Propane | $C_3H_8$ | 0 | 0.3702 | 0.3985 | 0.4821 | 0.5870 | 0.6782 | 0.7565 | 0.8243 | 0.8836 | 0.936 | 0.981 | 1.020 | 1.055 | 1.085 | 1.111 |
| n-Butane | $C_4H_{10}$ | 0 | 0.3731 | 0.4007 | 0.4812 | 0.5826 | 0.6717 | 0.7479 | 0.8136 | 0.8710 | 0.9207 | 0.9639 | 1.0014 | 1.0342 | 1.0626 | 1.0876 |
| n-Pentane | $C_5H_{12}$ | 0 | 0.3709 | 0.3982 | 0.4785 | 0.5790 | 0.6667 | 0.7417 | 0.8061 | 0.8620 | 0.9105 | 0.9526 | 0.9892 | 1.0211 | 1.0488 | 1.0728 |
| n-Hexane | $C_6H_{14}$ | 0 | 0.3697 | 0.3969 | 0.4767 | 0.5765 | 0.6636 | 0.7375 | 0.8009 | 0.8561 | 0.9038 | 0.9452 | 0.9810 | 1.0123 | 1.0394 | 1.0630 |
| n-Heptane | $C_7H_{16}$ | 0 | 0.3686 | 0.3959 | 0.4756 | 0.5749 | 0.6611 | 0.7344 | 0.7973 | 0.8517 | 0.899 | 0.940 | 0.975 | 1.006 | 1.033 | 1.056 |
| n-Octane | $C_8H_{18}$ | 0 | 0.3679 | 0.3952 | 0.4747 | 0.5735 | 0.6592 | 0.7322 | 0.7946 | 0.8485 | 0.895 | 0.936 | 0.971 | 1.001 | 1.027 | 1.050 |
| n-Nonane | $C_9H_{20}$ | 0 | 0.3674 | 0.3945 | 0.4739 | 0.5725 | 0.6578 | 0.7304 | 0.7924 | 0.8459 | 0.892 | 0.932 | 0.967 | 0.997 | 1.024 | 1.046 |
| n-Decane | $C_{10}H_{22}$ | 0 | 0.3669 | 0.3941 | 0.4733 | 0.5717 | 0.6568 | 0.7290 | 0.7906 | 0.8439 | 0.890 | 0.930 | 0.964 | 0.994 | 1.020 | 1.043 |
| n-Undecane | $C_{11}H_{24}$ | 0 | 0.3666 | 0.3937 | 0.4729 | 0.5709 | 0.6558 | 0.7278 | 0.7892 | 0.8422 | 0.888 | 0.928 | 0.962 | 0.992 | 1.018 | 1.040 |
| n-Dodecane | $C_{12}H_{26}$ | 0 | 0.3662 | 0.3934 | 0.4725 | 0.5704 | 0.6550 | 0.7268 | 0.7880 | 0.8408 | 0.886 | 0.926 | 0.960 | 0.990 | 1.016 | 1.038 |
| n-Tridecane | $C_{13}H_{28}$ | 0 | 0.3659 | 0.3931 | 0.4721 | 0.5700 | 0.6543 | 0.7259 | 0.7870 | 0.8396 | 0.885 | 0.924 | 0.958 | 0.988 | 1.014 | 1.036 |
| n-Tetradecane | $C_{14}H_{30}$ | 0 | 0.3658 | 0.3928 | 0.4718 | 0.5696 | 0.6538 | 0.7252 | 0.7861 | 0.8386 | 0.884 | 0.923 | 0.957 | 0.986 | 1.012 | 1.034 |
| n-Pentadecane | $C_{15}H_{32}$ | 0 | 0.3656 | 0.3926 | 0.4716 | 0.5692 | 0.6533 | 0.7246 | 0.7854 | 0.8377 | 0.883 | 0.922 | 0.956 | 0.985 | 1.011 | 1.033 |
| n-Hexadecane | $C_{16}H_{34}$ | 0 | 0.3654 | 0.3924 | 0.4714 | 0.5689 | 0.6529 | 0.7240 | 0.7847 | 0.8369 | 0.882 | 0.921 | 0.955 | 0.984 | 1.009 | 1.031 |
| n-Heptadecane | $C_{17}H_{36}$ | 0 | 0.3653 | 0.3923 | 0.4711 | 0.5686 | 0.6525 | 0.7236 | 0.7841 | 0.8362 | 0.881 | 0.920 | 0.954 | 0.983 | 1.008 | 1.030 |
| n-Octadecane | $C_{18}H_{38}$ | 0 | 0.3651 | 0.3922 | 0.4710 | 0.5684 | 0.6521 | 0.7232 | 0.7836 | 0.8356 | 0.881 | 0.919 | 0.953 | 0.982 | 1.007 | 1.029 |
| n-Nonadecane | $C_{19}H_{40}$ | 0 | 0.3650 | 0.3920 | 0.4708 | 0.5682 | 0.6518 | 0.7228 | 0.7831 | 0.8350 | 0.880 | 0.919 | 0.952 | 0.981 | 1.007 | 1.028 |
| n-Eicosane | $C_{20}H_{42}$ | 0 | 0.3649 | 0.3919 | 0.4707 | 0.5680 | 0.6516 | 0.7224 | 0.7827 | 0.8346 | 0.879 | 0.918 | 0.952 | 0.981 | 1.006 | 1.028 |

## TABLE 1v-G – PARAFFINS, C$_1$ TO C$_5$

### HEAT CAPACITY, $c_p^o$, FOR THE IDEAL GAS STATE, AT −273.16° TO 1200°C

November 30, 1944; February 28, 1949; December 31, 1952

Heat Capacity, $c_p^o$, in cal/g deg C

| Compound (gas) | Formula | Temperature in °C | | | | | | | | | | | | | | |
|---|---|---|---|---|---|---|---|---|---|---|---|---|---|---|---|---|
| | | −273.16 | −200 | −150 | −100 | −50 | 0 | 25 | 50 | 100 | 150 | 200 | 300 | 400 | 500 | 600 |
| Methane | CH$_4$ | 0 | 0.4955 | 0.4955 | 0.4965 | 0.5037 | 0.5204 | 0.5321 | 0.5474 | 0.5840 | 0.6255 | 0.6696 | 0.7588 | 0.8436 | 0.9215 | 0.9926 |
| Ethane | C$_2$H$_6$ | 0 | | 0.2947 | 0.3208 | 0.3550 | 0.3960 | 0.4186 | 0.4429 | 0.4937 | 0.5449 | 0.5946 | 0.6870 | 0.7686 | 0.8410 | 0.9051 |
| Propane | C$_3$H$_8$ | 0 | | 0.2397 | 0.2794 | 0.3240 | 0.3728 | 0.3985 | 0.4258 | 0.4814 | 0.5357 | 0.5867 | 0.6781 | 0.7565 | 0.8243 | 0.8836 |
| n-Butane | C$_4$H$_{10}$ | 0 | | | | | 0.3753 | 0.4007 | 0.4331 | 0.4812 | 0.5362 | 0.5826 | 0.6717 | 0.7479 | 0.8136 | 0.8710 |
| 2-Methylpropane (Isobutane) | " | 0 | | | | 0.3178 | 0.3704 | 0.3981 | 0.4261 | 0.4825 | 0.5367 | 0.5872 | 0.6772 | 0.7533 | 0.8184 | 0.8748 |
| n-Pentane | C$_5$H$_{12}$ | 0 | | | | | 0.3730 | 0.3982 | 0.4329 | 0.4785 | 0.5348 | 0.5790 | 0.6667 | 0.7417 | 0.8061 | 0.8620 |
| 2-Methylbutane (Isopentane) | " | 0 | | | | | 0.3656 | 0.3935 | 0.4218 | 0.4771 | 0.5300 | 0.5802 | 0.6698 | 0.7464 | 0.8117 | 0.8684 |
| 2,2-Dimethylpropane (Neopentane) | " | 0 | | | | 0.3168 | 0.3736 | 0.4029 | 0.4320 | 0.4900 | 0.5457 | 0.5975 | 0.6882 | 0.7637 | 0.8271 | 0.8814 |

Heat Capacity, $c_p^o$, in cal/g deg C

| Compound (gas) | Formula | Temperature in °C | | | | | |
|---|---|---|---|---|---|---|---|
| | | 700 | 800 | 900 | 1000 | 1100 | 1200 |
| Methane | CH$_4$ | 1.057 | 1.114 | 1.164 | 1.209 | 1.248 | 1.283 |
| Ethane | C$_2$H$_6$ | 0.961 | 1.011 | 1.054 | 1.092 | 1.125 | 1.154 |
| Propane | C$_3$H$_8$ | 0.936 | 0.981 | 1.020 | 1.055 | 1.085 | 1.111 |
| n-Butane | C$_4$H$_{10}$ | 0.921 | 0.964 | 1.001 | 1.034 | 1.063 | 1.088 |
| 2-Methylpropane (Isobutane) | " | 0.924 | 0.967 | 1.004 | 1.037 | 1.065 | 1.089 |
| n-Pentane | C$_5$H$_{12}$ | 0.910 | 0.953 | 0.989 | 1.021 | 1.049 | 1.073 |
| 2-Methylbutane (Isopentane) | " | 0.918 | 0.961 | 0.998 | 1.031 | 1.059 | 1.083 |
| 2,2-Dimethylpropane (Neopentane) | " | 0.928 | 0.969 | 1.004 | 1.034 | 1.061 | 1.084 |

TABLE 2v-G (PART 1) – PARAFFINS, $C_6$

HEAT CAPACITY, $C_p^o$, FOR THE IDEAL GAS STATE, AT -273.16° TO 1200°C

November 30, 1944; November 30, 1946; December 31, 1952

| Compound (gas) | Formula | Temperature in °C | | | | | | | | | | | | | | |
|---|---|---|---|---|---|---|---|---|---|---|---|---|---|---|---|---|
| | | -273.16 | 0 | 25 | 100 | 200 | 300 | 400 | 500 | 600 | 700 | 800 | 900 | 1000 | 1100 | 1200 |
| | | Heat Capacity, $C_p^o$, in cal/g deg C | | | | | | | | | | | | | | |
| n-Hexane | $C_6H_{14}$ | 0 | 0.3697 | 0.3969 | 0.4767 | 0.5765 | 0.6636 | 0.7375 | 0.8009 | 0.8561 | 0.9038 | 0.9452 | 0.9810 | 1.0123 | 1.0394 | 1.0630 |
| 2-Methylpentane | " | 0 | 0.3718 | 0.4000 | 0.482 | 0.584 | 0.671 | 0.745 | 0.807 | 0.861 | 0.907 | | | | | |
| 3-Methylpentane | " | 0 | 0.3697 | 0.3969 | 0.477 | 0.577 | 0.664 | 0.737 | 0.801 | 0.856 | 0.904 | | | | | |
| 2,2-Dimethylpentane | " | 0 | 0.3648 | 0.3935 | 0.478 | 0.583 | 0.674 | 0.749 | 0.813 | 0.865 | 0.912 | | | | | |
| 2,3-Dimethylpentane | " | 0 | 0.3607 | 0.3898 | 0.474 | 0.577 | 0.666 | 0.741 | 0.805 | 0.859 | 0.906 | | | | | |

TABLE 2v-G (PART 2) - PARAFFINS, C$_7$

HEAT CAPACITY, $C_p^o$, FOR THE IDEAL GAS STATE, AT -273.16° TO 1200°C

November 30, 1944; December 31, 1952

| Compound (gas) | Formula | Temperature in °C | | | | | | | | | | | | | | |
|---|---|---|---|---|---|---|---|---|---|---|---|---|---|---|---|---|
| | | -273.16 | 0 | 25 | 100 | 200 | 300 | 400 | 500 | 600 | 700 | 800 | 900 | 1000 | 1100 | 1200 |
| | | Heat Capacity, $C_p^o$, in cal/g deg C | | | | | | | | | | | | | | |
| n-Heptane | C$_7$H$_{16}$ | 0 | 0.3686 | 0.3959 | 0.4756 | 0.5749 | 0.6611 | 0.7344 | 0.7973 | 0.8517 | 0.899 | 0.940 | 0.975 | 1.006 | 1.033 | 1.056 |
| 2-Methylhexane | = | 0 | a | a | a | a | a | a | a | a | a | | | | | |
| 3-Methylhexane | = | 0 | a | a | a | a | a | a | a | a | a | | | | | |
| 3-Ethylpentane | = | 0 | a | a | a | a | a | a | a | a | a | | | | | |
| 2,2-Dimethylpentane | = | 0 | a | a | a | a | a | a | a | a | a | | | | | |
| 2,3-Dimethylpentane | = | 0 | a | a | a | a | a | a | a | a | a | | | | | |
| 2,4-Dimethylpentane | = | 0 | a | a | a | a | a | a | a | a | a | | | | | |
| 3,3-Dimethylpentane | = | 0 | a | a | a | a | a | a | a | a | a | | | | | |
| 2,2,3-Trimethylbutane | = | 0 | 0.3633 | 0.3925 | 0.4778 | 0.5832 | 0.6733 | 0.7480 | 0.8106 | 0.8640 | 0.910 | 0.950 | 0.984 | 1.015 | 1.040 | 1.062 |

a Until more data become available, the heat capacity of any branched-chain heptane may be taken as equal to that of the normal heptane. The meager data now available indicate that the difference in heat capacity between normal heptane and any of its isomers is not likely to exceed 3 percent.

TABLE 3v-G – PARAFFINS, $C_8$

HEAT CAPACITY, $C_p^o$, FOR THE IDEAL GAS STATE, AT -273.16° TO 1200°C

December 31, 1944; December 31, 1952

| Compound (gas) | Formula | Temperature in °C | | | | | | | | | | | | | | |
|---|---|---|---|---|---|---|---|---|---|---|---|---|---|---|---|---|
| | | -273.16 | 0 | 25 | 100 | 200 | 300 | 400 | 500 | 600 | 700 | 800 | 900 | 1000 | 1100 | 1200 |
| | | Heat Capacity, $C_p^o$, in cal/g deg C | | | | | | | | | | | | | | |
| n-Octane | $C_8H_{18}$ | 0 | 0.3679 | 0.3952 | 0.4747 | 0.5735 | 0.6592 | 0.7322 | 0.7946 | 0.8485 | 0.895 | 0.936 | 0.971 | 1.001 | 1.027 | 1.050 |
| 2-Methylheptane | = | 0 | a | a | a | a | a | a | a | a | a | | | | | |
| 3-Methylheptane | = | 0 | a | a | a | a | a | a | a | a | a | | | | | |
| 4-Methylheptane | = | 0 | a | a | a | a | a | a | a | a | a | | | | | |
| 3-Ethylhexane | = | 0 | a | a | a | a | a | a | a | a | a | | | | | |
| 2,2-Dimethylhexane | = | 0 | a | a | a | a | a | a | a | a | a | | | | | |
| 2,3-Dimethylhexane | = | 0 | a | a | a | a | a | a | a | a | a | | | | | |
| 2,4-Dimethylhexane | = | 0 | a | a | a | a | a | a | a | a | a | | | | | |
| 2,5-Dimethylhexane | = | 0 | a | a | a | a | a | a | a | a | a | | | | | |
| 3,3-Dimethylhexane | = | 0 | a | a | a | a | a | a | a | a | a | | | | | |
| 3,4-Dimethylhexane | = | 0 | a | a | a | a | a | a | a | a | a | | | | | |
| 2-Methyl-3-ethylpentane | = | 0 | a | a | a | a | a | a | a | a | a | | | | | |
| 3-Methyl-3-ethylpentane | = | 0 | a | a | a | a | a | a | a | a | a | | | | | |
| 2,2,3-Trimethylpentane | = | 0 | a | a | a | a | a | a | a | a | a | | | | | |
| 2,2,4-Trimethylpentane | = | 0 | a | a | a | a | a | a | a | a | a | | | | | |
| 2,3,3-Trimethylpentane | = | 0 | a | a | a | a | a | a | a | a | | | | | | |
| 2,3,4-Trimethylpentane | = | 0 | a | a | a | a | a | a | a | a | | | | | | |
| 2,2,3,3-Tetramethylbutane | = | 0 | 0.3712 | 0.4030 | 0.4936 | 0.6020 | 0.6924 | 0.7662 | 0.827 | 0.879 | 0.923 | | | | | |

a Until more data become available, the heat capacity of any branched-chain octane may be taken as equal to that of normal octane. The meager data now available indicate that the difference in heat capacity between normal octane and any of its isomers is not likely to exceed 3 percent.

TABLE 22v-G (PART 1) – NORMAL ALKYL CYCLOPENTANES, $C_5$ TO $C_{21}$
HEAT CAPACITY, $c_p^o$, FOR THE IDEAL GAS STATE, AT $-273.16^o$ TO $1200^oC$
October 31, 1947; December 31, 1952

| Compound (gas) | Formula | Temperature in °C — Heat Capacity, $c_p^o$, in cal/g deg C | | | | | | | | | | | | | | |
|---|---|---|---|---|---|---|---|---|---|---|---|---|---|---|---|---|
| | | -273.16 | 0 | 25 | 100 | 200 | 300 | 400 | 500 | 600 | 700 | 800 | 900 | 1000 | 1100 | 1200 |
| Cyclopentane | $C_5H_{10}$ | 0 | 0.2526 | 0.2826 | 0.3717 | 0.4835 | 0.5807 | 0.6622 | 0.7311 | 0.7896 | 0.8397 | 0.8832 | 0.9204 | 0.9526 | 0.9805 | 1.0048 |
| Methylcyclopentane | $C_6H_{12}$ | 0 | 0.2828 | 0.3118 | 0.3990 | 0.5072 | 0.6006 | 0.6786 | 0.7445 | 0.8007 | 0.8490 | 0.8908 | 0.9266 | 0.9577 | 0.9847 | 1.0083 |
| Ethylcyclopentane | $C_7H_{14}$ | 0 | 0.2817 | 0.3207 | 0.4179 | 0.5167 | 0.6057 | 0.6841 | 0.7501 | 0.8066 | 0.8555 | 0.8974 | 0.9334 | 0.9647 | 0.9917 | 1.0152 |
| n-Propylcyclopentane | $C_8H_{16}$ | 0 | 0.2918 | 0.3294 | 0.4241 | 0.5226 | 0.6107 | 0.6882 | 0.7532 | 0.8088 | 0.857 | 0.888 | 0.934 | 0.965 | 0.992 | 1.015 |
| n-Butylcyclopentane | $C_9H_{18}$ | 0 | 0.2998 | 0.3360 | 0.4290 | 0.5272 | 0.6147 | 0.6912 | 0.7556 | 0.8106 | 0.858 | 0.889 | 0.935 | 0.965 | 0.992 | 1.014 |
| n-Pentylcyclopentane | $C_{10}H_{20}$ | 0 | 0.3061 | 0.3414 | 0.4329 | 0.5309 | 0.6179 | 0.6937 | 0.7575 | 0.8121 | 0.859 | 0.900 | 0.935 | 0.965 | 0.992 | 1.014 |
| n-Hexylcyclopentane | $C_{11}H_{22}$ | 0 | 0.3112 | 0.3458 | 0.4361 | 0.5339 | 0.6205 | 0.6957 | 0.7590 | 0.8133 | 0.860 | 0.900 | 0.935 | 0.965 | 0.991 | 1.014 |
| n-Heptylcyclopentane | $C_{12}H_{24}$ | 0 | 0.3155 | 0.3495 | 0.4388 | 0.5365 | 0.6226 | 0.6974 | 0.7604 | 0.8143 | 0.861 | 0.901 | 0.936 | 0.966 | 0.991 | 1.014 |
| n-Octylcyclopentane | $C_{13}H_{26}$ | 0 | 0.3191 | 0.3526 | 0.4410 | 0.5386 | 0.6244 | 0.6988 | 0.7614 | 0.8151 | 0.862 | 0.901 | 0.936 | 0.966 | 0.991 | 1.014 |
| n-Nonylcyclopentane | $C_{14}H_{28}$ | 0 | 0.3223 | 0.3552 | 0.4430 | 0.5404 | 0.6260 | 0.7000 | 0.7624 | 0.8158 | 0.862 | 0.902 | 0.936 | 0.966 | 0.991 | 1.014 |
| n-Decylcyclopentane | $C_{15}H_{30}$ | 0 | 0.3250 | 0.3575 | 0.4446 | 0.5420 | 0.6274 | 0.7011 | 0.7632 | 0.8164 | 0.862 | 0.902 | 0.936 | 0.966 | 0.991 | 1.013 |
| n-Undecylcyclopentane | $C_{16}H_{32}$ | 0 | 0.3274 | 0.3595 | 0.4461 | 0.5434 | 0.6286 | 0.7019 | 0.7639 | 0.8170 | 0.863 | 0.902 | 0.936 | 0.966 | 0.991 | 1.013 |
| n-Dodecylcyclopentane | $C_{17}H_{34}$ | 0 | 0.3295 | 0.3613 | 0.4474 | 0.5446 | 0.6296 | 0.7028 | 0.7646 | 0.8175 | 0.863 | 0.902 | 0.936 | 0.966 | 0.991 | 1.013 |
| n-Tridecylcyclopentane | $C_{18}H_{36}$ | 0 | 0.3313 | 0.3629 | 0.4485 | 0.5457 | 0.6305 | 0.7035 | 0.7652 | 0.8179 | 0.864 | 0.903 | 0.937 | 0.966 | 0.991 | 1.013 |
| n-Tetradecylcyclopentane | $C_{19}H_{38}$ | 0 | 0.3330 | 0.3643 | 0.4495 | 0.5467 | 0.6314 | 0.7042 | 0.7656 | 0.8182 | 0.864 | 0.903 | 0.937 | 0.966 | 0.991 | 1.013 |
| n-Pentadecylcyclopentane | $C_{20}H_{40}$ | 0 | 0.3345 | 0.3656 | 0.4504 | 0.5476 | 0.6322 | 0.7048 | 0.7661 | 0.8186 | 0.864 | 0.903 | 0.937 | 0.966 | 0.991 | 1.013 |
| n-Hexadecylcyclopentane | $C_{21}H_{42}$ | 0 | 0.3358 | 0.3667 | 0.4513 | 0.5483 | 0.6328 | 0.7053 | 0.7665 | 0.8189 | 0.864 | 0.903 | 0.937 | 0.966 | 0.991 | 1.013 |

TABLE 6v-G – ALKYL CYCLOPENTANES, $C_5$ TO $C_7$

HEAT CAPACITY, $C_p^o$, FOR THE IDEAL GAS STATE, AT −273.16° TO 1200°C

April 30, 1949; December 31, 1952

Temperature in °C

Heat Capacity, $C_p^o$, in cal/g deg C

| Compound (gas) | Formula | −273.16 | 0 | 25 | 100 | 200 | 300 | 400 | 500 | 600 | 700 | 800 | 900 | 1000 | 1100 | 1200 |
|---|---|---|---|---|---|---|---|---|---|---|---|---|---|---|---|---|
| Cyclopentane | $C_5H_{10}$ | 0 | 0.2526 | 0.2826 | 0.3717 | 0.4835 | 0.5807 | 0.6622 | 0.7311 | 0.7896 | 0.8397 | 0.8832 | 0.9204 | 0.9526 | 0.9805 | 1.0048 |
| Methylcyclopentane | $C_6H_{12}$ | 0 | 0.2828 | 0.3118 | 0.3990 | 0.5072 | 0.6006 | 0.6786 | 0.7445 | 0.8007 | 0.8490 | 0.8908 | 0.9266 | 0.9577 | 0.9847 | 1.0083 |
| Ethylcyclopentane | $C_7H_{14}$ | 0 | 0.2817 | 0.3207 | 0.4179 | 0.5167 | 0.6057 | 0.6841 | 0.7501 | 0.8066 | 0.8555 | 0.8974 | 0.9334 | 0.9647 | 0.9917 | 1.0152 |
| 1,1-Dimethylcyclopentane | " | 0 | 0.2958 | 0.3245 | 0.4130 | 0.5229 | 0.6170 | 0.6951 | 0.7603 | 0.8155 | 0.8627 | 0.9030 | 0.9376 | 0.9678 | 0.9938 | 1.0161 |
| 1,cis-2-Dimethylcyclopentane | " | 0 | 0.2977 | 0.3265 | 0.4145 | 0.5234 | 0.6166 | 0.6938 | 0.7583 | 0.8131 | 0.8601 | 0.9005 | 0.9352 | 0.9654 | 0.9915 | 1.0141 |
| 1,trans-2-Dimethylcyclopentane | " | 0 | 0.2989 | 0.3274 | 0.4150 | 0.5235 | 0.6161 | 0.6933 | 0.7572 | 0.8115 | 0.8586 | 0.8991 | 0.9337 | 0.9641 | 0.9902 | 1.0129 |
| 1,cis-3-Dimethylcyclopentane | " | 0 | 0.2989 | 0.3274 | 0.4150 | 0.5235 | 0.6161 | 0.6933 | 0.7572 | 0.8115 | 0.8586 | 0.8991 | 0.9337 | 0.9641 | 0.9902 | 1.0129 |
| 1,trans-3-Dimethylcyclopentane | " | 0 | 0.2989 | 0.3274 | 0.4150 | 0.5235 | 0.6161 | 0.6933 | 0.7572 | 0.8115 | 0.8586 | 0.8991 | 0.9337 | 0.9641 | 0.9902 | 1.0129 |

TABLE 23v-G (PART 1) – NORMAL ALKYL CYCLOHEXANES, $C_6$ TO $C_{22}$
HEAT CAPACITY, $C_p^o$, FOR THE IDEAL GAS STATE, AT $-273.16^o$ TO $1200^oC$
November 30, 1947; December 31, 1952

| Compound (gas) | Formula | Temperature in °C — Heat Capacity, $C_p^o$, in cal/g deg C | | | | | | | | | | | | | | |
|---|---|---|---|---|---|---|---|---|---|---|---|---|---|---|---|---|
| | | -273.16 | 0 | 25 | 100 | 200 | 300 | 400 | 500 | 600 | 700 | 800 | 900 | 1000 | 1100 | 1200 |
| Cyclohexane | $C_6H_{12}$ | 0 | 0.2712 | 0.3018 | 0.3933 | 0.5107 | 0.6145 | 0.7023 | 0.7757 | 0.8371 | 0.8884 | 0.932 | 0.968 | 0.999 | 1.025 | 1.047 |
| Methylcyclohexane | $C_7H_{14}$ | 0 | 0.2979 | 0.3287 | 0.4201 | 0.5340 | 0.6328 | 0.7158 | 0.7853 | 0.8436 | 0.8926 | 0.934 | 0.969 | 0.999 | 1.025 | 1.046 |
| Ethylcyclohexane | $C_8H_{16}$ | 0 | 0.3078 | 0.3383 | 0.429 | 0.541 | 0.637 | 0.718 | 0.787 | 0.844 | 0.891 | 0.932 | 0.967 | 0.996 | 1.021 | 1.043 |
| n-Propylcyclohexane | $C_9H_{18}$ | 0 | 0.3190 | 0.3488 | 0.437 | 0.548 | 0.642 | 0.720 | 0.786 | 0.840 | 0.887 | 0.928 | 0.963 | 0.993 | 1.018 | 1.040 |
| n-Butylcyclohexane | $C_{10}H_{20}$ | 0 | 0.3235 | 0.3529 | 0.440 | 0.549 | 0.642 | 0.720 | 0.785 | 0.840 | 0.885 | 0.926 | 0.961 | 0.990 | 1.015 | 1.037 |
| n-Pentylcyclohexane | $C_{11}H_{22}$ | 0 | 0.3269 | 0.3562 | 0.443 | 0.551 | 0.642 | 0.719 | 0.784 | 0.838 | 0.884 | 0.924 | 0.959 | 0.988 | 1.013 | 1.035 |
| n-Hexylcyclohexane | $C_{12}H_{24}$ | 0 | 0.3303 | 0.3590 | 0.445 | 0.552 | 0.643 | 0.719 | 0.783 | 0.836 | 0.882 | 0.923 | 0.957 | 0.986 | 1.011 | 1.033 |
| n-Heptylcyclohexane | $C_{13}H_{26}$ | 0 | 0.3324 | 0.3614 | 0.447 | 0.551 | 0.643 | 0.719 | 0.782 | 0.836 | 0.881 | 0.922 | 0.956 | 0.984 | 1.010 | 1.031 |
| n-Octylcyclohexane | $C_{14}H_{28}$ | 0 | 0.3346 | 0.3634 | 0.448 | 0.554 | 0.643 | 0.719 | 0.782 | 0.836 | 0.880 | 0.920 | 0.955 | 0.983 | 1.008 | 1.030 |
| n-Nonylcyclohexane | $C_{15}H_{30}$ | 0 | 0.3368 | 0.3652 | 0.449 | 0.554 | 0.643 | 0.719 | 0.781 | 0.835 | 0.880 | 0.919 | 0.954 | 0.982 | 1.007 | 1.029 |
| n-Decylcyclohexane | $C_{16}H_{32}$ | 0 | 0.3383 | 0.3667 | 0.451 | 0.555 | 0.644 | 0.718 | 0.781 | 0.834 | 0.879 | 0.919 | 0.953 | 0.982 | 1.006 | 1.028 |
| n-Undecylcyclohexane | $C_{17}H_{34}$ | 0 | 0.3398 | 0.3681 | 0.452 | 0.556 | 0.644 | 0.718 | 0.780 | 0.833 | 0.878 | 0.918 | 0.952 | 0.980 | 1.005 | 1.027 |
| n-Dodecylcyclohexane | $C_{18}H_{36}$ | 0 | 0.3408 | 0.3692 | 0.453 | 0.556 | 0.644 | 0.718 | 0.780 | 0.833 | 0.878 | 0.917 | 0.951 | 0.980 | 1.004 | 1.026 |
| n-Tridecylcyclohexane | $C_{19}H_{38}$ | 0 | 0.3422 | 0.3703 | 0.453 | 0.556 | 0.644 | 0.718 | 0.780 | 0.833 | 0.877 | 0.917 | 0.950 | 0.979 | 1.004 | 1.025 |
| n-Tetradecylcyclohexane | $C_{20}H_{40}$ | 0 | 0.3435 | 0.3713 | 0.454 | 0.557 | 0.644 | 0.718 | 0.780 | 0.832 | 0.877 | 0.916 | 0.950 | 0.979 | 1.003 | 1.024 |
| n-Pentadecylcyclohexane | $C_{21}H_{42}$ | 0 | 0.3442 | 0.3722 | 0.455 | 0.558 | 0.644 | 0.718 | 0.780 | 0.832 | 0.877 | 0.916 | 0.950 | 0.978 | 1.003 | 1.024 |
| n-Hexadecylcyclohexane | $C_{22}H_{44}$ | 0 | 0.3450 | 0.3730 | 0.455 | 0.557 | 0.644 | 0.718 | 0.779 | 0.832 | 0.876 | 0.915 | 0.949 | 0.978 | 1.002 | 1.023 |

# TABLE 7v-G — ALKYL CYCLOHEXANES, $C_6$ TO $C_8$

## HEAT CAPACITY, $c_p^o$, FOR THE IDEAL GAS STATE, AT $-273.16^o$ TO $1200^oC$

November 30, 1947

| Compound (gas) | Formula | Temperature in °C |||||||||||||||
|---|---|---|---|---|---|---|---|---|---|---|---|---|---|---|---|---|
| | | Heat Capacity, $c_p^o$, in cal/g deg C |||||||||||||||
| | | -273.16 | 0 | 25 | 100 | 200 | 300 | 400 | 500 | 600 | 700 | 800 | 900 | 1000 | 1100 | 1200 |
| Cyclohexane | $C_6H_{12}$ | 0 | 0.2712 | 0.3018 | 0.3933 | 0.5107 | 0.6145 | 0.7023 | 0.7757 | 0.8371 | 0.8884 | 0.932 | 0.968 | 0.999 | 1.025 | 1.047 |
| Methylcyclohexane | $C_7H_{14}$ | 0 | 0.2979 | 0.3287 | 0.4201 | 0.5340 | 0.6328 | 0.7158 | 0.7853 | 0.8436 | 0.8926 | 0.934 | 0.969 | 0.999 | 1.025 | 1.046 |
| Ethylcyclohexane | $C_8H_{16}$ | 0 | 0.3078 | 0.3383 | 0.429 | 0.541 | 0.637 | 0.718 | 0.787 | 0.844 | 0.891 | 0.932 | 0.967 | 0.996 | 1.021 | 1.043 |
| 1,1-Dimethylcyclohexane | " | 0 | 0.299 | 0.329 | 0.420 | 0.535 | 0.636 | 0.721 | 0.792 | 0.850 | 0.899 | 0.940 | 0.975 | 1.004 | 1.030 | 1.050 |
| 1,cis-2-Dimethylcyclohexane | " | 0 | 0.303 | 0.333 | 0.424 | 0.538 | 0.636 | 0.718 | 0.787 | 0.844 | 0.892 | 0.933 | 0.968 | 0.997 | 1.022 | 1.044 |
| 1,trans-2-Dimethylcyclohexane | " | 0 | 0.308 | 0.339 | 0.431 | 0.544 | 0.642 | 0.723 | 0.790 | 0.847 | 0.895 | 0.935 | 0.969 | 0.998 | 1.023 | 1.045 |
| 1,cis-3-Dimethylcyclohexane | " | 0 | 0.306 | 0.335 | 0.425 | 0.538 | 0.637 | 0.721 | 0.790 | 0.848 | 0.897 | 0.938 | 0.973 | 1.003 | 1.028 | 1.049 |
| 1,trans-3-Dimethylcyclohexane | " | 0 | 0.306 | 0.335 | 0.424 | 0.537 | 0.634 | 0.716 | 0.784 | 0.841 | 0.889 | 0.930 | 0.965 | 0.994 | 1.020 | 1.042 |
| 1,cis-4-Dimethylcyclohexane | " | 0 | 0.306 | 0.335 | 0.424 | 0.537 | 0.634 | 0.716 | 0.784 | 0.841 | 0.889 | 0.930 | 0.965 | 0.994 | 1.020 | 1.042 |
| 1,trans-4-Dimethylcyclohexane | " | 0 | 0.305 | 0.336 | 0.428 | 0.542 | 0.641 | 0.723 | 0.791 | 0.849 | 0.897 | 0.937 | 0.971 | 1.000 | 1.025 | 1.046 |

TABLE 24v-G (PART 1) – NORMAL MONOOLEFINS (1-ALKENES), $C_2$ TO $C_{20}$
HEAT CAPACITY, $C_p^o$, FOR THE IDEAL GAS STATE, AT $-273.16^o$ TO $1200^oC$
March 31, 1946; December 31, 1952

Temperature in °C

Heat Capacity, $C_p^o$, in cal/g deg C

| Compound (gas) | Formula | -273.16 | 0 | 25 | 100 | 200 | 300 | 400 | 500 | 600 | 700 | 800 | 900 | 1000 | 1100 | 1200 |
|---|---|---|---|---|---|---|---|---|---|---|---|---|---|---|---|---|
| Ethene (Ethylene) | $C_2H_4$ | 0 | 0.3485 | 0.3711 | 0.4369 | 0.5197 | 0.5920 | 0.6538 | 0.7070 | 0.7535 | 0.7944 | 0.8303 | 0.8617 | 0.8894 | 0.9134 | 0.9345 |
| Propene (Propylene) | $C_3H_6$ | 0 | 0.3402 | 0.3629 | 0.4303 | 0.5160 | 0.5921 | 0.6581 | 0.7151 | 0.7649 | 0.8083 | 0.8460 | 0.8788 | 0.9076 | 0.9328 | 0.9546 |
| 1-Butene | $C_4H_8$ | 0 | 0.3390 | 0.3649 | 0.4388 | 0.5290 | 0.6073 | 0.6739 | 0.7310 | 0.7809 | 0.8240 | 0.8614 | 0.8942 | 0.9228 | 0.9475 | 0.9691 |
| 1-Pentene | $C_5H_{10}$ | 0 | 0.3478 | 0.3734 | 0.4469 | 0.5370 | 0.6161 | 0.6833 | 0.7409 | 0.7908 | 0.8337 | 0.8711 | 0.9037 | 0.9320 | 0.9567 | 0.9782 |
| 1-Hexene | $C_6H_{12}$ | 0 | 0.3499 | 0.3758 | 0.4502 | 0.5414 | 0.6211 | 0.6887 | 0.7466 | 0.7965 | 0.8395 | 0.8769 | 0.9096 | 0.9379 | 0.9624 | 0.9838 |
| 1-Heptene | $C_7H_{14}$ | 0 | 0.3518 | 0.3779 | 0.4527 | 0.5447 | 0.6248 | 0.6927 | 0.7505 | 0.8007 | 0.844 | 0.881 | 0.914 | 0.942 | 0.967 | 0.988 |
| 1-Octene | $C_8H_{16}$ | 0 | 0.3533 | 0.3793 | 0.4546 | 0.5471 | 0.6274 | 0.6955 | 0.7536 | 0.8037 | 0.847 | 0.885 | 0.917 | 0.945 | 0.970 | 0.991 |
| 1-Nonene | $C_9H_{18}$ | 0 | 0.3543 | 0.3805 | 0.4561 | 0.5490 | 0.6295 | 0.6978 | 0.7560 | 0.8061 | 0.849 | 0.886 | 0.920 | 0.947 | 0.972 | 0.993 |
| 1-Decene | $C_{10}H_{20}$ | 0 | 0.3552 | 0.3814 | 0.4573 | 0.5505 | 0.6313 | 0.6996 | 0.7578 | 0.8079 | 0.851 | 0.888 | 0.921 | 0.950 | 0.974 | 0.995 |
| 1-Undecene | $C_{11}H_{22}$ | 0 | 0.3558 | 0.3821 | 0.4583 | 0.5518 | 0.6326 | 0.7011 | 0.7593 | 0.8095 | 0.853 | 0.891 | 0.923 | 0.951 | 0.975 | 0.997 |
| 1-Dodecene | $C_{12}H_{24}$ | 0 | 0.3564 | 0.3828 | 0.4591 | 0.5528 | 0.6338 | 0.7023 | 0.7606 | 0.8109 | 0.854 | 0.891 | 0.924 | 0.952 | 0.977 | 0.998 |
| 1-Tridecene | $C_{13}H_{26}$ | 0 | 0.3569 | 0.3833 | 0.4598 | 0.5537 | 0.6347 | 0.7033 | 0.7617 | 0.8120 | 0.855 | 0.893 | 0.926 | 0.954 | 0.978 | 0.999 |
| 1-Tetradecene | $C_{14}H_{28}$ | 0 | 0.3573 | 0.3838 | 0.4604 | 0.5544 | 0.6356 | 0.7042 | 0.7626 | 0.8129 | 0.856 | 0.894 | 0.926 | 0.955 | 0.978 | 1.000 |
| 1-Pentadecene | $C_{15}H_{30}$ | 0 | 0.3578 | 0.3841 | 0.4609 | 0.5551 | 0.6362 | 0.7050 | 0.7634 | 0.8137 | 0.857 | 0.895 | 0.927 | 0.955 | 0.979 | 1.001 |
| 1-Hexadecene | $C_{16}H_{32}$ | 0 | 0.3580 | 0.3845 | 0.4613 | 0.5557 | 0.6369 | 0.7057 | 0.7642 | 0.8144 | 0.858 | 0.895 | 0.928 | 0.956 | 0.980 | 1.001 |
| 1-Heptadecene | $C_{17}H_{34}$ | 0 | 0.3583 | 0.3848 | 0.4617 | 0.5562 | 0.6374 | 0.7063 | 0.7648 | 0.8150 | 0.858 | 0.896 | 0.929 | 0.957 | 0.981 | 1.002 |
| 1-Octadecene | $C_{18}H_{36}$ | 0 | 0.3586 | 0.3851 | 0.4620 | 0.5566 | 0.6379 | 0.7068 | 0.7653 | 0.8156 | 0.859 | 0.897 | 0.929 | 0.957 | 0.982 | 1.003 |
| 1-Nonadecene | $C_{19}H_{38}$ | 0 | 0.3588 | 0.3853 | 0.4623 | 0.5570 | 0.6384 | 0.7073 | 0.7658 | 0.8161 | 0.859 | 0.897 | 0.930 | 0.958 | 0.982 | 1.003 |
| 1-Eicosene | $C_{20}H_{40}$ | 0 | 0.3590 | 0.3855 | 0.4626 | 0.5574 | 0.6388 | 0.7077 | 0.7663 | 0.8165 | 0.860 | 0.897 | 0.930 | 0.959 | 0.982 | 1.003 |

TABLE 8v-G (PART 1) – MONOOLEFINS, C$_2$ TO C$_5$

HEAT CAPACITY, $c_p^o$, FOR THE IDEAL GAS STATE, AT −273.16° TO 1200°C

April 30, 1946; December 31, 1952

| Compound (gas) | Formula | Temperature in °C | | | | | | | | | | | | | | |
|---|---|---|---|---|---|---|---|---|---|---|---|---|---|---|---|---|
| | | −273.16 | 0 | 25 | 100 | 200 | 300 | 400 | 500 | 600 | 700 | 800 | 900 | 1000 | 1100 | 1200 |
| | | Heat Capacity, $c_p^o$, in cal/g deg C | | | | | | | | | | | | | | |
| Ethene (Ethylene) | C$_2$H$_4$ | 0 | 0.3485 | 0.3711 | 0.4369 | 0.5197 | 0.5920 | 0.6538 | 0.7070 | 0.7535 | 0.7944 | 0.8303 | 0.8617 | 0.8894 | 0.9134 | 0.9245 |
| Propene (Propylene) | C$_3$H$_6$ | 0 | 0.3402 | 0.3629 | 0.4303 | 0.5160 | 0.5921 | 0.6581 | 0.7151 | 0.7649 | 0.8083 | 0.8460 | 0.8788 | 0.9076 | 0.9328 | 0.9546 |
| 1-Butene | C$_4$H$_8$ | 0 | 0.3390 | 0.3649 | 0.4388 | 0.5290 | 0.6073 | 0.6739 | 0.7310 | 0.7809 | 0.8240 | 0.8614 | 0.8942 | 0.9228 | 0.9475 | 0.9691 |
| cis-2-Butene | " | 0 | 0.3121 | 0.3362 | 0.4083 | 0.5005 | 0.5824 | 0.6530 | 0.7137 | 0.7661 | 0.8115 | 0.8509 | 0.8851 | 0.9149 | 0.9407 | 0.9631 |
| trans-2-Butene | " | 0 | 0.3518 | 0.3741 | 0.4404 | 0.5253 | 0.6015 | 0.6678 | 0.7255 | 0.7755 | 0.8194 | 0.8578 | 0.8909 | 0.9198 | 0.9449 | 0.9669 |
| 2-Methylpropene (Isobutene) | " | 0 | 0.3552 | 0.3796 | 0.4496 | 0.5355 | 0.6108 | 0.6758 | 0.7322 | 0.7816 | 0.8245 | 0.8620 | 0.8945 | 0.9229 | 0.9477 | 0.9693 |
| 1-Pentene | C$_5$H$_{10}$ | 0 | 0.3478 | 0.3734 | 0.4469 | 0.5370 | 0.6161 | 0.6833 | 0.7409 | 0.7908 | 0.8337 | 0.8711 | 0.9037 | 0.9320 | 0.9567 | 0.9782 |
| cis-2-Pentene | " | 0 | 0.3203 | 0.3468 | 0.4237 | 0.5189 | 0.6020 | 0.6713 | 0.7310 | 0.7825 | 0.8272 | 0.8658 | 0.8995 | 0.9285 | 0.9537 | 0.9758 |
| trans-2-Pentene | " | 0 | 0.3451 | 0.3696 | 0.4410 | 0.5303 | 0.6086 | 0.6757 | 0.7336 | 0.7840 | 0.8279 | 0.8658 | 0.8990 | 0.9278 | 0.9528 | 0.9746 |
| 2-Methyl-1-butene | " | 0 | 0.3544 | 0.3806 | 0.4553 | 0.5455 | 0.6226 | 0.6884 | 0.7451 | 0.7942 | 0.8370 | 0.8740 | 0.9064 | 0.9345 | 0.9590 | 0.9804 |
| 3-Methyl-1-butene | " | 0 | 0.3768 | 0.4042 | 0.4785 | 0.5636 | 0.6366 | 0.6997 | 0.7544 | 0.8016 | 0.8429 | 0.8792 | 0.9108 | 0.9384 | 0.9622 | 0.9832 |
| 2-Methyl-2-butene | " | 0 | 0.3330 | 0.3579 | 0.4303 | 0.5203 | 0.5997 | 0.6682 | 0.7276 | 0.7791 | 0.8239 | 0.8627 | 0.8965 | 0.9257 | 0.9511 | 0.9732 |

TABLE 8v-G (PART 2) — MONOOLEFINS, C₆

HEAT CAPACITY, $C_p^o$, FOR THE IDEAL GAS STATE, AT -273.16° TO 1200°C

May 31, 1946; December 31, 1952

Temperature in °C

Heat Capacity, $C_p^o$, in cal/g deg C

| Compound (gas) | Formula | -273.16 | 0 | 25 | 100 | 200 | 300 | 400 | 500 | 600 | 700 | 800 | 900 | 1000 | 1100 | 1200 |
|---|---|---|---|---|---|---|---|---|---|---|---|---|---|---|---|---|
| 1-Hexene | C₆H₁₂ | 0 | 0.3499 | 0.3758 | 0.4502 | 0.5414 | 0.6211 | 0.6887 | 0.7466 | 0.7965 | 0.8395 | 0.8769 | 0.9096 | 0.9370 | 0.9624 | 0.9838 |
| cis-2-Hexene | " | 0 | 0.3315 | 0.3570 | 0.432 | 0.528 | 0.610 | 0.679 | 0.739 | 0.791 | 0.835 | | | | | |
| trans-2-Hexene | " | 0 | 0.3522 | 0.3760 | 0.447 | 0.537 | 0.616 | 0.683 | 0.741 | 0.791 | 0.835 | | | | | |
| cis-3-Hexene | " | 0 | 0.3235 | 0.3511 | 0.430 | 0.527 | 0.612 | 0.681 | 0.740 | 0.791 | 0.835 | | | | | |
| trans-3-Hexene | " | 0 | 0.3510 | 0.3773 | 0.452 | 0.543 | 0.621 | 0.688 | 0.745 | 0.794 | 0.837 | | | | | |
| 2-Methyl-1-pentene | " | 0 | 0.3589 | 0.3851 | 0.460 | 0.549 | 0.627 | 0.694 | 0.751 | 0.801 | 0.843 | | | | | |
| 3-Methyl-1-pentene | " | 0 | 0.3800 | 0.4116 | 0.499 | 0.600 | 0.688 | 0.763 | 0.827 | 0.882 | 0.931 | | | | | |
| 4-Methyl-1-pentene | " | 0 | 0.3328 | 0.3592 | 0.436 | 0.529 | 0.610 | 0.677 | 0.736 | 0.785 | 0.829 | | | | | |
| 2-Methyl-2-pentene | " | 0 | 0.3322 | 0.3596 | 0.437 | 0.531 | 0.612 | 0.680 | 0.739 | 0.790 | 0.834 | | | | | |
| 3-Methyl-cis-2-pentene | " | 0 | 0.3322 | 0.3596 | 0.437 | 0.531 | 0.612 | 0.680 | 0.739 | 0.790 | 0.834 | | | | | |
| 3-Methyl-trans-2-pentene | " | 0 | 0.3322 | 0.3596 | 0.437 | 0.531 | 0.612 | 0.680 | 0.739 | 0.790 | 0.834 | | | | | |
| 4-Methyl-cis-2-pentene | " | 0 | 0.3517 | 0.3793 | 0.456 | 0.546 | 0.624 | 0.690 | 0.747 | 0.796 | 0.839 | | | | | |
| 4-Methyl-trans-2-pentene | " | 0 | 0.3755 | 0.4016 | 0.474 | 0.559 | 0.633 | 0.697 | 0.753 | 0.801 | 0.843 | | | | | |
| 2-Ethyl-1-butene | " | 0 | 0.3516 | 0.3793 | 0.457 | 0.550 | 0.629 | 0.695 | 0.751 | 0.801 | 0.844 | | | | | |
| 2,3-Dimethyl-1-butene | " | 0 | 0.3803 | 0.4075 | 0.482 | 0.568 | 0.640 | 0.704 | 0.759 | 0.806 | 0.847 | | | | | |
| 3,3-Dimethyl-1-butene | " | 0 | 0.3332 | 0.3592 | 0.436 | 0.531 | 0.615 | 0.683 | 0.742 | 0.788 | 0.831 | | | | | |
| 2,3-Dimethyl-2-butene | " | 0 | 0.3386 | 0.3622 | 0.434 | 0.525 | 0.605 | 0.673 | 0.733 | 0.784 | 0.828 | | | | | |

TABLE 11v-G (PART 1) – DIOLEFINS, $C_3$ TO $C_5$

HEAT CAPACITY, $c_p^o$, FOR THE IDEAL GAS STATE, AT $-273.16^o$ TO $1200^oC$

October 31, 1947; April 30, 1948

| Compound (gas) | Formula | Temperature in °C | | | | | | | | | | | | | | |
|---|---|---|---|---|---|---|---|---|---|---|---|---|---|---|---|---|
| | | -273.16 | 0 | 25 | 100 | 200 | 300 | 400 | 500 | 600 | 700 | 800 | 900 | 1000 | 1100 | 1200 |
| | | Heat Capacity, $c_p^o$, in cal/g deg C | | | | | | | | | | | | | | |
| Propadiene (Allene) | $C_3H_4$ | 0 | 0.3311 | 0.3520 | 0.4102 | 0.4783 | 0.5355 | 0.5835 | 0.6245 | 0.6602 | 0.6913 | 0.7182 | 0.7420 | 0.7625 | 0.7806 | 0.7964 |
| 1,2-Butadiene | $C_4H_6$ | 0 | 0.3328 | 0.3540 | 0.4146 | 0.4882 | 0.5524 | 0.6069 | 0.6541 | 0.6954 | 0.7312 | 0.7620 | 0.7888 | 0.8120 | 0.8324 | 0.8499 |
| 1,3-Butadiene | " | 0 | 0.3245 | 0.3515 | 0.4251 | 0.5080 | 0.5735 | 0.6262 | 0.6704 | 0.7083 | 0.7411 | 0.7698 | 0.7948 | 0.8167 | 0.8360 | 0.8526 |
| 1,2-Pentadiene | $C_5H_8$ | 0 | 0.3445 | 0.370 | 0.439 | 0.517 | 0.583 | 0.640 | 0.688 | 0.730 | 0.766 | 0.798 | 0.826 | 0.849 | 0.870 | 0.887 |
| 1,cis-3-Pentadiene | " | 0 | 0.304 | 0.332 | 0.408 | 0.497 | 0.569 | 0.629 | 0.678 | 0.721 | 0.757 | 0.789 | 0.817 | 0.841 | 0.862 | 0.881 |
| 1,trans-3-Pentadiene | " | 0 | 0.339 | 0.363 | 0.434 | 0.518 | 0.585 | 0.641 | 0.689 | 0.729 | 0.764 | 0.795 | 0.822 | 0.846 | 0.866 | 0.883 |
| 1,4-Pentadiene | " | 0 | 0.344 | 0.369 | 0.437 | 0.517 | 0.583 | 0.638 | 0.687 | 0.728 | 0.765 | 0.796 | 0.823 | 0.847 | 0.867 | 0.885 |
| 2,3-Pentadiene | " | 0 | 0.334 | 0.355 | 0.418 | 0.495 | 0.562 | 0.620 | 0.671 | 0.716 | 0.754 | 0.787 | 0.817 | 0.841 | 0.862 | 0.881 |
| 3-Methyl-1,2-butadiene | " | 0 | 0.347 | 0.370 | 0.434 | 0.510 | 0.576 | 0.632 | 0.681 | 0.724 | 0.760 | 0.792 | 0.820 | 0.844 | 0.865 | 0.884 |
| 2-Methyl-1,3-butadiene (Isoprene) | " | 0 | 0.340 | 0.367 | 0.443 | 0.525 | 0.592 | 0.647 | 0.694 | 0.733 | 0.768 | 0.799 | 0.825 | 0.848 | 0.869 | 0.886 |

TABLE 18v-G – ALKYL CYCLOPENTENES, C₅ TO C₇

HEAT CAPACITY, $C_p^o$, FOR THE IDEAL GAS STATE, AT -273.16° TO 1200°C

December 31, 1952

| Compound (gas) | Formula | Temperature in °C | | | | | | | | | | | | | | |
|---|---|---|---|---|---|---|---|---|---|---|---|---|---|---|---|---|
| | | -273.16 | 0 | 25 | 100 | 200 | 300 | 400 | 500 | 600 | 700 | 800 | 900 | 1000 | 1100 | 1200 |
| | | Heat Capacity, $C_p^o$, in cal/g deg C | | | | | | | | | | | | | | |
| Cyclopentene | $C_5H_8$ | 0 | 0.2399 | 0.2635 | 0.3402 | 0.4395 | 0.5254 | 0.5973 | 0.6576 | 0.7087 | 0.7520 | 0.7892 | 0.8210 | 0.8484 | 0.8720 | 0.8925 |
| 1-Methylcyclopentene | $C_6H_{10}$ | 0 | 0.269 | 0.293 | 0.369 | 0.465 | 0.549 | 0.620 | 0.679 | 0.729 | 0.772 | 0.810 | 0.841 | 0.868 | 0.892 | 0.913 |
| 3-Methylcyclopentene | " | 0 | 0.265 | 0.291 | 0.369 | 0.469 | 0.553 | 0.623 | 0.682 | 0.732 | 0.774 | 0.812 | 0.844 | 0.870 | 0.894 | 0.914 |
| 4-Methylcyclopentene | " | 0 | 0.265 | 0.291 | 0.370 | 0.467 | 0.551 | 0.622 | 0.680 | 0.732 | 0.774 | 0.811 | 0.842 | 0.869 | 0.892 | 0.913 |
| 1-Ethylcyclopentene | $C_7H_{12}$ | | | | | | | | | | | | | | | |
| 3-Ethylcyclopentene | " | | | | | | | | | | | | | | | |
| 4-Ethylcyclopentene | " | | | | | | | | | | | | | | | |
| 1,2-Dimethylcyclopentene | " | 0 | 0.291 | 0.315 | 0.390 | 0.484 | 0.567 | 0.635 | 0.694 | 0.744 | 0.787 | 0.824 | 0.856 | 0.884 | 0.908 | 0.929 |
| 1,3-Dimethylcyclopentene | " | 0 | 0.287 | 0.313 | 0.390 | 0.487 | 0.570 | 0.638 | 0.697 | 0.747 | 0.789 | 0.826 | 0.858 | 0.885 | 0.908 | 0.929 |
| 1,4-Dimethylcyclopentene | " | 0 | 0.288 | 0.312 | 0.389 | 0.486 | 0.569 | 0.637 | 0.696 | 0.746 | 0.788 | 0.825 | 0.857 | 0.884 | 0.907 | 0.928 |
| 1,5-Dimethylcyclopentene | " | 0 | 0.287 | 0.313 | 0.390 | 0.487 | 0.569 | 0.638 | 0.697 | 0.747 | 0.788 | 0.825 | 0.857 | 0.885 | 0.908 | 0.929 |
| 3,3-Dimethylcyclopentene | " | 0 | 0.280 | 0.306 | 0.386 | 0.488 | 0.576 | 0.649 | 0.710 | 0.760 | 0.804 | 0.840 | 0.871 | 0.897 | 0.920 | 0.940 |
| 3,cis-4-Dimethylcyclopentene | " | 0 | 0.283 | 0.310 | 0.390 | 0.490 | 0.575 | 0.645 | 0.703 | 0.753 | 0.794 | 0.831 | 0.862 | 0.889 | 0.912 | 0.932 |
| 3,trans-4-Dimethylcyclopentene | " | 0 | 0.286 | 0.312 | 0.391 | 0.489 | 0.573 | 0.642 | 0.699 | 0.749 | 0.791 | 0.828 | 0.859 | 0.886 | 0.909 | 0.930 |
| 3,cis-5-Dimethylcyclopentene | " | 0 | 0.286 | 0.312 | 0.391 | 0.489 | 0.573 | 0.642 | 0.699 | 0.749 | 0.791 | 0.828 | 0.859 | 0.886 | 0.909 | 0.930 |
| 3,trans-5-Dimethylcyclopentene | " | 0 | 0.286 | 0.312 | 0.391 | 0.489 | 0.573 | 0.642 | 0.699 | 0.749 | 0.791 | 0.828 | 0.859 | 0.886 | 0.909 | 0.930 |
| 4,4-Dimethylcyclopentene | " | | | | | | | | | | | | | | | |

TABLE 25v-G (PART 1) – NORMAL ACETYLENES (1-ALKYNES), $C_2$ TO $C_{20}$
HEAT CAPACITY, $C_p^o$, FOR THE IDEAL GAS STATE, AT $-273.16^o$ TO $1200^oC$
February 28, 1946; December 31, 1952

Temperature in $^oC$

Heat Capacity, $C_p^o$, in cal/g deg C

| Compound (gas) | Formula | -273.16 | 0 | 25 | 100 | 200 | 300 | 400 | 500 | 600 | 700 | 800 | 900 | 1000 | 1100 | 1200 |
|---|---|---|---|---|---|---|---|---|---|---|---|---|---|---|---|---|
| Ethyne (Acetylene) | $C_2H_2$ | 0 | 0.3857 | 0.4032 | 0.4470 | 0.4890 | 0.5200 | 0.5456 | 0.5679 | 0.5882 | 0.6068 | 0.6238 | 0.6392 | 0.6532 | 0.6658 | 0.6771 |
| Propyne (Methylacetylene) | $C_3H_4$ | 0 | 0.3430 | 0.3618 | 0.4148 | 0.4774 | 0.5311 | 0.5775 | 0.6176 | 0.6529 | 0.6840 | 0.7114 | 0.7353 | 0.7562 | 0.7746 | 0.7907 |
| 1-Butyne (Ethylacetylene) | $C_4H_6$ | 0 | 0.3379 | 0.3597 | 0.4209 | 0.4932 | 0.5550 | 0.6078 | 0.6534 | 0.6932 | 0.7279 | 0.7583 | 0.7848 | 0.8079 | 0.8281 | 0.8457 |
| 1-Pentyne | $C_5H_8$ | 0 | 0.3474 | 0.3697 | 0.4328 | 0.5087 | 0.5749 | 0.6311 | 0.6796 | 0.7216 | 0.7578 | 0.7896 | 0.8172 | 0.8412 | 0.8621 | 0.8804 |
| 1-Hexyne | $C_6H_{10}$ | 0 | 0.3499 | 0.3731 | 0.4388 | 0.5183 | 0.5870 | 0.6456 | 0.6958 | 0.7393 | 0.7768 | 0.8095 | 0.8380 | 0.8627 | 0.8841 | 0.9030 |
| 1-Heptyne | $C_7H_{12}$ | 0 | 0.3519 | 0.3755 | 0.4430 | 0.5249 | 0.5956 | 0.6558 | 0.7073 | 0.7518 | 0.790 | 0.824 | 0.853 | 0.878 | 0.900 | 0.919 |
| 1-Octyne | $C_8H_{14}$ | 0 | 0.3533 | 0.3773 | 0.4461 | 0.5299 | 0.6022 | 0.6635 | 0.7159 | 0.7611 | 0.800 | 0.834 | 0.863 | 0.889 | 0.911 | 0.931 |
| 1-Nonyne | $C_9H_{16}$ | 0 | 0.3544 | 0.3787 | 0.4486 | 0.5337 | 0.6072 | 0.6694 | 0.7225 | 0.7683 | 0.808 | 0.842 | 0.872 | 0.898 | 0.920 | 0.940 |
| 1-Decyne | $C_{10}H_{18}$ | 0 | 0.3552 | 0.3798 | 0.4507 | 0.5369 | 0.6111 | 0.6741 | 0.7278 | 0.7741 | 0.814 | 0.849 | 0.879 | 0.905 | 0.927 | 0.947 |
| 1-Undecyne | $C_{11}H_{20}$ | 0 | 0.3559 | 0.3808 | 0.4522 | 0.5394 | 0.6144 | 0.6779 | 0.7321 | 0.7788 | 0.819 | 0.854 | 0.884 | 0.911 | 0.933 | 0.953 |
| 1-Dodecyne | $C_{12}H_{22}$ | 0 | 0.3565 | 0.3815 | 0.4536 | 0.5415 | 0.6170 | 0.6811 | 0.7357 | 0.7827 | 0.823 | 0.858 | 0.889 | 0.915 | 0.938 | 0.958 |
| 1-Tridecyne | $C_{13}H_{24}$ | 0 | 0.3570 | 0.3822 | 0.4547 | 0.5433 | 0.6193 | 0.6838 | 0.7387 | 0.7860 | 0.827 | 0.862 | 0.893 | 0.919 | 0.942 | 0.962 |
| 1-Tetradecyne | $C_{14}H_{26}$ | 0 | 0.3574 | 0.3827 | 0.4556 | 0.5447 | 0.6213 | 0.6861 | 0.7413 | 0.7888 | 0.830 | 0.865 | 0.896 | 0.923 | 0.946 | 0.966 |
| 1-Pentadecyne | $C_{15}H_{28}$ | 0 | 0.3578 | 0.3832 | 0.4564 | 0.5461 | 0.6230 | 0.6881 | 0.7436 | 0.7913 | 0.832 | 0.868 | 0.899 | 0.926 | 0.949 | 0.969 |
| 1-Hexadecyne | $C_{16}H_{30}$ | 0 | 0.3581 | 0.3836 | 0.4572 | 0.5472 | 0.6245 | 0.6899 | 0.7456 | 0.7934 | 0.835 | 0.870 | 0.901 | 0.928 | 0.952 | 0.972 |
| 1-Heptadecyne | $C_{17}H_{32}$ | 0 | 0.3584 | 0.3839 | 0.4578 | 0.5482 | 0.6257 | 0.6914 | 0.7473 | 0.7953 | 0.837 | 0.873 | 0.904 | 0.931 | 0.954 | 0.974 |
| 1-Octadecyne | $C_{18}H_{34}$ | 0 | 0.3587 | 0.3843 | 0.4584 | 0.5491 | 0.6269 | 0.6928 | 0.7488 | 0.7970 | 0.839 | 0.874 | 0.906 | 0.933 | 0.956 | 0.976 |
| 1-Nonadecyne | $C_{19}H_{36}$ | 0 | 0.3589 | 0.3845 | 0.4589 | 0.5499 | 0.6280 | 0.6940 | 0.7502 | 0.7984 | 0.840 | 0.876 | 0.907 | 0.934 | 0.958 | 0.978 |
| 1-Eicosyne | $C_{20}H_{38}$ | 0 | 0.3591 | 0.3848 | 0.4593 | 0.5506 | 0.6289 | 0.6951 | 0.7514 | 0.7998 | 0.842 | 0.878 | 0.909 | 0.936 | 0.960 | 0.980 |

698

## TABLE 12v-G – ACETYLENES, C$_2$ TO C$_5$

### HEAT CAPACITY, $C_p^o$, FOR THE IDEAL GAS STATE, AT $-273.16^o$ TO $1200^o$C

January 31, 1946

| Compound (gas) | Formula | Temperature in °C — Heat Capacity, $C_p^o$, in cal/g deg C | | | | | | | | | | | | | | |
|---|---|---|---|---|---|---|---|---|---|---|---|---|---|---|---|---|
| | | -273.16 | 0 | 25 | 100 | 200 | 300 | 400 | 500 | 600 | 700 | 800 | 900 | 1000 | 1100 | 1200 |
| Ethyne (Acetylene) | C$_2$H$_2$ | 0 | 0.3857 | 0.4032 | 0.4470 | 0.4890 | 0.5200 | 0.5456 | 0.5679 | 0.5882 | 0.6068 | 0.6238 | 0.6392 | 0.6532 | 0.6658 | 0.6771 |
| Propyne (Methylacetylene) | C$_3$H$_4$ | 0 | 0.3430 | 0.3618 | 0.4148 | 0.4774 | 0.5311 | 0.5773 | 0.6176 | 0.6529 | 0.6840 | 0.7114 | 0.7353 | 0.7562 | 0.7746 | 0.7907 |
| 1-Butyne (Ethylacetylene) | C$_4$H$_6$ | 0 | 0.3379 | 0.3597 | 0.4209 | 0.4932 | 0.5550 | 0.6078 | 0.6534 | 0.6992 | 0.7279 | 0.7583 | 0.7848 | 0.8078 | 0.8281 | 0.8457 |
| 2-Butyne (Dimethylacetylene) | " | 0 | 0.3211 | 0.3444 | 0.3989 | 0.4694 | 0.5331 | 0.5888 | 0.6376 | 0.6802 | 0.7174 | 0.7496 | 0.7777 | 0.8021 | 0.8233 | 0.8418 |
| 1-Pentyne | C$_5$H$_8$ | 0 | 0.3543 | 0.3744 | 0.436 | 0.512 | 0.577 | 0.632 | 0.680 | 0.721 | 0.758 | 0.789 | 0.817 | 0.841 | 0.862 | 0.880 |
| 2-Pentyne | " | 0 | 0.3256 | 0.3463 | 0.407 | 0.484 | 0.552 | 0.611 | 0.662 | 0.707 | 0.745 | 0.779 | 0.808 | 0.834 | 0.856 | 0.875 |
| 3-Methyl-1-butyne | " | 0 | 0.3431 | 0.3673 | 0.434 | 0.513 | 0.579 | 0.636 | 0.684 | 0.725 | 0.761 | 0.792 | 0.819 | 0.843 | 0.864 | 0.882 |

TABLE 21v-G (PART 1) — NORMAL ALKYL BENZENES, C$_6$ TO C$_{22}$
HEAT CAPACITY, $c_p^o$, FOR THE IDEAL GAS STATE, AT −273.16° TO 1200°C
January 31, 1946; December 31, 1952

| Compound (gas) | Formula | Temperature in °C | | | | | | | | | | | | | | |
|---|---|---|---|---|---|---|---|---|---|---|---|---|---|---|---|---|
| | | −273.16 | 0 | 25 | 100 | 200 | 300 | 400 | 500 | 600 | 700 | 800 | 900 | 1000 | 1100 | 1200 |
| | | Heat Capacity, $c_p^o$, in cal/g deg C | | | | | | | | | | | | | | |
| Benzene | C$_6$H$_6$ | 0 | 0.2266 | 0.2499 | 0.3192 | 0.4005 | 0.4675 | 0.5217 | 0.5663 | 0.6034 | 0.6347 | 0.6613 | 0.6840 | 0.7034 | 0.7202 | 0.7347 |
| Methylbenzene (Toluene) | C$_7$H$_8$ | 0 | 0.2463 | 0.2691 | 0.3377 | 0.4200 | 0.4892 | 0.5461 | 0.5935 | 0.6332 | 0.6669 | 0.6956 | 0.7202 | 0.7413 | 0.7595 | 0.7752 |
| Ethylbenzene | C$_8$H$_{10}$ | 0 | 0.2655 | 0.2891 | 0.3600 | 0.4445 | 0.5150 | 0.5729 | 0.6210 | 0.6615 | 0.6959 | 0.7254 | 0.7507 | 0.7725 | 0.7913 | 0.8076 |
| n-Propylbenzene | C$_9$H$_{12}$ | 0 | 0.2780 | 0.3030 | 0.3739 | 0.4590 | 0.5708 | 0.5902 | 0.6396 | 0.6614 | 0.7166 | 0.7469 | 0.7730 | 0.7954 | 0.8148 | 0.8317 |
| n-Butylbenzene | C$_{10}$H$_{14}$ | 0 | 0.2866 | 0.3118 | 0.3836 | 0.4699 | 0.5430 | 0.6034 | 0.6537 | 0.6964 | 0.7325 | 0.7636 | 0.7903 | 0.8135 | 0.8333 | 0.8506 |
| n-Pentylbenzene | C$_{11}$H$_{16}$ | 0 | 0.2939 | 0.3192 | 0.3916 | 0.4788 | 0.5528 | 0.6140 | 0.6652 | 0.7085 | 0.7454 | 0.7771 | 0.8044 | 0.8279 | 0.8482 | 0.8658 |
| n-Hexylbenzene | C$_{12}$H$_{18}$ | 0 | 0.2999 | 0.3253 | 0.3982 | 0.4862 | 0.5609 | 0.6228 | 0.6746 | 0.7186 | 0.756 | 0.788 | 0.816 | 0.840 | 0.861 | 0.879 |
| n-Heptylbenzene | C$_{13}$H$_{20}$ | 0 | 0.3050 | 0.3304 | 0.4038 | 0.4924 | 0.5676 | 0.6302 | 0.6826 | 0.7271 | 0.765 | 0.798 | 0.826 | 0.850 | 0.871 | 0.889 |
| n-Octylbenzene | C$_{14}$H$_{22}$ | 0 | 0.3092 | 0.3348 | 0.4085 | 0.4977 | 0.5735 | 0.6365 | 0.6894 | 0.7343 | 0.773 | 0.806 | 0.834 | 0.859 | 0.880 | 0.898 |
| n-Nonylbenzene | C$_{15}$H$_{24}$ | 0 | 0.3129 | 0.3386 | 0.4125 | 0.5022 | 0.5784 | 0.6419 | 0.6952 | 0.7405 | 0.779 | 0.813 | 0.841 | 0.866 | 0.887 | 0.906 |
| n-Decylbenzene | C$_{16}$H$_{26}$ | 0 | 0.3161 | 0.3418 | 0.4162 | 0.5063 | 0.5828 | 0.6467 | 0.7003 | 0.7460 | 0.785 | 0.819 | 0.847 | 0.873 | 0.894 | 0.913 |
| n-Undecylbenzene | C$_{17}$H$_{28}$ | 0 | 0.3189 | 0.3448 | 0.4193 | 0.5098 | 0.5866 | 0.6509 | 0.7048 | 0.7508 | 0.790 | 0.824 | 0.853 | 0.878 | 0.900 | 0.919 |
| n-Dodecylbenzene | C$_{18}$H$_{30}$ | 0 | 0.3214 | 0.3473 | 0.4220 | 0.5129 | 0.5900 | 0.6546 | 0.7088 | 0.7550 | 0.795 | 0.828 | 0.858 | 0.883 | 0.905 | 0.924 |
| n-Tridecylbenzene | C$_{19}$H$_{32}$ | 0 | 0.3236 | 0.3496 | 0.4245 | 0.5156 | 0.5931 | 0.6579 | 0.7124 | 0.7588 | 0.799 | 0.833 | 0.862 | 0.888 | 0.910 | 0.929 |
| n-Tetradecylbenzene | C$_{20}$H$_{34}$ | 0 | 0.3257 | 0.3516 | 0.4268 | 0.5181 | 0.5958 | 0.6608 | 0.7155 | 0.7622 | 0.802 | 0.836 | 0.866 | 0.892 | 0.914 | 0.933 |
| n-Pentadecylbenzene | C$_{21}$H$_{36}$ | 0 | 0.3275 | 0.3535 | 0.4287 | 0.5204 | 0.5983 | 0.6635 | 0.7184 | 0.7652 | 0.805 | 0.840 | 0.870 | 0.895 | 0.918 | 0.937 |
| n-Hexadecylbenzene | C$_{22}$H$_{38}$ | 0 | 0.3291 | 0.3552 | 0.4305 | 0.5224 | 0.6005 | 0.6659 | 0.7210 | 0.7680 | 0.805 | 0.843 | 0.873 | 0.899 | 0.921 | 0.940 |

## TABLE 5v-G – ALKYL BENZENES, $C_6$ TO $C_9$

### HEAT CAPACITY, $C_p^o$, FOR THE IDEAL GAS STATE, AT $-273.16^o$ TO $1200^o$C

December 31, 1945

| Compound (gas) | Formula | Temperature in °C<br>Heat Capacity, $C_p^o$, in cal/g deg C | | | | | | | | | | | | | | |
|---|---|---|---|---|---|---|---|---|---|---|---|---|---|---|---|---|
| | | -273.16 | 0 | 25 | 100 | 200 | 300 | 400 | 500 | 600 | 700 | 800 | 900 | 1000 | 1100 | 1200 |
| Benzene | $C_6H_6$ | 0 | 0.2266 | 0.2499 | 0.3192 | 0.4005 | 0.4675 | 0.5217 | 0.5663 | 0.6034 | 0.6347 | 0.6613 | 0.6840 | 0.7034 | 0.7202 | 0.7347 |
| Methylbenzene (Toluene) | $C_7H_8$ | 0 | 0.2463 | 0.2691 | 0.3377 | 0.4200 | 0.4892 | 0.5461 | 0.5935 | 0.6332 | 0.6669 | 0.6956 | 0.7202 | 0.7413 | 0.7595 | 0.7752 |
| Ethylbenzene | $C_8H_{10}$ | 0 | 0.2655 | 0.2891 | 0.3600 | 0.4454 | 0.5150 | 0.5729 | 0.6210 | 0.6615 | 0.6959 | 0.7254 | 0.7507 | 0.7725 | 0.7913 | 0.8076 |
| 1,2-Dimethylbenzene (o-Xylene) | " | 0 | 0.2783 | 0.3000 | 0.3645 | 0.4432 | 0.5110 | 0.5680 | 0.6161 | 0.6570 | 0.6919 | 0.7218 | 0.7475 | 0.7697 | 0.7888 | 0.8054 |
| 1,3-Dimethylbenzene (m-Xylene) | " | 0 | 0.2649 | 0.2872 | 0.3542 | 0.4361 | 0.5061 | 0.5647 | 0.6137 | 0.6553 | 0.6906 | 0.7209 | 0.7468 | 0.7691 | 0.7883 | 0.8050 |
| 1,4-Dimethylbenzene (p-Xylene) | " | 0 | 0.2640 | 0.2856 | 0.3513 | 0.4326 | 0.5028 | 0.5616 | 0.6111 | 0.6530 | 0.6886 | 0.7192 | 0.7453 | 0.7678 | 0.7872 | 0.8040 |
| n-Propylbenzene | $C_9H_{12}$ | 0 | 0.2832 | 0.3056 | 0.376 | 0.461 | 0.532 | 0.591 | 0.640 | 0.681 | 0.716 | 0.747 | 0.773 | 0.795 | 0.815 | 0.831 |
| Isopropylbenzene | " | 0 | 0.2769 | 0.3017 | 0.375 | 0.461 | 0.534 | 0.593 | 0.642 | 0.683 | 0.718 | 0.748 | 0.774 | 0.797 | 0.816 | 0.833 |
| 1-Methyl-2-ethylbenzene | " | 0 | 0.2916 | 0.3140 | 0.381 | 0.462 | 0.531 | 0.589 | 0.638 | 0.679 | 0.715 | 0.745 | 0.771 | 0.794 | 0.813 | 0.830 |
| 1-Methyl-3-ethylbenzene | " | 0 | 0.2798 | 0.3027 | 0.372 | 0.456 | 0.527 | 0.586 | 0.636 | 0.678 | 0.714 | 0.744 | 0.771 | 0.793 | 0.813 | 0.830 |
| 1-Methyl-4-ethylbenzene | " | 0 | 0.2790 | 0.3014 | 0.369 | 0.453 | 0.524 | 0.583 | 0.633 | 0.676 | 0.712 | 0.743 | 0.769 | 0.792 | 0.812 | 0.829 |
| 1,2,3-Trimethylbenzene | " | 0 | 0.2859 | 0.3066 | 0.369 | 0.447 | 0.516 | 0.575 | 0.626 | 0.669 | 0.706 | 0.737 | 0.765 | 0.788 | 0.808 | 0.826 |
| 1,2,4-Trimethylbenzene | " | 0 | 0.2882 | 0.3087 | 0.370 | 0.448 | 0.517 | 0.576 | 0.627 | 0.670 | 0.707 | 0.738 | 0.765 | 0.789 | 0.809 | 0.826 |
| 1,3,5-Trimethylbenzene | " | 0 | 0.2771 | 0.2988 | 0.3636 | 0.4449 | 0.5160 | 0.5762 | 0.6270 | 0.6702 | 0.7072 | 0.7388 | 0.7660 | 0.7894 | 0.8096 | 0.8270 |

## TABLE 13v-G - STYRENES, $C_8$ and $C_9$

### HEAT CAPACITY, $C_p^o$, FOR THE IDEAL GAS STATE, AT -273.16 TO 1200°C

September 30, 1947

Heat Capacity, $C_p^o$, in cal/g deg C

| Compound (gas) | Formula | Temperature in °C | | | | | | | | | | | | | | |
|---|---|---|---|---|---|---|---|---|---|---|---|---|---|---|---|---|
| | | -273.16 | 0 | 25 | 100 | 200 | 300 | 400 | 500 | 600 | 700 | 800 | 900 | 1000 | 1100 | 1200 |
| Ethenylbenzene (Styrene; Vinylbenzene; Phenylethylene) | $C_8H_8$ | 0 | 0.2566 | 0.2802 | 0.3461 | 0.4228 | 0.4859 | 0.5372 | 0.5795 | 0.6149 | 0.6449 | 0.6705 | 0.6924 | 0.7112 | 0.7273 | 0.7414 |
| Isopropenylbenzene (α-Methylstyrene; 2-Phenyl-1-propene) | $C_9H_{10}$ | 0 | 0.271 | 0.294 | 0.358 | 0.434 | 0.498 | 0.552 | 0.597 | 0.635 | 0.667 | 0.695 | 0.719 | 0.739 | 0.756 | 0.772 |
| cis-1-Propenylbenzene (cis-β-Methylstyrene; cis-1-Phenyl-1-propene) | " | 0 | 0.271 | 0.294 | 0.358 | 0.434 | 0.498 | 0.552 | 0.597 | 0.635 | 0.667 | 0.695 | 0.719 | 0.739 | 0.756 | 0.772 |
| trans-1-Propenylbenzene (trans-β-Methylstyrene; trans-1-Phenyl-1-propene) | " | 0 | 0.273 | 0.295 | 0.361 | 0.438 | 0.503 | 0.556 | 0.600 | 0.638 | 0.669 | 0.697 | 0.720 | 0.741 | 0.758 | 0.772 |
| 1-Methyl-2-ethenylbenzene (o-Methylstyrene) | " | 0 | 0.271 | 0.294 | 0.358 | 0.434 | 0.498 | 0.552 | 0.597 | 0.635 | 0.667 | 0.695 | 0.719 | 0.739 | 0.756 | 0.772 |
| 1-Methyl-3-ethenylbenzene (m-Methylstyrene) | " | 0 | 0.271 | 0.294 | 0.358 | 0.434 | 0.498 | 0.552 | 0.597 | 0.635 | 0.667 | 0.695 | 0.719 | 0.739 | 0.756 | 0.772 |
| 1-Methyl-4-ethenylbenzene (p-Methylstyrene) | " | 0 | 0.271 | 0.294 | 0.358 | 0.434 | 0.498 | 0.552 | 0.597 | 0.635 | 0.667 | 0.695 | 0.719 | 0.739 | 0.756 | 0.772 |

Table 00w – O, H, N, C

HEAT OF FORMATION, $\Delta H_f^o$, AT 0° TO 5000°K

June 30, 1946; April 30, 1948; August 31, 1949

Temperature in °K

Heat of Formation, $\Delta H_f^o$, in kcal/mole

| Compound (gas, monatomic) | Formula | 0 | 298.16 | 300 | 400 | 500 | 600 | 700 | 800 | 900 | 1000 | 1100 | 1200 | 1300 | 1400 | 1500 |
|---|---|---|---|---|---|---|---|---|---|---|---|---|---|---|---|---|
| Oxygen | O | 58.586 | 59.159 | 59.162 | 59.325 | 59.470 | 59.598 | 59.713 | 59.817 | 59.910 | 59.997 | 60.077 | 60.152 | 60.222 | 60.289 | 60.352 |
| Hydrogen | H | 51.620 | 52.089 | 52.092 | 52.242 | 52.389 | 52.536 | 52.682 | 52.826 | 52.967 | 53.105 | 53.239 | 53.368 | 53.492 | 53.611 | 53.725 |
| Nitrogen | N | 85.120 | 85.565 | 85.568 | 85.716 | 85.862 | 86.002 | 86.135 | 86.260 | 86.377 | 86.487 | 86.589 | 86.685 | 86.776 | 86.863 | 86.945 |
| Carbon | C | 170.39 | 171.698 | 171.703 | 171.953 | 172.132 | 172.252 | 172.325 | 172.362 | 172.372 | 172.363 | 172.339 | 172.302 | 172.249 | 172.184 | 172.109 |

Temperature in °K

Heat of Formation, $\Delta H_f^o$, in kcal/mole

| Compound (gas, monatomic) | Formula | 1000 | 1250 | 1500 | 1750 | 2000 | 2250 | 2500 | 2750 | 3000 | 3500 | 4000 | 4500 | 5000 |
|---|---|---|---|---|---|---|---|---|---|---|---|---|---|---|
| Oxygen | O | 59.997 | 60.187 | 60.352 | 60.494 | 60.620 | 60.727 | 60.819 | 60.895 | 60.964 | 61.054 | 61.126 | 61.183 | 61.248 |
| Hydrogen | H | 53.105 | 53.430 | 53.725 | 53.987 | 54.220 | 54.428 | 54.615 | 54.781 | 54.931 | 55.191 | 55.406 | 55.586 | 55.735 |
| Nitrogen | N | 86.487 | 86.732 | 86.945 | 87.135 | 87.309 | 87.469 | 87.623 | 87.770 | 87.815 | 88.212 | 88.543 | 88.939 | 89.423 |
| Carbon | C | 172.363 | 172.277 | 172.109 | 171.889 | 171.64 | 171.38 | 171.09 | 170.79 | 170.47 | 169.84 | 169.16 | | |

TABLE 0w — O₂, H₂, OH, H₂O, N₂, NO, C, CO, CO₂
HEAT OF FORMATION, $\Delta H_f^\circ$, AT 0° TO 5000°K
July 31, 1944; August 31, 1946; June 30, 1949

Heat of Formation, $\Delta H_f^\circ$, in kcal/mole

| Compound | Formula | State | Temperature in °K | | | | | | | | | | | | | | |
|---|---|---|---|---|---|---|---|---|---|---|---|---|---|---|---|---|---|
| | | | 0 | 50 | 100 | 150 | 200 | 250 | 298.16 | 300 | 400 | 500 | 600 | 700 | 800 | 900 | 1000 |
| Oxygen | O₂ | gas | 0 | 0 | 0 | 0 | 0 | 0 | 0 | 0 | 0 | 0 | 0 | 0 | 0 | 0 | 0 |
| Hydrogen | H₂ | gas | 0 | 0 | 0 | 0 | 0 | 0 | 0 | 0 | 0 | 0 | 0 | 0 | 0 | 0 | 0 |
| Hydroxyl | OH | gas | 10.0 | | | | | | 10.06 | 10.063 | 10.069 | 10.059 | 10.036 | 10.003 | 9.963 | 9.919 | 9.875 |
| Water | H₂O | gas | -57.107 | | | | | | -57.7979 | -57.8028 | -58.040 | -58.273 | -58.493 | -58.696 | -58.882 | -59.055 | -59.214 |
| Nitrogen | N₂ | gas | 0 | 0 | 0 | | 0 | 0 | 0 | 0 | 0 | 0 | 0 | 0 | 0 | 0 | 0 |
| Nitric Oxide | NO | gas | 21.477 | | 21.528 | | 21.581 | 21.595 | 21.600 | 21.600 | 21.610 | 21.616 | 21.620 | 21.622 | 21.625 | 21.629 | 21.633 |
| Carbon | C | solid graphite | 0 | 0 | 0 | 0 | | | 0 | 0 | 0 | 0 | 0 | 0 | 0 | 0 | 0 |
| Carbon Monoxide | CO | gas | -27.2019 | | -26.8682 | | -26.5967 | -26.4933 | -26.4157 | -26.4131 | -26.317 | -26.295 | -26.330 | -26.407 | -26.511 | -26.635 | -26.768 |
| Carbon Dioxide | CO₂ | gas | -93.9686 | | | | | | -94.0518 | -94.0520 | -94.069 | -94.091 | -94.123 | -94.167 | -94.215 | -94.268 | -94.318 |

Heat of Formation, $\Delta H_f^\circ$, in kcal/mole

| Compound | Formula | State | Temperature in °K | | | | | | | | | | | | | | |
|---|---|---|---|---|---|---|---|---|---|---|---|---|---|---|---|---|---|
| | | | 1100 | 1200 | 1300 | 1400 | 1500 | 1750 | 2000 | 2250 | 2500 | 2750 | 3000 | 3500 | 4000 | 4500 | 5000 |
| Oxygen | O₂ | gas | 0 | 0 | 0 | 0 | 0 | 0 | 0 | 0 | 0 | 0 | 0 | 0 | 0 | 0 | 0 |
| Hydrogen | H₂ | gas | 0 | 0 | 0 | 0 | 0 | 0 | 0 | 0 | 0 | 0 | 0 | 0 | 0 | 0 | 0 |
| Hydroxyl | OH | gas | 9.851 | 9.788 | 9.748 | 9.712 | 9.676 | 9.591 | 9.515 | 9.441 | 9.368 | 9.291 | 9.209 | 9.036 | 8.858 | 8.681 | 8.526 |
| Water | H₂O | gas | -59.360 | -59.497 | -59.622 | -59.735 | -59.841 | -60.067 | -60.258 | -60.426 | -60.588 | -60.75 | -60.89 | -61.24 | -61.55 | -61.96 | -62.37 |
| Nitrogen | N₂ | gas | 0 | 0 | 0 | 0 | 0 | 0 | 0 | 0 | 0 | 0 | 0 | 0 | 0 | 0 | 0 |
| Nitric Oxide | NO | gas | 21.637 | 21.642 | 21.646 | 21.651 | 21.656 | 21.657 | 21.651 | 21.634 | 21.607 | 21.571 | 21.521 | 21.386 | 21.229 | 21.050 | 20.887 |
| Carbon | C | solid graphite | 0 | 0 | 0 | 0 | 0 | 0 | 0 | 0 | 0 | 0 | 0 | 0 | 0 | 0 | 0 |
| Carbon Monoxide | CO | gas | -26.909 | -27.056 | -27.212 | -27.376 | -27.545 | -27.99 | -28.46 | -28.94 | -29.45 | -29.98 | -30.56 | -31.74 | -33.04 | | |
| Carbon Dioxide | CO₂ | gas | -94.364 | -94.410 | -94.456 | -94.505 | -94.555 | -94.68 | -94.83 | -94.98 | -95.14 | -95.33 | -95.57 | -96.06 | -96.67 | | |

TABLE 20w (PART 1) — NORMAL PARAFFINS, $C_1$ TO $C_{20}$
HEAT OF FORMATION, $\Delta H_f°$, AT 0° TO 1500°K
November 30, 1945; December 31, 1952

Temperature in °K

Heat of Formation, $\Delta H_f°$, in kcal/mole

| Compound (gas) | Formula | 0 | 298.16 | 300 | 400 | 500 | 600 | 700 | 800 | 900 | 1000 | 1100 | 1200 | 1300 | 1400 | 1500 |
|---|---|---|---|---|---|---|---|---|---|---|---|---|---|---|---|---|
| Methane | $CH_4$ | -15.987 | -17.889 | -17.909 | -18.629 | -19.302 | -19.893 | -20.401 | -20.823 | -21.166 | -21.43 | -21.65 | -21.79 | -21.92 | -22.00 | -22.06 |
| Ethane | $C_2H_6$ | -16.517 | -20.236 | -20.258 | -21.419 | -22.437 | -23.28 | -23.98 | -24.53 | -24.97 | -25.28 | -25.50 | -25.64 | -25.72 | -25.75 | -25.73 |
| Propane | $C_3H_8$ | -19.482 | -24.820 | -24.848 | -26.358 | -27.622 | -28.66 | -29.49 | -30.12 | -30.58 | -30.90 | -31.09 | -31.16 | -31.19 | -31.14 | -31.06 |
| n-Butane | $C_4H_{10}$ | -23.67 | -30.15 | -30.18 | -32.00 | -33.51 | -34.73 | -35.70 | -36.42 | -36.94 | -37.26 | -37.43 | -37.46 | -37.41 | -37.29 | -37.13 |
| n-Pentane | $C_5H_{12}$ | -27.23 | -35.00 | -35.04 | -37.18 | -38.94 | -40.37 | -41.48 | -42.29 | -42.87 | -43.21 | -43.37 | -43.35 | -43.26 | -43.07 | -42.84 |
| n-Hexane | $C_6H_{14}$ | -30.91 | -39.96 | -40.01 | -42.46 | -44.48 | -46.11 | -47.36 | -48.28 | -48.90 | -49.27 | -49.40 | -49.35 | -49.20 | -48.95 | -48.64 |
| n-Heptane | $C_7H_{16}$ | -34.55 | -44.89 | -44.94 | -47.71 | -49.99 | -51.82 | -53.21 | -54.23 | -54.90 | -55.29 | -55.41 | -55.32 | -55.12 | -54.80 | -54.42 |
| n-Octane | $C_8H_{18}$ | -38.20 | -49.82 | -49.87 | -52.96 | -55.49 | -57.53 | -59.07 | -60.18 | -60.90 | -61.31 | -61.42 | -61.29 | -61.03 | -60.66 | -60.20 |
| n-Nonane | $C_9H_{20}$ | -41.84 | -54.74 | -54.81 | -58.22 | -61.00 | -63.23 | -64.92 | -66.12 | -66.91 | -67.33 | -67.43 | -67.25 | -66.95 | -66.51 | -65.98 |
| n-Decane | $C_{10}H_{22}$ | -45.49 | -59.67 | -59.74 | -63.47 | -66.51 | -68.94 | -70.78 | -72.07 | -72.91 | -73.35 | -73.44 | -73.22 | -72.87 | -72.37 | -71.76 |
| n-Undecane | $C_{11}H_{24}$ | -49.13 | -64.60 | -64.67 | -68.72 | -72.02 | -74.65 | -76.63 | -78.02 | -78.91 | -79.37 | -79.44 | -79.19 | -78.78 | -78.22 | -77.54 |
| n-Dodecane | $C_{12}H_{26}$ | -52.77 | -69.52 | -69.60 | -73.97 | -77.52 | -80.36 | -82.48 | -83.97 | -84.91 | -85.39 | -85.45 | -85.16 | -84.70 | -84.07 | -83.31 |
| n-Tridecane | $C_{13}H_{28}$ | -56.42 | -74.45 | -74.53 | -79.22 | -83.03 | -86.07 | -88.34 | -89.92 | -90.91 | -91.41 | -91.46 | -91.13 | -90.62 | -89.93 | -89.09 |
| n-Tetradecane | $C_{14}H_{30}$ | -60.06 | -79.38 | -79.47 | -84.48 | -88.54 | -91.77 | -94.19 | -95.86 | -96.92 | -97.43 | -97.47 | -97.09 | -96.54 | -95.78 | -94.87 |
| n-Pentadecane | $C_{15}H_{32}$ | -63.71 | -84.31 | -84.40 | -89.73 | -94.04 | -97.48 | -100.05 | -101.81 | -102.92 | -103.45 | -103.48 | -103.06 | -102.45 | -101.64 | -100.65 |
| n-Hexadecane | $C_{16}H_{34}$ | -67.35 | -89.23 | -89.33 | -94.98 | -99.55 | -103.19 | -105.90 | -107.76 | -108.92 | -109.47 | -109.49 | -109.03 | -108.37 | -107.49 | -106.43 |
| n-Heptadecane | $C_{17}H_{36}$ | -70.99 | -94.15 | -94.26 | -100.23 | -105.06 | -108.90 | -111.75 | -113.71 | -114.92 | -115.49 | -115.50 | -115.00 | -114.29 | -113.34 | -112.21 |
| n-Octadecane | $C_{18}H_{38}$ | -74.64 | -99.08 | -99.19 | -105.48 | -110.56 | -114.61 | -117.61 | -119.66 | -120.92 | -121.51 | -121.51 | -120.97 | -120.20 | -119.20 | -117.99 |
| n-Nonadecane | $C_{19}H_{40}$ | -78.28 | -104.00 | -104.13 | -110.74 | -116.07 | -120.31 | -123.46 | -125.60 | -126.93 | -127.53 | -127.52 | -126.93 | -126.12 | -125.05 | -123.77 |
| n-Eicosane | $C_{20}H_{42}$ | -81.93 | -108.93 | -109.06 | -115.99 | -121.58 | -126.02 | -129.32 | -131.55 | -132.93 | -133.55 | -133.53 | -132.90 | -132.04 | -130.91 | -129.55 |
| Increment per $CH_2$ group, applicable beyond n-hexane | | -3.644 | -4.926 | -4.932 | -5.252 | -5.507 | -5.708 | -5.854 | -5.948 | -6.002 | -6.020 | -6.009 | -5.968 | -5.917 | -5.854 | -5.779 |

TABLE 1w — PARAFFINS, C$_1$ TO C$_5$

HEAT OF FORMATION, $\Delta H_f°$, AT 0° TO 1500°K

August 31, 1944; February 28, 1949; December 31, 1952

| Compound (gas) | Formula | Temperature in °K — Heat of Formation, $\Delta H_f°$, in kcal/mole |||||||||||||||
|---|---|---|---|---|---|---|---|---|---|---|---|---|---|---|---|
| | | 0 | 100 | 150 | 200 | 250 | 298.16 | 300 | 350 | 400 | 450 | 500 | 600 | 700 | 800 | 900 |
| Methane | CH$_4$ | -15.987 | -16.640 | -16.914 | -17.209 | -17.543 | -17.889 | -17.903 | -18.266 | -18.629 | -18.974 | -19.302 | -19.893 | -20.401 | -20.823 | -21.166 |
| Ethane | C$_2$H$_6$ | -16.517 | -17.885 | -18.460 | -19.039 | -19.645 | -20.236 | -20.258 | -20.855 | -21.419 | -21.952 | -22.437 | -23.28 | -23.98 | -24.53 | -24.97 |
| Propane | C$_3$H$_8$ | -19.482 | -21.549 | -22.383 | -23.195 | -24.024 | -24.820 | -24.848 | -25.626 | -26.358 | -27.022 | -27.622 | -28.66 | -29.49 | -30.12 | -30.58 |
| $n$-Butane | C$_4$H$_{10}$ | -23.67 | | | -28.21 | -29.20 | -30.15 | -30.18 | -31.11 | -32.00 | -32.78 | -33.51 | -34.73 | -35.70 | -36.42 | -36.94 |
| 2-Methylpropane (Isobutane) | " | -25.30 | | | -30.17 | -31.19 | -32.15 | -32.19 | -33.12 | -34.00 | -34.78 | -35.48 | -36.67 | -37.61 | -38.30 | -38.80 |
| $n$-Pentane | C$_5$H$_{12}$ | -27.23 | | | -32.71 | -33.88 | -35.00 | -35.04 | -36.14 | -37.18 | -38.10 | -38.94 | -40.37 | -41.48 | -42.29 | -42.87 |
| 2-Methylbutane (Isopentane) | " | -28.81 | | | -34.55 | -35.79 | -36.92 | -36.96 | -38.07 | -39.12 | -40.04 | -40.88 | -42.28 | -43.34 | -44.15 | -44.66 |
| 2,2-Dimethylpropane (Neopentane) | " | -31.30 | | | -37.35 | -38.55 | -39.67 | -39.71 | -40.79 | -41.77 | -42.64 | -43.42 | -44.67 | -45.63 | -46.29 | -46.73 |

| Compound (gas) | Formula | Temperature in °K — Heat of Formation, $\Delta H_f°$, in kcal/mole ||||||
|---|---|---|---|---|---|---|---|
| | | 1000 | 1100 | 1200 | 1300 | 1400 | 1500 |
| Methane | CH$_4$ | -21.43 | -21.65 | -21.79 | -21.92 | -22.00 | -22.06 |
| Ethane | C$_2$H$_6$ | -25.28 | -25.50 | -25.64 | -25.72 | -25.75 | -25.73 |
| Propane | C$_3$H$_8$ | -30.90 | -31.09 | -31.16 | -31.19 | -31.14 | -31.06 |
| $n$-Butane | C$_4$H$_{10}$ | -37.26 | -37.43 | -37.46 | -37.41 | -37.29 | -37.13 |
| 2-Methylpropane (Isobutane) | " | -39.12 | -39.28 | -39.28 | -39.24 | -39.13 | -38.98 |
| $n$-Pentane | C$_5$H$_{12}$ | -43.21 | -43.37 | -43.35 | -43.26 | -43.07 | -42.84 |
| 2-Methylbutane (Isopentane) | " | -44.97 | -45.07 | -45.00 | -44.86 | -44.61 | -44.31 |
| 2,2-Dimethylpropane (Neopentane) | " | -46.96 | -47.01 | -46.90 | -46.70 | -46.42 | -46.12 |

TABLE 2w (PART 1) — PARAFFINS, C$_6$

HEAT OF FORMATION, $\Delta H_f°$, AT 0° TO 1500°K

September 30, 1944; November 30, 1946; December 31, 1952

Temperature in °K

Heat of Formation, $\Delta H_f°$, in kcal/mole

| Compound (gas) | Formula | 0 | 298.16 | 300 | 400 | 500 | 600 | 700 | 800 | 900 | 1000 | 1100 | 1200 | 1300 | 1400 | 1500 |
|---|---|---|---|---|---|---|---|---|---|---|---|---|---|---|---|---|
| n-Hexane | C$_6$H$_{14}$ | -30.91 | -39.96 | -40.01 | -42.46 | -44.48 | -46.11 | -47.36 | -48.28 | -48.90 | -49.27 | -49.40 | -49.35 | -49.20 | -48.95 | -48.64 |
| 2-Methylpentane | " | -32.08 | -41.66 | -41.71 | -44.13 | -46.06 | -47.65 | -48.82 | -49.73 | -50.28 | -50.59 | | | | | |
| 3-Methylpentane | " | -31.97 | -41.02 | -41.07 | -43.52 | -45.54 | -47.18 | -48.43 | -49.38 | -49.99 | -50.38 | | | | | |
| 2,2-Dimethylbutane | " | -34.65 | -44.35 | -44.46 | -46.90 | -48.83 | -50.40 | -51.60 | -52.38 | -52.97 | -53.20 | | | | | |
| 2,3-Dimethylbutane | " | -32.73 | -42.49 | -42.54 | -45.03 | -47.05 | -48.66 | -49.87 | -50.75 | -51.38 | -51.70 | | | | | |

TABLE 2w (PART 2) — PARAFFINS, C$_7$
HEAT OF FORMATION, $\Delta H_f^{\circ}$, AT 0° TO 1500°K
September 30, 1944; December 31, 1952

| Compound (gas) | Formula | Temperature in °K | | | | | | | | | | | | | | |
|---|---|---|---|---|---|---|---|---|---|---|---|---|---|---|---|---|
| | | 0 | 298.16 | 300 | 400 | 500 | 600 | 700 | 800 | 900 | 1000 | 1100 | 1200 | 1300 | 1400 | 1500 |
| | | Heat of Formation, $\Delta H_f^{\circ}$, in kcal/mole | | | | | | | | | | | | | | |
| n-Heptane | C$_7$H$_{16}$ | -34.55 | -44.89 | -44.94 | -47.71 | -49.99 | -51.82 | -53.21 | -54.23 | -54.90 | -55.29 | -55.41 | -55.32 | -55.12 | -54.80 | -54.42 |
| 2-Methylhexane | " | -35.77 | -46.60 | -46.66 | -49.30 | -51.45 | -53.09 | -54.33 | -55.25 | -55.91 | -56.33 | | | | | |
| 3-Methylhexane | " | -34.96 | -45.96 | -46.02 | -48.71 | -50.90 | -52.58 | -53.84 | -54.77 | -55.42 | -55.82 | | | | | |
| 3-Ethylpentane | " | -34.10 | -45.34 | -45.40 | -48.15 | -50.40 | -52.12 | -53.43 | -54.41 | -55.11 | -55.56 | | | | | |
| 2,2-Dimethylpentane | " | -38.00 | -49.29 | -49.35 | -52.02 | -54.14 | -55.72 | -56.87 | -57.69 | -58.25 | -58.56 | | | | | |
| 2,3-Dimethylpentane | " | -36.29 | -47.62 | -47.68 | -50.39 | -52.56 | -54.21 | -55.43 | -56.35 | -57.01 | -57.45 | | | | | |
| 2,4-Dimethylpentane | " | -36.98 | -48.30 | -48.36 | -51.02 | -53.13 | -54.70 | -55.85 | -56.69 | -57.27 | -57.64 | | | | | |
| 3,3-Dimethylpentane | " | -36.92 | -48.17 | -48.23 | -50.88 | -52.98 | -54.54 | -55.67 | -56.46 | -56.98 | -57.28 | | | | | |
| 2,2,3-Trimethylbutane | " | -37.71 | -48.96 | -49.02 | -51.78 | -53.99 | -55.68 | -56.94 | -57.86 | -58.43 | -58.66 | -58.72 | -58.54 | -58.36 | -57.94 | -57.46 |

TABLE 3w — PARAFFINS, C$_8$

HEAT OF FORMATION, $\Delta H_f°$, AT 0° TO 1500°K

October 31, 1944; December 31, 1952

| Compound (gas) | Formula | Temperature in °K |||||||||||||||
| | | Heat of Formation, $\Delta H_f°$, in kcal/mole |||||||||||||||
| | | 0 | 298.16 | 300 | 400 | 500 | 600 | 700 | 800 | 900 | 1000 | 1100 | 1200 | 1300 | 1400 | 1500 |
|---|---|---|---|---|---|---|---|---|---|---|---|---|---|---|---|---|
| n-Octane | C$_8$H$_{18}$ | -38.20 | -49.82 | -49.87 | -52.96 | -55.49 | -57.53 | -59.07 | -60.18 | -60.90 | -61.31 | -61.42 | -61.29 | -61.03 | -60.66 | -60.20 |
| 2-Methylheptane | = | -39.42 | -51.50 | -51.56 | -54.49 | -56.87 | -58.67 | -60.04 | -61.13 | -61.91 | -62.19 | | | | | |
| 3-Methylheptane | = | -38.64 | -50.82 | -50.88 | -53.84 | -56.23 | -58.03 | -59.40 | -60.49 | -61.27 | -61.57 | | | | | |
| 4-Methylheptane | = | -38.43 | -50.69 | -50.75 | -53.73 | -56.13 | -57.97 | -59.39 | -60.47 | -61.23 | -61.55 | | | | | |
| 3-Ethylhexane | = | -37.71 | -50.40 | -50.46 | -53.59 | -56.10 | -58.04 | -59.53 | -60.64 | -61.42 | -61.81 | | | | | |
| 2,2-Dimethylhexane | = | -41.23 | -53.71 | -53.77 | -56.72 | -59.06 | -60.85 | -62.16 | -63.02 | -63.66 | -63.96 | | | | | |
| 2,3-Dimethylhexane | = | -38.76 | -51.13 | -51.19 | -54.08 | -56.26 | -57.88 | -59.11 | -60.10 | -60.83 | -61.16 | | | | | |
| 2,4-Dimethylhexane | = | -39.74 | -52.44 | -52.51 | -55.50 | -57.92 | -59.72 | -61.06 | -62.10 | -62.86 | -63.23 | | | | | |
| 2,5-Dimethylhexane | = | -40.61 | -53.21 | -53.27 | -56.24 | -58.58 | -60.33 | -61.66 | -62.70 | -63.45 | -63.77 | | | | | |
| 3,3-Dimethylhexane | = | -39.90 | -52.61 | -52.68 | -55.65 | -58.03 | -59.78 | -61.04 | -61.93 | -62.54 | -62.84 | | | | | |
| 3,4-Dimethylhexane[a] | = | -38.61 | -50.91 | -50.97 | -53.99 | -56.42 | -58.29 | -59.74 | -60.78 | -61.44 | -61.80 | | | | | |
| 2-Methyl-3-ethylpentane | = | -37.96 | -50.48 | -50.54 | -53.46 | -55.77 | -57.52 | -58.87 | -59.95 | -60.70 | -60.93 | | | | | |
| 3-Methyl-3-ethylpentane | = | -38.68 | -51.38 | -51.45 | -54.32 | -56.65 | -58.42 | -59.74 | -60.65 | -61.18 | -61.29 | | | | | |
| 2,2,3-Trimethylpentane | = | -39.77 | -52.61 | -52.68 | -55.62 | -57.92 | -59.63 | -60.89 | -61.82 | -62.43 | -62.63 | | | | | |
| 2,2,4-Trimethylpentane | = | -40.73 | -53.57 | -53.64 | -56.58 | -58.88 | -60.59 | -61.85 | -62.78 | -63.39 | -63.59 | | | | | |
| 2,3,3-Trimethylpentane | = | -39.01 | -51.73 | -51.80 | -54.72 | -56.98 | -58.66 | -59.93 | -60.92 | -61.56 | -61.62 | | | | | |
| 2,3,4-Trimethylpentane | = | -39.12 | -51.97 | -52.04 | -54.97 | -57.18 | -58.83 | -60.11 | -61.17 | -61.91 | -62.03 | | | | | |
| 2,2,3,3-Tetramethylbutane | = | -41.24 | -53.99 | -54.05 | -56.97 | -59.20 | -60.83 | -61.97 | -62.74 | -63.13 | -63.24 | | | | | |

[a] See footnotes a and b of Table 3r.

TABLE 22w (PART 1) — NORMAL ALKYL CYCLOPENTANES, C$_5$ TO C$_{21}$

HEAT OF FORMATION, $\Delta H_f^\circ$, AT 0° TO 1500°K

March 31, 1947; December 31, 1952

| Compound (gas) | Formula | Temperature in °K — Heat of Formation, $\Delta H_f^\circ$, in kcal/mole | | | | | | | | | | | | | | |
|---|---|---|---|---|---|---|---|---|---|---|---|---|---|---|---|---|
| | | 0 | 298.16 | 300 | 400 | 500 | 600 | 700 | 800 | 900 | 1000 | 1100 | 1200 | 1300 | 1400 | 1500 |
| Cyclopentane | C$_5$H$_{10}$ | -10.68 | -18.46 | -18.50 | -20.80 | -22.67 | -24.12 | -25.25 | -26.06 | -26.61 | -26.91 | -27.01 | -26.97 | -26.81 | -26.57 | -26.25 |
| Methylcyclopentane | C$_6$H$_{12}$ | -16.62 | -25.50 | -25.54 | -28.07 | -30.11 | -31.68 | -32.88 | -33.74 | -34.29 | -34.58 | -34.65 | -34.52 | -34.30 | -33.97 | -33.56 |
| Ethylcyclopentane | C$_7$H$_{14}$ | -20.23 | -30.37 | -30.43 | -33.29 | -35.60 | -37.40 | -38.72 | -39.67 | -40.25 | -40.54 | -40.54 | -40.34 | -40.03 | -39.56 | -38.98 |
| n-Propylcyclopentane | C$_8$H$_{16}$ | -23.98 | -35.39 | -35.45 | -38.64 | -41.21 | -43.20 | -44.67 | -45.72 | -46.34 | -46.7 | -46.6 | -46.4 | -46.0 | -45.5 | -44.9 |
| n-Butylcyclopentane | C$_9$H$_{18}$ | -27.52 | -40.22 | -40.29 | -43.79 | -46.62 | -48.81 | -50.43 | -51.56 | -52.26 | -52.6 | -52.6 | -52.3 | -51.8 | -51.3 | -50.6 |
| n-Pentylcyclopentane | C$_{10}$H$_{20}$ | -31.16 | -45.15 | -45.22 | -49.04 | -52.13 | -54.52 | -56.28 | -57.51 | -58.26 | -58.6 | -58.6 | -58.3 | -57.7 | -57.2 | -56.4 |
| n-Hexylcyclopentane | C$_{11}$H$_{22}$ | -34.81 | -50.07 | -50.15 | -54.29 | -57.63 | -60.23 | -62.14 | -63.46 | -64.26 | -64.6 | -64.6 | -64.2 | -63.6 | -63.0 | -62.2 |
| n-Heptylcyclopentane | C$_{12}$H$_{24}$ | -38.45 | -55.00 | -55.09 | -59.55 | -63.14 | -65.93 | -67.99 | -69.40 | -70.27 | -70.7 | -70.6 | -70.2 | -69.6 | -68.8 | -67.9 |
| n-Octylcyclopentane | C$_{13}$H$_{26}$ | -42.10 | -59.92 | -60.02 | -64.80 | -68.65 | -71.64 | -73.85 | -75.35 | -76.27 | -76.7 | -76.6 | -76.2 | -75.5 | -74.7 | -73.7 |
| n-Nonylcyclopentane | C$_{14}$H$_{28}$ | -45.74 | -64.85 | -64.95 | -70.05 | -74.16 | -77.35 | -79.70 | -81.30 | -82.27 | -82.7 | -82.6 | -82.2 | -81.4 | -80.6 | -79.5 |
| n-Decylcyclopentane | C$_{15}$H$_{30}$ | -49.38 | -69.78 | -69.88 | -75.30 | -79.66 | -83.06 | -85.55 | -87.25 | -88.27 | -88.7 | -88.7 | -88.1 | -87.3 | -86.4 | -85.3 |
| n-Undecylcyclopentane | C$_{16}$H$_{32}$ | -53.03 | -74.70 | -74.81 | -80.55 | -85.17 | -88.77 | -91.41 | -93.20 | -94.27 | -94.7 | -94.7 | -94.1 | -93.2 | -92.2 | -91.1 |
| n-Dodecylcyclopentane | C$_{17}$H$_{34}$ | -56.67 | -79.63 | -79.75 | -85.81 | -90.68 | -94.47 | -97.26 | -99.14 | -100.28 | -100.8 | -100.7 | -100.1 | -99.2 | -98.1 | -96.8 |
| n-Tridecylcyclopentane | C$_{18}$H$_{36}$ | -60.32 | -84.55 | -84.68 | -91.06 | -96.18 | -100.18 | -103.12 | -105.09 | -106.28 | -106.8 | -106.7 | -106.0 | -105.1 | -104.0 | -102.6 |
| n-Tetradecylcyclopentane | C$_{19}$H$_{38}$ | -63.96 | -89.48 | -89.61 | -96.31 | -101.69 | -105.89 | -108.97 | -111.04 | -112.28 | -112.8 | -112.7 | -112.0 | -111.0 | -109.8 | -108.4 |
| n-Pentadecylcyclopentane | C$_{20}$H$_{40}$ | -67.60 | -94.41 | -94.54 | -101.56 | -107.20 | -111.60 | -114.82 | -116.99 | -118.28 | -118.8 | -118.7 | -118.0 | -116.9 | -115.6 | -114.2 |
| n-Hexadecylcyclopentane | C$_{21}$H$_{42}$ | -71.25 | -99.33 | -99.47 | -106.81 | -112.70 | -117.31 | -120.68 | -122.94 | -124.28 | -124.8 | -124.7 | -123.9 | -122.8 | -121.5 | -120.0 |
| Increment per CH$_2$ group, applicable beyond n-butylcyclopentane | | -3.644 | -4.926 | -4.932 | -5.252 | -5.507 | -5.708 | -5.854 | -5.948 | -6.002 | -6.02 | -6.01 | -5.97 | -5.92 | -5.85 | -5.78 |

711

TABLE 6w – ALKYL CYCLOPENTANES, $C_5$ TO $C_7$,
HEAT OF FORMATION, $\Delta H_f°$, AT 0° TO 1500°K
April 30, 1949; December 31, 1952

Heat of Formation, $\Delta H_f°$, in kcal/mole

| Compound (gas) | Formula | Temperature in °K | | | | | | | | | | | | | | |
|---|---|---|---|---|---|---|---|---|---|---|---|---|---|---|---|---|
| | | 0 | 298.16 | 300 | 400 | 500 | 600 | 700 | 800 | 900 | 1000 | 1100 | 1200 | 1300 | 1400 | 1500 |
| Cyclopentane | $C_5H_{10}$ | -10.68 | -18.46 | -18.50 | -20.80 | -22.67 | -24.12 | -25.25 | -26.06 | -26.61 | -26.91 | -27.01 | -26.97 | -26.81 | -26.57 | -26.25 |
| Methylcyclopentane | $C_6H_{12}$ | -16.62 | -25.50 | -25.54 | -28.07 | -30.11 | -31.68 | -32.88 | -33.74 | -34.29 | -34.58 | -34.65 | -34.52 | -34.30 | -33.97 | -33.56 |
| Ethylcyclopentane | $C_7H_{14}$ | -20.23 | -30.37 | -30.43 | -33.29 | -35.60 | -37.40 | -38.72 | -39.67 | -40.25 | -40.54 | -40.54 | -40.34 | -40.03 | -39.56 | -38.98 |
| 1,1-Dimethylcyclopentane | " | -22.69 | -33.05 | -33.10 | -35.92 | -38.14 | -39.79 | -41.04 | -41.91 | -42.39 | -42.59 | -42.55 | -42.29 | -41.94 | -41.49 | -40.94 |
| 1,cis-2-Dimethylcyclopentane | " | -20.66 | -30.96 | -31.01 | -33.84 | -36.05 | -37.72 | -38.96 | -39.83 | -40.36 | -40.58 | -40.57 | -40.33 | -39.99 | -39.54 | -39.03 |
| 1,trans-2-Dimethylcyclopentane | " | -22.39 | -32.67 | -32.72 | -35.54 | -37.75 | -39.41 | -40.67 | -41.58 | -42.09 | -42.33 | -42.35 | -42.11 | -41.78 | -41.36 | -40.85 |
| 1,cis-3-Dimethylcyclopentane | " | -21.65 | -31.93 | -31.98 | -34.80 | -37.01 | -38.67 | -39.93 | -40.84 | -41.35 | -41.59 | -41.61 | -41.37 | -41.04 | -40.62 | -40.11 |
| 1,trans-3-Dimethylcyclopentane | " | -22.19 | -32.47 | -32.52 | -35.34 | -37.55 | -39.21 | -40.47 | -41.38 | -41.89 | -42.13 | -42.15 | -41.91 | -41.58 | -41.16 | -40.65 |

TABLE 23w (PART 1) — NORMAL ALKYL CYCLOHEXANES, $C_6$ TO $C_{22}$
HEAT OF FORMATION, $\Delta H_f°$, AT 0° TO 1500°K
March 31, 1947; December 31, 1952

Heat of Formation, $\Delta H_f°$, in kcal/mole

| Compound (gas) | Formula | Temperature in °K | | | | | | | | | | | | | |
|---|---|---|---|---|---|---|---|---|---|---|---|---|---|---|---|
| | | 0 | 298.16 | 300 | 400 | 500 | 600 | 700 | 800 | 900 | 1000 | 1100 | 1200 | 1300 | 1400 | 1500 |
| Cyclohexane | $C_6H_{12}$ | -20.01 | -29.43 | -29.48 | -31.70 | -34.08 | -35.57 | -36.59 | -37.19 | -37.46 | -37.41 | -37.14 | -36.68 | -36.05 | -35.44 | -34.61 |
| Methylcyclohexane | $C_7H_{14}$ | -26.30 | -36.99 | -37.04 | -39.79 | -41.92 | -43.46 | -44.50 | -45.10 | -45.34 | -45.25 | -44.92 | -44.36 | -43.71 | -42.89 | -42.10 |
| Ethylcyclohexane | $C_8H_{16}$ | -28.94 | -41.05 | -41.10 | -44.13 | -46.50 | -48.22 | -49.35 | -49.98 | -50.25 | -50.17 | -49.84 | -49.25 | -48.51 | -47.69 | -46.71 |
| n-Propylcyclohexane | $C_9H_{18}$ | -32.62 | -46.20 | -46.26 | -49.6 | -52.1 | -54.0 | -55.2 | -56.0 | -56.3 | -56.2 | -55.9 | -55.3 | -54.5 | -53.5 | -52.5 |
| n-Butylcyclohexane | $C_{10}H_{20}$ | -36.09 | -50.95 | -51.01 | -54.6 | -57.4 | -59.5 | -60.9 | -61.8 | -62.1 | -62.0 | -61.7 | -61.1 | -60.2 | -59.1 | -58.1 |
| n-Pentylcyclohexane | $C_{11}H_{22}$ | -39.73 | -55.88 | -55.94 | -59.8 | -62.9 | -65.2 | -66.8 | -67.8 | -68.1 | -68.0 | -67.7 | -67.1 | -66.1 | -65.0 | -63.9 |
| n-Hexylcyclohexane | $C_{12}H_{24}$ | -43.38 | -60.80 | -60.87 | -65.1 | -68.4 | -70.9 | -72.6 | -73.7 | -74.1 | -74.0 | -73.7 | -73.0 | -72.0 | -70.8 | -69.7 |
| n-Heptylcyclohexane | $C_{13}H_{26}$ | -47.02 | -65.73 | -65.81 | -70.4 | -73.9 | -76.6 | -78.4 | -79.6 | -80.1 | -80.1 | -79.7 | -79.0 | -78.0 | -76.6 | -75.4 |
| n-Octylcyclohexane | $C_{14}H_{28}$ | -50.67 | -70.65 | -70.74 | -75.6 | -79.4 | -82.3 | -84.3 | -85.6 | -86.1 | -86.1 | -85.7 | -85.0 | -83.9 | -82.5 | -81.2 |
| n-Nonylcyclohexane | $C_{15}H_{30}$ | -54.31 | -75.58 | -75.67 | -80.8 | -85.0 | -88.0 | -90.2 | -91.6 | -92.1 | -92.1 | -91.8 | -91.0 | -89.8 | -88.4 | -87.0 |
| n-Decylcyclohexane | $C_{16}H_{32}$ | -57.95 | -80.51 | -80.60 | -86.1 | -90.5 | -93.8 | -96.0 | -97.5 | -98.1 | -98.1 | -97.8 | -96.9 | -95.7 | -94.2 | -92.8 |
| n-Undecylcyclohexane | $C_{17}H_{34}$ | -61.60 | -85.43 | -85.53 | -91.4 | -96.0 | -99.5 | -101.8 | -103.4 | -104.1 | -104.1 | -103.8 | -102.9 | -101.6 | -100.0 | -98.6 |
| n-Dodecylcyclohexane | $C_{18}H_{36}$ | -65.24 | -90.36 | -90.47 | -96.6 | -101.5 | -105.2 | -107.7 | -109.4 | -110.1 | -110.2 | -109.8 | -108.8 | -107.5 | -105.9 | -104.3 |
| n-Tridecylcyclohexane | $C_{19}H_{38}$ | -68.89 | -95.28 | -95.40 | -101.8 | -107.0 | -110.9 | -113.6 | -115.4 | -116.1 | -116.2 | -115.8 | -114.8 | -113.5 | -111.8 | -110.1 |
| n-Tetradecylcyclohexane | $C_{20}H_{40}$ | -72.53 | -100.21 | -100.33 | -107.1 | -112.5 | -116.6 | -119.4 | -121.3 | -122.1 | -122.2 | -121.8 | -120.8 | -119.4 | -117.6 | -115.9 |
| n-Pentadecylcyclohexane | $C_{21}H_{42}$ | -76.17 | -105.14 | -105.26 | -112.4 | -118.0 | -122.3 | -125.2 | -127.2 | -128.1 | -128.2 | -127.8 | -126.7 | -125.3 | -123.4 | -121.7 |
| n-Hexadecylcyclohexane | $C_{22}H_{44}$ | -79.82 | -110.06 | -110.19 | -117.6 | -123.5 | -128.0 | -131.1 | -133.2 | -134.1 | -134.2 | -133.8 | -132.7 | -131.2 | -129.3 | -127.5 |
| Increment per $CH_2$ group, applicable beyond n-butylcyclohexane | | -3.644 | -4.926 | -4.932 | -5.25 | -5.51 | -5.71 | -5.85 | -5.95 | -6.00 | -6.02 | -6.01 | -5.97 | -5.92 | -5.85 | -5.78 |

TABLE 7w – ALKYL CYCLOHEXANES, C$_6$ TO C$_8$
HEAT OF FORMATION, $\Delta Hf°$, AT 0° TO 1500°K

April 30, 1947

| Compound (gas) | Formula | Temperature in °K | | | | | | | | | | | | | | |
| --- | --- | --- | --- | --- | --- | --- | --- | --- | --- | --- | --- | --- | --- | --- | --- | --- |
| | | 0 | 298.16 | 300 | 400 | 500 | 600 | 700 | 800 | 900 | 1000 | 1100 | 1200 | 1300 | 1400 | 1500 |
| | | Heat of Formation, $\Delta Hf°$, in kcal/mole | | | | | | | | | | | | | | |
| Cyclohexane | C$_6$H$_{12}$ | -20.01 | -29.43 | -29.48 | -31.70 | -34.08 | -35.57 | -36.59 | -37.19 | -37.46 | -37.41 | -37.14 | -36.68 | -36.05 | -35.44 | -34.61 |
| Methylcyclohexane | C$_7$H$_{14}$ | -26.30 | -36.99 | -37.04 | -39.79 | -41.92 | -43.46 | -44.50 | -45.10 | -45.34 | -45.25 | -44.92 | -44.36 | -43.71 | -42.80 | -42.10 |
| Ethylcyclohexane | C$_8$H$_{16}$ | -28.94 | -41.05 | -41.10 | -44.13 | -46.50 | -48.22 | -49.35 | -49.98 | -50.25 | -50.17 | -49.84 | -49.25 | -48.51 | -47.69 | -46.71 |
| 1,1-Dimethylcyclohexane | " | -30.93 | -43.26 | -43.31 | -46.4 | -48.9 | -50.6 | -51.8 | -52.4 | -52.5 | -52.4 | -51.9 | -51.2 | -50.4 | -49.4 | -48.4 |
| 1,cis-2-Dimethylcyclohexane | " | -28.95 | -41.15 | -41.20 | -44.3 | -46.7 | -48.4 | -49.6 | -50.2 | -50.5 | -50.4 | -50.0 | -49.4 | -48.6 | -47.4 | -46.9 |
| 1,trans-2-Dimethylcyclohexane | " | -30.91 | -43.02 | -43.07 | -46.1 | -48.4 | -50.1 | -51.2 | -51.9 | -52.0 | -51.9 | -51.5 | -50.9 | -50.1 | -49.2 | -48.2 |
| 1,cis-3-Dimethylcyclohexane[a] | " | -32.02 | -44.16 | -44.21 | -47.3 | -49.7 | -51.4 | -52.5 | -53.1 | -53.3 | -53.2 | -52.8 | -52.1 | -51.2 | -50.4 | -49.3 |
| 1,trans-3-Dimethylcyclohexane[b] | " | -30.06 | -42.20 | -42.25 | -45.3 | -47.7 | -49.5 | -50.7 | -51.3 | -51.6 | -51.6 | -51.2 | -50.6 | -49.9 | -49.1 | -48.1 |
| 1,cis-4-Dimethylcyclohexane | " | -30.08 | -42.22 | -42.27 | -45.4 | -47.7 | -49.5 | -50.7 | -51.4 | -51.7 | -51.6 | -51.2 | -50.6 | -49.9 | -49.1 | -48.2 |
| 1,trans-4-Dimethylcyclohexane | " | -31.99 | -44.12 | -44.17 | -47.2 | -49.6 | -51.3 | -52.3 | -53.0 | -53.2 | -53.0 | -52.6 | -51.9 | -51.2 | -50.3 | -49.3 |

[a] Formerly labeled "trans"; see footnote b of Table 7a.

[b] Formerly labeled "cis"; see footnote c of Table 7a.

TABLE 24w (PART 1) — NORMAL MONOOLEFINS (1-ALKENES), C$_2$ TO C$_{20}$

HEAT OF FORMATION, $\Delta Hf^\circ$, AT 0° TO 1500°K

November 30, 1945; April 30, 1946; December 31, 1952

Temperature in °K

Heat of Formation, $\Delta Hf^\circ$, in kcal/mole

| Compound (gas) | Formula | 0 | 298.16 | 300 | 400 | 500 | 600 | 700 | 800 | 900 | 1000 | 1100 | 1200 | 1300 | 1400 | 1500 |
|---|---|---|---|---|---|---|---|---|---|---|---|---|---|---|---|---|
| Ethene (Ethylene) | C$_2$H$_4$ | 14.522 | 12.496 | 12.482 | 11.766 | 11.138 | 10.600 | 10.142 | 9.760 | 9.448 | 9.205 | 9.02 | 8.88 | 8.76 | 8.67 | 8.61 |
| Propene (Propylene) | C$_3$H$_6$ | 8.468 | 4.879 | 4.858 | 3.758 | 2.793 | 1.98 | 1.30 | 0.76 | 0.34 | 0.03 | -0.18 | -0.32 | -0.42 | -0.47 | -0.48 |
| 1-Butene | C$_4$H$_8$ | 4.96 | -0.03 | -0.06 | -1.49 | -2.70 | -3.70 | -4.51 | -5.15 | -5.62 | -5.95 | -6.16 | -6.26 | -6.31 | -6.29 | -6.24 |
| 1-Pentene | C$_5$H$_{10}$ | 1.13 | -5.00 | -5.03 | -6.77 | -8.22 | -9.41 | -10.37 | -11.10 | -11.62 | -11.95 | -12.14 | -12.20 | -12.18 | -12.08 | -11.94 |
| 1-Hexene | C$_6$H$_{12}$ | -2.54 | -9.96 | -10.00 | -12.06 | -13.76 | -15.16 | -16.26 | -17.08 | -17.66 | -18.01 | -18.19 | -18.19 | -18.13 | -17.97 | -17.77 |
| 1-Heptene | C$_7$H$_{14}$ | -6.18 | -14.89 | -14.93 | -17.31 | -19.27 | -20.87 | -22.11 | -23.03 | -23.66 | -24.03 | -24.20 | -24.16 | -24.05 | -23.82 | -23.55 |
| 1-Octene | C$_8$H$_{16}$ | -9.83 | -19.82 | -19.86 | -22.56 | -24.77 | -26.58 | -27.97 | -28.98 | -29.66 | -30.05 | -30.21 | -30.13 | -29.96 | -29.68 | -29.33 |
| 1-Nonene | C$_9$H$_{18}$ | -13.47 | -24.74 | -24.80 | -27.82 | -30.28 | -32.28 | -33.82 | -34.92 | -35.67 | -36.07 | -36.22 | -36.09 | -35.88 | -35.53 | -35.11 |
| 1-Decene | C$_{10}$H$_{20}$ | -17.12 | -29.67 | -29.73 | -33.07 | -35.79 | -37.99 | -39.68 | -40.87 | -41.67 | -42.09 | -42.23 | -42.06 | -41.80 | -41.39 | -40.89 |
| 1-Undecene | C$_{11}$H$_{22}$ | -20.76 | -34.60 | -34.66 | -38.32 | -41.30 | -43.70 | -45.53 | -46.82 | -47.67 | -48.11 | -48.24 | -48.03 | -47.72 | -47.24 | -46.66 |
| 1-Dodecene | C$_{12}$H$_{24}$ | -24.40 | -39.52 | -39.59 | -43.57 | -46.80 | -49.41 | -51.38 | -52.77 | -53.67 | -54.13 | -54.24 | -54.00 | -53.63 | -53.09 | -52.44 |
| 1-Tridecene | C$_{13}$H$_{26}$ | -28.05 | -44.45 | -44.52 | -48.82 | -52.31 | -55.12 | -57.24 | -58.72 | -59.67 | -60.15 | -60.25 | -59.97 | -59.55 | -58.95 | -58.22 |
| 1-Tetradecene | C$_{14}$H$_{28}$ | -31.69 | -49.36 | -49.46 | -54.08 | -57.82 | -60.82 | -63.09 | -64.66 | -65.68 | -66.17 | -66.26 | -65.93 | -65.47 | -64.80 | -64.00 |
| 1-Pentadecene | C$_{15}$H$_{30}$ | -35.34 | -54.31 | -54.39 | -59.33 | -63.32 | -66.53 | -68.95 | -70.61 | -71.68 | -72.19 | -72.27 | -71.90 | -71.38 | -70.66 | -69.78 |
| 1-Hexadecene | C$_{16}$H$_{32}$ | -38.98 | -59.23 | -59.32 | -64.58 | -68.83 | -72.24 | -74.80 | -76.56 | -77.68 | -78.21 | -78.28 | -77.87 | -77.30 | -76.51 | -75.56 |
| 1-Heptadecene | C$_{17}$H$_{34}$ | -42.62 | -64.15 | -64.25 | -69.83 | -74.34 | -77.95 | -80.65 | -82.51 | -83.68 | -84.23 | -84.29 | -83.84 | -83.22 | -82.36 | -81.34 |
| 1-Octadecene | C$_{18}$H$_{36}$ | -46.27 | -69.08 | -69.18 | -75.08 | -79.84 | -83.66 | -86.51 | -88.46 | -89.68 | -90.25 | -90.30 | -89.81 | -89.13 | -88.22 | -87.12 |
| 1-Nonadecene | C$_{19}$H$_{38}$ | -49.91 | -74.00 | -74.12 | -80.34 | -85.35 | -89.36 | -92.36 | -94.40 | -95.69 | -96.27 | -96.31 | -95.77 | -95.05 | -94.07 | -92.90 |
| 1-Eicosene | C$_{20}$H$_{40}$ | -53.56 | -78.93 | -79.05 | -85.59 | -90.86 | -95.07 | -98.22 | -100.35 | -101.69 | -102.29 | -102.32 | -101.74 | -100.97 | -99.93 | -98.68 |
| Increment per CH$_2$ group, applicable beyond 1-hexene | | -3.644 | -4.926 | -4.992 | -5.252 | -5.507 | -5.708 | -5.854 | -5.948 | -6.002 | -6.020 | -6.009 | -5.968 | -5.917 | -5.854 | -5.779 |

TABLE 8w (PART 1) – MONOOLEFINS, C$_2$ TO C$_5$

HEAT OF FORMATION, $\Delta H_f^{\circ}$, AT 0° TO 1500°K

December 31, 1944; March 31, 1945; October 31, 1945; April 30, 1946; December 31, 1952

| Compound (gas) | Formula | Temperature in °K — Heat of Formation, $\Delta H_f^{\circ}$, in kcal/mole | | | | | | | | | | | | | |
|---|---|---|---|---|---|---|---|---|---|---|---|---|---|---|---|
| | | 0 | 298.16 | 300 | 400 | 500 | 600 | 700 | 800 | 900 | 1000 | 1100 | 1200 | 1300 | 1400 | 1500 |
| Ethene (Ethylene) | C$_2$H$_4$ | 14.522 | 12.496 | 12.482 | 11.766 | 11.138 | 10.600 | 10.142 | 9.760 | 9.448 | 9.205 | 9.02 | 8.88 | 8.76 | 8.67 | 8.61 |
| Propene (Propylene) | C$_3$H$_6$ | 8.468 | 4.879 | 4.858 | 3.758 | 2.793 | 1.98 | 1.30 | 0.76 | 0.34 | 0.03 | -0.18 | -0.32 | -0.42 | -0.47 | -0.48 |
| 1-Butene | C$_4$H$_8$ | 4.96 | -0.03 | -0.06 | -1.49 | -2.70 | -3.70 | -4.51 | -5.15 | -5.62 | -5.95 | -6.16 | -6.26 | -6.31 | -6.29 | -6.24 |
| cis-2-Butene | " | 3.48 | -1.67 | -1.70 | -3.31 | -4.68 | -5.82 | -6.75 | -7.48 | -8.05 | -8.45 | -8.71 | -8.86 | -8.95 | -8.97 | -8.93 |
| trans-2-Butene | " | 2.24 | -2.67 | -2.70 | -4.12 | -5.34 | -6.38 | -7.22 | -7.89 | -8.39 | -8.73 | -8.96 | -9.08 | -9.14 | -9.14 | -9.09 |
| 2-Methylpropene (Isobutene) | " | 0.98 | -4.04 | -4.07 | -5.44 | -6.61 | -7.58 | -8.39 | -9.01 | -9.49 | -9.82 | -10.01 | -10.10 | -10.14 | -10.12 | -10.05 |
| 1-Pentene | C$_5$H$_{10}$ | -1.13 | -5.00 | -5.03 | -6.77 | -8.22 | -9.41 | -10.37 | -11.10 | -11.62 | -11.95 | -12.14 | -12.20 | -12.18 | -12.08 | -11.94 |
| cis-2-Pentene | " | -0.18 | -6.71 | -6.75 | -8.65 | -10.24 | -11.53 | -12.56 | -13.36 | -13.95 | -14.33 | -14.58 | -14.67 | -14.69 | -14.63 | -14.50 |
| trans-2-Pentene | " | -1.25 | -7.59 | -7.62 | -9.40 | -10.90 | -12.19 | -13.15 | -13.93 | -14.50 | -14.87 | -15.10 | -15.21 | -15.23 | -15.17 | -15.05 |
| 2-Methyl-1-butene | " | -2.30 | -8.68 | -8.72 | -10.39 | -11.79 | -12.92 | -13.83 | -14.53 | -15.04 | -15.36 | -15.51 | -15.56 | -15.53 | -15.41 | -15.26 |
| 3-Methyl-1-butene | " | -0.68 | -6.92 | -6.95 | -8.47 | -9.72 | -10.75 | -11.58 | -12.22 | -12.67 | -12.94 | -13.08 | -13.08 | -13.02 | -12.92 | -12.77 |
| 2-Methyl-2-butene | " | -3.63 | -10.17 | -10.21 | -12.06 | -13.63 | -14.94 | -15.99 | -16.81 | -17.42 | -17.83 | -18.08 | -18.19 | -18.22 | -18.17 | -18.07 |

TABLE 8w (PART 2) — MONOOLEFINS, C$_6$
HEAT OF FORMATION, $\Delta H_f^0$, AT 0° TO 1500°K
April 30, 1945; October 31, 1945; December 31, 1952

| Compound (gas) | Formula | Temperature in °K | | | | | | | | | | | | | | | |
|---|---|---|---|---|---|---|---|---|---|---|---|---|---|---|---|---|---|
| | | Heat of Formation, $\Delta H_f^0$, in kcal/mole | | | | | | | | | | | | | | | |
| | | 0 | 298.16 | 300 | 400 | 500 | 600 | 700 | 800 | 900 | 1000 | 1100 | 1200 | 1300 | 1400 | 1500 |
| 1-Hexene | C$_6$H$_{12}$ | -2.54 | -9.96 | -10.00 | -12.06 | -13.76 | -15.16 | -16.26 | -17.08 | -17.66 | -18.01 | -18.19 | -18.19 | -18.13 | -17.97 | -17.77 |
| cis-2-Hexene | " | -3.89 | -11.56 | -11.60 | -13.8 | -15.6 | -17.1 | -18.3 | -19.2 | -19.8 | -20.2 | | | | | |
| trans-2-Hexene | " | -5.08 | -12.56 | -12.60 | -14.7 | -16.4 | -17.8 | -19.0 | -19.5 | -20.5 | -20.9 | | | | | |
| cis-3-Hexene | " | -3.66 | -11.56 | -11.61 | -13.8 | -15.7 | -17.1 | -18.3 | -19.2 | -19.8 | -20.2 | | | | | |
| trans-3-Hexene | " | -4.91 | -12.56 | -12.60 | -14.7 | -16.4 | -17.7 | -18.8 | -19.7 | -20.2 | -20.7 | | | | | |
| 2-Methyl-1-pentene | " | -6.04 | -13.56 | -13.60 | -15.6 | -17.2 | -18.6 | -19.6 | -20.4 | -21.0 | -21.3 | | | | | |
| 3-Methyl-1-pentene | " | -3.48 | -11.02 | -11.06 | -12.8 | -14.0 | -14.8 | -15.2 | -15.4 | -15.3 | -14.9 | | | | | |
| 4-Methyl-1-pentene | " | -3.49 | -11.66 | -11.71 | -13.9 | -15.8 | -17.2 | -18.4 | -19.4 | -20.0 | -20.5 | | | | | |
| 2-Methyl-2-pentene | " | -6.99 | -14.96 | -15.01 | -17.2 | -19.0 | -20.5 | -21.6 | -22.5 | -23.2 | -23.6 | | | | | |
| 3-Methyl-cis-2-pentene | " | -6.35 | -14.32 | -14.37 | -16.5 | -18.3 | -19.8 | -21.0 | -21.9 | -22.5 | -22.9 | | | | | |
| 3-Methyl-trans-2-pentene | " | -6.35 | -14.32 | -14.37 | -16.5 | -18.3 | -19.8 | -21.0 | -21.9 | -22.5 | -22.9 | | | | | |
| 4-Methyl-cis-2-pentene | " | -5.42 | -13.26 | -13.30 | -15.3 | -17.0 | -18.3 | -19.4 | -20.2 | -20.8 | -21.2 | | | | | |
| 4-Methyl-trans-2-pentene | " | -6.67 | -14.26 | -14.30 | -16.2 | -17.7 | -19.0 | -20.0 | -20.8 | -21.3 | -21.6 | | | | | |
| 2-Ethyl-1-butene | " | -5.17 | -12.92 | -12.96 | -15.0 | -16.6 | -17.9 | -19.0 | -19.7 | -20.3 | -20.6 | | | | | |
| 2,3-Dimethyl-1-butene | " | -7.10 | -14.78 | -14.82 | -16.6 | -18.1 | -19.3 | -20.2 | -21.0 | -21.5 | -21.8 | | | | | |
| 3,3-Dimethyl-1-butene | " | -5.82 | -14.25 | -14.30 | -16.5 | -18.2 | -19.7 | -20.9 | -21.7 | -22.5 | -22.9 | | | | | |
| 2,3-Dimethyl-2-butene | " | -7.96 | -15.91 | -15.96 | -18.1 | -20.0 | -21.5 | -22.8 | -23.7 | -24.4 | -24.8 | | | | | |

TABLE 11w (PART 1) — DIOLEFINS, $C_3$ TO $C_5$

HEAT OF FORMATION, $\Delta H f^\circ$, AT 0° TO 1500°K

October 31, 1947; April 30, 1948; December 31, 1952

Temperature in °K

Heat of Formation, $\Delta H f^\circ$, in kcal/mole

| Compound (gas) | Formula | 0 | 298.16 | 300 | 400 | 500 | 600 | 700 | 800 | 900 | 1000 | 1100 | 1200 | 1300 | 1400 | 1500 |
|---|---|---|---|---|---|---|---|---|---|---|---|---|---|---|---|---|
| Propadiene (Allene) | $C_3H_4$ | 47.70 | 45.92 | 45.91 | 45.35 | 44.85 | 44.42 | 44.03 | 43.71 | 43.44 | 43.23 | 43.06 | 42.94 | 42.84 | 42.75 | 42.68 |
| 1,2-Butadiene | $C_4H_6$ | 42.00 | 38.77 | 38.75 | 37.78 | 37.00 | 36.31 | 35.72 | 35.25 | 34.88 | 34.62 | 34.43 | 34.32 | 34.26 | 34.22 | 34.21 |
| 1,3-Butadiene | " | 29.78 | 26.33 | 25.41 | 25.38 | 24.70 | 24.11 | 23.63 | 23.25 | 22.95 | 22.75 | 22.62 | 22.54 | 22.49 | 22.47 | 22.47 |
| 1,2-Pentadiene | $C_5H_8$ | 39.32 | 34.80 | 34.79 | 33.61 | 32.72 | 31.82 | 31.21 | 30.68 | 30.28 | 30.09 | 29.96 | 29.84 | 29.93 | 29.96 | 30.03 |
| 1,cis-3-Pentadiene (cis-Piperylene) | " | 23.73 | 18.70 | 18.69 | 17.29 | 16.16 | 15.27 | 14.49 | 13.97 | 13.52 | 13.19 | 13.04 | 12.93 | 12.91 | 12.97 | 12.93 |
| 1,trans-3-Pentadiene (trans-Piperylene) | " | 23.39 | 18.60 | 18.59 | 17.39 | 16.42 | 15.59 | 14.92 | 14.43 | 14.08 | 13.85 | 13.69 | 13.67 | 13.61 | 13.61 | 13.64 |
| 1,4-Pentadiene | " | 29.63 | 25.20 | 25.19 | 24.04 | 23.01 | 22.25 | 21.59 | 21.00 | 20.59 | 20.40 | 20.27 | 20.15 | 20.24 | 20.27 | 20.34 |
| 2,3-Pentadiene | " | 37.77 | 33.10 | 33.09 | 31.78 | 30.65 | 29.67 | 28.76 | 28.25 | 27.83 | 27.54 | 27.30 | 27.21 | 27.21 | 27.15 | 27.28 |
| 3-Methyl-1,2-butadiene | " | 35.64 | 31.00 | 30.96 | 29.76 | 28.72 | 27.90 | 27.18 | 26.60 | 26.15 | 25.91 | 25.72 | 25.68 | 25.73 | 25.72 | 25.74 |
| 2-Methyl-1,3-butadiene (Isoprene) | " | 22.98 | 18.10 | 18.09 | 16.90 | 16.01 | 15.24 | 14.66 | 14.18 | 13.85 | 13.54 | 13.50 | 13.50 | 13.46 | 13.48 | 13.53 |

TABLE 18w – ALKYL CYCLOPENTENES, C$_5$ TO C$_7$
HEAT OF FORMATION, $\Delta H_f^\circ$, AT 0° TO 1500°K
December 31, 1952

Temperature in °K

Heat of Formation, $\Delta H_f^\circ$, in kcal/mole

| Compound (gas) | Formula | 0 | 298.16 | 300 | 400 | 500 | 600 | 700 | 800 | 900 | 1000 | 1100 | 1200 | 1300 | 1400 | 1500 |
|---|---|---|---|---|---|---|---|---|---|---|---|---|---|---|---|---|
| Cyclopentene | C$_5$H$_8$ | 13.76 | 7.87 | 7.83 | 5.97 | 4.43 | 3.20 | 2.22 | 1.49 | 0.96 | 0.62 | 0.42 | 0.36 | 0.36 | 0.44 | 0.56 |
| 1-Methylcyclopentene | C$_6$H$_{10}$ | | | | | | | | | | | | | | | |
| 3-Methylcyclopentene | " | | | | | | | | | | | | | | | |
| 4-Methylcyclopentene | " | | | | | | | | | | | | | | | |
| 1-Ethylcyclopentene | C$_7$H$_{12}$ | | | | | | | | | | | | | | | |
| 3-Ethylcyclopentene | " | | | | | | | | | | | | | | | |
| 4-Ethylcyclopentene | " | | | | | | | | | | | | | | | |
| 1,2-Dimethylcyclopentene | " | | | | | | | | | | | | | | | |
| 1,3-Dimethylcyclopentene | " | | | | | | | | | | | | | | | |
| 1,4-Dimethylcyclopentene | " | | | | | | | | | | | | | | | |
| 1,5-Dimethylcyclopentene | " | | | | | | | | | | | | | | | |
| 3,3-Dimethylcyclopentene | " | | | | | | | | | | | | | | | |
| 3,cis-4-Dimethylcyclopentene | " | | | | | | | | | | | | | | | |
| 3,trans-4-Dimethylcyclopentene | " | | | | | | | | | | | | | | | |
| 3,cis-5-Dimethylcyclopentene | " | | | | | | | | | | | | | | | |
| 3,trans-5-Dimethylcyclopentene | " | | | | | | | | | | | | | | | |
| 4,4-Dimethylcyclopentene | " | | | | | | | | | | | | | | | |

TABLE 19w – ALKYL CYCLOHEXENES, $C_6$ TO $C_8$

HEAT OF FORMATION, $\Delta H_f^\circ$, AT $0^\circ$ TO $1500^\circ K$

December 31, 1952

Heat of Formation, $\Delta H_f^\circ$, in kcal/mole

| Compound (gas) | Formula | \multicolumn{15}{c}{Temperature in $^\circ K$} |
|---|---|---|
| | | 0 | 298.16 | 300 | 400 | 500 | 600 | 700 | 800 | 900 | 1000 | 1100 | 1200 | 1300 | 1400 | 1500 |
| Cyclohexene | $C_6H_{10}$ | 5.76 | -1.70 | -1.74 | -3.70 | -5.21 | -6.36 | -7.18 | -7.74 | -8.08 | -8.19 | -8.15 | -7.95 | -7.70 | -7.37 | -6.96 |
| 1-Methylcyclohexene | $C_7H_{12}$ | | | | | | | | | | | | | | | |
| 3-Methylcyclohexene | " | | | | | | | | | | | | | | | |
| 4-Methylcyclohexene | " | | | | | | | | | | | | | | | |
| 1-Ethylcyclohexene | $C_8H_{14}$ | | | | | | | | | | | | | | | |
| 3-Ethylcyclohexene | " | | | | | | | | | | | | | | | |
| 4-Ethylcyclohexene | " | | | | | | | | | | | | | | | |
| 1,2-Dimethylcyclohexene | " | | | | | | | | | | | | | | | |
| 1,3-Dimethylcyclohexene | " | | | | | | | | | | | | | | | |
| 1,4-Dimethylcyclohexene | " | | | | | | | | | | | | | | | |
| 1,5-Dimethylcyclohexene | " | | | | | | | | | | | | | | | |
| 1,6-Dimethylcyclohexene | " | | | | | | | | | | | | | | | |
| 3,3-Dimethylcyclohexene | " | | | | | | | | | | | | | | | |
| 3,cis-4-Dimethylcyclohexene | " | | | | | | | | | | | | | | | |
| 3,trans-4-Dimethylcyclohexene | " | | | | | | | | | | | | | | | |
| 3,cis-5-Dimethylcyclohexene | " | | | | | | | | | | | | | | | |
| 3,trans-5-Dimethylcyclohexene | " | | | | | | | | | | | | | | | |
| 3,cis-6-Dimethylcyclohexene | " | | | | | | | | | | | | | | | |
| 3,trans-6-Dimethylcyclohexene | " | | | | | | | | | | | | | | | |
| 4,4-Dimethylcyclohexene | " | | | | | | | | | | | | | | | |
| 4,cis-5-Dimethylcyclohexene | " | | | | | | | | | | | | | | | |
| 4,trans-5-Dimethylcyclohexene | " | | | | | | | | | | | | | | | |

TABLE 25w (PART 1) — NORMAL ACETYLENES (1-ALKYNES), $C_2$ TO $C_{20}$

HEAT OF FORMATION, $\Delta H_f^\circ$, AT 0° TO 1500°K

February 28, 1946; December 31, 1952

Heat of Formation, $\Delta H_f^\circ$, in kcal/mole

| Compound (gas) | Formula | Temperature in °K | | | | | | | | | | | | | | |
|---|---|---|---|---|---|---|---|---|---|---|---|---|---|---|---|---|
| | | 0 | 298.16 | 300 | 400 | 500 | 600 | 700 | 800 | 900 | 1000 | 1100 | 1200 | 1300 | 1400 | 1500 |
| Ethyne (Acetylene) | $C_2H_2$ | 54.329 | 54.194 | 54.193 | 54.134 | 54.049 | 53.931 | 53.787 | 53.627 | 53.462 | 53.304 | 53.151 | 53.003 | 52.851 | 52.698 | 52.548 |
| Propyne (Methylacetylene) | $C_3H_4$ | 46.017 | 44.319 | 44.309 | 43.775 | 43.280 | 42.829 | 42.423 | 42.069 | 41.769 | 41.53 | 41.34 | 41.19 | 41.06 | 40.95 | 40.86 |
| 1-Butyne (Ethylacetylene) | $C_4H_6$ | 42.74 | 39.48 | 39.46 | 38.57 | 37.78 | 37.10 | 36.52 | 36.04 | 35.66 | 35.38 | 35.17 | 35.05 | 34.95 | 34.90 | 34.86 |
| 1-Pentyne | $C_5H_8$ | 38.90 | 34.50 | 34.47 | 33.28 | 32.24 | 31.37 | 30.66 | 30.09 | 29.66 | 29.36 | 29.18 | 29.10 | 29.08 | 29.11 | 29.13 |
| 1-Hexyne | $C_6H_{10}$ | 35.26 | 29.55 | 29.54 | 28.03 | 26.73 | 25.66 | 24.81 | 24.14 | 23.66 | 23.34 | 23.17 | 23.13 | 23.16 | 23.26 | 23.35 |
| 1-Heptyne | $C_7H_{12}$ | 31.61 | 24.62 | 24.61 | 22.78 | 21.23 | 19.95 | 18.95 | 18.19 | 17.66 | 17.32 | 17.16 | 17.16 | 17.25 | 17.40 | 17.57 |
| 1-Octyne | $C_8H_{14}$ | 27.97 | 19.70 | 19.67 | 17.52 | 15.72 | 14.25 | 13.10 | 12.25 | 11.65 | 11.30 | 11.15 | 11.20 | 11.33 | 11.55 | 11.79 |
| 1-Nonyne | $C_9H_{16}$ | 24.32 | 14.77 | 14.74 | 12.27 | 10.21 | 8.54 | 7.24 | 6.30 | 5.65 | 5.28 | 5.14 | 5.23 | 5.41 | 5.69 | 6.01 |
| 1-Decyne | $C_{10}H_{18}$ | 20.68 | 9.85 | 9.81 | 7.02 | 4.70 | 2.83 | 1.39 | 0.35 | −0.35 | −0.74 | −0.86 | −0.74 | −0.50 | −0.16 | + 0.24 |
| 1-Undecyne | $C_{11}H_{20}$ | 17.04 | 4.92 | 4.88 | 1.77 | −0.80 | −2.88 | −4.46 | −5.60 | −6.35 | −6.76 | −6.87 | −6.71 | −6.42 | −6.01 | −5.54 |
| 1-Dodecyne | $C_{12}H_{22}$ | 13.39 | −0.01 | −0.05 | −3.48 | −6.31 | −8.59 | −10.32 | −11.55 | −12.35 | −12.78 | −12.88 | −12.67 | −12.34 | −11.87 | −11.32 |
| 1-Tridecyne | $C_{13}H_{24}$ | 9.75 | −4.93 | −4.99 | −8.74 | −11.82 | −14.29 | −16.17 | −17.49 | −18.36 | −18.80 | −18.89 | −18.64 | −18.26 | −17.72 | −17.10 |
| 1-Tetradecyne | $C_{14}H_{26}$ | 6.10 | −9.86 | −9.92 | −13.99 | −17.32 | −20.00 | −22.03 | −23.44 | −24.36 | −24.82 | −24.90 | −24.61 | −24.17 | −23.58 | −22.88 |
| 1-Pentadecyne | $C_{15}H_{28}$ | 2.46 | −14.78 | −14.85 | −19.24 | −22.83 | −25.71 | −27.88 | −29.39 | −30.36 | −30.84 | −30.91 | −30.58 | −30.09 | −29.43 | −28.66 |
| 1-Hexadecyne | $C_{16}H_{30}$ | −1.18 | −19.71 | −19.78 | −24.49 | −28.34 | −31.42 | −33.73 | −35.34 | −36.36 | −36.86 | −36.92 | −36.55 | −36.01 | −35.28 | −34.44 |
| 1-Heptadecyne | $C_{17}H_{32}$ | −4.83 | −24.64 | −24.71 | −29.74 | −33.84 | −37.13 | −39.59 | −41.29 | −42.36 | −42.88 | −42.93 | −42.51 | −41.92 | −41.14 | −40.22 |
| 1-Octadecyne | $C_{18}H_{34}$ | −8.47 | −29.56 | −29.65 | −35.00 | −39.35 | −42.83 | −45.44 | −47.23 | −48.37 | −48.90 | −48.94 | −48.48 | −47.84 | −46.99 | −46.00 |
| 1-Nonadecyne | $C_{19}H_{36}$ | −12.12 | −34.49 | −34.59 | −40.25 | −44.86 | −48.54 | −51.30 | −53.18 | −54.37 | −54.92 | −54.95 | −54.45 | −53.76 | −52.85 | −51.78 |
| 1-Eicosyne | $C_{20}H_{38}$ | −15.76 | −39.41 | −39.51 | −45.50 | −50.36 | −54.25 | −57.15 | −59.13 | −60.37 | −60.94 | −60.96 | −60.42 | −59.68 | −58.70 | −57.56 |
| Increment per $CH_2$ group, applicable beyond 1-pentyne | | −3.644 | −4.926 | −4.932 | −5.252 | −5.507 | −5.708 | −5.854 | −5.948 | −6.002 | −6.020 | −6.009 | −5.968 | −5.917 | −5.854 | −5.779 |

TABLE 12w — ACETYLENES, $C_2$ TO $C_5$
HEAT OF FORMATION, $\Delta H_f^{\circ}$, AT 0° TO 1500°K
April 30, 1945; December 31, 1952

Heat of Formation, $\Delta H_f^{\circ}$, in kcal/mole

| Compound (gas) | Formula | Temperature in °K | | | | | | | | | | | | | | |
|---|---|---|---|---|---|---|---|---|---|---|---|---|---|---|---|---|
| | | 0 | 298.16 | 300 | 400 | 500 | 600 | 700 | 800 | 900 | 1000 | 1100 | 1200 | 1300 | 1400 | 1500 |
| Ethyne (Acetylene) | $C_2H_2$ | 54.329 | 54.194 | 54.193 | 54.134 | 54.049 | 53.931 | 53.787 | 53.627 | 53.462 | 53.304 | 53.151 | 53.003 | 52.851 | 52.698 | 52.548 |
| Propyne (Methylacetylene) | $C_3H_4$ | 46.017 | 44.319 | 44.309 | 43.775 | 43.280 | 42.829 | 42.423 | 42.069 | 41.769 | 41.53 | 41.34 | 41.19 | 41.06 | 40.95 | 40.86 |
| 1-Butyne (Ethylacetylene) | $C_4H_6$ | 42.74 | 39.48 | 39.46 | 38.57 | 37.78 | 37.10 | 36.52 | 36.04 | 35.66 | 35.38 | 35.17 | 35.05 | 34.95 | 34.90 | 34.86 |
| 2-Butyne (Dimethylacetylene) | " | 38.09 | 34.97 | 34.96 | 33.95 | 33.03 | 32.23 | 31.55 | 30.98 | 30.52 | 30.19 | 29.93 | 29.77 | 29.63 | 29.55 | 29.49 |
| 1-Pentyne | $C_5H_8$ | 38.90 | 34.50 | 34.47 | 33.28 | 32.24 | 31.37 | 30.66 | 30.09 | 29.66 | 29.36 | 29.18 | 29.10 | 29.08 | 29.11 | 29.13 |
| 2-Pentyne | " | 35.48 | 30.80 | 30.77 | 29.41 | 28.20 | 27.17 | 26.30 | 25.62 | 25.07 | 24.69 | 24.44 | 24.28 | 24.19 | 24.16 | 24.17 |
| 3-Methyl-1-butyne | " | 37.37 | 32.60 | 32.57 | 31.37 | 30.37 | 29.55 | 28.84 | 28.30 | 27.89 | 27.60 | 27.44 | 27.37 | 27.36 | 27.37 | 27.38 |

TABLE 21w (PART 1) - NORMAL ALKYL BENZENES, $C_6$ TO $C_{22}$
HEAT OF FORMATION, $\Delta H_f°$, AT 0° TO 1500°K
November 30, 1945; December 31, 1952

| Compound (gas) | Formula | Temperature in °K | | | | | | | | | | | | | | |
|---|---|---|---|---|---|---|---|---|---|---|---|---|---|---|---|---|
| | | Heat of Formation, $\Delta H_f°$, in kcal/mole | | | | | | | | | | | | | | |
| | | 0 | 298.16 | 300 | 400 | 500 | 600 | 700 | 800 | 900 | 1000 | 1100 | 1200 | 1300 | 1400 | 1500 |
| Benzene | $C_6H_6$ | 24.000 | 19.820 | 19.796 | 18.554 | 17.536 | 16.711 | 16.040 | 15.510 | 15.100 | 14.818 | 14.63 | 14.52 | 14.45 | 14.41 | 14.39 |
| Methylbenzene (Toluene) | $C_7H_8$ | 17.500 | 11.950 | 11.919 | 10.327 | 9.005 | 7.932 | 7.067 | 6.399 | 5.895 | 5.564 | 5.36 | 5.27 | 5.22 | 5.23 | 5.27 |
| Ethylbenzene | $C_8H_{10}$ | 13.917 | 7.120 | 7.083 | 5.218 | 3.699 | 2.488 | 1.529 | 0.798 | 0.266 | -0.061 | -0.23 | -0.28 | -0.26 | -0.18 | -0.05 |
| n-Propylbenzene | $C_9H_{12}$ | 9.810 | 1.870 | 1.827 | -0.34 | -2.43 | -3.51 | -4.60 | -5.42 | -6.01 | -6.3 | -6.5 | -6.8 | -6.4 | -6.2 | -6.0 |
| n-Butylbenzene | $C_{10}H_{14}$ | 5.93 | -3.30 | -3.35 | -5.84 | -7.86 | -9.46 | -10.70 | -11.62 | -12.26 | -12.6 | -12.8 | -12.7 | -12.6 | -12.4 | -12.1 |
| n-Pentylbenzene | $C_{11}H_{16}$ | 2.28 | -8.23 | -8.28 | -11.10 | -13.37 | -15.17 | -16.56 | -17.57 | -18.26 | -18.6 | -18.8 | -18.7 | -18.5 | -18.2 | -17.8 |
| n-Hexylbenzene | $C_{12}H_{18}$ | -1.36 | -13.15 | -13.21 | -16.35 | -18.88 | -20.88 | -22.41 | -23.52 | -24.26 | -24.6 | -24.8 | -24.7 | -24.4 | -24.0 | -23.6 |
| n-Heptylbenzene | $C_{13}H_{20}$ | -5.01 | -18.08 | -18.14 | -21.60 | -24.38 | -26.59 | -28.27 | -29.47 | -30.26 | -30.6 | -30.8 | -30.6 | -30.3 | -29.9 | -29.4 |
| n-Octylbenzene | $C_{14}H_{22}$ | -8.65 | -23.00 | -23.08 | -26.86 | -29.89 | -32.29 | -34.12 | -35.41 | -36.27 | -36.7 | -36.8 | -36.6 | -36.3 | -35.8 | -35.1 |
| n-Nonylbenzene | $C_{15}H_{24}$ | -12.30 | -27.93 | -28.01 | -32.11 | -35.40 | -38.00 | -39.98 | -41.36 | -42.27 | -42.7 | -42.8 | -42.6 | -42.2 | -41.6 | -40.9 |
| n-Decylbenzene | $C_{16}H_{26}$ | -15.94 | -32.86 | -32.94 | -37.36 | -40.90 | -43.71 | -45.83 | -47.31 | -48.27 | -48.7 | -48.8 | -48.6 | -48.1 | -47.4 | -46.7 |
| n-Undecylbenzene | $C_{17}H_{28}$ | -19.58 | -37.78 | -37.87 | -42.61 | -46.41 | -49.42 | -51.68 | -53.26 | -54.27 | -54.7 | -54.9 | -54.5 | -54.0 | -53.3 | -52.5 |
| n-Dodecylbenzene | $C_{18}H_{30}$ | -23.23 | -42.71 | -42.80 | -47.86 | -51.92 | -55.13 | -57.54 | -59.21 | -60.27 | -60.7 | -60.9 | -60.5 | -59.9 | -59.2 | -58.3 |
| n-Tridecylbenzene | $C_{19}H_{32}$ | -26.87 | -47.63 | -47.74 | -53.12 | -57.43 | -60.83 | -63.39 | -65.15 | -66.28 | -66.8 | -66.9 | -66.5 | -65.9 | -65.0 | -64.0 |
| n-Tetradecylbenzene | $C_{20}H_{34}$ | -30.52 | -52.56 | -52.67 | -58.37 | -62.93 | -66.54 | -69.25 | -71.10 | -72.28 | -72.8 | -72.9 | -72.4 | -71.8 | -70.8 | -69.8 |
| n-Pentadecylbenzene | $C_{21}H_{36}$ | -34.15 | -57.49 | -57.60 | -63.62 | -68.44 | -72.25 | -75.10 | -77.05 | -78.28 | -78.8 | -78.9 | -78.4 | -77.7 | -76.7 | -75.6 |
| n-Hexadecylbenzene | $C_{22}H_{38}$ | -37.80 | -62.41 | -62.53 | -68.87 | -73.95 | -77.96 | -80.95 | -83.00 | -84.28 | -84.8 | -84.9 | -84.4 | -83.6 | -82.6 | -81.4 |
| Increment per $CH_2$ group, applicable beyond n-pentylbenzene | | -3.644 | -4.926 | -4.932 | -5.252 | -5.507 | -5.708 | -5.854 | -5.948 | -6.002 | -6.02 | -6.01 | -5.97 | -5.92 | -5.85 | -5.78 |

## TABLE 5w – ALKYL BENZENES, $C_6$ TO $C_9$
## HEAT OF FORMATION, $\Delta H_f^{\,0}$, AT 0° TO 1500°K
November 30, 1945

Temperature in °K — Heat of Formation, $\Delta H_f^{\,0}$, in kcal/mole

| Compound (gas) | Formula | 0 | 298.16 | 300 | 400 | 500 | 600 | 700 | 800 | 900 | 1000 | 1100 | 1200 | 1300 | 1400 | 1500 |
|---|---|---|---|---|---|---|---|---|---|---|---|---|---|---|---|---|
| Benzene | $C_6H_6$ | 24.000 | 19.820 | 19.796 | 18.554 | 17.536 | 16.711 | 16.040 | 15.510 | 15.100 | 14.818 | 14.63 | 14.52 | 14.45 | 14.41 | 14.39 |
| Methylbenzene (Toluene) | $C_7H_8$ | 17.500 | 11.950 | 11.919 | 10.327 | 9.005 | 7.932 | 7.067 | 6.399 | 5.895 | 5.564 | 5.36 | 5.27 | 5.22 | 5.23 | 5.27 |
| Ethylbenzene | $C_8H_{10}$ | 13.917 | 7.120 | 7.083 | 5.218 | 3.699 | 2.488 | 1.529 | 0.798 | 0.266 | -0.061 | -0.23 | -0.28 | -0.26 | -0.18 | -0.05 |
| 1,2-Dimethylbenzene (o-Xylene) | " | 11.096 | 4.540 | 4.506 | 2.711 | 1.189 | -0.062 | -1.076 | -1.858 | -2.434 | -2.799 | -3.01 | -3.08 | -3.09 | -3.04 | -2.92 |
| 1,3-Dimethylbenzene (m-Xylene) | " | 10.926 | 4.120 | 4.083 | 2.175 | 0.571 | -0.738 | -1.792 | -2.598 | -3.191 | -3.567 | -3.78 | -3.86 | -3.88 | -3.84 | -3.73 |
| 1,4-Dimethylbenzene (p-Xylene) | " | 11.064 | 4.290 | 4.253 | 2.317 | 0.680 | -0.665 | -1.751 | -2.586 | -3.207 | -3.607 | -3.84 | -3.94 | -3.97 | -3.94 | -3.84 |
| n-Propylbenzene | $C_9H_{12}$ | 9.810 | 1.870 | 1.827 | -0.31 | -2.06 | -3.44 | -4.52 | -5.34 | -5.95 | -6.30 | -6.5 | -6.5 | -6.4 | -6.2 | -6.0 |
| Isopropylbenzene | " | 9.250 | 0.940 | 0.895 | -1.28 | -3.01 | -4.37 | -5.44 | -6.24 | -6.80 | -7.13 | -7.3 | -7.2 | -7.2 | -7.0 | -6.8 |
| 1-Methyl-2-ethylbenzene | " | 8.092 | 0.290 | 0.250 | -1.82 | -3.54 | -4.93 | -6.03 | -6.88 | -7.48 | -7.84 | -8.0 | -8.0 | -8.0 | -7.9 | -7.7 |
| 1-Methyl-3-ethylbenzene | " | 7.593 | -0.460 | -0.503 | -2.68 | -4.49 | -5.93 | -7.08 | -7.95 | -8.57 | -8.94 | -9.1 | -9.2 | -9.1 | -9.0 | -8.8 |
| 1-Methyl-4-ethylbenzene | " | 7.241 | -0.780 | -0.823 | -3.03 | -4.87 | -6.35 | -7.53 | -8.43 | -9.08 | -9.47 | -9.7 | -9.7 | -9.7 | -9.6 | -9.4 |
| 1,2,3-Trimethylbenzene | " | 5.527 | -2.290 | -2.332 | -4.57 | -6.46 | -8.04 | -9.31 | -10.30 | -11.04 | -11.51 | -11.8 | -11.9 | -11.9 | -11.8 | -11.7 |
| 1,2,4-Trimethylbenzene | " | 4.468 | -3.330 | -3.372 | -5.59 | -7.46 | -9.02 | -10.28 | -11.26 | -11.98 | -12.45 | -12.7 | -12.8 | -12.8 | -12.7 | -12.6 |
| 1,3,5-Trimethylbenzene | " | 4.241 | -3.840 | -3.883 | -6.183 | -8.107 | -9.691 | -10.960 | -11.930 | -12.643 | -13.094 | -13.34 | -13.42 | -13.42 | -13.33 | -13.18 |

## TABLE 13w - STYRENES, $C_8$ and $C_9$

### HEAT OF FORMATION, $\Delta H_f^\circ$, FOR THE IDEAL GAS STATE, AT 0° TO 1500°K

September 30, 1947

Heat of Formation, $\Delta H_f^\circ$, in Kcal/mole

| Compound (gas) | Formula | Temperature in °K | | | | | | | | | | | | | | |
|---|---|---|---|---|---|---|---|---|---|---|---|---|---|---|---|---|
| | | 0 | 298.16 | 300 | 400 | 500 | 600 | 700 | 800 | 900 | 1000 | 1100 | 1200 | 1300 | 1400 | 1500 |
| Ethenylbenzene (Styrene; Vinylbenzene; Phenylethylene) | $C_8H_8$ | 40.34 | 35.22 | 35.19 | 33.83 | 32.72 | 31.81 | 31.08 | 30.51 | 30.09 | 29.83 | 29.69 | 29.65 | 29.61 | 29.63 | 29.68 |
| Isopropenylbenzene (α-Methylstyrene; 2-Phenyl-1-propene) | $C_9H_{10}$ | 33.33 | 27.00 | 26.94 | 25.23 | 23.80 | 22.66 | 21.73 | 20.99 | 20.45 | 20.13 | 19.93 | 19.90 | 19.88 | 19.95 | 19.93 |
| cis-1-Propenylbenzene (cis-β-Methylstyrene; cis-1-Phenyl-1-propene) | " | 35.33 | 29.00 | 28.94 | 27.23 | 25.80 | 24.66 | 23.73 | 22.99 | 22.45 | 22.13 | 21.93 | 21.90 | 21.83 | 21.95 | 21.93 |
| trans-1-Propenylbenzene (trans-β-Methylstyrene; trans-1-Phenyl-1-propene) | " | 34.45 | 28.00 | 27.97 | 26.31 | 24.92 | 23.78 | 22.92 | 22.19 | 21.66 | 21.45 | 21.27 | 21.26 | 21.21 | 21.35 | 21.35 |
| 1-Methyl-2-ethenylbenzene (o-Methylstyrene) | " | 34.63 | 28.30 | 28.24 | 26.53 | 25.10 | 23.96 | 23.03 | 22.29 | 21.75 | 21.43 | 21.23 | 21.20 | 21.13 | 21.25 | 21.23 |
| 1-Methyl-3-ethenylbenzene (m-Methylstyrene) | " | 33.93 | 27.60 | 27.54 | 25.83 | 24.40 | 23.26 | 22.33 | 21.59 | 21.05 | 20.73 | 20.53 | 20.50 | 20.43 | 20.55 | 20.53 |
| 1-Methyl-4-ethenylbenzene (p-Methylstyrene) | " | 33.73 | 27.40 | 27.34 | 25.63 | 24.20 | 23.06 | 22.13 | 21.39 | 20.85 | 20.53 | 20.33 | 20.30 | 20.23 | 20.35 | 20.33 |

Table 00x – O, H, N, C

FREE ENERGY OF FORMATION, $\Delta F_f{}^\circ$, AT 0° TO 5000°K

June 30, 1946: April 30, 1948: August 31, 1949

| Compound (gas, monatomic) | Formula | Temperature in °K |||||||||||||||
|---|---|---|---|---|---|---|---|---|---|---|---|---|---|---|---|---|
| | | Free Energy of Formation, $\Delta F_f{}^\circ$, in kcal/mole |||||||||||||||
| | | 0 | 298.16 | 300 | 400 | 500 | 600 | 700 | 800 | 900 | 1000 | 1100 | 1200 | 1300 | 1400 | 1500 |
| Oxygen | O | 58.586 | 54.994 | 54.969 | 53.547 | 52.085 | 50.596 | 49.085 | 47.561 | 46.023 | 44.476 | 42.919 | 41.356 | 39.788 | 38.215 | 36.634 |
| Hydrogen | H | 51.620 | 48.575 | 48.553 | 47.351 | 46.111 | 44.842 | 43.548 | 42.232 | 40.900 | 39.552 | 38.190 | 36.817 | 35.432 | 34.038 | 32.636 |
| Nitrogen | N | 85.120 | 81.471 | 81.446 | 80.050 | 78.616 | 77.154 | 75.668 | 74.164 | 72.646 | 71.114 | 69.571 | 68.020 | 66.461 | 64.895 | 63.324 |
| Carbon | C | 170.39 | 160.845 | 160.778 | 157.096 | 153.360 | 149.593 | 145.810 | 142.019 | 138.225 | 134.431 | 130.638 | 126.850 | 123.063 | 119.281 | 115.503 |

| Compound (gas, monatomic) | Formula | Temperature in °K ||||||||||||
|---|---|---|---|---|---|---|---|---|---|---|---|---|---|---|
| | | Free Energy of Formation, $\Delta F_f{}^\circ$, in kcal/mole ||||||||||||
| | | 1000 | 1250 | 1500 | 1750 | 2000 | 2250 | 2500 | 2750 | 3000 | 3500 | 4000 | 4500 | 5000 |
| Oxygen | O | 44.476 | 40.572 | 36.634 | 32.667 | 28.686 | 24.678 | 20.677 | 16.660 | 12.635 | 4.574 | -3.498 | -11.583 | -19.669 |
| Hydrogen | H | 39.552 | 36.124 | 32.636 | 29.100 | 25.529 | 21.928 | 18.308 | 14.670 | 11.014 | 3.670 | -3.702 | -11.101 | -18.523 |
| Nitrogen | N | 71.114 | 67.242 | 63.324 | 59.373 | 55.394 | 51.395 | 47.378 | 43.345 | 39.299 | 31.172 | 23.003 | 14.788 | 6.521 |
| Carbon | C | 134.431 | 124.955 | 115.503 | 106.09 | 96.70 | 87.36 | 78.02 | 68.75 | 59.49 | 41.02 | 22.68 | | |

TABLE 0x – $O_2$, $H_2$, OH, $H_2O$, $N_2$, NO, C, CO, $CO_2$
FREE ENERGY OF FORMATION, $\Delta F_f^\circ$, AT 0° TO 5000°K
July 31, 1944; August 31, 1946; June 30, 1949

Temperature in °K

Free Energy of Formation, $\Delta F_f^\circ$, in kcal/mole

| Compound | Formula | State | 0 | 50 | 100 | 150 | 200 | 250 | 298.16 | 300 | 400 | 500 | 600 | 700 | 800 | 900 | 1000 |
|---|---|---|---|---|---|---|---|---|---|---|---|---|---|---|---|---|---|
| Oxygen | $O_2$ | gas | 0 | 0 | 0 | 0 | 0 | 0 | 0 | 0 | 0 | 0 | 0 | 0 | 0 | 0 | 0 |
| Hydrogen | $H_2$ | gas | 0 | 0 | 0 | 0 | 0 | 0 | 0 | 0 | 0 | 0 | 0 | 0 | 0 | 0 | 0 |
| Hydroxyl | OH | gas. | 10.0 | | | | | | 8.93 | 8.928 | 8.546 | 8.165 | 7.789 | 7.416 | 7.049 | 6.669 | 6.333 |
| Water | $H_2O$ | gas | -57.107 | | | | | | -54.6351 | -54.6159 | -53.518 | -52.360 | -51.154 | -49.913 | -48.643 | -47.347 | -46.030 |
| Nitrogen | $N_2$ | gas | 0 | 0 | 0 | 0 | | 0 | 0 | 0 | 0 | 0 | 0 | 0 | 0 | 0 | 0 |
| Nitric Oxide | NO | gas | 21.477 | | 21.278 | | 21.008 | 20.864 | 20.719 | 20.714 | 20.418 | 20.120 | 19.820 | 19.517 | 19.218 | 18.917 | 18.614 |
| Carbon | C | solid graphite | 0 | 0 | 0 | 0 | | 0 | 0 | 0 | 0 | 0 | 0 | 0 | 0 | 0 | 0 |
| Carbon Monoxide | CO | gas | -27.2019 | | -28.7464 | | -30.7342 | -31.7819 | -32.8079 | -32.8464 | -35.007 | -37.184 | -39.358 | -41.526 | -43.677 | -45.816 | -47.942 |
| Carbon Dioxide | $CO_2$ | gas | -93.9686 | | | | | | -94.2598 | -94.2603 | -94.325 | -94.392 | -94.444 | -94.496 | -94.539 | -94.578 | -94.610 |

Temperature in °K

Free Energy of Formation, $\Delta F_f^\circ$, in kcal/mole

| Compound | Formula | State | 1100 | 1200 | 1300 | 1400 | 1500 | 1750 | 2000 | 2250 | 2500 | 2750 | 3000 | 3500 | 4000 | 4500 | 5000 |
|---|---|---|---|---|---|---|---|---|---|---|---|---|---|---|---|---|---|
| Oxygen | $O_2$ | gas | 0 | 0 | 0 | 0 | 0 | 0 | 0 | 0 | 0 | 0 | 0 | 0 | 0 | 0 | 0 |
| Hydrogen | $H_2$ | gas | 0 | 0 | 0 | 0 | 0 | 0 | 0 | 0 | 0 | 0 | 0 | 0 | 0 | 0 | 0 |
| Hydroxyl | OH | gas | 5.980 | 5.629 | 5.285 | 4.947 | 4.606 | 3.771 | 2.945 | 2.128 | 1.321 | 0.521 | -0.278 | -1.849 | -3.388 | -4.913 | -6.413 |
| Water | $H_2O$ | gas | -44.700 | -43.357 | -41.999 | -40.636 | -39.263 | -35.804 | -32.310 | -28.796 | -25.253 | -21.73 | -18.15 | -11.10 | -4.04 | +3.15 | 10.30 |
| Nitrogen | $N_2$ | gas | 0 | 0 | 0 | 0 | 0 | 0 | 0 | 0 | 0 | 0 | 0 | 0 | 0 | 0 | 0 |
| Nitric Oxide | NO | gas | 18.311 | 18.005 | 17.706 | 17.406 | 17.100 | 16.342 | 15.585 | 14.826 | 14.071 | 13.315 | 12.567 | 11.079 | 9.625 | 8.195 | 6.807 |
| Carbon | C | solid graphite | 0 | 0 | 0 | 0 | 0 | 0 | 0 | 0 | 0 | 0 | 0 | 0 | 0 | 0 | 0 |
| Carbon Monoxide | CO | gas | -50.053 | -52.151 | -54.235 | -56.308 | -58.370 | -63.47 | -68.51 | -73.49 | -78.41 | -83.27 | -88.10 | -97.59 | -106.91 | | |
| Carbon Dioxide | $CO_2$ | gas | -94.637 | -94.661 | -94.677 | -94.690 | -94.707 | -94.72 | -94.72 | -94.69 | -94.68 | -94.62 | -94.54 | -94.37 | -94.12 | | |

TABLE 20x (PART 1) – NORMAL PARAFFINS, $C_1$ TO $C_{20}$
FREE ENERGY OF FORMATION, $\Delta F_f^o$, AT 0° TO 1500°K
November 30, 1945; December 31, 1952

| Compound (gas) | Formula | Temperature in °K | | | | | | | | | | | | | | |
| --- | --- | --- | --- | --- | --- | --- | --- | --- | --- | --- | --- | --- | --- | --- | --- | --- |
| | | 0 | 298.16 | 300 | 400 | 500 | 600 | 700 | 800 | 900 | 1000 | 1100 | 1200 | 1300 | 1400 | 1500 |
| | | Free Energy of Formation, $\Delta F_f^o$, in kcal/mole | | | | | | | | | | | | | | |
| Methane | $CH_4$ | -15.987 | -12.140 | -12.105 | -10.048 | -7.841 | -5.49 | -3.05 | -0.55 | +2.01 | 4.61 | 7.22 | 9.85 | 12.50 | 15.14 | 17.79 |
| Ethane | $C_2H_6$ | -16.517 | -7.860 | -7.785 | -3.447 | +1.168 | +5.97 | +10.90 | +15.92 | 21.00 | 26.13 | 31.28 | 36.45 | 41.62 | 46.79 | 51.99 |
| Propane | $C_3H_8$ | -19.482 | -5.614 | -5.541 | +1.191 | 8.230 | 15.50 | 22.93 | 30.45 | 38.05 | 45.68 | 53.34 | 61.01 | 68.68 | 76.35 | 84.08 |
| n-Butane | $C_4H_{10}$ | -23.67 | -4.10 | -3.94 | +5.09 | 14.54 | 24.28 | 34.19 | 44.21 | 54.34 | 64.50 | 74.67 | 84.84 | 95.04 | 105.24 | 115.42 |
| n-Pentane | $C_5H_{12}$ | -27.23 | -2.00 | -1.80 | +9.60 | 21.51 | 33.76 | 46.20 | 58.77 | 71.46 | 84.18 | 96.91 | 109.63 | 122.39 | 135.13 | 147.86 |
| n-Hexane | $C_6H_{14}$ | -30.91 | -0.07 | +0.18 | 13.95 | 28.30 | 43.02 | 57.98 | 73.08 | 88.31 | 103.57 | 118.86 | 134.11 | 149.40 | 164.68 | 179.95 |
| n-Heptane | $C_7H_{16}$ | -34.55 | +1.94 | 2.23 | 18.34 | 35.14 | 52.35 | 69.83 | 87.45 | 105.23 | 123.05 | 140.88 | 158.66 | 176.51 | 194.32 | 212.12 |
| n-Octane | $C_8H_{18}$ | -38.20 | +3.95 | 4.29 | 22.77 | 42.02 | 61.73 | 81.74 | 101.90 | 122.24 | 142.62 | 163.00 | 183.33 | 203.73 | 224.09 | 244.44 |
| n-Nonane | $C_9H_{20}$ | -41.84 | +5.96 | 6.34 | 27.20 | 48.90 | 71.11 | 93.65 | 116.35 | 139.25 | 162.18 | 185.12 | 208.00 | 230.95 | 253.86 | 276.75 |
| n-Decane | $C_{10}H_{22}$ | -45.49 | +7.97 | 8.39 | 31.63 | 55.79 | 80.50 | 105.56 | 130.80 | 156.26 | 181.75 | 207.24 | 232.66 | 258.18 | 283.63 | 309.07 |
| n-Undecane | $C_{11}H_{24}$ | -49.13 | +9.98 | 10.44 | 36.06 | 62.67 | 89.88 | 117.47 | 145.25 | 173.27 | 201.31 | 229.36 | 257.33 | 285.40 | 313.40 | 341.38 |
| n-Dodecane | $C_{12}H_{26}$ | -52.77 | +11.98 | 12.50 | 40.50 | 69.55 | 99.26 | 129.38 | 159.70 | 190.28 | 220.88 | 251.48 | 282.00 | 312.62 | 343.16 | 373.70 |
| n-Tridecane | $C_{13}H_{28}$ | -56.42 | +13.99 | 14.55 | 44.93 | 76.43 | 108.64 | 141.29 | 174.16 | 207.28 | 240.45 | 273.60 | 306.67 | 339.84 | 372.93 | 406.02 |
| n-Tetradecane | $C_{14}H_{30}$ | -60.06 | +16.00 | 16.60 | 49.36 | 83.31 | 118.02 | 153.20 | 188.61 | 224.29 | 260.01 | 295.72 | 331.34 | 367.06 | 402.70 | 438.33 |
| n-Pentadecane | $C_{15}H_{32}$ | -63.71 | +18.01 | 18.66 | 53.79 | 90.20 | 127.41 | 165.11 | 203.06 | 241.30 | 279.58 | 317.84 | 356.00 | 394.29 | 432.47 | 470.65 |
| n-Hexadecane | $C_{16}H_{34}$ | -67.35 | +20.02 | 20.71 | 58.22 | 97.08 | 136.79 | 177.02 | 217.51 | 258.31 | 299.14 | 339.96 | 380.67 | 421.51 | 462.24 | 502.96 |
| n-Heptadecane | $C_{17}H_{36}$ | -70.99 | +22.03 | 22.76 | 62.65 | 103.96 | 146.17 | 188.93 | 231.96 | 275.32 | 318.71 | 362.08 | 405.34 | 448.73 | 492.01 | 535.28 |
| n-Octadecane | $C_{18}H_{38}$ | -74.64 | +24.04 | 24.82 | 67.08 | 110.84 | 155.55 | 200.84 | 246.41 | 292.33 | 338.28 | 384.20 | 430.01 | 475.95 | 521.78 | 567.60 |
| n-Nonadecane | $C_{19}H_{40}$ | -78.28 | +26.05 | 26.87 | 71.51 | 117.72 | 164.93 | 212.75 | 260.86 | 309.34 | 357.84 | 406.32 | 454.68 | 503.17 | 551.55 | 599.91 |
| n-Eicosane | $C_{20}H_{42}$ | -81.93 | +28.06 | 28.92 | 75.94 | 124.61 | 174.32 | 224.66 | 275.31 | 326.35 | 377.41 | 428.44 | 479.34 | 530.40 | 581.32 | 632.23 |
| Increment per $CH_2$ group, applicable beyond n-heptane | | -3.644 | +2.009 | 2.053 | 4.431 | 6.882 | 9.382 | 11.910 | 14.451 | 17.009 | 19.566 | 22.120 | 24.668 | 27.222 | 29.769 | 32.316 |

TABLE 1x - PARAFFINS, C₁ TO C₅

FREE ENERGY OF FORMATION, $\Delta F_f^o$, AT 0° TO 1500°K

August 31, 1944; February 28, 1949; December 31, 1952

| Compound (gas) | Formula | Temperature in °K |  |  |  |  |  |  |  |  |  |  |  |  |  |  |
|---|---|---|---|---|---|---|---|---|---|---|---|---|---|---|---|---|
|  |  | 0 | 100 | 150 | 200 | 250 | 298.16 | 300 | 350 | 400 | 450 | 500 | 600 | 700 | 800 | 900 |
|  |  | Free Energy of Formation, $\Delta F_f^o$, in kcal/mole |  |  |  |  |  |  |  |  |  |  |  |  |  |  |
| Methane | CH₄ | -15.987 |  |  |  | -12.987 | -12.140 | -12.105 | -11.113 | -10.048 | -8.969 | -7.841 | -5.49 | -3.05 | -0.55 | +2.01 |
| Ethane | C₂H₆ | -16.517 |  |  |  | -9.731 | -7.860 | -7.785 | -5.664 | -3.447 | -1.165 | +1.168 | 5.97 | 10.90 | 15.92 | 21.00 |
| Propane | C₃H₈ | -19.482 |  |  |  | -8.549 | -5.614 | -5.541 | -2.218 | +1.191 | 4.674 | 8.230 | 15.50 | 22.93 | 30.45 | 38.05 |
| n-Butane | C₄H₁₀ | -23.67 |  |  |  | -8.10 | -4.10 | -3.94 | +0.50 | 5.09 | 9.76 | 14.54 | 24.28 | 34.19 | 44.21 | 54.34 |
| 2-Methylpropane (Isobutane) | " | -25.30 |  |  |  | -9.17 | -5.00 | -4.83 | -0.20 | +4.57 | 9.44 | 14.39 | 24.48 | 34.74 | 45.12 | 55.59 |
| n-Pentane | C₅H₁₂ | -27.23 |  |  |  | -7.08 | -2.00 | -1.80 | +3.81 | 9.60 | 15.50 | 21.51 | 33.76 | 46.20 | 58.77 | 71.46 |
| 2-Methylbutane (Isopentane) | " | -28.81 |  |  |  | -8.70 | -3.54 | -3.33 | +2.35 | 8.22 | 14.21 | 20.26 | 32.63 | 45.19 | 57.88 | 70.68 |
| 2,2-Dimethylpropane (Neopentane) | " | -31.30 |  |  |  | -9.21 | -3.64 | -3.42 | +2.70 | 8.99 | 15.41 | 21.89 | 35.08 | 48.46 | 61.93 | 75.49 |

| Compound (gas) | Formula | Temperature in °K |  |  |  |  |  |
|---|---|---|---|---|---|---|---|
|  |  | 1000 | 1100 | 1200 | 1300 | 1400 | 1500 |
|  |  | Free Energy of Formation, $\Delta F_f^o$, in kcal/mole |  |  |  |  |  |
| Methane | CH₄ | 4.61 | 7.22 | 9.85 | 12.50 | 15.14 | 17.79 |
| Ethane | C₂H₆ | 26.13 | 31.28 | 36.45 | 41.62 | 46.79 | 51.99 |
| Propane | C₃H₈ | 45.68 | 53.34 | 61.01 | 68.68 | 76.35 | 84.08 |
| n-Butane | C₄H₁₀ | 64.50 | 74.67 | 84.84 | 95.04 | 105.24 | 115.42 |
| 2-Methylpropane (Isobutane) | " | 66.09 | 76.62 | 87.16 | 97.69 | 108.20 | 118.74 |
| n-Pentane | C₅H₁₂ | 84.18 | 96.91 | 109.63 | 122.39 | 135.13 | 147.86 |
| 2-Methylbutane (Isopentane) | " | 83.51 | 96.37 | 109.21 | 122.02 | 134.85 | 147.69 |
| 2,2-Dimethylpropane (Neopentane) | " | 89.08 | 102.68 | 116.27 | 129.88 | 143.44 | 157.00 |

TABLE 2x (PART 1) – PARAFFINS, $C_6$

FREE ENERGY OF FORMATION, $\Delta F_f°$, AT 0° TO 1500°K

September 30, 1944; November 30, 1946; December 31, 1952

Free Energy of Formation, $\Delta F_f°$, in kcal/mole

| Compound (gas) | Formula | 0 | 298.16 | 300 | 400 | 500 | 600 | 700 | 800 | 900 | 1000 | 1100 | 1200 | 1300 | 1400 | 1500 |
|---|---|---|---|---|---|---|---|---|---|---|---|---|---|---|---|---|
| | | | | | | | | | Temperature in °K | | | | | | |
| n-Hexane | $C_6H_{14}$ | -30.91 | -0.07 | +0.18 | 13.95 | 28.30 | 43.02 | 57.98 | 73.08 | 88.31 | 103.57 | 118.86 | 134.11 | 149.40 | 164.68 | 179.95 |
| 2-Methylpentane | " | -32.08 | -1.20 | -0.96 | +13.00 | 27.53 | 42.43 | 57.53 | 72.74 | 88.05 | 103.41 | 118.90 | 134.30 | 149.65 | 165.04 | 180.49 |
| 3-Methylpentane | " | -31.97 | -0.51 | -0.27 | +13.71 | 28.27 | 43.20 | 58.36 | 73.67 | 89.06 | 104.52 | 120.11 | 135.50 | 151.06 | 166.55 | 181.95 |
| 2,2-Dimethylbutane | " | -34.65 | -2.37 | -2.11 | +12.39 | 27.46 | 42.86 | 58.53 | 74.25 | 90.07 | 106.04 | 121.94 | 137.86 | 153.71 | 169.75 | 185.57 |
| 2,3-Dimethylbutane | " | -32.73 | -0.98 | -0.72 | +13.61 | 28.51 | 43.78 | 59.28 | 74.94 | 90.67 | 106.49 | 122.28 | 138.12 | 153.95 | 169.75 | 185.54 |

TABLE 2x (PART 2) — PARAFFINS, $C_7$
FREE ENERGY OF FORMATION, $\Delta F_f^{\circ}$, AT 0° TO 1500°K
September 30, 1944; December 31, 1952

Temperature in °K

Free Energy of Formation, $\Delta F_f^{\circ}$, in kcal/mole

| Compound (gas) | Formula | 0 | 298.16 | 300 | 400 | 500 | 600 | 700 | 800 | 900 | 1000 | 1100 | 1200 | 1300 | 1400 | 1500 |
|---|---|---|---|---|---|---|---|---|---|---|---|---|---|---|---|---|
| n-Heptane | $C_7H_{16}$ | -34.55 | +1.94 | 2.23 | 18.34 | 35.14 | 52.35 | 69.83 | 87.45 | 105.23 | 123.05 | 140.88 | 158.66 | 176.51 | 194.32 | 212.12 |
| 2-Methylhexane | " | -35.77 | +0.77 | 1.06 | 17.33 | 34.24 | 51.57 | 69.15 | 86.91 | 104.73 | 122.53 | | | | | |
| 3-Methylhexane | " | -34.96 | +1.10 | 1.39 | 17.57 | 34.40 | 51.68 | 69.21 | 86.87 | 104.59 | 122.29 | | | | | |
| 3-Ethylpentane | " | -34.10 | +2.57 | 2.84 | 19.28 | 36.41 | 54.02 | 71.94 | 89.94 | 108.11 | 126.10 | | | | | |
| 2,2-Dimethylpentane | " | -38.00 | +0.02 | 0.32 | 17.26 | 34.81 | 52.82 | 71.19 | 89.56 | 108.08 | 126.30 | | | | | |
| 2,3-Dimethylpentane | " | -36.29 | +0.16 | 0.45 | 16.83 | 33.90 | 51.43 | 69.24 | 87.17 | 105.18 | 123.16 | | | | | |
| 2,4-Dimethylpentane | " | -36.98 | +0.72 | 1.02 | 17.81 | 35.28 | 53.19 | 71.37 | 89.66 | 107.99 | 126.27 | | | | | |
| 3,3-Dimethylpentane | " | -36.92 | +0.63 | 0.93 | 17.64 | 35.02 | 52.84 | 70.92 | 89.10 | 107.34 | 125.53 | | | | | |
| 2,2,3-Trimethylbutane | " | -37.71 | +1.02 | 1.33 | 18.52 | 36.38 | 54.62 | 73.11 | 91.69 | 110.53 | 129.29 | 148.00 | 166.80 | 185.52 | 204.23 | 222.97 |

TABLE 3x -- PARAFFINS, $C_8$

FREE ENERGY OF FORMATION, $\Delta F_f^o$, AT 0° TO 1500°K

September 30, 1947; December 31, 1952

| Compound (gas) | Formula | Temperature in °K | | | | | | | | | | | | | | |
|---|---|---|---|---|---|---|---|---|---|---|---|---|---|---|---|---|
| | | 0 | 298.16 | 300 | 400 | 500 | 600 | 700 | 800 | 900 | 1000 | 1100 | 1200 | 1300 | 1400 | 1500 |
| | | Free Energy of Formation, $\Delta F_f^o$, in kcal/mole | | | | | | | | | | | | | | |
| n-Octane | $C_8H_{18}$ | -38.20 | +3.95 | 4.29 | 22.77 | 42.02 | 61.73 | 81.74 | 101.90 | 122.24 | 142.62 | 163.00 | 183.33 | 203.73 | 224.09 | 244.44 |
| 2-Methylheptane | " | -39.42 | +3.06 | 3.39 | 22.14 | 41.58 | 61.47 | 81.63 | 101.88 | 122.27 | 142.83 | | | | | |
| 3-Methylheptane | " | -38.64 | +3.29 | 3.62 | 22.21 | 41.50 | 61.27 | 81.31 | 101.44 | 121.68 | 142.07 | | | | | |
| 4-Methylheptane | " | -38.43 | +4.00 | 4.34 | 23.12 | 42.62 | 62.61 | 82.88 | 103.23 | 123.68 | 144.26 | | | | | |
| 3-Ethylhexane | " | -37.71 | +3.95 | 4.28 | 22.94 | 42.39 | 62.37 | 82.64 | 102.98 | 123.42 | 143.98 | | | | | |
| 2,2-Dimethylhexane | " | -41.23 | +2.56 | 2.91 | 22.18 | 42.20 | 62.71 | 83.48 | 104.30 | 125.21 | 146.27 | | | | | |
| 2,3-Dimethylhexane | " | -38.76 | +4.23 | 4.57 | 23.51 | 43.16 | 63.27 | 83.64 | 104.09 | 124.63 | 145.30 | | | | | |
| 2,4-Dimethylhexane | " | -39.74 | +2.80 | 3.14 | 22.05 | 41.72 | 61.89 | 82.32 | 102.84 | 123.43 | 144.07 | | | | | |
| 2,5-Dimethylhexane | " | -40.61 | +2.50 | 2.84 | 21.92 | 41.75 | 62.08 | 82.69 | 103.41 | 124.20 | 144.99 | | | | | |
| 3,3-Dimethylhexane | " | -39.90 | +3.17 | 3.51 | 22.63 | 42.50 | 62.85 | 83.47 | 104.16 | 124.93 | 145.76 | | | | | |
| 3,4-Dimethylhexane[a] | " | -38.61 | +4.14 | 4.47 | 23.43 | 43.08 | 63.16 | 83.54 | 104.04 | 124.72 | 145.41 | | | | | |
| 2-Methyl-3-ethylpentane | " | -37.96 | +5.08 | 5.43 | 24.47 | 44.24 | 64.47 | 84.96 | 105.52 | 126.21 | 147.09 | | | | | |
| 3-Methyl-3-ethylpentane | " | -38.68 | +4.76 | 5.11 | 24.32 | 44.30 | 64.77 | 85.48 | 106.22 | 127.05 | 148.01 | | | | | |
| 2,2,3-Trimethylpentane | " | -39.77 | +4.09 | 4.44 | 23.82 | 43.98 | 64.63 | 85.54 | 106.52 | 127.57 | 148.68 | | | | | |
| 2,2,4-Trimethylpentane | " | -40.73 | +3.27 | 3.62 | 23.07 | 43.28 | 64.00 | 84.97 | 105.97 | 127.04 | 148.18 | | | | | |
| 2,3,3-Trimethylpentane | " | -39.01 | +4.52 | 4.86 | 24.09 | 44.08 | 64.55 | 85.30 | 106.10 | 126.98 | 147.90 | | | | | |
| 2,3,4-Trimethylpentane | " | -39.12 | +4.52 | 4.87 | 24.16 | 44.24 | 64.77 | 85.60 | 106.46 | 127.48 | 148.49 | | | | | |
| 2,2,3,3-Tetramethylbutane | " | -41.24 | +5.27 | 5.63 | 26.00 | 46.97 | 68.41 | 89.99 | 111.78 | 133.64 | 155.47 | | | | | |

a See footnotes a and b of Table 3r.

TABLE 22x (PART 1) — NORMAL ALKYL CYCLOPENTANES, C5 TO C21
FREE ENERGY OF FORMATION, $\Delta Ff°$, AT 0° TO 1500°K
March 31, 1947; December 31, 1952

| Compound (gas) | Formula | Temperature in °K |||||||||||||||
|---|---|---|---|---|---|---|---|---|---|---|---|---|---|---|---|---|
| | | 0 | 298.16 | 300 | 400 | 500 | 600 | 700 | 800 | 900 | 1000 | 1100 | 1200 | 1300 | 1400 | 1500 |
| | | Free Energy of Formation, $\Delta Ff°$, in kcal/mole ||||||||||||||||
| Cyclopentane | $C_5H_{10}$ | -10.68 | +9.23 | 9.40 | 19.06 | 29.25 | 39.78 | 50.52 | 61.40 | 72.37 | 83.38 | 94.41 | 105.43 | 116.47 | 127.48 | 138.47 |
| Methylcyclopentane | $C_6H_{12}$ | -16.62 | +8.55 | 8.76 | 20.59 | 33.00 | 45.78 | 58.79 | 71.93 | 85.17 | 98.46 | 111.77 | 125.08 | 138.41 | 151.68 | 164.87 |
| Ethylcyclopentane | $C_7H_{14}$ | -20.23 | +10.66 | 10.91 | 25.08 | 39.91 | 55.15 | 70.63 | 86.26 | 102.06 | 117.89 | 133.76 | 149.61 | 165.44 | 181.36 | 197.19 |
| n-Propylcyclopentane | $C_8H_{16}$ | -23.98 | +12.56 | 12.85 | 29.41 | 46.68 | 64.42 | 82.43 | 100.60 | 118.95 | 137.3 | 155.7 | 174.2 | 192.6 | 211.2 | 229.4 |
| n-Butylcyclopentane | $C_9H_{18}$ | -27.52 | +14.67 | 15.01 | 33.94 | 53.67 | 73.91 | 94.45 | 115.16 | 136.07 | 157.0 | 177.9 | 199.0 | 219.9 | 241.2 | 261.8 |
| n-Pentylcyclopentane | $C_{10}H_{20}$ | -31.16 | +16.68 | 17.06 | 38.37 | 60.55 | 83.29 | 106.36 | 129.61 | 153.08 | 176.6 | 200.0 | 223.7 | 247.1 | 271.0 | 294.1 |
| n-Hexylcyclopentane | $C_{11}H_{22}$ | -34.81 | +18.69 | 19.12 | 42.80 | 67.43 | 92.67 | 118.27 | 144.06 | 170.09 | 196.1 | 222.1 | 248.4 | 274.3 | 300.7 | 326.4 |
| n-Heptylcyclopentane | $C_{12}H_{24}$ | -38.45 | +20.70 | 21.17 | 47.23 | 74.32 | 102.06 | 130.18 | 158.51 | 187.10 | 215.7 | 244.3 | 273.0 | 301.6 | 330.5 | 358.8 |
| n-Octylcyclopentane | $C_{13}H_{26}$ | -42.10 | +22.71 | 23.22 | 51.66 | 81.20 | 111.44 | 142.09 | 172.96 | 204.11 | 235.3 | 266.4 | 297.7 | 328.8 | 360.3 | 391.1 |
| n-Nonylcyclopentane | $C_{14}H_{28}$ | -45.74 | +24.72 | 25.28 | 56.10 | 88.08 | 120.82 | 154.00 | 187.42 | 221.12 | 254.8 | 288.5 | 322.4 | 356.0 | 390.0 | 423.4 |
| n-Decylcyclopentane | $C_{15}H_{30}$ | -49.38 | +26.72 | 27.33 | 60.53 | 94.96 | 130.20 | 165.91 | 201.87 | 238.12 | 274.4 | 310.6 | 347.1 | 383.2 | 419.8 | 455.7 |
| n-Undecylcyclopentane | $C_{16}H_{32}$ | -53.03 | +28.73 | 29.38 | 64.96 | 101.84 | 139.58 | 177.82 | 216.32 | 255.13 | 294.0 | 332.7 | 371.8 | 410.4 | 449.6 | 488.0 |
| n-Dodecylcyclopentane | $C_{17}H_{34}$ | -56.67 | +30.74 | 31.43 | 69.39 | 108.73 | 148.97 | 189.73 | 230.77 | 272.14 | 313.6 | 354.9 | 396.4 | 437.7 | 479.4 | 520.4 |
| n-Tridecylcyclopentane | $C_{18}H_{36}$ | -60.32 | +32.75 | 33.49 | 73.82 | 115.61 | 158.35 | 201.64 | 245.22 | 289.15 | 333.1 | 377.0 | 421.1 | 464.9 | 509.1 | 552.7 |
| n-Tetradecylcyclopentane | $C_{19}H_{38}$ | -63.96 | +34.76 | 35.54 | 78.25 | 122.49 | 167.73 | 213.55 | 259.67 | 306.16 | 352.7 | 399.1 | 445.8 | 492.1 | 538.9 | 585.0 |
| n-Pentadecylcyclopentane | $C_{20}H_{40}$ | -67.60 | +36.77 | 37.59 | 82.68 | 129.37 | 177.11 | 225.46 | 274.12 | 323.17 | 372.3 | 421.2 | 470.5 | 519.3 | 568.7 | 617.3 |
| n-Hexadecylcyclopentane | $C_{21}H_{42}$ | -71.25 | +38.78 | 39.65 | 87.11 | 136.25 | 186.49 | 237.37 | 288.57 | 340.18 | 391.8 | 443.3 | 495.2 | 546.5 | 598.4 | 649.6 |
| Increment per CH2 group, applicable beyond n-butylcyclopentane | | -3.644 | +2.009 | 2.053 | 4.431 | 6.882 | 9.382 | 11.910 | 14.451 | 17.009 | 19.57 | 22.12 | 24.68 | 27.22 | 29.77 | 32.32 |

TABLE 6x — ALKYL CYCLOPENTANES, C$_5$ TO C$_7$
FREE ENERGY OF FORMATION, $\Delta Ff^{o}$, AT 0° TO 1500°K
April 30, 1949; December 31, 1952

Free Energy of Formation, $\Delta Ff^{o}$, in kcal/mole

| Compound (gas) | Formula | Temperature in °K | | | | | | | | | | | | | | |
|---|---|---|---|---|---|---|---|---|---|---|---|---|---|---|---|---|
| | | 0 | 298.16 | 300 | 400 | 500 | 600 | 700 | 800 | 900 | 1000 | 1100 | 1200 | 1300 | 1400 | 1500 |
| Cyclopentane | C$_5$H$_{10}$ | −10.68 | +9.23 | 9.40 | 19.06 | 29.25 | 39.78 | 50.52 | 61.40 | 72.37 | 83.38 | 94.41 | 105.43 | 116.47 | 127.48 | 138.47 |
| Methylcyclopentane | C$_6$H$_{12}$ | −16.62 | +8.55 | 8.76 | 20.59 | 33.00 | 45.78 | 58.79 | 71.93 | 85.17 | 98.46 | 111.77 | 125.08 | 138.41 | 151.68 | 164.87 |
| Ethylcyclopentane | C$_7$H$_{14}$ | −20.23 | +10.66 | 10.91 | 25.08 | 39.91 | 55.15 | 70.63 | 86.26 | 102.06 | 117.89 | 133.76 | 149.63 | 165.44 | 181.36 | 197.19 |
| 1,1-Dimethylcyclopentane | " | −22.69 | +9.33 | 9.58 | 24.26 | 39.58 | 55.34 | 71.29 | 87.33 | 103.51 | 119.75 | 136.02 | 152.24 | 168.48 | 184.62 | 200.64 |
| 1,cis-2-Dimethylcyclopentane | " | −20.66 | +10.93 | 11.18 | 25.67 | 40.83 | 56.39 | 72.17 | 88.07 | 104.08 | 120.15 | 136.23 | 152.31 | 168.42 | 184.43 | 200.29 |
| 1,trans-2-Dimethylcyclopentane | " | −22.39 | +9.17 | 9.42 | 23.90 | 39.04 | 54.60 | 70.36 | 86.19 | 102.22 | 118.27 | 134.34 | 150.41 | 166.50 | 182.50 | 198.35 |
| 1,cis-3-Dimethylcyclopentane | " | −21.65 | +9.91 | 10.16 | 24.64 | 39.78 | 55.34 | 71.10 | 86.93 | 102.96 | 119.01 | 135.08 | 151.15 | 167.24 | 183.24 | 199.09 |
| 1,trans-3-Dimethylcyclopentane | " | −22.19 | +9.37 | 9.62 | 24.10 | 39.24 | 54.80 | 70.56 | 86.39 | 102.42 | 118.47 | 134.54 | 150.61 | 166.70 | 182.70 | 198.55 |

TABLE 23x (PART 1) — NORMAL ALKYL CYCLOHEXANES, C$_6$ TO C$_{22}$

FREE ENERGY OF FORMATION, $\Delta F_f^o$, AT 0° TO 1500°K

March 31, 1947; December 31, 1952

Free Energy of Formation, $\Delta F_f^o$, in kcal/mole

| Compound (gas) | Formula | 0 | 298.16 | 300 | 400 | 500 | 600 | 700 | 800 | 900 | 1000 | 1100 | 1200 | 1300 | 1400 | 1500 |
|---|---|---|---|---|---|---|---|---|---|---|---|---|---|---|---|---|
| Cyclohexane | C$_6$H$_{12}$ | −20.01 | +7.59 | 7.81 | 20.66 | 34.07 | 47.86 | 61.85 | 75.96 | 90.13 | 104.30 | 118.42 | 132.58 | 146.69 | 160.73 | 174.72 |
| Methylcyclohexane | C$_7$H$_{14}$ | −26.30 | +6.52 | 6.79 | 21.84 | 37.51 | 53.55 | 69.80 | 86.16 | 102.59 | 119.03 | 135.43 | 151.83 | 168.13 | 184.43 | 200.65 |
| Ethylcyclohexane | C$_8$H$_{16}$ | −28.94 | +9.38 | 9.69 | 27.12 | 45.19 | 63.72 | 82.50 | 101.37 | 120.28 | 139.23 | 158.17 | 177.11 | 195.93 | 214.71 | 233.36 |
| n-Propylcyclohexane | C$_9$H$_{18}$ | −32.62 | +11.31 | 11.66 | 31.5 | 52.1 | 73.1 | 94.4 | 115.8 | 137.3 | 158.8 | 180.3 | 201.8 | 223.2 | 244.5 | 265.8 |
| n-Butylcyclohexane | C$_{10}$H$_{20}$ | −36.09 | +13.49 | 13.89 | 36.1 | 59.1 | 82.6 | 106.5 | 130.4 | 154.5 | 178.5 | 202.7 | 226.6 | 250.6 | 274.5 | 298.3 |
| n-Pentylcyclohexane | C$_{11}$H$_{22}$ | −39.73 | +15.50 | 15.94 | 40.5 | 66.0 | 92.0 | 118.4 | 144.9 | 171.5 | 198.1 | 224.8 | 251.3 | 277.8 | 304.3 | 330.6 |
| n-Hexylcyclohexane | C$_{12}$H$_{24}$ | −43.38 | +17.51 | 18.00 | 45.0 | 72.9 | 101.4 | 130.3 | 159.3 | 188.5 | 217.6 | 246.9 | 275.9 | 305.0 | 334.0 | 362.9 |
| n-Heptylcyclohexane | C$_{13}$H$_{26}$ | −47.02 | +19.52 | 20.05 | 49.4 | 79.7 | 110.7 | 142.2 | 173.8 | 205.5 | 237.2 | 269.1 | 300.6 | 332.3 | 363.8 | 395.3 |
| n-Octylcyclohexane | C$_{14}$H$_{28}$ | −50.67 | +21.53 | 22.10 | 53.8 | 86.6 | 120.1 | 154.1 | 188.2 | 222.5 | 256.8 | 291.2 | 325.3 | 359.5 | 393.6 | 427.6 |
| n-Nonylcyclohexane | C$_{15}$H$_{30}$ | −54.31 | +23.54 | 24.16 | 58.2 | 93.5 | 129.5 | 166.0 | 202.6 | 239.6 | 276.4 | 313.3 | 350.0 | 386.7 | 423.4 | 459.9 |
| n-Decylcyclohexane | C$_{16}$H$_{32}$ | −57.95 | +25.54 | 26.21 | 62.7 | 100.4 | 138.9 | 178.0 | 217.1 | 256.6 | 295.9 | 335.4 | 374.6 | 413.9 | 453.1 | 492.2 |
| n-Undecylcyclohexane | C$_{17}$H$_{34}$ | −61.60 | +27.55 | 28.26 | 67.1 | 107.3 | 148.3 | 189.9 | 231.6 | 273.6 | 315.5 | 357.5 | 399.3 | 441.1 | 482.9 | 524.5 |
| n-Dodecylcyclohexane | C$_{18}$H$_{36}$ | −65.24 | +29.56 | 30.31 | 71.5 | 114.1 | 157.6 | 201.8 | 246.0 | 290.6 | 335.1 | 379.7 | 424.0 | 468.4 | 512.7 | 556.9 |
| n-Tridecylcyclohexane | C$_{19}$H$_{38}$ | −68.89 | +31.57 | 32.37 | 76.0 | 121.0 | 167.0 | 213.7 | 260.4 | 307.6 | 354.6 | 401.8 | 448.6 | 495.6 | 542.4 | 589.2 |
| n-Tetradecylcyclohexane | C$_{20}$H$_{40}$ | −72.53 | +33.58 | 34.42 | 80.4 | 127.9 | 176.4 | 225.6 | 274.9 | 324.6 | 374.2 | 423.9 | 473.3 | 522.8 | 572.2 | 621.5 |
| n-Pentadecylcyclohexane | C$_{21}$H$_{42}$ | −76.17 | +35.59 | 36.47 | 84.8 | 134.8 | 185.8 | 237.5 | 289.4 | 341.6 | 393.8 | 446.0 | 498.0 | 550.0 | 602.0 | 653.8 |
| n-Hexadecylcyclohexane | C$_{22}$H$_{44}$ | −79.82 | +37.60 | 38.53 | 89.3 | 141.7 | 195.2 | 249.4 | 303.9 | 358.6 | 413.3 | 468.1 | 522.6 | 577.2 | 631.7 | 686.1 |
| Increment per CH$_2$ group, applicable beyond n-butylcyclohexane | | −3.644 | +2.009 | 2.053 | 4.43 | 6.88 | 9.38 | 11.91 | 14.45 | 17.01 | 19.57 | 22.12 | 24.67 | 27.22 | 29.77 | 32.32 |

Temperature in °K

TABLE 7x – ALKYL CYCLOHEXANES, $C_6$ TO $C_8$

FREE ENERGY OF FORMATION, $\Delta F_f°$, AT 0° TO 1500°K

April 30, 1947 (Corrected)

| Compound (gas) | Formula | Temperature in °K | | | | | | | | | | | | | | |
|---|---|---|---|---|---|---|---|---|---|---|---|---|---|---|---|---|
| | | | | | | Free Energy of Formation, $\Delta F_f°$, in kcal/mole | | | | | | | | | | |
| | | 0 | 298.16 | 300 | 400 | 500 | 600 | 700 | 800 | 900 | 1000 | 1100 | 1200 | 1300 | 1400 | 1500 |
| Cyclohexane | $C_6H_{12}$ | -20.01 | +7.59 | 7.81 | 20.66 | 34.07 | 47.86 | 61.85 | 75.96 | 90.13 | 104.30 | 118.42 | 132.58 | 146.69 | 160.73 | 174.72 |
| Methylcyclohexane | $C_7H_{14}$ | -26.30 | +6.52 | 6.79 | 21.84 | 37.51 | 53.55 | 69.80 | 86.16 | 102.59 | 119.03 | 135.43 | 151.83 | 168.13 | 184.43 | 200.65 |
| Ethylcyclohexane | $C_8H_{16}$ | -28.94 | +9.38 | 9.69 | 27.12 | 45.19 | 63.72 | 82.50 | 101.37 | 120.28 | 139.23 | 158.17 | 177.11 | 195.93 | 214.71 | 233.36 |
| 1,1-Dimethylcyclohexane | " | -30.93 | +8.42 | 8.74 | 26.6 | 45.2 | 64.1 | 83.4 | 102.7 | 122.1 | 141.4 | 160.8 | 180.2 | 199.5 | 218.4 | 237.1 |
| 1,cis-2-Dimethylcyclohexane | " | -28.95 | +9.85 | 10.17 | 27.8 | 46.1 | 64.8 | 83.8 | 102.9 | 122.1 | 141.2 | 160.4 | 179.5 | 198.6 | 217.4 | 236.0 |
| 1,trans-2-Dimethylcyclohexane | " | -30.91 | +8.24 | 8.55 | 26.2 | 44.6 | 63.4 | 82.4 | 101.5 | 120.6 | 139.9 | 159.1 | 178.1 | 197.3 | 216.1 | 234.9 |
| 1,cis-3-Dimethylcyclohexane[a] | " | -32.02 | +7.13 | 7.44 | 25.2 | 43.6 | 62.4 | 81.4 | 100.6 | 119.8 | 139.0 | 158.3 | 177.5 | 196.6 | 215.6 | 234.5 |
| 1,trans-3-Dimethylcyclohexane[b] | " | -30.06 | +8.68 | 8.99 | 26.6 | 44.8 | 63.6 | 82.5 | 101.5 | 120.6 | 139.8 | 158.9 | 178.0 | 197.2 | 216.0 | 234.7 |
| 1,cis-4-Dimethylcyclohexane | " | -30.08 | +9.07 | 9.38 | 27.1 | 45.5 | 64.3 | 83.4 | 102.6 | 121.8 | 141.2 | 160.4 | 179.7 | 199.0 | 217.8 | 236.5 |
| 1,trans-4-Dimethylcyclohexane | " | -31.99 | +7.58 | 7.89 | 25.8 | 44.3 | 63.2 | 82.4 | 101.6 | 121.0 | 140.3 | 159.6 | 179.0 | 198.2 | 217.2 | 235.9 |

[a] Formerly labeled "trans"; see footnote b of Table 7a.

[b] Formerly labeled "cis"; see footnote c of Table 7a.

TABLE 24x (PART 1) — NORMAL MONOOLEFINS (1-ALKENES), $C_2$ TO $C_{20}$
FREE ENERGY OF FORMATION, $\Delta F_f^o$, AT $0^o$ TO $1500^o$K
November 30, 1945; April 30, 1946; December 31, 1952

| Compound (gas) | Formula | Temperature in °K | | | | | | | | | | | | | | |
|---|---|---|---|---|---|---|---|---|---|---|---|---|---|---|---|---|
| | | 0 | 298.16 | 300 | 400 | 500 | 600 | 700 | 800 | 900 | 1000 | 1100 | 1200 | 1300 | 1400 | 1500 |
| | | Free Energy of Formation, $\Delta F_f^o$, in kcal/mole | | | | | | | | | | | | | | |
| Ethene (Ethylene) | $C_2H_4$ | 14.522 | 16.282 | 16.305 | 17.675 | 19.245 | 20.918 | 22.676 | 24.490 | 26.354 | 28.249 | 30.16 | 32.09 | 34.03 | 35.97 | 37.92 |
| Propene (Propylene) | $C_3H_6$ | 8.468 | 14.990 | 15.051 | 18.610 | 22.450 | 26.46 | 30.59 | 34.81 | 39.10 | 43.43 | 47.78 | 52.15 | 56.52 | 60.90 | 65.28 |
| 1-Butene | $C_4H_8$ | 4.96 | 17.09 | 17.19 | 23.23 | 29.55 | 36.07 | 42.73 | 49.45 | 56.25 | 63.07 | 69.90 | 76.74 | 83.57 | 90.38 | 97.20 |
| 1-Pentene | $C_5H_{10}$ | 1.13 | 18.96 | 19.10 | 27.49 | 36.22 | 45.21 | 54.35 | 63.58 | 72.90 | 82.24 | 91.60 | 100.93 | 110.29 | 119.63 | 128.90 |
| 1-Hexene | $C_6H_{12}$ | -2.54 | +20.94 | 21.13 | 31.90 | 43.08 | 54.57 | 66.25 | 78.02 | 89.90 | 101.81 | 113.73 | 125.61 | 137.53 | 149.42 | 161.23 |
| 1-Heptene | $C_7H_{14}$ | -6.18 | +22.95 | 23.18 | 36.33 | 49.96 | 63.95 | 78.16 | 92.47 | 106.91 | 121.38 | 135.85 | 150.28 | 164.75 | 179.19 | 193.55 |
| 1-Octene | $C_8H_{16}$ | -9.83 | +24.96 | 25.24 | 40.76 | 56.84 | 73.33 | 90.07 | 106.92 | 123.92 | 140.94 | 157.97 | 174.95 | 191.97 | 208.96 | 225.86 |
| 1-Nonene | $C_9H_{18}$ | -13.47 | +26.97 | 27.29 | 45.19 | 63.73 | 82.72 | 101.98 | 121.37 | 140.93 | 160.51 | 180.09 | 199.61 | 219.20 | 238.73 | 258.18 |
| 1-Decene | $C_{10}H_{20}$ | -17.12 | +28.98 | 29.34 | 49.62 | 70.61 | 92.10 | 113.89 | 135.82 | 157.94 | 180.07 | 202.21 | 224.28 | 246.42 | 268.50 | 290.49 |
| 1-Undecene | $C_{11}H_{22}$ | -20.76 | +30.98 | 31.40 | 54.05 | 77.49 | 101.48 | 125.80 | 150.28 | 174.95 | 199.64 | 224.33 | 248.95 | 273.64 | 298.26 | 322.81 |
| 1-Dodecene | $C_{12}H_{24}$ | -24.40 | +32.99 | 33.45 | 58.49 | 84.37 | 110.86 | 137.71 | 164.73 | 191.95 | 219.21 | 246.45 | 273.62 | 300.86 | 328.03 | 355.13 |
| 1-Tridecene | $C_{13}H_{26}$ | -28.05 | +35.00 | 35.50 | 62.92 | 91.25 | 120.24 | 149.62 | 179.18 | 208.96 | 238.77 | 268.57 | 298.29 | 328.08 | 357.80 | 387.44 |
| 1-Tetradecene | $C_{14}H_{28}$ | -31.69 | +37.01 | 37.55 | 67.35 | 98.14 | 129.63 | 161.53 | 193.63 | 225.97 | 258.34 | 290.69 | 322.95 | 355.31 | 387.57 | 419.76 |
| 1-Pentadecene | $C_{15}H_{30}$ | -35.34 | +39.02 | 39.61 | 71.78 | 105.02 | 139.01 | 173.44 | 208.08 | 242.98 | 277.90 | 312.81 | 347.62 | 382.53 | 417.34 | 452.07 |
| 1-Hexadecene | $C_{16}H_{32}$ | -38.98 | +41.03 | 41.66 | 76.21 | 111.90 | 148.39 | 185.35 | 222.53 | 259.99 | 297.47 | 334.93 | 372.29 | 409.75 | 447.11 | 484.39 |
| 1-Heptadecene | $C_{17}H_{34}$ | -42.62 | +43.04 | 43.71 | 80.64 | 118.78 | 157.77 | 197.26 | 236.98 | 277.00 | 317.04 | 357.05 | 396.96 | 436.97 | 476.88 | 516.71 |
| 1-Octadecene | $C_{18}H_{36}$ | -46.27 | +45.05 | 45.77 | 85.07 | 125.66 | 167.15 | 209.17 | 251.43 | 294.01 | 336.60 | 379.17 | 421.63 | 464.19 | 506.65 | 549.02 |
| 1-Nonadecene | $C_{19}H_{38}$ | -49.91 | +47.06 | 47.82 | 89.50 | 132.55 | 176.54 | 221.08 | 265.88 | 311.02 | 356.17 | 401.29 | 446.29 | 491.42 | 536.42 | 581.34 |
| 1-Eicosene | $C_{20}H_{40}$ | -53.56 | +49.07 | 49.87 | 93.93 | 139.43 | 185.92 | 232.99 | 280.33 | 328.03 | 375.73 | 423.41 | 470.96 | 518.64 | 566.19 | 613.65 |
| Increment per $CH_2$ group, applicable beyond 1-hexene | | -3.644 | +2.009 | 2.053 | 4.431 | 6.882 | 9.382 | 11.910 | 14.451 | 17.009 | 19.566 | 22.120 | 24.668 | 27.222 | 29.769 | 32.316 |

TABLE 8x (PART 1) - MONOOLEFINS, $C_2$ TO $C_5$

FREE ENERGY OF FORMATION, $\Delta F_f^o$, AT 0° TO 1500°K

December 31, 1944; March 31, 1945; October 31, 1945; April 30, 1946; December 31, 1952

Temperature in °K

Free Energy of Formation, $\Delta F_f^o$, in kcal/mole

| Compound (gas) | Formula | 0 | 298.16 | 300 | 400 | 500 | 600 | 700 | 800 | 900 | 1000 | 1100 | 1200 | 1300 | 1400 | 1500 |
|---|---|---|---|---|---|---|---|---|---|---|---|---|---|---|---|---|
| Ethene (Ethylene) | $C_2H_4$ | 14.522 | 16.282 | 16.305 | 17.675 | 19.245 | 20.918 | 22.676 | 24.490 | 26.354 | 28.249 | 30.16 | 32.09 | 34.03 | 35.97 | 37.92 |
| Propene (Propylene) | $C_3H_6$ | 8.468 | 14.990 | 15.051 | 18.610 | 22.450 | 26.46 | 30.59 | 34.81 | 39.10 | 43.43 | 47.78 | 52.15 | 56.52 | 60.90 | 65.28 |
| 1-Butene | $C_4H_8$ | 4.96 | 17.09 | 17.19 | 23.23 | 29.55 | 36.07 | 42.73 | 49.45 | 56.25 | 63.07 | 69.90 | 76.74 | 83.57 | 90.38 | 97.20 |
| cis-2-Butene | " | 3.48 | 15.74 | 15.84 | 21.92 | 28.42 | 35.15 | 42.06 | 49.08 | 56.19 | 63.35 | 70.53 | 77.75 | 84.98 | 92.20 | 99.43 |
| trans-2-Butene | " | 2.24 | 15.05 | 15.15 | 21.31 | 27.83 | 34.56 | 41.45 | 48.44 | 55.53 | 62.66 | 69.81 | 76.98 | 84.16 | 91.32 | 98.50 |
| 2-Methylpropene (Isobutene) | " | 0.98 | 13.88 | 13.99 | 20.21 | 26.78 | 33.55 | 40.47 | 47.49 | 54.58 | 61.72 | 68.88 | 76.06 | 83.26 | 90.43 | 97.61 |
| 1-Pentene | $C_5H_{10}$ | +1.13 | 18.96 | 19.10 | 27.49 | 36.22 | 45.21 | 54.35 | 63.58 | 72.90 | 82.24 | 91.60 | 100.93 | 110.29 | 119.63 | 128.90 |
| cis-2-Pentene | " | -0.18 | +17.17 | 17.32 | 25.62 | 34.41 | 43.48 | 52.72 | 62.11 | 71.58 | 81.10 | 90.63 | 100.22 | 109.80 | 119.36 | 128.88 |
| trans-2-Pentene | " | -1.25 | +16.76 | 16.90 | 25.42 | 34.30 | 43.44 | 52.75 | 62.14 | 71.64 | 81.15 | 90.69 | 100.23 | 109.76 | 119.28 | 128.79 |
| 2-Methyl-1-butene | " | -2.30 | +15.51 | 15.66 | 24.03 | 32.82 | 41.85 | 51.06 | 60.37 | 69.76 | 79.20 | 88.65 | 98.14 | 107.63 | 117.10 | 126.53 |
| 3-Methyl-1-butene | " | -0.68 | +17.87 | 18.03 | 26.62 | 35.50 | 44.63 | 53.94 | 63.34 | 72.82 | 82.35 | 91.88 | 101.46 | 111.01 | 120.52 | 130.00 |
| 2-Methyl-2-butene | " | -3.67 | +14.26 | 14.42 | 22.92 | 31.85 | 41.08 | 50.49 | 60.05 | 69.69 | 79.40 | 89.12 | 98.87 | 108.63 | 118.42 | 128.17 |

TABLE 8x (PART 2) – MONOOLEFINS, $C_6$
FREE ENERGY OF FORMATION, $\Delta F_f^o$, AT 0° TO 1500°K
April 30, 1945; October 31, 1945; December 31, 1952

| Compound (gas) | Formula | Temperature in °K | | | | | | | | | | | | | | |
| --- | --- | --- | --- | --- | --- | --- | --- | --- | --- | --- | --- | --- | --- | --- | --- | --- |
| | | 0 | 298.16 | 300 | 400 | 500 | 600 | 700 | 800 | 900 | 1000 | 1100 | 1200 | 1300 | 1400 | 1500 |
| | | Free Energy of Formation, $\Delta F_f^o$, in kcal/mole | | | | | | | | | | | | | | |
| 1-Hexene | $C_6H_{12}$ | -2.54 | +20.94 | 21.13 | 31.90 | 43.08 | 54.57 | 66.25 | 78.02 | 89.90 | 101.81 | 113.73 | 125.61 | 137.53 | 149.42 | 161.23 |
| cis-2-Hexene | " | -3.89 | +19.16 | 19.35 | 30.0 | 41.2 | 52.7 | 64.5 | 76.4 | 88.3 | 100.4 | | | | | |
| trans-2-Hexene | " | -5.08 | +18.63 | 18.82 | 29.6 | 40.9 | 52.5 | 64.3 | 76.3 | 88.3 | 100.3 | | | | | |
| cis-3-Hexene | " | -3.66 | +19.66 | 19.86 | 30.7 | 42.0 | 53.7 | 65.7 | 77.7 | 89.9 | 102.1 | | | | | |
| trans-3-Hexene | " | -4.91 | +19.04 | 19.24 | 30.2 | 41.6 | 53.3 | 65.2 | 77.3 | 89.4 | 101.4 | | | | | |
| 2-Methyl-1-pentene | " | -6.04 | +17.47 | 17.66 | 28.4 | 39.6 | 51.1 | 62.7 | 74.6 | 86.5 | 98.5 | | | | | |
| 3-Methyl-1-pentene | " | -3.48 | +20.40 | 20.59 | 31.4 | 42.4 | 53.6 | 65.0 | 76.4 | 87.8 | 99.2 | | | | | |
| 4-Methyl-1-pentene | " | -3.49 | +20.45 | 20.65 | 31.7 | 43.1 | 54.8 | 66.8 | 78.9 | 90.3 | 103.2 | | | | | |
| 2-Methyl-2-pentene | " | -6.99 | +16.34 | 16.54 | 27.4 | 38.8 | 50.5 | 62.4 | 74.4 | 86.6 | 98.8 | | | | | |
| 3-Methyl-cis-2-pentene | " | -6.35 | +16.98 | 17.18 | 28.0 | 39.4 | 51.1 | 63.0 | 75.1 | 87.2 | 99.4 | | | | | |
| 3-Methyl-trans-2-pentene | " | -6.35 | +16.74 | 16.93 | 27.7 | 39.0 | 50.6 | 62.4 | 74.4 | 86.5 | 98.6 | | | | | |
| 4-Methyl-cis-2-pentene | " | -5.42 | +18.40 | 18.60 | 29.6 | 41.0 | 52.7 | 64.6 | 76.7 | 88.8 | 101.1 | | | | | |
| 4-Methyl-trans-2-pentene | " | -6.67 | +17.77 | 17.96 | 29.0 | 40.5 | 52.2 | 64.2 | 76.2 | 88.4 | 100.7 | | | | | |
| 2-Ethyl-1-butene | " | -5.17 | +18.51 | 18.71 | 29.6 | 40.9 | 52.5 | 64.4 | 76.3 | 88.4 | 100.5 | | | | | |
| 2,3-Dimethyl-1-butene | " | -7.10 | +17.43 | 17.63 | 28.7 | 40.2 | 52.0 | 64.0 | 76.0 | 88.2 | 100.4 | | | | | |
| 3,3-Dimethyl-1-butene | " | -5.82 | +19.53 | 19.73 | 31.2 | 43.3 | 55.5 | 68.1 | 80.6 | 93.2 | 106.0 | | | | | |
| 2,3-Dimethyl-2-butene | " | -7.96 | +16.52 | 16.72 | 27.9 | 39.7 | 51.8 | 64.1 | 76.6 | 89.2 | 101.8 | | | | | |

## TABLE 11x (PART 1) – DIOLEFINS, $C_3$ TO $C_5$
### FREE ENERGY OF FORMATION, $\Delta Ff°$, AT 0° TO 1500°K
October 31, 1947; April 30, 1948; December 31, 1952

Temperature in °K

Free Energy of Formation, $\Delta Ff°$, in kcal/mole

| Compound (gas) | Formula | 0 | 298.16 | 300 | 400 | 500 | 600 | 700 | 800 | 900 | 1000 | 1100 | 1200 | 1300 | 1400 | 1500 |
|---|---|---|---|---|---|---|---|---|---|---|---|---|---|---|---|---|
| Propadiene (Allene) | $C_3H_4$ | 47.70 | 48.37 | 48.38 | 49.29 | 50.33 | 51.48 | 52.68 | 53.93 | 55.23 | 56.50 | 57.86 | 59.25 | 60.62 | 61.98 | 63.35 |
| 1,2-Butadiene | $C_4H_6$ | 42.00 | 47.43 | 47.48 | 50.54 | 53.82 | 57.25 | 60.79 | 64.40 | 68.07 | 71.77 | 75.48 | 79.33 | 82.97 | 86.72 | 90.47 |
| 1,3-Butadiene | " | 29.78 | 36.01 | 36.07 | 39.46 | 43.05 | 46.78 | 50.60 | 54.48 | 58.40 | 62.36 | 66.32 | 70.30 | 74.28 | 78.25 | 82.24 |
| 1,2-Pentadiene | $C_5H_8$ | 39.32 | 50.29 | 50.38 | 55.77 | 61.44 | 67.28 | 73.21 | 79.27 | 85.41 | 91.53 | 97.70 | 103.85 | 109.96 | 116.16 | 122.22 |
| 1,cis-3-Pentadiene (cis-Piperylene) | " | 23.73 | 34.88 | 34.97 | 40.61 | 46.60 | 52.77 | 59.09 | 65.44 | 71.98 | 78.44 | 84.97 | 91.50 | 98.14 | 104.77 | 111.13 |
| 1,trans-3-Pentadiene (trans-Piperylene) | " | 23.39 | 35.07 | 35.17 | 40.87 | 46.91 | 53.09 | 59.38 | 65.74 | 72.18 | 78.70 | 85.18 | 91.64 | 98.19 | 104.71 | 111.09 |
| 1,4-Pentadiene | " | 29.63 | 40.69 | 40.78 | 46.16 | 51.85 | 57.71 | 63.66 | 69.66 | 75.81 | 81.94 | 88.12 | 94.28 | 100.53 | 106.61 | 112.83 |
| 2,3-Pentadiene | " | 37.77 | 49.22 | 49.31 | 54.94 | 60.84 | 66.99 | 73.27 | 79.64 | 86.11 | 92.58 | 99.12 | 105.66 | 112.18 | 118.67 | 125.32 |
| 3-Methyl-1,2-butadiene | " | 35.64 | 47.47 | 47.57 | 53.29 | 59.31 | 65.46 | 71.77 | 78.23 | 84.70 | 91.25 | 97.76 | 104.25 | 110.83 | 117.38 | 123.94 |
| 2-Methyl-1,3-butadiene (Isoprene) | " | 22.98 | 34.87 | 34.97 | 40.78 | 46.85 | 53.10 | 59.46 | 65.89 | 72.40 | 78.89 | 85.43 | 91.95 | 98.56 | 105.00 | 111.58 |

TABLE 18x – ALKYL CYCLOPENTENES, $C_5$ TO $C_7$

FREE ENERGY OF FORMATION, $\Delta F_f°$, AT 0° TO 1500°K

December 31, 1952

| Compound (gas) | Formula | \multicolumn{15}{c}{Temperature in °K} |
|---|---|---|---|---|---|---|---|---|---|---|---|---|---|---|---|---|
| | | 0 | 298.16 | 300 | 400 | 500 | 600 | 700 | 800 | 900 | 1000 | 1100 | 1200 | 1300 | 1400 | 1500 |
| | | \multicolumn{16}{c}{Free Energy of Formation, $\Delta F_f°$, in kcal/mole} |
| Cyclopentene | $C_5H_8$ | 13.76 | 26.48 | 26.60 | 33.14 | 40.12 | 47.37 | 54.82 | 62.37 | 70.02 | 77.72 | 85.44 | 93.17 | 100.9 | 108.6 | 116.3 |
| 1-Methylcyclopentene | $C_6H_{10}$ | | | | | | | | | | | | | | | |
| 3-Methylcyclopentene | " | | | | | | | | | | | | | | | |
| 4-Methylcyclopentene | " | | | | | | | | | | | | | | | |
| 1-Ethylcyclopentene | $C_7H_{12}$ | | | | | | | | | | | | | | | |
| 3-Ethylcyclopentene | " | | | | | | | | | | | | | | | |
| 4-Ethylcyclopentene | " | | | | | | | | | | | | | | | |
| 1,2-Dimethylcyclopentene | " | | | | | | | | | | | | | | | |
| 1,3-Dimethylcyclopentene | " | | | | | | | | | | | | | | | |
| 1,4-Dimethylcyclopentene | " | | | | | | | | | | | | | | | |
| 1,5-Dimethylcyclopentene | " | | | | | | | | | | | | | | | |
| 3,3-Dimethylcyclopentene | " | | | | | | | | | | | | | | | |
| 3,cis-4-Dimethylcyclopentene | " | | | | | | | | | | | | | | | |
| 3,trans-4-Dimethylcyclopentene | " | | | | | | | | | | | | | | | |
| 3,cis-5-Dimethylcyclopentene | " | | | | | | | | | | | | | | | |
| 3,trans-5-Dimethylcyclopentene | " | | | | | | | | | | | | | | | |
| 4,4-Dimethylcyclopentene | " | | | | | | | | | | | | | | | |

TABLE 19x - ALKYL CYCLOHEXENES, C₆ TO C₈

FREE ENERGY OF FORMATION, $\Delta F_f^o$, AT 0° TO 1500°K

December 31, 1952

Free Energy of Formation, $\Delta F_f^o$, in kcal/mole

| Compound (gas) | Formula | Temperature in °K | | | | | | | | | | | | | | |
|---|---|---|---|---|---|---|---|---|---|---|---|---|---|---|---|---|
| | | 0 | 298.16 | 300 | 400 | 500 | 600 | 700 | 800 | 900 | 1000 | 1100 | 1200 | 1300 | 1400 | 1500 |
| Cyclohexene | C₆H₁₀ | 5.76 | 25.12 | 25.28 | 34.60 | 44.36 | 54.38 | 64.58 | 74.86 | 85.22 | 95.60 | 105.96 | 116.30 | 126.66 | 136.99 | 147.29 |
| 1-Methylcyclohexene | C₇H₁₂ | | | | | | | | | | | | | | | |
| 3-Methylcyclohexene | " | | | | | | | | | | | | | | | |
| 4-Methylcyclohexene | " | | | | | | | | | | | | | | | |
| 1-Ethylcyclohexene | C₈H₁₄ | | | | | | | | | | | | | | | |
| 3-Ethylcyclohexene | " | | | | | | | | | | | | | | | |
| 4-Ethylcyclohexene | " | | | | | | | | | | | | | | | |
| 1,2-Dimethylcyclohexene | " | | | | | | | | | | | | | | | |
| 1,3-Dimethylcyclohexene | " | | | | | | | | | | | | | | | |
| 1,4-Dimethylcyclohexene | " | | | | | | | | | | | | | | | |
| 1,5-Dimethylcyclohexene | " | | | | | | | | | | | | | | | |
| 1,6-Dimethylcyclohexene | " | | | | | | | | | | | | | | | |
| 3,3-Dimethylcyclohexene | " | | | | | | | | | | | | | | | |
| 3,cis-4-Dimethylcyclohexene | " | | | | | | | | | | | | | | | |
| 3,trans-4-Dimethylcyclohexene | " | | | | | | | | | | | | | | | |
| 3,cis-5-Dimethylcyclohexene | " | | | | | | | | | | | | | | | |
| 3,trans-5-Dimethylcyclohexene | " | | | | | | | | | | | | | | | |
| 3,cis-6-Dimethylcyclohexene | " | | | | | | | | | | | | | | | |
| 3,trans-6-Dimethylcyclohexene | " | | | | | | | | | | | | | | | |
| 4,4-Dimethylcyclohexene | " | | | | | | | | | | | | | | | |
| 4,cis-5-Dimethylcyclohexene | " | | | | | | | | | | | | | | | |
| 4,trans-5-Dimethylcyclohexene | " | | | | | | | | | | | | | | | |

TABLE 25x (PART 1) – NORMAL ACETYLENES (1-ALKYNES), C$_2$ TO C$_{20}$

FREE ENERGY OF FORMATION, $\Delta F_f°$, AT 0° TO 1500°K

February 28, 1946; December 31, 1952

| Compound (gas) | Formula | Temperature in °K — Free Energy of Formation, $\Delta F_f°$, in kcal/mole | | | | | | | | | | | | | | |
|---|---|---|---|---|---|---|---|---|---|---|---|---|---|---|---|---|
| | | 0 | 298.16 | 300 | 400 | 500 | 600 | 700 | 800 | 900 | 1000 | 1100 | 1200 | 1300 | 1400 | 1500 |
| Ethyne (Acetylene) | C$_2$H$_2$ | 54.329 | 50.000 | 49.975 | 48.577 | 47.196 | 45.835 | 44.498 | 43.178 | 41.882 | 40.604 | 39.339 | 38.089 | 36.854 | 35.624 | 34.410 |
| Propyne (Methylacetylene) | C$_3$H$_4$ | 46.017 | 46.313 | 46.481 | 47.287 | 48.224 | 49.255 | 50.360 | 51.514 | 52.715 | 53.95 | 55.20 | 56.46 | 57.74 | 59.02 | 60.32 |
| 1-Butyne (Ethylacetylene) | C$_4$H$_6$ | 42.74 | 48.30 | 48.35 | 51.45 | 54.77 | 58.23 | 61.80 | 65.44 | 69.14 | 72.88 | 76.63 | 80.40 | 84.19 | 87.98 | 91.77 |
| 1-Pentyne | C$_5$H$_8$ | 38.90 | 50.16 | 50.25 | 55.70 | 61.42 | 67.35 | 73.40 | 79.54 | 85.78 | 92.05 | 98.32 | 104.59 | 110.90 | 117.21 | 123.45 |
| 1-Hexyne | C$_6$H$_{10}$ | 35.26 | 52.17 | 52.30 | 60.13 | 68.30 | 76.73 | 85.31 | 93.99 | 102.79 | 111.62 | 120.44 | 129.26 | 138.12 | 146.98 | 155.77 |
| 1-Heptyne | C$_7$H$_{12}$ | 31.61 | 54.18 | 54.36 | 64.56 | 75.18 | 86.11 | 97.22 | 108.44 | 119.80 | 131.18 | 142.56 | 153.93 | 165.34 | 176.75 | 188.08 |
| 1-Octyne | C$_8$H$_{14}$ | 27.97 | 56.19 | 56.41 | 68.99 | 82.07 | 95.50 | 109.13 | 122.89 | 136.81 | 150.75 | 164.68 | 178.59 | 192.57 | 206.52 | 220.40 |
| 1-Nonyne | C$_9$H$_{16}$ | 24.32 | 58.20 | 58.46 | 73.42 | 88.95 | 104.88 | 121.04 | 137.34 | 153.82 | 170.31 | 186.80 | 203.26 | 219.79 | 236.29 | 252.71 |
| 1-Decyne | C$_{10}$H$_{18}$ | 20.68 | 60.20 | 60.52 | 77.86 | 95.83 | 114.26 | 132.95 | 151.80 | 170.82 | 189.88 | 208.92 | 227.93 | 247.01 | 266.06 | 285.03 |
| 1-Undecyne | C$_{11}$H$_{20}$ | 17.04 | 62.21 | 62.57 | 82.29 | 102.71 | 123.64 | 144.86 | 166.25 | 187.83 | 209.45 | 231.04 | 252.60 | 274.23 | 295.82 | 317.35 |
| 1-Dodecyne | C$_{12}$H$_{22}$ | 13.39 | 64.22 | 64.62 | 86.72 | 109.59 | 133.02 | 156.77 | 180.70 | 204.84 | 229.01 | 253.16 | 277.27 | 301.45 | 325.59 | 349.66 |
| 1-Tridecyne | C$_{13}$H$_{24}$ | 9.75 | 66.23 | 66.67 | 91.15 | 116.48 | 142.41 | 168.68 | 195.15 | 221.85 | 248.58 | 275.28 | 301.93 | 328.68 | 355.36 | 381.98 |
| 1-Tetradecyne | C$_{14}$H$_{26}$ | 6.10 | 68.24 | 68.73 | 95.58 | 123.36 | 151.79 | 180.59 | 209.60 | 238.86 | 268.14 | 297.40 | 326.60 | 355.90 | 385.13 | 414.29 |
| 1-Pentadecyne | C$_{15}$H$_{28}$ | 2.46 | 70.25 | 70.78 | 100.01 | 130.24 | 161.17 | 192.50 | 224.05 | 255.87 | 287.71 | 319.52 | 351.27 | 383.12 | 414.90 | 446.61 |
| 1-Hexadecyne | C$_{16}$H$_{30}$ | -1.18 | 72.26 | 72.83 | 104.44 | 137.12 | 170.55 | 204.41 | 238.50 | 272.88 | 307.28 | 341.64 | 375.94 | 410.34 | 444.67 | 478.93 |
| 1-Heptadecyne | C$_{17}$H$_{32}$ | -4.83 | 74.27 | 74.89 | 108.87 | 144.00 | 179.93 | 216.32 | 252.95 | 289.89 | 326.84 | 363.76 | 400.61 | 437.56 | 474.44 | 511.24 |
| 1-Octadecyne | C$_{18}$H$_{34}$ | -8.47 | 76.28 | 76.94 | 113.30 | 150.89 | 189.32 | 228.23 | 267.40 | 306.90 | 346.41 | 385.88 | 425.27 | 464.79 | 504.21 | 543.56 |
| 1-Nonadecyne | C$_{19}$H$_{36}$ | -12.12 | 78.29 | 78.99 | 117.73 | 157.77 | 198.70 | 240.14 | 281.85 | 323.91 | 365.97 | 408.00 | 449.94 | 492.01 | 533.98 | 575.87 |
| 1-Eicosyne | C$_{20}$H$_{38}$ | -15.76 | 81.00 | 81.04 | 122.16 | 164.65 | 208.08 | 252.05 | 296.30 | 340.92 | 385.54 | 430.12 | 474.61 | 519.23 | 563.74 | 608.19 |
| Increment per CH$_2$ group, applicable beyond 1-pentyne | | -3.644 | +2.009 | 2.053 | 4.431 | 6.882 | 9.382 | 11.910 | 14.451 | 17.009 | 19.566 | 22.120 | 24.668 | 27.222 | 29.769 | 32.316 |

TABLE 12x – ACETYLENES, $C_2$ TO $C_5$
FREE ENERGY OF FORMATION, $\Delta F_f°$, AT 0° TO 1500°K
April 30, 1945; December 31, 1952

Temperature in °K

Free Energy of Formation, $\Delta F_f°$, in kcal/mole

| Compound (gas) | Formula | 0 | 298.16 | 300 | 400 | 500 | 600 | 700 | 800 | 900 | 1000 | 1100 | 1200 | 1300 | 1400 | 1500 |
|---|---|---|---|---|---|---|---|---|---|---|---|---|---|---|---|---|
| Ethyne (Acetylene) | $C_2H_2$ | 54.329 | 50.000 | 49.975 | 48.577 | 47.196 | 45.835 | 44.498 | 43.178 | 41.882 | 40.604 | 39.339 | 38.089 | 36.854 | 35.624 | 34.410 |
| Propyne (Methylacetylene) | $C_3H_4$ | 46.017 | 46.313 | 46.481 | 47.287 | 48.224 | 49.255 | 50.360 | 51.514 | 52.715 | 53.95 | 55.20 | 56.46 | 57.74 | 59.02 | 60.32 |
| 1-Butyne (Ethylacetylene) | $C_4H_6$ | 42.74 | 48.30 | 48.35 | 51.45 | 54.77 | 58.23 | 61.80 | 65.44 | 69.14 | 72.88 | 76.63 | 80.40 | 84.19 | 87.98 | 91.77 |
| 2-Butyne (Dimethylacetylene) | " | 38.09 | 44.32 | 44.38 | 47.68 | 51.22 | 54.94 | 58.78 | 62.70 | 66.70 | 70.74 | 74.80 | 78.89 | 82.99 | 87.09 | 91.20 |
| 1-Pentyne | $C_5H_8$ | 38.90 | 50.16 | 50.25 | 55.70 | 61.42 | 67.35 | 73.40 | 79.54 | 85.78 | 92.05 | 98.32 | 104.59 | 110.90 | 117.21 | 123.45 |
| 2-Pentyne | " | 35.48 | 46.41 | 46.51 | 51.96 | 57.74 | 63.75 | 69.92 | 76.19 | 82.55 | 88.96 | 95.39 | 101.84 | 108.32 | 114.79 | 121.26 |
| 3-Methyl-1-butyne | " | 37.37 | 49.12 | 49.23 | 54.96 | 60.97 | 67.17 | 73.50 | 79.92 | 86.40 | 92.93 | 99.47 | 106.04 | 112.61 | 119.15 | 125.68 |

TABLE 21x (PART 1) - NORMAL ALKYL BENZENES, C$_6$ TO C$_{22}$

FREE ENERGY OF FORMATION, $\Delta F_f^o$, AT 0° TO 1500°K

November 30, 1945; December 31, 1952

| Compound (gas) | Formula | Temperature in °K | | | | | | | | | | | | | | |
|---|---|---|---|---|---|---|---|---|---|---|---|---|---|---|---|---|
| | | 0 | 298.16 | 300 | 400 | 500 | 600 | 700 | 800 | 900 | 1000 | 1100 | 1200 | 1300 | 1400 | 1500 |
| | | Free Energy of Formation, $\Delta F_f^o$, in kcal/mole | | | | | | | | | | | | | | |
| Benzene | C$_6$H$_6$ | 24.000 | 30.989 | 31.058 | 35.008 | 39.242 | 43.663 | 48.211 | 52.838 | 57.537 | 62.270 | 67.02 | 71.79 | 76.57 | 81.34 | 86.11 |
| Methylbenzene (Toluene) | C$_7$H$_8$ | 17.500 | 29.228 | 29.335 | 35.390 | 41.811 | 48.477 | 55.306 | 62.236 | 69.255 | 76.320 | 83.40 | 90.50 | 97.61 | 104.71 | 111.81 |
| Ethylbenzene | C$_8$H$_{10}$ | 13.917 | 31.208 | 31.357 | 39.741 | 48.554 | 57.646 | 66.921 | 76.302 | 85.779 | 95.303 | 104.84 | 114.39 | 123.95 | 133.48 | 143.02 |
| n-Propylbenzene | C$_9$H$_{12}$ | 9.810 | 32.805 | 32.992 | 43.72 | 54.95 | 66.50 | 78.26 | 90.14 | 102.16 | 114.2 | 126.2 | 138.3 | 150.4 | 162.4 | 174.4 |
| n-Butylbenzene | C$_{10}$H$_{14}$ | 5.93 | 34.58 | 34.81 | 47.92 | 61.60 | 75.66 | 89.95 | 104.38 | 118.95 | 133.6 | 148.2 | 162.8 | 177.4 | 192.0 | 206.6 |
| n-Pentylbenzene | C$_{11}$H$_{16}$ | 2.28 | 36.54 | 36.82 | 52.29 | 68.41 | 84.96 | 101.76 | 118.72 | 135.83 | 153.0 | 170.2 | 187.3 | 204.4 | 221.6 | 238.7 |
| n-Hexylbenzene | C$_{12}$H$_{18}$ | -1.36 | 38.55 | 38.87 | 56.72 | 75.29 | 94.34 | 113.67 | 133.17 | 152.84 | 172.6 | 192.3 | 212.0 | 231.6 | 251.4 | 271.0 |
| n-Heptylbenzene | C$_{13}$H$_{20}$ | -5.01 | 40.56 | 40.93 | 61.15 | 82.17 | 103.72 | 125.58 | 147.62 | 169.85 | 192.1 | 214.4 | 236.6 | 258.8 | 281.1 | 303.3 |
| n-Octylbenzene | C$_{14}$H$_{22}$ | -8.65 | 42.57 | 42.98 | 65.58 | 89.06 | 113.11 | 137.49 | 162.07 | 186.86 | 211.7 | 236.6 | 261.3 | 286.1 | 310.9 | 335.7 |
| n-Nonylbenzene | C$_{15}$H$_{24}$ | -12.30 | 44.58 | 45.03 | 70.01 | 95.94 | 122.49 | 149.40 | 176.52 | 203.87 | 231.3 | 258.7 | 286.0 | 313.3 | 340.7 | 368.0 |
| n-Decylbenzene | C$_{16}$H$_{26}$ | -15.94 | 46.58 | 47.08 | 74.44 | 102.82 | 131.87 | 161.31 | 190.98 | 220.88 | 250.8 | 280.8 | 310.6 | 340.5 | 370.4 | 400.3 |
| n-Undecylbenzene | C$_{17}$H$_{28}$ | -19.58 | 48.59 | 49.14 | 78.88 | 109.70 | 141.25 | 173.22 | 205.43 | 237.88 | 270.4 | 302.9 | 335.3 | 367.7 | 400.2 | 432.6 |
| n-Dodecylbenzene | C$_{18}$H$_{30}$ | -23.23 | 50.60 | 51.19 | 83.31 | 116.58 | 150.63 | 185.13 | 219.88 | 254.89 | 290.0 | 325.0 | 360.0 | 394.9 | 430.0 | 464.9 |
| n-Tridecylbenzene | C$_{19}$H$_{32}$ | -26.87 | 52.61 | 53.24 | 87.74 | 123.47 | 160.02 | 197.04 | 234.33 | 271.90 | 309.6 | 347.2 | 384.7 | 422.2 | 459.8 | 497.3 |
| n-Tetradecylbenzene | C$_{20}$H$_{34}$ | -30.52 | 54.62 | 55.30 | 92.17 | 130.35 | 169.40 | 208.95 | 248.78 | 288.91 | 329.1 | 369.3 | 409.3 | 449.4 | 489.5 | 529.6 |
| n-Pentadecylbenzene | C$_{21}$H$_{36}$ | -34.15 | 56.63 | 57.35 | 96.60 | 137.23 | 178.78 | 220.86 | 263.23 | 305.92 | 348.7 | 391.4 | 434.0 | 476.6 | 519.3 | 561.9 |
| n-Hexadecylbenzene | C$_{22}$H$_{38}$ | -37.80 | 58.64 | 59.40 | 101.03 | 144.11 | 188.16 | 232.77 | 277.68 | 322.93 | 368.3 | 413.5 | 458.7 | 503.8 | 549.1 | 594.2 |
| Increment per CH$_2$ group, applicable beyond n-pentylbenzene | | -3.644 | +2.009 | 2.053 | 4.431 | 6.882 | 9.382 | 11.910 | 14.451 | 17.009 | 19.57 | 22.12 | 24.67 | 27.22 | 29.77 | 32.32 |

TABLE 5x – ALKYL BENZENES, $C_6$ TO $C_9$

FREE ENERGY OF FORMATION, $\Delta F_f^o$, AT 0° TO 1500°K

November 30, 1945

| Compound (gas) | Formula | Temperature in °K | | | | | | | | | | | | | | |
|---|---|---|---|---|---|---|---|---|---|---|---|---|---|---|---|---|
| | | Free Energy of Formation, $\Delta F_f^o$, in kcal/mole | | | | | | | | | | | | | | |
| | | 0 | 298.16 | 300 | 400 | 500 | 600 | 700 | 800 | 900 | 1000 | 1100 | 1200 | 1300 | 1400 | 1500 |
| Benzene | $C_6H_6$ | 24.000 | 30.989 | 31.058 | 35.008 | 39.242 | 43.663 | 48.211 | 52.838 | 57.537 | 62.270 | 67.02 | 71.79 | 76.57 | 81.34 | 86.11 |
| Methylbenzene (Toluene) | $C_7H_8$ | 17.500 | 29.228 | 29.335 | 35.390 | 41.811 | 48.477 | 55.306 | 62.236 | 69.255 | 76.320 | 83.40 | 90.50 | 97.61 | 104.71 | 111.81 |
| Ethylbenzene | $C_8H_{10}$ | 13.917 | 31.208 | 31.357 | 39.741 | 48.554 | 57.646 | 66.921 | 76.302 | 85.779 | 95.303 | 104.84 | 114.39 | 123.95 | 133.48 | 143.02 |
| 1,2-Dimethylbenzene (o-Xylene) | " | 11.096 | 29.177 | 29.329 | 37.883 | 46.852 | 56.103 | 65.548 | 75.110 | 84.777 | 94.494 | 104.23 | 113.99 | 123.76 | 133.50 | 143.24 |
| 1,3-Dimethylbenzene (m-Xylene) | " | 10.926 | 28.405 | 28.554 | 37.008 | 45.906 | 55.099 | 64.492 | 74.006 | 83.630 | 93.307 | 103.00 | 112.72 | 122.45 | 132.15 | 141.85 |
| 1,4-Dimethylbenzene (p-Xylene) | " | 11.064 | 28.952 | 29.104 | 37.688 | 46.724 | 56.060 | 65.604 | 75.275 | 85.058 | 94.897 | 104.76 | 114.64 | 124.54 | 134.40 | 144.27 |
| n-Propylbenzene | $C_9H_{12}$ | 9.810 | 32.810 | 33.000 | 43.73 | 54.94 | 66.48 | 78.22 | 90.09 | 102.07 | 114.08 | 126.1 | 138.2 | 150.3 | 162.3 | 174.3 |
| Isopropylbenzene | " | 9.250 | 32.738 | 32.934 | 43.96 | 55.46 | 67.29 | 79.33 | 91.48 | 103.74 | 116.06 | 128.4 | 140.7 | 153.1 | 165.4 | 177.6 |
| 1-Methyl-2-ethylbenzene | " | 8.092 | 31.323 | 31.514 | 42.26 | 53.48 | 65.02 | 76.78 | 88.65 | 100.64 | 112.67 | 124.7 | 136.8 | 148.9 | 160.9 | 173.0 |
| 1-Methyl-3-ethylbenzene | " | 7.593 | 30.217 | 30.406 | 41.05 | 52.20 | 63.68 | 75.38 | 87.20 | 99.14 | 111.14 | 123.2 | 135.2 | 147.2 | 159.2 | 171.2 |
| 1-Methyl-4-ethylbenzene | " | 7.241 | 30.281 | 30.472 | 41.25 | 52.54 | 64.16 | 76.02 | 88.00 | 100.10 | 112.26 | 124.4 | 136.6 | 148.8 | 161.0 | 173.2 |
| 1,2,3-Trimethylbenzene | " | 5.527 | 29.319 | 29.513 | 40.56 | 52.06 | 63.91 | 76.01 | 88.26 | 100.63 | 113.07 | 125.5 | 138.0 | 150.6 | 163.0 | 175.5 |
| 1,2,4-Trimethylbenzene | " | 4.468 | 27.912 | 28.104 | 39.02 | 50.39 | 62.11 | 74.07 | 86.17 | 98.41 | 110.71 | 123.0 | 135.4 | 147.8 | 160.1 | 172.4 |
| 1,3,5-Trimethylbenzene | " | 4.241 | 28.172 | 28.369 | 39.558 | 51.223 | 63.237 | 75.495 | 87.903 | 100.443 | 113.045 | 125.67 | 138.32 | 150.98 | 163.60 | 176.23 |

## TABLE 13x – STYRENES, $C_8$ and $C_9$

### FREE ENERGY OF FORMATION, $\Delta F_f^\circ$, FOR THE IDEAL GAS STATE, AT 0° TO 1500°K

September 30, 1947

Temperature, in °K

Free Energy of Formation, $\Delta F_f^\circ$, in Kcal/mole

| Compound (gas) | Formula | 0 | 298.16 | 300 | 400 | 500 | 600 | 700 | 800 | 900 | 1000 | 1100 | 1200 | 1300 | 1400 | 1500 |
|---|---|---|---|---|---|---|---|---|---|---|---|---|---|---|---|---|
| Ethenylbenzene (Styrene; Vinylbenzene; Phenylethylene) | $C_8H_8$ | 40.34 | 51.10 | 51.20 | 56.74 | 62.61 | 68.67 | 74.87 | 81.16 | 87.53 | 93.92 | 100.33 | 106.77 | 113.19 | 119.60 | 126.03 |
| Isopropenylbenzene (α-Methylstyrene; 2-Phenyl-1-propene) | $C_9H_{10}$ | 33.33 | 49.84 | 49.99 | 57.90 | 66.26 | 74.85 | 83.60 | 92.51 | 101.51 | 110.56 | 119.53 | 128.66 | 137.72 | 146.82 | 155.85 |
| cis-1-Propenylbenzene (cis-β-Methylstyrene; cis-1-Phenyl-1-propene) | " | 35.33 | 51.84 | 51.99 | 59.90 | 68.26 | 76.85 | 85.60 | 94.51 | 103.51 | 112.56 | 121.53 | 130.66 | 139.72 | 148.82 | 157.85 |
| trans-1-Propenylbenzene (trans-β-Methylstyrene; trans-1-Phenyl-1-propene) | " | 34.45 | 51.08 | 51.23 | 59.22 | 67.63 | 76.27 | 85.07 | 94.03 | 103.08 | 112.08 | 121.20 | 130.26 | 139.36 | 148.36 | 157.57 |
| 1-Methyl-2-ethenylbenzene (o-Methylstyrene) | " | 34.63 | 51.14 | 51.29 | 59.20 | 67.56 | 76.15 | 84.90 | 93.81 | 102.81 | 111.86 | 120.83 | 129.96 | 139.02 | 148.12 | 157.15 |
| 1-Methyl-3-ethenylbenzene (m-Methylstyrene) | " | 33.93 | 50.02 | 50.17 | 57.94 | 66.16 | 74.61 | 83.22 | 91.99 | 100.85 | 109.76 | 118.59 | 127.58 | 136.50 | 145.46 | 154.35 |
| 1-Methyl-4-ethenylbenzene (p-Methylstyrene) | " | 33.73 | 50.24 | 50.39 | 58.30 | 66.66 | 75.25 | 84.00 | 92.91 | 101.91 | 110.96 | 119.93 | 129.06 | 138.12 | 147.22 | 156.25 |

Table OOy - O, H, N, C

LOGARITHM OF EQUILIBRIUM CONSTANT OF FORMATION, $\log_{10} Kf$, AT 0° TO 5000°K

June 30, 1946; April 30, 1948; August 31, 1949

| Compound (gas, monatomic) | Formula | Temperature in °K | | | | | | | | | | | | | | |
|---|---|---|---|---|---|---|---|---|---|---|---|---|---|---|---|---|
| | | 0 | 298.16 | 300 | 400 | 500 | 600 | 700 | 800 | 900 | 1000 | 1100 | 1200 | 1300 | 1400 | 1500 |
| | | Logarithm of Equilibrium Constant of Formation, $\log_{10} Kf$ | | | | | | | | | | | | | | |
| Oxygen | O | | -40.31022 | -40.04460 | -29.25654 | -22.76620 | -18.42943 | -15.32498 | -12.99286 | -11.17574 | -9.72002 | -8.52720 | -7.53183 | -6.68892 | -5.96561 | -5.33746 |
| Hydrogen | H | | -35.60481 | -35.37064 | -25.87091 | -20.15490 | -16.33349 | -13.59607 | -11.53714 | -9.93179 | -8.64411 | -7.58754 | -6.70515 | -5.95662 | -5.31344 | -4.75505 |
| Nitrogen | N | | -59.71717 | -59.33243 | -43.73657 | -34.36273 | -28.10296 | -23.62447 | -20.26055 | -17.64059 | -15.54186 | -13.82240 | -12.36802 | -11.17299 | -10.13049 | -9.22619 |
| Carbon | C | | -117.8971 | -117.1249 | -86.6822 | -67.0326 | -54.4894 | -45.5234 | -38.7974 | -33.5661 | -29.3795 | -25.9551 | -23.1022 | -20.6886 | -18.6206 | -16.8206 |

| Compound (gas, monatomic) | Formula | Temperature in °K | | | | | | | | | | | | |
|---|---|---|---|---|---|---|---|---|---|---|---|---|---|---|
| | | 1000 | 1250 | 1500 | 1750 | 2000 | 2250 | 2500 | 2750 | 3000 | 3500 | 4000 | 4500 | 5000 |
| | | Logarithm of Equilibrium Constant of Formation, $\log_{10} Kf$ | | | | | | | | | | | | |
| Oxygen | O | -9.72002 | -7.09350 | -5.33746 | -4.07964 | -3.13463 | -2.39707 | -1.80756 | -1.32400 | -0.92045 | -0.28561 | 0.19112 | 0.56254 | 0.85971 |
| Hydrogen | H | -8.64411 | -6.31584 | -4.75505 | -3.6341 | -2.7836 | -2.1299 | -1.6005 | -1.1659 | -0.6024 | -0.2292 | 0.2023 | 0.5391 | 0.6096 |
| Nitrogen | N | -15.54186 | -11.75638 | -9.22619 | -7.41472 | -6.05308 | -4.99210 | -4.14173 | -3.44470 | -2.96290 | -1.94647 | -1.25692 | -0.71819 | -0.28505 |
| Carbon | C | -29.3795 | -21.8468 | -16.8206 | -13.2490 | -10.5668 | -8.4454 | -6.8208 | -5.4637 | -4.3338 | -2.5614 | -1.2391 | | |

TABLE Oy – $O_2$, $H_2$, OH, $H_2O$, $N_2$, NO, C, CO, $CO_2$

LOGARITHM OF EQUILIBRIUM CONSTANT OF FORMATION, $\log_{10} K_f$, AT 0° TO 5000°K

July 31, 1944; August 31, 1946; June 30, 1949

Logarithm of Equilibrium Constant of Formation, $\log_{10} K_f$

| Compound | Formula | State | Temperature in °K |||||||||||||||
|---|---|---|---|---|---|---|---|---|---|---|---|---|---|---|---|---|---|
| | | | 0 | 50 | 100 | 150 | 200 | 250 | 298.16 | 300 | 400 | 500 | 600 | 700 | 800 | 900 | 1000 |
| Oxygen | $O_2$ | gas | 0 | 0 | 0 | 0 | 0 | 0 | 0 | 0 | 0 | 0 | 0 | 0 | 0 | 0 | 0 |
| Hydrogen | $H_2$ | gas | 0 | 0 | 0 | 0 | 0 | 0 | 0 | 0 | 0 | 0 | 0 | 0 | 0 | 0 | 0 |
| Hydroxyl | OH | gas | infinite | | | | | | -6.546 | -6.50431 | -4.66916 | -3.56897 | -2.83704 | -2.31549 | -1.92561 | -1.62422 | -1.38407 |
| Water | $H_2O$ | gas | infinite | | | | | | 40.04724 | 39.78717 | 29.24052 | 22.88604 | 18.63268 | 15.58329 | 13.28854 | 11.49733 | 10.05973 |
| Nitrogen | $N_2$ | gas | 0 | 0 | 0 | 0 | 0 | 0 | 0 | 0 | 0 | 0 | 0 | 0 | 0 | 0 | 0 |
| Nitric Oxide | NO | gas | infinite | | -46.50248 | | -22.95620 | -18.23908 | -15.18688 | -15.08963 | -11.15555 | -8.79436 | -7.21929 | -6.09355 | -5.24995 | -4.59365 | -4.06805 |
| Carbon | C | solid graphite | 0 | 0 | 0 | 0 | 0 | 0 | 0 | 0 | 0 | 0 | 0 | 0 | 0 | 0 | 0 |
| Carbon Monoxide | CO | gas | infinite | | 62.82446 | | 38.58452 | 27.78357 | 24.04778 | 23.92832 | 19.12679 | 16.25296 | 14.33598 | 12.96488 | 11.93168 | 11.12555 | 10.47761 |
| Carbon Dioxide | $CO_2$ | gas | infinite | | | | | | 69.09124 | 66.66781 | 51.53639 | 41.25831 | 34.40082 | 29.50278 | 25.82659 | 22.96647 | 20.67680 |

Logarithm of Equilibrium Constant of Formation, $\log_{10} K_f$

| Compound | Formula | State | Temperature in °K |||||||||||||||
|---|---|---|---|---|---|---|---|---|---|---|---|---|---|---|---|---|---|
| | | | 1100 | 1200 | 1300 | 1400 | 1500 | 1750 | 2000 | 2250 | 2500 | 2750 | 3000 | 3500 | 4000 | 4500 | 5000 |
| Oxygen | $O_2$ | gas | 0 | 0 | 0 | 0 | 0 | 0 | 0 | 0 | 0 | 0 | 0 | 0 | 0 | 0 | 0 |
| Hydrogen | $H_2$ | gas | 0 | 0 | 0 | 0 | 0 | 0 | 0 | 0 | 0 | 0 | 0 | 0 | 0 | 00 | 0 |
| Hydroxyl | OH | gas | -1.18815 | -1.02517 | -0.88846 | -0.77215 | -0.67114 | -0.47094 | -0.32181 | -0.20670 | -0.11550 | -0.04139 | +0.02026 | 0.11548 | 0.18511 | 0.23861 | 0.28029 |
| Water | $H_2O$ | gas | 8.88088 | 7.89633 | 7.06060 | 6.34355 | 5.72047 | 4.47135 | 3.53063 | 2.79702 | 2.20755 | 1.7265 | 1.3222 | 0.6928 | 0.2207 | -0.1530 | -0.4502 |
| Nitrogen | $N_2$ | gas | 0 | 0 | 0 | 0 | 0 | 0 | 0 | 0 | 0 | 0 | 0 | 0 | 0 | 0 | 0 |
| Nitric Oxide | NO | gas | -3.63794 | -3.27909 | -2.97662 | -2.71720 | -2.49144 | -2.04086 | -1.70303 | -1.44008 | -1.23005 | -1.05816 | -0.91549 | -0.69177 | -0.52589 | -0.39802 | -0.29753 |
| Carbon | C | solid graphite | 0 | 0 | 0 | 0 | 0 | 0 | 0 | 0 | 0 | 0 | 0 | 0 | 0 | 0 | 0 |
| Carbon Monoxide | CO | gas | 9.94451 | 9.49779 | 9.11764 | 8.78999 | 8.50442 | 7.9264 | 7.4863 | 7.1382 | 6.8545 | 6.6176 | 6.4180 | 6.0937 | 5.8412 | | |
| Carbon Dioxide | $CO_2$ | gas | 18.80244 | 17.23996 | 15.91649 | 14.78164 | 13.79867 | 11.8290 | 10.3504 | 9.1974 | 8.2768 | 7.5196 | 6.8871 | 5.8927 | 5.1424 | | . |

TABLE 20y (PART 1) — NORMAL PARAFFINS, $C_1$ TO $C_{20}$

LOGARITHM OF EQUILIBRIUM CONSTANT OF FORMATION, $\log_{10} K_f$, AT 0° TO 1500°K

November 30, 1945; December 31, 1952

| Compound (gas) | Formula | Temperature in °K | | | | | | | | | | | | | | |
| --- | --- | --- | --- | --- | --- | --- | --- | --- | --- | --- | --- | --- | --- | --- | --- | --- |
| | | 0 | 298.16 | 300 | 400 | 500 | 600 | 700 | 800 | 900 | 1000 | 1100 | 1200 | 1300 | 1400 | 1500 |
| | | | Logarithm of Equilibrium Constant of Formation, $\log_{10} K_f$ | | | | | | | | | | | | | |
| Methane | $CH_4$ | infinite | 8.8985 | 8.8184 | 5.4899 | 3.3473 | 2.0004 | 0.9529 | 0.1500 | -0.4881 | -1.0075 | -1.4345 | -1.7936 | -2.1006 | -2.3638 | -2.5923 |
| Ethane | $C_2H_6$ | infinite | 5.7613 | 5.6713 | 1.8833 | -0.5105 | -2.1749 | -3.4019 | -4.3480 | -5.1004 | -5.7104 | -6.2147 | -6.6377 | -6.9972 | -7.3048 | -7.5744 |
| Propane | $C_3H_8$ | infinite | 4.1150 | 4.0366 | -0.6507 | -3.5973 | -5.6469 | -7.1584 | -8.3182 | -9.2395 | -9.9839 | -10.5966 | -11.1106 | -11.5457 | -11.9182 | -12.2499 |
| n-Butane | $C_4H_{10}$ | infinite | 3.0052 | 2.8702 | -2.7810 | -6.3553 | -8.8439 | -10.6745 | -12.0774 | -13.1954 | -14.0963 | -14.8354 | -15.4513 | -15.9775 | -16.4285 | -16.8165 |
| n-Pentane | $C_5H_{12}$ | infinite | 1.4660 | 1.3313 | -5.2451 | -9.4019 | -12.2969 | -14.4241 | -16.0550 | -17.3526 | -18.3973 | -19.2540 | -19.9661 | -20.5754 | -21.0945 | -21.5429 |
| n-Hexane | $C_6H_{14}$ | infinite | 0.051 | -0.131 | -7.622 | -12.370 | -15.670 | -18.102 | -19.964 | -21.444 | -22.635 | -23.615 | -24.424 | -25.116 | -25.707 | -26.218 |
| n-Heptane | $C_7H_{16}$ | infinite | -1.422 | -1.627 | -10.020 | -15.359 | -19.068 | -21.802 | -23.890 | -25.553 | -26.892 | -27.990 | -28.896 | -29.674 | -30.334 | -30.905 |
| n-Octane | $C_8H_{18}$ | infinite | -2.894 | -3.122 | -12.441 | -18.367 | -22.485 | -25.520 | -27.838 | -29.683 | -31.169 | -32.385 | -33.389 | -34.250 | -34.982 | -35.614 |
| n-Nonane | $C_9H_{20}$ | infinite | -4.367 | -4.618 | -14.862 | -21.375 | -25.903 | -29.239 | -31.786 | -33.814 | -35.446 | -36.780 | -37.882 | -38.826 | -39.629 | -40.323 |
| n-Decane | $C_{10}H_{22}$ | infinite | -5.839 | -6.113 | -17.283 | -24.383 | -29.320 | -32.957 | -35.733 | -37.934 | -39.723 | -41.174 | -42.375 | -43.402 | -44.276 | -45.032 |
| n-Undecane | $C_{11}H_{24}$ | infinite | -7.312 | -7.609 | -19.704 | -27.391 | -32.737 | -36.676 | -39.681 | -42.074 | -44.000 | -45.569 | -46.868 | -47.978 | -48.923 | -49.741 |
| n-Dodecane | $C_{12}H_{26}$ | infinite | -8.785 | -9.105 | -22.125 | -30.400 | -36.154 | -40.394 | -43.629 | -46.204 | -48.277 | -49.964 | -51.361 | -52.554 | -53.569 | -54.450 |
| n-Tridecane | $C_{13}H_{28}$ | infinite | -10.257 | -10.600 | -24.546 | -33.408 | -39.572 | -44.112 | -47.577 | -50.335 | -52.554 | -54.359 | -55.854 | -57.130 | -58.216 | -59.159 |
| n-Tetradecane | $C_{14}H_{30}$ | infinite | -11.730 | -12.096 | -26.967 | -36.416 | -42.989 | -47.831 | -51.525 | -54.465 | -56.831 | -58.754 | -60.347 | -61.706 | -62.863 | -63.868 |
| n-Pentadecane | $C_{15}H_{32}$ | infinite | -13.202 | -13.591 | -29.388 | -39.424 | -46.406 | -51.549 | -55.472 | -58.595 | -61.108 | -63.148 | -64.840 | -66.282 | -67.511 | -68.577 |
| n-Hexadecane | $C_{16}H_{34}$ | infinite | -14.675 | -15.087 | -31.809 | -42.432 | -49.824 | -55.268 | -59.420 | -62.726 | -65.385 | -67.543 | -69.333 | -70.858 | -72.158 | -73.286 |
| n-Heptadecane | $C_{17}H_{36}$ | infinite | -16.148 | -16.583 | -34.230 | -45.440 | -53.241 | -58.986 | -63.368 | -66.856 | -69.662 | -71.938 | -73.826 | -75.434 | -76.805 | -77.995 |
| n-Octadecane | $C_{18}H_{38}$ | infinite | -17.620 | -18.078 | -36.651 | -48.448 | -56.658 | -62.704 | -67.316 | -70.986 | -73.939 | -76.333 | -78.319 | -80.010 | -81.452 | -82.704 |
| n-Nonadecane | $C_{19}H_{40}$ | infinite | -19.093 | -19.574 | -39.072 | -51.456 | -60.076 | -66.423 | -71.264 | -75.117 | -78.216 | -80.728 | -82.812 | -84.586 | -86.100 | -87.413 |
| n-Eicosane | $C_{20}H_{42}$ | infinite | -20.565 | -21.069 | -41.493 | -54.464 | -63.493 | -70.141 | -75.211 | -79.247 | -82.493 | -85.122 | -87.305 | -89.162 | -90.747 | -92.122 |
| Increment per $CH_2$ group, applicable beyond n-heptane | | infinite | -1.4726 | -1.4956 | -2.4210 | -3.0081 | -3.4173 | -3.7184 | -3.9478 | -4.1303 | -4.2770 | -4.3948 | -4.4930 | -4.5760 | -4.6471 | -4.7090 |

TABLE 1y – PARAFFINS, $C_1$ TO $C_5$

LOGARITHM OF EQUILIBRIUM CONSTANT OF FORMATION, $\log_{10} Kf$, AT 0° TO 1500°K

August 31, 1944; February 28, 1949; December 31, 1952

| Compound (gas) | Formula | Temperature in °K — Logarithm of Equilibrium Constant of Formation, $\log_{10} Kf$ | | | | | | | | | | | | | | |
|---|---|---|---|---|---|---|---|---|---|---|---|---|---|---|---|---|
| | | 0 | 100 | 150 | 200 | 250 | 298.16 | 300 | 350 | 400 | 450 | 500 | 600 | 700 | 800 | 900 |
| Methane | $CH_4$ | infinite | | | | 11.3534 | 8.8985 | 8.8184 | 6.9993 | 5.4899 | 4.3558 | 3.4273 | 2.0004 | 0.9529 | 0.1500 | -0.4881 |
| Ethane | $C_2H_6$ | infinite | | | | 8.5064 | 5.7613 | 5.6713 | 3.5366 | 1.8833 | 0.5656 | -0.5105 | -2.1749 | -3.4019 | -4.3480 | -5.1004 |
| Propane | $C_3H_8$ | infinite | | | | 7.4734 | 4.1150 | 4.0366 | 1.3852 | -0.6507 | -2.2699 | -3.5973 | -5.6469 | -7.1584 | -8.3182 | -9.2395 |
| n-Butane | $C_4H_{10}$ | infinite | | | | 7.0809 | 3.0052 | 2.8702 | -0.3122 | -2.7810 | -4.7400 | -6.3553 | -8.8439 | -10.6745 | -12.0774 | -13.1954 |
| 2-Methylpropane (Isobutane) | " | infinite | | | | 8.0163 | 3.6649 | 3.5186 | -0.1249 | -2.4969 | -4.5846 | -6.2898 | -8.9167 | -10.8462 | -12.3260 | -13.4989 |
| n-Pentane | $C_5H_{12}$ | infinite | | | | 6.1893 | 1.4660 | 1.3113 | -2.3790 | -5.2451 | -7.5277 | -9.4019 | -12.2969 | -14.4241 | -16.0550 | -17.3526 |
| 2-Methylbutane (Isopentane) | " | infinite | | | | 7.6054 | 2.5948 | 2.4259 | -1.4674 | -4.4911 | -6.9012 | -8.8555 | -11.8853 | -14.1088 | -15.8119 | -17.1632 |
| 2,2-Dimethylpropane (Neopentane) | " | infinite | | | | 8.0509 | 2.6681 | 2.4915 | -1.6878 | -4.9119 | -7.4838 | -9.5680 | -12.7778 | -15.1298 | -16.9184 | -18.3313 |

| Compound (gas) | Formula | Temperature in °K — Logarithm of Equilibrium Constant of Formation, $\log_{10} Kf$ | | | | | |
|---|---|---|---|---|---|---|---|
| | | 1000 | 1100 | 1200 | 1300 | 1400 | 1500 |
| Methane | $CH_4$ | -1.0075 | -1.4345 | -1.7936 | -2.1006 | -2.3638 | -2.5923 |
| Ethane | $C_2H_6$ | -5.7104 | -6.2147 | -6.6377 | -6.9972 | -7.3048 | -7.5744 |
| Propane | $C_3H_8$ | -9.9839 | -10.5966 | -11.1106 | -11.5457 | -11.9182 | -12.2499 |
| n-Butane | $C_4H_{10}$ | -14.0963 | -14.8354 | -15.4513 | -15.9775 | -16.4285 | -16.8165 |
| 2-Methylpropane (Isobutane) | " | -14.4438 | -15.2228 | -15.8738 | -16.4230 | -16.8906 | -17.3002 |
| n-Pentane | $C_5H_{12}$ | -18.3973 | -19.2540 | -19.9661 | -20.5754 | -21.0945 | -21.5429 |
| 2-Methylbutane (Isopentane) | " | -18.2509 | -19.1467 | -19.8896 | -20.5132 | -21.0508 | -21.5181 |
| 2,2-Dimethylpropane (Neopentane) | " | -19.4683 | -20.4005 | -21.1755 | -21.8846 | -22.3918 | -22.8747 |

TABLE 2y (PART 1) – PARAFFINS, $C_6$

LOGARITHM OF EQUILIBRIUM CONSTANT OF FORMATION, $\log_{10} Kf$, AT 0° TO 1500°K

September 30, 1944; November 30, 1946; December 31, 1952

| Compound (gas) | Formula | Temperature in °K | | | | | | | | | | | | | | |
|---|---|---|---|---|---|---|---|---|---|---|---|---|---|---|---|---|
| | | 0 | 298.16 | 300 | 400 | 500 | 600 | 700 | 800 | 900 | 1000 | 1100 | 1200 | 1300 | 1400 | 1500 |
| | | Logarithm of Equilibrium Constant of Formation, $\log_{10} Kf$ | | | | | | | | | | | | | | |
| n-Hexane | $C_6H_{14}$ | infinite | 0.051 | −0.131 | −7.622 | −12.370 | −15.670 | −18.102 | −19.964 | −21.444 | −22.635 | −23.615 | −24.424 | −25.116 | −25.707 | −26.218 |
| 2-Methylpentane | " | infinite | 0.880 | 0.699 | −7.103 | −12.033 | −15.455 | −17.961 | −19.871 | −21.381 | −22.600 | −23.623 | −24.459 | −25.158 | −25.764 | −26.297 |
| 3-Methylpentane | " | infinite | 0.374 | 0.197 | −7.491 | −12.357 | −15.735 | −18.220 | −20.125 | −21.626 | −22.842 | −23.863 | −24.678 | −25.395 | −25.999 | −26.510 |
| 2,2-Dimethylbutane | " | infinite | 1.737 | 1.537 | −6.769 | −12.003 | −15.612 | −18.274 | −20.284 | −21.872 | −23.175 | −24.227 | −25.107 | −25.841 | −26.499 | −27.037 |
| 2,3-Dimethylbutane | " | infinite | 0.718 | 0.524 | −7.436 | −12.462 | −15.947 | −18.508 | −20.472 | −22.017 | −23.273 | −24.294 | −25.155 | −25.881 | −26.499 | −27.033 |

## TABLE 2y (PART 2) - PARAFFINS, C₇

LOGARITHM OF EQUILIBRIUM CONSTANT OF FORMATION, $\log_{10} Kf$, AT 0° TO 1500°K

September 30, 1944; December 31, 1952

| Compound (gas) | Formula | Temperature in °K | | | | | | | | | | | | | | |
|---|---|---|---|---|---|---|---|---|---|---|---|---|---|---|---|---|
| | | 0 | 298.16 | 300 | 400 | 500 | 600 | 700 | 800 | 900 | 1000 | 1100 | 1200 | 1300 | 1400 | 1500 |
| | | Logarithm of Equilibrium Constant of Formation, $\log_{10} Kf$ | | | | | | | | | | | | | | |
| n-Heptane | C₇H₁₆ | infinite | -1.422 | -1.627 | -10.020 | -15.359 | -19.068 | -21.802 | -23.890 | -25.553 | -26.892 | -27.990 | -28.896 | -29.674 | -30.334 | -30.905 |
| 2-Methylhexane | " | infinite | -0.564 | -0.772 | -9.468 | -14.966 | -18.784 | -21.589 | -23.742 | -25.432 | -26.778 | | | | | |
| 3-Methylhexane | " | infinite | -0.806 | -1.013 | -9.600 | -15.036 | -18.824 | -21.608 | -23.732 | -25.398 | -26.726 | | | | | |
| 3-Ethylpentane | " | infinite | -1.884 | -2.069 | -10.534 | -15.914 | -19.676 | -22.460 | -24.570 | -26.252 | -27.559 | | | | | |
| 2,2-Dimethylpentane | " | infinite | -0.015 | -0.233 | -9.430 | -15.215 | -19.239 | -22.226 | -24.466 | -26.245 | -27.602 | | | | | |
| 2,3-Dimethylpentane | " | infinite | -0.117 | -0.328 | -9.195 | -14.818 | -18.733 | -21.618 | -23.814 | -25.541 | -26.916 | | | | | |
| 2,4-Dimethylpentane | " | infinite | -0.528 | -0.743 | -9.731 | -15.421 | -19.374 | -22.283 | -24.494 | -26.223 | -27.596 | | | | | |
| 3,3-Dimethylpentane | " | infinite | -0.462 | -0.677 | -9.638 | -15.307 | -19.247 | -22.142 | -24.341 | -26.066 | -27.434 | | | | | |
| 2,2,3-Trimethylbutane | " | infinite | -0.748 | -0.969 | -10.119 | -15.901 | -19.895 | -22.826 | -25.048 | -26.840 | -28.256 | -29.404 | -30.378 | -31.188 | -31.881 | -32.486 |

## TABLE 3y — PARAFFINS, C$_8$

### LOGARITHM OF EQUILIBRIUM CONSTANT OF FORMATION, log$_{10}$ $K_f$, AT 0° TO 1500°K

October 31, 1944; December 31, 1952

| Compound (gas) | Formula | Temperature in °K | | | | | | | | | | | | | | |
|---|---|---|---|---|---|---|---|---|---|---|---|---|---|---|---|---|
| | | 0 | 298.16 | 300 | 400 | 500 | 600 | 700 | 800 | 900 | 1000 | 1100 | 1200 | 1300 | 1400 | 1500 |
| | | Logarithm of Equilibrium Constant of Formation, log$_{10}$ $K_f$ | | | | | | | | | | | | | | |
| n-Octane | C$_8$H$_{18}$ | infinite | -2.894 | -3.122 | -12.441 | -18.367 | -22.485 | -25.520 | -27.888 | -29.683 | -31.169 | -32.385 | -33.389 | -34.250 | -34.982 | -35.614 |
| 2-Methylheptane | " | infinite | -2.243 | -2.470 | -12.097 | -18.174 | -22.390 | -25.486 | -27.832 | -29.691 | -31.215 | | | | | |
| 3-Methylheptane | " | infinite | -2.412 | -2.637 | -12.135 | -18.139 | -22.317 | -25.386 | -27.712 | -29.548 | -31.049 | | | | | |
| 4-Methylheptane | " | infinite | -2.932 | -3.162 | -12.632 | -18.629 | -22.805 | -25.876 | -28.201 | -30.033 | -31.528 | | | | | |
| 3-Ethylhexane | " | infinite | -2.895 | -3.118 | -12.534 | -18.529 | -22.718 | -25.801 | -28.133 | -29.970 | -31.467 | | | | | |
| 2,2-Dimethylhexane | " | infinite | -1.876 | -2.120 | -12.118 | -18.445 | -22.842 | -26.063 | -28.493 | -30.405 | -31.967 | | | | | |
| 2,3-Dimethylhexane | " | infinite | -3.101 | -3.329 | -12.845 | -18.865 | -23.046 | -26.113 | -28.436 | -30.264 | -31.755 | | | | | |
| 2,4-Dimethylhexane | " | infinite | -2.052 | -2.287 | -12.047 | -18.236 | -22.543 | -25.701 | -28.094 | -29.973 | -31.486 | | | | | |
| 2,5-Dimethylhexane | " | infinite | -1.832 | -2.069 | -11.976 | -18.249 | -22.612 | -25.817 | -28.250 | -30.160 | -31.687 | | | | | |
| 3,3-Dimethylhexane | " | infinite | -2.324 | -2.557 | -12.364 | -18.577 | -22.893 | -26.060 | -28.455 | -30.337 | -31.856 | | | | | |
| 3,4-Dimethylhexane[a] | " | infinite | -3.035 | -3.259 | -12.803 | -18.832 | -23.005 | -26.083 | -28.422 | -30.285 | -31.778 | | | | | |
| 2-Methyl-3-ethylpentane | " | infinite | -3.724 | -3.956 | -13.370 | -19.337 | -23.483 | -26.526 | -28.827 | -30.648 | -32.146 | | | | | |
| 3-Methyl-3-ethylpentane | " | infinite | -3.489 | -3.723 | -13.288 | -19.363 | -23.592 | -26.688 | -29.018 | -30.852 | -32.347 | | | | | |
| 2,2,3-Trimethylpentane | " | infinite | -2.998 | -3.235 | -13.015 | -19.223 | -23.541 | -26.707 | -29.100 | -30.978 | -32.494 | | | | | |
| 2,2,4-Trimethylpentane | " | infinite | -2.397 | -2.637 | -12.605 | -18.917 | -23.312 | -26.528 | -28.949 | -30.849 | -32.384 | | | | | |
| 2,3,3-Trimethylpentane | " | infinite | -3.313 | -3.540 | -13.162 | -19.267 | -23.512 | -26.632 | -28.985 | -30.835 | -32.323 | | | | | |
| 2,3,4-Trimethylpentane | " | infinite | -3.313 | -3.548 | -13.200 | -19.337 | -23.592 | -26.725 | -29.083 | -30.956 | -32.452 | | | | | |
| 2,2,3,3-Tetramethylbutane | " | infinite | -3.863 | -4.101 | -14.206 | -20.530 | -24.918 | -28.096 | -30.536 | -32.452 | -33.978 | | | | | |

a See footnotes a and b of Table 3r.

TABLE 22y (PART 1) – NORMAL ALKYL CYCLOPENTANES, C$_5$ TO C$_{21}$

LOGARITHM OF EQUILIBRIUM CONSTANT OF FORMATION, $\log_{10} Kf$, AT 0° TO 1500°K

March 31, 1947; December 31, 1952

| Compound (gas) | Formula | Temperature in °K | | | | | | | | | | | | | | |
|---|---|---|---|---|---|---|---|---|---|---|---|---|---|---|---|---|
| | | 0 | 298.16 | 300 | 400 | 500 | 600 | 700 | 800 | 900 | 1000 | 1100 | 1200 | 1300 | 1400 | 1500 |
| | | Logarithm of Equilibrium Constant of Formation, $\log_{10} Kf$ | | | | | | | | | | | | | | |
| Cyclopentane | C$_5$H$_{10}$ | Infinite | − 6.7643 | − 6.8490 | −10.4144 | −12.7851 | −14.4897 | −15.7722 | −16.7736 | −17.5731 | −18.2238 | −18.7571 | −19.2005 | −19.5796 | −19.9002 | −20.1753 |
| Methylcyclopentane | C$_6$H$_{12}$ | Infinite | − 6.2649 | − 6.3801 | −11.2501 | −14.4250 | −16.6770 | −18.3549 | −19.6492 | −20.6813 | −21.5189 | −22.2064 | −22.7795 | −23.2694 | −23.6775 | −24.0218 |
| Ethylcyclopentane | C$_7$H$_{14}$ | Infinite | − 7.8136 | − 7.9478 | −13.7029 | −17.4444 | −20.0881 | −22.0514 | −23.5735 | −24.7832 | −25.7645 | −26.5753 | −27.2473 | −27.8126 | −28.3112 | −28.7302 |
| n-Propylcyclopentane | C$_8$H$_{16}$ | Infinite | − 9.206 | − 9.361 | −16.069 | −20.404 | −23.465 | −25.796 | −27.492 | −28.885 | −30.006 | −30.934 | −31.726 | −32.379 | −32.969 | −33.423 |
| n-Butylcyclopentane | C$_9$H$_{18}$ | Infinite | −10.753 | −10.935 | −18.544 | −23.459 | −26.921 | −29.488 | −31.471 | −33.042 | −34.312 | −35.345 | −36.242 | −36.968 | −37.652 | −38.144 |
| n-Pentylcyclopentane | C$_{10}$H$_{20}$ | Infinite | −12.226 | −12.430 | −20.965 | −26.467 | −30.339 | −33.207 | −35.429 | −37.172 | −38.589 | −39.740 | −40.735 | −41.544 | −42.304 | −42.853 |
| n-Hexylcyclopentane | C$_{11}$H$_{22}$ | Infinite | −13.698 | −13.926 | −23.386 | −29.475 | −33.756 | −36.925 | −39.367 | −41.302 | −42.866 | −44.135 | −45.228 | −46.120 | −46.941 | −47.562 |
| n-Heptylcyclopentane | C$_{12}$H$_{24}$ | Infinite | −15.171 | −15.421 | −25.807 | −32.483 | −37.173 | −40.643 | −43.315 | −45.433 | −47.143 | −48.529 | −49.721 | −50.696 | −51.593 | −52.271 |
| n-Octylcyclopentane | C$_{13}$H$_{26}$ | Infinite | −16.643 | −16.917 | −28.228 | −35.491 | −40.591 | −44.362 | −47.263 | −49.563 | −51.420 | −52.924 | −54.214 | −55.272 | −56.245 | −56.980 |
| n-Nonylcyclopentane | C$_{14}$H$_{28}$ | Infinite | −18.116 | −18.413 | −30.649 | −38.499 | −44.008 | −48.030 | −51.210 | −53.693 | −55.697 | −57.319 | −58.707 | −59.848 | −60.881 | −61.689 |
| n-Decylcyclopentane | C$_{15}$H$_{30}$ | Infinite | −19.588 | −19.908 | −33.070 | −41.507 | −47.425 | −51.799 | −55.158 | −57.824 | −59.974 | −61.714 | −63.200 | −64.424 | −65.533 | −66.398 |
| n-Undecylcyclopentane | C$_{16}$H$_{32}$ | Infinite | −21.061 | −21.404 | −35.491 | −44.516 | −50.842 | −55.517 | −59.106 | −61.954 | −64.251 | −66.109 | −67.693 | −69.000 | −70.185 | −71.107 |
| n-Dodecylcyclopentane | C$_{17}$H$_{34}$ | Infinite | −22.534 | −22.899 | −37.912 | −47.524 | −54.260 | −59.235 | −63.054 | −66.084 | −68.528 | −70.503 | −72.186 | −73.576 | −74.837 | −75.816 |
| n-Tridecylcyclopentane | C$_{18}$H$_{36}$ | Infinite | −24.006 | −24.395 | −40.333 | −50.532 | −57.677 | −62.954 | −67.002 | −70.215 | −72.805 | −74.898 | −76.679 | −78.152 | −79.473 | −80.525 |
| n-Tetradecylcyclopentane | C$_{19}$H$_{38}$ | Infinite | −25.479 | −25.891 | −42.754 | −53.540 | −61.094 | −66.672 | −70.949 | −74.345 | −77.082 | −79.293 | −81.172 | −82.728 | −84.125 | −85.234 |
| n-Pentadecylcyclopentane | C$_{20}$H$_{40}$ | Infinite | −26.952 | −27.386 | −45.175 | −56.548 | −64.512 | −70.391 | −74.897 | −78.475 | −81.359 | −83.688 | −85.665 | −87.304 | −88.777 | −89.943 |
| n-Hexadecylcyclopentane | C$_{21}$H$_{42}$ | Infinite | −28.424 | −28.882 | −47.596 | −59.556 | −67.929 | −74.109 | −78.845 | −82.606 | −85.636 | −88.083 | −90.158 | −91.880 | −93.413 | −94.652 |
| Increment per CH$_2$ group, applicable beyond n-butylcyclopentane | | Infinite | − 1.4726 | − 1.4956 | − 2.4210 | − 3.0081 | − 3.4173 | − 3.7184 | − 3.9478 | − 4.1303 | − 4.2770 | − 4.3948 | − 4.4930 | − 4.5760 | − 4.6471 | − 4.7090 |

## TABLE 6y – ALKYL CYCLOPENTANES, $C_5$ TO $C_7$

### LOGARITHM OF EQUILIBRIUM CONSTANT OF FORMATION, $\log_{10} Kf$, AT 0° TO 1500°K

April 30, 1949; December 31, 1952

| Compound (gas) | Formula | Temperature in °K | | | | | | | | | | | | | | |
|---|---|---|---|---|---|---|---|---|---|---|---|---|---|---|---|---|
| | | 0 | 298.16 | 300 | 400 | 500 | 600 | 700 | 800 | 900 | 1000 | 1100 | 1200 | 1300 | 1400 | 1500 |
| | | Logarithm of Equilibrium Constant of Formation, $\log_{10} Kf$ | | | | | | | | | | | | | | |
| Cyclopentane | $C_5H_{10}$ | infinite | -6.7643 | -6.8490 | -10.4114 | -12.7851 | -14.4897 | -15.7722 | -16.7736 | -17.5731 | -18.2238 | -18.7571 | -19.2005 | -19.5796 | -19.9002 | -20.1753 |
| Methylcyclopentane | $C_6H_{12}$ | infinite | -6.2649 | -6.3801 | -11.2501 | -14.4250 | -16.6770 | -18.3549 | -19.6492 | -20.6813 | -21.5189 | -22.2064 | -22.7795 | -23.2694 | -23.6775 | -24.0218 |
| Ethylcyclopentane | $C_7H_{14}$ | infinite | -7.8136 | -7.9478 | -13.7029 | -17.4444 | -20.0881 | -22.0514 | -23.5735 | -24.7832 | -25.7645 | -26.5753 | -27.2473 | -27.8126 | -28.3112 | -28.7302 |
| 1,1-Dimethylcyclopentane | " | infinite | -6.8372 | -6.9791 | -13.2550 | -17.3002 | -20.1566 | -22.2561 | -23.8567 | -25.1361 | -26.1704 | -27.0036 | -27.7258 | -28.3238 | -28.8208 | -29.2335 |
| 1,cis-2-Dimethylcyclopentane | " | infinite | -8.0107 | -8.1413 | -14.0255 | -17.8445 | -20.5399 | -22.5337 | -24.0595 | -25.2729 | -26.2579 | -27.0664 | -27.7393 | -28.3132 | -28.7903 | -29.1818 |
| 1,trans-2-Dimethylcyclopentane | " | infinite | -6.7224 | -6.8651 | -13.0564 | -17.0648 | -19.8865 | -21.9662 | -23.5465 | -24.8213 | -25.8483 | -26.6914 | -27.3930 | -27.9912 | -28.4890 | -28.8986 |
| 1,cis-3-Dimethylcyclopentane | " | infinite | -7.2648 | -7.4042 | -13.4607 | -17.3882 | -20.1561 | -22.1972 | -23.7487 | -25.0009 | -26.0101 | -26.8384 | -27.5277 | -28.1156 | -28.6046 | -29.0064 |
| 1,trans-3-Dimethylcyclopentane | " | infinite | -6.8690 | -7.0108 | -13.1657 | -17.1522 | -19.9594 | -22.0286 | -23.6011 | -24.8598 | -25.8921 | -26.7311 | -27.4294 | -28.0248 | -28.5203 | -28.9278 |

TABLE 23y (PART 1) - NORMAL ALKYL CYCLOHEXANES, $C_6$ TO $C_{22}$

LOGARITHM OF EQUILIBRIUM CONSTANT OF FORMATION, $\log_{10} Kf$, AT 0° TO 1500°K

March 31, 1947; December 31, 1952

| Compound (gas) | Formula | Temperature in °K — Logarithm of Equilibrium Constant of Formation, $\log_{10} Kf$ | | | | | | | | | | | | | | |
|---|---|---|---|---|---|---|---|---|---|---|---|---|---|---|---|---|
| | | 0 | 298.16 | 300 | 400 | 500 | 600 | 700 | 800 | 900 | 1000 | 1100 | 1200 | 1300 | 1400 | 1500 |
| Cyclohexane | $C_6H_{12}$ | Infinite | - 5.5605 | - 5.6931 | -11.2861 | -14.8932 | -17.4318 | -19.3103 | -20.7501 | -21.8852 | -22.7943 | -23.5277 | -24.1458 | -24.6613 | -25.0905 | -25.4571 |
| Methylcyclohexane | $C_7H_{14}$ | Infinite | - 4.7819 | - 4.9487 | -11.9344 | -16.3959 | -19.5065 | -21.7937 | -23.5374 | -24.9110 | -26.0133 | -26.9077 | -27.6521 | -28.2657 | -28.7908 | -29.2345 |
| Ethylcyclohexane | $C_8H_{16}$ | Infinite | - 6.8744 | - 7.0592 | -14.8200 | -19.7522 | -23.2097 | -25.7561 | -27.6926 | -29.2075 | -30.4279 | -31.4213 | -32.2567 | -32.9304 | -33.5168 | -33.9999 |
| n-Propylcyclohexane | $C_9H_{18}$ | Infinite | - 8.290 | - 8.494 | -17.210 | -22.773 | -26.626 | -29.473 | -31.635 | -33.340 | -34.705 | -35.822 | -36.752 | -37.523 | -38.168 | -38.726 |
| n-Butylcyclohexane | $C_{10}H_{20}$ | Infinite | - 9.888 | -10.119 | -19.724 | -25.832 | -30.087 | -33.250 | -35.623 | -37.517 | -39.011 | -40.272 | -41.269 | -42.129 | -42.851 | -43.462 |
| n-Pentylcyclohexane | $C_{11}H_{22}$ | Infinite | -11.360 | -11.615 | -22.145 | -28.840 | -33.504 | -36.968 | -39.571 | -41.647 | -43.288 | -44.667 | -45.762 | -46.705 | -47.503 | -48.171 |
| n-Hexylcyclohexane | $C_{12}H_{24}$ | Infinite | -12.833 | -13.110 | -24.566 | -31.848 | -36.922 | -40.687 | -43.519 | -45.778 | -47.565 | -49.062 | -50.255 | -51.281 | -52.139 | -52.880 |
| n-Heptylcyclohexane | $C_{13}H_{26}$ | Infinite | -14.306 | -14.606 | -26.987 | -34.856 | -40.339 | -44.405 | -47.466 | -49.908 | -51.842 | -53.456 | -54.748 | -55.857 | -56.791 | -57.589 |
| n-Octylcyclohexane | $C_{14}H_{28}$ | Infinite | -15.778 | -16.101 | -29.408 | -37.864 | -43.756 | -48.124 | -51.414 | -54.038 | -56.119 | -57.851 | -59.241 | -60.433 | -61.443 | -62.298 |
| n-Nonylcyclohexane | $C_{15}H_{30}$ | Infinite | -17.251 | -17.597 | -31.829 | -40.872 | -47.174 | -51.842 | -55.362 | -58.168 | -60.396 | -62.246 | -63.734 | -65.009 | -66.095 | -67.007 |
| n-Decylcyclohexane | $C_{16}H_{32}$ | Infinite | -18.724 | -19.093 | -34.250 | -43.881 | -50.591 | -55.560 | -59.310 | -62.299 | -64.673 | -66.641 | -68.227 | -69.585 | -70.731 | -71.716 |
| n-Undecylcyclohexane | $C_{17}H_{34}$ | Infinite | -20.196 | -20.588 | -36.671 | -46.889 | -54.008 | -59.279 | -63.258 | -66.429 | -68.950 | -71.036 | -72.720 | -74.161 | -75.385 | -76.425 |
| n-Dodecylcyclohexane | $C_{18}H_{36}$ | Infinite | -21.669 | -22.084 | -39.092 | -49.897 | -57.425 | -62.997 | -67.205 | -70.559 | -73.227 | -75.430 | -77.213 | -78.737 | -80.035 | -81.134 |
| n-Tridecylcyclohexane | $C_{19}H_{38}$ | Infinite | -23.141 | -23.579 | -41.513 | -52.905 | -60.843 | -66.716 | -71.153 | -74.690 | -77.504 | -79.825 | -81.706 | -83.313 | -84.671 | -85.843 |
| n-Tetradecylcyclohexane | $C_{20}H_{40}$ | Infinite | -24.614 | -25.075 | -43.934 | -55.913 | -64.260 | -70.434 | -75.101 | -78.820 | -81.781 | -84.220 | -86.199 | -87.889 | -89.323 | -90.552 |
| n-Pentadecylcyclohexane | $C_{21}H_{42}$ | Infinite | -26.087 | -26.571 | -46.355 | -58.921 | -67.677 | -74.152 | -79.049 | -82.950 | -86.058 | -88.615 | -90.692 | -92.465 | -93.975 | -95.261 |
| n-Hexadecylcyclohexane | $C_{22}H_{44}$ | Infinite | -27.559 | -28.066 | -48.776 | -61.929 | -71.095 | -77.871 | -82.997 | -87.081 | -90.335 | -93.010 | -95.185 | -97.041 | -98.611 | -99.970 |
| Increment per $CH_2$ group, applicable beyond n-butylcyclohexane | | Infinite | - 1.4726 | - 1.4956 | - 2.4210 | - 3.0081 | - 3.4173 | - 3.7184 | - 3.9478 | - 4.1303 | - 4.2770 | - 4.3948 | - 4.4930 | - 4.5760 | - 4.6471 | - 4.7090 |

TABLE 7y – ALKYL CYCLOHEXANES, $C_6$ TO $C_8$

LOGARITHM OF EQUILIBRIUM CONSTANT OF FORMATION, $\log_{10} K_f$, AT 0° TO 1500°K

April 30, 1947

| Compound (gas) | Formula | Temperature in °K | | | | | | | | | | | | | | |
|---|---|---|---|---|---|---|---|---|---|---|---|---|---|---|---|---|
| | | 0 | 298.16 | 300 | 400 | 500 | 600 | 700 | 800 | 900 | 1000 | 1100 | 1200 | 1300 | 1400 | 1500 |
| | | Logarithm of Equilibrium Constant of Formation, $\log_{10} K_f$ | | | | | | | | | | | | | | |
| Cyclohexane | $C_6H_{12}$ | infinite | -5.5605 | -5.6931 | -11.2861 | -14.8892 | -17.4318 | -19.3103 | -20.7501 | -21.8852 | -22.7943 | -23.5277 | -24.1458 | -24.6613 | -25.0905 | -25.4571 |
| Methylcyclohexane | $C_7H_{14}$ | infinite | -4.7819 | -4.9487 | -11.9344 | -16.3959 | -19.5065 | -21.7937 | -23.5374 | -24.9110 | -26.0133 | -26.9077 | -27.6521 | -28.2657 | -28.7908 | -29.2345 |
| Ethylcyclohexane | $C_8H_{16}$ | infinite | -6.8744 | -7.0592 | -14.8200 | -19.7522 | -23.2097 | -25.7561 | -27.6926 | -29.2075 | -30.4279 | -31.4243 | -32.2567 | -32.9394 | -33.5168 | -33.9999 |
| 1,1-Dimethylcyclohexane | " | infinite | -6.174 | -6.363 | -14.541 | -19.735 | -23.359 | -26.031 | -28.045 | -29.642 | -30.911 | -31.947 | -32.813 | -33.544 | -34.146 | -34.628 |
| 1,cis-2-Dimethylcyclohexane | " | infinite | -7.225 | -7.408 | -15.186 | -20.163 | -23.622 | -26.168 | -28.105 | -29.642 | -30.863 | -31.859 | -32.692 | -33.396 | -33.974 | -34.435 |
| 1,trans-2-Dimethylcyclohexane[a] | " | infinite | -6.038 | -6.227 | -14.334 | -19.503 | -23.083 | -25.731 | -27.723 | -29.298 | -30.566 | -31.601 | -32.445 | -33.176 | -33.755 | -34.259 |
| 1,cis-3-Dimethylcyclohexane[a] | " | infinite | -5.228 | -5.423 | -13.749 | -19.040 | -22.722 | -25.428 | -27.485 | -29.094 | -30.389 | -31.446 | -32.350 | -33.055 | -33.670 | -34.185 |
| 1,trans-3-Dimethylcyclohexane[b] | " | infinite | -6.363 | -6.549 | -14.510 | -19.590 | -23.152 | -25.756 | -27.737 | -29.286 | -30.555 | -31.573 | -32.425 | -33.144 | -33.736 | -34.230 |
| 1,cis-4-Dimethylcyclohexane | " | infinite | -6.650 | -6.836 | -14.831 | -19.887 | -23.429 | -26.034 | -27.994 | -29.586 | -30.856 | -31.875 | -32.727 | -33.447 | -34.038 | -34.533 |
| 1,trans-4-Dimethylcyclohexane | " | infinite | -5.552 | -5.746 | -14.071 | -19.359 | -23.039 | -25.722 | -27.756 | -29.384 | -30.657 | -31.714 | -32.597 | -33.322 | -33.937 | -34.430 |

a Formerly labeled "trans"; see footnote b of Table 7a.

b Formerly labeled "cis"; see footnote c of Table 7a.

TABLE 24y (PART 1) - NORMAL MONOOLEFINS (1-ALKENES), $C_2$ TO $C_{20}$

LOGARITHM OF EQUILIBRIUM CONSTANT OF FORMATION, $\log_{10} Kf$, AT 0° TO 1500°K

November 30, 1945; April 30, 1946; December 31, 1952

| Compound (gas) | Formula | Temperature in °K | | | | | | | | | | | | | | |
|---|---|---|---|---|---|---|---|---|---|---|---|---|---|---|---|---|
| | | 0 | 298.16 | 300 | 400 | 500 | 600 | 700 | 800 | 900 | 1000 | 1100 | 1200 | 1300 | 1400 | 1500 |
| | | Logarithm of Equilibrium Constant of Formation, $\log_{10} Kf$ | | | | | | | | | | | | | | |
| Ethene (Ethylene) | $C_2H_4$ | Infinite | -11.9345 | -11.8781 | -9.6571 | -8.4119 | -7.6193 | -7.0797 | -6.6903 | -6.3996 | -6.1738 | -5.9918 | -5.8440 | -5.7206 | -5.6151 | -5.5249 |
| Propene (Propylene) | $C_3H_6$ | Infinite | -10.9875 | -10.9648 | -10.1677 | -9.8128 | -9.6375 | -9.5519 | -9.5093 | -9.4942 | -9.4909 | -9.4922 | -9.4970 | -9.5027 | -9.5066 | -9.5117 |
| 1-Butene | $C_4H_8$ | Infinite | -12.5267 | -12.5227 | -12.6921 | -12.9161 | -13.1383 | -13.3407 | -13.5089 | -13.6592 | -13.7858 | -13.8877 | -13.9761 | -14.0492 | -14.1088 | -14.1618 |
| 1-Pentene | $C_5H_{10}$ | Infinite | -13.8974 | -13.9142 | -15.0196 | -15.8315 | -16.4675 | -16.9686 | -17.3690 | -17.7023 | -17.9733 | -18.1990 | -18.3816 | -18.5412 | -18.6748 | -18.7805 |
| 1-Hexene | $C_6H_{12}$ | Infinite | -15.3487 | -15.3930 | -17.4291 | -18.8300 | -19.8768 | -20.6839 | -21.3138 | -21.8304 | -22.2503 | -22.5958 | -22.8764 | -23.1206 | -23.3252 | -23.4909 |
| 1-Heptene | $C_7H_{14}$ | Infinite | -16.821 | -16.889 | -19.850 | -21.838 | -23.294 | -24.402 | -25.262 | -25.961 | -26.527 | -26.991 | -27.369 | -27.697 | -27.972 | -28.200 |
| 1-Octene | $C_8H_{16}$ | Infinite | -18.294 | -18.384 | -22.271 | -24.846 | -26.711 | -28.121 | -29.209 | -30.091 | -30.804 | -31.385 | -31.862 | -32.273 | -32.620 | -32.909 |
| 1-Nonene | $C_9H_{18}$ | Infinite | -19.766 | -19.880 | -24.692 | -27.854 | -30.129 | -31.839 | -33.157 | -34.221 | -35.081 | -35.780 | -36.355 | -36.849 | -37.267 | -37.618 |
| 1-Decene | $C_{10}H_{20}$ | Infinite | -21.239 | -21.375 | -27.113 | -30.862 | -33.546 | -35.558 | -37.105 | -38.352 | -39.358 | -40.175 | -40.848 | -41.425 | -41.914 | -42.327 |
| 1-Undecene | $C_{11}H_{22}$ | Infinite | -22.712 | -22.871 | -29.534 | -33.870 | -36.963 | -39.276 | -41.053 | -42.482 | -43.635 | -44.570 | -45.341 | -46.001 | -46.560 | -47.036 |
| 1-Dodecene | $C_{12}H_{24}$ | Infinite | -24.184 | -24.367 | -31.955 | -36.879 | -40.381 | -42.994 | -45.001 | -46.612 | -47.912 | -48.965 | -49.834 | -50.577 | -51.207 | -51.745 |
| 1-Tridecene | $C_{13}H_{26}$ | Infinite | -25.657 | -25.862 | -34.376 | -39.887 | -43.798 | -46.713 | -48.948 | -50.742 | -52.189 | -53.359 | -54.327 | -55.153 | -55.854 | -56.454 |
| 1-Tetradecene | $C_{14}H_{28}$ | Infinite | -27.130 | -27.358 | -36.797 | -42.895 | -47.215 | -50.431 | -52.896 | -54.873 | -56.466 | -57.754 | -58.820 | -59.729 | -60.502 | -61.163 |
| 1-Pentadecene | $C_{15}H_{30}$ | Infinite | -28.602 | -28.853 | -39.218 | -45.903 | -50.632 | -54.150 | -56.844 | -59.003 | -60.743 | -62.149 | -63.313 | -64.305 | -65.149 | -65.872 |
| 1-Hexadecene | $C_{16}H_{32}$ | Infinite | -30.075 | -30.349 | -41.639 | -48.911 | -54.050 | -57.868 | -60.792 | -63.133 | -65.020 | -66.544 | -67.806 | -68.881 | -69.796 | -70.581 |
| 1-Heptadecene | $C_{17}H_{34}$ | Infinite | -31.547 | -31.845 | -44.060 | -51.919 | -57.467 | -61.586 | -64.740 | -67.264 | -69.297 | -70.939 | -72.299 | -73.457 | -74.443 | -75.290 |
| 1-Octadecene | $C_{18}H_{36}$ | Infinite | -33.020 | -33.340 | -46.481 | -54.927 | -60.884 | -65.305 | -68.687 | -71.394 | -73.574 | -75.333 | -76.792 | -78.033 | -79.091 | -79.999 |
| 1-Nonadecene | $C_{19}H_{38}$ | Infinite | -34.492 | -34.836 | -48.902 | -57.935 | -64.302 | -69.023 | -72.635 | -75.524 | -77.851 | -79.728 | -81.285 | -82.609 | -83.738 | -84.708 |
| 1-Eicosene | $C_{20}H_{40}$ | Infinite | -35.965 | -36.331 | -51.323 | -60.943 | -67.719 | -72.742 | -76.583 | -79.655 | -82.128 | -84.123 | -85.778 | -87.185 | -88.385 | -89.417 |
| Increment per $CH_2$ group, applicable beyond 1-hexene | | Infinite | -1.4726 | -1.4956 | -2.4210 | -3.0081 | -3.4173 | -3.7184 | -3.9478 | -4.1303 | -4.2770 | -4.3948 | -4.4930 | -4.5760 | -4.6471 | -4.7090 |

## TABLE 8y (PART 1) - MONOOLEFINS, C₂ TO C₅

LOGARITHM OF EQUILIBRIUM CONSTANT OF FORMATION, $\log_{10} Kf$, AT 0° TO 1500°K

December 31, 1944; March 31, 1945; October 31, 1945; April 30, 1946; December 31, 1952

| Compound (gas) | Formula | Temperature in °K — Logarithm of Equilibrium Constant of Formation, $\log_{10} Kf$ | | | | | | | | | | | | | | |
|---|---|---|---|---|---|---|---|---|---|---|---|---|---|---|---|---|
| | | 0 | 298.16 | 300 | 400 | 500 | 600 | 700 | 800 | 900 | 1000 | 1100 | 1200 | 1300 | 1400 | 1500 |
| Ethene (Ethylene) | C₂H₄ | Infinite | -11.9345 | -11.8781 | -9.6571 | -8.4119 | -7.6193 | -7.0797 | -6.6903 | -6.3996 | -6.1738 | -5.9918 | -5.8440 | -5.7206 | -5.6151 | -5.5249 |
| Propene (Propylene) | C₃H₆ | Infinite | -10.9875 | -10.9648 | -10.1677 | -9.8128 | -9.6375 | -9.5519 | -9.5093 | -9.4942 | -9.4909 | -9.4922 | -9.4970 | -9.5027 | -9.5066 | -9.5117 |
| 1-Butene | C₄H₈ | Infinite | -12.5267 | -12.5227 | -12.6921 | -12.9161 | -13.1383 | -13.3407 | -13.5089 | -13.6592 | -13.7838 | -13.8877 | -13.9761 | -14.0492 | -14.1088 | -14.1618 |
| cis-2-Butene | " | Infinite | -11.5372 | -11.5393 | -11.9764 | -12.4222 | -12.8032 | -13.1316 | -13.4079 | -13.6446 | -13.8450 | -14.0128 | -14.1600 | -14.2862 | -14.3929 | -14.4868 |
| trans-2-Butene | " | Infinite | -12.0314 | -12.0366 | -11.6431 | -12.1643 | -12.5883 | -12.9411 | -13.2330 | -13.4843 | -13.6942 | -13.8698 | -14.0198 | -14.1484 | -14.2555 | -14.3512 |
| 2-Methylpropene (Isobutene) | " | Infinite | -10.1738 | -10.1916 | -11.0421 | -11.7054 | -12.2204 | -12.6351 | -12.9735 | -13.2537 | -13.4887 | -13.6850 | -13.8522 | -13.9971 | -14.1166 | -14.2216 |
| 1-Pentene | C₅H₁₀ | Infinite | -13.8974 | -13.9142 | -15.0196 | -15.8315 | -16.4675 | -16.9686 | -17.3690 | -17.7023 | -17.9733 | -18.1990 | -18.3816 | -18.5412 | -18.6748 | -18.7805 |
| cis-2-Pentene | " | Infinite | -12.5874 | -12.6191 | -13.9997 | -15.0403 | -15.8357 | -16.4601 | -16.9665 | -17.3806 | -17.7236 | -18.0069 | -18.2524 | -18.4581 | -18.6329 | -18.7779 |
| trans-2-Pentene | " | Infinite | -12.2848 | -12.3115 | -13.8887 | -14.9923 | -15.8228 | -16.4691 | -16.9756 | -17.3963 | -17.7351 | -18.0182 | -18.2541 | -18.4521 | -18.6202 | -18.7644 |
| 2-Methyl-1-butene | " | Infinite | -11.3680 | -11.4073 | -13.1269 | -14.3451 | -15.2451 | -15.9408 | -16.4929 | -16.9409 | -17.3094 | -17.6130 | -17.8741 | -18.0943 | -18.2793 | -18.4355 |
| 3-Methyl-1-butene | " | Infinite | -13.1017 | -13.1337 | -14.5425 | -15.5156 | -16.2580 | -16.8408 | -17.3034 | -17.6825 | -17.9984 | -18.2545 | -18.4778 | -18.6621 | -18.8146 | -18.9408 |
| 2-Methyl-2-butene | " | Infinite | -10.4531 | -10.5041 | -12.5227 | -13.9214 | -14.9632 | -15.7635 | -16.4047 | -16.9228 | -17.3526 | -17.7063 | -18.0064 | -18.2621 | -18.4860 | -18.6741 |

TABLE 8y (PART 2) – MONOOLEFINS, C6

LOGARITHM OF EQUILIBRIUM CONSTANT OF FORMATION, $\log_{10} K_f$, AT 0° TO 1500°K

April 30, 1945; October 31, 1945; December 31, 1952

| Compound (gas) | Formula | Temperature in °K | | | | | | | | | | | | | | |
|---|---|---|---|---|---|---|---|---|---|---|---|---|---|---|---|---|
| | | Logarithm of Equilibrium Constant of Formation, $\log_{10} K_f$ | | | | | | | | | | | | | | |
| | | 0 | 298.16 | 300 | 400 | 500 | 600 | 700 | 800 | 900 | 1000 | 1100 | 1200 | 1300 | 1400 | 1500 |
| 1-Hexene | $C_6H_{12}$ | Infinite | -15.3487 | -15.3930 | -17.4291 | -18.8300 | -19.8768 | -20.6839 | -21.3138 | -21.8304 | -22.2503 | -22.5958 | -22.8764 | -23.1206 | -23.3252 | -23.4909 |
| cis-2-Hexene | " | Infinite | -14.0440 | -14.0963 | -16.3910 | -18.0083 | -19.1957 | -20.1376 | -20.8712 | -21.4419 | -21.9421 | | | | | |
| trans-2-Hexene | " | Infinite | -13.6555 | -13.7102 | -16.1725 | -17.8771 | -19.1229 | -20.0751 | -20.8439 | -21.4419 | -21.9203 | | | | | |
| cis-3-Hexene | " | Infinite | -14.4094 | -14.4646 | -16.7566 | -18.3784 | -19.5768 | -20.4970 | -21.2287 | -21.8205 | -22.3040 | | | | | |
| trans-3-Hexene | " | Infinite | -13.9560 | -14.0161 | -16.5003 | -18.1831 | -19.4143 | -20.3561 | -21.1171 | -21.7090 | -22.1607 | | | | | |
| 2-Methyl-1-pentene | " | Infinite | -12.8053 | -12.8651 | -15.5168 | -17.3089 | -18.6129 | -19.5756 | -20.3795 | -21.0048 | -21.5269 | | | | | |
| 3-Methyl-1-pentene | " | Infinite | -14.9529 | -14.9996 | -17.1559 | -18.5328 | -19.5235 | -20.2936 | -20.8712 | -21.3205 | -21.6799 | | | | | |
| 4-Methyl-1-pentene | " | Infinite | -14.9896 | -15.0433 | -17.3198 | -18.8388 | -19.9606 | -20.8556 | -21.5542 | -21.9275 | -22.5540 | | | | | |
| 2-Methyl-2-pentene | " | Infinite | -11.9780 | -12.0461 | -14.9509 | -16.9386 | -18.3774 | -19.4687 | -20.3302 | -21.0209 | -21.5874 | | | | | |
| 3-Methyl-cis-2-pentene | " | Infinite | -12.4471 | -12.5123 | -15.3006 | -17.2183 | -18.6105 | -19.6685 | -20.5050 | -21.1763 | -21.7273 | | | | | |
| 3-Methyl-trans-2-pentene | " | Infinite | -12.2697 | -12.3353 | -15.1236 | -17.0413 | -18.4335 | -19.4915 | -20.3280 | -20.9993 | -21.5503 | | | | | |
| 4-Methyl-cis-2-pentene | " | Infinite | -13.4903 | -13.5519 | -16.1567 | -17.9059 | -19.1914 | -20.1730 | -20.9472 | -21.5665 | -22.0864 | | | | | |
| 4-Methyl-trans-2-pentene | " | Infinite | -13.0216 | -13.0864 | -15.8569 | -17.6895 | -19.0243 | -20.0378 | -20.8301 | -21.4740 | -22.0000 | | | | | |
| 2-Ethyl-1-butene | " | Infinite | -13.5690 | -13.6292 | -16.1492 | -17.8819 | -19.1405 | -20.1003 | -20.8539 | -21.4611 | -21.9553 | | | | | |
| 2,3-Dimethyl-1-butene | " | Infinite | -12.7782 | -12.8449 | -15.7069 | -17.5844 | -18.9418 | -19.9712 | -20.7737 | -21.4175 | -21.9475 | | | | | |
| 3,3-Dimethyl-1-butene | " | Infinite | -14.3152 | -14.3731 | -17.0467 | -18.9262 | -20.2156 | -21.2615 | -22.0186 | -22.6318 | -23.1660 | | | | | |
| 2,3-Dimethyl-2-butene | " | Infinite | -12.1073 | -12.1779 | -15.2525 | -17.3503 | -18.8661 | -20.0122 | -20.9180 | -21.6491 | -22.2478 | | | | | |

## TABLE 11y (PART 1) – DIOLEFINS, C$_3$ TO C$_5$
### LOGARITHM OF EQUILIBRIUM CONSTANT OF FORMATION, $\log_{10} Kf$, AT 0° TO 1500°K
September 30, 1947; April 30, 1948; December 31, 1952

Temperature in °K

Logarithm of Equilibrium Constant of Formation, $\log_{10} Kf$

| Compound (gas) | Formula | 0 | 298.16 | 300 | 400 | 500 | 600 | 700 | 800 | 900 | 1000 | 1100 | 1200 | 1300 | 1400 | 1500 |
|---|---|---|---|---|---|---|---|---|---|---|---|---|---|---|---|---|
| Propadiene (Allene) | C$_3$H$_4$ | Infinite | -35.4519 | -35.2462 | -26.9916 | -22.0008 | -18.7503 | -16.4479 | -14.7338 | -13.3413 | -12.3488 | -11.5024 | -10.7904 | -10.1907 | -9.6747 | -9.2306 |
| 1,2-Butadiene | C$_4$H$_6$ | Infinite | -34.7655 | -34.5887 | -27.6134 | -23.5244 | -20.8530 | -18.9792 | -17.5930 | -16.5294 | -15.6851 | -14.9963 | -14.4478 | -13.9483 | -13.5374 | -13.1813 |
| 1,3-Butadiene | " | Infinite | -26.3948 | -26.2766 | -21.5597 | -18.8169 | -17.0394 | -15.7978 | -14.8830 | -14.1813 | -13.6286 | -13.1764 | -12.8032 | -12.4874 | -11.5908 | -11.9822 |
| 1,2-Pentadiene | C$_5$H$_8$ | Infinite | -36.861 | -36.705 | -30.469 | -26.854 | -24.507 | -22.857 | -21.555 | -20.741 | -20.004 | -19.412 | -18.913 | -18.486 | -18.134 | -17.807 |
| 1,cis-3-Pentadiene (cis-Piperylene) | " | Infinite | -25.563 | -25.477 | -22.190 | -20.367 | -19.221 | -18.448 | -17.877 | -17.479 | -17.142 | -16.882 | -16.664 | -16.499 | -16.355 | -16.191 |
| 1,trans-3-Pentadiene (trans-Piperylene) | " | Infinite | -25.707 | -25.624 | -22.332 | -20.502 | -19.337 | -18.538 | -17.959 | -17.528 | -17.199 | -16.924 | -16.689 | -16.507 | -16.346 | -16.185 |
| 1,4-Pentadiene | " | Infinite | -29.824 | -29.712 | -25.219 | -22.663 | -21.021 | -19.875 | -19.030 | -18.410 | -17.908 | -17.508 | -17.171 | -16.901 | -16.643 | -16.439 |
| 2,3-Pentadiene | ." | Infinite | -36.074 | -35.925 | -30.017 | -26.592 | -24.401 | -22.875 | -21.756 | -20.910 | -20.233 | -19.693 | -19.243 | -18.859 | -18.526 | -18.259 |
| 3-Methyl-1,2-butadiene | " | Infinite | -34.797 | -34.657 | -29.114 | -25.923 | -23.843 | -22.407 | -21.371 | -20.568 | -19.942 | -19.423 | -18.986 | -18.632 | -18.324 | -18.058 |
| 2-Methyl-1,3-butadiene (Isoprene) | " | Infinite | -25.560 | -25.477 | -22.284 | -20.476 | -19.341 | -18.563 | -18.000 | -17.581 | -17.241 | -16.973 | -16.746 | -16.569 | -16.392 | -16.257 |

TABLE 18y – ALKYL CYCLOPENTENES, C$_5$ TO C$_7$

LOGARITHM OF EQUILIBRIUM CONSTANT OF FORMATION, $\log_{10} Kf$, AT 0° TO 1500°K

December 31, 1952

| Compound (gas) | Formula | Temperature in °K | | | | | | | | | | | | | | |
|---|---|---|---|---|---|---|---|---|---|---|---|---|---|---|---|---|
| | | 0° | 298.16 | 300 | 400 | 500 | 600 | 700 | 800 | 900 | 1000 | 1100 | 1200 | 1300 | 1400 | 1500 |
| | | Logarithm of Equilibrium Constant of Formation, $\log_{10} Kf$ | | | | | | | | | | | | | | |
| Cyclopentene | C$_5$H$_8$ | infinite | -19.410 | -19.378 | -18.107 | -17.536 | -17.254 | -17.115 | -17.098 | -17.003 | -16.985 | -16.975 | -16.968 | -16.963 | -16.953 | -16.945 |
| 1-Methylcyclopentene | C$_6$H$_{10}$ | | | | | | | | | | | | | | | |
| 3-Methylcyclopentene | " | | | | | | | | | | | | | | | |
| 4-Methylcyclopentene | " | | | | | | | | | | | | | | | |
| 1-Ethylcyclopentene | C$_7$H$_{12}$ | | | | | | | | | | | | | | | |
| 3-Ethylcyclopentene | " | | | | | | | | | | | | | | | |
| 4-Ethylcyclopentene | " | | | | | | | | | | | | | | | |
| 1,2-Dimethylcyclopentene | " | | | | | | | | | | | | | | | |
| 1,3-Dimethylcyclopentene | " | | | | | | | | | | | | | | | |
| 1,4-Dimethylcyclopentene | " | | | | | | | | | | | | | | | |
| 1,5-Dimethylcyclopentene | " | | | | | | | | | | | | | | | |
| 3,3-Dimethylcyclopentene | " | | | | | | | | | | | | | | | |
| 3,cis-4-Dimethylcyclopentene | " | | | | | | | | | | | | | | | |
| 3,trans-4-Dimethylcyclopentene | " | | | | | | | | | | | | | | | |
| 3,cis-5-Dimethylcyclopentene | " | | | | | | | | | | | | | | | |
| 3,trans-5-Dimethylcyclopentene | " | | | | | | | | | | | | | | | |
| 4,4-Dimethylcyclopentene | " | | | | | | | | | | | | | | | |

TABLE 19y - ALKYL CYCLOHEXENES, $C_6$ TO $C_8$
LOGARITHM OF EQUILIBRIUM CONSTANT OF FORMATION, $\log_{10} Kf$, AT 0° TO 1500°K
December 31, 1952

| Compound (gas) | Formula | Temperature in °K | | | | | | | | | | | | | | |
|---|---|---|---|---|---|---|---|---|---|---|---|---|---|---|---|---|
| | | 0 | 298.16 | 300 | 400 | 500 | 600 | 700 | 800 | 900 | 1000 | 1100 | 1200 | 1300 | 1400 | 1500 |
| | | | | | | Logarithm of Equilibrium Constant of Formation, $\log_{10} Kf$ | | | | | | | | | | |
| Cyclohexene | $C_6H_{10}$ | infinite | 18.412 | 18.416 | 18.904 | 19.389 | 19.808 | 20.163 | 20.451 | 20.694 | 20.893 | 21.052 | 21.181 | 21.293 | 21.385 | 21.460 |
| 1-Methylcyclohexene | $C_7H_{12}$ | | | | | | | | | | | | | | | |
| 3-Methylcyclohexene | " | | | | | | | | | | | | | | | |
| 4-Methylcyclohexene | " | | | | | | | | | | | | | | | |
| 1-Ethylcyclohexene | $C_8H_{14}$ | | | | | | | | | | | | | | | |
| 3-Ethylcyclohexene | " | | | | | | | | | | | | | | | |
| 4-Ethylcyclohexene | " | | | | | | | | | | | | | | | |
| 1,2-Dimethylcyclohexene | " | | | | | | | | | | | | | | | |
| 1,3-Dimethylcyclohexene | " | | | | | | | | | | | | | | | |
| 1,4-Dimethylcyclohexene | " | | | | | | | | | | | | | | | |
| 1,5-Dimethylcyclohexene | " | | | | | | | | | | | | | | | |
| 1,6-Dimethylcyclohexene | " | | | | | | | | | | | | | | | |
| 3,3-Dimethylcyclohexene | " | | | | | | | | | | | | | | | |
| 3,cis-4-Dimethylcyclohexene | " | | | | | | | | | | | | | | | |
| 3,trans-4-Dimethylcyclohexene | " | | | | | | | | | | | | | | | |
| 3,cis-5-Dimethylcyclohexene | " | | | | | | | | | | | | | | | |
| 3,trans-5-Dimethylcyclohexene | " | | | | | | | | | | | | | | | |
| 3,cis-6-Dimethylcyclohexene | " | | | | | | | | | | | | | | | |
| 3,trans-6-Dimethylcyclohexene | " | | | | | | | | | | | | | | | |
| 4,4-Dimethylcyclohexene | " | | | | | | | | | | | | | | | |
| 4,cis-5-Dimethylcyclohexene | " | | | | | | | | | | | | | | | |
| 4,trans-5-Dimethylcyclohexene | " | | | | | | | | | | | | | | | |

TABLE 25y (PART 1) — NORMAL ACETYLENES (1-ALKYNES), $C_2$ TO $C_{20}$

LOGARITHM OF EQUILIBRIUM CONSTANT OF FORMATION, $\log_{10} Kf$, AT 0° TO 1500°K

February 28, 1946; December 31, 1952

Temperature in °K

Logarithm of Equilibrium Constant of Formation, $\log_{10} Kf$

| Compound (gas) | Formula | 0 | 298.16 | 300 | 400 | 500 | 600 | 700 | 800 | 900 | 1000 | 1100 | 1200 | 1300 | 1400 | 1500 |
|---|---|---|---|---|---|---|---|---|---|---|---|---|---|---|---|---|
| Ethyne (Acetylene) | $C_2H_2$ | Infinite | -36.6490 | -36.4058 | -26.5406 | -20.6290 | -16.6952 | -13.8925 | -11.7978 | -10.1702 | -8.8738 | -7.8158 | -6.9369 | -6.1956 | -5.5611 | -5.0134 |
| Propyne (Methylacetylene) | $C_3H_4$ | Infinite | -33.9469 | -33.8610 | -25.8360 | -21.0781 | -17.9409 | -15.7228 | -14.0728 | -12.8007 | -11.7897 | -10.9660 | -10.2830 | -9.7072 | -9.2137 | -8.7879 |
| 1-Butyne (Ethylacetylene) | $C_4H_6$ | Infinite | -35.4032 | -35.2225 | -28.1106 | -23.9396 | -21.2100 | -19.2946 | -17.8771 | -16.7893 | -15.9277 | -15.2248 | -14.6426 | -14.1534 | -13.741 | -13.3707 |
| 1-Pentyne | $C_5H_8$ | Infinite | -36.7666 | -36.6067 | -30.4327 | -26.8463 | -24.5319 | -22.9162 | -21.7290 | -20.8300 | -20.1172 | -19.5341 | -19.0482 | -18.6437 | -18.2971 | -17.9864 |
| 1-Hexyne | $C_6H_{10}$ | Infinite | -38.239 | -38.102 | -32.854 | -29.854 | -27.949 | -26.635 | -25.677 | -24.960 | -24.394 | -23.929 | -23.541 | -23.220 | -22.944 | -22.695 |
| 1-Heptyne | $C_7H_{12}$ | Infinite | -39.712 | -39.598 | -35.275 | -32.862 | -31.366 | -30.353 | -29.625 | -29.091 | -28.671 | -28.324 | -28.034 | -27.796 | -27.592 | -27.404 |
| 1-Octyne | $C_8H_{14}$ | Infinite | -41.184 | -41.094 | -37.696 | -35.871 | -34.784 | -34.071 | -33.572 | -33.221 | -32.948 | -32.718 | -32.527 | -32.372 | -32.239 | -32.113 |
| 1-Nonyne | $C_9H_{16}$ | Infinite | -42.657 | -42.589 | -40.117 | -38.879 | -38.201 | -37.790 | -37.520 | -37.351 | -37.225 | -37.113 | -37.020 | -36.948 | -36.886 | -36.822 |
| 1-Decyne | $C_{10}H_{18}$ | Infinite | -44.130 | -44.085 | -42.538 | -41.887 | -41.618 | -41.508 | -41.468 | -41.482 | -41.502 | -41.508 | -41.513 | -41.524 | -41.533 | -41.531 |
| 1-Undecyne | $C_{11}H_{20}$ | Infinite | -45.602 | -45.580 | -44.959 | -44.895 | -45.036 | -45.227 | -45.416 | -45.612 | -45.779 | -45.903 | -46.006 | -46.100 | -46.179 | -46.240 |
| 1-Dodecyne | $C_{12}H_{22}$ | Infinite | -47.075 | -47.076 | -47.380 | -47.903 | -48.453 | -48.945 | -49.364 | -49.742 | -50.056 | -50.298 | -50.499 | -50.676 | -50.826 | -50.949 |
| 1-Tridecyne | $C_{13}H_{24}$ | Infinite | -48.547 | -48.572 | -49.801 | -50.911 | -51.870 | -52.663 | -53.311 | -53.872 | -54.333 | -54.692 | -54.992 | -55.252 | -55.473 | -55.658 |
| 1-Tetradecyne | $C_{14}H_{26}$ | Infinite | -50.020 | -50.067 | -52.222 | -53.919 | -55.288 | -56.382 | -57.259 | -58.003 | -58.610 | -59.087 | -59.485 | -59.828 | -60.121 | -60.367 |
| 1-Pentadecyne | $C_{15}H_{28}$ | Infinite | -51.493 | -51.563 | -54.643 | -56.927 | -58.705 | -60.100 | -61.207 | -62.133 | -62.887 | -63.482 | -63.978 | -64.404 | -64.768 | -65.076 |
| 1-Hexadecyne | $C_{16}H_{30}$ | Infinite | -52.965 | -53.058 | -57.064 | -59.935 | -62.122 | -63.819 | -65.155 | -66.263 | -67.164 | -67.877 | -68.471 | -68.980 | -69.415 | -69.785 |
| 1-Heptadecyne | $C_{17}H_{32}$ | Infinite | -54.438 | -54.554 | -59.485 | -62.944 | -65.540 | -67.537 | -69.103 | -70.394 | -71.441 | -72.272 | -72.964 | -73.556 | -74.062 | -74.494 |
| 1-Octadecyne | $C_{18}H_{34}$ | Infinite | -55.910 | -56.050 | -61.906 | -65.952 | -68.957 | -71.255 | -73.050 | -74.524 | -75.718 | -76.666 | -77.457 | -78.132 | -78.710 | -79.203 |
| 1-Nonadecyne | $C_{19}H_{36}$ | Infinite | -57.383 | -57.545 | -64.327 | -68.960 | -72.374 | -74.974 | -76.998 | -78.654 | -79.995 | -81.061 | -81.950 | -82.708 | -83.357 | -83.912 |
| 1-Eicosyne | $C_{20}H_{38}$ | Infinite | -58.856 | -59.041 | -66.748 | -61.968 | -75.791 | -78.692 | -80.946 | -82.784 | -84.272 | -85.456 | -86.443 | -87.284 | -88.003 | -88.621 |
| Increment per $CH_2$ group, applicable beyond 1-pentyne | | Infinite | -1.4726 | -1.4956 | -2.4210 | -3.0081 | -3.4173 | -3.7184 | -3.9478 | -4.1303 | -4.2770 | -4.3948 | -4.4930 | -4.5760 | -4.6471 | -4.7090 |

TABLE 12y – ACETYLENES, $C_2$ TO $C_5$
LOGARITHM OF EQUILIBRIUM CONSTANT OF FORMATION, $\log_{10} Kf$, AT 0° TO 1500°K
April 30, 1945; December 31, 1952

| Compound (gas) | Formula | Temperature in °K | | | | | | | | | | | | | | |
|---|---|---|---|---|---|---|---|---|---|---|---|---|---|---|---|---|
| | | 0 | 298.16 | 300 | 400 | 500 | 600 | 700 | 800 | 900 | 1000 | 1100 | 1200 | 1300 | 1400 | 1500 |
| | | Logarithm of Equilibrium Constant of Formation, $\log_{10} Kf$ | | | | | | | | | | | | | | |
| Ethyne (Acetylene) | $C_2H_2$ | infinite | -36.6490 | -36.4058 | -26.5406 | -20.6290 | -16.6952 | -13.8925 | -11.7978 | -10.1702 | -8.8738 | -7.8158 | -6.9369 | -6.1956 | -5.5611 | -5.0134 |
| Propyne (Methylacetylene) | $C_3H_4$ | infinite | -33.9469 | -33.8610 | -25.8360 | -21.0781 | -17.9409 | -15.7228 | -14.0728 | -12.8007 | -11.7897 | -10.9660 | -10.2830 | -9.7072 | -9.2137 | -8.7879 |
| 1-Butyne (Ethylacetylene) | $C_4H_6$ | infinite | -35.4032 | -35.2225 | -28.1106 | -23.9996 | -21.2100 | -19.2946 | -17.8771 | -16.7893 | -15.9277 | -15.2248 | -14.6426 | -14.1534 | -13.7341 | -13.3707 |
| 2-Butyne (Dimethylacetylene) | " | infinite | -32.4859 | -32.3304 | -26.0508 | -22.3880 | -20.0116 | -18.3517 | -17.1286 | -16.1968 | -15.4600 | -14.8612 | -14.3676 | -13.9517 | -13.5952 | -13.2876 |
| 1-Pentyne | $C_5H_8$ | infinite | -36.7666 | -36.6067 | -30.4327 | -26.8463 | -24.5319 | -22.9162 | -21.7290 | -20.8300 | -20.1172 | -19.5341 | -19.0482 | -18.6437 | -18.2971 | -17.9864 |
| 2-Pentyne | " | infinite | -34.0177 | -33.8792 | -28.3891 | -25.2377 | -23.2205 | -21.8297 | -20.8130 | -20.0457 | -19.4412 | -18.9519 | -18.5480 | -18.2095 | -17.9186 | -17.6668 |
| 3-Methyl-1-butyne | " | infinite | -36.0061 | -35.8614 | -30.0299 | -26.6495 | -24.4662 | -22.9486 | -21.8318 | -20.9810 | -20.3088 | -19.7622 | -19.3118 | -18.9315 | -18.6004 | -18.3115 |

## TABLE 21 y (PART 1) – NORMAL ALKYL BENZENES, $C_6$ TO $C_{22}$
### LOGARITHM OF EQUILIBRIUM CONSTANT OF FORMATION, $\log_{10} Kf$, AT 0° TO 1500°K
November 30, 1945; December 31, 1952

| Compound (gas) | Formula | Temperature in °K |  |  |  |  |  |  |  |  |  |  |  |  |  |  |
|---|---|---|---|---|---|---|---|---|---|---|---|---|---|---|---|---|
|  |  | 0 | 298.16 | 300 | 400 | 500 | 600 | 700 | 800 | 900 | 1000 | 1100 | 1200 | 1300 | 1400 | 1500 |
|  |  | Logarithm of Equilibrium Constant of Formation, $\log_{10} Kf$ |  |  |  |  |  |  |  |  |  |  |  |  |  |  |
| Benzene | $C_6H_6$ | Infinite | -22.7143 | -22.6252 | -19.1271 | -17.1521 | -15.9040 | -15.0519 | -14.4345 | -13.9716 | -13.6088 | -13.3153 | -13.0738 | -12.8717 | -12.6971 | -12.5461 |
| Methylbenzene (Toluene) | $C_7H_8$ | Infinite | -21.4236 | -21.3698 | -19.3356 | -18.2752 | -17.6574 | -17.2671 | -17.0018 | -16.8171 | -16.6794 | -16.5699 | -16.4825 | -16.4102 | -16.3455 | -16.2900 |
| Ethylbenzene | $C_8H_{10}$ | Infinite | -22.8750 | -22.8428 | -21.7132 | -21.2223 | -20.9972 | -20.8934 | -20.8442 | -20.8296 | -20.8281 | -20.8294 | -20.8333 | -20.8368 | -20.8362 | -20.8375 |
| n-Propylbenzene | $C_9H_{12}$ | Infinite | -24.046 | -24.034 | -23.887 | -24.018 | -24.222 | -24.434 | -24.625 | -24.808 | -24.958 | -25.073 | -25.188 | -25.284 | -25.351 | -25.410 |
| n-Butylbenzene | $C_{10}H_{14}$ | Infinite | -25.347 | -25.359 | -26.182 | -26.925 | -27.559 | -28.083 | -28.515 | -28.885 | -29.198 | -29.444 | -29.650 | -29.823 | -29.972 | -30.101 |
| n-Pentylbenzene | $C_{11}H_{16}$ | Infinite | -26.783 | -26.823 | -28.570 | -29.902 | -30.946 | -31.770 | -32.432 | -32.984 | -33.438 | -33.815 | -34.112 | -34.362 | -34.593 | -34.778 |
| n-Hexylbenzene | $C_{12}H_{18}$ | Infinite | -28.256 | -28.319 | -30.991 | -32.910 | -34.363 | -35.488 | -36.380 | -37.114 | -37.715 | -38.210 | -38.605 | -38.938 | -39.245 | -39.487 |
| n-Heptylbenzene | $C_{13}H_{20}$ | Infinite | -29.728 | -29.814 | -33.412 | -35.918 | -37.781 | -39.207 | -40.328 | -41.245 | -41.992 | -42.605 | -43.098 | -43.514 | -43.881 | -44.196 |
| n-Octylbenzene | $C_{14}H_{22}$ | Infinite | -31.201 | -31.310 | -35.833 | -38.926 | -41.198 | -42.925 | -44.275 | -45.375 | -46.269 | -46.999 | -47.591 | -48.090 | -48.533 | -48.905 |
| n-Nonylbenzene | $C_{15}H_{24}$ | Infinite | -32.673 | -32.805 | -38.254 | -41.934 | -44.615 | -46.644 | -48.223 | -49.505 | -50.546 | -51.394 | -52.084 | -52.666 | -53.185 | -53.614 |
| n-Decylbenzene | $C_{16}H_{26}$ | Infinite | -34.146 | -34.301 | -40.675 | -44.942 | -48.032 | -50.362 | -52.171 | -53.636 | -54.823 | -55.789 | -56.577 | -57.242 | -57.821 | -58.323 |
| n-Undecylbenzene | $C_{17}H_{28}$ | Infinite | -35.619 | -35.797 | -43.096 | -47.951 | -51.450 | -54.080 | -56.119 | -57.766 | -59.100 | -60.184 | -61.070 | -61.818 | -62.473 | -63.032 |
| n-Dodecylbenzene | $C_{18}H_{30}$ | Infinite | -37.091 | -37.292 | -45.517 | -50.959 | -54.867 | -57.799 | -60.067 | -61.896 | -63.377 | -64.579 | -65.563 | -66.394 | -67.125 | -67.741 |
| n-Tridecylbenzene | $C_{19}H_{32}$ | Infinite | -38.564 | -38.788 | -47.938 | -53.967 | -58.284 | -61.517 | -64.014 | -66.026 | -67.654 | -68.973 | -70.056 | -70.970 | -71.777 | -72.450 |
| n-Tetradecylbenzene | $C_{20}H_{34}$ | Infinite | -40.036 | -40.283 | -50.359 | -56.975 | -61.702 | -65.236 | -67.962 | -70.157 | -71.931 | -73.368 | -74.549 | -75.546 | -76.413 | -77.159 |
| n-Pentadecylbenzene | $C_{21}H_{36}$ | Infinite | -41.509 | -41.779 | -52.780 | -59.983 | -65.119 | -68.954 | -71.910 | -74.287 | -76.208 | -77.763 | -79.042 | -80.122 | -81.065 | -81.868 |
| n-Hexadecylbenzene | $C_{22}H_{38}$ | Infinite | -42.982 | -43.215 | -55.201 | -62.991 | -68.536 | -72.672 | -75.858 | -78.417 | -80.485 | -82.158 | -83.535 | -84.698 | -85.717 | -86.577 |
| Increment per $CH_2$ group, applicable beyond n-pentylbenzene | | Infinite | -1.4726 | -1.4956 | -2.4210 | -3.0081 | -3.4173 | -3.7184 | -3.9478 | -4.1303 | -4.2770 | -4.3948 | -4.4930 | -4.5760 | -4.6471 | -4.7090 |

TABLE 5y – ALKYL BENZENES, $C_6$ TO $C_9$

LOGARITHM OF EQUILIBRIUM CONSTANT OF FORMATION, $\log_{10} Kf$, AT 0° TO 1500°K

November 30, 1945

Temperature in °K

Logarithm of Equilibrium Constant of Formation, $\log_{10} Kf$

| Compound (gas) | Formula | 0 | 298.16 | 300 | 400 | 500 | 600 | 700 | 800 | 900 | 1000 | 1100 | 1200 | 1300 | 1400 | 1500 |
|---|---|---|---|---|---|---|---|---|---|---|---|---|---|---|---|---|
| Benzene | $C_6H_6$ | infinite | -22.7143 | -22.6252 | -19.1271 | -17.1521 | -15.9040 | -15.0519 | -14.4345 | -13.9716 | -13.6088 | -13.3153 | -13.0738 | -12.8717 | -12.6971 | -12.5461 |
| Methylbenzene (Toluene) | $C_7H_8$ | infinite | -21.4236 | -21.3698 | -19.3356 | -18.2752 | -17.6574 | -17.2671 | -17.0018 | -16.8171 | -16.6794 | -16.5699 | -16.4825 | -16.4102 | -16.3455 | -16.2900 |
| Ethylbenzene | $C_8H_{10}$ | infinite | -22.8750 | -22.8428 | -21.7132 | -21.1223 | -20.9972 | -20.8934 | -20.8442 | -20.8296 | -20.8281 | -20.8294 | -20.8333 | -20.8368 | -20.8362 | -20.8375 |
| 1,2-Dimethylbenzene (o-Xylene) | " | infinite | -21.3860 | -21.3655 | -20.6980 | -20.4786 | -20.4351 | -20.4646 | -20.5188 | -20.5864 | -20.6513 | -20.7081 | -20.7601 | -20.8051 | -20.8399 | -20.8692 |
| 1,3-Dimethylbenzene (m-Xylene) | " | infinite | -20.8202 | -20.8014 | -20.2201 | -20.0651 | -20.0699 | -20.1349 | -20.2172 | -20.3077 | -20.3919 | -20.4646 | -20.5296 | -20.5853 | -20.6290 | -20.6670 |
| 1,4-Dimethylbenzene (p-Xylene) | " | infinite | -21.2214 | -21.2018 | -20.5912 | -20.4227 | -20.4194 | -20.4821 | -20.5638 | -20.6545 | -20.7393 | -20.8128 | -20.8788 | -20.9358 | -20.9808 | -21.0202 |
| n-Propylbenzene | $C_9H_{12}$ | infinite | -24.049 | -24.040 | -23.894 | -24.012 | -24.215 | -24.422 | -24.610 | -24.785 | -24.932 | -25.056 | -25.168 | -25.262 | -25.336 | -25.395 |
| Isopropylbenzene | " | infinite | -23.996 | -23.992 | -24.016 | -24.241 | -24.510 | -24.768 | -24.991 | -25.192 | -25.364 | -25.509 | -25.631 | -25.732 | -25.812 | -25.880 |
| 1-Methyl-2-ethylbenzene | " | infinite | -22.960 | -22.958 | -23.090 | -23.377 | -23.684 | -23.970 | -24.218 | -24.437 | -24.624 | -24.780 | -24.914 | -25.027 | -25.119 | -25.199 |
| 1-Methyl-3-ethylbenzene | " | infinite | -22.149 | -22.150 | -22.428 | -22.816 | -23.194 | -23.533 | -23.822 | -24.075 | -24.289 | -24.468 | -24.620 | -24.749 | -24.853 | -24.945 |
| 1-Methyl-4-ethylbenzene | " | infinite | -22.195 | -22.198 | -22.537 | -22.964 | -23.371 | -23.733 | -24.040 | -24.308 | -24.535 | -24.723 | -24.885 | -25.021 | -25.133 | -25.232 |
| 1,2,3-Trimethylbenzene | " | infinite | -21.490 | -21.500 | -22.159 | -22.754 | -23.279 | -23.731 | -24.110 | -24.436 | -24.712 | -24.942 | -25.140 | -25.310 | -25.450 | -25.571 |
| 1,2,4-Trimethylbenzene | " | infinite | -20.459 | -20.473 | -21.319 | -22.025 | -22.622 | -23.124 | -23.541 | -23.897 | -24.196 | -24.445 | -24.657 | -24.839 | -24.990 | -25.121 |
| 1,3,5-Trimethylbenzene | " | infinite | -20.6497 | -20.6666 | -21.6131 | -22.3891 | -23.0336 | -23.5702 | -24.0136 | -24.3904 | -24.7055 | -24.9678 | -25.1916 | -25.3815 | -25.5390 | -25.6761 |

TABLE 13y - STYRENES, $C_8$ and $C_9$

LOGARITHM OF EQUILIBRIUM CONSTANT OF FORMATION, $\log_{10} Kf$, AT $0°$ TO $1500°K$

September 30, 1947

| Compound (gas) | Formula | Temperature in $°K$ | | | | | | | | | | | | | | |
|---|---|---|---|---|---|---|---|---|---|---|---|---|---|---|---|---|
| | | Logarithm of Equilibrium Constant of Formation, $\log_{10} Kf$ | | | | | | | | | | | | | | |
| | | 0 | 298.16 | 300 | 400 | 500 | 600 | 700 | 800 | 900 | 1000 | 1100 | 1200 | 1300 | 1400 | 1500 |
| Ethenylbenzene (Styrene; Vinylbenzene; Phenylethylene) | $C_8H_8$ | Infinite | -37.4532 | -37.2963 | -31.0030 | -27.3649 | -25.0117 | -23.3762 | -22.1729 | -21.2543 | -20.5264 | -19.9330 | -19.4456 | -19.0295 | -18.6705 | -18.3630 |
| Isopropenylbenzene (α-Methylstyrene; 2-Phenyl-1-propene) | $C_9H_{10}$ | Infinite | -36.531 | -36.416 | -31.636 | -28.963 | -27.266 | -26.101 | -25.272 | -24.649 | -24.162 | -23.749 | -23.433 | -23.153 | -22.919 | -22.707 |
| cis-1-Propenylbenzene (cis-β-Methylstyrene; cis-1-Phenyl-1-propene) | " | Infinite | -37.998 | -37.874 | -32.729 | -29.837 | -27.994 | -26.726 | -25.818 | -25.134 | -24.600 | -24.146 | -23.797 | -23.490 | -23.231 | -22.998 |
| trans-1-Propenylbenzene (trans-β-Methylstyrene; trans-1-Phenyl-1-propene) | " | Infinite | -37.440 | -37.380 | -32.357 | -29.562 | -27.783 | -26.560 | -25.687 | -25.030 | -24.495 | -24.081 | -23.724 | -23.429 | -23.159 | -22.958 |
| 1-Methyl-2-ethenylbenzene (o-Methylstyrene) | " | Infinite | -37.484 | -37.364 | -32.346 | -29.531 | -27.739 | -26.507 | -25.627 | -24.965 | -24.446 | -24.007 | -23.670 | -23.352 | -23.122 | -22.896 |
| 1-Methyl-3-ethenylbenzene (m-Methylstyrene) | " | Infinite | -36.665 | -36.548 | -31.658 | -28.919 | -27.176 | -25.982 | -25.130 | -24.488 | -23.988 | -23.562 | -23.236 | -22.948 | -22.706 | -22.488 |
| 1-Methyl-4-ethenylbenzene (p-Methylstyrene) | " | Infinite | -36.825 | -36.708 | -31.855 | -29.138 | -27.411 | -26.226 | -25.381 | -24.746 | -24.250 | -23.888 | -23.506 | -23.220 | -22.981 | -22.765 |

TABLE 20z (PART 1) - NORMAL PARAFFINS, $C_1$ TO $C_{20}$
HEAT AND ENTROPY OF FUSION, FREEZING POINTS, AND CRYOSCOPIC CONSTANTS
December 31, 1952

| Compound | Formula | Crystalline Form[a] | Freezing Point in air at 1 atm | | Freezing Point at satn. press. (triple point) | Freezing Point at satn. press. less Freezing Point in air at 1 atm[b] | Heat of Fusion $\Delta Hm^o$ | Entropy of Fusion $\Delta Sm^o$ | Cryoscopic Constants[c] | |
|---|---|---|---|---|---|---|---|---|---|---|
| | | | °C | °K | °K | °K | kcal/mole | cal/deg mole | A | B |
| | | | | | | | | | mole fraction | mole fraction/deg |
| Methane | $CH_4$ | I | | | 90.68 | | 0.225 | 2.48 | 0.0138 | 0.0057 |
| Ethane | $C_2H_6$ | I | | | 89.89 | | 0.6834 | 7.603 | 0.04256 | 0.0095 |
| Propane | $C_3H_8$ | I | | | 85.47 | | 0.8422 | 9.854 | 0.05802 | 0.0073 |
| n-Butane | $C_4H_{10}$ | I | -138.350 | 134.810 | 134.83 | 0.02 | 1.114 | 8.263 | 0.03085 | 0.0048 |
| n-Pentane | $C_5H_{12}$ | I | -129.721 | 143.439 | 143.49 | 0.05 | 2.006 | 13.98 | 0.04906 | 0.0042 |
| n-Hexane | $C_6H_{14}$ | I | -95.348 | 177.812 | 177.84 | 0.03 | 3.114 | 17.51 | 0.04956 | 0.0039 |
| n-Heptane | $C_7H_{16}$ | I | -90.610 | 182.550 | 182.57 | 0.02 | 3.354 | 18.37 | 0.05065 | 0.0033 |
| n-Octane | $C_8H_{18}$ | I | -56.795 | 216.365 | 216.38 | 0.01 | 4.957 | 22.91 | 0.05329 | 0.0031 |
| n-Nonane | $C_9H_{20}$ | I | -53.519 | 219.641 | 219.66 | 0.02 | 3.697 | 16.83 | 0.03856 | |
| n-Decane | $C_{10}H_{22}$ | I | -29.661 | 243.499 | 243.51 | 0.01 | 6.863 | 28.18 | 0.05825 | |
| n-Undecane | $C_{11}H_{24}$ | I | -25.594 | 247.566 | 247.59 | 0.02 | 5.301 | 21.41 | 0.04352 | |
| n-Dodecane | $C_{12}H_{26}$ | I | -9.587 | 263.573 | 263.61 | 0.04 | 8.803 | 33.40 | 0.06377 | |
| n-Tridecane | $C_{13}H_{28}$ | I | -5.392 | 267.768 | 267.79 | 0.02 | 6.811 | 25.44 | 0.04780 | |
| n-Tetradecane | $C_{14}H_{30}$ | I | +5.863 | 279.023 | 279.03 | 0.01 | 10.772 | 38.606 | 0.06963 | |
| n-Pentadecane | $C_{15}H_{32}$ | I | +9.926 | 283.086 | 283.11 | 0.02 | 8.267 | 29.20 | 0.05191 | |
| n-Hexadecane | $C_{16}H_{34}$ | I | +18.165 | 291.325 | 291.34 | 0.01 | 12.750 | 43.766 | 0.07560 | |
| n-Heptadecane | $C_{17}H_{36}$ | I | +21.980 | 295.140 | 295.16 | 0.02 | 9.676 | 32.784 | 0.0559 | |
| n-Octadecane | $C_{18}H_{38}$ | I | +28.180 | 301.340 | 301.36 | 0.02 | 14.815 | 49.164 | 0.0821 | |
| n-Nonadecane | $C_{19}H_{40}$ | I | +32.1 | 305.2 | 305.4 | 0.02 | 12.0 | 36.0 | 0.0594 | |
| n-Eicosane | $C_{20}H_{42}$ | I | +36.8 | 309.9 | 310.1 | 0.02 | 16.8 | 54.2 | 0.0880 | |

[a] See footnote a of Table 1z.  [b] See footnote b of Table 1z.  [c] See footnote c of Table 1z.

TABLE 1z – PARAFFINS, $C_1$ TO $C_5$

## HEAT AND ENTROPY OF FUSION, FREEZING POINTS, AND CRYOSCOPIC CONSTANTS

December 31, 1944; November 30, 1949; December 31, 1952

| Compound | Formula | Crystalline Form[a] | Freezing Point in air at 1 atm | | Freezing Point at satn. press. (triple point) | Freezing Point at satn. press. less Freezing Point in air at 1 atm[b] | Heat of Fusion $\Delta Hm^\circ$ | Entropy of Fusion $\Delta Sm^\circ$ | Cryoscopic Constants[c] | |
|---|---|---|---|---|---|---|---|---|---|---|
| | | | °C | °K | °K | °K | kcal/mole | cal/deg mole | $A$ | $B$ |
| | | | | | | | | | mole fraction/deg | |
| Methane | $CH_4$ | I | | | 90.68 | | 0.225 | 2.48 | 0.0138 | 0.0057 |
| Ethane | $C_2H_6$ | I | | | 89.89 | | 0.6834 | 7.603 | 0.04256 | 0.0095 |
| Propane | $C_3H_8$ | I | | | 85.47 | | 0.8422 | 9.854 | 0.05802 | 0.0073 |
| n-Butane | $C_4H_{10}$ | I | −138.350 | 134.810 | 134.83 | 0.02 | 1.114 | 8.26 | 0.03085 | 0.0048 |
| 2-Methylpropane (Isobutane) | " | I | −159.600 | 113.560 | | | 1.085 | 9.55 | 0.04234 | 0.0057 |
| n-Pentane | $C_5H_{12}$ | I | −129.721 | 143.439 | 143.49 | 0.05 | 2.006 | 13.98 | 0.04906 | 0.0042 |
| 2-Methylbutane (Isopentane) | " | I | −159.900 | 113.260 | | | 1.231 | 10.87 | 0.04829 | 0.0058 |
| 2,2-Dimethylpropane (Neopentane) | " | I | −16.550 | 256.610 | | | 0.7782 | 3.033 | 0.00595 | 0.000 |

a When a given hydrocarbon has more than one crystalline form, the several forms will be labeled I, II, III, etc., in order of decreasing temperature of the freezing point. Forms other than I will be, at their respective freezing point, in metastable equilibrium with the undercooled liquid, and will be unstable with respect to transition to some other solid form at the same temperature and pressure (one atmosphere). Such metastable forms are indicated by a letter u in parentheses following the Roman numeral.

b For compounds having a value of the cryoscopic constant $A$ greater than about 0.03 and a freezing point above about −100°C, the value of the freezing point at saturation pressure is usually higher by a small amount (of the order of 0.010°C) than the freezing point in air at one atmosphere.

c For use in the equation, $-\ln N_1 = A(T_1^* - T)[1 + B(T_1^* - T) + \ldots]$, which relates the temperature and the composition of a liquid solution for a system in which the liquid phase (consisting of the major component and one or more other components) is in thermodynamic equilibrium with a solid phase consisting of crystals of the major component alone. Here $N_1$ is the mole fraction of the major component in the liquid phase; $T_1^*$ is the freezing point in degrees Kelvin of the major component when pure ($N_1 = 1$) in air at 1 atmosphere: $T$ is the freezing point in degrees Kelvin of an actual sample of the substance ($N_1 < 1$); $A = \Delta Hm_1/RT_1^{*2}$; $B = 1/T_1^* - \Delta C_pm_1/2\Delta Hm_1$; $\Delta Hm_1$ is the heat of fusion per mole of the major component at the temperature $T_1^*$; and $\Delta C_pm_1$ is the heat capacity per mole of the liquid less that of the solid for the major component in the pure state at the temperature $T_1^*$. The freezing point of a given sample of a substance is defined as the temperature at which an infinitesimal amount of crystals of the major component is in equilibrium with the sample in liquid phase. For calculating the purity, $p$, in mole percent, the following equation may be used: $\log_{10} p = 2.00000 - (A/2.30259)(T_1^* - T)[1 + B(T_1^* - T)]$.

## TABLE 2z (PART 1) — PARAFFINS, $C_6$
### HEAT AND ENTROPY OF FUSION, FREEZING POINTS, AND CRYOSCOPIC CONSTANTS

January 31, 1945; March 31, 1945; December 31, 1952

| Compound | Formula | Crystal-line Form[a] | Freezing Point in air at 1 atm | | Freezing Point at satn. press. (triple point) | Freezing Point at satn. press. less Freezing Point in air at 1 atm[b] | Heat of Fusion | Entropy of Fusion | Cryoscopic Constants[c] | |
|---|---|---|---|---|---|---|---|---|---|---|
| | | | °C | °K | °K | °K | $\Delta H_m°$ | $\Delta S_m°$ | A | B |
| | | | | | | | kcal/mole | cal/deg mole | mole fraction/deg | |
| n-Hexane | $C_6H_{14}$ | I | − 95.348 | 177.812 | 177.84 | 0.03 | 3.114 | 17.51 | 0.04956 | 0.0039 |
| 2-Methylpentane | " | I | −153.670 | 119.490 | 119.55 | 0.06 | 1.500 | 12.55 | 0.05287 | 0.005 |
| 3-Methylpentane | " | | | | | | | | | |
| 2,2-Dimethylbutane | " | I | − 99.870 | 173.290 | 174.28 | 0.99 | 0.1385 | 0.7992 | 0.002321 | 0.000 |
| 2,3-Dimethylbutane | " | I | −128.538 | 144.622 | 145.19 | 0.57 | 0.194 | 1.34 | 0.00467 | |

a See footnote a of Table 1z.    b See footnote b of Table 1z.    c See footnote c of Table 1z.

TABLE 2z (PART 2) — PARAFFINS, $C_7$

HEAT AND ENTROPY OF FUSION, FREEZING POINTS, AND CRYOSCOPIC CONSTANTS

January 31, 1945; December 31, 1952

| Compound | Formula | Crystal-line Form[a] | Freezing Point in air at 1 atm | | Freezing Point at satn. press. (triple point) | Freezing Point at satn. press. less Freezing Point in air at 1 atm[b] | Heat of Fusion $\Delta H_m^\circ$ | Entropy of Fusion $\Delta S_m^\circ$ | Cryoscopic Constants[c] | |
|---|---|---|---|---|---|---|---|---|---|---|
| | | | °C | °K | °K | °K | kcal/mole | cal/deg mole | A | B |
| | | | | | | | | | mole fraction | mole fraction/deg |
| n-Heptane | $C_7H_{16}$ | I | − 90.610 | 182.550 | 182.57 | 0.02 | 3.354 | 18.37 | 0.05065 | 0.0033 |
| 2-Methylhexane | " | I | −118.276 | 154.884 | 154.91 | 0.03 | 2.195 | 14.17 | 0.04605 | 0.0036 |
| 3-Methylhexane | " | | | | | | | | | |
| 3-Ethylpentane | " | I | −118.604 | 154.556 | 154.59 | 0.03 | 2.282 | 14.75 | 0.04807 | 0.0039 |
| 2,2-Dimethylpentane | " | I | −123.811 | 149.349 | 149.43 | 0.08 | 1.392 | 9.32 | 0.03140 | 0.0036 |
| 2,3-Dimethylpentane | " | | | | | | | | | |
| 2,4-Dimethylpentane | " | I | −119.242 | 153.918 | 153.98 | 0.06 | 1.635 | 10.62 | 0.03473 | 0.0038 |
| 3,3-Dimethylpentane | " | I | −134.46 | 138.70 | | | 1.689 | 12.18 | 0.04418 | 0.0040 |
| " | " | II(u) | −134.95 | 138.21 | | | | | | |
| " | " | III(u) | −135.36 | 137.80 | | | | | | |
| 2,2,3-Trimethylbutane | " | I | − 24.912 | 248.248 | 248.53 | 0.28 | 0.5404 | 2.177 | 0.00441 | 0.0033 |

[a] See footnote a of Table 1z.  [b] See footnote b of Table 1z.  [c] See footnote c of Table 1z.

TABLE 3z – PARAFFINS, C$_8$

HEAT AND ENTROPY OF FUSION, FREEZING POINTS, AND CRYOSCOPIC CONSTANTS

August 31, 1945; December 31, 1952

| Compound | Formula | Crystalline Form[a] | Freezing Point in air at 1 atm | | Freezing Point at satn. press. (triple point) | Freezing Point at satn. press. less Freezing Point in air at 1 atm[b] | Heat of Fusion | Entropy of Fusion | Cryoscopic Constants[c] | |
|---|---|---|---|---|---|---|---|---|---|---|
| | | | °C | °K | °K | °K | $\Delta H_m°$ | $\Delta S_m°$ | A | B |
| | | | | | | | kcal/mole | cal/deg mole | mole fraction/deg | |
| n-Octane | C$_8$H$_{18}$ | I | − 56.795 | 216.365 | 216.38 | 0.01 | 4.957 | 22.91 | 0.05329 | 0.0031 |
| 2-Methylheptane | " | I | −109.040 | 164.120 | | | 2.45 | 14.94 | 0.0458 | |
| 3-Methylheptane | " | I | −120.50 | 152.66 | | | 2.72 | 17.80 | 0.0587 | |
| 4-Methylheptane | " | I | −120.955 | 152.205 | | | 2.59 | 17.03 | 0.0563 | |
| 3-Ethylhexane | " | | | | | | | | | |
| 2,2-Dimethylhexane | " | I | −121.18 | 151.98 | | | 1.62 | 10.69 | 0.0354 | |
| 2,3-Dimethylhexane | " | | | | | | | | | |
| 2,4-Dimethylhexane | " | | | | | | | | | |
| 2,5-Dimethylhexane | " | I | − 91.200 | 181.960 | | | 3.07 | 16.89 | 0.0467 | |
| 3,3-Dimethylhexane | " | I | −126.10 | 147.06 | | | 1.7 | 12. | 0.04 | |
| 3,4-Dimethylhexane | " | | | | | | | | | |
| 2-Methyl-3-ethylpentane | " | I | −114.960 | 158.200 | | | 2.71 | 17.10 | 0.0544 | |
| 3-Methyl-3-ethylpentane | " | I | − 90.870 | 182.290 | | | 2.59 | 14.20 | 0.0392 | |
| 2,2,3-Trimethylpentane | " | I | −112.27 | 160.89 | | | 2.06 | 12.82 | 0.0401 | |
| 2,2,4-Trimethylpentane | " | I | −107.380 | 165.780 | | | 2.202 | 13.28 | 0.04031 | 0.0043 |
| 2,3,3-Trimethylpentane | " | I | −100.70 | 172.46 | | | 0.37 | 2.12 | 0.0062 | |
| 2,3,4-Trimethylpentane | " | I | −109.210 | 163.950 | | | 2.215 | 13.51 | 0.04147 | 0.0035 |
| 2,2,3,3-Tetramethylbutane | " | I | +100.69 | 373.85 | 373.97 | 0.12 | 1.802 | 4.820 | 0.00649 | |

a See footnote a of Table 1z.  b See footnote b of Table 1z.  c See footnote c of Table 1z.

TABLE 4z, Page 1 — PARAFFINS, C$_9$
HEAT AND ENTROPY OF FUSION, FREEZING POINTS, AND CRYOSCOPIC CONSTANTS
December 31, 1952

| Compound | Formula | Crystal-line Form[a] | Freezing Point in air at 1 atm | | Freezing Point at satn. press. (triple point) | Freezing Point at satn. press. less Freezing Point in air at 1 atm[b] | Heat of Fusion | Entropy of Fusion | Cryoscopic Constants[c] | |
|---|---|---|---|---|---|---|---|---|---|---|
| | | | °C | °K | °K | °K | $\Delta Hm^0$ | $\Delta Sm^0$ | A | B |
| | | | | | | | kcal/mole | cal/deg mole | mole fraction/deg | |
| n-Nonane | C$_9$H$_{20}$ | I | − 53.519 | 219.641 | 219.66 | 0.02 | 3.697 | 16.83 | 0.03856 | |
| 2-Methyloctane | " | I | − 80.4 | 192.7 | | | | | | |
| 3-Methyloctane | " | I | −107.6 | 165.5 | | | | | | |
| 4-Methyloctane | " | I | −113.2 | 159.9 | | | | | | |
| 3-Ethylheptane | " | | | | | | | | | |
| 4-Ethylheptane | " | I | −113.00 | 160.16 | | | 2.14 | 13.4 | 0.042 | |
| 2,2-Dimethylheptane | " | | | | | | | | | |
| 2,3-Dimethylheptane | " | | | | | | | | | |
| 2,4-Dimethylheptane | " | | | | | | | | | |
| 2,5-Dimethylheptane | " | I | −102.9 | 170.2 | | | | | | |
| 2,6-Dimethylheptane | " | | | | | | | | | |
| 3,3-Dimethylheptane | " | | | | | | | | | |
| 3,4-Dimethylheptane | " | | | | | | | | | |
| 3,5-Dimethylheptane | " | | | | | | | | | |
| 4,4-Dimethylheptane | " | | | | | | | | | |

a See footnote a of Table 1z.   b See footnote b of Table 1z.   c See footnote c of Table 1z.

TABLE 4z, Page 2 — PARAFFINS, C$_9$

## HEAT AND ENTROPY OF FUSION, FREEZING POINTS, AND CRYOSCOPIC CONSTANTS
December 31, 1952

| Compound | Formula | Crystal- line Form[a] | Freezing Point in air at 1 atm °C | Freezing Point in air at 1 atm °K | Freezing Point at satn. press. (triple point) °K | Freezing Point at satn. press. less Freezing Point in air at 1 atm[b] °K | Heat of Fusion ΔHm° kcal/mole | Entropy of Fusion ΔSm° cal/deg mole | Cryoscopic Constants[c] A mole fraction/deg | Cryoscopic Constants[c] B |
|---|---|---|---|---|---|---|---|---|---|---|
| 2-Methyl-3-ethylhexane | C$_9$H$_{20}$ | | | | | | | | | |
| 2-Methyl-4-ethylhexane | " | | | | | | | | | |
| 3-Methyl-3-ethylhexane | " | | | | | | | | | |
| 3-Methyl-4-ethylhexane | " | | | | | | | | | |
| 2,2,3-Trimethylhexane | " | I | -120.0 | 153.1 | | | 2.8 | 18. | 0.06 | |
| 2,2,4-Trimethylhexane | " | I | -105.780 | 167.380 | | | 1.48 | 8.81 | 0.0265 | |
| 2,2,5-Trimethylhexane | " | I | -116.800 | 156.360 | | | 2.17 | 13.89 | 0.0447 | |
| 2,3,3-Trimethylhexane | " | I | -127.8 | 145.3 | | | | | | |
| 2,3,4-Trimethylhexane | " | I | -113.380 | 159.780 | | | 2.71 | 16.99 | 0.0535 | |
| 2,3,5-Trimethylhexane | " | I | -101.20 | 171.96 | | | 1.94 | 11.3 | 0.033 | |
| 2,4,4-Trimethylhexane | " | I | | | | | | | | |
| 3,3,4-Trimethylhexane | " | I | | | | | | | | |
| 3,3-Diethylpentane | " | I | -33.110 | 240.050 | 240.12 | 0.07 | 2.55 | 10.6 | 0.0223 | |
| 2,2-Dimethyl-3-ethylpentane | " | I | -99.2 | 173.9 | | | | | | |
| 2,3-Dimethyl-3-ethylpentane | " | I | | | | | | | | |
| 2,4-Dimethyl-3-ethylpentane | " | I | -122.2 | 150.9 | | | | | | |
| 2,2,3,3-Tetramethylpentane | " | I | -9.90 | 263.26 | | | 0.555 | 2.11 | 0.00403 | |
| 2,2,3,4-Tetramethylpentane | " | I | -121.09 | 152.07 | | | 0.124 | 0.82 | 0.0027 | |
| 2,2,4,4-Tetramethylpentane | " | I | -66.54 | 206.62 | | | 2.32 | 11.21 | 0.0273 | |
| 2,3,3,4-Tetramethylpentane | " | I | -102.123 | 171.037 | | | 2.14 | 12.54 | 0.0369 | |

[a] See footnote a of Table 1z.    [b] See footnote b of Table 1z.    [c] See footnote c of Table 1z.

TABLE 6z – ALKYL CYCLOPENTANES, $C_5$ TO $C_7$

HEAT AND ENTROPY OF FUSION, FREEZING POINTS, AND CRYOSCOPIC CONSTANTS

April 30, 1946; May 31, 1947; August 31, 1949; December 31, 1952

| Compound | Formula | Crystalline Form[a] | Freezing Point in air at 1 atm (°C) | Freezing Point in air at 1 atm (°K) | Freezing Point at satn. press. (triple point) (°K) | Freezing Point at satn. press. less Freezing Point in air at 1 atm[b] (°K) | Heat of Fusion $\Delta Hm°$ (kcal/mole) | Entropy of Fusion $\Delta Sm°$ (cal/deg mole) | Cryoscopic Constants[c] A (mole fraction/deg) | Cryoscopic Constants[c] B (mole fraction/deg) |
|---|---|---|---|---|---|---|---|---|---|---|
| Cyclopentane | $C_5H_{10}$ | I | – 93.879 | 179.281 | 179.71 | 0.43 | 0.1455 | 0.812 | 0.00228 | 0.00 |
| Methylcyclopentane | $C_6H_{12}$ | I | –142.455 | 130.705 | 130.73 | 0.02 | 1.6560 | 12.670 | 0.04878 | 0.0046 |
| Ethylcyclopentane | $C_7H_{14}$ | I | –138.446 | 134.714 | 134.73 | 0.02 | 1.6418 | 12.187 | 0.04553 | |
| " | " | II(u) | –139.14 | 134.02 | 134.03 | 0.01 | 1.8892 | 14.096 | 0.05293 | |
| 1,1-Dimethylcyclopentane | " | I | – 69.795 | 203.365 | 203.68 | 0.31 | 0.2578 | 1.268 | 0.00314 | |
| 1,cis-2-Dimethylcyclopentane | " | I | – 53.896 | 219.264 | 219.45 | 0.19 | 0.3961 | 1.896 | 0.00415 | |
| 1,trans-2-Dimethyocyclopentane | " | I | –117.58 | 155.58 | 155.70 | 0.12 | 1.540 | 9.90 | 0.03202 | 0.003 |
| 1,cis-3-Dimethylcyclopentane | " | I | –133.975 | 139.185 | 139.27 | 0.08 | 1.738 | 12.49 | 0.04515 | |
| 1,trans-3-Dimethylcyclopentane | " | I | –133.702 | 139.458 | 139.48 | 0.02 | 1.7682 | 12.679 | 0.04575 | |

a See footnote a of Table 1z.    b See footnote b of Table 1z.    c See footnote c of Table 1z.

TABLE 7z – ALKYL CYCLOHEXANES, $C_6$ TO $C_8$

HEAT AND ENTROPY OF FUSION, FREEZING POINTS, AND CRYOSCOPIC CONSTANTS

March 31, 1947; August 31, 1949; December 31, 1952

| Compound | Formula | Crystalline Form[a] | Freezing Point in air at 1 atm | | Freezing Point at satn. press. (triple point) | Freezing Point at satn. press. less Freezing Point in air at 1 atm[b] | Heat of Fusion $\Delta Hm^{o}$ | Entropy of Fusion $\Delta Sm^{o}$ | Cryoscopic Constants[c] | |
|---|---|---|---|---|---|---|---|---|---|---|
| | | | °C | °K | °K | °K | kcal/mole | cal/deg mole | A | B |
| | | | | | | | | | mole fraction/deg | |
| Cyclohexane | $C_6H_{12}$ | I | + 6.554 | 279.714 | 279.83 | 0.12 | 0.6398 | 2.287 | 0.00411 | 0.00072 |
| Methylcyclohexane | $C_7H_{14}$ | I | -126.593 | 146.567 | 146.58 | 0.01 | 1.6134 | 11.008 | 0.03779 | 0.0032 |
| Ethylcyclohexane | $C_8H_{16}$ | I | -111.323 | 161.837 | 161.84 | 0.00 | 1.9917 | 12.307 | 0.03827 | 0.00308 |
| 1,1-Dimethylcyclohexane | " | I | - 33.495 | 239.665 | 239.81 | 0.14 | 0.4834 | 2.017 | 0.00424 | 0.00174 |
| 1,cis-2-Dimethylcyclohexane | " | I | - 50.023 | 223.137 | 223.28 | 0.14 | 0.3932 | 1.762 | 0.00397 | 0.00133 |
| 1,trans-2-Dimethylcyclohexane | " | I | - 88.194 | 184.966 | 184.99 | 0.02 | 2.4908 | 13.466 | 0.03664 | 0.00336 |
| 1,cis-3-Dimethylcyclohexane | " | I | - 75.573 | 197.587 | 197.59 | 0.00 | 2.5861 | 13.088 | 0.03333 | 0.00345 |
| 1,trans-3-Dimethylcyclohexane | " | I | - 90.108 | 183.052 | 183.06 | 0.01 | 2.358 | 12.88 | 0.0354 | 0.0031 |
| 1,cis-4-Dimethylcyclohexane | " | I | - 87.436 | 185.724 | 185.73 | 0.01 | 2.2244 | 11.977 | 0.03245 | 0.00272 |
| 1,trans-4-Dimethylcyclohexane | " | I | - 36.962 | 236.198 | 236.22 | 0.02 | 2.9472 | 12.478 | 0.02658 | 0.00296 |

a See footnote a of Table 1z.   b See footnote b of Table 1z.   c See footnote c of Table 1z.

TABLE 8z (PART 1) – MONOOLEFINS, C₂ TO C₅

## HEAT AND ENTROPY OF FUSION, FREEZING POINTS, AND CRYOSCOPIC CONSTANTS

January 31, 1945; December 31, 1952

| Compound | Formula | Crystalline Form a | Freezing Point in air at 1 atm °C | Freezing Point in air at 1 atm °K | Freezing Point at satn. press. (triple point) °K | Freezing Point at satn. press. less Freezing Point in air at 1 atm b °K | Heat of Fusion $\Delta Hm°$ kcal/mole | Entropy of Fusion $\Delta Sm°$ cal/deg mole | Cryoscopic Constants c A mole fraction/deg | Cryoscopic Constants c B |
|---|---|---|---|---|---|---|---|---|---|---|
| Ethene (Ethylene) | $C_2H_4$ | I | (−169.15)d | | 104.01 | | 0.8008 | 7.699 | 0.03725 | 0.0130 |
| Propene (Propylene) | $C_3H_6$ | I | (−185.25)d | | 87.91 | | 0.7176 | 8.163 | 0.04673 | 0.0054 |
| 1-Butene | $C_4H_8$ | I | (−185.35)d | | 87.81 | | 0.9197 | 10.474 | 0.06002 | 0.0045 |
| cis-2-Butene | " | I | −138.910 | 134.250 | 134.26 | 0.01 | 1.7468 | 13.012 | 0.04877 | 0.0052 |
| trans-2-Butene | " | I | −105.550 | 167.610 | 167.61 | 0.00 | 2.3319 | 13.913 | 0.04177 | 0.0058 |
| 2-Methylpropene (Isobutene) | " | I | −140.350 | 132.810 | 132.81 | 0.00 | 1.4175 | 10.673 | 0.04044 | 0.005 |
| 1-Pentene | $C_5H_{10}$ | I | −165.220 | 107.940 | | | 1.388 | 12.86 | 0.05995 | 0.0048 |
| cis-2-Pentene | " | I | −151.390 | 121.770 | 121.80 | 0.03 | 1.6997 | 13.958 | 0.05768 | 0.0048 |
| trans-2-Pentene | " | I | −140.244 | 132.916 | 132.95 | 0.03 | 1.9960 | 15.017 | 0.05685 | 0.0052 |
| 2-Methyl-1-butene | " | I | −137.560 | 135.600 | | | 1.8906 | 13.933 | 0.05167 | 0.0043 |
| 3-Methyl-1-butene | " | I | −168.528 | 104.632 | 104.72 | 0.09 | 1.2809 | 12.242 | 0.05888 | 0.0047 |
| 2-Methyl-2-butene | " | I | −133.768 | 139.392 | 139.42 | 0.03 | 1.8158 | 13.027 | 0.04703 | 0.0048 |

a See footnote a of Table 1z.   b See footnote b of Table 1z.   c See footnote c of Table 1z.   d At saturation pressure (triple point).

TABLE 5z - ALKYL BENZENES, $C_6$ TO $C_9$

## HEAT AND ENTROPY OF FUSION, FREEZING POINTS, AND CRYOSCOPIC CONSTANTS

January 31, 1945; August 31, 1945; December 31, 1952

| Compound | Formula | Crystalline Form[a] | Freezing Point in air at 1 atm | | Freezing Point at satn. press. (triple point) | Freezing Point at satn. press. less Freezing Point in air at 1 atm[b] | Heat of Fusion | Entropy of Fusion | Cryoscopic Constants[c] | |
|---|---|---|---|---|---|---|---|---|---|---|
| | | | °C | °K | °K | °K | $\Delta Hm°$ | $\Delta Sm°$ | A | B |
| | | | | | | | kcal/mole | cal/deg mole | mole fraction | /deg |
| Benzene | $C_6H_6$ | I | + 5.533 | 278.693 | | | 2.351 | 8.436 | 0.01523 | 0.0032 |
| Methylbenzene (Toluene) | $C_7H_8$ | I | - 94.991 | 178.169 | | | 1.582 | 8.879 | 0.02508 | 0.0019 |
| Ethylbenzene | $C_8H_{10}$ | I | - 94.975 | 178.185 | | | 2.190 | 12.291 | 0.03471 | 0.0029 |
| 1,2-Dimethylbenzene (o-Xylene) | " | I | - 25.182 | 247.978 | | | 3.250 | 13.106 | 0.02659 | 0.0030 |
| 1,3-Dimethylbenzene (m-Xylene) | " | I | - 47.872 | 225.288 | | | 2.765 | 12.273 | 0.02741 | 0.0027 |
| 1,4-Dimethylbenzene (p-Xylene) | " | I | + 13.263 | 286.423 | | | 4.090 | 14.280 | 0.02509 | 0.0028 |
| n-Propylbenzene | $C_9H_{12}$ | I | - 99.500 | 173.660 | | | 2.04 | 11.7 | 0.034 | 0.003 |
| " | " | II(u) | -101.55 | 171.61 | | | 1.87 | 10.9 | 0.032 | 0.003 |
| Isopropylbenzene | " | I | - 96.035 | 177.125 | | | 1.7 | 10. | 0.028 | 0.003 |
| 1-Methyl-2-ethylbenzene | " | I | - 80.833 | 192.327 | | | 2.54 | 13.2 | 0.0346 | 0.003 |
| " | " | II(u) | - 86.556 | 186.604 | | | 2.28 | 12.2 | 0.033 | 0.003 |
| 1-Methyl-3-ethylbenzene | " | I | - 95.55 | 177.61 | | | 1.82 | 10.2 | 0.029 | 0.003 |
| " | " | II(u) | - 96.96 | 176.20 | | | 1.79 | 10.2 | 0.029 | 0.003 |
| 1-Methyl-4-ethylbenzene | " | I | - 62.350 | 210.810 | | | 3.04 | 14.4 | 0.0344 | 0.003 |
| 1,2,3-Trimethylbenzene | " | I | - 25.375 | 247.785 | | | 2.00 | 8.07 | 0.0164 | 0.003 |
| 1,2,4-Trimethylbenzene | " | I | - 43.80 | 229.36 | | | 2.95 | 12.9 | 0.0282 | 0.0028 |
| " | " | II(u) | - 49.00 | 224.16 | | | | | | |
| 1,3,5-Trimethylbenzene | " | I | - 44.720 | 228.440 | | | 2.3 | 10. | 0.022 | 0.003 |
| " | " | II(u) | - 49.79 | 223.37 | | | 2.0 | 8. | 0.020 | 0.003 |
| " | " | III(u) | - 51.68 | 221.48 | | | 1.9 | 8.6 | 0.020 | 0.003 |

a See footnote a of Table 1z.    b See footnote b of Table 1z.    c See footnote c of Table 1z.

TABLE 14z – ALKYL BENZENES, $C_{10}$

HEAT AND ENTROPY OF FUSION, FREEZING POINTS, AND CRYOSCOPIC CONSTANTS

December 31, 1952

| Compound | Formula | Crystalline Form[a] | Freezing Point in air at 1 atm | | Freezing Point at satn. press. (triple point) | Freezing Point at satn. press. less Freezing Point in air at 1 atm[b] | Heat of Fusion $\Delta Hm^{o}$ | Entropy of Fusion $\Delta Sm^{o}$ | Cryoscopic Constants[c] | |
|---|---|---|---|---|---|---|---|---|---|---|
| | | | °C | °K | °K | °K | kcal/mole | cal/deg mole | A | B |
| | | | | | | | | | mole fraction/deg | |
| n-Butylbenzene (1-Phenylbutane) | $C_{10}H_{14}$ | I | -87.970 | 185.190 | | | 2.624 | 14.17 | 0.0385 | |
| Isobutylbenzene (1-Phenyl-2-methylpropane) | " | I | -51.48 | 221.68 | | | 2.99 | 13.48 | 0.0306 | |
| sec-Butylbenzene (2-Phenylbutane) | " | I | -75.470 | 197.690 | | | 2.35 | 11.90 | 0.0303 | |
| tert-Butylbenzene (2-Phenyl-2-methylpropane) | " | I | -57.850 | 215.310 | | | 2.004 | 9.31 | 0.02175 | |
| 1-Methyl-2-propylbenzene | " | I | -60.2 | 212.9 | | | | | | |
| 1-Methyl-3-propylbenzene | " | I | -63.6 | 209.5 | | | | | | |
| 1-Methyl-4-propylbenzene | " | I | -71.540 | 201.620 | | | 2.39 | 11.86 | 0.0296 | |
| 1-Methyl-2-isopropylbenzene (o-Cymene) | " | II(u) | -75.24 | 197.92 | | | | | | |
| " | " | III(u) | -81.53 | 191.63 | | | | | | |
| 1-Methyl-3-isopropyobenzene (m-Cymene) | " | I | -63.745 | 209.415 | | | 3.27 | 15.60 | 0.0375 | |
| 1-Methyl-4-isopropylbenzene (p-Cymene) | " | I | -67.935 | 205.225 | | | 2.308 | 11.25 | 0.02758 | |
| 1,2-Diethylbenzene | " | I | -31.240 | 241.920 | | | 3.48 | 14.37 | 0.0299 | |
| 1,3-Diethylbenzene | " | I | -83.920 | 189.240 | | | 2.63 | 13.88 | 0.0369 | |
| 1,4-Diethylbenzene | " | I | -42.850 | 230.310 | | | 2.53 | 10.98 | 0.0240 | |
| 1,2-Dimethyl-3-ethylbenzene | " | I | -49.38 | 223.78 | | | | | | |
| 1,2-Dimethyl-4-ethylbenzene | " | I | -66.98 | 206.18 | | | | | | |
| 1,3-Dimethyl-2-ethylbenzene | " | I | -16.28 | 256.88 | | | | | | |
| 1,3-Dimethyl-4-ethylbenzene | " | I | -62.90 | 210.26 | | | | | | |
| 1,3-Dimethyl-5-ethylbenzene | " | I | -84.325 | 188.835 | | | 2.14 | 11.33 | 0.0302 | |
| 1,4-Dimethyl-2-ethylbenzene | " | I | -53.68 | 219.48 | | | | | | |
| 1,2,3,4-Tetramethylbenzene (Prehnitene) | " | I | - 6.25 | 266.91 | | | 2.68 | 10.1 | 0.0190 | |
| 1,2,3,5-Tetramethylbenzene (Isodurene) | " | I | -23.685 | 249.475 | | | 2.8 | 11. | 0.023 | |
| 1,2,4,5-Tetramethylbenzene (Durene) | " | I | +79.240 | 352.400 | | | 5.020 | 14.24 | 0.02034 | |

a See footnote a of Table 1z.　　b See footnote b of Table 1z.　　c See footnote c of Table 1z.

SPECIFIC REFERENCES
FOR TABLES 20a (PART 1), 20a-E (PART 1), AND 20b (PART 1)

June 30, 1948; December 31, 1950; October 31, 1952

| Compound | REFERENCES FOR | | | | |
|---|---|---|---|---|---|
| | Boiling Point | Refractive Index | Density | Freezing Point | Refractive Dispersion |
| Methane | 57,60,61,62 | | | 62,63,64,65,66,67, 81,107,108 | |
| Ethane | 57,68,69,70 | | | 63,68,69 | |
| Propane | 57,71,72,73,74,75 | | 56,59 | 71,74,75 | |
| n-Butane | 55,57,58,77 | | 55,56,59 | 2,5,58,101 | |
| n-Pentane | 4,8,9,13,15,18,20, 30,41,78,79,80,85, 98,100 | 3,4,8,9,11,15,18, 20,30,41,80,84,100 | 4,8,9,18,20,30,37, 56,59,83,84 | 1,8,9,11,15,20,24, 78,79,87,109 | 6,9,20,84 |
| n-Hexane | 9,13,15,18,20,30, 41,80,86,97,98,99, 100 | 3,9,11,15,18,20,25, 30,41,80,84,97,99, 100,113 | 9,11,18,20,25,30, 37,84,97,99,113 | 2,9,11,15,20,24, 26,80,87,109 | 6,9,10,11,20,84 |
| n-Heptane | 8,9,13,15,18,20,41, 80,86,88,89,90,91, 92,93,102 | 8,9,11,15,18,20,30, 41,80,84,88,89,90, 91,92,106 | 8,9,10,11,18,20,30, 37,83,84,88,90,91, 92,94 | 8,9,11,15,18,20, 24,80,87,88,90,91, 105 | 6,9,20,84,95,96, 106 |
| n-Octane | 9,13,15,16,18,20, 30,41,86 | 9,11,15,16,18,20, 30,41,84,113 | 9,11,16,18,20,30, 37,83,84 | 8,9,11,15,16,18, 20,24,82 | 6,9,10,11,20,84 |
| n-Nonane | 8,9,11,12,13,15,18, 20,30,37,41,80,86, 102 | 8,9,11,12,15,18,20, 30,41,46,80,106 | 8,9,10,11,15,18,20, 30,37 | 1,9,11,12,15,18,20, 80,82 | 6,9,20,106 |
| n-Decane | 8,9,13,15,18,31,41, 41,42,114 | 8,9,11,15,18,21,31, 41,42,114 | 8,9,11,18,21,31,37, 42,114 | 8,9,11,15,18,31,34, 110 | 6,9 |
| n-Undecane | 6,9,30,105 | 6,9,15,16,21,30 | 6,9,16,21,30,37 | 9,15,16,105 | 6,9,10 |
| n-Dodecane | 6,9,13,14,17,23 | 7,9,14,15,17,19,21, 23,30,38 | 6,7,9,14,17,19,21, 23,30,37 | 7,9,14,15,17,34, 36,109 | 6,9,14 |
| n-Tridecane | 6,17,29 | 6,7,16,17,30 | 6,7,16,17,30 | 7,16,17,29,105 | 6,30 |
| n-Tetradecane | 6 | 6,7,22,30 | 6,7,30 | 7,22,27,29,32,105 | 6 |
| n-Pentadecane | 6,103 | 6,7,30,38,43 | 6,7,29,30,43,112 | 7,29,47,105 | 6,30 |
| n-Hexadecane | 6,104,105 | 7,19,20,22,23,30, 38,105 | 7,19,20,23,30,105 | 7,19,20,22,23,30, 36,49,52,105 | 6,19,20,30,105 |
| n-Heptadecane | 6 | 6,7,16,45,111 | 6,7,16,29,44,45 | 7,16,29,32,33,36, 44,52,105,115 | 6,105 |
| n-Octadecane | 6 | 6,7,22,39,40 | 6,7,29,39,40 | 7,22,29,33,35,39, 50,52,105 | 6,105 |
| n-Nonadecane | 6 | 6 | 6,29,54 | 6,29,32,33,35,48 | 6 |
| n-Eicosane | 6 | 6,7,53 | 6,7,29,53 | 7,28,29,32,33,35, 48,51 | 6 |

REFERENCES

1. Parks and Huffman[1]
2. Huffman, Parks, and Barmore[1]
3. Wibaut and Langedijk[1]
4. Howard, Mears, Fookson, Pomerantz, and Brooks[1]
5. Glasgow and Rossini[1]
6. American Petroleum Institute Research Project 44[1]
7. Schiessler, Herr, Rytina, Weisel, Fischl, McLaughlin, and Kuehner[1]
8. American Petroleum Institute Research Project 45[1]
9. Shepard, Henne, and Midgley[1]
10. Forziati and Rossini[1]
11. Forziati, Glasgow, Willingham, and Rossini[1]
12. Streiff, Murphy, Cahill, Flanagan, Sedlak, Willingham, and Rossini[1]
13. Willingham, Taylor, Pignocco, and Rossini[1]
14. Mair and Streiff[2]
15. Mair[1]
16. Schmidt, Schoeller, and Eberlein[1]
17. Horie and Morikawa[1]
18. Birch, Fidler, and Lowry[1]
19. Deanesly and Carleton[1]
20. Wibaut, Hoog, Langedijk, Overhoff, Smittenberg, Benninga, Bouman, van Dijk, Gaade, Geldof, Hackmann, Jonker, Papp, and Zuiderweg[1]
21. Dornte and Smyth[1]
22. van Hook and Silver[1]
23. Evans[1]
24. Huffman and others[1]
25. Waddington and Douslin[1]
26. Douslin and Huffman[2]
27. Parks and Light[1]
28. Parks, Huffman, and Thomas[1]
29. Kraft[1]
30. Vogel[2]
31. Simon[1]
32. Vorländer and Selke[1]
33. Müller and Saville[1]

SPECIFIC REFERENCES

FOR TABLES 20a (PART 1), 20a-E (PART 1) AND 20b (PART 1) (Continued)

June 30, 1948; December 31, 1950; October 31, 1952

REFERENCES

34. Seyer[2]
35. Seyer, Patterson, and Keays[1]
36. Ralston, Hoerr, and Crews[1]
37. Quayle, Day, and Brown[1]
38. Berger[1]
39. Hetling and Shchekin[1]
40. Dover and Hensley[1]
41. McArdle and Robertson[1]
42. Bried and Hennion[1]
43. Badin[1]
44. Semmler and Feldstein[1]
45. Bertram[1]
46. Fenske, Braun, Wiegand, Quiggle, McCormick, and Rank[1]
47. Skraup and Nieten[1]
48. Hildebrand[1] and Wachter[1]
49. Smith, J.C.[1]
50. Fischer[1]
51. Sherk, Augur, and Soffer[1]
52. Carey and Smith[1]
53. Eykman[2]
54. Eykman[3]
55. Benoliel[1]
56. Cragoe[1]
57. Cragoe[2]
58. Aston and Messerly[2]
59. Natural Gasoline Association of America[1]
60. Frank and Clusius[1]
61. Keyes, Taylor, and Smith[1]
62. Henning and Stock[1]
63. Clusius and Wiegand[1]
64. Clusius[1]
65. Eucken and Karwot[1]
66. Wiebe and Brevoort[1]
67. Freeth and Verschoyle[1]
68. Witt and Kemp[1]
69. Wiebe, Hubbard, and Brevoort[1]
70. Loomis and Walters[1]
71. Hartick and Edse[1]
72. Dana, Jenkins, Burdick, and Timm[1]
73. Francis and Robbins[1]
74. Hicks-Bruun and Bruun[1]
75. Kemp and Egan[1]
76. Coffin and Maass[1]
77. Coffin and Maass[2]
78. Messerly and Kennedy[1]
79. Timmermans and Hennaut-Roland[2]
80. Smittenberg, Hoog, and Henkes[1]
81. Parks and Huffman[2]

82. Streiff, Murphy, Sedlak, Willingham, and Rossini[1]
83. Geist and Cannon[1]
84. Garrett[1]
85. Wojciechowski[1]
86. Wojciechowski[3]
87. Glasgow, Murphy, Willingham, and Rossini[1]
88. Edgar and Calingaert[1]
89. Davies and Gilbert[1]
90. Brooks[1]
91. Brooks, Howard, and Crafton[2]
92. Butler[1]
93. Smith, E.R.[1]
94. Reno and Katz[1]
95. Grosse and Wackher[1]
96. Smyth and Stoops[1]
97. Cramer and Mulligan[1]
98. Lamb and Roper[1]
99. Lemons and Felsing[1]
100. Griswold, van Berg, and Kasch[1]
101. Glasgow, Krouskop, Beadle, Axilrod, and Rossini[1]
102. Forziati, Norris, and Rossini[1]
103. Spengler[1]
104. Schrader and Dreisbach[1]
105. American Petroleum Institute Research Project 6[1]
106. Forziati[1]
107. Frank[1]
108. Scott[1]
109. Streiff and Rossini[1]
110. Brooks[2]
111. Bradley and Shellard[1]
112. Pannicker, Rao, and Simonsen[1]
113. Boord, Henne, Greenlee, Perilstein, and Derfer[1]
114. Bruun and Hicks-Bruun[3]
115. Doolittle and Peterson[1]

SPECIFIC REFERENCES

FOR TABLES 20a (PART 2), 20a-E (PART 2), AND 20b (PART 2)

December 31, 1950

| Compound | REFERENCES FOR | | | | |
|---|---|---|---|---|---|
| | Boiling Point | Refractive Index | Density | Freezing Point | Refractive Dispersion |
| n–Heneicosane | 1 | 1 | 1 | 2,3,4 | 1 |
| n–Docosane | 1 | 1 | 1 | 2,5,6,7 | 1 |
| n–Tricosane | 1 | 1 | 1 | 2,3,4 | 1 |
| n–Tetracosane | 1 | 1 | 1 | 2,3,5,8 | 1 |
| n–Pentacosane | 1 | 1 | 1 | 1 | 1 |
| n–Hexacosane | 1 | 1 | 1 | 5,8,9,10 | 1 |
| n–Heptacosane | 1 | 1 | 1 | 2,11,12 | 1 |
| n–Octacosane | 1 | 1 | 1 | 2,3,5,8,11,13,14 | 1 |
| n–Nonacosane | 1 | 1 | 1 | 2,8,12 | 1 |
| n–Triacontane | 1 | 1 | 1 | 2,3,5,9,10,12 | 1 |
| n–Hentriacontane | 1 | 1 | 1 | 2,3,12 | 1 |
| n–Dotriacontane | 1 | 1 | 1 | 2,5,12,15,16 | 1 |
| n–Tritriacontane | 1 | 1 | 1 | 1 | 1 |
| n–Tetratriacontane | 1 | 1 | 1 | 3,5,10,12 | 1 |
| n–Pentatriacontane | 1 | 1 | 1 | 2,3,10,12,17 | 1 |
| n–Hexatriacontane | 1 | 1 | 1 | 3,12,13,17 | 1 |
| n–Heptatriacontane | 1 | 1 | 1 | 1 | 1 |
| n–Octatriacontane | 1 | 1 | 1 | 1 | 1 |
| n–Nonatriacontane | 1 | 1 | 1 | 18 | 1 |
| n–Tetracontane | 1 | 1 | 1 | 3,17 | 1 |

REFERENCES

1. American Petroleum Institute Research Project 44[1]
2. Krafft[1]
3. Mazee[1]
4. Strating and Backer[1]
5. Seyer, Patterson, and Keays[1]
6. Robinson[1]
7. Francis and Wood[1]
8. Schiessler, Herr, Rytima, Weisel, Fischl, McLaughlin, and Kuehner[1]
9. Schmidt, Schoeller, and Eberlein[1]
10. Garner, van Bibber, and King[1]
11. Mueller and Saville[1]
12. Piper, Chibnall, Hopkins, Pollard, Smith, and Williams[1]
13. Doolittle and Peterson[1]
14. Nieman and Wagner[1]
15. Hildebrand and Wachter[1]
16. Schluback and Goes[1]
17. Backer and Strating[1]
18. Stenhagen and Tägström[1]

SPECIFIC REFERENCES

FOR TABLES 1a, 1a-E AND 1b

June 30, 1945; June 30, 1948; October 31, 1952

| Compound | REFERENCES FOR | | | | |
|---|---|---|---|---|---|
| | Boiling Point | Refractive Index | Density | Freezing Point | Refractive Dispersion |
| Methane | 1 | 1 | 1 | 1 | 1 |
| Ethane | 1 | 1 | 1 | 1 | 1 |
| Propane | 1 | 1 | 1 | 1 | 1 |
| n-Butane | 1 | 1 | 1 | 1 | 1 |
| 2-Methylpropane (Isobutane) | 2,4,10,12,13,14,15 | 29 | 2,8,29,33 | 10,11,16,34 | |
| n-Pentane | 1 | 1 | 1 | 1 | 1 |
| 2-Methylbutane (Isopentane) | 6,9,14,17,18,19,20,25,26 | 6,7,9,17,19,20,24,28 | 3,6,9,20,23 | 6,9,17,22,25,26,27,28 | 7,9 |
| 2,2-Dimethylpropane (Neopentane) | 2,5,6 | 30 | 2,30,33 | 2,5,6,21,31 | 32 |

REFERENCES

1. See references for Tables 20a (Part 1), 20a-E (Part 1), and 20b (Part 1).
2. Benoliel[1]
3. Cragoe[1]
4. Cragoe[2]
5. Aston and Messerly[1]
6. Howard, Mears, Fookson, Pomerantz, and Brooks[1]
7. Garrett[1]
8. Natural Gasoline Association of America[1]
9. Wibaut, Hoog, Langedijk, Overhoff, Smittenberg, Benninga, Bouman, van Dijk, Gaade, Geldof, Hackman, Jonker, Paap, and Zuiderweg[1]
10. Coffin and Mass[1]
11. Glasgow, Krouskop, Beadle, Axilrod, and Rossini[1]
12. Hückel and Rossmann[1]
13. Peters and Lohmar[1]
14. Lamb and Roper[1]
15. Aston, Kennedy, and Schumann[1]
16. Parks, Shomate, Kennedy, and Crawford[1]
17. Smittenberg, Hoog, and Henkes[1]
18. Willingham, Taylor, Pignocco, and Rossini[1]
19. McArdle and Robertson[1]
20. American Petroleum Institute Research Project 45[1]
21. Birch, Fidler, and Lowry[1]
22. Glasgow, Murphy, Willingham, and Rossini[1]
23. Geist and Cannon[1]
24. Wibaut and Langedijk[1]
25. Guthrie and Huffman[1]
26. Schumann, Aston, and Sagenkahn[1]
27. Timmermans and Martin[1]
28. Forziati, Glasgow, Willingham, and Rossini[1]
29. Wackher, Linn, and Grosse[1]
30. Horton[1]
31. Streiff, Zimmerman, Soule, Butt, Sedlak, Willingham, and Rossini[1]
32. American Petroleum Institute Research Project 44[1]
33. Phibbs[1]
34. American Petroleum Institute Research Project 6[1]

## SPECIFIC REFERENCES
### FOR TABLES 2a (PART 1), 2a-E (PART 1), AND 2b (PART 1)
#### May 31, 1947; December 31, 1948; October 31, 1952

| Compound | REFERENCES FOR | | | | |
|---|---|---|---|---|---|
| | Boiling Point | Refractive Index | Density | Freezing Point | Refractive Dispersion |
| n-Hexane | 1 | 1 | 1 | 1 | 1 |
| 2-Methylpentane | 3,4,6,7,8,9,10, 12,15,16,17,32 | 4,5,6,7,8,9,10, 13,15,16,17,19,30 | 4,5,6,7,8,9,10, 15,29,32 | 2,4,5,9,20,33 | 7,21 |
| 3-Methylpentane | 3,4,6,7,8,9,11, 12,17,32 | 4,5,6,7,8,9,13, 17,19,30 | 4,5,6,7,8,9,18, 29,32 | | 7,21 |
| 2,2-Dimethylbutane | 3,4,6,7,8,12,13, 16,17,22,23,24, 25,27,32 | 4,5,6,7,8,13,16, 17,19,22,23,24, 26,27,30,31 | 4,5,6,7,8,22,23, 24,27,31,32 | 2,4,5,7,13,20,22, 23,24,25,33 | 7,21 |
| 2,3-Dimethylbutane | 3,6,7,8,9,12,13, 14,15,16,17,22,32 | 5,6,7,8,9,13,15, 16,17,19,22,28,30 | 5,6,7,8,9,15,22, 28,29,32 | 2,5,7,9,13,20,22, 33 | 7,21 |

### REFERENCES

1. See references for Tables 20a (Part 1), 20a-E (Part 1), and 20b (Part 1).
2. Glasgow, Murphy, Willingham, and Rossini[1]
3. Willingham, Taylor, Pignocco, and Rossini[1]
4. Howard, Mears, Fookson, Pomerantz, and Brooks[1]
5. Forziati, Glasgow, Willingham, and Rossini[1]
6. Birch, Fidler, and Lowry[1]
7. Wibaut, Hoog, Langedijk, Overhoff, Smittenberg, Benninga, Bouman, van Dijk, Gaade, Geldof, Hackmann, Jonker, Paap, and Zuiderweg[1]
8. Cramer and Mulligan[1]
9. Bruun, Hicks-Bruun, and Faulconer[1]
10. Maman[1]
11. Shepard, Henne, and Midgley[1]
12. Wojciechowski[3]
13. Smittenberg, Hoog, and Henkes[1]
14. Lamb and Roper[1]
15. Lemons and Felsing[1]
16. McArdle and Robertson[1]
17. Griswold, van Berg, and Kasch[1]
18. Quayle, Day, and Brown[1]
19. Wibaut and Langedijk[1]
20. Douslin and Huffman[2]
21. Forziati and Rossini[1]
22. Brooks, Howard, and Crafton[2]
23. Hicks-Bruun, Bruun, and Faulconer[1]
24. van Risseghem[2]
25. Timmermans[1]
26. van Grosse[1]
27. Liberman, Lukina, Solovova, and Kazanskiĭ[1]
28. Bazhulin, Bokshtein, Liberman, Lukina, Margolis, Solovova, and Kazanskiĭ[1]
29. Geist and Cannon[1]
30. American Petroleum Institute Research Project 45[1]
31. Waddington and Douslin[1]
32. Kay[2]
33. American Petroleum Institute Research Project 6[1]

## SPECIFIC REFERENCES
### FOR TABLES 2a (PART 2), 2a-E (PART 2), AND 2b (PART 2)
#### May 31, 1947; December 31, 1948; October 31, 1952

| Compound | REFERENCES FOR | | | | |
|---|---|---|---|---|---|
| | Boiling Point | Refractive Index | Density | Freezing Point | Refractive Dispersion |
| n-Heptane | 1 | 1 | 1 | 1 | 1 |
| 2-Methylhexane | 5,6,7,8,9,18,31 | 5,6,7,8,9,14,20,21,30 | 5,6,7,18,20,30 | 5,7,8,14,18,22,29 | 5,19,20,30 |
| 3-Methylhexane | 6,7,9,11,18,31 | 6,7,9,14,18,20,30 | 6,7,18,20,30 | | 19,20,30 |
| 3-Ethylpentane | 6,7,9,10,11,18,25,31 | 6,7,9,10,14,18,20,27,30 | 6,7,10,18,20,27,30 | 10,14,18,22,29 | 19,20,30 |
| 2,2-Dimethylpentane | 2,3,4,6,7,8,9,11,12,18,23,26,31 | 2,5,6,7,8,9,12,14,17,18,20,21,23,26,30 | 2,5,6,7,18,20,23,30 | 5,7,8,14,18,22,29 | 5,19,20,30 |
| 2,3-Dimethylpentane | 4,5,6,7,8,9,11,12,15,16,18,26,30 | 4,5,6,7,8,9,12,14,15,16,18,20,21,26,30 | 4,5,6,7,15,16,18,20,30 | | 5,19,20,30 |
| 2,4-Dimethylpentane | 4,5,6,7,8,9,12,16,23,31 | 4,5,6,7,8,9,12,14,15,16,18,20,21,23,30 | 4,5,6,7,16,18,23,30 | 4,5,7,8,14,18,22,29 | 5,19,20,30 |
| 3,3-Dimethylpentane | 2,3,5,7,8,9,16,17,18,31 | 2,5,7,8,9,14,17,18,20,21,30 | 2,5,6,7,16,17,18,20,30 | 5,7,8,14,18 | 5,19,20,30 |
| 2,2,3-Trimethylbutane | 5,6,7,8,9,10,11,12,18,23,25,31 | 5,6,7,8,9,10,12,13,16,18,20,21,23,30 | 5,6,7,10,13,16,18,20,23,30 | 5,6,7,8,10,18,22,24,28,29 | 5,13,19,20,30 |

### REFERENCES

1. See references for Tables 20a (Part 1), 20a-E (Part 1), and 20b (Part 1).
2. Forziati, Glasgow, Willingham, and Rossini[1]
3. Willingham, Taylor, Pignocco, and Rossini[1]
4. Howard, Mears, Fookson, Pomerantz, and Brooks[1]
5. Wibaut, Hoog, Langedijk, Overhoff, Smittenberg, Benninga, Bouman, van Dijk, Gaade, Geldof, Hackmann, Jonker, Paap, and Zuiderweg[1]
6. Birch, Fidler, and Lowry[1]
7. Edgar and Calingaert[1]
8. Smittenberg, Hoog, and Henkes[1]
9. Davies and Gilbert[1]
10. Brooks, Howard, and Crafton[1]
11. Wojciechowski[3]
12. McArdle and Robertson[1]
13. Garrett[1]
14. Streiff, Murphy, Sedlak, Willingham, and Rossini[1]
15. Cline[1]
16. Bazhulin, Bokshtein, Liberman, Lukina, Margolis, Solovova, and Kazanskii[1]
17. Liberman, Lukina, Solovova, and Kazanskii[1]
18. American Petroleum Institute Research Project 45[1]
19. Smyth and Stoops[1]
20. Forziati and Rossini[1]
21. Wibaut and Langedijk[1]
22. Huffman and others[1]
23. Fawcett[1]
24. Streiff, Zimmerman, Soule, Butt, Sedlak, Willingham, and Rossini[1]
25. Smith, E.R.[1]
26. Cramer and Miller[1]
27. Boesekin and Wildschut[1]
28. Glasgow, Murphy, Willingham, and Rossini[1]
29. Waddington and others[1]
30. Forziati and Rossini[2]
31. Forziati, Norris, and Rossini[1]

SPECIFIC REFERENCES

FOR TABLES 3a, 3a-E, AND 3b

May 31, 1947; December 31, 1948; October 31, 1952

| Compound | REFERENCES FOR | | | | |
|---|---|---|---|---|---|
| | Boiling Point | Refractive Index | Density | Freezing Point | Refractive Dispersion |
| n-Octane | 1 | 1 | 1 | 1 | 1 |
| 2-Methylheptane | 3,7 | 6,7,10,37 | 5,7,10,15,37 | 2,10 | 6,11,13 |
| 3-Methylheptane | 3,8 | 6,7,10,37 | 5,6,8,10,15,37 | 2,10,37 | 6,8,11,13 |
| 4-Methylheptane | 3,6,17 | 6,10,16,17,37 | 5,6,10,15,16,17,37 | 2,10,16,17 | 6,11,13 |
| 3-Ethylhexane | 3 | 10 | 5,10,15 | | 11,13 |
| 2,2-Dimethylhexane | 3,18 | 10,18 | 5,10,18 | 2,10 | 11,13 |
| 2,3-Dimethylhexane | 3,8,9,17,19 | 8,9,10,17,19 | 5,8,9,10,17,19 | | 8,11,13 |
| 2,4-Dimethylhexane | 3,7 | 7,10 | 5,7,10 | | 11,13 |
| 2,5-Dimethylhexane | 3,7,8,20 | 7,8,10,20 | 7,8,10,20 | 2,10 | 8,11,13 |
| 3,3-Dimethylhexane | 3 | 10 | 5,10 | 2,10 | 11,13 |
| 3,4-Dimethylhexane | 3,7,8,9 | 7,8,9,10 | 5,7,8,9,10 | | 8,11,13 |
| 2-Methyl-3-ethylpentane | 3,4,9 | 4,6,9,10,37 | 4,5,6,9,10,37 | 2,4,10 | 6,11,13 |
| 3-Methyl-3-ethylpentane | 3,8,18 | 6,8,10,18,37 | 5,6,8,10,18,37 | 2,8,10,17 | 6,8,11,13 |
| 2,2,3-Trimethylpentane | 3,7,8,9,22 | 7,8,9,10,22 | 5,7,8,10,22,35 | 2,4,10,22 | 8,11,13 |
| 2,2,4-Trimethylpentane | 3,7,8,12,14,21,23,24,32,33 | 6,7,8,10,14,21,23,25,33 | 5,6,7,8,10,21,23,25,32,33,35 | 7,8,10,21,23,26,32,33,36 | 6,8,11,13,25,30,31 |
| 2,3,3-Trimethylpentane | 3,4,7,19 | 4,7,10,19 | 4,5,7,10,19 | 2,4,10,17 | 11,13 |
| 2,3,4-Trimethylpentane | 3,7,9,23 | 6,7,9,10,23,37 | 5,7,9,10,23 | 2,10,23,29 | 6,11,13 |
| 2,2,3,3-Tetramethylbutane | 27,28 | 28 | 28 | 9,28,34 | 11,13 |

REFERENCES

1. See references for Tables 20a (Part 1), 20a-E (Part 1), and 20b (Part 1).
2. Streiff, Murphy, Sedlak, Willingham, and Rossini[1]
3. Willingham, Taylor, Pignocco, and Rossini[1]
4. Howard, Mears, Fookson, Pomerantz, and Brooks[1]
5. Geist and Cannon[1]
6. Garrett[1]
7. Birch, Fidler, and Lowry[1]
8. Wibaut, Hoog, Langedijk, Overhoff, Smittenberg, Benninga, Bouman, van Dijk, Gaade, Geldof, Hackmann, Jonker, Paap, and Zuiderweg[1]
9. Bazhulin, Bokshtein, Liberman, Lukina, Margolis, Solovova, and Kazanskiĭ[1]
10. Forziati, Glasgow, Willingham, and Rossini[1]
11. Forziati and Rossini[1]
12. Wojciechowski[1]
13. American Petroleum Institute Research Project 44[1]
14. McArdle and Robertson[1]
15. Quayle, Day, and Brown[1]
16. Butler[1]
17. American Petroleum Institute Research Project 45[1]
18. Liberman, Lukina, Solovova, and Kazanskiĭ[1]
19. Cline[1]
20. Turk[1]
21. Brooks[1]
22. Brooks, Howard, and Crafton[1]
23. Brooks, Howard, and Crafton[2]
24. Smith, E.R.[1]
25. Tilton[1]
26. Glasgow, Murphy, Willingham, and Rossini[1]
27. Henry[1]
28. Calingaert, Soroos, Hnizda, and Shapiro[1]
29. Pitzer and Scott[1]
30. Grosse and Wackher[1]
31. Smyth and Stoops[1]

| SPECIFIC REFERENCES | | |
|---|---|---|
| FOR TABLES 3a, 3a-E, AND 3b (Continued) | | |
| May 31, 1947; December 31, 1948; October 31, 1952 | | |
| REFERENCES | | |
| 32. Kay and Warzel[1]<br>33. Pomerantz[1]<br>34. Scott, Douslin, Gross, Oliver, and Huffman[1]<br>35. Lauer[1]<br>36. American Petroleum Institute Research Project 6[1]<br>37. Boord, Henne, Greenlee, Perilstein, and Derfer[1] | | |

| | SPECIFIC REFERENCES | | | | |
|---|---|---|---|---|---|
| | FOR TABLES 4a, 4a-E, AND 4b | | | | |
| | May 31, 1947; March 31, 1949; October 31, 1952 | | | | |
| | REFERENCES FOR | | | | |
| Compound | Boiling Point | Refractive Index | Density | Freezing Point | Refractive Dispersion |
| *n*-Nonane | 1 | 1 | 1 | 1 | 1 |
| 2-Methyloctane | 3,5,19 | 3,5,12,19,24,28 | 3,5,19,28 | 3,5 | 14 |
| 3-Methyloctane | 3,9,28 | 3,9,24,28 | 3,9,28 | 3 | 14 |
| 4-Methyloctane | 3,28,29 | 3,24,28,29 | 3,28,29 | 3,29 | 14 |
| 3-Ethylheptane | 5,19,28 | 5,12,19,24 | 5,19,28 | 5,19 | 14 |
| 4-Ethylheptane | 2,9,20,21,24 | 2,9,20,21,24 | 2,9,20,21 | | 14 |
| 2,2-Dimethylheptane | 6,13,24 | 6,12,13,24 | 6,13 | 13,37 | 14 |
| 2,3-Dimethylheptane | 5,22,24,25 | 4,5,22,24,25,26 | 4,5,22,25 | 5 | 14 |
| 2,4-Dimethylheptane | 7,8,10,18,24,25,27 | 7,8,10,24,25,26,27 | 7,8,10,18,25,27 | | 14 |
| 2,5-Dimethylheptane | 7,8,18,24 | 7,8,24,26 | 7,8,18 | | 14 |
| 2,6-Dimethylheptane | 11,17,21,24 | 11,17,21,24,26 | 11,17,21 | 17 | 14 |
| 3,3-Dimethylheptane | 6,16 | 6,12,16 | 6,16 | | 14 |
| 3,4-Dimethylheptane | 2,9,12,15,24 | 2,9,12,15,24 | 2,9,15 | | 14 |
| 3,5-Dimethylheptane | 2,9,12 | 2,9,12 | 2,9 | | 14 |
| 4,4-Dimethylheptane | 2,9,12,24 | 2,9,12,24 | 2,9 | | 14 |
| 2-Methyl-3-ethylhexane | 2,9,12,24,30 | 2,9,12,24,30 | 2,9,30 | | 14 |
| 2-Methyl-4-ethylhexane | 2,9,12,24 | 2,9,12,24 | 2,9 | | 14 |
| 3-Methyl-3-ethylhexane | 2,9,12,24 | 2,9,12,24 | 2,9 | | 14 |
| 3-Methyl-4-ethylhexane | 2,9,12,24,31 | 2,9,12 | 2,9 | | 14 |
| 2,2,3-Trimethylhexane | 2,9,30,32,33 | 2,9,26,30,32,33 | 2,9,30,32 | | 14 |
| 2,2,4-Trimethylhexane | 12,33,34,35,36 | 12,33,34,35,36,37 | 34,35,36 | 34,35,38 | 14 |
| 2,2,5-Trimethylhexane | 12,13,16,23,34,35,39,40 | 12,13,16,34,35,39,40,41,42,43 | 13,16,34,35,39,40,42,43 | 13,34,35,41 | 42,43 |
| 2,3,3-Trimethylhexane | 2,9,22,33,44 | 2,9,12,22,33,44,45 | 2,9,22 | 38 | 14 |
| 2,3,4-Trimethylhexane | 2,9,12,13,33 | 2,9,12,13,33 | 2,9,13 | | 14 |
| 2,3,5-Trimethylhexane | 13,22,33,35,39,46 | 13,22,33,35,37,39,45,46,47 | 13,22,35,39,46,47 | 35 | 14 |
| 2,4,4-Trimethylhexane | 2,9,12,23,30,48,49 | 2,9,12,30,41,42,43,48,49 | 2,9,30,42,43,48,49 | 41 | 42,43 |
| 3,3,4-Trimethylhexane | 2,9,12,30,33,50 | 2,9,12,30,33,50 | 2,9,30,50 | 38 | 14 |
| 3,3-Diethylpentane | 13,23,44,51,52 | 13,42,43,44,51,52 | 13,42,43,51,52 | 13,41,51,52,53 | 42,43,53,54 |
| 2,2-Dimethyl-3-ethylpentane | 12,35 | 12,35 | 35 | 35 | 14 |
| 2,3-Dimethyl-3-ethylpentane | 2,9 | 2,9 | 2,9 | | 42 |
| 2,4-Dimethyl-3-ethylpentane | 12,30,35 | 12,24,28,30,35 | 28,30,35 | 35 | 14 |
| 2,2,3,3-Tetramethylpentane | 13,23,35 | 13,35,42,43 | 13,35,42,43 | 13,35,41 | 42,43 |
| 2,2,3,4-Tetramethylpentane | 12,23 | 12,42,43 | 42,43 | 41 | 42,43 |
| 2,2,4,4-Tetramethylpentane | 5,23,55,56 | 5,12,42,43,55 | 5,42,43,55 | 5,41,55 | 42,43 |
| 2,3,3,4-Tetramethylpentane | 12,23,35,57 | 12,35,42,43,57 | 35,42,43,57 | 41 | 42,43 |

SPECIFIC REFERENCES

FOR TABLES 4a, 4a–E, AND 4b (Continued)

May 31, 1947; March 31, 1949; October 31, 1952

REFERENCES

1. See references for Tables 20a (Part 1), 20a–E (Part 1), and 20b (Part 1).
2. Francis[1]
3. White and Glasgow[1]
4. White and Glasgow[2]
5. Whitmore and Southgate[1]
6. Marker and Oakwood[1]
7. Tuot[1]
8. Clarke and Biggs[1]
9. Taylor, Pignocco, and Rossini[1]
10. Jacquemain[1]
11. Vogel[2]
12. Fenske, Braun, Wiegand, Quiggle, McCormick, and Rank[1]
13. American Petroleum Institute Research Project 45[1]
14. American Petroleum Institute Research Project 44[1]
15. Henne and Chanan[1]
16. Noller[1]
17. White, Rose, Calingaert, and Soroos[1]
18. Richards and Shipley[1]
19. Whitmore and Orem[1]
20. Oberreit[1]
21. Butler[1]
22. Cline[1]
23. Forziati, Norris, and Rossini[1]
24. Jamison, Leslie, and Turner[1]
25. Levina, Fainzil'berg, and Itenberg[1]
26. Braun, Spooner, and Fenske[1]
27. Levina, Kleimenova, and Shusherina[1]
28. Bazhulin, Ukholin, Bulanova, Koperina, Plate, and Kazanskii[1]
29. Slabey and Wise[2]
30. Whitmore and others[1]
31. Gleim[1]
32. Schlesman[1]
33. Streiff and Rossini[1]
34. Brooks, Cleaton, and Carter[1]
35. Howard, Mears, Fookson, Pomerantz, and Brooks[1]
36. Moersch[1]
37. American Petroleum Institute Research Project 6[1]
38. Streiff, Zimmerman, Soule, Butt, Sedlak, Willingham, and Rossini[1]
39. Turk[1]
40. Birch, Fidler, and Lowry[1]
41. Streiff, Murphy, Cahill, Flanagan, Sedlak, Willingham, and Rossini[1]
42. Forziati and Rossini[1]
43. Forziati and Rossini[2]
44. Buck, Elsner, Forbes, Morrell, Smith, and Wallsgrove[1]
45. Buck, Elsner, Henshall, Moore, Murray, Morrell, Muller, Plant, Smith, and Wallsgrove[1]
46. Petrov, Koptev, and Kaplan[1]
47. Levina, Tantsyreva, Fainzil'berg, and Mezentsova[1]
48. Levina and Kagan[1]
49. Fawcett and Johnson[1]
50. Pomerantz, Mears, and Howard[1]
51. Morgan, Carter, and Buck[1]
52. Horton[1]
53. Waddington and others[1]
54. Mathot[1]
55. Howard[1]
56. Smith, E.R.[1]
57. Enyeart[1]

| | SPECIFIC REFERENCES FOR TABLES 17a, 17a-E, AND 17b October 31, 1950; October 31, 1952 | | | | |
|---|---|---|---|---|---|
| Compound | REFERENCES FOR | | | | |
| | Boiling Point | Refractive Index | Density | Freezing Point | Refractive Dispersion |
| $n$-Decane | 1 | 1 | 1 | 1 | 1 |
| 2-Methylnonane | 3 | 3 | 3,4,5 | 3,6 | |
| 3-Methylnonane | 3 | 3,49 | 3,4,7 | 3,6 | |
| 4-Methylnonane | 3 | 3 | 3,5,8,9 | 3 | |
| 5-Methylnonane | 3,10,11,12 | 3,10 | 3,5,7,10,12 | 3,6 | |
| 3-Ethyloctane | 13,63 | 13,63 | 13,63 | | |
| 4-Ethyloctane | 13,63 | 13,63 | 13,63 | | |
| 2,2-Dimethyloctane | 13,63 | 14 | 14 | | |
| 2,3-Dimethyloctane | 15,50,51 | 15,50,51 | 15,51 | | |
| 2,4-Dimethyloctane | 16,17,18,51 | 16,17,18,51 | 8,16,17,18 | | |
| 2,5-Dimethyloctane | 9,19 | 19 | 19 | | |
| 2,6-Dimethyloctane | 20,21,22,23,24,25, 26,27,28,29,30 | 21,22,24,25,26,27, 28 | 20,21,22,24,25,26, 27,28,30 | | |
| 2,7-Dimethyloctane | 2,31,32,33,34,35, 36,37,38 | 2,31,32,35,36,38 | 2,31,32,34,35,36, 38 | 2,29 | 32 |
| 3,3-Dimethyloctane | 9,39 | 39 | 9,39 | | |
| 3,4-Dimethyloctane | 13,63 | 40 | 13,63 | | |
| 3,5-Dimethyloctane | 13,63 | 13,63 | 13,63 | | |
| 3,6-Dimethyloctane | 41 | 41,42 | 41,42 | | |
| 4,4-Dimethyloctane | 13,63 | 13,63 | 13,63 | | |
| 4,5-Dimethyloctane | 32,43,44,45 | 32,43,44,50 | 32,43,44 | | 32 |
| 4-Propylheptane | 46 | 46 | 46 | | |
| 4-Isopropylheptane | 46,50 | 46,50 | 46 | | |
| 2-Methyl-3-ethylheptane | 13,63 | 13,63 | 13,63 | | |
| 2-Methyl-4-ethylheptane | 13,63 | 13,63 | 13,63 | | |
| 2-Methyl-5-ethylheptane | 47 | 47 | 47 | | |
| 3-Methyl-3-ethylheptane | 14,48 | 14,48,52 | 14,52 | | |
| 3-Methyl-4-ethylheptane | 13,63 | 13,63 | 13,63 | | |
| 3-Methyl-5-ethylheptane | 13,63 | 13,63 | 13,63 | | |
| 4-Methyl-3-ethylheptane | 13,63 | 13,63 | 13,63 | | |
| 4-Methyl-4-ethylheptane | 13,63 | 13,63 | 13,63 | | |
| 2,2,3-Trimethylheptane | 13,63 | 13,63 | 13,63 | | |
| 2,2,4-Trimethylheptane | 53,59 | 53,59 | 53 | | |
| 2,2,5-Trimethylheptane | 13,63 | 13,63 | 13,63 | | |
| 2,2,6-Trimethylheptane | 22,54 | 22,54,60 | 22 | | |
| 2,3,3-Trimethylheptane | 15 | 15 | 15 | | |
| 2,3,4-Trimethylheptane | 13,63 | 13,63 | 13,63 | | |
| 2,3,5-Trimethylheptane | 16 | 16 | 16 | | |
| 2,3,6-Trimethylheptane | 15,54 | 15,54 | 15 | | |
| 2,4,4-Trimethylheptane | 13,63 | 13,63 | 13,63 | | |
| 2,4,5-Trimethylheptane | 13,63 | 40 | 13,63 | | |
| 2,4,6-Trimethylheptane | 16,18,46,57 | 16,18,46,57 | 16,18,46 | | |
| 2,5,5-Trimethylheptane | 43,44 | 43,44 | 43,44 | | |
| 3,3,4-Trimethylheptane | 13,63 | 13,63 | 13,63 | | |
| 3,3,5-Trimethylheptane | 55,56,61 | 55,56,61,62 | 55,56,61,62 | | |
| 3,4,4-Trimethylheptane | 13,63 | 13,63 | 13,63 | | |
| 3,4,5-Trimethylheptane | 13,63 | 13,63 | 13,63 | | |
| 2-Methyl-3-isopropylhexane | 13,63 | 13,63 | 13,63 | | |
| 3,3-Diethylhexane | 48 | 13,63 | 13,63 | | |

| SPECIFIC REFERENCES FOR TABLES 17a, 17a-E, AND 17b (Continued) October 31, 1950; October 31, 1952 | | | | | |
|---|---|---|---|---|---|
| | REFERENCES FOR | | | | |
| Compound | Boiling Point | Refractive Index | Density | Freezing Point | Refractive Dispersion |
| 3,4-Diethylhexane | 32,58 | 32,58 | 32,58 | | 32 |
| 2,2-Dimethyl-3-ethylhexane | 13,63 | 13,63 | 13,63 | | |
| 2,2-Dimethyl-4-ethylhexane | 13,59 | 13,59 | 13,63 | | |
| 2,3-Dimethyl-3-ethylhexane | 13,63 | 13,63 | 13,63 | | |
| 2,3-Dimethyl-4-ethylhexane | 13,63 | 13,63 | 13,63 | | |
| 2,4-Dimethyl-3-ethylhexane | 13,63 | 13,63 | 13,63 | | |
| 2,4-Dimethyl-4-ethylhexane | 13,63 | 13,63 | 13,63 | | |
| 2,5-Dimethyl-3-ethylhexane | 13,63 | 13,63 | 13,63 | | |
| 3,3-Dimethyl-4-ethylhexane | 13,63 | 13,63 | 13,63 | | |
| 3,4-Dimethyl-3-ethylhexane | 13,63 | 13,63 | 13,63 | | |
| 2,2,3,3-Tetramethylhexane | 54,64 | 54,64 | 64 | 64 | |
| 2,2,3,4-Tetramethylhexane | 54,55,56 | 54,56 | 56 | | |
| 2,2,3,5-Tetramethylhexane | 54 | 10,54,69 | 10,54 | | |
| 2,2,4,4-Tetramethylhexane | 13 | 13 | 13 | | |
| 2,2,4,5-Tetramethylhexane | 54,64 | 54,64 | 54,64 | | |
| 2,2,5,5-Tetramethylhexane | 64,65,66,67 | 64,65,66,67 | 64,65 | 64,65 | |
| 2,3,3,4-Tetramethylhexane | 61,68 | 61,68 | 61,68 | | |
| 2,3,3,5-Tetramethylhexane | 13,69 | 13,69 | 13,63 | | |
| 2,3,4,4-Tetramethylhexane | 61,68 | 61,68 | 61,68 | | |
| 2,3,4,5-Tetramethylhexane | 13,63 | 13,63 | 13,63 | | |
| 3,3,4,4-Tetramethylhexane | 54,64 | 54,64 | 64 | | |
| 2,4-Dimethyl-3-isopropylpentane | 64 | 64 | 64 | 64 | |
| 2-Methyl-3,3-diethylpentane | 13,63 | 13,63 | 13,63 | | |
| 2,2,3-Trimethyl-3-ethylpentane | 13,63 | 13,63 | 13,63 | | |
| 2,2,4-Trimethyl-3-ethylpentane | 13,61 | 13,61 | 13,61 | | |
| 2,3,4-Trimethyl-3-ethylpentane | 55,61 | 13,55,61 | 13,61 | | |
| 2,2,3,3,4-Pentamethylpentane | 64 | 64 | 64 | 64 | |
| 2,2,3,4,4-Pentamethylpentane | 64 | 64 | 64 | 64 | |

REFERENCES

1. See references for Tables 20a (Part 1), 20a-E (Part 1), and 20b (Part 1).
2. Boord, Henne, Greenlee, Perilstein, and Derfer[1]
3. Calingaert and Soroos[1]
4. Birch, Pin, and Tait[1]
5. Geist and Cannon[1]
6. Parks, West, and Moore[1]
7. Levene and Taylor[1]
8. Levene and Marker[1]
9. Levene and Marker[2]
10. Petrov, Koptev, and Kaplan[1]
11. Levene and Marker[3]
12. Levene and Cretcher[1]
13. American Petroleum Institute Research Project 44[1]
14. Campbell and Eby[3]
15. Cline[1]
16. Tuot[1]
17. Jacquemain[2]
18. Levina, Kleimenova, and Shusherina[1]
19. Kazowskii and Sergienko[1]
20. Kishner[5]
21. Kishner[6]
22. Kishner[7]
23. Lamb and Roper[1]
24. Enklaar[3]
25. Escourrou[1]
26. Asahina[1]
27. Vavon[1]
28. Enklaar[1]
29. Timmermans[5]
30. Willstatter and Meyer[1]
31. Ivanova, Savinova, and Zhakhovskaya[1]
32. Vogel[2]
33. Spath[1]
34. Lachowicz[1]
35. von Auwers and Eisenlohr[2]
36. Kazanskii and Plate[1]
37. Timmermans[6]
38. Brooks and Humphrey[1]
39. Marker and Oakwood[1]
40. Shine and Turner[1]
41. Dupont[2]
42. Hardin and Sikorsky[1]

SPECIFIC REFERENCES
FOR TABLES 17a, 17a-E, AND 17b (Continued)
October 31, 1950; October 31, 1952

REFERENCES

43. Henne and Chanan[1]
44. American Petroleum Institute Research Project 45[1]
45. Festraete[1]
46. Butler[1]
47. Gleim[1]
48. Buck, Elsner, Forbes, Morrell, Smith, and Wallsgrove[1]
49. Letsinger and Traynham[1]
50. Buck, Elsner, Henshall, Moore, Morrell, Muller, Murray, Plant, Smith, and Wallsgrove[1]
51. Levina, Fainzilberg, and Itenberg[1]
52. Desty and Fidler[1]
53. Moersch and Whitmore[1]
54. Fenske, Braun, Wiegand, Quiggle, McCormick, and Rank[1]
55. Johnson, G.C.[1]
56. Drake and Welsh[1]
57. Kinney and Spliethoff[1]
58. Koch and Hilberath[1]
59. Braun, Spooner, and Fenske[1]
60. Hickenbottom, Porter, Edwards, Schlucterer, and Spitzer[1]
61. Pomerantz, Mears, and Howard[1]
62. Levina and Shusherina[1]
63. Taylor, Pignocco, and Rossini[1]
64. Howard, Mears, Fookson, Pomerantz, and Brooks[1]
65. Hennion and Banigan[1]
66. Whitmore, Popkin, and Pfister[1]
67. Whitmore, Popkin, Bernstein, and Wilkins[1]
68. Johnson, G.C.[2]
69. Whitmore, Goldsmith, Cook, Yarze, and Ecke[1]

| SPECIFIC REFERENCES | | | | | |
|---|---|---|---|---|---|
| FOR TABLES 22a (PART 1), 22a-E (PART 1), AND 22b (PART 1) | | | | | |
| December 31, 1948; June 30, 1949; September 30, 1951 (Corrected) | | | | | |

| Compound | REFERENCES FOR | | | | |
|---|---|---|---|---|---|
| | Boiling Point | Refractive Index | Density | Freezing Point | Refractive Dispersion |
| Cyclopentane | 2,5,7,8,9,10,24, 25,39 | 1,2,3,5,8,12,25, 26,39,40 | 1,2,3,4,5,8,24,25, 40 | 2,5,7,11,12,27,41 | 3,5,23,25,40 |
| Methylcyclopentane | 2,5,6,8,10,13,14, 24,30 | 1,2,3,5,8,9,12,13, 14,15,26,30,39 | 1,2,3,4,5,6,8,13, 14,15,24,30,39,40 | 5,6,11,27,37 | 3,5,22,23 |
| Ethylcyclopentane | 2,6,8,13,16,17,19, 20,23,24,28,29,30, 39,45 | 2,3,6,8,13,15,16, 17,19,20,22,23,28, 29,30,39,44 | 2,3,4,6,8,13,15, 19,20,23,25,28,29, 30 | 6,11,18,20,21,42 | 3,6,22,23,44 |
| n–Propylcyclopentane | 2,6,10,15,20,21, 23,28,29,30,39,45 | 1,2,3,6,20,21,23, 28,29,30,31,39,44 | 1,2,3,4,6,20,23, 28,29,30,31 | 1,18,20,21,30 | 21,23,44 |
| n–Butylcyclopentane | 6,8,29,30,32,37, 46 | 6,8,20,29,30,32, 37,46 | 6,20,29,30,32 | 6,13,18,20,43 | 6,33 |
| n–Pentylcyclopentane | 33,47 | 33,35 | 33,35,38 | 38 | 38 |
| n–Hexylcyclopentane | 33,34 | 33,34 | 33,34 | 38 | 38 |
| n–Heptylcyclopentane | 33 | 33,38 | 33,38 | 38 | 38 |
| n–Octylcyclopentane | 38 | 34,36,38 | 34,36,38 | 36,38 | 38 |
| n–Nonylcyclopentane | 38 | 38 | 38 | 38 | 38 |
| n–Decylcyclopentane | 20,38 | 36,37 | 36,37 | 36,37 | 37,38 |
| n–Undecylcyclopentane | 38 | 38 | 38 | 38 | 38 |
| n–Dodecylcyclopentane | 38 | 36,38 | 36,38 | 36,38 | 38 |
| n–Tridecylcyclopentane | 38 | 38 | 38 | 38 | 38 |
| n–Tetradecylcyclopentane | 38 | 36,38 | 36,38 | 36,38 | 38 |
| n–Pentadecylcyclopentane | 38 | 38 | 38 | 38 | 38 |
| n–Hexadecylcyclopentane | 38 | 36,38 | 36,38 | 36,38 | 38 |

## REFERENCES

1. Forziati, Glasgow, Willingham, and Rossini[1]
2. Birch, Fidler, and Lowry[1]
3. Garrett[1]
4. Geist and Cannon[1]
5. Wibaut, Hoog, Langedijk, Overhoff, Smittenberg, Benninga, Bouman, van Dijk, Gaade, Geldof, Hackmann, Jonker, Paap, and Zuiderweg[1]
6. Chavanne and Becker[1]
7. Aston, Fink, and Schumann[1]
8. Evans, E.B.[2]
9. Griswold, van Berg, and Kasch[1]
10. Willingham, Taylor, Pignocco, and Rossini[1]
11. Glasgow, Murphy, Willingham, and Rossini[1]
12. Smittenberg, Hoog, and Henkes[1]
13. Crane[1]
14. Griswold and Ludwig[1]
15. Moore, Renquist, and Parks[1]
16. Turner and Lesslie[1]
17. McArdle and Robertson[1]
18. Timmermans[2]
19. Greenlee[1]
20. American Petroleum Institute Research Project 45[1]
21. Streiff, Murphy, Cahill, Flanagan, Sedlak, Willingham, and Rossini[1]
22. Grosse and Wackher[1]
23. Forziati and Rossini[2]
24. Kay[1]
25. Vogel[1]
26. Wibaut and Langedijk[1]
27. Douslin and Huffman[1]
28. Zelinsky, Kazanskiĭ, and Platé[1]
29. Pines and Ipatieff[1]
30. Crane, Boord, and Henne[1]
31. Turova–Pollak and Polyakova[1]
32. Kazanskiĭ and Platé[1]
33. Platé[1]
34. Zelinsky, Michlina, and Eventowa[1]
35. Stratford[1]

## SPECIFIC REFERENCES

FOR TABLES 22a (PART 1), 22a-E (PART 1), AND 22b (PART 1) (Continued)

December 31, 1948; June 30, 1949; September 30, 1951 (Corrected)

### REFERENCES

36. Schmidt and Gemassmer[1]
37. American Petroleum Institute Research Project 6[1]
38. American Petroleum Institute Research Project 44[1]
39. Fenske, Braun, Wiegand, Quiggle, McCormick, and Rank[1]
40. Timmermans and Hennaut-Roland[4]
41. Streiff, Murphy, Zimmerman, Soule, Sedlak, Willingham, and Rossini[1]
42. Huffman and others[1]
43. Streiff, Zimmerman, Soule, Butt, Sedlak, Willingham, and Rossini[1]
44. Forziati[1]
45. Forziati, Norris, and Rossini[1]
46. Garner and Evans[1]
47. Bazhulin, Sterin, Bulanova, Solovova, Turova-Pollak, and Kazanskii[1]
48. Boord, Henne, Greenlee, Perilstein, and Derfer[1]

| | SPECIFIC REFERENCES |||||
| :---: | :---: | :---: | :---: | :---: | :---: |
| | FOR TABLES 22a (PART 2), 22a-E (PART 2), AND 22b (PART 2)<br>September 30, 1951 |||||
| | REFERENCES FOR |||||
| Compound | Boiling<br>Point | Refractive<br>Index | Density | Freezing<br>Point | Refractive<br>Dispersion |
| n-Heptadecylcyclopentane | 1 | 1 | 1 | 1 | 1 |
| n-Octadecylcyclopentane | 1 | 1 | 1 | 1 | 1 |
| n-Nonadecylcyclopentane | 1 | 1 | 1 | 1 | 1 |
| n-Eicosylcyclopentane | 1 | 1 | 1 | 1 | 1 |
| n-Heneicosylcyclopentane | 1 | 1 | 1 | 1 | 1 |
| n-Docosylcyclopentane | 1 | 1 | 1 | 1 | 1 |
| n-Tricosylcyclopentane | 1 | 1 | 1 | 1 | 1 |
| n-Tetracosylcyclopentane | 1 | 1 | 1 | 1 | 1 |
| n-Pentacosylcyclopentane | 1 | 1 | 1 | 1 | 1 |
| n-Hexacosylcyclopentane | 1 | 1 | 1 | 1 | 1 |
| n-Heptacosylcyclopentane | 1 | 1 | 1 | 1 | 1 |
| n-Octacosylcyclopentane | 1 | 1 | 1 | 1 | 1 |
| n-Nonacosylcyclopentane | 1 | 1 | 1 | 1 | 1 |
| n-Triacontylcyclopentane | 1 | 1 | 1 | 1 | 1 |
| n-Hentriacontylcyclopentane | 1 | 1 | 1 | 1 | 1 |
| n-Dotriacontylcyclopentane | 1 | 1 | 1 | 1 | 1 |
| n-Tritriacontylcyclopentane | 1 | 1 | 1 | 1 | 1 |
| n-Tetratriacontylcyclopentane | 1 | 1 | 1 | 1 | 1 |
| n-Pentatriacontylcyclopentane | 1 | 1 | 1 | 1 | 1 |
| n-Hexatriacontylcyclopentane | 1 | 1 | 1 | 1 | 1 |

REFERENCES

1. American Petroleum Institute Research
   Project 44[1]

| | SPECIFIC REFERENCES FOR TABLES 6a, 6a–E AND 6b May 31, 1947; June 30, 1949 (Corrected) | | | | |
|---|---|---|---|---|---|
| Compound | REFERENCES FOR | | | | |
| | Boiling Point | Refractive Index | Density | Freezing Point | Refractive Dispersion |
| Cyclopentane | 1 | 1 | 1 | 1 | 1 |
| Methylcyclopentane | 1 | 1 | 1 | 1 | 1 |
| Ethylcyclopentane | 1 | 1 | 1 | 1 | 1 |
| 1,1–Dimethylcyclopentane | 3,10,11,12,13,14,17,19 | 3,10,11,12,13,14,17,19,21 | 3,11,12,13,17 | 3,10,11,12,22 | 17 |
| 1,cis-2–Dimethylcyclopentane | 3,4,6,17,18,19,21 | 3,4,6,17,19,21 | 3,4,6,17,18 | 4,6,10,18,22 | 4,6,17 |
| 1,trans-2–Dimethylcyclopentane | 3,4,6,15,17,18,19,21 | 3,4,6,15,17,18,19,21 | 3,4,6,15,17 | 2,4,6,10,15,18,22 | 4,6,17 |
| 1,cis-3–Dimethylcyclopentane | 9,17,21 | 9,17,21 | 9,17 | 9,20,21,22 | 17 |
| 1,trans-3–Dimethylcyclopentane | 5,7,8,15,16,17,21 | 5,7,15,17,21 | 5,7,15,16,17 | 2,5,15,20,22 | 5,17 |

REFERENCES

1. See references for Tables 22a (Part 1), 22a–E (Part 1), and 22b (Part 1).
2. Huffman, Parks, and Barmore[1]
3. Birch, Fidler, and Lowry[1]
4. Chiurdoglu[1]
5. Chavanne[1]
6. Chavanne[2]
7. Evans, E.B.[2]
8. Turner and Lesslie[1]
9. American Petroleum Institute Research Project 45[1]
10. Streiff, Murphy, Cahill, Flanagan, Sedlak, Willingham, and Rossini[1]
11. Bruun and Hicks-Bruun[1]
12. Chavanne, Miller, and Cornet[1]
13. Kishner[3]
14. Henshall[1]
15. Glasgow[1]
16. Chavanne and Miller[1]
17. Forziati and Rossini[1]
18. Chiurdoglu[2]
19. Whitmore and others[1]
20. Streiff, Zimmerman, Soule, Butt, Sedlak, Willingham, and Rossini[1]
21. Fenske, Braun, Wiegand, Quiggle, McCormick, and Rank[1]
22. Huffman and others[1]

## SPECIFIC REFERENCES

### FOR TABLES 15a, 15a–E, AND 15b

#### May 31, 1947; June 30, 1949

| Compound | REFERENCES FOR | | | | |
|---|---|---|---|---|---|
| | Boiling Point | Refractive Index | Density | Freezing Point | Refractive Dispersion |
| n–Propylcyclopentane | 1 | 1 | 1 | 1 | 1 |
| Isopropylcyclopentane | 3,5,7,8,10,13,19,20,22 | 5,6,7,8,11,13,20,22 | 5,6,7,8,11,12,20 | 3,4,6,20 | 5,11 |
| 1–Methyl–1–ethylcyclopentane | 5,22,23 | 5,22,23 | 5,23 | 21 | 5 |
| 1–Methyl–cis–2–ethylcyclopentane | 5,9 | 5,9 | 5,9 | 21 | 5 |
| 1–Methyl–trans–2–ethylcyclopentane | 5,9,24 | 9,24 | 5,9 | 9 | 2 |
| 1–Methyl–cis–3–ethylcyclopentane | 14,15,22,24 | 14,22,24 | 14,24 | | 2 |
| 1–Methyl–trans–3–ethylcyclopentane | 24 | 24 | 24 | 24 | 2 |
| 1,1,2–Trimethylcyclopentane | 5,7,15,16,22 | 5,7,15,16,22 | 5,7,16, | 4,7 | 5 |
| 1,1,3–Trimethylcyclopentane | 3,5,7,17,18,22 | 3,5,7,17,18,22 | 3,5,7,17,18 | 4 | 5 |
| 1–cis–2–cis–3–Trimethylcyclopentane | 22,24 | 22,24 | 24 | 25 | 2 |
| 1–cis–2–trans–3–Trimethylcyclopentane | 22,24 | 22,24 | 24 | 21 | 2 |
| 1–trans–2–cis–3–Trimethylcyclopentane | 22,24 | 22,24 | 24 | 25 | 2 |
| 1–cis–2–cis–4–Trimethylcyclopentane | 2 | 2 | 2 | | 2 |
| 1–cis–2–trans–4–Trimethylcyclopentane | 5,22 | 5,22 | 5 | 4 | 5 |
| 1–trans–2–cis–4–Trimethylcyclopentane | 5,22 | 5,22 | 5 | 4 | 5 |

## REFERENCES

1. See references for tables 22a and 22b.
2. American Petroleum Institute Research Project 44[1]
3. American Petroleum Institute Research Project 45[1]
4. Streiff, Murphy, Cahill, Flanagan, Sedlak, Willingham, and Rossini[1]
5. Forziati and Rossini[2]
6. Forziati, Glasgow, Willingham, and Rossini[1]
7. Birch, Fidler, and Lowry[1]
8. Pines and Ipatieff[1]
9. Chiurdoglu[2]
10. Willingham, Taylor, Pignocco, and Rossini[1]

11. Garrett[1]
12. Geist and Cannon[1]
13. Kazanskii and Tatevosyan[1]
14. Zelinsky[1]
15. Turner and Lesslie[1]
16. Crossley and Renouf[1]
17. McKinley, Stevens, and Baldwin[1]
18. Zelinsky and Uspensky[1]
19. Streiff, Zimmerman, Soule, Butt, Sedlak, Willingham, and Rossini[1]
20. Crane, Boord, and Henne[1]
21. Streiff, Murphy, Zimmerman, Soule, Sedlak, Willingham, and Rossini[1]
22. Fenske, Braun, Wiegand, Quiggle, McCormick, and Rank[1]

23. Plate and Zabezhenskaya[1]
24. American Petroleum Institute Research Project 6[1]

SPECIFIC REFERENCES

FOR TABLES 23a (PART 1), 23a-E (PART 1), AND 23b (PART 1)

December 31, 1948; September 30, 1951; October 31, 1952

| Compound | REFERENCES FOR | | | | |
|---|---|---|---|---|---|
| | Boiling Point | Refractive Index | Density | Freezing Point | Refractive Dispersion |
| Cyclohexane | 3,4,6,8,10,11,12 | 1,4,5,6,8,9,11,12, 13,14,51,52 | 1,4,5,6,7,8,13,14, 15,51,53 | 2,4,6,8,9,13,16,23, 36 | 5,6,21,22 |
| Methylcyclohexane | 3,4,6,8,12,17,24 | 1,4,5,6,8,9,12,13, 17,18,25,51 | 1,4,5,6,7,8,13,15, 18,24,51 | 2,4,6,26,36 | 5,6,18,21,22 |
| Ethylcyclohexane | 3,4,8,12,19,20 | 1,4,5,8,12,20 | 1,4,5,7,8 | 2,19,20,27,36 | 5,22 |
| n-Propylcyclohexane | 3,8,12,22,28,29, 35,47 | 5,8,12,22,28,29, 32,35,50 | 5,8,12,22,28,35, 45,49 | 19,35,37 | 5,48,50 |
| n-Butylcyclohexane | 8,30,31,32,33,34. 35,37,38,47 | 8,12,22,31,32,33, 34,35,37,38,50 | 8,22,30,31,32,33, 34,35,38,46,49 | 19,35,37 | 50 |
| n-Pentylcyclohexane | 12,31,32,33,34 | 12,31,32,33,34 | 31,32,34,44,46 | 44 | 44 |
| n-Hexylcyclohexane | 12,31 | 31,41 | 31,41,44,46 | 44 | 44 |
| n-Heptylcyclohexane | 44 | 38,44 | 38,44 | 38,44 | 44 |
| n-Octylcyclohexane | 44 | 39,40 | 39,40 | 40 | 44 |
| n-Nonylcyclohexane | 12,44 | 12 | 44 | 44 | 44 |
| n-Decylcyclohexane | 44 | 36,44 | 36,44 | 36,44,55 | 48 |
| n-Undecylcyclohexane | 44 | 44 | 44 | 44 | 44 |
| n-Dodecylcyclohexane | 44 | 38,44 | 38,44 | 38,44 | 44 |
| n-Tridecylcyclohexane | 44 | 44 | 44 | 44 | 44 |
| n-Tetradecylcyclohexane | 44 | 44 | 44 | 38 | 44 |
| n-Pentadecylcyclohexane | 44 | 42,44 | 42,44 | 44 | 44 |
| n-Hexadecylcyclohexane | 44 | 44 | 44 | 38,43 | 44 |

REFERENCES

1. Forziati, Glasgow, Willingham, and Rossini[1]
2. Glasgow, Murphy, Willingham, and Rossini[1]
3. Willingham, Taylor, Pignocco, and Rossini[1]
4. Birch, Fidler, and Lowry[1]
5. Garrett[1]
6. Wibaut, Hoog, Langedijk, Overhoff, Smittenberg, Benninga, Bouman, van Dijk, Gaade, Geldof, Hackmann, Jonker, Paap, and Zuiderweg[2]
7. Geist and Cannon[1]
8. Evans[2]
9. Smittenberg, Hoog, and Henkes[1]
10. Scatchard, Wood, and Mochel[1]
11. Griswold, van Berg, and Kasch[1]
12. Smith and Pennekamp[1]
13. Moore, Renquist, and Parks[1]
14. Waterman and Leendertse[1]
15. Massart[1]
16. Ruehrwein and Huffman[1]
17. McArdle and Robertson[1]
18. Tilton[1]
19. Timmermans[2]
20. Streiff, Murphy, Cahill, Flanagan, Sedlak, Willingham, and Rossini[1]
21. Grosse and Wackher[1]
22. Forziati and Rossini[1]
23. Aston, Szasz, and Fink
24. Kay[1]
25. Calingaert[1]
26. Douslin and Huffman[1]
27. Huffman and others[1]
28. Lozovoi, D'yakowa, and Stepantseva[1]
29. Levina and Trakhtenberg[1]
30. Douris[1]
31. Bourguel[2]
32. Lozovoi, D'yakowa, and Stepantseva[2]
33. Stratford[1]
34. Signaigo and Cramer[1]
35. American Petroleum Institute Research Project 45[1]
36. American Petroleum Institute Research Project 6[1]

SPECIFIC REFERENCES

FOR TABLES 23a (PART 1), 23a-E (PART 1), AND 23b (PART 1) (Continued)

December 31, 1948; September 30, 1951; October 31, 1952

| REFERENCES | | |
|---|---|---|
| 37. Streiff, Murphy, Zimmerman, Soule, Sedlak, Willingham, and Rossini[1] | | |
| 38. Schmidt and Grosser[1] | | |
| 39. Waterman, Leendertse, and van Krevelen[1] | | |
| 40. Schiessler, Herr, Rytina, Weisel, Fischl, McLaughlin, and Kuehner[1] | | |
| 41. Nenitzescu and Cioranescu[1] | | |
| 42. Haagen-Smit[1] | | |
| 43. Van Romburgh, Van Veen, and Haagen-Smit[1] | | |
| 44. American Petroleum Institute Research Project 44[1] | | |
| 45. Cannon[1] | | |
| 46. Aranda[1] | | |
| 47. Forziati, Norris, and Rossini[1] | | |
| 48. Eisenlohr and Gohr[1] | | |
| 49. Forziati and Rossini[2] | | |
| 50. Forziati[1] | | |
| 51. Timmermans and Martin[2] | | |
| 52. Seyer and Barrow[1] | | |
| 53. Rotingantz and Nagornow[1] | | |
| 54. Huffman, Todd, and Oliver[1] | | |
| 55. Waddington and others[1] | | |

| | SPECIFIC REFERENCES | | | | |
|---|---|---|---|---|---|
| | FOR TABLES 23a (PART 2), 23a-E (PART 2), AND 23b (PART 2) | | | | |
| | September 30, 1951 | | | | |
| | REFERENCES FOR | | | | |
| Compound | Boiling Point | Refractive Index | Density | Freezing Point | Refractive Dispersion |
| n–Heptadecylcyclohexane | 1 | 1 | 1 | 1 | 1 |
| n–Octadecylcyclohexane | 1 | 1 | 1 | 1 | 1 |
| n–Nonadecylcyclohexane | 1 | 1 | 1 | 1 | 1 |
| n–Eicosylcyclohexane | 1 | 1 | 1 | 1 | 1 |
| n–Heneicosylcyclohexane | 1 | 1 | 1 | 1 | 1 |
| n–Docosylcyclohexane | 1 | 1 | 1 | 1 | 1 |
| n–Tricosylcyclohexane | 1 | 1 | 1 | 1 | 1 |
| n–Tetracosylcyclohexane | 1 | 1 | 1 | 1 | 1 |
| n–Pentacosylcyclohexane | 1 | 1 | 1 | 1 | 1 |
| n–Hexacosylcyclohexane | 1 | 1 | 1 | 1 | 1 |
| n–Heptacosylcyclohexane | 1 | 1 | 1 | 1 | 1 |
| n–Octacosylcyclohexane | 1 | 1 | 1 | 1 | 1 |
| n–Nonacosylcyclohexane | 1 | 1 | 1 | 1 | 1 |
| n–Triacontylcyclohexane | 1 | 1 | 1 | 1 | 1 |
| n–Hentriacontylcyclohexane | 1 | 1 | 1 | 1 | 1 |
| n–Dotriacontylcyclohexane | 1 | 1 | 1 | 1 | 1 |
| n–Tritriacontylcyclohexane | 1 | 1 | 1 | 1 | 1 |
| n–Tetratriacontylcyclohexane | 1 | 1 | 1 | 1 | 1 |
| n–Pentatriacontylcyclohexane | 1 | 1 | 1 | 1 | 1 |
| n–Hexatriacontylcyclohexane | 1 | 1 | 1 | 1 | 1 |

REFERENCES

1. American Petroleum Institute Research Project 44[1]

| | SPECIFIC REFERENCES | | | | |
|---|---|---|---|---|---|
| | FOR TABLES 7a, 7a–E AND 7b | | | | |
| | May 31, 1947; June 30, 1949; October 31, 1952 | | | | |
| Compound | REFERENCES FOR | | | | |
| | Boiling Point | Refractive Index | Density | Freezing Point | Refractive Dispersion |
| Cyclohexane | 1 | 1 | 1 | 1 | 1 |
| Methylcyclohexane | 1 | 1 | 1 | 1 | 1 |
| Ethylcyclohexane | 1 | 1 | 1 | 1 | 1 |
| 1,1–Dimethylcyclohexane | 3,4,5,6,7,8,9 | 3,4,5,6,7,8,9 | 3,4,6,7,8,9 | 4,6,7,8,12,13,20 | 3,7 |
| 1,cis-2–Dimethylcyclohexane | 7,10,11 | 7,10,14,17 | 7,10,14,17,18 | 7,10,12,13,20 | 7,14,15,16 |
| 1,trans-2–Dimethylcyclohexane | 7,10,11 | 7,10,14,17 | 7,10,14,17,18 | 7,10,12,13,20 | 7,14,15,16 |
| 1,cis-3–Dimethylcyclohexane | 2,7,11,19 | 2,7,17,19 | 2,7,17,18,19 | 7,10,12,17,19,20,21 | 7,15 |
| 1,trans-3–Dimethylcyclohexane | 2,7,11 | 2,7,10,17 | 2,7,17,18 | 7,12,17,20,21 | 7,15 |
| 1,cis-4–Dimethylcyclohexane | 7,10,11 | 7,10,13,14,17 | 7,10,14,17,18 | 7,10,12,13,20 | 7,14,15 |
| 1,trans-4–Dimethylcyclohexane | 7,10,11 | 7,10,14,17 | 7,10,14,17,18 | 7,10,12,13,20 | 7,14,15 |

REFERENCES

1. See references for Tables 23a (Part 1), 23a–E (Part 1), and 23b (Part 1).
2. Mousseron and Granger[1]
3. Forziati and Rossini[2]
4. Evans, G.L.[1]
5. Turner and Lesslie[1]
6. Shortridge, Craig, Greenlee, Derfer, and Boord[1]
7. Miller, O.[3]
8. Chavanne, Miller, and Cornet[1]
9. Zelinsky, Packindorff, and Khokhlova[1]
10. American Petroleum Institute Research Project 45[1]
11. Willingham, Taylor, Pignocco, and Rossini[1]
12. Huffman and others[1]
13. Streiff, Murphy, Cahill, Flanagan, Sedlak, Willingham, and Rossini[1]
14. Garrett[1]
15. American Petroleum Institute Research Project 6[1]
16. Miller, O.[2]
17. Forziati, Glasgow, Willingham, and Rossini[1]
18. Geist and Cannon[1]
19. Birch, Fidler, and Lowry[1]
20. Huffman, Todd, and Oliver[1]
21. Streiff, Murphy, Zimmerman, Soule, Sedlak, Willingham, and Rossini[1]

# SPECIFIC REFERENCES

## FOR TABLES 24a (PART 1), 24a-E (PART 1), AND 24b (PART 1)

February 28, 1949; December 31, 1950; October 31, 1952

| Compound | REFERENCES FOR | | | | |
|---|---|---|---|---|---|
| | Boiling Point | Refractive Index | Density | Freezing Point | Refractive Dispersion |
| Ethene | 4,6,7,8,21 | | | 6,7 | |
| Propene | 3,4,9,10,11,21 | | 1 | 9,12 | |
| 1-Butene | 2,3,4,13,14,21,86 | | 1,2 | 14 | |
| 1-Pentene | 5,15,16,17,18,19,20,75,83,88,90 | 9,16,20,90 | 16,20,76,77,83,90 | 5,74,92 | 87,90 |
| 1-Hexene | 18,19,20,24,25,26,27,28,29,30,31,46,85,90 | 20,24,25,27,28,29,31,46,51,85,90 | 19,20,24,25,26,27,28,29,31,46,51,77,85,90 | 20,25,26,29,31,74,93 | 25,27,29,31,51,87,90 |
| 1-Heptene | 4,16,17,18,20,25,27,31,32,33,34,35,78,79,90 | 16,17,20,25,27,31,32,33,34,35,51,78,79,90 | 16,20,25,27,31,32,34,35,51,77,78,90 | 20,25,31,33,36,74,93 | 25,27,31,51,87,90 |
| 1-Octene | 25,27,37,38,39,40,41,42,43,44,79,85,90 | 20,25,27,37,38,39,40,41,42,43,44,51,79,85,90 | 20,25,27,37,38,39,40,41,42,43,44,51,79,85,90 | 20,25,37,39,41,84,93 | 25,27,44,51,87,90 |
| 1-Nonene | 20,45,46,47,48,90 | 20,45,46,47,49,50,51,90 | 20,45,46,49,50,51,77,90 | 20,46,49,89 | 51,87,90 |
| 1-Decene | 18,52,85,90 | 49,50,51,85,90 | 49,50,51,85,90 | 49,89 | 51,87,90 |
| 1-Undecene | 20,53,90 | 20,49,90 | 20,49,90 | 20,49,89 | 90 |
| 1-Dodecene | 54,90 | 49,50,51,56,85,90 | 49,50,51,54,56,67,85,90 | 49,67 | 51,87,90 |
| 1-Tridecene | 22 | 49,57,58,91 | 49,57,58 | 23,49,57,58 | 22 |
| 1-Tetradecene | 20,48 | 20,48,50,56,85 | 20,48,67,85 | 20,23,67 | 22,85 |
| 1-Pentadecene | 46,48 | 46,49,57,58,59,91 | 46,49,57,58,59 | 23,46,49,57,58,59 | 22 |
| 1-Hexadecene | 20,55,75 | 23,50,51,54,55,59,60,61,62,63,64,65,81,85 | 23,50,51,54,59,60,64,65,67,69,81,85 | 23,55,59,60,63,64,65,67,70,71,72,82,93 | 23,51,65 |
| 1-Heptadecene | 22 | 49,57,58 | 49,57,58 | 49,57,58 | 22 |
| 1-Octadecene | 22 | 51,66 | 51,66,67 | 67,73 | 22,51 |
| 1-Nonadecene | 46 | 46 | 46,57 | 46,57 | 22 |
| 1-Eicosene | 68 | 22 | 68 | 22 | 22 |

## REFERENCES

1. Cragoe[1]
2. Benoliel[1]
3. Kistiakowsky, Ruhoff, Smith, and Vaughan[1]
4. Lamb and Roper[1]
5. Streiff, Murphy, Sedlak, Willingham, and Rossini[1]
6. Kistiakowsky, Romeyn, Ruhoff, Smith, and Vaughan[1]
7. Egan and Kemp[1]
8. Henning and Stock[1]
9. Powell and Giauque[1]
10. Crawford, Kistiakowsky, Rice, Wells, and Wilson[1]
11. Ashdown, Harris, and Armstrong[1]
12. Huffman, Parks, and Barmore[1]
13. Lucas and Dillon[1]
14. Aston, Fink, Bestul, Pace, and Szasz[1]
15. Whitmore and Simpson[1]
16. Sherrill, Mayer, and Walter[1]
17. Stewart, Dod, and Stenmark[1]
18. Mulliken, Wakeman, and Gerry[1]
19. Dykstra, Lewis, and Boord[1]
20. American Petroleum Institute Research Project 45[1]
21. Cragoe[2]
22. American Petroleum Institute Research Project 44[1]
23. American Petroleum Institute Research Project 6[1]
24. Schmitt and Boord[2]
25. Campbell and Eby[2]
26. van Risseghem, Gredy, and Piaux[1]
27. van Pelt and Wibaut[1]
28. Whitmore, Fenske, Quiggle, Bernstein, Carney, Lawroski, Popkin, Wagner, Wheeler, and Whitaker[1]
29. van Risseghem[6]
30. Weinstein and Lucas[1]
31. Waterman and DeKok[1]
32. Soday and Boord[1]
33. Kistiakowsky, Ruhoff, Smith, and Vaughan[2]
34. Campbell and Young[1]
35. Appleby, Dobratz, and Kapranos[1]

## SPECIFIC REFERENCES
### FOR TABLES 24a (PART 1), 24a-E (PART 1) AND 24b (PART 1) (Continued)
February 28, 1949; December 31, 1950; October 31, 1952

### REFERENCES

36. Parks, Todd, and Shomate[1]
37. Henne and Greenlee[1]
38. Dietrich[1]
39. Henne, Chanan, and Turk[1]
40. Mavity[1]
41. Cleveland[1]
42. Whitmore and Herndon[1]
43. Meshcheryakov[1]
44. Waterman and Te Nuyl[1]
45. Wilkinson[1]
46. Spengler[1]
47. Bourguel[2]
48. Pictet and Potok[1]
49. Schmidt, Schoeller, and Eberlein[1]
50. Maman[1]
51. Wibaut and Geldof[1]
52. Grosjean[1]
53. Ross and Leather[1]
54. Evans[2]
55. Gault and Altchidjean[1]
56. Kressilchik[1]
57. Kozacik and Reid[1]
58. Schiessler, Herr, Rytina, Weisel, Fischl, McLaughlin, and Kuehner[1]
59. Asinger and Eckoldt[1]
60. Suida and Drahowzal[1]
61. Berger[1]
62. Klages[2]
63. Langedijk and Stedehouder[1]
64. Waterman and Leendertse[2]
65. Waterman, van't Spijker, and van Westen[1]
66. Dover and Hensley[1]
67. Krafft[1]
68. Engler and Höfer[1]
69. Eykman[4]
70. Ubbelohde[1]
71. Seyer and Huggert[1]
72. Messer[1]
73. Meyer and Streuli[1]
74. Streiff, Zimmerman, Soule, Butt, Sedlak, Willingham, and Rossini[1]
75. Ward and Fulweiler[1]
76. Ewell and Hardy[1]
77. Ouayle[1]
78. Griffith[1]
79. Fenske, Braun, Wiegand, Quiggle, McCormick, and Rank[1]
80. Asinger[1]
81. Schoorl[1]
82. Langedijk and Brezesinska[1]

83. Day, Nicholson, and Felsing[1]
84. Streiff, Murphy, Zimmerman, Sedlak, Willingham, and Rossini[1]
85. Jeffery and Vogel[1]
86. Kozlov[1]
87. Geldof and Wibaut[1]
88. Scott, Waddington, Smith, and Huffman[1]
89. Streiff, Soule, Kennedy, Janes, Sedlak, Willingham, and Rossini[1]
90. Forziati, Camin, and Rossini[2]
91. Lagemann[1]
92. Todd, Oliver, and Huffman[1]
93. Waddington and others[1]

| | SPECIFIC REFERENCES FOR TABLES 24a (PART 2), 24a-E (PART 2), AND 24b (PART 2) December 31, 1950 | | | | |
|---|---|---|---|---|---|
| Compound | REFERENCES FOR | | | | |
| | Boiling Point | Refractive Index | Density | Freezing Point | Refractive Dispersion |
| 1-Heneicosene | 1 | 1 | 1,2 | 2 | 1 |
| 1-Decosene | 1 | 1 | 1 | 3 | 1 |
| 1-Tricosene | 1 | 1 | 1 | 1 | 1 |
| 1-Tetracosene | 1 | 1 | 1 | 1 | 1 |
| 1-Pentacosene | 1 | 1 | 1 | 1 | 1 |
| 1-Hexacosene | 1 | 1 | 1 | 1 | 1 |
| 1-Heptacosene | 1 | 1 | 1 | 4 | 1 |
| 1-Octacosene | 1 | 1 | 1 | 1 | 1 |
| 1-Nonacosene | 1 | 1 | 1 | 1 | 1 |
| 1-Triacontene | 1 | 1 | 1 | 1 | 1 |
| 1-Hentriacontene | 1 | 1 | 1 | 5 | 1 |
| 1-Dotriacontene | 1 | 1 | 1 | 1 | 1 |
| 1-Tritriacontene | 1 | 1 | 1 | 1 | 1 |
| 1-Tetratriacontene | 1 | 1 | 1 | 1 | 1 |
| 1-Pentatriacontene | 1 | 1 | 1 | 1 | 1 |
| 1-Hexatriacontene | 1 | 1 | 1 | 1 | 1 |
| 1-Heptatriacontene | 1 | 1 | 1 | 1 | 1 |
| 1-Octatriacontene | 1 | 1 | 1 | 1 | 1 |
| 1-Nonatriacontene | 1 | 1 | 1 | 1 | 1 |
| 1-Tetracontene | 1 | 1 | 1 | 1 | 1 |

REFERENCES

1. American Petroleum Institute Research Project 44[1]
2. Schmidt, Schoeller, and Eberlein[1]
3. Braun, Teuffert, and Weissbach[1]
4. Brodie[1]
5. Pummerer and Kranz[1]

| | SPECIFIC REFERENCES FOR TABLES 8a (PART 1), 8a–E (PART 1), AND 8b (PART 1) May 31, 1947; October 31, 1952 | | | | |
|---|---|---|---|---|---|
| | REFERENCES FOR | | | | |
| Compound | Boiling Point | Refractive Index | Density | Freezing Point | Refractive Dispersion |
| Ethene (Ethylene) | 1 | | | 1 | |
| Propene (Propylene) | 1 | | 1 | 1 | |
| 1-Butene | 1 | | 1 | 1 | |
| cis-2-Butene | 2,3,4,19,24,26 | | 2,10 | 3,20,26,31,49 | |
| trans-2-Butene | 2,3,4,19,21,24 | | 2,10 | 3,20,21,31,49 | |
| 2-Methylpropene (Isobutene) | 2,3,4,22,24 | | 2,10 | 3,20,22,27,31,49 | |
| 1-Pentene | 1 | 1 | 1 | 1 | 1 |
| cis-2-Pentene | 5,6,7,8,15,28,29,30,32,51 | 5,6,7,9,28,29,30,50,51 | 5,6,7,8,29,30,51 | 5,7,9,12,50 | 25,30 |
| trans-2-Pentene | 5,6,7,8,9,15,28,30,33,34,35 | 5,6,7,9,28,30,33,34,35 | 6,7,8,28,30,34,35 | 5,7,9,12,28 | 25 |
| 2-Methyl-1-butene | 8,9,16,18,36,37,38,39 | 9,11,13,18,36,37,38,39 | 8,11,13,17,18,37 | 9,12,18,28 | 25 |
| 3-Methyl-1-butene | 6,7,8,9,15,23,40,41,42,43,48 | 6,7,40,41,42,43 | 6,7,8,41,43 | 9,12,31 | 25,43 |
| 2-Methyl-2-butene | 4,6,7,8,9,16,28,36,38,39,43,44,45,46,47 | 6,7,9,11,13,14,28,36,38,39,43,44,45,46,47 | 6,7,8,11,28,47 | 7,9,12,28,31,36,43 | 25 |

**REFERENCES**

1. See references for Tables 24a (Part 1), 24a–E (Part 1), and 24b (Part 1).
2. Benoliel[1]
3. Kistiakowsky, Ruhoff, Smith, and Vaughan[1]
4. Lamb and Roper[1]
5. Lucas and Prater[1]
6. Carr and Walter[1]
7. Norris and Reuter[1]
8. Ewell and Hardy[1]
9. Streiff, Murphy, Sedlak, Willingham, and Rossini[1]
10. Cragoe[1]
11. Desty and Fidler[1]
12. Todd, Oliver, and Huffman[1]
13. Laren and Frost[1]
14. Obolentsev[1]
15. Waddington and others[1]
16. Scott, Waddington, Smith, and Huffman[1]
17. Derfer, Greenlee, and Boord[1]
18. Slabey[1]
19. Young, Dillon and Lucas[1]
20. Todd and Parks[1]
21. Guttman and Pitzer[1]
22. Coffin and Maass[3]
23. Whitmore and Simpson[1]
24. Cragoe[2]
25. American Petroleum Institute Research Project 44[1]
26. Scott, Ferguson, and Brickwedde[1]
27. Rands, Scott and Brickwedde[1]
28. American Petroleum Institute Research Project 45[1]
29. Sherrill and Launspach[1]
30. Sherrill and Matlack[1]
31. Glasgow and Rossini[1]
32. Gredy[1]
33. Lauer and Stodola[1]
34. Sherrill, Baldwin, and Haas[1]
35. Sherrill, Otto, and Pickett[1]
36. Kistiakowsky, Ruhoff, Smith, and Vaughan[2]
37. Sherrill and Walter[1]
38. Church, Whitmore, and McGrew[1]
39. Whitmore, Rowland, Wrenn, and Kilmer[1]

## SPECIFIC REFERENCES

FOR TABLES 8a (PART 1), 8a-E (PART 1), AND 8b (PART 1) (Continued)

May 31, 1947; October 31, 1952

### REFERENCES

40. Dolliver, Gresham, Kistiakowsky, and Vaughan[1]
41. Whitmore, Popkin, Bernstein, and Wilkins[1]
42. Gredy[2]
43. Leendertse, Tulleners, and Waterman[1]
44. Whitmore and Mosher[1]
45. Whitmore and Stahly[1]
46. Michael and Weiner[1]
47. Thompson and Sherrill[1]
48. Smith, E.A.[1]
49. Glasgow, Krouskop, Beadle, Axilrod, and Rossini[1]
50. American Petroleum Institute Research Project 6[1]
51. Hoff, Greenlee, and Boord[1]

808

# SPECIFIC REFERENCES

FOR TABLES 8a (PART 2), 8a-E (PART 2), AND 8b (PART 2)

May 31, 1947; October 31, 1952

| Compound | REFERENCES FOR | | | | |
|---|---|---|---|---|---|
| | Boiling Point | Refractive Index | Density | Freezing Point | Refractive Dispersion |
| 1-Hexene | 1 | 1 | 1 | 1 | 1 |
| cis-2-Hexene | 2,4,14,21,24,25,48 | 2,4,14,21,25,48,49 | 2,4,14,25,48 | 4,14,26,48,50 | 2,4,14,47 |
| trans-2-Hexene | 2,4,14,17,21,24,30 | 2,4,14,17 | 2,4,14,17,21,49 | 4,14,17,30,51 | 2,4,14,47 |
| cis-3-Hexene | 2,3,6,18,19,21,27,48 | 2,3,6,18,19,21,27,48 | 2,3,6,18,19,27,48 | 3,26,48,50 | 4,18,47 |
| trans-3-Hexene | 2,3,6,18,21,27 | 2,3,6,18,21,27,30,49 | 2,3,6,18,27,30 | 3,30,51 | 4,18,47 |
| 2-Methyl-1-pentene | 2,10,20,21 | 2,10,20 | 2,10,20 | 50 | 47 |
| 3-Methyl-1-pentene | 2,21,28,29,30,52 | 2,21,28,29,30,52 | 2,28,29,30 | 51,57 | 47 |
| 4-Methyl-1-pentene | 2,16,17,21,22,52 | 2,16,21,30,49,52,53 | 2,16,22,30,53 | 50,57 | 2,16,47 |
| 2-Methyl-2-pentene | 2,13,15,17,21,30,31,32,52,53 | 2,13,15,20,30,31,32,52,53,54 | 2,13,15,30,31,32,52,53 | 13,30,51 | 2,15,47 |
| 3-Methyl-cis-2-pentene | 2,7,12,19,21,33,34,35 | 2,7,21,30,33,34,35,52,56 | 2,7,34,35 | 7,30,51 | 2,47 |
| 3-Methyl-trans-2-pentene | 2,7,12,19,21,33,34,35 | 2,7,21,30,33,34,35,52,56 | 2,7,34,35 | 7,50 | 2,47 |
| 4-Methyl-cis-2-pentene | 2,5,11,17,19,21,23,30,49 | 2,21,23,30,49,53 | 2,23,30 | 50 | 47 |
| 4-Methyl-trans-2-pentene | 2,5,19,21 | 2,21,30,49,52 | 2,52 | 50 | 47 |
| 2-Ethyl-1-butene | 2,9,10,20,21,35,36,55 | 2,9,10,20,21,35,36,49,52,55,56 | 2,9,10,20,35,36,52,55 | 51,55 | 9,47 |
| 2,3-Dimethyl-1-butene | 2,7,8,20,21,37,38,39 | 2,7,8,20,21,37,38,39,52,56 | 2,7,8,20,38 | 7,21,38 | 47 |
| 3,3-Dimethyl-1-butene | 8,38,39,40,41,42,43,46 | 8,38,39,40,41,42,43,46,52,58 | 8,38,41,43,52 | 8,44,46 | 47 |
| 2,3-Dimethyl-2-butene | 6,7,8,21,30,37,38,39,52,59,60 | 6,7,8,21,30,37,38,39,52,56 | 7,8,30,38,52,58 | 7,8,21,30,37,38,45,60 | 38,47 |

## REFERENCES

1. See references for Tables 24a (Part 1), 24a-E (Part 1), and 24b (Part 1).
2. Schmitt and Boord[2]
3. Campbell and Eby[1]
4. Campbell and Eby[2]
5. van Risseghem, Gredy, and Piaux[1]
6. Carr and Walter[1]
7. Howard, Mears, Fookson, Pomerantz, and Brooks[1]
8. Brooks, Howard, and Crafton[2]
9. van Pelt and Wibaut[1]
10. Whitmore, Fenske, Quiggle, Bernstein, Carney, Lawroski, Popkin, Wagner, Wheeler, and Whitaker[1]
11. van Risseghem[2]
12. van Risseghem[4]
13. van Risseghem[5]
14. van Risseghem[6]
15. van Risseghem[7]
16. van Risseghem[8]
17. van Risseghem[10]
18. van Risseghem[11]
19. van Risseghem[12]
20. Schmitt and Boord[1]
21. American Petroleum Institute Research Project 6[1]
22. Dykstra, Lewis, and Boord[1]
23. Mullikan, Wakeman, and Gerry[1]
24. Stewart, Dod, and Stenmark[1]
25. Gredy[1]
26. Henne and Greenlee[1]
27. Gibson[1]
28. Whitmore and Carney[1]
29. Taylor, Pignocco, and Rossini[1]
30. American Petroleum Institute Research Project 45[1]
31. Rudel[1]
32. Nasarov[1]
33. Whitmore and Mosher[1]
34. Horney[1]
35. Hull[1]
36. Colonge[1]
37. Kistiakowsky, Ruhoff, Smith, and Vaughan[2]
38. Schurman and Boord[1]

SPECIFIC REFERENCES
FOR TABLES 8a (PART 2), 8a—E (PART 2), AND 8b (PART 2), (Continued)
May 31, 1947; October 31, 1952

REFERENCES

39. Laughlin, Nash, and Whitmore[1]
40. Dolliver, Gresham, Kistiakowsky, and Vaughan[1]
41. Fomin and Sochanski[1]
42. Birch, Fidler, and Lowry[1]
43. Wibaut and Gitsels[2]
44. Kennedy, Shomate, and Parks[1]
45. Parks, Todd, and Shomate[1]
46. Streiff, Murphy, Cahill, Soule, Sedlak, Willingham, and Rossini[1]
47. American Petroleum Institute Research Project 44[1]
48. Hoff, Greenlee, and Boord[1]
49. Braun, Spooner, and Fenske[1]
50. Streiff, Soule, Kennedy, Janes, Sedlak, Willingham, and Rossini[1]
51. Streiff, Zimmerman, Soule, Butt, Sedlak, Willingham, and Rossini[1]
52. Koch[1]
53. Spengler[1]
54. Whitmore, Whitmore, and Cook[1]
55. Derfer, Greenlee, and Boord[1]
56. Miller and Lovell[1]
57. Boord, Henne, Greenlee, Perilstein, and Derfer[1]
58. Waldmann and Petru[1]
59. Kelso, Greenlee, Derfer, and Boord[1]
60. Waddington and others[1]

| | SPECIFIC REFERENCES |
| --- | --- |
| | FOR TABLES 9a, 9a–E, AND 9b |
| | May 31, 1947; October 31, 1952 |

| Compound | REFERENCES FOR | | | | |
| --- | --- | --- | --- | --- | --- |
| | Boiling Point | Refractive Index | Density | Freezing Point | Refractive Dispersion |
| 1-Heptene | 1 | 1 | 1 | 1 | 1 |
| cis-2-Heptene | 2,3,4,7 | 2,3,4,7 | 2,4,7 | | 18 |
| trans-2-Heptene | 2,3,4,7,8,12 | 2,3,4,7,8,12 | 2,4,7,12 | 8,12 | 18 |
| cis-3-Heptene | 12 | 12 | 12 | | 18 |
| trans-3-Heptene | 8,12 | 8,12 | 12 | 8,12 | 18 |
| 2-Methyl-1-hexene | 2,7,8,9,12 | 2,7,8,9,12 | 2,7,12 | 8 | 18 |
| 3-Methyl-1-hexene | 2,7 | 2,7 | 2,7 | | 18 |
| 4-Methyl-1-hexene | 2,7,8,12 | 2,7,8,12 | 2,7,12 | 8 | 18 |
| 5-Methyl-1-hexene | 2,8,10,11,12 | 2,7,8,10,12 | 2,10,11,12 | | 18 |
| 2-Methyl-2-hexene | 2,5,12,13,14,19 | 2,5,12,14,19 | 2,5,6,12,14,19 | 8 | 18 |
| 3-Methyl-cis-2-hexene | 2,7,15,16 | 2,7,15,16 | 2,7,16 | | 18 |
| 3-Methyl-trans-2-hexene | 2,7,15,16 | 2,7,15,16 | 2,7,16 | | 18 |
| 4-Methyl-cis-2-hexene | 2,7,12 | 2,7,12 | 2,7,12 | | 18 |
| 4-Methyl-trans-2-hexene | 2,7,12 | 2,7,12 | 2,7,12 | 12 | 18 |
| 5-Methyl-cis-2-hexene | 2,5,7 | 2,5,7 | 2,5,7 | | 18 |
| 5-Methyl-trans-2-hexene | 2,5,7 | 2,5,7 | 2,5,7 | | 18 |
| 2-Methyl-cis-3-hexene | 2,7 | 2,7 | 2,7 | | 18 |
| 2-Methyl-trans-3-hexene | | | | | 18 |
| 3-Methyl-cis-3-hexene | 12 | 12 | 12 | | 18 |
| 3-Methyl-trans-3-hexene | 12 | 12 | 12 | | 18 |
| 2-Ethyl-1-pentene | 2,7 | 2,7 | 2,7 | | 18 |
| 3-Ethyl-1-pentene | 7,32 | 7,32 | 7,32 | | 18 |
| 2,3-Dimethyl-1-pentene | 2,7,12 | 2,7,12 | 2,7,12 | 12 | 18 |
| 2,4-Dimethyl-1-pentene | 2,7,19 | 2,7,12 | 2,7,12 | 19 | 18 |
| 3,3-Dimethyl-1-pentene | 7,14,26 | 7,14,26 | 7,14,26 | | 18 |
| 3,4-Dimethyl-1-pentene | 7,24 | 7,24 | 7 | | 18 |
| 4,4-Dimethyl-1-pentene | 9,10,12,19,25,34,35 | 9,10,12,19,23,25,34,35 | 10,12,19,35 | 12,19,25,34 | 18 |
| 3-Ethyl-2-pentene | 2,8,12,13,16,36,37 | 2,8,9,12,16,28,29,36,37 | 2,12,16,29,36 | | 2,18 |
| 2,3-Dimethyl-2-pentene | 12,13,16,19,27,30,31,38 | 16,19,27,30,38 | 16,19,27,30,38 | 27 | 18 |
| 2,4-Dimethyl-2-pentene | 12,13,19,33,37,39,40,41 | 12,19,33,39,40,41 | 12,19,33,39,40,41 | | 18,40,41 |
| 3,4-Dimethyl-cis-2-pentene | 2,7,16 | 2,7,16 | 2,7,16 | | 18 |
| 3,4-Dimethyl-trans-2-pentene | | | | | 18 |
| 4,4-Dimethyl-cis-2-pentene | 8,9,12 | 8,9,12 | 12 | 8,12 | 18 |
| 4,4-Dimethyl-trans-2-pentene | 9,12,25 | 9,12,25 | 12 | 12,25 | 18 |
| 3-Methyl-2-ethyl-1-butene | 2,7 | 2,7 | 2,7 | | 18 |
| 2,3,3-Trimethyl-1-butene | 8,12,19,20,21,22,27,30 | 8,12,19,20,21,22,27,30 | 12,19,20,21,22 | 12,19,20,21,25 | 18,21 |

## REFERENCES

1. See references for Tables 24a (Part 1), 24a–E (Part 1), and 24b (Part 1).
2. Soday and Boord[1]
3. Stewart, Dod, and Stenmark[1]
4. Gredy[1]
5. Tuot[2]
6. Obolentsev[1]
7. Taylor, Pignocco, and Rossini[1]
8. American Petroleum Institute Research Project 6[1]
9. Braun, Spooner, and Fenske[1]
10. Mulliken, Wakeman, and Gerry[1]
11. Dykstra, Lewis, and Boord[1]
12. American Petroleum Institute Research Project 45[1]
13. Edgar, Calingaert, and Marker[1]
14. Rudel[1]
15. Horney[1]

SPECIFIC REFERENCES
FOR TABLES 9a, 9a–E, AND 9b (Continued)
May 31, 1947; October 31, 1952

REFERENCES

16. Nasarov[1]
17. Favorski and Zalusky–Kibardine[1]
18. American Petroleum Institute Research Project 44[1]
19. Boord, Henne, Greenlee, Perilstein, and Derfer[1]
20. Brooks, Howard, and Crafton[2]
21. Chavanne and Lejeune[1]
22. Meshcheryakov[1]
23. Schmerling[1]
24. Keulemans, Kwantes, and van Bavel[1]
25. Streiff, Soule, Kennedy, Janes, Sedlak, Willingham, and Rossini[1]
26. Schurman and Boord[1]
27. Cline[1]
28. Buck, Elsner, Henshall, Moore, Murray, Müller, Morrell, Plant, Smith, and Wallsgrove[1]
29. Böeseken and Wildschut[1]
30. Pomerantz, Mears, and Howard[1]
31. Miller and Lovell[1]
32. Prevost and Daujat[1]
33. Wibaut, van Pelt, Santilhano, and Beuskens[1]
34. Dolliver, Gresham, Kistiakowsky, and Vaughan[1]
35. Whitmore and Homeyer[1]
36. Carr and Walter[1]
37. Birch, Fidler and Lowry[1]
38. Pariselle and Simon[1]
39. Deux[1]
40. de Graef[1]
41. van Pelt and Wibaut[1]

812

| | REFERENCES FOR | | | | |
|---|---|---|---|---|---|
| Compound | Boiling Point | Refractive Index | Density | Freezing Point | Refractive Dispersion |
| 1-Octene | 1 | 1 | 1 | 1 | 1 |
| cis-2-Octene | 2,3,4,6,7,8,11,15 | 2,3,4,6,7,8,11,13,14,15 | 2,3,4,6,7,8,11,14,15 | 2,6,7,14 | 6,26 |
| trans-2-Octene | 2,3,4,6,7,8,9,11 | 2,3,4,6,7,8,9,11,13 | 2,3,4,6,7,8,9,11 | 2,6,7,9 | 6,26 |
| cis-3-Octene | 2,5,8,16,17 | 2,5,8,16,17 | 2,5,8,16,17 | | 6,16,26 |
| trans-3-Octene | 2,5,8,9,16,17,18,25 | 2,5,8,9,16,17,18,25,27 | 2,5,8,9,16,17,18,25 | 2,5,18,25 | 6,16,26 |
| cis-4-Octene | 2,5,8,14,19,20 | 2,5,8,14,19,20 | 2,5,8,14,19,20 | 2,5,14,19,20 | 6,26 |
| trans-4-Octene | 2,4,5,8,9,18,20,25,28 | 2,4,5,8,9,18,20,25,27,28,29,30 | 2,4,5,8,9,18,20,25,29,30 | 2,5,9,18,20,25,28 | 6,26 |
| 2-Methyl-1-heptene | 7,8,10,21,31 | 7,8,10,21,31 | 7,8,10,31 | 7,10,31 | 26 |
| 3-Methyl-1-heptene | 4,7,12 | 4,12 | 4,12 | | 26 |
| 4-Methyl-1-heptene | 3,7,12 | 3,7,12 | 3,7,12 | | 26 |
| 5-Methyl-1-heptene | 3,12 | 3,12 | 3,12 | | 26 |
| 6-Methyl-1-heptene | 3,7,10,22,27,31 | 3,7,10,22,31 | 3,7,10,22,29,31 | | 26 |
| 2-Methyl-2-heptene | 17,21,23,24,31,33 | 17,21,23,24,31,32,33 | 17,23,24,31 | | 26 |
| 3-Methyl-cis-2-heptene / 3-Methyl-trans-2-heptene | 12,24,69,70 | 12,24,69,70 | 12,24,69 | | 26 |
| 4-Methyl-cis-2-heptene / 4-Methyl-trans-2-heptene | 3,7,12,34,37 | 3,7,12,34,37 | 3,7,12,37 | | 26 |
| 5-Methyl-cis-2-heptene / 5-Methyl-trans-2-heptene | 12 | 12 | 12 | | 26 |
| 6-Methyl-cis-2-heptene / 6-Methyl-trans-2-heptene | 3,12,25,31 | 3,12,25,31 | 3,12,25,31 | | 26 |
| 2-Methyl-cis-3-heptene / 2-Methyl-trans-3-heptene | 8,12 | 8,12,29,30 | 8,12,29,30 | | 26 |
| 3-Methyl-cis-3-heptene / 3-Methyl-trans-3-heptene | 12,35,36 | 12,35,36 | 12,35,36 | | 26 |
| 4-Methyl-cis-3-heptene / 4-Methyl-trans-3-heptene | 12 | 12 | 12 | | 26 |
| 5-Methyl-cis-3-heptene / 5-Methyl-trans-3-heptene | 8,12 | 8,12 | 8,12 | | 26 |
| 6-Methyl-cis-3-heptene / 6-Methyl-trans-3-heptene | 8,12,17 | 8,12,17 | 8,12,17 | | 26 |
| 2-Ethyl-1-hexene | 8,12,38 | 8,12,38 | 8,12,38 | | 26,38,43 |
| 3-Ethyl-1-hexene | 8,12 | 8,12 | 8,12 | | 26 |
| 4-Ethyl-1-hexene | 12 | 12 | 12 | | 26 |
| 2,3-Dimethyl-1-hexene | 12,25,31,35,39 | 12,25,31,35,39 | 12,25,31,35,39 | | 26 |
| 2,4-Dimethyl-1-hexene | 12,39 | 12,39 | 12,39 | | 26 |
| 2,5-Dimethyl-1-hexene | 12,39 | 12,39 | 12,39 | | 26 |
| 3,3-Dimethyl-1-hexene | 12,23,35 | 12,23,35 | 12,23,35 | | 26 |
| 3,4-Dimethyl-1-hexene | 3,12 | 3,12 | 3,12 | | 26 |
| 3,5-Dimethyl-1-hexene | 3,12 | 3,12 | 3,12 | | 26 |
| 4,4-Dimethyl-1-hexene | 3,12,44 | 3,12,44 | 3,12,44 | | 26 |
| 4,5-Dimethyl-1-hexene | 12,35 | 12,35 | 12,35 | | 26 |
| 5,5-Dimethyl-1-hexene | 12,23,45 | 12,23,45 | 12,23,45 | | 26 |
| 3-Ethyl-cis-2-hexene / 3-Ethyl-trans-2-hexene | 12,24 | 12,24 | 12,24 | | 26 |

SPECIFIC REFERENCES FOR TABLES 10a, 10a-E, AND 10b May 31, 1947; October 31, 1952

| | SPECIFIC REFERENCES | | | | |
|---|---|---|---|---|---|
| | FOR TABLES 10a, 10a-E, AND 10b (Continued) | | | | |
| | May 31, 1947; October 31, 1952 | | | | |

| Compound | REFERENCES FOR | | | | |
|---|---|---|---|---|---|
| | Boiling Point | Refractive Index | Density | Freezing Point | Refractive Dispersion |
| 4-Ethyl-*cis*-2-hexene / 4-Ethyl-*trans*-2-hexene | 3,12 | 3,12 | 3,12 | * | 26 |
| 2,3-Dimethyl-2-hexene | 12,25,31,35,40,41, 42,46,70 | 12,25,31,35,40,41, 42,46,70 | 12,25,31,35,40,41, 42,46 | 25,40 | 26 |
| 2,4-Dimethyl-2-hexene | 12,21,35,45,70 | 12,35,45,70 | 12,35,45,70 | | 26 |
| 2,5-Dimethyl-2-hexene | 12,17,23,24,47 | 12,17,23,24,47 | 12,17,23,24,47 | | 26 |
| 3,4-Dimethyl-*cis*-2-hexene / 3,4-Dimethyl-*trans*-2-hexene | 12,32 | 12,32 | 12,32 | | 26 |
| 3,5-Dimethyl-*cis*-2-hexene / 3,5-Dimethyl-*trans*-2-hexene | 12,24,32,48 | 12,24,32,48 | 12,24,48 | | 26 |
| 4,4-Dimethyl-*cis*-2-hexene / 4,4-Dimethyl-*trans*-2-hexene | 12,49,51 | 12,49,51 | 12,49,51 | | 26 |
| 4,5-Dimethyl-*cis*-2-hexene / 4,5-Dimethyl-*trans*-2-hexene | 3,12,52 | 3,12,52 | 3,12 | | 26 |
| 5,5-Dimethyl-*cis*-2-hexene | 45 | 45 | 45 | | 26 |
| 5,5-Dimethyl-*trans*-2-hexene | 45 | 45 | 45 | | 26 |
| 3-Ethyl-3-hexene | 12 | 12 | 12 | | 26 |
| 2,2-Dimethyl-*cis*-3-hexene | 12,25,31,42,49,54 | 12,25,31,42,49,54 | 12,25,31,42,49 | | 26 |
| 2,2-Dimethyl-*trans*-3-hexene | 25,31,54 | 25,31,54 | 25,31 | | 26 |
| 2,3-Dimethyl-*cis*-3-hexene / 2,3-Dimethyl-*trans*-3-hexene | 12 | 12 | 12 | | 26 |
| 2,4-Dimethyl-*cis*-3-hexene | 45 | 45 | 45 | | 26 |
| 2,4-Dimethyl-*trans*-3-hexene | 45 | 45 | 45 | | 26 |
| 2,5-Dimethyl-*cis*-3-hexene / 2,5-Dimethyl-*trans*-3-hexene | 12,35,50 | 12,35,50 | 12,35,50 | | 26 |
| 3,4-Dimethyl-*cis*-3-hexene / 3,4-Dimethyl-*trans*-3-hexene | 12 | 12 | 12 | | 26 |
| 2-*n*-Propyl-1-pentene | 12,39 | 12,39 | 12,39 | | 26 |
| 2-Isopropyl-1-pentene | 12,39 | 12,39 | 12,39 | | 26 |
| 3-Methyl-2-ethyl-1-pentene | 12,39 | 12,39 | 12,39 | | 26 |
| 4-Methyl-2-ethyl-1-pentene | 8,12,39 | 8,12,39 | 8,12,39 | | 26 |
| 2-Methyl-3-ethyl-1-pentene | 12,39 | 12,39 | 12,39 | | 26 |
| 3-Methyl-3-ethyl-1-pentene | 12,35 | 12,35 | 12,35 | | 26 |
| 4-Methyl-3-ethyl-1-pentene | 12,45 | 12,45 | 12,45 | | 26 |
| 2,3,3-Trimethyl-1-pentene | 12,39,40,53,56, 58,64,65 | 12,39,40,52,53, 56,58,65 | 12,39,40,52,53, 56,58,65 | 40 | 26 |
| 2,3,4-Trimethyl-1-pentene | 12,39 | 12,39 | 12,39 | | 26 |
| 2,4,4-Trimethyl-1-pentene | 31,54,57,58,59, 60,61,66 | 31,54,57,58,59, 60,61,67 | 31,57,58,67 | 57,58,62,67,68 | 26 |
| 3,3,4-Trimethyl-1-pentene | 12,23 | 12,23,63 | 12,23 | | 26 |
| 3,4,4-Trimethyl-1-pentene | 3,12 | 3,12 | 3,12 | | 26 |
| 2-Methyl-3-ethyl-2-pentene | 12,33,35,41 | 12,33,35,41 | 12,35,41 | | 26 |
| 4-Methyl-3-ethyl-*cis*-2-pentene | 45 | 45 | 45 | | 26 |
| 4-Methyl-3-ethyl-*trans*-2-pentene | 45 | 45 | 45 | | 26 |
| 2,3,4-Trimethyl-2-pentene | 55,58,63 | 55,58,63,65,66 | 58,63 | 58 | 26 |
| 2,4,4-Trimethyl-2-pentene | 32,38,54,57,58, 59,61,66,67 | 32,38,54,57,58, 59,61,67 | 32,38,57,58,67 | 54,57,58,62 | 26,38 |
| 3,4,4-Trimethyl-*cis*-2-pentene / 3,4,4-Trimethyl-*trans*-2-pentene | 32,52,53,56,58 | 32,52,53,56,58 | 32,56,58 | | 26 |

SPECIFIC REFERENCES
FOR TABLES 10a, 10a–E, AND 10b (Continued)
May 31, 1947; October 31, 1952

| Compound | REFERENCES FOR | | | | |
|---|---|---|---|---|---|
| | Boiling Point | Refractive Index | Density | Freezing Point | Refractive Dispersion |
| 3–Methyl–2–isopropyl–1–butene | 12,39,55,63 | 12,39,55,63,66 | 12,39,63 | | 26 |
| 3,3–Dimethyl–2–ethyl–1–butene | 12,64 | 12,66 | 12 | | 26 |

## REFERENCES

1. See references for Tables 24a (Part 1) 24a–E (Part 1), and 24b (Part 1).
2. Henne and Greenlee[1]
3. Dietrich[1]
4. Gibson[1]
5. Campbell and Eby[1]
6. Campbell and Eby[2]
7. Henne, Chanan, and Turk[1]
8. Mavity[1]
9. Cleveland[1]
10. Cleveland[2]
11. Whitmore and Herndon[1]
12. Taylor, Pignocco, and Rossini[1]
13. University of Chicago[1]
14. Hoff, Greenlee, and Boord[1]
15. Gredy[1]
16. Wibaut and Gitsels[1]
17. Tuot[2]
18. Campbell and McDermott[1]
19. Campbell and Young[1]
20. Young, Jasaitis, and Levanas[1]
21. Birch, Fidler, and Lowry[1]
22. Brooks and Humphrey[1]
23. Rudel[1]
24. Hull[1]
25. American Petroleum Institute Research Project 45[1]
26. American Petroleum Institute Research Project 44[1]
27. Braun, Spooner, and Fenske[1]
28. Streiff, Soule, Kennedy, Janes, Sedlak, Willingham, and Rossini[1]
29. Seifert[1]
30. Goubeau and Seifert[1]
31. Boord, Henne, Greenlee, Perilstein, and Derfer[1]
32. Kishner[9]
33. Buck, Elsner, Henshall, Moore, Morrell, Müller, Murray, Plant, Smith, and Wallgrove[1]
34. Komarewsky and Kritchevsky[1]
35. Reid[1]
36. Mescheryakov[1]
37. Mulliken, Wakeman, and Gerry[1]
38. van Pelt and Wibaut[1]
39. Kuykendall[1]
40. Cline[1]
41. Nasarov[1]
42. Henne and Matuszak[1]
43. Grosse and Wackher[1]
44. Liberman and Kazanskiĭ[2]
45. Whitmore, Whitmore, and Cook[1]
46. Levina, Fainzil'berg, and Itenberg[1]
47. Levina, Skvarchenko, Viktorova, Tatevskiĭ, and Treshchova[1]
48. Tuot[1]
49. Schurman and Boord[1]
50. Levina, Skvarchenko, Treshchova, and Tatevskiĭ[1]
51. Levina, Fainzil'berg, Tautsyreva, and Treshchova[1]
52. Pomerantz, Mears, and Howard[1]
53. Whitmore and Laughlin[1]
54. American Petroleum Institute Research Project 6[1]
55. Whitmore and Laughlin[2]
56. Whitmore and Laughlin[3]
57. Tongberg, Pickens, Fenske, and Whitmore[1]
58. Howard, Mears, Fookson, Pomerantz, and Brooks[1]
59. Dolliver, Gresham, Kistiakowsky, and Vaughan[1]
60. Whitmore and Houk[1]
61. Whitmore, Rowland, Wrenn, and Kilmer[1]
62. Parks, Todd, and Shomate[1]
63. Wiest[1]
64. Clarke and Jones[1]
65. Miller and Lovell[1]
66. Fenske, Braun, Wiegand, Quiggle, McCormick, and Rank[1]
67. Pomerantz[1]
68. Streiff, Zimmerman, Soule, Butt, Sedlak, Willingham, and Rossini[1]
69. Tuot[3]
70. Horney[1]

SPECIFIC REFERENCES
FOR TABLES 11a (PART 1), 11a-E (PART 1), AND 11b (PART 1)
May 31, 1947; September 30, 1951; October 31, 1952

| Compound | REFERENCES FOR | | | | |
|---|---|---|---|---|---|
| | Boiling Point | Refractive Index | Density | Freezing Point | Refractive Dispersion |
| Propadiene (Allene) | 1,2,3,4 | | | 1,4 | |
| 1,2-Butadiene | 5,34,39 | | 5,33 | 6,39 | |
| 1,3-Butadiene | 1,2,7,10,11,28,38,40 | | 7,10,12,18 | 1,6,10,13,36,37,38,41 | |
| 1,2-Pentadiene | 14,35 | 14,35 | 14,35 | 36 | 14,35 |
| 1,cis-3-Pentadiene | 8,9,15,16,17,19,35 | 8,9,15,16,19,20,35 | 8,9,16,19,20,35 | 36 | 9,35 |
| 1,trans-3-Pentadiene | 8,9,15,16,35 | 8,9,15,16,20,35 | 8,9,16,20,35 | 15,36 | 9,35 |
| 1,4-Pentadiene | 1,2,21,22,23,35 | 21,22,33,35 | 21,22,23,33,35 | 1,24,36 | 33,35 |
| 2,3-Pentadiene | 35 | 35 | 33,35 | 36 | 35 |
| 3-Methyl-1,2-butadiene | 25 | 25,33 | 25,33 | | |
| 2-Methyl-1,3-butadiene (Isoprene) | 9,26,27,28,29,35 | 9,26,29,30,35 | 9,26,29,31,35 | 26,29,36,37 | 9,26,29,35 |

REFERENCES

1. Kistiakowsky, Ruhoff, Smith, and Vaughan[3]
2. Lamb and Roper[1]
3. Livingston and Heisig[1]
4. Lespieau and Chavanne[1]
5. Hurd and Meinert[1]
6. Glasgow and Rossini[1]
7. Benoliel[1]
8. Craig[1]
9. Farmer and Warren[1]
10. Meyers, Scott, Brickwedde, and Rands[1]
11. Prevost[3]
12. Cragoe[1]
13. Garner, Adams, and Stuchell[1]
14. Bouis[1]
15. Dolliver, Gresham, Kistiakowsky, and Vaughan[1]
16. Prevost[1]
17. Mulliken, Wakeman, and Gerry[1]
18. Buck[1]
19. Harries and Duvel[1]
20. Ward[1]
21. Shoemaker and Boord[1]
22. Kogerman[1]
23. Dykstra, Lewis, and Boord[1]
24. Parks, Todd, and Shomate[1]
25. von Auwers[1]
26. Bekkedahl, Wood, and Wojciechowski[1]
27. Whitby and Crozier[1]
28. Heisig[1]
29. Enklaar[1]
30. Glazebrook[1]
31. Forziati and Rossini[1]
32. von Auwers and Westerman[1]
33. American Petroleum Institute Research Project 44[1]
34. Streiff, Murphy, Cahill, Soule, Sedlak, Willingham, and Rossini[1]
35. Forziati, Camin and Rossini[2]
36. Streiff, Soule, Kennedy, Janes, Sedlak, Willingham, and Rossini[1]
37. Glasgow, Krouskop, Beadle, Axilrod, and Rossini[1]
38. Scott, Meyers, Rands, Brickwedde, and Bekkedahl[1]
39. Aston and Szasz[1]
40. Meyers, Scott, Brickwedde, and Vaughan[1]
41. Streiff, Murphy, Zimmerman, Soule, Sedlak, Willingham, and Rossini[1]

| | SPECIFIC REFERENCES | | | | |
|---|---|---|---|---|---|
| | FOR TABLES 11a (PART 2), 11a-E (PART 2), AND 11b (PART 2) | | | | |
| | May 31, 1947; October 31, 1952 | | | | |
| Compound | REFERENCES FOR | | | | |
| | Boiling Point | Refractive Index | Density | Freezing Point | Refractive Dispersion |
| 1,2-Hexadiene | 1,27 | 1,27 | 1,27 | | 1 |
| 1,cis-3-Hexadiene | 2,3,4,28,29 | 2,3,4,28,29 | 2,3,4,29 | | 2,26 |
| 1,trans-3-Hexadiene | | | | | |
| 1,cis-4-Hexadiene | 4,5,29,30,31 | 4,5,29,30,31 | 4,5,29,30,31 | | |
| 1,trans-4-Hexadiene | | | | | |
| 1,5-Hexadiene | 6,7,8,9,10,32,34,35 | 7,9,32,35,36 | 7,9,10,35,36 | 6,7,43 | |
| 2,3-Hexadiene | 11 | 11 | 11 | 11 | |
| cis-2,cis-4-Hexadiene | 3,4,12,13,14,15,16,17,28,29,35,36,37 | 3,4,12,13,14,15,16,17,28,29,35,36 | 3,4,12,13,14,15,16,17,29,35,36 | | 13,14,26 |
| cis-2,trans-4-Hexadiene | | | | | |
| trans-2,trans-4-Hexadiene | | | | | |
| 3-Methyl-1,2-pentadiene | 26 | 26 | 26 | | |
| 4-Methyl-1,2-pentadiene | 1 | 1 | 1 | | 1 |
| 2-Methyl-1,cis-3-pentadiene | 2,12,13,14 | 2,12,13,14 | 2,12,13,14 | | 2,13,14,26 |
| 2-Methyl-1,trans-3-pentadiene | | | | | |
| 3-Methyl-1,cis-3-pentadiene | 12,13,18,38,39 | 12,13,18,39 | 12,13 | | 13,26 |
| 3-Methyl-1,trans-3-pentadiene | | | | | |
| 4-Methyl-1,3-pentadiene | 12,13,19,20 | 12,13,19,20 | 12,13,19,20 | | 13,26 |
| 2-Methyl-1,4-pentadiene | 19 | 19,26 | 19,26 | | |
| 3-Methyl-1,4-pentadiene | 26 | 26 | 26 | | |
| 2-Methyl-2,3-pentadiene | 26 | 26 | 26 | | |
| 2-Ethyl-1,3-butadiene | 21,26,40,41 | 26,41 | 26,41 | | 26 |
| 2,3-Dimethyl-1,3-butadiene | 8,12,13,14,22,23,24,25,32,42 | 12,13,14,22,25,28,32,42 | 12,13,14,25,42 | 14,22,43 | 13,14,26 |

## REFERENCES

1. Bouis[1]
2. van Keersbilck[1]
3. Henne and Turk[1]
4. Prevost[2]
5. Shoemaker and Boord[1]
6. Kistiakowsky, Ruhoff, Smith, and Vaughan[3]
7. Cortese[1]
8. Winstein and Lucas[1]
9. Henne, Chanan, and Turk[1]
10. Merling[1]
11. van Risseghem[9]
12. Whitby and Gallay[1]
13. Farmer and Warren[1]
14. Enklaar[1]
15. Prevost[1]
16. van Pelt and Wibaut[1]
17. Henne and Chanan[1]
18. Fisher and Chittenden[1]
19. Wiest[1]
20. Bachman and Goebel[1]
21. Pariselle and Simon[1]
22. Dolliver, Gresham, Kistiakowsky and Vaughan[1]
23. Allen and Bell[1]
24. Birch, Fidler and Lowry[1]
25. Lebedev[1]
26. American Petroleum Institute Research Project 44[1]
27. Hennion and Sheehan[1]
28. Braun, Spooner, and Fenske[1]
29. Paul and Tchelitcheff[1]
30. Riobe[1]
31. Riobe[2]
32. American Petroleum Institute Research Project 6[1]
33. Boord, Henne, Greenlee, Perilstein, and Derfer[1]
34. Bateman and Koch[1]
35. Tatevskii, Treshchova, Skvarchenko, and Levina[1]
36. Plate and Batuev[1]
37. Prevost[5]
38. Nazarov, Azerbaev, and Rakcheeva[1]
39. Marvel and Williams[2]

SPECIFIC REFERENCES

FOR TABLES 11a (PART 2), 11a–E (PART 2), AND 11b (PART 2) (Continued)

May 31, 1947; October 31, 1952

REFERENCES

40. Zalmanovitch[1]
41. Marvel, Myers, and Saunders[1]
42. Howard, Mears, Fookson, Pomerantz, and Brooks[2]
43. Streiff, Soule, Kennedy, Janes, Sedlak, Willingham, and Rossini[1]

# SPECIFIC REFERENCES
## FOR TABLES 18a, 18a-E AND 18b
### October 31, 1950; October 31, 1952

| Compound | REFERENCES FOR | | | | |
|---|---|---|---|---|---|
| | Boiling Point | Refractive Index | Density | Freezing Point | Refractive Dispersion |
| Cyclopentene | 1,2,3,4,5,6,7,8,9,10,14 | 1,2,3,4,5,6,8,9,10,11,12,13,14 | 2,3,4,5,6,8,9,10,11,12,14 | 1,6,15 | 6,10,14 |
| 1-Methylcyclopentene | 4,16,17,18,19,20,21,22,23,24,42 | 4,11,12,13,14,18,19,20,21,22,23,24,25,42 | 4,11,16,18,19,20,22,23,24,42 | 23,42 | 19 |
| 3-Methylcyclopentene | 4,18,21,22,24,26,27,28,29,30,31 | 4,18,21,22,24,26,27,28,29,30,31 | 4,18,24,26,27,28,29,30,31 | | 29 |
| 4-Methylcyclopentene | 4,18,24,27 | 18,24,27 | 4,18,24,27 | | |
| 1-Ethylcyclopentene | 13,22,32,33,34,35 | 13,22,32,33,34,35 | 13,32,33,34,35 | 13,32 | 32 |
| 3-Ethylcyclopentene | 22,31 | 22,31 | 22,31 | | |
| 4-Ethylcyclopentene | 41 | 41 | 41 | | |
| 1,2-Dimethylcyclopentene | 2,22,33,36,37,38,39 | 2,19,22,33,36,37,38,39 | 2,19,33,36,37,38,39 | 2,38,40 | 38 |
| 1,3-Dimethylcyclopentene | 41 | 41 | 41 | | |
| 1,4-Dimethylcyclopentene | 41,43 | 41,43 | 41 | | |
| 1,5-Dimethylcyclopentene | 41 | 22,38 | 22,38 | 38,40 | 38 |
| 3,3-Dimethylcyclopentene | 19,33,36 | 33,36 | 33,36 | | |
| 3,*cis*-4-Dimethylcyclopentene | | 21 | 41 | | |
| 3,*trans*-4-Dimethylcyclopentene | | | | | |
| 3,*cis*-5-Dimethylcyclopentene | | | | | |
| 3,*trans*-5-Dimethylcyclopentene | | | | | |
| 4,4-Dimethylcyclopentene | 41 | 41 | 41 | | |

## REFERENCES

1. Dolliver, Gresham, Kistiakowsky, and Vaughan[1]
2. Birch, Fidler and Lowry[1]
3. Carr and Stücklen[1]
4. Mousseron[1]
5. Hückel and Harder[1]
6. American Petroleum Institute Research Project 6[1]
7. Meiser[1]
8. Harries and Tank[1]
9. Philipov[1]
10. von Auwers[5]
11. Godchot and Cauquil[2]
12. Godchot[1]
13. American Petroleum Institute Research Project 45[1]
14. Vogel[1]
15. Huffman and others[1]
16. Markownikov[1]
17. Markownikov[2]
18. Zelinskii[2]
19. Chavanne and de Vogel[1]
20. Tatevosyan, Melikyan, and Terzyan[1]
21. Fenske, Braun, Wiegand, Quiggle, McCormick, and Rank[1]
22. Adkins and Roebuck[1]
23. Boord, Henne, Greenlee, Perilstein, and Derfer[1]
24. Cook[1]
25. Lutz, Bearse, Leonard, and Cronton[1]
26. Semmler[1]
27. Godchot, Mousseron, and Richaud[1]
28. von Braun, Kamp, and Kopp[1]
29. Vogel[1]
30. Crane[1]
31. Crane, Boord, and Henne[1]
32. Chavanne and Becker[1]
33. von Auwers and Moosbrugger[1]
34. Wallach and Martius[1]
35. Hückel, Kumetat, and Severin[1]
36. Kishner[4]
37. Chavanne[2]

SPECIFIC REFERENCES
FOR TABLES 18a, 18a-E AND 18b (Continued)
October 31, 1950; October 31, 1952

REFERENCES

38. Chiurdoglu[1]
39. Turova-Pollak and Vsevolozhskaya[1]
40. Timmermans[4]
41. American Petroleum Institute Research Project 44[1]
42. Timmermans and Hennaut-Roland[4]
43. Braun, Spooner, and Fenske[1]

820

| | SPECIFIC REFERENCES | | | | |
|---|---|---|---|---|---|
| | FOR TABLES 19a, 19a–E, AND 19b | | | | |
| | October 31, 1950 | | | | |
| Compound | REFERENCES FOR | | | | |
| | Boiling Point | Refractive Index | Density | Freezing Point | Refractive Dispersion |
| Cyclohexene | 1,2,3,4,5,6,7,8,9,10 | 1,2,3,5,6,7,8,10,11,12,13,14 | 1,3,4,6,8,14,15 | 8,12,16,17,61 | 1,8,10 |
| 1-Methylcyclohexene | 1,2,6,9,18,19 | 1,2,12,14,18,19,20,21 | 1,2,14,19 | 19 | 1,21 |
| 3-Methylcyclohexene | 9,22,23 | 9,20,22,23,24 | 9,22,23,24 | | |
| 4-Methylcyclohexene | 9,12,24,25,26 | 9,12,20,24,26,27 | 12,24,25,27,28,29,30,31,32,33 | 12 | |
| 1-Ethylcyclohexene | 2,18,34,35,36,37 | 2,18,34,35,36 | 2,34,35,36 | | 34 |
| 3-Ethylcyclohexene | 22,23 | 22,23 | 22,23 | | |
| 4-Ethylcyclohexene | 60 | 60 | 60 | | |
| 1,2-Dimethylcyclohexene | 36,38,39,40,41,42 | 36,39,40,41,42,43,44 | 36,38,39,40,41,42,44 | | 43,44 |
| 1,3-Dimethylcyclohexene | 38,43,45,46,47 | 43,45,46,47 | 38,43,45,46,47 | | 43 |
| 1,4-Dimethylcyclohexene | 2,31,38,39,40,43,44,47,48,49,50 | 2,27,31,33,38,39,40,43,44,47,49,50,51 | 2,27,31,33,38,39,40,43,44,48,49,51 | 43,59 | 43,44 |
| 1,5-Dimethylcyclohexene | 2,36,40,44,46,52 | 2,36,44,46 | 2,36,40,44,46 | | 44 |
| 1,6-Dimethylcyclohexene | 60 | 60 | 60 | | |
| 3,3-Dimethylcyclohexene | 53,54 | 53,54 | 53,54 | | |
| 3,cis-4-Dimethylcyclohexene | | | | | |
| 3,trans-4-Dimethylcyclohexene | | | | | |
| 3,cis-5-Dimethylcyclohexene | | | | | |
| 3,trans-5-Dimethylcyclohexene | | | | | |
| 3,cis-6-Dimethylcyclohexene | | | | | |
| 3,trans-6-Dimethylcyclohexene | | | | | |
| 4,4-Dimethylcyclohexene | 53,55,56,57,58 | 53,55,57,58 | 53,55,56,57,58 | 58 | 55 |
| 4,cis-5-Dimethylcyclohexene | | | | | |
| 4,trans-5-Dimethylcyclohexene | | | | | |

REFERENCES

1. Vogel[1]
2. Kazanskii and Glushner[1]
3. Carr and Stücklen[1]
4. Friend and Hargreaves[2]
5. Shell Development Company[1]
6. Hückel and Harder[1]
7. University of Chicago[1]
8. American Petroleum Institute Research Project 6[1]
9. Adkins and Roebuck[1]
10. Waterman and van Westen[1]
11. Herington[1]
12. American Petroleum Institute Research Project 45[1]

13. Fenske, Braun, Wiegand, Quiggle, McCormick and Rank[1]
14. Adkins and Roebuck[1]
15. American Petroleum Institute Research Project 42[1]
16. Huffman and others[1]
17. Nametkin[1]
18. Rice and Murphy[1]
19. Boord, Henne, Greenlee, Perilstein, and Derfer[1]
20. University of Minnesota[1]
21. von Auwers and Ellinger[1]
22. Berlande[1]
23. Berlande[2]

24. Godchot, Mousseron, and Granger[1]
25. Midgley and Henne[2]
26. Birch[1]
27. Godchot[1]
28. Markownikov[4]
29. Markownikov[5]
30. Eykman[7]
31. Nametkin and Bruessoff[1]
32. Zelinskii[3]
33. Godchot and Cauquil[2]
34. von Auwers and Ellinger[1]
35. Wallach and Mendelsohn–Bartholdy[1]
36. Signaigo and Cramer[1]
37. Bergman and Bergman[1]
38. Sabatier and Mailhe[2]

SPECIFIC REFERENCES

FOR TABLES 19a, 19a–E, AND 19b (Continued)

October 31, 1950

| REFERENCES |
|---|

39. Zelinskii and Gorskii[1]

40. Wallach[2]

41. Meerwein[1]

42. Meerwein and Fleischhauer[1]

43. Chiurdoglu[3]

44. von Auwers, Hinterseber, and Treppman[1]

45. Ruzicka, Koolhaas, and Wind[1]

46. Mousseron and Paulet[1]

47. Mousseron, Richaud, and Granger[1]

48. Sabatier and Mailhe[4]

49. Zelinskii and Pavlov[1]

50. Mousseron, Winternitz, and Jacquier[1]

51. Zelinskii and Gorskii[2]

52. Subov[1]

53. Zelinskii, Pockindorff and Khokhlova[1]

54. Chavanne, Miller, and Cornet[1]

55. Crossley and Renouf[2]

56. von Auwers and Lange[1]

57. Hibbit and Linstead[1]

58. Evans, G. L.[1]

59. Timmermans[4]

60. American Petroleum Institute Research
    Project 44[1]

61. Streiff, Zimmerman, Soule, Butt, Sedlak,
    Willingham, and Rossini[1]

| | SPECIFIC REFERENCES FOR TABLES 25a (PART 1), 25a-E (PART 1), AND 25b (PART 1) April 30, 1949; September 30, 1951; October 31, 1952 | | | | |
|---|---|---|---|---|---|
| Compound | REFERENCES FOR | | | | |
| | Boiling Point | Refractive Index | Density | Freezing Point | Refractive Dispersion |
| Ethyne (Acetylene) | 1,3 | | | 1,4 | |
| Propyne (Methylacetylene) | 1,5,6,7,8,9,10,11,12 | | | 1,5,6,8 | |
| 1-Butyne (Ethylacetylene) | 1,6,11,12,13,14,15,20,21 | | 1,15 | 1,6,14,15,48 | |
| 1-Pentyne | 2,6,11,16,17,18,19,26 | 6,11,16,19,26 | 2,6,11,16,17,19,26 | 2,6,18,19,26 | 38 |
| 1-Hexyne | 6,22,23,24,25,26,27,28,29 | 6,23,24,26,42 | 6,22,23,24,26 | 6,22,23,26 | 22,23,42 |
| 1-Heptyne | 6,23,24,26,28,31,32,35,36,37,39,51 | 23,24,26,35,36,39,51 | 6,23,24,26,30,34,35,39 | 6,23,26,35 | 23,36,39 |
| 1-Octyne | 6,23,26,28,36,37,39,40,41,50 | 6,23,26,35,36,39,40,41,50,51 | 6,23,26,35,39,40 | 6,23,26,30,35,40 | 23,36,39 |
| 1-Nonyne | 28,36,38 | 36,38,51 | 30,36,38 | 30,38 | 38 |
| 1-Decyne | 30,38,51 | 36,38,51 | 30,31,36,38 | 30,31 | 38 |
| 1-Undecyne | 30,32,38,43 | 38 | 30,38 | 30,38 | 38 |
| 1-Dodecyne | 38 | 38,45 | 38,45 | 38 | 38 |
| 1-Tridecyne | 38 | 38,51 | 38 | 38,51 | 38 |
| 1-Tetradecyne | 38 | 38 | 38 | 38 | 38 |
| 1-Pentadecyne | 38 | 38,46,51 | 38,46 | 38,51 | 38 |
| 1-Hexadecyne | 38 | 38,51 | 47 | 37,47,51 | 38 |
| 1-Heptadecyne | 38 | 38 | 38 | 38 | 38 |
| 1-Octadecyne | 38 | 38,51 | 38,47 | 31,33,47,51 | 38 |
| 1-Nonadecyne | 38 | 38 | 38 | 38,49 | 38 |
| 1-Eicosyne | 38,44 | 38 | 38,44 | 38 | 38 |

REFERENCES

1. Morehouse and Maass[1]
2. Morehouse and Maass[2]
3. Burrell and Robertson[1]
4. Maass and Russell[1]
5. Conn, Kistiakowsky, and Smith[1]
6. American Petroleum Institute Research Project 45[1]
7. Meinert and Hurd[1]
8. Lespieau and Chavanne[1]
9. Heisig and Hurd[1]
10. Heisig[1]
11. Krieger and Wenzke[1]
12. Lamb and Roper[1]
13. Hurd and Meinert[1]
14. Picon[1]

15. Dupont[1]
16. Bouis[1]
17. Picon[2]
18. Bourguel[1]
19. Greenlee[1]
20. American Petroleum Institute Research Project 6[1]
21. Aston, Mastrangelo, and Moessen[1]
22. Van Risseghem[6]
23. Campbell and Eby[2]
24. Campbell and O'Connor[1]
25. Welt[1]
26. Henne and Greenlee[2]
27. Lebeau and Picon[1]
28. Bourguel[3]

29. Grignard, Lapayre, and Tchéou Faki[1]
30. Noerdlinger[1]
31. Picon[3]
32. Meunier and Desparmet[1]
33. Meyer and Streuli[1]
34. Prevost[4]
35. Landrieu and Baylocq[1]
36. Truchet[1]
37. Mulliken, Wakeman, and Gerry[1]
38. American Petroleum Institute Research Project 44[1]
39. Moureu[1]
40. Cleveland[1]
41. University of Chicago[1]
42. Straus and Kuehnel[1]

SPECIFIC REFERENCES
FOR TABLES 25a (PART 1), 25a–E (PART 1), AND 25b (PART 1) (Continued)

April 30, 1949; September 30, 1951; October 31 1952

| REFERENCES | | |
|---|---|---|
| 43. Bruylants[1] | | |
| 44. Lippman and Hawliczk[1] | | |
| 45. Vaughn[1] | | |
| 46. Ryden, Glavis, and Marvel[1] | | |
| 47. Krafft and Reuter[1] | | |
| 48. Streiff, Zimmerman, Soule, Butt, Sedlak, Willingham, and Rossini[1] | | |
| 49. Coffman, Chien–Yu Tsao, Schniepp, and Marvel[1] | | |
| 50. Mulliken[1] | | |
| 51. Elsner and Paul[1] | | |

| | REFERENCES FOR | | | | |
|---|---|---|---|---|---|
| Compound | Boiling Point | Refractive Index | Density | Freezing Point | Refractive Dispersion |
| 1-Heneicosyne | 1 | 1 | 1 | 1 | 1 |
| 1-Docosyne | 1 | 1 | 1 | 1 | 1 |
| 1-Tricosyne | 1 | 1 | 1 | 1 | 1 |
| 1-Tetracosyne | 1 | 1 | 1 | 1 | 1 |
| 1-Pentacosyne | 1 | 1 | 1 | 1 | 1 |
| 1-Hexacosyne | 1 | 1 | 1 | 1 | 1 |
| 1-Heptacosyne | 1 | 1 | 1 | 1 | 1 |
| 1-Octacosyne | 1 | 1 | 1 | 1 | 1 |
| 1-Nonacosyne | 1 | 1 | 1 | 1 | 1 |
| 1-Triacontyne | 1 | 1 | 1 | 1 | 1 |
| 1-Hentriacontyne | 1 | 1 | 1 | 1 | 1 |
| 1-Dotriacontyne | 1 | 1 | 1 | 1 | 1 |
| 1-Tritriacontyne | 1 | 1 | 1 | 1 | 1 |
| 1-Tetratriacontyne | 1 | 1 | 1 | 1 | 1 |
| 1-Pentatriacontyne | 1 | 1 | 1 | 1 | 1 |
| 1-Hexatriacontyne | 1 | 1 | 1 | 1 | 1 |
| 1-Heptatriacontyne | 1 | 1 | 1 | 1 | 1 |
| 1-Octatriacontyne | 1 | 1 | 1 | 1 | 1 |
| 1-Nonatriacontyne | 1 | 1 | 1 | 1 | 1 |
| 1-Tetracontyne | 1 | 1 | 1 | 1 | 1 |

SPECIFIC REFERENCES FOR TABLES 25a (PART 2), 25a-E (PART 2), AND 25b (PART 2). September 30, 1951

REFERENCES

1. American Petroleum Institute Research Project 44[1]

| Compound | REFERENCES FOR | | | | |
|---|---|---|---|---|---|
| | Boiling Point | Refractive Index | Density | Freezing Point | Refractive Dispersion |
| Ethyne (Acetylene) | 1 | | | 1 | |
| Propyne (Methylacetylene) | 1 | | | 1 | |
| 1-Butyne (Ethylacetylene) | 1 | | 1 | 1 | |
| 2-Butyne (Dimethylacetylene) | 6,7,8,10,11,13,14 | 6,10 | 6,7,10 | 6,7,10,12,15 | |
| 1-Pentyne | 1 | 1 | 1 | 1 | |
| 2-Pentyne | 3,4,5,6 | 3,4,5,6 | 4,5,6 | 4,6 | |
| 3-Methyl-1-butyne | 2,9 | 2,9 | 2 | 9 | |

**SPECIFIC REFERENCES**

FOR TABLES 12a, 12a-E, AND 12b

May 31, 1947; October 31, 1950; October 31, 1952

REFERENCES

1. See references for Tables 25a (Part 1), 25a-E (Part 1), and 25b (Part 1).
2. Gredy[2]
3. Greenlee[1]
4. van Ressighem[1]
5. Sherrill and Launspach[1]
6. Henne and Greenlee[1]
7. Morehouse and Maass[1]
8. Wislicenus[1]
9. American Petroleum Institute Research Project 45[1]
10. Heisig and Davis[1]
11. Heisig[1]
12. Yost, Osborne and Garner[1]
13. Conn, Kistiakowsky, and Smith[1]
14. American Petroleum Institute Research Project 6[1]
15. Streiff, Murphy, Zimmerman, Soule, Sedlak, Willingham, and Rossini[1]

| SPECIFIC REFERENCES<br>FOR TABLES 21a (PART 1), 21a-E (PART 1), AND 21b (PART 1)<br>June 30, 1948; September 30, 1951; (Corrected) | | | | | |
|---|---|---|---|---|---|
| | **REFERENCES FOR** | | | | |
| Compound | Boiling Point | Refractive Index | Density | Freezing Point | Refractive Dispersion |
| Benzene | 3,4,7,8,9,11,12, 13,14,15,16,18, 35,64,65,70 | 1,4,6,7,8,9,13,15, 16,17,18,35,64,68, 80 | 1,4,5,8,9,18,19, 35,64,75,76,77,78 | 2,4,7,8,13,35,64, 69 | 1,6,30,32,68 |
| Methylbenzene (Toluene) | 3,7,8,9,12,16,20, 35,70 | 1,4,7,8,9,16,17, 33,35,68 | 1,4,5,8,9,19,21, 33,35,75,79 | 2,4,7,8,22,35,69 | 1,26,30,32,33,68 |
| Ethylbenzene | 3,4,8,9,16,20,23, 24,35,70 | 1,4,6,8,9,16,17, 23,24,35,40,68, 73,74,81 | 1,4,5,8,9,19,23, 24,35,75,81 | 2,4,8,23,24,31,35, 69 | 1,6,30,32,34,40, 68,73 |
| n-Propylbenzene | 3,4,9,16,25,27, 35,70 | 4,6,9,16,17,25, 27,29,35,40,68, 73,74,81 | 1,4,5,8,9,19,25, 27,29,35,75,81 | 2,4,25,28,29,35 | 1,6,30,34,68 |
| n-Butylbenzene | 1,4,16,36,37,38, 70 | 1,4,16,36,37,39, 40,41,42,68,73,81 | 1,4,19,37,41,42, 75 | 2,4,36,37,38,69 | 1,68,73 |
| n-Pentylbenzene | 10,16,43,46,47, 52,58,66,81 | 10,16,42,43,44, 46,47,50,52,73,74 | 10,42,43,44,46, 47,50,52,58,66 | 10,43 | 10,43,52,73 |
| n-Hexylbenzene | 10,16,43,44,45, 49,58,81 | 10,16,42,43,44, 45,49,51,73,81 | 10,42,43,45,49,58 | 10,43 | 10,43,73 |
| n-Heptylbenzene | 10,49,58,60,62 | 10,42,48,49,50, 62 | 10,42,45,49,50, 58,62 | 10 | 10,48 |
| n-Octylbenzene | 10,48,56 | 10,42,46,48,56, 59,67 | 10,42,46,56,59, 67 | 10,54,56,67 | 10,48 |
| n-Nonylbenzene | 10,16,44,53,57,58 | 10,16,44,50,53 | 10,50,58 | 10 | 10 |
| n-Decylbenzene | 10 | 10,69 | 10,69 | 10,69 | 10,69 |
| n-Undecylbenzene | 10,53 | 10 | 10 | 10 | 10 |
| n-Dodecylbenzene | 10 | 10,42,49,50,55,72 | 10,42,49,50,55 | 10,50,55 | 10 |
| n-Tridecylbenzene | 10 | 10 | 10 | 10 | 10 |
| n-Tetradecylbenzene | 10 | 10,42,49 | 10,42,49,50 | 10 | 10 |
| n-Pentadecylbenzene | 10 | 10 | 10 | 10 | 10 |
| n-Hexadecylbenzene | 10 | 10,42,48,49,61 | 10,42,49,52,61,63 | 10,52,61,63,71 | 10,48,52,61 |

**REFERENCES**

1. Forziati and Rossini[1]
2. Glasgow, Murphy, Willingham, and Rossini[1]
3. Willingham, Taylor, Pignocco, and Rossini[1]
4. Birch, Fidler, and Lowry[1]
5. Geist and Cannon[1]
6. Garrett[1]
7. Smittenberg, Hoog, and Henkes[1]
8. Timmermans and Martin[1]
9. Forziati, Glasgow, Willingham, and Rossini[1]
10. American Petroleum Institute Research Project 44[1]
11. Smith, E.R.[1]
12. Zmaczynski[1]
13. Kistiakowsky, Ruhoff, Smith, and Vaughan[1]
14. Scatchard, Wood, and Mochel[1]
15. Griswold, van Berg, and Kasch[1]
16. Smith and Pennekamp[1]
17. von Auwers and Kolligs[1]
18. Griswold and Ludwig[1]
19. Massart[1]
20. de la Mare and Robertson[1]
21. Burlew[1]
22. Mair, Glasgow, and Rossini[1]
23. White and Rose[2]
24. Hammond and McArdle[1]
25. Timmermans and Hennaut-Roland[1]
26. Timmermans and Martin[2]
27. McKenna and Sowa[1]
28. Streiff, Murphy, Sedlak, Willingham, and Rossini[1]
29. Hirschler and Faulconer[1]
30. von Auwers[2]
31. Guthrie, Spitzer, and Huffman[1]
32. Grosse and Wackher[1]
33. Tilton[1]
34. Cotton and Mouton[1]
35. Gibbons, Thompson, Reynolds, Wright, Chanan, Lamberti, Hipsher, and Karabinos[1]
36. Streiff, Murphy, Cahill, Flanagan, Sedlak, Willingham, and Rossini[1]

SPECIFIC REFERENCES

FOR TABLES 21a (PART 1), 21a–E (PART 1), AND 21b (PART 1) (Continued)
June 30, 1948; September 30, 1951 (Corrected)

| REFERENCES | | |
|---|---|---|
| 37. American Petroleum Institute Research Project 45[1] | | |
| 38. Huffman, Parks, and Barmore[1] | | |
| 39. Turner and Lesslie[1] | | |
| 40. Calingaert[1] | | |
| 41. Hennion and Auspos[1] | | |
| 42. Schmidt, Hopp, and Schoeller[1] | | |
| 43. Simon[1] | | |
| 44. Smith and Pennekamp[2] | | |
| 45. Denisenko[1] | | |
| 46. D'yakowa and Lozovoi[1] | | |
| 47. Ipatieff and Schmerling[1] | | |
| 48. Eisenlohr and Schulz[1] | | |
| 49. Gilman and Meals[1] | | |
| 50. Ju, Shen, and Wood[1] | | |
| 51. Kimel and Cope[1] | | |
| 52. Larsen, Thorpe, and Armfield[1] | | |
| 53. Morton, Davidson, and Best[1] | | |
| 54. Paquette, Lingafelter, and Tartar[1] | | |
| 55. Petrov and Lapteva[1] | | |
| 56. Petrov, Lapteva, and Pchelinka[1] | | |
| 57. Sabatier and Mailhe[1] | | |
| 58. Shen, Wood, and Garner[1] | | |
| 59. Waterman, Leendertse, and van Krevelan[1] | | |
| 60. Waygand and Mensdorf[1] | | |
| 61. Wibaut, Overhoff, and Jonker[1] | | |
| 62. Braun and Deutsch[1] | | |
| 63. Krafft and Göttig[1] | | |
| 64. Wojciechowski[2] | | |
| 65. Swietoslowski and Usakiewicj[1] | | |
| 66. Buehler, Gardner, and Clemens[1] | | |
| 67. Schiessler, Herr, Rytina, Weisel, Fischl, McLaughlin, and Kuehner[1] | | |
| 68. Forziati[1] | | |
| 69. American Petroleum Institute Research Project 6[1] | | |
| 70. Forziati, Norris, and Rossini[1] | | |
| 71. Krafft[3] | | |
| 72. Schmidt and Grosser[1] | | |
| 73. Vogel[3] | | |
| 74. Maman[1] | | |
| 75. Forziati and Rossini[2] | | |
| 76. Young[2] | | |
| 77. Pesca[1] | | |
| 78. Cohen and Buij[1] | | |
| 79. Mason and Washburn[1] | | |
| 80. Tilicheev, Peshkov, and Yuganova[2] | | |
| 81. Bryce-Smith and Turner[1] | | |

828

| | REFERENCES FOR | | | | |
|---|---|---|---|---|---|
| Compound | Boiling Point | Refractive Index | Density | Freezing Point | Refractive Dispersion |
| n-Heptadecylbenzene | 1 | 1 | 1 | 1 | 1 |
| n-Octadecylbenzene | 1 | 1 | 1 | 1,2,3,4 | 1 |
| n-Nonadecylbenzene | 1 | 1 | 1 | 1 | 1 |
| n-Eicosylbenzene | 1 | 1 | 1 | 1,5,6 | 1 |
| n-Heneicosylbenzene | 1 | 1 | 1 | 1 | 1 |
| n-Docosylbenzene | 1 | 1 | 1 | 1 | 1 |
| n-Tricosylbenzene | 1 | 1 | 1 | 1 | 1 |
| n-Tetracosylbenzene | 1 | 1 | 1 | 1 | 1 |
| n-Pentacosylbenzene | 1 | 1 | 1 | 1 | 1 |
| n-Hexacosylbenzene | 1 | 1 | 1 | 1 | 1 |
| n-Heptacosylbenzene | 1 | 1 | 1 | 1 | 1 |
| n-Octacosylbenzene | 1 | 1 | 1 | 1 | 1 |
| n-Nonacosylbenzene | 1 | 1 | 1 | 1 | 1 |
| n-Triacontylbenzene | 1 | 1 | 1 | 1 | 1 |
| n-Hentriacontylbenzene | 1 | 1 | 1 | 1 | 1 |
| n-Dotriacontylbenzene | 1 | 1 | 1 | 1 | 1 |
| n-Tritriacontylbenzene | 1 | 1 | 1 | 1 | 1 |
| n-Tetratriacontylbenzene | 1 | 1 | 1 | 1 | 1 |
| n-Pentatriacontylbenzene | 1 | 1 | 1 | 1 | 1 |
| n-Hexatriacontylbenzene | 1 | 1 | 1 | 1 | 1 |

SPECIFIC REFERENCES
FOR TABLES 21a (PART 2), 21a-E (PART 2) AND 21b (PART 2)
September 30, 1951

REFERENCES

1. American Petroleum Institute Research Project 44[1]
2. Krafft[3]
3. Larsen, Thorpe, and Armfield[1]
4. Laidler and Szayma[1]
5. Sherk, Augur, and Soffer[1]
6. American Petroleum Institute Research Project 42[1]

SPECIFIC REFERENCES
FOR TABLES 5a, 5a–E, AND 5b
May 31, 1947; October 31, 1950 (Corrected)

| Compound | REFERENCES FOR | | | | |
|---|---|---|---|---|---|
| | Boiling Point | Refractive Index | Density | Freezing Point | Refractive Dispersion |
| Benzene | 1 | 1 | 1 | 1 | 1 |
| Methylbenzene (Toluene) | 1 | 1 | 1 | 1 | 1 |
| Ethylbenzene | 1 | 1 | 1 | 1 | 1 |
| 1,2-Dimethylbenzene (o-Xylene) | 2,4,5,6,7,8 | 3,7 | 3,7,17 | 15,18 | 3,7 |
| 1,3-Dimethylbenzene (m-Xylene) | 2,4,6,7,12 | 3,7 | 3,7,17 | 15,18,19,26,28,29,30 | 3,7 |
| 1,4-Dimethylbenzene (p-Xylene) | 2,4,6,7,13 | 3,7 | 3,7,9,17 | 4,5,18,19,23,26,28,29,31,32,33 | 3,7 |
| n-Propylbenzene | 1 | 1 | 1 | 1 | 1 |
| Isopropylbenzene | 2,5,6,7,15 | 3,7 | 3,7,17 | 10,11,18,20,21,23 | 3,7 |
| 1-Methyl-2-ethylbenzene | 2,5,7,13 | 3,7 | 3,7,17 | 10,14,19 | 3,7 |
| 1-Methyl-3-ethylbenzene | 2,7,13 | 3,7 | 3,7,17 | 10,14,16,19 | 3,7 |
| 1-Methyl-4-ethylbenzene | 2,7,13 | 3,7 | 3,7,17 | 10,14,19,33 | 3,7 |
| 1,2,3-Trimethylbenzene | 2,5,7,12 | 3,7 | 3,7,17 | 10,14,18,19,22 | 3,7 |
| 1,2,4-Trimethylbenzene | 2,7 | 3,7 | 3,7,17 | 10,14,16,18,19,22,25,27 | 3,7 |
| 1,3,5-Trimethylbenzene | 2,4,5,7,16 | 3,7 | 3,7,17 | 10,14,16,18,19,22 | 3,7 |

REFERENCES

1. See references for Tables 21a (Part 1), 21a–E (Part 1), and 21b (Part 1).
2. Forziati, Norris and Rossini[1]
3. Forziati and Rossini[2]
4. Stuckey and Saylor[1]
5. Fenske, Braun, Wiegand, Quiggle, McCormick and Rank[1]
6. Willingham, Taylor, Pignocco, and Rossini[1]
7. Forziati and Rossini[1]
8. Wojeiechowski[2]
9. Bryce-Smith and Turner[1]
10. Hirschler and Faulconer[1]
11. White and Rose[3]
12. Reynolds, Ebersole, Lamberti, Chanan, and Ordin[1]
13. Boord, Henne, Greenlee, Perilstein and Derfer[1]
14. Streiff, Murphy, Sedlak, Willingham, and Rossini[1]
15. American Petroleum Institute Research Project 6[1]
16. American Petroleum Institute Research Project 45[1]
17. See references for Tables 5d and 5d–E.
18. Glasgow, Murphy, Willingham and Rossini[1]
19. Birch, Fidler, and Lowry[1]
20. Smittenberg, Hoog, and Henkes[1]
21. Trojan[1]
22. Mair and Schicktanz[1]
23. Gibbons, Thompson, Reynolds, Wright, Chanan, Lamberti, Hipsher, and Karabinos[1]
24. Mair, Glasgow, and Rossini[1]
25. Smith and Lund[1]
26. Hammond and McArdle[1]
27. Huffman, Parks, and Barmore[1]
28. White and Rose[1]
29. Pitzer and Scott[2]
30. Timmermans and Hennaut-Roland[1]
31. Chapas[1]
32. Timmermans and Martin[2]
33. Schmidt and Schoeller[1]

| | SPECIFIC REFERENCES | | | | |
|---|---|---|---|---|---|
| | FOR TABLES 14a, 14a-E, AND 14b | | | | |
| | May 31, 1947; April 30, 1952 | | | | |

| Compound | REFERENCES FOR | | | | |
|---|---|---|---|---|---|
| | Boiling Point | Refractive Index | Density | Freezing Point | Refractive Dispersion |
| *n*-Butylbenzene (1-Phenylbutane) | 1 | 1 | 1 | 1 | 1 |
| Isobutylbenzene (1-Phenyl-2-methylpropane) | 2,3,4,5,8,13,14,15, 51,55,57 | 2,4,5,8,10,11,14, 16,51,55,57,60 | 2,4,11,12,14,15,51, 57 | 2,6,51,55,57 | 50,60 |
| *sec*-Butylbenzene (2-Phenylbutane) | 2,3,4,5,13,17,18, 19,51,55,57 | 2,4,5,10,11,17,19, 51,55,57,60 | 2,4,11,12,17,51,57 | 2,6,18,51,55,57 | 50,60 |
| *tert*-Butylbenzene (2-Phenyl-2-methylpropane) | 2,3,4,5,8,13,17,19, 20,21,22,23,24,25, 26,51,57 | 2,4,5,8,10,11,16, 17,19,20,24,25,51, 55,57,60 | 2,4,11,12,17,20,21, 22,24,25,51,57 | 2,6,22,55,57 | 50,60 |
| 1-Methyl-2-propylbenzene | 9,57 | 27,28,57 | 9,28,57 | 57 | 9,50 |
| 1-Methyl-3-propylbenzene | 9,57 | 27,57 | 9,57 | | 9,27,50 |
| 1-Methyl-4-propylbenzene | 3,29,56,57 | 3,27,29,57 | 3,9,29,56,57 | 3,29,57 | 9,27,50 |
| 1-Methyl-2-isopropylbenzene (*o*-Cymene) | 2,3,9,30,54,57,58 | 2,3,9,30,54,57,58, | 2,3,9,30,57 | 2,54,57 | 9,50 |
| 1-Methyl-3-isopropylbenzene (*m*-Cymene) | 2,8,9,31,32,54,57 | 2,8,9,31,32,57,58 | 2,9,31,32,57 | 2,54,57 | 9,50 |
| 1-Methyl-4-isopropylbenzene (*p*-Cymene) | 2,3,7,9,19,26,32, 33,34,35,36,37,38, 51,54,57 | 2,3,9,14,19,26,27, 32,33,34,36,38,39, 51,54,57 | 2,9,14,26,32,33,34, 36,51,57 | 2,7,32,51,54,57 | 9,50 |
| 1,2-Diethylbenzene | 2,3,13,40,52,54, 57 | 2,3,40,52,57,60 | 2,3,12,40,52,57 | 2,52,57,59 | 50,60 |
| 1,3-Diethylbenzene | 2,3,13,41,42,53, 54,57 | 2,3,4,41,42,53,57, 60 | 2,3,12,41,42,53, 57 | 2,3,53,57,59 | 50,60 |
| 1,4-Diethylbenzene | 2,3,13,52,54,57 | 2,3,52,57,60 | 2,3,12,52,57 | 2,3,57,59 | 9,50,60 |
| 1,2-Dimethyl-3-ethylbenzene | 2,3,4,54,57 | 2,3,4,54,57 | 2,3,4,54,57 | 2,3,57 | 50 |
| 1,2-Dimethyl-4-ethylbenzene | 2,4,43,54,57 | 2,4,54,57 | 2,4,43,54,57 | 2,57 | 50 |
| 1,3-Dimethyl-2-ethylbenzene | 2,4,54,57 | 2,4,44,54,57 | 2,4,54,57 | 2,57 | 50 |
| 1,3-Dimethyl-4-ethylbenzene | 2,4,54,57 | 2,4,44,54,57 | 2,4,54,57 | 2,57 | 50 |
| 1,3-Dimethyl-5-ethylbenzene | 2,4,54,57 | 2,4,54,57 | 2,4,54,57 | 2,54,57 | 50 |
| 1,4-Dimethyl-2-ethylbenzene | 2,4,54,57 | 2,4,44,54,57 | 2,4,54,57 | 2,57 | 50 |
| 1,2,3,4-Tetramethylbenzene (Prehnitene) | 45,46,57 | 38,44,46,47 | 46 | 7,46,48 | 9,50 |
| 1,2,3,5-Tetramethylbenzene (Isodurene) | 3,45,54,57 | 3,38,47,57 | 3,57 | 3,7,47,48 | 50 |
| 1,2,4,5-Tetramethylbenzene (Durene) | 45,57 | 50 | 50 | 38,48,49 | 50 |

REFERENCES

1. See references for tables 21a, 21a-E, and 21b.
2. Birch, Fidler, and Lowry[1]
3. American Petroleum Institute Research Project 45[1]
4. Forziati and Rossini[1]
5. Smith and Pennekamp[1]
6. Glasgow, Murphy, Willingham, and Rossini[1]
7. Huffman, Parks, and Barmore[1]
8. Turner and Lesslie[1]
9. von Auwers[2]
10. Calingaert[1]
11. Hennion and Auspos[1]
12. Forziati, Camin, and Rossini[2]
13. Forziati, Norris, and Rossini[1]
14. Perkins[1]
15. Zelinskii and Gaverdovskaya[1]
16. Urry and Kharasch[1]
17. McKenna and Sowa[1]
18. Timmermanns[2]
19. Simon and Hart[1]
20. Grosse and Ipatieff[1]
21. Richards and Shipley[2]
22. Huffman, Parks, and Daniels[1]
23. de la Mare and Robertson[1]
24. Smith, R. A.[1]
25. Huston, Fox, and Binder[1]
26. Hennion and Kurtz[1]
27. von Auwers and Kolligs[1]
28. Kuhn and Deutsch[1]
29. Schmidt and Schoeller[1]
30. Desseigne[1]
31. Lacourt[2]
32. Richter and Wolff[2]
33. Welsh and Hennion[1]
34. Lacourt[1]
35. McVicker, Marsh, and Stewart[1]
36. LeFevre, LeFevre, and Robertson[1]
37. Kobe, Okabe, Ramstad, and Huemmer[1]
38. Smith and Pennekamp[2]
39. Schorger[1]

SPECIFIC REFERENCES
FOR TABLES 14a, 14a-E, AND 14b (Continued)

May 31, 1947; April 30, 1952

| REFERENCES | | |
|---|---|---|
| 40. Fries and Bestian[1]<br>41. Copenhaven and Reid[1]<br>42. Ipatieff, Pines, and Komarsky[1]<br>43. Kruber[1]<br>44. Smith and Kiess[1]<br>45. MacDougall and Smith[1]<br>46. Mair and Streiff[1]<br>47. Smith and Cass[2]<br>48. Smith and MacDougall[1]<br>49. Fuson and McKusick[1]<br>50. American Petroleum Institute Research<br>    Project 44[1]<br>51. Buess, Karabinos, Kunz, and Gibbons[1]<br>52. Karabinos, Serijan, and Gibbons[1]<br>53. Gibbons, Thompson, Reynolds, Wright,<br>    Chanan, Lamberti, Hipsher, and<br>    Karabinos[1]<br>54. American Petroleum Institute Research<br>    Project 6[1]<br>55. Streiff, Murphy, Cahill, Flanagan,<br>    Sedlak, Willingham, and Rossini[1]<br>56. Boord, Henne, Greenlee, Perilstein,<br>    and Derfer[1]<br>57. Birch, Dean, Fidler, and Lowry[1]<br>58. Fenske, Braun, Wiegand, Quiggle,<br>    McCormick, and Rank[1]<br>59. Streiff, Zimmerman, Soule, Butt,<br>    Sedlak, Willingham, and Rossini[1]<br>60. Forziati[1] | | |

832

| | SPECIFIC REFERENCES<br>FOR TABLES 26a, 26a-E, AND 26b<br>April 30, 1952 | | | | |
|---|---|---|---|---|---|
| Compound | REFERENCES FOR | | | | |
| | Boiling Point | Refractive Index | Density | Freezing Point | Refractive Dispersion |
| n–Pentylbenzene | 1 | 1 | 1 | 1 | 1 |
| 2-Phenylpentane | 2,3,4,5,7,8,9,10 | 2,8,11 | 2,3 | | 2 |
| 3-Phenylpentane | 2,3,4,11 | 2,3 | 2,3 | | 2 |
| 1-Phenyl-2-methylbutane | 2,3 | 2,3,10,27,28,29,30.31 | 2,3,27,28,29,30,31,43,44 | | 2 |
| 1-Phenyl-3-methylbutane | 2,3,8,12,13,14 | 2,3,8,12,13,24 | 2,8,12,14,45 | | |
| 2-Phenyl-2-methylbutane | 2,15 | 2,15,25 | 2,15,46,47,48 | | 2,51 |
| 2-Phenyl-3-methylbutane | 2,3,8,9,16 | 2,3,8,16,32 | 2,3,8,16,32 | | 2 |
| 1-Phenyl-2,2-dimethylpropane | 2,3,8 | 2,3,8 | 2,3,8 | | |
| 1-Methyl-2-n-butylbenzene | 2 | 2,26,33 | 2,26 | | |
| 1-Methyl-3-n-butylbenzene | 2 | 2,26 | 2,26 | | |
| 1-Methyl-4-n-butylbenzene | 2 | 2,26,33,34,35,36 | 2,26,34,36 | | |
| 1-Methyl-2-sec-butylbenzene | 2 | 2 | 2 | | 2 |
| 1-Methyl-3-sec-butylbenzene | 2,17,18 | 2,18 | 2 | | 2 |
| 1-Methyl-4-sec-butylbenzene | 2,17,19 | 2,18,19,37,38,39 | 2,38,39 | | 2 |
| 1-Methyl-2-isobutylbenzene | 2 | 2 | 2 | | 2 |
| 1-Methyl-3-isobutylbenzene | 2 | 2 | 2 | | 2 |
| 1-Methyl-4-isobutylbenzene | 2,20 | 2 | 2 | | |
| 1-Methyl-2-tert-butylbenzene | 2,21 | 2,21 | 2,21 | 21 | |
| 1-Methyl-3-tert-butylbenzene | 2,21,22 | 2,21,22 | 2,21 | 22 | |
| 1-Methyl-4-tert-butylbenzene | 2,21,22 | 2,21,22,39,40,41,42 | 2,21 | 22 | 2,42 |
| 1-Ethyl-2-n-propylbenzene | 2 | 2 | 2 | | |
| 1-Ethyl-3-n-propylbenzene | 2 | 2 | 2 | | |
| 1-Ethyl-4-n-propylbenzene | 2,23 | 2 | 2 | | |
| 1-Ethyl-2-isopropylbenzene | 2 | 2 | 2 | | 2 |
| 1-Ethyl-3-isopropylbenzene | 2 | 2 | 2 | | 2 |
| 1-Ethyl-4-isopropylbenzene | 2 | 2,38 | 2,49 | | 2 |
| 1,2-Dimethyl-3-n-propylbenzene | 2 | 2 | 2 | | 2 |
| 1,2-Dimethyl-4-n-propylbenzene | 2 | 2 | 2 | | 2,54 |
| 1,3-Dimethyl-2-n-propylbenzene | 2 | 2 | 2 | | 2 |
| 1,3-Dimethyl-4-n-propylbenzene | 2 | 2 | 2 | | 2 |
| 1,3-Dimethyl-5-n-propylbenzene | 2,15 | 2,15 | 2,15 | 15 | 2 |
| 1,4-Dimethyl-2-n-propylbenzene | 2 | 2 | 2,50,62 | | 2 |
| 1,2-Dimethyl-3-isopropylbenzene | 2 | 2 | 2 | | 2 |
| 1,2-Dimethyl-4-isopropylbenzene | 2 | 2,52 | 2 | | 2 |
| 1,3-Dimethyl-2-isopropylbenzene | 2 | 2 | 2 | | 2 |
| 1,3-Dimethyl-4-isopropylbenzene | 2 | 2,53 | 2 | | 2 |
| 1,3-Dimethyl-5-isopropylbenzene | 2 | 2,7 | 2 | | 2 |
| 1,4-Dimethyl-2-isopropylbenzene | 2 | 2 | 2 | | 2 |
| 1-Methyl-2,3-diethylbenzene | 2 | 2 | 2 | | 2 |
| 1-Methyl-2,4-diethylbenzene | 2 | 2 | 2 | | 2 |
| 1-Methyl-2,5-diethylbenzene | 2 | 2 | 2 | | 2 |
| 1-Methyl-2,6-diethylbenzene | 2 | 2 | 2 | | 2 |
| 1-Methyl-3,4-diethylbenzene | 2 | 2 | 2 | | 2 |
| 1-Methyl-3,5-diethylbenzene | 2 | 2,57 | 2,57 | 57 | 2 |
| 1,2,3-Trimethyl-4-ethylbenzene | 2 | 2 | 2 | | 2 |
| 1,2,3-Trimethyl-5-ethylbenzene | 2 | 2 | 2 | | 2 |
| 1,2,4-Trimethyl-3-ethylbenzene | 2,55 | 2,55 | 2,55 | | 2 |

SPECIFIC REFERENCES

FOR TABLES 26a, 26a-E, AND 26b (Continued)

April 30, 1952

| Compound | REFERENCES FOR | | | | |
|---|---|---|---|---|---|
| | Boiling Point | Refractive Index | Density | Freezing Point | Refractive Dispersion |
| 1,2,4-Trimethyl-5-ethylbenzene | 2,55 | 2,55 | 2,49,54,55,59 | 55 | 2,54,59 |
| 1,2,4-Trimethyl-6-ethylbenzene | 2 | 2 | 2 | | 2 |
| 1,3,5-Trimethyl-2-ethylbenzene | 2,55 | 2,55,58 | 2,49,55,59 | 55 | 2,59 |
| Pentamethylbenzene | 2,56 | 2,54 | 2,54 | 60,61 | 2,54,63,64 |

REFERENCES

1. See references for tables 21a, 21a-E, and 21b
2. American Petroleum Institute Research Project 44[1]
3. Ipatieff and Schmerling[1]
4. Denisenko[1]
5. Denisenko[2]
6. Stephens and Roduta[1]
7. Klages[3]
8. Bygden[1]
9. Huston and Hsieh[1]
10. Khromov[1]
11. Huston and Kaye[1]
12. Klages[4]
13. Smith and Pennekamp[1]
14. Claisen, Kremers, Rath, and Tietze[1]
15. American Petroleum Institute Research Project 45[1]
16. Klages[5]
17. Shoesmith and McGechen[1]
18. Barkenbus, Hopkins, and Allen[1]
19. Wallach[3]
20. Wallach[4]
21. Serijan, Hipsher, and Gibbons[1]
22. American Petroleum Institute Research Project 6[1]
23. Widman[1]
24. Martin[2]
25. Ipatieff and Carson[1]
26. Niemczycki[1]
27. Levene and Kuna[1]
28. von Braun and Deutsch[1]
29. Tafel and Jurgens[1]
30. Rothen and Levene[1]
31. Letsinger[1]
32. Ipatieff, Pines, and Schmerling[1]
33. Kozak[1]
34. Schmidt and Schoeller[1]
35. Marvel, Hager, and Coffman[1]
36. Schorigin, Issaguljanz, and Gussewa[1]
37. Simons and Hart[1]
38. Welsh and Hennion[1]
39. Hennion and Kurtz[1]
40. Simons and Archer[1]
41. Baker and Groves[1]
42. Lacourt[1]
43. Levene and Marker[4]
44. Zelinskii and Gaverdovskaya[1]
45. Gilman and Beaber[1]
46. Howes and Nash[1]
47. Huston and Barrett[1]
48. Konovalov and Egorov[1]
49. Klages and Keil[1]
50. Quayle and others[1]
51. Legge[1]
52. Klages[6]
53. Nightingale and Carton[1]
54. von Auwers and Ziegler[1]
55. Smith and Kiess[1]
56. MacDougall and Smith[1]
57. Gibbons, Thompson, Reynolds, Wright, Chanan, Lamberti, Hipsher, and Karabinos[1]
58. Fuson, Denton, and Kneisley[1]
59. von Auwers[2]
60. Smith and MacDougall[1]
61. Parks, West, Naylor, Fujii, and McClaine[1]
62. Lester and Suratt[1]
63. Eykman[6]
64. Dutoit and Friederick[1]

834

| | SPECIFIC REFERENCES | | | | |
|---|---|---|---|---|---|
| | FOR TABLES 13a, 13a–E AND 13b | | | | |
| | May 31, 1947; June 30, 1948; October 31, 1952 | | | | |
| Compound | REFERENCES FOR | | | | |
| | Boiling Point | Refractive Index | Density | Freezing Point | Refractive Dispersion |
| Ethenylbenzene (Styrene; Vinylbenzene; Phenylethylene) | 1,2,3,4,5,32 | 1,2,3,5,6,17,32 | 1,2,3,5,7 | 6,8,9 | 2,17 |
| Isopropenylbenzene (α–Methylstyrene; 2–Phenyl–1–propene) | 2,10,11,12,13,31,32 | 2,11,12,13,31,32,34 | 2,11,12,13,31,32 | 13,32 | 2 |
| cis–1–Propenylbenzene (cis–β–Methylstyrene; cis–1–Phenyl–1–propene) | 2,14,15,16 | 2,14,16,33 | 2,14,16 | | 2 |
| trans–1–Propenylbenzene (trans–β–Methylstyrene; trans–1–Phenyl–1–propene) | | | | | |
| 1–Methyl–2–ethenylbenzene (o–Methylstyrene) | 18,29 | 3,29,35 | 3,29,35 | | 30 |
| 1–Methyl–3–ethenylbenzene (m–Methylstyrene) | 22 | 3,21,35 | 3,28,35 | | 30 |
| 1–Methyl–4–ethenylbenzene (p–Methylstyrene) | 12,19,20,24,25 | 3,20,23,26,27,35 | 3,12,20,23,27,35 | | 30 |

REFERENCES

1. Patnode and Scheiber[1]
2. von Auwers and Eisenlohr[1]
3. Shoryqin and Shorygina[1]
4. Garner, Adams, and Stuchell[1]
5. Goldfinger, Josefowitz, and Mark[1]
6. Smoker and Burchfield[1]
7. Cragoe and Peffer[1]
8. Glasgow, Krouskop, Beadle, Axilrod, and Rossini[1]
9. Guttman, Westrum, and Pitzer[1]
10. Harries[1]
11. Tiffeneau[1]
12. Klages[1]
13. Dreisbach[1]
14. Campbell and O'Connor[1]
15. Tiffeneau[2]
16. Levina[1]
17. Forziati and Rossini[1]
18. Emde[1]
19. Gauthier and Gauthier[1]
20. Klages and Keil[1]
21. Marvel, Overberger, Allen, Johnston, Saunders, and Young[1]
22. Müller[1]
23. Otto and Wenzke[1]
24. Sabetay[1]
25. Schramm[1]
26. Mowry, Renoll, and Huber[1]
27. von Auwers[3]
28. Titley[1]
29. von Auwers[4]
30. American Petroleum Institute Research Project 44[1]
31. Balandin and Marukjan[1]
32. Stull[2]
33. Kharasch, Lambert, and Urry[1]
34. Bachmann and Hellman[2]
35. Kutz, Nickels, McGovern, and Corson[2]

835

SPECIFIC REFERENCES

FOR TABLES 30a, 30a-E, and 30b

October 31, 1952

| Compound | Boiling Point | Refractive Index | Density | Freezing Point | Refractive Dispersion |
|---|---|---|---|---|---|
| | | | REFERENCES FOR | | |
| Naphthalene | 1,2,3,4,5,26 | 1 | 1,6 | 1,4,5,6,7,8,9,10,11,12,26 | 1 |
| 1-Methylnaphthalene | 1,6,13,14,15,16,17,18,20,21,22,26 | 1,6,14,15,16,17,19,20,21,22,23,24,25 | 1,6,15,16,18,19,20 | 1,6,14,17,18,20,26 | 1 |
| 1-Ethylnaphthalene | 17,18,20,27,28,29,30,31,32,33,34,35,36,37,38 | 17,20,22,27,35,39 | 18,20,22,27,28,34,35,36 | 17,20,22,34,36,37 | 40 |
| 1-n-Propylnaphthalene | 22 | 40 | 40 | 17,22,40 | 21,40 |
| 1-n-Butylnaphthalene | 20 | 20,22 | 20 | 20 | 21,40 |
| 1-n-Pentylnaphthalene | 22 | 22,40 | 40 | 40 | 40 |
| 1-n-Hexylnaphthalene | 22 | 22,40 | 40 | 40 | 40 |
| 1-n-Heptylnaphthalene | 40 | 40,43 | 40,43 | 40,43 | 40 |
| 1-n-Octylnaphthalene | 40 | 40,41 | 40 | 40,41 | 21,40 |
| 1-n-Nonylnaphthalene | 40 | 40,43 | 40,43 | 40,43 | 40 |
| 1-n-Decylnaphthalene | 40 | 40,41 | 40 | 40,41 | 40 |
| 1-n-Undecylnaphthalene | 40 | 25,42,43 | 42,43 | 40,42,43 | 40 |
| 1-n-Dodecylnaphthalene | 40 | 40 | 40 | 40,41 | 40 |

REFERENCES

1. Mair and Streiff[2]
2. Taylor and Taylor[1]
3. van Liempt[1]
4. Triebs[1]
5. Trusty[1]
6. Evans[3]
7. Chuang, Tien, and Ma[1]
8. Lassettre and Dickinson[1]
9. Wright and Wallace[1]
10. von Christiani and Pailer[1]
11. Huntenberg[1]
12. Nenitzescu and Cioranescu[2]
13. Larsen, Thorpe, and Armfield[1]
14. Coulson[2]
15. Pokravskaya[1]
16. Grummit and Buck[1]
17. Morrell, Pickering, and Smith[1]
18. Luther[1]
19. Arbusov[1]
20. Hipsher and Wise[1]
21. Luther and Wächter[1]
22. Bailey, Pickering, and Smith[1]
23. Andreev and Petrov[1]
24. Adkins and Davis[1]
25. Braun, Spooner, and Fenske[1]
26. American Petroleum Institute Research Project 6[1]
27. Kutz, Nickels, McGovern, and Corson[1]
28. Carnelutti[1]
29. Roux[1]
30. Clemmensen[1]
31. Marchetti[1]
32. Gilman and Hoyle[1]
33. Fröschl and Harlass[1]
34. Coscing[1]
35. Levy[1]
36. Fittig and Remsen[1]
37. Stull[3]
38. Tatevosyan and Vardanyan[1]
39. Hickenbottom, Porter, Edwards, Schlüchterer, and Spitzer[1]
40. American Petroleum Institute Research Project 44[1]
41. Bannister and Elsner[1]
42. American Petroleum Institute Research Project 42[1]
43. Anderson and Smith[1]

| | SPECIFIC REFERENCES | | | | |
|---|---|---|---|---|---|
| | FOR TABLES 31a, 31a–E, AND 31b | | | | |
| | October 31, 1952 | | | | |
| Compound | REFERENCES FOR | | | | |
| | Boiling Point | Refractive Index | Density | Freezing Point | Refractive Dispersion |
| Naphthalene | 1,17 | 1 | 1 | 1 | 1 |
| 2–Methylnaphthalene | 2,3,4,5,6,17 | 2,5,7,17 | 2,6,7 | 2,3,4,5,6,7,17 | 2 |
| 2–Ethylnaphthalene | 5,6,8,9,10,11,12, 13,14,15 | 5,10,12,13,15,18, 19 | 6,10,12,13,15 | 5,6,9,10,12,13,19, 20,21,22 | 16 |
| 2–n–Propylnaphthalene | 19 | 5,19,22 | 6,19,23 | 5,6,19,22 | 16 |
| 2–n–Butylnaphthalene | 19 | 19,22,24 | 6,19,24,25 | 16,19,22 | 16 |
| 2–n–Pentylnaphthalene | 19 | 19,22 | 6,19,25 | 16,19,22 | 16 |
| 2–n–Hexylnaphthalene | 16,19 | 19,22 | 6,19,26 | 16,19,22 | 16 |
| 2–n–Heptylnaphthalene | 16 | 16,22,28 | 6,16,28 | 16,22,28 | 16 |
| 2–n–Octylnaphthalene | 16 | 16,22,27 | 6,16 | 16,22,27 | 16 |
| 2–n–Nonylnaphthalene | 16 | 16,22,28 | 6,16,28 | 16,22,28 | 16 |
| 2–n–Decylnaphthalene | 16 | 16,22,25,27 | 6,16,25 | 16,22,25,27 | 16 |
| 2–n–Undecylnaphthalene | 16 | 16,28 | 16,28 | 28 | 16 |
| 2–n–Dodecylnaphthalene | 16 | 16,22 | 6,16 | 22,27 | 16 |

REFERENCES

1. See references for Tables 30a, 30a–E, and 30b.
2. Mair and Streiff[2]
3. Coulson[2]
4. Nenitzescu, Isacescu, and Isopescu[1]
5. Morrell, Pickering, and Smith[1]
6. Luther[1]
7. Evans[3]
8. Roux[1]
9. Coscina[1]
10. Levy[1]
11. Brunel[1]
12. Levy[2]
13. Orlov[1]
14. von Auwers and Fruhling[1]
15. Kutz, Nickels, McGovern, and Corson[1]
16. American Petroleum Institute Research Project 44[1]
17. American Petroleum Institute Research Project 6[1]
18. Hickenbottom, Porter, Edwards, Schlüchterer, and Spitzer[1]
19. Bailey, Pickering, and Smith[1]
20. Claus and Feist[1]
21. Adkins and Davis[1]
22. Kölbel and Fritsch[1]
23. Levina and Kulikov[1]
24. Petrov and Andreev[1]
25. Hart and Robinson[1]
26. Mikeska[1]
27. Bannister and Elsner[1]
28. Anderson and Smith[1]

| | SPECIFIC REFERENCES FOR TABLES 27a, 27a-E, AND 27b February 28, 1949; October 31, 1952 | | | | |
|---|---|---|---|---|---|
| Compound | REFERENCES FOR | | | | |
| | Boiling Point | Refractive Index | Density | Freezing Point | Refractive Dispersion |
| Naphthalene | 1 | 1 | 1 | 1 | 1 |
| 1-Methylnaphthalene | 1 | 1 | 1 | 1 | 1 |
| 2-Methylnaphthalene | 2 | 2 | 2 | 2 | 2 |
| 1-Ethylnaphthalene | 1 | 1 | 1 | 1 | 1 |
| 2-Ethylnaphthalene | 2 | 2 | 2 | 2 | 2 |
| 1,2-Dimethylnaphthalene | 28,29,30 | 24,26,29 | 24,25,26 | 29,30 | 3 |
| 1,3-Dimethylnaphthalene | 4,29,31 | 4,29 | 3,4 | 4,29 | 3 |
| 1,4-Dimethylnaphthalene | 5,29,32,34 | 5,29 | 3,5 | 5,29,33,35,36,37 | 3 |
| 1,5-Dimethylnaphthalene | 29,40 | | | 29,31,39,40,41,42,43 | |
| 1,6-Dimethylnaphthalene | 8,26,29,44,45,46,47 | 29,38,47 | 44,47 | 29 | 3 |
| 1,7-Dimethylnaphthalene | 6,29,34 | 6,29 | 6 | 29,31 | 3 |
| 1,8-Dimethylnaphthalene | 29 | | | 29 | |
| 2,3-Dimethylnaphthalene | 7,29 | | | 9,10,25,29,34,37,44 | |
| 2,6-Dimethylnaphthalene | 7,8,29,44 | | | 8,11,12,13,14,17,21,29,44,45,48 | |
| 2,7-Dimethylnaphthalene | 19,29,44 | | | 8,12,15,16,18,20,22,23,27,29,44 | |

REFERENCES

1. See references for Tables 30a, 30a-E, and 30b.
2. See references for Tables 31a, 31a-E, and 31b.
3. American Petroleum Institute Research Project 44[1]
4. Evans and Smith[1]
5. American Petroleum Institute Research Project 45[1]
6. Kruber and Schade[2]
7. Kruber[3]
8. Nenitzescu, Isacescu, and Isopescu[1]
9. Windaus and Thiele[1]
10. Thiele and Trautmann[1]
11. Baeyer and Villiger[1]
12. de Lazlo[1]
13. Kuhn and Winterstein[1]
14. Mayer and Schiffner[1]
15. Kariyone and Nonaka[1]
16. Ruzicka, Brüngger, Egli, Ehmann, Furter, and Hösli[1]
17. Royer[1]
18. Ruzicka, Ehmann, and Moergeli[1]
19. Coulson[3]
20. Ruzicka, Hösli, and Ehmann[1]
21. Ruzicka, Hofmann, and Frei[1]
22. Ruzicka, Furter, and Leuenberger[1]
23. Noller[2]
24. Meyer and Sieglitz[1]
25. Schroeter, Lichtenstadt, and Irineu[1]
26. von Auwers and Fruhling[1]
27. Sengupta[1]
28. Kruber and Schade[1]
29. Bailey, Bryant, Hancock, Morrell, and Smith[1]
30. Darzens and Levy[1]
31. Vesely and Struza[1]
32. Cannizzaro[1]
33. Robinson and Thompson[1]
34. Barnett and Sanders[1]
35. Meyer and Fricke[1]
36. Vesely and Sturza[2]
37. Wibaut and van Dijk[1]
38. Braun, Spooner, and Fenske[1]
39. Anderson and Short[1]

| SPECIFIC REFERENCES |
|---|
| FOR TABLES 27a, 27a-E, AND 27b (Continued) |
| February 28, 1949; October 31, 1952 |

| REFERENCES | | |
|---|---|---|
| 40. Kruber[2] | | |
| 41. Butz, Gaddis, Butz, and Davis[1] | | |
| 42. Butz[1] | | |
| 43. Linstead and Thomas[1] | | |
| 44. Weissgerber and Kruber[1] | | |
| 45. Charlampowiszowna[1] | | |
| 46. Kipping and Wild[1] | | |
| 47. Seidel, Müller, and Schinz[1] | | |
| 48. Hall[1] | | |

| SPECIFIC REFERENCES<br>FOR TABLES 28a, 28a–E, AND 28b<br>August 31, 1949; October 31, 1952 | | | | | |
|---|---|---|---|---|---|
| | REFERENCES FOR | | | | |
| Compound | Boiling<br>Point | Refractive<br>Index | Density | Freezing<br>Point | Refractive<br>Dispersion |
| 1,2,3,4–Tetrahydronaphthalene | 1,2,3,4,5,6,7,8,9,<br>10,11,12,13,14,22 | 2,3,4,5,6,10,13,<br>14 | 2,3,4,5,6,10,12,<br>13,17 | 2,24 | 2 |
| 1–Methyl–[1,2,3,4–tetrahydronaphthalene] | 15,16,22 | 15,16 | 15,16 | | |
| 2–Methyl–[1,2,3,4–tetrahydronaphthalene] | 23 | 23 | 23 | | |
| 5–Methyl–[1,2,3,4–tetrahydronaphthalene] | 2 | 2 | 2 | 2 | 2 |
| 6–Methyl–[1,2,3,4–tetrahydronaphthalene] | 2,17,18 | 2,17,18,19 | 2,18,19 | 2 | 2,18 |
| 1–Ethyl–[1,2,3,4–tetrahydronaphthalene] | 15 | 15 | 15 | | |
| 2–Ethyl–[1,2,3,4–tetrahydronaphthalene] | 20 | 20 | 20 | | |
| 5–Ethyl–[1,2,3,4–tetrahydronaphthalene] | 23 | 23 | 23 | | |
| 6–Ethyl–[1,2,3,4–tetrahydronaphthalene] | 12,18,20 | 12,18,20 | 12,18,20 | | 18 |
| 1,1–Dimethyl–<br>[1,2,3,4–tetrahydronaphthalene] | 21 | 19,21,25,26 | 19,21,25 | | |
| 1,cis–2–Dimethyl–<br>[1,2,3,4–tetrahydronaphthalene] | 15 | 15 | 15 | | |
| 1,trans–2–Dimethyl–<br>[1,2,3,4–tetrahydronaphthalene] | 15 | 15 | 15 | | |
| 1,cis–3–Dimethyl–<br>[1,2,3,4–tetrahydronaphthalene] | 23 | 23 | 23 | | |
| 1,trans–3–Dimethyl–<br>[1,2,3,4–tetrahydronaphthalene] | 23 | 23 | 23 | | |
| 1,cis–4–Dimethyl–<br>[1,2,3,4–tetrahydronaphthalene] | 23 | 23,27 | 23 | | |
| 1,trans–4–Dimethyl–<br>[1,2,3,4–tetrahydronaphthalene] | 23 | 23,27 | 23 | | |
| 2,2–Dimethyl–<br>[1,2,3,4–tetrahydronaphthalene] | 23 | 28 | 28 | | |
| 2,cis–3–Dimethyl–<br>[1,2,3,4–tetrahydronaphthalene] | 9,29 | 23 | 23 | 29 | |
| 2,trans–3–Dimethyl–<br>[1,2,3,4–tetrahydronaphthalene] | 9,29 | 23 | 23 | 29 | |
| 1,5–Dimethyl–<br>[1,2,3,4–tetrahydronaphthalene] | 23 | 23 | 23 | | |
| 1,6–Dimethyl–<br>[1,2,3,4–tetrahydronaphthalene] | 23 | 19 | 19 | | |
| 1,7–Dimethyl–<br>[1,2,3,4–tetrahydronaphthalene] | 23 | 23 | 23 | | |
| 1,8–Dimethyl–<br>[1,2,3,4–tetrahydronaphthalene] | 23 | 23 | 23 | | |
| 2,5–Dimethyl–<br>[1,2,3,4–tetrahydronaphthalene] | 23 | 23 | 30 | | |
| 2,6–Dimethyl–<br>[1,2,3,4–tetrahydronaphthalene] | 31 | 23 | 23 | 31 | |
| 2,7–Dimethyl–<br>[1,2,3,4–tetrahydronaphthalene] | 31 | 23 | 23 | | |
| 2,8–Dimethyl–<br>[1,2,3,4–tetrahydronaphthalene] | 23 | 23 | 23 | | |
| 5,6–Dimethyl–<br>[1,2,3,4–tetrahydronaphthalene] | 23 | 17 | 23 | | |
| 5,7–Dimethyl–<br>[1,2,3,4–tetrahydronaphthalene] | 18,33 | 18,33 | 18,33 | 33 | 18 |
| 5,8–Dimethyl–<br>[1,2,3,4–tetrahydronaphthalene] | 32 | 23 | 23 | | |
| 6,7–Dimethyl–<br>[1,2,3,4–tetrahydronaphthalene] | 32 | 17 | 23 | 32 | |

SPECIFIC REFERENCES

FOR TABLES 28a, 28a-E, AND 28b (Continued)

August 31, 1949; October 31, 1952

REFERENCES

1. Herz and Schuftan[1]
2. Mair and Streiff[1]
3. Nametkin and Rosenberg[1]
4. Lozovoi, D'yakowa, and Stepantseva[2]
5. Ross and Leather [1]
6. von Auwers[5]
7. Roth and von Auwers[1]
8. Meyer and Fricke[1]
9. Madinaveitia[1]
10. Evans[3]
11. Larsen, Thorpe, and Armfield[1]
12. Kutz, Nickels, McGovern, and Corson[1]
13. Balandin and Marukjan[2]
14. Leroux[1]
15. Roblin, Davidson, and Bogert[1]
16. Hock and Lang[1]
17. Smith and Lo[1]
18. Krollpfeiffer and Schaeffer[1]
19. Linstead and Thomas[1]
20. Levy[2]
21. Bogert, Davidson, and Apfelbaum[1]
22. Andreev and Petrov[1]
23. American Petroleum Institute Research
    Project 44[1]
24. American Petroleum Institute Research
    Project 6[1]
25. Colonge and Chambion[1]
26. Adkins and Davis[1]
27. American Petroleum Institute Research
    Project 45[1]
28. Sengupta[1]
29. Coulson[4]
30. Mayer and Schulte[1]
31. Coulson[3]
32. Barnett and Sanders[1]
33. Evans and Smith[1]

| | SPECIFIC REFERENCES |
| --- | --- |
| | FOR TABLES 29a (PART 1), 29a-E (PART 1) AND 29b (PART 1) |
| | October 31, 1950 (Corrected) |

| Compound | REFERENCES FOR | | | | |
| --- | --- | --- | --- | --- | --- |
| | Boiling Point | Refractive Index | Density | Freezing Point | Refractive Dispersion |
| *cis*–decahydronaphthalene | 1,4,6,8,9,10,11,12 | 4,6,8,9,11,12,14, | 1,4,6,8,9,12,14,15,16,18 | 4,9,10,11,14,17,24 | |
| *trans*–decahydronaphthalene | 1,2,3,4,5,6,7,8,9,10,11,12,13 | 1,2,3,4,5,6,7,8,9,11,12,13,14 | 1,2,3,4,5,6,7,8,9,12,14,15,16,17,18 | 4,9,10,11,14,17,24 | |
| 1–Methyl–[*cis*–decahydronaphthalene] | 20 | | | | |
| 1–Methyl–[*trans*–decahydronaphthalene] | 19,20 | 19 | | | |
| 2–Methyl–[*cis*–decahydronaphthalene] | 20 | | | | |
| 2–Methyl–[*trans*–decahydronaphthalene] | 6,20,21 | | | | |
| 9–Methyl–[*cis*–decahydronaphthalene] | 20,22,23 | 22,23 | 22,23 | | |
| 9–Methyl–[*trans*–decahydronaphthalene] | 6,20 | 6 | | | |

1. Eisenlohr and Polenske[1]
2. Zelinskii and Turova-Pollak[1]
3. Hückel[4]
4. Hückel[2]
5. Zelinskii[5]
6. Ruzicka, Koolhaas, and Wind[1]
7. Zelinskii and Turova-Pollak[2]
8. Prokopetz[1]
9. Seyer and Walker[1]
10. Seyer and Mann[1]
11. American Petroleum Institute Research Project 6[1]
12. Fenske, Myers and Quiggle[1]
13. Struck and Kinney[1]
14. Seyer and Barrow[1]
15. Zelinskii[4]
16. Hückel, Kumetat and Severin[1]
17. Hückel[3]
18. Hückel[1]
19. English and Cavaglieri[1]
20. American Petroleum Institute Research Project 44[1]
21. Barret and Linstead[1]
22. Hibbit and Linstead[1]
23. Linstead, Millidge and Walpole[1]
24. Streiff, Soule, Kennedy, Janes, Sedlak, Willingham, and Rossini[1]

| | SPECIFIC REFERENCES | | | | |
| | FOR TABLES 29a (PART 2) AND 29b (PART 2) | | | | |
| | October 31, 1950 | | | | |

| | REFERENCES FOR | | | | |
|---|---|---|---|---|---|
| Compound | Boiling Point | Refractive Index | Density | Freezing Point | Refractive Dispersion |
| 1-Ethyl-[cis-decahydronaphthalene] | 1 | | | | |
| 1-Ethyl-[trans-decahydronaphthalene] | 1 | | | | |
| 2-Ethyl-[cis-decahydronaphthalene] | 1 | | | | |
| 2-Ethyl-[trans-decahydronaphthalene] | 1 | | | | |
| 9-Ethyl-[cis-decahydronaphthalene] | 1 | 1 | 1 | | |
| 9-Ethyl-[trans-decahydronaphthalene] | 1 | 1 | 1 | | |
| 1,1-Dimethyl-[cis-decahydronaphthalene] | | | | | |
| 1,1-Dimethyl-[trans-decahydronaphthalene] | | | | | |
| 1,cis-2-Dimethyl-[cis-decahydronaphthalene] | | | | | |
| 1,cis-2-Dimethyl-[trans-decahydronaphthalene] | | | | | |
| 1,trans-2-Dimethyl-[cis-decahydronaphthalene] | | | | | |
| 1,trans-2-Dimethyl-[trans-decahydronaphthalene] | | | | | |
| 1,cis-3-Dimethyl-[cis-decahydronaphthalene] | | | | | |
| 1,cis-3-Dimethyl-[trans-decahydronaphthalene] | | | | | |
| 1,trans-3-Dimethyl-[cis-decahydronaphthalene] | | | | | |
| 1,trans-3-Dimethyl-[trans-decahydronaphthalene] | | | | | |
| 1,cis-4-Dimethyl-[cis-decahydronaphthalene] | | | | | |
| 1,cis-4-Dimethyl-[trans-decahydronaphthalene] | | | | | |
| 1,trans-4-Dimethyl-[cis-decahydronaphthalene] | | | | | |
| 1,trans-4-Dimethyl-[trans-decahydronaphthalene] | | | | | |
| 1,cis-5-Dimethyl-[cis-decahydronaphthalene] | | | | | |
| 1,cis-5-Dimethyl-[trans-decahydronaphthalene] | | | | | |
| 1,trans-5-Dimethyl-[cis-decahydronaphthalene] | | | | | |
| 1,trans-5-Dimethyl-[trans-decahydronaphthalene] | | | | | |
| 1,cis-6-Dimethyl-[cis-decahydronaphthalene] | | | | | |
| 1,cis-6-Dimethyl-[trans-decahydronaphthalene] | | | | | |
| 1,trans-6-Dimethyl-[cis-decahydronaphthalene] | | | | | |
| 1,trans-6-Dimethyl-[trans-decahydronaphthalene] | | | | | |
| 1,cis-7-Dimethyl-[cis-decahydronaphthalene] | | | | | |
| 1,cis-7-Dimethyl-[trans-decahydronaphthalene] | | | | | |
| 1,trans-7-Dimethyl-[cis-decahydronaphthalene] | | | | | |
| 1,trans-7-Dimethyl-[trans-decahydronaphthalene] | | | | | |

| REFERENCES | | |
|---|---|---|
| 1. American Petroleum Institute Research Project 44[1] | | |

843

| Compound | REFERENCES FOR | | | | |
|---|---|---|---|---|---|
| | Boiling Point | Refractive Index | Density | Freezing Point | Refractive Dispersion |
| 1,*cis*-8-Dimethyl-[*cis*-decahydronaphthalene] | | | | | |
| 1,*cis*-8-Dimethyl-[*trans*-decahydronaphthalene] | | | | | |
| 1,*trans*-8-Dimethyl-[*cis*-decahydronaphthalene] | | | | | |
| 1,*trans*-8-Dimethyl-[*trans*-decahydronaphthalene] | | | | | |
| 1,9-Dimethyl-[*cis*-decahydronaphthalene] | | | | | |
| 1,9-Dimethyl-[*trans*-decahydronaphthalene] | | | | | |
| 1,10-Dimethyl-[*cis*-decahydronaphthalene] | 1,2 | 2 | 2 | | |
| 1,10-Dimethyl-[*trans*-decahydronaphthalene] | 1,2 | 2 | 2 | | |
| 2,2-Dimethyl-[*cis*-decahydronaphthalene] | | | | | |
| 2,2-Dimethyl-[*trans*-decahydronaphthalene] | | | | | |
| 2,*cis*-3-Dimethyl-[*cis*-decahydronaphthalene] | | | | | |
| 2,*cis*-3-Dimethyl-[*trans*-decahydronaphthalene] | | | | | |
| 2,*trans*-3-Dimethyl-[*cis*-decahydronaphthalene] | | | | | |
| 2,*trans*-3-Dimethyl-[*trans*-decahydronaphthalene] | | | | | |
| 2,*cis*-6-Dimethyl-[*cis*-decahydronaphthalene] | | | | | |
| 2,*cis*-6-Dimethyl-[*trans*-decahydronaphthalene] | | | | | |
| 2,*trans*-6-Dimethyl-[*cis*-decahydronaphthalene] | | | | | |
| 2,*trans*-6-Dimethyl-[*trans*-decahydronaphthalene] | | | | | |
| 2,*cis*-7-Dimethyl-[*cis*-decahydronaphthalene] | | | | | |
| 2,*cis*-7-Dimethyl-[*trans*-decahydronaphthalene] | | | | | |
| 2,*trans*-7-Dimethyl-[*cis*-decahydronaphthalene] | | | | | |
| 2,*trans*-7-Dimethyl-[*trans*-decahydronaphthalene] | | | | | |
| 2,9-Dimethyl-[*cis*-decahydronaphthalene] | | | | | |
| 2,9-Dimethyl-[*trans*-decahydronaphthalene] | | | | | |
| 2,10-Dimethyl-[*cis*-decahydronaphthalene] | | | | | |
| 2,10-Dimethyl-[*trans*-decahydronaphthalene] | | | | | |
| 9,10-Dimethyl-[*cis*-decahydronaphthalene] | | | | | |
| 9,10-Dimethyl-[*trans*-decahydronaphthalene] | | | | | |

SPECIFIC REFERENCES
FOR TABLES 29a (PART 3) AND 29b (PART 3)
October 31, 1950

REFERENCES

1. American Petroleum Institute Research Project 44[1]
2. Ruzicka, Koolhaas, and Wind[2]

| | SPECIFIC REFERENCES | | | | |
| --- | --- | --- | --- | --- | --- |
| | FOR TABLES 101a, 101a–E and 101b | | | | |
| | April 30, 1952 | | | | |
| | REFERENCES FOR | | | | |
| Compound | Boiling Point | Refractive Index | Density | Freezing Point | Refractive Dispersion |
| Methanethiol (Methyl mercaptan) | 3 | | 4,9 | 3 | |
| Ethanethiol (Ethyl mercaptan) | 2,4,5,6,7,8,9 | 2,7,8,16,17 | 2,16 | 2,5 | 2,7 |
| 1-Propanethiol (n-Propyl mercaptan) | 4,5,7,10,11,12,13 | 4,5,7,11,12,17,18 | 4,5,11,18 | 2 | 7,11 |
| 1-Butanethiol (n-Butyl mercaptan) | 2,4,5,7,11,12,14 | 2,7,11,14,17 | 2,4,11 | 2,5 | 2,7 |
| 1-Pentanethiol | 2,4 | 2,7,14 | 2,4 | 2 | 2,7 |
| 1-Hexanethiol | 4,7,15 | 4,7,19 | 4,13 | 23 | 1 |
| 1-Heptanethiol | 4,7,15 | 2,4,7 | 2,4,13 | 2,23 | 7 |
| 1-Octanethiol | 4,7,15 | 4,7 | 4,13 | 23 | 1 |
| 1-Nonanethiol | 4 | 4,20 | 4,13 | 23 | 1 |
| 1-Decanethiol | 1 | 20 | 1,20,22 | 1 | 1 |
| 1-Undecanethiol | 1 | 1 | 1,22 | 1 | 1 |
| 1-Dodecanethiol | 1 | 1 | 1,22 | 1 | 1 |
| 1-Tridecanethiol | 1 | 1 | 1,22 | 1 | 1 |
| 1-Tetradecanethiol | 1 | 1 | 1,22 | 1 | 1 |
| 1-Pentadecanethiol | 1 | 1 | 1 | 1 | 1 |
| 1-Hexadecanethiol | 1 | 1 | 1 | 24,25,26,27 | 1 |
| 1-Heptadecanethiol | 1 | 1 | 1 | 1 | 1 |
| 1-Octadecanethiol | 1 | 1 | 1 | 1 | 1 |
| 1-Nonadecanethiol | 1 | 1 | 1 | 1 | 1 |
| 1-Eicosanethiol | 1 | 1 | 1 | 1 | 1 |

REFERENCES

1. American Petroleum Institute Research Project 44[1]
2. American Petroleum Institute Research Project 48A[1]
3. Russel, Osborne, and Yost[1]
4. Ellis and Reid[1]
5. Denyer, Fidler, and Lowry[1]
6. Vogel and Cowan[1]
7. Vogel[4]
8. Hunter and Partington[1]
9. Berthoud and Brum[1]
10. Taylor and Layng[1]
11. Mathias[2]
12. Vaughn and Rust[1]
13. Bingham and Fornwalt[1]
14. Walls and Smyth[1]
15. Backer, Terpstra, and Dijkstra[1]
16. Nasini[1]
17. Bezzi[1]
18. Selker and Kemp[1]
19. Nametkin and Sosnira[1]
20. Tits–Skvortsova, Levina, Leonova, and Karaseva[1]
21. Gorin, Dougherty and Tobolsky[1]
22. Noller and Gordon[1]
23. Teets[1]
24. Denison and Condit[1]
25. Baer and Carmack[1]
26. Flaschentroger and Wannschaff[1]
27. Backer and Kramer[1]

SPECIFIC REFERENCES

FOR TABLES 102a, 102a-E, AND 102b

April 30, 1952; December 31, 1952

| Compound | REFERENCES FOR | | | | |
|---|---|---|---|---|---|
| | Boiling Point | Refractive Index | Density | Freezing Point | Refractive Dispersion |
| 2-Propanethiol (Isopropyl mercaptan) | 2 | 2,5,6 | 2,4,5,8 | 2 | 2 |
| 2-Butanethiol (*sec*-Butyl mercaptan) | 2,3 | 5 | 4,5 | 2,4 | 5 |
| 2-Pentanethiol | 4 | 4 | 4,8 | 2,4 | 1 |
| 2-Hexanethiol | 4 | 4 | 4,8 | 4 | 1 |
| 2-Heptanethiol | 4 | 4,7 | 4,8 | 4 | 1 |
| 2-Octanethiol | 4 | 4,7 | 4,8 | 4 | 1 |
| 2-Nonanethiol | 4 | 4 | 4,8 | 4 | 1 |
| 2-Decanethiol | 1 | 1 | 1 | 1 | 1 |
| 2-Undecanethiol | 1 | 1 | 1 | 1 | 1 |
| 2-Dodecanethiol | 1 | 1 | 1 | 1 | 1 |
| 2-Tridecanethiol | 1 | 1 | 1 | 1 | 1 |
| 2-Tetradecanethiol | 1 | 1 | 1 | 1 | 1 |
| 2-Pentadecanethiol | 1 | 1 | 1 | 1 | 1 |
| 2-Hexadecanethiol | 1 | 1 | 1 | 1 | 1 |
| 2-Heptadecanethiol | 1 | 1 | 1 | 1 | 1 |
| 2-Octadecanethiol | 1 | 1 | 1 | 1 | 1 |
| 2-Nonadecanethiol | 1 | 1 | 1 | 1 | 1 |
| 2-Eicosanethiol | 1 | 1 | 1 | 1 | 1 |

REFERENCES

1. American Petroleum Institute Research Project 44[1]

2. American Petroleum Institute Research Project 48[1]

3. Denyer, Fidler and Lowry[1]

4. Ellis and Reid[1]

5. Mathias[2]

6. Vogel[4]

7. Jones and Reid[1]

8. Bingham and Fornwalt[1]

| | REFERENCES FOR | | | | |
|---|---|---|---|---|---|
| Compound | Boiling Point | Refractive Index | Density | Freezing Point | Refractive Dispersion |
| Methanethiol (Methyl mercaptan) | 1 | | 1 | 1 | 1 |
| Ethanethiol (Ethyl Mercaptan) | 1 | 1 | 1 | 1 | 1 |
| 1-Propanethiol (n-Propyl mercaptan) | 1 | 1 | 1 | 1 | 1 |
| 2-Propanethiol (Isopropyl mercaptan) | 2 | 2 | 2 | 2 | 2 |
| 1-Butanethiol (n-Butyl mercaptan) | 1 | 1 | 1 | 1 | 1 |
| 2-Butanethiol (sec-Butyl mercaptan) | 2 | 2 | 2 | 2 | 2 |
| 2-Methyl-1-propanethiol (Isobutyl mercaptan) | 5 | 5, 10, 11, 16 | 5, 10, 11, 16 | | 10, 16 |
| 2-Methyl-2-propanethiol (tert-Butyl mercaptan) | 4, 5 | 4 | 4 | 4 | 4 |
| 1-Pentanethiol | 1 | 1 | 1 | 1 | 1 |
| 2-Pentanethiol | 2 | 2 | 2 | 2 | 2 |
| 3-Pentanethiol | 6 | 4 | 4 | 4 | |
| 2-Methyl-1-butanethiol | 7, 8, 9 | 3 | 3 | | |
| 3-Methyl-1-butanethiol | 10, 11, 12, 13, 14, 15 | 3, 11 | 11 | | 10 |
| 2-Methyl-2-butanethiol | 4 | 17 | 3 | | |
| 3-Methyl-2-butanethiol | | 4 | 4 | | |
| 2,2-Dimethyl-1-propanethiol | | | | 4 | |

SPECIFIC REFERENCES
FOR TABLES 103a, 103a-E, AND 103b
April 30, 1952

REFERENCES

1. See references for Tables 101a, 101a-E, and 101b.

2. See references for Tables 102a, 102a-E, and 102b.

3. American Petroleum Institute Research Project 44[1]

4. American Petroleum Institute Research Project 48A[1]

5. Denyer, Fidler, and Lowry[1]

6. Mailhe[1]

7. Hardin and Sikorsky[1]

8. Votocek and Vesely[1]

9. Levene and Mikeska[1]

10. Vogel[4]

11. Nasini, R[1]

12. Sabatier and Mailhe[5]

13. Bottomley[1]

14. Adams, Bremlet, and Tendwick[1]

15. Nord[1]

16. Mathias[2]

17. Ipatieff and Friedman[1]

| | SPECIFIC REFERENCES<br>FOR TABLES 104a, 104a–E, AND 104b<br>October 31, 1952 | | | | |
|---|---|---|---|---|---|
| | REFERENCES FOR | | | | |
| Compound | Boiling Point | Refractive Index | Density | Freezing Point | Refractive Dispersion |
| Benzenethiol (Thiophenol) | 2,3 | 7,8,9,10,11,12 | 8,10,11,14 | 15 | 7,11 |
| 2–Methylbenzenethiol (o–Methylthiophenol) | 2 | 1 | 1 | 2,16,17 | |
| 3–Methylbenzenethiol (m–Methylthiophenol) | 2 | 1,13 | 2 | | |
| 4–Methylbenzenethiol (p–Methylthiophenol) | 2 | | | 2,7,17,18,19,20,21,22,23 | |
| 2–Ethylbenzenethiol (o–Ethylthiophenol) | 4,5 | 1,4 | 1,4 | | |
| 3–Ethylbenzenethiol (m–Ethylthiophenol) | 1 | 1 | 1 | | |
| 4–Ethylbenzenethiol (p–Ethylthiophenol) | 1 | 1 | 1 | | |
| 2,3–Dimethylbenzenethiol (2,3–Dimethylthiophenol) | | | | | |
| 2,4–Dimethylbenzenethiol (2,4–Dimethylthiophenol) | 6 | | | | |
| 2,5–Dimethylbenzenethiol (2,5–Dimethylthiophenol) | 6,7 | | | | |
| 2,6–Dimethylbenzenethiol (2,6–Dimethylthiophenol) | | | | | |
| 3,4–Dimethylbenzenethiol (3,4–Dimethylthiophenol) | | | | | |
| 3,5–Dimethylbenzenethiol (3,5–Dimethylthiophenol) | | | | | |

REFERENCES

1. American Petroleum Institute Research Project 44[1]
2. Bourgeois[2]
3. Brand and Kranz[1]
4. Fricke and Spilker[2]
5. Hansch and Blondon[1]
6. Gatterman[1]
7. Taboury[2]
8. Vogel[4]
9. Gilman and Fullhart[1]
10. Hunter and Partington[2]
11. Eisenlohr[1]
12. Haresnape, Fidler, and Lowry[1]
13. Tarbell and Fukushima[2]
14. Walden and Swinne[1]
15. Parks, Todd, and Moore[1]
16. Hübner and Post[1]
17. Vallin[1]
18. Fischer, E.[1]
19. Field and Grunwald[1]
20. Knüsli[1]
21. Rosenmund and Harms[1]
22. Strating and Backer[2]
23. Backer and Kramer[1]

848

| Compound | REFERENCES FOR | | | | |
|---|---|---|---|---|---|
| | Boiling Point | Refractive Index | Density | Freezing Point | Refractive Dispersion |
| 2–Thiapropane (Dimethyl sulfide) | 3,4,5 | 2 | 2 | 2,5 | 2,7 |
| 2–Thiabutane (Methyl ethyl sulfide) | 6 | 2,7 | 2 | 2,6 | 2 |
| 2–Thiapentane (Methyl n–propyl sulfide) | 2,3,4 | 4 | 4 | 10 | 2,10 |
| 2–Thiahexane | 2,7 | 2,7 | 2,4,7 | 2 | 7 |
| 2–Thiaheptane | 8 | 1 | 1 | 1 | 1 |
| 2–Thiaoctane | 9 | 2 | 2 | 2 | 1 |
| 2–Thianonane | 1 | 2 | 2 | 2 | 1 |
| 2–Thiadecane | 1 | 1 | 1 | 1 | 1 |
| 2–Thiaundecane | 1 | 1 | 1 | 1 | 1 |
| 2–Thiadodecane | 1 | 1 | 1 | 2 | 1 |
| 2–Thiatridecane | 1 | 1 | 1 | 1 | 1 |
| 2–Thiatetradecane | 1 | 1 | 1 | 1 | 1 |
| 2–Thiapentadecane | 1 | 1 | 1 | 1 | 1 |
| 2–Thiahexadecane | 1 | 1 | 1 | 1 | 1 |
| 2–Thiaheptadecane | 1 | 1 | 1 | 1 | 1 |
| 2–Thiaoctadecane | 1 | 1 | 1 | 11 | 1 |
| 2–Thianonadecane | 1 | 1 | 1 | 1 | 1 |
| 2–Thiaeicosane | 1 | 1 | 1 | 1 | 1 |
| 2–Thiaheneicosane | 1 | 1 | 1 | 1 | 1 |

SPECIFIC REFERENCES FOR TABLES 105a, 105a–E, AND 105b
April 30, 1952; December 31, 1952

REFERENCES

1. American Petroleum Institute Research Project 44[1]
2. American Petroleum Institute Research Project 48[1]
3. White, Barnard–Smith, and Fidler[1]
4. Desty and Fidler[1]
5. Osborne, Doescher, and Yost[1]
6. Scott, Finke, McCullough, Gross, Williamson, Waddington, and Huffman[1]
7. Vogel and Cowan[1]
8. Blackburn and Challenger[1]
9. Braun, Teuffert, and Weissbach[1]
10. McAllan, Cullum, Dean, and Fidler[1]
11. Kuhn and Dann[1]

SPECIFIC REFERENCES

FOR TABLES 107a, 107a–E, AND 107b

April 30, 1952; December 31, 1952

| Compound | REFERENCES FOR | | | | |
|---|---|---|---|---|---|
| | Boiling Point | Refractive Index | Density | Freezing Point | Refractive Dispersion |
| 2–Thiapropane (Dimethyl sulfide) | 1 | 1 | 1 | 1 | 1 |
| 2–Thiabutane (Methyl ethyl sulfide) | 1 | 1 | 1 | 1 | 1 |
| 2–Thiapentane (Methyl *n*–propyl sulfide) | 1 | 1 | 1 | 1 | 1 |
| 3–Thiapentane (Diethyl sulfide) | 3 | 3,10 | 3,9 | 3 | 3 |
| 3–Methyl–2–thiabutane (Methyl isopropyl sulfide) | 5,6 | 6 | 8 | 3,8 | 8 |
| 2–Thiahexane | 1 | 1 | 1 | 1 | 1 |
| 3–Thiahexane | 5 | 4,8 | 8 | 8 | 8 |
| 3–Methyl–2–thiapentane | 2 | 2 | 2 | | |
| 4–Methyl–2–thiapentane | 7 | 7 | 7 | 3 | 7 |
| 2–Methyl–3–thiapentane | 5 | 8 | 8 | 8 | 8 |
| 3,3–Dimethyl–2–thiabutane | 3 | 3,7 | 3,7 | 3 | 7 |

REFERENCES

1. See references for Tables 105a, 105a–E, and 105b.
2. American Petroleum Institute Research Project 44[1]
3. American Petroleum Institute Research Project 48[1]
4. Haresnape, Fidler, and Lowry[1]
5. White, Barnard–Smith, and Fidler[1]
6. Desty and Fidler[1]
7. Vogel and Cowan[1]
8. McAllan, Cullum, Dean, and Fidler[1]
9. Timmermans and Hennaut–Roland[3]
10. Bezzi[1]

| | REFERENCES FOR | | | | |
|---|---|---|---|---|---|
| Compound | Boiling Point | Refractive Index | Density | Freezing Point | Refractive Dispersion |
| 2-Thiaheptane | 1 | 1 | 1 | 1 | 1 |
| 3-Thiaheptane | 2 | 2 | 2 | 2 | 2 |
| 4-Thiaheptane | 4 | 7, 8, 9, 11, 12, 13, 14 | 10, 12, 13, 14, 17 | 14, 18 | 12, 14 |
| 3-Methyl-2-thiahexane | 3 | | | | |
| 4-Methyl-2-thiahexane | 5 | 3 | 5 | | |
| 5-Methyl-2-thiahexane | 6 | | | | |
| 2-Methyl-3-thiahexane | 4 | 14 | 14 | | 14 |
| 4-Methyl-3-thiahexane | 4 | 14 | 14 | | 14 |
| 5-Methyl-3-thiahexane | 4 | 14, 15, 16 | 14, 16 | | 14 |
| 3,3-Dimethyl-2-thiapentane | | | | | |
| 3,4-Dimethyl-2-thiapentane | | | | | |
| 4,4-Dimethyl-2-thiapentane | | | | | |
| 2,2-Dimethyl-3-thiapentane | 4 | 12, 14 | 12, 14 | 14 | 12, 14 |
| 2,4-Dimethyl-3-thiapentane | 4 | 10, 12, 14 | 10, 12, 14 | 14 | 14 |

**SPECIFIC REFERENCES**
**FOR TABLES 108a, 108a-E, AND 108b**
April 30, 1952

## REFERENCES

1. See references for tables 105a, 105a-E, and 105b.
2. See references for tables 106a, 106a-E, and 106b.
3. American Petroleum Institute Research Project 44[1]
4. White, Barnard-Smith, and Fidler[1]
5. Brjuchonenko[1]
6. Obermeyer[1]
7. Haresnape, Fidler, and Lowry[1]
8. Nametkin and Sosnina[2]
9. Vaughan and Rust[1]
10. Ayers and Agruss[1]
11. Bezzi[1]

12. Vogel and Cowan[1]
13. Selker and Kemp[1]
14. McAllan, Cullum, Dean, and Fidler[1]
15. Ipatieff and Friedman[1]
16. Wuyts[3]
17. Strecker and Spitaler[1]
18. Timmermans[6]

| | SPECIFIC REFERENCES FOR TABLES 109a, 109a-E, AND 109b October 31, 1952 | | | | |
|---|---|---|---|---|---|
| | REFERENCES FOR | | | | |
| Compound | Boiling Point | Refractive Index | Density | Freezing Point | Refractive Dispersion |
| (1-Thiaethyl)-benzene (Methyl phenyl sulfide) | 2,3,4,5,6 | 2,4,12,13,14 | 2,12,14 | | 2,12 |
| (1-Thiapropyl)-benzene (Ethyl phenyl sulfide) | 2,3,4,7,8,9,10 | 2,4 | 2 | | 2 |
| 2-Methyl-(1-thiaethyl)-benzene | | | | | |
| 3-Methyl-(1-thiaethyl)-benzene | | 1,15 | 1 | | |
| 4-Methyl-(1-thiaethyl)-benzene | 4,11 | 1,11 | 1,11 | | 11 |

REFERENCES

1. American Petroleum Institute Research Project 44[1]
2. Vogel[4]
3. Kahovec and Reitz[1]
4. Taboury[2]
5. Bourgeois and Abraham[1]
6. Obermeyer[1]
7. Stadler[1]
8. Gilman and Beaber[2]
9. Hepworth and Clapham[1]
10. Wuyts[3]
11. von Auwers and Arndt[1]
12. Brand and Krantz[1]
13. Barnard, Fabian, and Koch[1]
14. Suter and Hansen[1]

15. Tarbell and Fukushima[1]

## SPECIFIC REFERENCES
### FOR TABLES 110a, 110a-E, AND 110b
#### October 31, 1952

| Compound | REFERENCES FOR | | | | |
|---|---|---|---|---|---|
| | Boiling Point | Refractive Index | Density | Freezing Point | Refractive Dispersion |
| (1-Thiabutyl)-benzene (n-Propyl phenyl sulfide) | 2 | 1,2,8 | 2,8 | | 8 |
| (2-Methyl-1-thiapropyl)-benzene (Isopropyl phenyl sulfide) | 2 | 1,2,8 | 2,8 | | 8 |
| 2-Methyl-(1-thiapropyl)-benzene | | | | | |
| 3-Methyl-(1-thiapropyl)-benzene | 3 | 1,3 | 1,3 | | |
| 4-Methyl-(1-thiapropyl)-benzene | 4,5,6 | 1 | 1,6 | | |
| 2-Ethyl-(1-thiaethyl)-benzene | 7 | 1,9 | 1,7 | | |
| 3-Ethyl-(1-thiaethyl)-benzene | | | | | |
| 4-Ethyl-(1-thiaethyl)-benzene | | | | | |
| 2,3-Dimethyl-(1-thiaethyl)-benzene | | | | | |
| 2,4-Dimethyl-(1-thiaethyl)-benzene | | 1 | 10 | | 10 |
| 2,5-Dimethyl-(1-thiaethyl)-benzene | | | | | |
| 2,6-Dimethyl-(1-thiaethyl)-benzene | | | | | |
| 3,4-Dimethyl-(1-thiaethyl)-benzene | | | | | |
| 3,5-Dimethyl-(1-thiaethyl)-benzene | | | | | |

## REFERENCES

1. American Petroleum Institute Research Project 44[1]
2. Ipatieff, Pines, and Friedman[1]
3. Illuminati and Gilman[1]
4. Taboury[3]
5. Gilman and Beaber[1]
6. Otto[1]
7. Fricke and Spilker[2]
8. Vogel[4]
9. Fricke and Spilker[3]
10. Krollpfeiffer[2]

<table>
<tr><td colspan="6" align="center">SPECIFIC REFERENCES<br>FOR TABLES 111a, 111a-E, AND 111b<br>October 31, 1952</td></tr>
<tr><td rowspan="2">Compound</td><td colspan="5" align="center">REFERENCES FOR</td></tr>
<tr><td>Boiling Point</td><td>Refractive Index</td><td>Density</td><td>Freezing Point</td><td>Refractive Dispersion</td></tr>
<tr><td>Thiacyclopropane (Ethylene sulfide)</td><td>9</td><td>1,2,7,8</td><td>1,2,8</td><td>2</td><td>2</td></tr>
<tr><td>2-Methylthiacyclopropane</td><td>2,3</td><td>1,2,4</td><td>1,2</td><td>2</td><td>2</td></tr>
<tr><td>2-Ethylthiacyclopropane</td><td>4</td><td>1,4</td><td>1,4</td><td></td><td></td></tr>
<tr><td>2,2-Dimethylthiacyclopropane</td><td>5,6</td><td>1,5,6</td><td></td><td></td><td></td></tr>
<tr><td>2,cis-3-Dimethylthiacyclopropane</td><td></td><td></td><td></td><td></td><td></td></tr>
<tr><td>2,trans-3-Dimethylthiacyclopropane</td><td></td><td></td><td></td><td></td><td></td></tr>
</table>

REFERENCES

1. American Petroleum Institute Research Project 44[1]
2. Sunner[1]
3. Davies and Savige[1]
4. Delépine and Jaffeux[1]
5. Snyder, Stewart, and Ziegler[1]
6. Culvenor, Davies, and Pausacker[1]
7. Delépine[1]
8. Günthard and Gäuman[1]
9. American Petroleum Institute Research Project 48A[1]

| | SPECIFIC REFERENCES FOR TABLES 112a, 112a-E, AND 112b October 31, 1952 | | | | |
|---|---|---|---|---|---|
| Compound | REFERENCES FOR | | | | |
| | Boiling Point | Refractive Index | Density | Freezing Point | Refractive Dispersion |
| Thiacyclopentane (Tetrahydrothiophene) | 2,17 | 5,17 | 17 | 12,17 | 4,5,12,17 |
| 2-Methylthiacyclopentane | 2 | 12,13,14 | 12,13,15 | 12 | 12 |
| 3-Methylthiacyclopentane | 2 | 12,14 | 12,14 | 12 | 12 |
| 2-Ethylthiacyclopentane | 14,16 | 1,14,16 | 1,14,16 | | |
| 3-Ethylthiacyclopentane | 14 | 1,14 | 1,14 | | |
| 2,2-Dimethylthiacyclopentane | | | | | |
| 2,cis-3-Dimethylthiacyclopentane | | | | | |
| 2,trans-3-Dimethylthiacyclopentane | | | | | |
| 2,cis-4-Dimethylthiacyclopentane | | | | | |
| 2,trans-4-Dimethylthiacyclopentane | | | | | |
| 2,cis-5-Dimethylthiacyclopentane | 2 | 12 | 12 | 12 | |
| 2,trans-5-Dimethylthiacyclopentane | 2 | 12 | 12 | 12 | |
| 3,3-Dimethylthiacyclopentane | | | | | |
| 3,cis-4-Dimethylthiacyclopentane | | | | | |
| 3,trans-4-Dimethylthiacyclopentane | | | | | |

REFERENCES

1. American Petroleum Institute Research Project 44[1]
2. White, Barnard-Smith, and Fidler[1]
3. Birch and McAllan[1]
4. Sunner[1]
5. Robles[1]
6. Haresnape, Fidler, and Lowry[1]
7. Tarbell and Weaver[1]
8. Yur'ev and Bugorkova[1]
9. Yur'ev and Tronova[1]
10. Yur'ev, Dubrovina, and Tregubov[1]
11. Desty and Fidler[1]
12. Whitehead, Dean, and Fidler[1]
13. Yur'ev[1]
14. Yur'ev and Gragerov[1]

15. Griskevich-Trackhimovskii[1]
16. Yur'ev, Gusev, Tronova, and Yurilin[1]
17. American Petroleum Institute Research Project 48A[1]

| SPECIFIC REFERENCES FOR TABLES 113a, 113a-E, AND 113b October 31, 1952 | | | | | |
|---|---|---|---|---|---|
| Compound | REFERENCES FOR | | | | |
| | Boiling Point | Refractive Index | Density | Freezing Point | Refractive Dispersion |
| Thiacyclohexane | 1 | 2,3,4 | 2,4,5,6 | 2,7 | 2,4 |
| 2-Methylthiacyclohexane | 1 | 2 | 2,8 | 2 | 2 |
| 3-Methylthiacyclohexane | 1 | 2 | 2 | 2 | 2 |
| 4-Methylthiacyclohexane | 1 | 2 | 2 | 2 | 2 |
| 2-Ethylthiacyclohexane | | | | | |
| 3-Ethylthiacyclohexane | | | | | |
| 4-Ethylthiacyclohexane | | | | | |
| 2,2-Dimethylthiacyclohexane | | | | | |
| 2,cis-3-Dimethylthiacyclohexane | | | | | |
| 2,trans-3-Dimethylthiacyclohexane | | | | | |
| 2,cis-4-Dimethylthiacyclohexane | | | | | |
| 2,trans-4-Dimethylthiacyclohexane | | | | | |
| 2,cis-5-Dimethylthiacyclohexane | | | | | |
| 2,trans-5-Dimethylthiacyclohexane | | | | | |
| 2,cis-6-Dimethylthiacyclohexane | | | | | |
| 2,trans-6-Dimethylthiacyclohexane | | | | | |
| 3,3-Dimethylthiacyclohexane | | | | | |
| 3,cis-4-Dimethylthiacyclohexane | | | | | |
| 3,trans-4-Dimethylthiacyclohexane | | | | | |
| 3,cis-5-Dimethylthiacyclohexane | | | | | |
| 3,trans-5-Dimethylthiacyclohexane | | | | | |
| 4,4-Dimethylthiacyclohexane | | | | | |

REFERENCES

1. White, Barnard-Smith, and Fidler[1]
2. Whitehead, Dean, and Fidler[1]
3. Haresnape, Fidler, and Lowry[1]
4. Sunner[1]
5. Clarke, H.[1]
6. Hepworth[1]
7. American Petroleum Institute Research Project 48A[1]
8. Griskevich-Trokhimovskiĭ[1]

| | SPECIFIC REFERENCES FOR TABLES 114a, 114a–E, AND 114b | | | | |
| | April 30, 1952; December 31, 1952 | | | | |
| Compound | REFERENCES FOR | | | | |
| | Boiling Point | Refractive Index | Density | Freezing Point | Refractive Dispersion |
|---|---|---|---|---|---|
| Thiophene | 1,19,20,21 | 1,22 | 1,25 | 1,19,20 | 1,14,19,22,23,24 |
| 2–Methylthiophene | 21 | 5,26,27,28 | 2,14,27,29 | 1 | 14,27 |
| 3–Methylthiophene | 1,21 | 1 | 1 | 1 | 1,27 |
| 2–Ethylthiophene | 3,5,8,9,14,29 | 5 | 14 | | 14 |
| 3–Ethylthiophene | 4,8,9 | 1 | 1 | 1 | |
| 2,3–Dimethylthiophene | 5,6,18 | 5,6,18 | 6 | 6 | |
| 2,4–Dimethylthiophene | 18 | 18 | 7 | | |
| 2,5–Dimethylthiophene | 1,8,10,11,18 | 1,5,16,17,18 | 1,14,16,17 | 1 | 14 |
| 3,4–Dimethylthiophene | 7,8,9,12,13,14,15 | 13 | 7 | | 14 |

REFERENCES

1. American Petroleum Institute Research Project 48[1]
2. Nasini[1]
3. Meyer and Kreis[1]
4. Gerlach[1]
5. King and Nord[1]
6. Shepard[1]
7. Zelinskii[7]
8. McKittrick[1]
9. van Arkel[1]
10. Messinger[1]
11. Charles and Freiser[1]
12. Linstead, Noble, and Wright[1]
13. Shepard, Henne, and Midgley[2]
14. von Auwers and Kohlhaas[1]

15. Steinkopf[1]
16. Nasini and Carrara[1]
17. Opolski[1]
18. Hartough[1]
19. Fawcett and Rasmussen[1]
20. Waddington, Knowlton, Scott, Oliver, Todd, Hubbard, Smith, and Huffman[1]
21. White, Barnard–Smith, and Fidler[1]
22. Brühl[1]
23. Cotton and Mouton[1]
24. Knops[1]
25. Coulson, Hales, and Herington[1]
26. Desty and Fidler[1]
27. Fawcett[2]
28. Yur'ev[2]

29. Keswani and Freiser[1]

SPECIFIC REFERENCES
FOR TABLES 115a, 115a-E, AND 115b
April 30, 1952

| Compound | REFERENCES FOR | | | | |
|---|---|---|---|---|---|
| | Boiling Point | Refractive Index | Density | Freezing Point | Refractive Dispersion |
| 2-Propylthiophene | 1 | 1 | 1 | | 1 |
| 3-Propylthiophene | 2 | 2 | 2 | | 2 |
| 2-Isopropylthiophene | 4,5 | 4,12 | 4,12 | | 4 |
| 3-Isopropylthiophene | 4,5,6 | 4 | 4 | | 4 |
| 2-Methyl-3-ethylthiophene | 7 | | | | |
| 2-Methyl-4-ethylthiophene | 8 | 8 | 8 | 8 | |
| 2-Methyl-5-ethylthiophene | 8,9,10 | 8,9,10 | 8,10 | 8,10 | |
| 3-Methyl-2-ethylthiophene | 7 | 7 | 7 | | |
| 3-Methyl-4-ethylthiophene | | | | | |
| 3-Methyl-5-ethylthiophene | | | | | |
| 2,3,4-Trimethylthiophene | 11 | 11 | 3 | | |
| 2,3,5-Trimethylthiophene | 11 | 9,11,13 | 13 | | |

REFERENCES

1. See references for tables 112a, 112a-E, and 112b.
2. See references for tables 113a, 113a-E, and 113b.
3. American Petroleum Institute Research Project 44[1]
4. Scheibler and Schmidt[1]
5. Leclere and Leclere[1]
6. Thiele[1]
7. Steinkopf, Merckoll, and Strauch[1]
8. Shepard[1]
9. King and Nord[1]
10. Midgley, Henne, and Shepard[1]
11. Hartough[1]
12. Kutz and Corson[1]
13. Youtz and Perkins[1]

## SPECIFIC REFERENCES
### FOR TABLES 20c (PART 1), 20c-E (PART 1), AND 20c-K (PART 1)
#### May 31, 1947; October 31, 1952

| Compound | REFERENCES FOR Viscosity | Compound | REFERENCES FOR Viscosity |
|---|---|---|---|
| Methane | 1,6,8,10,11 | | |
| Ethane | 1,6,7,8 | | |
| Propane | 1,6,7,9 | | |
| n–Butane | 1,9 | | |
| n–Pentane | 1,2,3,4,5,12,26,27 | | |
| n–Hexane | 1,2,3,4,12,13,19,20,26,27 | | |
| n–Heptane | 1,2,3,4,5,12,16,18,26,27,28 | | |
| n–Octane | 1,2,3,4,13,14,15,26,27 | | |
| n–Nonane | 1,4,17,26 | | |
| n–Decane | 1,4,17,27 | | |
| n–Undecane | 1,4,15,17,26 | | |
| n–Dodecane | 1,4,17,21,22,27 | | |
| n–Tridecane | 1,15,21,26 | | |
| n–Tetradecane | 1,21,23,27 | | |
| n–Pentadecane | 1,21 | | |
| n–Hexadecane | 1,21,22,23,29 | | |
| n–Heptadecane | 1,15,21,24,26 | | |
| n–Octadecane | 1,21,23,25 | | |
| n–Nonadecane | 1 | | |
| n–Eicosane | 1,21 | | |

### REFERENCES

1. American Petroleum Institute Research Project 44[1]
2. Geist and Cannon[1]
3. Thorpe and Rodger[1]
4. Shepard, Henne, and Midgley[1]
5. Timmermans and Hennaut-Roland[3]
6. Gerf and Galkov[1]
7. Galkov and Gerf[1]
8. Gerf and Galkov[2]
9. Lipkin, Davison, and Kurtz[1]
10. Bresler and Landerman[1]
11. Rudenko and Shubnikov[1]
12. Khalilov[2]
13. Timmermans and Martin[3]
14. Madge[1]
15. Schmidt, Schoeller, and Eberlein[1]
16. Smyth and Stoops[1]
17. Bingham and Fornwalt[1]
18. Lewis[1]
19. Andrade and Rotherham[1]
20. Drapier[1]
21. American Petroleum Institute Research Project 42[1]
22. Evans[1]
23. Engler-Höfer[1]
24. Karrer and Ferri[1]
25. Dover and Hensley[1]
26. Doolittle and Peterson[1]
27. Giller and Drickamer[1]
28. California Research Corporation[1]
29. Nederbragt and Boelhouwer[1]

| | SPECIFIC REFERENCES<br>FOR TABLES 1c, 1c–E, AND 1c–K<br>October 31, 1948; October 31, 1952 | | | |
|---|---|---|---|---|
| Compound | REFERENCES FOR | Compound | REFERENCES FOR | |
| | Viscosity | | Viscosity | |
| Methane | 1 | | | |
| Ethane | 1 | | | |
| Propane | 1 | | | |
| *n*–Butane | 1 | | | |
| 2–Methylpropane (Isobutane) | 2,3 | | | |
| *n*–Pentane | 1 | | | |
| 2–Methylbutane (Isopentane) | 4,5,6,7 | | | |
| 2,2–Dimethylpropane (Neopentane) | 8 | | | |

REFERENCES

1. See references for Tables 20c (Part 1) 20c–E (Part 1), and 20c–K (Part 1).
2. Sage, Yale, and Lacey[1]
3. Lipkin, Davison, and Kurtz[1]
4. Geist and Cannon[1]
5. Timmermans and Martin[2]
6. Thorpe and Rodger[1]
7. Thorpe and Rodger[2]
8. Phibbs[1]

| | SPECIFIC REFERENCES FOR TABLES 22c, 22c-E, AND 22c-K December 31, 1948 | | | |
|---|---|---|---|---|
| Compound | REFERENCES FOR | Compound | REFERENCES FOR | |
| | Viscosity | | Viscosity | |
| Cyclopentane | 1,2,3,5,6,7,8 | | | |
| Methylcyclopentane | 1,2,3,5,6,7,8 | | | |
| Ethylcyclopentane | 1,2,3 | | | |
| n-Propylcyclopentane | 1,2,3 | | | |
| n-Butylcyclopentane | 1,3 | | | |
| n-Pentylcyclopentane | 1 | | | |
| n-Hexylcyclopentane | 1 | | | |
| n-Heptylcyclopentane | 1 | | | |
| n-Octylcyclopentane | 1,4 | | | |
| n-Nonylcyclopentane | 1 | | | |
| n-Decylcyclopentane | 1,4 | | | |
| n-Undecylcyclopentane | 1 | | | |
| n-Dodecylcyclopentane | 1,4 | | | |
| n-Tridecylcyclopentane | 1 | | | |
| n-Tetradecylcyclopentane | 1,4 | | | |
| n-Pentadecylcyclopentane | 1 | | | |
| n-Hexadecylcyclopentane | 1,4 | | | |

REFERENCES

1. American Petroleum Institute Research Project 44[1]
2. Geist and Cannon[1]
3. Evans[2]
4. Schmidt and Gemassmer[1]
5. Chavanne and van Ressighem[1]
6. Hugel[1]
7. Godchot[1]
8. Godchot and Cauquil[1]

SPECIFIC REFERENCES
FOR TABLES 23c, 23c-E, AND 23c-K
December 31, 1948

| Compound | REFERENCES FOR | Compound | REFERENCES FOR |
|---|---|---|---|
| | Viscosity | | Viscosity |
| Cyclohexane | 1,2,3,5,6,7,8,10,11,12,13,14,15, 16 | | |
| Methylcyclohexane | 1,2,3,5,6,7,8,9,11,14,15 | | |
| Ethylcyclohexane | 1,2,3,17 | | |
| n–Propylcyclohexane | 1,2,3 | | |
| n–Butylcyclohexane | 1,3,4 | | |
| n–Pentylcyclohexane | 1 | | |
| n–Hexylcyclohexane | 1 | | |
| n–Heptylcyclohexane | 1,4 | | |
| n–Octylcyclohexane | 1,18 | | |
| n–Nonylcyclohexane | 1 | | |
| n–Decylcyclohexane | 1 | | |
| n–Undecylcyclohexane | 1 | | |
| n–Dodecylcyclohexane | 1,4 | | |
| n–Tridecylcyclohexane | 1 | | |
| n–Tetradecylcyclohexane | 1,4 | | |
| n–Pentadecylcyclohexane | 1 | | |
| n–Hexadecylcyclohexane | 1,4,19,20 | | |

REFERENCES

1. American Petroleum Institute Research Project 44[1]
2. Geist and Cannon[1]
3. Evans[2]
4. Schmidt and Grosser[1]
5. Chavanne and van Ressighem[1]
6. Hugel[1]
7. Godchot[1]
8. Godchot and Cauquil[1]
9. Timmermans and Martin[1]
10. Timmermans and Martin[2]
11. Friend and Hargreaves[1]
12. Linke[1]
13. Vorlander and Fischer[1]
14. Vorlander and Walter[1]
15. Tausz and Staab[1]
16. Drapier[1]
17. Ubbelohde and Agthe[1]
18. Schiessler, Herr, Rytina, Weisel, Fischl, McLaughlin, and Kuehner[1]
19. Larsen, Thorpe, and Armfield[1]
20. Fuel Research Board of Great Britain[1]

SPECIFIC REFERENCES
FOR TABLES 24c, 24c-E, AND 24c-K
August 31, 1949

| Compound | REFERENCES FOR | Compound | REFERENCES FOR |
|---|---|---|---|
| | Viscosity | | Viscosity |
| Ethene | 1,8,10 | | |
| Propene | 1,8,9 | | |
| 1-Butene | 1 | | |
| 1-Pentene | 1 | | |
| 1-Hexene | 1 | | |
| 1-Heptene | 1 | | |
| 1-Octene | 1 | | |
| 1-Nonene | 1,2 | | |
| 1-Decene | 1,2 | | |
| 1-Undecene | 1,2 | | |
| 1-Dodecene | 1,2,3 | | |
| 1-Tridecene | 1,2,4 | | |
| 1-Tetradecene | 1 | | |
| 1-Pentadecene | 1,2,4,5 | | |
| 1-Hexadecene | 1,3,6 | | |
| 1-Heptadecene | 1,2,4 | | |
| 1-Octadecene | 1,7 | | |
| 1-Nonadecene | 1 | | |
| 1-Eicosene | 1 | | |

REFERENCES

1. American Petroleum Institute Research Project 44[1]
2. Schmidt, Schoeller, and Eberlein[1]
3. Evans, E.B.[2]
4. Schiessler, Herr, Rytina, Weisel, Fischl, McLaughlin, and Kuehner[1]
5. Landa and Landova[1]
6. Suida and Drahowzal[1]
7. Dover and Hensley[1]
8. Gerf and Galkov[1]
9. Galkov and Gerf[1]
10. Rudenko and Shubnikov[1]

| | SPECIFIC REFERENCES FOR TABLES 21c, 21c-E, AND 21c-K October 31, 1948 | | | | |
|---|---|---|---|---|---|
| Compound | REFERENCES FOR | | Compound | REFERENCES FOR | |
| | Viscosity | | | Viscosity | |
| Benzene | 1,2,3,12,15,16,17,18,19,20,21,22, 23,29,30,31,32,33,34,35,36,37,38, 39,40,41,42,43,44,45,46,47 | | | | |
| Methylbenzene | 1,2,3,12,16,19,20,22,23,29,31,37, 42,43,45,46,47,48,49,50 | | | | |
| Ethylbenzene | 1,2,3,4,5,12,29,30 | | | | |
| n-Propylbenzene | 1,2,5,11,27,29 | | | | |
| n-Butylbenzene | 1,5,13,27,28 | | | | |
| n-Pentylbenzene | 1,5,6,7,10 | | | | |
| n-Hexylbenzene | 1,5,6,7,10 | | | | |
| n-Heptylbenzene | 1,5,6,7 | | | | |
| n-Octylbenzene | 1,5,9 | | | | |
| n-Nonylbenzene | 1,6,7 | | | | |
| n-Decylbenzene | 1 | | | | |
| n-Undecylbenzene | 1 | | | | |
| n-Dodecylbenzene | 1,5,6,8,14 | | | | |
| n-Tridecylbenzene | 1 | | | | |
| n-Tetradecylbenzene | 1,5,6,8 | | | | |
| n-Pentadecylbenzene | 1 | | | | |
| n-Hexadecylbenzene | 1,5,24,25,26 | | | | |

## REFERENCES

1. American Petroleum Institute Research Project 44[1]
2. Geist and Cannon[1]
3. Thorpe and Rodger[1]
4. Thorpe and Rodger[2]
5. Schmidt, Hopp, and Schoeller[1]
6. Ju, Shen, and Wood[2]
7. Shen, Wood, and Garner[2]
8. Ju, Wood, and Garner[1]
9. Schiessler, Herr, Rytina, Weisel, Fischl, McLaughlin, and Kuekner[1]
10. Simon[1]
11. Timmermans and Hennaut-Roland[1]
12. Timmermans and Martin[2]
13. Timmermans and Martin[3]
14. Petrov and Lapteva[1]
15. Meyer and Mylius[1]
16. Heydweiller[1]
17. Khalilov[2]
18. Madge[1]
19. Dessart[1]
20. Miller[1]
21. Martin[1]
22. Lemonde[1]
23. de Kolossowsky[1]
24. Fuel Research Board of Great Britain[1]
25. Neyman-Pilat and Pilat[1]
26. Larsen, Thorpe, and Armfield[1]
27. Evans[3]
28. Thole[1]
29. Dunstan, Hilditch, and Thole[1]
30. Gartenmeister[1]
31. Linke[1]
32. Linke[2]
33. Kireev and Skvortsova[1]
34. Deželić[1]
35. Sălceanu[1]
36. Shalberov and Ostroumov[1]
37. Tausz and Staab[1]
38. Faust[1]
39. Kurnakov[1]
40. Watson, Wien, and Murphy[1]
41. Muchin[1]
42. Pushin and Pintner[1]
43. Lewis[1]

864

| SPECIFIC REFERENCES |||
| :---: | :---: | :---: |
| FOR TABLES 21c, 21c–E, AND 21c–K – (Continued) |||
| October 31, 1948 |||
| REFERENCES |||
| 44.  Dunstan and Stubbs[1] | | |
| 45.  Kendall and Monroe[1] | | |
| 46.  Linebarger[1] | | |
| 47.  Schaaf[1] | | |
| 48.  Zeidler and Schuster[1] | | |
| 49.  Houseman and Keulegan[1] | | |
| 50.  Il'in and Ivanov[1] | | |

| | SPECIFIC REFERENCES<br>FOR TABLES 5c, 5c-E, AND 5c-K<br>November 30, 1949 | | | | |
|---|---|---|---|---|---|
| Compound | REFERENCES FOR | Compound | REFERENCES FOR | | |
| | Viscosity | | Viscosity | | |
| Benzene | 1 | | | | |
| Methylbenzene | 1 | | | | |
| Ethylbenzene | 1 | | | | |
| 1,2-Dimethylbenzene | 2,3,4,5 | | | | |
| 1,3-Dimethylbenzene | 2,3,4,5,6,7,8,9 | | | | |
| 1,4-Dimethylbenzene | 2,3,4,5,10 | | | | |
| n-Propylbenzene | 1 | | | | |
| Isopropylbenzene | 2,4 | | | | |
| 1-Methyl-2-ethylbenzene | | | | | |
| 1-Methyl-3-ethylbenzene | | | | | |
| 1-Methyl-4-ethylbenzene | 2,11 | | | | |
| 1,2,3-Trimethylbenzene | | | | | |
| 1,2,4-Trimethylbenzene | 2,8 | | | | |
| 1,3,5-Trimethylbenzene | | | | | |

## REFERENCES

1. See references for table 21c.
2. American Petroleum Institute Research Project 44[1]
3. Kremann, Gugl, and Meingast[1]
4. Geist and Cannon[1]
5. Thorpe and Rodger[1]
6. Timmermans and Hennaut-Roland[1]
7. Houseman and Keulegan[1]
8. de Carli[1]
9. Miller, C[1]
10. Timmermans and Martin[2]
11. Schmidt and Schoeller[1]

| | SPECIFIC REFERENCES<br>FOR TABLES 20d (PART 1) AND 20d-E (PART 1)<br>June 30, 1949; October 31, 1952 | | | |
|---|---|---|---|---|
| Compound | REFERENCES FOR | Compound | REFERENCES FOR | |
| | Density as a<br>Function of Temperature | | Density as a<br>Function of Temperature | |
| Methane | 1,2 | | | |
| Ethane | 1,3 | | | |
| Propane | 1,3,4,11,12,24,26 | | | |
| n-Butane | 1,4,10,11,12,24,26 | | | |
| n-Pentane | 1,4,5,6,7,11,22,27 | | | |
| n-Hexane | 1,5,6,7,8,14,22 | | | |
| n-Heptane | 1,5,6,7,8,13,15,22,25,27 | | | |
| n-Octane | 1,5,6,7,8,14,22,27 | | | |
| n-Nonane | 1,6,8,9,20,22,25,27 | | | |
| n-Decane | 1,6,8,9,20,22,23 | | | |
| n-Undecane | 1,6,8,9,16,20,22,27 | | | |
| n-Dodecane | 1,6,8,9,20,21,22 | | | |
| n-Tridecane | 1,9,16,21,22,27 | | | |
| n-Tetradecane | 1,9,16,21,22 | | | |
| n-Pentadecane | 1,9,16,21,22 | | | |
| n-Hexadecane | 1,9,16,19,21,22 | | | |
| n-Heptadecane | 1,9,16,21,27 | | | |
| n-Octadecane | 1,9,16,17,21 | | | |
| n-Nonadecane | 1,9,16,17 | | | |
| n-Eicosane | 1,9,16,17,18,21 | | | |

| REFERENCES | | |
|---|---|---|
| 1. American Petroleum Institute Research Project 44[1] | 14. Timmermans and Martin[3] | |
| 2. Keyes, Taylor, and Smith[1] | 15. Timmermans and Hennaut-Roland[3] | |
| 3. Maass and Wright[1] | 16. Krafft[1] | |
| 4. Cragoe[1] | 17. Eykman[3] | |
| 5. Geist and Cannon[1] | 18. Eykman[5] | |
| 6. Dornte and Smyth[1] | 19. Evans, E.B.[1] | |
| 7. Garrett[1] | 20. Bingham and Fornwalt[1] | |
| 8. Quayle, Day, and Brown[1] | 21. Schiessler, Herr, Rytina, Weisel, Fischl, McLaughlin, and Kuehner[1] | |
| 9. Calingaert, Beatty, Kuder, and Thomson[1] | 22. Vogel[2] | |
| 10. Coffin and Maass[1] | 23. Simon[1] | |
| 11. Natural Gasoline Association of America[2] | 24. Lipkin, Davison, and Kurtz[1] | |
| 12. Van der Vet[1] | 25. Forziati and Rossini[2] | |
| 13. Smyth and Stoops[1] | 26. Dana, Jenkins, Burdick, and Timm[1] | |
| | 27. Doolittle and Peterson[1] | |

| | SPECIFIC REFERENCES | | | |
|---|---|---|---|---|
| | FOR TABLES 1d AND 1d-E | | | |
| | October 31, 1950; October 31, 1952 | | | |
| Compound | REFERENCES FOR | Compound | REFERENCES FOR | |
| | Density as a Function of Temperature | | Density as a Function of Temperature | |
| Methane | 1 | | | |
| Ethane | 1 | | | |
| Propane | 1 | | | |
| *n*-Butane | 1 | | | |
| 2-Methylpropane (Isobutane) | 2,3,4,5,6,7,8 | | | |
| *n*-Pentane | 1 | | | |
| 2-Methylbutane (Isopentane) | 2,3,9,10,11,12,13 | | | |
| 2,2-Dimethylpropane (Neopentane) | 2,14 | | | |

REFERENCES

1. See references for Tables 20d (Part 1) and 20d-E (Part 1).
2. American Petroleum Institute Research Project 44[1]
3. Cragoe[1]
4. Natural Gasoline Association of America[2]
5. Wackher, Linn, and Grosse[1]
6. Coffin and Maass[1]
7. Dana, Jenkins, Burdick, and Timm[1]
8. Van der Vet[1]
9. Geist and Cannon[1]
10. Howard, Mears, Fookson, Pomerantz, and Brooks[1]
11. Wibaut, Hoog, Langedijk, Overhoff, Smittenberg, Benninga, Bouman, van Dijk, Gaade, Geldof, Hackman, Jonker, Paap, and Zuiderweg[1]
12. Young[2]
13. Timmermans and Martin[2]
14. Phibbs[2]

868

| | SPECIFIC REFERENCES | | | |
|---|---|---|---|---|
| | FOR TABLES 2d (PART 1) AND 2d-E (PART 1) | | | |
| | October 31, 1950; October 31, 1952 | | | |

| Compound | REFERENCES FOR | Compound | REFERENCES FOR |
|---|---|---|---|
| | Density as a Function of Temperature | | Density as a Function of Temperature |
| *n*-Hexane | 1 | | |
| 2-Methylpentane | 2,3,4,5,6,7,8,9,10,12.13 | | |
| 3-Methylpentane | 2,4,5,6,8,9,10,12,13,14 | | |
| 2,2-Dimethylbutane | 2,5,6,7,8,9,11,12,13 | | |
| 2,3-Dimethylbutane | 2,3,4,5,6,7,8,10,11,12,13,15 | | |

REFERENCES

1. See references for Tables 20d (Part 1) and 20d-E (Part 1).
2. American Petroleum Institute Research Project 44[1]
3. Lemons and Felsing[1]
4. Bridgman[1]
5. Chavanne and van Ressighem[1]
6. van Ressighem[2]
7. Schmerling, Friedman, and Ipatieff[1]
8. Bruun, Hicks-Bruun, and Faulconer[1]
9. Howard, Mears, Pomerantz, and Brooks[1]
10. Geist and Cannon[1]
11. Brooks, Howard, and Crafton[2]
12. Wibaut, Hoog, Langedijk, Overhoff, Smittenberg, Benninga, Bouman, van Dijk, Gaade, Geldof, Hackmann, Jonker, Paap, and Zuiderweg[1]
13. Forziati, Glasgow, Willingham, and Rossini[1]
14. Quayle, Day, and Brown[1]
15. Young[2]

| | SPECIFIC REFERENCES<br>FOR TABLES 2d (PART 2) AND 2d–E (PART 2)<br>October 31, 1950; October 31, 1952 | | | |
|---|---|---|---|---|
| Compound | REFERENCES FOR | Compound | REFERENCES FOR | |
| | Density as a<br>Function of Temperature | | Density as a<br>Function of Temperature | |
| *n*–Heptane | 1 | | | |
| 2–Methylhexane | 2,8,9,16 | | | |
| 3–Methylhexane | 2,8,10 | | | |
| 3–Ethylpentane | 2,8,11,12 | | | |
| 2,2–Dimethylpentane | 2,8,9,10,11,16 | | | |
| 2,3–Dimethylpentane | 2,5,8,9,13,16 | | | |
| 2,4–Dimethylpentane | 2,5,7,8,9,10,13,16 | | | |
| 3,3–Dimethylpentane | 2,8,9,16 | | | |
| 2,2,3–Trimethylbutane | 2,3,4,6,7,8,9,14,15,16 | | | |

## REFERENCES

1. See references for Tables 20d (Part 1) and 20d–E (Part 1).
2. American Petroleum Institute Research Project 44[1]
3. Chavanne and van Ressighem[1]
4. Schmerling, Friedman, and Ipatieff[1]
5. Howard, Mears, Pomerantz, and Brooks[1]
6. Geist and Cannon[1]
7. Brooks, Howard, and Crafton[2]
8. Forziati and Rossini[1]
9. Manzoni and Ansidei[1]
10. de Graef[2]
11. Smyth and Stoops[1]
12. Brooks, Howard, and Crafton[1]
13. Chavanne and de Graef[1]
14. Garrett[1]
15. Chavanne and Lejeune[1]
16. Wibaut, Hoog, Langedijk, Overhoff, Smittenberg, Benninga, Bouman, van Dijk, Gaade, Geldof, Hackmann, Jonker, Paap, and Zuiderweg[1]

| | SPECIFIC REFERENCES | | | |
| --- | --- | --- | --- | --- |
| | FOR TABLES 3d AND 3d-E | | | |
| | October 31, 1950; October 31, 1952 | | | |
| Compound | REFERENCES FOR | Compound | REFERENCES FOR | |
| | Density as a Function of Temperature | | Density as a Function of Temperature | |
| n-Octane | 1 | | | |
| 2-Methylheptane | 2,3,4,5 | | | |
| 3-Methylheptane | 2,3,4,5,6,7,19 | | | |
| 4-Methylheptane | 2,3,4,5,19 | | | |
| 3-Ethylhexane | 2,3,4,5 | | | |
| 2,2-Dimethylhexane | 2,3,4 | | | |
| 2,3-Dimethylhexane | 2,3,4,6,7 | | | |
| 2,4-Dimethylhexane | 2,3,4 | | | |
| 2,5-Dimethylhexane | 2,3,4,6,8,9,10 | | | |
| 3,3-Dimethylhexane | 2,3,4 | | | |
| 3,4-Dimethylhexane | 2,3,4,6,9,11 | | | |
| 2-Methyl-3-ethylpentane | 2,3,4,12,19 | | | |
| 3-Methyl-3-ethylpentane | 2,3,4,6,7 | | | |
| 2,2,3-Trimethylpentane | 2,3,4,6,7,12,13,14 | | | |
| 2,2,4-Trimethylpentane | 2,3,4,6,7,13,15,16,17,19,20 | | | |
| 2,3,3-Trimethylpentane | 2,3,4,12 | | | |
| 2,3,4-Trimethylpentane | 2,3,4,11,16 | | | |
| 2,2,3,3-Tetramethylbutane | 2,18 | | | |

## REFERENCES

1. See references for Tables 20d (Part 1) and 20d-E (Part 1).
2. American Petroleum Institute Research Project 44[1]
3. Forziati, Glasgow, Willingham, and Rossini[1]
4. Geist and Cannon[1]
5. Quayle, Day, and Brown[1]
6. Wibaut, Hoog, Langedijk, Overhoff, Smittenberg, Benninga, van Dijk, Gaade, Geldof, Hackman, Jonker, Paap, and Zuiderweg[1]
7. Manzoni and Ansidei[1]
8. Young[2]
9. Vogel[2]
10. Timmermans and Hennaut-Roland[2]
11. Schmerling, Friedman, and Ipatieff[1]
12. Howard, Mears, Fookson, Pomerantz, and Brooks[1]
13. Lauer[1]
14. Brooks, Howard, and Crafton[1]
15. Brooks[1]
16. Brooks, Howard, and Crafton[2]
17. Smyth and Stoops[1]
18. Seyer, Bennett, and Williams[1]
19. Garrett[1]
20. Kay and Warzel[1]

SPECIFIC REFERENCES

FOR TABLES 24d (PART 1) AND 24d-E (PART 1)

October 31, 1952

| Compound | REFERENCES FOR Density as a Function of Temperature | Compound | REFERENCES FOR Density as a Function of Temperature |
|---|---|---|---|
| Ethene (Ethylene) | 2,3,4,5 | | |
| Propene (Propylene) | 1,2,6 | | |
| 1–Butene | 1,6,7,8,12 | | |
| 1–Pentene | 9,10,11 | | |
| 1–Hexene | 9,10,11,13,14,15,19 | | |
| 1–Heptene | 9,10,11,14,17 | | |
| 1–Octene | 9,10,11,14,15,17, | | |
| 1–Nonene | 9,10,11,14,17 | | |
| 1–Decene | 9,10,11,14,15,17,20 | | |
| 1–Undecene | 9,11 | | |
| 1–Dodecene | 9,10,11,14,15,21,22 | | |
| 1–Tridecene | 11,23,24 | | |
| 1–Tetradecene | 11,15,21 | | |
| 1–Pentadecene | 11,17,23,24,25 | | |
| 1–Hexadecene | 9,10,11,14,15,16,21,22,26,27 | | |
| 1–Heptadecene | 11,24 | | |
| 1–Octadecene | 11,18,21 | | |
| 1–Nonadecene | 11,23 | | |
| 1–Eicosene | 11 | | |

REFERENCES

1. Cragoe[1]
2. Maass and Wright[1]
3. Ladenburg and Krügel[1]
4. Mathias, Crommelin, and Watts[1]
5. Maass and McIntosh[1]
6. Natural Gasoline Association of America[1]
7. Benoliel[1]
8. Coffin and Maass[1]
9. Forziati, Camin, and Rossini[2]
10. Wibaut and Geldof[1]
11. American Petroleum Institute Research Project 44[1]
12. Wackler, Linn, and Gross[1]
13. van Risseghem[6]
14. Geldof and Wibaut[1]
15. Jeffery and Vogel[1]
16. Eykman[5]
17. Lagemann[1]
18. Dover and Hensley[1]
19. Drapier[1]
20. Grosjean[1]
21. Krafft[2]
22. Evans[2]
23. Kozacik and Ried[1]
24. Schiessler, Herr, Rytina, Weisel, Fischl, McLaughlin, and Kuehner[1]
25. Landa and Landova[1]
26. Eykman[4]
27. Schoorl[1]

SPECIFIC REFERENCES

FOR TABLES 5d AND 5d-E

November 30, 1949; October 31, 1952

| Compound | REFERENCES FOR Density as a Function of Temperature | Compound | REFERENCES FOR Density as a Function of Temperature |
|---|---|---|---|
| Benzene | 1 | | |
| Methylbenzene (Toluene) | 1 | | |
| Ethylbenzene | 1 | | |
| 1,2-Dimethylbenzene (o-Xylene) | 2,3,4,5,6,7,8,9,10,11,37,38,39,40 | | |
| 1,3-Dimethylbenzene (m-Xylene) | 2,3,4,5,6,7,8,9,11,12,13,14,15, 19,37,40,41 | | |
| 1,4-Dimethylbenzene (p-Xylene) | 2,3,4,5,6,7,8,9,11,12,16,34,37,40 | | |
| n-Propylbenzene | 1 | | |
| Isopropylbenzene | 2,4,12,17,18,19,20,37 | | |
| 1-Methyl-2-ethylbenzene | 2,21,22,37 | | |
| 1-Methyl-3-ethylbenzene | 2,21,37 | | |
| 1-Methyl-4-ethylbenzene | 2,21,24,25,26,27,28,29,30,37 | | |
| 1,2,3-Trimethylbenzene | 2,32,37 | | |
| 1,2,4-Trimethylbenzene | 2,4,13,35,37 | | |
| 1,3,5-Trimethylbenzene | 2,4,8,11,13,23,26,31,36,37 | | |

## REFERENCES

1. See references for Tables 21d (Part 1), and 21d-E (Part 1).
2. American Petroleum Institute Research Project 44[1]
3. Massart[1]
4. Perkin[2]
5. Kreman, Meingast, and Gugl[1]
6. Heil[1]
7. Richards, Speyers, and Carver[1]
8. Morgan and Daghlian[1]
9. Pinette[1]
10. Landolt and Jahn[1]
11. Patterson[1]
12. Geist and Cannon[1]
13. Azim, Bhatnagar, and Mathur[1]
14. Tyrer[1]
15. Walden and Swinne[1]
16. Block[1]
17. Vogel[3]
18. Silva[1]
19. White and Rose[3]
20. Troyan[1]
21. von Auwers[2]
22. von Auwers[6]
23. Tischenko[1]
24. Tsukervanik and Vikrova[1]
25. Le Fèvre, Le Fèvre and Robertson[1]
26. Schiff[1]
27. Krollpfeiffer[1]
28. Schiff[2]
29. von Auwers and Keil[1]
30. Klages and Keil[1]
31. von Auwers and Müller[2]
32. Smith and Spillane[1]
33. von Auwers and Wieners[1]
34. Timmermans and Martin[2]
35. Biron[1]
36. Garner and Evans[1]
37. Forziati and Rossini[2]
38. Chavanne, Katzenstein, and Pahlavouni[1]
39. Miller, O.[1]
40. Hammond and McArdle[1]
41. Timmermans and Hennaut-Roland[1]

| | SPECIFIC REFERENCES | | |
|---|---|---|---|
| | FOR TABLE 20e (PART 1) | | |
| | October 31, 1952 | | |

| Compound | REFERENCES FOR Surface Tension as a Function of Temperature | Compound | REFERENCES FOR Surface Tension as a Function of Temperature |
|---|---|---|---|
| Methane | 1 | | |
| Ethane | 2 | | |
| Propane | 2 | | |
| n-Butane | 3 | | |
| n-Pentane | 1 | | |
| n-Hexane | 4,5,6,7,8,9,10 | | |
| n-Heptane | 6,8,10,11,12 | | |
| n-Octane | 4,6,8,9,10,13,14 | | |
| n-Nonane | 6,8,10,13 | | |
| n-Decane | 6,8,9 | | |
| n-Undecane | 6,8 | | |
| n-Dodecane | 6,8 | | |
| n-Tridecane | 8 | | |
| n-Tetradecane | 8 | | |
| n-Pentadecane | 8 | | |
| n-Hexadecane | 8 | | |
| n-Heptadecane | 1 | | |
| n-Octadecane | 1 | | |
| n-Nonadecane | 1 | | |
| n-Eicosane | 1 | | |

## REFERENCES

1. American Petroleum Institute Research Project 44[1]
2. Maass and Wright[1]
3. Coffin and Maass[1]
4. Harkins and Cheng[1]
5. Morgan and Chazal[1]
6. Quayle, Day, and Brown[1]
7. Schiff[2]
8. Vogel[2]
9. Hennaut-Roland and Lek[1]
10. Wibaut, Hoog, Langedijk, Overhoff, Smittenberg, Benninga, Bouman, van Dijk, Gaade, Geldof, Hackmann, Jonker, Paap, and Zuiderweg[1]

11. Timmermans and Hennaut-Roland[3]
12. Edgar and Calingaert[1]
13. Quayle and others[1]
14. Richards, Speyers, and Carver[1]

| | SPECIFIC REFERENCES FOR TABLE 1e October 31, 1952 | | | |
|---|---|---|---|---|

| Compound | REFERENCES FOR | Compound | REFERENCES FOR |
|---|---|---|---|
| | Surface Tension as a Function of Temperature | | Surface Tension as a Function of Temperature |
| Methane | 1 | | |
| Ethane | 1 | | |
| Propane | 1 | | |
| $n$–Butane | 1 | | |
| 2–Methylpropane (Isobutane) | 2 | | |
| $n$–Pentane | 1 | | |
| 2–Methylbutane (Isopentane) | 3,4 | | |
| 2,2–Dimethylpropane (Neopentane) | | | |

| REFERENCES |
|---|

1. See references for Table 20e (Part 1).
2. Coffin and Maass[1]
3. Hennaut-Roland and Lek[1]
4. Wibaut, Hoog, Langedijk, Overhoff, Smittenberg, Benninga, Bouman, van Dijk, Gaade, Geldof, Hackmann, Jonker, Paap, and Zuiderweg[1]

| | SPECIFIC REFERENCES | | | |
|---|---|---|---|---|
| | FOR TABLE 2e (PART 1) | | | |
| | October 31, 1952 | | | |
| Compound | REFERENCES FOR | Compound | REFERENCES FOR |
| | Surface Tension as a Function of Temperature | | Surface Tension as a Function of Temperature |
| n-Hexane | 1 | | |
| 2-Methylpentane | 2,3,5 | | |
| 3-Methylpentane | 4,5 | | |
| 2,2-Dimethylbutane | 2,3,5 | | |
| 2,3-Dimethylbutane | 2,3,5 | | |

### REFERENCES

1. See references for Table 20e (Part 1).
2. American Petroleum Institute Research Project 44[1]
3. Taylor, Pignocco, and Rossini[1]
4. Quayle, Day, and Brown[1]
5. Wibaut, Hoog, Langedijk, Overhoff, Smittenberg, Benninga, van Dijk, Gaade, Geldof, Hackman, Jonker, Paap, and Zuiderweg[1]

876

## SPECIFIC REFERENCES
### FOR TABLE 2e (PART 2)
October 31, 1952

| Compound | REFERENCES FOR Surface Tension as a Function of Temperature | Compound | REFERENCES FOR Surface Tension as a Function of Temperature |
|---|---|---|---|
| $n$-Heptane | 1 | | |
| 2-Methylhexane | 2 | | |
| 3-Methylhexane | 2 | | |
| 3-Ethylpentane | 2 | | |
| 2,2-Dimethylpentane | 2 | | |
| 2,3-Dimethylpentane | 2 | | |
| 2,4-Dimethylpentane | 2 | | |
| 3,3-Dimethylpentane | 2 | | |
| 2,2,3-Trimethylbutane | 2 | | |

## REFERENCES

1. See references for Table 20e (PART 1).
2. Quayle and others[1].

| | SPECIFIC REFERENCES FOR TABLE 3e October 31, 1952 | | | | |
|---|---|---|---|---|---|

| Compound | REFERENCES FOR Surface Tension as a Function of Temperature | Compound | REFERENCES FOR Surface Tension as a Function of Temperature |
|---|---|---|---|
| n–Octane | 1 | | |
| 2–Methylheptane | 2,3 | | |
| 3–Methylheptane | 2 | | |
| 4–Methylheptane | 2 | | |
| 3–Ethylhexane | 2 | | |
| 2,2–Dimethylhexane | 2 | | |
| 2,3–Dimethylhexane | 2 | | |
| 2,4–Dimethylhexane | 2 | | |
| 2,5–Dimethylhexane | 2,3,4,5 | | |
| 3,3–Dimethylhexane | 2 | | |
| 3,4–Dimethylhexane | 2,4 | | |
| 2–Methyl–3–ethylpentane | 2 | | |
| 3–Methyl–3–ethylpentane | 2 | | |
| 2,2,3–Trimethylpentane | 2 | | |
| 2,2,4–Trimethylpentane | 2 | | |
| 2,3,3–Trimethylpentane | 2 | | |
| 2,3,4–Trimethylpentane | 2 | | |
| 2,2,3,3–Tetramethylbutane | | | |

REFERENCES

1. See references for Table 20e (Part 1).
2. Quayle and others[1]
3. Richards, Speyers and Carver[1]
4. Vogel[2]
5. Schiff[2]

| | SPECIFIC REFERENCES FOR TABLE 5e October 31, 1952 | | | |
|---|---|---|---|---|
| Compound | REFERENCES FOR | Compound | REFERENCES FOR | |
| | Surface Tension as a Function of Temperature | | Surface Tension as a Function of Temperature | |
| Benzene | 2,3,4,5,6,7,8,9,10,11,12,13,14, 15,16,17,18,26 | | | |
| Methylbenzene (Toluene) | 3,5,7,8,9,12,13,19,20,21,22,23, 27 | | | |
| Ethylbenzene | 9,12,13,14,17,19 | | | |
| 1,2-Dimethylbenzene (o-Xylene) | 7,9,14 | | | |
| 1,3-Dimethylbenzene (m-Xylene) | 7,9,13,14,16,24,25 | | | |
| 1,4-Dimethylbenzene (p-Xylene) | 4,7,9,11,13,14 | | | |
| n-Propylbenzene | 4,7,9,13,19,24 | | | |
| Isopropylbenzene | 1,9,19 | | | |
| 1-Methyl-2-ethylbenzene | 9 | | | |
| 1-Methyl-3-ethylbenzene | 9 | | | |
| 1-Methyl-4-ethylbenzene | 1,7,9 | | | |
| 1,2,3-Trimethylbenzene | 9 | | | |
| 1,2,4-Trimethylbenzene | 1,9,11 | | | |
| 1,3,5-Trimethylbenzene | 7,9,11,16,25 | | | |

### REFERENCES

1. American Petroleum Institute Research Project 44[1]
2. Morgan and Griggs[1]
3. Kremann and Meingast[1]
4. Donaldson and Quayle[1]
5. Transue, Washburn, and Kahler[1]
6. Sugden[1]
7. Schiff[2]
8. Richards and Carver[1]
9. Quayle and Others[1]
10. Walden and Swinne[1]
11. Jaeger[1]
12. Buehler, Gardner, and Clemens[2]
13. Hennaut-Roland and Lek[1]
14. Richards, Speyers, and Carver[1]
15. Morino[1]
16. Renard and Guye[1]
17. Kistiadowsky[3]
18. Harkins and Cheng[1]
19. Vogel[3]
20. Tonomura[1]
21. Ramsay and Aston[1]
22. Satterly and Collingwood[1]
23. Richards and Coombs[1]
24. Timmermans and Hennaut-Roland[1]
25. Dutoit and Friederich[1]
26. Sugden[2]
27. Sugden[3]

| SPECIFIC REFERENCES FOR TABLE 20i June 30, 1949 | | | |
|---|---|---|---|
| Compound | REFERENCES FOR | | |
| | Critical Temperature | Critical Pressure | Critical Density |
| Methane | 7,9,12,19,20,29,33,36,38 | 7,9,12,19,20,29,33,38 | 6,7,9,20 |
| Ethane | 5,8,12,13,22,23,26,27,28,30,37 | 5,8,12,13,22,23,27,28,30 | 5,22 |
| Propane | 3,11,13,24,25,27,32,34 | 3,11,13,24,27,32,34 | 3,10,11,32 |
| n-Butane | 4,14,15,35 | 4,15,35 | 4,10,15 |
| n-Pentane | 1,31,39,40 | 1,31,39,40 | 1,10,31,39,40 |
| n-Hexane | 16,40 | 16,40 | 16,40 |
| n-Heptane | 2,17,18,21,40 | 2,17,18,40 | 2,17,40 |
| n-Octane | 40 | 40 | 40 |
| n-Nonane | 41 | 41 | 41 |
| n-Decane | 41 | 41 | 41 |
| n-Undecane | 41 | 41 | 41 |
| n-Dodecane | 41 | 41 | 41 |
| n-Tridecane | 41 | 41 | 41 |
| n-Tetradecane | 41 | 41 | 41 |
| n-Pentadecane | 41 | 41 | 41 |
| n-Hexadecane | 41 | 41 | 41 |
| n-Heptadecane | 41 | 41 | 41 |
| n-Octadecane | 41 | 41 | 41 |
| n-Nonadecane | 41 | 41 | 41 |
| n-Eicosane | 41 | 41 | 41 |

## REFERENCES

1. Beattie, Douslin, and Levine[1]
2. Beattie and Kay[1]
3. Beattie, Poffenberger, and Hadlock[1]
4. Beattie, Simard, and Su[1]
5. Beattie, Su, and Simard[1]
6. Cardoso[1]
7. Cardoso[2]
8. Cardoso and Bell[1]
9. Corcoran, Bowles, and Lacey[1]
10. Cragoe[1]
11. Deschner and Brown[1]
12. Dewar[2]
13. Hainlen[1]
14. Harand[1]
15. Kay[2]
16. Kay[3]
17. Kay[4]
18. Keyes[1]
19. Keyes[2]
20. Keyes, Taylor, and Smith[1]
21. Khalilov[2]
22. Kuenen[1]
23. Kuenen[2]
24. Lebeau[1]
25. Maass and Wright[1]
26. Mason, Naldrett, and Maass[1]
27. Olszewski[1]
28. Olszewski[2]
29. Olszewski[3]
30. Prins[1]
31. Sage and Lacey[1]
32. Sage, Schaafsma, and Lacey[1]
33. Sarrau[1]
34. Scheeline and Gilliland[1]
35. Seibert and Burrell[1]
36. Wiebe and Brevoort[1]
37. Wiebe, Hubbard, and Brevoort[1]
38. Wroblewski[1]
39. Young[1]
40. Young[2]
41. American Petroleum Institute Research Project 44[1]

## SPECIFIC REFERENCES
## FOR TABLE 1i
October 31, 1948

| Compound | REFERENCES FOR | | |
| --- | --- | --- | --- |
| | Critical Temperature | Critical Pressure | Critical Density |
| Methane | 7,9,12,17,18,26,32,35,37 | 7,9,12,17,18,26,32,37 | 6,7,9,18 |
| Ethane | 5,8,12,13,19,20,23,24,25,28,36 | 5,8,12,13,19,20,24,25,28 | 5,19 |
| Propane | 3,11,13,21,22,24,31,33 | 3,11,13,21,24,31,33 | 3,10,11,14,31 |
| Butane | 4,15,16,34 | 4,16,34 | 4,10,16 |
| 2-Methylpropane | 1,14,15,34 | 1,14,34 | 10,14 |
| Pentane | 2,30,38,39 | 2,30,38,39 | 2,10,30,38,39 |
| 2-Methylbutane | 39 | 39 | 10,27,29,39 |
| 2,2-Dimethylpropane | 2 | 2 | 2 |

## REFERENCES

1. Beattie[1]
2. Beattie, Douslin, and Levine[1]
3. Beattie, Poffenberger, and Hadlock[1]
4. Beattie, Simard, and Su[1]
5. Beattie, Su, and Simard[1]
6. Cardoso[1]
7. Cardoso[2]
8. Cardoso and Bell[1]
9. Corcoran, Bowles, and Lacey[1]
10. Cragoe[1]
11. Deschner and Brown[1]
12. Dewar[2]
13. Hainlen[1]
14. Beattie[3]
15. Harand[1]
16. Kay[2]
17. Keyes[2]
18. Keyes, Taylor, and Smith[1]
19. Kuenen[1]
20. Kuenen[2]
21. Lebeau[1]
22. Maass and Wright[1]
23. Mason, Naldrett, and Maass[1]
24. Olszewski[1]
25. Olszewski[2]
26. Olszewski[3]
27. Predvotitelev[1]
28. Prins[1]
29. Rose-Innes and Young[1]
30. Sage and Lacey[1]
31. Sage, Schaafsma, and Lacey[1]
32. Sarrau[1]
33. Scheeline and Gilliland[1]
34. Seibert and Burrell[1]
35. Wiebe and Brevoort[1]
36. Wiebe, Hubbard, and Brevoort[1]
37. Wroblewski[1]
38. Young[1]
39. Young[2]

| Compound | SPECIFIC REFERENCES FOR TABLE 2i (PART 1) October 31, 1948 REFERENCES FOR | | |
| --- | --- | --- | --- |
| | Critical Temperature | Critical Pressure | Critical Density |
| n–Hexane | 1,2 | 1,2 | 1,2 |
| 2-Methylpentane | 2 | 2 | 2 |
| 3-Methylpentane | 2 | 2 | 2 |
| 2,2-Dimethylbutane | 2 | 2 | 2 |
| 2,3-Dimethylbutane | 1,2 | 1,2 | 1,2 |

REFERENCES

1. Young[2]
2. Kay[3]

| | SPECIFIC REFERENCES<br>FOR TABLE 2i (PART 2)<br>October 31, 1948 | | |
|---|---|---|---|
| Compound | REFERENCES FOR | | |
| | Critical Temperature | Critical Pressure | Critical Density |
| n–Heptane | 1,2,3,4,5 | 1,2,3,5 | 1,2,5 |
| 2–Methylhexane | 3 | 3 | 6 |
| 3–Methylhexane | 3 | 3 | 6 |
| 3–Ethylpentane | 3 | 3 | 6 |
| 2,2–Dimethylpentane | 3 | 3 | 6 |
| 2,3–Dimethylpentane | 3 | 3 | 6 |
| 2,4–Dimethylpentane | 3 · | 3 | 6 |
| 3,3–Dimethylpentane | 6 | 6 | |
| 2,2,3–Trimethylbutane | 3 | 3 | 6 |

| REFERENCES | | |
|---|---|---|
| 1. Beattie and Kay[1]<br>2. Kay[4]<br>3. Keyes[1]<br>4. Khalilov[2]<br>5. Young[2]<br>6. American Petroleum Institute Research<br>    Project 44[1] | | |

| Compound | REFERENCES FOR | | |
|---|---|---|---|
| | Critical Temperature | Critical Pressure | Critical Density |
| n-Octane | 1 | 1 | 1 |
| 2-Methylheptane | 2 | 2 | 2 |
| 3-Methylheptane | 2 | 2 | 2 |
| 4-Methylheptane | 2 | 2 | 2 |
| 3-Ethylhexane | 2 | 2 | 2 |
| 2,2-Dimethylhexane | 2 | 2 | 2 |
| 2,3-Dimethylhexane | 2 | 2 | 2 |
| 2,4-Dimethylhexane | 2 | 2 | 2 |
| 2,5-Dimethylhexane | 1,2 | 1,2 | 2 |
| 3,3-Dimethylhexane | 2 | 2 | 2 |
| 3,4-Dimethylhexane | 2 | 2 | 2 |
| 2-Methyl-3-ethylpentane | 2 | 2 | 2 |
| 3-Methyl-3-ethylpentane | 2 | 2 | 2 |
| 2,2,3-Trimethylpentane | 2 | 2 | 2 |
| 2,2,4-Trimethylpentane | 3 | 3 | 3 |
| 2,3,3-Trimethylpentane | 2 | 2 | 2 |
| 2,3,4-Trimethylpentane | 2 | 2 | 2 |
| 2,2,3,3-Tetramethylbutane | 4 | 4 | 2 |

SPECIFIC REFERENCES FOR TABLE 3i, February 28, 1949

REFERENCES

1. Young[2]
2. American Petroleum Institute Research Project 44[1]
3. Beattie and Edwards[1]
4. Felsing, Cuellar, and Newton[1]

| Compound | REFERENCES FOR | | |
|---|---|---|---|
| | Critical Temperature | Critical Pressure | Critical Density |

SPECIFIC REFERENCES
FOR TABLE 6i
August 31, 1949

| Compound | Critical Temperature | Critical Pressure | Critical Density |
|---|---|---|---|
| Cyclopentane | 1 | 1 | 1 |
| Methylcyclopentane | 1 | 1 | 1 |
| Ethylcyclopentane | 1 | 1 | 1 |
| 1,1-Dimethylcyclopentane | 2 | 2 | 2 |
| 1,cis-2-Dimethylcyclopentane | 2 | 2 | 2 |
| 1,trans-2-Dimethylcyclopentane | 2 | 2 | 2 |
| 1,cis-3-Dimethylcyclopentane | 2 | 2 | 2 |
| 1,trans-3-Dimethylcyclopentane | 2 | 2 | 2 |

REFERENCES

1. Kay[5]
2. American Petroleum Institute Project
   Project 44[1]

| Compound | REFERENCES FOR | | |
|---|---|---|---|
| | Critical Temperature | Critical Pressure | Critical Density |
| Ethene | 1,2,3,4,5,6,7,8,10,11,12 | 2,3,4,6,9,10,11,12 | 1,3,6 |
| Propene | 5,15,16,17,18,19 | 16,17,18 | 13,17,18 |
| 1-Butene | 14,20,22,23 | 14,22,23 | 13,14 |
| cis-2-Butene | 13,20 | 13 | 13 |
| trans-2-Butene | 13 | 13 | 13 |
| 2-Methylpropene | 20,24,25,26 | 24,25,26 | 13,24 |
| 1-Pentene | 21,27 | 27 | |
| cis-2-Pentene | | | |
| trans-2-Pentene | | | |
| 2-Methyl-1-butene | | | |
| 3-Methyl-1-butene | | | |
| 2-Methyl-2-butene | | | |

SPECIFIC REFERENCES
FOR TABLE 8i (PART 1)
October 31, 1948

REFERENCES

1. Cailletet and Mathias[1]
2. Cardoso and Arni[1]
3. Dacey, McIntosh, and Maass[1]
4. Dewar[2]
5. Maass and Wright[1]
6. McIntosh, Dacey, and Maass[1]
7. McIntosh and Maass[1]
8. Naldrett and Maass[1]
9. Olszewski[4]
10. Olszewski[2]
11. Sarrau[2]
12. Van der Waals[1]
13. Cragoe[1]
14. Beattie[3]
15. Marsden and Maass[1]
16. Seibert and Burrell[1]
17. Souders[1]
18. Vaughan and Graves[1]
19. Winkler and Maass[1]
20. Coffin and Maass[1]
21. Pawlewski[1]
22. Kellogg Company[1]
23. Olds, Sage, and Lacey[1]
24. Beattie, Ingersoll, and Stockmayer[1]
25. Benedict[1]
26. Scheeline and Gilliland[1]
27. Day, Nicholson, and Felsing[1]

| | REFERENCES FOR | | |
|---|---|---|---|
| Compound | Critical Temperature | Critical Pressure | Critical Density |

SPECIFIC REFERENCES
FOR TABLE 11i (PART 1)
October 31, 1948

| Compound | Critical Temperature | Critical Pressure | Critical Density |
|---|---|---|---|
| Propadiene | 2 | | |
| 1,2-Butadiene | | | |
| 1,3-Butadiene | 1,3 | 3 | 3 |
| 1,2-Pentadiene | | | |
| 1-cis-3-Pentadiene | | | |
| 1-trans-3-Pentadiene | | | |
| 1,4-Pentadiene | | | |
| 2,3-Pentadiene | | | |
| 3-Methyl-1,2-butadiene | | | |
| 2-Methyl-1,3-butadiene | | | |

REFERENCES

1. Garner, Adams, and Stuchell[1]
2. Lespiau and Chavanne[1]
3. Scott, Meyers, Rands, Brickwedde, and Bekkedahl[1]

| Compound | REFERENCES FOR | | |
|---|---|---|---|
| | Critical Temperature | Critical Pressure | Critical Density |
| Ethyne | 1,2,3,4,5,6,7,8 | 1,2,3,5,6,8 | 7,8 |
| 1-Propyne | 9,10,11 | | |
| 1-Butyne | 10 | | |
| 2-Butyne | 10 | | |
| 1-Pentyne | 10 | | |
| 2-Pentyne | | | |
| 3-Methyl-1-butyne | | | |

SPECIFIC REFERENCES
FOR TABLE 12i
October 31, 1948

REFERENCES

1. Ansdell[1]
2. Cardoso and Baumé[1]
3. Cardoso and Baumé[2]
4. Dewar[1]
5. Dewar[2]
6. Kuenen[2]
7. Mathias[1]
8. McIntosh[1]
9. Maass and Wright[1]
10. Morehouse and Maass[1]
11. Lespiau and Chavanne[1]

888

| | SPECIFIC REFERENCES FOR TABLE 5i April 30, 1949 | | |
|---|---|---|---|
| Compound | REFERENCES FOR | | |
| | Critical Temperature | Critical Pressure | Critical Density |
| Benzene | 1,3,4,5,6,7 | 1,3,5,6,10 | 5,10 |
| Methylbenzene | 1,4,7,8 | 1 | 11 |
| Ethylbenzene | 1 | 1 | 11 |
| 1,2-Dimethylbenzene | 1,2,4 | 1 | 11 |
| 1,3-Dimethylbenzene | 1,2 | 1 | 11 |
| 1,4-Dimethylbenzene | 1,2,4 | 1 | 11 |
| n-Propylbenzene | 1 | 1 | 11 |
| Isopropylbenzene | 1 | 1 | 11 |
| 1-Methyl-2-ethylbenzene | 11 | 11 | 11 |
| 1-Methyl-3-ethylbenzene | 11 | 11 | 11 |
| 1-Methyl-4-ethylbenzene | 11 | 11 | 11 |
| 1,2,3-Trimethylbenzene | 11 | 11 | 11 |
| 1,2,4-Trimethylbenzene | 1,11 | 1 | 11 |
| 1,3,5-Trimethylbenzene | 1,2 | 1 | 11 |

REFERENCES

1. Altschul[1]
2. Brown[1]
3. Dewar[2]
4. Fischer and Reichel[1]
5. Gornowski, Amick, and Hixson[1]
6. Esso Laboratories[1]
7. Harand[1]
8. Pawlewski[1]
9. Starobinets and Pamfilov[1]
10. Young[2]
11. American Petroleum Institute Research Project 44[1]

| Compound | REFERENCES FOR Vapor Pressures and Boiling Points[a] | Compound | REFERENCES FOR Vapor Pressures and Boiling Points[a] |
|---|---|---|---|
| Methane | 1,2,3,17,18 | | |
| Ethane | 1,4,24 | | |
| Propane | 1,5,15 | | |
| n-Butane | 1,6,11,15 | | |
| n-Pentane | 7,8,19 | | |
| n-Hexane | 7,20 | | |
| n-Heptane | 7,9,10,13,21 | | |
| n-Octane | 7,22 | | |
| n-Nonane | 7,13 | | |
| n-Decane | 7 | | |
| n-Undecane | 23 | | |
| n-Dodecane | 7 | | |
| n-Tridecane | 14 | | |
| n-Tetradecane | 12,14 | | |
| n-Pentadecane | 12,14 | | |
| n-Hexadecane | 14,16,23 | | |
| n-Heptadecane | 12,14,16 | | |
| n-Octadecane | 12,14,16 | | |
| n-Nonadecane | 12,14 | | |
| n-Eicosane | 14 | | |

SPECIFIC REFERENCES
FOR TABLES 20k (PART 1) AND 20k-E (PART 1)
February 28, 1949; December 31, 1952

[a] For the references to the normal boiling point, see the references to the corresponding "a" table.

## REFERENCES

1. Cragoe[2]
2. Freeth and Verschoyle[1]
3. Clusius and Weygand[1]
4. Loomis and Walters[1]
5. Kemp and Egan[1]
6. Aston and Messerly[2]
7. Willingham, Taylor, Pignocco, and Rossini[1]
8. Messerly and Kennedy[1]
9. Smith, E.R.[1]
10. Calingaert[1]
11. Wackher, Linn, and Grosse[1]
12. Krafft[1]
13. Forziati, Norris, and Rossini[1]
14. American Petroleum Institute Research Project 44[1]
15. Dana, Jenkins, Burdick, and Timm[1]
16. Bradley and Shellard[1]
17. Henning and Stock[1]
18. Keyes, Taylor, and Smith[1]
19. Young[1]
20. Thomas and Young[1]
21. Young[3]
22. Young[4]
23. American Petroleum Institute Research Project 6[1]
24. Burrell and Robertson[1]

| SPECIFIC REFERENCES |||||
| --- |
| FOR TABLES 1k AND 1k-E ||||| 
| May 31, 1947; December 31, 1952 |||||

| Compound | REFERENCES FOR | | Compound | REFERENCES FOR |
| --- | --- | --- | --- | --- |
| | Vapor Pressures and Boiling Points[a] | | | Vapor Pressures and Boiling Points[a] |
| Methane | 1 | | | |
| Ethane | 1 | | | |
| Propane | 1 | | | |
| n-Butane | 1 | | | |
| 2-Methylpropane (Isobutane) | 2,4,8,9,11,12 | | | |
| n-Pentane | 1 | | | |
| 2-Methylbutane (Isopentane) | 5,6 | | | |
| 2,2-Dimethylpropane (Neopentane) | 3,7,10 | | | |

[a] For the references to the normal boiling point, see the references to the corresponding "a" table.

| REFERENCES |||
| --- |

1. See references for Tables 20k (Part 1), and 20k-E (Part 1).
2. Cragoe[2]
3. Aston and Messerly[1]
4. Aston, Kennedy, and Schumann[1]
5. Willingham, Taylor, Pignocco, and Rossini[1]
6. Schumann, Aston, and Sagenkahn[1]
7. Benoliel[1]
8. Dana, Jenkins, Burdick, and Timm[1]
9. Wackher, Linn, and Grosse[1]
10. Whitmore and Fleming[1]
11. Hückel and Rossmann[1].
12. Burrell and Robertson[2]

891

| Compound | REFERENCES FOR Vapor Pressures and Boiling Points[a] | | Compound | REFERENCES FOR Vapor Pressures and Boiling Points[a] |
|---|---|---|---|---|
| n–Hexane | 1 | | | |
| 2–Methylpentane | 2 | | | |
| 3–Methylpentane | 2 | | | |
| 2,2–Dimethylbutane | 2,3 | | | |
| 2,3–Dimethylbutane | 2 | | | |

SPECIFIC REFERENCES
FOR TABLES 2k (PART 1) AND 2k–E (PART 1)
May 31, 1947; December 31, 1952

[a] For the references to the normal boiling point, see the references to the corresponding "a" table.

REFERENCES

1. See references for Table 20k.
2. Willingham, Taylor, Pignocco, and Rossini[1]
3. Nicolini and Laffitte[1]

| | SPECIFIC REFERENCES<br>FOR TABLES 2k (PART 2) AND 2k-E (PART 2)<br>May 31, 1947; December 31, 1948; December 31, 1952 | | | |
|---|---|---|---|
| | REFERENCES FOR | | REFERENCES FOR |
| Compound | Vapor Pressures and Boiling Points[a] | Compound | Vapor Pressures and Boiling Points[a] |
| $n$-Heptane | 1 | | |
| 2-Methylhexane | 3,4,6 | | |
| 3-Methylhexane | 3,4,6 | | |
| 3-Ethylpentane | 3,5,6 | | |
| 2,2-Dimethylpentane | 2,3,6 | | |
| 2,3-Dimethylpentane | 3,6 | | |
| 2,4-Dimethylpentane | 3,4,6 | | |
| 3,3-Dimethylpentane | 2,3,6 | | |
| 2,2,3-Trimethylbutane | 3,5,6 | | |

[a] For the references to the normal boiling point, see the references to the corresponding "a" table.

| REFERENCES | | |
|---|---|---|
| 1. See references for Tables 20k (Part 1) and 20k-E (Part 1).<br>2. Willingham, Taylor, Pignocco, and Rossini[1]<br>3. Forziati, Norris, and Rossini[1]<br>4. Calingaert and Thomson[1]<br>5. Smith, E.R.[2]<br>6. Calingaert[1] | | |

## SPECIFIC REFERENCES
### FOR TABLES 3k AND 3k-E
May 31, 1947; December 31, 1952

| Compound | REFERENCES FOR Vapor Pressures and Boiling Points[a] | Compound | REFERENCES FOR Vapor Pressures and Boiling Points[a] |
|---|---|---|---|
| n–Octane | 1 | | |
| 2–Methylheptane | 2 | | |
| 3–Methylheptane | 2 | | |
| 4–Methylheptane | 2 | | |
| 3–Ethylhexane | 2 | | |
| 2,2–Dimethylhexane | 2 | | |
| 2,3–Dimethylhexane | 2 | | |
| 2,4–Dimethylhexane | 2 | | |
| 2,5–Dimethylhexane | 2 | | |
| 3,3–Dimethylhexane | 2 | | |
| 3,4–Dimethylhexane | 2 | | |
| 2–Methyl–3–ethylpentane | 2 | | |
| 3–Methyl–3–ethylpentane | 2 | | |
| 2,2,3–Trimethylpentane | 2 | | |
| 2,2,4–Trimethylpentane | 2,3,5 | | |
| 2,3,3–Trimethylpentane | 2 | | |
| 2,3,4–Trimethylpentane | 2 | | |
| 2,2,3,3–Tetramethylbutane | 4,6 | | |

[a] For the references to the normal boiling point, see the references to the corresponding "a" table.

## REFERENCES

1. See references for Tables 20k (Part 1) and 20k–E (Part 1).
2. Willingham, Taylor, Pignocco, and Rossini[1]
3. Smith, E.R.[1]
4. Calingaert, Soroos, Hnizda, and Shapiro[1]
5. Nicolini and Laffitte[1]
6. Scott, Douslin, Gross, Oliver, and Huffman[1]

| | SPECIFIC REFERENCES<br>FOR TABLES 4k AND 4k-E<br>November 30, 1949 (Corrected) | | | |
|---|---|---|---|---|
| Compound | REFERENCES FOR | Compound | REFERENCES FOR |
| | Vapor Pressures<br>and Boiling Points[a] | | Vapor Pressures<br>and Boiling Points[a] |
| *n*–Nonane | 1 | 2,3–Dimethyl–3–ethylpentane | 3 |
| 2–Methyloctane | 3 | 2,4–Dimethyl–3–ethylpentane | 3 |
| 3–Methyloctane | 3 | 2,2,3,3–Tetramethylpentane | 2 |
| 4–Methyloctane | 3 | 2,2,3,4–Tetramethylpentane | 2 |
| 3–Ethylheptane | 3 | 2,2,4,4–Tetramethylpentane | 2,4 |
| 4–Ethylheptane | 3 | 2,3,3,4–Tetramethylpentane | 2 |
| 2,2–Dimethylheptane | 3 | | |
| 2,3–Dimethylheptane | 3 | | |
| 2,4–Dimethylheptane | 3 | | |
| 2,5–Dimethylheptane | 3 | | |
| 2,6–Dimethylheptane | 3 | | |
| 3,3–Dimethylheptane | 3 | | |
| 3,4–Dimethylheptane | 3 | | |
| 3,5–Dimethylheptane | 3 | | |
| 4,4–Dimethylheptane | 3 | | |
| 2–Methyl–3–ethylhexane | 3 | | |
| 2–Methyl–4–ethylhexane | 3 | | |
| 3–Methyl–3–ethylhexane | 3 | | |
| 3–Methyl–4–ethylhexane | 3 | | |
| 2,2,3–Trimethylhexane | 3 | | |
| 2,2,4–Trimethylhexane | 3 | | |
| 2,2,5–Trimethylhexane | 2 | | |
| 2,3,3–Trimethylhexane | 3 | | |
| 2,3,4–Trimethylhexane | 3 | | |
| 2,3,5–Trimethylhexane | 3 | | |
| 2,4,4–Trimethylhexane | 2 | | |
| 3,3,4–Trimethylhexane | 3 | | |
| 3,3–Diethylpentane | 2 | | |
| 2,2–Dimethyl–3–ethylpentane | 3 | | |

[a] For the references to the normal boiling point, see the references to the corresponding "a" table.

| REFERENCES | | |
|---|---|---|
| 1. See references for Tables 20k (Part 1)<br>   and 20k-E (Part 1).<br>2. Forziati, Norris, and Rossini[1]<br>3. American Petroleum Institute Research<br>   Project 44[1]<br>4. Smith, E.R.[2] | | |

## SPECIFIC REFERENCES
### FOR TABLES 22k (PART 1) AND 22k-E (PART 1)
#### October 31, 1950 (Corrected)

| Compound | REFERENCES FOR Vapor Pressures and Boiling Points[a] | Compound | REFERENCES FOR Vapor Pressures and Boiling Points[a] |
|---|---|---|---|
| Cyclopentane | 2,3,5 | | |
| Methylcyclopentane | 2,4,5 | | |
| Ethylcyclopentane | 1,5 | | |
| n-Propylcyclopentane | 1,2 | | |
| n-Butylcyclopentane | 12 | | |
| n-Pentylcyclopentane | 12 | | |
| n-Hexylcyclopentane | 12 | | |
| n-Heptylcyclopentane | 12 | | |
| n-Octylcyclopentane | 7,8,12 | | |
| n-Nonylcyclopentane | 12 | | |
| n-Decylcyclopentane | 6,12 | | |
| n-Undecylcyclopentane | 12 | | |
| n-Dodecylcyclopentane | 9,10,11,12 | | |
| n-Tridecylcyclopentane | 12 | | |
| n-Tetradecylcyclopentane | 12 | | |
| n-Pentadecycyclopentane | 12 | | |
| n-Hexadecylcyclopentane | 12 | | |

[a] For the references to the normal boiling point, see the references to the corresponding "a" table.

### REFERENCES

1. Forziati, Norris, and Rossini[1]
2. Willingham, Taylor, Pignocco, and Rossini[1]
3. Aston, Fink, and Schumann[1]
4. Schmitt[1]
5. Kay[5]
6. American Petroleum Institute Research Project 6[1]
7. Zelinskiĭ, Michlina, and Eventova[1]
8. Schmidt, and Gemassmer[1]
9. von Braun, Kamp, and Kopp[1]
10. Smith, L.[1]
11. Doss[1]
12. American Petroleum Institute Research Project 44[1]

896

| | SPECIFIC REFERENCES<br>FOR TABLES 6k AND 6k-E<br>May 31, 1947; August 31, 1949; December 31, 1952 | | | |
|---|---|---|---|---|
| | REFERENCES FOR | | | REFERENCES FOR |
| Compound | Vapor Pressures<br>and Boiling Points[a] | | Compound | Vapor Pressures<br>and Boiling Points[a] |
| Cyclopentane | 1 | | | |
| Methylcyclopentane | 1 | | | |
| Ethylcyclopentane | 1 | | | |
| 1,1-Dimethylcyclopentane | 2 | | | |
| 1,cis-2-Dimethylcyclopentane | 2 | | | |
| 1,trans-2-Dimethylcyclopentane | 2 | | | |
| 1,cis-3-Dimethylcyclopentane | 2 | | | |
| 1,trans-3-Dimethylcyclopentane | 2 | | | |

[a] For the references to the normal boiling point, see the references to the corresponding "a" table.

REFERENCES

1. See references for Tables 22k (Part 1) and 22k-E (Part 1).
2. Forziati, Norris, and Rossini[1]

| | SPECIFIC REFERENCES FOR TABLES 15k AND 15k-E August 31, 1949; December 31, 1952 | | | |
|---|---|---|---|---|
| Compound | REFERENCES FOR | Compound | REFERENCES FOR | |
| | Vapor Pressures and Boiling Points[a] | | Vapor Pressures and Boiling Points[a] | |
| n-Propylcyclopentane | 1,2 | | | |
| Isopropylcyclopentane | 1,2 | | | |
| 1-Methyl-1-ethylcyclopentane | 1 | | | |
| 1-Methyl-cis-2-ethylcyclopentane | 1 | | | |
| 1-Methyl-trans-2-ethylcyclopentane | 3 | | | |
| 1-Methyl-cis-3-ethylcyclopentane | 3 | | | |
| 1-Methyl-trans-3-ethylcyclopentane | 3 | | | |
| 1,1,2-Trimethylcyclopentane | 1 | | | |
| 1,1,3,-Trimethylcyclopentane | 1 | | | |
| 1,cis-2,cis-3-Trimethylcyclopentane | 3,4 | | | |
| 1,cis-2,trans-3-Trimethylcyclopentane | 3 | | | |
| 1,trans-2,cis-3-Trimethylcyclopentane | 3,4 | | | |
| 1,cis-2,cis-4-Trimethylcyclopentane | 3 | | | |
| 1,cis-2,trans-4-Trimethylcyclopentane | 1 | | | |
| 1,trans-2,cis-4-Trimethylcyclopentane | 1 | | | |

[a] For the references to the normal boiling point, see the references to the corresponding "a" table.

REFERENCES

1. Forziati, Norris, and Rossini[1]
2. Willingham, Taylor, Pignocco, and Rossini[1]
3. American Petroleum Institute Research Project 44[1]
4. American Petroleum Institute Research Project 6[1]

# SPECIFIC REFERENCES
## FOR TABLES 7k AND 7k-E
### May 31, 1947; December 31, 1952

| Compound | REFERENCES FOR Vapor Pressures and Boiling Points[a] | Compound | REFERENCES FOR Vapor Pressures and Boiling Points[a] |
|---|---|---|---|
| Cyclohexane | 1,2,3 | | |
| Methylcyclohexane | 1,6 | | |
| Ethylcyclohexane | 1 | | |
| 1,1-Dimethylcyclohexane | 4,5 | | |
| 1,cis-2-Dimethylcyclohexane | 1 | | |
| 1,trans-2-Dimethylcyclohexane | 1 | | |
| 1,cis-3-Dimethylcyclohexane | 1 | | |
| 1,trans-3-Dimethylcyclohexane | 1 | | |
| 1,cis-4-Dimethylcyclohexane | 1 | | |
| 1,trans-4-Dimethylcyclohexane | 1 | | |

[a] For the references to the normal boiling point, see the references to the corresponding "a" table.

## REFERENCES

1. Willingham, Taylor, Pignocco, and Rossini[1]
2. Scatchard, Wood, and Mochel[1]
3. Aston, Szasz, and Fink[1]
4. Forziati, Norris, and Rossini[1]
5. American Petroleum Institute Research Project 44[1]
6. Stuckey and Saylor[1]

| | REFERENCES FOR | Compound | REFERENCES FOR |
|---|---|---|---|
| Compound | Vapor Pressures and Boiling Points[a] | | Vapor Pressures and Boiling Points[a] |
| Ethene (Ethylene) | 1,2,3,5,15 | | |
| Propene (Propylene) | 1,4,5 | | |
| 1-Butene | 1,5,6,12,13 | | |
| 1-Pentene | 7,8 | | |
| 1-Hexene | 8 | | |
| 1-Heptene | 8,11,14 | | |
| 1-Octene | 8 | | |
| 1-Nonene | 8 | | |
| 1-Decene | 8 | | |
| 1-Undecene | 8 | | |
| 1-Dodecene | 8 | | |
| 1-Tridecene | 9,10 | | |
| 1-Tetradecene | 9 | | |
| 1-Pentadecene | 9,10 | | |
| 1-Hexadecene | 9 | | |
| 1-Heptadecene | 9,10 | | |
| 1-Octadecene | 9 | | |
| 1-Nonadecene | 9 | | |
| 1-Eicosene | 9 | | |

SPECIFIC REFERENCES
FOR TABLES 24k (PART 1) AND 24k-E (PART 1)
September 30, 1951 (Corrected)

[a] For the references to the normal boiling point, see the references to the corresponding "a" table.

REFERENCES

1. Cragoe[2]
2. Egan and Kemp[1]
3. Henning and Stock[1]
4. Powell and Giauque[1]
5. Lamb and Roper[1]
6. Benoliel[1]
7. Scott, Waddington, Smith, and Huffman[1]
8. Forziati, Camin, and Rossini[1]
9. American Petroleum Institute Research Project 44[1]
10. Schiessler, Herr, Rytina, Weisel, Fischl, McLaughlin, and Kuehner[1]
11. Lister[1]
12. Aston, Fink, Bestul, Pace, and Szasz[1]
13. Coffin and Maass[1]
14. Bent, Cuthbertson, Dorfman, and Leary[1]
15. Burrell and Robertson[2]

## SPECIFIC REFERENCES
FOR TABLES 8k (PART 1) AND 8k-E (PART 1)
October 31, 1950; December 31, 1952

| Compound | REFERENCES FOR Vapor Pressures and Boiling Points[a] | Compound | REFERENCES FOR Vapor Pressures and Boiling Points[a] |
|---|---|---|---|
| Ethene (Ethylene) | 1 | | |
| Propene (Propylene) | 1 | | |
| 1-Butene | 1 | | |
| cis-2-Butene | 4,5,6,8 | | |
| trans-2-Butene | 4,5,6,7 | | |
| 2-Methylpropene (Isobutene) | 4,5,9 | | |
| 1-Pentene | 1 | | |
| cis-2-Pentene | 2 | | |
| trans-2-Pentene | 2 | | |
| 2-Methyl-1-butene | 3 | | |
| 3-Methyl-1-butene | 1 | | |
| 2-Methyl-2-butene | 3,4 | | |

[a] For the references to the normal boiling point, see the references to the corresponding "a" table.

## REFERENCES

1. See references for Tables 24k (Part 1) and 24k-E (Part 1).
2. Waddington and others[1]
3. Scott, Waddington, Smith, and Huffman[1]
4. Lamb and Roper[1]
5. Cragoe[2]
6. Kistiakowsky, Ruhoff, Smith, and Vaughan[1]
7. Guttman and Pitzer[1]
8. Scott, Ferguson, and Brickwedde[1]
9. Coffin and Maass[3]

Carnegie Institute of Technology

| | SPECIFIC REFERENCES<br>FOR TABLE 11k (PART 1) AND 11k—E (PART 1)<br>September 30, 1951; December 31, 1952 | | | |
|---|---|---|---|---|
| | REFERENCES FOR | | | REFERENCES FOR |
| Compound | Vapor Pressures and Boiling Points[a] | | Compound | Vapor Pressures and Boiling Points[a] |
| Propadiene (Allene) | 1,2,3 | | | |
| 1,2-Butadiene | 4,6 | | | |
| 1,3-Butadiene | 5,9 | | | |
| 1,2-Pentadiene | 8 | | | |
| 1,cis-3-Pentadiene | 8 | | | |
| 1,trans-3-Pentadiene | 8 | | | |
| 1,4-Pentadiene | 3,8 | | | |
| 2,3-Pentadiene | 8 | | | |
| 3-Methyl-1,2-butadiene | 7 | | | |
| 2-Methyl-1,3-butadiene (Isoprene) | 8 | | | |

[a] For the references to the normal boiling point, see the references to the corresponding "a" table.

## REFERENCES

1. Livingston and Heisig[1]
2. Kistiakowsky, Ruhoff, Smith, and Vaughan[3]
3. Lamb and Roper[1]
4. Aston and Szasz[1]
5. Scott, Meyers, Rands, Brickwedde, and Bekkedahl[1]
6. American Petroleum Institute Research Project 6[1]
7. American Petroleum Institute Research Project 44[1]
8. Forziati, Camin and Rossini[1]
9. Heisig[2]

SPECIFIC REFERENCES

FOR TABLES 5k AND 5k-E

May 31, 1947; April 30, 1949; December 31, 1952

| Compound | REFERENCES FOR Vapor Pressures and Boiling Points[a] | Compound | REFERENCES FOR Vapor Pressures and Boiling Points[a] |
|---|---|---|---|
| Benzene | 1,2,3,4,5,6,7,8,9,10,11,14,15 | | |
| Methylbenzene (Toluene) | 1,2,7,8 | | |
| Ethylbenzene | 1,2,4,12,16 | | |
| 1,2-Dimethylbenzene (o-Xylene) | 1,2,4,8,13 | | |
| 1,3-Dimethylbenzene (m-Xylene) | 1,2,4,8,13 | | |
| 1,4-Dimethylbenzene (p-Xylene) | 1,2,4,8,13 | | |
| n-Propylbenzene | 1,2 | | |
| Isopropylbenzene | 1,2,17 | | |
| 1-Methyl-2-ethylbenzene | 1 | | |
| 1-Methyl-3-ethylbenzene | 1 | | |
| 1-Methyl-4-ethylbenzene | 1 | | |
| 1,2,3-Trimethylbenzene | 1,18,19 | | |
| 1,2,4-Trimethylbenzene | 1,18 | | |
| 1,3,5-Trimethylbenzene | 1,4,13,18 | | |

[a] For the references to the normal boiling point, see the references to the corresponding "a" table.

REFERENCES

1. Forziati, Norris, and Rossini[1]
2. Willingham, Taylor, Pignocco, and Rossini[1]
3. Smith, E.R.[2]
4. Stuckey and Saylor[1]
5. Scatchard, Wood, and Mochel[1]
6. Osborne and Ginnings[1]
7. Zmaczynski[1]
8. Pitzer and Scott[2]
9. Stull[1]
10. Huffman, Parks, and Daniels[1]
11. Fiock, Ginnings, and Holton[1]
12. Guttman, Westrum, and Pitzer[1]
13. Kassel[4]
14. Rodulescu[1]
15. Mali[1]
16. Scott and Brickwedde[1]
17. Kobe, Okabe, Ramstad, and Huemmer[1]
18. Sears[1]
19. Smith and Spillane[1]

903

| | SPECIFIC REFERENCES | | | |
|---|---|---|---|---|

SPECIFIC REFERENCES
FOR TABLES 14k AND 14k-E
April 30, 1949; December 31, 1952

| Compound | REFERENCES FOR Vapor Pressures and Boiling Points[a] | Compound | REFERENCES FOR Vapor Pressures and Boiling Points[a] |
|---|---|---|---|
| n-Butylbenzene | 1 | | |
| Isobutylbenzene | 1 | | |
| sec-Butylbenzene | 1 | | |
| tert-Butylbenzene | 1 | | |
| 1-Methyl-2-propylbenzene | 2 | | |
| 1-Methyl-3-propylbenzene | 2 | | |
| 1-Methyl-4-propylbenzene | 2 | | |
| 1-Methyl-2-isopropylbenzene | 2 | | |
| 1-Methyl-3-isopropylbenzene | 2,3 | | |
| 1-Methyl-4-isopropylbenzene | 2,4 | | |
| 1,2-Diethylbenzene | 1 | | |
| 1,3-Diethylbenzene | 1 | | |
| 1,4-Diethylbenzene | 1 | | |
| 1,2-Dimethyl-3-ethylbenzene | 2,3 | | |
| 1,2-Dimethyl-4-ethylbenzene | 2,3 | | |
| 1,3-Dimethyl-2-ethylbenzene | 2,3 | | |
| 1,3-Dimethyl-4-ethylbenzene | 2,3 | | |
| 1,3-Dimethyl-5-ethylbenzene | 2,3 | | |
| 1,4-Dimethyl-2-ethylbenzene | 2,3 | | |
| 1,2,3,4-Tetramethylbenzene | 5,6 | | |
| 1,2,3,5-Tetramethylbenzene | 2,3,6 | | |
| 1,2,4,5-Tetramethylbenzene | 2,6 | | |

[a] For the references to the normal boiling point, see the references to the corresponding "a" table.

REFERENCES

1. Forziati, Norris, and Rossini[1]
2. American Petroleum Institute Research Project 44[1]
3. American Petroleum Institute Research Project 6[1]
4. Kobe, Okabe, and Ramstead[1]
5. Mair and Streiff[1]
6. MacDougall and Smith[1]

| | SPECIFIC REFERENCES<br>FOR TABLES 27k AND 27k-E<br>August 31, 1949; December 31, 1952 | | | |
|---|---|---|---|---|
| Compound | REFERENCES FOR | Compound | REFERENCES FOR |
| | Vapor Pressures<br>and Boiling Points[a] | | Vapor Pressures<br>and Boiling Points[a] |
| Naphthalene | 1,2,3,4,5,6,7,8,9,11,12,13,14 | | |
| 1-Methylnaphthalene | 1,2,11 | | |
| 2-Methylnaphthalene | 1,2,11 | | |
| 1-Ethylnaphthalene | 2,10 | | |
| 2-Ethylnaphthalene | 2,10 | | |

[a] For the references to the normal boiling point, see the references to the corresponding "a" table.

## REFERENCES

1. American Petroleum Institute Research Project 6[1]
2. American Petroleum Institute Research Project 44[1]
3. Beckmann and Lieshe[1]
4. Burk[1]
5. Crafts[1]
6. Crafts[2]
7. Eppley[1]
8. Finck and Wilhelm[1]
9. Jacquerod and Wassmer[1]
10. Kutz, Nickels, McGovern, and Corson[1]
11. Mair and Streiff[2]
12. Mortimer and Murphy[1]
13. Nelson and Senseman[1]
14. Waidner and Burgess[1]

| | SPECIFIC REFERENCES<br>FOR TABLE 20m<br>April 30, 1949 | | | |
|---|---|---|---|---|
| Compound | REFERENCES FOR | Compound | REFERENCES FOR |
| | Heat of Vaporization | | Heat of Vaporization |
| Methane | 2,3 | | |
| Ethane | 4 | | |
| Propane | 5,6 | | |
| n–Butane | 6,7 | | |
| n–Pentane | 8,9,10,11 | | |
| n–Hexane | 8,12,13,14 | | |
| n–Heptane | 8,15,16 | | |
| n–Octane | 1,8 | | |
| n–Nonane | 1,8 | | |
| n–Decane | 1,8 | | |
| n–Undecane | 1 | | |
| n–Dodecane | 1 | | |
| n–Tridecane | 1 | | |
| n–Tetradecane | 1 | | |
| n–Pentadecane | 1 | | |
| n–Hexadecane | 1 | | |
| n–Heptadecane | 1 | | |
| n–Octadecane | 1 | | |
| n–Nonadecane | 1 | | |
| n–Eicosane | 1 | | |

## REFERENCES

1. American Petroleum Institute Research Project 44[1]
2. Frank and Clusius[2]
3. Osborne and others[1]
4. Witt and Kemp[1]
5. Kemp and Egan[1]
6. Dana, Jenkins, Burdick, and Timm[1]
7. Aston and Messerly[2]
8. Osborne and Ginnings[2]
9. Messerly and Kennedy[1]
10. Pitzer[5]
11. Sage, Evans, and Lacey[1]
12. Waddington and Douslin[1]
13. Mathews[1]
14. Lemons and Felsing[1]
15. Pitzer[4]
16. Waddington, Todd, and Huffman[1]

| | SPECIFIC REFERENCES | | | |
|---|---|---|---|---|
| | FOR TABLE 1m | | | |
| | May 31, 1947 | | | |

| Compound | REFERENCES FOR | Compound | REFERENCES FOR |
|---|---|---|---|
| | Heat of Vaporization | | Heat of Vaporization |
| Methane | 1,2 | | |
| Ethane | 3 | | |
| Propane | 4,13,14 | | |
| n-Butane | 5,13,14 | | |
| 2-Methylpropane (Isobutane) | 6,13,14 | | |
| n-Pentane | 7,8,9,10,13 | | |
| 2-Methylbutane (Isopentane) | 11,13 | | |
| 2,2-Dimethylpropane (Neopentane) | 12,13 | | |

## REFERENCES

1. Frank and Clusius[2]
2. Osborne and others[1]
3. Witt and Kemp[1]
4. Kemp and Egan[1]
5. Aston, and Messerly[2]
6. Aston, Kennedy, and Schumann[1]
7. Osborne and Ginnings[1]
8. Messerly and Kennedy[1]
9. Pitzer[5]
10. Sage, Evans, and Lacey[1]
11. Schumann, Aston, and Sagenkahn[1]
12. Aston and Messerly[1]
13. American Petroleum Institute Research Project 44[1]
14. Dana, Jenkins, Burdick, and Timm[1]

| | REFERENCES FOR | | REFERENCES FOR |
| Compound | Heat of Vaporization | Compound | Heat of Vaporization |
|---|---|---|---|
| | | SPECIFIC REFERENCES | |

**SPECIFIC REFERENCES**
**FOR TABLE 2m**
**May 31, 1947**

| Compound | REFERENCES FOR Heat of Vaporization | Compound | REFERENCES FOR Heat of Vaporization |
|---|---|---|---|
| n-Hexane | 1,2,3,4,9 | | |
| 2-Methylpentane | 1,3,5,9 | | |
| 3-Methylpentane | 1,5,9 | | |
| 2,2-Dimethylbutane | 1,2,6,7,9 | | |
| 2,3-Dimethylbutane | 1,3,5,9 | | |
| n-Heptane | 1,8,9,10 | | |
| 2-Methylhexane | 9 | | |
| 3-Methylhexane | 9 | | |
| 3-Ethylpentane | 1,9 | | |
| 2,2-Dimethylpentane | 1,9 | | |
| 2,3-Dimethylpentane | 1,9 | | |
| 2,4-Dimethylpentane | 1,9 | | |
| 3,3-Dimethylpentane | 1,9 | | |
| 2,2,3-Trimethylbutane | 1,9,10 | | |

**REFERENCES**

1. Osborne and Ginnings[1]
2. Waddington and Douslin[1]
3. Lemons and Felsing[1]
4. Mathews[1]
5. Huffman and others[1]
6. Pitzer[5]
7. Kilpatrick and Pitzer[1]
8. Pitzer[4]
9. American Petroleum Institute Research Project 44[1]
10. Waddington, Todd, and Huffman[1]

| | SPECIFIC REFERENCES | | | |
|---|---|---|---|---|
| | FOR TABLE 3m | | | |
| | May 31, 1947 | | | |
| Compound | REFERENCES FOR | Compound | REFERENCES FOR | |
| | Heat of Vaporization | | Heat of Vaporization | |
| $n$-Octane | 1,5 | | | |
| 2-Methylheptane | 1,5 | | | |
| 3-Methylheptane | 1,5 | | | |
| 4-Methylheptane | 1,2,5 | | | |
| 3-Ethylhexane | 1,5 | | | |
| 2,2-Dimethylhexane | 1,5 | | | |
| 2,3-Dimethylhexane | 1,5 | | | |
| 2,4-Dimethylhexane | 1,5 | | | |
| 2,5-Dimethylhexane | 1,5 | | | |
| 3,3-Dimethylhexane | 1,5 | | | |
| 3,4-Dimethylhexane | 1,5 | | | |
| 2-Methyl-3-ethylpentane | 1,5 | | | |
| 3-Methyl-3-ethylpentane | 1,5 | | | |
| 2,2,3-Trimethylpentane | 1,5 | | | |
| 2,2,4-Trimethylpentane | 1,3,5 | | | |
| 2,3,3-Trimethylpentane | 1,5 | | | |
| 2,3,4-Trimethylpentane | 1,4,5 | | | |
| 2,2,3,3-Tetramethylbutane | 5 | | | |

REFERENCES

1. Osborne and Ginnings[1]
2. Mathews[1]
3. Pitzer[4]
4. Pitzer and Scott[1]
5. American Petroleum Institute Research Project 44[1]

SPECIFIC REFERENCES
FOR TABLE 4m
May 31, 1947

| Compound | REFERENCES FOR Heat of Vaporization | Compound | REFERENCES FOR Heat of Vaporization |
|---|---|---|---|
| *n*–Nonane | 1,2 | 2,2,3,3–Tetramethylpentane | 2 |
| 2–Methyloctane | 2 | 2,2,3,4–Tetramethylpentane | 2 |
| 3–Methyloctane | 2 | 2,2,4,4–Tetramethylpentane | 2 |
| 4–Methyloctane | 2 | 2,3,3,4–Tetramethylpentane | 2 |
| 3–Ethylheptane | 2 | | |
| 4–Ethylheptane | 2 | | |
| 2,2–Dimethylheptane | 2 | | |
| 2,3–Dimethylheptane | 2 | | |
| 2,4–Dimethylheptane | 2 | | |
| 2,5–Dimethylheptane | 2 | | |
| 2,6–Dimethylheptane | 2 | | |
| 3,3–Dimethylheptane | 2 | | |
| 3,4–Dimethylheptane | 2 | | |
| 3,5–Dimethylheptane | 2 | | |
| 4,4–Dimethylheptane | 2 | | |
| 2–Methyl–3–ethylhexane | 2 | | |
| 2–Methyl–4–ethylhexane | 2 | | |
| 3–Methyl–3–ethylhexane | 2 | | |
| 3–Methyl–4–ethylhexane | 2 | | |
| 2,2,3–Trimethylhexane | 2 | | |
| 2,2,4–Trimethylhexane | 2 | | |
| 2,2,5–Trimethylhexane | 1,2 | | |
| 2,3,3–Trimethylhexane | 2 | | |
| 2,3,4–Trimethylhexane | 2 | | |
| 2,3,5–Trimethylhexane | 1,2 | | |
| 2,4,4–Trimethylhexane | 2 | | |
| 3,3,4–Trimethylhexane | 2 | | |
| 3,3–Diethylpentane | 2 | | |
| 2,2–Dimethyl–3–ethylpentane | 2 | | |
| 2,3–Dimethyl–3–ethylpentane | 2 | | |
| 2,4–Dimethyl–3–ethylpentane | 2 | | |

REFERENCES

1. Osborne and Ginnings[1]
2. American Petroleum Institute Research Project 44[1]

910

| | SPECIFIC REFERENCES | | | |
|---|---|---|---|---|
| | FOR TABLE 6m | | | |
| | May 31, 1947; October 31, 1948 | | | |

| Compound | REFERENCES FOR | Compound | REFERENCES FOR |
|---|---|---|---|
| | Heat of Vaporization | | Heat of Vaporization |
| Cyclopentane | 1, 2, 3, 5 | | |
| Methylcyclopentane | 4, 5 | | |
| Ethylcyclopentane | 5 | | |
| 1,1-Dimethylcyclopentane | 5 | | |
| cis-1,2-Dimethylcyclopentane | 5 | | |
| trans-1,2-Dimethylcyclopentane | 5 | | |
| cis-1,3-Dimethylcyclopentane | 5 | | |
| trans-1,3-Dimethylcyclopentane | 5 | | |

REFERENCES

1. Aston, Fink, and Schumann[1]
2. Spitzer and Pitzer[1]
3. Huffman and others[1]
4. Osborne and Ginnings[2]
5. American Petroleum Institute Research
   Project 44[1]

## SPECIFIC REFERENCES
### FOR TABLE 7m
May 31, 1947

| Compound | REFERENCES FOR | Compound | REFERENCES FOR |
|---|---|---|---|
| | Heat of Vaporization | | Heat of Vaporization |
| Cyclohexane | 1,2,3,4,5 | | |
| Methylcyclohexane | 1,2,4,5 | | |
| Ethylcyclohexane | 1,5 | | |
| 1,1-Dimethylcyclohexane | 5 | | |
| 1,cis-2-Dimethylcyclohexane | 1,5 | | |
| 1,trans-2-Dimethylcyclohexane | 1,5 | | |
| 1,cis-3-Dimethylcyclohexane | 1,5 | | |
| 1,trans-3-Dimethylcyclohexane | 1,5 | | |
| 1,cis-4-Dimethylcyclohexane | 1,5 | | |
| 1,trans-4-Dimethylcyclohexane | 1,5 | | |

### REFERENCES

1. Osborne and Ginnings[1]
2. Spitzer and Pitzer[1]
3. Aston, Szasz, and Fink[1]
4. Mathews[1]
5. American Petroleum Institute Research Project 44[1]

912

| | SPECIFIC REFERENCES FOR TABLE 8m (PART 1) May 31, 1947 | | | |
|---|---|---|---|---|
| Compound | REFERENCES FOR Heat of Vaporization | | Compound | REFERENCES FOR Heat of Vaporization |
| Ethene | 1 | | | |
| Propene | 2 | | | |
| 1-Butene | 3,7 | | | |
| cis-2-Butene | 4,7 | | | |
| trans-2-Butene | 5,7 | | | |
| 2-Methylpropene | 6,7 | | | |

REFERENCES

1. Egan and Kemp[1]
2. Powell and Giauque[1]
3. Aston, Fink, Bestul, Pace, and Szasz[1]
4. Scott, Ferguson, and Brickwedde[1]
5. Guttman and Pitzer[1]
6. Rands, Scott, and Brickwedde[1]
7. American Petroleum Institute Research Project 44[1]

| | SPECIFIC REFERENCES | | | |
|---|---|---|---|---|
| | FOR TABLE 5m | | | |
| | May 31, 1947 | | | |

| Compound | REFERENCES FOR | Compound | REFERENCES FOR |
|---|---|---|---|
| | Heat of Vaporization | | Heat of Vaporization |
| Benzene | 1,2,3,4,5,8 | | |
| Methylbenzene (Toluene) | 1,4,5,8 | | |
| Ethylbenzene | 1,4,6,8 | | |
| 1,2-Dimethylbenzene (o-Xylene) | 1,4,7,8 | | |
| 1,3-Dimethylbenzene (m-Xylene) | 1,4,7,8 | | |
| 1,4-Dimethylbenzene (p-Xylene) | 1,4,7,8 | | |
| n-Propylbenzene | 1,8 | | |
| Isopropylbenzene | 1,8 | | |
| 1-Methyl-2-ethylbenzene | 8 | | |
| 1-Methyl-3-ethylbenzene | 8 | | |
| 1-Methyl-4-ethylbenzene | 8 | | |
| 1,2,3-Trimethylbenzene | 1,8 | | |
| 1,2,4-Trimethylbenzene | 1,8 | | |
| 1,3,5-Trimethylbenzene | 1,8 | | |

## REFERENCES

1. Osborne and Ginnings[1]
2. Waddington and Douslin[1]
3. Fiock, Ginnings, and Holton[1]
4. Mathews[1]
5. Kolossovsky and Theodorowitsch[1]
6. Scott and Brickwedde[1]
7. Pitzer and Scott[2]
8. American Petroleum Institute Research
   Project 44[1]

SPECIFIC REFERENCES

FOR THE "n" TABLES

May 31, 1947

The values of the heats of combustion, $-\Delta Hc^{\circ}$, at 25°C, in the n tables are calculated from the selected values of the standard heats of formation, $\Delta Hf^{\circ}$, at 25°C, for the hydrocarbons and for carbon dioxide ($CO_2$) and water ($H_2O$), as given in the p tables. The specific references for the p tables are given in the appropriate place in this section. The specific references for that n table for which the corresponding p table has not yet been issued are as follows: Table 9n, Prosen and Rossini[9].

SPECIFIC REFERENCES
FOR TABLE Op

May 31, 1947

| Compound | REFERENCES FOR | | |
| --- | --- | --- | --- |
| | Heat of Formation | Entropy. | Free Energy of Formation |
| | At 25$^\circ$C | At 25$^\circ$C | At 25$^\circ$C |
| Oxygen | 3 | 1 | 2 |
| Hydrogen | 3 | 1 | 2 |
| Water | 3,6 | 1,6 | 2,6 |
| Nitrogen | 3 | 1 | 2 |
| Carbon (graphite) | 3,4,5 | 1 | 2 |
| Carbon monoxide | 3,6 | 1,6 | 2,6 |
| Carbon dioxide | 3,4,5,6 | 1,6 | 2,6 |

REFERENCES

1. See references for Table Ot.
2. See references for Table Ox.
3. Wagman, Kilpatrick, Taylor, Pitzer, and Rossini[1]
4. Prosen, Jessup, and Rossini[1]
5. Prosen and Rossini[5]
6. National Bureau of Standards[1]

916

| | REFERENCES FOR | | |
|---|---|---|---|
| Compound | Heat of Formation | Entropy | Free Energy of Formation |
| | At 25°C | At 25°C | At 25°C |
| Methane | 3,4,5,6,8 | 1 | 2 |
| Ethane | 3,4,5,6,8 | 1 | 2 |
| Propane | 3,4,5,6,8 | 1 | 2 |
| n-Butane | 3,4,5,6,8,20 | 1 | 2 |
| n-Pentane | 3,4,5,6,7,8 | 1 | 2 |
| n-Hexane | 7,8,9,10,11,12 | 1 | 2 |
| n-Heptane | 7,8,9,13,14,15 | 1 | 2 |
| n-Octane | 7,8,9,12,13,16,17,18 | 1 | 2 |
| n-Nonane | 7,8,9 | 1 | 2 |
| n-Decane | 7,8,9 | 1 | 2 |
| n-Undecane | 8,9 | 1 | 2 |
| n-Dodecane | 7,8,9 | 1 | 2 |
| n-Tridecane | 8 | 1 | 2 |
| n-Tetradecane | 8 | 1 | 2 |
| n-Pentadecane | 8 | 1 | 2 |
| n-Hexadecane | 7,8,19 | 1 | 2 |
| n-Heptadecane | 8 | 1 | 2 |
| n-Octadecane | 8 | 1 | 2 |
| n-Nonadecane | 8 | 1 | 2 |
| n-Eicosane | 8 | 1 | 2 |

**SPECIFIC REFERENCES FOR TABLE 20p (PART 1)** — May 31, 1947; December 31, 1952

### REFERENCES

1. See references for Table 20t (Part 1).
2. See references for Table 20x (Part 1).
3. Rossini[4]
4. Rossini[8]
5. Rossini[18]
6. Rossini[21]
7. Prosen and Rossini[4]
8. Prosen and Rossini[8]
9. Jessup[1]
10. Prosen and Rossini[2]
11. Stohman, Kleber, and Langbein[3]
12. Zubov[1]
13. Jessup[4]
14. Davies and Gilbert[1]
15. Louguinine[1]
16. Prosen and Rossini[7]
17. Richards and Jesse[1]
18. Banse and Parks[1]
19. Richardson and Parks[1]
20. Prosen, Maron, and Rossini[2]

# SPECIFIC REFERENCES
## FOR TABLE 1p
May 31, 1947; December 31, 1952

| Compound | REFERENCES FOR | | |
|---|---|---|---|
| | Heat of Formation | Entropy | Free Energy of Formation |
| | At 25°C | At 25°C | At 25°C |
| Methane | 1 | 2 | 3 |
| Ethane | 1 | 2 | 3 |
| Propane | 1 | 2 | 3 |
| n-Butane | 1,15 | 2 | 3 |
| 2-Methylpropane (Isobutane) | 4,5,6,7,8,9,10,11 | 2 | 3 |
| n-Pentane | 1 | 2 | 3 |
| 2-Methylbutane (Isopentane) | 4,5,6,7,12,13,14 | 2 | 3 |
| 2,2-Dimethylpropane (Neopentane) | 4,5,6,7,8,9,10,11,12 | 2 | 3 |

## REFERENCES

1. See references for Table 20p (Part 1).
2. See references for Table 1t.
3. See references for Table 1x.
4. Rossini[4]
5. Rossini[8]
6. Rossini[18]
7. Rossini[21]
8. Thomsen[1]
9. Thomsen[2]
10. Thomsen[3]
11. Thomsen[4]
12. Knowlton and Rossini[1]
13. Roth and Macheleidt[1]
14. Roth and Fahlke[1]
15. Prosen, Maron, and Rossini[2]

SPECIFIC REFERENCES

FOR TABLE 2p (PART 1)

May 31, 1947; December 31, 1952

| Compound | REFERENCES FOR | | |
| --- | --- | --- | --- |
| | Heat of Formation | Entropy | Free Energy of Formation |
| | At 25°C | At 25°C | At 25°C |
| n-Hexane | 1 | 2 | 3 |
| 2-Methylpentane | 4 | 2 | 3 |
| 3-Methylpentane | 4 | 2 | 3 |
| 2,2-Dimethylbutane | 4 | 2 | 3 |
| 2,3-Dimethylbutane | 4,5,6 | 2 | 3 |

REFERENCES

1. See references for Table 20p (Part 1).
2. See references for Table 2t (Part 1).
3. See references for Table 2x (Part 1).
4. Prosen and Rossini[2]
5. Prosen and Rossini[3]
6. Thomsen[4]

SPECIFIC REFERENCES
FOR TABLE 2p (PART 2)

May 31, 1947; December 31, 1952

| Compound | REFERENCES FOR | | |
| --- | --- | --- | --- |
| | Heat of Formation | Entropy | Free Energy of Formation |
| | At 25°C | At 25°C | At 25°C |
| n–Heptane | 1 | 2 | 3 |
| 2–Methylhexane | 4,5,6 | 2 | 3 |
| 3–Methylhexane | 4,5,6 | 2 | 3 |
| 3–Ethylpentane | 4,5,6 | 2 | 3 |
| 2,2–Dimethylpentane | 4,5,6 | 2 | 3 |
| 2,3–Dimethylpentane | 4,5,6 | 2 | 3 |
| 2,4–Dimethylpentane | 4,5,6 | 2 | 3 |
| 3,3–Dimethylpentane | 4,5,6 | 2 | 3 |
| 2,2,3–Trimethylbutane | 4,5,6 | 2 | 3 |

REFERENCES

1. See references for Table 20p (Part 1).
2. See references for Table 2t (Part 2).
3. See references for Table 2x (Part 2).
4. Prosen and Rossini[3]
5. Jessup[4]
6. Davies and Gilbert[1]

920

| | REFERENCES FOR | | |
|---|---|---|---|
| Compound | Heat of Formation | Entropy | Free Energy of Formation |
| | At 25°C | At 25°C | At 25°C |
| *n*–Octane | 1 | 2 | 3 |
| 2–Methylheptane | 4,5 | 2 | 3 |
| 3–Methylheptane | 4 | 2 | 3 |
| 4–Methylheptane | 4 | 2 | 3 |
| 3–Ethylhexane | 4,5 | 2 | 3 |
| 2,2–Dimethylhexane | 4 | 2 | 3 |
| 2,3–Dimethylhexane | 4 | 2 | 3 |
| 2,4–Dimethylhexane | 4 | 2 | 3 |
| 2,5–Dimethylhexane | 4,5 | 2 | 3 |
| 3,3–Dimethylhexane | 4 | 2 | 3 |
| 3,4–Dimethylhexane | 4,5 | 2 | 3 |
| 2–Methyl–3–ethylpentane | 4 | 2 | 3 |
| 3–Methyl–3–ethylpentane | 4 | 2 | 3 |
| 2,2,3–Trimethylpentane | 4 | 2 | 3 |
| 2,2,4–Trimethylpentane | 4,6 | 2 | 3 |
| 2,3,3–Trimethylpentane | 4 | 2 | 3 |
| 2,3,4–Trimethylpentane | 4 | 2 | 3 |
| 2,2,3,3–Tetramethylbutane | 4,6 | 2 | 3 |

The table title and references:

**SPECIFIC REFERENCES**
**FOR TABLE 3p**
May 31, 1947; December 31, 1952

**REFERENCES**

1. See references for Table 20p (Part 1).
2. See references for Table 3t.
3. See references for Table 3x.
4. Prosen and Rossini[7]
5. Richards and Jesse[1]
6. Jessup[4]

| Compound | Heat of Formation At 25°C | Entropy At 25°C | Free Energy of Formation At 25°C |
|---|---|---|---|
| Cyclohexane | 3, 5, 7, 8, 9, 10 | 1 | 2 |
| Methylcyclohexane | 3, 5, 9 | 1 | 2 |
| Ethylcyclohexane | 3, 4, 5, 6 | 1 | 2 |
| 1,1-Dimethylcyclohexane | 4, 6 | 1 | 2 |
| cis-1,2-Dimethylcyclohexane | 4, 6 | 1 | 2 |
| trans-1,2-Dimethylcyclohexane | 4, 6 | 1 | 2 |
| cis-1,3-Dimethylcyclohexane | 4, 6 | 1 | 2 |
| trans-1,3-Dimethylcyclohexane | 4, 6 | 1 | 2 |
| cis-1,4-Dimethylcyclohexane | 4, 6 | 1 | 2 |
| trans-1,4-Dimethylcyclohexane | 4, 6 | 1 | 2 |

SPECIFIC REFERENCES FOR TABLE 7p October 31, 1948

REFERENCES

1. See references for table 7t.
2. See references for table 7x.
3. Johnson, Prosen, and Rossini[2]
4. Johnson, Prosen, and Rossini[4]
5. Prosen, Johnson, and Rossini[2]
6. Prosen, Johnson, and Rossini[3]
7. Richards and Barry[1]
8. Roth and von Auwers[1]
9. Moore, Renquist, and Parks[1]
10. Huffman and others[1]

| | SPECIFIC REFERENCES | | |
| | FOR TABLE 22p (Part 1) | | |
| | April 30, 1949; December 31, 1952 | | |

| Compound | REFERENCES FOR | | |
| | Heat of Formation | Entropy | Free Energy of Formation |
| | At 25°C | At 25°C | At 25°C |
| Cyclopentane | 3,4,5 | 1 | 2 |
| Methylcyclopentane | 3,4,6,7 | 1 | 2 |
| Ethylcyclopentane | 3,4,6 | 1 | 2 |
| n-Propylcyclopentane | 3,4, | 1 | 2 |
| n-Butylcyclopentane | 4 | 1 | 2 |
| n-Pentylcyclopentane | 4 | 1 | 2 |
| n-Hexylcyclopentane | 4 | 1 | 2 |
| n-Heptylcyclopentane | 4 | 1 | 2 |
| n-Octylcyclopentane | 4 | 1 | 2 |
| n-Nonylcyclopentane | 4 | 1 | 2 |
| n-Decylcyclopentane | 4 | 1 | 2 |
| n-Undecylcyclopentane | 4 | 1 | 2 |
| n-Dodecylcyclopentane | 4 | 1 | 2 |
| n-Tridecylcyclopentane | 4 | 1 | 2 |
| n-Tetradecylcyclopentane | 4 | 1 | 2 |
| n-Pentadecylcyclopentane | 4 | 1 | 2 |
| n-Hexadecylcyclopentane | 4 | 1 | 2 |

REFERENCES

1. See references for Table 22t (Part 1).
2. See references for Table 22x (Part 1).
3. Johnson, Prosen, and Rossini[2]
4. Prosen, Johnson, and Rossini[2]
5. Spitzer and Huffman[1]
6. Moore, Renquist, and Parks[1]
7. Zubov[1]

| | REFERENCES FOR | | |
|---|---|---|---|
| Compound | Heat of Formation | Entropy | Free Energy of Formation |
| | At 25°C | At 25°C | At 25°C |
| Cyclopentane | 3 | 1 | 2 |
| Methylcyclopentane | 3 | 1 | 2 |
| Ethylcyclopentane | 3 | 1 | 2 |
| 1,1-Dimethylcyclopentane | 4 | 1 | 2 |
| 1, cis-2-Dimethylcyclopentane | 4 | 1 | 2 |
| 1, trans-2-Dimethylcyclopentane | 4 | 1 | 2 |
| 1, cis-3-Dimethylcyclopentane | 4 | 1 | 2 |
| 1, trans-3-Dimethylcyclopentane | 4 | 1 | 2 |

SPECIFIC REFERENCES FOR TABLE 6p — April 30, 1949; December 31, 1952

REFERENCES

1. See references for Table 6t.
2. See references for Table 6x.
3. See references for Table 22p (Part 1).
4. Johnson, Prosen, and Rossini[5]

| | SPECIFIC REFERENCES<br>FOR TABLE 23p (PART 1)<br>April 30, 1949; December 31, 1952 | | |
|---|---|---|---|
| | REFERENCES FOR | | |
| Compound | Heat of Formation | Entropy | Free Energy of Formation |
| | At 25°C | At 25°C | At 25°C |
| Cyclohexane | 3,4,5,6,7,8 | 1 | 2 |
| Methylcyclohexane | 3,4,7 | 1 | 2 |
| Ethylcyclohexane | 3,4,9,10 | 1 | 2 |
| n–Propylcyclohexane | 3,4 | 1 | 2 |
| n–Butylcyclohexane | 3,4 | 1 | 2 |
| n–Fentylcyclohexane | 4 | 1 | 2 |
| n–Hexylcyclohexane | 4 | 1 | 2 |
| n–Heptylcyclohexane | 4 | 1 | 2 |
| n–Octylcyclohexane | 4 | 1 | 2 |
| n–Nonylcyclohexane | 4 | 1 | 2 |
| n–Decylcyclohexane | 4 | 1 | 2 |
| n–Undecylcyclohexane | 4 | 1 | 2 |
| n–Dodecylcyclohexane | 4 | 1 | 2 |
| n–Tridecylcyclohexane | 4 | 1 | 2 |
| n–Tetradecylcyclohexane | 4 | 1 | 2 |
| n–Fentadecylcyclohexane | 4 | 1 | 2 |
| n–Hexadecylcyclohexane | 4 | 1 | 2 |

REFERENCES

1. See references for Table 23t (Part 1).
2. See references for Table 23x (Part 1).
3. Johnson, Prosen, and Rossini[2]
4. Frosen, Johnson, and Rossini[2]
5. Richards and Barry[1]
6. Roth and von Auwers[1]
7. Moore, Renquist, and Farks[1]
8. Huffran and others[1]
9. Johnson, Prosen, and Rossini[4]
10. Frosen, Johnson, and Rossini[3]

| | REFERENCES FOR | | |
|---|---|---|---|
| Compound | Heat of Formation | Entropy | Free Energy of Formation |
| | At 25°C | At 25°C | At 25°C |
| Ethene (Ethylene) | 3,4,7,8,9,10,11 | 1 | 2 |
| Propene (Propylene) | 3,7,8,9,10,12 | 1 | 2 |
| 1-Butene | 3,4,6 | 1 | 2 |
| 1-Pentene | 3 | 1 | 2 |
| 1-Hexene | 3 | 1 | 2 |
| 1-Heptene | 3,5 | 1 | 2 |
| 1-Octene | 3 | 1 | 2 |
| 1-Nonene | 3 | 1 | 2 |
| 1-Decene | 3 | 1 | 2 |
| 1-Undecene | 3 | 1 | 2 |
| 1-Dodecene | 3 | 1 | 2 |
| 1-Tridecene | 3 | 1 | 2 |
| 1-Tetradecene | 3 | 1 | 2 |
| 1-Pentadecene | 3 | 1 | 2 |
| 1-Hexadecene | 3 | 1 | 2 |
| 1-Heptadecene | 3 | 1 | 2 |
| 1-Octadecene | 3 | 1 | 2 |
| 1-Nonadecene | 3 | 1 | 2 |
| 1-Eicosene | 3 | 1 | 2 |

**SPECIFIC REFERENCES**
FOR TABLE 24p (PART 1)
May 31, 1947; December 31, 1952

**REFERENCES**

1. See references for Table 24t (Part 1).
2. See references for Table 24x (Part 1).
3. Prosen and Rossini[9]
4. Kistiakowsky, Romeyn, Ruhoff, Smith, and Vaughan[1]
5. Kistiakowsky, Ruhoff, Smith, and Vaughan[2]
6. Prosen, Maron, and Rossini[2]
7. Berthelot and Matignon[1]
8. Rossini and Knowlton[1]
9. Thomsen[2]
10. Thomsen[4]
11. Mixter[1]
12. Kistiakowsky, Ruhoff, Smith, and Vaughan[1]

| | SPECIFIC REFERENCES FOR TABLE 8p (FART 1) May 31, 1947; December 31, 1952 | | |
|---|---|---|---|
| | REFERENCES FOR | | |
| Compound | Heat of Formation | Entropy | Free Energy of Formation |
| | At 25°C | At 25°C | At 25°C |
| Ethene (Ethylene) | 1 | 2 | 3 |
| Propene (Fropylene) | 1 | 2 | 3 |
| 1-Butene | 1 | 2 | 3 |
| cis-2-Butene | 4,5,6 | 2 | 3 |
| trans-2-Butene | 4,5,6 | 2 | 3 |
| 2-Methylpropene (Isobutene) | 4,5,6,7,8,9,10 | 2 | 3 |
| 1-Pentene | 1 | 2 | 3 |
| cis-2-Fentene | 4 | 2 | 3 |
| trans-2-Pentene | 4 | 2 | 3 |
| 2-Methyl-1-butene | 4,11 | 2 | 3 |
| 3-Methyl-1-butene | 4,12 | 2 | 3 |
| 2-Methyl-2-butene | 4,7,8,9,10,11,13 | 2 | 3 |

REFERENCES

1. See references for Table 24p (Part 1).
2. See references for Table 8t (Fart 1).
3. See references for Table 8x (Part 1).
4. Frosen and Rossini[9]
5. Kistiakowsky, Ruhoff, Smith, and Vaughan[1]
6. Frosen, Maron, and Rossini[2]
7. Thomsen[1]
8. Thomsen[2]
9. Thomsen[3]
10. Thomsen[4]
11. Kistiakowsky, Ruhoff, Smith, and Vaughan[2]
12. Dolliver, Gresham, Kistiakowsky, and Vaughan[1]
13. Zubov[1]

| | REFERENCES FOR | | |
|---|---|---|---|
| Compound | Heat of Formation At 25°C | Entropy At 25°C | Free Energy of Formation At 25°C |
| 1-Hexene | 1 | 2 | 3 |
| cis-2-Hexene | 4 | 2 | 3 |
| trans-2-Hexene | 4 | 2 | 3 |
| cis-3-Hexene | 4 | 2 | 3 |
| trans-3-Hexene | 4 | 2 | 3 |
| 2-Methyl-1-pentene | 4 | 2 | 3 |
| 3-Methyl-1-pentene | 4 | 2 | 3 |
| 4-Methyl-1-pentene | 4 | 2 | 3 |
| 2-Methyl-2-pentene | 4 | 2 | 3 |
| 3-Methyl-cis-2-pentene | 4 | 2 | 3 |
| 3-Methyl-trans-2-pentene | 4 | 2 | 3 |
| 4-Methyl-cis-2-pentene | 4 | 2 | 3 |
| 4-Methyl-trans-2-pentene | 4 | 2 | 3 |
| 2-Ethyl-1-butene | 4 | 2 | 3 |
| 2,3-Dimethyl-1-butene | 4,5 | 2 | 3 |
| 3,3-Dimethyl-1-butene | 4,5 | 2 | 3 |
| 2,3-Dimethyl-2-butene | 4,5 | 2 | 3 |

**SPECIFIC REFERENCES FOR TABLE 8p (PART 2)** — May 31, 1947; December 31, 1952

REFERENCES

1. See references for Table 24p (Part 1).
2. See references for Table 8t (Part 2).
3. See references for Table 8x (Part 2).
4. Frosen and Rossini[9]
5. Kistiakowsky, Ruhoff, Smith, and Vaughan[2]

| SPECIFIC REFERENCES FOR TABLE 11p (PART 1) February 28, 1949; December 31, 1952 | | | |
|---|---|---|---|
| Compound | REFERENCES FOR | | |
| | Heat of Formation At 25°C | Entropy At 25°C | Free Energy of Formation At 25°C |
| Propadiene | 4,7 | 1 | 2 |
| 1,2-Butadiene | 6,7,8 | 1 | 2 |
| 1,3-Butadiene | 3,4,6,7,8 | 1 | 2 |
| 1,2-Pentadiene | 7,8 | 1 | 2 |
| 1-cis-3-Pentadiene | 5,7 | 1 | 2 |
| 1-trans-3-Pentadiene | 5,7 | 1 | 2 |
| 1,4-Pentadiene | 4,7 | 1 | 2 |
| 2,3-Pentadiene | 7 | 1 | 2 |
| 3-Methyl-1,2-butadiene | 7 | 1 | 2 |
| 2-Methyl-1,3-butadiene | 7 | 1 | 2 |

REFERENCES

1. See references for Table 11t (Part 1).
2. See references for Table 11x (Part 1).
3. Prosen and Rossini[6]
4. Kistiakowsky, Ruhoff, Smith, and Vaughan[3]
5. Dolliver, Gresham, Kistiakowsky, and Vaughan[1]
6. Prosen, Maron, and Rossini[1]
7. Kilpatrick, Beckett, Prosen, Pitzer, and Rossini[1]
8. Frosen, Maron, and Rossini[2]

| | REFERENCES FOR | | |
|---|---|---|---|
| SPECIFIC REFERENCES<br>FOR TABLE 18p<br>December 31, 1952 | | | |
| Compound | Heat of Formation | Entropy | Free Energy of Formation |
| | At 25°C | At 25°C | At 25°C |
| Cyclopentene | 1 | 2 | 3 |
| 1-Methylcyclopentene | | 4 | |
| 3-Methylcyclopentene | | 4 | |
| 4-Methylcyclopentene | | 4 | |
| 1-Ethylcyclopentene | | | |
| 3-Ethylcyclopentene | | | |
| 4-Ethylcyclopentene | | | |
| 1,2-Dimethylcyclopentene | | 4 | |
| 1,3-Dimethylcyclopentene | | 4 | |
| 1,4-Dimethylcyclopentene | | 4 | |
| 1,5-Dimethylcyclopentene | | 4 | |
| 3,3-Dimethylcyclopentene | | 4 | |
| 3,cis-4-Dimethylcyclopentene | | 4 | |
| 3,trans-4-Dimethylcyclopentene | | 4 | |
| 3,cis-5-Dimethylcyclopentene | | 4 | |
| 3,trans-5-Dimethylcyclopentene | | 4 | |
| 4,4-Dimethylcyclopentene | | | |

REFERENCES

1. Epstein, Fitzer, and Rossini[1]
2. See references for Table 18t.
3. See references for Table 18x.
4. American Petroleum Institute Research
   Project 50[1]

| | REFERENCES FOR | | |
|---|---|---|---|
| Compound | Heat of Formation | Entropy | Free Energy of Formation |
| | At 25°C | At 25°C | At 25°C |
| Ethyne (Acetylene) | 3,4,5,6,7,8,9,10,11 | 1 | 2 |
| Propyne (Methylacetylene) | 3,11 | 1 | 2 |
| 1-Butyne (Ethylacetylene) | 3,11,12 | 1 | 2 |
| 1-Pentyne | 3,11 | 1 | 2 |
| 1-Hexyne | 3 | 1 | 2 |
| 1-Heptyne | 3,13 | 1 | 2 |
| 1-Octyne | 3 | 1 | 2 |
| 1-Nonyne | 3 | 1 | 2 |
| 1-Decyne | 3 | 1 | 2 |
| 1-Undecyne | 3 | 1 | 2 |
| 1-Dodecyne | 3 | 1 | 2 |
| 1-Tridecyne | 3 | 1 | 2 |
| 1-Tetradecyne | 3 | 1 | 2 |
| 1-Pentadecyne | 3 | 1 | 2 |
| 1-Hexadecyne | 3 | 1 | 2 |
| 1-Heptadecyne | 3 | 1 | 2 |
| 1-Octadecyne | 3 | 1 | 2 |
| 1-Nonadecyne | 3 | 1 | 2 |
| 1-Eicosyne | 3 | 1 | 2 |

SPECIFIC REFERENCES
FOR TABLE 25p (PART 1)
May 31, 1947; December 31, 1952

## REFERENCES

1. See references for Table 25t (Part 1).
2. See references for Table 25x (Part 1).
3. American Petroleum Institute Research Project 44[1]
4. Berthelot[2]
5. Thomsen[1]
6. Thomsen[2]
7. Thomsen[3]
8. Thomsen[4]
9. Berthelot and Matignon[1]
10. Mixter[2]
11. Wagman, Kilpatrick, Pitzer, and Rossini[1]
12. Prosen, Maron, and Rossini[2]
13. Moureu and André[1]

SPECIFIC REFERENCES

FOR TABLE 12p

May 31, 1947; December 31, 1952

| Compound | REFERENCES FOR | | |
| --- | --- | --- | --- |
| | Heat of Formation | Entropy | Free Energy of Formation |
| | At 25°C | At 25°C | At 25°C |
| Ethyne (Acetylene) | 1 | 2 | 3 |
| Propyne (Methylacetylene) | 1 | 2 | 3 |
| 1-Butyne (Ethylacetylene) | 1 | 2 | 3 |
| 2-Butyne (Dimethylacetylene) | 4,5 | 2 | 3 |
| 1-Pentyne | 1 | 2 | 3 |
| 2-Fentyne | 4,5 | 2 | 3 |
| 3-Methyl-1-butyne | 4,5 | 2 | 3 |

REFERENCES

1. See references for Table 25p (Part 1).
2. See references for Table 12t.
3. See references for Table 12x.
4. Frosen, Maron, and Rossini[2]
5. Wagman, Kilpatrick, Pitzer, and Rossini[1]

## SPECIFIC REFERENCES
### FOR TABLE 21p (PART 1)
May 31, 1947; December 31, 1952

| Compound | REFERENCES FOR | | |
| --- | --- | --- | --- |
| | Heat of Formation | Entropy | Free Energy of Formation |
| | At 25°C | At 25°C | At 25°C |
| Benzene | 3,4,5,6,7,8,9,10,11,12,13,14, 15 | 1 | 2 |
| Methylbenzene (Toluene) | 3,4,11,12,13,16,17,18 | 1 | 2 |
| Ethylbenzene | 3,4,12,19,20,21 | 1 | 2 |
| n-Propylbenzene | 3,4,12,22,23,24 | 1 | 2 |
| n-Butylbenzene | 3 | 1 | 2 |
| n-Pentylbenzene | 3 | 1 | 2 |
| n-Hexylbenzene | 3 | 1 | 2 |
| n-Heptylbenzene | 3 | 1 | 2 |
| n-Octylbenzene | 3 | 1 | 2 |
| n-Nonylbenzene | 3 | 1 | 2 |
| n-Decylbenzene | 3 | 1 | 2 |
| n-Undecylbenzene | 3 | 1 | 2 |
| n-Dodecylbenzene | 3 | 1 | 2 |
| n-Tridecylbenzene | 3 | 1 | 2 |
| n-Tetradecylbenzene | 3 | 1 | 2 |
| n-Pentadecylbenzene | 3 | 1 | 2 |
| n-Hexadecylbenzene | 3 | 1 | 2 |

### REFERENCES

1. See references for Table 21t (Part 1).
2. See references for Table 21x (Part 1).
3. Prosen, Johnson, and Rossini[1]
4. Prosen, Gilmont, and Rossini[1]
5. Berthelot[1]
6. Stohman, Rodatz, and Herzberg[1]
7. Stohman, Kleber, and Langbein[1]
8. Richards, Henderson, and Frevert[1]
9. Richards, Henderson, and Frevert[2]
10. Richards and Jesse[1]
11. Roth and von Auwers[1]
12. Richards and Barry[1]
13. Richards and Davis[2]
14. Berthelot[3]
15. Thomsen[4]
16. Stohman, Rodatz, and Herzberg[2]
17. Schmidlin[1]
18. Richards and Davis[1]
19. Jesse[1]
20. Moureu and André[1]
21. von Auwers and Kolligs[2]
22. Johnson, Prosen, and Rossini[1]
23. Genvresse[1]
24. Huffman and others[1]

| | REFERENCES FOR | | |
|---|---|---|---|
| SPECIFIC REFERENCES FOR TABLE 5p May 31, 1947 | | | |
| Compound | Heat of Formation At 25°C | Entropy At 25°C | Free Energy of Formation At 25°C |
| Benzene | 1 | 1 | 1 |
| Methylbenzene (Toluene) | 1 | 1 | 1 |
| Ethylbenzene | 1 | 1 | 1 |
| 1,2-Dimethylbenzene (o-Xylene) | 3,4,9,10 | 6 | 2 |
| 1,3-Dimethylbenzene (m-Xylene) | 3,4,7,8,10 | 6 | 2 |
| 1,4-Dimethylbenzene (p-Xylene) | 3,4,7,10 | 6 | 2 |
| n-Propylbenzene | 1 | 1 | 1 |
| Isopropylbenzene | 3,5,9,11,12 | 6 | 2 |
| 1-Methyl-2-ethylbenzene | 3,5 | 6 | 2 |
| 1-Methyl-3-ethylbenzene | 3,5 | 6 | 2 |
| 1-Methyl-4-ethylbenzene | 3,5 | 6 | 2 |
| 1,2,3-Trimethylbenzene | 3,5 | 6 | 2 |
| 1,2,4-Trimethylbenzene | 3,5,9 | 6 | 2 |
| 1,3,5-Trimethylbenzene | 3,5,9,10 | 6 | 2 |

REFERENCES

1. See references for Table 21p.
2. See references for Table 5x.
3. Prosen, Johnson, and Rossini[1]
4. Prosen, Gilmont, and Rossini[1]
5. Johnson, Prosen, and Rossini[1]
6. See references for Table 5t.
7. Richards and Jesse[1]
8. Roth and von Auwers[1]
9. Richards and Barry[1]
10. Stohmann, Rodatz, and Herzberg[2]
11. Genvresse[1]
12. Huffman and others[1]

| | SPECIFIC REFERENCES FOR TABLE 13p February 28, 1949 | | |
|---|---|---|---|
| Compound | REFERENCES FOR | | |
| | Heat of Formation | Entropy | Free Energy of Formation |
| | At 25°C | At 25°C | At 25°C |
| Ethenylbenzene | 3,4,6,7,8,9,10,11,12,13 | 1 | 2 |
| Isopropenylbenzene | 5,6 | 1 | 2 |
| cis-1-Propenylbenzene | 6 | 1 | 2 |
| trans-1-Propenylbenzene | 6 | 1 | 2 |
| 1-Methyl-2-ethenylbenzene | 6 | 1 | 2 |
| 1-Methyl-3-ethenylbenzene | 6 | 1 | 2 |
| 1-Methyl-4-ethenylbenzene | 6 | 1 | 2 |

REFERENCES

1. See references for table 13t.
2. See references for table 13x.
3. Prosen and Rossini[6]
4. Prosen, Gilmont, and Rossini[1]
5. Johnson, Prosen, and Rossini[5]
6. Kilpatrick, Beckett, Prosen, Pitzer, and Rossini[1]
7. Stohmann, Kleber, and Langbein[2]
8. von Auwers, Roth, and Eisenlohr[1]
9. von Auwers, Roth, and Eisenlohr[2]
10. Lemoult[1]
11. Moureu and André[1]
12. Landrieu, Baylocq, and Johnson[1]
13. Luchinsky[1]

SPECIFIC REFERENCES
FOR THE "q" TABLES
May 31, 1947

The values of the standard heat of vaporization, $\Delta H v^\circ$, standard entropy of vaporization, $\Delta S v^\circ$, and standard free energy of vaporization, $\Delta F v^\circ$, all at $25^\circ C$, given in the q tables are calculated from the values of the heats of vaporization, $\Delta H v$, at saturation pressure and $25^\circ C$, given in the corresponding m tables, the values of the vapor pressures at $25^\circ C$ derived from the corresponding k tables, and unpublished calculations of the American Petroleum Institute Research Project 44[1]. The specific references for the k and m tables are given in the appropriate places in this section.

SPECIFIC REFERENCES

FOR TABLES 00r, 00s, 00t, 00u, 00v, 00w, 00x, AND 00y

May 31, 1947; April 30, 1948; August 31, 1949

| Compound | r $(H^o - H^o_0)/T$ | s $(F^o - H^o_0)/T$ | t $S^o$ | u $(H^o - H^o_0)$ | v $C_p^o$ | w $\Delta H_f^o$ | x $\Delta F_f^o$ | y $\log_{10} K_f$ |
|---|---|---|---|---|---|---|---|---|
| Oxygen | 1 | 1 | 1 | 1 | 1 | 1 | 1 | 1 |
| Hydrogen | 1 | 1 | 1 | 1 | 1 | 1 | 1 | 1 |
| Nitrogen | 1 | 1 | 1 | 1 | 1 | 1 | 1 | 1 |
| Carbon | 1 | 1 | 1 | 1 | 1 | 1 | 1 | 1 |

REFERENCES

1. National Bureau of Standards[1]

SPECIFIC REFERENCES

FOR TABLES Or, Os, Ot, Ou, Ov, Ow, Ox, AND Oy

May 31, 1947; June 30, 1949

| Compound | Formula | REFERENCES FOR TABLE O | | | | | | | |
| | | r $(H^o-H^o_0)/T$ | s $(F^o-H^o_0)/T$ | t $S^o$ | u $(H^o-H^o_0)$ | v $C_p^o$ | w $\Delta H_f^o$ | x $\Delta F_f^o$ | y $\log_{10} K_f$ |
|---|---|---|---|---|---|---|---|---|---|
| Oxygen | $O_2$ | 1,4,7,42,44 | 1,3,4,5,6,42,44 | 1,3,4,5,42,44 | 1,4,7,42,44 | 1,3,4,5,8,42,44 | 1,42 | 1,42 | 1,42 |
| Hydrogen | $H_2$ | 1,7,9,11,42,43 | 1,9,10,11,42,43 | 1,9,11,12,13,42,43 | 1,7,9,11,42,43 | 1,9,11,12,42,43 | 1,42 | 1,42 | 1,42 |
| Hydroxyl | OH | 2,7,14,42 | 2,14,42 | 2,13,14,15,42 | 2,7,14,42 | 2,14,42 | 2,14,16,17,18,19,20,42 | 2,42 | 2,42 |
| Water | $H_2O$ | 1,7,23,24,42 | 1,10,21,22,23,24,42 | 1,12,13,21,22,23,24,25,42 | 1,7,23,24,42 | 1,8,12,22,23,24,42 | 1,42 | 1,42 | 1,42 |
| Nitrogen | $N_2$ | 1,7,27,42 | 1,26,42 | 1,26,27,42 | 1,7,27,42 | 1,42 | 1,42 | 1,42 | 1,42 |
| Nitric Oxide | NO | 2,42 | 2,5,28,29,42 | 2,5,28,29,42 | 2,42 | 2,5,28,29,42 | 2,28,29,42 | 2,42 | 2,42 |
| Carbon (graphite) | C | 1,42 | 1,42 | 1,42 | 1,42 | 1,30,31,32,33,34,35,42 | 1,42 | 1,42 | 1,42 |
| Carbon Monoxide | CO | 1,7,27,37,42 | 1,5,36,37,42 | 1,5,12,13,27,36,37,42 | 1,7,27,37,42 | 1,5,12,27,37,42 | 1,42 | 1,42 | 1,42 |
| Carbon Dioxide | $CO_2$ | 1,7,38,42 | 1,21,38,42 | 1,12,21,39,40,41,42 | 1,7,38,42 | 1,12,38,42 | 1,42 | 1,42 | 1,42 |

REFERENCES

1. Wagman, Kilpatrick, Taylor, Pitzer, and Rossini[1]
2. American Petroleum Institute Research Project 44[1]
3. Johnston and Walker[1]
4. Johnston and Walker[2]
5. Gordon and Barnes[2]
6. Shand and Spurr[1]
7. Lewis and von Elbe[1]
8. Trautz and Adler[1]
9. Giauque[1]
10. Libby[1]
11. Davis and Johnston[1]
12. Gordon and Barnes[1]
13. Zeise[1]
14. Johnston and Dawson[1]
15. Villars[1]
16. Tanaka and Koana[1]
17. Johnston, Dawson, and Walker[1]
18. Riechemeier, Seuftleben, and Pastorff[1]
19. Lewis and von Elbe[2]
20. Dwyer and Oldenberg[1]
21. Gordon[1]
22. Gordon[2]
23. Wilson[1]
24. Gordon[3]
25. Giauque and Ashley[1]
26. Giauque and Clayton[1]
27. Johnston and Davis[1]
28. Johnston and Chapman[1]
29. Witmer[1]
30. Nernst[1]

| SPECIFIC REFERENCES | | |
|---|---|---|
| FOR TABLES Or, Os, Ot, Ou, Ov, Ow, Ox, AND Oy (Continued) | | |
| May 31, 1947; June 30, 1949 | | |
| REFERENCES | | |
| 31. Worthing[1] | | |
| 32. Magnus[2] | | |
| 33. Schlapfer and Debrunner[1] | | |
| 34. Jacobs and Parks[1] | | |
| 35. Magnus[1] | | |
| 36. Clayton and Giauque[1] | | |
| 37. Kassel[1] | | |
| 38. Kassel[3] | | |
| 39. Badger and Woo[1] | | |
| 40. Giauque and Egan[1] | | |
| 41. Rodebush[1] | | |
| 42. National Bureau of Standards[1] | | |
| 43. Woolley, Scott, and Brickwedde[1] | | |
| 44. Woolley[1] | | |

SPECIFIC REFERENCES

FOR TABLES 20r, 20s, 20t, 20u, 20u-E, 20u-G, 20v, 20v-E, 20v-G, 20w, 20x, AND 20y (PARTS 1)

May 31, 1947; December 31, 1952

| Compound | r $(H^o-H_0^o)/T$ | s $(F^o-H_0^o)/T$ | t $S^o$ | u,u-E,u-G $(H^o-H_0^o)$ | v,v-E,v-G $C_p^o$ | w $\Delta H_f^o$ | x $\Delta F_f^o$ | y $\log_{10}K_f$ |
|---|---|---|---|---|---|---|---|---|
| Methane | 1,6 | 1,6 | 1,6,8 | 1,6 | 1,6,13,14,15,16 | 2,3,4,6 | 2,6 | 6 |
| Ethane | 1,6 | 1,6 | 1,6,9 | 1,6 | 1,6,17,18,19 | 2,3,4,6 | 2,6 | 6 |
| Propane | 1,6 | 1,6 | 1,6,10 | 1,6 | 1,6,19,20,21 | 2,3,4,6 | 2,6 | 6 |
| n-Butane | 1,6,7,37 | 1,6,37 | 1,6,7,11,37 | 1,6,7,37 | 1,6,7,19,22,37 | 2,3,4,6 | 2,6 | 5,6,26,27,28 |
| n-Pentane | 1,6,7,37 | 1,6,37 | 1,6,7,12,37 | 1,6,7,37 | 1,6,7,23,24,25,37 | 2,3,4,6 | 2,6 | 5,6,28,29 |
| n-Hexane | 7,37 | 7,37 | 7,30,37 | 7,37 | 7,23,31,37 | 3,4,7 | 2,6 | 6,28 |
| n-Heptane | 1,37 | 1,37 | 1,32,33,34,37 | 1,37 | 1,23,35,37 | 2,3,4 | 2 | 6 |
| n-Octane | 1,37 | 1,37 | 1,34,36,37 | 1,37 | 1,37 | 2,3,4 | 2 | 6 |
| n-Nonane | 1,37 | 1,37 | 1,37 | 1,37 | 1,37 | 2,3,4 | 2 | 6 |
| n-Decane | 1,37 | 1,37 | 1,37 | 1,37 | 1,37 | 2,3,4 | 2 | 6 |
| n-Undecane | 1,37 | 1,37 | 1,37 | 1,37 | 1,37 | 2,3,4 | 2 | 6 |
| n-Dodecane | 1,37 | 1,37 | 1,37 | 1,37 | 1,37 | 2,3,4 | 2 | 6 |
| n-Tridecane | 1,37 | 1,37 | 1,37 | 1,37 | 1,37 | 2,3,4 | 2 | 6 |
| n-Tetradecane | 1,37 | 1,37 | 1,37 | 1,37 | 1,37 | 2,3,4 | 2 | 6 |
| n-Pentadecane | 1,37 | 1,37 | 1,37 | 1,37 | 1,37 | 2,3,4 | 2 | 6 |
| n-Hexadecane | 1,37 | 1,37 | 1,37 | 1,37 | 1,37 | 2,3,4 | 2 | 6 |
| n-Heptadecane | 1,37 | 1,37 | 1,37 | 1,37 | 1,37 | 2,3,4 | 2 | 6 |
| n-Octadecane | 1,37 | 1,37 | 1,37 | 1,37 | 1,37 | 2,3,4 | 2 | 6 |
| n-Nonadecane | 1,37 | 1,37 | 1,37 | 1,37 | 1,37 | 2,3,4 | 2 | 6 |
| n-Eicosane | 1,37 | 1,37 | 1,37 | 1,37 | 1,37 | 2,3,4 | 2 | 6 |

REFERENCES

1. Pitzer[7]
2. Prosen, Pitzer, and Rossini[2]
3. Prosen and Rossini[8]
4. See references for Table 20p (Part 1).
5. Montgomery, McAteer, and Franke[1]
6. American Petroleum Institute Research Project 44[1]
7. Pitzer and Kilpatrick[1]
8. Frank and Clusius[1]
9. Witt and Kemp[1]
10. Kemp and Egan[1]
11. Aston and Messerly[1]
12. Messerly and Kennedy[1]
13. Eucken and Fried[1]
14. Heuse[1]
15. Eucken and Lude[1]
16. Millar[1]
17. Wiebe, Hubbard, and Brevoort[1]
18. Eucken and Weigert[1]
19. Dailey and Felsing[1]
20. Kistiakowsky and Rice[1]
21. Kistiakowsky, Lacher, and Ransom[1]
22. Templeton, Davies, and Felsing[1]
23. Bennewitz and Rossner[1]
24. Pitzer[5]
25. Eucken and Sarstedt[1]
26. Montgomery, McAteer, and Horne[1]
27. Moldarskii and Nizorkina[1]
28. Schuit, Hoog, and Verheus[1]
29. Moldarskii and Nizorkina[2]
30. Douslin and Huffman[2]
31. Waddington and Douslin[1]
32. Pitzer[4]
33. Huffman, Parks, and Thomas[1]

SPECIFIC REFERENCES
FOR TABLES 20r, 20s, 20t, 20u, 20u-E, 20u-G, 20v, 20v-E, 20v-G, 20w, 20x, AND 20y (PARTS 1) (Continued)

May 31, 1947; December 31, 1952

REFERENCES

34. Parks, Huffman, and Thomas[1]
35. Waddington, Todd, and Huffman[1]
36. Huffman, Parks, and Barmore[1]
37. American Petroleum Institute Research Project 50[1]

SPECIFIC REFERENCES

FOR TABLES 1r, 1s, 1t, 1u, 1u-E, 1u-G, 1v, 1v-E, 1v-G, 1w, 1x, AND 1y

May 31, 1947; February 28, 1949; December 31, 1952

| Compound | r $(H^{\circ}-H^{\circ}_0)/T$ | s $(F^{\circ}-H^{\circ}_0)/T$ | t $S^{\circ}$ | u,u-E,u-G $(H^{\circ}-H^{\circ}_0)$ | v,v-E,v-G $C_p^{\circ}$ | w $\Delta H_f^{\circ}$ | x $\Delta F_f^{\circ}$ | y $\log_{10}K_f$ |
|---|---|---|---|---|---|---|---|---|
| Methane | 1 | 1 | 1 | 1 | 1 | 1 | 1 | 1 |
| Ethane | 1 | 1 | 1 | 1 | 1 | 1 | 1 | 1 |
| Propane | 1 | 1 | 1 | 1 | 1 | 1 | 1 | 1 |
| n-Butane | 1 | 1 | 1 | 1 | 1 | 1 | 1 | 1 |
| 2-Methylpropane (Isobutane) | 2,3 | 2,3 | 2,3,4 | 2,3 | 2,3,5 | 3,6,7,8 | 3,7 | 3,9,10,11,12 |
| n-Pentane | 1 | 1 | 1 | 1 | 1 | 1 | 1 | 1 |
| 2-Methylbutane (Isopentane) | 2,3,17 | 2,3,17 | 2,3,13,14,17 | 2,3,17 | 2,3,17 | 3,6,7,8 | 3,7 | 3,9,12,15 |
| 2,2-Dimethylpropane (Neopentane) | 2,3 | 2,3 | 2,3,16 | 2,3 | 2,3 | 3,6,7,8 | 3,7 | 3 |

REFERENCES

1. See references for Tables 20r, 20s, 20t, 20u, 20u-E, 20u-G, 20v, 20v-E, 20v-G, 20w, 20x, and 20y (Parts 1).
2. Pitzer and Kilpatrick[1]
3. American Petroleum Institute Research Project 44[1]
4. Aston, Kennedy, and Schumann[1]
5. Dailey and Felsing[2]
6. Prosen, Pitzer, and Rossini[2]
7. Prosen and Rossini[8]
8. See references for Table 1p.
9. Montgomery, McAteer, and Franke[1]
10. Montgomery, McAteer, and Horne[1]
11. Moldarskiĭ and Nizovakina[1]
12. Schuit, Hoog, and Verheus[1]
13. Schumann, Aston, and Sagenkahn[1]
14. Guthrie and Huffman[1]
15. Moldarskiĭ and Nizovakina[2]
16. Aston and Messerly[1]
17. Scott, McCullough, Williamson, and Waddington[1]

## SPECIFIC REFERENCES

### FOR TABLES 2r, 2s, 2t, 2u, 2u-E, 2u-G, 2v, 2v-E, 2v-G, 2w, 2x, AND 2y (PARTS 1)

May 31, 1947; December 31, 1952

| Compound | r $(H^o - H_0^o)/T$ | s $(F^o - H_0^o)/T$ | t $S^o$ | u, u-E, u-G $(H^o - H_0^o)$ | v, v-E, v-G $C_p^o$ | w $\Delta H_f^o$ | x $\Delta F_f^o$ | y $\log_{10} K_f$ |
|---|---|---|---|---|---|---|---|---|
| *n*-Hexane | 1 | 1 | 1 | 1 | 1 | 1 | 1 | 1 |
| 2-Methylpentane | 2 | 2,14 | 2,3,14 | 2 | 2 | 2,8,9 | 10,11 | 10,12,13 |
| 3-Methylpentane | 2,14 | 2,14 | 2,14 | 2,14 | 2,14 | 2,8,9 | 10,11 | 10,12,13 |
| 2,2-Dimethylbutane | 2,14 | 2,14 | 2,3,4,14 | 2,14 | 2,5,6,7,14 | 2,8,9 | 10,11 | 10 |
| 2,3-Dimethylbutane | 2,15 | 2,15 | 2,3,15 | 2,15 | 2,15 | 2,8,9 | 10,11 | 10,12 |

### REFERENCES

1. See references for Tables 20r, 20s, 20t, 20u, 20u-E, 20u-G, 20v, 20v-E, 20v-G, 20w, 20x, and 20y (Parts 1).
2. Pitzer and Kilpatrick[1]
3. Douslin and Huffman[2]
4. Kilpatrick and Pitzer[1]
5. Waddington and Douslin[1]
6. Pitzer[5]
7. Eucken and Sarstedt[1]
8. Prosen and Rossini[8]
9. See references for Table 2p (Part 1).
10. American Petroleum Institute Research Project 44[1]
11. Prosen, Pitzer, and Rossini[2]
12. Schuit, Hoog, and Verheus[1]
13. Montgomery[1]
14. American Petroleum Institute Research Project 50[1]
15. Scott, McCullough, Williamson, and Waddington[1]

SPECIFIC REFERENCES

FOR TABLES 2r, 2s, 2t, 2u, 2u-E, 2u-G, 2v, 2v-E, 2v-G, 2w, 2x, AND 2y (PARTS 2)

May 31, 1947; December 31, 1952

| Compound | r $(H^o-H^o_0)/T$ | s $(H^o-H^o_0)$ | t $S^o$ | u, u-E, u-G $(H^o-H^o_0)$ | v, v-E, v-G $C_p^o$ | w $\Delta H_f^o$ | x $\Delta F_f^o$ | y $\log_{10}K_f$ |
|---|---|---|---|---|---|---|---|---|
| n-Heptane | 1 | 1 | 1 | 1 | 1 | 1 | 1 | 1 |
| 2-Methylhexane | 2,3,10 | 2,3,10 | 2,3,4,10 | 2,3,10 | 2,3,10 | 7,8,9 | 7 | 2 |
| 3-Methylhexane | 2,3 | 2,3 | 2,3,5 | 2,3 | 2,3 | 7,8,9 | 7 | 2 |
| 3-Ethylpentane | 2,3,10 | 2,3,10 | 2,3,5,10 | 2,3,10 | 2,3,10 | 7,8,9 | 7 | 2 |
| 2,2-Dimethylpentane | 2,3,10 | 2,3,10 | 2,3,5,10 | 2,3,10 | 2,3,10 | 7,8,9 | 7 | 2 |
| 2,3-Dimethylpentane | 2,3 | 2,3 | 2,3,5 | 2,3 | 2,3 | 7,8,9 | 7 | 2 |
| 2,4-Dimethylpentane | 2,3 | 2,3 | 2,3,5 | 2,3 | 2,3 | 7,8,9 | 7 | 2 |
| 3,3-Dimethylpentane | 2,3 | 2,3 | 2,3,5 | 2,3 | 2,3 | 7,8,9 | 7 | 2 |
| 2,2,3-Trimethylbutane | 2,3,11 | 2,3,11 | 2,3,5,11 | 2,3,11 | 2,3,6,11 | 7,8,9 | 7 | 2 |

REFERENCES

1. See references for Tables 20r, 20s, 20t, 20u, 20u-E, 20u-G, 20v, 20v-E, 20w, 20x, and 20y (Parts 1).
2. American Petroleum Institute Research Project 44[1]
3. Pitzer[3]
4. Parks, Huffman, and Thomas[1]
5. Huffman, Parks, and Thomas[1]
6. Waddington, Todd, and Huffman[1]
7. Prosen, Pitzer, and Rossini[2]
8. Prosen and Rossini[8]
9. See references for Table 2p (Part 2).
10. American Petroleum Institute Research Project 50[1]
11. Waddington, and others[1]

SPECIFIC REFERENCES

FOR TABLES 3r, 3s, 3t, 3u, 3u-E, 3u-G, 3v, 3v-E, 3v-G, 3w, 3x, AND 3y

May 31, 1947; December 31, 1952

| Compound | r $(H°-H°_0)/T$ | s $(F°-H°_0)/T$ | t $S°$ | u,u-E,u-G $(H°-H°_0)$ | v,v-E,v-G $C_p°$ | w $\Delta H_f°$ | x $\Delta F_f°$ | y $\log_{10} K_f$ |
|---|---|---|---|---|---|---|---|---|
| n-Octane | 1 | 1 | 1 | 1 | 1 | 1 | 1 | 1 |
| 2-Methylheptane | 2,3 | 4 | 2,3 | 2,3 | 2,3 | 5,8,9 | 5 | 2 |
| 3-Methylheptane | 2,3 | 4 | 2,3 | 2,3 | 2,3 | 5,8,9 | 5 | 2 |
| 4-Methylheptane | 2,3 | 4 | 2,3 | 2,3 | 2,3 | 5,8,9 | 5 | 2 |
| 3-Ethylhexane | 2,3 | 4 | 2,3 | 2,3 | 2,3 | 5,8,9 | 5 | 2 |
| 2,2-Dimethylhexane | 2,3 | 4 | 2,3 | 2,3 | 2,3 | 5,8,9 | 5 | 2 |
| 2,3-Dimethylhexane | 2,3 | 4 | 2,3 | 2,3 | 2,3 | 5,8,9 | 5 | 2 |
| 2,4-Dimethylhexane | 2,3 | 4 | 2,3 | 2,3 | 2,3 | 5,8,9 | 5 | 2 |
| 2,5-Dimethylhexane | 2,3 | 4 | 2,3 | 2,3 | 2,3 | 5,8,9 | 5 | 2 |
| 3,3-Dimethylhexane | 2,3 | 4 | 2,3 | 2,3 | 2,3 | 5,8,9 | 5 | 2 |
| 3,4-Dimethylhexane | 2,3 | 4 | 2,3 | 2,3 | 2,3 | 5,8,9 | 5 | 2 |
| 2-Methyl-3-ethylpentane | 2,3 | 4 | 2,3 | 2,3 | 2,3 | 5,8,9 | 5 | 2 |
| 3-Methyl-3-ethylpentane | 2,3 | 4 | 2,3 | 2,3 | 2,3 | 5,8,9 | 5 | 2 |
| 2,2,3-Trimethylpentane | 2,3 | 4 | 2,3 | 2,3 | 2,3 | 5,8,9 | 5 | 2 |
| 2,2,4-Trimethylpentane | 2,3 | 4,10 | 2,3,6,7,10 | 2,3 | 2,3 | 5,8,9 | 5 | 2 |
| 2,3,3-Trimethylpentane | 2,3 | 4 | 2,3 | 2,3 | 2,3 | 5,8,9 | 5 | 2 |
| 2,3,4-Trimethylpentane | 2,3 | 4,10 | 2,3,10 | 2,3 | 2,3 | 5,8,9 | 5 | 2 |
| 2,2,3,3-Tetramethylbutane | 2,3,11 | 4,11 | 2,3,11 | 2,3,11 | 2,3,11 | 5,8,9 | 5 | 2 |

REFERENCES

1. See references for Tables 20r, 20s, 20t, 20u, 20u-E, 20u-G, 20v, 20v-E, 20v-G, 20w, 20x, and 20y (Parts 1).
2. American Petroleum Institute Research Project 44[1]
3. Pitzer[3]
4. Prosen, Pitzer, and Rossini[1]
5. Prosen, Pitzer, and Rossini[2]
6. Parks, Huffman, and Thomas[1]
7. Pitzer[4]
8. Prosen and Rossini[8]
9. See references for Table 3p.
10. American Petroleum Institute Research Project 50[1]
11. Scott, Douslin, Gross, Oliver, and Huffman[1]

SPECIFIC REFERENCES

FOR TABLES 22r, 22s, 22t, 22u, 22u-G, 22v, 22v-E, 22v-G, 22w, 22x, AND 22y (PARTS 1)

May 31, 1947; December 31, 1952

| Compound | r $(H^o-H_0^o)/T$ | s $(F^o-H_0^o)/T$ | t $S^o$ | u,u-E,u-G $(H^o-H_0^o)$ | v,v-E,v-G $C_p^o$ | w $\Delta H_f^o$ | x $\Delta F_f^o$ | y $\log_{10} K_f$ |
|---|---|---|---|---|---|---|---|---|
| Cyclopentane | 1 | 1 | 1,4,5 | 1 | 1,7 | 1,3,8 | 1 | 1 |
| Methylcyclopentane | 2 | 2 | 2,4,6 | 2 | 2 | 2,3,8 | 2 | 2,9,10,11 |
| Ethylcyclopentane | 2,12 | 2,12 | 2,12,13 | 2,12 | 2,12 | 2,3,8 | 2 | 2 |
| n-Propylcyclopentane | 2,12 | 2,12 | 2,12 | 2,12 | 2,12 | 2,3,8 | 2 | 2 |
| n-Butylcyclopentane | 2,12 | 2,12 | 2,12 | 2,12 | 2,12 | 2,3,8 | 2 | 2 |
| n-Pentylcyclopentane | 2,12 | 2,12 | 2,12 | 2,12 | 2,12 | 2,3,8 | 2 | 2 |
| n-Hexylcyclopentane | 2,12 | 2,12 | 2,12 | 2,12 | 2,12 | 2,3,8 | 2 | 2 |
| n-Heptylcyclopentane | 2,12 | 2,12 | 2,12 | 2,12 | 2,12 | 2,3,8 | 2 | 2 |
| n-Octylcyclopentane | 2,12 | 2,12 | 2,12 | 2,12 | 2,12 | 2,3,8 | 2 | 2 |
| n-Nonylcyclopentane | 2,12 | 2,12 | 2,12 | 2,12 | 2,12 | 2,3,8 | 2 | 2 |
| n-Decylcyclopentane | 2,12 | 2,12 | 2,12 | 2,12 | 2,12 | 2,3,8 | 2 | 2 |
| n-Undecylcyclopentane | 2,12 | 2,12 | 2,12 | 2,12 | 2,12 | 2,3,8 | 2 | 2 |
| n-Dodecylcyclopentane | 2,12 | 2,12 | 2,12 | 2,12 | 2,12 | 2,3,8 | 2 | 2 |
| n-Tridecylcyclopentane | 2,12 | 2,12 | 2,12 | 2,12 | 2,12 | 2,3,8 | 2 | 2 |
| n-Tetradecylcyclopentane | 2,12 | 2,12 | 2,12 | 2,12 | 2,12 | 2,3,8 | 2 | 2 |
| n-Pentadecylcyclopentane | 2,12 | 2,12 | 2,12 | 2,12 | 2,12 | 2,3,8 | 2 | 2 |
| n-Hexadecylcyclopentane | 2,12 | 2,12 | 2,12 | 2,12 | 2,12 | 2,3,8 | 2 | 2 |

REFERENCES

1. Kilpatrick, Spitzer, and Pitzer[1]
2. Kilpatrick, Werner, Beckett, Pitzer, and Rossini[1]
3. Prosen, Johnson, and Rossini[2]
4. Douslin and Huffman[1]
5. Aston, Fink, and Schumann[1]
6. Huffman, Parks, and Barmore[1]
7. Spitzer and Pitzer[1]
8. See references for Table 22p (Part 1).
9. Glasebrook and Lovell[1]
10. Arbuzov and Zelinskii[1]
11. Mizusima, Morino, and Huzisino[1]
12. American Petroleum Institute Research Project 50[1]
13. Huffman and others[1]

## SPECIFIC REFERENCES

FOR TABLES 6r, 6s, 6t, 6u, 6u-E, 6u-G, 6v, 6v-E, 6v-G, 6w, 6x, AND 6y

April 30, 1949; December 31, 1952

| Compound | r $(H^o-H_0^o)/T$ | s $(F^o-H_0^o)/T$ | t $S^o$ | u, u-E, u-G $(H^o-H_0^o)$ | v, v-E, v-G $C_p^o$ | w $\Delta H_f^o$ | x $\Delta F_f^o$ | y $\log_{10} K_f$ |
|---|---|---|---|---|---|---|---|---|
| Cyclopentane | 1 | 1 | 1 | 1 | 1 | 2 | 1 | 1 |
| Methylcyclopentane | 1 | 1 | 1 | 1 | 1 | 2 | 1 | 1 |
| Ethylcyclopentane | 1 | 1 | 1 | 1 | 1 | 2 | 1 | 1 |
| 1,1-Dimethylcyclopentane | 3 | 3 | 3 | 3 | 3 | 4 | 3 | 3 |
| 1,cis-2-Dimethylcyclopentane | 3 | 3 | 3 | 3 | 3 | 4 | 3 | 3 |
| 1,trans-2-Dimethylcyclopentane | 3 | 3 | 3 | 3 | 3 | 4 | 3 | 3 |
| 1,cis-3-Dimethylcyclopentane | 3 | 3 | 3 | 3 | 3 | 4 | 3 | 3 |
| 1,trans-3-Dimethylcyclopentane | 3 | 3 | 3 | 3 | 3 | 4 | 3 | 3 |

## REFERENCES

1. See references for Tables 22r, 22s, 22t, 22u, 22v, 22x, and 22y (Parts 1).
2. See references for Table 22p (Part 1).
3. Epstein, Barrow, Pitzer, and Rossini[1].
4. See references for Table 6p.

## SPECIFIC REFERENCES

FOR TABLES 23r, 23s, 23t, 23u, 23u-E, 23u-G, 23v, 23v-E, 23v-G, 23w, 23x, AND 23y (PARTS 1)
May 31, 1947; December 31, 1952

| Compound | r $(H^o-H^o_0)/T$ | s $(F^o-H^o_0)/T$ | t $S^o$ | u,u-E,u-G $(H^o-H^o_0)$ | v,v-E,v-G $C_p^o$ | w $\Delta H_f^o$ | x $\Delta H_f^o$ | y $\log_{10}K_f$ |
|---|---|---|---|---|---|---|---|---|
| Cyclohexane | 1 | | 1,5,6,7 | 1 | 1,11,12,13 | 3,4 | 2 | 2,14,15,16,17 |
| Methylcyclohexane | 1 | | 1,8,9 | 1 | 1,11,12,13 | 3,4 | 2 | 2 |
| Ethylcyclohexane | 1 | | 1,10 | 1 | 1 | 3,4 | 2 | 2 |
| n-Propylcyclohexane | 2,18 | | 2,18 | 2,18 | 2,18 | 2,3,4 | 2 | 2 |
| n-Butylcyclohexane | 2,18 | | 2,18 | 2,18 | 2,18 | 2,3,4 | 2 | 2 |
| n-Pentylcyclohexane | 2,18 | | 2,18 | 2,18 | 2,18 | 2,3,4 | 2 | 2 |
| n-Hexylcyclohexane | 2,18 | | 2,18 | 2,18 | 2,18 | 2,3,4 | 2 | 2 |
| n-Heptylcyclohexane | 2,18 | | 2,18 | 2,18 | 2,18 | 2,3,4 | 2 | 2 |
| n-Octylcyclohexane | 2,18 | | 2,18 | 2,18 | 2,18 | 2,3,4 | 2 | 2 |
| n-Nonylcyclohexane | 2,18 | | 2,18 | 2,18 | 2,18 | 2,3,4 | 2 | 2 |
| n-Decylcyclohexane | 2,18 | | 2,18 | 2,18 | 2,18 | 2,3,4 | 2 | 2 |
| n-Undecylcyclohexane | 2,18 | | 2,18 | 2,18 | 2,18 | 2,3,4 | 2 | 2 |
| n-Dodecylcyclohexane | 2,18 | | 2,18 | 2,18 | 2,18 | 2,3,4 | 2 | 2 |
| n-Tridecylcyclohexane | 2,18 | | 2,18 | 2,18 | 2,18 | 2,3,4 | 2 | 2 |
| n-Tetradecylcyclohexane | 2,18 | | 2,18 | 2,18 | 2,18 | 2,3,4 | 2 | 2 |
| n-Pentadecylcyclohexane | 2,18 | | 2,18 | 2,18 | 2,18 | 2,3,4 | 2 | 2 |
| n-Hexadecylcyclohexane | 2,18 | | 2,18 | 2,18 | 2,18 | 2,3,4 | 2 | 2 |

## REFERENCES

1. Beckett, Pitzer, and Spitzer[1]
2. Kilpatrick, Werner, Beckett, Pitzer, and Rossini[1]
3. Prosen, Johnson, and Rossini[2]
4. See references for Table 23p (Part 1).
5. Ruehrwein and Huffman[1]
6. Aston, Szasz, and Fink[1]
7. Parks, Huffman, and Thomas[1]
8. Douslin and Huffman[1]
9. Parks and Huffman[2]
10. Huffman, Todd, and Oliver[1]
11. Montgomery and DeVries[1]
12. Bennewitz and Rossner[1]
13. Spitzer and Pitzer[1]
14. Schuit, Hoog, and Verheus[1]
15. Glasebrook and Lovell[1]
16. Arbuzov and Zelinski[1]
17. Mizusima, Morino, and Huzisino[1]
18. American Petroleum Institute Research Project 50[1]

SPECIFIC REFERENCES

FOR TABLES 7r, 7s, 7t, 7u, 7u-E, 7u-G, 7v, 7v-E, 7v-G, 7w, 7x, AND 7y

May 31, 1947 (Corrected)

| Compound | r $(H^o - H^o_0)/T$ | s $(F^o - H^o_0)/T$ | t $S^o$ | u,u-E,u-G $(H^o - H^o_0)$ | v,v-E,v-G $C_p^o$ | w $\Delta H_f^o$ | x $\Delta F_f^o$ | y $\log_{10} K_f$ |
|---|---|---|---|---|---|---|---|---|
| Cyclohexane | 2 | 2 | 2 | 2 | 2 | 2 | 2 | 2 |
| Methylcyclohexane | 2 | 2 | 2 | 2 | 2 | 2 | 2 | 2 |
| Ethylcyclohexane | 2 | 2 | 2 | 2 | 2 | 2 | 2 | 2 |
| 1,1-Dimethylcyclohexane | 1 | 1 | 1,4 | 1 | 1 | 3,6 | 5 | 5 |
| 1,cis-2-Dimethylcyclohexane | 1 | 1 | 1,4 | 1 | 1 | 3,6 | 5 | 5 |
| 1,trans-2-Dimethylcyclohexane | 1 | 1 | 1,4 | 1 | 1 | 3,6 | 5 | 5 |
| 1,cis-3-Dimethylcyclohexane | 1 | 1 | 1,4 | 1 | 1 | 3,6 | 5 | 5 |
| 1,trans-3-Dimethylcyclohexane | 1 | 1 | 1,4 | 1 | 1 | 3,6 | 5 | 5 |
| 1,cis-4-Dimethylcyclohexane | 1 | 1 | 1,4 | 1 | 1 | 3,6 | 5 | 5 |
| 1,trans-4-Dimethylcyclohexane | 1 | 1 | 1,4 | 1 | 1 | 3,6 | 5 | 5 |

REFERENCES

1. Beckett, Pitzer, and Spitzer[1]
2. See references for Tables 23r, 23s, 23t, 23u, 23u-E, 23u-G, 23v, 23v-E, 23v-G, 23w, 23x, and 23y
3. Prosen, Johnson, and Rossini[3]
4. Huffman, Todd, and Oliver[1]
5. Kilpatrick, Werner, Beckett, Pitzer, and Rossini[1]
6. See references for Table 7p.

## SPECIFIC REFERENCES

FOR TABLES 24r, 24s, 24t, 24u, 24u-E, 24u-G, 24v, 24v-E, 24v-G, 24w, 24x, AND 24y (PARTS 1)

May 31, 1947; December 31, 1952

| Compound | r $(H^o - H_0^o)/T$ | s $(F^o - H_0^o)/T$ | t $S^o$ | u,u-E,u-G $(H^o - H_0^o)$ | v,v-E,v-G $C_p^o$ | w $\Delta H_f^o$ | x $\Delta F_f^o$ | y $\log_{10} K_f$ |
|---|---|---|---|---|---|---|---|---|
| Ethene (Ethylene) | 1 | 1 | 1,2 | 1 | 1,5 | 7,8,9 | 7 | 7 |
| Propene (Propylene) | 1 | 1 | 1,3 | 1,15 | 1,6 | 7,8,9 | 7 | 7 |
| 1-Butene | 1,15 | 1,15 | 1,4,15 | 1,15 | 1,4,15 | 7,8,9 | 7 | 7,10,11,12,13 |
| 1-Pentene | 7 | 7 | 7 | 7 | 7 | 7,8,9 | 7 | 7,14 |
| 1-Hexene | 7 | 7 | 7 | 7 | 7 | 7,8,9 | 7 | 7 |
| 1-Heptene | 7,15 | 7,15 | 7,15 | 7,15 | 7,15 | 7,8,9 | 7 | 7 |
| 1-Octene | 7,15 | 7,15 | 7,15 | 7,15 | 7,15 | 7,8,9 | 7 | 7 |
| 1-Nonene | 7,15 | 7,15 | 7,15 | 7,15 | 7,15 | 7,8,9 | 7 | 7 |
| 1-Decene | 7,15 | 7,15 | 7,15 | 7,15 | 7,15 | 7,8,9 | 7 | 7 |
| 1-Undecene | 7,15 | 7,15 | 7,15 | 7,15 | 7,15 | 7,8,9 | 7 | 7 |
| 1-Dodecene | 7,15 | 7,15 | 7,15 | 7,15 | 7,15 | 7,8,9 | 7 | 7 |
| 1-Tridecene | 7,15 | 7,15 | 7,15 | 7,15 | 7,15 | 7,8,9 | 7 | 7 |
| 1-Tetradecene | 7,15 | 7,15 | 7,15 | 7,15 | 7,15 | 7,8,9 | 7 | 7 |
| 1-Pentadecene | 7,15 | 7,15 | 7,15 | 7,15 | 7,15 | 7,8,9 | 7 | 7 |
| 1-Hexadecene | 7,15 | 7,15 | 7,15 | 7,15 | 7,15 | 7,8,9 | 7 | 7 |
| 1-Heptadecene | 7,15 | 7,15 | 7,15 | 7,15 | 7,15 | 7,8,9 | 7 | 7 |
| 1-Octadecene | 7,15 | 7,15 | 7,15 | 7,15 | 7,15 | 7,8,9 | 7 | 7 |
| 1-Nonadecene | 7,15 | 7,15 | 7,15 | 7,15 | 7,15 | 7,8,9 | 7 | 7 |
| 1-Eicosene | 7,15 | 7,15 | 7,15 | 7,15 | 7,15 | 7,8,9 | 7 | 7 |

## REFERENCES

1. Kilpatrick and Pitzer[2]
2. Egan and Kemp[1]
3. Powell and Giauque[1]
4. Aston, Fink, Bestul, Pace, and Szasz[1]
5. Bureik, Eyster, and Yost[1]
6. Kistiakowsky and Rice[1]
7. Kilpatrick, Prosen, Pitzer, and Rossini[1]
8. Prosen and Rossini[9]
9. See references for Table 24p (Part 1).
10. Frey and Huppke[1]
11. Shell Development Company[1]
12. Kistiakowsky[1]
13. Turkevich[1]
14. Ewell and Hardy[1]
15. American Petroleum Institute Research Project 50[1]

SPECIFIC REFERENCES

FOR TABLES 8r, 8s, 8t, 8u, 8u-E, 8u-G, 8v, 8v-E, 8v-G, 8w, 8x, AND 8y (PARTS 1)

May 31, 1947; December 31, 1952

| Compound | r $(H^o-H^o_0)/T$ | s $(F^o-H^o_0)/T$ | t $S^o$ | u,u-E,u-G $(H^o-H^o_0)$ | v,v-E,v-G $C^o_p$ | w $\Delta H_f^o$ | x $\Delta H_f^o$ | y $\log_{10}K_f$ |
|---|---|---|---|---|---|---|---|---|
| Ethene (Ethylene) | 1 | 1 | 1 | 1 | 1 | 1 | 1 | 1 |
| Propene (Propylene) | 1 | 1 | 1 | 1 | 1 | 1 | 1 | 1 |
| 1-Butene | 1 | 1 | 1 | 1 | 1 | 1 | 1 | 1 |
| cis-2-Butene | 2 | 2 | 2,3 | 2 | 2,3,6 | 8,9,10 | 8 | 8,11,12,13 |
| trans-2-Butene | 2 | 2 | 2,4 | 2 | 2,6 | 8,9,10 | 8 | 8,11,12,13 |
| 2-Methylpropene (Isobutene) | 2 | 2 | 2,5 | 2 | 2,7 | 8,9,10 | 8 | 8,11 |
| 1-Pentene | 1 | 1 | 1 | 1 | 1 | 1 | 1 | 1 |
| cis-2-Pentene | 8 | 8 | 8 | 8 | 8 | 8,9,10 | 8 | 8,14 |
| trans-2-Pentene | 8 | 8 | 8 | 8 | 8 | 8,9,10 | 8 | 8,14 |
| 2-Methyl-1-butene | 8 | 8 | 8 | 8 | 8 | 8,9,10 | 8 | 8,14 |
| 3-Methyl-1-butene | 8 | 8 | 8 | 8 | 8 | 8,9,10 | 8 | 8,14 |
| 2-Methyl-2-butene | 8,15 | 8,15 | 8,15 | 8,15 | 8,15 | 8,9,10 | 8 | 8,14 |

REFERENCES

1. See references for Tables 24r, 24s, 24t, 24u, 24u-E, 24u-G, 24v, 24v-E, 24v-G, 24w, 24x, and 24y (Parts 1).
2. Kilpatrick and Pitzer[2]
3. Scott, Ferguson, and Brickwedde[1]
4. Guttman and Pitzer[1]
5. Rands, Scott, and Brickwedde[1]
6. Kistiakowsky and Rice[2]
7. Scott and Mellors[1]
8. Kilpatrick, Prosen, Pitzer, and Rossini[1]
9. Prosen and Rossini[9]
10. See references for Table 8p (Part 1).
11. Frey and Huppke[1]
12. Shell Development Company[1]
13. Turkevich[1]
14. Ewell and Hardy[1]
15. Scott, Waddington, Smith, and Huffman[1]

SPECIFIC REFERENCES

FOR TABLES 8r, 8s, 8t, 8u, 8u-E, 8u-G, 8v, 8v-E, 8v-G, 8w, 8x, AND 8y (PARTS 2)

May 31, 1947; December 31, 1952

| Compound | r | s | t | u, u-E, u-G | v, v-E, v-G | w | x | y |
|---|---|---|---|---|---|---|---|---|
| | $(H^o - H^o_0)/T$ | $(F^o - H^o_0)/T$ | $S^o$ | $(H^o - H^o_0)$ | $C_p^o$ | $\Delta H_f^o$ | $\Delta F_f^o$ | $\log_{10} K_f$ |
| 1-Hexene | 7 | 7 | 7 | 7 | 7 | 7 | 7 | 7 |
| cis-2-Hexene | 1 | 1 | 1 | 1 | 1 | 1,2,3 | 1 | 1 |
| trans-2-Hexene | 1 | 1 | 1 | 1 | 1 | 1,2,3 | 1 | 1 |
| cis-3-Hexene | 1 | 1 | 1 | 1 | 1 | 1,2,3 | 1 | 1 |
| trans-3-Hexene | 1 | 1 | 1 | 1 | 1 | 1,2,3 | 1 | 1 |
| 2-Methyl-1-pentene | 1 | 1 | 1 | 1 | 1 | 1,2,3 | 1 | 1 |
| 3-Methyl-1-pentene | 1 | 1 | 1 | 1 | 1 | 1,2,3 | 1 | 1 |
| 4-Methyl-1-pentene | 1 | 1 | 1 | 1 | 1 | 1,2,3 | 1 | 1 |
| 2-Methyl-2-pentene | 1 | 1 | 1 | 1 | 1 | 1,2,3 | 1 | 1 |
| 3-Methyl-cis-2-pentene | 1 | 1 | 1 | 1 | 1 | 1,2,3 | 1 | 1 |
| 3-Methyl-trans-2-pentene | 1 | 1 | 1 | 1 | 1 | 1,2,3 | 1 | 1 |
| 4-Methyl-cis-2-pentene | 1 | 1 | 1 | 1 | 1 | 1,2,3 | 1 | 1 |
| 4-Methyl-trans-2-pentene | 1 | 1 | 1 | 1 | 1 | 1,2,3 | 1 | 1 |
| 2-Ethyl-1-butene | 1 | 1 | 1 | 1 | 1 | 1,2,3 | 1 | 1 |
| 2,3-Dimethyl-1-butene | 1 | 1 | 1 | 1 | 1 | 1,2,3 | 1 | 1,4,5,6 |
| 3,3-Dimethyl-1-butene | 1 | 1 | 1 | 1 | 1 | 1,2,3 | 1 | 1,4,5,6 |
| 2,3-Dimethyl-2-butene | 1 | 1 | 1 | 1 | 1 | 1,2,3 | 1 | 1,4,5,6 |

REFERENCES

1. Kilpatrick, Prosen, Pitzer, and Rossini[1]
2. Prosen and Rossini[9]
3. See references for Table 8p (Part 2).
4. Whitmore and Meunier[1]
5. Cramer and Glasebrook[1]
6. Brooks, Howard, and Crafton[2]
7. See references for Tables 24r, 24s, 24t, 24u, 24u-E, 24u-G, 24v, 24v-E, 24v-G, 24w, 24x, and 24y (Parts 1).

SPECIFIC REFERENCES

FOR TABLES 11r, 11s, 11t, 11u, 11u-E, 11u-G, 11v, 11v-E, 11v-G, 11w, 11x, AND 11y (PARTS 1)

October 31, 1947; April 30, 1948; December 31, 1952

| Compound | r $(H^o-H^o_0)/T$ | s $(F^o-H^o_0)/T$ | t $S^o$ | u,u-E,u-G $(H^o-H^o_0)$ | v,v-E,v-G $C_p^o$ | w $\Delta Hf^o$ | x $\Delta Ff^o$ | y $\log_{10}Kf$ |
|---|---|---|---|---|---|---|---|---|
| Propadiene (Allene) | 1 | 1 | 1 | 1,11 | 1,11 | 3,6,7 | 1 | 1 |
| 1,2-Butadiene | 1 | 1 | 1,9 | 1,11 | 1,11 | 3,10 | 1 | 1 |
| 1,3-Butadiene | 1,2 | 1,2 | 1,2,12 | 1,11 | 1,2,11,13,14 | 3,5,6,7,10 | 1 | 1 |
| 1,2-Pentadiene | 1 | 1 | 1 | 1,11 | 1,11 | 3 | 1 | 1 |
| 1,cis-3-pentadiene (cis-Piperylene) | 1 | 1 | 1 | 1,11 | 1,11 | 3,6,8 | 1 | 1 |
| 1,trans-3-Pentadiene (trans-Piperylene) | 1 | 1 | 1 | 1,11 | 1,11 | 3,6,8 | 1 | 1 |
| 1,4-Pentadiene | 1 | 1 | 1 | 1,11 | 1,11 | 3,6,7 | 1 | 1 |
| 2,3-Pentadiene | 1 | 1 | 1 | 1,11 | 1,11 | 3 | 1 | 1 |
| 3-Methyl-1,2-butadiene | 1 | 1 | 1,4 | 1,11 | 1,11 | 3 | 1 | 1 |
| 2-Methyl-1,3-butadiene (Isoprene) | 1 | 1 | 1 | 1,11 | 1,11 | 3 | 1 | 1 |

REFERENCES

1. Kilpatrick, Beckett, Prosen, Pitzer, and Rossini[1]
2. Aston, Szasz, Woolley, and Brickwedde[1]
3. See references for Table 11p (Part 1).
4. Bekkedahl and Wood[1]
5. Prosen and Rossini[6]
6. Rossini[21]
7. Kistiakowsky, Ruhoff, Smith, and Vaughan[3]
8. Dolliver, Gresham, Kistiakowsky, and Vaughan[1]
9. Aston and Szasz[1]
10. Prosen, Maron, and Rossini[1]
11. American Petroleum Institute Research Project 44[1]
12. Scott, Meyers, Rands, Brickwedde, and Bekkedahl[1]
13. Scott and Mellors[1]
14. Templeton, Davies, and Felsing[1]

SPECIFIC REFERENCES

FOR TABLES 18r, 18s, 18t, 18u, 18u-E, 18u-G, 18v, 18v-E, 18v-G, 18w, 18x, AND 18y

December 31, 1952

| Compound | r | s | t | u, u-E, u-G | v, v-E, v-G | w | x | y |
|---|---|---|---|---|---|---|---|---|
| | $(H^o - H_0^o)/T$ | $(F^o - H_0^o)/T$ | $S^o$ | $(H^o - H_0^o)$ | $C_p^o$ | $\Delta H_f^o$ | $\Delta F_f^o$ | $\log_{10} K_f$ |
| Cyclopentene | 1 | 1 | 1 | 1 | 1 | 3 | 4 | 4 |
| 1-Methylcyclopentene | 2 | 2 | 2 | 2 | 2 | | | |
| 3-Methylcyclopentene | 2 | 2 | 2 | 2 | 2 | | | |
| 4-Methylcyclopentene | 2 | 2 | 2 | 2 | 2 | | | |
| 1-Ethylcyclopentene | | | | | | | | |
| 3-Ethylcyclopentene | | | | | | | | |
| 4-Ethylcyclopentene | | | | | | | | |
| 1,2-Dimethylcyclopentene | 2 | 2 | 2 | 2 | 2 | | | |
| 1,3-Dimethylcyclopentene | 2 | 2 | 2 | 2 | 2 | | | |
| 1,4-Dimethylcyclopentene | 2 | 2 | 2 | 2 | 2 | | | |
| 1,5-Dimethylcyclopentene | 2 | 2 | 2 | 2 | 2 | | | |
| 3,3-Dimethylcyclopentene | 2 | 2 | 2 | 2 | 2 | | | |
| 3,cis-4-Dimethylcyclopentene | 2 | 2 | 2 | 2 | 2 | | | |
| 3,trans-4-Dimethylcyclopentene | 2 , | 2 | 2 | 2 | 2 | | | |
| 3,cis-5-Dimethylcyclopentene | 2 | 2 | 2 | 2 | 2 | | | |
| 3,trans-5-Dimethylcyclopentene | 2 | 2 | 2 | 2 | 2 | | | |
| 4,4-Dimethylcyclopentene | 2 | | | | | | | |

REFERENCES

1. Beckett, Freeman, and Pitzer[1]
2. American Petroleum Institute Research Project 50[1]
3. See references for Table 18p.
4. American Petroleum Institute Research Project 44[1]

SPECIFIC REFERENCES

FOR TABLES 19r, 19s, 19t, 19u, 19u-E, 19u-G, 19v, 19v-E, 19v-G, 19w, 19x, AND 19y

December 31, 1952

| Compound | r | s | t | u,u-E,u-G | v,v-E,v-G | w | x | y |
|---|---|---|---|---|---|---|---|---|
| | $(H^o-H^o_0)/T$ | $(F^o-H^o_0)/T$ | $S^o$ | $(H^o-H^o_0)$ | $C_p^o$ | $\Delta Hf^o$ | $\Delta Ff^o$ | $\log_{10} Kf$ |
| Cyclohexene | 2 | 2 | 2 | 2 | 2 | 1 | 1 | 1 |
| 1-Methylcyclohexene | | | | | | | | |
| 3-Methylcyclohexene | | | | | | | | |
| 4-Methylcyclohexene | | | | | | | | |
| 1-Ethylcyclohexene | | | | | | | | |
| 3-Ethylcyclohexene | | | | | | | | |
| 4-Ethylcyclohexene | | | | | | | | |
| 1,2-Dimethylcyclohexene | | | | | | | | |
| 1,3-Dimethylcyclohexene | | | | | | | | |
| 1,4-Dimethylcyclohexene | | | | | | | | |
| 1,5-Dimethylcyclohexene | | | | | | | | |
| 1,6-Dimethylcyclohexene | | | | | | | | |
| 3,3-Dimethylcyclohexene | | | | | | | | |
| 3,cis-4-Dimethylcyclohexene | | | | | | | | |
| 3,trans-4-Dimethylcyclohexene | | | | | | | | |
| 3,cis-5-Dimethylcyclohexene | | | | | | | | |
| 3,trans-5-Dimethylcyclohexene | | | | | | | | |
| 3,cis-6-Dimethylcyclohexene | | | | | | | | |
| 3,trans-6-Dimethylcyclohexene | | | | | | | | |
| 4,4-Dimethylcyclohexene | | | | | | | | |
| 4,cis-5-Dimethylcyclohexene | | | | | | | | |
| 4,trans-5-Dimethylcyclohexene | | | | | | | | |

REFERENCES

1. American Petroleum Institute Research Project 441

2. Beckett, Freeman, and Pitzer[1]

SPECIFIC REFERENCES

FOR TABLES 25r, 25s, 25t, 25u, 25u-E, 25u-G, 25v, 25v-E, 25v-G, 25w, 25x, AND 25y (PARTS 1)

May 31, 1947; December 31, 1952

| Compound | r $(H^o-H_0^o)/T$ | s $(F^o-H_0^o)/T$ | t $S^o$ | u, u-E, u-G $(H^o-H_0^o)$ | v, v-E, v-G $C_p^o$ | w $\Delta H_f^o$ | x $\Delta F_f^o$ | y $\log_{10} K_f$ |
|---|---|---|---|---|---|---|---|---|
| Ethyne (Acetylene) | 2 | 2 | 2 | 2 | 2 | 2,4 | 2 | 2 |
| Propyne (Methylacetylene) | 2 | 2 | 2 | 2 | 1,2 | 2,4 | 2 | 2 |
| 1-Butyne (Ethylacetylene) | 2 | 2 | 2 | 2 | 2 | 2,4 | 2 | 2 |
| 1-Pentyne | 2,3 | 2,3 | 2,3 | 2,3 | 2,3 | 2,4 | 2 | 2 |
| 1-Hexyne | 2,3,5 | 2,3,5 | 2,3,5 | 2,3,5 | 2,3,5 | 4,5 | 2,5 | 2,5 |
| 1-Heptyne | 2,3,5 | 2,3,5 | 2,3,5 | 2,3,5 | 2,3,5 | 4,5 | 2,5 | 2,5 |
| 1-Octyne | 2,3,5 | 2,3,5 | 2,3,5 | 2,3,5 | 2,3,5 | 4,5 | 2,5 | 2,5 |
| 1-Nonyne | 2,3,5 | 2,3,5 | 2,3,5 | 2,3,5 | 2,3,5 | 4,5 | 2,5 | 2,5 |
| 1-Decyne | 2,3,5 | 2,3,5 | 2,3,5 | 2,3,5 | 2,3,5 | 4,5 | 2,5 | 2,5 |
| 1-Undecyne | 2,3,5 | 2,3,5 | 2,3,5 | 2,3,5 | 2,3,5 | 4,5 | 2,5 | 2,5 |
| 1-Dodecyne | 2,3,5 | 2,3,5 | 2,3,5 | 2,3,5 | 2,3,5 | 4,5 | 2,5 | 2,5 |
| 1-Tridecyne | 2,3,5 | 2,3,5 | 2,3,5 | 2,3,5 | 2,3,5 | 4,5 | 2,5 | 2,5 |
| 1-Tetradecyne | 2,3,5 | 2,3,5 | 2,3,5 | 2,3,5 | 2,3,5 | 4,5 | 2,5 | 2,5 |
| 1-Pentadecyne | 2,3,5 | 2,3,5 | 2,3,5 | 2,3,5 | 2,3,5 | 4,5 | 2,5 | 2,5 |
| 1-Hexadecyne | 2,3,5 | 2,3,5 | 2,3,5 | 2,3,5 | 2,3,5 | 4,5 | 2,5 | 2,5 |
| 1-Heptadecyne | 2,3,5 | 2,3,5 | 2,3,5 | 2,3,5 | 2,3,5 | 4,5 | 2,5 | 2,5 |
| 1-Octadecyne | 2,3,5 | 2,3,5 | 2,3,5 | 2,3,5 | 2,3,5 | 4,5 | 2,5 | 2,5 |
| 1-Nonadecyne | 2,3,5 | 2,3,5 | 2,3,5 | 2,3,5 | 2,3,5 | 4,5 | 2,5 | 2,5 |
| 1-Eicosyne | 2,3,5 | 2,3,5 | 2,3,5 | 2,3,5 | 2,3,5 | 4,5 | 2,5 | 2,5 |

REFERENCES

1. Kistiakowsky and Rice[2]
2. Wagman, Kilpatrick, Pitzer, and Rossini[1]
3. American Petroleum Institute Research Project 50[1]
4. See references for Table 25p (Part 1).
5. American Petroleum Institute Research Project 44[1]

## SPECIFIC REFERENCES

### FOR TABLES 12r, 12s, 12t, 12u, 12u-E, 12u-G, 12v, 12v-E, 12v-G, 12w, 12x, AND 12y

May 31, 1947

| Compound | r $(H^o-H_0^o)/T$ | s $(F^o-H_0^o)/T$ | t $S^o$ | u,u-E,u-G $(H^o-H_0^o)$ | v,v-E,v-G $C_p^o$ | w $\Delta H_f^o$ | x $\Delta F_f^o$ | y $\log_{10}K_f$ |
|---|---|---|---|---|---|---|---|---|
| Ethyne (Acetylene) | 1 | 1 | 1 | 1 | 1 | 1,4 | 1 | 1 |
| Propyne (Methylacetylene) | 1 | 1 | 1 | 1 | 1,3 | 1,4 | 1 | 1 |
| 1-Butyne (Ethylacetylene) | 1 | 1 | 1 | 1 | 1 | 1,4 | 1 | 1 |
| 2-Butyne (Dimethylacetylene) | 1 | 1 | 1,2 | 1 | 1,3 | 1,4 | 1 | 1 |
| 1-Pentyne | 1 | 1 | 1 | 1 | 1 | 1,4 | 1 | 1 |
| 2-Pentyne | 1 | 1 | 1 | 1 | 1 | 1,4 | 1 | 1 |
| 3-Methyl-1-butyne | 1 | 1 | 1 | 1 | 1 | 1,4 | 1 | 1 |

REFERENCES

1. Wagman, Kilpatrick, Pitzer, and Rossini[1]
2. Osborne, Garner, and Yost[1]
3. Kistiakowsky and Rice[2]
4. See references for Table 12p.

SPECIFIC REFERENCES

FOR TABLES 21r, 21s, 21t, 21u, 21u-E, 21u-G, 21v, 21v-E, 21v-G, 21w, 21x, AND 21y (PARTS 1)

May 31, 1947; December 31, 1952

| Compound | r $(H^o-H^o_0)/T$ | s $(F^o-H^o_0)/T$ | t $S^o$ | u,u-E,u-G $(H^o-H^o_0)$ | v,v-E,v-G $C_p^o$ | w $\Delta H_f^o$ | x $\Delta F_f^o$ | y $\log_{10}K_f$ |
|---|---|---|---|---|---|---|---|---|
| Benzene | 1 | 1 | 1,2 | 1 | 1,6,7 | 1,9,10 | 1 | 1 |
| Methylbenzene (Toluene) | 1 | 1 | 1,3 | 1 | 1,6,7 | 1,9,10 | 1 | 1 |
| Ethylbenzene | 1 | 1 | 1,4,5 | 1 | 1,8 | 1,9,10 | 1 | 1 |
| n-Propylbenzene | 1,11 | 1,11 | 1,11 | 1,11 | 1,11 | 1,9,10 | 1 | 1 |
| n-Butylbenzene | 1,11 | 1,11 | 1,11 | 1,11 | 1,11 | 1,9,10 | 1 | 1 |
| n-Pentylbenzene | 1,11 | 1,11 | 1,11 | 1,11 | 1,11 | 1,9,10 | 1 | 1 |
| n-Hexylbenzene | 1,11 | 1,11 | 1,11 | 1,11 | 1,11 | 1,9,10 | 1 | 1 |
| n-Heptylbenzene | 1,11 | 1,11 | 1,11 | 1,11 | 1,11 | 1,9,10 | 1 | 1 |
| n-Octylbenzene | 1,11 | 1,11 | 1,11 | 1,11 | 1,11 | 1,9,10 | 1 | 1 |
| n-Nonylbenzene | 1,11 | 1,11 | 1,11 | 1,11 | 1,11 | 1,9,10 | 1 | 1 |
| n-Decylbenzene | 1,11 | 1,11 | 1,11 | 1,11 | 1,11 | 1,9,10 | 1 | 1 |
| n-Undecylbenzene | 1,11 | 1,11 | 1,11 | 1,11 | 1,11 | 1,9,10 | 1 | 1 |
| n-Dodecylbenzene | 1,11 | 1,11 | 1,11 | 1,11 | 1,11 | 1,9,10 | 1 | 1 |
| n-Tridecylbenzene | 1,11 | 1,11 | 1,11 | 1,11 | 1,11 | 1,9,10 | 1 | 1 |
| n-Tetradecylbenzene | 1,11 | 1,11 | 1,11 | 1,11 | 1,11 | 1,9,10 | 1 | 1 |
| n-Pentadecylbenzene | 1,11 | 1,11 | 1,11 | 1,11 | 1,11 | 1,9,10 | 1 | 1 |
| n-Hexadecylbenzene | 1,11 | 1,11 | 1,11 | 1,11 | 1,11 | 1,9,10 | 1 | 1 |

REFERENCES

1. Taylor, Wagman, Williams, Pitzer, and Rossini[1]
2. Ahlberg, Blanchard, and Lundberg[1]
3. Kelley[1]
4. Guthrie, Spitzer, and Huffman[1]
5. Scott and Brickwedde[1]
6. Pitzer and Scott[2]
7. Montgomery and DeVries[1]
8. Scott and Mellors[1]
9. Prosen, Johnson, and Rossini[3]
10. See references for Table 21p (Part 1).
11. American Petroleum Institute Research Project 50[1]

## SPECIFIC REFERENCES

### FOR TABLES 5r, 5s, 5t, 5u, 5u-E, 5u-G, 5v, 5v-E, 5v-G, 5w, 5x, AND 5y

May 31, 1947

| Compound | r $(H^o-H^o_0)/T$ | s $(F^o-H^o_0)/T$ | t $S^o$ | u,u-E,u-G $-(H^o-H^o_0)$ | v,v-E,v-G $C^o_p$ | w $\Delta H_f^o$ | x $\Delta F_f^o$ | y $\log_{10}K_f$ |
|---|---|---|---|---|---|---|---|---|
| Benzene | 2 | 2 | 2 | 2 | 2 | 2 | 2 | 2 |
| Methylbenzene (Toluene) | 2 | 2 | 2 | 2 | 2 | 2 | 2 | 2 |
| Ethylbenzene | 2 | 2 | 2 | 2 | 2 | 2 | 2 | 2 |
| 1,2-Dimethylbenzene (o-Xylene) | 1 | 1,3 | 1,3 | 1 | 1,3 | 1,4,5 | 1 | 1 |
| 1,3-Dimethylbenzene (m-Xylene) | 1 | 1,3 | 1,3 | 1 | 1,3 | 1,4,5 | 1 | 1 |
| 1,4-Dimethylbenzene (p-Xylene) | 1 | 1,3 | 1,3 | 1 | 1,3 | 1,4,5 | 1 | 1 |
| n-Propylbenzene | 2 | 2 | 2 | 2 | 2 | 2 | 2 | 2 |
| Isopropylbenzene | 1 | 1 | 1 | 1 | 1 | 1,4,5 | 1 | 1 |
| 1-Methyl-2-ethylbenzene | 1 | 1 | 1 | 1 | 1 | 1,4,5 | 1 | 1 |
| 1-Methyl-3-ethylbenzene | 1 | 1 | 1 | 1 | 1 | 1,4,5 | 1 | 1 |
| 1-Methyl-4-ethylbenzene | 1 | 1 | 1 | 1 | 1 | 1,4,5 | 1 | 1 |
| 1,2,3-Trimethylbenzene | 1 | 1 | 1 | 1 | 1 | 1,4,5 | 1 | 1 |
| 1,2,4-Trimethylbenzene | 1 | 1 | 1 | 1 | 1 | 1,4,5 | 1 | 1 |
| 1,3,5-Trimethylbenzene | 1 | 1 | 1 | 1 | 1 | 1,4,5 | 1. | 1 |

### REFERENCES

1. Taylor, Wagman, Williams, Pitzer, and Rossini[1]
2. See references for Tables 21r, 21s, 21t, 21u, 21u-E, 21u-G, 21v, 21v-E, 21v-G, 21w, 21x, and 21y.
3. Pitzer and Scott[2]
4. Prosen, Johnson, and Rossini[3]
5. See references for Table 7p.

SPECIFIC REFERENCES

FOR TABLES 13r, 13s, 13t, 13u, 13u-E, 13u-G, 13v, 13v-E, 13v-G, 13w, 13x, AND 13y

September 30, 1947

| Compound | r $(H^o-H_0^o)/T$ | s $(F^o-H_0^o)/T$ | t $S^o$ | u,u-E,u-G $(H^o-H_0^o)$ | v,v-E,v-G $C_p^o$ | w $\Delta H_f^o$ | x $\Delta F_f^o$ | y $\log_{10}K_f$ |
|---|---|---|---|---|---|---|---|---|
| Ethenylbenzene (Styrene; Vinylbenzene; Phenylethylene) | 2 | 2 | 1,2 | 2,6 | 1,2,3,6 | 4,7 | 5,6 | 5,6 |
| Isopropenylbenzene (α-Methylstyrene; 2-Phenyl-1-propene) | 2 | 2 | 2 | 2,6 | 2,6 | 4 | 6 | 6 |
| cis-1-Propenylbenzene (cis-β-Methylstyrene; cis-1-Phenyl-1-propene) | 2 | 2 | 2 | 2,6 | 2,6 | 8 | 6 | 6 |
| trans-1-Propenylbenzene (trans-β-Methylstyrene; trans-1-Phenyl-1-propene) | 2 | 2 | 2 | 2,6 | 2,6 | 8 | 6 | 6 |
| 1-Methyl-2-ethenylbenzene (o-Methylstyrene) | 2 | 2 | 2 | 2,6 | 2,6 | 8 | 6 | 6 |
| 1-Methyl-3-ethenylbenzene (m-Methylstyrene) | 2 | 2 | 2 | 2,6 | 2,6 | 8 | 6 | 6 |
| 1-Methyl-4-ethenylbenzene (p-Methylstyrene) | 2 | 2 | 2 | 2,6 | 2,6 | 8 | 6 | 6 |

REFERENCES

1. Pitzer, Guttman, and Westrum[1]
2. Beckett and Pitzer[1]
3. Scott and Mellors[1]
4. Prosen and Rossini[6]
5. Ghosh, Guha, and Roy[1]
6. American Petroleum Institute Research Project 44[1]
7. Dolliver, Gresham, Kistiakowsky, and Vaughan[1]
8. Kilpatrick, Beckett, Prosen, Pitzer, and Rossini[1]

## SPECIFIC REFERENCES[a]
### FOR TABLE 20z (PART 1)
#### December 31, 1952

| Compound | REFERENCES FOR | |
| --- | --- | --- |
| | Heat of Fusion | Cryoscopic Constants |
| Methane | 1 | 15 |
| Ethane | 2,3 | 15 |
| Propane | 4 | 15 |
| n–Butane | 5,6 | 15,17 |
| n–Pentane | 7,8,9 | 15 |
| n–Hexane | 6,10,11,12 | 15 |
| n–Heptane | 11,13,16 | 15,17 |
| n–Octane | 6,11,16 | 15 |
| n–Nonane | 16 | 15,18 |
| n–Decane | 16 | 15 |
| n–Undecane | 16 | 14,15 |
| n–Dodecane | 16 | 14,15 |
| n–Tridecane | 16 | 14,15 |
| n–Tetradecane | 16 | 14,15 |
| n–Pentadecane | 16 | 14,15 |
| n–Hexadecane | 16 | 14,15 |
| n–Heptadecane | 15 | 14 |
| n–Octadecane | 15 | 14 |
| n–Nonadecane | 15 | 15 |
| n–Eicosane | 15 | 15 |

[a] References for freezing points are given in the specific references for the corresponding "a" table.

### REFERENCES

1. Clusius[1]
2. Witt and Kemp[1]
3. Wiebe, Hubbard, and Brevoort[1]
4. Kemp and Egan[1]
5. Aston and Messerly[2]
6. Huffman, Parks, and Barmore[1]
7. Messerly and Kennedy[1]
8. Parks and Huffman[1]
9. Huffman and others[1]
10. Douslin and Huffman[2]
11. Parks, Huffman, and Thomas[1]
12. Stull[1]
13. Pitzer[4]
14. American Petroleum Institute Research Project 6[1]
15. American Petroleum Institute Research Project 44[1]
16. Waddington and others[1]
17. Glasgow, Krouskop, Beadle, Axilrod, and Rossini[1]
18. Streiff, Murphy, Cahill, Flanagan, Sedlak; Willingham, and Rossini[1]

## SPECIFIC REFERENCES[a]
### FOR TABLE 1z
May 31, 1947; November 30, 1949; December 31, 1952

| Compound | REFERENCES FOR | |
| --- | --- | --- |
| | Heat of Fusion | Cryoscopic Constants |
| Methane | 1 | 1 |
| Ethane | 1 | 1 |
| Propane | 1 | 1 |
| *n*–Butane | 1 | 1 |
| 2–Methylpropane (Isobutane) | 2,3 | 11,12 |
| *n*–Pentane | 4,5,10 | 11 |
| 2–Methylbutane (Isopentane) | 6,7,8 | 11 |
| 2,2–Dimethylpropane (Neopentane) | 9 | 11 |

[a] References for freezing points are given in the specific references for the corresponding "a" table.

### REFERENCES

1. See references for Table 20z (Part 1).
2. Parks, Shomate, Kennedy, and Crawford[1]
3. Aston, Kennedy, and Schumann[1]
4. Messerly and Kennedy[1]
5. Parks and Huffman[1]
6. Schumann, Aston, and Sagenkahn[1]
7. Guthrie and Huffman[1]
8. Parks, Huffman, and Thomas[1]
9. Aston and Messerly[1]
10. Huffman and others[1]
11. American Petroleum Institute Research Project 44[1]
12. Glasgow, Krouskop, Beadle, Axilrod, and Rossini[1]

SPECIFIC REFERENCES[a]

FOR TABLE 2z (PART 1)

May 31, 1947; December 31, 1952

| Compound | REFERENCES FOR | |
| --- | --- | --- |
| | Heat of Fusion | Cryoscopic Constants |
| *n*-Hexane | 1 | 1 |
| 2-Methylpentane | 2,3 | 5 |
| 3-Methylpentane | | |
| 2,2-Dimethylbutane | 2,3,4 | 5 |
| 2,3-Dimethylbutane | 2 | 5 |

[a] References for freezing points are given in the specific references for the corresponding "a" table.

REFERENCES

1. See references for Table 20z (Part 1).
2. Douslin and Huffman[2]
3. Stull[1]
4. Kilpatrick and Pitzer[1]
5. American Petroleum Institute Research Project 44[1]

## SPECIFIC REFERENCES[a]
### FOR TABLE 2z (PART 2)
May 31, 1947; December 31, 1952

| Compound | REFERENCES FOR | |
| --- | --- | --- |
| | Heat of Fusion | Cryoscopic Constants |
| $n$-Heptane | 1 | 1 |
| 2-Methylhexane | 2,4 | 5 |
| 3-Methylhexane | | |
| 3-Ethylpentane | 3,4 | 5 |
| 2,2-Dimethylpentane | 3,4 | 5 |
| 2,3-Dimethylpentane | | |
| 2,4-Dimethylpentane | 3,4 | 5 |
| 3,3-Dimethylpentane | 3 | 5 |
| 2,2,3-Trimethylbutane | 3,4 | 5 |

[a] References for freezing points are given in the specific references for the corresponding "a" table.

### REFERENCES

1. See references for Table 20z (Part 1).
2. Parks, Huffman, and Thomas[1]
3. Huffman, Parks, and Thomas[1]
4. Waddington and others[1]
5. American Petroleum Institute Research Project 44[1]

SPECIFIC REFERENCES[a]
FOR TABLE 3z

May 31, 1947; December 31, 1952

| Compound | REFERENCES FOR | |
| --- | --- | --- |
| | Heat of Fusion | Cryoscopic Constants |
| n-Octane | 1 | 1 |
| 2-Methylheptane | 4 | 3 |
| 3-Methylheptane | 4 | 3 |
| 4-Methylheptane | 4 | 3 |
| 3-Ethylhexane | | |
| 2,2-Dimethylhexane | 4 | 3 |
| 2,3-Dimethylhexane | | |
| 2,4-Dimethylhexane | | |
| 2,5-Dimethylhexane | 4 | 3 |
| 3,3-Dimethylhexane | 4 | 4 |
| 3,4-Dimethylhexane | | |
| 2-Methyl-3-ethylpentane | 4 | 3 |
| 3-Methyl-3-ethylpentane | 4 | 3 |
| 2,2,3-Trimethylpentane | 4 | 3 |
| 2,2,4-Trimethylpentane | 2 | 4 |
| 2,3,3-Trimethylpentane | 4 | 3 |
| 2,3,4-Trimethylpentane | 5 | 4 |
| 2,2,3,3-Tetramethylbutane | 6,7 | 4 |

[a] References for freezing points are given in the specific references for the corresponding "a" table.

REFERENCES

1. See references for Table 20z (Part 1).
2. Parks, Huffman, and Thomas[1]
3. Streiff, Murphy, Sedlak, Willingham, and Rossini[1]
4. American Petroleum Institute Research Project 44[1]
5. Pitzer and Scott[1]
6. Parks and Huffman[2]
7. Scott, Douslin, Gross, Oliver, and Huffman[1]

SPECIFIC REFERENCES[a]

FOR TABLE 4z, Page 1

December 31, 1952

| Compound | REFERENCES FOR | |
|---|---|---|
| | Heat of Fusion | Cryoscopic Constants |
| *n*–Nonane | 1 | 1 |
| 2–Methyloctane | | |
| 3–Methyloctane | | |
| 4–Methyloctane | | |
| 3–Ethylheptane | | |
| 4–Ethylheptane | | |
| 2,2–Dimethylheptane | 2 | 3 |
| 2,3–Dimethylheptane | | |
| 2,4–Dimethylheptane | | |
| 2,5–Dimethylheptane | | |
| 2,6–Dimethylheptane | | |
| 3,3–Dimethylheptane | | |
| 3,4–Dimethylheptane | | |
| 3,5–Dimethylheptane | | |
| 4,4–Dimethylheptane | | |

[a] References for freezing points are given in the specific references for the corresponding "a" table.

REFERENCES

1. See references for Table 20z (Part 1).
2. American Petroleum Institute Research Project 44[1]
3. American Petroleum Institute Research Project 6[1]

SPECIFIC REFERENCES[a]
FOR TABLE 4z, Page 2
December 31, 1952

| Compound | REFERENCES FOR | |
| | Heat of Fusion | Cryoscopic Constants |
| --- | --- | --- |
| 2-Methyl-3-ethylhexane | | |
| 2-Methyl-4-ethylhexane | | |
| 3-Methyl-3-ethylhexane | | |
| 3-Methyl-4-ethylhexane | | |
| 2,2,3-Trimethylhexane | | |
| 2,2,4-Trimethylhexane | 1 | 2 |
| 2,2,5-Trimethylhexane | 1 | 3 |
| 2,3,3-Trimethylhexane | 1 | 2 |
| 2,3,4-Trimethylhexane | | |
| 2,3,5-Trimethylhexane | | |
| 2,4,4-Trimethylhexane | 1 | 3 |
| 3,3,4-Trimethylhexane | 1 | 2 |
| 3,3-Diethylpentane | 1 | 3 |
| 2,2-Dimethyl-3-ethylpentane | | |
| 2,3-Dimethyl-3-ethylpentane | | |
| 2,4-Dimethyl-3-ethylpentane | | |
| 2,2,3,3-Tetramethylpentane | 1 | 3 |
| 2,2,3,4-Tetramethylpentane | 1 | 3 |
| 2,2,4,4-Tetramethylpentane | 1 | 3 |
| 2,3,3,4-Tetramethylpentane | 1 | 3 |

[a] References for freezing points are given in the specific references for the corresponding "a" table.

REFERENCES

1. American Petroleum Institute Research Project 44[1]
2. Streiff, Zimmerman, Soule, Butt, Sedlak, Willingham, and Rossini[1]
3. Streiff, Murphy, Cahill, Flanagan, Sedlak, Willingham, and Rossini[1]

SPECIFIC REFERENCES[a]

FOR TABLE 6z

May 31, 1947; August 31, 1949; December 31, 1952

| Compound | REFERENCES FOR | |
| --- | --- | --- |
| | Heat of Fusion | Cryoscopic Constants |
| Cyclopentane | 1,2,3 | 6 |
| Methylcyclopentane | 2,4 | 6 |
| Ethylcyclopentane | 5 | 6 |
| 1,1-Dimethylcyclopentane | 5 | 6,7 |
| 1,cis-2-Dimethylcyclopentane | 5 | 6,7 |
| 1,trans-2-Dimethylcyclopentane | 4 | 6 |
| 1,cis-3-Dimethylcyclopentane | 5 | 6,8 |
| 1,trans-3-Dimethylcyclopentane | 5 | 6,7 |

[a] References for freezing points are given in the specific references for the corresponding "a" table.

REFERENCES

1. Aston, Fink, and Schumann[1]
2. Douslin and Huffman[1]
3. Jacobs and Parks[1]
4. Huffman, Parks, and Barmore[1]
5. Huffman and others[1]
6. American Petroleum Institute Research Project 44[1]
7. Streiff, Murphy, Cahill, Flanagan, Sedlak, Willingham, and Rossini[1]
8. Streiff, Zimmerman, Soule, Butt, Sedlak, Willingham, and Rossini[1]

SPECIFIC REFERENCES[a]

FOR TABLE 7z

May 31, 1947; August 31, 1949; December 31, 1952

| Compound | REFERENCES FOR | |
|---|---|---|
| | Heat of Fusion | Cryoscopic Constants |
| Cyclohexane | 1,2,3,4 | 8,9 |
| Methylcyclohexane | 5,6 | 8,9 |
| Ethylcyclohexane | 7 | 8,9 |
| 1,1-Dimethylcyclohexane | 7 | 8,10 |
| 1,cis-2-Dimethylcyclohexane | 7 | 8,10 |
| 1,trans-2-Dimethylcyclohexane | 7 | 8,10 |
| 1,cis-3-Dimethylcyclohexane | 7 | 8,11 |
| 1,trans-3-Dimethylcyclohexane | 7 | 8,11 |
| 1,cis-4-Dimethylcyclohexane | 7 | 8,10 |
| 1,trans-4-Dimethylcyclohexane | 7 | 8,10 |

[a] References for freezing points are given in the specific references for the corresponding "a" table.

REFERENCES

1. Parks, Huffman, and Thomas[1]
2. Ruehrwein and Huffman[1]
3. Aston, Szasz, and Fink[1]
4. Ziegler and Andrews[1]
5. Parks and Huffman[1]
6. Douslin and Huffman[1]
7. Huffman, Todd, and Oliver[1]
8. American Petroleum Institute Research Project 44[1]
9. American Petroleum Institute Research Project 6[1]
10. Streiff, Murphy, Cahill, Flanagan, Sedlak, Willingham, and Rossini[1]
11. Streiff, Murphy, Zimmerman, Soule, Sedlak, Willingham, and Rossini[1]

SPECIFIC REFERENCES[a]
FOR TABLE 8z (PART 1)
May 31, 1947; December 31, 1952

| Compound | REFERENCES FOR | |
| --- | --- | --- |
| | Heat of Fusion | Cryoscopic Constants |
| Ethene | 1,2 | 10 |
| Propene | 3,4 | 10 |
| 1-Butene | 5 | 10 |
| cis-2-Butene | 6,7 | 10,11 |
| trans-2-Butene | 6,8 | 10,11 |
| 2-Methylpropene | 6,9 | 10,11 |
| 1-Pentene | 12 | 10 |
| cis-2-Pentene | 12 | 10 |
| trans-2-Pentene | 12 | 10,14 |
| 2-Methyl-1-butene | 12 | 10,14 |
| 3-Methyl-1-butene | 12 | 10,14 |
| 2-Methyl-2-butene | 12,13 | 10 |

[a] References for freezing points are given in the specific references for the corresponding "a" table.

### REFERENCES

1. Egan and Kemp[1]
2. Eucken and Hauck[1]
3. Huffman, Parks, and Barmore[1]
4. Powell and Giauque[1]
5. Aston, Fink, Bestul, Pace, and Szasz[1]
6. Todd and Parks[1]
7. Scott, Ferguson, and Brickwedde[1]
8. Guttman and Pitzer[1]
9. Rands, Scott, and Brickwedde[1]
10. American Petroleum Institute Research Project 44[1]
11. Glasgow, Krouskop, Beadle, Axilrod, and Rossini[1]
12. Todd, Oliver, and Huffman[1]
13. Parks and Huffman[1]
14. Streiff, Murphy, Sedlak, Willingham, and Rossini[1]

| | SPECIFIC REFERENCES[a] | |
|---|---|---|
| | FOR TABLE 5z | |
| | May 31, 1947; December 31, 1952 | |

| Compound | REFERENCES FOR | |
|---|---|---|
| | Heat of Fusion | Cryoscopic Constants |
| Benzene | 1,2,3 | 11 |
| Methylbenzene (Toluene) | 2,3,4 | 11 |
| Ethylbenzene | 1,5,6 | 11 |
| 1,2-Dimethylbenzene (o-Xylene) | 1,7 | 11 |
| 1,3-Dimethylbenzene (m-Xylene) | 1,7 | 11 |
| 1,4-Dimethylbenzene (p-Xylene) | 1,7 | 11 |
| n-Propylbenzene | 11 | 8,12 |
| Isopropylbenzene | 11 | 12 |
| 1-Methyl-2-ethylbenzene | 11 | 8 |
| 1-Methyl-3-ethylbenzene | 11 | 8 |
| 1-Methyl-4-ethylbenzene | 11 | 8 |
| 1,2,3-Trimethylbenzene | 9 | 8,11,12 |
| 1,2,4-Trimethylbenzene | 9,10 | 8,11,12 |
| 1,3,5-Trimethylbenzene | 9 | 11 |

[a] References for freezing points are given in the specific references for the corresponding "a" table.

REFERENCES

1. Huffman, Parks, and Daniels[1]
2. Stull[1]
3. Ziegler and Andrews[1]
4. Kelley[1]
5. Guthrie, Spitzer, and Huffman[1]
6. Scott and Brickwedde[1]
7. Pitzer and Scott[2]
8. Streiff, Murphy, Sedlak, Willingham, and Rossini[1]
9. Rossini[12]
10. Huffman, Parks, and Barmore[1]
11. American Petroleum Institute Research Project 44[1]
12. Glasgow, Murphy, Willingham, and Rossini[1]

## SPECIFIC REFERENCES[a]
### FOR TABLE 14z
### December 31, 1952

| Compound | REFERENCES FOR | |
| --- | --- | --- |
| | Heat of Fusion | Cryoscopic Constants |
| *n*–Butylbenzene (1–Phenylbutane) | 3,4 | 1 |
| Isobutylbenzene (1–Phenyl–2–methylpropane) | 1 | 6,7 |
| *sec*–Butylbenzene (2–Phenylbutane) | 1 | 2,6,7 |
| *tert*–Butylbenzene (2–Phenyl–2–methylpropane) | 4,8 | 1 |
| 1–Methyl–2–propylbenzene | | |
| 1–Methyl–3–propylbenzene | | |
| 1–Methyl–4–propylbenzene | | |
| 1–Methyl–2–isopropylbenzene (*o*–Cymene) | 1 | 2 |
| 1–Methyl–3–isopropylbenzene (*m*–Cymene) | 1 | 2 |
| 1–Methyl–4–isopropylbenzene (*p*–Cymene) | 3,4 | 1 |
| 1,2–Diethylbenzene | 1 | 5 |
| 1,3–Diethylbenzene | 1 | 2,5 |
| 1,4–Diethylbenzene | 1 | 5 |
| 1,2–Dimethyl–3–ethylbenzene | | |
| 1,2–Dimethyl–4–ethylbenzene | | |
| 1,3–Dimethyl–2–ethylbenzene | | |
| 1,3–Dimethyl–4–ethylbenzene | | |
| 1,3–Dimethyl–5–ethylbenzene | 1 | 2 |
| 1,4–Dimethyl–2–ethylbenzene | | |
| 1,2,3,4–Tetramethylbenzene (Prehnitene) | 3,4 | 1 |
| 1,2,3,5–Tetramethylbenzene (Isodurene) | 3,4,9 | 1 |
| 1,2,4,5–Tetramethylbenzene (Durene) | 4,9,10,11 | 1 |

[a] References for freezing points are given in the specific references for the corresponding "a" table.

### REFERENCES

1. American Petroleum Institute Research Project 44[1]
2. American Petroleum Institute Research Project 6[1]
3. Huffman, Parks, and Barmore[1]
4. Parks and Huffman[2]
5. Streiff, Zimmerman, Soule, Butt, Sedlak, Willingham, and Rossini[1]
6. Glasgow, Murphy, Willingham, and Rossini[1]
7. Streiff, Murphy, Cahill, Flanagan, Sedlak, Willingham, and Rossini[1]
8. Huffman, Parks, and Daniels[1]
9. Smith and MacDougall[1]
10. Ferry and Thomas[1]
11. Eibert[1]

GENERAL LIST OF REFERENCES
A (Page 1)
As of December 31, 1952

Adam
    1. Phil. Mag. 8, 539 (1929)

Adams, Bramlet, and Tendwick
    1. J. Am. Chem. Soc. 42, 2369 (1920)

Adams and Marshall
    1. J. Am. Chem. Soc. 67, 279 (1945)

Addison
    1. J. Chem. Soc. 535 (1943)

Adkins and Cramer
    1. J. Am. Chem. Soc. 53, 1425 (1931)

Adkins and Davis
    1. J. Am. Chem. Soc. 71, 2955 (1949)

Adkins and England
    1. J. Am. Chem. Soc. 71, 2958 (1949)

Adkins and Roebuck
    1. J. Am. Chem. Soc. 70, 4041 (1948)

Ador and Rilliet
    1. Ber. 12, 329 (1879)

Adrienz
    1. Ber. 6, 439 (1873)

Affleck and Dougherty
    1. J. Org. Chem. 15, 865 (1950)

Ahlberg, Blanchard, and Lundberg
    1. J. Chem. Phys. 5, 539 (1937)

Ahrens and Moźd'eński
    1. Z. angew. Chem. 21, 1411 (1908)

Akhmatov
    1. Kolloid-Z 66, 266 (1934)
    2. J. Phys. Chem. (U.S.S.R.) 5, 812 (1934)

Alder and Vogt
    1. Ann. 564, 120 (1949)

Alexander and Mudrak
    1. J. Am. Chem. Soc. 72, 3194 (1950)

Alexander and Perkins
    1. J. Am. Chem. Soc. 71, 1786 (1949)

Ali
    1. Proc. Ind. Assoc. Cult. Sci. 9, 155 (1925)

Allen and Bell
    1. Organic Synthesis 22, 39 (1942)

Altschul
    1. Z. physik. Chem. 11, 577 (1893)

Amemiya
    1. J. Chem. Soc. Japan 63, 1225 (1942)

American Petroleum Institute Research Project 6, Carnegie
    Institute of Technology, Pittsburgh, Pennsylvania,
    F. D. Rossini
    1. Unpublished

American Petroleum Institute Research Project 42, Pennsylvania
    State College, State College, Pennsylvania, R. W. Schiessler
    1. Unpublished

American Petroleum Institute Research Project 44, Carnegie
    Institute of Technology, Pittsburgh, Pennsylvania,
    F. D. Rossini
    1. Unpublished

American Petroleum Institute Research Project 45, Ohio State
    University, Columbus, Ohio, C. E. Boord
    1. Unpublished

American Petroleum Institute Research Project 48, U. S. Bureau
    of Mines, Bartlesville, Oklahoma, H. M. Smith
    1. Unpublished

American Petroleum Institute Research Project 50, University of
    California, Berkeley, California, K. S. Pitzer
    1. Unpublished

Anderson
    1. Proc. Am. Petrol. Inst. Sec. III 28, 181 (1948)

Anderson and Erskine
    1. Ind. Eng. Chem. 16, 263 (1944)

Anderson and Short
    1. J. Chem. Soc. 485 (1933)

Anderson and Smith
    1. J. Inst. Petroleum 38, 415 (1952)

Andrade and Rotherham
    1. Proc. Phys. Soc. (London) 48, 261 (1936)

Andreev
    1. J. Gen. Chem. (U.S.S.R.) 17, 1645 (1947)

Andreev, Meshcheryakov, and Petrov
    1. J. Phys. Chem. (U.S.S.R.) 19, 705 (1946)

Andreev and Petrov
    1. J. Applied Chem. (U.S.S.R.) 21, 134 (1948)

Ansdell
    1. Proc. Roy. Soc. 29, 209 (1879)

Appleby, Dobraty, and Kapranos
    1. J. Am. Chem. Soc. 66, 1938 (1944)

Appleby, Sartor, Lee, and Kapranos
    1. J. Am. Chem. Soc. 70, 1552 (1948)

Aranda
    1. Anales soc. espān. fiś. quim. 35, 186 (1937)

GENERAL LIST OF REFERENCES
A (Page 2)
As of December 31, 1952

Arbuzov
1. Compt. rend. acad. sci. U.R.S.S. **39**, 311 (1943)

Arbuzov and Zelinskiĭ
1. Compt. rend. acad. sci. U.R.S.S. **30**, 721 (1941)

van Arkel
1. Rec. trav. chim. **52**, 733 (1933)

Armstrong, Grove, Hammick, and Thompson
1. J. Chem. Soc. 1700 (1948)

Armstrong, Little, and Doak
1. Ind. Eng. Chem. **36**, 628 (1944)

Arnold, Smith, and Dobson
1. J. Org. Chem. **15**, 1256 (1950)

Asahina
1. Acta Phytochim. (Japan) **1**, 67 (1922)

Ashdown, Harris, and Armstrong
1. J. Am. Chem. Soc. **58**, 850 (1936)

Asinger
1. Ber. **77**, 73 (1944)

Asinger and Eckoldt
1. Ber. **76**, 585 (1943)

Aston
1. Unpublished. Pennsylvania State College, State College, Pennsylvania

Aston, Fink, Bestul, Pace, and Szasz
1. J. Am. Chem. Soc. **68**, 52 (1946)

Aston, Fink, and Schumann
1. J. Am. Chem. Soc. **65**, 341 (1943)

Aston, Kennedy, and Schumann
1. J. Am. Chem. Soc. **62**, 2059 (1940)

Aston, Mastrangelo, and Moessen
1. J. Am. Chem. Soc. **72**, 5287 (1950)

Aston and Messerly
1. J. Am. Chem. Soc. **58**, 2354 (1936)
2. J. Am. Chem. Soc. **62**, 1917 (1940)

Aston and Szasz
1. J. Am. Chem. Soc. **69**, 3108 (1947)

Aston, Szasz, and Fink
1. J. Am. Chem. Soc. **65**, 1135, 2481 (1943)

Aston, Szasz, Wooley, and Brickwedde
1. J. Chem. Phys. **14**, 67 (1946)

Autenrieth
1. Ann. **254**, 222 (1889)

Autenrieth and Geyer
1. Ber. **41**, 4249 (1908)

Autenrieth and Wolff
1. Ber. **32**, 1368 (1899)

von Auwers
1. Ber. **51**, 1126 (1918)
2. Ann. **419**, 92 (1919)
3. Ber. **45**, 2764 (1912)
4. Ann. **413**, 253 (1917)
5. Ber. **46**, 2988 (1913)
6. Ann. **415**, 98 (1918)
7. Ann. **410**, 287 (1915)
8. Ann. **420**, 84 (1920)
9. Ann. **420**, 97 (1919)
10. Ann. **408**, 212 (1915)

von Auwers and Arndt
1. Ber. **42**, 537 (1909)

von Auwers and Beger
1. Ber. **27**, 1733 (1894)

von Auwers and Eisenlohr
1. J. prakt. Chem. **82**, 65 (1910)
2. Z. physik Chem. **83**, 429 (1913)

von Auwers and Ellinger
1. Ann. **387**, 200 (1912)

von Auwers and Fruhling
1. Ann. **422**, 193 (1921)

von Auwers, Hinterseher, and Treppman
1. Ann. **410**, 257 (1915)

von Auwers and Keil
1. Ber. **36**, 1861 (1903)

von Auwers and Kohlhaas
1. J. prakt. Chem. **108**, 321 (1924)

von Auwers and Kolligs
1. Ber. **55**, 21 (1922)
2. Ber. **55**, 3872 (1922)

von Auwers and Lange
1. Ann. **409**, 149 (1915)

von Auwers and Moosbrugger
1. Ann. **387**, 167 (1912)

von Auwers and Müller
1. Ber. **44**, 1606 (1911)
2. Ber. **44**, 1595 (1911)

von Auwers, Roth, and Eisenlohr
1. Ann. **373**, 267 (1910)
2. Ann. **385**, 102 (1911)

von Auwers and Thies
1. Ber. **53**, 2285 (1920)

von Auwers and Westerman
1. Ber. **54**, 2993 (1921)

GENERAL LIST OF REFERENCES
A (Page 3)
As of December 31, 1952

von Auwers and Wieners
    1. Ber, **58**, 2815 (1925)

von Auwers and Ziegler
    1. Ann. **425**, 217 (1921)

Ayers and Agruss
    1. J. Am. Chem. Soc. **61**, 83 (1939)

Azim, Bhatnagar, and Mathur
    1. Phil. Mag. **16**, 860 (1933)
    2. Phil. Mag. **16**, 580 (1933)

GENERAL LIST OF REFERENCES
B (Page 1)
As of December 31, 1952

Bachman and Goebel
1. J. Am. Chem. Soc. **64**, 787 (1942)

Bachman and Hellman
1. J. Am. Chem. Soc. **70**, 1772 (1948)

Backer and Blaas
1. Rec. trav. chim. **61**, 785 (1942)

Backer and Dijkstra
1. Rec. trav. **chim.** **51**, 289 (1932)

Backer and Dost
1. Rec. trav. chim. **68**, 1143 (1949)

Backer and de Jong
1. Rec. trav. chim. **67**, 884 (1948)

Backer and Keuning
1. Rec. trav. chim. **53**, 808 (1934)
2. Rec. trav. chim. **52**, 499 (1933)

Backer and Kramer
1. Rec. trav. chim. **53**, 1101 (1934)

Backer and Stedehouder
1. Rec. trav. chim. **52**, 437 (1933)

Backer, Stevens, and Dost
1. Rec. trav. chim. **67**, 451 (1948)

Backer and Strating
1. Rec. trav. chim. **59**, 933 (1940)

Backer and Tamsma
1. Rec. trav. chim. **57**, 1183 (1938)

Backer, Terpstra, and Dijkstra
1. Rec. trav. chim. **51**, 1166 (1932)

Bader, Cross, Heilbron, and Jones
1. J. Chem. Soc. 619 (1949)

Badger
1. J. Chem. Phys. **2**, 128 (1934)
2. J. Chem. Phys. **3**, 710 (1935)

Badger and Bauer
1. J. Chem. Phys. **5**, 599 (1937)

Badger, Cook, and Croslie
1. J. Chem. Soc. 1432 (1947)

Badger and Woo
1. J. Am. Chem. Soc. **54**, 3523 (1932)

Badin
1. J. Am. Chem. Soc. **65**, 1812 (1943)

Baer and Carmack
1. J. Am. Chem. Soc. **71**, 1215 (1949)

Baeyer
1. Ann. **155**, 275 (1870)

Baeyer and Villiger
1. Ber. **32**, 2429 (1899)

Bailey, Bryant, Hancock, Morrell, and Smith
1. J. Inst. Petroleum **33**, 503 (1947)

Bailey, Pickering, and Smith
1. J. Inst. Petroleum **35**, 103 (1949)

Baker and Groves
1. J. Chem. Soc. 1144 (1939)

Balandin and Marukjan
1. Compt. rend. acad. sci. U.R.S.S. **48**, 482 (1946)
2. Compt. rend. acad. sci. U.R.S.S. **55**, 121 (1947)
3. Bull. acad. sci. U.R.S.S. Classe sci. chim. 451 (1948)

Bales and Nickelson
1. J. Chem. Soc. **121**, 2137 (1922)

Bamburger
1. Ber. **30**, 366 (1897)

Bannister and Elsner
1. J. Chem. Soc. 1055 (1951)
2. J. Chem. Soc. 1061 (1951)

Banse and Parks
1. J. Am. Chem. Soc. **55**, 3223 (1933)

Barbandy
1. Bull. soc. chim. **39**, 371 (1926)

Barber and Smiles
1. J. Chem. Soc. 1141 (1928)

Barbier and Grignard
1. Bull. soc. chim. **31**, 840 (1904)

Barbot
1. Bull. soc. chim. **47**, 1314 (1930)

Bargellini and Melacini
1. Gazz. chim. ital. **38**, 567 (1908)
2. Atti accad. nazl. Lincei. Classe sci. fis. mat. e nat. **17**, 26 (1908)

Barkenbus, Hopkins, and Allen
1. J. Am. Chem. Soc. **61**, 2452 (1939)

Barnard, Fabian, and Koch
1. J. Chem. Soc. 2443 (1949)

Barnett and Sanders
1. J. Chem. Soc. 434 (1933)

Barrett and Linstead
1. J. Chem. Soc. 1069 (1935)

Barrow
1. J. Chem. Phys. **19**, 345 (1951)

Barrow and McClellan
1. J. Am. Chem. Soc. **73**, 573 (1951)

GENERAL LIST OF REFERENCES
B (Page 2)
As of December 31, 1952

Bartleson, Burk, and Lankelma
1. J. Am. Chem. Soc. 68, 2513 (1946)

Bartoli and Stracciati
1. Nuovo Cimento 8, 195 (1885)

Bate
1. Proc. Phys. Soc. (London) 53, 403 (1941)

Bateman and Koch
1. J. Chem. Soc. 602 (1944)

Baumann
1. Ber. 19, 2803 (1886)

Baumann and Fromm
1. Ber. 28, 907 (1895)

Baumé and Germann
1. Compt. rend. 153, 569 (1911)

Baxter, Guichard, Hönigschmid, and Whytlaw-Gray
1. J. Am. Chem. Soc. 63, 845 (1941)

Baxter, Guichard, and Whytlaw-Gray
1. J. Am. Chem. Soc. 69, 731 (1947)

Bazhulin, Bokshteĭn, Liberman, Lukina, Margolis, Solovova, and Kazanskiĭ
1. Bull. acad. sci. U.R.S.S. Classe sci. chim. 198 (1943)

Bazhulin, Sterin, Bulanova, Solovova, Turova-Pollak, and Kazanakiĭ
1. Bull. acad. sci. U.R.S.S. Classe sci. chim. 7 (1946)

Bearden and Watts
1. Phys. Rev. 81, 73 (1951)

Beattie
1. Technical Report No. CR-1117, April, 1946, Office of Rubber Reserve, Reconstruction Finance Corporation, Washington, D. C.

Beattie and others
1. Unpublished. Massachusetts Institute of Technology, Cambridge, Massachusetts

Beattie, Douslin, and Levine
1. Unpublished. Massachusetts Institute of Technology, Cambridge, Massachusetts
2. J. Chem. Phys. 19, 948 (1951)

Beattie and Edwards
1. J. Am. Chem. Soc. 70, 3382 (1948)

Beattie, Edwards, and Marple
1. J. Chem. Phys. 17, 576 (1949)

Beattie, Ingersoll, and Stockmayer
1. J. Am. Chem. Soc. 64, 546 (1942)

Beattie and Kay
1. J. Am. Chem. Soc. 59, 1586 (1937)

Beattie, Poffenberger, and Hadlock
1. J. Chem. Phys. 3, 96 (1935)

Beattie, Simard, and Su
1. J. Am. Chem. Soc. 61, 24 (1939)

Beattie, Su, and Simard
1. J. Am. Chem. Soc. 61, 924 (1934)

Bechler
1. J. prakt. Chem. 8, 67 (1873)

Becke
1. Ber. 23, 3191 (1890)

Beckett, Freeman, and Pitzer
1. J. Am. Chem. Soc. 70, 4227 (1948)

Beckett and Pitzer
1. J. Am. Chem. Soc. 68, 2213 (1946)

Beckett, Pitzer, and Spitzer
1. J. Am. Chem. Soc. 69, 2488 (1947)

Beckmann and Lieshe
1. Z. physik. Chem. 89, 111 (1915)

Bekkedahl and Wood
1. J. Research Natl. Bur. Standards 19, 55 (1937)

Bekkedahl, Wood, and Wojciechowski
1. J. Research Natl. Bur. Standards 17, 883 (1936)

Bell, Bennett, and Hock
1. J. Chem. Soc. 1803 (1927)

Bender, Furukawa, and Hyndman
1. Ind. Eng. Chem. 44, 387 (1952)

Benedict
1. Unpublished. Petroleum Research Laboratory, The M. W. Kellogg Company, Jersey City, New Jersey

Bennett and Berry
1. J. Chem. Soc. 127, 910 (1928)

Bennett and Gudgeon
1. J. Chem. Soc. 1891 (1938)

Bennett and Hafez
1. J. Chem. Soc. 287 (1941)

Bennewitz and Rossner
1. Z. physik. Chem. B39, 126 (1938)

Benoliel
1. Thesis. Pennsylvania State College, State College, Pennsylvania (1941)

Benson
1. Ind. Eng. Chem. Anal. Ed. 13, 502 (1941)

Berger
1. Rec. trav. chim. 57, 1029 (1938)

GENERAL LIST OF REFERENCES
B (Page 3)
As of December 31, 1952

Bergman and Bergman
   1. J. Am. Chem. Soc. 59, 1443 (1937)

Bergmann and Szmuszkowicz
   1. J. Am. Chem. Soc. 70, 2748 (1948)

Bergmann and Weizmann
   1. J. Org. Chem. 9, 352 (1944)

Berlande
   1. Compt. rend. 213, 437 (1941)
   2. Bull. soc. chim. 9, 642 (1942)

Berry and Reid
   1. J. Am. Chem. Soc. 49, 3142 (1927)

Bert and Anglade
   1. Compt. rend. 189, 645 (1929)

Berthelot
   1. Ann. chim. phys. 13, 1 (1878)
   2. Ann. chim. phys. 23, 176 (1881)
   3. Ann. chim. phys. 23, 193 (1881)

Berthelot and Matignon
   1. Ann. chim. phys. 30, 547 (1893)

Berthoud and Brum
   1. J. chim. phys. 21, 143 (1924)

Bertram
   1. Chem. Weekblad 33, 457 (1936)

Bettendorff and Wullner
   1. Ann. Physik 133, 293 (1868)

Bezdrik, Friedländer, and Koeniger
   1. Ber. 41, 231 (1908)

Bezzi
   1. Gazz. chim. ital. 65, 698 (1930)

Bezzi and Lanza
   1. Gazz. chim. ital. 80, 180 (1950)

Bhatnagar and Singh
   1. J. Indian Chem. Soc. 7, 663 (1930)
   2. J. chim. phys. 25, 21 (1928)

Bicher and Katz
   1. Ind. Eng. Chem. 35, 754 (1943)

Bichowsky and Rossini
   1. "The Thermochemistry of Chemical Substances," Rheinhold
      Publishing Corporation, New York (1936)

Billeter
   1. Ber. 8, 462 (1875)

Bingham and Fornwalt
   1. J. Rheology 1, 372 (1930)

Bingham, White, Thomas, and Caldwell
   1. Z. physik Chem. 83, 641 (1913)

Birch
   1. J. Chem. Soc. 1642 (1947)
   2. J. Chem. Soc. 809 (1945)

Birch, Dean, Fidler, and Lowry
   1. J. Am. Chem. Soc. 71, 1362 (1949)

Birch, Fidler, and Lowry
   1. Unpublished. Anglo-Iranian Oil Company, Ltd.,
      Sunbury, England

Birch, Gripp, McAllan, and Nathan
   1. J. Chem. Soc. 1363 (1952)

Birch and McAllan
   1. Nature 165, 899 (1950)

Birch and Norris
   1. J. Chem. Soc. 127, 898 (1925)

Birch, Pin, and Tait
   1. J. Soc. Chem. Ind. 55, 335 (1936)

Birge
   1. Rev. Modern Phys. 1, 1 (1929)
   2. Rev. Modern Phys. 13, 233 (1941)
   3. Am. J. Phys. 13, 63 (1945)

Biron
   1. J. Russ. Phys. Chem. Soc. 42, 167 (1910)

Bjelouss
   1. Ber. 45, 625 (1912)

Blackburn and Challenger
   1. J. Chem. Soc. 1872 (1938)

Blaise and Montagne
   1. Compt. rend. 181, 122 (1925)

Blanksma
   1. Rec. trav. chim. 20, 121 (1901)

Bleekrode
   1. Rec. trav. chim. 4, 77 (1885)

Block
   1. Z. physik. Chem. 78, 385 (1912)

Bloomfield
   1. Rubber Chem. and Technol. 22, 348 (1949)
   2. J. Chem. Soc. 1547 (1947)

Blyumenfel'd
   1. Bull. acad. sci. U.R.S.S. Sér. phys. 12, 595 (1948)

Böeseken, I.
   1. Rec. trav. chim. 24, 209 (1905)

Böeseken, J.
   1. Rec. trav. chim. 29, 315 (1910)

Böeseken and Wildschut
   1. Rec. trav. chim. 51, 168 (1932)

GENERAL LIST OF REFERENCES

B (Page 4)

As of December 31, 1952

Bogert, Davidson, and Apfelbaum
1. J. Am. Chem. Soc. 56, 959 (1934)

Bogert and Mandelbaum
1. J. Am. Chem. Soc. 45, 3045 (1923)

Böhme
1. Ber. 69, 1610 (1936)

Böhme, Fischer, and Frank
1. Ann. 563, 54 (1949)

Böhme and Krause
1. Ber. 82, 426 (1949)

Boord, Henne, Greenlee, Perilstein, and Derfer
1. Ind. Eng. Chem. 41, 609 (1949)

Borgellini and Melacini
1. Gazz. chim. ital. 38, 567 (1908)

Borgstrom and McIntire
1. Ind. Eng. Chem. 23, 321 (1931)

Borsche and Lange
1. Ber. 39, 393 (1906)

Borsche and Niemann
1. Ann. 499, 59 (1932)

Borsche and Pommet
1. Ber. 54, 102 (1921)

Bost and Conn
1. Oil Gas J. 32, 17 (1933)

Bost and Everett
1. J. Am. Chem. Soc. 62, 1752 (1940)

Bottomley
1. Refiner Natural Gasoline Mfr. 20, 526 (1941)

Bouis
1. Ann. chim. 9, 402 (1928)

Bouknight and Smith
1. J. Am. Chem. Soc. 61, 28 (1939)

Bourgeois
1. Ber. 28, 2312 (1895)
2. Rec. trav. chim. 18, 435 (1899)

Bourgeois and Abraham
1. Rec. trav. chim. 30, 407 (1911)

Bourguel
1. Compt. rend. 176, 751 (1923)
2. Bull. soc. chim. 41, 1475 (1927)
3. Ann. chim. 3, 191 (1925)
4. Bull. soc. chim. 45, 403 (1929)

Bradley and Shellard
1. Proc. Roy. Soc. (London) A198, 239 (1949)

Brand and Kranz
1. J. prakt. Chem. 115, 143 (1927)

von Braun
1. Ber. 45, 1563 (1912)
2. Ber. 42, 4568 (1909)
3. Ber. 36, 2259 (1903)
4. Ber. 58, 2165 (1925)
5. Ber. 43, 3220 (1910)

von Braun, Braundsdorf, Engelbertz, Hahn, Hahn, Hainbach,
Kredel, and Larbig
1. Ber. 56, 2332 (1923)

von Braun and Deutsch
1. Ber. 45, 2171 (1912)

von Braun and Engelbertz
1. Ber. 56, 1573 (1923)

von Braun, Hahn, and Seeman
1. Ber. 55, 1687 (1922)

von Braun, Kamp, and Kopp
1. Ber. 70, 1750 (1937)

von Braun and Kirschbaum
1. Ber. 53, 1399 (1920)

von Braun and Manz
1. Ann. 468, 258 (1929)
2. Ber. 67, 1696 (1934)

von Braun, May, and Michaelis
1. Ann. 490, 189 (1931)

von Braun and Murjahn
1. Ber. 59, 1202 (1926)

von Braun and Plate
1. Ber. 67, 281 (1934)

Braun, Spooner, and Fenske
1. Anal. Chem. 22, 1074 (1950)

von Braun, Teuffert, and Weissbach
1. Ann. 472, 121 (1929)

von Braun and Trumple
1. Ber. 43, 545 (1910)

von Braun and Weissbach
1. Ber. 62, 2416 (1929)

von Braun and Zobel
1. Ber. 56, 2142 (1923)

Bresler and Landerman
1. J. Exptl. Theoret. Phys. (U.S.S.R.) 10, 250 (1940)

Bridgman
1. Proc. Am. Acad. Arts and Sciences 66, 185 (1931)
2. Proc. Am. Acad. Arts and Sciences 61, 55 (1926)
3. Proc. Nat. Acad. Sci. 11, 604 (1925)

GENERAL LIST OF REFERENCES
B (Page 5)
As of December 31, 1952

Bried and Hennion
1. J. Am. Chem. Soc. **60**, 1717 (1938)

Briscoe, Peel, and Robinson
1. J. Chem. Soc. 368 (1929)

Brjuchonenko
1. J. prakt. Chem. **59**, 45 (1899)

Brockway and Cross
1. J. Am. Chem. Soc. **58**, 2407 (1936)

Brodie
1. Ann. **67**, 180 (1848)

Bromby, Peters, and Rowe
1. J. Chem. Soc. 144 (1943)

Brooks
1. J. Research Natl. Bur. Standards **21**, 847 (1938)
2. Unpublished. National Bureau of Standards, Washington, D. C.

Brooks, Cleaton, and Carter
1. J. Research Natl. Bur. Standards **19**, 319 (1937)

Brooks, Howard and others
1. Unpublished. National Bureau of Standards, Washington, D. C.

Brooks, Howard, and Crafton
1. J. Research Natl. Bur. Standards **23**, 637 (1939)
2. J. Research Natl. Bur. Standards **24**, 33 (1940)

Brooks, Howard, and Wehrle
1. J. Am. Chem. Soc. **72**, 1289 (1950)

Brooks and Humphrey
1. J. Am. Chem. Soc. **40**, 822 (1918)

Brooks and Spinks
1. J. Research Natl. Bur. Standards **9**, 781 (1932)

Broun and Voronkov
1. Doklady Akad. Nauk. S.S.S.R. **59**, 1293 (1948)

Broun, Voronkov, and Katova
1. J. Gen. Chem. (U.S.S.R.) **20**, 726 (1950)

Brown
1. J. Chem. Soc. **89**, 311 (1906)

Brown and Carr
1. Ind. Eng. Chem. **18**, 718 (1926)

Brown, Durand, and Marvel
1. J. Am. Chem. Soc. **58**, 1594 (1936)

Brown and Moggridge
1. J. Chem. Soc. 816 (1946)

Brühl
1. Z. physik. Chem. **22**, 373 (1897)

Brunel
1. Ber. **17**, 1179 (1884)

Bruner
1. Ind. Eng. Chem. **41**, 2860 (1949)

Bruson and Kroeger
1. J. Am. Chem. Soc. **62**, 36 (1940)

Bruson and Riener
1. J. Am. Chem. Soc. **70**, 2809 (1948)

Bruun
1. Ind. Eng. Chem. Anal. Ed. **1**, 212 (1929)
2. Ind. Eng. Chem. Anal. Ed. **2**, 187 (1930)
3. J. Chem. Education **8**, 1930 (1931)

Bruun and Faulconer
1. Ind. Eng. Chem. Anal. Ed. **9**, 192 (1937)

Bruun and Hicks-Bruun
1. J. Research Natl. Bur. Standards **5**, 933 (1930)
2. J. Research Natl. Bur. Standards **10**, 465 (1933)
3. J. Research Natl. Bur. Standards **8**, 583 (1932)
4. J. Research Natl. Bur. Standards **6**, 869 (1931)
5. J. Research Natl. Bur. Standards **7**, 607 (1931)
6. J. Research Natl. Bur. Standards **9**, 53 (1932)
7. J. Research Natl. Bur. Standards **9**, 269 (1932)

Bruun, Hicks-Bruun, and Faulconer
1. J. Am. Chem. Soc. **59**, 2355 (1937)

Bruun, Leslie, and Schicktanz
1. J. Research Natl. Bur. Standards.**6**, 363 (1931)

Bruun and Schicktanz
1. J. Research Natl. Bur. Standards **7**, 851 (1931)

Bruylants
1. Ber. **8**, 413 (1875)

Bryce-Smith and Turner
1. J. Chem. Soc. 1975 (1950)

Buck
1. Unpublished. Shell Development Company, Emeryville, California

Buck, Elsner, Forbes, Morrell, Smith, and Wallsgrove
1. J. Inst. Petroleum **34**, 339 (1948)

Buck, Elsner, Henshall, Moore, Murray, Müller, Morrell, Plant, Smith, and Wallsgrove
1. J. Inst. Petroleum **35**, 631 (1949)

Buckland and Seyer
1. Unpublished. University of California, Berkeley, California

Buckley and Ray
1. J. Chem. Soc. 1154 (1949)

GENERAL LIST OF REFERENCES

B (Page 6)

As of December 31, 1952

Buehler, Gardner, and Clemens
1. J. Org. Chem. 2, 174 (1937)
2. J. Org. Chem. 2, 167 (1937)

Buess, Karabinos, Kunz, and Gibbons
1. Technical Note No. 1021. National Advisory Committee
    for Aeronautics. Aircraft Engine Research Laboratory,
    Cleveland, Ohio

Burcik, Eyster, and Yost
1. J. Chem. Phys. 9, 118 (1941)

Burgess
1. J. Research Natl. Bur. Standards 1, 635 (1928)

Burk
1. Gas-u. Wasserfach 67, 523 (1924)

Burlew
1. J. Am. Chem. Soc. 62, 690 (1940)

Burrell and Robertson
1. J. Am. Chem. Soc. 37, 2482 (1915)
2. J. Am. Chem. Soc. 37, 1893 (1915)

Burriel
1. Anales soc. espãn. fís. quím. 29, 89 (1931)

Burton and Davy
1. J. Chem. Soc. 52 (1947)

Butler
1. Thesis. Ohio State University, Columbus, Ohio (1941)

Butz
1. J. Am. Chem. Soc. 62, 2557 (1940)

Butz, Gaddis, Butz, and Davis
1. J. Org. Chem. 5, 379 (1940)

Buu-Hoï, Bihan, Binon, and Xuang
1. J. Org. Chem. 16, 988 (1951)

Buu-Hoi and Cagniant
1. Ber. 76, 1269 (1943)
2. Rev. sci. 80, 271 (1942)

Buu-Hoï, Hoan, and Khôi
1. Rec. trav. chim. 69, 1053 (1950)

Bygden
1. Ber. 45, 3479 (1912)

GENERAL LIST OF REFERENCES
C (Page 1)
As of December 31, 1952

Caesar
1. J. Am. Chem. Soc. **70**, 3623 (1948)

Caesar and Branton
1. Ind. Eng. Chem. **44**, 122 (1952)

Cagniant
1. Bull. soc. chim. 28 (1950)
2. Compt. rend. **229**, 1342 (1949)
3. Compt. rend. **230**, 100 (1950)

Cagniant and Deluzarche
1. Compt. rend. **223**, 1012 (1946)

Cagniant, Deluzarche, and Chatelus
1. Compt. rend. **224**, 1064 (1947)

Cahours and Hofman
1. Ann. **102**, 293 (1857)

Cailletet
1. Compt. rend. **94**, 1224 (1882)

Cailletet and Mathias
1. Compt. rend. **102**, 1202 (1886)

Calcott, Tinker, and Weinmayr
1. J. Am. Chem. Soc. **61**, 1010 (1939)

California Research Corporation, Richmond, California
1. Unpublished

Calingaert
1. Unpublished. Ethyl Corporation, Detroit, Michigan
2. Bull. soc. chim. Belg. **31**, 109 (1922)

Calingaert, Beatty, Kuder, and Thomson
1. Ind. Eng. Chem. **33**, 103 (1941)

Calingaert and Soroos
1. J. Am. Chem. Soc. **58**, 635 (1936)

Calingaert, Soroos, Hnizda, and Shapiro
1. J. Am. Chem. Soc. **66**, 1389 (1944)

Calingaert and Thomson
1. Unpublished. Ethyl Corporation, Detroit, Michigan

Campbell and Eby
1. J. Am. Chem. Soc. **63**, 216 (1941)
2. J. Am. Chem. Soc. **63**, 2683 (1941)
3. J. Am. Chem. Soc. **62**, 1800 (1940)

Campbell and McDermott
1. J. Am. Chem. Soc. **67**, 282 (1945)

Campbell and O'Connor
1. J. Am. Chem. Soc. **61**, 2897 (1939)

Campbell and Young
1. J. Am. Chem. Soc. **65**, 965 (1943)

Cannizzaro
1. Gazz. chim. ital. **26**, 13 (1896)

Capellar
1. Helv. chim. acta **11**, 166 (1928)

Capelle
1. Bull. soc. chim. 3, 150 (1908)

Cardoso
1. Arch. Sci. Phys. Nat. **39**, 403 (1915)
2. Arch. Sci. Phys. Nat. **36**, 97 (1913)

Cardoso and Arni
1. J. chim. phys. 10, 504 (1912)

Cardoso and Baume
1. Compt. rend. **151**, 141 (1910)
2. J. chim. phys. 10, 509 (1912)

Cardoso and Bell
1. J. chim. phys. 10, 497 (1912)

Carey and Smith
1. J. Chem. Soc. 346 (1933)

de Carli
1. Atti accad. naz. Lincei Classe sci. fis. mat. e nat.
   **14**, 200 (1931)

Cardwell
1. J. Chem. Soc. 1059 (1950)

Carius
1. Ann. **119**, 313 (1861)

Carlson
1. Ber. **40**, 4191 (1907)

Carnelutti
1. Ber. **13**, 1671 (1880)

Carney
1. Petroleum Refiner **21**, 274 (1942)

Carr and Stücklen
1. J. Chem. Phys. **6**, 55 (1938)

Carr and Walter
1. J. Chem. Phys. **4**, 756 (1936)

Challenger and Greenwood
1. Biochem. J. **44**, 87 (1949)

Challenger and Harrison
1. J. Inst. Petroleum Tech. **21**, 135 (1935)

Challenger, Haslam, Bramhall, and Walkden
1. J. Inst. Petroleum Tech. **12**, 106 (1926)

Challenger and Rawlings
1. J. Chem. Soc. 868 (1937)

Chapas
1. Thesis. Paris (1932)

Charlampowicz and Marchlewski
1. Bull. intern. acad. polonaise **A**, 376 (1930)

GENERAL LIST OF REFERENCES
C (Page 2)
As of December 31, 1952

Charles and Freiser
1. J. Am. Chem. Soc. 72, 2233 (1950)

Charnock and Moggridge
1. J. Chem. Soc. 815 (1946)

Charon
1. Ann. chim. phys. 17, 197 (1899)

Chavanne
1. Bull. soc. chim. Belg. 35, 283 (1926)
2. Bull. soc. chim. Belg. 39, 402 (1930)

Chavanne and Becker
1. Bull. soc. chim. Belg. 36, 591 (1927)

Chavanne and de Graef
1. Bull. soc. chim. Belg. 33, 366 (1924)

Chavanne, Katzenstein, and Pahlavouni
1. Bull. soc. chim. Belg. 41, 209 (1932)

Chavanne and Lejeune
1. Bull. soc. chim. Belg. 31, 98 (1922)

Chavanne and Miller
1. Bull. soc. chim. Belg. 39, 287 (1930)

Chavanne, Miller, and Cornet
1. Bull. soc. chim. Belg. 40, 673 (1931)

Chavanne and van Risseghem
1. Bull. soc. chim. Belg. 31, 87 (1922)

Chavanne and Simon
1. Ann. chim. anal. chim. appl. 2, 76 (1920)

Chavanne and de Vogel
1. Bull. soc. chim. Belg. 37, 141 (1928)

Chiurdoglu
1. Bull. soc. chim. Belg. 47, 363 (1938)
2. Bull. soc. chim. Belg. 53, 45 (1944)
3. Bull. soc. chim. Belg. 47, 241 (1938)
4. Bull. soc. chim. Belg. 53, 55 (1944)
5. Bull. sci. acad. roy. Belg. 17, 1404 (1931)
6. Bull. soc. chim. Belg. 42, 347 (1933)
7. Bull. soc. chim. Belg. 43, 35 (1934)

Chmelewsky and Friedländer
1: Ber. 46, 1903 (1913)

Chraszczewska
1. Roczniki Chem. 5, (1–3), 33 (1925)

von Christiani and Pailer
1. Mikrochim. Acta I, 26 (1937)

Chuang, Tien, and Ma
1. Ber. 69, 1494 (1936)

Chugaev and Il'in
1. Z. anorg. u. allgem. Chem. 135, 143 (1924)

Church, Whitmore, and McGrew
1. J. Am. Chem. Soc. 56, 182 (1934)

Claesson
1. J. prakt. Chem. 15, 174 (1877)

Claisen, Kremers, Rath, and Tietze
1. J. prakt. Chem. 105, 65 (1922)

Clarke, H.
1. J. Chem. Soc. 101, 1804 (1912)

Clarke, L.
1. J. Am. Chem. Soc. 31, 558 (1909)
2. J. Am. Chem. Soc. 33, 520 (1911)

Clarke and Biggs
1. J. Am. Chem. Soc. 34, 54 (1912)
2. J. Am. Chem. Soc. 34, 60 (1912)

Clarke and Jones
1. J. Am. Chem. Soc. 34, 171 (1912)

Clarke and Riegel
1. J. Am. Chem. Soc. 34, 674 (1912)

Claus
1. Ber. 8, 530 (1875)

Claus and Feist
1. Ber. 19, 3180 (1886)

Clayton and Giauque
1. J. Am. Chem. Soc. 55, 5071 (1933)

Cleaves, Carver, and Hibbard
1. Technical Note No. 1608. National Advisory Committee
for Aeronautics, Flight Propulsion Research Laboratory,
Cleveland, Ohio.

Clemence and Leffler
1. J. Am. Chem. Soc. 70, 2439 (1948)

Clemmensen
1. Ber. 46, 1841 (1913)

Cleveland
1. J. Chem. Phys. 11, 1 (1943)
2. J. Chem. Phys. 11, 227 (1943)
3. J. Chem. Phys. 12, 53 (1944)

Cleveland and Murray
1. J. Chem. Phys. 10, 174 (1942)

Cline
1. Thesis. Ohio State University, Columbus, Ohio (1940)

Clusius
1. Z. physik. Chem. B3, 41 (1929)

Clusius and Weigand
1. Z. physik. Chem. B46, 1 (1940)

GENERAL LIST OF REFERENCES
C (Page 3)
As of December 31, 1952

Coe and Godfrey
1. J. Applied Phys. **15**, 625 (1944)

Coffin and Maass
1. J. Am. Chem. Soc. **50**, 1427 (1928)
2. J. Am. Chem. Soc. **50**, 1433 (1928)
3. Trans. Roy. Soc. Chem. **21**, 33 (1927)

Coffman, Tsao, Schniepp, and Marvel
1. J. Am. Chem. Soc. **55**, 3792 (1933)

Cohen and Buÿ
1. Z. physik. Chem. **B35**, 270 (1937)

Collin, Hilditch, Marsh, and McLeod
1. J. Soc. Chem. Ind. **52**, 2721 (1933)

Colonge
1. Bull. soc. chim. **9**, 730 (1942)

Colonge and Chambion
1. Bull. soc. chim. 1002 (1947)

Conn, Kistiakowsky, and Smith
1. J. Am. Chem. Soc. **61**, 1868 (1939)

Cook, J.W.
1. J. Chem. Soc. 456 (1932)

Cook, N.C.
1. Unpublished. Pennsylvania State College, State
   College, Pennsylvania

Cope and Bailey
1. J. Am. Chem. Soc. **70**, 2305 (1948)

Cope and Fenton
1. J. Am. Chem. Soc. **73**, 1676 (1951)

Cope, Morrison, and Field
1. J. Am. Chem. Soc. **72**, 59 (1950)

Copenhaver and Reid
1. J. Am. Chem. Soc. **49**, 3157 (1927)

Corcoran, Bowles, Sage, and Lacey
1. Ind. Eng. Chem. **37**, 825 (1945)

Cortese
1. J. Am. Chem. Soc. **51**, 2266 (1929)

Cosby and Sutherland
1. Refiner **20**, 471 (1941)
2. J. Am. Chem. Soc. **64**, 1360 (1801)

Coscing
1. Petroleum Z. **34**, No. 20, 1 (1938)

Cotton and Mouton
1. Ann. chim. phys. **28**, 209 (1913)

Coulson
1. J. Soc. Chem. Ind. **60**, 123 (1941)
2. J. Soc. Chem. Ind. **62**, 177 (1943)
3. J. Chem. Soc. 77 (1935)
4. J. Chem. Soc. 1305 (1938)

Crafts
1. Bull. soc. chim. **39**, 277 (1883)
2. J. chim. phys. **11**, 429 (1913)
3. Ann. **124**, 110 (1862)

Cragoe
1. National Bureau of Standards LC-736 (1943)
2. Unpublished. National Bureau of Standards.
   Washington, D. C.
3. J. Research Natl. Bur. Standards **26**, 495 (1941)

Cragoe and Peffer
1. Unpublished. National Bureau of Standards,
   Washington, D. C.

Craig
1. J. Am. Chem. Soc. **65**, 1006 (1943)

Cram
1. J. Am. Chem. Soc. **71**, 3883 (1949)

Cramer and Glasbrook
1. J. Am. Chem. Soc. **61**, 230 (1939)

Cramer and Miller
1. J. Am. Chem. Soc. **62**, 1452 (1940)

Cramer and Mulligan
1. J. Am. Chem. Soc. **58**, 373 (1936)

Crane
1. Thesis. Ohio State University, Columbus, Ohio (1941)

Crane, Boord, and Henne
1. J. Am. Chem. Soc. **67**, 1237 (1945)

Crawford
1. J. Chem. Phys. **7**, 555 (1939)
2. J. Chem. Phys. **8**, 526 (1940)

Crawford, Kistiakowsky, Rice, Wells, and Wilson
1. J. Am. Chem. Soc. **61**, 2980 (1939)

Crittenden
1. Unpublished. National Bureau of Standards,
   Washington, D. C.

Crombie and Harper
1. J. Chem. Soc. 1707 (1950)

Crossley and Renouf
1. J. Chem. Soc. **89**, 26 (1906)
2. J. Chem. Soc. **87**, 1487 (1905)

GENERAL LIST OF REFERENCES
C (Page 4)
As of December 31, 1952

Cullinane and Chard
    1. J. Chem. Soc. 804 (1948)

Culvenor and Davies
    1. Australian J. Sci. Research 1, 236 (1948)

Culvenor, Davies, and Heath
    1. J. Chem. Soc. 282 (1949)

Culvenor, Davies, and Pausacker
    1. J. Chem. Soc. 1050 (1946)

Cunneen
    1. J. Chem. Soc. 134 (1947)

Curtis
    1. J. Research Natl. Bur. Standards 33, 235 (1944)

Curtis, Moon, and Sparks
    1. J. Research Natl. Bur. Standards 16, 1 (1936)
    2. J. Research Natl. Bur. Standards 21, 375 (1938)
    3. J. Wash. Acad. Sci. 29, 313 (1939)

GENERAL LIST OF REFERENCES

D (Page 1)

As of December 31, 1952

Dacey, McIntosh, and Maass
1. Can. J. Research 17, 206 (1939)

Dailey and Felsing
1. J. Am. Chem. Soc. 65, 42 (1943)
2. J. Am. Chem. Soc. 65, 44 (1943)

Dalgliesh and Mann
1. J. Chem. Soc. 559 (1947)

Damerell
1. J. Am. Chem. Soc. 49, 2988 (1928)

Dana, Jenkins, Burdick, and Timm
1. Refrig. Eng. 12, 387 (1926)

Darzens and Levy
1. Compt. rend. 202, 73 (1936)

Darzens and Rost
1. Compt. rend. 146, 933 (1908)

Davies and Gilbert
1. J. Am. Chem. Soc. 63, 2730 (1941)

Davies and Oxford
1. J. Chem. Soc. 224 (1931)

Davies and Savige
1. J. Chem. Soc. 317 (1950)

Davis and Degering
1. Proc. Indiana Acad. Sci. 56, 116 (1946)

Davis and Johnston
1. J. Am. Chem. Soc. 56, 1045 (1934)

Dawson
1. J. Am. Chem. Soc. 55, 2070 (1933)

Day, Nicholson, and Felsing
1. J. Am. Chem. Soc. 70, 1784 (1948)

Deanesly and Carleton
1. J. Phys. Chem. 45, 1104 (1941)
2. J. Research Natl. Bur. Standards 21, 375 (1938)

Delépine
1. Compt. rend. 171, 36 (1920)

Delépine and Jaffeux
1. Compt. rend. 172, 158 (1921)

Deluchat
1. Ann. chim. 1, 181 (1934)

Demmerle
1. Chem. Eng. News 24, 2020 (1946)

Denisenko
1. J. Gen. Chem. (U.S.S.R.) 9, 1068 (1939)
2. Ber. 69, 1353 (1936)

Denison and Condit
1. Ind. Eng. Chem. 37, 1102 (1945)

Denyer, Fidler, and Lowry
1. Ind. Eng. Chem. 41, 2727 (1949)

Derfer, Greenlee, and Boord
1. J. Am. Chem. Soc. 71, 175 (1949)

Deschner and Brown
1. Ind. Eng. Chem. 32, 836 (1940)
2. Ind. Eng. Chem. 33, 263 (1941)

Dessart
1. Bull. soc. chim. Belg. 35, 9 (1926)

Desseigne
1. Compt. rend. 200, 466 (1935)

Desty and Fidler
1. Ind. Eng. Chem. 43, 905 (1951)

Deux
1. Compt. rend. 208, 523 (1939)
2. Compt. rend. 208, 528 (1939)

Dev and Guha
1. J. Indian Chem. Soc. 25, 13 (1948)

Dewar
1. Proc. Roy. Soc. (London) 30, 538 (1880)
2. Phil. Mag. 18, 210 (1884)

Dewey and Harper
1. J. Research Natl. Bur. Standards 21, 457 (1938)

Deželić
1. Bull. soc. chim. roy. Yougoslav 8, 139 (1937)

Dice, Loveless, and Cates
1. J. Am. Chem. Soc. 71, 3546 (1949)

Dietrich
1. Thesis. Ohio State University, Columbus, Ohio (1933)

Dilthey and Hurtig
1. Ber. 67, 495 (1934)

Dilthey, Neuhaus, Reis, and Schommer
1. J. prakt. Chem. 124, 81 (1930)

Doeuvre
1. Bull. soc. chim. 39, 988 (1926)

Dolliver, Gresham, Kistiakowsky, and Vaughn
1. J. Am. Chem. Soc. 59, 831 (1937)

Donaldson and Quayle
1. J. Am. Chem. Soc. 72, 35 (1950)

Doolittle and Peterson
1. Unpublished. Union Carbide and Carbon Corporation, South Charleston, West Virginia
2. J. Am. Chem. Soc. 73, 2145 (1951)

Dornte and Smyth
1. J. Am. Chem. Soc. 52, 3546 (1930)

GENERAL LIST OF REFERENCES
D (Page 2)
As of December 31, 1952

Doss
    1. "Physical Constants of the Principal Hydrocarbons,"
       4th Edition, The Texas Company, New York, New York
       (1943)

Douglass and Johnson
    1. J. Am. Chem. Soc. **60**, 1486 (1938)

Douris
    1. Compt. rend. **157**, 55 (1913)

Douslin and Huffman
    1. J. Am. Chem. Soc. **68**, 173 (1946)
    2. J. Am. Chem. Soc. **68**, 1704 (1946)

Dover and Hensley
    1. Ind. Eng. Chem. **27**, 337 (1935)

Dow
    1. Physics **6**, 71 (1935)

Downes, Gill, and Lions
    1. J. Am. Chem. Soc. **72**, 3464 (1950)

Drake and Duvall
    1. J. Am. Chem. Soc. **58**, 1688 (1936)

Drake and Veitch
    1. J. Am. Chem. Soc. **57**, 2623 (1935)

Drake and Welch
    1. J. Am. Chem. Soc. **60**, 488 (1938)

Drapier
    1. Bull. acad. sci. Belg. 621 (1911)

Dreisbach
    1. Unpublished. Dow Chemical Company, Midland, Michigan

Dros, Tulleners, and Waterman
    1. J. Inst. Petroleum Tech. **19**, 784 (1933)

DuMond and Cohen
    1. Rev. Modern Physics **20**, 82 (1948)
    2. Phys. Rev. **82**, 555 (1951)

Dunstan, Hilditch, and Thole
    1. J. Chem. Soc. **103**, 140 (1913)

Dunstan and Stubbs
    1. J. Chem. Soc. **93**, 1919 (1908)

Dupont
    1. Compt. rend. **148**, 1522 (1909)
    2. Compt. rend. **156**, 1623 (1913)
    3. Bull. soc. chim. **3**, 1030 (1936)

Dutoit and Friederich
    1. Arch. sci. phys. nat. **9**, 105 (1900)

Dwyer and Oldenberg
    1. J. Chem. Phys. **12**, 351 (1944)

D'yakowa and Lozovoï
    1. J. Gen. Chem. (U.S.S.R.) **9**, 26 (1939)

Dykstra, Lewis, and Boord
    1. J. Am. Chem. Soc. **52**, 3398 (1930)

GENERAL LIST OF REFERENCES
E (Page 1)
As of December 31, 1952

Ebel, Brunner, and Mangelli
    1. Helv. Chim. Acta 12, 19 (1929)

Eberhard
    1. Ber. 27, 2919 (1894)

Ebersole
    1. Technical Note No. 1020. National Advisory Committee
       for Aeronautics, Washington, D. C.
    2. Technical Note No. 1164. National Advisory Committee
       for Aeronautics, Washington, D. C.

Eckman and Rossini
    1. J. Research Natl. Bur. Standards 3, 597 (1929)

Edgar and Calingaert
    1. J. Am. Chem. Soc. 51, 1540 (1929)
    2. J. Am. Chem. Soc. 51, 1883 (1929)

Edgar, Calingaert, and Marker
    1. J. Am. Chem. Soc. 51, 1483 (1929)

Edmister
    1. Ind. Eng. Chem. 30, 353 (1938)

Edson, Powell, and Fisher
    1. Ind. Eng. Chem. 40, 1526 (1948)

Edwards and Bonilla
    1. Ind. Eng. Chem. 36, 1038 (1944)

Egan and Kemp
    1. J. Am. Chem. Soc. 59, 1264 (1937)

Eglinton and Whiting
    1. J. Chem. Soc. 3650 (1950)

Egloff
    1. "Physical Constants of Hydrocarbons," Vol. I,
       "Paraffins, Olefins, Acetylenes, and Other Aliphatic
       Hydrocarbons," Reinhold Publishing Corporation, New
       York (1939)
    2. "Physical Constants of Hydrocarbons," Vol. II,
       "Cyclanes, Cyclenes, Cyclynes, and Other Alicyclic
       Hydrocarbons," Reinhold Publishing Corporation, New
       York (1940)
    3. "Physical Constants of Hydrocarbons," Vol. III,
       "Mononuclear Aromatic Hydrocarbons," Reinhold
       Publishing Corporation, New York (1946)
    4. "Physical Constants of Hydrocarbons," Vol. IV,
       "Polynuclear Aromatic Hydrocarbons," Reinhold
       Publishing Corporation, New York (1947)

Eibert
    1. Thesis. Washington University, St. Louis, Missouri
       (1944)

Eisenlohr
    1. Ber. 44, 3207 (1911)
    2. Fortschr. Chem. Physik u. physik. Chem. B18,521 (1925)

Eisenlohr and Polenske
    1. Ber. 57, 1639 (1924)

Eisenlohr and Schulz
    1. Ber. 57, 1815 (1924)

Elbs and Christ
    1. J. prakt. Chem. 106, 17 (1923)

Ellis and Reid
    1. J. Am. Chem. Soc. 54, 1684 (1932)

Elsner and Paul
    1. J. Chem. Soc. 893 (1951)

Emde
    1. Ann. 391, 88 (1912)

Emerson and Patrick
    1. J. Org. Chem. 13, 729 (1948)

Engler
    1. Ber. 11, 930 (1878)

Engler and Höfer
    1. Das Erdöl,Vol.I,p53, Hirzel Co., Leipzig, Germany (1909)

English and Cavaglieri
    1. J. Am. Chem. Soc. 65, 1088 (1943)

Enklaar
    1. Rec. trav. chim. 36, 215 (1916)
    2. Rec. trav. chim. 36, 247 (1916)
    3. Ber. 41, 2084 (1908)

Enyeart
    1. Abs. Doc. Diss. 5, 201 (1942) Pennsylvania State
       College, State College, Pennsylvania

Eppley
    1. J. Franklin Inst. 205, 383 (1928)

Epstein, Barrow, Pitzer, and Rossini
    1. J. Research Natl. Bur. Standards 43, 245 (1949)

Epstein, Mair, Willingham, and Rossini
    1. J. Research Natl. Bur. Standards 42, 139 (1949)

Epstein, Pitzer, and Rossini
    1. J. Research Natl. Bur. Standards 42, 379 (1949)

Epstein and Rossini
    1. Chem. Eng. News 26, 2959 (1948)
    2. Chem. Eng. News 28, 1910 (1950)

Erlenmeyer and Wanklyn
    1. Ann. 135, 129 (1865)

Esafov
    1. J. Gen. Chem. (U.S.S.R.) 17, 1453 (1947)
    2. J. Gen. Chem. (U.S.S.R.) 19, 1063 (1949)

Esafov and Molchanova
    1. J. Gen. Chem. (U.S.S.R.) 16, 1885 (1946)

GENERAL LIST OF REFERENCES

E (Page 2)

As of December 31, 1952

Escales and Baumann
1. Ber. **19**, 1787 (1886)

Escourrou
1. Bull. soc. chim. **43**, 1101 (1928)

Esso Laboratories
1. Unpublished. Standard Oil Development Company,
Elizabeth, New Jersey

Estermann
1. Z. physik. Chem. **B1**, 134 (1928)

Eucken and Fried
1. Physik. **29**, 41 (1924)

Eucken and Hauck
1. Z. physik. Chem. **134**, 161 (1928)

Eucken and Karwot
1. Z. physik. Chem. **112**, 467 (1924)

Eucken and Lüde
1. Z. physik, Chem. **B5**, 413 (1929)

Eucken and Sarstedt
1. Z. physik. Chem. **B50**, 143 (1941)

Eucken and Weigert
1. Z. physik. Chem. **B23**, 265 (1933)

Evans, E.B.
1. J. Inst. Petroleum Tech. **24**, 38 (1938)
2. J. Inst. Petroleum Tech. **24**, 321 (1938)
3. J. Inst. Petroleum Tech. **24**, 537 (1938)
4. Proceedings Second World Petroleum Congress, Paris
**2**, sect. 2, 934 (1937)

Evans, G.L.
1. Abs. Doc. Diss. **55**, 99 (1949) Ohio State University,
Columbus, Ohio

Evans, Greenlee, Derfer, and Boord
1. J. Am. Chem. Soc. **71**, 361 (1949)

Evans and Smith
1. J. Inst. Petroleum **37**, 80 (1951)

Ewell and Hardy
1. J. Am. Chem. Soc. **63**, 3460 (1941)

Eykman
1. Chem. Zentr. **II**, 1205 (1907)
2. Recherches Refractometriques (1919)
3. Rec. trav. chim. **15**, 52 (1896)
4. Chem. Weekblad **3**, 701 (1906)
5. Rec. trav. chim. **14**, 185 (1895)
6. Rec. trav. chim. **12**, 157 (1893)
7. Chem. Weekblad **4**, 41 (1907)
8. Chem. Weekblad **8**, 653 (1911)

GENERAL LIST OF REFERENCES
F (Page 1)
As of December 31, 1952

Farmer and Moore
1. J. Chem. Soc. 131 (1951)

Farmer and Shipley
1. Rubber Chem. and Technol. 20, 341 (1947)
2. J. Chem. Soc. 1519 (1947)

Farmer and Warren
1. J. Chem. Soc. 3221 (1931)

Fasbender
1. Ber. 21, 1473 (1888)

Faust
1. Z. physik. Chem. 79, 97 (1912)
2. Z. anorg. allgem. Chem. 154, 61 (1926)

Favorski and Zalusky—Kibardine
1. Bull. soc. chim. 37, 1227 (1925)

Fawcett
1. Unpublished. Socony—Vacuum Laboratories, Paulsboro, New Jersey
2. J. Am. Chem. Soc. 68, 1420 (1946)

Fawcett and Rasmussen
1. J. Am. Chem. Soc. 67, 1705 (1945)

Fehnel and Carmack
1. J. Am. Chem. Soc. 71, 84 (1949)

Felsing, Cuellar, and Newton
1. J. Am. Chem. Soc. 69, 1972 (1947)

Fenske, Braun, Wiegand, Quiggle, McCormick, and Rank
1. Anal. Chem. 19, 700 (1947)

Fenske, Myers, and Quiggle
1. Ind. Eng. Chem. 42, 649 (1950)

Fenske, Quiggle, and Tongberg
1. Ind. Eng. Chem. 24, 408 (1932)

Fenton and Ingold
1. J. Chem. Soc. 3129 (1928)

Ferguson
1. Proc. Phys. Soc. (London) 44, 511 (1932)

Ferguson and Vogel
1. Proc. Phys. Soc. (London) 38, 193 (1926)

Fernholz, Ansbacher, and MacPhillamy
1. J. Am. Chem. Soc. 62, 430 (1940)

Ferretto
1. Gazz. chim. ital. 30, 297 (1900)

Ferry and Thomas
1. J. Phys. Chem. 37, 253 (1933)

Festraete
1. Bull. soc. chim. Belg. 41, 333 (1932)

Fichter and Braun
1. Ber. 47, 1526 (1914)

Fichter and Sjöstedt
1. Ber. 43, 3422 (1910)

Field and Grunwald
1. J. Org. Chem. 16, 946 (1951)

Fieser, Berliner, Bondhus, Chang, Dauben, Ettlinger, Fawaz, Fields, Heidelberger, Heymann, Vaughan, Wilson, Wilson, Wu, Leffler, Hamlin, Matson, Moore, Moore, and Zaugg
1. J. Am. Chem. Soc. 70, 3212 (1948)

Fieser and Price
1. J. Am. Chem. Soc. 58, 1838 (1936)

Fieser and Szmuszkovicz
1. J. Am. Chem. Soc. 70, 3352 (1948)

Finck and Wilhelm
1. J. Am. Chem. Soc. 47, 1577 (1925)

Finckh
1. Ber. 27, 1239 (1894)

Fiock, Ginnings, and Holton
1. J. Research Natl. Bur. Standards 6, 881 (1931)

Fischer, E.
1. Ber. 48, 93 (1915)

Fischer, L.
1. Bull. soc. chim. Belg. 49, 129 (1940)

Fischer and Klemm
1. Z. physik. Chem. A147, 275 (1930)

Fischer and Reichel
1. Mikrochemie ver. Mikrochim. Acta 31, 102 (1943)

Fisher and Chittenden
1. Ind. Eng. Chem. 22, 869 (1930)

Fittica
1. Ann. 172, 303 (1874)

Fittig and Feist
1. Ann. 255, 108 (1889)

Fittig and Remsen
1. Ann. 155, 112 (1870)

Flaschenträger and Wannschaff
1. Ber. 67, 1122 (1934)

Flesch
1. Ber. 6, 478 (1873)

Flowers and Miller
1. J. Am. Chem. Soc. 69, 1388 (1947)

Fodor and Wein
1. J. Chem. Soc. 684 (1948)

GENERAL LIST OF REFERENCES
F (Page 2)
As of December 31, 1952

Föhl
1. Ber. **28**, 2459 (1895)

Fomin and Sochanski
1. Ber. **46**, 244 (1913)

Fore and Bost
1. J. Am. Chem. Soc. **59**, 2557 (1937)

Forst
1. Ann. **178**, 370 (1875)

Forster
1. Thesis. Pennsylvania State College, State College,
Pennsylvania

Forziati
1. J. Research Natl. Bur. Standards **44**, 373 (1950)

Forziati, Camin, and Rossini
1. J. Research Natl. Bur. Standards **45**, 406 (1950)

Forziati, Glasgow, Willingham, and Rossini
1. J. Research Natl. Bur. Standards **36**, 129 (1946)

Forziati, Mair, and Rossini
1. J. Research Natl. Bur. Standards **35**, 513 (1945)

Forziati, Norris, and Rossini
1. J. Research Natl. Bur. Standards **43**, 555 (1949)

Forziati and Rossini
1. J. Research Natl. Bur. Standards **43**, 473 (1949)
2. J. Research Natl. Bur. Standards **39**, 425 (1947)

Forziati, Willingham, Mair, and Rossini
1. Proc. Am. Petroleum Inst. III **24**, 34 (1943)

Francis
1. Ind. Eng. Chem. **35**, 442 (1943)
2. Oil Gas J. **30**, No. 10, 102 (1931)

Francis and Robbins
1. J. Am. Chem. Soc. **55**, 4339 (1933)

Francis and Wood
1. J. Chem. Soc. **129**, 1420 (1926)

Frank and Clusius
1. Z. physik. Chem. **B36**, 291 (1937)
2. Z. physik. Chem. **B42**, 395 (1939)

Frank–Kamenetzky and Markovich
1. Acta Physicochim. U.R.S.S. **17**, 308 (1942)

Freeth and Verschoyle
1. Proc. Roy. Soc. (London) **A130**, 453 (1931)

Frey and Huppke
1. Ind. Eng. Chem. **25**, 54 (1933)

Fricke and Spilker
1. Ber. **58**, 24 (1925)
2. Ber. **58**, 1589 (1925)
3. Ber. **59**, 349 (1926)

Fridau
1. Ann. **83**, 1 (1852)

Friedburg
1. J. Am. Chem. Soc. **12**, 85 (1890)

Friedmann
1. J. Inst. Petroleum **37**, 239 (1951)

Friend and Hargreaves
1. Phil. Mag. **35**, 57 (1944)
2. Phil. Mag. **35**, 136 (1944)

Fries and Bestian
1. Ber. **69**, 715 (1936)

Fries and Küster
1. Ann. **470**, 20 (1929)

Fromm
1. Ber. **41**, 3403 (1908)

Fromm and Siebert
1. Ber. **55**, 1014 (1922)

Fröschl and Harlass
1. Sitzber. Akad. Wiss. Wien, Math. naturw. Klasse Abt.
**IIb 140**, 703 (1931)

von Fuchs and Anderson
1. Ind. Eng. Chem. **29**, 319 (1937)

Fuel Research Board of Great Britain, London, England
1. Report of Director (F.S. Sinnatt), (1934)

Fulton and Robinson
1. J. Chem. Soc. 200 (1939)

Fuson, Denton, and Kneisley
1. J. Am. Chem. Soc. **63**, 2652 (1941)

Fuson and McKusick
1. J. Am. Chem. Soc. **65**, 62 (1943)

GENERAL LIST OF REFERENCES

G (Page 1)

As of December 31, 1952

Gabriel and Deutsch
1. Ber. 13, 386 (1880)

Galkov and Gerf
1. J. Tech. Phys. (U.S.S.R.) 11, 613 (1941)

Gallaway and Barker
1. J. Chem. Phys. 10, 88 (1942)

Garner, Adams, and Stuchell
1. Petroleum Refiner 21, 321 (1942)

Garner, van Bibber, and King
1. J. Chem. Soc. 1533 (1931)

Garner and Evans
1. J. Inst. Petroleum Tech. 18, 751 (1932)

Garrett
1. Unpublished. Ohio State University, Columbus, Ohio

Gartenmeister
1. Z. physik. Chem. 6, 529 (1890)

Gatterman
1. Ber. 32, 1136 (1899)

Gatterman and Lockhart
1. Ber. 26, 2808 (1893)

Gault and Altchidjean
1. Ann. chim. 2, 209 (1924)

Gauthier and Gauthier
1. Bull. soc. chim. 53, 323 (1933)

Geist
1. Thesis, Pennsylvania State College, State College,
   Pennsylvania (1942)

Geist and Cannon
1. Ind. Eng. Chem. Anal. Ed. 18, 611 (1946)

Geldof and Wibaut
1. Rec. trav. chim. 67, 105 (1948)

Genvresse
1. Bull. soc. chim. 9, 219 (1893)

Gerf and Galkov
1. J. Tech. Phys. (U.S.S.R.) 10, 725 (1940)
2. J. Tech. Phys. (U.S.S.R.) 11, 801 (1941)

Gerlach
1. Ann. 267, 145 (1892)

Ghosh, Guha, and Roy
1. Current Sci. 14, 269 (1945)

Giauque
1. J. Am. Chem. Soc. 52, 4816 (1930)

Giauque and Ashley
1. Phys. Rev. 43, 81 (1933)

Giauque and Clayton
1. J. Am. Chem. Soc. 55, 4875 (1933)

Giauque and Egan
1. J. Chem. Phys. 5, 45 (1937)

Gibbons
1. Thesis. Ohio State University, Columbus, Ohio (1941)

Gibbons, Thompson, Reynolds, Wright, Chanan, Lamberti, Hipsher,
and Karabinos
1. J. Am. Chem. Soc. 68, 1130 (1946)

Gibson, D.
1. J. Chem. Soc. 12 (1930)

Gibson, J.
1. Thesis. Ohio State University, Columbus, Ohio (1938)

Giller and Drickamer
1. Ind. Eng. Chem. 41, 2067 (1949)

Gilman and Beaber
1. J. Am. Chem. Soc. 47, 518 (1925)
2. J. Am. Chem. Soc. 47, 1449 (1925)

Gilman and Fullhart
1. J. Am. Chem. Soc. 71, 1478 (1949)

Gilman and Heck
1. J. Am. Chem. Soc. 50, 2229 (1928)

Gilman and Hoyle
1. J. Am. Chem. Soc. 44, 2621 (1922)

Gilman and King
1. J. Am. Chem. Soc. 47, 1136 (1925)

Gilman and Meals
1. J. Org. Chem. 8, 140 (1943)

Gilman, Smith, and Parker
1. J. Am. Chem. Soc. 47, 851 (1925)

Gilman and Webb
1. J. Am. Chem. Soc. 71, 4062 (1949)

Glasebrook
1. Unpublished. Hercules Powder Co., Wilmington, Delaware

Glasebrook and Lovell
1. J. Am. Chem. Soc. 61, 1717 (1939)

Glasgow
1. J. Research Natl. Bur. Standards 24, 509 (1940)
2. J. Research Natl. Bur. Standards 46, 43 (1951)

Glasgow, Krouskop, Beadle, Axilrod, and Rossini
1. Anal. Chem. 20, 410 (1948)

Glasgow, Krouskop, Sedlak, Willingham, and Rossini
1. Anal. Chem. 21, 688 (1949)

Glasgow, Krouskop, and Rossini
1. Anal. Chem. 22, 1521 (1950)

GENERAL LIST OF REFERENCES

G (Page 2)

As of December 31, 1952

Glasgow, Murphy, Willingham, and Rossini
1. J. Research Natl. Bur. Standards **37**, 141 (1946)

Glasgow and Schicktanz
1. J. Research Natl. Bur. Standards **19**, 593 (1937)

Glasgow, Streiff, and Rossini
1. J. Research Natl. Bur. Standards **35**, 355 (1945)
2. Am. Soc. Testing Materials, Standards on Petroleum Products, Committee D-2, Year Book, p510 (1947)

Glasgow, Streiff, Willingham, and Rossini
1. Proc. Am. Petroleum Inst. **III 26**, 127 (1946)

Glasgow, Willingham, and Rossini
1. J. Research Natl. Bur. Standards **38**, 621 (1947)
2. Ind. Eng. Chem. **41**, 2292 (1949)
3. J. Research Natl. Bur. Standards **44**, 141 (1950)
4. J. Research Natl. Bur. Standards **44**, 411 (1950)

Glass and Reid
1. J. Am. Chem. Soc. **51**, 3428 (1929)

Gleim
1. Thesis. Pennsylvania State College, State College, Pennsylvania (1941)

Glenn
1. Thesis. Pennsylvania State College, State College, Pennsylvania (1941)

Gluud
1. Ber. **52**, 1039 (1919)

Godchot
1. Bull. soc. chim. **1**, 1153 (1934)

Godchot and Cauquil
1. Compt. rend. **192**, 1560 (1931)
2. Compt. rend. **191**, 1326 (1930)

Godchot, Mousseron, and Granger
1. Compt. rend. **198**, 480 (1934)

Godchot, Mousseron, and Richaud
1. Compt. rend. **200**, 1599 (1935)

Goering, Abell, and Aycock
1. J. Am. Chem. Soc. **74**, 3588 (1952)

Goldfinger, Josefowitz, and Mark
1. J. Am. Chem. Soc. **65**, 1432 (1943)

Goodman and Wise
1. J. Am. Chem. Soc. **72**, 3076 (1950)
2. J. Am. Chem. Soc. **73**, 850 (1951)
3. Technical Note No. 2260, National Advisory Committee for Aeronautics, Lewis Flight Propulsion Laboratory, Cleveland, Ohio

Gordon
1. J. Chem. Phys. **1**, 308 (1933)
2. J. Chem. Phys. **2**, 65 (1934)
3. J. Chem. Phys. **2**, 549 (1934)
4. J. Chem. Phys. **6**, 219 (1938)

Gordon and Barnes
1. J. Phys. Chem. **36**, 1143 (1932)
2. J. Chem. Phys. **1**, 297 (1933)

Gorin, Dougherty, and Tobolsky
1. J. Am. Chem. Soc. **71**, 3551 (1949)

Gornowski, Amick, and Hixon
1. Ind. Eng. Chem. **39**, 1348 (1947)

Goubeau and Seifert
1. Monatsh. **79**, 475 (1948)

Gough, Hunter, and Kenyon
1. J. Chem. Soc. 2052 (1926)

Grabowsky and Saytzeff
1. Ann. **171**, 257 (1874)

de Graef
1. Bull. soc. chim. Belg. **40**, 315 (1931)
2. Bull. soc. chim. Belg. **34**, 427 (1925)

Gray and Gutekunst
1. J. Am. Chem. Soc. **42**, 856 (1920)

Gredy
1. Bull. soc. chim. **2**, 1029 (1935)
2. Bull. soc. chim. **2**, 1951 (1935)

Greenlee
1. Thesis, Ohio State University, Columbus, Ohio (1942)

Greensfelder, Voge, and Good
1. Ind. Eng. Chem. **37**, 1168 (1945)

Gregg, Alderman, and Mayo
1. J. Am. Chem. Soc. **70**, 3740 (1948)

Griffith
1. J. Chem. Soc. 715 (1945)

Grignard, Lapayre, and Tchéou Faki
1. Compt. rend. **187**, 517 (1928)

Grignard and Zorn
1. Compt. rend. **150**, 1177 (1910)

Grigorowitsch and Pawlow
1. J. Russ. Phys. Chem. Soc. **23**, 172 (1891)

Grishevich-Trokhimovskiĭ
1. J. Russ. Phys. Chem. Soc. **48**, 901 (1916)

Griswold and Ludwig
1. Ind. Eng. Chem. **35**, 117 (1943)

GENERAL LIST OF REFERENCES
G (Page 3)
As of December 31, 1952

Griswold, van Berg, and Kasch
1. Ind. Eng. Chem. 35, 854 (1943)

Grosjean
1. Ber. 25, 478 (1892)

Grosse and Ipatieff
1. J. Am. Chem. Soc. 57, 2415 (1935)
2. J. Am. Chem. Soc. 61, 640 (1939)

Grosse and Wackher
1. Ind. Eng. Chem. Anal. Ed. 11, 614 (1939)

Grünewald
1. Ber. 20, 2585 (1887)

Grummit and Buck
1. J. Am. Chem. Soc. 65, 296 (1943)

Grützmacher
1. Z. Physik 28, 342 (1924)

Guerbert
1. Compt. rend. 118, 286 (1894)

Guha and Chakladar
1. J. Indian Chem. Soc. 2, 318 (1925)

Günthard and Gäumann
1. Helv. Chim. Acta 33, 1985 (1950)

Guthrie and Huffman
1. J. Am. Chem. Soc. 65, 1139 (1943)

Guthrie, Spitzer, and Huffman
1. J. Am. Chem. Soc. 66, 2120 (1944)

Guttman
1. Thesis. University of California, Berkeley,
   California (1943)

Guttman and Pitzer
1. J. Am. Chem. Soc. 67, 324 (1945)

Guttman, Westrum, and Pitzer
1. J. Am. Chem. Soc. 65, 1246 (1943)

GENERAL LIST OF REFERENCES
H (Page 1)
As of December 31, 1952

Haagen–Smit
1. Koninkl. Akad. Wetterschap Amsterdam **34**, 165 (1931)

Haak and Wibaut
1. Rec. trav. chim. **69**, 1382 (1950)

Hachmuth, Hanson, and Smith
1. Trans. Am. Inst. Chem. Engrs. **42**, 975 (1946)

Haensel and Ipatieff
1. Ind. Eng. Chem. **35**, 632 (1943)

Hagelberg
1. Ber. **23**, 1083 (1890)

Hainlen
1. Ann. **282**, 236 (1894)
2. Ann. **282**, 245 (1894)

Hall
1. J. Soc. Chem. Ind. **54**, 208 (1935)

Hall and Reid
1. J. Am. Chem. Soc. **65**, 1466 (1943)

Hammond and McArdle
1. Ind. Eng. Chem. **35**, 809 (1943)

Hampson, Farmer, and Sutton
1. Proc. Roy. Soc. (London) **A143**, 147 (1933)

Hanna and Smith
1. J. Am. Chem. Soc. **21**, 381 (1899)

Hanney and Smyth
1. J. Am. Chem. Soc. **68**, 244 (1946)

Hansch and Blondon
1. J. Am. Chem. Soc. **70**, 1561 (1948)

Hansch and Lindwall
1. J. Org. Chem. **10**, 381 (1945)

Hanson
1. Trans. Am. Inst. Chem. Engrs. **42**, 959 (1946)

Harand
1. Monatsh. **65**, 153 (1935)

Haraszti
1. J. prakt. Chem. **149**, 301 (1937)

Hardin and Sikorsky
1. J. chim. phys. **6**, 179 (1908)

Hardy
1. Proc. Roy. Soc. **88**, 303 (1913)

Haresnape, Fidler, and Lowry
1. Ind. Eng. Chem. **41**, 2691 (1949)

Harkins and Cheng
1. J. Am. Chem. Soc. **43**, 35 (1921)

Harkins and Ewing
1. J. Am. Chem. Soc. **41**, 1977 (1919)

Harries
1. Ann. **390**, 265 (1912)

Harries and Duvel
1. Ber. **410**, 54 (1915)

Harries and Seitz
1. Ann. **395**, 253 (1913)

Harries and Tank
1. Ber. **41**, 1701 (1908)

Hart and Robinson
1. J. Am. Chem. Soc. **70**, 3731 (1948)

Hartick and Edse
1. Z. physik. Chem. **A182**, 220 (1938)

Hartough
1. J. Am. Chem. Soc. **73**, 4033 (1951)

Hauptmann and Campos
1. J. Am. Chem. Soc. **72**, 1405 (1950)

Haworth, Lindley, and Woodcock
1. J. Chem. Soc. 369 (1947)

Headington
1. Unpublished. Atlantic Refining Company, Philadelphia, Pennsylvania

Heil
1. Phys. Rev. **39**, 666 (1932)

Heisig
1. J. Am. Chem. Soc. **53**, 3245 (1931)

Heisig and Davis
1. J. Am. Chem. Soc. **57**, 339 (1935)

Heisig and Hurd
1. J. Am. Chem. Soc. **55**, 3485 (1933)

Henbest, Jones and Walls
1. J. Chem. Soc. 2696 (1949)

Hennaut-Roland and Lek
1. Bull. soc. chim. Belg. **40**, 177 (1931)

Henne and Chanan
1. J. Am. Chem. Soc. **66**, 395 (1944)

Henne, Chanan, and Turk
1. J. Am. Chem. Soc. **63**, 3474 (1941)

Henne and Greenlee
1. J. Am. Chem. Soc. **65**, 2020 (1943)
2. J. Am. Chem. Soc. **67**, 484 (1945)

Henne and Matuszak
1. J. Am. Chem. Soc. **66**, 1649 (1944)

Henne and Turk
1. J. Am. Chem. Soc. **64**, 826 (1942)

GENERAL LIST OF REFERENCES
H (Page 2)
As of December 31, 1952

Henning and Stock
1. Z. Physik 4, 226 (1921)

Hennion and Auspos
1. J. Am. Chem. Soc. 65, 1603 (1943)

Hennion and Banigan
1. J. Am. Chem. Soc. 69, 1202 (1946)

Hennion and Kurtz
1. J. Am. Chem. Soc. 65, 1001 (1943)

Hennion and Pillar
1. J. Am. Chem. Soc. 72, 5317 (1950)

Hennion and Sheehan
1. J. Am. Chem. Soc. 71, 1964 (1949)

Henry
1. Compt. rend. 142, 1075 (1906)

Henshall
1. J. Soc. Chem. Ind. 62, 127 (1943)

Hepworth
1. J. Chem. Soc. 119, 1254 (1921)

Hepworth and Clapham
1. J. Chem. Soc. 119, 1188 (1921)

Herington
1. Trans. Faraday Soc. 40, 481 (1944)

Herz and Schuftan
1. Z. physik. Chem. 101, 269 (1922)

Herzberg
1. "Infrared and Raman Spectra of Polyatomic Molecules,"
   D. Van Nostrand Co., New York, N.Y. (1945)

Herzberg, Patat, and Verleger
1. J. Phys. Chem. 41, 123 (1937)

Herzenberg and Ruhemann
1. Ber. 60, 889 (1927)

Herzenberg and von Winterfeld
1. Ber. 64, 1036 (1931)

Hetting and Shchekin
1. J. Gen. Chem. (U.S.S.R.) 13, 717 (1943)

Heuse
1. Ann. phys. 59, 86 (1919)

Hewett
1. J. Chem. Soc. 293 (1940)

Hey and Morris
1. J. Chem. Soc. 48 (1948)

Heydweiller
1. Ann. Physik. 59, 193 (1896)

Hibbit and Linstead
1. J. Chem. Soc. 470, (1936)

Hickenbottom, Porter, Edwards, Schlüchterer, and Spitzer
1. J. Inst. Petroleum 35, 621 (1949)

Hicks-Bruun
1. J. Research Natl. Bur. Standards 5, 575 (1930)

Hicks-Bruun and Bruun
1. J. Am. Chem. Soc. 58, 810 (1936)
2. J. Research Natl. Bur. Standards 7, 799 (1931)
3. J. Research Natl. Bur. Standards 8, 525 (1932)

Hicks-Bruun, Bruun, and Faulconer
1. J. Am. Chem. Soc. 61, 3100 (1939)

Hilbert and Johnson
1. J. Am. Chem. Soc. 51, 1526 (1929)

Hildebrand and Wachter
1. J. Am. Chem. Soc. 51, 2487 (1929)

Hilditch
1. Z. Electrochem. 18, 929 (1912)

Hilditch and Dunstan
1. Z. Electrochem. 18, 881 (1912)

Hinsberg
1. Ber. 69, 492 (1936)

Hipsher and Wise
1. Unpublished. National Advisory Committee for Aeronautics,
   Lewis Flight Propulsion Laboratory, Cleveland, Ohio

Hischler and Faulconer
1. J. Am. Chem. Soc. 68, 210 (1946)

Hock and Lang
1. Ber. 75, 300 (1942)

Hoff, Greenlee, and Boord
1. J. Am. Chem. Soc. 73, 3325 (1951)

Hoffman and Arnoldi
1. Ber. 39, 339 (1906)

Hoggarth
1. J. Chem. Soc. 110 (1947)

Holliman and Mann
1. J. Chem. Soc. 37 (1945)

Holmberg
1. Arkiv Kemi, Mineral. Geol. A20, No. 1, 14pp (1945)
2. Arkiv Kemi, Mineral. Geol. A13, No. 8, 9pp. (1939)
3. Arkiv Kemi, Mineral. Geol. A12, No. 14, 10pp. (1937)
4. Arkiv Kemi, Mineral. Geol. B21, No. 7, 7pp. (1945)
5. Ann. 359, 81 (1908)

Holmes, Alcock, Demianiw, Robinson, Rooney, and Sundberg
1. Can. J. Research 26B, 248 (1948)

GENERAL LIST OF REFERENCES
H (Page 3)
As of December 31, 1952

Hoog, Smittenberg, and Visser
1. Proceedings Second World Petroleum Congress, Paris, 2, sect. 2, 498 (1937)

van Hook and Silver
1. J. Chem. Phys. 10, 686 (1942)

Hookway
1. J. Chem. Soc. 1932 (1950)

Hopff and Ohlinger
1. Ber. 76, 1250 (1944)

Horie and Morikawa
1. J. Soc. Chem. Ind. 41, 401 (1938)

Horney
1. Thesis, Ohio State University, Columbus, Ohio (1937)

Horton
1. J. Am. Chem. Soc. 69, 182 (1947)
2. J. Org. Chem. 14, 761 (1949)

Hosking and Brandt
1. Ber. 68, 1286 (1935)

Houben and Doescher
1. Ber. 39, 3506 (1906)

Houseman and Keulegan
1. Report No. 398, National Advisory Committee for Aeronautics, Washington, D. C. (1931)

Houtman, Steenis, and Heertjes
1. Rec. trav. chim. 65, 781 (1946)

Howard
1. J. Research Natl. Bur. Standards 24, 677 (1940)

Howard, Mears, Fookson, Pomerantz, and Brooks
1. J. Research Natl. Bur. Standards 38, 365 (1947)

Huang-Minlon
1. J. Am. Chem. Soc. 71, 3301 (1949)

Hubbard and Brown
1. Ind. Eng. Chem. 35, 1276 (1943)

Hübner and Post
1. Ann. 169, 1 (1873)

Hückel
1. Suomen Kemistilehti 17B, 7 (1944)
2. Ann. 441, 1 (1925)
3. Ann. 533, 1 (1937)
4. Ber. 58, 1449 (1925)

Hückel and Harder
1. Ber. 80, 357 (1947)

Hückel, Kumetat, and Severin
1. Ann. 518, 184 (1935)

Hückel and Rossmann
1. J. prakt. Chem. 136, 30 (1933)

Huffman and others
1. Unpublished. U.S. Bureau of Mines, Bartlesville, Oklahoma

Huffman, Eaton, and Oliver
1. J. Am. Chem. Soc. 70, 2911 (1948)

Huffman, Parks, and Barmore
1. J. Am. Chem. Soc. 53, 3876 (1931)

Huffman, Parks, and Daniels
1. J. Am. Chem. Soc. 62, 1547 (1930)

Huffman, Parks, and Thomas
1. J. Am. Chem. Soc. 52, 3241 (1930)

Huffman, Todd, and Oliver
1. J. Am. Chem. Soc. 71, 584 (1949)

Hugel
1. Chimie et Industrie 26, 1282 (1932)

Hull
1. Thesis, Ohio State University, Columbus, Ohio (1935)

Huntenberg
1. J. prakt. Chem. 145, 23 (1936)

Hunter
1. J. Phys. Chem. 10, 330 (1906)

Hunter and Maass
1. J. Am. Chem. Soc. 51, 153 (1929)

Hunter and Partington
1. J. Chem. Soc. 2062 (1931)
2. J. Chem. Soc. 2812 (1932)

Hunter and Sorenson
1. J. Am. Chem. Soc. 54, 3364 (1932)

Hurd and Greengard
1. J. Am. Chem. Soc. 52, 3356 (1930)

Hurd and Meinert
1. J. Am. Chem. Soc. 53, 289 (1931)

Huston and Awuapara
1. J. Org. Chem. 9, 401 (1944)

Huston and Barrett
1. J. Org. Chem. 11, 657 (1946)

Huston, Fox, and Binder
1. J. Org. Chem. 3, 251 (1938)

Huston, Goerner, Breining, Bostwick, Cline, and Snyder
1. J. Am. Chem. Soc. 70, 1090 (1948)

Huston, Guile, Sculati, and Wasson
1. J. Org. Chem. 6, 252 (1941)

Huston and Hsieh
1. J. Am. Chem. Soc. 58, 429 (1936)

GENERAL LIST OF REFERENCES
H (Page 4)
As of December 31, 1952

Huston and Kaye
1. J. Am. Chem. Soc. **64**, 1576 (1942)

Huston and Kranz
1. J. Org. Chem. **13**, 63 (1948)

Huston and Smith
1. J. Org. Chem. **15**, 1074 (1950)

GENERAL LIST OF REFERENCES

As of December 31, 1952

Il'in and Ivanov
    1. Kolloid-Z. **71**, 267 (1935)

Illuminati and Gilman
    1. J. Am. Chem. Soc. **71**, 3349 (1949)

Inatome, Greenlee, Derfer, and Boord
    1. J. Am. Chem. Soc. **74**, 292 (1952)

Ingle
    1. Ber. **27**, 2526 (1894)

Ingold, Jessop, Kuriyam, and Mandour
    1. J. Chem. Soc. 533 (1933)

International Critical Tables
    1. **III**, 208,262,263
    2. **V**, 10
    3. **VII**, 12,34

Ipatiev
    1. Ber. **44**, 2978 (1911)
    2. Ber. **43**, 3383 (1910)

Ipatieff and Carson
    1. J. Am. Chem. Soc. **59**, 1417 (1937)

Ipatieff and Friedman
    1. J. Am. Chem. Soc. **61**, 71 (1939)

Ipatieff, Pines, and Friedman
    1. J. Am. Chem. Soc. **60**, 2731 (1938)

Ipatieff, Pines, and Komarewsky
    1. Ind. Eng. Chem. **28**, 222 (1936)

Ipatieff, Pines, and Olberg
    1. J. Am. Chem. Soc. **68**, 1709 (1946)

Ipatieff, Pines, and Schmerling
    1. J. Am. Chem. Soc. **60**, 353 (1938)

Ipatieff and Schmerling
    1. J. Am. Chem. Soc. **60**, 1476 (1938)

Ishikawa and Savo
    1. Bull. Inst. Phys. Chem. Research (Tokyo) **22**, 903 (1943)

van Itterbeek
    1. Physica **7**, 831 (1940)

Ivanov, Savinova, and Zhakhovskaya
    1. Doklady Akad, Nauk, S.S.S.R. **59**, 703 (1948)

GENERAL LIST OF REFERENCES

J

As of December 31, 1952

Jacobs and Parks
1. J. Am. Chem. Soc. 56, 1513 (1934)

Jacquemain
1. Ann. chim. 19, 522 (1944)
2. Compt. rend. 215, 179 (1942)

Jacquerod and Wassmer
1. Ber. 37, 2531 (1904)

Jaeger
1. Z. anorg. Chem. 101, 1 (1917)

Jaffeux and Delépine
1. Compt. rend. 172, 158 (1921)

Jamison, Lesslie, and Turner
1. J. Inst. Petroleum 35, 590 (1949)

Jasper
1. Unpublished. Wayne University, Detroit, Michigan

Jawarsky
1. Z. Chem. 8, 222 (1865)

Jeffery and Vogel
1. J. Chem. Soc. 658 (1948)

Jesse
1. J. Am. Chem. Soc. 34, 1337 (1912)

Jessup
1. J. Research Natl. Bur. Standards 18, 115 (1937)
2. J. Research Natl. Bur. Standards 21, 475 (1938)
3. J. Research Natl. Bur. Standards 29, 247 (1942)
4. Unpublished. National Bureau of Standards, Washington, D. C.

Jessup and Green
1. J. Research Natl. Bur. Standards 13, 469 (1934)

Johns and Hixon
1. J. Am. Chem. Soc. 56, 1333 (1934)

Johnson
1. J. Am. Chem. Soc. 69, 146 (1947)

Johnson and Fawcett
1. J. Am. Chem. Soc. 68, 1416 (1946)

Johnson and LeTourneau
1. J. Am. Chem. Soc. 75, 000 (1953)

Johnson, Prosen, and Rossini
1. J. Research Natl. Bur. Standards 35, 141 (1945)
2. J. Research Natl. Bur. Standards 36, 463 (1946)
3. J. Research Natl. Bur. Standards 38, 419 (1947)
4. J. Research Natl. Bur. Standards 39, 49 (1947)
5. Unpublished. National Bureau of Standards, Washington, D. C.
6. J. Research Natl. Bur. Standards 42, 251 (1949)

Johnston and Chapman
1. J. Am. Chem. Soc. 55, 153 (1933)

Johnston and Davis
1. J. Am. Chem. Soc. 56, 271 (1934)

Johnston and Dawson
1. J. Am. Chem. Soc. 55, 2744 (1933)

Johnston, Dawson, and Walker
1. Phys. Rev. 43, 473 (1933)

Johnston and Walker
1. J. Am. Chem. Soc. 55, 172 (1933)
2. J. Am. Chem. Soc. 57, 682 (1935)

Jones and Reid
1. J. Am. Chem. Soc. 60, 2452 (1938)

Ju, Shen, and Wood
1. J. Chem. Soc. 514 (1940)
2. J. Inst. Petroleum 26, 519 (1940)

Ju, Wood, and Garner
1. J. Inst. Petroleum 28, 159 (1942)

GENERAL LIST OF REFERENCES
K (Page 1)
As of December 31, 1952

Kahovec and Reitz
1. Monatsh. 69, 363 (1936)

Karabinos and Lamberti
1. Technical Note No. 1019, National Advisory Committee
for Aeronautics, Aircraft Engine Research Laboratory,
Cleveland, Ohio

Karabinos, Serijan, and Gibbons
1. J. Am. Chem. Soc. 68, 2107 (1946)

Kariyone and Nonaka
1. Pharm. Soc. Japan 57, 20 (1937)

Karrer and Ferri
1. Helv. Chim. Acta 17, 358 (1934)

Karrer and Schmid
1. Helv. Chim. Acta 27, 1275 (1944)

Kasansky and Platé
1. Ber. 69, 1862 (1936)

Kassel
1. J. Chem. Phys. 1, 576 (1933)
2. J. Am. Chem. Soc. 55, 1351 (1933)
3. J. Am. Chem. Soc. 56, 1838 (1934)
4. J. Am. Chem. Soc. 58, 670 (1936)

Katz and Saltman
1. Ind. Eng. Chem. 31, 91 (1939)

Kay
1. Unpublished. Standard Oil Co. (Indiana), Whiting,
Indiana
2. Ind. Eng. Chem. 32, 358 (1940)
3. J. Am. Chem. Soc. 68, 1336 (1946)
4. Ind. Eng. Chem. 33, 590 (1941)
5. J. Am. Chem. Soc. 69, 1273 (1947)

Kay and Warzel
1. Ind. Eng. Chem. 43, 1150 (1951)

Kazanskiĭ and Eliseena
1. J. Gen. Chem. (U.S.S.R.) 6, 888 (1936)

Kazanskiĭ and Glushnev
1. J. Gen. Chem. (U.S.S.R.) 8, 642 (1938)

Kazanskiĭ and Platé
1. Ber. 69, 1862 (1936)

Kazanskiĭ and Sergienko
1. J. Gen. Chem. (U.S.S.R.) 9, 447 (1939)

Kazanskiĭ and Tatevosyan
1. J. Gen. Chem. (U.S.S.R.) 9, 2248 (1939)

van Keersbilck
1. Bull. soc. chim. Belg. 38, 205 (1929)

Keffler
1. J. Am. Chem. Soc. 56, 1259 (1934)

Kehrmann and Sava
1. Ber. 45, 2895 (1912)

Kelley
1. J. Am. Chem. Soc. 51, 2738 (1929)

Kellogg Company, Jersey City, New Jersey
1. Unpublished.

Kelso, Greenlee, Derfer, and Boord
1. J. Am. Chem. Soc. 74, 287 (1952)

Kemp and Egan
1. J. Am. Chem. Soc. 60, 1521 (1938)

Kendall and Monroe
1. J. Am. Chem. Soc. 39, 1795 (1917)

Kennedy, Shomate, and Parks
1. J. Am. Chem. Soc. 60, 1507 (1938)

Kenyon, Phillips, Pittman, Shackelton, Kahn, Yortson, Cochinaras
1. J. Chem. Soc. 1072 (1935)

Keskin, Miller, and Nord
1. J. Org. Chem. 16, 199 (1951)

Keswani and Freiser
1. J. Am. Chem. Soc. 71, 1789 (1949)

Keulemans, Kwantes, and van Bavel
1. Rec. trav. chim. 67, 298 (1948)

Keyes
1. Unpublished. Massachusetts Institute of Technology,
Cambridge, Massachusetts
2. Trans Am. Soc. Mech. Engrs. 70, 641 (1948)

Keyes, Taylor, and Smith
1. J. Math. Phys. 1, 211 (1922)

Khalilov
1. J. Tech. Phys. (U.S.S.R.) 8, 1249 (1938)
2. J. Exptl. Theoret. Phys. (U.S.S.R.) 9, 335 (1939)

Kharasch and Eberly
1. J. Am. Chem. Soc. 63, 625 (1941)

Kharasch, Jerome, and Urry
1. J. Org. Chem. 15, 966 (1950)

Kharasch, Lambert, and Urry
1. J. Org. Chem. 10, 298 (1945)

Kharasch and Zavist
1. J. Am. Chem. Soc. 73, 964 (1951)

Khromov
1. J. Gen. Chem. (U.S.S.R.) 7, 350 (1937)

GENERAL LIST OF REFERENCES
K (Page 2)
As of December 31, 1952

Kierstead and Turkerrich
    1. J. Chem. Phys. 12, 24 (1944)

Kilpatrick, Beckett, Prosen, Pitzer, and Rossini
    1. J. Research Natl. Bur. Standards 42, 225 (1949)

Kilpatrick and Pitzer
    1. J. Am. Chem. Soc. 68, 1066 (1946)
    2. J. Research Natl. Bur. Standards 37, 163 (1946)
    3. J. Research Natl. Bur. Standards 38, 191 (1947)

Kilpatrick, Prosen, Pitzer, and Rossini
    1. J. Research Natl. Bur. Standards 36, 559 (1946)

Kilpatrick, Spitzer, and Pitzer
    1. J. Am. Chem. Soc. 69, 2483 (1947)

Kilpatrick, Werner, Beckett, Pitzer, and Rossini
    1. J. Research Natl. Bur. Standards, 39, 523 (1947)

Kimel and Cope
    1. J. Am. Chem. Soc. 65, 1998 (1943)

King and McMillan
    1. J. Am. Chem. Soc. 68, 1369 (1946)

King and Nord
    1. J. Org. Chem. 14, 638 (1949)

Kinney and Spiethoff
    1. J. Org. Chem. 14, 71 (1949)

Kiplinger
    1. J. Am. Chem. Soc. 42, 472 (1920)

Kipnis and Ornfelt
    1. J. Am. Chem. Soc. 71, 3571 (1949)

Kipping and Herkin
    1. J. Chem. Soc. 57, 25 (1890)

Kipping and Wild
    1. J. Chem. Soc. 1239 (1940)

Kireev and Skvortsova
    1. J. Phys. Chem. (U.S.S.R.) 7, 63 (1936)

Kishner
    1. J. Soc. chim. St. Petersbourg 37, 514 (1905)
    2. J. Soc. chim. St. Petersbourg 40, 995 (1908)
    3. Chem. Zentr. 84, 2132 (1913)
    4. J. Russ. Phys. Chem. Soc. 40, 994 (1908)
    5. J. Russ. Phys. Chem. Soc. 43, 959 (1911)
    6. J. Russ. Phys. Chem. Soc. 45, 1786 (1913)
    7. J. Russ. Phys. Chem. Soc. 50, 15 (1920)
    8. J. Russ. Phys. Chem. Soc. 44, 854 (1912)
    9. J. Russ. Phys. Chem. Soc. 45, 973 (1913)

Kistiakowsky
    1. J. Am. Chem. Soc. 58, 766 (1936)
    2. Ann. Inst. Polytech-Petrograd 1, 450 (1904)
    3. J. Russ. Phys. Chem. Soc. 32, 70 (1902)

Kistiakowsky, Lacher, and Ransom
    1. J. Chem. Phys. 8, 970 (1940)

Kistiakowsky and Nickle
    1. J. Chem. Phys. 10, 78 (1942)
    2. J. Chem. Phys. 10, 146 (1942)

Kistiakowsky and Rice
    1. J. Chem. Phys. 8, 610 (1940)
    2. J. Chem. Phys. 8, 618 (1940)

Kistiakowsky, Romeyn, Ruhoff, Smith, and Vaughan
    1. J. Am. Chem. Soc. 57, 65 (1935)

Kistiakowsky, Ruhoff, Smith, and Vaughan
    1. J. Am. Chem. Soc. 57, 876 (1935)
    2. J. Am. Chem. Soc. 58, 137 (1936)
    3. J. Am. Chem. Soc. 58, 146 (1936)

Klages
    1. Ber. 35, 2245 (1902)
    2. Ber. 36, 3584 (1903)
    3. Ber. 35, 2633 (1902)
    4. Ber. 37, 2301 (1904)
    5. Ber. 36, 3688 (1903)
    6. Ber. 39, 2306 (1906)

Klages and Keil
    1. Ber. 36, 1632 (1903)

Klepper
    1. Chimie et industrie, Special No., 261 (1929)

Kloetzel
    1. J. Am. Chem. Soc. 62, 1708 (1940)

Kloetzel, Dayton, and Herzog
    1. J. Am. Chem. Soc. 72, 273 (1950)

Klos, Neiman-Pilyat, and Pilyat
    1. J. Applied Chem. (U.S.S.R.) 13, 1369 (1940)

Knops
    1. Ann. 248, 175 (1888)

Knoevenagel
    1. Ann. 297, 159 (1897)
    2. Ann. 297, 113 (1897)

Knoevenagel and Fischer
    1. Ann. 297, 185 (1897)

Knowlton and Rossini
    1. J. Research Natl. Bur. Standards 22, 415 (1939)
    2. J. Research Natl. Bur. Standards 19, 605 (1937)
    3. J. Research Natl. Bur. Standards 43, 113 (1949)

Knüsli
    1. Gazz. chim. ital. 79, 621 (1949)

Kobe, Okabe, Ramstad, and Huemmer
    1. J. Am. Chem. Soc. 63, 3251 (1941)

Koch
1. Unpublished. Kaiser-Wilhelm Institute, Mülheim (Ruhr), Germany (1948)

Koch and Hilberath
1. Ber. 73, 1171 (1940)

Koch and Steinbrink
1. Brennstoff-Chem. 19, 277 (1936)

Kogerman
1. J. Am. Chem. Soc. 52, 5060 (1930)

Kohlrausch and Köppl
1. Z. physik. Chem. B26, 209 (1934)

Kohlrausch and Pongrantz
1. Sitzber. Akak. Wiss. Wien, Math. nauturw. Klasse 143, abt. IIb, 358 (1934)

Kohlrauch and Stockmair
1. Z. physik. Chem. B29, 296 (1935)

Kölbel and Fritsch
1. Brennstoff-Chem. 30, 73 (1949)

Kolossovsky
1. Bull. soc. chim. Belg. 34, 228 (1925)

Kolossovsky and Theodorowitsch
1. Bull. soc. chim. 2, 692 (1935)

Komarewsky and Kritchevsky
1. J. Am. Chem. Soc. 65, 547 (1943)

Komarewsky and Shand
1. J. Am. Chem. Soc. 66, 1118 (1944)

Kondakov and Schindelmeiser
1. J. prakt Chem. 61, 477 (1900)

Konovalov
1. Ber. 28, 1852 (1895)
2. J. Russ. Chem. Soc. 23, 446 (1891)
3. J. Russ. Chem. Soc. 19, 255 (1887)

Konovalov and Egorov
1. J. Russ. Phys. Chem. Soc. 30, 1031 (1898)

Koperina and Kazanskiĭ
1. Bull. acad. sci. U.R.S.S., Classe sci. chim. 302 (1948)

Korchung
1. Naturwissenschaften 31, 384 (1943)

Kotake, Fukui, and Terashima
1. J. Chem. Soc. Japan 65, 423 (1944)

Kozacik and Reid
1. J. Am. Chem. Soc. 60, 2436 (1938)

Kozak
1. Anz. Akad. Wiss. Krakaw 407 (1906)

Kozlov
1. Neftyanoe Khoz. 26, 47 (1948)

Krafft
1. Ber. 15, 1698 (1882)
2. Ber. 16, 3018 (1883)
3. Ber. 19, 2982 (1886)
4. Ber. 29, 2232 (1896)
5. Ber. 40, 4779 (1907)
6. Ber. 15, 1718 (1882)
7. Chem. Ztg. 7, 153 (1883)

Krafft and Göttig
1. Ber. 21, 3180 (1888)

Krafft and Reuter
1. Ber. 25, 2250 (1892)

Krafft and Vorster
1. Ber. 26, 2813 (1893)

Krafft and Weilandt
1. Ber. 29, 1316 (1896)

Kraft and Schönherr
1. Ber. 22, 821 (1889)

Krapiwin
1. Bull. soc. naturalistes, Moscow 22, 134 (1918)

Krase and Goodman
1. Ind. Eng. Chem. 22, 13 (1930)

Krassilchik
1. Ann. combustibles liquides 10, 923 (1935)

Krekeler
1. Ber. 19, 3266 (1886)

Kremann, Gugl, and Meingast
1. Sitzber. Adad. Wiss. Wien, Math. naturw. Klasse Abt. IIb, 123, 863 (1914)

Kremann and Meingast
1. Monatsh. 35, 1332 (1914)

Kremann, Meingast, and Gugl
1. Sitzber. Adad. Wiss. Wien, Math. naturw. Klasse Abt. IIb, 123, 731 (1914)

Krieger and Wenzke
1. J. Am. Chem. Soc. 60, 2115 (1938)

Krollpfeiffer
1. Ann. 430, 161 (1923)
2. Ber. 58, 1677 (1925)

Krollpfeiffer, Hartmann, and Schmidt
1. Ann. 563, 15 (1949)

Krollpfeiffer and Schaeffer
1. Ber. 56, 620 (1923)

GENERAL LIST OF REFERENCES
K (Page 4)
As of December 31, 1952

Krollpfeiffer, Schneider, and Wissner
    1. Ann. **566**, 139 (1950)

Krollpfeiffer, Schultze, Schlumbohm, and Sommermeyer
    1. Ber. **58**, 1654 (1925)

Kruber
    1. Ber. **57**, 1008 (1924)
    2. Ber. **72**, 1970 (1939)
    3. Ber. **62**, 3044 (1929)
    4. Brennstoff Chem. **13**, 187 (1932)
    5. Ber. **69**, 1722 (1936)

Kruber and Schade
    1. Ber. **68**, 11 (1935)
    2. Ber. **69**, 1722 (1936)

Kuenen .
    1. Phil. Mag. **3**, 628 (1902)
    2. Phil. Mag. **44**, 174 (1897)

Kuenen and Visser
    1. Proc. Roy. Acad. Sci. Amersterdam **16**, 355 (1913)
    2. Communs. Phys. Lab. Univ. Leiden **168**, No. 138a

Kues and Paal
    1. Ber. **19**, 555 (1886)

Kuhn and Dann
    1. Ber. **73**, 1092 (1940)
    2. Ann. **547**, 293 (1941)

Kuhn and Deutsch
    1. Ber. **65**, 43 (1932)

Kuhn and Winterstein
    1. Ber. **66**, 429 (1933)

Kurnakov
    1. Z. anorg. Chem. **135**, 81 (1924)

Kurnakov, Krothov, and Okunanu
    1. J. Russ. Phys. Chem. Soc. **49**, 583 (1915)

Kuroda and Ishino
    1. Bull. Inst. Phys. Chem. Research (Tokyo) **22**, 858 (1943)

Kutz and Corson
    1. J. Am. Chem. Soc. **68**, 1477 (1946)

Kutz, Nickels, McGovern, and Corson
    1. J. Am. Chem. Soc. **70**, 4026, (1948)
    2. J. Org. Chem. **16**, 699 (1951)

Kuwata, Tomiyama, and Takao
    1. Bull. Chem. Soc. Japan **22**, 66 (1949)

Kuykendall
    1. Thesis..Ohio State University, Columbus, Ohio (1935)

GENERAL LIST OF REFERENCES
L (Page 1)
As of December 31, 1952

Laakso
    1. Suomen Kemistilehti B13, 8 (1940)

Lachowicz
    1. Ann. 220, 168 (1883)

Lacourt
    1. Bull. soc. chim. Belg. 38, 1 (1929)
    2. Bull. soc. chim. Belg. 39, 132 (1930)

Ladenburg and Krügel
    1. Ber. 33, 637 (1900)
    2. Ber. 32, 46 (1899)

Lagemann
    1. J. Chem. Phys. 16, 247 (1948)

Laidler and Szayna
    1. J. Inst. Petroleum Tech. 20, 163 (1934)

Lamb and Roper
    1. J. Am. Chem. Soc. 62, 806 (1940)

Lamberti, Reynolds, and Chanan
    1. Technical Note No. 1163, National Advisory Committee for
      Aeronautics, Washington, D. C.

Lamneck and Wise
    1. Technical Note No. 2230, National Advisory Committee for
      Aeronautics, Lewis Flight Propulsion Laboratory,
      Cleveland, Ohio

Landa
    1. Collection Czechoslov. Chem. Commun. 3, 367 (1931)

Landa and Landova
    1. Collection Czechoslov. Chem. Commun. 2, 31 (1930)

Landa and Riedl
    1. Collection Czechoslov. Chem. Commun. 2, 520 (1930)

Landa and Sliva
    1. Collection Czechoslov. Chem. Commun. 4, 538 (1932)

Landolt—Börnstein
    1. "Physikalisch—Chemische Tabellen," 4th ed., Berlin,
      (1912)

Landolt and Jahn
    1. Z. physik. Chem. 10, 289 (1892)

Landrieu and Baylocq
    1. Bull. soc. chim. 45, 217 (1929)

Landrieu, Baylocq, and Johnson
    1. Bull. soc. chim. 45, 36 (1929)

Langedijk and Brezesinska
    1. Rec. trav. chim. 57, 1050 (1938)

Langedijk and Stedehouder
    1. Rec. trav. chim. 56, 526 (1937)

Larin and Frost
    1. Compt. rend. scad. sci. U.R.S.S. 59, 1297 (1948)

Larsen, Thorpe, and Armfield
    1. Ind. Eng. Chem. 34, 183 (1942)

Lassettre and Dickinson
    1. J. Am. Chem. Soc. 61, 54 (1939)

Lauer
    1. J. Chem. Phys. 16, 612 (1948)

Lauer and Stodola
    1. J. Am. Chem. Soc. 56, 1215 (1934)

Laughlin, Nash, and Whitmore
    1. J. Am. Chem. Soc. 56, 1395 (1934)

de Lazlo
    1. Z. physik. Chem. 118, 369 (1925)

Le Beau
    1. Bull. soc. chim. 33, 1137 (1905)

Le Beau and Picon
    1. Compt. rend. 156, 1077 (1913)

Lebedev and Orlov
    1. J. Gen. Chem. (U.S.S.R.) 5, 1589 (1935)

Lecher
    1. Ber. 58, 414 (1925)
    2. Ber. 48, 524 (1915)

Lecher and Siefken
    1. Ber. 59, 1314 (1926)

Lecher and Wittwer
    1. Ber. 55, 1474 (1922)

Leclère and Leclère
    1. Compt. rend. 194, 286 (1932)

Lee and Dougherty
    1. J. Org. Chem. 4, 48 (1939)

L'Ecuyer and Turcotte
    1. Can. J. Research 25B, 575 (1947)

Lederer
    1. Allgem. Öl—u. Fett—Ztg. 27, 237 (1930)

Leendertse, Tulleners, and Waterman
    1. Rec. trav. chim. 52, 515 (1933)

Le Fevre, Le Fevre, and Robertson
    1. J. Chem. Soc. 480 (1935)

Legge
    1. J. Am. Chem. Soc. 69, 2079 (1947)

Lemonde
    1. Ann. phys. 9, 539 (1939)

GENERAL LIST OF REFERENCES
L (Page 2)
As of December 31, 1952

Lemons and Felsing
1. J. Am. Chem. Soc. 65, 46 (1943)

Lemoult
1. Compt. rend. 152, 1402 (1911)

Leroux
1. Compt. rend. 139, 672 (1904)

Leslie
1. J. Research Natl. Bur. Standards 8, 591 (1932)
2. J. Research Natl. Bur. Standards 10, 609 (1933)
3. J. Research Natl. Bur. Standards 13, 589 (1934)
4. J. Research Natl. Bur. Standards 15, 41 (1935)
5. J. Research Natl. Bur. Standards 17, 761 (1936)
6. J. Research Natl. Bur. Standards 22, 153 (1939)

Leslie and Heuer
1. J. Research Natl. Bur. Standards 18, 639 (1937)
2. J. Research Natl. Bur. Standards 21, 515 (1938)

Leslie and Schicktanz
1. J. Research Natl. Bur. Standards 6, 377 (1931)

Leslie and White
1. J. Research Natl. Bur. Standards 15, 211 (1935)

Lespieau and Chavanne
1. Compt. rend. 140, 1035 (1905)

Lespieau and Deluchat
1. Compt. rend. 190, 683 (1930)

Lespieau and Wiemann
1. Bull. soc. chim. 45, 627 (1929)

Lester and Suratt
1. J. Am. Chem. Soc. 71, 2262 (1949)

Letsinger
1. J. Am. Chem. Soc. 70, 406 (1948)

Letsinger and Traynham
1. J. Am. Chem. Soc. 72, 849 (1950)

Levene and Cretcher
1. J. Biol. Chem. 33, 505 (1918)

Levene and Kuna
1. J. Biol. Chem. 110, 323 (1935)

Levene and Marker
1. J. Biol. Chem. 91, 761 (1931)
2. J. Biol. Chem. 95, 1 (1932)
3. J. Biol. Chem. 106, 173 (1934)
4. J. Biol. Chem. 110, 299 (1935)

Levene and Mikeska
1. J. Biol. Chem. 84, 571 (1929)
2. J. Biol. Chem. 75, 587 (1927)
3. J. Biol. Chem. 70, 365 (1926)

Levene, Mikeska, and Passoth
1. J. Biol. Chem. 88, 27 (1930)

Levene and Taylor
1. J. Biol. Chem. 54, 351 (1922)

Levina
1. J. Gen. Chem. (U.S.S.R.) 9, 2287 (1939)

Levina and Egorova
1. J. Gen. Chem. (U.S.S.R.) 16, 821 (1946)

Levina, Faĭnzil'berg, and Itenberg
1. Doklady Akad. Nauk S.S.S.R. 75, 39 (1950)

Levina, Faĭnzil'berg, Tantsyreva, and Treshchova
1. Bull. acad. sci. U.R.S.S. Classe sci. chim. 321 (1951)

Levina, Faĭnzil'berg, Tatevskiĭ, and Treshchova
1. J. Gen. Chem. (U.S.S.R.) 21, 233 (1951)

Levina, Gladshtein, and Akishin
1. J. Gen. Chem. (U.S.S.R.) 19, 1077 (1949)

Levina and Kagan
1. J. Gen. Chem. (U.S.S.R.) 11, 523 (1941)

Levina, Kleĭmenova, and Shusherina
1. J. Gen. Chem. (U.S.S.R.) 17, 117 (1947)

Levina and Kulikov
1. J. Gen. Chem. (U.S.S.R.) 19, 1724 (1949)
2. J. Gen. Chem. (U.S.S.R.) 17, 1189 (1947)

Levina, Skvarchenko, Kagan, and Treshchova
1. J. Gen. Chem. (U.S.S.R.) 19, 62 (1949)

Levina, Skvarchenko, Tatevskiĭ, and Treshchova
1. J. Gen. Chem. (U.S.S.R.) 20, 684 (1950)

Levina, Skvarchenko, Treshchova, and Tatevskiĭ
1. J. Gen. Chem. (U.S.S.R.) 20, 419 (1950)

Levina, Skvarchenko, Viktorova, Tatevskiĭ, and Treshchova
1. J. Gen. Chem. (U.S.S.R.) 20, 690 (1950)

Levina, Tantsyreva, Faĭnzil'berg, and Mezentsova
1. Bull. acad. sci. U.R.S.S. Classe sci. chim. 161 (1951)

Levina and Trakhtenberg
1. J. Gen. Chem. (U.S.S.R.) 6, 764 (1936)

Levy
1. Compt. rend. 193, 174 (1931)
2. Ann. chim. 9, 1 (1938)

Lewis
1. J. Am. Chem. Soc. 47, 626 (1925)

Lewis and von Elbe
1. J. Am. Chem. Soc. 57, 2737 (1935)
2. J. Chem. Phys. 3, 63 (1935)

GENERAL LIST OF REFERENCES
L (Page 3)
As of December 31, 1952

Lewis and Randall
1. "Thermodynamics and the Free Energy of Chemical
   Substances," McGraw-Hill Book Co., Inc., New York (1923)

Libby
1. J. Chem. Phys. **11**, 101 (1943)

Liberman and Kazanskiĭ
1. Bull. acad. sci. U.R.S.S. Classe sci. chim. 77 (1946)
2. Compt. rend. acad. sci. U.R.S.S. **40**, 353 (1943)

Liberman, Lukina, Solovova, and Kazanskiĭ
1. Compt. rend. acad. sci. U.R.S.S. **40**, 70 (1943)

Liddel and Kasper
1. J. Research Natl. Bur. Standards **11**, 599 (1933)

van Liempt
1. Rec. trav. chim. **37**, 694 (1938)

Lien, McCaulay, and Evering
1. Ind. Eng. Chem. **41**, 2698 (1949)

Linebarger
1. Am. J. Sci. **2**, 331 (1896)

Linke
1. Z. physik. Chem. **A188**, 17 (1941)
2. Z. physik. Chem. **A188**, 191 (1941)
3. Z. physik. Chem. **A187**, 227 (1940)

Linsk
1. J. Am. Chem. Soc. **72**, 4257 (1950)

Linstead, Millidge, and Walpole
1. J. Chem. Soc. 1140 (1937)

Linstead, Noble, and Wright
1. J. Chem. Soc. 911 (1937)

Linstead and Thomas
1. J. Chem. Soc. 1131 (1940)

Lipkin, Davison, and Kurtz
1. Ind. Eng. Chem. **34**, 976 (1942)

Lippman and Hawliczk
1. Ber. **12**, 69 (1879)

Lister
1. J. Am. Chem. Soc. **63**, 143 (1941)

Livingston and Heisig
1. J. Am. Chem. Soc. **52**, 2409 (1930)

Loevenich, Losen, and Dierichs
1. Ber. **60**, 950 (1927)

Loevenich, Utsch, Moldrickx, and Schaeffer
1. Ber. **62**, 3084 (1929)

Loomis and Walters
1. J. Am. Chem. Soc. **48**, 2051 (1926)

Louguinine
1. Compt. rend. **93**, 274 (1881)

Lowry and Allsopp
1. Proc. Roy. Soc. (London) **A113**, 36 (1931)

Lowry and Nasini
1. Proc. Roy. Soc. (London) **A123**, 686 (1926)

Lozovoi, D'yakova, and Stepantseva
1. J. Gen. Chem. (U.S.S.R.) **7**, 1119 (1937)
2. J. Gen. Chem. (U.S.S.R.) **9**, 540 (1939)

Lucas and Dillon
1. J. Am. Chem. Soc. **50**, 1460 (1928)

Lucas, Dillon, and Young
1. J. Am. Chem. Soc. **52**, 1949 (1930)

Lucas and Prater
1. J. Am. Chem. Soc. **59**, 1682 (1937)

Lumbroso
1. Compt. rend. **228**, 77 (1949)

Lumsden
1. J. Chem. Soc. **91**, 24 (1907)

Lunshof, van Steenis, and Waterman
1. Rec. trav. chim. **66**, 348 (1947)

Luschinsky
1. Z. physik. Chem. **A182**, 384 (1938)

Luther
1. Unpublished. Schleicher and Schuell Company, New York,
   New York

Luther and Koebel
1. Brennstoff-Chem. **30**, 300 (1949)

Luther and Wächter
1. Ber. **82**, 161 (1949)

Lüttringhaus, König, and Böttcher
1. Ann. **560**, 201 (1947)

Lutz, Bearse, Leonard, and Croxton
1. J. Am. Chem. Soc. **70**, 4139 (1948)

GENERAL LIST OF REFERENCES

M (Page 1)

As of December 31, 1952

MacDougall and Smith
1. J. Am. Chem. Soc. **52**, 1998 (1930)

McAllan, Cullum, Dean, and Fidler
1. J. Am. Chem. Soc. **73**, 3627 (1951)

McArdle and Robertson
1. Ind. Eng. Chem. Anal. Ed. **15**, 484 (1943)

McIntosh
1. J. Phys. Chem. **11**, 306 (1907)

McIntosh, Dacey, and Maass
1. Can. J. Research **17B**, 241 (1939)

McIntosh and Maass
1. Can. J. Research **16B**, 289 (1938)

McKee
1. Ind. Eng. Chem. **20**, 1169 (1928)

McKenna and Sowa
1. J. Am. Chem. Soc. **59**, 470 (1937)

McKinley, Stevens, and Baldwin
1. J. Am. Chem. Soc. **67**, 1455 (1945)

McKittrick
1. Ind. Eng. Chem. **21**, 585 (1929)

McMillan and King
1. J. Am. Chem. Soc. **70**, 4143 (1948)

McVicker, Marsh, and Stewart
1. J. Chem. Soc. **125**, 1743 (1924)
2. J. Chem. Soc. **127**, 1001 (1925)

Maass and McIntosh
1. J. Am. Chem. Soc. **36**, 737 (1914)

Maass and Russell
1. J. Am. Chem. Soc. **40**, 1561 (1918)

Maass and Wright
1. J. Am. Chem. Soc. **43**, 1098 (1921)

Mabery
1. Am. Chem. J. **13**, 233 (1891)

Madge
1. J. Phys. Chem. **34**, 1599 (1930)

Madinaveitia
1. Anales soc. españ. fís. y quím. **32**, 1100 (1934)

Madorsky and Wood
1. Unpublished. National Bureau of Standards, Washington, D. C.

Maess and von Müffling
1. Angew. Chem. **50**, 759 (1937)

Magnus
1. Ann. Physik **48**, 983 (1915)
2. Ann. Physik **70**, 303 (1923)

Magnus and Hodler
1. Ann. Physik **80**, 808 (1926)

Mailhe
1. Bull. soc. chim. **15**, 327 (1914)

Mailhe and Murat
1. Bull. soc. chim. **7**, 288 (1910)
2. Bull. soc. chim. **7**, 1083 (1910)

Mair
1. J. Research Natl. Bur. Standards **9**, 457 (1932)
2. J. Research Natl. Bur. Standards **14**, 345 (1935)
3. J. Research Natl. Bur. Standards **34**, 435 (1945)
4. Ann. N.Y. Acad. Sci. **49**, 218 (1948)
5. Ind. Eng. Chem. **42**, 1355 (1950)

Mair and Forziati
1. J. Research Natl. Bur. Standards **32**, 151 (1944)
2. J. Research Natl. Bur. Standards **32**, 165 (1944)

Mair, Gaboriault, and Rossini
1. Ind. Eng. Chem. **39**, 1072 (1947)

Mair, Glasgow, and Rossini
1. J. Research Natl. Bur. Standards **26**, 591 (1941)
2. J. Research Natl. Bur. Standards **27**, 39 (1941)

Mair and Rossini
1. Am. Soc. Testing Materials, Standards on Petroleum Products, Committee D2, Year Book, p486 (1947)
2. "Science of Petroleum," Vol. V, Part I, p126, Oxford University Press, New York, 1950

Mair and Schicktanz
1. J. Research Natl. Bur. Standards **11**, 665 (1933)
2. Ind. Eng. Chem. **28**, 1056 (1936)
3. Ind. Eng. Chem. **28**, 1446 (1936)

Mair, Schicktanz, and Rose
1. J. Research Natl. Bur. Standards **15**, 557 (1935)

Mair and Streiff
1. J. Research Natl. Bur. Standards **27**, 343 (1941)
2. J. Research Natl. Bur. Standards **24**, 395 (1940)

Mair, Sweetman, and Rossini
1. Ind. Eng. Chem. **41**, 2224 (1949)

Mair, Termini, Willingham, and Rossini
1. J. Research Natl. Bur. Standards **37**, 229 (1946)

Mair, Westhaver, and Rossini
1. Ind. Eng. Chem. **42**, 1279 (1950)

Mair and White
1. J. Research Natl. Bur. Standards **15**, 51 (1935)

Mair and Willingham
1. Ind. Eng. Chem. **28**, 1452 (1936)
2. J. Research Natl. Bur. Standards **21**, 535 (1938)
3. J. Research Natl. Bur. Standards **22**, 519 (1939)

GENERAL LIST OF REFERENCES

M (Page 2)

As of December 31, 1952

Mair, Willingham, and Streiff
    1. J. Research Natl. Bur. Standards **21**, 565 (1938)
    2. J. Research Natl. Bur. Standards **21**, 581 (1938)

Maman
    1. Pub. sci. tech. ministére air (France) **66**, 32 (1935)
    2. Compt. rend. **207**, 1401 (1938)

Mann and Purdie
    1. J. Chem. Soc. 1549 (1935)

Mannich and Fresenius
    1. Arch. Pharm. **274**, 461 (1936)

Manzoni—Ansidei
    1. Boll. sci. facoltá chim. ind. Bologna 201 (1940)

Marchetti
    1. Gazz. chim. ital. **11**, 439 (1881)

Märcker
    1. Ann. **136**, 75 (1865)
    2. Ann. **140**, 86 (1866)

de la Mare and Robertson
    1. J. Chem. Soc. 279 (1943)

Marker and Oakwood
    1. J. Am. Chem. Soc. **60**, 2598 (1938)

Markownikov
    1. J. Russ. Phys. Chem. Soc. **31**, 214 (1899)
    2. Ann. **307**, 335 (1899)
    3. J. Russ. Phys. Chem. Soc. **36**, 58 (1904)
    4. Ann. **336**, 310 (1904)
    5. J. Russ. Phys. Chem. Soc. **35**, 389 (1903)
    6. Ann. **301**, 127 (1898)

Markownikov and Oglobin
    1. J. Russ. Phys. Chem. Soc. **15**, 331 (1883)

Marsden and Maass
    1. Can. J. Research **13B**, 296 (1935)

Martin, E.
    1. Sitzb. Akad. Wiss. Wien, Math. natur—w. Klasse. Abt IIA,
       **123**, 2491 (1914)

Martin, F.
    1. Bull. soc. chim. Belg. **34**, 82 (1925)
    2. Ann. office natl. combustibles liquides **12**, 97 (1937)

Marvel and Chambers
    1. J. Am. Chem. Soc. **70**, 993 (1948)

Marvel and Fuller
    1. J. Am. Chem. Soc. **74**, 1506 (1952)

Marvel, Hager, and Coffman
    1. J. Am. Chem. Soc. **49**, 2323 (1927)

Marvel and Hein
    1. J..Am. Chem. Soc. **70**, 1895 (1948)

Marvel and Johnson
    1. J. Org. Chem. **13**, 822 (1948)

Marvel, Myers, and Saunders
    1. J. Am. Chem. Soc. **70**, 1694 (1948)

Marvel, Overberger, Allen, Johnston, Saunders, and Young
    1. J. Am. Chem. Soc. **68**, 736 (1946)

Marvel and Williams
    1. J. Am. Chem. Soc. **61**, 2714 (1939)
    2. J. Am. Chem. Soc. **70**, 3842 (1948)

Mason, Naldrett, and Maass
    1. Can J. Research **18B**, 103 (1940)

Mason and Paxton
    1. J. Am. Chem. Soc. **61**, 67 (1939)

Mason and Washburn
    1. J. Phys. Chem. **40**, 481 (1936)

Massart
    1. Bull. soc. chim. Belg. **45**, 76 (1936)

Masson, H.
    1. Compt. rend. **132**, 483 (1901)

Masson, O.
    1. J. Chem. Soc. **49**, 233 (1886)

Mathews
    1. J. Am. Chem. Soc. **48**, 562 (1926)

Mathias, E.
    1. Compt. rend. **148**, 1102 (1909)

Mathias, S.
    1. J. Am. Chem. Soc. **72**, 1897 (1950)

Mathias, Crommelin, and Watts
    1. Ann. Phys. **11**, 343 (1929)

Mathot
    1. Bull. soc. chim. Belg. **59**, 111 (1950)

Mathus and Gibon
    1. Bull. soc. chim. Belg. **34**, 303 (1925)

Matsubasa and Perkin
    1. J. Chem. Soc. **87**, 661 (1905)

Mauthner
    1. Ber. **39**, 3593 (1906)

Mavity
    1. Thesis. Ohio State University, Columbus, Ohio (1931)

Mayer and Mayer
    1. "Statistical Mechanics," John Wiley & Sons, New York
       (1940)

Mayer and Schiffner
    1. Ber. **67**, 67 (1934)

GENERAL LIST OF REFERENCES

M (Page 3)

As of December 31, 1952

Mayer and Schulte
1. Ber. **55**, 2164 (1922)

Mazee
1. Rec. trav. chim. **67**, 197 (1948)

Meadows and Reid
1. J. Am. Chem. Soc. **56**, 2177 (1934)

Mecke and Ziegler
1. Z. Physik **101**, 405 (1936)

Meerwein
1. Ann. **405**, 129 (1914)
2. Ann. **405**, 142 (1914)

Meerwein and Fleischhauer
1. Ann. **417**, 263 (1918)

Meinert and Hurd
1. J. Am. Chem. Soc. **52**, 4544 (1930)

Meiser
1. Ber. **32**, 2049 (1899)

Melpolder, Woodbridge, and Headington
1. J. Am. Chem. Soc. **70**, 935 (1948)
2. Presented before the Division of Petroleum Chemistry, American Chemical Society, New York, New York, September, 1947

Merling
1. Ann. **264**, 310 (1891)

Meshcheryakov
1. Bull. acad. sci. U.R.S.S., classe sci. chim. 157 (1941)

Messer
1. Chem. News **138**, 292 (1929)

Messerly and Kennedy
1. J. Am. Chem. Soc. **62**, 2988 (1940)

Messinger
1. Ber. **18**, 563 (1885)

Meunier and Desparmet
1. Bull. soc. chim. **35**, 481 (1924)

Meyer
1. Ber. **16**, 1465 (1883)
2. Ber. **19**, 3259 (1886)

Meyer and Bernhaver
1. Sitzber. Akad. Wiss. Wien, Math. naturw. Klasse **138**, Abt. IIb, 721 (1929)

Meyer and Fricke
1. Ber. **47**, 2765 (1914)

Meyer and Kreis
1. Ber. **17**, 787 (1884)

Meyer and Mylius
1. Z. physik. Chem. **95**, 349 (1920)

Meyer and Sieglitz
1. Ber. **55**, 1835 (1922)

Meyer and Streuli
1. Helv. Chim. Acta **20**, 1179 (1937)

Meyers, Scott, Brickwedde, and Rands
1. Unpublished. National Bureau of Standards, Washington, D. C.

Michael and Weiner
1. J. Org. Chem. **4**, 531 (1939)

Michels and Wassenaar
1. Physica **16**, 221 (1950)

Midgley and Henne
1. J. Am. Chem. Soc. **51**, 1215 (1929)
2. J. Am. Chem. Soc. **51**, 1218 (1929)

Midgley, Henne, and Shepard
1. J. Am. Chem. Soc. **54**, 2957 (1932)

Mikeska
1. Ind. Eng. Chem. **28**, 970 (1936)

Mikeska and Cohen
1. J. Org. Chem. **6**, 787 (1941)

Mikeska, Smith, and Lieber
1. J. Org. Chem. **2**, 499 (1938)

Milazzo
1. Gazz. chim. ital. **74**, 58 (1944)

Millar
1. J. Am. Chem. Soc. **45**, 874 (1923)

Miller, C.
1. Proc. Roy. Soc. (London) **A106**, 724 (1924)

Miller, O.
1. Bull. soc. chim. Belg. **41**, 217 (1932)
2. Bull. soc. chim. Belg. **42**, 238 (1933)
3. Bull. soc. chim. Belg. **44**, 513 (1935)

Miller, Crossley, and Moore
1. J. Am. Chem. Soc. **64**, 2322 (1942)

Miller and Lovell
1. Ind. Eng. Chem. **40**, 1138 (1948)

Miller and Piaux
1. Compt. rend. **197**, 412 (1933)

Mixter
1. Am. J. Sci. **12**, 347 (1901)
2. Am. J. Sci. **22**, 13 (1906)

GENERAL LIST OF REFERENCES
M (Page 4)
As of December 31, 1952

Mizusima, Morino, and Huzisino
1. J. Chem. Soc. Japan 62, 587 (1941)

Mochel, Agre, and Hanford
1. J. Am. Chem. Soc. 70, 2268 (1948)

Möhlau and Berger
1. Ber. 26, 1994 (1893)

Moersch
1. Abs. Doc. Diss. 5, 301 (1942) Pennsylvania State
College, State College, Pennsylvania

Moersch and Whitmore
1. J. Am. Chem. Soc. 71, 819 (1949)

Möslinger
1. Ann. 185, 26 (1877)

Mohler and Sorge
1. Helv. Chim. Acta 23, 1200 (1940)

Moldavskiĭ and Nizovkina
1. J. Gen. Chem. (U.S.S.R.) 9, 1652 (1939)
2. J. Gen. Chem. (U.S.S.R.) 10, 1183 (1940)

Moldavskiĭ, Nizovkina, and Sharkova
1. J. Gen. Chem. (U.S.S.R.) 16, 427 (1946)

Montagne
1. Ann. chim. phys. 13, 40 (1930)

Montgomery
1. Unpublished. Gulf Research and Development Company,
Pittsburgh, Pennsylvania

Montgomery, McAteer, and Franke
1. J. Am. Chem. Soc. 59, 1768 (1937)
2. Presented before the Division of Petroleum Chemistry,
American Chemical Society, Baltimore, Maryland,
April 1939

Montgomery, McAteer, and Horne
1. Unpublished. Gulf Research and Development Company,
Pittsburgh, Pennsylvania

Montgomery and de Vries
1. J. Am. Chem. Soc. 64, 2375 (1942)

Moore and Greensfelder
1. J. Am. Chem. Soc. 69, 2008 (1947)

Moore, Renquist, and Parks
1. J. Am. Chem. Soc. 62, 1505 (1940)

Morehouse and Maass
1. Can. J. Research 5B, 306 (1931)
2. Can. J. Research 11B, 637 (1934)

Morgan, Carter, and Duck
1. J. Chem. Soc. 127, 1252 (1925)

Morgan and Chazal
1. J. Am. Chem. Soc. 35, 1821 (1913)

Morgan and Daghlian
1. Z. physik. Chem. 78, 169 (1912)
2. J. Am. Chem. Soc. 33, 672 (1911)

Morgan and Dow
1. Phys. Rev. 54, 312 (1938)

Morgan and Griggs
1. J. Am. Chem. Soc. 39, 2261 (1917)

Morino
1. Sci. Papers Inst. Phys. Chem. Research (Tokyo) 23, 49
(1933)

Morrell, Pickering, and Smith
1. J. Inst. Petroleum 34, 677 (1948)

Mortimer and Murphy
1. Ind. Eng. Chem. 15, 1140 (1923)

Morton, Davidson, and Best
1. J. Am. Chem. Soc. 64, 2239 (1942)

Moureu
1. Ann. chim. 7, 536 (1906)

Moureu and André
1. Ann. chim. 1, 113 (1914)

Moury, Dazzi, Renoll, and Shortridge
1. J. Am. Chem. Soc. 70, 1916 (1948)

Mousseron
1. Compt. rend. 215, 201 (1942)
2. Bull. soc. chim. 218 (1946)
3. Compt. rend. 216, 812 (1943)

Mousseron, Bousquet, and Marret
1. Bull. soc. chim. 15, 84 (1948)

Mousseron and Granger
1. Bull. soc. chim. Belg. 5, 1618 (1938)
2. Compt. rend. 207, 367 (1938)

Mousseron and Paulet
1. Parfumerie moderne 33, 101 (1939)

Mousseron, Richaud, and Granger
1. Bull. soc. chim. 218 (1946)

Mousseron, Winternitz, and Jacquier
1. Compt. rend. 224, 1062 (1947)

Mowry, Renall, and Huber
1. J. Am. Chem. Soc. 68, 1105 (1946)

Muchin
1. Z. Electrochem. 19, 819 (1913)

GENERAL LIST OF REFERENCES
M (Page 5)

As of December 31, 1952

Mueller, E. F.
  1. "Temperature, Its Measurement and Control in Science and
     Industry." pp. 162–179. Reinhold Publishing Corporation,
     New York (1941)

Müller, W.
  1. Ber. **20**, 1212 (1887)

Mueller and Rossini
  1. Am. J. Physics **12**, 1 (1944)

Müller and Saville
  1. J. Chem. Soc. **127**, 599 (1925)

Müller and Schütz
  1. Ber. **71**, 692 (1938)

Mueller and Stimson
  1. J. Research Natl. Bur. Standards **13**, 699 (1934)

Muglioni
  1. Chim. ind. agr. biol. **15**, 695 (1939)

Mulliken
  1. Unpublished. University of Chicago, Chicago, Illinois

Mulliken, Wakeman, and Gerry
  1. J. Am. Chem. Soc. **57**, 1605 (1935)

**Mumford and Phillips**
  1. J. Chem. Soc. 75 (1950)

Murat
  1. Ann. chim. phys. **16**, 117 (1909)

Murphy and Duggan
  1. J. Am. Chem. Soc. **71**, 3347 (1949)

Murray and Gallaway
  1. J. Am. Chem. Soc. **70**, 3867 (1948)

Muset
  1. Bull. classe. sci. Acad. roy. Belg. 775 (1906)

GENERAL LIST OF REFERENCES
N (Page 1)
As of December 31, 1952

Nagornov and Rotinyantz
1. Ann. inst. anal. phys. chim. (U.S.S.R.) **3**, 162 (1926)

Naldrett and Maass
1. Can. J. Research **18B**, 118 (1940)

Nametkin
1. J. Russ. Phys. Chem. Soc. **55-6**, 47 (1924-5)

Nametkin and Bruessoff
1. Ber. **56**, 1807 (1923)

Nametkin and Rosenberg
1. Bull. acad. sci. U.R.S.S., classe sci. tech. No. **11-12**, 3 (1943)

Nametkin and Sosnina
1. Doklady Akad. Nauk, S.S.S.R. **62**, 775 (1948)
2. Doklady Akad. Nauk. S.S.S.R. **63**, 391 (1948)

Nametkin and Volodina
1. J. Gen. Chem. (U.S.S.R.) **17**, 325 (1947)

Nasini, A.
1. Proc. Roy. Soc. (London) **A123**, 704 (1929)

Nasini, R.
1. Ber. **15**, 2878 (1882)

Nasini and Carrara
1. Gazz. chim. ital. **24**, 256 (1894)

Nasini and Scala
1. Gazz. chim. ital. **17**, 74 (1887)

National Bureau of Standards
1. Unpublished
2. Miscellaneous Publication M121, January, 1926, "Units of weight and measure; definitions and tables of equivalents."
3. Technical News Bulletin **31**, 49 (1947)

National Research Council
1. Report of the Committee on Physical Chemistry, Washington, D. C., July, 1951

Natural Gasoline Association of America, Petroleum Technical Committee
1. Ind. Eng. Chem. **34**, 1240 (1942)

Naylor
1. J. Chem. Soc. 2749 (1949)

Nazarov
1. Ber. **70**, 606 (1937)

Nazarov, Azerbaev, and Rakcheeva
1. J. Gen. Chem. (U.S.S.R.) **18**, 407 (1948)

Nazarov and Kotlyarevskiĭ
1. J. Gen. Chem. (U.S.S.R.) **20**, 1441 (1950)
2. J. Gen. Chem. (U.S.S.R.) **20**, 1449 (1950)

Nazarov, Kuznetsova, and Gurvich
1. J. Gen. Chem. (U.S.S.R.) **19**, 2164 (1949)

Nazarov and Zaretskaya
1. J. Gen. Chem. (U.S.S.R.) **18**, 665 (1948)

Nazzaro and Bullock
1. J. Am. Chem. Soc. **68**, 2121 (1946)

Nederbragt and Boelhouwer
1. Physica **13**, 305 (1937)

Nederbragt and de Jong
1. Rec. trav. chim. **65**, 831 (1946)

Nekrasov and Melnikow
1. Ber. **62**, 2091 (1929)

Nelson and Senseman
1. Ind. Eng. Chem. **14**, 58 (1922)

Nenitzescu and Cioränescu
1. Ber. **69**, 1820 (1936)
2. Ber. **69**, 1040 (1936)

Nenitzescu, Isǎcescu, and Isopescu
1. Oesterr. Chem.-Ztg. **42**, 350 (1939)

Nernst
1. Ann. Physik **36**, 395 (1911)

Nernst and Lindemann
1. Z. Elektrochem. **17**, 817 (1911)

Newman and Mangham
1. J. Am. Chem. Soc. **71**, 3342 (1949)

Neyman-Pilat and Pilat
1. Ind. Eng. Chem. **33**, 1382 (1941)

Nickels and Heintzelman
1. Unpublished. Mellon Institute of Industrial Research, Koppers Fellowship, Pittsburgh, Pennsylvania, 1950
2. J. Org. Chem. **15**, 1142 (1950)

Nicolini and Laffitte
1. Compt. rend. **229**, 757 (1949)
2. Compt. rend. **229**, 935 (1949)

Niemann and Wagner
1. J. Org. Chem. **7**, 227 (1942)

Niemczycki
1. Anz. Akad. Wiss. Krakau 473 (1899)

Nightingale and Carton
1. J. Am. Chem. Soc. **62**, 280 (1940)

Nissan and Clark
1. Nature **143**, 722 (1939)

Noerdlinger
1. Chem. Fabrik Flörsheim, Chem. Zentr. **83**, 210 (1912)

GENERAL LIST OF REFERENCES

N (Page 2)

As of December 31, 1952

Noller
1. J. Am. Chem. Soc. 51, 594 (1929)
2. J. Am. Chem. Soc. 56, 1582 (1934)

Noller and Gordon
1. J. Am. Chem. Soc. 55, 1091 (1933)

Nord
1. Ber. 52, 1207 (1919)

Norris and Reuter
1. J. Am. Chem. Soc. 49, 2624 (1927)

Norris and Rubinstein
1. J. Am. Chem. Soc. 61, 1163 (1939)

GENERAL LIST OF REFERENCES

O

As of December 31, 1952

Obermeyer
    1. Ber. 20, 2918 (1887)

Oberreit
    1. Ber. 29, 1998 (1896)

Obolentsev
    1. J. Applied Chem. (U.S.S.R.) 23, 1223 (1950)

O'Connor and Sowa
    1. J. Am. Chem. Soc. 60, 125 (1938)

Oddo and Barabini
    1. Gazz. chim. ital. 20, 719 (1890)

Olds, Sage, and Lacey
    1. Ind. Eng. Chem. 38, 301 (1946)

Olivier and Witt
    1. Rec. trav. chim. 57, 90 (1938)

Olszewski
    1. Bull. intern. acad. sci. Cracovie 27 (1889)
    2. Phil. Mag. 39, 203 (1895)
    3. Compt. rend. 100, 940 (1885)
    4. Compt. rend. 99, 133 (1884)

Opolski
    1. Anz. Akad. Wiss. Krakow 727 (1904)

Orchin and Reggel
    1. J. Am. Chem. Soc. 69, 505 (1947)

Orchin, Reggel, and Friedel
    1. J. Am. Chem. Soc. 73, 1454 (1951)

Orlov
    1. Ber. 60, 1950 (1927)

Osborne and others
    1. Unpublished. National Bureau of Standards,
       Washington, D. C.

Osborne, Garner, and Yost
    1. J. Am. Chem. Soc. 63, 3492 (1941)

Osborne and Ginnings
    1. Unpublished. National Bureau of Standards,
       Washington, D. C.
    2. J. Research Natl. Bur. Standards 39, 453 (1947)

Osborne, Doescher, and Yost
    1. J. Am. Chem. Soc. 64, 169 (1942)

Osborne, Stimson, and Ginnings
    1. J. Research Natl. Bur. Standards 23, 197 (1939)

Othmer, Savitt, Krasner, Goldberg, and Markowitz
    1. Ind. Eng. Chem. 41, 572 (1949)

Ott, Marple, and Hearne
    1. Ind. Eng. Chem. 33, 115 (1941)

Otto
    1. Ber. 13, 1272 (1880)

Otto and Lüders
    1. Ber. 13, 1283 (1880)

Otto and Rössing
    1. Ber. 19, 3132 (1886)

Otto and Wenzke
    1. J. Am. Chem. Soc. 57, 294 (1935)

Overberger and Cope
    1. J. Am. Chem. Soc. 69, 976 (1947)

Ozatyan
    1. Doklady Akad. Nauk, S.S.S.R. 59, 901 (1948)

GENERAL LIST OF REFERENCES
P (Page 1)
As of December 31, 1952

Paal
1. Ber. **18**, 2251 (1885)

Paal and Püschel
1. Ber. **20**, 2557 (1887)

Palfray, Sabetay, and Sontag
1. Compt. rend. **194**, 102 (1932)

Pannicker, Rao, and Simonsen
1. J. Indian Inst. Sci. **A9**, 133 (1926)

Paquette, Lingafelter, and Tartar
1. J. Am. Chem. Soc. **65**, 687 (1943)

Pariselle and Simon
1. Compt. rend. **173**, 86 (1921)

Parks and Huffman
1. J. Am. Chem. Soc. **52**, 4381 (1930)
2. Ind. Eng. Chem. **23**, 1138 (1931)

Parks, Huffman, and Thomas
1. J. Am. Chem. Soc. **52**, 1032 (1930)

Parks and Light
1. J. Am. Chem. Soc. **56**, 1511 (1934)

Parks, Moore, Renquist, Naylor, McClaine, Fujii, and Halton
1. J. Am. Chem. Soc. **71**, 3386 (1949)

Parks, Shomate, Kennedy, and Crawford
1. J. Chem. Phys. **5**, 359 (1937)

Parks, Todd, and Moore
1. J. Am. Chem. Soc. **58**, 398 (1936)

Parks, Todd, and Shomate
1. J. Am. Chem. Soc. **58**, 2505 (1936)

Parks, West, and Moore
1. J. Am. Chem. Soc. **63**, 1133 (1941)

Parks, West, Naylor, Fujii, and McClaine
1. J. Am. Chem. Soc. **68**, 2524 (1946)

Parr
1. Ind. Eng. Chem. **4**, 746 (1912)

Patel, Sen-Gupta, and Chakravarti
1. J. Indian Inst. Sci. **13A**, 73 (1930)

Patnode and Scheiber
1. J. Am. Chem. Soc. **61**, 3449 (1939)

Patterson
1. J. Chem. Soc. **81**, 1097 (1902)

Paul and Normann
1. Compt. rend. **216**, 689 (1943)
2. Bull. soc. chim. **11**, 365 (1944)

Paul and Tchelitcheff
1. Compt. rend. **223**, 1136 (1946)

Pauling, Springall, and Palmer
1. J. Am. Chem. Soc. **61**, 927 (1939)

Pawlewski
1. Ber. **16**, 2633 (1883)

Pazschke
1. J. prakt. Chem. **2**, 418 (1870)

Peel and Robinson
1. J. Chem. Soc. 2068 (1928)

Peffer and Mulligan
1. National Bureau of Standards Circular C434, "Testing of glass volumetric apparatus"

van Pelt and Wibaut
1. Rec. trav. chim. **60**, 55 (1941)

Perkin
1. J. Chem. Soc. **77**, 267 (1900)
2. J. Chem. Soc. **69**, 1025 (1896)

Pesca
1. Gazz. chim. ital. **65**, 440 (1935)

Peter
1. Ber. **17**, 1341 (1884)

Peters and Lohmar
1. Beiheft Z. Ver. deut. Chem. No. 2, Angew. Chem. **50**, 40 (1937)

Petrov
1. Bull. acad. sci. U.R.S.S. Classe sci. chim. 533 (1941)

Petrov and Andreev
1. J. Gen. Chem. (U.S.S.R.) **12**, 95 (1942)

Petrov and Kaplan
1. J. Gen. Chem. (U.S.S.R.) **12**, 99 (1942)

Petrov, Koptev, and Kaplan
1. Bull. acad. sci. U.R.S.S., Classe sci. chim. 152 (1944)

Petrov and Lapteva
1. J. Gen. Chem. (U.S.S.R.) **8**, 207 (1938)

Petrov, Lapteva, and Pchelinka
1. J. Gen. Chem. (U.S.S.R.) **14**, 495 (1944)

Petrov and Ol'dekop
1. J. Gen. Chem. (U.S.S.R.) **18**, 859 (1948)

Petrov and Vittekh
1. Bull. acad. sci. U.R.S.S., Classe sci. chim. 238 (1944)

Phibbs
1. J. Chem. Phys. **19**, 1420 (1951)
2. Unpublished. E. I. duPont de Nemours and Company

Philipov
1. J. Russ. Phys. Chem. Soc. **46**, 1141 (1914)

GENERAL LIST OF REFERENCES
P (Page 2)
As of December 31, 1952

Phillips
1. Org. Synthesis 12, 72 (1932)

Piccard and Brewster
1. J. Am. Chem. Soc. 43, 2628 (1921)

Pickering
1. J. Phys. Chem. 28, 97 (1924)

Picon
1. Compt. rend. 158, 1184 (1914)
2. Compt. rend. 158, 1346 (1914)
3. Compt. rend. 169, 32 (1919)

Pictet and Bouvier
1. Ber. 48, 926 (1915)

Pictet and Potok
1. Helv. Chim. Acta 2, 508 (1919)

Pines and Ipatieff
1. J. Am. Chem. Soc. 61, 1076 (1939)

Pines, Kvetinskas, and Vesely
1. J. Am. Chem. Soc. 72, 1568 (1950)

Pines, Weizmann, and Ipatieff
1. J. Am. Chem. Soc. 70, 3859 (1948)

Pinette
1. Ann. 243, 32 (1888)

Piper, Chibnall, Hopkins, Pollard, Smith, and Williams
1. Biochem. J. 25, 2072 (1931)

Pisati and Patterno
1. Gazz. chim. ital. 3, 551 (1873)

Pitzer
1. J. Chem. Phys. 6, 68 (1938)
2. J. Chem. Phys. 8, 711 (1940)
3. Chem. Rev. 27, 39 (1940)
4. J. Am. Chem. Soc. 62, 1224 (1940)
5. J. Am. Chem. Soc. 63, 2413 (1941)
6. J. Chem. Phys. 12, 310 (1944)
7. Ind. Eng. Chem. 36, 829 (1944)
8. J. Chem. Phys. 14, 239 (1946)

Pitzer and Beckett
1. J. Am. Chem. Soc. 69, 977 (1947)

Pitzer, Guttman, and Westrum
1. J. Am. Chem. Soc. 68, 2209 (1946)

Pitzer and Gwinn
1. J. Chem. Phys. 10, 428 (1942)

Pitzer and Kilpatrick
1. Chem. Rev. 39, 435 (1946)

Pitzer and Scott
1. J. Am. Chem. Soc. 63, 2419 (1941)
2. J. Am. Chem. Soc. 65, 803 (1943)

Platé
1. Compt. rend. acad. sci. U.R.S.S. 24, 257 (1939)

Platé and Batuev
1. Doklady Akad. Nauk. S.S.S.R. 59, 1305 (1948)

Platé and Meyervitch
1. Bull. acad. sci. U.R.S.S., Classe sci. chim. 219 (1947)

Platé and Zabezhenskaya
1. Bull. acad. sci. U.R.S.S., Classe sci. chim. 651 (1946)

Pokravskaya
1. J. Gen. Chem. (U.S.S.R.) 13, 579 (1943)

Pollak and Schadler
1. Monatsch. 39, 179 (1918)

Pomerantz
1. J. Research Natl. Bur. Standards 48, 76 (1952)

Pomerantz, Mears, and Howard
1. J. Research Natl. Bur. Standards 42, 617 (1949)

Powell and Giauque
1. J. Am. Chem. Soc. 61, 2366 (1939)

Predvotitelev
1. Z. Physik 36, 557 (1926)

Prevost
1. Ann. chim. 10, 113 (1928)
2. Bull. soc. chim. 8, 89 (1941)
3. Compt. rend. 186, 1209 (1928)
4. Compt. rend. 187, 946 (1928)
5. Bull. soc. chim. 11, 218 (1944)

Prevost and Daujat
1. Bull. soc. chim. 47, 588 (1930)

Pribam and Handl
1. Anz. Akad. Wiss. Wien, Abt. IIB, 80, 17 (1879)

Price and Ciskowski
1. J. Am. Chem. Soc. 60, 2499 (1938)

Price and Smiles
1. J. Chem. Soc. 2372 (1928)

Price and Zomlefer
1. J. Am. Chem. Soc. 72, 14 (1950)

Prins
1. Proc. Acad. Sci. Amsterdam 17, 1095 (1915)

Prokopetz
1. J. Applied Chem. (U.S.S.R.) 8, 1214 (1935)

Prosen, Gilmont, and Rossini
1. J. Research Natl. Bur. Standards 34, 65 (1945)

Prosen, Jessup, and Rossini
1. J. Research Natl. Bur. Standards 33, 447 (1944)

GENERAL LIST OF REFERENCES
P (Page 3)
As of December 31, 1952

Prosen, Johnson, and Rossini
1. J. Research Natl. Bur. Standards **36**, 455 (1946)
2. J. Research Natl. Bur. Standards **37**, 51 (1946)
3. J. Research Natl. Bur. Standards **39**, 173 (1947)
4. J. Am. Chem. Soc. **69**, 2068 (1947)
5. J. Am. Chem. Soc. **72**, 626 (1950)

Prosen, Maron, and Rossini
1. J. Research Natl. Bur. Standards **42**, 269 (1949)
2. J. Research Natl. Bur. Standards **45**, 106 (1951)

Prosen, Pitzer, and Rossini
1. J. Research Natl. Bur. Standards **34**, 255 (1945)
2. J. Research Natl. Bur. Standards **34**, 403 (1945)

Prosen and Rossini
1. J. Am. Chem. Soc. **62**, 2250 (1940)
2. J. Research Natl. Bur. Standards **27**, 289 (1941)
3. J. Research Natl. Bur. Standards **27**, 519 (1941)
4. J. Research Natl. Bur. Standards **33**, 255 (1944)
5. J. Research Natl. Bur. Standards **33**, 439 (1944)
6. J. Research Natl. Bur. Standards **34**, 59 (1945)
7. J. Research Natl. Bur. Standards **34**, 163 (1945)
8. J. Research Natl. Bur. Standards **34**, 263 (1945)
9. J. Research Natl. Bur. Standards **36**, 269 (1946)

Puchkov and Nikolaeva
1. J. Gen. Chem. (U.S.S.R.) **8**, 1939 (1938)

Pummerer
1. Ber. **43**, 1401 (1910)

Pummerer and Kranz
1. Ber. **62**, 2620 (1929)

Purgotti
1. Gazz. chim. ital. **20**, 24 (1890)

Pushin and Pintner
1. Z. physik. Chem. **A142**, 211 (1929)

GENERAL LIST OF REFERENCES
Q
As of December 31, 1952

Quayle and Others
    1. Unpublished. Emory University, Atlanta, Georgia

Quayle, Day, and Brown
    1. J. Am. Chem. Soc. **66**, 938 (1944)

GENERAL LIST OF REFERENCES
R (Page 1)
As of December 31, 1952

Radcliffe and Simpkin
    1. J. Soc. Chem. Ind. **40**, 119T, (1921)

Radloff
    1. Ber. **11**, 32 (1878)

Ralston, Hoerr, and Crews
    1. J. Org. Chem. **9**, 319 (1944)

Ramsay and Aston
    1. Z. physik. Chem. **15**, 89 (1894)

Ramsay and Shields
    1. Phil. Trans. **184**, 647 (1893)

Randall and Rossini
    1. J. Am. Chem. Soc. **51**, 323 (1929)

Rands, Scott, and Brickwedde
    1. Unpublished. National Bureau of Standards,
       Washington, D. C.

Rechenberg
    1. Z. physik. Chem. **99**, 87 (1921)

Reid
    1. Thesis, Ohio State University, Columbus, Ohio (1938)

Reid and Jelinek
    1. J. Org. Chem. **15**, 448 (1950)

Reihlen, von Friedolsheim, and Oswald
    1. Ann. **465**, 72 (1928)

Renard
    1. Ann. chim. **1**, 223 (1884)

Renard and Guye
    1. J. chim. phys. **5**, 81 (1907)

Reno and Katz
    1. Ind. Eng. Chem. **35**, 1091 (1943)

de Resséquier
    1. Bull. soc. chim. **15**, 183 (1914)

Reymann
    1. Ber. **7**, 1287 (1874)

Reynolds, Ebersole, Lamberti, Chanan, and Ordin
    1. Ind. Eng. Chem. **40**, 1751 (1948)

Rheinboldt, Mott, and Motzkus
    1. J. prakt. Chem. **134**, 257 (1932)

Rice and Murphy
    1. J. Am. Chem. Soc. **66**, 765 (1944)

Richards and Barry
    1. J. Am. Chem. Soc. **37**, 993 (1915)

Richards and Carver
    1. J. Am. Chem. Soc. **43**, 827 (1921)

Richards and Coombs
    1. J. Am. Chem. Soc. **37**, 1656 (1915)

Richards and Matthews
    1. J. Am. Chem. Soc. **30**, 8 (1908)

Richards and Davis
    1. J. Am. Chem. Soc. **39**, 341 (1917)
    2. J. Am. Chem. Soc. **42**, 1599 (1920)

Richards, Henderson, and Frevert
    1. Proc. Am. Acad. **42**, 573 (1907)
    2. Z. physik. Chem. **59**, 532 (1907)

Richards and Jesse
    1. J. Am. Chem. Soc. **32**, 268 (1910)

Richards and Shipley
    1. J. Am. Chem. Soc. **38**, 996 (1916)
    2. J. Am. Chem. Soc. **41**, 2002 (1919)

Richards, Speyers, and Carver
    1. J. Am. Chem. Soc. **46**, 1196 (1924)

Richardson and Parks
    1. J. Am. Chem. Soc. **61**, 3543 (1939)

Richter and Wolff
    1. Ber. **63**, 1714 (1930)
    2. Ber. **63**, 1721 (1930)

Riding and Thomas
    1. J. Chem. Soc. **123**, 3271 (1923)

Riechemeier, Seuftleben, and Pastorff
    1. Ann. Physik **19**, 202 (1934)

Riobé
    1. Compt. rend. **226**, 1625 (1948)
    2. Ann. chim. **4**, 593 (1949)

van Risseghem
    1. Compt. rend. **158**, 1696 (1914)
    2. Bull. soc. chim. Belg. **30**, 8 (1921)
    3. Bull. soc. chim. Belg. **31**, 65 (1922)
    4. Bull. soc. chim. Belg. **31**, 213 (1922)
    5. Bull. soc. chim. Belg. **32**, 144 (1923)
    6. Bull. soc. chim. Belg. **35**, 328 (1926)
    7. Bull. soc. chim. Belg. **42**, 219 (1933)
    8. Bull. soc. chim. Belg. **42**, 229 (1933)
    9. Bull. soc. chim. Belg. **44**, 593 (1935)
   10. Bull. soc. chim. Belg. **47**, 47 (1938)
   11. Bull. soc. chim. Belg. **47**, 221 (1938)
   12. Bull. soc. chim. Belg. **47**, 261 (1938)

van Risseghem, Gredy, and Piaux
    1. Compt. rend. **196**, 938 (1933)

Ritter and Sharpe
    1. J. Am. Chem. Soc. **59**, 2351 (1937)

GENERAL LIST OF REFERENCES
R (Page 2)
As of December 31, 1952

Robertson, Fox, and Martin
1. Proc. Roy. Soc. (London) 157, 579 (1936)

Robinson
1. J. Chem. Soc. 125, 226 (1924)

Robinson and Thompson
1. J. Chem. Soc. 2015 (1932)

Robles
1. Rec. trav. chim. 58, 111 (1939)

Roblin, Davidson, and Bogert
1. J. Am. Chem. Soc. 57, 151 (1935)

Rodebush
1. Phys. Rev. 40, 113 (1932)

van Romburgh, van Veen, and Haagen-Smit
1. Koninkl. Akad. Wetenschap. Amsterdam 33, 690 (1930)

Rosa and Babcock
1. Bull. Bur. Standards 4, 121 (1907-8) S73

Rose
1. J. Research Natl. Bur. Standards 19, 143 (1937)
2. J. Research Natl. Bur. Standards 20, 129 (1938)

Rose and White
1. J. Research Natl. Bur. Standards 15, 151 (1935)
2. J. Research Natl. Bur. Standards 21, 167 (1938)

Rose-Innes and Young
1. Phil. Mag. 47, 353 (1899)

Rosenmund and Harms
1. Ber. 53, 2226 (1920)

Ross and Leather
1. Analyst 31, 284 (1906)

Rossini
1. Bur. Standards J. Research 4, 313 (1930)
2. Proc. Natl. Acad. Sci. 16, 694 (1930)
3. Bur. Standards J. Research 6, 1 (1931)
4. Bur. Standards J. Research 6, 37 (1931)
5. Bur. Standards J. Research 6, 791 (1931)
6. Bur. Standards J. Research 6, 847 (1931)
7. Bur. Standards J. Research 7, 47 (1931)
8. Bur. Standards J. Research 7, 329 (1931)
9. Proc. Natl. Acad. Sci. 17, 343 (1931)
10. Bur. Standards J. Research 8, 119 (1932)
11. Bur. Standards J. Research 9, 679 (1932)
12. Bur. Standards J. Research 11, 553 (1933)
13. Bur. Standards J. Research 12, 735 (1934)
14. Proc. Natl. Acad. Sci. 20, 323 (1934)
15. J. Research Natl. Bur. Standards 13, 21 (1934)
16. J. Research Natl. Bur. Standards 13, 189 (1934)
17. J. Chem. Phys. 3, 438 (1935)
18. J. Research Natl. Bur. Standards 15, 357 (1935)
19. J. Research Natl. Bur. Standards 17, 629 (1936)
20. J. Research Natl. Bur. Standards 22, 407 (1939)
21. Chem. Rev. 27, 1 (1940)
22. "Chemical Thermodynamics," John Wiley and Sons, Inc., New York, 1950
23. Proc. Am. Petroleum Inst. 16M III, 47 (1935)
24. Proc. Am. Petroleum Inst. 16M III, 63 (1935)
25. Proc. Am. Petroleum Inst. 17 III, 59 (1936)
26. Proc. Am. Petroleum Inst. 18 III, 36 (1937)
27. Proc. Am. Petroleum Inst. 19 III, 99 (1938)
28. Record Chem. Progress 3, 53 (1942)
29. Petroleum Engr. 14, 223 (1943)
30. Chem. Eng. News 25, 230 (1947)
31. Anal. Chem. 20, 110 (1948)
32. J. Wash. Acad. Sci. 39, 249 (1949)
33. "Recent Advances in Analytical Chemistry," A chapter p157, Interscience Publishers, Inc., New York, 1949
34. "Chemical Thermodynamics; Fractionating Processes; Hydrocarbons in Petroleum." Reilly Lecture Series, University of Notre Dame, Notre Dame, Indiana, 1950
35. "Science of Petroleum." A chapter in Vol. V, Part I, Oxford University Press, New York, 1950
36. Proceedings of the Third World Petroleum Congress, section VI; p1, E.J. Brill Company, Leiden, Netherlands, 1951
37. Proceedings of the Third World Petroleum Congress, section VI; p157, E.J. Brill Company, Leiden, Netherlands 1951
38. Applied Spectroscopy 6, 3 (1951)
39. J. Chem. Phys. 2, 145 (1934)
40. J. Wash. Acad. Sci. 25, 399 (1935)
41. Chem. Rev. 18, 233 (1936)
42. Ind. Eng. Chem. 29, 1424 (1937)
43. "Thermodynamics, thermochemistry and chemical equilibrium," Chemical Engineers Handbook, Second Edition, section 5, 1941
44. "Chemical Background for Engine Research." A chapter "Chemical Thermodynamics of Hydrocarbons," Interscience Publishers, New York, 1942
45. Trans. Am. Soc. Mech. Engrs. 70, 625 (1948)
46. "Physical Chemistry of Hydrocarbons," A chapter. Vol I, chapter 9, Academic Press, New York, 1949
47. "Annual Survey of American Chemistry." A chapter. Vol 5, Chapter IV, Chemical Catalog Company, New York 1931
48. "Annual Survey of American Chemistry." A chapter, Vol 6, chapter IV, Chemical Catalog Company, New York 1932
49. "Annual Survey of American Chemistry." A chapter, Vol Vol 7, chapter IV, Chemical Catalog Company, New York, 1933

GENERAL LIST OF REFERENCES
R (Page 3)
As of December 31, 1952

Rossini and Deming
1. J. Wash. Acad. Sci. 29, 416 (1939)

Rossini and Frandsen
1. J. Research Natl. Bur. Standards 9, 733 (1932)

Rossini and Glasgow
1. J. Research Natl. Bur. Standards 23, 509 (1939)

Rossini, Gucker, Johnston, Pauling, and Vinal
1. J. Am. Chem. Soc. 74, 2699 (1952)

Rossini and Jessup
1. J. Research Natl. Bur. Standards 21, 491 (1938)

Rossini and Knowlton
1. J. Research Natl. Bur. Standards 19, 249 (1937)
2. J. Research Natl. Bur. Standards 19, 339 (1937)
3. J. Chem. Phys. 6, 569 (1938)
4. J. Chem. Phys. 6, 168 (1938)

Rossini, Knowlton, and Johnston
1. J. Research Natl. Bur. Standards 24, 369 (1940)

Rossini and Mair
1. Proc. Am. Petroleum Inst. 22 III, 7 (1941)
2. "Advances in Chemistry Series." A chapter, Vol 5, p334,
American Chemical Society, Washington, D. C. 1951

Rossini, Mair, Forziati, Glasgow, and Willingham
1. Proc. Am. Petroleum Inst. 23 III, 7 (1942)

Rossini, Mair, and Glasgow
1. Proc. Am. Petroleum Inst. 21 III, 43 (1940)

Rossini, Mair, and Glasgow
1. Record Chem. Progress 10, 121 (1949)

Rossini and Pitzer
1. Science 105, 647 (1947)

Rossini, Pitzer, Taylor, Ebert, Kilpatrick, Beckett, Williams,
and Werner
1. "Selected Values of Properties of Hydrocarbons."
National Bureau Standards Circular 461. U.S. Government
Printing Office, Washington, D. C., 1947

Rossini and Prosen
1. J. Am. Chem. Soc. 62, 2250 (1940)

Rossini, Prosen, and Pitzer
1. J. Research Natl. Bur. Standards 27, 529 (1941)

Rossini, Wagman, Evans, Levine, and Jaffe
1. "Selected Values of Chemical Thermodynamic Properties."
National Bureau Standards Circular 500, U.S. Government
Printing Office, Washington, D. C.

Rossini, Wagman, Evans, and Prosen
1. "Annual Review of Physical Chemistry." A chapter. Vol I,
p1, Annual Review, Inc., Stanford, California, 1950

Roth and von Auwers
1. Ann. 407, 145 (1915)

Roth and Macheleidt
1. Unpublished dissertation, Braunschweig, 1921, Landolt-
Bornstein, Physikalisch-chemische Tabellen, 5th ed.,
Vol. II, p1588, Berlin, Julius Springer (1923)

Roth and Pahlke
1. Z. angew. Chem. 49, 618 (1936)

Rothen and Levene
1. J. Chem. Phys. 7, 975 (1939)

Rothstein
1. J. Chem. Soc. 1550 (1940)

Rotinyantz and Nagornov
1. Z. physik. Chem. A169, 20 (1934)

Roux
1. Ann. chim. phys. 12, 289 (1887)

Roy
1. Proc. Natl. Inst. Sci. India 12, 137 (1946)

Rudel
1. Thesis. Ohio State University, Columbus, Ohio (1938)

Rudenko
1. J. Exptl. Theoret. Phys. (U.S.S.R.) 9, 1078 (1939)

Rudenko and Shubnikov
1. Physik. Z. Sowjetunion 8, 179 (1935)

Ruehrwein and Huffman
1. J. Am. Chem. Soc. 65, 1620 (1943)

Ruhemann
1. Ber. 46, 3384 (1913)

Ruigh and Erickson
1. J. Am. Chem. Soc. 61, 915 (1939)

Russel, Osborne and Yost
1. J. Am. Chem. Soc. 64, 166 (1942)

Ruston and Rudorf
1. Bull. soc. chim. Belg. 56, 97 (1947)

Ruzicka, Brüngger, Egli, Ehmann, Furter, and Hösli
1. Helv. Chim. Acta 15, 1496 (1932)

Ruzicka and Capato
1. Ann. 453, 62 (1927)

Ruzicka and Ehmann
1. Helv. Chim. Acta 15, 140 (1932)

Ruzicka, Ehmann, and Morgeli
1. Helv. Chim. Acta 16, 314 (1933)

Ruzicka, Furter, and Leuenberger
1. Helv. Chim. Acta 20, 791 (1937)

GENERAL LIST OF REFERENCES
R (Page 4)
As of December 31, 1952

Ruzicka, Hösli, and Ehmann
1. Helv. Chim. Acta **17**, 442 (1934)

Ruzicka, Hofmann, and Frei
1. Helv. Chim. Acta **19**, 386 (1936)

Ruzicka, Koolhaas, and Wind
1. Helv. Chim. Acta **14**, 1151 (1931)
2. Helv. Chim. Acta **14**, 1171 (1931)

Ruzicka, Plattner, and Wild
1. Helv. Chim. Acta **29**, 1611 (1946)

Ryden, Glavis, and Marvel
1. J. Am. Chem. Soc. **59**, 1014 (1937)

Rytina, Schiessler, and Whitmore
1. J. Am. Chem. Soc. **71**, 751 (1949)

GENERAL LIST OF REFERENCES
S (Page 1)

As of December 31, 1952

Sabatier and Mailhe
1. Compt. rend. **158**, 830 (1914)
2. Compt. rend. **141**, 20 (1905)
3. Compt. rend. **137**, 240 (1903)
4. Compt. rend. **142**, 438 (1906)
5. Compt. rend. **150**, 1217 (1910)
6. Compt. rend. **140**, 350 (1905)

Sabatier and Senderens
1. Ann. chim. phys. **4**, 358 (1905)
2. Compt. rend. **132**, 1254 (1901)
3. Compt. rend. **132**, 566 (1901)

Sabétay
1. Bull. soc. chim. **45**, 69 (1929)
2. Compt. rend. **192**, 1109 (1931)

Sage, Evans, and Lacey
1. Ind. Eng. Chem. **31**, 763 (1939)

Sage and Lacey
1. Ind. Eng. Chem. **34**, 730 (1942)
2. Ind. Eng. Chem. **30**, 829 (1938)

Sage, Schaafsma, and Lacey
1. Ind. Eng. Chem. **26**, 1218 (1934)

Sage, Yale, and Lacey
1. Ind. Eng. Chem. **31**, 223 (1939)

Sah and Brüll
1. Ber. **73**, 1430 (1940)

Sâlceanu
1. Compt. rend. **208**, 1797 (1939)

Sâlceanu and McCormick
1. Compt. rend. **208**, 1278 (1939)

Sarrau
1. Compt. rend. **94**, 718 (1882)
2. Compt. rend. **94**, 845 (1882)

Satterly and Collingwood
1. Trans. Roy. Soc. Can. **25 III**, 205 (1931)

Saytzeff
1. Ann. **139**, 354 (1866)

Scatchard, Wood, and Mochel
1. J. Am. Chem. Soc. **61**, 3206 (1939)

Schaaf
1. Z. physik. Chem. **126**, 237 (1923)

Schaeffer and Stirton
1. J. Am. Chem. Soc. **69**, 2071 (1947)

Scheeline and Gilleland
1. Ind. Eng. Chem. **31**, 1050 (1939)

Scheibler and Rettig
1. Ber. **59**, 1194 (1926)

Scheibler and Schmidt
1. Ber. **54**, 139 (1921)

Schenck and Kintzinger
1. Rec. trav. chim. **42**, 759 (1923)

Schicktanz
1. J. Research Natl. Bur. Standards **11**, 89 (1933)
2. J. Research Natl. Bur. Standards **12**, 259 (1934)
3. J. Research Natl. Bur. Standards **14**, 685 (1935)
4. J. Research Natl. Bur. Standards **18**, 129 (1937)
5. J. Research Natl. Bur. Standards **20**, 83 (1938)

Schiessler, Cosby, Clark, Rowland, Sloatman, and Herr
1. Petroleum Refiner **21**, 383 (1942)

Schiessler, Herr, Rytina, Weisel, Fischl, McLaughlin, and Kuehner
1. Proc. Am. Petroleum Inst. **26 III**, 254 (1946)

Schiff
1. Ann. **220**, 71 (1883)
2. Ann. **223**, 47 (1884)
3. Ber. **18**, 1601 (1885)

Schläpfer and Debrunner
1. Helv. Chim. Acta **7**, 31 (1924)

Schleicher
1. Ber. **19**, 672 (1886)

Schlesman
1. Unpublished. Socony-Vacuum Laboratories, Paulsboro, New Jersey

Schluback and Goes
1. Ber. **55**, 2889 (1922)

Schmerling
1. J. Am. Chem. Soc. **67**, 1438 (1945)

Schmerling, Friedman, and Ipatieff
1. J. Am. Chem. Soc. **62**, 2446 (1940)

Schmid and Margulies
1. Sitzber. Akad. Wiss. Wien, Math. naturw. Klasse Abt. **IIB**, **144**, 81 (1935)

Schmidlin
1. Ann. chim. phys. **7**, 245 (1906)

Schmidt
1. Ber. **75**, 1399 (1942)

Schmidt and Gemassmer
1. Ber. **73**, 359 (1940)

Schmidt and Grosser
1. Ber. **73**, 930 (1940)
2. Ber. **75**, 833 (1942)

Schmidt, Hopp, and Schoeller
1. Ber. 72, 1893 (1939)

Schmidt and Schoeller
1. Ber. 74, 258 (1941)

Schmidt, Schoeller, and Eberlein
1. Ber. 74, 1313 (1941)

Schmitt
1. Compt. rend. 199, 1299 (1934)

Schmitt and Boord
1. J. Am. Chem. Soc. 53, 2427 (1931)
2. J. Am. Chem. Soc. 54, 751 (1932)

Schniepp and Geller
1. J. Am. Chem. Soc. 67, 54 (1945)

Schoorl
1. Rec. trav. chim. 57, 719 (1938)

Schorger
1. J. Am. Chem. Soc. 39, 2671 (1917)

Schrader and Dreisbach
1. Unpublished. Dow Chemical Company, Midland, Michigan, 1950

Schramm
1. Ber. 24, 1332 (1891)

Schroeter
1. Ann. 426, 1 (1922)

Schroeter, Lichtenstadt, and Irineu
1. Ber. 51, 1587 (1918)

Schuit, Hoog, and Verheus
1. Rec. trav. chim. 59, 793 (1940)

Schultze
1. Ber. 17, 843 (1884)

Schulze, Short, and Crouch
1. Ind. Eng. Chem. 42, 916 (1950)

Schumann, Aston, and Sagenkahn
1. J. Am. Chem. Soc. 64, 1039 (1942)

Schurman and Boord
1. J. Am. Chem. Soc. 55, 4932 (1933)

Schwab and Wichers
1. J. Research Natl. Bur. Standards 25, 747 (1940)

Schwarzenbach and Epprecht
1. Helv. Chim. Acta 19, 169 (1936)

von Schweinitz
1. Ber. 19, 644 (1886)

Scott
1. Unpublished. National Bureau of Standards, Washington, D. C.

Scott and Brickwedde
1. J. Research Natl. Bur. Standards 35, 501 (1945)

Scott, Douslin, Gross, Oliver, and Huffman
1. J. Am. Chem. Soc. 74, 883 (1952)

Scott, Ferguson, and Brickwedde
1. J. Research Natl. Bur. Standards 33, 1 (1944)

Scott, Finke, Gross, Guthrie, and Huffman
1. J. Am. Chem. Soc. 72, 2424 (1950)

Scott, Finke, McCullough, Gross, Williamson, Waddington, and Huffman
1. J. Am. Chem. Soc. 73, 261 (1951)

Scott, McCullough, Williamson, and Waddington
1. J. Am. Chem. Soc. 73, 1707 (1951)

Scott and Mellors
1. J. Research Natl. Bur. Standards 34, 243 (1945)

Scott, Meyers, Rand, Brickwedde, and Bekkedahl
1. J. Research Natl. Bur. Standards 35, 39 (1945)

Scott, Waddington, Smith, and Huffman
1. J. Am. Chem. Soc. 71, 2769 (1949)

Seibert and Burrell
1. J. Am. Chem. Soc. 37, 2683 (1915)

Seidell, Müller, and Schinz
1. Helv. Chim. Acta 27, 738 (1944)

Seifert
1. Monatsh. 79, 198 (1948)

Selker and Kemp
1. Ind. Eng. Chem. 36, 16 (1944)

Semmler
1. Ber. 26, 774 (1893)
2. Ann. 241, 90 (1887)

Semmler and Feldstein
1. Ber. 47, 2687 (1914)

Sen
1. J. Indian Chem. Soc. 12, 647 (1936)

Sengupta
1. J. prakt. Chem. 151, 82 (1938)

Serijan, Hipsher, and Gibbons
1. J. Am. Chem. Soc. 71, 873 (1949)

Serijan and Wise
1. J. Am. Chem. Soc. 73, 5191 (1951)

Serijan, Wise, and Gibbons
1. J. Am. Chem. Soc. 71, 2265 (1949)

Seyer
1. J. Am. Chem. Soc. 53, 3588 (1931)
2. J. Am. Chem. Soc. 60, 827 (1938)

GENERAL LIST OF REFERENCES
S (Page 3)
As of December 31, 1952

Seyer and Barrow
1. J. Am. Chem. Soc. 70, 802 (1948)

Seyer, Bennett, and Williams
1. J. Am. Chem. Soc. 71, 3447 (1949)

Seyer and Davenport
1. J. Am. Chem. Soc. 63, 2425 (1941)

Seyer and Fordyce
1. J. Am. Chem. Soc. 58, 2029 (1950)

Seyer and Huggert
1. Trans. Roy. Soc. Canada 18, 213 (1924)

Seyer and Leslie
1. J. Am. Chem. Soc. 64, 1912 (1942)

Seyer and Mann
1. J. Am. Chem. Soc. 67, 328 (1945)

Seyer, Patterson, and Keays
1. J. Am. Chem. Soc. 66, 179 (1944)

Seyer and Walker
1. J. Am. Chem. Soc. 60, 2125 (1938)

Shalberov and Ostreumov
1. J. Phys. Chem. (U.S.S.R.) 7, 552 (1936)

Shand and Spurr
1. J. Am. Chem. Soc. 65, 179 (1943)

Shell Development Company
1. Unpublished. Emeryville, California

Shen, Wood, and Garner
1. J. Chem. Soc. 698 (1939)
2. J. Inst. Petroleum 25, 698 (1939)

Shepard
1. J. Am. Chem. Soc. 54, 2951 (1932)

Shepard, Henne, and Midgley
1. J. Am. Chem. Soc. 53, 1948 (1931)
2. J. Am. Chem. Soc. 56, 1355 (1934)

Shepherd and Bailey
1. J. Research Natl. Bur. Standards 26, 347 (1941)

Sheppard
1. Trans. Faraday Soc. 46, 429 (1950)

Sherk, Augur, and Soffer
1. J. Am. Chem. Soc. 67, 2239 (1945)

Sherrill, Baldwin, and Haas
1. J. Am. Chem. Soc. 51, 3034 (1929)

Sherrill and Launspach
1. J. Am. Chem. Soc. 60, 2562 (1938)

Sherrill and Matlock
1. J. Am. Chem. Soc. 59, 2134 (1937)

Sherrill, Mayer, and Walter
1. J. Am. Chem. Soc. 56, 926 (1934)

Sherrill, Otto, and Pickett
1. J. Am. Chem. Soc. 51, 3023 (1929)

Sherrill and Walter
1. J. Am. Chem. Soc. 58, 742 (1936)

Shine and Turner
1. J. Am. Chem. Soc. 71, 2589 (1949)

Shoemaker and Boord
1. J. Am. Chem. Soc. 53, 1505 (1931)

Shoesmith and McGechen
1. J. Chem. Soc. 2231 (1930)

Shortridge, Craig, Greenlee, Derfer, and Boord
1. J. Am. Chem. Soc. 70, 946 (1948)

Shorygin
1. Ber. 58, 2036 (1925)

Shorygin, Issguljanz, and Gussewa
1. Ber. 66, 1426 (1933)

Shorygin and Shorygina
1. J. Gen. Chem. (U.S.S.R.) 5, 551 (1935)

Signaigo and Cramer
1. J. Am. Chem. Soc. 55, 3326 (1933)

Silsbee and Gross
1. J. Research Natl. Bur. Standards 27, 269 (1941)

Silva
1. Bull. soc. chim. 43, 317 (1885)

de Simo, McMillan, and Cheney
1. Unpublished. Shell Development Company, Emeryville, California

Simon
1. Bull. soc. chim. Belg. 38, 47 (1929)

Simons and Archer
1. J. Am. Chem. Soc. 60, 2952 (1938)

Simons, Archer, and Randall
1. J. Am. Chem. Soc. 61, 1821 (1939)

Simons and Hart
1. J. Am. Chem. Soc. 66, 1309 (1944)

Skita
1. Ber. 53, 1792 (1920)

Skita and Ritter
1. Ber. 44, 668 (1911)

Skita and Schneck
1. Ber. 55, 144 (1922)

GENERAL LIST OF REFERENCES
S (Page 4)
As of December 31, 1952

Skraup and Nieten
1. Ber. 57, 1294 (1924)

Slabey
1. Technical Note No. 1023, National Advisory Committee for
Aeronautic, Aircraft Engine Research Laboratory,
Cleveland, Ohio
2. J. Am. Chem. Soc. 69, 475 (1947)
3. J. Am. Chem. Soc. 68, 1335 (1946)

Slabey and Wise
1. J. Am. Chem. Soc. 74, 1473 (1952)
2. J. Am. Chem. Soc. 74, 3887 (1952)

Slomp
1. Thesis. Ohio State University, Columbus, Ohio (1951)

Slotta and Franke
1. Ber. 63, 678 (1930)

Small, Bailey, and Cavallito
1. J. Am. Chem. Soc. 69, 1710 (1947)

de Smet
1. Naturw. Tijdschr. 15, 215 (1933)

Smith, E.A.
1. Unpublished. Catalytic Development Corporation, Marcus
Hook, Pennsylvania

Smith, E.R.
1. J. Research Natl. Bur. Standards 24, 229 (1940)
2. J. Research Natl. Bur. Standards 26, 129 (1941)

Smith, G.W.
1. J. Phys. Chem. 48, 168 (1944)

Smith, J.C.
1. J. Am. Chem. Soc. 737 (1932)

Smith, L.
1. Unpublished. University of Minnesota, Minneapolis,
Minnesota

Smith, R.A.
1. J. Am. Chem. Soc. 59, 899 (1937)

Smith and Brown
1. Ind. Eng. Chem. 35, 705 (1943)

Smith and Cass
1. J. Am. Chem. Soc. 54, 1603 (1932)
2. J. Am. Chem. Soc. 54, 1611 (1932)

Smith and Kiess
1. J. Am. Chem. Soc. 61, 989 (1939)

Smith and Lo
1. J. Am. Chem. Soc. 70, 2209 (1948)

Smith and Lund
1. J. Am. Chem. Soc. 52, 4144 (1930)

Smith and MacDougall
1. J. Am. Chem. Soc. 51, 3001 (1929)

Smith and Pennekamp
1. J. Am. Chem. Soc. 67, 276 (1945)
2. J. Am. Chem. Soc. 67, 279 (1945)

Smith and Spillane
1. J. Am. Chem. Soc. 62, 2639 (1940)

Smittenberg, Hoog, and Henkes
1. J. Am. Chem. Soc. 60, 17 (1938)

Smoker and Burchfield
1. Ind. Eng. Chem. Anal. Ed. 15, 128 (1943)

Smyth and Stoops
1. J. Am. Chem. Soc. 50, 1883 (1928)

Snyder, Stewart, Allen, and Dearborn
1. J. Am. Chem. Soc. 68, 1425 (1946)

Snyder, Stewart, and Ziegler
1. J. Am. Chem. Soc. 69, 2672 (1947)

Soday and Boord
1. J. Am. Chem. Soc. 55, 3293 (1933)

Soffer, Strauss, Trail, and Sherk
1. J. Am. Chem. Soc. 69, 1684 (1949)

Sokolov
1. J. Fuss. Phys. Chem. Soc. 599 (1887)
2. J. prakt. Chem. 39, 444 (1889)

Sokolov and Sorinskiĭ
1. Compt. rend. acad. sci. U.R.S.S. 4, 135 (1935)

Sontag
1. Ann. chim. 1, 359 (1934)

Sörensen and Sörensen
1. Acta Chemica Scandinavica 2, 166 (1948)

Sorm, Sormová, and Šedivý
1. Collection Czechoslav. Chem. Communs. 12, 554 (1947)

Soroos and Willis
1. J. Am. Chem. Soc. 63, 881 (1941)

Souders
1. Unpublished. Shell Development Company, Emeryville,

Späth
1. Sitzber. Akad. Wiss. Wien, Math. naturw. Klasse
Abt. IIB, 122, 1207 (1913)

Speakman
1. J. Chem. Soc. 1449 (1933)

Spengler
1. Unpublished. Institut für Kohleforschung, Prague,
Czechoslovakia

GENERAL LIST OF REFERENCES
S (Page 5)
As of December 31, 1952

Speziale
1. Org. Synthesis **30**, 35 (1950)

Spiegler and Tinker
1. J. Am. Chem. Soc. **61**, 940 (1939)

Spitzer and Huffman
1. J. Am. Chem. Soc. **69**, 211 (1947)

Spitzer and Pitzer
1. J. Am. Chem. Soc. **68**, 2537 (1946)

Spring and Legros
1. Ber. **15**, 1938 (1882)

Srinivasan
1. Phil. Mag. **32**, 253 (1941)

Stadler
1. Ber. **17**, 2075 (1884)

Starobinets and Pamfilov
1. J. Gen. Chem. (U.S.S.R.) **11**, 493 (1941)

Staudinger, Schlenker, and Goldstein
1. Helv. Chim. Acta **4**, 355 (1921)

Staudinger and Siegwart
1. Ber. **49**, 1918 (1911)

Stehman, Cook, Percival, and Whitmore
1. J. Am. Chem. Soc. **72**, 4165 (1950)

Steinkopf
1. Ann. **403**, 1 (1914)
2. Ann. **430**, 78 (1923)

Steinkopf, Barlag, and Petersdorff
1. Ann. **540**, 7 (1939)

Steinkopf and Boëtius
1. Ann. **546**, 208 (1941)

Steinkopf, Frömmel, and Leo
1. Ann. **546**, 199 (1941)

Steinkopf, and Freund
1. Ber. **47**, 417 (1914)

Steinkopf and Hanske
1. Ann. **541**, 238 (1939)

Steinkopf, Leitsmann, and Hofmann
1. Ann. **546**, 180 (1941)

Steinkopf, Merckoll, and Strauch
1. Ann. **545**, 45 (1940)

Steinkopf, Poulsson, and Herdy
1. Ann. **536**, 128 (1938)

Steinkopf and Roch
1. Ann. **482**, 254 (1930)

Steinkopf and Schubart
1. Ann. **424**, 1 (1921)

Steinkopf, Schubart, and Schmidt
1. Ber. **61**, 678 (1928)

Stenhagen and Tägström
1. J. Am. Chem. Soc. **66**, 845 (1944)

Stenhouse
1. Proc. Roy. Soc. (London) **17**, 63 (1864)
2. Proc. Roy. Soc. (London) **14**, 353 (1862)

Stenzil and Fichter
1. Helv. Chim. Acta **17**, 669 (1934)

Stephens and Roduta
1. J. Am. Chem. Soc. **57**, 2380 (1935)

Stevens, D.R.
1. Ind. Eng. Chem. **35**, 655 (1943)

Stevens, P.G.
1. J. Am. Chem. Soc. **67**, 407 (1945)

Stewart, Dod, and Stenmark
1. J. Am. Chem. Soc. **59**, 1765 (1937)

Stimson
1. J. Research Natl. Bur. Standards **42**, 209 (1949)

Stockmayer, Kavanagh, and Mickley
1. J. Chem. Phys. **12**, 408 (1944)

Stohmann, Kleber, and Langbein
1. J. prakt. Chem. **40**, 77 (1889)
2. Z. physik. Chem. **6**, 338 (1890)
3. J. prakt. Chem. **43**, 1 (1891)

Stohmann, Rodatz, and Herzberg
1. J. prakt. Chem. **33**, 241 (1886)
2. J. prakt. Chem. **35**, 22 (1887)

Stratford
1. Ann. combustibles liquides **4**, 83 (1929)

Strating and Backer
1. Rec. trav. chim. **55**, 903 (1936)
2. Rec. trav. chim. **69**, 638 (1950)

Straus and Kühnel
1. Ber. **65**, 154 (1932)

Strecker and Spitaler
1. Ber. **59**, 1754 (1926)

Streiff, Mair, and Rossini
1. Ind. Eng. Chem. **41**, 2037 (1949)

Streiff, Murphy, Cahill, Flanagan, Sedlak, Willingham, and Rossini
1. J. Research Natl. Bur. Standards **38**, 53 (1947)

Streiff, Murphy, Cahill, Soule, Sedlak, Willingham, and Rossini
1. Unpublished. Carnegie Institute of Technology, Pittsburgh, Pennsylvania

GENERAL LIST OF REFERENCES
S (Page 6)
As of December 31, 1952

Streiff, Murphy, Sedlak, Willingham, and Rossini
1. J. Research Natl. Bur. Standards 37, 331 (1946)

Streiff, Murphy, Zimmerman, Soule, Sedlak, Willingham, and
Rossini
1. J. Research Natl. Bur. Standards 39, 321 (1947)

Streiff and Rossini
1. Unpublished. Carnegie Institute of Technology,
Pittsburgh, Pennsylvania
2. J. Research Natl. Bur. Standards 32, 185 (1944)
3. J. Research Natl. Bur. Standards 39, 303 (1947)

Streiff, Soule, Kennedy, Janes, Sedlak, Willingham, and
Rossini
1. J. Research Natl. Bur. Standards 45, 173 (1950)

Streiff, Zimmerman, Soule, Butt, Sedlak, Willingham, and
Rossini
1. J. Research Natl. Bur. Standards 41, 323 (1948)

Strönholm
1. Ber. 33, 823 (1900)

Struck and Kinney
1. Ind. Eng. Chem. 42, 77 (1950)

Stuckey and Saylor
1. J. Am. Chem. Soc. 62, 2922 (1940)

Stull
1. J. Am. Chem. Soc. 59, 2726 (1937)
2. Unpublished. Dow Chemical Company, Midland, Michigan
3. Ind. Eng. Chem. 39, 532 (1947)

Stutz and Shriner
1. J. Am. Chem. Soc. 55, 1242 (1933)

Subkov
1. J. Russ. Phys. Chem. Soc. 33, 711 (1901)

Subov
1. J. Russ. Phys. Chem. Soc. 45, 242 (1913)

Sugden
1. J. Chem. Soc. 121, 858 (1922)
2. J. Chem. Soc. 125, 32 (1924)
3. J. Chem. Soc. 125, 1177 (1924)

Suida and Drahowzal
1. Ber. 75, 991 (1942)

Suida and Gemassmer
1. Ber. 72, 1168 (1939)

Sulzbacher and Bergmann
1. J. Org. Chem. 13, 303 (1948)

Sunner
1. Thesis. University of Lund, Lund, Sweden (1949)

Suter and Hansen
1. J. Am. Chem. Soc. 54, 4100 (1932)

Swietoslowski
1. J. Am. Chem. Soc. 42, 1092 (1920)

Swietoslowski and Usakiewicj
1. Roczniki Chem. 13, 495 (1933)

Swindells, Coe, and Godfrey
1. J. Research Natl. Bur. Standards 48, 1 (1952)

Szmuszkovicz and Modest
1. J. Am. Chem. Soc. 72, 571 (1950)

GENERAL LIST OF REFERENCES
T (Page 1)
As of December 31, 1952

Taboury
1. Bull. soc. chim. **29**, 761 (1903)
2. Ann. chim. phys. **15**, 5 (1908)
3. Bull. soc. chim. **31**, 1183 (1904)
4. Compt. rend. **138**, 982 (1904)

Tafel and Jurgens
1. Ber. **42**, 2548 (1909)

Tamele, Ott, Marple, and Hearne
1. Ind. Eng. Chem. **33**, 115 (1941)

Tanaka and Koana
1. Proc. Phys.-Math. Soc. Japan **16**, 365 (1934)

Tarbell and Fukushima
1. J. Am. Chem. Soc. **68**, 1456 (1946)
2. Org. Synthesis **27**, 81 (1947)

Tarbell, Fukushima, and Dam
1. J. Am. Chem. Soc. **67**, 1643 (1945)

Tarbell and Lindstrom
1. J. Am. Chem. Soc. **68**, 1930 (1946)

Tarbell and Weaver
1. J. Am. Chem. Soc. **63**, 2939 (1941)

Tatarenko and Tsukervanik
1. J. Gen. Chem. (U.S.S.R.) **18**, 106 (1948)

Tatevosyan, Melikyan, and Terzyan
1. J. Gen. Chem. (U.S.S.R.) **17**, 981 (1947)

Tatevosyan and Vardanyan
1. J. Gen. Chem. (U.S.S.R.) **19**, 332 (1949)

Tatevskiĭ, Treshchova, Skavarchenko, and Levina
1. J. Gen. Chem. (U.S.S.R.) **23**, 657 (1949)

Tausz and Staab
1. Petroleum Z. **26**, 1129 (1930)

Taylor, W.H.
1. J. Am. Chem. Soc. **58**, 2649 (1936)
2. J. Am. Chem. Soc. **57**, 1065 (1935)

Taylor, W.J.
1. J. Research Natl. Bur. Standards **35**, 151 (1945)
2. J. Chem. Phys. **11**, 532 (1943)
3. J. Chem. Phys. **14**, 570 (1946)
4. J. Chem. Phys. **15**, 412 (1947)
5. J. Chem. Phys. **16**, 257 (1948)

Taylor and Layng
1. J. Chem. Phys. **1**, 798 (1933)

Taylor, Pignocco, and Rossini
1. J. Research Natl. Bur. Standards **34**, 413 (1945)

Taylor and Pitzer
1. J. Research Natl. Bur. Standards **38**, 1 (1947)

Taylor and Rossini
1. J. Research Natl. Bur. Standards **32**, 197 (1944)

Taylor and Taylor
1. J. Am. Chem. Soc. **61**, 503 (1939)

Taylor, Wagman, Williams, Pitzer, and Rossini
1. J. Research Natl. Bur. Standards **37**, 95 (1946)

Tcherniac
1. J. Chem. Soc. **115**, 1071 (1919)

Teets
1. J. Am. Chem. Soc. **56**, 1143 (1934)

Templeton, Davies, and Felsing
1. J. Am. Chem. Soc. **66**, 2033 (1944)
2. Unpublished. University of Texas, Austin, Texas

Thiele
1. Ann. **267**, 133 (1892)

Thiele and Trautmann
1. Ber. **68**, 2245 (1935)

Thierry
1. J. Chem. Soc. **127**, 2756 (1925)

Thole
1. J. Chem. Soc. **105**, 2004 (1914)

Thomas
1. Bull. soc. chim. **5**, 730 (1909)

Thompson and Sherrill
1. J. Am. Chem. Soc. **58**, 745 (1936)

Thomsen
1. "Thermochemische Untersuchungen," Vol. **I**, J.A. Barth, Leipzig (1882-86)
2. "Thermochemische Untersuchungen," Vol. **II**, J.A. Barth, Leipzig (1882-86)
3. "Thermochemische Untersuchungen," Vol. **III**, J.A. Barth, Leipzig (1882-86)
4. "Thermochemische Untersuchungen," Vol. **IV**, J.A. Barth, Leipzig (1882-86)

Thomson
1. Chem. Rev. **38**, 1 (1946)

Thorpe and Larsen
1. Ind. Eng. Chem. **34**, 853 (1942)

Thorpe and Rodger
1. Trans. Roy. Soc. (London) **A185**, 397 (1894)
2. Trans. Roy. Soc. (London) **A189**, 71 (1897)
3. Trans. Roy. Soc. (London) **A185**, 522 (1894)

Tiffeneau
1. Ann. chim. phys. **10**, 145 (1907)
2. Compt. rend. **139**, 481 (1904)

Tilicheev

1. Khim. Tverdogo Topliva **9**, 181 (1938)

Tilicheev, Peshkov, and Yuganova

1. J. Gen. Chem. (U.S.S.R.) **21**, 1229 (1951)
2. Zhur. Anal. Khim **4**, 298 (1949)

Tilton

1. Unpublished. National Bureau of Standards, Washington, D. C.

Timmermans

1. Bull. soc. chim. Belg. **31**, 389 (1922)
2. Bull. soc. chim. Belg. **36**, 502 (1927)
3. Bureau International des Etalons Physicochimique, University of Brussels, Brussels, Belgium
4. Unpublished. University of Brussels, Brussels, Belgium
5. Bull. soc. chim. Belg. **30**, 62 (1921)
6. Bull. soc. chim. Belg. **25**, 300 (1911)
7. Proc. Akad. Sci. Amsterdam **13**, 507 (1910)
8. J. chim. phys. **23**, 747 (1926)
9. J. chim. phys. **25**, 411 (1928)

Timmermans and Hennaut-Roland

1. J. chim. phys. **27**, 401 (1930)
2. J. chim. phys. **29**, 529 (1932)
3. J. chim. phys. **32**, 501, 589 (1935)
4. J. chim. phys. **34**, 693 (1937)
5. Anal. soc. españ. fis. quim. **27**, 460 (1929)

Timmermans and Mataar

1. Bull. soc. chim. Belg. **30**, 213 (1921)

Timmermans and Martin

1. J. chim. phys. **23**, 733 (1926)
2. J. chim. phys. **23**, 747 (1926)
3. J. chim. phys. **25**, 411 (1928)

Tischenko

1. Bull. soc. chim. **53**, 1428 (1933)

Titani

1. Bull. Chem. Soc. Japan **5**, 99 (1930)
2. Bull. Inst. Phys. Chem. Research (Tokyo) **8**, 433 (1929)

Titley

1. J. Chem. Soc. 508 (1926)

Tits-Skvortsova, Levina, Leonova, and Karaseva

1. J. Gen. Chem. (U.S.S.R.) **21**, 242 (1951)

Todd, Oliver, and Huffman

1. J. Am. Chem. Soc. **69**, 1519 (1947)

Todd and Parks

1. J. Am. Chem. Soc. **58**, 134 (1936)

Tolman

1. "The Principles of Statistical Mechanics," Oxford University Press, New York, New York (1938)

Tongberg, Pickens, Fenske, and Whitmore

1. J. Am. Chem. Soc. **54**, 3706 (1932)

Tonomura

1. Sci. Repts. Tohuko Imp. Univ. **22**, 104 (1933)

Tonomura and Vehara

1. Bull. Chem. Soc. Japan **6**, 255 (1931)

Toussaint and Hennion

1. J. Am. Chem. Soc. **62**, 1145 (1940)

Transue, Washburn, and Kahler

1. J. Am. Chem. Soc. **64**, 274 (1942)

Trautz and Adler

1. Z. Physik **89**, 1 (1934)

Triebs

1. Ber. **71**, 612 (1938)

Trieschmann

1. Z. physik. Chem. **B29**, 328 (1935)

Trotter and Thompson

1. J. Chem. Soc. 481 (1946)

Troyan

1. J. Am. Chem. Soc. **64**, 3056 (1942)

Truchet

1. Ann. chim. **16**, 309 (1931)

Trusty

1. Petroleum Refiner **22**, 95 (1943)

Tsakalotos and Guye

1. J. chim. phys. **8**, 340 (1910)

Tsukervanik and Terent'eva

1. J. Gen. Chem. (U.S.S.R.) **7**, 637 (1937)

Tsukervanik and Vikrova

1. J. Gen. Chem. (U.S.S.R.) **7**, 632 (1937)

Tucker and Reid

1. J. Am. Chem. Soc. **55**, 775 (1933)

Tuot

1. Compt. rend. **197**, 1434 (1933)
2. Compt. rend. **211**, 561 (1940)
3. Bull. soc. chim. **9**, 899 (1942)

Tuot and Guyard

1. Bull. soc. chim. **14**, 1086 (1947)

Turk

1. Thesis. Ohio State University, Columbus, Ohio (1941)

Turkevich

1. J. Chem. Phys. **12**, 461 (1944)

Turner and Lesslie

1. Unpublished. University of Cambridge, Cambridge, England

GENERAL LIST OF REFERENCES
T (Page 3)
As of December 31, 1952

Turova-Pollak and Polyakova
    1. J. Gen. Chem. (U.S.S.R.) **9**, 233 (1939)

Turova-Pollak and Vsevolozhskaya
    1. J. Gen. Chem. (U.S.S.R.) **11**, 817 (1941)

Tyrer
    1. J. Chem. Soc. **105**, 2534 (1914)

GENERAL LIST OF REFERENCES
U
As of December 31, 1952

Ubbelohde
1. Trans. Faraday Soc. **34**, 282 (1938)

Ubbelohde and Agthe
1. In C. Engler and H. Höfer, Das Erdöl, Vol. **I**,
   S. Hirzel Company, Leipzig (1909)

Ufimtsev
1. J. Gen. Chem. (U.S.S.R.) **13**, 516 (1943)

University of Chicago
1. Unpublished. The Physics Department, University of
   Chicago, Chicago, Illinois

University of Minnesota
1. Unpublished. School of Chemistry, University of
   Minnesota, Minneapolis, Minnesota

Urry and Kharasch
1. J. Am. Chem. Soc. **66**, 1438 (1944)

GENERAL LIST OF REFERENCES

V

As of December 31, 1952

Vallin
1. Ber. **19**, 2952 (1886)

Van Hook and Silver
1. J. Chem. Phys. **10**, 686 (1942)

Van der Vet
1. Proceedings Second World Petroleum Congress, Paris,
**2**, sect. 2, 515 (1937)

Van Volkenburgh, Greenlee, Derfer, and Boord
1. J. Am. Chem. Soc. **71**, 172 (1949)

Van der Waals
1. Beibl. Ann. Physik **4**, 704 (1880)

Vaughan and Graves
1. Ind. Eng. Chem. **32**, 1252 (1940)

Vaughan and Rust
1. J. Org. Chem. **7**, 472 (1942)

Vaughn
1. J. Am. Chem. Soc. **55**, 3453 (1933)

Vavon
1. Ann. chim. phys. **1**, 169 (1914)

Vavon and Mottez
1. Compt. rend. **218**, 557 (1944)

Veksler
1. J. Exptl. Theoret. Phys. (U.S.S.R.) **9**, 616 (1939)

Verley
1. Bull. soc. chim. **19**, 67 (1898)

Veselý and Šturza
1. Chem. Listy **26**, 495 (1932)
2. Collection Czechoslov. Chem. Communs. **3**, 430 (1931)
3. Collection Czechoslov. Chem. Communs. **4**, 139 (1932)

Villard
1. Compt. rend. **120**, 1262 (1895)

Villars
1. Proc. Natl. Acad. Sci. **16**, 396 (1930)

Voge and May
1. J. Am. Chem. Soc. **68**, 550 (1946)

Vogel
1. J. Chem. Soc. 1323 (1938)
2. J. Chem. Soc. 133 (1946)
3. J. Chem. Soc. 607 (1948)
4. J. Chem. Soc. 1820 (1948)

Vogel and Cowan
1. J. Chem. Soc. 16 (1943)

Vogt
1. Ann. **119**, 142 (1861)

Vorländer and Fischer
1. Ber. **65**, 1756 (1932)

Vorländer and Selke
1. Z. physik. Chem. **129**, 435 (1927)

Vorländer and Walter
1. Z. physik. Chem. **118**, 1 (1925)

Voronkov, Broun, Karpenko, and Gol'shtein
1. J. Gen. Chem. (U.S.S.R.) **19**, 1356 (1949)

Voronkov and Gol'shtein
1. J. Gen. Chem. (U.S.S.R.) **20**, 1218 (1950)

Voswinkel
1. Ber. **22**, 315 (1889)

Votoček and Veselý
1. Ber. **47**, 1516 (1914)

Wackher, Linn, and Grosse
1. Ind. Eng. Chem. **37**, 464 (1945)

Waddington and others
1. Unpublished. U.S. Bureau of Mines, Bartlesville,
Oklahoma

Waddington and Douslin
1. J. Am. Chem. Soc. **69**, 2275 (1947)

Waddington, Knowlton, Scott, Oliver, Todd, Hubbard, Smith, and
Huffman
1. J. Am. Chem. Soc. **71**, 797 (1949)

Waddington, Todd, and Huffman
1. J. Am. Chem. Soc. **69**, 22 (1947)

Wagman, Kilpatrick, Pitzer, and Rossini
1. J. Research Natl. Bur. Standards **35**, 467 (1945)

Wagman, Kilpatrick, Taylor, Pitzer, and Rossini
1. J. Research Natl. Bur. Standards **34**, 143 (1945)

Wagman and Rossini
1. J. Research Natl. Bur. Standards **32**, 95 (1944)

Waidner and Burgess
1. Chem. News **103**, 25 (1911)

Walden
1. Z. physik. Chem. **66**, 388 (1909)
2. Z. physik. Chem. **82**, 271 (1913)

Walden and Swinne
1. Z. physik. Chem. **79**, 700 (1912)

Waldmann and Petru
1. Ber. **83**, 287 (1950)

Walker
1. J. Chem. Soc. 193 (1950)

Wallach
1. Ann. **289**, 337 (1895)
2. Ann. **396**, 264 (1913)
3. Ann. **414**, 195 (1917–1918)
4. Nachr. Ges. Wiss. Göttingen 1 (1915)
5. Ann. **347**, 316 (1906)

Wallach and Martius
1. Ann. **365**, 272 (1909)

Wallach and Mendelsohn-Bartholdy
1. Ann. **360**, 48 (1908)

Walls and Smyth
1. J. Chem. Phys. **1**, 337 (1933)

Ward
1. Unpublished. United Gas Improvement Company,
Philadelphia, Pennsylvania
2. Ind. Eng. Chem. Anal. Ed. **6**, 395 (1934)

Ward and Fulweiler
1. Ind. Eng. Chem. Anal. Ed. **6**, 396 (1934)

Ward and Kurtz
1. Ind. Eng. Chem. Anal. Ed. **10**, 559 (1938)

Washburn
1. J. Research Natl. Bur. Standards **10**, 525 (1933)
2. J. Research Natl. Bur. Standards **4**, 221 (1930)
3. Ind. Eng. Chem. **22**, 985 (1930)
4. J. Research Natl. Bur. Standards **5**, 867 (1930)
5. National Bureau of Standards, Letter Circular LC–289
(1930)
6. Ind. Eng. Chem. **25**, 891 (1933)
7. Proc. Am. Petroleum Inst. **III 14**, 111 (1933)

Washburn, Bruun, and Hicks
1. J. Research Natl. Bur. Standards **2**, 467 (1929)

Waterman and de Kok
1. Rec. trav. chim. **52**, 251 (1933)
2. Rec. trav. chim. **52**, 298 (1933)

Waterman and Leendertse
1. J. Inst. Petroleum **25**, 89 (1939)
2. Trans. Faraday Soc. **35**, 985 (1939)

Waterman, Leendertse, and de Kok
1. Rec. trav. chim. **53**, 1151 (1933)

Waterman, Leendertse, and van Krevelen
1. J. Inst. Petroleum **25**, 801 (1939)

Waterman and Te Nuyl
1. Rec. trav. chim. **51**, 533 (1932)

Waterman, van't Spijker, and van Westen
1. Rec. trav. chim. **48**, 1103 (1929)

Waterman and van Westen
1. Rec. trav. chim. **48**, 637 (1929)

Watson, Wien, and Murphy
1. Ind. Eng. Chem. **28**, 605 (1936)

Weber
1. Ann. Physik **154**, 367 (1875)
2. Ann. Physik **154**, 553 (1875)

Wedekind and Schenk
1. Ber. **54**, 1604 (1921)

Weibull
1. Arkiv Kemi, Mineral. Geol. 23A, No. 18, 25 (1946)

Weinmayr
1. J. Am. Chem. Soc. **72**, 918 (1950)

Weissgerber
1. Ber. **61**, 2111 (1928)

Weissgerber and Kruber
1. Ber. **52**, 346 (1919)

GENERAL LIST OF REFERENCES

W (Page 2)

As of December 31, 1952

Weissgerber and Seidler
1. Ber. **60**, 2088 (1927)

Welsh and Hennion
1. J. Am. Chem. Soc. **63**, 2603 (1941)

Welt
1. Ber. **30**, 1494 (1904)

Wenner, Thomas, Cooter, and Kotter
1. J. Wash. Acad. Sci. **29**, 313 (1939)

Westlake and Dougherty
1. J. Am. Chem. Soc. **64**, 149 (1942)

Westlake, Laquer, and Smyth
1. J. Am. Chem. Soc. **72**, 436 (1950)

Weygand and Mensdorf
1. Ber. **68**, 1830 (1935)

Wheeler, Tartan, and Lingafelter
1. J. Am. Chem. Soc. **67**, 2115 (1945)

Whitby and Crozier
1. Can. J. Research **6**, 203 (1932)

Whitby and Gallay
1. Can. J. Research **6**, 261 (1932)

White, Barnard-Smith, and Fidler
1. Ind. Eng. Chem. **44**, 1430 (1952)

White and Glasgow
1. J. Research Natl. Bur. Standards **19**, 423 (1937)
2. J. Research Natl. Bur. Standards **22**, 137 (1939)

White and Rose
1. J. Research Natl. Bur. Standards **9**, 711 (1932)
2. J. Research Natl. Bur. Standards **10**, 639 (1933)
3. J. Research Natl. Bur. Standards **21**, 151 (1938)
4. J. Research Natl. Bur. Standards **7**, 907 (1931)
5. J. Research Natl. Bur. Standards **13**, 799 (1934)
6. J. Research Natl. Bur. Standards **17**, 943 (1936)

White, Rose, Calingaert, and Soroos
1. J. Research Natl. Bur. Standards **22**, 315 (1939)

Whitehead, Dean, and Fidler
1. J. Am. Chem. Soc. **73**, 3632 (1951)

Whitmore and others
1. Unpublished. Pennsylvania State College, State College, Pennsylvania

Whitmore and Carney
1. J. Am. Chem. Soc. **63**, 2633 (1941)

Whitmore and Church
1. J. Am. Chem. Soc. **54**, 3710 (1932)

Whitmore, Fenske, Quiggle, Bernstein, Carney, Lawroski, Popkin, Wagner, Wheeler, and Whitaker
1. J. Am. Chem. Soc. **62**, 795 (1940)

Whitmore and Fleming
1. J. Am. Chem. Soc. **55**, 3803 (1933)

Whitmore, Goldsmith, Cook, Yarze, and Ecke
1. J. Am. Chem. Soc. **72**, 53 (1950)

Whitmore and Herndon
1. J. Am. Chem. Soc. **55**, 3428 (1933)

Whitmore and Homeyer
1. J. Am. Chem. Soc. **55**, 4555 (1933)

Whitmore and Houk
1. J. Am. Chem. Soc. **54**, 3714 (1932)

Whitmore and James
1. J. Am. Chem. Soc. **65**, 2088 (1943)

Whitmore and Laughlin
1. J. Am. Chem. Soc. **54**, 4014 (1932)
2. J. Am. Chem. Soc. **54**, 4392 (1932)
3. J. Am. Chem. Soc. **55**, 3732 (1933)

Whitmore and Meunier
1. J. Am. Chem. Soc. **55**, 3721 (1933)

Whitmore and Mosher
1. J. Am. Chem. Soc. **63**, 1120 (1941)
2. J. Am. Chem. Soc. **68**, 281 (1946)

Whitmore and Orem
1. J. Am. Chem. Soc. **60**, 2573 (1938)

Whitmore, Popkin, Bernstein, and Wilkins
1. J. Am. Chem. Soc. **63**, 124 (1941)

Whitmore, Popkin, and Pfister
1. J. Am. Chem. Soc. **61**, 1616 (1939)

Whitmore, Rowland, Wrenn, and Kilmer
1. J. Am. Chem. Soc. **64**, 2970 (1942)

Whitmore and Simpson
1. J. Am. Chem. Soc. **55**, 3811 (1933)

Whitmore and Southgate
1. J. Am. Chem. Soc. **60**, 2571 (1938)

Whitmore and Stahly
1. J. Am. Chem. Soc. **55**, 4153 (1933)

Whitmore, Whitmore, and Cook
1. J. Am. Chem. Soc. **72**, 51 (1950)

Whitmore and Wrenn
1. J. Am. Chem. Soc. **53**, 3136 (1931)

Whitner and Reid
1. J. Am. Chem. Soc. **43**, 638 (1921)

Whittaker
1. Biochem. J. **41**, 56 (1947)

Wibaut and van Dijk
1. Rec. trav. chim. **65**, 413 (1946)

GENERAL LIST OF REFERENCES
W (Page 3)
As of December 31, 1952

Wibaut and Geldof
1. Rec. trav. chim. **65**, 125 (1946)

Wibaut and Gitsels
1. Rec. trav. chim. **59**, 947 (1940)
2. Rec. trav. chim. **60**, 241 (1941)

Wibaut, Hoog, Langedijk, Overhoff, Smittenberg, Benniga, Bouman,
    van Dijk, Gaade, Geldof, Hackmann, Jonker, Paap, and Zuiderweg
1. Rec. trav. chim. **58**, 329 (1939)

Wibaut and Langedijk
1. Rec. trav. chim. **59**, 1220 (1940)

Wibaut, Overhoff, and Jonker
1. Rec. trav. chim. **62**, 31 (1943)

Wibaut and van Pelt
1. Rec. trav. chim. **57**, 1055 (1938)

Wibaut, van Pelt, Santilhano, and Beuskens
1. Rec. trav. chim. **61**, 265 (1942)

Widman
1. Ber. **23**, 3080 (1890)
2. Ber. **24**, 456 (1891)

Wiebe and Brevoort
1. J. Am. Chem. Soc. **52**, 622 (1930)

Wiebe, Hubbard, and Brevoort
1. J. Am. Chem. Soc. **52**, 611 (1930)

Wiest
1. Thesis. Ohio State University, Columbus, Ohio (1940)

van Wijk, van der Veen, Brinkman, and Seeder
1. Physica **7**, 45 (1940)

Wijkander
1. Physik Ber. **3**, 8 (1879)

Wilkinson
1. J. Chem. Soc. 3057 (1931)

Willingham
1. J. Research Natl. Bur. Standards **22**, 321 (1939)

Willingham and Rossini
1. J. Research Natl. Bur. Standards **33**, 383 (1944)
2. J. Research Natl. Bur. Standards **37**, 15 (1946)
3. Proc. Am. Petroleum Inst. III **26**, 63 (1946)

Willingham and Sedlak
1. J. Research Natl. Bur. Standards **45**, 315 (1950)

Willingham, Sedlak, Westhaver, and Rossini
1. Ind. Eng. Chem. **39**, 706 (1947)

Willingham, Taylor, Pignocco, and Rossini
1. J. Research Natl. Bur. Standards **35**, 219 (1945)

Willson and Suckert
1. J. Franklin Inst. **139**, 327 (1895)

Willstäter and Mever
1. Ber. **41**, 1478 (1908)

Wilson
1. J. Chem. Phys. **4**, 526 (1936)

Windaus and Thiele
1. Ann. **521**, 160 (1935)

Winkler and Maass
1. Can. J. Research **9**, 613 (1933)
2. Can. J. Research **9**, 65 (1933)

Winssinger
1. Bull. soc. chim. **48**, 108 (1887)

Winstein and Lucas
1. J. Am. Chem. Soc. **60**, 838 (1938)

Wise, Serijan, and Goodman
1. Technical Note No. 2081. National Advisory Committee for
    Aeronautics, Flight Propulsion Laboratory, Cleveland,
    Ohio (1950)

Wislicenus
1. Ann. **313**, 207 (1900)

Witmer
1. J. Am. Chem. Soc. **56**, 2229 (1934)

Witt and Kemp
1. J. Am. Chem. Soc. **59**, 273 (1937)

Wojciechowski
1. J. Research Natl. Bur. Standards **17**, 453 (1936)
2. J. Research Natl. Bur. Standards **19**, 347 (1937)
3. Przemysl Chem. **23**, 129 (1939)
4. Proc. Am. Acad. Arts Sci. **73**, 361 (1940)

Woods and Plapinger
1. J. Am. Chem. Soc. **73**, 5603 (1951)

Woods and Schwartzman
1. J. Am. Chem. Soc. **70**, 3394 (1948)

Woolley
1. J. Research Natl. Bur. Standards **40**, 163 (1948)

Woolley, Scott, and Brickwedde
1. J. Research Natl. Bur. Standards **41**, 379 (1948)

Woolsey
1. J. Am. Chem. Soc. **59**, 1577 (1937)

Worthing
1. Phys. Rev. **12**, 199 (1918)

Wright and Wallace
1. J. Chem. Soc. 1279 (1936)

Wroblewski
1. Compt. rend. **99**, 136 (1884)

GENERAL LIST OF REFERENCES
W (Page 4)
As of December 31, 1952

Wu

1. J. Chem. Phys. **8**, 489 (1940)

Wuyts

1. Ber. **36**, 863 (1903)
2. Bull. soc. chim. **5**, 409 (1909)
3. Bull. soc. chim. **35**, 166 (1906)

GENERAL LIST OF REFERENCES
Y
As of December 31, 1952

Yost, Osborne, and Garner
    1. J. Am. Chem. Soc. **63**, 3492 (1941)

Young
    1. J. Chem. Soc. **71**, 446 (1897)
    2. Sci. Proc. Roy. Dublin Soc. **12**, 374 (1910)

Young, Dillon, and Lucas
    1. J. Am. Chem. Soc. **51**, 2528 (1929)

Young, Jasaitis, and Levanas
    1. J. Am. Chem. Soc. **59**, 403 (1937)

Young and Thomas
    1. J. Chem. Soc. **71**, 448 (1897)

Youtz and Perkins
    1. J. Am. Chem. Soc. **51**, 3508 (1929)
    2. J. Am. Chem. Soc. **51**, 3511 (1929)

Yur'ev
    1. J. Gen. Chem. (U.S.S.R.) **8**, 1934 (1938)

Yur'ev and Bugorkova
    1. J. Gen. Chem. (U.S.S.R.) **19**, 720 (1949)

Yur'ev, Dubrovina, and Tregubov
    1. J. Gen. Chem. (U.S.S.R.) **16**, 843 (1946)

Yur'ev and Gragerov
    1. J. Gen. Chem. (U.S.S.R.) **19**, 724 (1949)

Yur'ev, Gusev, Tronova, and Yurilin
    1. J. Gen. Chem. (U.S.S.R.) **11**, 344 (1941)

Yur'ev and Levi
    1. Doklady Akad. Nauk S.S.S.R. **73**, 953 (1950)

Yur'ev and Novitskiĭ
    1. Doklady Akad. Nauk. S.S.S.R. **63**, 285 (1948)

Yur'ev and Tronova
    1. J. Gen. Chem. (U.S.S.R.) **21**, 256 (1951)

Yur'ev, Tronova, L'vova, and Bukshpan
    1. J. Gen. Chem. (U.S.S.R.) **11**, 1128 (1941)

GENERAL LIST OF REFERENCES

Z

As of December 31, 1952

Zalmanovitch
    1. J. Gen. Chem. (U.S.S.R.) **17**, 2103 (1947)

Zeidler and Schuster
    1. Farben-Ztg. **47**, 318 (1942)

Zeise
    1. Z. Elektrochem. **39**, 895 (1933)

Zelikov
    1. Ber. **37**, 1374 (1904)

Zelinskiĭ
    1. Ber. **35**, 2677 (1902)
    2. Ber. **35**, 2488 (1902)
    3. Ber. **57**, 2055 (1924)
    4. Ber. **57**, 2062 (1924)
    5. Ber. **62**, 1658 (1929)
    6. Ber. **56**, 1718 (1923)
    7. Ber. **20**, 2017 (1887)
    8. Ber. **21**, 1835 (1888)

Zelinskiĭ and Dworshantschik
    1. J. Russ. Phys. Chem. Soc. **35**, 563 (1903)

Zelinskiĭ and Gaverdovskaya
    1. Ber. **61**, 1049 (1928)

Zelinskiĭ and Gorskiĭ
    1. Ber. **41**, 2630 (1908)
    2. J. Russ. Phys. Chem. Soc. **40**, 1399 (1908)

Zelinskiĭ, Kasanskiĭ, and Platé
    1. Ber. **68**, 1869 (1935)

Zelinskiĭ, Michlina, and Eventova
    1. Ber. **66**, 1422 (1933)

Zelinskiĭ, Pakendorf, and Khoklova
    1. Ber. **68**, 98 (1935)

Zelinskiĭ and Pavlov
    1. Ber. **57**, 1066 (1924)

Zelinskiĭ and Reformatskiĭ
    1. Ber. **29**, 214 (1896)

Zelinskiĭ and Turova-Pollak
    1. Ber. **58**, 1292 (1925)
    2. Ber. **65**, 1299 (1932)

Zelinskiĭ and Uspenskiĭ
    1. Ber. **35**, 1470 (1913)

Zelinskiĭ and Zelikov
    1. Ber. **34**, 3249 (1901)

Ziegler and Andrews
    1. J. Am. Chem. Soc. **64**, 2482 (1942)

Ziegler, Dersch, and Wollthan
    1. Ann. **511**, 13 (1934)

Ziegler and Ditzel
    1. Ann. **473**, 194 (1929)

Zincke and Dahm
    1. Ber. **45**, 3457 (1912)

Zincke and Eismayer
    1. Ber. **51**, 751 (1918)

Zmaczynski
    1. J. chim. phys. **27**, 503 (1930)

Zubov
    1. J. Russ. Phys. Chem. Soc. **30**, 926 (1898)
    2. J. Russ. Phys. Chem. Soc. **33**, 708 (1901)
    3. J. Russ. Phys. Chem. Soc. **35**, 815 (1903)
    4. J. Russ. Phys. Chem. Soc. **45**, 242 (1913)

## INDEX OF PROPERTIES

INDEX OF COMPOUNDS

PUBLICATIONS

Page 1

1. Application of Polya's theorem to optical, geometrical, and structural isomerism. W.J.Taylor. J. Chem. Phys. $\underline{11}$, 532 (1943).

2. The calory and the joule in thermodynamics and thermochemistry. E.F.Mueller and F.D.Rossini. Am. J. Phys. $\underline{12}$, 1-7 (1944).

3. Theoretical analysis of certain time-temperature freezing and melting curves as applied to hydrocarbons. W.J.Taylor and F.D.Rossini. J. Research Natl. Bur. Standards $\underline{32}$, 197-213 (1944).

4. Heats of formation and combustion of 1,3-butadiene and styrene. E.J.Prosen and F.D.Rossini. J. Research Natl. Bur. Standards $\underline{34}$, 59-63 (1945).

5. Heats, free energies, and equilibrium constants of some reactions involving $O_2$, $H_2$, $H_2O$, C, CO, $CO_2$, and $CH_4$. D.D.Wagman, J.E.Kilpatrick, W.J.Taylor, K.S.Pitzer, and F.D.Rossini. J. Research Natl. Bur. Standards $\underline{34}$, 143-161 (1945).

6. Free energies and equilibria of isomerization of the 18 octanes. E.J.Prosen, K.S.Pitzer, and F.D.Rossini. J. Research Natl. Bur. Standards $\underline{34}$, 255-261 (1945).

7. Heats of combustion and formation of the paraffin hydrocarbons at 25°C. E.J.Prosen and F.D.Rossini. J. Research Natl. Bur. Standards $\underline{34}$, 263-269 (1945).

8. Heats and free energies of formation of the paraffin hydrocarbons in the gaseous state to 1500°K. E.J.Prosen, K.S.Pitzer, and F.D.Rossini. J. Research Natl. Bur. Standards $\underline{34}$, 403-411 (1945).

9. Method for calculating the properties of hydrocarbons and its application to the refractive indices, densities, and boiling points of the paraffin and monoolefin hydrocarbons. W.J.Taylor, J.M.Pignocco, and F.D.Rossini. J. Research Natl. Bur. Standards $\underline{34}$, 413-434 (1945).

10. Method of Lagrangian curvilinear interpolation. W.J.Taylor. J. Research Natl. Bur. Standards $\underline{35}$, 151-155 (1945).

11. Vapor pressures and boiling points of some paraffin, alkylcyclopentane, alkyl-cyclohexane, and alkylbenzene hydrocarbons. C.B.Willingham, W.J.Taylor, J.M. Pignocco, and F.D.Rossini. J. Research Natl. Bur. Standards $\underline{35}$, 219-244 (1945).

12. Heats, equilibrium constants, and free energies of formation of the acetylene hydrocarbons through the pentynes, to 1500°K. D.D.Wagman, J.E.Kilpatrick, K.S.Pitzer, and F.D.Rossini. J. Research Natl. Bur. Standards $\underline{35}$, 467-496 (1945).

13. Heat of formation, hydrogenation, and combustion of the monoolefin hydrocarbons through the hexenes, and of the higher 1-alkenes, in the gaseous state at 25°C. E.J.Prosen and F.D.Rossini. J. Research Natl. Bur. Standards $\underline{36}$, 269-275 (1946).

14. Heats of combustion and formation at 25°C of the alkylbenzenes through $C_{10}H_{14}$, and of the higher normal monoalkylbenzenes. E.J.Prosen, W.H.Johnson, and F.D.Rossini. J. Research Natl. Bur. Standards $\underline{36}$, 455-461 (1946).

15. Heats, equilibrium constants, and free energies of formation of the monoolefin hydrocarbons. J.E.Kilpatrick, E.J.Prosen, K.S.Pitzer, and F.D.Rossini. J. Research Natl. Bur. Standards $\underline{36}$, 559-612 (1946).

16. Heats of formation and combustion of the normal alkylcyclopentanes and cyclohexanes and the increment per $CH_2$ group for several homologous series of hydrocarbons. E.J.Prosen, W.H.Johnson, and F.D.Rossini. J. Research Natl. Bur. Standards $\underline{37}$, 51-56 (1946).

17. Heats, equilibrium constants, and free energies of formation of the alkylbenzenes. W.J.Taylor, D.D.Wagman, M.G.Williams, K.S.Pitzer, and F.D.Rossini. J. Research Natl. Bur. Standards $\underline{37}$, 95-122 (1946).

18. Heat content, free energy function, entropy, and heat capacity of ethylene, propylene, and the four butenes to 1500°K. J.E.Kilpatrick and K.S.Pitzer. J. Research Natl. Bur. Standards $\underline{37}$, 163-171 (1946).

19. Upper and lower bounds to Rayleigh's frequency for a vibrating system. W.J.Taylor. J. Chem. Phys. $\underline{14}$, 570-571 (1946).

20. The thermodynamics of styrene and its methyl derivatives. C.W.Beckett and K.S. Pitzer. J. Am. Chem. Soc. $\underline{68}$, 2213 (1946).

21. The entropies and related properties of branched paraffin hydrocarbons. K.S. Pitzer and J.E.Kilpatrick. Chem. Revs. $\underline{39}$, 435-447 (1946).

22. Vibrational frequencies of semirigid molecules: A general method and values for ethylbenzene. W.J.Taylor and K.S.Pitzer. J. Research Natl. Bur. Standards $\underline{38}$, 1-17 (1947).

23. Normal coordinate analysis of the vibrational frequencies of ethylene, propylene, cis-2-butene, trans-2-butene, and isobutene. J.E.Kilpatrick and K.S.Pitzer. J. Research Natl. Bur. Standards $\underline{38}$, 191-209 (1947).

24. Tautomerism in cyclohexane derivatives; reassignment of configuration of the 1,3-dimethylcyclohexanes. K.S.Pitzer and C.W.Beckett. J. Am. Chem. Soc. $\underline{69}$, 977 (1947).

25. Relabeling of the cis and trans isomers of 1,3-dimethylcyclohexane. F.D.Rossini and K.S.Pitzer. Science $\underline{105}$, 647 (1947).

26. Average square length and radius of unbranched long-chain molecules with restricted internal rotation. W.J.Taylor. J. Chem. Phys. $\underline{15}$, 412-413 (1947).

27. Heats of formation and isomerization of the eight $C_8H_{12}$ alkylcyclohexanes in the liquid and gaseous states. E.J.Prosen, W.H.Johnson, and F.D.Rossini. J. Research Natl. Bur. Standards $\underline{39}$, 173-175 (1947).

28. Thermodynamics and molecular structure of cyclopentane. J.E.Kilpatrick, K.S. Pitzer, and R.Spitzer. J. Am. Chem. Soc. $\underline{69}$, 2483-2488 (1947).

29. The thermodynamic properties and molecular structure of cyclohexane, methylcyclohexane, ethylcyclohexane and the seven dimethylcyclohexanes. C.W.Beckett, K.S.Pitzer, and R.Spitzer. J. Am. Chem. Soc. $\underline{69}$, 2488-2495 (1947).

30. Heats, equilibrium constants, and free energies of formation of the alkylcyclopentanes, and alkylcyclohexanes. J.E.Kilpatrick, H.G.Werner, C.W.Beckett, K.S. Pitzer, and F.D.Rossini. J. Research Natl. Bur. Standards $\underline{39}$, 523-543 (1947).

31. "Selected values of properties of hydrocarbons." F.D.Rossini, K.S.Pitzer, W.J. Taylor, J.P.Ebert, J.E.Kilpatrick, C.W.Beckett, M.G.Williams, and H.G.Werner. Book, 483 + xiii pages. Natl. Bur. Standards Circular C461. U.S.Government Printing Office, Washington, 1947.

32. Average length and radius of normal paraffin hydrocarbon molecules. W.J.Taylor. J. Chem. Phys. $\underline{16}$, 257-267 (1948).

33. Naming of cis and trans isomers of hydrocarbons containing olefin double bonds. M.B.Epstein and F.D.Rossini. Chem. Eng. News $\underline{26}$, 2959 (1948).

34. The thermodynamic properties and molecular structure of cyclopentene and cyclohexene. C.W.Beckett, N.K.Freeman, and K.S.Pitzer. J. Am. Chem. Soc. $\underline{70}$, 4227-4230 (1948).

35. Heats, equilibrium constants, and free energies of formation of the $C_3$ to $C_5$ diolefins, styrene, and the methylstyrenes. J.E.Kilpatrick, C.W.Beckett, E.J. Prosen, K.S.Pitzer, and F.D.Rossini. J. Research Natl. Bur. Standards $\underline{42}$, 225-240 (1949).

36. Heats, equilibrium constants, and free energies of formation of cyclopentene and cyclohexene. M.B.Epstein, K.S.Pitzer, and F.D.Rossini. J. Research Natl. Bur. Standards $\underline{42}$, 379-382 (1949).

37. Excusion in chemical thermodynamics. F.D.Rossini. J. Wash. Acad. Sci. $\underline{39}$, 249-269 (1949).

38. Heats, equilibrium constants, and free energies of formation of the dimethyl-cyclopentanes. M.B.Epstein, G.M.Barrow, K.S.Pitzer, and F.D.Rossini. J. Research Natl. Bur. Standards $\underline{43}$, 245-250 (1949).

39. Chemical thermodynamic equilibria among hydrocarbons. F.D.Rossini. A chapter, pp. 363-434, in Volume 1 of "Physical chemistry of hydrocarbons", Academic Press, New York, 1950.

40. Note on the naming of geometric isomers of polyalkyl monocycloalkanes. M.B. Epstein and F.D.Rossini. Chem. Eng. News $\underline{28}$, 1910 (1950).

41. Chemical thermodynamic properties of hydrocarbons. F.D.Rossini. A chapter, pp. 153-181, in Volume V, Part 1, of "Science of petroleum", Oxford University Press, New York, 1950.

42. Thermochemistry and the thermodynamic properties of substances. F.D.Rossini, D.D.Wagman, W.H.Evans, and E.J.Prosen. A chapter, pp. 1-40, in Volume 1 of "Annual review of physical chemistry", Annual Review, Inc., Stanford, California, 1950.

43. Chemical thermodynamics; fractionating processes; hydrocarbons in petroleum. F.D.Rossini. Book, 164 + iv pages. Reilly Lecture Series, University of Notre Dame, Notre Dame, Indiana, 1950.

44. The thermodynamic properties of naphthalene. G.M.Barrow and A.L.McClellan. J. Am. Chem. Soc. $\underline{73}$, 573 (1951).

45. Remarks on the interpretation of the $CH_2$ vibrational frequencies of n-paraffins. G.M.Barrow. J. Chem. Phys. $\underline{19}$, 345 (1951).

46. Compilation of data on the properties of hydrocarbons and related compounds. F.D. Rossini. Proceedings of the Third World Petroleum Congress, Section VI; pp. 157-239. E.J. Brill Company, Leiden, Netherlands, 1951.

47. American Petroleum Institute spectral data and standard samples. F.D.Rossini. Applied Spectroscopy $\underline{6}$, 3-13 (1951).

48. Infrared spectra of naphthalene crystals, vapor, and solutions. G.C.Pimentel and A.L.McClellan. J. Chem. Phys. $\underline{20}$, 270-277 (1952).

49. Status of the values of the fundamental constants for physcial chemistry as of July 1, 1951. F.D.Rossini, F.T.Gucker,Jr., H.L.Johnston, L. Pauling, and G.W. Vinal. J. Am. Chem. Soc. $\underline{74}$, 2699-2701 (1952).

50. The structure of cyclooctatetraene. W.B.Person, G.C.Pimentel, and K.S.Pitzer. Jointly with API Research Project 50. J. Am. Chem. Soc. $\underline{74}$, 3437-3438 (1952).

51. A decade of progress in selecting data on hydrocarbons and related compounds. A report on API Research Project 44. W.E.Kuhn and F.D.Rossini. Proc. Am. Petroleum Inst. (III) $\underline{33}$, 000 (1952).

52. Thermodynamic properties and the characteristic $CH_2$ frequencies of n-paraffins. W.B.Person and G.C.Pimentel. Jointly with API Research Project 50. J. Am. Chem. Soc. $\underline{75}$, 532-538 (1953).

53. The thermodynamic properties of the three monomethylcyclopentenes and nine dimethylcyclopentenes. H.J.Hrostowski and G.C.Pimentel. Jointly with API Research Project 50. J. Am. Chem. Soc. $\underline{75}$, 539-542 (1953).